Pre-Algebra

Program Highlights

Vertically Aligned Content	Sample Page(s)
• PreK-12 Alignment	T10
• Research Base for Glencoe Mathematics	T12
• NCTM Focal Points	T14
• Program Philosophy	T16

Balanced Instruction Delivers Rich, Rigorous Content to All Students	Sample Page(s)
• Chapter 0, Preparing for Pre-Algebra	P1–P23
• Friendly Lesson Design	61–66
• Engaging Algebra and Graphing Technology Labs	439–440
• Step-by-Step Selected Solutions	43, R11
• Looking Ahead to Algebra	LA0–LA29

Right Amount of Rigor	Sample Page(s)
• Leveled Exercise Sets	367
• Multiple Representations	36, 513
• **H**igher **O**rder **T**hinking Problems (H.O.T. Problems)	157
• Leveled Resources	605, 609

Assessment and Tiered Intervention	Sample Page(s)
• Diagnostic Teaching	393
• Formative Assessment	81
• Summative Assessment	318–323
• Tier 1-3 Response to Intervention (RtI)	329, 356, 387

State-of-the-Art Technology	Sample Page(s)
• Personal Tutors for Each Example	61
• Math Online at glencoe.com	270
• FREE! Hotmath.com Online Tutorials	R11

Refer to the back of this endsheet for your *QuickPass* Code.

More Than Just a Textbook

Internet Resources

StudentWorks™ *Plus* Online This interactive **eBook** includes the complete Student Edition with audio, Math in Motion, Personal Tutor, Self-Check Quizzes, and much more – all at point of use!

Step 1 **Connect to** Math Online glencoe.com

Step 2 **Connect to resources by using simple and convenient**  **codes.**

"PA" for "Pre-Algebra" — **PA5167c1** — Enter the appropriate chapter number. c1 = Chapter 1

This edition, ISBN 978-0-07-888516-7

For Students

Connect to the Student Edition **eBook** that contains all of the following online resources. You don't need to take your textbook home every night.

- Personal Tutor
- Self-Check Quizzes
- Chapter Readiness Quizzes
- Math in Motion: Animation
- Math in Motion: BrainPOP®
- Math in Motion: Interactive Lab
- Extra Examples
- Chapter Test Practice
- Standardized Test Practice
- Study to Go
- Vocabulary Review Games
- Graphing Calculator Keystrokes
- Multilingual eGlossary
- Scavenger Hunts
- Workbooks

Hotmath.com

For Teachers

- Teaching Today
- **Advance Tracker**
  - Diagnostic, formative, and summative assessment
  - Progress reports
  - Differentiated instruction
- State Resources
- Professional Development at www.mhpd.com
  - Video Clips
  - Online Credit Courses
- Research
  - White Papers
  - Efficacy Studies

For Parents

Connect to www.glencoe.com to access the **StudentWorks Plus Online** and all of the resources for students and teachers listed above.

CONTENTS IN BRIEF

Focal Points and Connections
See page iv for key.

About the Cover

Nothing beats a hole-in-one in miniature golf! The next time you are playing miniature golf, think about the math you use—from keeping score to estimating distance. But there is more math than that! When you putt the ball in a straight line, the line can represent a linear function. You will learn more about linear functions in Chapter 8.

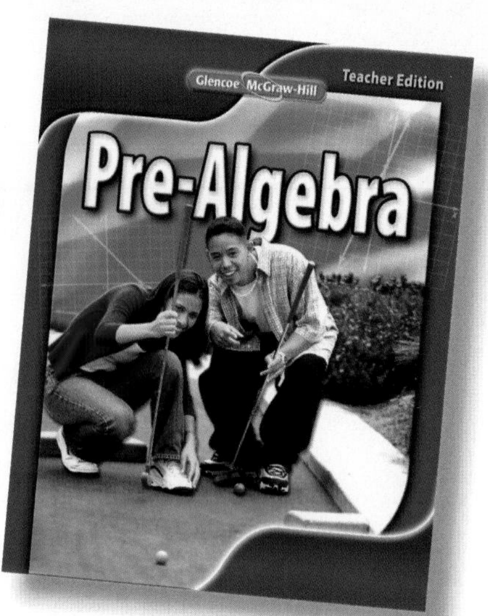

Image Credits:
T3 image100/Alamy; **T8** Bloom Works Inc./Alamy; **T13** Michael Newman/PhotoEdit; **T14** Jose Luis Pelaez, Inc./CORBIS;

The McGraw-Hill Companies

Glencoe

Send all inquiries to:
Glencoe/McGraw-Hill
8787 Orion Place
Columbus, OH 43240-4027

ISBN: 978-0-07-888516-7 (Teacher Edition)
MHID: 0-07-888516-7 (Teacher Edition)
ISBN: 978-0-07-888515-0 (Student Edition)
MHID: 0-07-888515-9 (Student Edition)

Printed in the United States of America.

5 6 7 8 9 10 SCI 17 16 15 14 13 12 11

Benefits of Student Edition Organization

Glencoe/McGraw-Hill's ***Pre-Algebra*** Student Edition has a 4-part organization that is front-loaded for standardized test success.

1. **Chapter 0** gets students ready for Pre-Algebra with a review of topics from previous courses that are prerequisites for Pre-Algebra.
2. **Chapters 1–13** Each chapter has coherent groups of lessons focused on related grade level math standards and the NCTM Focal Points.
3. **Preparing for Standardized Tests** provides test success tips, step-by-step solutions for standards-based questions, and a practice section in each chapter.
4. **Looking Ahead to Algebra 1** prepares students for success in Algebra 1 with lessons on several key math standards from Algebra 1.

The organization and pacing of ***Pre-Algebra*** helps ensure in-depth coverage of all grade 8 standards, success on your state test, and a good start for Algebra 1.

The School Year

About 167 School Days

Teach **Chapters 1–13.**

Use **Preparing for Standardized Tests** throughout the year to prepare students for success on your state test.

Your State Test

About 8 School Days

Teach
Looking Ahead to Algebra 1.

Pacing Guide Each chapter includes multiple days for review and assessment.	
Chapter 1	14 days
Chapter 2	13 days
Chapter 3	9 days
Chapter 4	10 days
Chapter 5	9 days
Chapter 6	13 days
Chapter 7	13 days
Chapter 8	15 days
Chapter 9	13 days
Chapter 10	12 days
Chapter 11	14 days
Chapter 12	16 days
Chapter 13	16 days
Total:	167 days
State Test	
Looking Ahead to Algebra 1	8 days

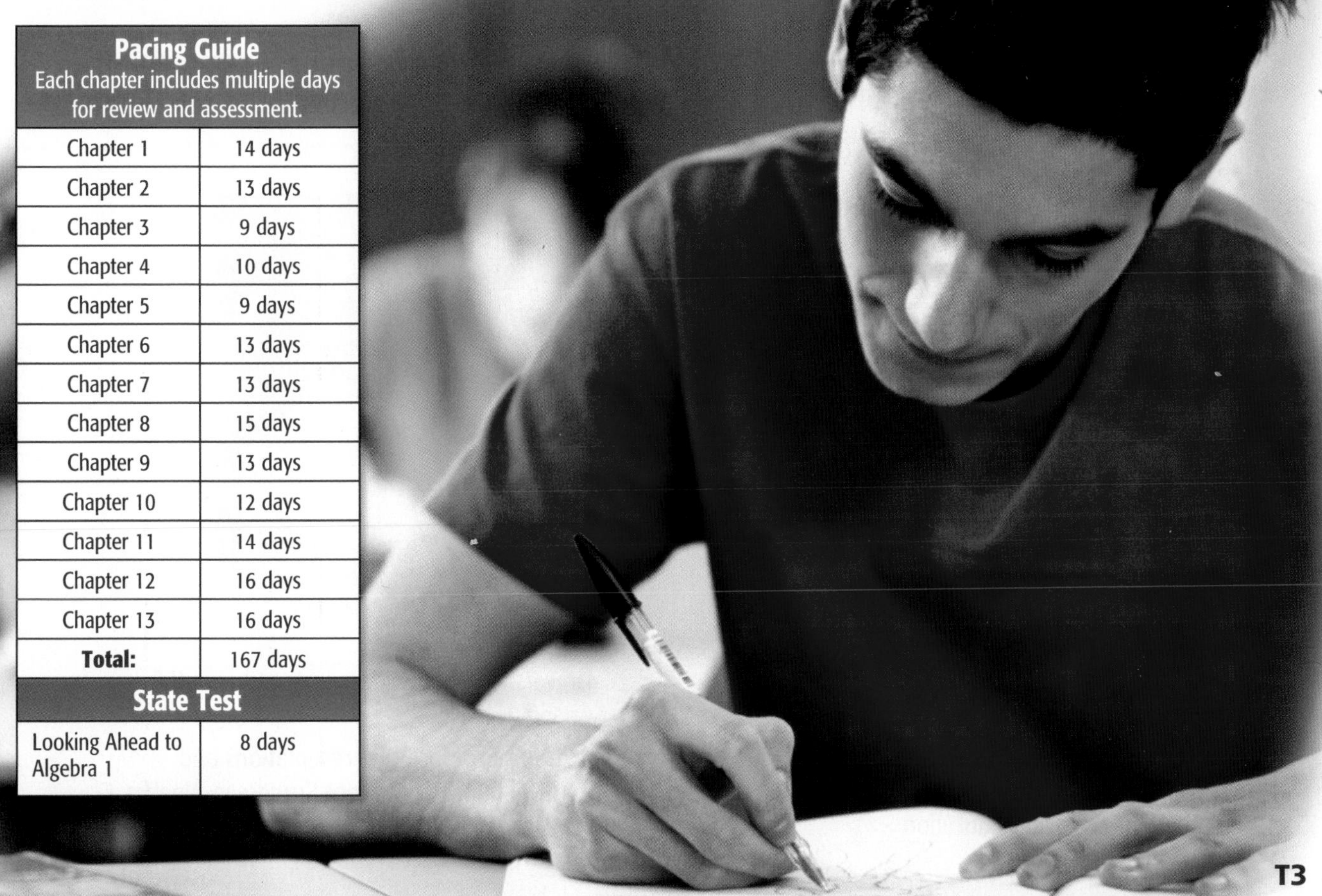

image 100/Alamy

Macmillan/McGraw-Hill and Glencoe/McGraw-Hill K–12 Mathematics Lead Authors

Our lead authors ensure that the Macmillan/McGraw-Hill and Glencoe/McGraw-Hill mathematics programs are truly vertically aligned by beginning with the end in mind—success in Algebra 1 and beyond. By "backmapping" the content from the high school programs, all of our mathematics programs are well articulated in their scope and sequence, ensuring that the content in each program provides a solid foundation for moving forward. These authors also worked closely with the entire K–12 author team to ensure vertical alignment of the instructional approach and visual design.

Dr. John A. Carter, Ph.D.
Assistant Principal for Teaching and Learning
Adlai E. Stevenson High School
Lincolnshire, Illinois

Areas of Expertise: Using technology and manipulatives to visualize concepts; Mathematics Achievement of English-Language Learners

Dr. Gilbert J. Cuevas, Ph.D.
Professor of Mathematics Education
Texas State University–San Marcos
San Marcos, Texas

Areas of Expertise: Applying concepts and skills in mathematically rich contexts; Mathematical Representations

Dr. Roger Day, Ph.D.
Mathematics Department Chairperson
Pontiac Township High School
Pontiac, Illinois

Areas of Expertise: Understanding and applying probability and statistics; Mathematics Teacher Education

Dr. Carol Malloy, Ph.D.
Associate Professor
University of North Carolina at Chapel Hill
Chapel Hill, NC

Areas of Expertise: Representations and critical thinking; Student Success in Algebra 1

Additional Pre-Algebra Authors

The entire Pre-Algebra author team strives to create a program that can be used by all types of Pre-Algebra teachers with all types of Pre-Algebra students. Each author brings their special expertise to making a program that will contribute to the success of every student who uses this instructional resource.

Rhonda J. Molix-Bailey
Mathematics Consultant
Mathematics by Design
DeSoto, Texas

Areas of Expertise: Geometry; Geometry in grades K–12 mathematics

Jack Price, Ed.D.
Professor Emeritus
California State Polytechnic University
Pomona, California

Areas of Expertise: Proportionality; Probability, statistics, and geometry in K–12 mathematics; Pre-Service Teacher Education

Teri Willard, Ed.D.
Assistant Professor
Department of Mathematics
Central Washington University
Ellensburg, Washington

Areas of Expertise: Functions; Functions in grades 6–12 mathematics

Contributing Author

This program is the beneficiary of the imagination of Dinah Zike through the contribution of the Foldables Study Organizers.

Dinah Zike
Educational Consultant
Dinah-Might Activities, Inc.
San Antonio, Texas

Math Online Meet the Authors at **glencoe.com**

Consultants

Glencoe/McGraw-Hill wishes to thank the following professionals for their feedback. They were instrumental in providing valuable input toward the development of this program in these specific areas.

Mathematical Content

Viken Hovsepian
Professor of Mathematics
Rio Hondo College
Whittier, California

Grant A. Fraser, Ph.D.
Professor of Mathematics
California State University, Los Angeles
Los Angeles, California

Arthur K. Wayman, Ph.D.
Professor of Mathematics Emeritus
California State University, Long Beach
Long Beach, California

Gifted and Talented

Shelbi K. Cole
Research Assistant
University of Connecticut
Storrs, Connecticut

College Readiness

Robert Lee Kimball, Jr.
Department Head, Math and Physics
Wake Technical Community College
Raleigh, North Carolina

English-Language Learners

Susana Davidenko
State University of New York
Cortland, New York

Alfredo Gómez
Mathematics/ESL teacher
George W. Fowler High School
Syracuse, New York

Graphing Calculator

Ruth M. Casey
T^3 National Instructor
Frankfort, Kentucky

Jerry Cummins
Former President
National Council of Supervisors of Mathematics
Western Springs, Illinois

Mathematical Fluency

Robert M. Capraro
Associate Professor
Texas A&M University
College Station, Texas

Pre-AP

Dixie Ross
Lead Teacher for Advanced Placement Mathematics
Pflugerville High School
Pflugerville, Texas

Reading and Writing

ReLeah Cossett Lent
Author and Educational Consultant
Morganton, Georgia

Lynn T. Havens
Director of Project CRISS
Kalispell, Montana

Reviewers

Each Reviewer reviewed at least two chapters of the Student Edition, giving feedback and suggestions for improving the effectiveness of the mathematics instruction.

Sherri Abel
Mathematics Teacher
Eastside High School
Taylors, South Carolina

Kelli Ball, NBCT
Mathematics Teacher
Owasso 7th Grade Center
Owasso, Oklahoma

Cynthia A. Burke
Mathematics Teacher
Sherrard Junior High School
Wheeling, West Virginia

Patrick M. Cain, Sr.
Assistant Principal
Stanhope Elmore High School
Millbrook, Alabama

Robert D. Cherry
Mathematics Instructor
Wheaton Warrenville South High School
Wheaton, Illinois

Tammy Cisco
8th Grade Mathematics/Algebra Teacher
Celina Middle School
Celina, Ohio

Amber L. Contrano
High School Teacher
Naperville Central High School
Naperville, Illinois

Catherine Creteau
Mathematics Department
Delaware Valley Regional High School
Frenchtown, New Jersey

Glenna L. Crockett
Mathematics Department Chair
Fairland High School
Fairland, Oklahoma

Jami L. Cullen
Mathematics Teacher/Leader
Hilltonia Middle School
Columbus, Ohio

Franco DiPasqua
Director of K–12 Mathematics
West Seneca Central Schools
West Seneca, New York

Kendrick Fearson
Mathematics Department Chair
Amos P. Godby High School
Tallahassee, Florida

Lisa K. Gleason
Mathematics Teacher
Gaylord High School
Gaylord, Michigan

Debra Harley
Director of Math & Science
East Meadow School District
Westbury, New York

Tracie A. Harwood
Mathematics Teacher
Braden River High School
Bradenton, Florida

Bonnie C. Hill
Mathematics Department Chair
Triad High School
Troy, Illinois

Clayton Hutsler
Teacher
Goodwyn Junior High School
Montgomery, Alabama

Gureet Kaur
7th Grade Mathematics Teacher
Quail Hollow Middle School
Charlotte, North Carolina

Rima Seals Kelley, NBCT
Mathematics Teacher/Department Chair
Deerlake Middle School
Tallahassee, Florida

Holly W. Loftis
8th Grade Mathematics Teacher
Greer Middle School
Lyman, South Carolina

Katherine Lohrman
Teacher, Math Specialist, New Teacher Mentor
John Marshall High School
Rochester, New York

Carol Y. Lumpkin
Mathematics Educator
Crayton Middle School
Columbia, South Carolina

Ron Mezzadri
Supervisor of Mathematics K–12
Fair Lawn Public Schools
Fair Lawn, New Jersey

Bonnye C. Newton
SOL Resource Specialist
Amherst County Public Schools
Amherst, Virginia

Kevin Olsen
Mathematics Teacher
River Ridge High School
New Port Richey, Florida

Kara Painter
Mathematics Teacher
Downers Grove South High School
Downers Grove, Illinois

Sheila L. Ruddle, NBCT
Mathematics Teacher, Grades 7 and 8
Pendleton County Middle/High School
Franklin, West Virginia

Angela H. Slate
Mathematics Teacher/Grade 7, Pre-Algebra, Algebra
LeRoy Martin Middle School
Raleigh, North Carolina

Cathy Stellern
Mathematics Teacher
West High School
Knoxville, Tennessee

Dr. Maria J. Vlahos
Mathematics Division Head for Grades 6–12
Barrington High School
Barrington, Illinois

Susan S. Wesson
Mathematics Consultant/Teacher (Retired)
Pilot Butte Middle School
Bend, Oregon

Mary Beth Zinn
Mathematics Teacher
Chippewa Valley High Schools
Clinton Township, Michigan

Mathematics Teacher Handbook

Focus on Pre-Algebra

- Rigorous mathematics content
- In-depth Algebra 1 preparation
- Aligned to grades 7 and 8 NCTM Focal Points
- Multiple Representations
- Next-generation technology

Bloom Works Inc./Alamy

Table of Contents

Welcome to PreK–12 Mathematics

True Vertical Alignment in 3 Ways

1 Content Design

Vertical content alignment is a process that ensures you and your students experience an articulated, coherent sequence of content from grade level to grade level. This provides you with the assurance that content is introduced, reinforced, and assessed at appropriate times in the series, eliminating gaps and unnecessary duplication. You are able to target your instruction to student needs because you are not teaching content intended to be covered later or that students have previously mastered.

2 Instructional Design

Our strong vertical alignment in instructional approach from PreKindergarten through Algebra 2 provides a smooth transition for students from elementary to middle school to high school. Our common vocabulary, technology, manipulatives, and lesson planning reduces the confusion students often encounter when transitioning between grade levels without this built-in articulation.

3 Visual Design

The student pages have a consistent visual design from grade to grade. This aids students' transition from elementary school to middle school and from middle school to Algebra 2. Students are more likely to succeed when they are already familiar with how to navigate student pages.

Grades PreK–2

Grades 3–5

Teacher Handbook

5 Keys to Success

1 Backmapping

According to College Board research, about 80% of students who successfully complete Algebra 1 and Geometry by 10th grade attend and succeed in college (Changing the Odds: Factors Increasing Access to College, 1990). ***Math Connects*** **K–8** and the ***Glencoe Mathematics*** high school series were conceived and developed by backmapping with the final result in mind–student success in Algebra 1 and beyond.

2 Balanced, In-Depth Content

The content was developed to specifically target the skills and topics that give students the most difficulty, such as Problem Solving, in each grade span.

Grades K–2	Grades 3–5
1. Problem Solving 2. Money 3. Time 4. Measurement 5. Fractions 6. Computation	1. Problem Solving 2. Fractions 3. Measurement 4. Decimals 5. Time 6. Algebra
Grades 6–8	**Grades 9–12**
1. Fractions 2. Problem Solving 3. Measurement 4. Algebra 5. Computation	1. Problem Solving 2. Fractions 3. Algebra 4. Geometry 5. Computation 6. Probability

– *K-12 Math Market Analysis Survey,* Open Book Publishing, 2006

3 Ongoing Assessment

Diagnostic, formative, and summative assessment includes: data-driven instruction; intervention options; and performance tracking, as well as remediation, acceleration, and enrichment tools throughout the program.

4 Intervention and Differentiated Instruction

A three-tiered Response to Intervention (RtI) is provided.

TIER 1 **Daily Intervention** Options for Differentiated Instruction in the Teacher Edition address concepts for different modalities or learning styles.

TIER 2 **Strategic Intervention** Teachers can use the myriad of intervention tips and ancillary materials, such as the *Strategic Intervention Guide* (1–5) and *Study Guide and Intervention* (6–8).

TIER 3 **Intensive Intervention** For students who are two or more years below grade level, ***Math Triumphs*** provides step-by-step instruction, vocabulary support, and data-driven decision making to help students succeed.

5 Professional Development

Many opportunities are included for teacher professional development. Additional learning opportunities in various formats–video, online, and on-site instruction–are fully aligned and articulated from Kindergarten through Algebra 2.

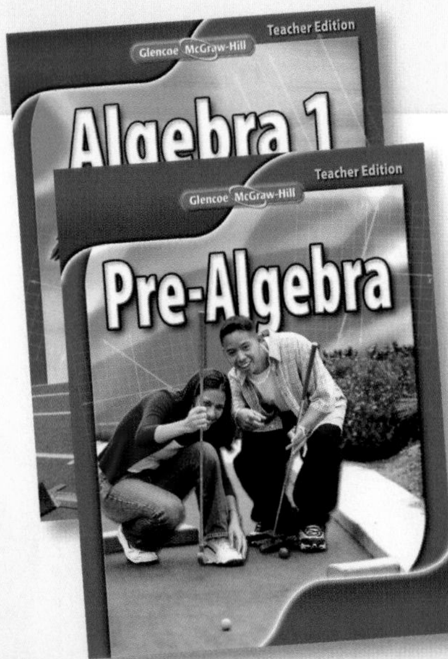

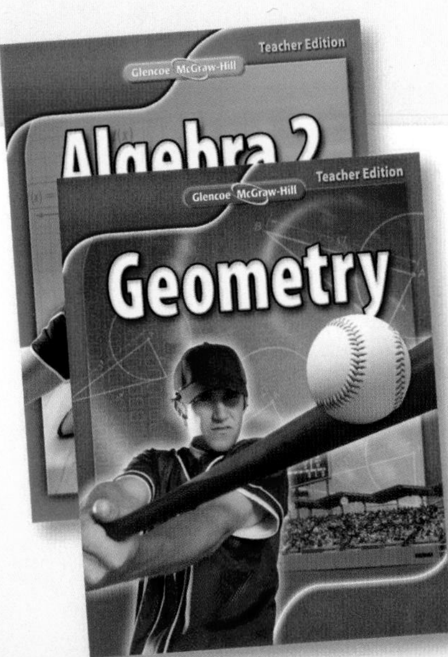

Grades 6–8 | Pre-Algebra and Algebra 1 | Geometry and Algebra 2

The Research Base for Glencoe *Pre-Algebra*

Continuous research with teachers, students, academicians, and leading experts helps to build a solid foundation for all of our PreK–12 programs, including **Glencoe *Pre-Algebra***.

1 Program Development Research

- Evaluating state and local standards
- Qualitative market research
- Academic content research

For more detailed information about our classroom research results, please consult the Glencoe *Pre-Algebra Program Efficacy Research Report.*

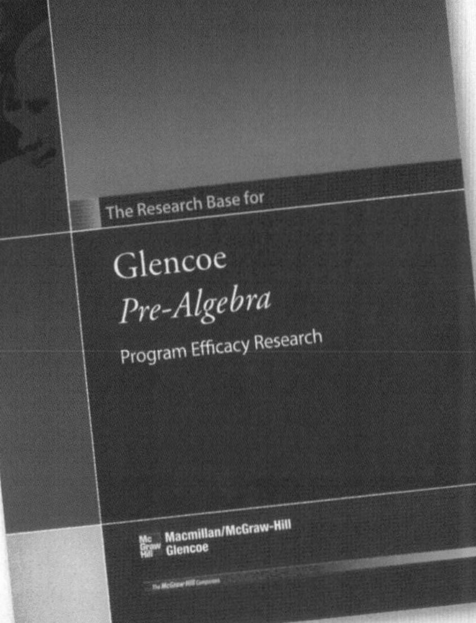

2 Formative Research

- Pedagogical research base
- Classroom field tests
- Teacher advisory boards
- Academic consultants and reviewers

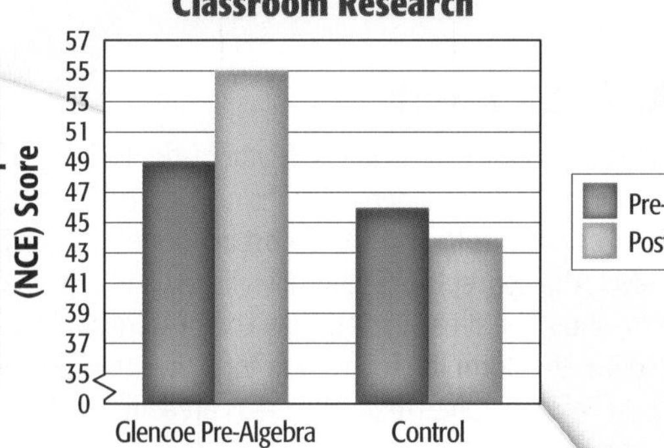

The average Normal Curve Equivalent (NCE) score among students using **Glencoe *Pre-Algebra*** increased. For students using another program, NCEs decreased.

3 Summative Research

- Evidence of increased test scores
- Quasi-experimental program efficacy research
- Longitudinal studies
- Qualitative program evaluations

Access all of our current research at glencoe.com.

Teacher Handbook

NCTM Focal Points

The NCTM Focal Points

In 2006, the National Council of Teachers of Mathematics (NCTM) released the Curriculum Focal Points for Pre-Kindergarten through Grade 8 Mathematics. These Curriculum Focal Points focus on the most important mathematical topics for each grade level. The concepts are vertically-aligned and expect a level of depth, complexity, and rigor at each level. They comprise related ideas, concepts, skills, and procedures that form the foundation for understanding and lasting learning. The Focal Points emphasize depth versus breadth. The Focal Points will be addressed and highlighted throughout our PreK–8 and Pre-Algebra series.

NCTM Focal Points for Grade 8	Supporting Chapters in *Math Connects*
Algebra	Chapters 1, 3, 4, 5, 7, 8
Geometry and *Measurement*	Chapters 6, 10, 11, 12
Data Analysis and *Number and Operations* and *Algebra*	Chapters 2, 13
Connections to the Focal Points	
Algebra	Chapters 8, 9
Geometry	Chapter 8
Data Analysis	Chapters 1, 8, 13
Number and Operations	Chapters 9, 10

For a complete listing of the Grade 7 Focal Points, see pages FP0–FP1.

What is the benefit to you in your classroom?

These Focal Points identify content for each grade level that should be mastered in order for your students to have true mathematical understanding–being able to not only calculate the answer, but to explain the answer and how to apply the calculation. The NCTM Focal Points were used as the basis in the development of ***Pre-Algebra.*** The authors have incorporated the Focal Points into the content to assist you in building depth of understanding.

Jose Luis Pelaez, Inc./CORBIS

KEY

G8-FP1 Grade 8 Focal Point 1	**G8-FP5C** Grade 8 Focal Point 5 Connection
G8-FP2 Grade 8 Focal Point 2	**G8-FP6C** Grade 8 Focal Point 6 Connection
G8-FP3 Grade 8 Focal Point 3	**G8-FP7C** Grade 8 Focal Point 7 Connection
G8-FP4C Grade 8 Focal Point 4 Connection	

The Curriculum Focal Points identify key mathematical ideas for this grade. They are not discrete topics or a checklist to be mastered; rather, they provide a framework for the majority of instruction at a particular grade level and the foundation for future mathematics study. The complete document may be viewed at www.nctm.org/focalpoints.

G8-FP1 ***Algebra:*** **Analyzing and representing linear functions and solving linear equations and systems of linear equations**
Students use linear functions, linear equations, and systems of linear equations to represent, analyze, and solve a variety of problems. They recognize a proportion $\left(\frac{y}{x} = k, \text{ or } y = kx\right)$ as a special case of a linear equation of the form $y = mx + b$, understanding that the constant of proportionality (k) is the slope and the resulting graph is a line through the origin. Students understand that the slope (m) of a line is a constant rate of change, so if the input, or x-coordinate, changes by a specific amount, a, the output, or y-coordinate, changes by the amount ma. Students translate among verbal, tabular, graphical, and algebraic representations of functions (recognizing that tabular and graphical representations are usually only partial representations), and they describe how such aspects of a function as slope and y-intercept appear in different representations. Students solve systems of two linear equations in two variables and relate the systems to pairs of lines that intersect, are parallel, or are the same line in the plane. Students use linear equations, systems of linear equations, linear functions, and their understanding of the slope of a line to analyze situations and solve problems.

G8-FP2 ***Geometry*** and ***Measurement:*** **Analyzing two- and three-dimensional space and figures by using distance and angle**
Students use fundamental facts about distance and angles to describe and analyze figures and situations in two- and three-dimensional space and to solve problems, including those with multiple steps. They prove that particular configurations of lines give rise to similar triangles because of the congruent angles created when a transversal cuts parallel lines. Students apply this reasoning about similar triangles to solve a variety of problems, including those that ask them to find heights and distances. They use facts about the angles that are created when a transversal cuts parallel lines to explain why the sum of the measures of the angles in a triangle is 180 degrees, and they apply this fact about triangles to find unknown measures of angles. Students explain why the Pythagorean theorem is valid by using a variety of methods–for example, by decomposing a square in two different ways. They apply the Pythagorean theorem to find distances between points in the Cartesian coordinate plane to measure lengths and analyze polygons and polyhedra.

G8-FP3 ***Data Analysis*** and ***Number and Operations*** and ***Algebra:*** **Analyzing and summarizing data sets**
Students use descriptive statistics, including mean, median, and range, to summarize and compare data sets, and they organize and display data to pose and answer questions. They compare the information provided by the mean and the median and investigate the different effects that changes in data values have on these measures of center. They understand that a measure of center alone does not thoroughly describe a data set because very different data sets can share the same measure of center. Students select the mean or the median as the appropriate measure of center for a given purpose.

Connections to the Focal Points

G8-FP4C ***Algebra:*** Students encounter some nonlinear functions (such as the inverse proportions that they studied in grade 7 as well as basic quadratic and exponential functions) whose rates of change contrast with the constant rate of change of linear functions. They view arithmetic sequences, including those arising from patterns or problems, as linear functions whose inputs are counting numbers. They apply ideas about linear functions to solve problems involving rates such as motion at a constant speed.

G8-FP5C ***Geometry:*** Given a line in a coordinate plane, students understand that all "slope triangles"–triangles created by a vertical "rise" line segment (showing the change in y), a horizontal "run" line segment (showing the change in x), and a segment of the line itself–are similar. They also understand the relationship of these similar triangles to the constant slope of a line.

G8-FP6C ***Data Analysis:*** Building on their work in previous grades to organize and display data to pose and answer questions, students now see numerical data as an aggregate, which they can often summarize with one or several numbers. In addition to the median, students determine the 25th and 75th percentiles (1st and 3rd quartiles) to obtain information about the spread of data. They may use box-and-whisker plots to convey this information. Students make scatterplots to display bivariate data, and they informally estimate lines of best fit to make and test conjectures.

G8-FP7C ***Number and Operations:*** Students use exponents and scientific notation to describe very large and very small numbers. They use square roots when they apply the Pythagorean theorem.

Program Philosophy

Balanced Instruction, Vertically Aligned from Grade PreK through Algebra 2

The vertical alignment of ***Math Connects*** PreK–8 through ***Algebra 2*** incorporates a balance of instruction throughout. These programs provide students a balanced approach to mathematics by:

- investigating concepts and building conceptual understanding.
- developing, reinforcing, and mastering computational and procedural skills.
- applying mathematics to problem-solving situations.

This sequence of Student Edition pages illustrates the vertically-aligned development of the conceptual understanding and corresponding computational and procedural skills for an important algebra topic.

Primary Students use two-color counters to model addition sentences. This activity forms a basis for future understanding of and success in solving algebraic equations.

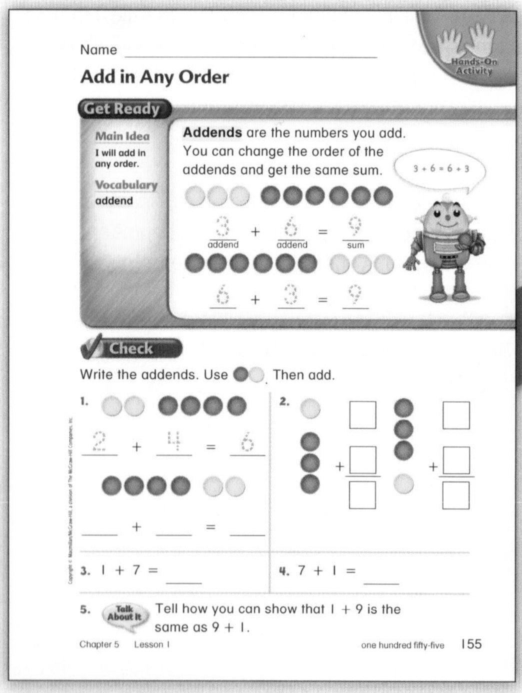

Name ______________________

Add in Any Order

Hands-On Activity

Get Ready

Main Idea
I will add in any order.

Vocabulary
addend

Addends are the numbers you add. You can change the order of the addends and get the same sum.

3 + 6 = 6 + 3

3 + 6 = 9
addend addend sum

6 + 3 = 9

Check

Write the addends. Use counters. Then add.

1. 2 + 4 = 6

___ + ___ = ___

2.

3. 1 + 7 = ____

4. 7 + 1 = ____

5. Talk About It Tell how you can show that 1 + 9 is the same as 9 + 1.

Chapter 5 Lesson 1 one hundred fifty-five 155

Math Connects, Grade 1, Student Edition, page 155

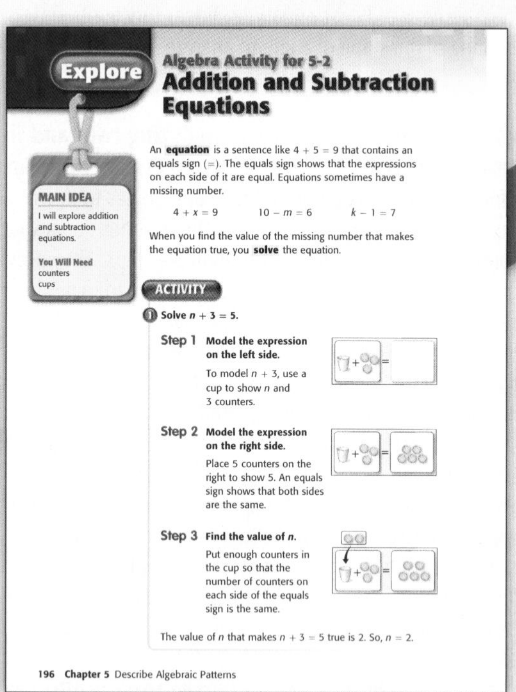

Explore

Algebra Activity for 5-2

Addition and Subtraction Equations

MAIN IDEA
I will explore addition and subtraction equations.

You Will Need
counters
cups

An **equation** is a sentence like $4 + 5 = 9$ that contains an equals sign (=). The equals sign shows that the expressions on each side of it are equal. Equations sometimes have a missing number.

$4 + x = 9$ $10 - m = 6$ $k - 1 = 7$

When you find the value of the missing number that makes the equation true, you **solve** the equation.

ACTIVITY

1 **Solve $n + 3 = 5$.**

Step 1 Model the expression on the left side.
To model $n + 3$, use a cup to show n and 3 counters.

Step 2 Model the expression on the right side.
Place 5 counters on the right to show 5. An equals sign shows that both sides are the same.

Step 3 Find the value of n.
Put enough counters in the cup so that the number of counters on each side of the equals sign is the same.

The value of n that makes $n + 3 = 5$ true is 2. So, $n = 2$.

196 **Chapter 5** Describe Algebraic Patterns

Math Connects, Grade 4, Student Edition, page 196

Intermediate Students build on their experience with counters to using cups and counters to model and solve addition and subtraction equations. The exercises are designed to help students bridge the gap from using cups and counters to solving equations symbolically.

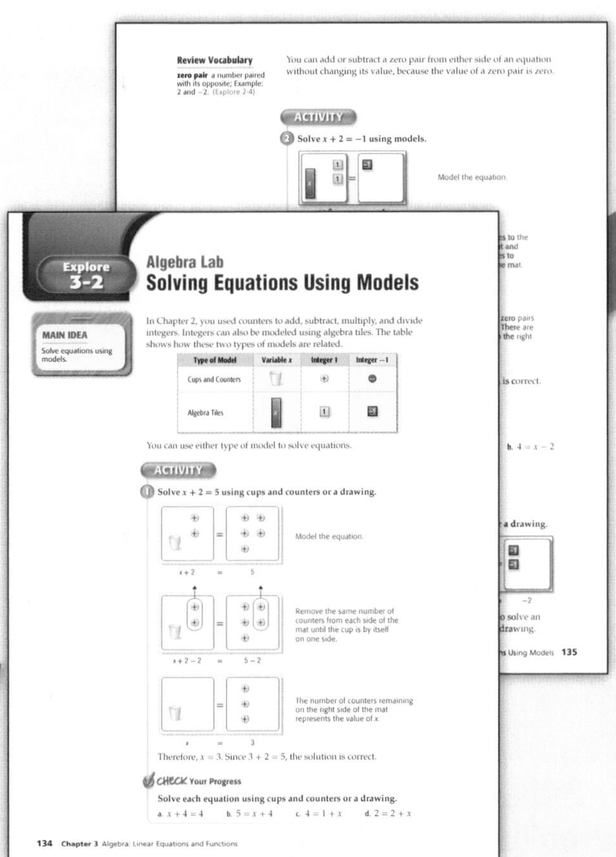

Review Vocabulary

zero pair a number paired with its opposite; Example: 2 and −2. (Explore 2-4)

You can add or subtract a zero pair from either side of an equation without changing its value, because the value of a zero pair is zero.

ACTIVITY

2 Solve $x + 2 = -1$ using models.

Model the equation.

Explore 3-2

Algebra Lab
Solving Equations Using Models

MAIN IDEA

Solve equations using models.

In Chapter 2, you used counters to add, subtract, multiply, and divide integers. Integers can also be modeled using algebra tiles. The table shows how these two types of models are related.

Type of Model	Variable x	Integer 1	Integer −1
Cups and Counters			
Algebra Tiles			

You can use either type of model to solve equations.

ACTIVITY

1 Solve $x + 2 = 5$ using cups and counters or a drawing.

Model the equation.

$x + 2 = 5$

Remove the same number of counters from each side of the mat until the cup is by itself on one side.

$x + 2 - 2 = 5 - 2$

The number of counters remaining on the right side of the mat represents the value of x.

$x = 3$

Therefore, $x = 3$. Since $3 + 2 = 5$, the solution is correct.

CHECK Your Progress

Solve each equation using cups and counters or a drawing.

a. $x + 4 = 4$ b. $5 = x + 4$ c. $4 = 1 + x$ d. $2 = 2 + x$

134 Chapter 3 Algebra: Linear Equations and Functions

h. $4 = x - 2$

135

Math Connects, Course 2,
Student Edition, pages 134–135

Middle School Students represent the variable x as a cup, as a counter, or as a written x. In this Algebra Lab, students make the transition from cups and counters to the more abstract algebra tiles. In the next lesson, students solve simple equations symbolically.

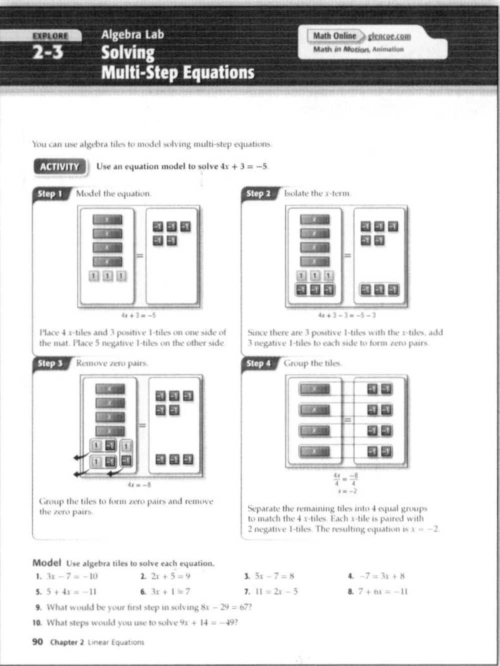

EXPLORE 2-3

Algebra Lab
Solving Multi-Step Equations

Math Online glencoe.com
Math in Motion, Animation

You can use algebra tiles to model solving multi-step equations.

ACTIVITY **Use an equation model to solve $4x + 3 = -5$.**

Step 1 Model the equation.

$4x + 3 = -5$

Place 4 x-tiles and 3 positive 1-tiles on one side of the mat. Place 5 negative 1-tiles on the other side.

Step 2 Isolate the x-term.

$4x + 3 - 3 = -5 - 3$

Since there are 3 positive 1-tiles with the x-tiles, add 3 negative 1-tiles to each side to form zero pairs.

Step 3 Remove zero pairs.

$4x = -8$

Group the tiles to form zero pairs and remove the zero pairs.

Step 4 Group the tiles.

$\frac{4x}{4} = \frac{-8}{4}$

$x = -2$

Separate the remaining tiles into 4 equal groups to match the 4 x-tiles. Each x-tile is paired with 2 negative 1-tiles. The resulting equation is $x = -2$.

Model **Use algebra tiles to solve each equation.**

1. $3x - 7 = -10$
2. $2x + 5 = 9$
3. $5x - 7 = 8$
4. $-7 = 3x + 8$
5. $5 + 4x = -11$
6. $3x + 1 = 7$
7. $11 = 2x - 5$
8. $7 + 6x = -11$
9. What would be your first step in solving $8x - 29 = 67$?
10. What steps would you use to solve $9x + 14 = -49$?

90 Chapter 2 Linear Equations

Algebra 1,
Student Edition, page 90

Algebra 1 Students continue the use of algebra tiles to investigate solving multi-step equations. In the next lesson, students apply the procedure developed in the Algebra Lab to a symbolic approach.

Continuity of Instruction The instructional sequence described demonstrates the power of backward mapping from the desired result, success in Algebra 1 and beyond. This process of development avoids gaps and overlaps between grade levels and ensures that at each grade level the concepts and skills are built on the strong foundation developed in previous grades. The same approach was used across all strands throughout the entire PreK–12 series.

Program Philosophy

Balanced Approach

- Concepts
- Skills
- Problem solving

Relevant Problem Solving

Students are provided with ongoing opportunities to apply their math skills and solve problems using visual thinking, logical reasoning, number sense, and algebra.

Problem-Solving Strategies

Problem-Solving Strategy Lessons help students learn different problem-solving strategies for attacking word problems.

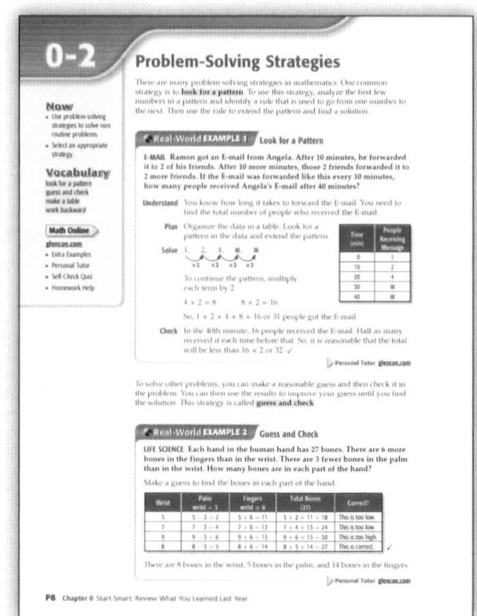

0-2 Problem-Solving Strategies

Now
- Use problem-solving strategies to solve non routine problems.
- Select an appropriate strategy.

Vocabulary
look for a pattern
guess and check
make a table
work backward

Math Online
glencoe.com
- Extra Examples
- Personal Tutor
- Self-Check Quiz
- Homework Help

There are many problem-solving strategies in mathematics. One common strategy is to **look for a pattern**. To use this strategy, analyze the first few numbers in a pattern and identify a rule that is used to go from one number to the next. Then use the rule to extend the pattern and find a solution.

Real-World EXAMPLE 1 Look for a Pattern

E-MAIL Ramon got an E-mail from Angela. After 10 minutes, he forwarded it to 2 of his friends. After 10 more minutes, those 2 friends forwarded it to 2 more friends. If the E-mail was forwarded like this every 10 minutes, how many people received Angela's E-mail after 40 minutes?

Understand You know how long it takes to forward the E-mail. You need to find the total number of people who received the E-mail.

Plan Organize the data in a table. Look for a pattern in the data and extend the pattern.

Time (min)	People Receiving Message
0	1
10	2
20	4
30	■
40	■

Solve 1, 2, 4, ■, ■ (×2 ×2 ×2 ×2)

To continue the pattern, multiply each term by 2.

$4 \times 2 = 8$ $8 \times 2 = 16$

So, $1 + 2 + 4 + 8 + 16$ or 31 people got the E-mail.

Check In the 40th minute, 16 people received the E-mail. Half as many received it each time before that. So, it is reasonable that the total will be less than 16×2 or 32. ✓

Personal Tutor glencoe.com

To solve other problems, you can make a reasonable guess and then check it in the problem. You can then use the results to improve your guess until you find the solution. This strategy is called **guess and check**.

Real-World EXAMPLE 2 Guess and Check

LIFE SCIENCE Each hand in the human hand has 27 bones. There are 6 more bones in the fingers than in the wrist. There are 3 fewer bones in the palm than in the wrist. How many bones are in each part of the hand?

Make a guess to find the bones in each part of the hand.

Wrist	Palm wrist − 3	Fingers wrist + 6	Total Bones (27)	Correct?
5	5 − 3 = 2	5 + 6 = 11	5 + 2 + 11 = 18	This is too low.
7	7 − 3 = 4	7 + 6 = 13	7 + 4 + 13 = 24	This is too low.
9	9 − 3 = 6	9 + 6 = 15	9 + 6 + 15 = 30	This is too high.
8	8 − 3 = 5	8 + 6 = 14	8 + 5 + 14 = 27	This is correct. ✓

There are 8 bones in the wrist, 5 bones in the palm, and 14 bones in the fingers.

Personal Tutor glencoe.com

P8 Chapter 0 Start Smart: Review What You Learned Last Year

Pre-Algebra
Student Edition, page P8

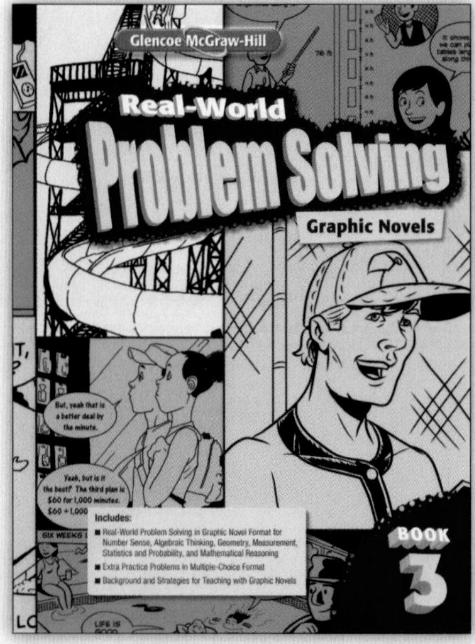

Real-World Problem Solving, Book 3

Real-World Problem Solving Graphic Novels

Motivating, teen-relevant problem solving in graphic novel format provides practice with number sense, algebraic thinking, geometry, measurement, statistics and probability, and mathematical reasoning.

H.O.T. Problems

H.O.T. Problems require students to use **Higher Order Thinking** skills to solve problems.

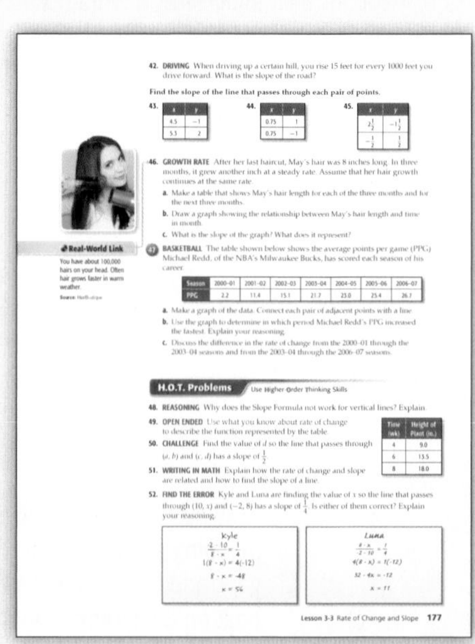

42. **DRIVING** When driving up a certain hill, you rise 15 feet for every 1000 feet you drive forward. What is the slope of the road?

Find the slope of the line that passes through each pair of points.

43.

x	y
4.5	−1
5.5	2

44.

x	y
0.75	1
0.75	−1

45.

x	y
$2\frac{1}{2}$	$-1\frac{1}{2}$
$-\frac{1}{2}$	$\frac{1}{2}$

46. **GROWTH RATE** After her last haircut, May's hair was 8 inches long. In three months, it grew another inch at a steady rate. Assume that her hair growth continues at the same rate.
    a. Make a table that shows May's hair length for each of the three months and for the next three months.
    b. Draw a graph showing the relationship between May's hair length and time in month.
    c. What is the slope of the graph? What does it represent?

Real-World Link
You have about 100,000 hairs on your head. Often hair grows faster in warm weather.

47. **BASKETBALL** The table shown below shows the average points per game (PPG) Michael Redd, of the NBA's Milwaukee Bucks, has scored each season of his career.

Season	2000–01	2001–02	2002–03	2003–04	2004–05	2005–06	2006–07
PPG	2.2	11.4	15.1	21.7	23.0	25.4	26.7

    a. Make a graph of the data. Connect each pair of adjacent points with a line.
    b. Use the graph to determine in which period Michael Redd's PPG increased the fastest. Explain your reasoning.
    c. Discuss the difference in the rate of change from the 2000–01 through the 2003–04 seasons and from the 2003–04 through the 2006–07 seasons.

H.O.T. Problems Use Higher Order Thinking Skills

48. **REASONING** Why does the Slope Formula not work for vertical lines? Explain.
49. **OPEN ENDED** Use what you know about rate of change to describe the function represented by the table.

Time (wk)	Height of Plant (in.)
4	9.0
6	13.5
8	18.0

50. **CHALLENGE** Find the value of d so the line that passes through (a, b) and (c, d) has a slope of $\frac{1}{2}$.
51. **WRITING IN MATH** Explain how the rate of change and slope are related and how to find the slope of a line.
52. **FIND THE ERROR** Kyle and Luna are finding the value of x so the line that passes through $(10, x)$ and $(-2, 8)$ has a slope of $\frac{1}{4}$. Is either of them correct? Explain your reasoning.

Kyle
$\frac{-2-10}{8-x} = \frac{1}{4}$
$1(8-x) = 4(-12)$
$8 - x = -48$
$x = 56$

Luna
$\frac{8-x}{-2-10} = \frac{1}{4}$
$4(8-x) = 1(-12)$
$32 - 4x = -12$
$x = 11$

Lesson 3-3 Rate of Change and Slope 177

Algebra 1
Student Edition, page 177

Multiple Representations

Problems using **Multiple Representations** help students visualize concepts and increase understanding. Verbal, numerical, algebraic, tabular, graphical, and analytical representations can be found throughout.

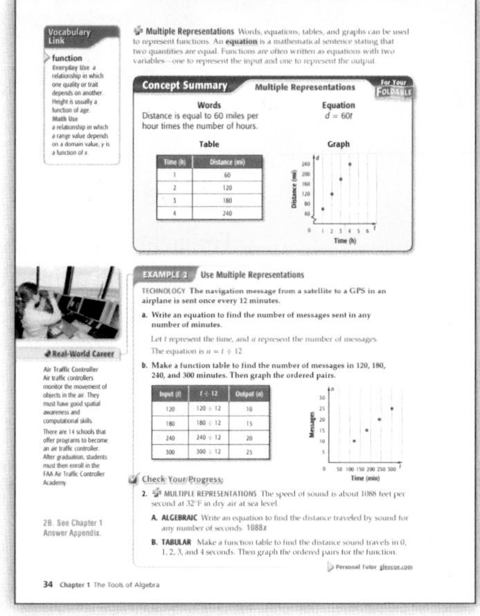

Vocabulary Link

function
Everyday Use a relationship in which one quality or trait depends on another. Height is usually a function of age.
Math Use a relationship in which a range value depends on a domain value, *y* is a function of *x*.

Multiple Representations Words, equations, tables, and graphs can be used to represent functions. An **equation** is a mathematical sentence stating that two quantities are equal. Functions are often written as equations with two variables—one to represent the input and one to represent the output.

Concept Summary Multiple Representations — For Your FOLDABLE

Words
Distance is equal to 60 miles per hour times the number of hours.

Equation
$d = 60t$

Table

Time (h)	Distance (mi)
1	60
2	120
3	180
4	240

Graph

EXAMPLE 2 Use Multiple Representations

TECHNOLOGY **The navigation message from a satellite to a GPS in an airplane is sent once every 12 minutes.**

a. Write an equation to find the number of messages sent in any number of minutes.

Let *t* represent the time, and *n* represent the number of messages. The equation is $n = t \div 12$.

b. Make a function table to find the number of messages in 120, 180, 240, and 300 minutes. Then graph the ordered pairs.

Input (t)	$t \div 12$	Output (n)
120	$120 \div 12$	10
180	$180 \div 12$	15
240	$240 \div 12$	20
300	$300 \div 12$	25

Real-World Career

Air Traffic Controller
Air traffic controllers monitor the movement of objects in the air. They must have good spatial awareness and computational skills.
There are 14 schools that offer programs to become an air traffic controller. After graduation, students must then enroll in the FAA Air Traffic Controller Academy.

Check Your Progress

2. MULTIPLE REPRESENTATIONS The speed of sound is about 1088 feet per second at 32°F in dry air at sea level.

A. **ALGEBRAIC** Write an equation to find the distance traveled by sound for any number of seconds. 1088*x*

B. **TABULAR** Make a function table to find the distance sound travels in 0, 1, 2, 3, and 4 seconds. Then graph the ordered pairs for the function.

2B. See Chapter 1 Answer Appendix.

Personal Tutor glencoe.com

34 Chapter 1 The Tools of Algebra

Pre-Algebra
Student Edition, page 34

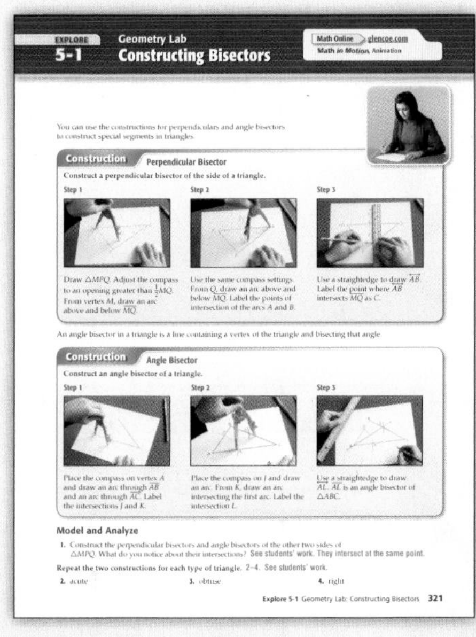

EXPLORE 5-1 Geometry Lab
Constructing Bisectors

Math Online glencoe.com
Math in Motion, Animation

You can use the constructions for perpendiculars and angle bisectors to construct special segments in triangles.

Construction Perpendicular Bisector

Construct a perpendicular bisector of the side of a triangle.

Step 1 Draw $\triangle MPQ$. Adjust the compass to an opening greater than $\frac{1}{2}MQ$. From vertex *M*, draw an arc above and below $\overline{MQ}$.

Step 2 Use the same compass settings. From *Q*, draw an arc above and below $\overline{MQ}$. Label the points of intersection of the arcs *A* and *B*.

Step 3 Use a straightedge to draw $\overleftrightarrow{AB}$. Label the point where $\overleftrightarrow{AB}$ intersects $\overline{MQ}$ as *C*.

An angle bisector in a triangle is a line containing a vertex of the triangle and bisecting that angle.

Construction Angle Bisector

Construct an angle bisector of a triangle.

Step 1 Place the compass on vertex *A* and draw an arc through $\overline{AB}$ and an arc through $\overline{AC}$. Label the intersections *J* and *K*.

Step 2 Place the compass on *J* and draw an arc. From *K*, draw an arc intersecting the first arc. Label the intersection *L*.

Step 3 Use a straightedge to draw $\overrightarrow{AL}$. $\overrightarrow{AL}$ is an angle bisector of $\triangle ABC$.

Model and Analyze

1. Construct the perpendicular bisectors and angle bisectors of the other two sides of $\triangle MPQ$. What do you notice about their intersections? See students' work. They intersect at the same point.

Repeat the two constructions for each type of triangle. 2–4. See students' work.

2. acute 3. obtuse 4. right

Explore 5-1 Geometry Lab: Constructing Bisectors 321

Geometry
Student Edition, page 321

Hands-On Labs

Some labs introduce mathematical topics, while others extend topics just presented. **Algebra, Geometry, Measurement, Statistics,** and **Probability** labs use models to bridge the gap between concrete understanding and mathematical symbolism.

Math in Motion

Math in Motion are online illustrations of key concepts through Animations, Interactive Labs, and BrainPOPs®.

Graphing Technology Labs

Graphing calculator labs allow students to gain understanding of mathematics through graphical representations.

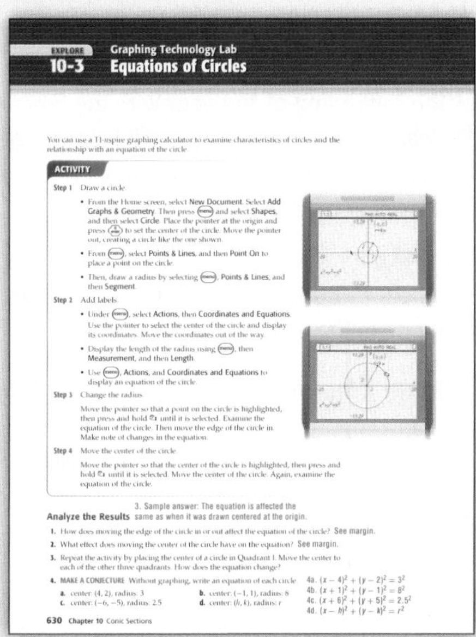

EXPLORE 10-3 Graphing Technology Lab
Equations of Circles

You can use a TI-nspire graphing calculator to examine characteristics of circles and the relationship with an equation of the circle.

ACTIVITY

Step 1 Draw a circle.
- From the Home screen, select New Document. Select Add Graphs & Geometry. Then press (menu) and select Shapes, and then select Circle. Place the pointer at the origin and press (enter) to set the center of the circle. Move the pointer out, creating a circle like the one shown.
- From (menu), select Points & Lines, and then Point On to place a point on the circle.
- Then, draw a radius by selecting (menu), Points & Lines, and then Segment.

Step 2 Add labels.
- Under (menu), select Actions, then Coordinates and Equations. Use the pointer to select the center of the circle and display its coordinates. Move the coordinates out of the way.
- Display the length of the radius using (menu), then Measurement, and then Length.
- Use (menu), Actions, and Coordinates and Equations to display an equation of the circle.

Step 3 Change the radius.
Move the pointer so that a point on the circle is highlighted, then press and hold until it is selected. Examine the equation of the circle. Then move the edge of the circle in. Make note of changes in the equation.

Step 4 Move the center of the circle.
Move the pointer so that the center of the circle is highlighted, then press and hold until it is selected. Move the center of the circle. Again, examine the equation of the circle.

Analyze the Results 3. Sample answer: The equation is affected the same as when it was drawn centered at the origin.

1. How does moving the edge of the circle in or out affect the equation of the circle? See margin.
2. What effect does moving the center of the circle have on the equation? See margin.
3. Repeat the activity by placing the center of a circle in Quadrant I. Move the center to each of the other three quadrants. How does the equation change?
4. MAKE A CONJECTURE Without graphing, write an equation of each circle.
   a. center: (4, 2), radius: 3
   b. center: (−1, 1), radius: 8
   c. center: (−6, −5), radius: 2.5
   d. center: (*h*, *k*), radius: *r*

4a. $(x-4)^2 + (y-2)^2 = 3^2$
4b. $(x+1)^2 + (y-1)^2 = 8^2$
4c. $(x+6)^2 + (y+5)^2 = 2.5^2$
4d. $(x-h)^2 + (y-k)^2 = r^2$

630 Chapter 10 Conic Sections

Algebra 2
Student Edition, page 630

Comprehensive Assessment System

Data-Driven Decision Making

Frequent and meaningful assessment of student progress is offered within the curriculum structure and printed teacher support materials. See pages T22 and T23 for digital assessment solutions.

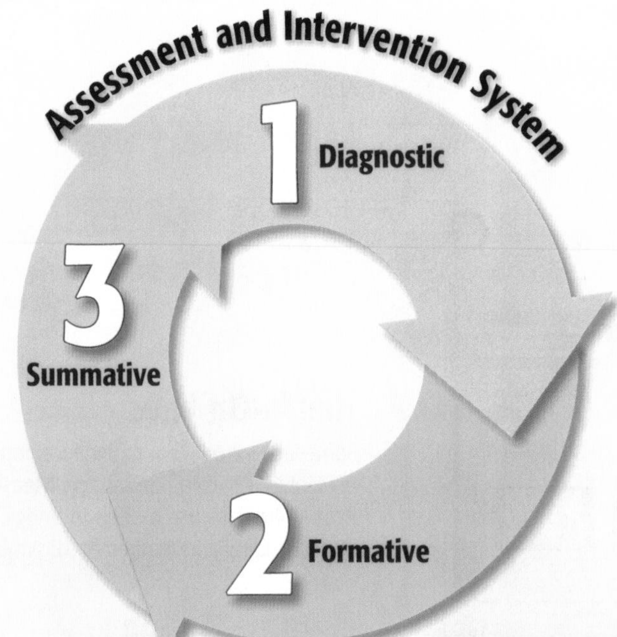

1 Diagnostic

Initial Assessment Assess students' knowledge **at the beginning of the year** with the *Diagnostic and Placement Tests*. This booklet will help you determine whether your students need additional materials and resources to meet grade-level standards.

Entry–Level Assessment Assess students' prior knowledge **at the beginning of a chapter or lesson** with one of the following options.

Student Edition
- Get Ready

Teacher Edition
- Differentiated Instruction
- 5-Minute Check

Additional Resources
- Chapter Resource Masters, Anticipation Guide

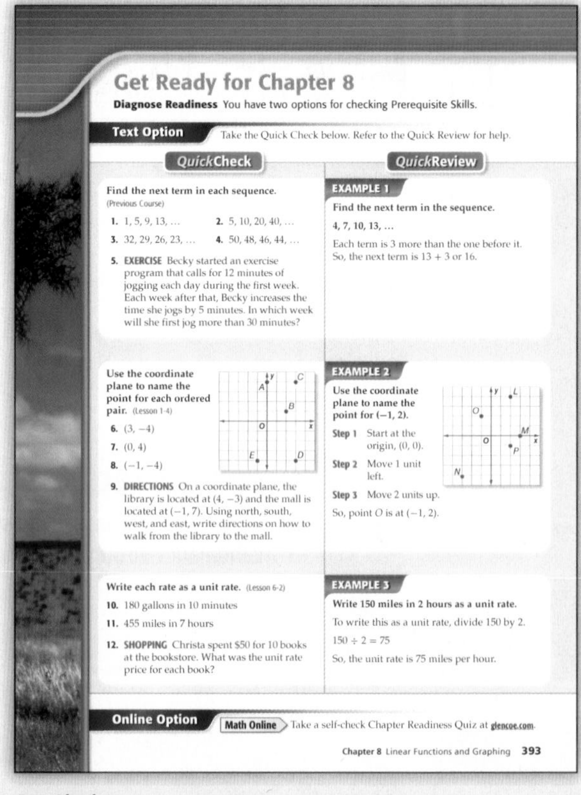

Get Ready for Chapter 8

Diagnose Readiness You have two options for checking Prerequisite Skills.

Text Option Take the Quick Check below. Refer to the Quick Review for help.

*Quick*Check

Find the next term in each sequence. (Previous Course)

1. 1, 5, 9, 13, …
2. 5, 10, 20, 40, …
3. 32, 29, 26, 23, …
4. 50, 48, 46, 44, …
5. **EXERCISE** Becky started an exercise program that calls for 12 minutes of jogging each day during the first week. Each week after that, Becky increases the time she jogs by 5 minutes. In which week will she first jog more than 30 minutes?

Use the coordinate plane to name the point for each ordered pair. (Lesson 1-4)

6. (3, −4)
7. (0, 4)
8. (−1, −4)
9. **DIRECTIONS** On a coordinate plane, the library is located at (4, −3) and the mall is located at (−1, 7). Using north, south, west, and east, write directions on how to walk from the library to the mall.

Write each rate as a unit rate. (Lesson 6-2)

10. 180 gallons in 10 minutes
11. 455 miles in 7 hours
12. **SHOPPING** Christa spent $50 for 10 books at the bookstore. What was the unit rate price for each book?

*Quick*Review

EXAMPLE 1

Find the next term in the sequence.

4, 7, 10, 13, …

Each term is 3 more than the one before it. So, the next term is 13 + 3 or 16.

EXAMPLE 2

Use the coordinate plane to name the point for (−1, 2).

Step 1 Start at the origin, (0, 0).

Step 2 Move 1 unit left.

Step 3 Move 2 units up.

So, point *O* is at (−1, 2).

EXAMPLE 3

Write 150 miles in 2 hours as a unit rate.

To write this as a unit rate, divide 150 by 2.

150 ÷ 2 = 75

So, the unit rate is 75 miles per hour.

Online Option Math Online Take a self-check Chapter Readiness Quiz at glencoe.com.

Chapter 8 Linear Functions and Graphing 393

Pre-Algebra
Student Edition, page 393

2 Formative

Progress Monitoring Determine if students are progressing adequately as you teach each lesson. Use the assessments to differentiate lesson instruction and practice.

Student Edition

- Check Your Understanding
- Find the Error
- Writing in Math
- Mid-Chapter Quiz
- Study Guide and Review
- Foldables®

Teacher Edition

- Differentiated Instruction
- Step 4 (Assess) of the Teaching Plan
- Response to Intervention

Additional Resources

Chapter Resource Masters

- Mid-Chapter Test
- 4 Quizzes
- Standardized Test Practice

CHAPTER 4 **Mid-Chapter Quiz**
Lessons 4-1 through 4-4

Math Online glencoe.com
Math *in Motion*, Animation

Write an equation in slope-intercept form for each graph shown. (Lesson 4-1)

1.

2.

Graph each equation. (Lesson 4-1)

3. $y = 2x + 3$
4. $y = \frac{1}{3}x - 2$

5. BOATS The sign below describes the charge to rent a pontoon boat. Write an equation in slope-intercept form for the total rental cost C for a boat used for t hours. (Lesson 4-1)

Pontoon Boat Rentals
$60 per hour
plus
$20 cleaning fee

Write an equation of a line with the given conditions. (Lesson 4-2)

6. (2, 5); slope 3
7. (−3, −1), slope $\frac{1}{2}$
8. (−3, 4), (1, 12)
9. (−1, 6), (2, 4)
10. (2, 1), slope 0

11. MULTIPLE CHOICE Write an equation of a line that passes through the point (0, 0) and has slope −4. (Lesson 4-2)
    A $y = x - 4$
    B $y = x + 4$
    C $y = -4x$
    D $y = 4 - x$

Write an equation in point-slope form for the line that passes through each point with the given slope. (Lesson 4-3)

12. (1, 4), $m = 6$
13. (−2, −1), $m = -3$
14. Write an equation in point-slope form for the line that passes through the point (8, 3) and has slope −2. (Lesson 4-3)
15. Write the equation $y + 3 = \frac{1}{2}(x - 5)$ in standard form. (Lesson 4-3)
16. Write the equation $y + 4 = -7(x - 3)$ in slope-intercept form. (Lesson 4-3)

Write each equation in standard form. (Lesson 4-3)

17. $y - 5 = -2(x - 3)$
18. $y + 4 = \frac{2}{3}(x - 3)$

Write each equation in slope-intercept form. (Lesson 4-3)

19. $y - 3 = 4(x + 3)$
20. $y + 1 = \frac{1}{2}(x - 8)$

21. MULTIPLE CHOICE Determine whether the graphs of the pair of equations are *parallel*, *perpendicular*, or *neither*. (Lesson 4-4)

$$y = -6x + 8$$
$$3x + \frac{1}{2}y = -3$$

    F parallel
    G perpendicular
    H neither
    J not enough information

Write an equation in slope-intercept form for the line that passes through the given point and is perpendicular to the graph of the equation. (Lesson 4-4)

22. (3, −4); $y = -\frac{1}{3}x - 5$
23. (0, −3); $y = -2x + 4$
24. (−4, −5); $-4x + 5y = -6$
25. (−1, −4); $-x - 2y = 0$

244 Chapter 4 Linear Functions and Relations

Algebra 1
Student Edition, page 244

3 Summative

Summative Evaluation Assess student success in learning the concepts in each chapter.

Student Edition

- Practice Test
- Standardized Test Practice
- Foldables™

Teacher Edition

- Response to Intervention

Additional Resources

Chapter Resource Masters

- Vocabulary Test
- 6 Leveled Chapter Tests
- Extended Response Test

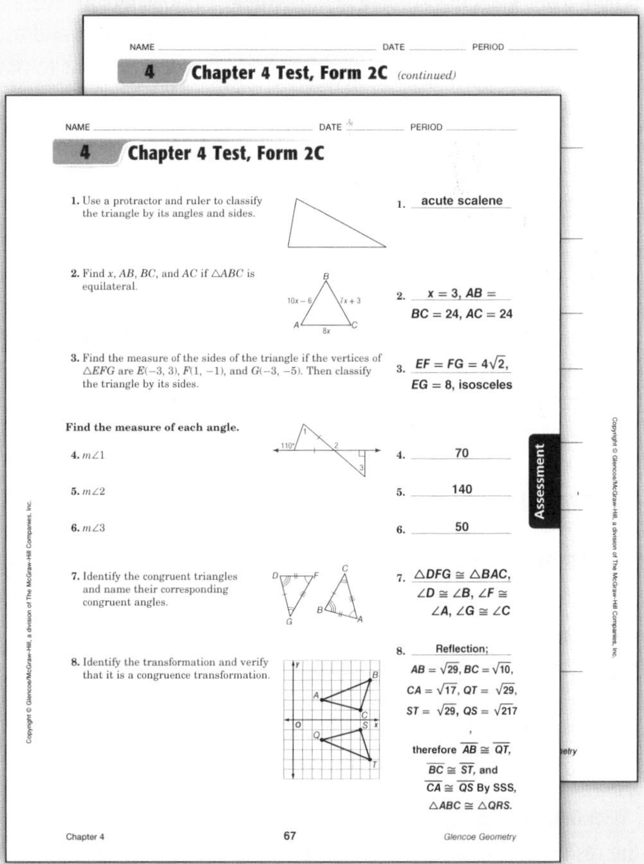

NAME ______ DATE ______ PERIOD ______

4 **Chapter 4 Test, Form 2C** *(continued)*

NAME ______ DATE ______ PERIOD ______

4 **Chapter 4 Test, Form 2C**

1. Use a protractor and ruler to classify the triangle by its angles and sides. — 1. acute scalene

2. Find x, AB, BC, and AC if $\triangle ABC$ is equilateral. — 2. $x = 3$, $AB = BC = 24$, $AC = 24$

3. Find the measure of the sides of the triangle if the vertices of $\triangle EFG$ are $E(-3, 3)$, $F(1, -1)$, and $G(-3, -5)$. Then classify the triangle by its sides. — 3. $EF = FG = 4\sqrt{2}$, $EG = 8$, isosceles

Find the measure of each angle.

4. $m\angle 1$ — 4. 70
5. $m\angle 2$ — 5. 140
6. $m\angle 3$ — 6. 50

7. Identify the congruent triangles and name their corresponding congruent angles. — 7. $\triangle DFG \cong \triangle BAC$, $\angle D \cong \angle B$, $\angle F \cong \angle A$, $\angle G \cong \angle C$

8. Identify the transformation and verify that it is a congruence transformation. — 8. Reflection; $AB = \sqrt{29}$, $BC = \sqrt{10}$, $CA = \sqrt{17}$, $QT = \sqrt{29}$, $ST = \sqrt{29}$, $QS = \sqrt{217}$, therefore $\overline{AB} \cong \overline{QT}$, $\overline{BC} \cong \overline{ST}$, and $\overline{CA} \cong \overline{QS}$ By SSS, $\triangle ABC \cong \triangle QRS$.

Assessment

Chapter 4 67 Glencoe Geometry

Geometry
Chapter 4 Resource Masters, pages 67–68

Comprehensive Assessment System

Data-Driven Decision Making

Digital assessment options are provided to create, customize, administer, and instantly score a variety of assessments. These digital solutions offer the same quality assessments and reporting as the print resources in easy-to-use technology tools.

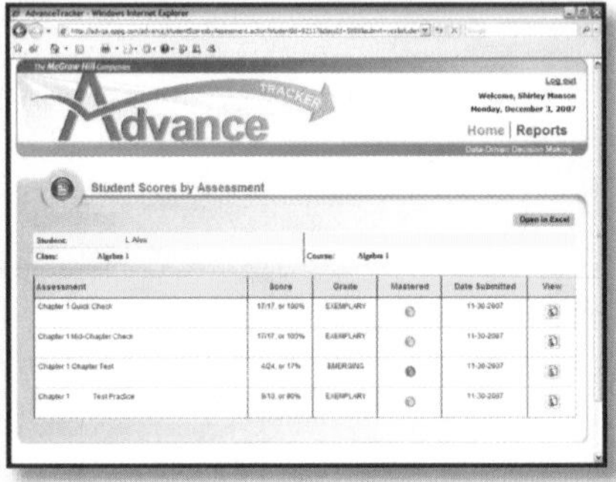

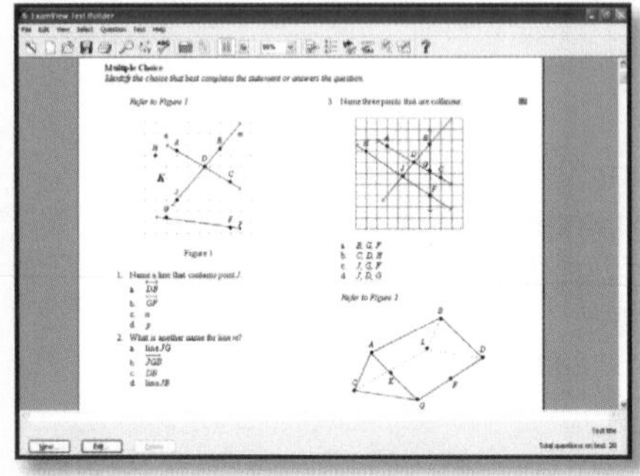

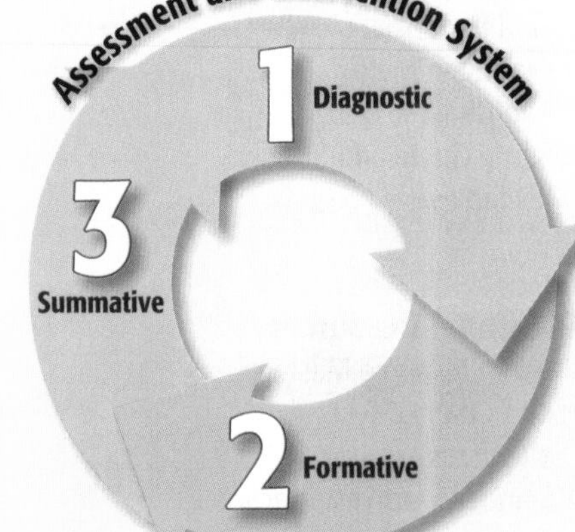

Advance Tracker helps teachers administer online tests, diagnose student achievement, and create prescriptive reports for a student or class.

Exam*View*® Assessment Suite allows teachers to create and customize their own assessment and assignments. Print in one or two columns to match state test.

1 Diagnostic

Initial Assessment Assess students' knowledge **at the beginning of the year** with the *Diagnostic and Placement Tests.* These assessments will help you determine whether your students need additional materials and resources to meet grade-level standards.

- Diagnostic and Placement Tests

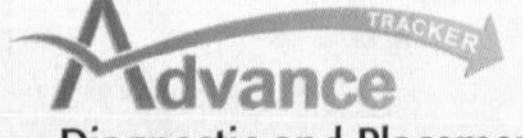

- Diagnostic and Placement Tests

Entry-Level Assessment Assess students' prior knowledge **at the beginning of a chapter or lesson.**

Math Online glencoe.com Students can complete online tests and the results are emailed to the teacher.

- Chapter Readiness

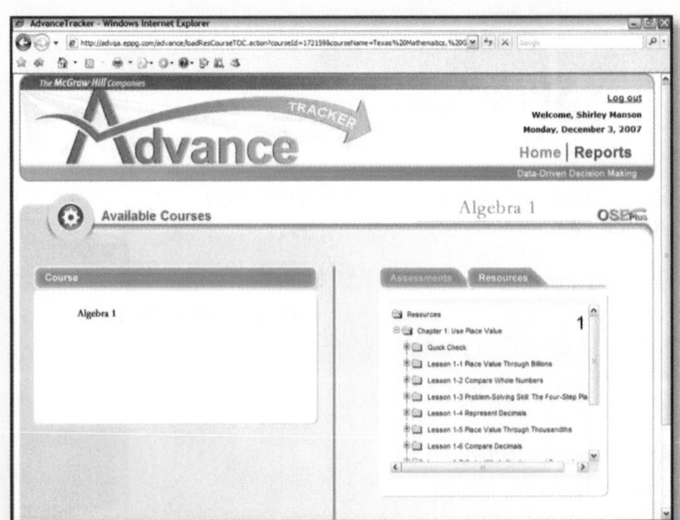

Algebra 1, Advance Tracker

2 Formative

Progress Monitoring Determine if students are progressing adequately as you teach each lesson. Use the assessments to differentiate lesson instruction and practice.

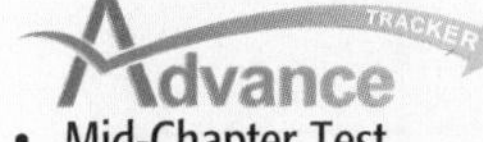

- Mid-Chapter Test
- Study Guide and Review

MindJogger, Super DVD

Math Online glencoe.com

- Self-Check Quizzes

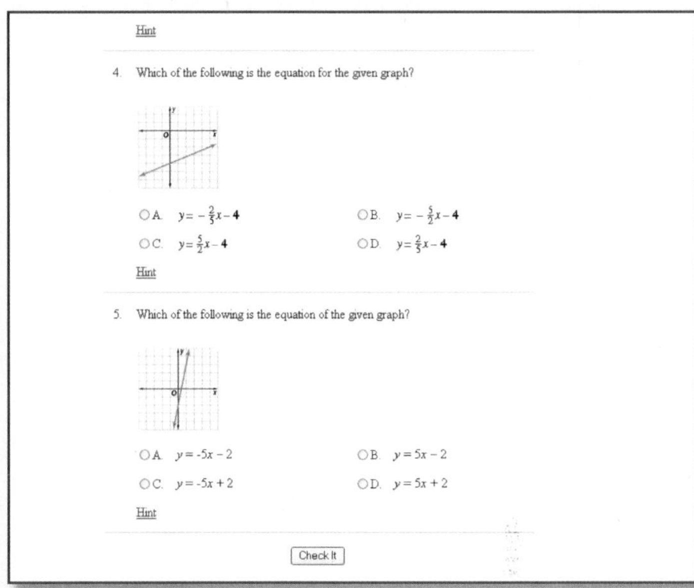

Pre-Algebra, Self-Check Quiz

3 Summative

Summative Evaluation Assess students' success in learning the concepts in each chapter.

- Chapter Tests
- Cumulative Standardized Test Practice

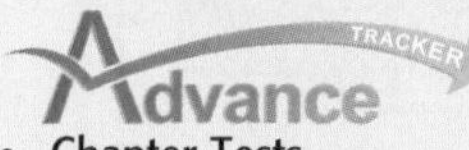

- Chapter Tests
- Cumulative Standardized Test Practice

Math Online glencoe.com

- Chapter Tests

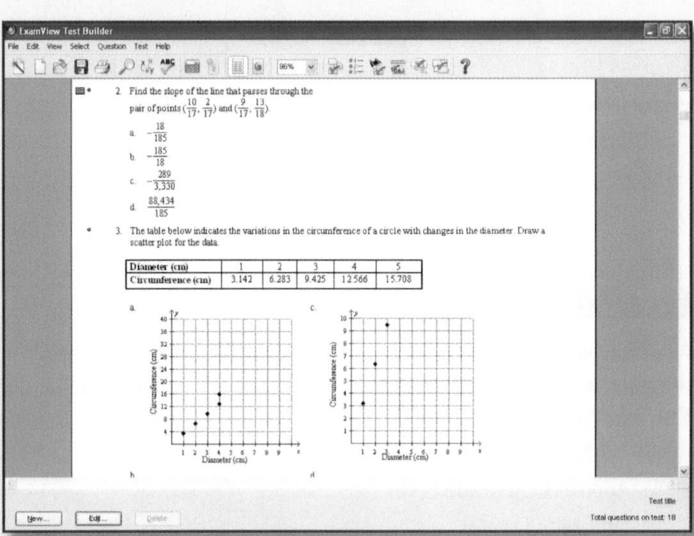

Algebra 2, ExamView® Assessment Suite

Teacher Handbook

Differentiated Instruction

Reaching All Learners

Every chapter and lesson includes suggestions for identifying and meeting your students' needs. Strategies include differentiation in pacing and student grouping, alternate approaches, ways to enhance instruction with manipulatives, questions to promote higher-order thinking, and language hints.

Personalize instruction for:

- AL Students who are approaching grade level
- ELL English language learners
- BL Students who are beyond grade level

CHAPTER 2 **Differentiated Instruction**

Option 1 Reaching All Learners AL OL BL ELL

AUDITORY/MUSICAL Have students clap twice each second for 5 seconds. Then have students clap twice each second for 10 seconds. Write the following on the board, leaving space between the equations:

Point out that each value in the second equation is double the first, but the equation is still true. Write × 2 under each side of the first equation.

Explain that when you perform the same operation on each side of a true equation, the result is a true equation.

INTRAPERSONAL Have students make a list of four items and their prices. The items can be in the price range of their choosing. Then have students calculate the price of each item after a discount of 15%.

Option 2 Approaching Level AL

Explain to students that often class scores do not all carry the same weight toward the final grade. Tell students that homework counts 10%, quizzes count 30%, tests count 40%, and the final exam counts 20%. Have students compute the final grade for a homework average of 86%, quiz average of 89%, test average of 95%, and final exam of 98%. 0.929 or 92.9% Ask students to determine if this weighted average is greater than or less than the non-weighted average? greater than

Option 3 English Learners ELL

Have students make study cards for the key concepts in this chapter. On one side of the card, students write the name of the concept. On the flip side, students give an example of how the concept is used.

Option 4 Beyond Level BL

The study of number theory can be quite interesting for students. Ask pairs of students to write and solve their own consecutive integer problems, using Example 3 in Lesson 2-3 as a guide. Then have pairs "teach" the class how to solve their problem.

Chapter 2 Linear Equations 72F

Algebra 1
Teacher Edition, page 72F

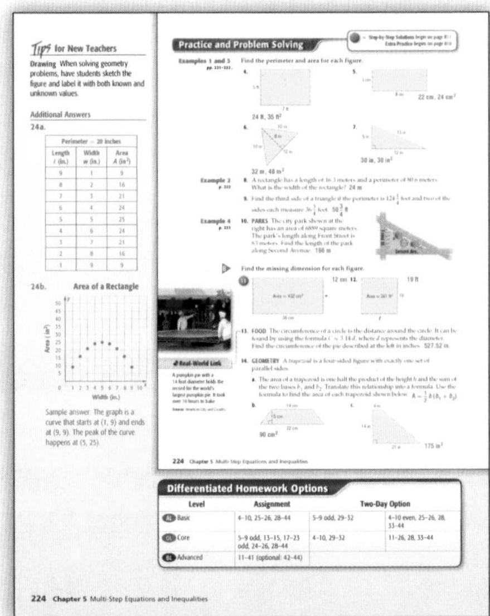

Differentiated Homework Options

Level	Assignment	Two-Day Option	
AL Basic	4–10, 25–26, 28–44	5–9 odd, 29–32	4–10 even, 25–26, 28, 33–44
OL Core	5–9 odd, 13–15, 17–23 odd, 24–26, 28–44	4–10, 29–32	11–26, 28, 33–44
BL Advanced	11–41 (optional: 42–44)		

224 Chapter 5 Multi-Step Equations and Inequalities

Pre-Algebra
Teacher Edition, page 224

Leveled Exercise Sets

The assignments for each lesson are leveled for students.

- AL Approaching Grade Level
- OL On Grade Level
- BL Beyond Grade Level

Leveled Resources

All of the blackline masters and transparencies that accompany the program, as well as all of the Teacher Edition pages, are available on the **TeacherWorks Plus™ CD-ROM.** Resources and assignments are leveled for students who are:

- AL Approaching Grade Level
- OL On Grade Level
- BL Beyond Grade Level
- ELL English Language Learners

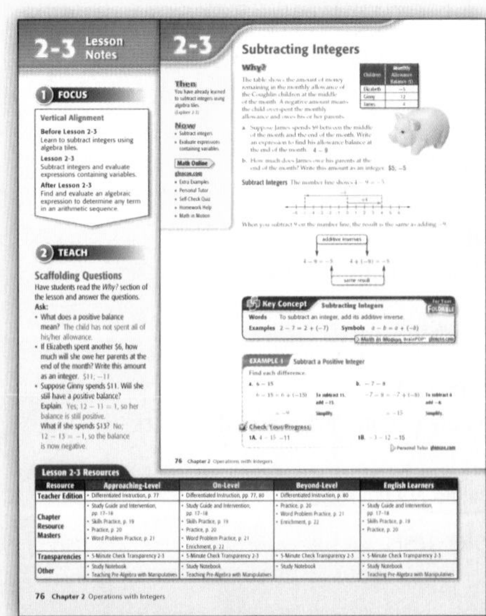

Lesson 2-3 Resources

Resource	Approaching-Level	On-Level	Beyond-Level	English Learners
Teacher Edition	• Differentiated Instruction, p. 77	• Differentiated Instruction, pp. 77, 80	• Differentiated Instruction, p. 80	
Chapter Resource Masters	• Study Guide and Intervention, pp. 17–18 • Skills Practice, p. 19 • Practice, p. 20 • Word Problem Practice, p. 21	• Study Guide and Intervention, pp. 17–18 • Skills Practice, p. 19 • Practice, p. 20 • Word Problem Practice, p. 21 • Enrichment, p. 22	• Practice, p. 20 • Word Problem Practice, p. 21 • Enrichment, p. 22	• Study Guide and Intervention, pp. 17–18 • Skills Practice, p. 19 • Practice, p. 20
Transparencies	• 5-Minute Check Transparency 2-3	• 5-Minute Check Transparency 2-3	• 5-Minute Check Transparency 2-3	• 5-Minute Check Transparency 2-3
Other	• Study Notebook • Teaching Pre-Algebra with Manipulatives	• Study Notebook • Teaching Pre-Algebra with Manipulatives	• Study Notebook	• Study Notebook • Teaching Pre-Algebra with Manipulatives

76 Chapter 2 Operations with Integers

Pre-Algebra
Teacher Edition, page 76

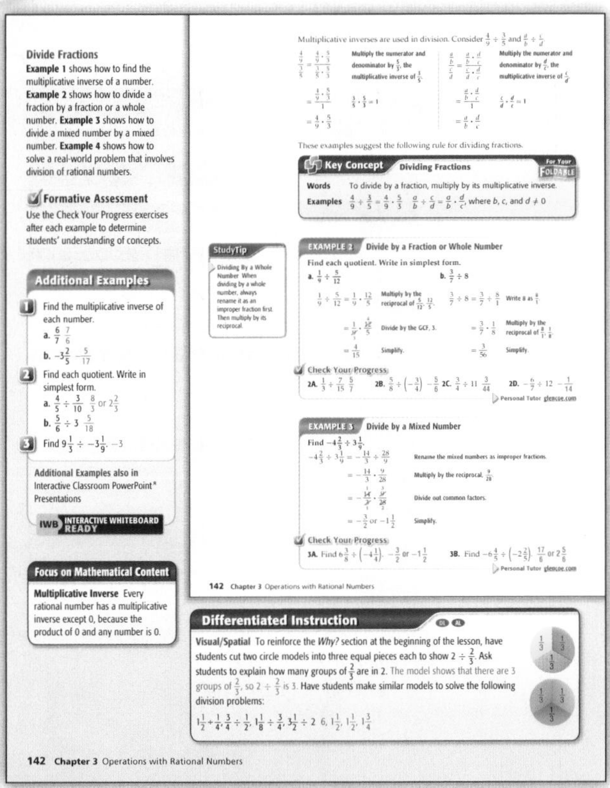

Divide Fractions
Example 1 shows how to find the multiplicative inverse of a number. **Example 2** shows how to divide a fraction by a fraction or a whole number. **Example 3** shows how to divide a mixed number by a mixed number. **Example 4** shows how to solve a real-world problem that involves division of rational numbers.

Formative Assessment
Use the Check Your Progress exercises after each example to determine students' understanding of concepts.

Additional Examples

1. Find the multiplicative inverse of each number.
   a. $\frac{6}{7}$ $\frac{7}{6}$
   b. $-3\frac{2}{5}$ $-\frac{5}{17}$
2. Find each quotient. Write in simplest form.
   a. $\frac{4}{5} \div \frac{3}{10}$ $\frac{8}{3}$ or $2\frac{2}{3}$
   b. $\frac{5}{6} \div 3$ $\frac{5}{18}$
3. Find $9\frac{1}{3} \div -3\frac{1}{9}$. -3

Additional Examples also in Interactive Classroom PowerPoint® Presentations

IWB INTERACTIVE WHITEBOARD READY

Focus on Mathematical Content
Multiplicative Inverse Every rational number has a multiplicative inverse except 0, because the product of 0 and any number is 0.

Multiplicative inverses are used in division. Consider $\frac{4}{9} \div \frac{3}{5}$ and $\frac{a}{b} \div \frac{c}{d}$.

$\frac{\frac{4}{9}}{\frac{3}{5}} = \frac{\frac{4}{9} \cdot \frac{5}{3}}{\frac{3}{5} \cdot \frac{5}{3}}$ **Multiply the numerator and denominator by $\frac{5}{3}$, the multiplicative inverse of $\frac{3}{5}$.**

$= \frac{\frac{4}{9} \cdot \frac{5}{3}}{1}$ $\frac{3}{5} \cdot \frac{5}{3} = 1$

$= \frac{4}{9} \cdot \frac{5}{3}$

$\frac{\frac{a}{b}}{\frac{c}{d}} = \frac{\frac{a}{b} \cdot \frac{d}{c}}{\frac{c}{d} \cdot \frac{d}{c}}$ **Multiply the numerator and denominator by $\frac{d}{c}$, the multiplicative inverse of $\frac{c}{d}$.**

$= \frac{\frac{a}{b} \cdot \frac{d}{c}}{1}$ $\frac{c}{d} \cdot \frac{d}{c} = 1$

$= \frac{a}{b} \cdot \frac{d}{c}$

These examples suggest the following rule for dividing fractions.

Key Concept Dividing Fractions — For Your FOLDABLE

Words To divide by a fraction, multiply by its multiplicative inverse.
Examples $\frac{4}{9} \div \frac{3}{5} = \frac{4}{9} \cdot \frac{5}{3}$ $\frac{a}{b} \div \frac{c}{d} = \frac{a}{b} \cdot \frac{d}{c}$, where b, c, and $d \neq 0$

StudyTip
Dividing By a Whole Number When dividing by a whole number, always rename it as an improper fraction first. Then multiply by its reciprocal.

EXAMPLE 2 Divide by a Fraction or Whole Number

Find each quotient. Write in simplest form.

a. $\frac{1}{9} \div \frac{5}{12}$

$\frac{1}{9} \div \frac{5}{12} = \frac{1}{9} \cdot \frac{12}{5}$ Multiply by the reciprocal of $\frac{5}{12}$, $\frac{12}{5}$.

$= \frac{1}{\cancel{9}_3} \cdot \frac{\cancel{12}^4}{5}$ Divide by the GCF, 3.

$= \frac{4}{15}$ Simplify.

b. $\frac{3}{7} \div 8$

$\frac{3}{7} \div 8 = \frac{3}{7} \div \frac{8}{1}$ Write 8 as $\frac{8}{1}$.

$= \frac{3}{7} \cdot \frac{1}{8}$ Multiply by the reciprocal of $\frac{8}{1}$, $\frac{1}{8}$.

$= \frac{3}{56}$ Simplify.

Check Your Progress
2A. $\frac{1}{3} \div \frac{7}{15}$ $\frac{5}{7}$ **2B.** $\frac{5}{8} \div \left(-\frac{3}{4}\right)$ $-\frac{5}{6}$ **2C.** $\frac{3}{4} \div 11$ $\frac{3}{44}$ **2D.** $-\frac{6}{7} \div 12$ $-\frac{1}{14}$

Personal Tutor glencoe.com

EXAMPLE 3 Divide by a Mixed Number

Find $-4\frac{2}{3} \div 3\frac{1}{9}$.

$-4\frac{2}{3} \div 3\frac{1}{9} = -\frac{14}{3} \div \frac{28}{9}$ Rename the mixed numbers as improper fractions.

$= -\frac{14}{3} \cdot \frac{9}{28}$ Multiply by the reciprocal, $\frac{9}{28}$.

$= -\frac{\cancel{14}^1}{\cancel{3}_1} \cdot \frac{\cancel{9}^3}{\cancel{28}_2}$ Divide out common factors.

$= -\frac{3}{2}$ or $-1\frac{1}{2}$ Simplify.

Check Your Progress
3A. Find $6\frac{3}{8} \div \left(-4\frac{1}{4}\right)$. $-\frac{3}{2}$ or $-1\frac{1}{2}$ **3B.** Find $-6\frac{4}{5} \div \left(-2\frac{2}{5}\right)$. $\frac{17}{6}$ or $2\frac{5}{6}$

Personal Tutor glencoe.com

142 Chapter 3 Operations with Rational Numbers

Differentiated Instruction OL AL

Visual/Spatial To reinforce the *Why?* section at the beginning of the lesson, have students cut two circle models into three equal pieces each to show $2 \div \frac{2}{3}$. Ask students to explain how many groups of $\frac{2}{3}$ are in 2. The model shows that there are 3 groups of $\frac{2}{3}$, so $2 \div \frac{2}{3}$ is 3. Have students make similar models to solve the following division problems:

$1\frac{1}{2} \div \frac{1}{4}$, $\frac{3}{4} \div \frac{1}{2}$, $1\frac{1}{8} \div \frac{3}{4}$, $3\frac{1}{2} \div 2$ 6, $1\frac{1}{2}$, $1\frac{1}{2}$, $1\frac{3}{4}$

142 Chapter 3 Operations with Rational Numbers

Pre-Algebra
Teacher Edition, page 142

Meeting Students' Needs

Diagnostic Teaching Every chapter and lesson includes suggestions for identifying and meeting your students' needs. Strategies include differentiation in pacing and student grouping, alternate approaches, ways to enhance instruction with manipulatives, questions to promote higher order thinking, and language hints.

Personalize instruction for:

- Struggling students
- English language learners
- Students with special needs
- Students who are above or beyond grade level in their comprehension of mathematics

Advanced Learners

Acceleration and Enrichment Resources and assignments that are coded for students who are above or beyond level may be used with advanced learners. The **Enrichment Masters** provide students with valuable opportunities for extending your lessons. **Differentiated Instruction** in the Teacher Edition provides additional opportunities for extension.

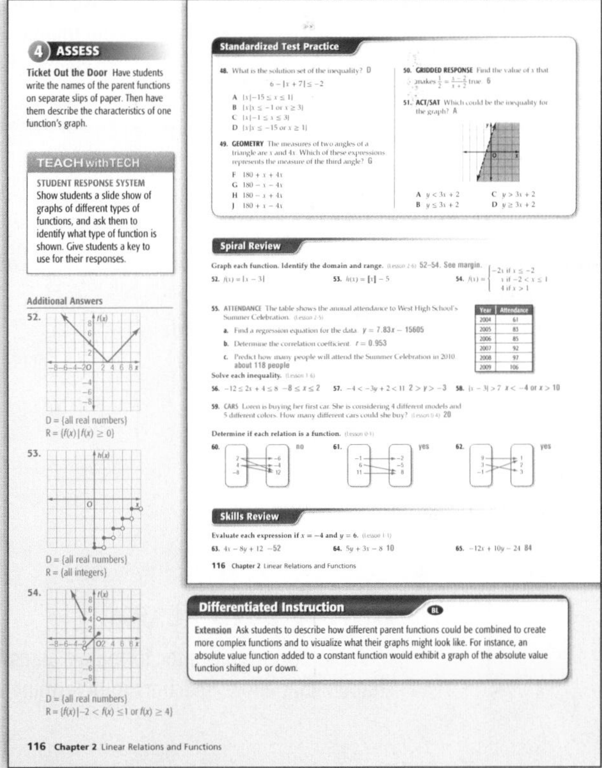

4 ASSESS

Ticket Out the Door Have students write the names of the parent functions on separate slips of paper. Then have them describe the characteristics of one function's graph.

TEACH with TECH
STUDENT RESPONSE SYSTEM Show students a slide show of graphs of different types of functions, and ask them to identify what type of function is shown. Give students a key to use for their responses.

Additional Answers

52. D = {all real numbers}
R = $\{f(x) \mid f(x) \geq 0\}$

53. D = {all real numbers}
R = {all integers}

54. D = {all real numbers}
R = $\{f(x) \mid -2 < f(x) \leq 1 \text{ or } f(x) \geq 4\}$

Standardized Test Practice

48. What is the solution set of the inequality? D

$6 - |x + 7| \leq -2$

A $\{x \mid -15 \leq x \leq 1\}$
B $\{x \mid x \leq -1 \text{ or } x \geq 3\}$
C $\{x \mid -1 \leq x \leq 3\}$
D $\{x \mid x \leq -15 \text{ or } x \geq 1\}$

49. GEOMETRY The measures of two angles of a triangle are x and $4x$. Which of these expressions represents the measure of the third angle? G

F $180 + x + 4x$
G $180 - x - 4x$
H $180 - x + 4x$
J $180 + x - 4x$

50. GRIDDED RESPONSE Find the value of x that makes $\frac{1}{2} = \frac{x-2}{x+2}$ true. 6

51. ACT/SAT Which could be the inequality for the graph? A

A $y < 3x + 2$
B $y \leq 3x + 2$
C $y > 3x + 2$
D $y \geq 3x + 2$

Spiral Review

Graph each function. Identify the domain and range. (Lesson 2-6) 52–54. See margin.

52. $f(x) = |x - 3|$ **53.** $h(x) = [\![x]\!] - 5$ **54.** $f(x) = \begin{cases} -2x \text{ if } x \leq -2 \\ x \text{ if } -2 < x \leq 1 \\ 4 \text{ if } x > 1 \end{cases}$

55. ATTENDANCE The table shows the annual attendance to West High School's Summer Celebration. (Lesson 2-5)

Year	Attendance
2004	61
2005	83
2006	85
2007	92
2008	97
2009	106

a. Find a regression equation for the data. $y = 7.83x - 15605$
b. Determine the correlation coefficient. $r = 0.953$
c. Predict how many people will attend the Summer Celebration in 2010. about 118 people

Solve each inequality. (Lesson 1-6)

56. $-12 \leq 2x + 4 \leq 8$ $-8 \leq x \leq 2$ **57.** $-4 < -3y + 2 < 11$ $2 > y > -3$ **58.** $|x - 3| > 7$ $x < -4$ or $x > 10$

59. CARS Loren is buying her first car. She is considering 4 different models and 5 different colors. How many different cars could she buy? (Lesson 0-4) 20

Determine if each relation is a function. (Lesson 0-1)

60. no **61.** yes **62.** yes

Skills Review

Evaluate each expression if $x = -4$ and $y = 6$. (Lesson 1-1)

63. $4x - 8y + 12$ -52 **64.** $5y + 3x - 8$ 10 **65.** $-12x + 10y - 24$ 84

116 Chapter 2 Linear Relations and Functions

Differentiated Instruction BL

Extension Ask students to describe how different parent functions could be combined to create more complex functions and to visualize what their graphs might look like. For instance, an absolute value function added to a constant function would exhibit a graph of the absolute value function shifted up or down.

116 Chapter 2 Linear Relations and Functions

Algebra 2
Teacher Edition, page 116

Response to Intervention

Tiered Intervention

A comprehensive approach to intervention is provided throughout the Teacher Editions, beginning with a diagnostic review and continuing with prescriptions at all three RtI levels.

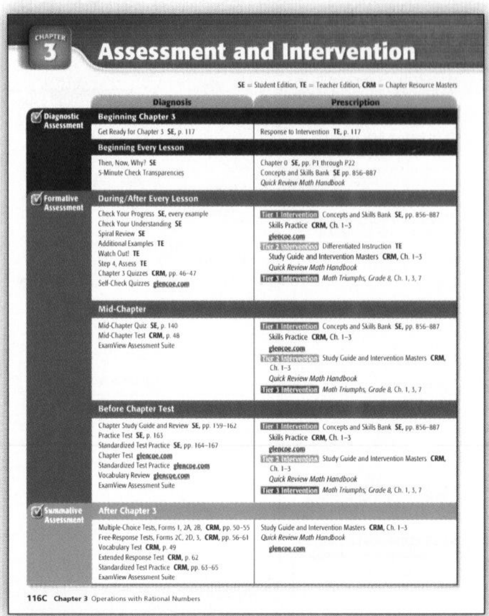

CHAPTER 3

Assessment and Intervention

SE = Student Edition, **TE** = Teacher Edition, **CRM** = Chapter Resource Masters

	Diagnosis	Prescription
Diagnostic Assessment	**Beginning Chapter 3**	
	Get Ready for Chapter 3 **SE**, p. 117	Response to Intervention **TE**, p. 117
	Beginning Every Lesson	
	Then, Now, Why? **SE** 5-Minute Check Transparencies	Chapter 0 **SE**, pp. P1 through P22 Concepts and Skills Bank **SE** pp. 856–887 *Quick Review Math Handbook*
Formative Assessment	**During/After Every Lesson**	
	Check Your Progress **SE**, every example Check Your Understanding **SE** Spiral Review **SE** Additional Examples **TE** Watch Out! **TE** Step 4, Assess **TE** Chapter 3 Quizzes **CRM**, pp. 46–47 Self-Check Quizzes **glencoe.com**	Tier 1 Intervention Concepts and Skills Bank **SE**, pp. 856–887 Skills Practice **CRM**, Ch. 1–3 **glencoe.com** Tier 2 Intervention Differentiated Instruction **TE** Study Guide and Intervention Masters **CRM**, Ch. 1–3 *Quick Review Math Handbook* Tier 3 Intervention *Math Triumphs, Grade 8*, Ch. 1, 3, 7
	Mid-Chapter	
	Mid-Chapter Quiz **SE**, p. 140 Mid-Chapter Test **CRM**, p. 48 ExamView Assessment Suite	Tier 1 Intervention Concepts and Skills Bank **SE**, pp. 856–887 Skills Practice **CRM**, Ch. 1–3 **glencoe.com** Tier 2 Intervention Study Guide and Intervention Masters **CRM**, Ch. 1–3 *Quick Review Math Handbook* Tier 3 Intervention *Math Triumphs, Grade 8*, Ch. 1, 3, 7
	Before Chapter Test	
	Chapter Study Guide and Review **SE**, pp. 159–162 Practice Test **SE**, p. 163 Standardized Test Practice **SE**, pp. 164–167 Chapter Test **glencoe.com** Standardized Test Practice **glencoe.com** Vocabulary Review **glencoe.com** ExamView Assessment Suite	Tier 1 Intervention Concepts and Skills Bank **SE**, pp. 856–887 Skills Practice **CRM**, Ch. 1–3 **glencoe.com** Tier 2 Intervention Study Guide and Intervention Masters **CRM**, Ch. 1–3 *Quick Review Math Handbook* Tier 3 Intervention *Math Triumphs, Grade 8*, Ch. 1, 3, 7
Summative Assessment	**After Chapter 3**	
	Multiple-Choice Tests, Forms 1, 2A, 2B, **CRM**, pp. 50–55 Free-Response Tests, Forms 2C, 2D, 3, **CRM**, pp. 56–61 Vocabulary Test **CRM**, p. 49 Extended Response Test **CRM**, p. 62 Standardized Test Practice **CRM**, pp. 63–65 ExamView Assessment Suite	Study Guide and Intervention Masters **CRM**, Ch. 1–3 *Quick Review Math Handbook* **glencoe.com**

116C Chapter 3 Operations with Rational Numbers

Pre-Algebra 1
Teacher Edition, page 116C

Assessment and Intervention

Each chapter includes diagnosis and prescription suggestions for each of the three tiers of intervention.

Leveled exercise sets and leveled resources

Study Guide and Intervention and differentiated instruction options

TIER 3 Intensive Intervention, ***Math Triumphs***

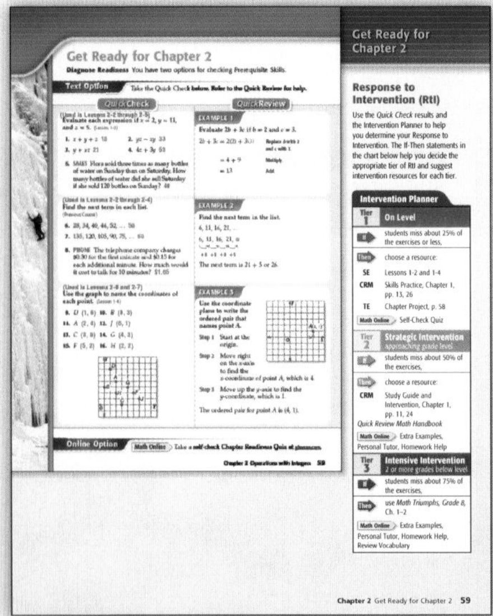

Get Ready for Chapter 2

Response to Intervention (RtI)

Use the *Quick Check* results and the Intervention Planner to help you determine your Response to Intervention. The If-Then statements in the chart below help you decide the appropriate tier of RtI and suggest intervention resources for each tier.

Intervention Planner

Tier 1 On Level
If students miss about 25% of the exercises or less,
Then choose a resource:
SE Lessons 1-2 and 1-4
CRM Skills Practice, Chapter 1, pp. 13, 26
TE Chapter Project, p. 58
Math Online Self-Check Quiz

Tier 2 Strategic Intervention approaching grade level
If students miss about 50% of the exercises,
Then choose a resource:
CRM Study Guide and Intervention, Chapter 1, pp. 11, 24
Quick Review Math Handbook
Math Online Extra Examples, Personal Tutor, Homework Help

Tier 3 Intensive Intervention 2 or more grades below level
If students miss about 75% of the exercises,
Then use *Math Triumphs, Grade 8*, Ch. 1–2
Math Online Extra Examples, Personal Tutor, Homework Help, Review Vocabulary

Chapter 2 Get Ready for Chapter 2 59

Pre-Algebra
Teacher Edition, page 59

Beginning Each Chapter

Based on the results of the *Quick Check* at the beginning of each chapter, the Intervention Planner provides suggestions for intervening with your students. The If-Then statements help you decide which tier of RtI to use.

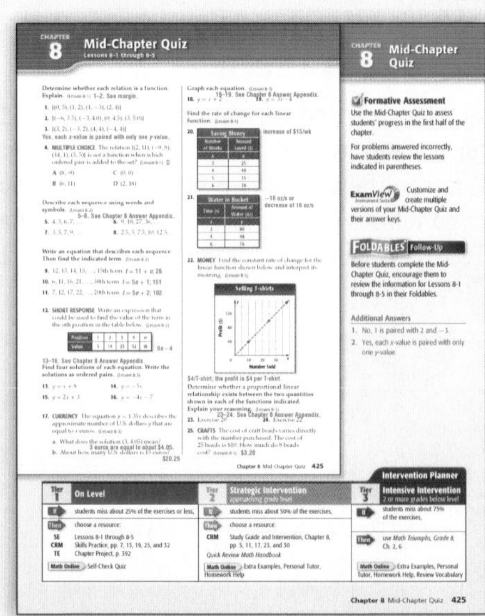

CHAPTER 8 Mid-Chapter Quiz

Formative Assessment
Use the Mid-Chapter Quiz to assess students' progress in the first half of the chapter.

For problems answered incorrectly, have students review the lessons indicated in parentheses.

ExamView Assessment Suite Customize and create multiple versions of your Mid-Chapter Quiz and their answer keys.

FOLDABLES Follow-Up
Before students complete the Mid-Chapter Quiz, encourage them to review the information for Lessons 8-1 through 8-5 in their Foldables.

Additional Answers
1. No, 1 is paired with 2 and −3.
2. Yes, each x-value is paired with only one y-value.

Intervention Planner

Tier 1 On Level	Tier 2 Strategic Intervention approaching grade level	Tier 3 Intensive Intervention 2 or more grades below level
If students miss about 25% of the exercises or less,	If students miss about 50% of the exercises,	If students miss about 75% of the exercises,
Then choose a resource: SE Lessons 8-1 through 8-5 CRM Skills Practice, pp. 7, 13, 19, 25, and 32 TE Chapter Project, p. 392 Math Online Self-Check Quiz	Then choose a resource: CRM Study Guide and Intervention, Chapter 8, pp. 5, 11, 17, 23, and 30 *Quick Review Math Handbook* Math Online Extra Examples, Personal Tutor, Homework Help	Then use *Math Triumphs, Grade 8*, Ch. 2, 6 Math Online Extra Examples, Personal Tutor, Homework Help, Review Vocabulary

Chapter 8 Mid-Chapter Quiz 425

Pre-Algebra
Teacher Edition, page 425

During Each Lesson

Multiple opportunities for formative assessment are included in each chapter that allows teachers to determine if intervention is needed.

After the Chapter

If students are still struggling after completing the chapter, students are provided with several options to help them get back on track.

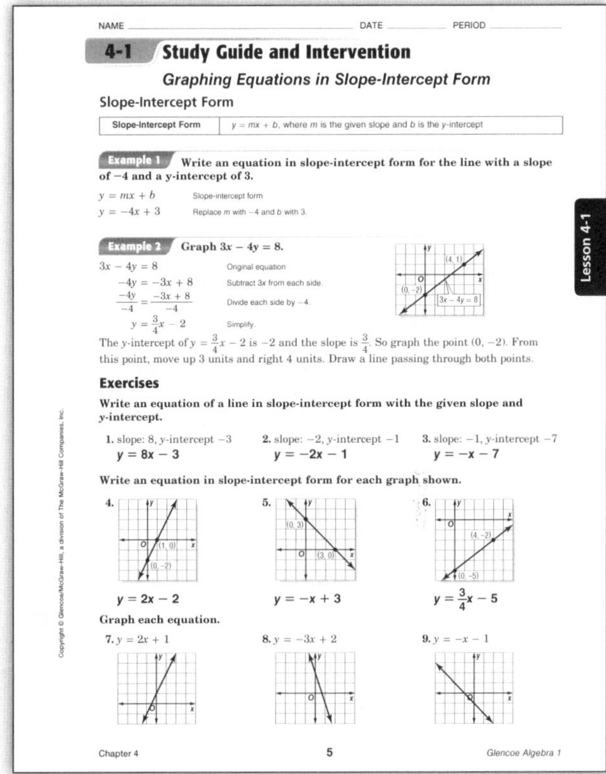

NAME ______ DATE ______ PERIOD ______

4-1 Study Guide and Intervention

Graphing Equations in Slope-Intercept Form

Slope-Intercept Form

Slope-Intercept Form	$y = mx + b$, where m is the given slope and b is the y-intercept

Example 1 **Write an equation in slope-intercept form for the line with a slope of −4 and a y-intercept of 3.**

$y = mx + b$ Slope-intercept form
$y = -4x + 3$ Replace m with −4 and b with 3.

Example 2 **Graph $3x - 4y = 8$.**

$3x - 4y = 8$ Original equation
$-4y = -3x + 8$ Subtract $3x$ from each side.
$\frac{-4y}{-4} = \frac{-3x + 8}{-4}$ Divide each side by −4.
$y = \frac{3}{4}x - 2$ Simplify.

The y-intercept of $y = \frac{3}{4}x - 2$ is −2 and the slope is $\frac{3}{4}$. So graph the point (0, −2). From this point, move up 3 units and right 4 units. Draw a line passing through both points.

Exercises

Write an equation of a line in slope-intercept form with the given slope and y-intercept.

1. slope: 8, y-intercept −3 — $y = 8x - 3$
2. slope: −2, y-intercept −1 — $y = -2x - 1$
3. slope: −1, y-intercept −7 — $y = -x - 7$

Write an equation in slope-intercept form for each graph shown.

4. $y = 2x - 2$
5. $y = -x + 3$
6. $y = \frac{3}{4}x - 5$

Graph each equation.

7. $y = 2x + 1$
8. $y = -3x + 2$
9. $y = -x - 1$

Lesson 4-1

Chapter 4 5 Glencoe Algebra 1

Algebra 1
Chapter 4 Resource Master, page 5

Study Guide and Intervention Masters

Reinforce important mathematical skills by providing additional worked-out examples and problems. This Tier 2 RtI addresses students' needs up to one year below grade level.

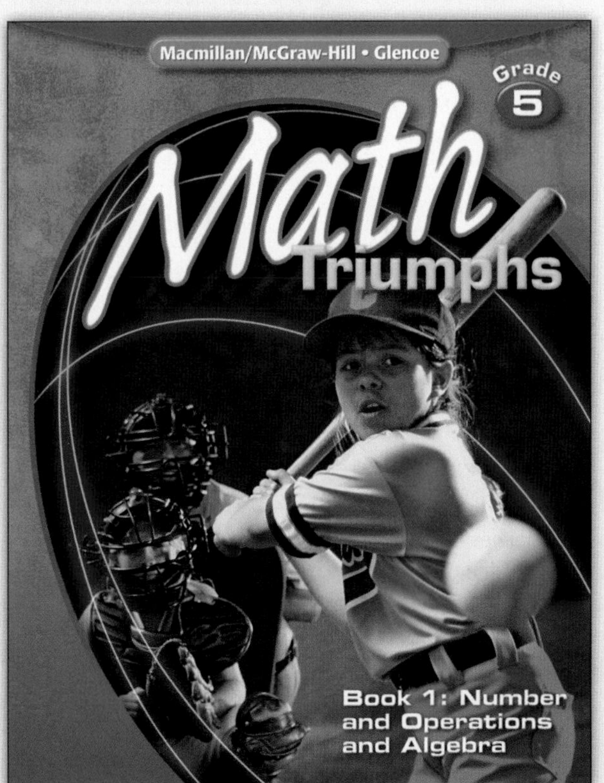

Math Triumphs
Grade 5, Book 1

Math Triumphs

For students who are two or more years below grade level, ***Math Triumphs*** provides step-by-step instruction, vocabulary support, and data-driven decision making to help students succeed.

Planning for Success

Ease of Use

A strong instructional model is provided that includes differentiated instructional options, reteaching, reinforcement, and extension options, Tips for New Teachers to help address various learners, Advanced items, and assessment linked with instruction.

Convenient Lesson Planning at Your Fingertips

The **Chapter Planner** helps you plan your instruction by showing the objectives to be covered, suggested pacing, and coverage of Focal Points.

TeacherWorks™ Plus

This electronic lesson planner contains multi-purpose management software including the Teacher Edition pages, program blackline masters, and daily calendars that make planning a snap.

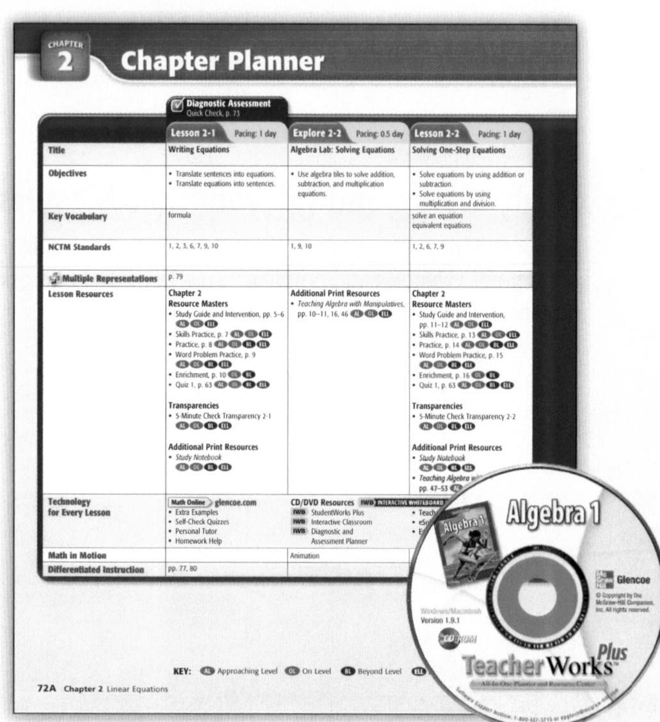

CHAPTER 2 **Chapter Planner**

Diagnostic Assessment — Quick Check, p. 73

	Lesson 2-1 (Pacing: 1 day)	Explore 2-2 (Pacing: 0.5 day)	Lesson 2-2 (Pacing: 1 day)
Title	**Writing Equations**	**Algebra Lab: Solving Equations**	**Solving One-Step Equations**
Objectives	• Translate sentences into equations. • Translate equations into sentences.	• Use algebra tiles to solve addition, subtraction, and multiplication equations.	• Solve equations by using addition or subtraction. • Solve equations by using multiplication and division.
Key Vocabulary	formula		solve an equation equivalent equations
NCTM Standards	1, 2, 3, 6, 7, 9, 10	1, 9, 10	1, 2, 6, 7, 9
Multiple Representations	p. 79		
Lesson Resources	**Chapter 2 Resource Masters** • Study Guide and Intervention, pp. 5–6 AL OL ELL • Skills Practice, p. 7 AL OL ELL • Practice, p. 8 AL OL BL ELL • Word Problem Practice, p. 9 AL OL BL ELL • Enrichment, p. 10 OL BL • Quiz 1, p. 63 AL OL BL ELL **Transparencies** • 5-Minute Check Transparency 2-1 AL OL BL ELL **Additional Print Resources** • *Study Notebook* AL OL BL ELL	**Additional Print Resources** • *Teaching Algebra with Manipulatives*, pp. 10–11, 16, 46 AL OL ELL	**Chapter 2 Resource Masters** • Study Guide and Intervention, pp. 11–12 AL OL ELL • Skills Practice, p. 13 AL OL ELL • Practice, p. 14 AL OL BL ELL • Word Problem Practice, p. 15 AL OL BL ELL • Enrichment, p. 16 OL BL • Quiz 1, p. 63 AL OL BL ELL **Transparencies** • 5-Minute Check Transparency 2-2 AL OL BL ELL **Additional Print Resources** • *Study Notebook* AL OL BL ELL • *Teaching Algebra w*… pp. 47–53
Technology for Every Lesson	Math Online glencoe.com • Extra Examples • Self-Check Quizzes • Personal Tutor • Homework Help	CD/DVD Resources IWB INTERACTIVE WHITEBOARD IWB StudentWorks Plus IWB Interactive Classroom IWB Diagnostic and Assessment Planner	• Teach… • eS… • E…
Math in Motion		Animation	
Differentiated Instruction	pp. 77, 80		

KEY: AL Approaching Level OL On Level BL Beyond Level ELL

72A Chapter 2 Linear Equations

Algebra 1
Teacher Edition, page 72A

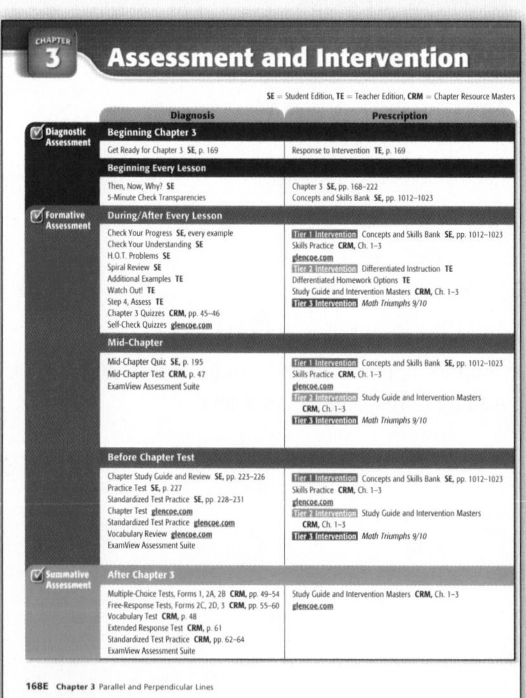

CHAPTER 3 **Assessment and Intervention**

SE = Student Edition, **TE** = Teacher Edition, **CRM** = Chapter Resource Masters

	Diagnosis	Prescription
Diagnostic Assessment	**Beginning Chapter 3**	
	Get Ready for Chapter 3 **SE**, p. 169	Response to Intervention **TE**, p. 169
	Beginning Every Lesson	
	Then, Now, Why? **SE** 5-Minute Check Transparencies	Chapter 3 **SE**, pp. 168–222 Concepts and Skills Bank **SE**, pp. 1012–1023
Formative Assessment	**During/After Every Lesson**	
	Check Your Progress **SE**, every example Check Your Understanding **SE** H.O.T. Problems **SE** Spiral Review **SE** Additional Examples **TE** Watch Out! **TE** Step 4, Assess **TE** Chapter 3 Quizzes **CRM**, pp. 45–46 Self-Check Quizzes glencoe.com	Tier 1 Intervention Concepts and Skills Bank **SE**, pp. 1012–1023 Skills Practice **CRM**, Ch. 1–3 glencoe.com Tier 2 Intervention Differentiated Instruction **TE** Differentiated Homework Options **TE** Study Guide and Intervention Masters **CRM**, Ch. 1–3 Tier 3 Intervention *Math Triumphs 9/10*
	Mid-Chapter	
	Mid-Chapter Quiz **SE**, p. 195 Mid-Chapter Test **CRM**, p. 47 ExamView Assessment Suite	Tier 1 Intervention Concepts and Skills Bank **SE**, pp. 1012–1023 Skills Practice **CRM**, Ch. 1–3 glencoe.com Tier 2 Intervention Study Guide and Intervention Masters **CRM**, Ch. 1–3 Tier 3 Intervention *Math Triumphs 9/10*
	Before Chapter Test	
	Chapter Study Guide and Review **SE**, pp. 223–226 Practice Test **SE**, p. 227 Standardized Test Practice **SE**, pp. 228–231 Chapter Test glencoe.com Standardized Test Practice glencoe.com Vocabulary Review glencoe.com ExamView Assessment Suite	Tier 1 Intervention Concepts and Skills Bank **SE**, pp. 1012–1023 Skills Practice **CRM**, Ch. 1–3 glencoe.com Tier 2 Intervention Study Guide and Intervention Masters **CRM**, Ch. 1–3 Tier 3 Intervention *Math Triumphs 9/10*
Summative Assessment	**After Chapter 3**	
	Multiple-Choice Tests, Forms 1, 2A, 2B **CRM**, pp. 49–54 Free-Response Tests, Forms 2C, 2D, 3 **CRM**, pp. 55–60 Vocabulary Test **CRM**, p. 48 Extended Response Test **CRM**, p. 61 Standardized Test Practice **CRM**, pp. 62–64 ExamView Assessment Suite	Study Guide and Intervention Masters **CRM**, Ch. 1–3 glencoe.com

168E Chapter 3 Parallel and Perpendicular Lines

Geometry,
Teacher Edition, page 168E

Vertical Alignment

Topics are presented to build upon prior grade level skills and concepts and to serve as a foundation for future topics.

Professional Development

Targeted professional development has been articulated throughout the program. Actual classroom video clips are especially helpful when planning lessons and differentiating instruction. See page T32 for more information.

Four-Step Teaching Plan

Organize your instruction as you **Focus** and **Teach** and help your students **Practice** and **Assess** what they've learned.

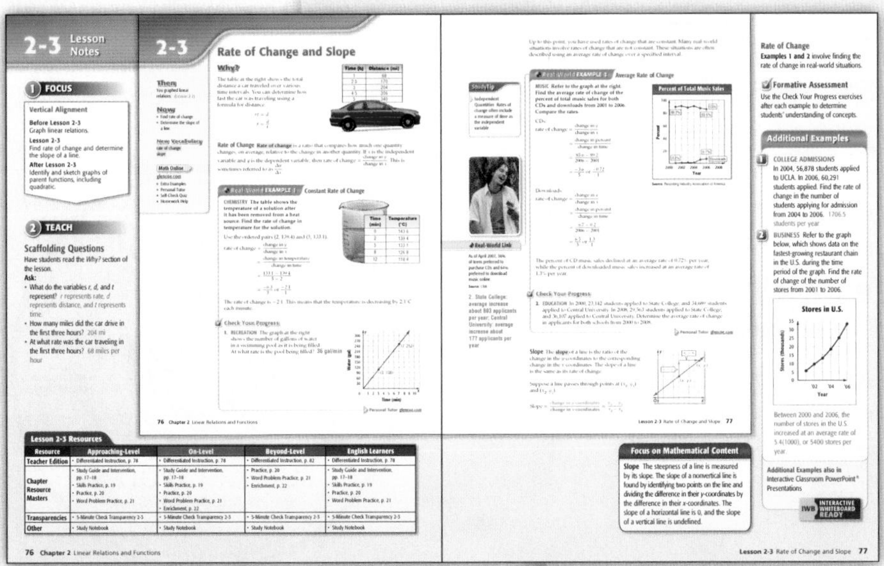

Algebra 2
Teacher Edition, pages 76–77

Vertical Alignment

Vertical Alignment at the beginning of each lesson shows the objectives that lead into and follow the current lesson's content for a coherent PreK–12 scope and sequence.

Scaffolding Questions

Each lesson contains **Scaffolding Questions** for you to use to help students investigate and understand the main ideas of the lesson.

Additional Examples

Each **Additional Example** mirrors the example in the Student Edition. The Additional Examples are also available as a PowerPoint® presentation on the **Interactive Classroom** CD-ROM.

Differentiated Homework Options

Because most classrooms include students with a wide range of ability levels, **Differentiated Homework Options** allow you to customize your assignments.

Assessment Activities

Formative Assessment activities provide alternate ways to determine student comprehension at the end of each lesson.

- **Ticket Out the Door** Students must answer the given question and hand it to the teacher as they leave the classroom.
- **Yesterday's News** Students connect what they learned today to yesterday's lesson.
- **Crystal Ball** Students predict how today's lesson will relate to the next lesson.
- **Name the Math** Students tell what mathematics is used in a problem.

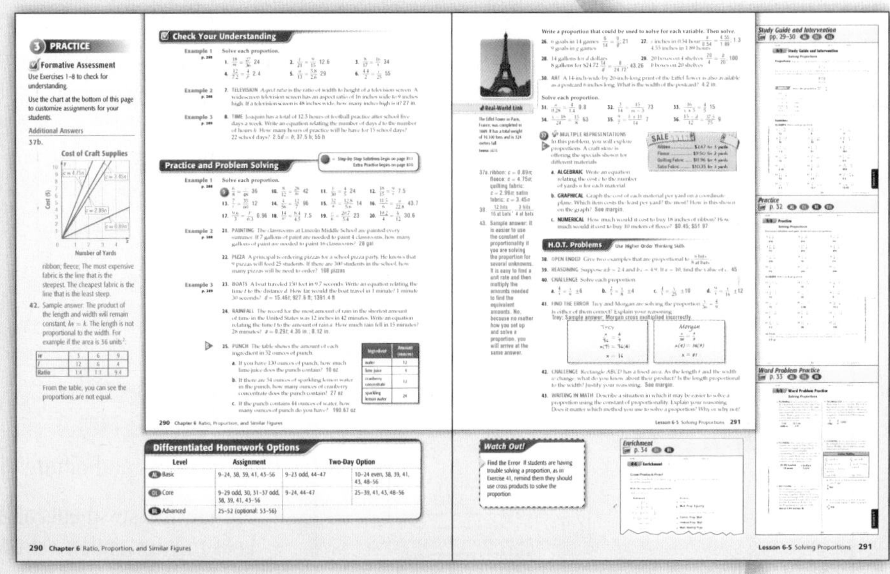

Pre-Algebra
Teacher Edition, pages 290–291

Planning for Success

State-of-the-Art Technology

Fully integrated technology resources are provided for teachers, students, and parents.

For Teachers

TeacherWorks™ Plus is your all-in-one planner and resource center.

- entire Teacher Edition
- all print ancillaries
- electronic lesson planner

Exam*View*® Assessment Suite allows teachers to create and customize their own assessment and assignments.

New features:
- correlated to state standards
- online content update
- one- or two-column formatting

Use **Interactive Classroom** to guide instruction using PowerPoint ™.

- in-class examples
- 5-Minute Check Transparencies
- Math in Motion
- links to **Math Online**

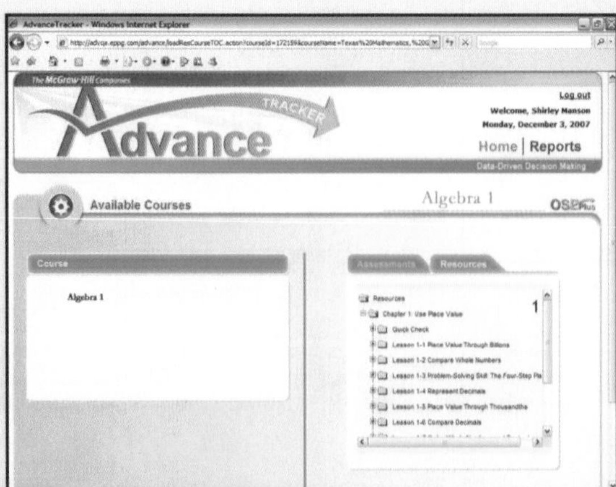

Algebra 1

Advance Tracker Learner Management System helps you track progress and differentiate your instruction.

- formative assessments aligned to standards
- links to intervention help

For Students

StudentWorks™ Plus is your students' backpack solution.

- entire Student Edition
- all student worksheets
- links to **Math Online**

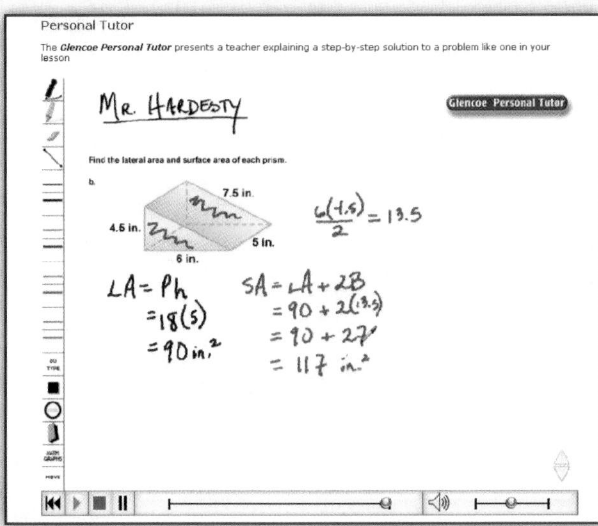

Pre-Algebra
Web site, Personal Tutor

Math Online provides a wealth of resources–convenient for students and parents!

- self-check quizzes
- Personal Tutor
- Math in Motion
- eGlossary (14 languages)
- and much, much more!

Math Online The **eBook** is easy to use, easy to read, and packed with features.

- links to online study tools and resources right from the page
- includes audio

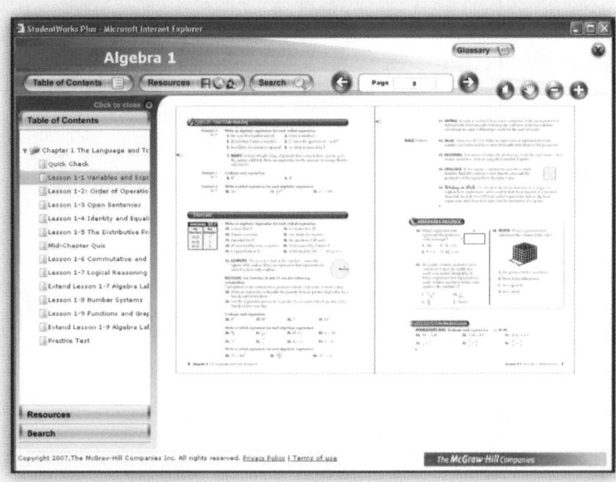

Algebra 1
eBook, pages 8–9

Math Online Students can access a link to **Hotmath.com** at **glencoe.com**. There, they will find complete step-by-step solutions to most odd-numbered exercises.

PreK–12 Data-Driven Professional Development

McGraw-Hill Professional Development (MHPD) provides a comprehensive plan for mathematics that is fully aligned and articulated with ***Math Connects PreK–8*** and the ***Glencoe Mathematics*** high school series.

Professional Development Needs	Online Courses	DVD Workshops	Video Library	Program Walkthroughs	Ready-Access Math
Has immediate classroom application	✓	✓	✓	✓	✓
Builds content knowledge	✓	✓			✓
Promotes best teaching practices		✓	✓		
Supports new and experienced teachers	✓	✓	✓	✓	✓
Allows customization of courses	✓	✓			✓
Can be self-paced	✓	✓		✓	✓
Adaptable for various timeframes	✓	✓	✓	✓	✓
Is grade-level specific			✓	✓	✓
Promotes a learning community	✓	✓			✓
Provides vertically-aligned content	✓	✓	✓		✓
Helps with RtI (Response to Intervention), Tiers 1–3	✓	✓	✓		✓

Use students' mathematics achievement data to help develop a targeted Professional Development Plan.

Accredited Online Courses

(available for purchase)

- Watch video clips of math classrooms. Complete interactive exercises. Develop electronic portfolios.
- Complete each 3- to 5-hour online module one segment at a time.
- University credit (additional tuition charge)

DVD Workshops

- Watch video clips of classroom mathematics lessons and commentaries by leading educators.
- Complete lessons and activities.

MHPD Online

- Access this online Professional Development resource for K–12 educators.
- Link to relevant Web sites.
- Download grade-level student resources.

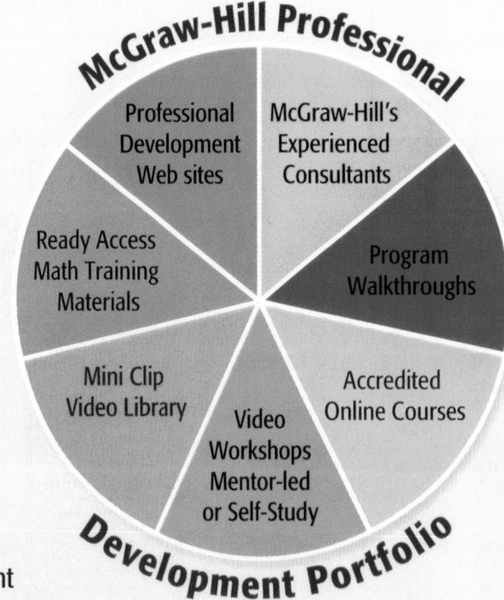

Video Library Math Online

- Access hundreds of video clips.
- See clips that illustrate mathematics content and instructional strategies.
- Watch demonstrations or commentaries by math specialists.

Program Walkthroughs

- Walk through program features of the Student Edition, Teacher Edition, and program ancillaries, including technology options.
- Online or video-enhanced DVD

Ready-Access Math, Personalized Professional Development

- Access training materials for nearly 300 mathematics professional development lessons.
- Create a customized sequence of professional development sessions.
- Deliver 45–60 minute after-school professional development sessions.

Teacher Edition

Glencoe McGraw-Hill

Pre-Algebra

Welcome to *Pre-Algebra*

Authors

Carter • Cuevas • Day • Malloy • Molix-Bailey • Price • Willard

McGraw Hill Glencoe

CHAPTER 0

Start Smart: Preparing for Pre-Algebra

Jack Sullivan/Alamy

Chapter 0 Support

Helping You Learn

- **Vocabulary** P8, P12, P18
- **Exercises** P7, P10, P13, P15, P17, P19, P21

Math Online

- **Personal Tutor** P7, P8, P9, P12, P13, P14, P16, P18, P19, P20, P21
- **Self-Check Quizzes** P6, P8, P12, P14, P16, P18, P20
- **Extra Examples** P6, P8, P12, P14, P16, P18, P20
- **Homework Help** P6, P8, P12, P14, P16, P18, P20

Unit 1
Rational Numbers and Equations

CHAPTER 1

The Tools of Algebra

Anthony-Masterson/Getty Images

Chapter 1 Support

Helping You Learn

- **New Vocabulary** 5, 10, 18, 25, 33, 40
- **Key Concepts** 6, 11, 18, 19, 34, 41
- **Check Your Progress** 5, 6, 7, 11, 12, 19, 20, 26, 27, 33, 34, 40, 41, 42
- **Check Your Understanding** 7, 13, 21, 35, 42
- **Multiple Representations** 8, 14, 28, 29, 35, 36, 44
- **H.O.T. Problems** 9, 14, 22, 29, 36, 45
- **Skills Check** 15, 23, 30, 37, 46

Math Online

- **Math in Motion: Animation** 3, 25
- **Math in Motion: Interactive Labs** 17
- **Personal Tutor** 5, 6, 7, 12, 13, 19, 20, 26, 27, 33, 34, 40, 41, 42
- **Self-Check Quizzes** 5, 11, 18, 25, 33, 40
- **Extra Examples** 5, 11, 18, 25, 33, 40
- **Homework Help** 5, 11, 18, 25, 33, 40

Preparing for Testing

- **Extended Response** 16, 37, 57
- **Multiple Choice** 9, 16, 21, 23, 24, 30, 37, 46, 53, 55, 56
- **Short/Gridded Response** 9, 23, 30, 57
- **Worked Out Example** 20

Table of Contents

Unit 1
Rational Numbers and Equations

CHAPTER 2

Operations with Integers

Visionsof America/Joe Sohm/Getty Images

Chapter 2 Support

Helping You Study

- **New Vocabulary** 61, 69, 76, 90, 96, 101
- **Key Concepts** 63, 69, 70, 71, 76, 83, 84, 90, 91, 101
- **Check Your Progress** 61, 62, 63, 69, 70, 71, 76, 77, 78, 83, 84, 85, 90, 91, 92, 96, 97, 102, 103
- **Check Your Understanding** 64, 72, 78, 85, 92, 98
- **Multiple Representations** 66, 79, 87, 94, 99, 105
- **H.O.T. Problems** 65, 73, 79, 87, 94, 99, 105
- **Skills Check** 66, 74, 80, 88, 95, 100, 106

Math Online

- **Math in Motion: Animation** 59, 82
- **Math in Motion: BrainPOPs** 76
- **Math in Motion: Interactive Labs** 96
- **Personal Tutor** 61, 62, 63, 69 70, 71, 72, 76, 77, 78, 83, 84, 85, 90, 91, 92, 96, 97, 102, 103,
- **Self-Check Quizzes** 61, 69, 76, 83, 90, 96, 101
- **Extra Examples** 61, 69, 76, 83, 90, 96, 101
- **Homework Help** 61, 69, 76, 83, 90, 96, 101

Preparing for Testing

- **Extended Response** 66, 74, 95, 100, 115
- **Multiple Choice** 66, 74, 80, 81, 88, 95, 100, 102, 106, 111, 113, 114
- **Short/Gridded Response** 80, 88, 106, 113, 115
- **Worked Out Example** 102

Table of Contents

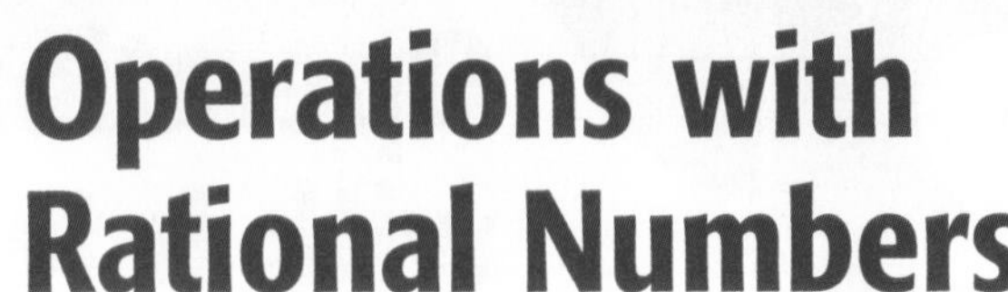

Unit 1
Rational Numbers and Equations

CHAPTER 3

Operations with Rational Numbers

George Tiedemann/GT Images/CORBIS

Chapter 3 Support

Helping You Study

Math Online

Preparing for Testing

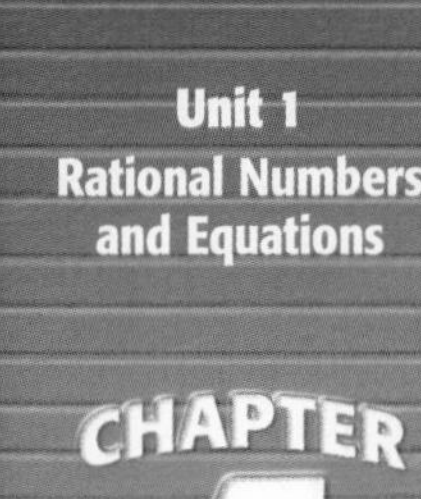

Expressions and Equations

Chapter 4 Support

Helping You Study

- **New Vocabulary** 171, 178, 184, 199
- **Key Concepts** 171, 184, 185, 191, 193
- **Check Your Progress** 171, 172, 173, 178, 179, 180, 185, 186, 191, 192, 193, 199, 200, 201, 205, 206
- **Check Your Understanding** 173, 180, 187, 194, 202, 207
- **Multiple Representations** 175, 182, 188, 195, 203, 208
- **H.O.T. Problems** 175, 182, 188, 195, 203, 208
- **Skills Check** 176, 183, 189, 196, 204, 209

Math Online

- **Math in Motion: Animation** 169, 191
- **Math in Motion: BrainPOPs** 171
- **Math in Motion: Interactive Labs** 191
- **Personal Tutor** 171, 172, 173, 178, 179, 180, 185, 186, 191, 192, 193, 199, 200, 201, 205
- **Self-Check Quizzes** 171, 184, 191, 199, 205, 206
- **Extra Examples** 171, 184, 191, 199, 205, 206,
- **Homework Help** 171, 184, 191, 199, 205, 206

Preparing for Testing

- **Extended Response** 176, 196, 209, 217
- **Multiple Choice** 176, 183, 189, 190, 196, 202, 204, 209, 213, 215, 216
- **Short/Gridded Response** 183, 189, 204, 217
- **Worked Out Example** 201

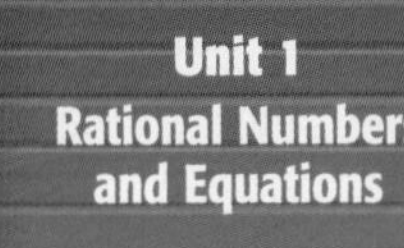

Multi-Step Equations and Inequalities

Alaska Stock

Chapter 5 Support

Helping You Study

- **New Vocabulary** 221, 234, 248
- **Key Concepts** 221, 222, 235, 241, 242, 244
- **Check Your Progress** 221, 222, 223, 229, 230, 234, 235, 236, 241, 242, 243, 244, 248, 249, 250
- **Check Your Understanding** 223, 231, 237, 244, 251
- **Multiple Representations** 225, 246
- **H.O.T. Problems** 225, 232, 238, 246, 252
- **Skills Check** 226, 233, 239, 247, 253

Math Online

- **Math in Motion: Animation** 219
- **Personal Tutor** 221, 222, 223, 229, 230, 231, 234, 235, 236, 241, 242, 243, 244, 248, 249, 250
- **Self-Check Quizzes** 221, 229, 234, 241, 248
- **Extra Examples** 221, 229, 234, 241, 248
- **Homework Help** 221, 229, 234, 241, 248

Preparing for Testing

- **Extended Response** 247, 261
- **Multiple Choice** 226, 233, 239, 240, 247, 251, 253, 257, 258, 259, 260
- **Short/Gridded Response** 226, 233, 239, 253, 261
- **Worked Out Example** 249

Table of Contents

Unit 2
Proportions and Similarity

CHAPTER 6

Ratio, Proportion, and Similar Figures

Steffen Schmidt/epa/CORBIS

Chapter 6 Support

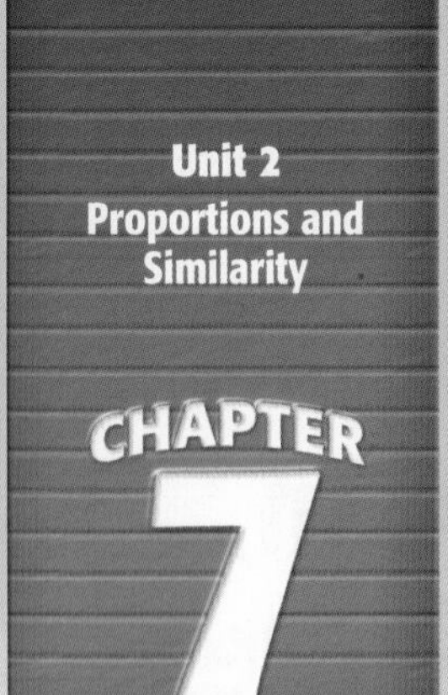

Percent

Chapter 7 Support

Helping You Study

Math Online

Preparing for Testing

Unit 3
Linear and Nonlinear Functions

CHAPTER 8

Linear Functions and Graphing

Chapter 8 Support

Helping You Study

- **New Vocabulary** 395, 401, 406, 412, 418, 429, 433, 441, 448, 453
- **Key Concepts** 401, 408, 414, 420, 421, 428, 433
- **Check Your Progress** 395, 396, 397, 401, 402, 406, 407, 408, 412, 413, 414, 419, 420, 421, 427, 428, 429, 433, 434, 435, 441, 442, 443, 448, 449, 453, 454, 455
- **Check Your Understanding** 397, 403, 409, 415, 422, 429, 435, 444, 450, 455
- **Multiple Representations** 404, 410, 430, 437, 446, 451, 456
- **H.O.T. Problems** 399, 404, 410, 416, 423, 430, 437, 446, 451, 456

Math Online

- **Math in Motion: Animation** 393
- **Math in Motion: BrainPOPs** 433
- **Math in Motion: Interactive Labs** 406
- **Personal Tutor** 395, 396, 397, 401, 402, 406, 407, 408, 412, 413, 414, 419, 420, 421, 427, 428, 429, 433, 434, 435, 441, 442, 443, 448, 449, 453, 454, 455
- **Self-Check Quizzes** 395, 401, 406, 412, 418, 427, 433, 441, 448, 453
- **Extra Examples** 395, 401, 406, 412, 418, 427, 433, 441, 448, 453
- **Homework Help** 395, 401, 406, 412, 418, 427, 433, 441, 448, 453

Preparing for Testing

- **Extended Response** 400, 411, 424, 438, 452, 455, 464, 465, 467
- **Multiple Choice** 400, 405, 411, 417, 424, 425, 431, 438, 447, 452, 457, 463, 466
- **Short/Gridded Response** 405, 417, 425, 431, 447, 457, 466
- **Worked Out Example** 454

Powers and Nonlinear Functions

James Marshall/CORBIS

Chapter 9 Support

Table of Contents

Unit 4
Two- and Three-Dimensional Space

CHAPTER 10

Real Numbers and Right Triangles

Bilderbuch/Design Pics/CORBIS

Chapter 10 Support

Helping You Study

Math Online

Preparing for Testing

Table of Contents

Distance and Angle

Chapter 11 Support

Helping You Study

- **New Vocabulary** 589, 598, 605, 611, 617, 624, 631, 636, 644
- **Key Concepts** 589, 590, 598, 611, 618, 624, 625, 626, 631, 636, 638, 645
- **Check Your Progress** 590, 591, 599, 600, 605, 606, 607, 612, 617, 618, 619, 624, 625, 626, 631, 632, 637, 638, 644, 645
- **Check Your Understanding** 592, 601, 608, 613, 620, 627, 633, 638, 646
- **Multiple Representations** 594, 609, 614, 621, 629, 634, 640, 648
- **H.O.T. Problems** 594, 603, 609, 614, 621, 629, 634, 640, 648

Math Online

- **Math in Motion:** Animation 587, 611
- **Math in Motion: Interactive Labs** 631
- **Personal Tutor** 590, 591, 599, 600, 605, 606, 607, 612, 617, 618, 619, 624, 625, 626, 631, 632, 637, 638, 644, 645,
- **Self-Check Quizzes** 589, 598, 605, 611, 617, 624, 631, 636, 644
- **Extra Examples** 589, 598, 605, 611, 617, 624, 631, 636, 644
- **Homework Help** 589, 598, 605, 611, 617, 624, 631, 636, 644

Preparing for Testing

- **Extended Response** 595, 604, 610, 630, 635, 641, 659
- **Multiple Choice** 595, 604, 610, 615, 620, 622, 623, 630, 635, 641, 649, 655, 658
- **Short/ Gridded Response** 615, 622, 649, 656, 657, 659
- **Worked Out Example 618**

Unit 4
Two- and Three-Dimensional Space

CHAPTER 12

Surface Area and Volume

Chapter 12 Support

Unit 5
Data Sets

CHAPTER 13

Statistics and Probability

Greg Von Doersten/Aurora/Getty Images

Chapter 13 Support

Christian Liewig/Liewig Media Sports/CORBIS

Looking Ahead to Algebra 1

Student Handbook

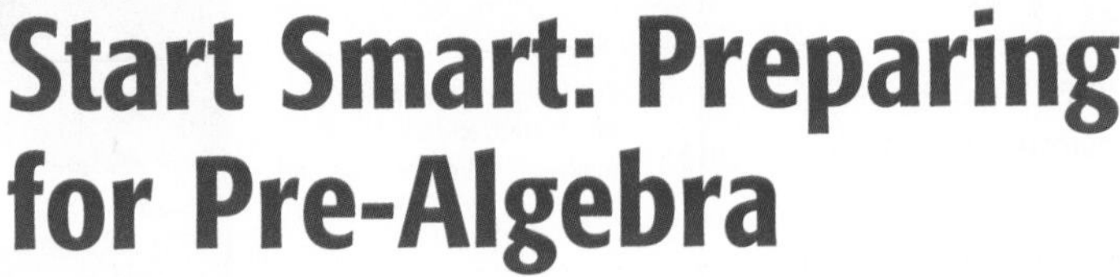

Start Smart: Preparing for Pre-Algebra

Chapter 0 contains lessons on topics from previous courses. You can use this chapter in various ways.

- Begin the school year by taking the Pretest. If you need additional review, complete the lessons in this chapter. To verify that you have successfully reviewed the topics, take the Posttest.
- As you work through the text, you may find that there are topics you need to review. When this happens, complete the individual lessons that you need.
- Use this chapter for reference. When you have questions about any of these topics, flip back to this chapter to review definitions or key concepts.

CHAPTER 0 Notes

Using Chapter 0

The concepts presented in Chapter 0 are review from previous courses. You may wish to use all or some of the chapter at the beginning of the school year to refresh students' skills. Or you may wish to begin with Chapter 1 and use the Chapter 0 lessons as needed to reinforce prerequisite skills as you progress through the program.

CHAPTER 0 Start Smart: Preparing for Pre-Algebra

Then

You have already written, interpreted, and used mathematical expressions and equations. (Previous Course)

Now

- Use the four-step plan to solve problems.
- Add, subtract, multiply, and divide decimals.
- Write a verbal rule to represent a pattern or sequence.

Why?

BEGINNINGS You are getting ready to start Pre-Algebra. Like the beginning of a race, you need to be prepared for what is ahead. This chapter will "rev-up" your skills!

P2 **Chapter 0** Start Smart: Preparing for Pre-Algebra

Get Started on Chapter 0

You will review several concepts, skills, and vocabulary terms as you study this chapter. To get ready, identify important terms and organize your resources.

FOLDABLES® Study Organizer

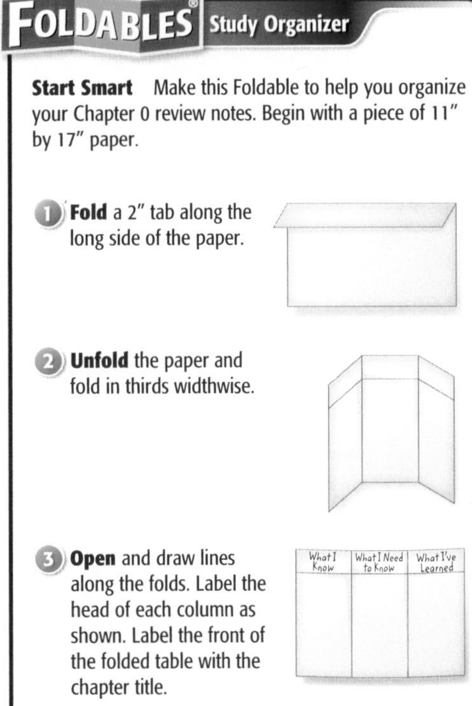

Start Smart Make this Foldable to help you organize your Chapter 0 review notes. Begin with a piece of 11″ by 17″ paper.

1. **Fold** a 2″ tab along the long side of the paper.
2. **Unfold** the paper and fold in thirds widthwise.
3. **Open** and draw lines along the folds. Label the head of each column as shown. Label the front of the folded table with the chapter title.

Math Online

- Study the chapter online
- Explore **Math in Motion**
- Get extra help from your own **Personal Tutor**
- Use **Extra Examples** from additional help
- Take a **Self-Check Quiz**
- **Review Vocabulary** in fun ways

New Vocabulary

English		Español
look for a pattern	• p. P8 •	buscar un patrón
guess and check	• p. P8 •	adivina y verifica
make a table	• p. P9 •	trabajar a la inverse
work backward	• p. P9 •	hacer una tabla
decimal	• p. P12 •	decimal
annex	• p. P12 •	anexionar
customary system	• p. P18 •	sistema inglés
metric system	• p. P18 •	sistema métrico
data	• p. P20 •	datos
pictograph	• p. P20 •	pictograma
line graph	• p. P20 •	gráfica lineal
bar graph	• p. P21 •	gráfica de barras

Review Vocabulary

centimeter • centímetro a metric unit of length that is equal to one-hundredth of a meter

inch • pulgada customary unit of length, there are 12 inches in one foot

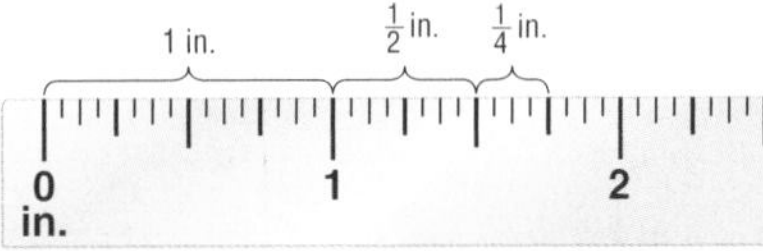

millimeter • milímetro a metric unit of length that is equal to one-thousandth of a meter

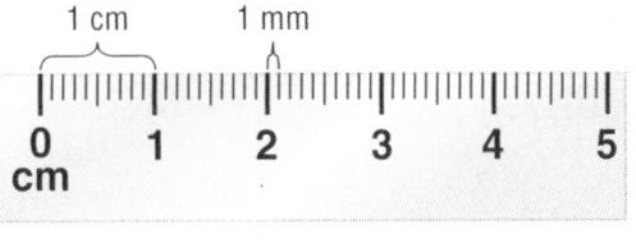

Multilingual eGlossary glencoe.com

FOLDABLES® Study Organizer

Each chapter of *Glencoe Pre-Algebra* features a Foldable Study Organizer students can make to organize their notes. Encourage students to use these tools to make their study time more productive.

Chapter 0 Get Started on Chapter 0 P3

CHAPTER 0 Pretest

Using the Pretest

The Chapter 0 Pretest assesses students' understanding of the concepts presented in Chapter 0. You may use the pretest to determine whether students need to complete each lesson in Chapter 0 before beginning the content in Chapter 1.

CHAPTER 0 Pretest

Use any problem-solving strategy to solve each problem.

1. **STAMPS** Suppose stamps for postcards cost \$0.26 and stamps for first-class letters cost \$0.41. Diego wanted to send postcards and letters to 10 friends. If he had \$3.35 for stamps and spends all of it, how many postcards and how many letters could he send? **5 postcards and 5 letters**

2. **PATTERNS** If the pattern below continues, where will the heart be in the 20th figure? **top**

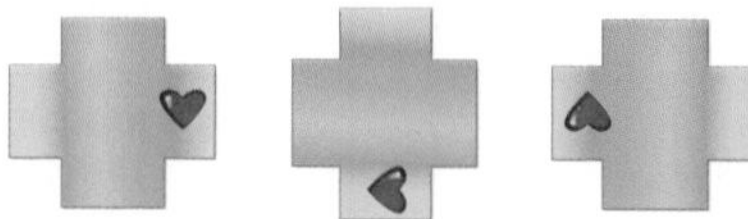

3. **WATER** A 500-gallon bathtub is being filled with water. Eighty gallons of water are in the bathtub after 4 minutes. How long will it take to fill the bathtub? **25 min**

4. **GEOGRAPHY** The table shows the areas of the five Great Lakes.
   a. About how many times larger is Lake Superior than Lake Ontario? **about 4 times**
   b. How many square miles do the Great Lakes cover altogether? **94,267 mi^2**

Great Lakes

Name	Area (sq mi)
Lake Superior	31,698
Lake Huron	23,011
Lake Michigan	22,316
Lake Erie	9922
Lake Ontario	7320

5. **WORK** Two workers can make two chairs in two days. How many chairs can 8 workers working at the same rate make in 20 days? **80 chairs**

Find each sum or difference.

6. 9.5 + 8.6 **18.1**
7. 11.25 + 13.46 **24.71**
8. 48.64 + 52.91 **101.55**
9. 39.45 + 42.4 **81.85**
10. 178.96 + 201.841 **380.801**
11. 3054.2 + 514.67 **3568.87**
12. 8.7 − 5.4 **3.3**
13. 142.67 − 98.59 **44.08**
14. 267.84 − 192.41 **75.43**
15. 58.6 − 31.65 **26.95**
16. 237.42 − 98.6 **138.82**
17. 982 − 457.28 **524.72**

18. **SALES** An MP3 player is on sale for \$149.98. If the original price of the MP3 player was \$225.49, how much money will you save? **\$75.51**

Find each product or quotient.

19. 9.4 × 5 **47**
20. 7.5 × 4.3 **32.25**
21. 12.6 × 18.2 **229.32**
22. 24 × 6.9 **165.6**
23. 42.3 × 5.24 **221.652**
24. 9.865 × 4.3 **42.4195**
25. 12.4 ÷ 5 **2.48**
26. 36.98 ÷ 8.6 **4.3**
27. 38.7828 ÷ 6.84 **5.67**
28. 840.9744 ÷ 12.96 **64.89**
29. 1877.9904 ÷ 6.24 **300.96**
30. 782.8886 ÷ 42.41 **18.46**

31. **BOWLING** Xavier's bowling average is 185.4 and Lola's average is 122.9. About how many times greater is Xavier's average than Lola's? **about 1.5 times**

Write a verbal rule to describe each pattern or sequence. Then find the tenth term.

32–35. See margin.

32.

Number of Tanks	Number of Fish
1	7
2	14
3	21

33.

Number of Cars Washed	Money Earned ($)
1	10
2	15
3	20

34. 8, 9, 10, 11, ...

35. 4, 9, 14, 19, ...

Find the perimeter of each figure.

36. 36 in.

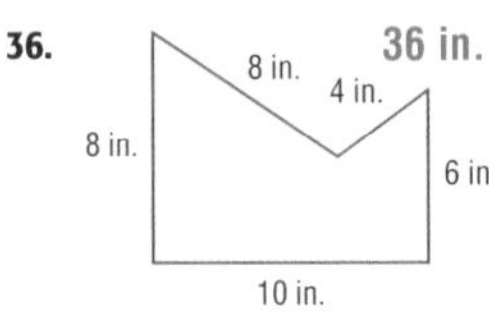

37. 101 cm

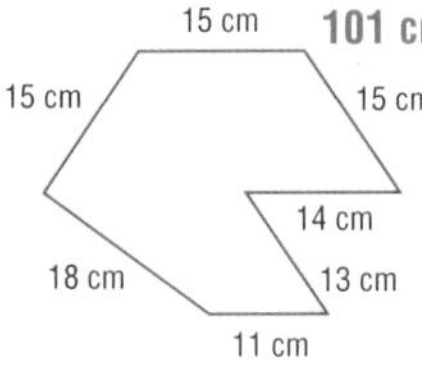

38. 88 ft

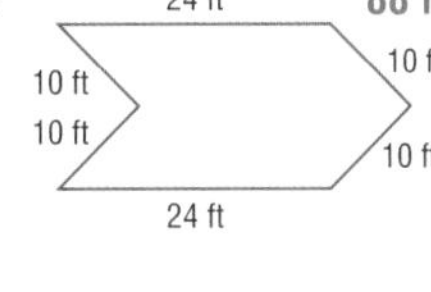

Write the customary unit that you would use to measure each length.

39. width of a video game system inch

40. length of a car yard

41. distance between cities mile

42. height of a door foot

Complete.

43. 6160 yd = ■ mi 3.5

44. ■ in. = 6 ft 72

45. ■ ft = 45 yd 135

46. 2 mi = ■ yd 3520

47. ■ yd = 20 ft $6\frac{2}{3}$

48. 2784 mm = ■ cm 278.4

49. 6.4 km = ■ m 6400

50. ■ m = 210 cm 2.1

51. ■ cm = 4.3 m 430

52. CELL PHONES The pictograph shows the number of students in each class that have a cell phone. How many times as many students have a cell phone in Mr. Watkins' class as in Mr. Hernandez' class? 1.6 times

Class	Number of Students
Mr. Watkins	
Ms. Thompson	
Mr. Hernandez	
Miss Sweeney	

= 4 students

53. TICKETS The Drama Club is selling tickets for the school play. The bar graph shows the number of tickets sold each day for one week. How many tickets were sold Wednesday through Friday? 148 tickets

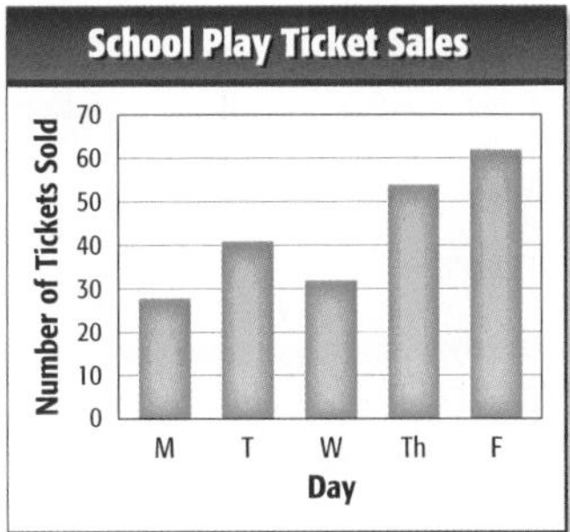

Additional Answers

32. Sample answer: the number of fish is equal to 7 times the number of tanks; 70 fish.

33. Sample answer: the money earned is equal to 5 times the number of cars washed plus five; $55.

34. Sample answer: the value of the term is equal to seven more than the term number; 17.

35. Sample answer: the value of the term is equal to one less than five times the term number; 49.

0-1 Lesson Notes

1 FOCUS

Vertical Alignment

Lesson 0-1
Use the four-step plan to solve problems.

After Lesson 0-1
Solve real-world problems using problem-solving strategies.

2 TEACH

Example 1 shows how to use the four-step plan to solve a real-world problem.

Additional Example

1 **SCHOOL** The table below shows the number of students who signed up for after-school activities. About how many times greater is the number of students who signed up for volleyball than the number of students who signed up for jazz band? about 5.4 times

Activity	Number of Students
Cheerleading	56
Jazz Band	16
Photography	28
Volleyball	87

0-1 A Plan for Problem Solving

Now
- Use the four-step plan to solve problems.

Math Online

glencoe.com
- Extra Examples
- Personal Tutor
- Self-Check Quiz
- Homework Help

INSTANT MESSAGING The graphic shows the results of a class survey about which instant messaging abbreviations students use most. About how many times as great is the number of students who use TTYL as the number of students who use WTG?

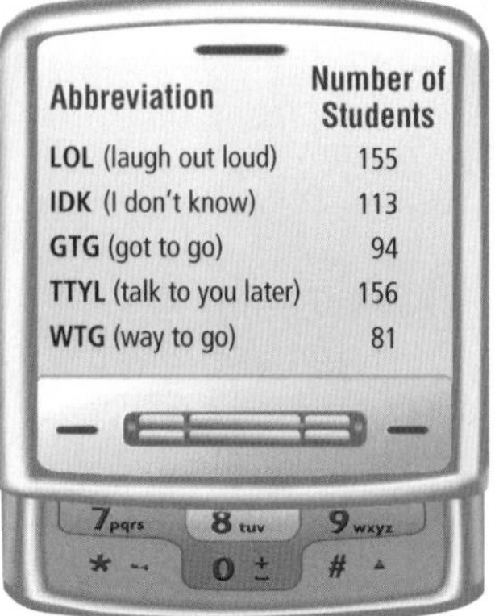

Abbreviation	Number of Students
LOL (laugh out loud)	155
IDK (I don't know)	113
GTG (got to go)	94
TTYL (talk to you later)	156
WTG (way to go)	81

It is often helpful to have an organized plan to solve math problems. The following four steps can be used to solve any math problem.

Understand
- Read the problem quickly to gain a general understanding of it.
- Ask, "What facts do I know?"
- Ask, "What do I need to find out?"
- Ask, "Is there enough information to solve the problem? Is there extra information?"

Plan
- Reread the problem to identify relevant facts.
- Determine how the facts relate to one another.
- Make a plan and choose a strategy for solving it. There may be several strategies that you can use.
- Estimate what you think the answer should be.

Solve
- Use your plan to solve the problem.
- If your plan does not work, revise it or make a new plan.

Check
- Reread the problem. Is there another solution?
- Examine your answer carefully.
- Ask, "Is my answer reasonable and close to my estimate?"
- Ask, "Does my answer make sense?"
- If your answer is not reasonable, make a new plan and solve the problem another way.
- You may also want to check your answer by solving the problem again in a different way.

TEACH with TECH

INTERACTIVE WHITEBOARD Step through examples of different problem-solving strategies using your interactive whiteboard. Save your lesson notes as a pdf. You can print or e-mail notes to absent students.

P6 **Chapter 0** Start Smart: Preparing for Pre-Algebra

Real-World Link

According to a recent survey, 75% of all online teens use instant messaging. Of these, 48% say that they send more than one instant message per day.

Source: Pew Internet and American Life Project

Real-World EXAMPLE 1 The Four-Step Plan

INSTANT MESSAGING Refer to the information at the top of the previous page.

Use the four-step plan to find *about* how many times as many students use TTYL than WTG.

Understand You know that 156 students use TTYL and 81 students use WTG. You need to find *about* how many times as great the number who use TTYL is as the number who use WTG.

Plan Divide the number of students that use TTYL by the number that use WTG. Since the question asks for *about* how many, you can estimate.

Solve $160 \div 80 = 2$

So, about twice as many students use TTYL as use WTG.

Check Multiply 81 by 2. Since $162 \approx 160$, the answer is reasonable. ✓

Personal Tutor glencoe.com

Exercises

Use the four-step plan to solve each problem.

1. **PIZZA** For today's lunch, the school cafeteria is offering make your own pizzas with the options shown at the right. How many different pizzas can be ordered with one cheese and one topping? **16 pizzas**

Pizza Options		
Crust	**Cheese**	**Toppings**
thin	mozzarella	pepperoni
deep dish	cheddar	sausage
		onions
		mushrooms

2. **MONEY** Antonia bought a video game system for $323.96. She paid in 12 equal installments. About how much did she pay each month? **about $27**

3. **GEOMETRY** Megan has 1200 sugar cubes. What is the largest cube she could build with the sugar cubes? **$10 \times 10 \times 10$**

4. **COFFEE** The sales of Café Mocha's coffee of the month are shown.

   a. How many more cups of this kind of coffee did Café Mocha sell in January than in April? **350 cups**

   b. If Café Mocha charges $1.98 for each cup of coffee, about how much money did Café Mocha take in on coffee of the month in March? **about $1180**

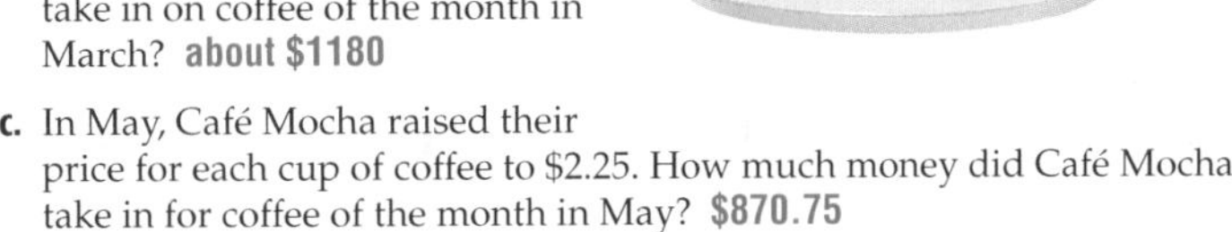

Coffee of the Month Sales

Month	Number of Cups Sold
January	850
February	765
March	587
April	500
May	387

   c. In May, Café Mocha raised their price for each cup of coffee to $2.25. How much money did Café Mocha take in for coffee of the month in May? **$870.75**

Watch Out!

Preventing Errors Some students may be tempted to skip the fourth step of the plan, but the fourth step is crucial for detecting and correcting errors.

3 ASSESS

Formative Assessment

Use Exercises 1–4 to assess whether students understand how to use the four-step plan to solve problems.

Name the Math

Ask students to give a brief description of the four steps in the four-step plan.

Lesson 0-1 A Plan for Problem Solving P7

Lesson Notes

1 FOCUS

Vertical Alignment

Lesson 0-2
Select and use problem-solving strategies to solve appropriate problems.

After Lesson 0-2
Use problem-solving strategies to solve problems involving patterns and sequences, ratios, counting principles, and probabilities.

2 TEACH

Example 1 shows how to use the *look for a pattern* strategy to solve problems. **Example 2** shows how to use the *guess and check* strategy. **Example 3** shows how to use the *make a table* strategy. **Example 4** shows how to use the *work backward* strategy.

Additional Example

1 **DINING** A server at a restaurant sets one table with 4 place settings, including plates, tableware, and glasses. If two tables are pushed together, the server sets 6 place settings, and if three tables are pushed together, the server sets 8 place settings. How many place settings will a server set for six tables pushed together? 14

0-2 Problem-Solving Strategies

Now
- Use problem-solving strategies to solve non routine problems.
- Select an appropriate strategy.

Vocabulary
look for a pattern
guess and check
make a table
work backward

Math Online
glencoe.com
- Extra Examples
- Personal Tutor
- Self-Check Quiz
- Homework Help

There are many problem-solving strategies in mathematics. One common strategy is to **look for a pattern**. To use this strategy, analyze the first few numbers in a pattern and identify a rule that is used to go from one number to the next. Then use the rule to extend the pattern and find a solution.

Real-World EXAMPLE 1 Look for a Pattern

E-MAIL Ramon got an E-mail from Angela. After 10 minutes, he forwarded it to 2 of his friends. After 10 more minutes, those 2 friends forwarded it to 2 more friends. If the E-mail was forwarded like this every 10 minutes, how many people received Angela's E-mail after 40 minutes?

Understand You know how long it takes to forward the E-mail. You need to find the total number of people who received the E-mail.

Plan Organize the data in a table. Look for a pattern in the data and extend the pattern.

Time (min)	People Receiving Message
0	1
10	2
20	4
30	■
40	■

Solve 1, 2, 4, ■, ■
×2 ×2 ×2 ×2

To continue the pattern, multiply each term by 2.

$4 \times 2 = 8$ $\quad 8 \times 2 = 16$

So, $1 + 2 + 4 + 8 + 16$ or 31 people got the E-mail.

Check In the 40th minute, 16 people received the E-mail. Half as many received it each time before that. So, it is reasonable that the total will be less than 16×2 or 32. ✓

Personal Tutor glencoe.com

To solve other problems, you can make a reasonable guess and then check it in the problem. You can then use the results to improve your guess until you find the solution. This strategy is called **guess and check**.

Real-World EXAMPLE 2 Guess and Check

LIFE SCIENCE Each hand in the human hand has 27 bones. There are 6 more bones in the fingers than in the wrist. There are 3 fewer bones in the palm than in the wrist. How many bones are in each part of the hand?

Make a guess to find the bones in each part of the hand.

Wrist	Palm wrist − 3	Fingers wrist + 6	Total Bones (27)	Correct?
5	$5 - 3 = 2$	$5 + 6 = 11$	$5 + 2 + 11 = 18$	This is too low.
7	$7 - 3 = 4$	$7 + 6 = 13$	$7 + 4 + 13 = 24$	This is too low.
9	$9 - 3 = 6$	$9 + 6 = 15$	$9 + 6 + 15 = 30$	This is too high.
8	$8 - 3 = 5$	$8 + 6 = 14$	$8 + 5 + 14 = 27$	This is correct. ✓

There are 8 bones in the wrist, 5 bones in the palm, and 14 bones in the fingers.

Personal Tutor glencoe.com

Another strategy for solving problems is to **make a table**. A table allows you to organize information in an understandable way.

Real-World EXAMPLE 3 Make a Table

SNACKS A vending machine accepts dollars, and each item in the machine costs 65 cents. If the machine gives only nickels, dimes, and quarters, what combinations of those coins are possible as change for one dollar?

The machine will give back \$1.00 – \$0.65 or 35 cents in change in a combinations of nickels, dimes, and quarters.

Make a table showing different combinations of nickels, dimes, and quarters that total 35 cents. Organize the table by starting with the combinations that include the most quarters.

quarters	dimes	nickels
1	1	0
1	0	2
0	3	1
0	2	3
0	1	5
0	0	7

The total for each combination of these coins is 35 cents. There are 6 combinations possible.

Personal Tutor glencoe.com

Real-World Link

More than 50% of the vending machines in the United States sell cold drinks and about 20% of the machines sell snacks.

Source: Vencoa

In most problems, a set of conditions or facts is given and an end result must be found. However, some problems start with the result and ask for something that happened earlier. The **work backward** strategy can be used to solve problems like this.

To use the work backward strategy, start with the end result and *undo* each step.

Real-World EXAMPLE 4 Work Backward

MONEY Kendrick spent half of the money he had this morning on lunch. After lunch, he loaned his friend a dollar. Now he has \$1.50. How much money did Kendrick start with in the morning?

Start with the end result, \$1.50, and work backward to find Kendrick's starting amount.

Kendrick now has \$1.50. ⟶ \$1.50

Undo the \$1 he loaned to his friend. ⟶ +1.00

\$2.50

Undo the half he spent for lunch. ⟶ × 2

\$5.00

The amount Kendrick started with was \$5.00.

Check Kendrick started with \$5. If he spent half of that on lunch and loaned his friend \$1.00, he would have \$1.50 left. The solution is correct. ✓

Personal Tutor glencoe.com

Additional Examples

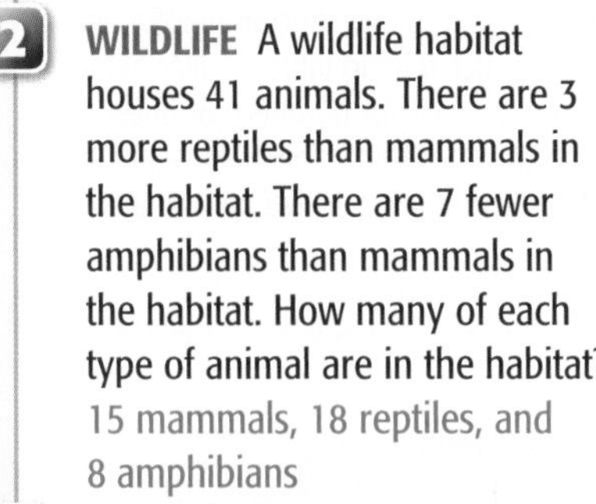

2 **WILDLIFE** A wildlife habitat houses 41 animals. There are 3 more reptiles than mammals in the habitat. There are 7 fewer amphibians than mammals in the habitat. How many of each type of animal are in the habitat? 15 mammals, 18 reptiles, and 8 amphibians

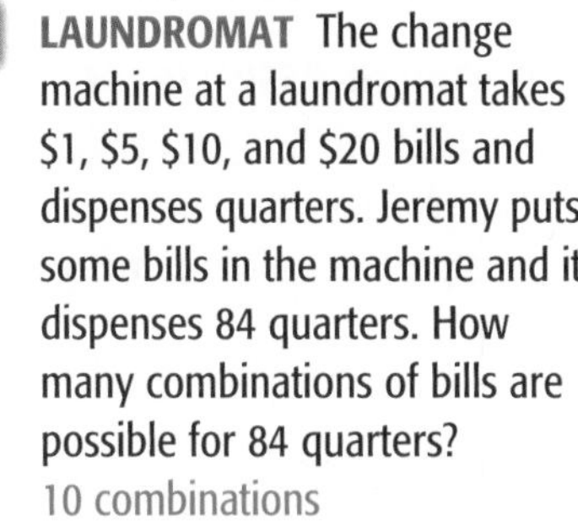

3 **LAUNDROMAT** The change machine at a laundromat takes \$1, \$5, \$10, and \$20 bills and dispenses quarters. Jeremy puts some bills in the machine and it dispenses 84 quarters. How many combinations of bills are possible for 84 quarters? 10 combinations

\$20	\$10	\$5	\$1
1	0	0	1
0	2	0	1
0	1	2	1
0	1	1	6
0	1	0	11
0	0	4	1
0	0	3	6
0	0	2	11
0	0	1	16
0	0	0	21

4 **TICKETS** Kayla bought a book of tickets for rides at the carnival. She had one-third of the tickets left after she rode the Hammer and the Tilt-a-Whirl. She used 12 tickets to ride the Ferris wheel. Now she has 13 tickets. How many tickets were in the book of tickets Kayla bought? 75 tickets

TEACH with TECH

STUDENT RESPONSE SYSTEM Present students with a problem to solve, and ask the class which problem-solving strategy they think should be used. Assign each type of strategy a letter, A, B, C, D, etc., and have students vote. Use the strategy that receives the most votes to solve the problem. If possible, show how to use another strategy to solve the same problem.

Watch Out!

Preventing Errors Encourage students to organize data in tables or lists before using the *look for a pattern* or *guess and check* strategy. The table will help them track their calculations and avoid errors.

3 ASSESS

Formative Assessment

Use Exercises 1–19 to assess whether students understand how to select and then use a problem-solving strategy to solve a problem.

Additional Answers

5.

Total Number of Cards	Amount Traded	Amount Received	New Total
55	8	5	52
52	6	4	50
50	5	3	48
48	12	9	45

6.

First Die	Second Die	Total
1	1	2
1	2	3
1	3	4
1	4	5
1	5	6
1	6	7
2	1	3
2	2	4
...		

Exercises

Solve each problem by looking for a pattern.

1. **MEASUREMENT** What is the perimeter of the twelfth figure? **28**

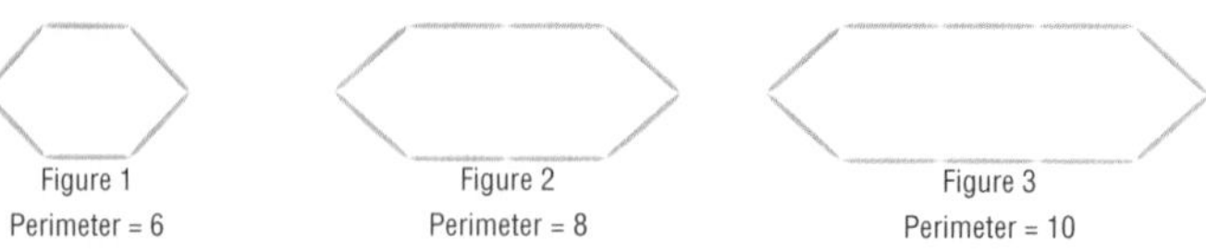

2. **SCIENCE** A ball bounces back 0.6 of its height on every bounce. If a ball is dropped from 200 feet, how high does it bounce on the fifth bounce? Round to the nearest tenth. **15.6 ft**

Use the guess and check strategy to solve each problem.

3. **NUMBER SENSE** The product of two consecutive odd integers is 783. What are the integers? **27 and 29**

4. **MUSIC** Rafael is burning a CD for Selma. The CD will hold 35 minutes of music. Which songs should he select from the list to record the maximum time on the CD without going over?

Song	A	B	C	D	E
Time	5 min 4 s	9 min 10 s	4 min 12 s	3 min 9 s	3 min 44 s
Song	F	G	H	I	J
Time	4 min 30 s	5 min 0 s	7 min 21 s	4 min 33 s	5 min 58 s

Songs A, B, C, D, E, G, and I run for a total of 34 minutes 52 seconds.

Solve each problem by making a table. **5–6. See margin for tables.**

5. **CARDS** Jorge had 55 football cards. He traded 8 cards for 5 from Elise. He traded 6 more for 4 from Leon and 5 for 3 from Bret. Finally, he traded 12 cards for 9 from Ginger. How many cards does Jorge have now? **45 cards**

Real-World Link

The first trading cards were made around 1887 and were made from a cloth-like material and measured 1.5 inches by 2 inches. Today, these are among the rarest and most valuable trading cards.

Source: Trading Card Central

6. **GAMES** The cubes at the right are each numbered 1 through 6. During a game, both are rolled and the faces landing up are added. How many ways can a person playing the game roll a sum less than 8? **21 ways**

Solve each problem by working backward.

7. **MONEY** Tia used half of her allowance to buy a ticket to the class play. Then she spent $1.75 for ice cream. Now she has $2.25 left. How much is her allowance? **$8**

8. **TIME** To catch a 7:30 A.M. bus, Don needs 30 minutes to shower and dress, 15 minutes for breakfast, and 10 minutes to walk to the bus stop. To catch the bus, what is his latest possible wake-up time? **6:35 A.M.**

P10 Chapter 0 Start Smart: Preparing for Pre-Algebra

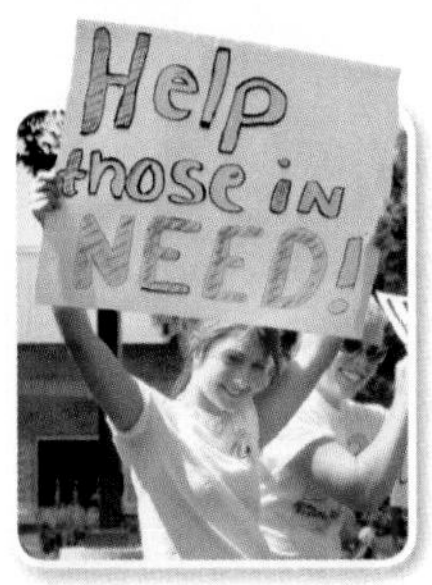

Real-World Link

The top five fundraising activities for schools are
1) candy bars
2) catalogs
3) cookie dough
4) discount cards
5) scratch-off tickets

Source: Fundraiser Help

StudyTip

Strategies Other problem solving strategies include
- draw a diagram
- make a model
- solve a simpler problem
- use logical reasoning

16. 1st hour: 5;
2nd hour: 9;
3rd hour: 13;
4th hour: 17;
5th hour: 21;
6th hour: 25;
7th hour: 29;
8th hour: 33;
9th hour: 37;
10th hour: 41

Use any strategy to solve each problem.

9. **FUNDRAISING** The Science Club sold candy bars and soft pretzels to raise money for an animal shelter. They raised a total of $62.75. They made 25¢ profit on each candy bar and 30¢ profit on each pretzel sold. How many of each did they sell? **Sample answer: 125 candy bars and 105 pretzels**

Help Support the Friends with Paws Shelter! Buy a candy bar or soft pretzel today!

10. **STOCKS** Mr. and Mrs. Delgado each own an equal number of shares of a stock. Mr. Delgado sells one-third of his shares for $2700. What was the total value of Mr. and Mrs. Delgado's stock before the sale? **$16,200**

11. **MONEY** Odell has the same number of quarters, dimes, and nickels. In all he has $4 in change. How many of each coin does he have? **10**

12. **GAMES** Three counters are used for a board game. If the counters are tossed, how many ways can at least one counter with Side A turn up? **6 ways**

Counters	Side 1	Side 2
Counter 1	A	B
Counter 2	A	C
Counter 3	B	C

13. **NUMBER SENSE** A certain number is multiplied by 3, and then 5 is added to the result. The final answer is 41. What is the number? **12**

14. **TRAVEL** Courtney travels south on her bicycle riding 8 miles per hour. One hour later, her friend Horacio starts riding his bicycle from the same location. If he travels south at 10 miles per hour, how long will it take him to catch Courtney? **4 hours**

15. **GAMES** The spinner is used to play a certain game. On your turn, you must spin the spinner twice. How many different combinations of colors could you spin? List all possible combinations. **16 combinations. See margin for table.**

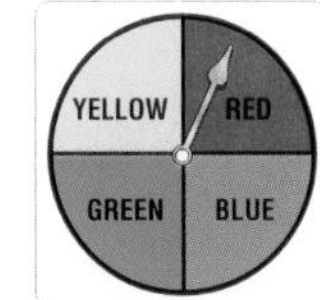

16. **FIRES** A forest fire spread to 41 acres in 10 hours. Each hour the fire spread to four more acres than the previous hour. How many acres were consumed during each hour of the fire?

17. **MONEY** Lawanda put $15 of her paycheck into her savings account. Then she spent one-half of what was left on clothes. She paid $24 for a concert ticket and later spent one-half of what was then left on a book. When she got home, she had $14 left. What was the amount of Lawanda's paycheck? **$119**

18. **AGE** Brianne is three times as old as Camila. Four years from now she will be just two times as old as Camila. How old are Brianne and Camila now? **12 and 4**

19. **MONEY** Anita sold tickets to the school musical. At the end of the day, she filled out a register like the one at the right to make her deposit. If she deposited a total of 12 bills, how many of each bill did she deposit? **Sample answer: 3 $5 bills, 2 $10 bills, and 7 $20 bills**

Deposit	
Type of Bill	Number Deposited
$1	0
$5	■
$10	■
$20	■
Total	$175

Yesterday's News

Ask students to explain how yesterday's lesson on using a four-step plan helped them with today's lesson on problem-solving strategies.

Additional Answer

15.

First Spin	Second Spin
red	red
red	blue
red	green
red	yellow
blue	red
blue	blue
blue	green
blue	yellow
green	red
green	blue
green	green
green	yellow
yellow	red
yellow	blue
yellow	green
yellow	yellow

Lesson 0-2 Problem-Solving Strategies P11
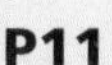

0-3 Lesson Notes

1 FOCUS

Vertical Alignment

Lesson 0-3
Add and subtract decimals.
Multiply and divide decimals.

After Lesson 0-3
Solve equations involving decimals.

2 TEACH

Example 1 shows how to add and subtract decimals to solve a real-world problem. **Example 2** shows how to multiply decimals. **Example 3** shows how to divide decimals.

Additional Examples

1 **HIKING** The table shows the length of the trails Nikki hiked at Yosemite National Park.

Trail Name	Length (km)
Bridalveil Fall	0.8
Mirror Lake	3.22
Four Mile	15.45
Nevada Fall	11.3

a. Find the total number of kilometers Nikki hiked. 30.77 km

b. How much longer is the Nevada Fall trail than the Mirror Lake trail? 8.08 km

2 Find 1.18 × 3.6. 4.248

0-3 Number and Operations

Now
- Add and subtract decimals.
- Multiply and divide decimals.

Review Vocabulary
decimal
annex

Math Online
glencoe.com
- Extra Examples
- Personal Tutor
- Self-Check Quiz
- Homework Help

A **decimal** is a number that has a digit in the tenths place, hundredths place, and beyond. To add or subtract decimals, line up the decimal points first.

Real-World EXAMPLE 1 Add and Subtract Decimals

SPORTS **The table shows the scores for each event for the two champions of the 2007 Southeastern Conference (SEC) Gymnastics Championships.**

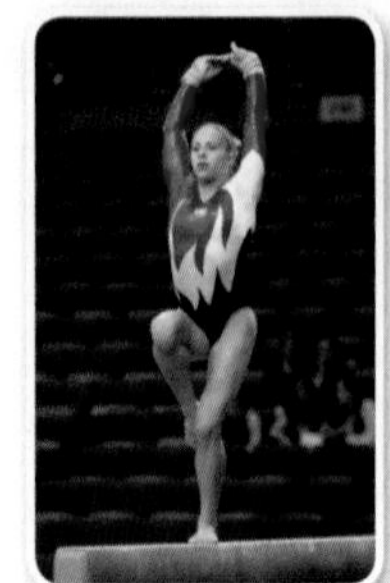

2007 SEC Gymnastics Championships

Event	Courtney Kupets	Katie Heenan
Bars	9.925	9.85
Beam	9.825	9.9
Floor	9.875	9.9
Vault	9.975	9.95

a. Find the all-around score for each champion.

The all-around score is found by adding together the four event scores.

Courtney Kupets: 9.925 + 9.825 + 9.875 + 9.975 = 39.600

Line up the decimal points. Add as with whole numbers.

Katie Heenan: 9.85 + 9.90 + 9.90 + 9.95 = 39.60

Annex a zero to align the columns.

So, both women had an all-around score of 39.6.

b. How much greater was Katie's beam score than Courtney's?

Find the difference between the scores.

9.900 − 9.825 = 0.075

Annex zeros. **Subtract as with whole numbers.**

So, Katie's beam score was 0.075 more than Courtney's.

Personal Tutor glencoe.com

EXAMPLE 2 Multiply Decimals

Find 4.5 × 2.7.

Multiply as with whole numbers. To place the decimal point, find the sum of the number of decimal places in each factor. The product has the same number of decimal places.

4.5 ← one decimal place
× 2.7 ← one decimal place
315
+ 90
12.15 ← two decimal places

Personal Tutor glencoe.com

EXAMPLE 3 Divide Decimals

Divide 0.086 ÷ 0.04.

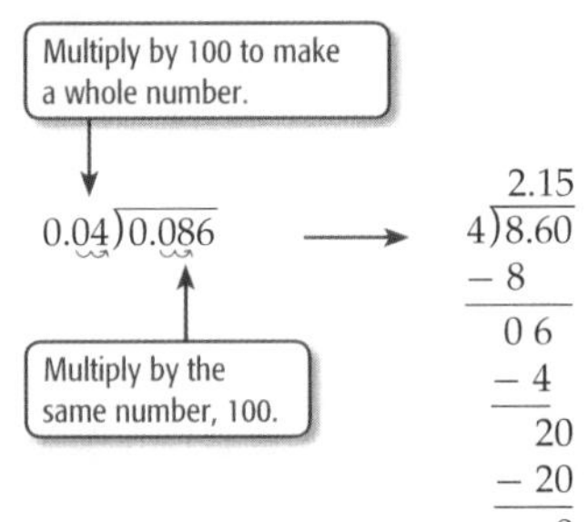

Multiply by 100 to make a whole number.
0.04)0.086
Multiply by the same number, 100.

$$\begin{array}{r} 2.15 \\ 4\overline{)8.60} \\ -8 \\ \hline 06 \\ -4 \\ \hline 20 \\ -20 \\ \hline 0 \end{array}$$

Place the decimal point.
Divide as with whole numbers.

Annex a zero to continue.

The quotient is 2.15.

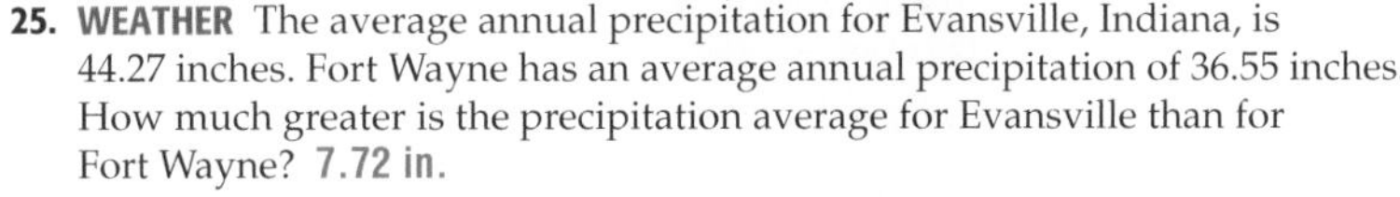

Personal Tutor glencoe.com

StudyTip

Powers of 10 To multiply by 100, move the decimal point two places to the right.

Exercises

Find each sum or difference.

1. 17.8 + 22.29 **40.09**
2. 32.34 + 15.19 **47.53**
3. 6.651 + 13.76 **20.411**
4. 45 – 31.52 **13.48**
5. 113.6 – 41.8 **71.8**
6. 178.4 – 147.3 **31.1**
7. 0.37 + 2.548 **2.918**
8. \$8.74 + \$3.15 **\$11.89**
9. \$92.71 + \$115.23 **\$207.94**
10. 36.17 – 20 **16.17**
11. \$17.00 – \$4.61 **\$12.39**
12. \$98.10 – \$20.10 **\$78.00**

Find each product or quotient.

13. 5.7 × 9.4 **53.58**
14. 7.34 × 7.6 **55.784**
15. 21.5 × 4.9 **105.35**
16. 13.02 ÷ 4.2 **3.1**
17. 5.082 ÷ 2.42 **2.1**
18. 0.1485 ÷ 1.35 **0.11**
19. 145.2 × 27.5 **3993**
20. 1.723 × 2.49 **4.29027**
21. 8.42 × 0.137 **1.15354**
22. 25.334 ÷ 5.3 **4.78**
23. 100.1 ÷ 14.3 **7**
24. 1864.3 ÷ 3.62 **515**

25. **WEATHER** The average annual precipitation for Evansville, Indiana, is 44.27 inches. Fort Wayne has an average annual precipitation of 36.55 inches. How much greater is the precipitation average for Evansville than for Fort Wayne? **7.72 in.**

26. **SWIMMING** A record time for the 400-meter medley relay was set by the four swimmers shown. The times for each leg that they swam are shown.

Swimmer	Leg	Time (s)
Aaron Peirsol	backstroke	53.45
Brendan Hansen	breaststroke	59.37
Ian Crocker	butterfly	50.28
Jason Lezak	freestyle	47.58

a. What was the total time of the world record? **210.68 s or 3 min 30.68 s**

b. How much faster did Jason Lezak swim his leg than Aaron Peirsol? **5.87 s**

c. Refer to the information at the left. How much faster is the world record time than the gold medal winning time in the 1960 Olympics? **34.72 s**

Real-World Link

The 400-meter medley relay was introduced as an Olympic sport in 1960. The gold medal winning time that year was 245.4 seconds.

Additional Example

3 Divide 0.034 ÷ 0.02 1.7

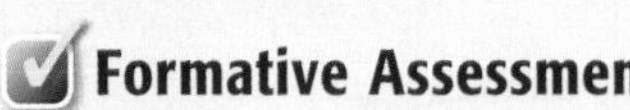

Tips for New Teachers

Estimation Encourage students to estimate sums, differences, products, and quotients. Estimation can help avoid errors made in annexing zeros, in aligning decimal points, and in placing decimal points.

3 ASSESS

Formative Assessment

Use Exercises 1–26 to assess whether students understand how to add, subtract, multiply, and divide decimals.

Ticket Out the Door

Have students find the sum, difference, product, and quotient of 2.4 and 0.08. 2.48; 2.32; 0.192; 30

0-4 Lesson Notes

1 FOCUS

Vertical Alignment

Lesson 0-4
Write a verbal rule to represent a pattern or sequence. Find any term value in a pattern or sequence.

After Lesson 0-4
Write equations to describe arithmetic sequences. Use equations to extend a sequence and find terms in a sequence.

2 TEACH

Example 1 shows how to write a verbal rule for a pattern or sequence. **Example 2** shows how to find terms in a pattern or sequence. **Example 3** shows how to find a rule for a pattern or sequence.

Additional Examples

1. Write a verbal rule to find the number of squares in any figure below. Then find the number of squares in the 12th figure.

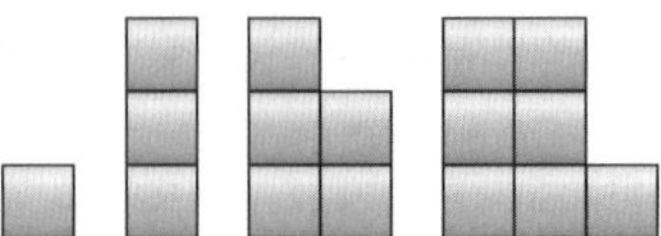

The number of squares is one less than twice the figure number; 23 squares

2. Find the 20th term in the sequence 4, 7, 10, 13, ... 61

0-4 Algebra

Now
- Write a verbal rule to represent a pattern or sequence.
- Find any term value in a pattern or sequence.

Math Online
glencoe.com
- Extra Examples
- Personal Tutor
- Self-Check Quiz
- Homework Help

The world around you is made up of patterns and sequences. Tables, rules, formulas, and algebraic expressions can model these relationships.

EXAMPLE 1 Write a Rule

Write a verbal rule to find the number of dots in any figure below. Then find the number of dots in the 15th figure.

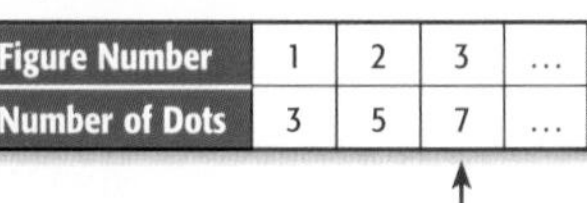

Figure	● ●●	●● ●●●	●●● ●●●●	●●●● ●●●●●
Figure Number	1	2	3	4
Number of Dots	3	5	7	9

You can draw each figure or you can look for a pattern and write a rule.

Make a table to organize the information.

Figure Number	1	2	3	...
Number of Dots	3	5	7	...

$2 \cdot 3 + 1 = 7$

The number of dots is *one more than the twice the figure number.*

So, the 15th figure would have $2 \cdot 15 + 1$ or 31 dots.

Personal Tutor glencoe.com

EXAMPLE 2 Find Terms

Find the 25th term in the sequence 4, 8, 12, 16, ...

The value of each term is 4 times its position in the sequence.

Position	1	2	3	4	...
Value of Term	4	8	12	16	...

So, the 25th term would have a value of $4 \cdot 25$ or 100.

Personal Tutor glencoe.com

EXAMPLE 3 Find a Rule

Describe how to find the number of diagonals that can be drawn from any one vertex in the polygons shown. Then find the number of diagonals from one vertex in a 10-sided polygon.

Draw the diagonals from a single vertex.

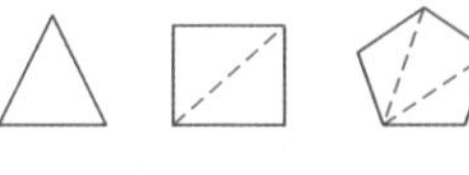

Number of Sides	3	4	5	...
Number of Diagonals	0	1	2	...

The number of diagonals is *three less than the number of sides.*

So, there are $10 - 3$ or 7 diagonals that can be drawn.

Personal Tutor glencoe.com

Additional Answers

1. Sample answer: the number of bracelets made is equal to 25 times the number of hours; 500 bracelets.
2. Sample answer: the number of dollars paid is equal to 10 times the number of lawns mowed plus five; $205.
3. Sample answer: the value of the term is equal to three more than the term number; 23.
4. Sample answer: the value of the term is equal to two less than five times the term number; 98.

Exercises

Write a verbal rule to describe each pattern or sequence. Then find the 20th term in each. 1–4. See margin.

1.

Time (hours)	Bracelets Made
1	25
2	50
3	75

2.

Number of Lawns	Dollars Paid
1	15
2	25
3	35

3. 4, 5, 6, 7, ...

4. 3, 8, 13, 18, ...

5. **MOVIES** Tickets at the local movie theater cost $6.50 per ticket.

   a. Copy and complete the table that shows the relationship between the number of tickets purchased and the total cost. See margin.

Number of Tickets	1	2	3	4	5
Total Cost ($)	6.50	■	■	■	■

   b. Write a rule that describes the relationship between the number of tickets and the total cost. Sample answer: The total cost is 6.5 times the number of tickets.

   c. How much will it cost to purchase 8 tickets? $52.00

Real-World Link

The average ticket price for a movie in the United States is about $6.60 per ticket.

Source: National Association of Theatre Owners

6. **CONSTRUCTION** Micah is tiling his kitchen floor with blue and white tiles. He surrounds each pair of blue tiles with white tiles. Four copies of this design are shown below.

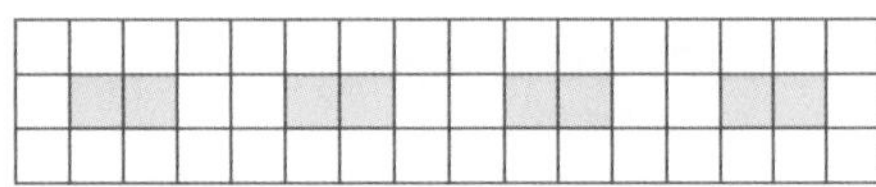

   a. Copy and complete the table to show the number of white tiles needed for each given amount of blue tiles. See margin.

Blue Tiles	2	4	6	8	20	100
White Tiles	10	■	■	■	■	■

   b. Write a rule that describes the relationship between the number of white tiles and the number of blue tiles. Sample answer: The number of white tiles is 5 times the number of blue tiles.

   c. How many blue tiles were used if 800 white tiles were used? 160 blue tiles

7. **PATTERNS** Look at the sequence of cubes below.

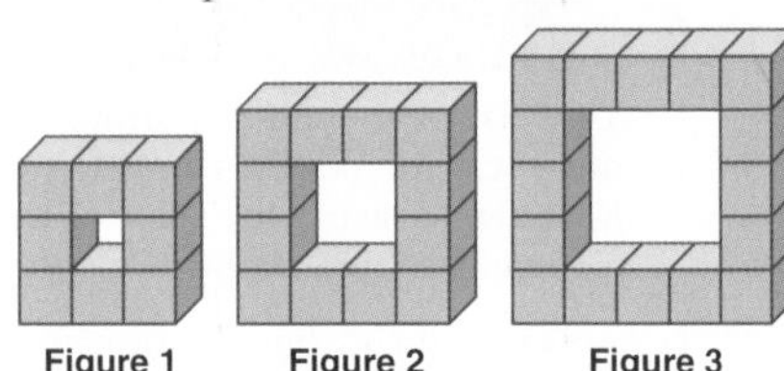

   a. Make a table that shows the number of cubes in each figure. See margin.

   b. Write a rule for the number of cubes in each figure. Sample answer: The number of cubes is four more than four times the term number.

   c. How many cubes would be in the tenth figure of the pattern? 44 cubes

StudyTip

Patterns In these Exercises, you are using both the Make a Table and Look for a Pattern problem solving strategies.

Additional Answers

5a.

Number of Tickets	1	2	3	4	5
Total Cost ($)	6.50	13.00	19.50	26.00	32.50

6a.

Blue Tiles	2	4	6	8	20	100
White Tiles	10	20	30	40	100	500

7a.

Term Number	1	2	3
Number of Cubes	8	12	16

Additional Example

3 The figures below are triangles made from connecting rods. Describe how to find the number of rods and triangles for any figure. Then find the number of rods in a figure that has 15 triangles.

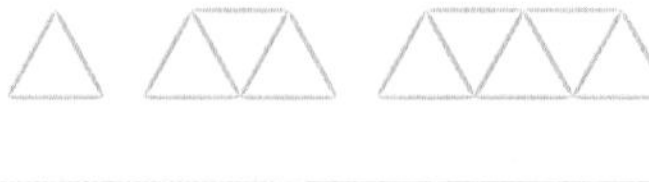

Number of Triangles	1	3	5	...
Number of Rods	3	7	11	...

The number of rods in each figure is one more than two times the number of triangles; 31 rods in a figure of 15 triangles.

Watch Out!

Common Misconceptions Some students may think that a verbal rule can involve only one operation. Remind them that rules used to describe patterns or sequences may involve more than one operation. The rule must apply to all of the terms in the pattern or sequence.

3 ASSESS

Formative Assessment

Use Exercises 1–7 to assess whether students understand how to write a rule to find a term in a pattern or sequence, and then find a term.

Yesterday's News

Have students write a sentence on how the problem-solving strategy *look for a pattern* connects with today's lesson on writing a verbal rule to find a term in a pattern.

Lesson 0-4 Algebra P15

0-5 Lesson Notes

1 FOCUS

Vertical Alignment

Lesson 0-5
Find the perimeter of a figure. Measure sides of figures to find the perimeter.

After Lesson 0-5
Find the perimeter of composite figures. Explore the relationship between perimeter and area.

2 TEACH

Example 1 shows how to solve a real-world problem involving perimeter. **Example 2** shows how to find the perimeter of a regular polygon. **Example 3** shows how to find perimeter to solve a real-world problem.

Additional Examples

1. **VOLLEYBALL** The length of a volleyball court is 59 feet. The width is 29.5 feet. How much masking tape, in feet, will Diego need if he tapes the dimensions of a volleyball court on a playground? 177 feet
2. Find the perimeter of the regular polygon shown with side lengths of 1.2 millimeters. 8.4 mm

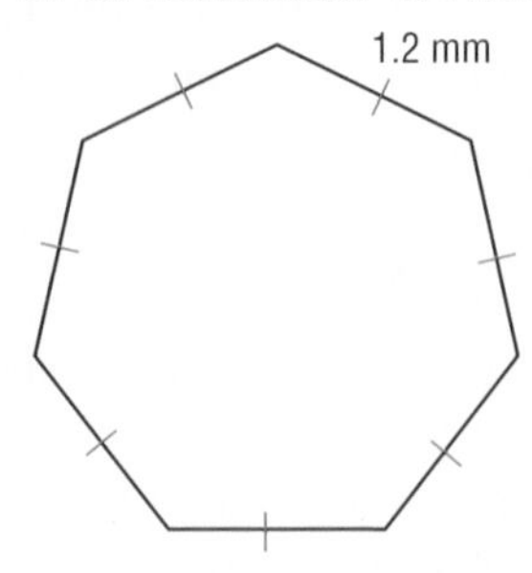

0-5 Geometry

Now
- Find the perimeter of a figure.
- Measure sides of figures to find the perimeter.

Math Online
glencoe.com
- Extra Examples
- Personal Tutor
- Self-Check Quiz
- Homework Help

Perimeter is the distance around any closed figure. While the figure itself is two-dimensional, the perimeter is only one dimension: length. You can find the perimeter by adding the measures of all of the sides of the figure.

Real-World EXAMPLE 1 Find Perimeter

BASEBALL The distance between each base on a Little League baseball diamond is 60 feet. Find the total distance you will run if you hit a home run.

To find the total distance run, find the perimeter of the baseball diamond.

60 feet + 60 feet + 60 feet + 60 feet = 240 feet

You will run a total of 240 feet.

Personal Tutor glencoe.com

A figure like a baseball diamond that has equal sides and equal angles is a regular figure. You can find the perimeter of a regular figure by multiplying the side length by the number of sides.

EXAMPLE 2 Perimeter of a Regular Polygon

Find the perimeter of a regular octagon with side lengths of 2 centimeters.

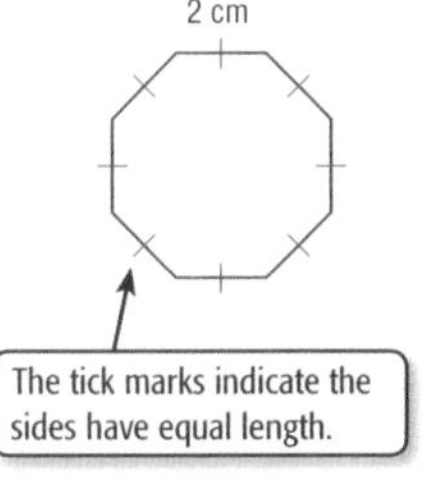

The tick marks indicate the sides have equal length.

A regular octagon has 8 sides of equal length.

Multiply 8 by 2 centimeters to get the perimeter.

$8 \cdot 2 = 16$

So, the octagon has a perimeter of 16 centimeters.

Personal Tutor glencoe.com

Real-World EXAMPLE 3 Find the Perimeter

SCRAPBOOKING Laila is putting the letter shown at the right into a scrapbook. She wants to put a decorative trim around the letter. Measure the sides of the letter to the nearest millimeter to determine how much trim she will need.

Use a centimeter ruler to measure each side of the letter to the nearest millimeter. Then add the six lengths.

6 mm + 21 mm + 16 mm + 6 mm + 10 mm + 15 mm = 74 mm

Laila will need 74 millimeters of trim for the letter.

Personal Tutor glencoe.com

TEACH with TECH

BLOG Have students create a blog entry in your secure class blog to name real-world applications of perimeter.

Exercises

Find the perimeter of each figure.

1. 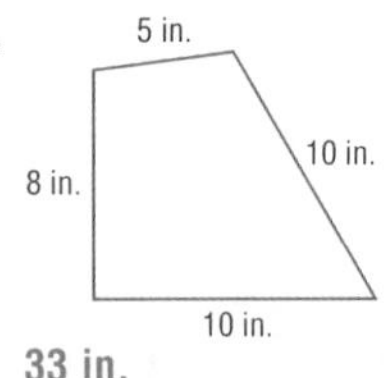

33 in.

2. 11 cm, 4 cm, 5 cm, 7 cm, 10 cm, 12 cm, 6 cm
55 cm

3. 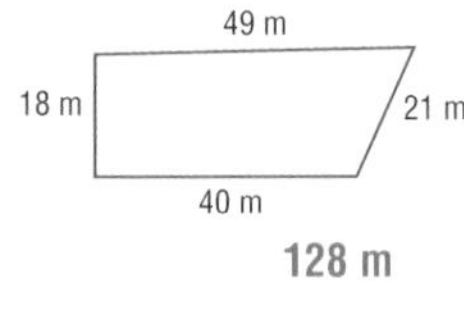

128 m

Find the perimeter of each regular polygon.

4. 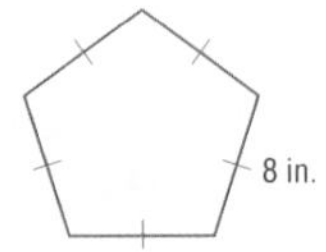

40 in.

5. $1\frac{1}{8}$ ft
$11\frac{1}{4}$ ft

6. 4.5 cm
72 cm

Measure the sides of each figure to the nearest millimeter. Then find the perimeter.

7. 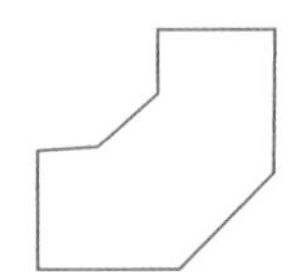
76 mm

8. 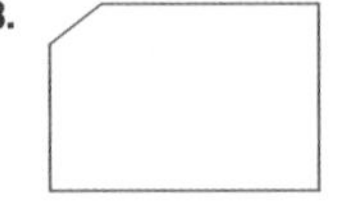
78 mm

9. 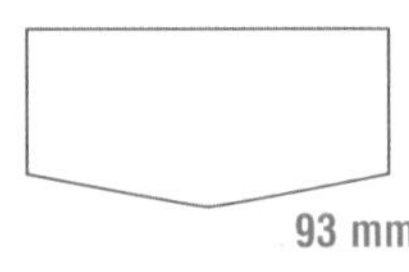
93 mm

Measure the sides of each figure to the nearest $\frac{1}{16}$ inch. Then find the perimeter.

10. 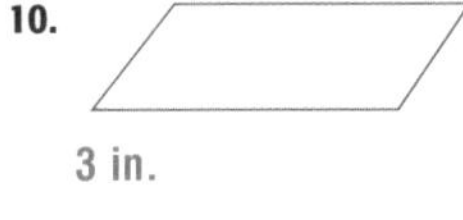
3 in.

11. 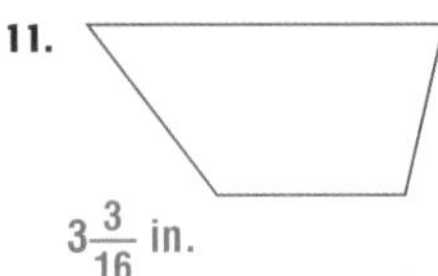
$3\frac{3}{16}$ in.

12. 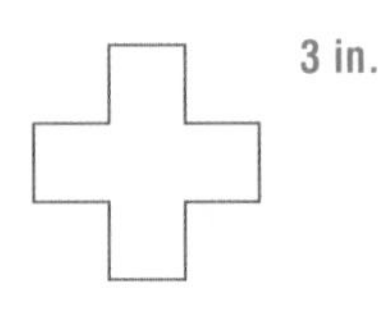
3 in.

13. **GEOMETRY** Measure one side of the square to the nearest inch.
    a. Draw a square that has sides that are twice the length of the square. See students' work.
    b. Draw two more squares, one with side lengths that are three times as great as the original and one with side lengths that are four times great as the original. Record the side length and perimeter of each square in a table like the one shown below.

Side Length	Perimeter
1 in. ■	4 in. ■
2 in. ■	8 in. ■
3 in. ■	12 in ■
4 in. ■	16 in ■

    c. What happens to the perimeter of a square if the side length is doubled? tripled? quadrupled? it doubles; it triples; it quadruples
    d. Predict the perimeter if the original side length is multiplied by 8. 32 in.

Watch Out!

Rulers Be sure to use the correct ruler when measuring length. Use the metric side for Exercises 7–9 and the customary side for Exercises 10–12.

Additional Example

3 **NAME CARDS** Jasmine is making a name card in the shape below. She wants to put ribbon around the border of the name card. Measure the sides of the shape to the nearest millimeter to determine how much ribbon Jasmine needs. 161 mm

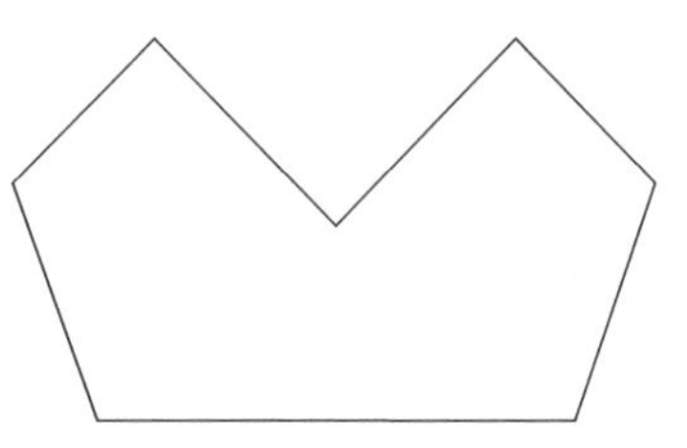

Watch Out!

Preventing Errors Though the sides of a figure may appear to be the same length, they may actually be different lengths. Unless a figure is a regular polygon or has tick marks to indicate congruent sides, each side should be measured to determine its length.

3 ASSESS

Formative Assessment

Use Exercises 1–13 to assess whether students understand how to find the perimeter of a figure and a regular polygon, and how to measure the sides of a figure and then find the perimeter.

Crystal Ball

Have students write a sentence on how they think today's lesson on measuring perimeter will help with the next lesson on estimating and measuring objects.

0-6 Lesson Notes

1 FOCUS

Vertical Alignment

Lesson 0-6
Convert within measurement systems. Estimate and measure objects.

After Lesson 0-6
Convert within measurement systems using dimensional analysis. Convert between measurement systems.

2 TEACH

Example 1 shows how to estimate and then measure the customary length of an object. **Example 2** shows how to estimate and then measure the metric length of an object. **Example 3** shows how to convert measurements within a system.

Additional Examples

1. Estimate the customary length of the pencil. Then measure to find the actual length. estimate: 2 in.; actual: $1\frac{15}{16}$ in.

2. Estimate the metric length of the fly's wingspan. Then measure to find the actual length. estimate: 3 cm; actual: 3.2 cm or 32 mm

0-6 Measurement

Now
- Convert within measurement systems.
- Estimate and measure objects.

Vocabulary
customary system
metric system

Math Online
glencoe.com
- Extra Examples
- Personal Tutor
- Self-Check Quiz
- Homework Help

A regulation baseball bat is about 3 feet long. But the world's largest bat is 40 yards long. Yards and feet are measurements of length. There are two common systems of measurement, the customary system and the metric system. The most common units for measuring length are shown.

Customary System	
Unit	**Model**
1 inch (in.)	width of a quarter
1 foot (ft) = 12 in.	height of a textbook
1 yard (yd) = 3 ft	length from nose to fingertip
1 mile (mi) = 1760 yd	10 city blocks
Metric System	
Unit	**Model**
millimeter (mm)	thickness of a coin
centimeter (cm) = 10 mm	half the width of a penny
meter (m) = 100 cm	width of a doorway
kilometer (km) = 1000 m	six city blocks

EXAMPLE 1 Estimate and Measure Length

Estimate the customary length of the key. Then measure to find the actual length.

The length of the key is about the width of two quarters. An appropriate estimate is about 2 inches long.

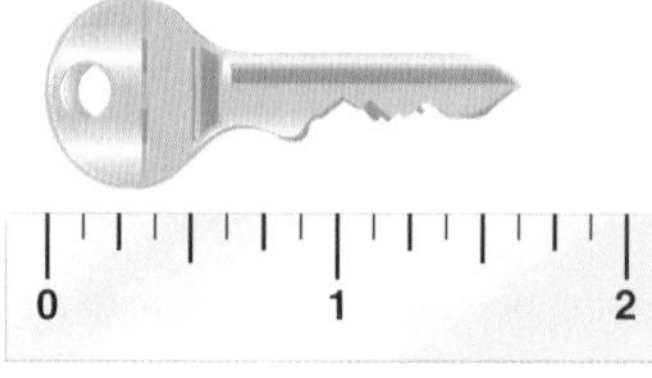

The key is $1\frac{5}{8}$ inches long.

Personal Tutor glencoe.com

StudyTip

Conversions When converting a larger unit to a smaller unit, multiply. When converting a smaller unit to a larger unit, divide.

EXAMPLE 2 Estimate and Measure Length

Estimate the metric length of the caterpillar. Then measure to find the actual length.

The caterpillar is about $2\frac{1}{2}$ pennies wide.
An appropriate estimate is about 5 centimeters long.

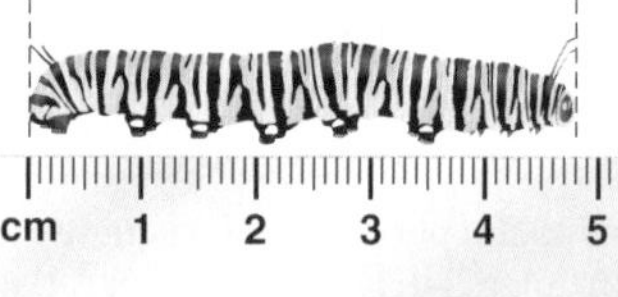

The caterpillar is 48 millimeters or 4.8 centimeters long.

Personal Tutor glencoe.com

TEACH with TECH

WEB SEARCH Show your students that a search engine can be used to find Web sites that contain unit conversion tables and perform simple unit conversions. For example, search for "18 inches to feet."

EXAMPLE 3 Convert Measurements

Complete each conversion.

a. ■ **yd = 129 ft**

Since 1 yard = 3 feet, divide 129 by 3.

129 ÷ 3 = 43

So, 43 yard = 129 feet.

b. ■ **in. = 4.5 ft**

Since 12 inches = 1 foot, multiply 12 by 4.5.

12 × 4.5 = 54

So, 54 inches = 4.5 feet

c. ■ **mm = 13 cm**

Since 10 millimeter = 1 centimeter, multiply 13 by 10.

13 × 10 = 130

So, 130 millimeter = 13 centimeter.

d. ■ **m = 175 cm**

Since 1 meter = 100 centimeter, divide 175 by 100.

175 ÷ 100 = 1.75

So, 1.75 meter = 175 centimeter.

Personal Tutor glencoe.com

Exercises

Write the customary unit of length that you would use to measure each of the following.

1. height of a box of cereal in.
2. length of a truck yd
3. distance across Tennessee mi
4. height of a classroom ft

Write the metric unit of length that you would use to measure each of the following.

5. length of a toothbrush cm
6. thickness of a dime mm
7. length of the Mississippi River km
8. depth of a pond m
9. Estimate the customary length of the paperclip. Then measure to find actual length. $1\frac{1}{2}$ in.; $1\frac{1}{4}$ in.
10. Estimate the metric length of the fish. Then measure to find the actual length. 4 cm; 4.4 cm

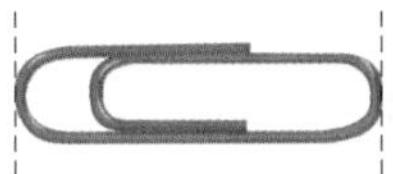

Watch Out!

Rulers Be sure to use the correct ruler when measuring length. Use the customary side for Exercise 9 and the metric side for Exercise 10.

Complete.

11. ■ mi = 3080 yd 1.75
12. 12 ft = ■ in. 144
13. ■ in. = 5.25 ft 63
14. 4400 yd = ■ mi 2.5
15. ■ ft = 51 yd 153
16. 18 in. = ■ ft 1.5
17. ■ cm = 7.5 m 750
18. 5.7 km = ■ m 5700
19. ■ mm = 54 cm 540
20. 4.75 m = ■ cm 475
21. ■ m = 740 cm 7.4
22. 1675 mm = ■ cm 167.5

Additional Example

3 Complete each conversion.

a. ■ mi = 4,400 yd 2.5 mi

b. ■ ft = 3.75 yd 11.25 ft

c. ■ m = 0.8 km 800 m

d. ■ mm = 76 cm 760 mm

Tips for New Teachers

Measuring Length Remind students to check that one end of the object is aligned with 0 on the ruler. If necessary, add guidelines to the ends of the object to help make the measurement easier and more accurate.

3 ASSESS

Formative Assessment

Use Exercises 1–22 to assess whether students know how to convert measurements within the customary and metric systems and know how to measure length in both systems.

Yesterday's News

Ask students to write a sentence on how yesterday's concept on measuring perimeter helped with today's lesson on measuring length in the customary and metric systems.

0-7 Lesson Notes

1 FOCUS

Vertical Alignment

Lesson 0-7
Make and interpret pictographs, line graphs, and bar graphs.

After Lesson 0-7
Use graphs to represent, compare, and analyze data.

2 TEACH

Example 1 shows how to read and interpret pictographs. **Example 2** shows how to read and interpret line graphs. **Example 3** shows how to read and interpret bar graphs.

Additional Example

1 **WEATHER** The pictograph shows the number of cloudy days from March through June. How many times greater is the number of cloudy days in April than in June? about 2.4 times

Month	Number of Cloudy Days
March	☁☁☁☁☁◐
April	☁☁☁☁☁☁
May	☁☁☁☁◐
June	☁☁◐

☁ = 2 cloudy days

Tips for New Teachers

Making Pictographs Remind students that half a symbol should be a whole number, so the value of each symbol should be an even number.

0-7 Data Analysis

Now
- Read and interpret pictographs, line graphs, and bar graphs.
- Make pictographs, line graphs, and bar graphs.

Review Vocabulary
data
pictograph
line graph
bar graph

Math Online
glencoe.com
- Extra Examples
- Personal Tutor
- Self-Check Quiz
- Homework Help

Data are pieces of information that are often numerical and can be displayed using tables and graphs.

A **pictograph** compares data by using picture symbols.

Real-World EXAMPLE 1 Pictographs

DRIVER PERMITS The pictograph shows the number of students in each homeroom that have their driving permit. How many times as great is the number of students who have their driver's permits in homeroom 16 as in homeroom 14?

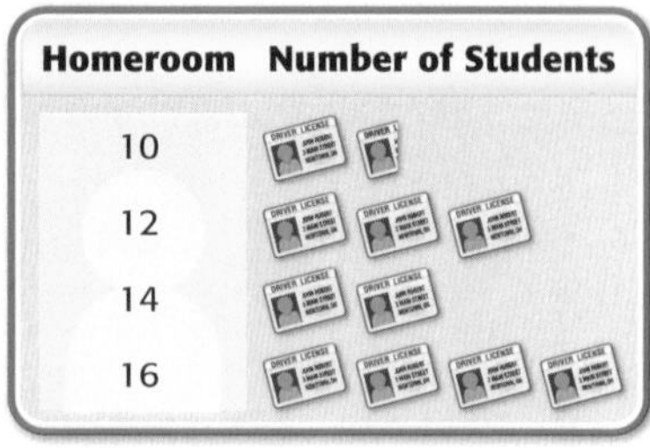

Homeroom
Number of Students
10
12
14
16

= 2 students

In homeroom 16, 8 students have their permits. In homeroom 14, 4 students have their permits.

To find how many times as many students in homeroom 16 have their permits as homeroom 14, divide.

$8 \div 4 = 2$

So, two times as many students in homeroom 16 have their permits as in homeroom 14.

Personal Tutor glencoe.com

Line graphs show how a data set changes over a period of time. By examining the direction of the connected lines, you can describe the trend in the data.

Real-World EXAMPLE 2 Line Graphs

ANIMALS The line graph shows the growth of a baby Asian elephant at the National Zoo in Washington, D.C. Find about how much weight the elephant gained from 10 months to 12 months.

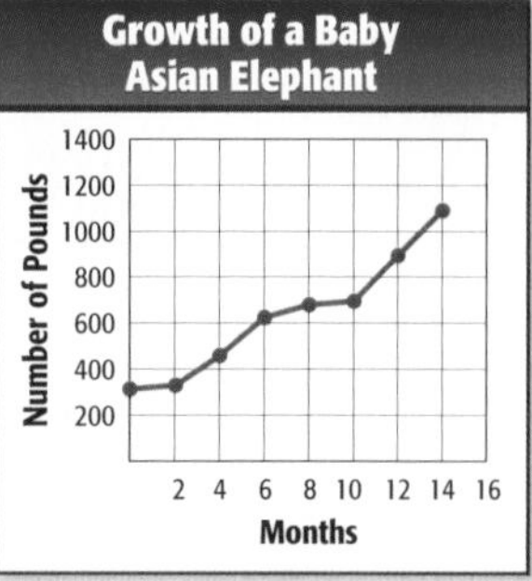

Look at the graph. At ten months, the elephant weighed about 700 pounds. At twelve months, the elephant weighed about 900 pounds.

$900 - 700 = 200$

So, the elephant gained about 200 pounds between the ages of 10 months and 12 months.

Personal Tutor glencoe.com

Real-World Link

There are almost 50,000 shopping malls nationwide. Connecticut has the greatest number of malls per person. For every 1000 people in Connecticut, there are 0.238 malls.

Source: National Research Bureau

Bar graphs are used to compare categories of data. The height of each bar represents the frequency of each category of data.

Real-World EXAMPLE 3 Bar Graphs

SHOPPING The bar graph shows the approximate number of shopping malls in the states with the most shopping malls. About how many more malls are in California than in Illinois?

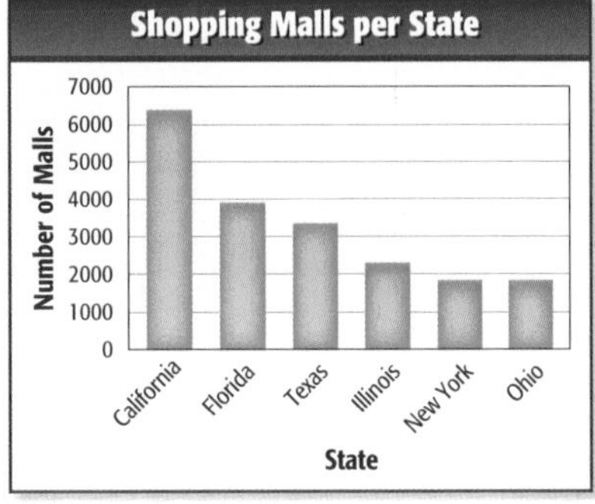

Source: National Research Bureau

There are about 6500 malls in California and about 2500 malls in Illinois.

$6500 - 2500 = 4000$

So, there are about 4000 more malls in California than in Illinois.

Personal Tutor glencoe.com

Exercises

For Exercises 1–3, refer to the pictograph in Example 1.

1. How many more students would have to have their driver's permit in homeroom 10 to exceed the number of students who have their permit in homeroom 12? 4 students
2. What is the total number of students who have their driver's permit shown in the graph? 21 students
3. Write a question that could be answered using the pictograph. Have a classmate answer your question.

For Exercises 4–6, refer to the line graph in Example 2.

4. Describe the change in the elephant's weight from 2 months to 14 months. Sample answer: The weight of the elephant is increasing.
5. Predict the elephant's weight by the 16th month. Sample answer: 1300 pounds
6. For which two-month period did the elephant have the greatest weight change?

For Exercises 7–9, refer to the bar graph in Example 3.

7. What can be determined about the number of malls in New York and Ohio? Sample answer: There are about the same number of malls in New York and Ohio.
8. About how many times as many malls are in California as in Ohio? Sample answer: about 3 times
9. Use the Internet or another source to find the number of malls in your state. Then write a question that compares the data in the bar graph to the data you found. See students' work.

3. Sample answer: Which homeroom had the greatest number of students with their driver's permit? Homeroom 16

6. Either the 10- to 12-month period or the 12- to 14-month period. The weight gain appears to be about the same in these two periods.

Additional Examples

2 EARTHQUAKES The line graph shows the number of U.S. earthquakes from 2002 to 2007. About how many fewer earthquakes occurred in 2006 than 2005? about 1000

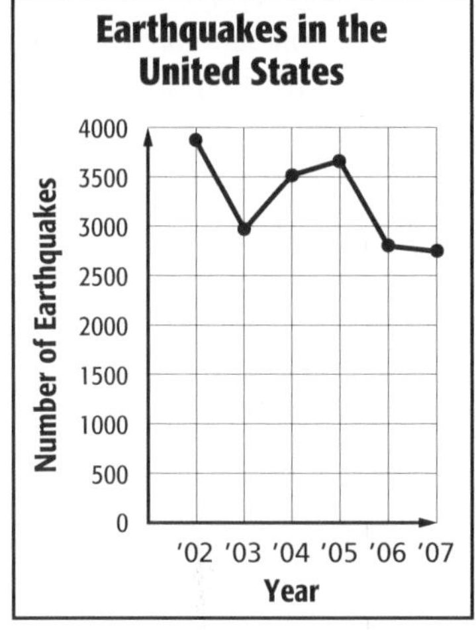

3 PETS The bar graph shows the results of a 2007 pet survey. About how many more cats than horses are owned as pets? about 75 million

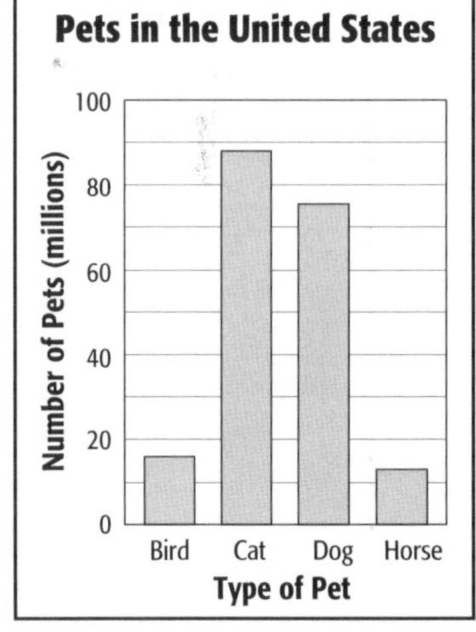

Name the Math

Ask students to explain how to read data on a pictograph, line graph, or bar graph.

3 ASSESS

Formative Assessment

Use Exercises 1–9 to assess whether students can read and interpret pictographs, line graphs, and bar graphs.

Using the Posttest

Use the Chapter 0 Posttest to assess students' understanding of the concepts after you have presented the lessons in Chapter 0. If students are still having difficulty with one or more concepts, refer to *Math Triumphs* for strategies for reteaching.

Additional Answer

2. 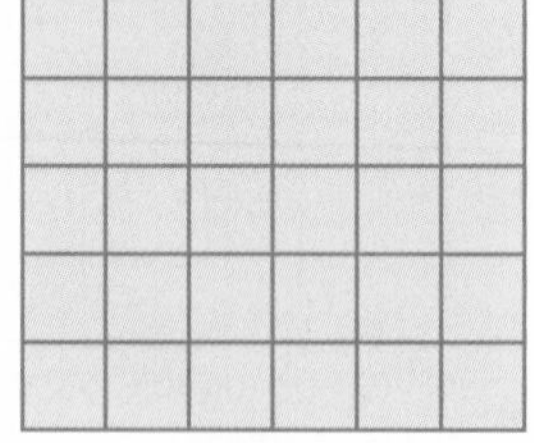

CHAPTER 0 Posttest

Use any problem-solving strategy to solve each problem.

1. **GO-KARTS** The length of Fun Center's go-kart track is 843 feet. If Nadia circled the track 9 times, how many feet did she travel? **7587 ft**

2. **PATTERNS** Draw the fifth figure in the pattern below. **See margin.**

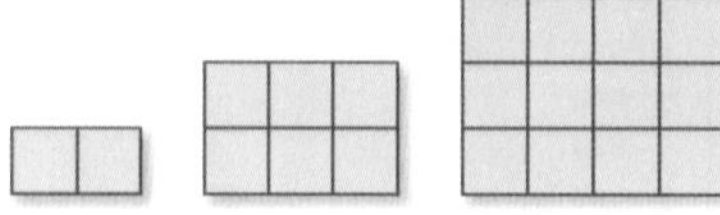

3. **GAMES** Find the number of squares of any size in the game board shown at the right. **204 squares**

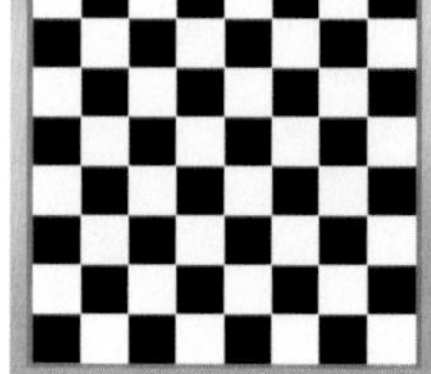

4. **SUPPLIES** An art supply store sells 5 different sized canvases. The surface area of the middle-size canvas is 3.5 times larger than the surface area of the extra-small canvas. If the surface area of the extra-small canvas is 81 square inches, what is the surface area of the middle-sized canvas? **283.5 in^2**

5. **MONEY** How many ways can you make change for a dollar using only quarters, dimes, and nickels? **29 ways**

6. **NUMBER SENSE** The product of two consecutive even integers is 1088. What are the integers? **32 and 34**

Find each sum or difference.

7. $6.5 + 2.3$ **8.8**
8. $25.72 + 18.67$ **44.39**
9. $59.04 + 77.84$ **136.88**
10. $25.54 + 36.7$ **62.24**
11. $257.76 + 345.487$ **603.247**
12. $4865.7 + 705.76$ **5571.46**
13. $5.3 - 4.7$ **0.6**
14. $458.07 - 67.75$ **390.32**
15. $851.79 - 570.85$ **280.94**
16. $73.2 - 42.86$ **30.34**
17. $569.43 - 97.1$ **472.33**
18. $852 - 469.72$ **382.28**

19. **SALES** A digital camera is on sale for \$139.99. If the original price of the camera was \$175.59, how much money will you save? **\$35.60**

20. **TEMPERATURE** A city's average high temperature during the month of May is 64.5°F. Its average low for the same month is 35.9°F. Find the difference between the average high and average low temperature. **28.6°**

Find each product or quotient.

21. 4.7×6 **28.2**
22. 6.2×3.9 **24.18**
23. 43.8×76.3 **3341.94**
24. 49×3.7 **181.3**
25. 82.7×6.72 **555.744**
26. 6.535×3.7 **24.1795**
27. $28.8 \div 4$ **7.2**
28. $92.4 \div 5.5$ **16.8**
29. $156.3408 \div 9.87$ **15.84**
30. $382.1565 \div 36.57$ **10.45**
31. $2542 \div 8.64$ **294.212963**
32. $6482.84 \div 46.22$ **140.2604933**

33. **MOVIES** The all-time top grossing movie earned approximately 1.835 million dollars. The tenth all-time grossing movie earned about 0.915 million dollars. About how many times as much did the top movie make as the tenth? **about 2 times**

Write a verbal rule to describe each pattern or sequence. Then find the 10th term in each. 34–37. See margin.

34.

Number of Teams	Number of Players
1	7
2	14
3	21

35.

Number of People	Bracelets Made
1	15
2	25
3	35

36. 6, 7, 8, 9, ...

37. 6, 11, 16, 21, ...

Find the perimeter of each figure.

38.

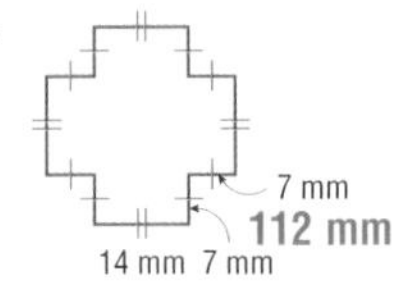

112 mm

39.

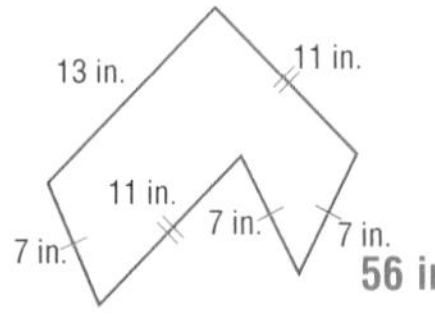

56 in.

40. 4 cm, 6 cm, 5 cm, 9 cm, 4 cm, 2 cm, 5 cm

35 cm

Write the metric unit of length that you would use to measure each of the following.

41. width of a DVD player centimeter

42. length of a school bus meter

43. distance between state capitals kilometer

44. height of a room meter

Complete.

45. 7040 yd = ■ mi 4

46. ■ in. = 12 ft 144

47. ■ ft = 72 yd 216

48. 10 ft = ■ in. 120

49. 3.5 mi = ■ yd 6160

50. ■ yd = 30 ft 10

51. 1656 mm = ■ cm 165.6

52. 4.8 km = ■ m 4800

53. ■ m = 620 cm 6.2

54. 5.72 m = ■ cm 572

55. ■ mm = 43 cm 430

56. ■ cm = 3.9 m 390

57. VIDEO GAMES The pictograph shows the number of students in each grade that have a video game system. About how many times as great is the number of students who have a video game system in eighth grade as in seventh grade? 1.4 times

Grade	Number of Students
Sixth	🎮 ½🎮
Seventh	🎮 🎮 ½🎮
Eighth	🎮 🎮 🎮 ¼🎮

🎮 = 50 students

58. CELL PHONES The local cell phone store is having a sale on cell phones. The graph shows the number of cell phones sold each day for one week. How does the number of phones sold Sunday through Thursday compare to the number of phones sold Friday and Saturday? They are the same.

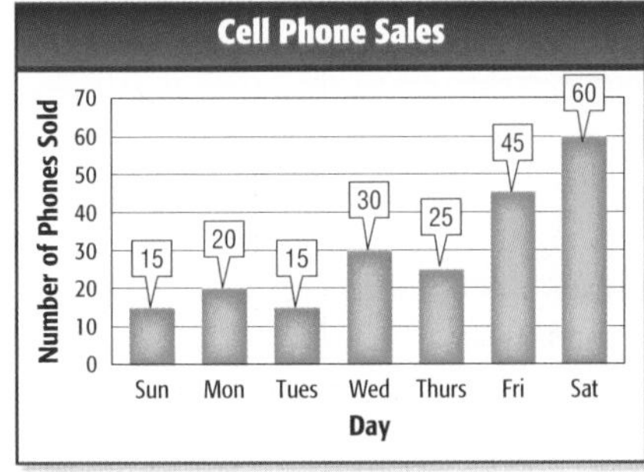

Additional Answers

34. Sample answer: the number of players is equal to 7 times the number of teams; 70 players.

35. Sample answer: the bracelets made are equal to 10 times the number of people plus five; 105 bracelets.

36. Sample answer: the value of the term is equal to five more than the term number; 15.

37. Sample answer: the value of the term is equal to one more than five times the term number; 51.

CHAPTER 1

Chapter Planner

Diagnostic Assessment
Quick Check, p. 3

	Lesson 1-1 Pacing: 1 day	Explore 1-2 Pacing: 1 day	Lesson 1-2 Pacing: 1 day
Title	**Words and Expressions**	**Algebra Lab: Rules and Expressions**	**Variables and Expressions**
Objectives	• Translate verbal phrases into numerical expressions. • Use the order of operations to evaluate expressions.	• Determine rules for a given pattern.	• Translate verbal phrases into algebraic expressions. • Evaluate expressions containing variables.
Key Vocabulary	numerical expression evaluate order of operations		algebra variable algebraic expression defining a variable
NCTM Focal Points	G8–FP1, G8–FP6C For the complete wording of the focal points for grades 7 and 8 please see pages iv, v, FP0, and FP1.		
Multiple Representations	p. 8		p. 15
Lesson Resources	**Chapter 1 Resource Masters** • Study Guide and Intervention, pp. 5–6 AL OL ELL • Skills Practice, p. 7 AL OL ELL • Practice, p. 8 AL OL BL ELL • Word Problem Practice, p. 9 AL OL BL • Enrichment, p. 10 OL BL **Transparencies** • 5-Minute Check Transparency 1-1 AL OL BL ELL **Additional Print Resources** • *Study Notebook* AL OL BL ELL	**Materials:** • grid paper • toothpicks	**Chapter 1 Resource Masters** • Study Guide and Intervention, pp. 11–12 AL OL ELL • Skills Practice, p. 13 AL OL ELL • Practice, p. 14 AL OL BL ELL • Word Problem Practice, p. 15 AL OL BL • Enrichment, p. 16 OL BL • Graphing Calculator, p. 17 AL OL BL ELL • Quiz 1, p. 46 AL OL BL ELL **Transparencies** • 5-Minute Check Transparency 1-2 AL OL BL ELL **Additional Print Resources** • *Study Notebook* AL OL BL ELL
Technology for Every Lesson	Math Online glencoe.com • Extra Examples • Self-Check Quizzes • Personal Tutor	**CD/DVD Resources** IWB INTERACTIVE WHITEBOARD READY IWB StudentWorks Plus IWB Interactive Classroom IWB Diagnostic and Assessment Planner	• TeacherWorks Plus • eSolutions Manual Plus • ExamView Assessment Suite
Math in Motion		p. 10	
Differentiated Instruction	pp. 6, 9		pp. 13, 16

KEY:   Approaching Level  On Level 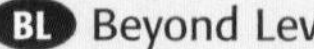 Beyond Level  English Learners

Suggested Pacing			
Time Periods	Instruction	Review & Assessment	Total
45-minute	12	2	14
90-minute	6	1	7

The Tools of Algebra

Extend 1-2 Pacing: 1 day	Lesson 1-3 Pacing: 1 day	Lesson 1-4 Pacing: 1 day	Explore 1-5 Pacing: 1 day
Spreadsheet Lab: Expressions and Spreadsheets	**Properties**	**Ordered Pairs and Relations**	**Algebra Lab: Relations and Functions**
• Determine rules for a given pattern.	• Identify and use properties of addition and multiplication. • Use properties of addition and multiplication to simplify algebraic expressions.	• Use ordered pairs to locate points. • Use graphs to represent relations.	• Identify a function.
	properties counterexample simplify deductive reasoning	coordinate system *y*-axis; *x*-axis coordinate plane origin ordered pair relation domain; range	
		p. 29	
Materials: • spreadsheet software	**Chapter 1 Resource Masters** • Study Guide and Intervention, pp. 18–19 AL OL ELL • Skills Practice, p. 20 AL OL ELL • Practice, p. 21 AL OL BL ELL • Word Problem Practice, p. 22 AL OL BL • Enrichment, p. 23 OL BL • Quiz 2, p. 46 AL OL BL ELL **Transparencies** • 5-Minute Check Transparency 1-3 AL OL BL ELL **Additional Print Resources** • *Study Notebook* AL OL BL ELL	**Chapter 1 Resource Masters** • Study Guide and Intervention, pp. 24–25 AL OL ELL • Skills Practice, p. 26 AL OL ELL • Practice, p. 27 AL OL BL ELL • Word Problem Practice, p. 28 AL OL BL • Enrichment, p. 29 OL BL • Quiz 3, p. 47 AL OL BL ELL **Transparencies** • 5-Minute Check Transparency 1-4 AL OL BL ELL **Additional Print Resources** • *Study Notebook* AL OL BL ELL	**Materials:** • grid paper • centimeter cubes
Math Online glencoe.com • Extra Examples • Self-Check Quizzes • Personal Tutor	**CD/DVD Resources** IWB INTERACTIVE WHITEBOARD READY IWB StudentWorks Plus IWB Interactive Classroom IWB Diagnostic and Assessment Planner	• TeacherWorks Plus • eSolutions Manual Plus • ExamView Assessment Suite	
		p. 27	p. 31
	pp. 19, 23	pp. 26, 30	

Formative Assessment
Mid-Chapter Quiz, p. 24

CHAPTER 1

Chapter Planner

	Lesson 1-5 Pacing: 1 day	Extend 1-5 Pacing: 1 day	Explore 1-6 Pacing: 1 day
Title	**Words, Equations, Tables, and Graphs**	**Graphing Technology Lab: Function Tables**	**Algebra Lab: Scatter Plots**
Objectives	• Use multiple representations to represent functions. • Translate among different verbal, tabular, graphical, and algebraic representations of functions.	• Use a graphing calculator to create function tables.	• Use a scatter plot to investigate the relationship between two sets of data.
Key Vocabulary	function function rule function table equation		
NCTM Focal Points			
Multiple Representations	pp. 34, 35	p. 38	
Lesson Resources	**Chapter 1 Resource Masters** • Study Guide and Intervention, pp. 30–31 AL OL ELL • Skills Practice, p. 32 AL OL ELL • Practice, p. 33 AL OL BL ELL • Word Problem Practice, p. 34 AL OL BL • Enrichment, p. 35 OL BL • Graphing Calculator, p. 36 AL OL BL ELL • Quiz 4, p. 47 AL OL BL ELL **Transparencies** • 5-Minute Check Transparency 1-5 AL OL BL ELL **Additional Print Resources** • *Study Notebook* AL OL BL ELL	**Materials:** • TI-Nspire calculator	**Materials:** • grid paper • centimeter ruler or tape measure
Technology for Every Lesson	Math Online **glencoe.com** • Extra Examples • Self-Check Quizzes • Personal Tutor	**CD/DVD Resources** IWB INTERACTIVE WHITEBOARD READY IWB StudentWorks Plus IWB Interactive Classroom IWB Diagnostic and Assessment Planner	• TeacherWorks Plus • eSolutions Manual Plus • ExamView Assessment Suite
Math in Motion			p. 39
Differentiated Instruction	pp. 34, 37		

KEY: AL Approaching Level OL On Level BL Beyond Level ELL English Learners

Lesson 1-6 Pacing: 1 day	Extend 1-6 Pacing: 1 day
Scatter Plots	**Graphing Technology Lab: Scatter Plot**
• Construct scatter plots. • Analyze trends in scatter plots.	• Use a graphing calculator to graph scatter plots.
scatter plot	
pp. 44, 46	
Chapter 1 Resource Masters • Study Guide and Intervention, pp. 37–38 AL OL ELL • Skills Practice, p. 39 AL OL ELL • Practice, p. 40 AL OL BL ELL • Word Problem Practice, p. 41 AL OL BL • Enrichment, p. 42 OL BL • Graphing Calculator, p. 43 AL OL BL ELL **Transparencies** • 5-Minute Check Transparency 1-6 AL OL BL ELL **Additional Print Resources** • *Study Notebook* AL OL BL ELL	**Materials:** • graphing calculator

Math Online glencoe.com
- Extra Examples
- Self-Check Quizzes
- Personal Tutor

CD/DVD Resources IWB INTERACTIVE WHITEBOARD READY
- IWB StudentWorks Plus
- IWB Interactive Classroom
- IWB Diagnostic and Assessment Planner
- TeacherWorks Plus
- eSolutions Manual Plus
- ExamView Assessment Suite

pp. 42, 46	

Summative Assessment
- Study Guide and Review, pp. 49–52
- Practice Test, p. 53

CHAPTER 1 Assessment and Intervention

SE = Student Edition, **TE** = Teacher Edition, **CRM** = Chapter Resource Masters

	Diagnosis	Prescription
Diagnostic Assessment	**Beginning Chapter 1**	
	Get Ready for Chapter 1 **SE,** p. 3	Intervention **TE,** p. 3
	Beginning Every Lesson	
	Then, Now, Why? **SE** 5-Minute Check Transparencies	Chapter 0 **SE,** pp. P1 through P22 Concepts and Skills Bank **SE,** pp. 856–887 *Quick Review Math Handbook*
Formative Assessment	**During/After Every Lesson**	
	Check Your Progress **SE,** every example Check Your Understanding **SE** H.O.T. Problems **SE** Spiral Review **SE** Additional Examples **TE** Watch Out! **TE** Step 4, Assess **TE** Chapter 1 Quizzes **CRM,** pp. 46–47 Self-Check Quizzes **glencoe.com**	**Tier 1 Intervention** Concepts and Skills Bank **SE,** pp. 856–887 Skills Practice **CRM,** Ch. 1 **glencoe.com** **Tier 2 Intervention** Differentiated Instruction **TE** Study Guide and Intervention Masters **CRM,** Ch. 1 *Quick Review Math Handbook* **Tier 3 Intervention** *Math Triumphs, Grade 8,* Ch. 2, 3, 9
	Mid-Chapter	
	Mid-Chapter Quiz **SE,** p. 24 Mid-Chapter Test **CRM,** p. 48 ExamView Assessment Suite	**Tier 1 Intervention** Concepts and Skills Bank **SE,** pp. 856–887 Skills Practice **CRM,** Ch. 1 **glencoe.com** **Tier 2 Intervention** Study Guide and Intervention Masters **CRM,** Ch. 1 *Quick Review Math Handbook* **Tier 3 Intervention** *Math Triumphs, Grade 8,* Ch. 2, 3, 9
	Before Chapter Test	
	Chapter Study Guide and Review **SE,** pp. 49–52 Practice Test **SE,** p. 53 Standardized Test Practice **SE,** pp. 54–57 Chapter Test **glencoe.com** Standardized Test Practice **glencoe.com** Vocabulary Review **glencoe.com** ExamView Assessment Suite	**Tier 1 Intervention** Concepts and Skills Bank **SE,** pp. 856–887 Skills Practice **CRM,** Ch. 1 **glencoe.com** **Tier 2 Intervention** Study Guide and Intervention Masters **CRM,** Ch. 1 *Quick Review Math Handbook* **Tier 3 Intervention** *Math Triumphs, Grade 8,* Ch. 2, 3, 9
Summative Assessment	**After Chapter 1**	
	Multiple-Choice Tests, Forms 1, 2A, 2B, **CRM,** pp. 50–55 Free-Response Tests, Forms 2C, 2D, 3, **CRM,** pp. 56–61 Vocabulary Test **CRM,** p. 49 Extended Response Test **CRM,** p. 62 Standardized Test Practice **CRM,** pp. 63–65 ExamView Assessment Suite	Study Guide and Intervention Masters **CRM,** Ch. 1 *Quick Review Math Handbook* **glencoe.com**

Differentiated Instruction

Option 1 Reaching All Learners AL OL BL ELL

VISUAL/SPATIAL Some students find simplifying complicated expressions intimidating. To help students visualize the step-by-step process of simplifying, ask them to make a mobile. At the top, place an expression requiring several steps to simplify. From this expression, hang a card showing the first step in simplifying the expression. Continue hanging cards showing each successive step until the value is reached at the bottom.

LOGICAL Write the following symbols on the board:

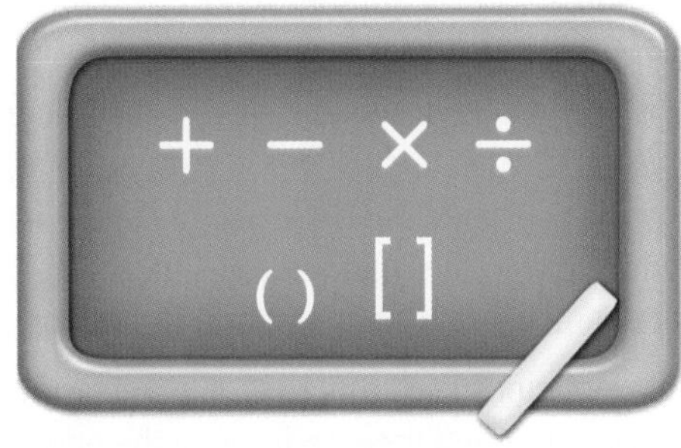

Have students use at least three of the symbols and any numbers to write an expression that has a value of 27. Sample answer: $24 + 18 \div (3 \times 2)$

Ask students to make up their own problems and then exchange them with other students to solve.

Option 2 Approaching Level AL

Have students work in small groups. Ask each group to think of an example for at least four different properties of numbers, such as $44 + 87 = 87 + 44$ or $12 \times 1 = 12$. Groups then take turns calling out one of the examples, while the other group confers and then names the property. Have each of the groups play each other in rounds.

After each round, ask groups to go over any of the properties they missed so that they can do better in the next round.

Option 3 English Learners ELL

Have students discuss and then write on separate index cards a list of as many verbal phrases as they can for each of the following algebraic expressions:

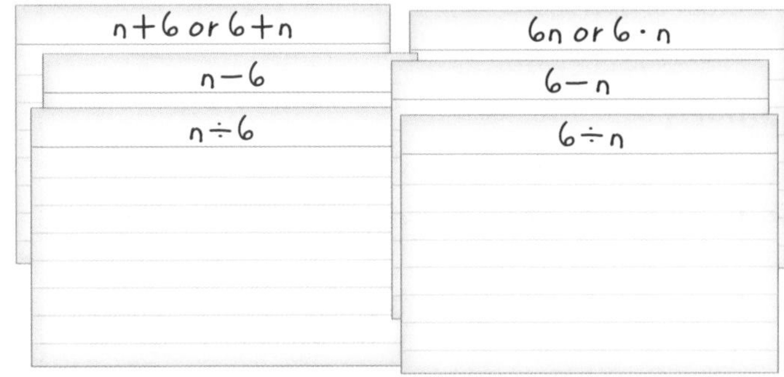

Students can use the cards to help translate verbal phrases into algebraic expressions.

Word Wall Extend the vocabulary chart to include all new words or phrases in the chapter. You can include words that are not just used in mathematics. For each word or phrase, show:

- Multiple meanings of words.
- How words are used within a sentence. Students can write the sentences to help with grammar, usage, etc.
- Cultural context that may not be understood by students.
- Illustrations, graphs, and diagrams to make the concepts and vocabulary more comprehensible.

Option 4 Beyond Level BL

Ask students to prepare a quiz of ten questions covering ordered pairs, relations, and scatter plots. Each question should include directions and each quiz should have a solution key. Students can exchange their questions. Discussions about the strengths and weaknesses of the questions can be conducted following the activity.

Focus on Mathematical Content

Vertical Alignment

Before Chapter 1

Related Topics before Pre-Algebra

- select tools to solve problems
- use order of operations

Chapter 1

Related Topics from Pre-Algebra

- use variables, expressions, and equations to model real-world problems
- predict, find, and justify solutions to application problems using appropriate tables, graphs, and algebraic equations
- locate and name points on a coordinate graph
- draw conclusions and make predictions using scatter plots

After Chapter 1

Preparation for Algebra 1

- represent relationships among quantities, using concrete models
- investigate methods for solving linear equations
- look for patterns and represent generalizations algebraically

Lesson-by-Lesson Preview

1-1 Words and Expressions

When evaluating an expression, use the order of operations to find its numerical value:

Step 1 Simplify the expressions inside grouping symbols.

Step 2 Do all multiplications and/or divisions from left to right.

Step 3 Do all additions and/or subtractions from left to right.

To facilitate translating verbal phrases into expressions, develop a list of words that correspond to mathematical operations.

1-2 Variables and Expressions

Algebra is a language of symbols. A variable is a placeholder for any value. Any letter, such as x, can be used as a variable. Mathematicians usually avoid the use of i and e for variables because they have other mathematical meanings (i is used with imaginary numbers and e with natural logarithms).

Evaluate expressions such as $4x + 2y$ by replacing the variables with known values and then performing the operations using the order of operations.

1-3 Properties

In algebra, properties are statements that are true for any numbers.

- The Commutative Property of Addition or Multiplication states that the order in which numbers are added or multiplied does not change the sum or product. So, $3 + 8 = 8 + 3$ and $3 \cdot 8 = 8 \cdot 3$.
- The Associative Property of Addition or Multiplication states that the way in which numbers are grouped when added or multiplied does not change the sum or product. So, $(3 + 8) + 2 = 3 + (8 + 2)$ and $(3 \cdot 8) \cdot 2 = 3 \cdot (8 \cdot 2)$.

The following properties are also true:

- Additive Identity Property: When 0 is added to any number, the sum is the number, e.g., $9 + 0 = 9$.
- Multiplicative Identity Property: When any number is multiplied by 1, the product is the number, e.g., $9 \times 1 = 9$.
- Multiplicative Property of Zero: When any number is multiplied by 0, the product is 0, e.g., $9 \times 0 = 0$.

You can use the properties of numbers to find sums and products mentally and to simplify expressions.

1-4 Ordered Pairs and Relations

The Cartesian coordinate system is used to locate points.

- The coordinate system is formed by two perpendicular number lines that intersect at their zero points.
- An ordered pair of numbers is used to locate a point on a coordinate plane. The first number is the x-coordinate and tells where the point is located on the x-axis. The second number is the y-coordinate and tells where the point is located on the y-axis.
- A set of ordered pairs such as {(1, 4), (2, 6), (3, 8), (4, 7)} is a relation. The domain of the relation is the set of x-coordinates. The range is the set of y-coordinates.
- A relation can be shown as a set of ordered pairs, as a table, or as a graph.

Ordered pairs: (0, 0), (2, 3), (4, 2), (5, 4)

Table and graph of ordered pairs:

x	y
0	0
2	3
4	2
5	4

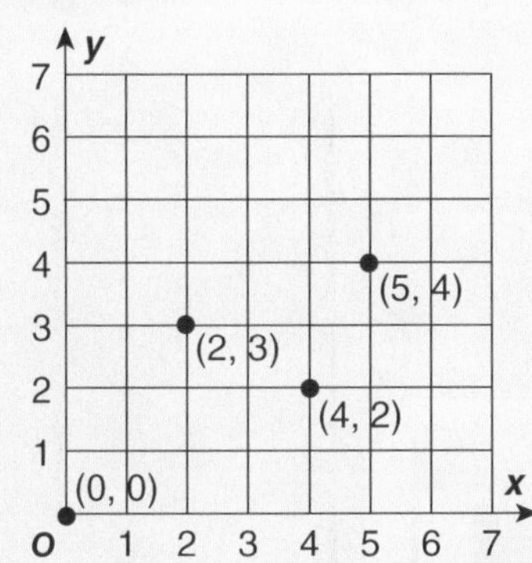

1-5 Words, Equations, Tables, and Graphs

A function is a special relation in which each member of the domain is paired with exactly one member of the range. Functions can be described using words, equations, tables, or graphs. Functions are usually written as equations with two variables in which x represents the input and y represents the output. A function table organizes the x-coordinate of the input, the function rule, and the y-coordinate of the output. The x- and y-coordinates in the function table can be plotted on a graph.

1-6 Scatter Plots

A scatter plot is a graph that shows the relationship between two sets of data. In a scatter plot, two sets of data are graphed as ordered pairs on a coordinate system. Two sets of data can have:

- a positive relationship: as x increases, y increases

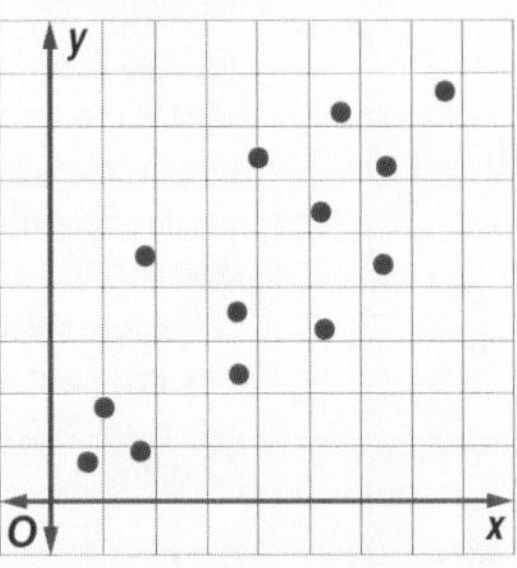

- a negative relationship: as x increases, y decreases

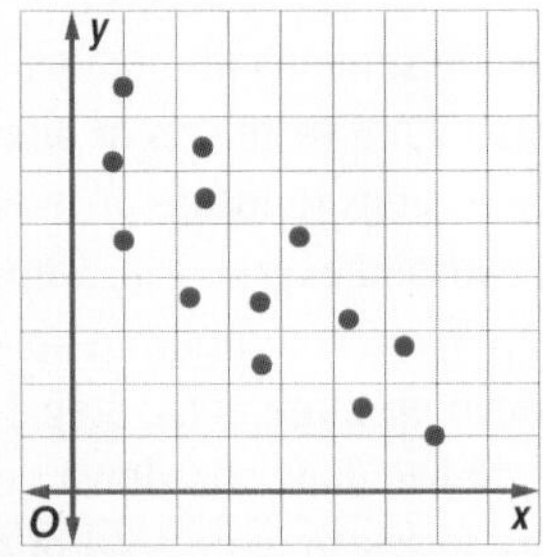

- no relationship: no obvious pattern

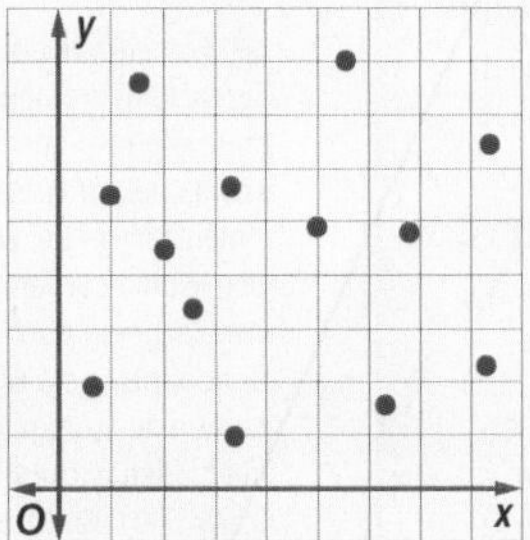

Scatter plots can be used to spot trends, draw conclusions, and make predictions.

Professional Development

Targeted professional development has been articulated throughout McGraw-Hill's mathematics program. The **McGraw-Hill Professional Development Video Library** provides short videos that support key topics. For more information, visit **glencoe.com.**

Model Lessons

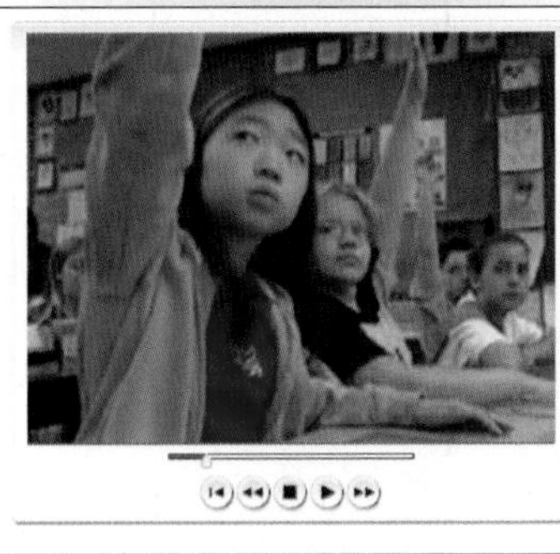

Instructional Strategies

CHAPTER 1 Notes

Chapter Project

Find the Coordinates

Students use what they have learned about the tools of algebra to create and solve a geocache-type game, using *x*- and *y*-coordinates and puzzles for the cache.

- Divide students into teams. Have each team write sets of directions in three steps to locate ordered pairs on a coordinate grid, e.g., Step 1: Start at (2, 1), move right three units; Step 2: Move up three units; Step 3: Move right five units and down one unit. Ask teams to write a set of directions for each of six ordered pairs, using one or two moves for each step. Each set of directions should be written on a separate note card.
- Have teams write a puzzle for each of the six ordered pairs, with one puzzle per note card, and answers in a separate document. Each puzzle should involve one of the concepts in the chapter, such as writing or evaluating an expression, representing a situation as an equation, table, or graph, naming properties, or creating a scatter plot.
- Have teams exchange games. Each team is given a coordinate grid and one set of directions. After they locate and label the ordered pair, the team receives the puzzle. After they solve the puzzle, they receive a new set of directions. They continue until they locate the six sets of ordered pairs and solve the six puzzles.

CHAPTER 1 The Tools of Algebra

Then
In previous courses, you have performed mathematical operations and evaluated numerical expressions.

Now
In Chapter 1, you will:
- Translate verbal phrases into numerical expressions.
- Evaluate expressions and use the order of operations.
- Identify and use properties of addition and multiplication.
- Use words, tables, equations, and graphs to represent relations and functions.

Why?
TECHNOLOGY
Geocaching is a new adventure game where participants bury a container, or *cache*, somewhere in the world. They then list the coordinates of their cache on a website. Other participants use a Global Positioning System, or GPS, to find hidden caches. There are nearly 500,000 active caches hidden worldwide.

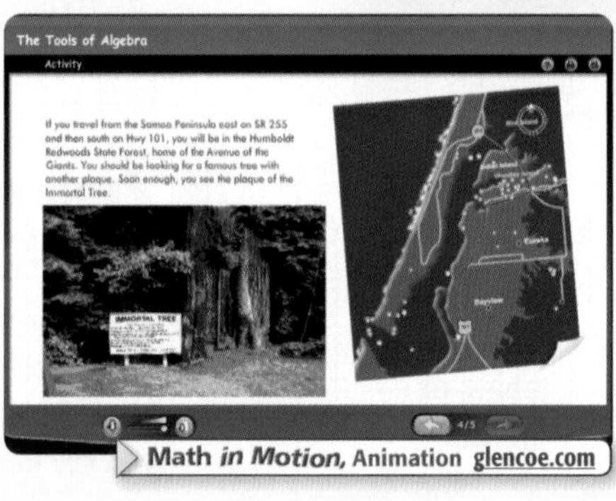

Math *in Motion*, Animation glencoe.com

Key Vocabulary Introduce the key vocabulary in the chapter using the routine below.

Define: An algebraic expression is an expression that contains at least one mathematical operation, one variable, and one number.

Example: $x + 5$

Ask: What is the variable? *x* What is the operation? addition What is 5? a number

Diagnose students' readiness for each chapter by using either the in-text **Quick Check** or the online **Chapter Readiness Quiz.** Then use the **Intervention Planner** to choose the correct program resource to reinforce each student's prerequisite skills.

Get Ready for Chapter 1

Diagnose Readiness You have two options for checking Prerequisite Skills.

Text Option Take the Quick Check below. Refer to the Quick Review for help.

*Quick*Check

(Used in Lesson 1-1)

Find each sum or difference. (Previous Course) 1–6. See margin.

1. 5.8 + 4.2 **2.** 7.1 + 6.5 **3.** 1.3 + 2.6

4. 9.4 – 4.2 **5.** 8.6 – 1.1 **6.** 5.7 – 3.5

7. **LUNCH** Calvin has $7.80. He spends $3.30 on lunch. How much money does Calvin have left? **$4.50**

8. **MONEY** Phil has $9.50. His sister gives him the $3.75 she owes him. How much money does Phil have now? **$13.25**

(Used in Lessons 1-1 through 1-4)

Estimate each sum, difference, product, or quotient. (Previous Course) **9–12. See margin.**

9. 1600 + 192 **10.** 524 – 349

11. 119 × 63 **12.** 1210 ÷ 398

13. **ANIMALS** The Siberian Tiger is the largest cat in the world. It can run as fast as 50 miles per hour. At that rate, about how far can it travel in 4 hours? **Sample answer: 200 mi**

14. **BABYSITTING** Ginny earns $5 per hour babysitting. Estimate how much she will earn in 4.75 hours. **Sample answer: $25**

(Used in Lessons 1-5 and 1-6)

Write the number that represents each given point on the number line. (Previous Course)

A B C D
0 1 2 3 4 5 6 7 8 9 10

15. *A* **1** **16.** *B* **3** **17.** *C* **4** **18.** *D* **6**

19. **TEMPERATURE** The low temperature yesterday was 32°F. Graph this temperature on a number line. **See margin.**

*Quick*Review

EXAMPLE 1

Find 11.9 – 2.15.

$$\begin{array}{r} \overset{8\,10}{11.\not9\not0} \\ -\ 2.15 \\ \hline 9.75 \end{array}$$

Annex a zero to align the decimal points. Subtract.

11.9 – 2.15 = 9.75

EXAMPLE 2

Estimate 117 + 51.

$$\begin{array}{r} 117 \\ +\ 51 \\ \hline \end{array} \longrightarrow \begin{array}{r} 120 \\ +\ 50 \\ \hline 170 \end{array}$$

Round to the nearest ten. Add.

$117 + 51 \approx 170$

EXAMPLE 3

Write the number that represents point *A* on the number line.

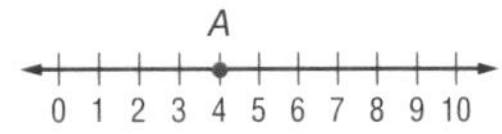

The number line starts at 0 and increases by 1. So point *A* is at 4.

Online Option Math Online Take a self-check Chapter Readiness Quiz at glencoe.com.

Chapter 1 The Tools of Algebra 3

Additional Answers

1. 10

2. 13.6

3. 3.9

4. 5.2

5. 7.5

6. 2.2

9. Sample answer: 1790

10. Sample answer: 170

11. Sample answer: 7200

12. Sample answer: 3

19. [number line from 28 to 38 with a point at 32]

Get Ready for Chapter 1

Response to Intervention (RtI)

Use the *Quick Check* results and the Intervention Planner to help you determine your Response to Intervention. The If-Then statements in the chart below help you decide the appropriate tier of RtI and suggest intervention resources for each tier.

Intervention Planner

Tier 1 On Level

If students miss about 25% of the exercises or less,

Then choose a resource:

SE Chapter 0, pp. P11–P12

TE Chapter Project, p. 2

Math Online Self-Check Quiz

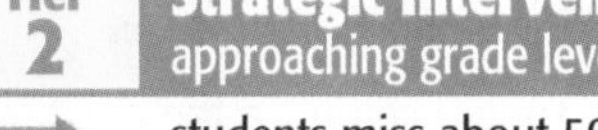
Tier 2 Strategic Intervention approaching grade level

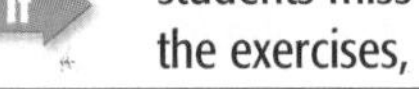
If students miss about 50% of the exercises,

Then choose a resource:

SE Concept and Skills Bank, pp. 856–887

Quick Review Math Handbook

Math Online Extra Examples, Personal Tutor, Homework Help

Tier 3 Intensive Intervention 2 or more years below grade level

If students miss about 75% of the exercises,

Then use *Math Triumphs, Grade 8,* Ch. 2, 3, 9

Math Online Extra Examples, Personal Tutor, Homework Help, Review Vocabulary

CHAPTER 1
Notes

FOLDABLES® Study Organizer

Dinah Zike's Foldables®

Focus Students write notes about algebraic concepts, properties, and vocabulary for each lesson of this chapter.

Teach Have students make and label the tabs for each lesson of their Foldables as illustrated. Encourage students to write a real-world problem for each lesson or concept that they cover in this chapter. Suggest that they record new vocabulary terms and include a definition and example for each.

When to Use It Encourage students to add to their Foldable as they work through the chapter, and use them to review for the chapter test.

Differentiated Instruction

CRM Student-Built Glossary, pp. 1–2 Students should complete the chart by providing a definition of each term and an example as they progress through Chapter 1. This study tool can also be used to review for the chapter test.

Get Started on Chapter 1

You will learn several new concepts, skills, and vocabulary terms as you study Chapter 1. To get ready, identify important terms and organize your resources. You may wish to refer to **Chapter 0** to review prerequisite skills.

FOLDABLES® Study Organizer

The Tools of Algebra Make this Foldable to help you organize your Chapter 1 notes about algebra. Begin with seven sheets of notebook paper.

1. **Staple** the seven sheets together to form a booklet.

2. **Cut** a tab on the second page the width of the white space. On the third page, make the tab 2 lines longer, and so on.

3. **Write** the chapter title on the cover and label each tab with the lesson number.

Math Online glencoe.com

- Study the chapter online
- Explore **Math in Motion**
- Get extra help from your own **Personal Tutor**
- Use **Extra Examples** for additional help
- Take a **Self-Check Quiz**
- **Review Vocabulary** in fun ways

New Vocabulary

English		Español
numerical expression	• p. 5 •	expresión numérica
order of operations	• p. 6 •	orden de las operaciones
algebra	• p. 11 •	álgebra
variable	• p. 11 •	variable
algebraic expression	• p. 11 •	expresión algebraica
counterexample	• p. 19 •	contraejemplo
simplify	• p. 20 •	reducir
y-axis	• p. 25 •	efe *y*
coordinate plane	• p. 25 •	plano de coordenadas
origin	• p. 25 •	origen
x-axis	• p. 25 •	eje *x*
ordered pair	• p. 25 •	par ordenado
function	• p. 33 •	función
function rule	• p. 33 •	regla de funciones
function table	• p. 33 •	tabla de funciones
equation	• p. 34 •	ecuación

Review Vocabulary

difference • (Previous Course) • diferencia the answer to a subtraction problem

operations • (Previous Course) • operación common words that indicate different operations

Operations			
+	−	×	÷
plus	minus	times	divide
the sum of	difference between	the product of	quotient
increased by	decreased by	of	divided by
more than	less than		among

quotient • (Previous Course) • cociente the answer to a division problem

Multilingual eGlossary glencoe.com

1-1 Words and Expressions

Why?

Lisa and Patty want their friends to make ice cream at their birthday party. Each friend will need the following ingredients for one small batch of ice cream.

Homemade Ice Cream
$\frac{1}{4}$ cup sugar
$\frac{1}{2}$ cup milk
$\frac{1}{2}$ cup whipping cream
$\frac{1}{4}$ teaspoon vanilla
3 cups ice
1 cup salt

a. Determine how much ice is needed to make one batch of ice cream. **3 c**

b. How many cups of ice will be needed for 9 people at the party? **27 c**

c. If there are 12 people at the party, how many cups of ice are needed? **36 c**

d. Describe how you will determine the number of cups of ice needed for any number of friends. **multiply the number of guests by 3**

Then
You have already performed mathematical operations. (Previous Course)

Now
- Translate verbal phrases into numerical expressions.
- Use the order of operations to evaluate expressions.

New Vocabulary
numerical expression
evaluate
order of operations

Math Online
glencoe.com
- Extra Examples
- Personal Tutor
- Self-Check Quiz
- Homework Help

Translate Verbal Phrases into Expressions To find the number of cups of ice for 9 friends, Lisa and Patty can use the numerical expression 9 × 3. **Numerical expressions** contain a combination of numbers and operations such as addition, subtraction, multiplication, and division.

EXAMPLE 1 Translate Phrases into Expressions

Write a numerical expression for each verbal phrase.

a. the total amount of money if you have nine dollars and twelve dollars

Phrase the sum of nine and twelve

Expression 9 + 12

b. the age difference between fifteen years old and ten years old

Phrase the difference of fifteen and 10

Expression 15 – 10

Check Your Progress

1A. the cost of ten yo-yos if each costs three dollars **10 × 3**

1B. the number of students in each group if fifteen students are divided into five equal groups **15 ÷ 5**

Personal Tutor glencoe.com

1-1 Lesson Notes

1 FOCUS

Vertical Alignment

Before Lesson 1-1
Perform mathematical operations.

Lesson 1-1
Translate verbal phrases into numerical expressions.
Use the order of operations to evaluate expressions.

After Lesson 1-1
Find and evaluate an algebraic expression to determine any term in an arithmetic sequence.

2 TEACH

Scaffolding Questions

Have students read the *Why?* section of the lesson and answer the questions.

Ask:
- How many cups of milk would be needed for 4 people at the party? 2 cups of milk
- How could you determine the amount needed for any ingredient? Multiply the number of guests by the amount of the ingredient needed.
- Which items in the recipe would be the most difficult measurements to determine for 9 people? The sugar and vanilla would be the most difficult because the recipe calls for fourths.

Lesson 1-1 Resources

Resource	Approaching-Level	On-Level	Beyond-Level	English Learners
Teacher Edition	• Differentiated Instruction, p. 6		• Differentiated Instruction, p. 9	• Differentiated Instruction, p. 6
Chapter Resource Masters	• Study Guide and Intervention, pp. 5–6 • Skills Practice, p. 7 • Practice, p. 8 • Word Problem Practice, p. 9	• Study Guide and Intervention, pp. 5–6 • Skills Practice, p. 7 • Practice, p. 8 • Word Problem Practice, p. 9 • Enrichment, p. 10	• Practice, p. 8 • Word Problem Practice, p. 9 • Enrichment, p. 10	• Study Guide and Intervention, pp. 5–6 • Skills Practice, p. 7 • Practice, p. 8
Transparencies	• 5-Minute Check Transparency 1-1	• 5-Minute Check Transparency 1-1	• 5-Minute Check Transparency 1-1	• 5-Minute Check Transparency 1-1
Other	• Study Notebook • Teaching Pre-Algebra with Manipulatives	• Study Notebook • Teaching Pre-Algebra with Manipulatives	• Study Notebook	• Study Notebook • Teaching Pre-Algebra with Manipulatives

Translate Verbal Phrases Into Numerical Expressions

Example 1 shows how to translate verbal phrases into numerical expressions.

Formative Assessment

Use the Check Your Progress exercises after each example to determine students' understanding of concepts.

Additional Example

1 Write a numerical expression for each verbal phrase.

a. eighteen marbles divided equally among six friends $18 \div 6$

b. the total number of photos if there are nine photos in the camera plus four more $9 + 4$

Additional Examples also in Interactive Classroom PowerPoint® Presentations

IWB INTERACTIVE WHITEBOARD READY

Order of Operations

Example 2 shows how to use the order of operations when evaluating numerical expressions. **Example 3** shows how to write and evaluate an expression.

Additional Example

2 Evaluate each expression.

a. $17 + 36 \div 9$ 21

b. $24 \div 8 \times 3$ 9

c. $5(4 + 6) - 7 \cdot 7$ 1

d. $3[(18 - 6) + 2(4)]$ 60

e. $\frac{49 + 31}{19 - 14}$ 16

Tips for New Teachers

Differences and Quotients In this course, *the difference of 15 and 3* means to start with 15 and subtract 3, so the expression is $15 - 3$. Similarly, *the quotient of 15 and 3* means to start with 15 and divide by 3, so the expression is $15 \div 3$.

Order of Operations To **evaluate** an expression, you find its numerical value. If a numerical expression has more than one operation, use the order of operations. The **order of operations** are the rules to follow when evaluating an expression with more than one operation.

StudyTip

Grouping Symbols Grouping symbols include:
- parentheses ( ),
- brackets [ ], and
- fraction bars, as in $\frac{6 + 4}{2}$, which means $(6 + 4) \div 2$.

Key Concept Order of Operations — For Your FOLDABLE

Step 1	Evaluate the expressions inside grouping symbols.
Step 2	Multiply and/or divide in order from left to right.
Step 3	Add and/or subtract in order from left to right.

EXAMPLE 2 Evaluate Expressions

Evaluate each expression.

a. $20 - 3 \times 5$

$20 - 3 \times 5 = 20 - 15$ — Multiply 3 and 5 first.

$= 5$ — Subtract 15 from 20.

b. $30 \div 5 \times 3$

$30 \div 5 \times 3 = 6 \times 3$ — Divide 30 by 5.

$= 18$ — Multiply 6 and 3.

Watch Out! In Example 2b, you divide before you multiply because division comes first in order from left to right.

c. $4(10 - 7) + 2 \cdot 3$

$4(10 - 7) + 2 \cdot 3 = 4(3) + 2 \cdot 3$ — Evaluate (10 − 7) first.

$= 12 + 2 \cdot 3$ — 4(3) means 4 × 3 or 12.

$= 12 + 6$ — 2 • 3 means 2 × 3 or 6.

$= 18$ — Add 12 and 6.

d. $5[11 - (7 + 5) \div 4]$

$5[11 - (7 + 5) \div 4] = 5[11 - 12 \div 4]$ — Evaluate (7 + 5).

$= 5(11 - 3)$ — Divide 12 by 4.

$= 5(8)$ — Subtract 3 from 11.

$= 40$ — Multiply 5 and 8.

e. $\frac{60 - 15}{2 + 7}$

$\frac{60 - 15}{2 + 7} = (60 - 15) \div (2 + 7)$ — Rewrite as a division expression.

$= 45 \div 9$ — Evaluate (60 − 15) and (2 + 7).

$= 5$ — Divide 45 by 9.

Check Your Progress

2A. $6 - 3 + 5$ 8

2B. $24 \div 3 \times 9$ 72

2C. $2[(10 - 3) + 6(5)]$ 74

2D. $\frac{19 - 7}{25 - 22}$ 4

Personal Tutor glencoe.com

Differentiated Instruction

If students have trouble translating numerical expressions from verbal phrases,

Then pair them with other students as mentors to read verbal phrases aloud. AL ELL

Web addresses, or URLs, are provided to point students to online assets such as **Personal Tutor, Extra Examples,** and **Self-Check Quizzes.**

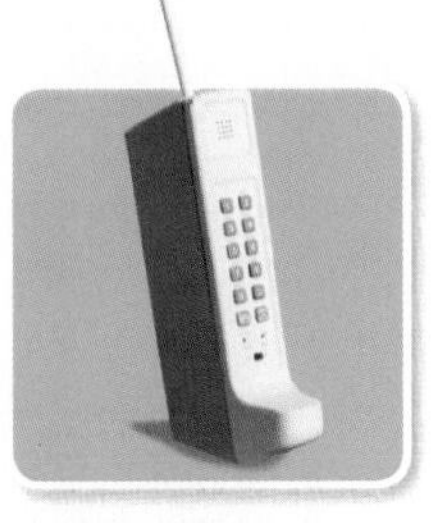

Real-World Link

The first call on a portable cellular phone was made in 1973. The phone weighed 28 ounces and was 13 inches by 1.75 inches by 3.5 inches.

Real-World EXAMPLE 3 Write Expressions to Solve Problems

CELL PHONES A cell phone company charges $20 per month and $0.15 for each call made or received. Write and evaluate an expression to find the cost for 40 calls. Then make a table showing the cost for 40, 50, 60, and 70 calls.

Understand You know how much the company charges per month. You need to find how much it will cost for 40, 50, 60, and 70 calls.

Plan Write an expression to find each cost. Organize the results in a table.

Solve First, write an expression for 40 calls.

Words	$20 per month	and	$0.15 for each call made or received
Expression	20	+	0.15 • 40

$20 + 0.15 \cdot 40 = 20 + 6$ **Multiply.**

$= 26$ **Add.**

So, 40 calls will cost $26. Make a table showing the costs for 40, 50, 60, and 70 calls.

Number of Calls	Expression	Cost ($)
40	20 + 0.15 • 40	26.00
50	20 + 0.15 • 50	27.50
60	20 + 0.15 • 60	29.00
70	20 + 0.15 • 70	30.50

Check Look for a pattern in the costs. As the number of calls increases by 10, the cost increases by $1.50. ✓

Check Your Progress

3. **CELL PHONES** The same phone company offers another plan where they charge $15 per month and $0.25 for each call made or received. Write and then evaluate an expression to find the cost for 40 calls during one month. Then make a table showing the cost for 40, 50, 60, and 70 calls. See Chapter 1 Answer Appendix.

Personal Tutor glencoe.com

Check Your Understanding

Example 1 p. 5 — **Write a numerical expression for each verbal phrase.**

1. the cost of six electronic hand-held games if each costs eight dollars 6×8
2. the cost of one box of cereal if four boxes cost twelve dollars $12 \div 4$

Example 2 p. 6 — **Evaluate each expression.**

3. $18 + 2 \times 4$ 26
4. $2 \times 9 \div 3$ 6
5. $4(6) + 9$ 33
6. $6(17 - 8)$ 54
7. $4[6(2) - 3]$ 36
8. $3[(20 - 7) + 1]$ 42
9. $\frac{15-5}{6-4}$ 5
10. $\frac{34+18}{27-14}$ 4

Example 3 p. 7

11. **TOURS** A tour bus costs $75 plus $6 for each passenger. Write and evaluate an expression to find the total cost for 25 passengers. Then make a table showing the cost for 25, 30, 35, and 40 passengers. $75 + 6(25)$; $225 See Chapter 1 Answer Appendix for table.

Focus on Mathematical Content

Order of Operations The order of operations is followed when there is more than one operation in the expression. When there is only subtraction and addition, or multiplication and division, the problem is worked from left to right.

Additional Example

3 **EARNINGS** Madison earns an allowance of $5 per week. She also earns $8 per hour baby-sitting, and usually baby-sits 6 hours each week. Write and evaluate an expression for the total amount of money she earns in one week. Then make a table showing what she will earn if she baby-sits 7, 8, and 9 hours a week. $5 + 8 \times 6$; $53

Number of Hours	Expression	Earnings ($)
7	5 + 8 × 7	61
8	5 + 8 × 8	69
9	5 + 8 × 9	77

Tips for New Teachers

Problem-Solving Tell students that sometimes it is helpful to look for a pattern when using a table. Point out that in Example 3, as the number of calls increases by 10, the cost increases by $1.50. The pattern can be applied to easily find smaller or larger costs.

Differentiated Homework Options

Level	Assignment	Two-Day Option	
AL Basic	12–31, 34–36, 38–42	13–31 odd, 39–42	12–30 even, 34–36, 38
OL Core	13–31 odd, 33, 34–36, 38–42	12–31, 39–42	32–36, 38
BL Advanced	32–42		

3 PRACTICE

Formative Assessment

Use Exercises 1–11 to check for understanding.

Use the table at the left to customize assignments for your students.

Practice and Problem Solving

● = **Step-by-Step Solutions** begin on page R11.
Extra Practice begins on page 810.

Example 1 p. 5

Write a numerical expression for each verbal phrase.

12. the height difference between fourteen and nine inches **14 – 9**

13. the total number of fish if you had eight and bought four more **8 + 4**

14. the number of weeks until vacation if vacation is twenty-eight days away **28 ÷ 7**

15. the total length of songs on a CD if each of nine songs is three minutes long **9 × 3**

16. the total money earned if Lee sold four scarves at twenty dollars each **4 × 20**

17. the number of people left to play if ten of fifteen have played **15 – 10**

Example 2 p. 6

Evaluate each expression.

18. $3 \cdot 6 - 4$ **14**

19. $18 - 4 \times 2$ **10**

20. $16 \div 4 + 15$ **19**

21. $2[3 + 7(4)]$ **62**

22. $6 + 4(3)$ **18**

23. $12(11) - 56$ **76**

24. $8[(12 - 5) + 4]$ **88**

25. $4(8) \div (8 - 6)$ **16**

26. $\frac{28 + 12}{13 - 5}$ **5**

27. $7[8(3) \div (15 - 9)]$ **28**

28. $\frac{5 + 9}{10 - 3}$ **2**

29. $\frac{16 - 8}{15 - 11}$ **2**

Example 3 p. 7

30. TILING A decorative floor pattern has one red square tile surrounded by 12 blue tiles. Write and evaluate an expression to show how many total tiles (red and blue) are needed if there are 15 red tiles. Then make a table showing the total number of tiles if there are 15, 20, 25, or 30 red tiles. **15 + 12(15); 195 tiles**

30–31. See Chapter 1 Answer Appendix for tables.

31. FINANCIAL LITERACY To place an ad in a newspaper, it costs \$8 plus \$0.75 for each line. Write and evaluate an expression to find the total cost for an ad that has 6 lines. Then make a table showing the cost if there are 6, 10, 14, and 18 lines in the ad. **8 + 6(0.75); \$12.50**

32. ZOO The table shows the prices of admission to the local zoo.

a. Write an expression that can be used to find the total cost of admission for 4 adults, 3 children, and 1 senior. **4(8) + 3(5) + 4**

b. Find the total cost. **\$51**

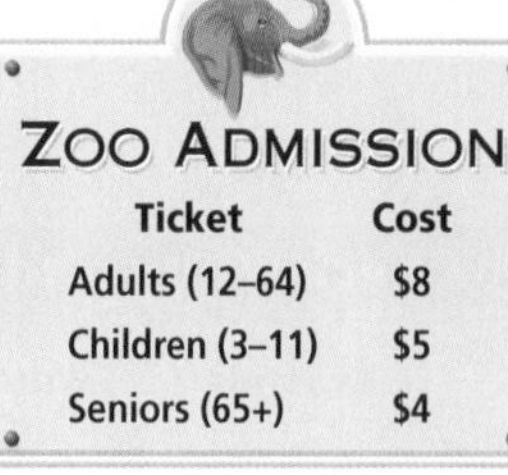

ZOO ADMISSION

Ticket	Cost
Adults (12–64)	\$8
Children (3–11)	\$5
Seniors (65+)	\$4

33. MULTIPLE REPRESENTATIONS In this problem, you will investigate expressions using a toothpick sequence.

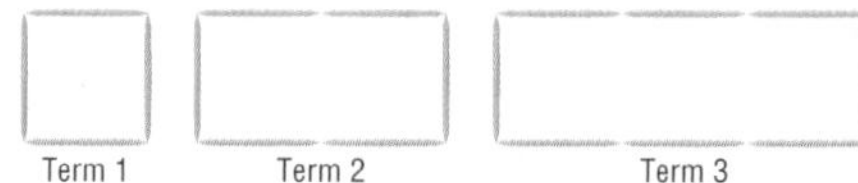

33a. See margin.

a. TABULAR Make a table showing term number and number of toothpicks.

b. VERBAL Write a verbal rule to find the number of toothpicks for any term. **The number of toothpicks is two more than twice the term number.**

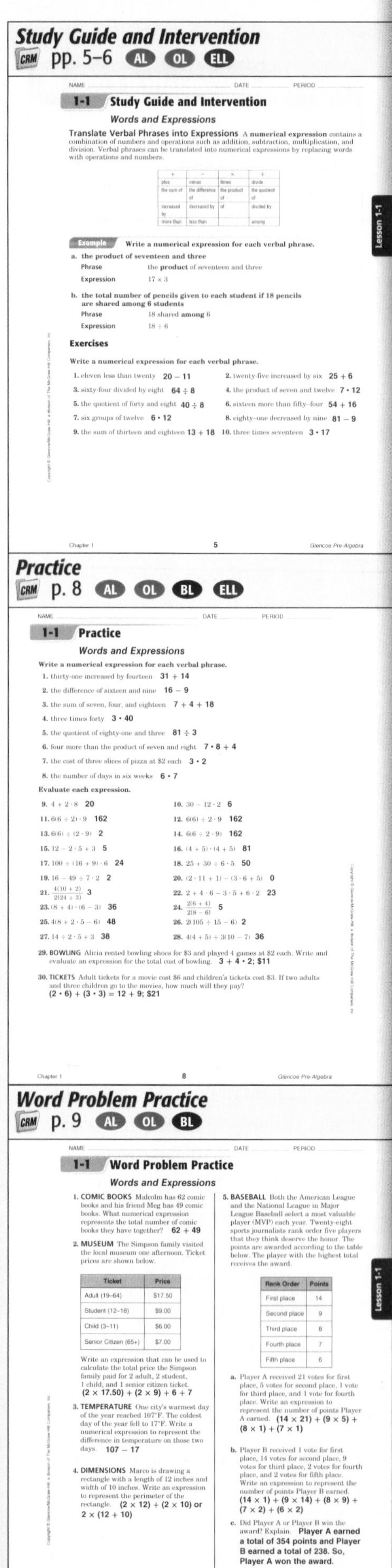

Study Guide and Intervention
CRM pp. 5–6 AL OL ELL

NAME ______ DATE ______ PERIOD ______

1-1 Study Guide and Intervention

Words and Expressions

Translate Verbal Phrases into Expressions A **numerical expression** contains a combination of numbers and operations such as addition, subtraction, multiplication, and division. Verbal phrases can be translated into numerical expressions by replacing words with operations and numbers.

+	−	×	÷
plus	minus	times	divide
the sum of	the difference of	the product of	the quotient of
increased by	decreased by	of	divided by
more than	less than		among

Example Write a numerical expression for each verbal phrase.

a. the product of seventeen and three

Phrase: the **product** of seventeen and three

Expression: 17 × 3

b. the total number of pencils given to each student if 18 pencils are shared among 6 students

Phrase: 18 shared **among** 6

Expression: 18 ÷ 6

Exercises

Write a numerical expression for each verbal phrase.

1. eleven less than twenty **20 − 11**
2. twenty-five increased by six **25 + 6**
3. sixty-four divided by eight **64 ÷ 8**
4. the product of seven and twelve **7 • 12**
5. the quotient of forty and eight **40 ÷ 8**
6. sixteen more than fifty-four **54 + 16**
7. six groups of twelve **6 • 12**
8. eighty-one decreased by nine **81 − 9**
9. the sum of thirteen and eighteen **13 + 18**
10. three times seventeen **3 • 17**

Lesson 1-1

Chapter 1 5 Glencoe Pre-Algebra

Practice
CRM p. 8 AL OL BL ELL

NAME ______ DATE ______ PERIOD ______

1-1 Practice

Words and Expressions

Write a numerical expression for each verbal phrase.

1. thirty-one increased by fourteen **31 + 14**
2. the difference of sixteen and nine **16 − 9**
3. the sum of seven, four, and eighteen **7 + 4 + 18**
4. three times forty **3 • 40**
5. the quotient of eighty-one and three **81 ÷ 3**
6. four more than the product of seven and eight **7 • 8 + 4**
7. the cost of three slices of pizza at \$2 each **3 • 2**
8. the number of days in six weeks **6 • 7**

Evaluate each expression.

9. $4 + 2 \cdot 8$ **20**
10. $30 - 12 \cdot 2$ **6**
11. $6(6 + 2) \cdot 9$ **162**
12. $6(6) + 2 \cdot 9$ **162**
13. $6(6) \div (2 \cdot 9)$ **2**
14. $6(6 \div 2 \cdot 9)$ **162**
15. $12 - 2 \cdot 5 + 3$ **5**
16. $(4 + 5) \cdot (4 + 5)$ **81**
17. $100 \div (16 + 9) \cdot 6$ **24**
18. $25 + 30 \div 6 \cdot 5$ **50**
19. $16 - 49 \div 7 \cdot 2$ **2**
20. $(2 \cdot 11 + 1) - (3 \cdot 6 + 5)$ **0**
21. $\frac{4(10 + 2)}{2(24 \div 3)}$ **3**
22. $2 + 4 \cdot 6 - 3 \cdot 5 + 6 \cdot 2$ **23**
23. $(8 + 4) \cdot (6 - 3)$ **36**
24. $\frac{2(6 + 4)}{2(8 - 6)}$ **5**
25. $4(8 + 2 \cdot 5 - 6)$ **48**
26. $2(105 \div 15 - 6)$ **2**
27. $14 \div 2 \cdot 5 + 3$ **38**
28. $4(4 + 5) \div 3(10 - 7)$ **36**

29. **BOWLING** Alicia rented bowling shoes for \$3 and played 4 games at \$2 each. Write and evaluate an expression for the total cost of bowling. **3 + 4 • 2; \$11**

30. **TICKETS** Adult tickets for a movie cost \$6 and children's tickets cost \$3. If two adults and three children go to the movies, how much will they pay? **(2 • 6) + (3 • 3) = 12 + 9; \$21**

Chapter 1 8 Glencoe Pre-Algebra

Word Problem Practice
CRM p. 9 AL OL BL

NAME ______ DATE ______ PERIOD ______

1-1 Word Problem Practice

Words and Expressions

1. **COMIC BOOKS** Malcolm has 62 comic books and his friend Meg has 49 comic books. What numerical expression represents the total number of comic books they have together? **62 + 49**

2. **MUSEUM** The Simpson family visited the local museum one afternoon. Ticket prices are shown below.

Ticket	Price
Adult (19–64)	\$17.50
Student (12–18)	\$9.00
Child (3–11)	\$6.00
Senior Citizen (65+)	\$7.00

Write an expression that can be used to calculate the total price the Simpson family paid for 2 adult, 2 student, 1 child, and 1 senior citizen ticket. **(2 × 17.50) + (2 × 9) + 6 + 7**

3. **TEMPERATURE** One city's warmest day of the year reached 107°F. The coldest day of the year fell to 17°F. Write a numerical expression to represent the difference in temperature on those two days. **107 − 17**

4. **DIMENSIONS** Marco is drawing a rectangle with a length of 12 inches and width of 10 inches. Write an expression to represent the perimeter of the rectangle. **(2 × 12) + (2 × 10) or 2 × (12 + 10)**

5. **BASEBALL** Both the American League and the National League in Major League Baseball select a most valuable player (MVP) each year. Twenty-eight sports journalists rank order five players that they think deserve the honor. The points are awarded according to the table below. The player with the highest total receives the award.

Rank Order	Points
First place	14
Second place	9
Third place	8
Fourth place	7
Fifth place	6

a. Player A received 21 votes for first place, 5 votes for second place, 1 vote for third place, and 1 vote for fourth place. Write an expression to represent the number of points Player A earned. **(14 × 21) + (9 × 5) + (8 × 1) + (7 × 1)**

b. Player B received 1 vote for first place, 14 votes for second place, 9 votes for third place, 2 votes for fourth place, and 2 votes for fifth place. Write an expression to represent the number of points Player B earned. **(14 × 1) + (9 × 14) + (8 × 9) + (7 × 2) + (6 × 2)**

c. Did Player A or Player B win the award? Explain. **Player A earned a total of 354 points and Player B earned a total of 238. So, Player A won the award.**

Lesson 1-1

Chapter 1 9 Glencoe Pre-Algebra

8 Chapter 1 The Tools of Algebra

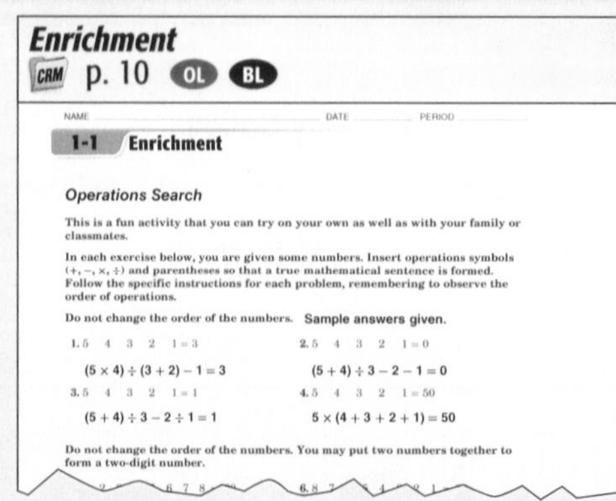

Enrichment
CRM p. 10 OL BL

NAME ______ DATE ______ PERIOD ______

1-1 Enrichment

Operations Search

This is a fun activity that you can try on your own as well as with your family or classmates.

In each exercise below, you are given some numbers. Insert operations symbols (+, −, ×, ÷) and parentheses so that a true mathematical sentence is formed. Follow the specific instructions for each problem, remembering to observe the order of operations.

Do not change the order of the numbers. **Sample answers given.**

1. 5 4 3 2 1 = 3 **(5 × 4) ÷ (3 + 2) − 1 = 3**
2. 5 4 3 2 1 = 0 **(5 + 4) ÷ 3 − 2 − 1 = 0**
3. 5 4 3 2 1 = 1 **(5 + 4) ÷ 3 − 2 ÷ 1 = 1**
4. 5 4 3 2 1 = 50 **5 × (4 + 3 + 2 + 1) = 50**

Do not change the order of the numbers. You may put two numbers together to form a two-digit number.

Multiple Representations In Exercise 33, students use a physical model with toothpicks and a table of values to determine the rule for a number sequence.

35b. Sample answer:
$64 - (20 \div 4) + 6$
$= 64 - 5 + 6$
$= 59 + 6$
$= 65$

36. Sample answer: First evaluate $(1 + 3)$. Since this is 4, the expression is now $4^2 + 4 \div 2$. Now follow order of operations.
$4^2 + 4 \div 2$
$= 4 \cdot 4 + 4 \div 2$
$= 16 + 4 \div 2$
$= 16 + 2$
$= 18$

37b. $508 + 350 = 858$ cm

37c. 90 in. $\approx 90(2.54)$ or about 230 cm; $858 \div 230 \approx 3.73$; about 4 packages of 90 inch trim

H.O.T. Problems

Use Higher-Order Thinking Skills

34. OPEN ENDED Write two different expressions, each with more than one operation, that have a value of 20. Sample answer: $(6 \times 3) + 2$; $(8 \times 5) - 20$

35. REASONING Use the expression $64 - 20 \div 4 + 6$.

a. Where should the parentheses be placed so that the value of the expression is 17? around $(64 - 20)$

b. Place different parentheses in the expression to find an answer other than 17. Then evaluate the new expression.

36. WRITING IN MATH The numerical expression 3^2 means to write 2 factors of 3 and multiply. So, $3^2 = 3 \cdot 3$ or 9. Likewise, $2^3 = 2 \cdot 2 \cdot 2$ or 8. Using this information, how would you evaluate the expression $(1 + 3)^2 + 4 \div 2$? Explain your reasoning.

37. CHALLENGE Leah bought two packages of special decorative trim for a craft project. One package contains 350 centimeters of trim. The second package contains 200 inches of trim.

a. If one inch $\approx$ 2.54 centimeters, write and evaluate an expression to find the number of centimeters in 200 inches. 200(2.54); 508 cm

b. Find the total number of centimeters of trim in the two packages.

c. How many packages of trim containing 90 inches each will Leah need to buy to have about the same amount of trim from part **b**? Explain.

38. WRITING IN MATH Explain why the rules for the order of operations are important. Support your answer with two numerical examples. See margin.

Standardized Test Practice

39. Rusty is evaluating $96 \div 3 \times 4 + 7$ as shown below. C

$$96 \div 3 \times 4 + 7$$
$$3 \times 4 = 12$$
$$96 \div 12 = 8$$
$$8 + 7 = 15$$

What should Rusty have done differently in order to evaluate the expression correctly?

A multiplied $(96 \div 3)$ by $(4 + 7)$

B divided 96 by (3×11)

C multiplied $(96 \div 3)$ by 4 and added 7

D divided 96 by $(4 + 7)$

40. Evaluate $7[12 - (6 - 2) \div 4]$. H

F 7 H 77

G 14 J 83

41. Aman is a musician. He charges \$50 for each of the first three hours he plays and \$24.95 for each additional hour. Which expression *cannot* be used to find the total amount he charges if he plays for 7 hours? B

A $4 \times \$24.95 + 3 \times \$50$

B $7(\$50 + \$24.95)$

C $\$50 + \$50 + \$50 + 4(\$24.95)$

D $3(\$50) + 4(\$24.95)$

42. SHORT RESPONSE Max wants to buy 5 hats and 4 T-shirts. Write an expression to find the total cost of 5 hats and 4 T-shirts.

Hats	\$15
T-shirts	\$20

Sample answer: $5(\$15) + 4(\$20)$

Differentiated Instruction

BL

Extension Tell students that variables are letters that are used to represent values in a numerical expression. Ask them to evaluate the expression $42 \div (7 \cdot k) \times 9$ when $k = 2$. 27

4 ASSESS

Name the Math Have students name the mathematical procedures for each step in evaluating the expression $3 + 4 \times 5 - 2$.

TEACH with TECH

STUDENT RESPONSE SYSTEM You can use your SRS software to assess students' understanding of the order of operations. Create a short quiz of several expressions (such as $6 \times 5 - 4 \div 2 + 1$). Ask students which operation to perform first, second, etc. Develop a key: A = add, B = subtract, C = multiply, and D = divide. You will be able to track how many students understand the order of operations.

Teach with Tech features throughout the Teacher Edition offer tips on using various types of technology such as interactive whiteboards, document cameras, blogs, and more, to enhance your teaching.

Additional Answers

33a.

Term Number	Number of Toothpicks
1	4
2	6
3	8

38. Sample answer: Without the order of operations, any expression that contains more than one operation could have many different solutions. For example, when following the order of operations, the expression $12 + 4 \times 4 = 12 + 16$ or 28. When you do the math from left to right, the expression $12 + 4 \times 4 = 16 \times 4$ or 64.

EXPLORE 1-2 Lesson Notes

 FOCUS

Objective Determine rules for a given pattern.

Materials for Each Student

- grid paper
- toothpicks (optional)

Teaching Tip

The use of grid paper may help some students visually extend a pattern or create a new one.

2 TEACH

Working in Cooperative Groups

Arrange students in pairs, mixing abilities. Have each pair complete the Activity. Suggest that students take turns drawing the next figure.

Ask:

- What would the sixth term model look like?

- What is the connection between the term number and the number of toothpicks? 2 greater, 3 greater, then 4 greater…

Practice Have students complete Exercises 1–4.

 ASSESS

 **Formative Assessment**

Use Exercise 3 to assess whether students comprehend how to determine a rule for a given pattern.

EXPLORE 1-2 Algebra Lab

Rules and Expressions

Math Online glencoe.com
Math *in Motion*, Animation

Objective
Determine rules for a given pattern.

Numerical patterns can often be defined by a rule. You can then use the rule to find any term in the pattern.

ACTIVITY 1

The pattern below is made from toothpicks. The first term uses 3 toothpicks, the second term uses 5 toothpicks, and the third term uses 7 toothpicks.

Step 1 Draw the next two terms in the pattern.

Step 2 Copy and complete the table to show the number of toothpicks needed if the pattern continues.

Term Number	1	2	3	4	5	6	7
Number of Toothpicks	3	5	7	■ 9	■ 11	■ 13	■ 15

+2 +2 +2

Step 3 Describe a rule you could use to find the number of toothpicks for any figure.

Since the number of toothpicks increases by 2 for each term, multiply the term number by 2. Then add 1 to get the number of toothpicks in the figure.

Analyze the Results

1. Using your rule, how many toothpicks would be needed for the twelfth term? the thirtieth term? **25 toothpicks; 61 toothpicks**

For Exercises 2 and 3, use the tile pattern below.

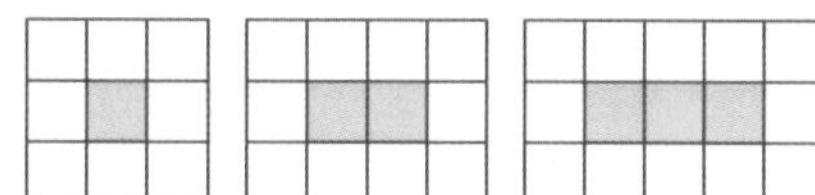

2. Make a table to show how many white tiles are needed for each blue tile. **See margin.**
3. Describe a rule that could be used to find the number of white tiles needed for any figure. **Sample answer: Multiply the number of blue tiles by 2 and add 6.**
4. Create a pattern of your own. Share your pattern with another student and ask him or her to write a rule to describe your pattern. **See students' work.**

From Concrete to Abstract

Return to the Activity. Ask students to write an expression to find the number of toothpicks for the 100th term. $2 \times 100 + 1$

Extending the Concept

Ask:

- How could you describe a rule without using words? use numbers, operations, and variables

Additional Answer

2.

blue tiles	1	2	3
white tiles	8	10	12

1-2 Variables and Expressions

Why?

Marin received $100 from her grandfather for her birthday. She wants to use the money to buy an MP3 player for $69 and download some songs that are $0.88 each from the Internet with the rest of the money.

Total Cost of MP3 Player and Songs		
Number of Songs	Cost to Download Songs	Total Cost
0	0 × 0.88 or $0	69 + 0 or $69
1	1 × 0.88 or $0.88	69 + 0.88 or $69.88
5	5 × 0.88 or $4.40	69 + 4.40 or $73.40
10	10 × 0.88 or $8.80	69 + 8.80 or $77.80

a. Suppose Marin wants to download 15 songs. What would be the total cost of the player and the songs? **$82.20**

b. How can you find the cost of 20 songs? **See Chapter 1 Answer Appendix.**

c. If we used the letter s to represent *any number of songs*, what expression could be used to represent the total cost of the MP3 player and the songs? **$69 + 0.88s$**

Then

You have already written numerical expressions. (Lesson 1-1)

Now

- Translate verbal phrases into algebraic expressions.
- Evaluate expressions containing variables.

New Vocabulary

algebra
variable
algebraic expression
defining a variable

Math Online

glencoe.com

- Extra Examples
- Personal Tutor
- Self-Check Quiz
- Homework Help

Algebraic Expressions and Verbal Phrases **Algebra** is a branch of mathematics that uses symbols. A variable is often used in algebra. A **variable** is a letter or symbol used to represent an unknown value. In the example above, s was used to represent *any number of songs*. Any letter can be used as a variable.

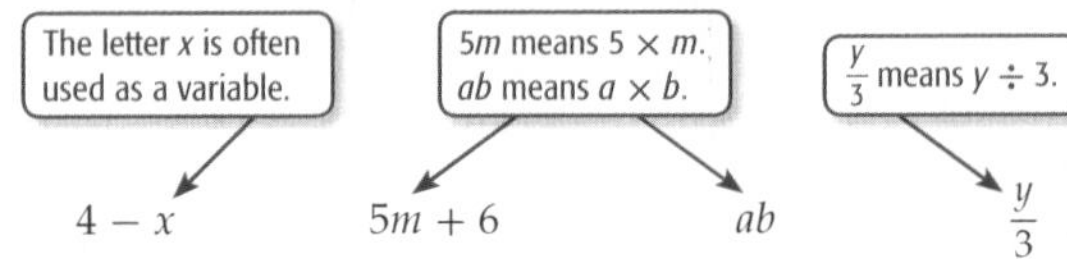

An expression like $5m + 6$ is an **algebraic expression** because it contains at least one variable and at least one mathematical operation.

The first step in translating verbal phrases into algebraic expressions is to choose a variable and a quantity for the variable to represent. This is called **defining a variable**. All of the steps involved in writing algebraic expressions are shown below.

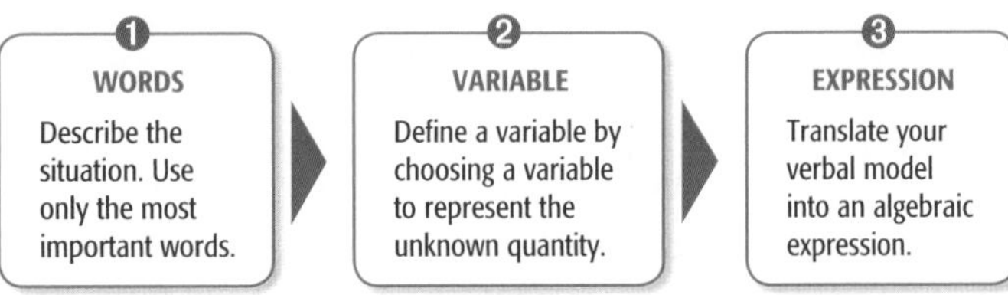

1 WORDS
Describe the situation. Use only the most important words.
2 VARIABLE
Define a variable by choosing a variable to represent the unknown quantity.
3 EXPRESSION
Translate your verbal model into an algebraic expression.

1-2 Lesson Notes

1 FOCUS

Vertical Alignment

Before Lesson 1-2
Write numerical expressions.

Lesson 1-2
Translate verbal phrases into algebraic expressions.
Evaluate expressions containing variables.

After Lesson 1-2
Determine rules for a given pattern.

2 TEACH

Scaffolding Questions

Have students read the *Why?* section of the lesson and answer the questions.

Ask:

- What does the 0.88 in the expression $69 + 0.88s$ represent? the cost of a song
- Which value varies in the expression: the cost of the MP3 player or the number of songs she wants to purchase? the number of songs she wants to purchase
- How can you use the expression to find the total cost to buy the MP3 player and download 30 songs? Substitute 30 for s and evaluate the expression.

Lesson 1-2 Resources

Resource	Approaching-Level	On-Level	Beyond-Level	English Learners
Teacher Edition	• Differentiated Instruction, p. 13	• Differentiated Instruction, p. 13	• Differentiated Instruction, p. 16	• Differentiated Instruction, p. 13
Chapter 1 Resource Masters	• Study Guide and Intervention, pp. 11–12 • Skills Practice, p. 13 • Practice, p. 14 • Word Problem Practice, p. 15 • Graphing Calculator, p. 17	• Study Guide and Intervention, pp. 11–12 • Skills Practice, p. 13 • Practice, p. 14 • Word Problem Practice, p. 15 • Enrichment, p. 16 • Graphing Calculator, p. 17	• Practice, p. 14 • Word Problem Practice, p. 15 • Enrichment, p. 16 • Graphing Calculator, p. 17	• Study Guide and Intervention, pp. 11–12 • Skills Practice, p. 13 • Practice, p. 14 • Graphing Calculator, p. 17
Transparencies	• 5-Minute Check Transparency 1-2	• 5-Minute Check Transparency 1-2	• 5-Minute Check Transparency 1-2	• 5-Minute Check Transparency 1-2
Other	• Study Notebook • Teaching Pre-Algebra with Manipulatives	• Study Notebook • Teaching Pre-Algebra with Manipulatives	• Study Notebook	• Study Notebook • Teaching Pre-Algebra with Manipulatives

Algebraic Expressions and Verbal Phrases

Example 1 shows how to translate verbal expressions into algebraic expressions.

Formative Assessment

Use the Check Your Progress exercises after each example to determine students' understanding of concepts.

Additional Example

1 Translate each phrase into an algebraic expression.

a. 35 more than the number of tickets sold $t + 35$

b. the difference of six times a number and 10 $6n - 10$

Additional Examples also in Interactive Classroom PowerPoint® Presentations

IWB INTERACTIVE WHITEBOARD READY

Evaluate Expressions

Examples 2 and 3 show how to evaluate an expression by replacing the variable or variables with known values, and then using the order of operations. **Example 4** shows how to write and evaluate an expression to solve a real-world problem.

Additional Example

2 Evaluate $x - y + 6$ if $x = 27$ and $y = 12$. 21

Focus on Mathematical Content

Defining Variables The first step in translating a verbal phrase is to decide what variable to use and what the variable will represent. Because the variable is a placeholder for an unknown value, look for the value in the verbal expression that is unknown.

Math History Link

Al-Khwarizmi (c 780–850) Al-Khwarizmi is considered to be the father of algebra. He wrote a book titled *Al-Kitab al-Jabr wa-l-Muqabala* in approximately 820 A.D. The word *algebra* is derived from this title.

Examples illustrate all of the concepts taught in the lesson and closely mirror the exercises in the exercise sets. Check Your Progress exercises give students an opportunity to try a similar problem on their own.

EXAMPLE 1 Translate Phrases into Algebraic Expressions

Translate each phrase into an algebraic expression.

a. three dollars more than the cost of a sandwich

Words	three dollars more than the cost of a sandwich
Variable	Let c represent the cost of the sandwich.
Expression	$3 + c$

b. Mari had \$2 and made \$6 an hour babysitting.

Words	two more than six dollars per hour
Variable	Let n represent the number of hours.
Expression	$2 + 6n$

Check Your Progress

1A. two miles less than the athlete ran $a - 2$

1B. five points more than the points scored by field goals if each field goal is worth 3 points $5 + 3n$

Personal Tutor glencoe.com

Evaluate Expressions To evaluate an algebraic expression, replace the variable(s) with known values and then use the order of operations. When you replace a variable with a number, you are using the **Substitution Property of Equality.**

Key Concept Substitution Property of Equality

For Your FOLDABLE

Words If two quantities are equal, then one quantity can be replaced by the other.

Symbols For all numbers a and b, if $a = b$, then a may be replaced by b.

EXAMPLE 2 Evaluate Expressions

Evaluate $d + 5 - f$ if $d = 16$ and $f = 18$.

$d + 5 - f = 16 + 5 - 18$	Replace d with 16 and f with 18.
$= 21 - 18$	Add 16 and 5.
$= 3$	Subtract 18 from 21.

Check Your Progress

2A. Evaluate $6 - e + f$ if $e = 3$ and $f = 9$. 12

2B. Evaluate $7k + h$ if $k = 4$ and $h = 10$. 38

Personal Tutor glencoe.com

Watch Out!

Preventing Errors Using a · or a × sign to represent multiplication with a variable can cause confusion. Tell students there is a special notation to represent multiplication. The expression $4 \times n$ can be written as $4n$. The number should always come before the letter when showing multiplication.

EXAMPLE 3 Evaluate Expressions

Evaluate each expression if $r = 1$, $s = 5$, and $t = 8$.

a. $6s + 2t$

$6s + 2t = 6(5) + 2(8)$ — Replace s with 5 and t with 8.

$= 30 + 16$ or 46 — Multiply. Then add.

b. $\frac{st}{20}$

$\frac{st}{20} = st \div 20$ — Rewrite as a division expression.

$= (5 \cdot 8) \div 20$ — Replace s with 5 and t with 8.

$= 40 \div 20$ or 2 — Multiply. Then divide.

c. $r + (40 - 3t)$

$r + (40 - 3t) = 1 + (40 - 3 \cdot 8)$ — Replace r with 1 and t with 8.

$= 1 + (40 - 24)$ — Multiply 3 and 8.

$= 1 + 16$ or 17 — Subtract 24 from 40. Then add 1 and 16.

Check Your Progress

Evaluate each expression if $a = 4$, $b = 8$, and $c = 12$.

3A. $3a + 2c$ **36** **3B.** $\frac{ab}{16}$ **2** **3C.** $c + (5b - 2a)$ **44**

Personal Tutor glencoe.com

Real-World EXAMPLE 4 Use Expressions to Solve Problems

Real-World Link

In a recent year, 72.6 million adults in the United States went boating. This is about 25% of the entire population.

Source: National Marine Manufacturers Association

BOATS A company rents a house boat for \$200 plus an extra \$30 per day.

a. Write an expression that can be used to find the total cost to rent a house boat.

Words	two hundred dollar rental fee	plus	thirty dollars per day
Variable	Let d represent the		number of days.
Expression	200	+	$30d$

The expression is $200 + 30d$.

b. Suppose the Gregoran family wants to rent a house boat for six days. What will be the total cost?

$200 + 30d = 200 + 6(30)$ — Replace d with 6.

$= 200 + 180$ or 380 — Multiply. Then add.

The total cost will be \$380.

Check Your Progress

4. SALES At a garage sale, Georgia found some used DVDs and CDs that she wanted to buy. Each DVD was marked at \$5 and each CD was marked at \$3. Write an expression to find the total cost to buy some DVDs and CDs. Then find the cost of buying 4 DVDs and 7 CDs. **$5d + 3c$; \$41**

Personal Tutor glencoe.com

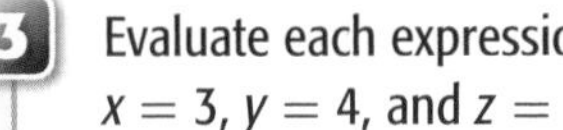

Tips for New Teachers

Multiplying Make sure that students remember that $4x$ means 4 times x. If $x = 3$, $4x = 12$, not 43.

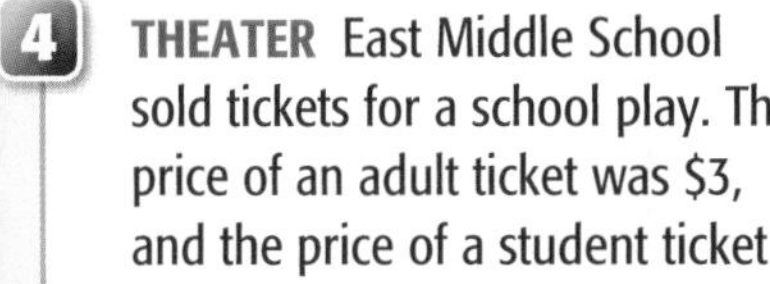

Additional Examples

3 Evaluate each expression if $x = 3$, $y = 4$, and $z = 7$.

a. $6y - 4x$ 12

b. $\frac{(z - x)}{y}$ 1

c. $5z + (x + 4y) - 15$ 39

4 **THEATER** East Middle School sold tickets for a school play. The price of an adult ticket was \$3, and the price of a student ticket was \$1.

a. Write an expression that represents the total amount of money collected. $3a + 1s$

b. Suppose 70 adult tickets and 85 student tickets were sold. How much money was collected? \$295

Differentiated Instruction

students have trouble evaluating expressions,

make a set of expression cards with numbers, operation symbols, and variables. Put one character on each card. Some students will hold number cards, some will hold symbol cards, and others will hold variable cards. Ask four or five students at a time to line up, making an expression using their cards. Have students with numbers interchange places with students who have variables, and so on, to create many different combinations and expressions. Evaluate the expressions.

3 PRACTICE

Formative Assessment

Use Exercises 1–11 to check for understanding.

Use the chart at the bottom of this page to customize assignments for your students.

Additional Answers

38. Plan C; Sample answer: Plan A costs 0.1×750 or \$75, plan B costs $\$29.99 + 250 \times \$0.08$ or \$49.99, and plan D costs \$49.99. Since plan C costs \$39.99, it is less than all of the other plans.

43. $2n + 4$; $2(n + 2)$; Sample answer: The first expression represents the top multiplied by two to give the top and bottom, then add 4 for the sloped sides. The second expression represents half of the figure, then multiply by two to get the whole figure.

44. addition then multiplication; Sample answer: Order of operations tells us to evaluate what is inside the parentheses first. Since the addition is inside the parentheses, it is first. Then you multiply the value of a by the value of $x + y$.

Watch Out!

Find the Error Exercise 42 shows a common error made by students. Suggest that students replace *the number* with *10,* which makes the phrase *five less than 10.* This allows a student a more concrete example to better understand the order when writing an expression. This exercise also reinforces the concept that subtraction is not commutative.

Check Your Understanding

Example 1 p. 12

Translate each phrase into an algebraic expression.

1. four dollars less than the cost of the sweater $c - 4$
2. 13 more students than teachers $13 + t$
3. money earned babysitting at \$10 per hour $10h$
4. 30 pencils divided among some students $30 \div s$

Examples 2 and 3 pp. 12–13

ALGEBRA Evaluate each expression if $g = 6$, $h = 10$, and $j = 5$.

5. $h + 15$ 25
6. $g - 3$ 3
7. $20 - h + g$ 16
8. $22 - 3j$ 7
9. $\frac{gh}{j}$ 12
10. $4g + (3h - 4j)$ 34

Example 4 p. 13

11. **CAPACITY** One pint of liquid is the same as 16 fluid ounces.
    a. Suppose the number of pints of liquid is represented by p. Write an expression to find the number of fluid ounces. $16p$
    b. How many fluid ounces is 5 pints? 80 fl oz

Practice and Problem Solving

● = **Step-by-Step Solutions** begin on page R11. **Extra Practice** begins on page 810.

Example 1 p. 12

Translate each phrase into an algebraic expression.

12. three times as many balloons $3b$
13. twenty-four pieces of candy divided among some students $24 \div s$
14. the number of people increased by thirteen $p + 13$
15. the number of inches in any number of feet $12n$
16. four more than the number of weeks in a group of days $\frac{n}{7} + 4$
17. four less than the amount of cents in a number of dimes $10n - 4$

Examples 2 and 3 pp. 12–13

ALGEBRA Evaluate each expression if $a = 9$, $b = 4$, and $c = 11$.

18. $b + 9$ 13
19. $13 - a$ 4
20. $2c - 5$ 17
21. $18 + 4b$ 34
22. $\frac{ab}{6}$ 6
23. $\frac{8a}{b}$ 18
24. $5c - 4a$ 19
25. $7b - 2c$ 6
26. $45 - \frac{bc}{2}$ 23
27. $\frac{ac}{3} - 15$ 18
28. $4b + 3c - 5a$ 4
29. $6c - 2a + 6b$ 72

Example 4 p. 13

30. **PHOTOGRAPHY** A studio charges a sitting fee of \$25 plus \$7 for each portrait sheet ordered. Write an expression that can be used to find the total cost to have photographs taken. Then find the cost of purchasing twelve portrait sheets. $25 + 7s$; \$109

31. **MEASUREMENT** One gallon of water is equal to 231 cubic inches. Write an expression for the number of gallons of water in any number of cubic inches of water. $\frac{w}{231}$

ALGEBRA Evaluate each expression if $x = 9$, $y = 4$, and $z = 12$.

32. $7z - (y + x)$ 71
33. $(8y + 5) - 2z$ 13
34. $(5z - 4x) + 3y$ 36
35. $6x - (z - 2y)$ 50
36. $2x + (4z - 13) - 5$ 48
37. $(29 - 3y) + 4z - 7$ 58

Differentiated Homework Options

Level	Assignment	Two-Day Option	
AL Basic	12–31, 41, 42, 44–64	13–31 odd, 45–48	12–30 even, 41, 42, 44, 49–64
OL Core	13–37 odd, 38–42, 44–64	12–31, 45–48	32–42, 44, 49–64
BL Advanced	32–60, (optional: 61–64)		

38. FINANCIAL LITERACY After the included minutes have been used, a cell phone company charges an additional \$0.08 per minute. Plan A uses a flat rate of \$0.10 per minute for all calls. Which plan is the least costly if a person uses 750 minutes per month? Explain. **See margin.**

Plan	Monthly Fee	Included Minutes
A	\$0	None
B	\$29.99	500
C	\$39.99	1000
D	\$49.99	1500

Real-World Link

The largest apple crop in the United States was in 1998. Approximately 277.3 million bushels were harvested.

Source: U.S. Apple Association

39. FOOD One bushel of apples from a dwarf apple tree is equal to 42 pounds. Write an expression to find the number of pounds of apples in any number of bushels. If one tree can produce 6 bushels, how many pounds of apples will an orchard of 100 trees produce? **$42b$; $100 \cdot 42 \cdot 6$ or 25,200 lb**

40. MULTIPLE REPRESENTATIONS In this problem, you will use algebra to describe a relationship. Jacinda used the table below to help convert measurements while she was cooking.

Number of Cups (c)	4	8	12	16
Number of Quarts (q)	1	2	3	4

a. **VERBAL** Write an expression in words that describes the relationship between the number of quarts and the number of cups. **There are four cups in one quart.**

b. **ALGEBRAIC** Write an algebraic expression that represents the number of quarts in c cups. **$c \div 4$**

c. **NUMERICAL** Use the expression in part **b** to find the number of quarts in 100 cups. **25**

H.O.T. Problems Use Higher-Order Thinking Skills

41. OPEN ENDED Write an algebraic expression that has two different variables and two different operations: addition, subtraction, multiplication, or division. Then write a real-world problem that uses the expression.

41. Sample answer: $6a + c$; $a = 4$, $c = 8$; \$32 total cost for 4 items costing \$6 each and an \$8 item.

42. FIND THE ERROR John and Ramon are writing an algebraic expression for the phrase *five less than a number*. Is either of them correct? Explain.

John	Ramon
Let n represent the number.	Let n represent the number.
$5 - n$	$n - 5$

42. Ramon; Sample answer: Five less than a number means subtract 5 from the number.

43. CHALLENGE Franco constructed the objects below using toothpicks.

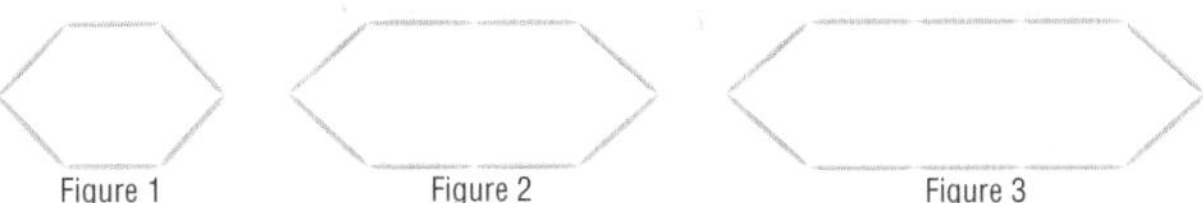

Figure 1 Figure 2 Figure 3

Write two different rules that relate the figure number to the number of toothpicks in each figure. Explain how you arrived at your answers. **See margin.**

Problem-Solving Tip

Make a Table You can make a table to organize the information in Exercise 43. You can find the pattern involved by comparing the number of sides to the number of toothpicks.

44. WRITING IN MATH Cassandra needs to evaluate the expression $a(x + y)$. After she replaces the variables with numerical values, in which order should she perform the operations of addition and multiplication? Explain. **See margin.**

Multiple Representations In Exercise 40, students use a table along with verbal, numerical, and algebraic expressions to model the relations between customary measures of capacity.

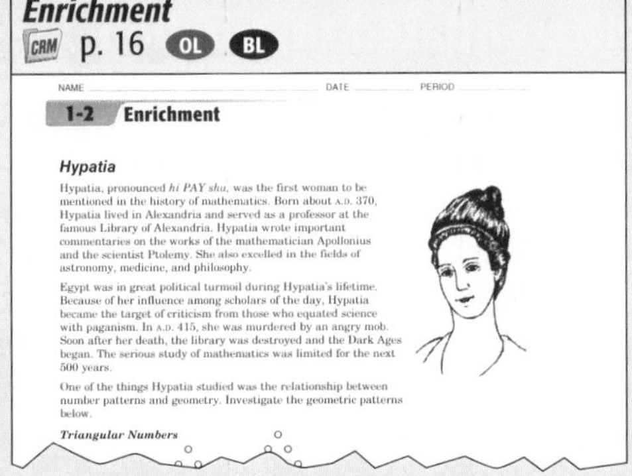

Enrichment
CRM p. 16 OL BL

NAME ______ DATE ______ PERIOD ______

1-2 Enrichment

Hypatia

Hypatia, pronounced *hi PAY sha*, was the first woman to be mentioned in the history of mathematics. Born about A.D. 370, Hypatia lived in Alexandria and served as a professor at the famous Library of Alexandria. Hypatia wrote important commentaries on the works of the mathematician Apollonius and the scientist Ptolemy. She also excelled in the fields of astronomy, medicine, and philosophy.

Egypt was in great political turmoil during Hypatia's lifetime. Because of her influence among scholars of the day, Hypatia became the target of criticism from those who equated science with paganism. In A.D. 415, she was murdered by an angry mob. Soon after her death, the library was destroyed and the Dark Ages began. The serious study of mathematics was limited for the next 500 years.

One of the things Hypatia studied was the relationship between number patterns and geometry. Investigate the geometric patterns below.

Triangular Numbers

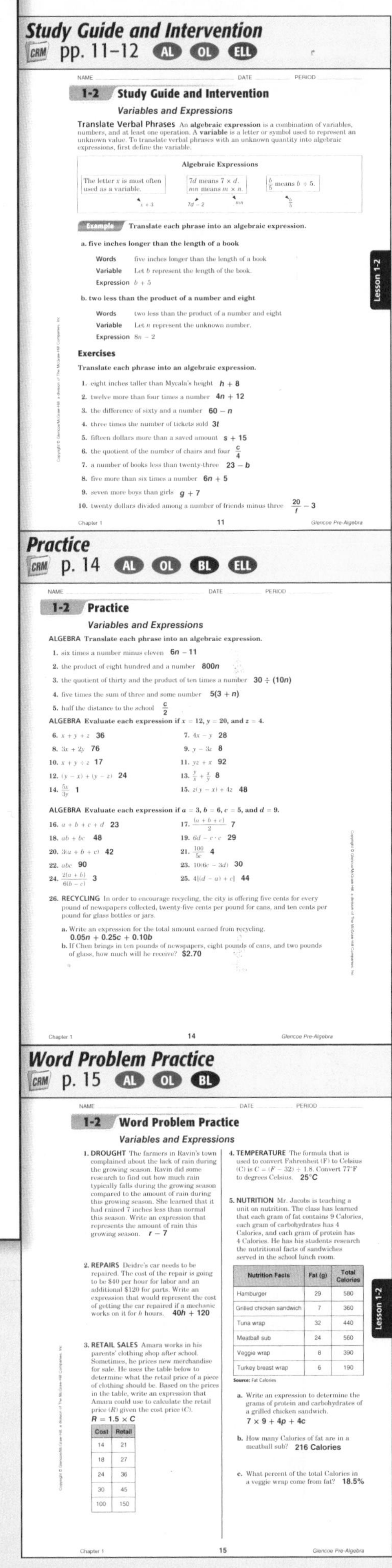

Study Guide and Intervention
CRM pp. 11–12 AL OL ELL

NAME ______ DATE ______ PERIOD ______

1-2 Study Guide and Intervention

Variables and Expressions

Translate Verbal Phrases An **algebraic expression** is a combination of variables, numbers, and at least one operation. A **variable** is a letter or symbol used to represent an unknown value. To translate verbal phrases with an unknown quantity into algebraic expressions, first define the variable.

Algebraic Expressions

The letter x is most often used as a variable.	$7d$ means $7 \times d$. mn means $m \times n$.	$\frac{b}{5}$ means $b \div 5$.
$x + 3$	$7d - 2$, mn	$\frac{b}{5}$

Example Translate each phrase into an algebraic expression.

a. five inches longer than the length of a book

Words five inches longer than the length of a book
Variable Let b represent the length of the book.
Expression $b + 5$

b. two less than the product of a number and eight

Words two less than the product of a number and eight
Variable Let n represent the unknown number.
Expression $8n - 2$

Exercises

Translate each phrase into an algebraic expression.

1. eight inches taller than Mycala's height **$h + 8$**
2. twelve more than four times a number **$4n + 12$**
3. the difference of sixty and a number **$60 - n$**
4. three times the number of tickets sold **$3t$**
5. fifteen dollars more than a saved amount **$s + 15$**
6. the quotient of the number of chairs and four **$\frac{c}{4}$**
7. a number of books less than twenty-three **$23 - b$**
8. five more than six times a number **$6n + 5$**
9. seven more boys than girls **$g + 7$**
10. twenty dollars divided among a number of friends minus three **$\frac{20}{f} - 3$**

Chapter 1 11 Glencoe Pre-Algebra

Practice
CRM p. 14 AL OL BL ELL

NAME ______ DATE ______ PERIOD ______

1-2 Practice

Variables and Expressions

ALGEBRA Translate each phrase into an algebraic expression.

1. six times a number minus eleven **$6n - 11$**
2. the product of eight hundred and a number **$800n$**
3. the quotient of thirty and the product of ten times a number **$30 \div (10n)$**
4. five times the sum of three and some number **$5(3 + n)$**
5. half the distance to the school **$\frac{c}{2}$**

ALGEBRA Evaluate each expression if $x = 12$, $y = 20$, and $z = 4$.

6. $x + y + z$ **36**
7. $4x - y$ **28**
8. $3x + 2y$ **76**
9. $y - 3z$ **8**
10. $x + y \div z$ **17**
11. $yz + x$ **92**
12. $(y - x) + (y - z)$ **24**
13. $\frac{y}{x} + \frac{x}{y}$ **8**
14. $\frac{5x}{3y}$ **1**
15. $z(y - x) + 4z$ **48**

ALGEBRA Evaluate each expression if $a = 3$, $b = 6$, $c = 5$, and $d = 9$.

16. $a + b + c + d$ **23**
17. $\frac{(a + b + c)}{2}$ **7**
18. $ab + bc$ **48**
19. $6d - c \cdot c$ **29**
20. $3(a + b + c)$ **42**
21. $\frac{100}{5c}$ **4**
22. abc **90**
23. $10(6c - 3d)$ **30**
24. $\frac{2(a + b)}{6(b - c)}$ **3**
25. $4[(d - a) + c]$ **44**

26. **RECYCLING** In order to encourage recycling, the city is offering five cents for every pound of newspapers collected, twenty-five cents per pound for cans, and ten cents per pound for glass bottles or jars.

a. Write an expression for the total amount earned from recycling. **$0.05n + 0.25c + 0.10b$**

b. If Chen brings in ten pounds of newspapers, eight pounds of cans, and two pounds of glass, how much will he receive? **\$2.70**

Chapter 1 14 Glencoe Pre-Algebra

Word Problem Practice
CRM p. 15 AL OL BL

NAME ______ DATE ______ PERIOD ______

1-2 Word Problem Practice

Variables and Expressions

1. **DROUGHT** The farmers in Ravin's town complained about the lack of rain during the growing season. Ravin did some research to find out how much rain typically falls during the growing season compared to the amount of rain during this growing season. She learned that it had rained 7 inches less than normal this season. Write an expression that represents the amount of rain this growing season. **$r - 7$**

2. **REPAIRS** Deidre's car needs to be repaired. The cost of the repair is going to be \$40 per hour for labor and an additional \$120 for parts. Write an expression that would represent the cost of getting the car repaired if a mechanic works on it for h hours. **$40h + 120$**

3. **RETAIL SALES** Amara works in his parents' clothing shop after school. Sometimes, he prices new merchandise for sale. He uses the table below to determine what the retail price of a piece of clothing should be. Based on the prices in the table, write an expression that Amara could use to calculate the retail price (R) given the cost price (C). **$R = 1.5 \times C$**

Cost	Retail
14	21
18	27
24	36
30	45
100	150

4. **TEMPERATURE** The formula that is used to convert Fahrenheit (F) to Celsius (C) is $C = (F - 32) \div 1.8$. Convert 77°F to degrees Celsius. **25°C**

5. **NUTRITION** Mr. Jacobs is teaching a unit on nutrition. The class has learned that each gram of fat contains 9 Calories, each gram of carbohydrates has 4 Calories, and each gram of protein has 4 Calories. He has his students research the nutritional facts of sandwiches served in the school lunch room.

Nutrition Facts	Fat (g)	Total Calories
Hamburger	29	580
Grilled chicken sandwich	7	360
Tuna wrap	32	440
Meatball sub	24	560
Veggie wrap	8	390
Turkey breast wrap	6	190

Source: Fat Calories

a. Write an expression to determine the grams of protein and carbohydrates of a grilled chicken sandwich. **$7 \times 9 + 4p + 4c$**

b. How many Calories of fat are in a meatball sub? **216 Calories**

c. What percent of the total Calories in a veggie wrap come from fat? **18.5%**

Chapter 1 15 Glencoe Pre-Algebra

4 ASSESS

Yesterday's News Tell students to write how yesterday's lesson on the order of operations and translating verbal phrases into numerical expressions helped them with today's lesson on translating and evaluating algebraic expressions.

Formative Assessment

Check for student understanding of the concepts in Lessons 1-1 and 1-2.

CRM Quiz 1, p. 46

Standardized Test Practice

45. What word phrase is equivalent to the expression $5x + 9$? **C**

A I have five cents more than nine nickels

B I have nine cents plus five cents

C I have nine cents more than five nickels

D I have nine cents less than five nickels

46. Which rule describes the ordered pairs in this table? **H**

x	y
1	1
2	4
3	7
4	10

F $y = x$

G $y = 2x$

H $y = 3x - 2$

J $y = 2x + 2$

47. What is "9 more than the product of five and a number n" written as an algebraic expression? **B**

A $5 + 9n$

B $9 + 5n$

C $5 + 9 \div n$

D $9 + n \div 5$

48. EXTENDED RESPONSE At a video store, DVDs cost $4 to rent for two days, and games cost $3 to rent for one day.

a. Complete the table below to show how much Ava will pay to rent one DVD and one game for the number of days given.

Number of Days	Total Cost ($)
2	■ **10**
4	■ **20**
6	■ **30**

b. How much will Ava pay to rent 4 DVDs and 3 games for 10 days? **b. $4 \cdot 5 \cdot 4 + 3 \cdot 3 \cdot 10 = \$170$**

Spiral Review

Find the value of each expression. (Lesson 1-1)

49. $3 \cdot 6 - 4$ **14**

50. $12 - 3 \times 3$ **3**

51. $9 + 18 \div 3$ **15**

52. $56 \div (7 \cdot 2) \times 6$ **24**

53. $75 \div (7 + 8) - 3$ **2**

54. $70 - (16 \div 2 + 21)$ **41**

55. $\frac{45 - 18}{9 \div 3}$ **9**

56. $\frac{8 \div 8 + 11}{15 - 4(3)}$ **4**

57. $4(20 - 13) + 4 \times 5$ **48**

HOCKEY The final standings of a hockey league are shown. A win is worth three points, and a tie is worth 1 point. Zero points are given for a loss. (Lesson 1-1)

Team	Wins	Losses	Ties
Knights	14	9	7
Huskies	11	9	10
Wildcats	10	9	11
Mustangs	9	10	11
Panthers	10	14	6

58. How many points do the Wildcats have? **41 points**

59. How many points do the Huskies have? **43 points**

60. How many more points do the Knights have than the Panthers? **13 points**

Skills Review

Find each difference. (Previous Course)

61. $47 - 24$ **23**

62. $58 - 32$ **26**

63. $93 - 61$ **32**

64. $154 - 107$ **47**

Differentiated Instruction

Extension Present the following problem to students: Company A charges $63 per day to lease a car, plus $0.24 per mile driven. Write an expression for the cost to lease the car. $63n + 0.24m$; n = number of days leased; m = miles driven How much does it cost to rent the car for two days and drive 50 miles? $138 Company B charges $55 per day to lease, plus $0.33 per mile driven over 20 miles. Write an expression for the cost to lease this car. $55n + 0.33(m - 20)$ How much does it cost to rent the car for two days and drive 50 miles? $119.90 Which company is less expensive to lease a car for two days and drive 50 miles? Company B

Differentiated Instruction Extension activities help you cultivate skills that students will need to have success in higher mathematics.

Spreadsheet Lab
Expressions and Spreadsheets

Math Online glencoe.com

Math *in Motion,* Animation

One of the most common computer applications is a spreadsheet program. A **spreadsheet** is a table that performs calculations. It is organized into boxes called **cells**, which are named by a letter and a number. In the spreadsheet below, cell B2 is highlighted.

An advantage of using a spreadsheet is that values in the spreadsheet are recalculated when a number is changed. You can use a spreadsheet to investigate patterns in data.

ACTIVITY 1

Here's a number trick! Pick any number. Double it. Then add four and divide by two. Then subtract the original number. I guarantee you the answer is 2.

You can use a spreadsheet to test different numbers. Suppose we start with the number 15.

I Know The Answer!.xls

◇	A	B	C
1	Think of any number.	15	15
2	Double it.	=B1*2	30
3	Add 4.	=B2+4	34
4	Divide by 2.	=B3/2	17
5	Subtract the original number.	=B4-B1	2
6			

Sheet 1 / Sheet 2 / Sheet 3

The spreadsheet takes the value in B1,doubles it, and enters the value in B2. Note the * is the symbol for multiplication.

The spreadsheet takes the value in B3, divides by 2, and enters the value in B4. Note that / is the symbol for division.

The result is 2.

Exercises

To change information in a spreadsheet, move the cursor to the cell you want to access and click the mouse. Then type in the information and press Enter. Find the result when each value is entered in B1.

1. 7 2
2. 10 2
3. 50 2
4. 115 2
5. 1200 2
6. 2132 2

7. **MAKE A CONJECTURE** What is the result if a decimal is entered in B1? a negative number? 2, 2

8. **WRITING IN MATH** Explain why the result is always 2. Write an expression that describes your answer. **8–9. See Chapter 1 Answer Appendix.**

9. Make up your own mind-reading trick. Enter it into a spreadsheet to show that it works. Write an expression to describe the trick.

EXTEND 1-2 Lesson Notes

1 FOCUS

Objective Determine rules for a given pattern.

Materials for Each Pair

- spreadsheet software

Teaching Tips

Ask students to locate specific cells. Review the formulas in the example so students understand what they mean.

2 TEACH

Working in Cooperative Groups

Arrange students in pairs, mixing abilities. Have each pair work through the Activity.

Ask:

- Suppose in the Activity there was a value of 5 in C5. Where would the formula for that cell be? B5 What would the formula be? = B4 − B1
- Suppose we enter a value of 5 into B1. What will result in C2? 10 C3? 14 C4? 7 C5? 2

Practice Have students complete Exercises 1–9.

3 ASSESS

Formative Assessment

Use Exercise 8 to assess whether students comprehend how to determine a rule for a given pattern.

From Concrete to Abstract

Ask student pairs to create a spreadsheet similar to the one in the Activity. Tell students to trade the values from C1 and C5 of their spreadsheet with another student pair. Each pair will create a new spreadsheet based on the values provided. Have student pairs that switched values discuss their results.

1-3 Lesson Notes

1 FOCUS

Vertical Alignment

Before Lesson 1-3
Evaluate numerical and algebraic expressions.

Lesson 1-3
Identify and use properties of addition and multiplication.
Use properties of addition and multiplication to simplify algebraic expressions.

After Lesson 1-3
Write and solve equations.

2 TEACH

Scaffolding Questions

Have students read the *Why?* section of the lesson and answer the questions.

Ask:

- Is $7 + 5$ equal to $5 + 7$? Yes, the value of each expression is 12.
- Is $7 - 5$ equal to $5 - 7$? No, the value of each expression is different.
- What are two conjectures that you can make about the order of adding or subtracting two numbers? Order does not matter for addition; order does matter for subtraction.

Scaffolding Questions give direction and momentum to the lesson, clarify its purpose, and keep students on task.

1-3 Properties

Then
You have already evaluated numerical and algebraic expressions. (Lessons 1-1 and 1-2)

Now
- Identify and use properties of addition and multiplication.
- Use properties of addition and multiplication to simplify algebraic expressions.

New Vocabulary
properties
counterexample
simplify
deductive reasoning

Math Online
glencoe.com
- Extra Examples
- Personal Tutor
- Self-Check Quiz
- Homework Help

Why?

When you make a peanut butter and jelly sandwich, do you spread the peanut butter first or the jelly? The order does not matter because in the end you have a tasty sandwich.

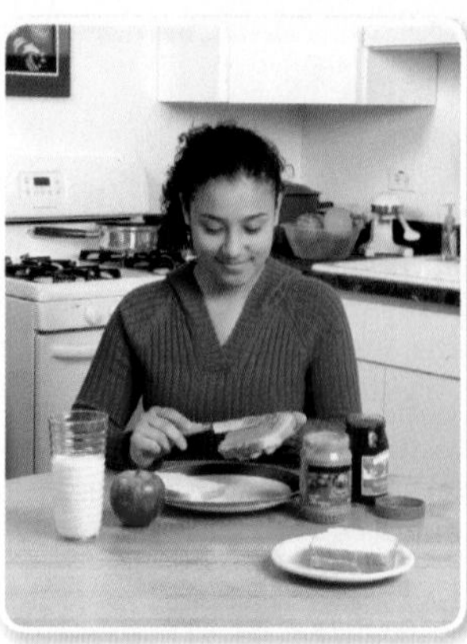

a. Name two other activities where order does not matter. **a–b. See Chapter 1 Answer Appendix.**

b. Name two activities where order *does* matter.

c. Name a mathematical operation in which you can switch the numbers and still have the same value. **addition or multiplication**

Properties of Addition and Multiplication In algebra, **properties** are statements that are true for any numbers. For example, the expression $30 + 10$ and $10 + 30$ have the same value, 40. This illustrates the **Commutative Property of Addition**.

Likewise, $30 \cdot 10$ and $10 \cdot 30$ have the same value, 300. This illustrates the **Commutative Property of Multiplication**.

Key Concept Commutative Properties — For Your FOLDABLE

Words The order in which numbers are added or multiplied does not change the sum or product.

Symbols For any numbers a and b, $a + b = b + a$.
For any numbers a and b, $a \cdot b = b \cdot a$.

Examples
$6 + 9 = 9 + 6$
$15 = 15$

$4 \cdot 7 = 7 \cdot 4$
$28 = 28$

Suppose you want to evaluate the expression $16 + (14 + 58)$. Since $4 + 6$ is 10, it is easier to use mental math by grouping the numbers as $(16 + 14) + 58$. This illustrates the **Associative Property of Addition**. There is also an **Associative Property of Multiplication**.

Key Concept Associative Properties — For Your FOLDABLE

Words The order in which numbers are grouped when added or multiplied does not change the sum or product.

Symbols For any numbers a, b, and c, $(a + b) + c = a + (b + c)$.
For any numbers a, b, and c, $(a \cdot b) \cdot c = a \cdot (b \cdot c)$.

Examples
$(3 + 6) + 1 = 3 + (6 + 1)$
$9 + 1 = 3 + 7$
$10 = 10$

$(5 \cdot 9) \cdot 2 = 5 \cdot (9 \cdot 2)$
$45 \cdot 2 = 5 \cdot 18$
$90 = 90$

Lesson 1-3 Resources

Resource	Approaching-Level	On-Level	Beyond-Level	English Learners
Teacher Edition		• Differentiated Instruction, p. 19	• Differentiated Instruction, pp. 19, 23	
Chapter Resource Masters	• Study Guide and Intervention, pp. 18–19 • Skills Practice, p. 20 • Practice, p. 21 • Word Problem Practice, p. 22	• Study Guide and Intervention, pp. 18–19 • Skills Practice, p. 20 • Practice, p. 21 • Word Problem Practice, p. 22 • Enrichment, p. 23	• Practice, p. 21 • Word Problem Practice, p. 22 • Enrichment, p. 23	• Study Guide and Intervention, pp. 18–19 • Skills Practice, p. 20 • Practice, p. 21
Transparencies	• 5-Minute Check Transparency 1-3	• 5-Minute Check Transparency 1-3	• 5-Minute Check Transparency 1-3	• 5-Minute Check Transparency 1-3
Other	• Study Notebook • Teaching Pre-Algebra with Manipulatives	• Study Notebook • Teaching Pre-Algebra with Manipulatives	• Study Notebook	• Study Notebook • Teaching Pre-Algebra with Manipulatives

In addition to the Commutative and Associative Properties, the following properties are also true for any numbers.

Key Concept — **Number Properties** — For Your FOLDABLE

Property	Words	Symbols	Examples
Additive Identity	When 0 is added to any number, the sum is the number.	For any number a, $a + 0 = 0 + a = a$	$5 + 0 = 5$ $0 + 5 = 5$
Multiplicative Identity	When any number is multiplied by 1, the product is the number.	For any number a, $a \cdot 1 = 1 \cdot a = a$.	$8 \cdot 1 = 8$ $1 \cdot 8 = 8$
Multiplicative Property of Zero	When any number is multiplied by 0, the product is 0.	For any number a, $a \cdot 0 = 0 \cdot a = 0$	$3 \cdot 0 = 0$ $0 \cdot 3 = 0$

ReadingMath

Identity The word identity means *sameness of essential character*. The additive identity, 0, and multiplicative identity, 1, allow the original number to remain the same.

Do these properties apply to subtraction or division? One way to find out is to look for a counterexample. A **counterexample** is an example that shows a conjecture is not true.

EXAMPLE 1 Find a Counterexample

Is division of whole numbers associative? If not, give a counterexample.

The Associative Property of Multiplication states $(a \cdot b) \cdot c = a \cdot (b \cdot c)$. Check $(a \div b) \div c \stackrel{?}{=} a \div (b \div c)$.

$(27 \div 9) \div 3 \stackrel{?}{=} 27 \div (9 \div 3)$ **Pick values for a, b, and c.**

$(3) \div 3 \stackrel{?}{=} 27 \div (3)$ **Simplify.**

$1 \neq 9$ **Simplify.**

We found a counterexample. So, division of whole numbers is not associative.

StudyTip

Counterexample You can disprove a statement by finding only one counterexample.

Check Your Progress

1. Is subtraction of decimals associative? If not, give a counterexample. no; $(7.1 - 4.8) - 1.2 \neq 7.1 - (4.8 - 1.2)$

Personal Tutor glencoe.com

EXAMPLE 2 Identify Properties

Name the property shown by each statement.

a. $4 + (a + 3) = (a + 3) + 4$

The order of the numbers and variables changed. This is the Commutative Property of Addition.

b. $1 \cdot (3c) = 3c$

The expression was multiplied by 1 and remained the same. This is the Multiplicative Identity Property.

Check Your Progress

2A. $d + 0 = d$ Identity (+)

2B. $8 \cdot 1 = 8$ Identity (×)

2C. $14 + (9 + 10) = (14 + 9) + 10$ Associative (+)

2D. $5 \times 7 \times 2 = 7 \times 2 \times 5$ Commutative (×)

Personal Tutor glencoe.com

Properties of Addition and Multiplication

Example 1 shows how to find a counterexample that demonstrates that a conjecture is not true. **Example 2** shows how to identify properties of numbers.

TEACH with TECH

AUDIO RECORDING Have students work in pairs to record themselves stating and describing the properties from the lesson in their own words.

Formative Assessment

Use the Check Your Progress exercises after each example to determine students' understanding of concepts.

Additional Examples

1. Is division of whole numbers commutative? If not, give a counterexample. No; $12 \div 6 \neq 6 \div 12$

2. Name the property shown by each statement.
   a. $3 \cdot 10 \cdot 2 = 3 \cdot 2 \cdot 10$ Commutative Property of Multiplication
   b. $(2 + 5) + m = 2 + (5 + m)$ Associative Property of Addition

Additional Examples also in Interactive Classroom PowerPoint® Presentations

IWB INTERACTIVE WHITEBOARD READY

Differentiated Instruction

students need enrichment activities,

provide additional mathematical conjectures for student pairs to work on. Have one student try to list examples to support the conjecture and the other student try to list counterexamples. Then have the pair use their findings to determine whether the conjecture is true or false.

*Additional Examples, which are included for every example in the Student Edition, exactly parallel the examples in the text. Step-by-step solutions for these examples are included in **Interactive Classroom.***

Focus on Mathematical Content

Commutative and Associative Properties The operations of multiplication and addition are related because multiplication is repeated addition. Multiplication and addition are the only operations where the order or the grouping can be changed within the problem and the sum or product remains the same. Ask students if the quotient of $36 \div 9$ is the same if the order of the values is switched to $9 \div 36$. no Explain. The order of the numbers affects the outcome in division.

Simplify Algebraic Expressions

Example 3 shows how to simplify algebraic expressions using the Associative and Commutative Properties. **Example 4** shows how to identify properties.

Additional Examples

3 Simplify each expression.

a. $12 + (x + 18)$ $30 + x$

b. $5 \cdot (3 \cdot r)$ $15r$

4 **STANDARDIZED TEST PRACTICE** Which of the following is an example of the Associative Property of Addition? B

A $18 + 0 = 18$

B $9 + (5 + 3) = (9 + 5) + 3$

C $19 + 3 + 7 = 3 + 19 + 7$

D $14 \cdot (5 \cdot 3) = (14 \cdot 5) \cdot 3$

New teachers, or teachers new to teaching mathematics, may especially appreciate the **Tips for New Teachers**.

Simplify Algebraic Expressions To **simplify** an algebraic expression, perform all possible operations. You can use the properties you learned in this lesson. Using facts, properties, or rules to reach valid conclusions is called **deductive reasoning**.

EXAMPLE 3 Simplify Algebraic Expressions

Simplify each expression.

a. $(3 + e) + 7$

$(3 + e) + 7 = (e + 3) + 7$	**Commutative Property of Addition**
$= e + (3 + 7)$	**Associative Property of Addition**
$= e + 10$	**Simplify.**

b. $8 \cdot (x \cdot 5)$

$8 \cdot (x \cdot 5) = 8 \cdot (5 \cdot x)$	**Commutative Property of Multiplication**
$= (8 \cdot 5) \cdot x$	**Associative Property of Multiplication**
$= 40x$	**Simplify.**

Check Your Progress

3A. $12 \cdot (10 \cdot z)$ $120z$

3B. $10 + (p + 18)$ $28 + p$

Personal Tutor glencoe.com

Test-TakingTip

Multiple Choice Eliminate the options you know are incorrect. If possible, circle the word, phrase or number that makes the option incorrect.

STANDARDIZED TEST EXAMPLE 4

Which of the following is an example of the Commutative Property of Addition?

A $(3 \cdot 4) + 5 = 5 + (3 \cdot 4)$

B $(7 + 8) + 2 = 7 + (8 + 2)$

C $8 \cdot 9 = 9 \cdot 8$

D $1 + 0 = 1$

Read the Test Item

You need to identify the correct expression.

Solve the Test Item

The Identity Property of Addition shows that any number added to zero is equal to that number. So, option D can be eliminated.

The Associative Property of Addition deals with grouping of individual terms. The factors are grouped in different ways on each side of the statement. So, option B can be eliminated.

Option C can be eliminated because it shows the Commutative Property of Multiplication.

The answer is A.

Check Your Progress

4. Which of the following is an example of the Identity Property of Multiplication? H

F $10 \cdot 1 = 1 \cdot 10$

G $(5 \cdot 6) \cdot 3 = 3 \cdot (5 \cdot 6)$

H $8 \cdot 1 = 8$

J $4 \cdot 4 = 16$

Personal Tutor glencoe.com

Tips for New Teachers

Counterexamples One counterexample can prove a conjecture false. However, an infinite number of true examples cannot prove a conjecture true.

Tips for New Teachers

Inductive Reasoning In inductive reasoning, conclusions are made based on past events or patterns.

Check Your Understanding

Example 1 p. 19

1. Is subtraction of whole numbers commutative? If not, give a counterexample. No; $10 - 6 \neq 6 - 10$

Example 2 p. 19

Name the property shown by each statement.

2. $8 \cdot 4 = 4 \cdot 8$ Commutative (×)
3. $6 \cdot 1 = 6$ Identity (×)
4. $9 + 3 + 20 = 3 + 9 + 20$ Commutative (+)
5. $7 + 0 = 7$ Identity (+)
6. $13 + 12 = 12 + 13$ Commutative (+)
7. $6 \times (1 \times 9) = (6 \times 1) \times 9$ Associative (×)

Example 3 p. 20

ALGEBRA Simplify each expression.

8. $(12 + m) + 4$ $16 + m$
9. $3 + (k + 8)$ $11 + k$
10. $(15 + s) + 4$ $19 + s$
11. $8 \cdot (x \cdot 5)$ $40x$
12. $(10 \cdot r) \cdot 5$ $50r$
13. $(12 \cdot a) \cdot 6$ $72a$

Example 4 p. 20

14. **MULTIPLE CHOICE** Which of the following is an example of the Identity Property of Addition? D

A $3 + 4 = 4 + 3$
B $7 + 7 = 14$
C $(5 + 2) + 6 = 5 + (2 + 6)$
D $12 + 0 = 12$

Practice and Problem Solving

 = **Step-by-Step Solutions** begin on page R11. **Extra Practice** begins on page 810.

Example 1 p. 19

State whether each conjecture is true. If not, give a counterexample.

15. The sum of two odd numbers is always odd. No; $13 + 15 = 28$
16. The product of odd numbers is always even. No; $3 \times 5 = 15$

Example 2 p. 19

Name the property shown by each statement.

17. $0 + 14 = 14$ Identity (+)
18. $8 \cdot 1 = 8$ Identity (×)
19. $15 + 17 = 17 + 15$ Commutative (+)
20. $(2 \cdot 8) \cdot 5 = 2 \cdot (8 \cdot 5)$ Associative (×)
21. $14 \times 0 \times 3 = 0$ Multiplicative (0)
22. $4 + (9 + 2) = (4 + 9) + 2$ Associative (+)
23. $7 + x + 11 = x + 7 + 11$ Commutative (+)
24. $5k \times 1 = 5k$ Identity (×)

Example 3 p. 20

ALGEBRA Simplify each expression.

25. $(d + 12) + 16$ $d + 28$
26. $14 + (27 + m)$ $41 + m$
27. $(54 + p) + 16$ $70 + p$
28. $(r + 32) + 24$ $r + 56$
29. $(8 \cdot s) \cdot 9$ $72s$
30. $g \cdot (5 \cdot 7)$ $35g$
31. $11 \cdot (t \cdot 4)$ $44t$
32. $15b(5)$ $75b$
33. $6(12c)$ $72c$
34. $(7 + p) + 13$ $20 + p$
35. $29 + (1 + t)$ $30 + t$
36. $4 \cdot (x \cdot 2)$ $8x$

37. **BASKETBALL** Use the table to write an expression that shows how many total baskets the Cavaliers made during the season. Simplify the expression. $1978 + f$

Cavaliers' Baskets

Free Throws	1484
2-Point Field Goals	f
3-Point Field Goals	494

38. **HOMEWORK** Moreno likes to do her social studies homework before she does her math homework. Is doing social studies homework and math homework commutative? Explain. See margin.

*Check Your Understanding exercises are intended to be completed in class. **Example references** show students where to look back for review. In the Exercises, **Homework Help** boxes function in the same way.*

3 PRACTICE

Formative Assessment

Use Exercises 1–14 to check for understanding.

Use the chart at the bottom of this page to customize assignments for your students.

Watch Out!

Find the Error In Exercise 46, point out to students that neither Meghan nor Alejandro used the Associative or Commutative Properties of Multiplication to group and associate the numbers and variables in the expression before simplifying. Suggest that students use these properties of multiplication to write the steps for simplifying the expression. They can then use the steps to identify any errors Meghan or Alejandro may have made.

Additional Answer

38. Yes; the order in which she does her homework doesn't matter as long as it all gets done.

Differentiated Homework Options

Level	Assignment	Two-Day Option	
AL Basic	15–36, 44–46, 48–71	15–35 odd, 49–52	16–36 even, 44–46, 48, 53–71
OL Core	15–35 odd, 37–39, 41, 43–46, 48–71	15–36, 49–52	37–46, 48, 53–71
BL Advanced	37–63, (optional: 64–71)		

Study Guide and Intervention
CRM pp. 18–19 AL OL ELL

NAME ________ DATE ________ PERIOD ________

1-3 Study Guide and Intervention

Properties

Properties of Addition and Multiplication In algebra, there are certain statements called **properties** that are true for any numbers.

Property	Explanations	Example
Commutative Property of Addition	$a + b = b + a$	$6 + 3 = 3 + 6$ $9 = 9$
Commutative Property of Multiplication	$a \cdot b = b \cdot a$	$4 \cdot 5 = 5 \cdot 4$ $20 = 20$
Associative Property of Addition	$(a + b) + c =$ $a + (b + c)$	$(3 + 4) + 7 = 3 + (4 + 7)$ $14 = 14$
Associative Property of Multiplication	$(a \cdot b) \cdot c =$ $a \cdot (b \cdot c)$	$(2 \cdot 5) \cdot 8 = 2 \cdot (5 \cdot 8)$ $80 = 80$
Additive Identity	$a + 0 = 0 + a = a$	$10 + 0 = 0 + 10 = 10$
Multiplicative Identity	$a \cdot 1 = 1 \cdot a = a$	$5 \cdot 1 = 1 \cdot 5 = 5$
Multiplicative Property of Zero	$a \cdot 0 = 0 \cdot a = 0$	$15 \cdot 0 = 0 \cdot 15 = 0$

Example 1 Is subtraction of whole numbers associative? If not, give a counterexample.

$(9 - 4) - 2 \stackrel{?}{=} 9 - (4 - 2)$ State the conjecture
$5 - 2 \stackrel{?}{=} 9 - 2$ Simplify.
$3 \neq 7$ Simplify.

This is a counterexample. So, subtraction of whole numbers is not associative.

Example 2 Name the property shown by the statement.

$15 \times b = b \times 15$ The order of the numbers and variables changed. This is the Commutative Property of Multiplication.

Exercises

1. State whether the following conjecture is true or false: The multiplicative identity applies to division also. If false, give a counterexample. **Sample answer: False; $4 \div 1 = 4$, not 1.**

Name the property shown by each statement.

2. $75 + 25 = 25 + 75$ **Commutative Property of Addition**
3. $2 \cdot (3 \cdot 4) = (2 \cdot 3) \cdot 4$ **Associative Property of Multiplication**
4. $14 \cdot 1 = 14$ **Multiplicative Identity**
5. $p \cdot 0 = 0$ **Multiplicative Property of Zero**

Chapter 1 18 Glencoe Pre-Algebra

Practice
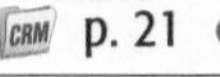    

CRM p. 21 AL OL BL ELL

NAME ________ DATE ________ PERIOD ________

1-3 Practice

Properties

Name the property shown by each statement.

1. $55 + 6 = 6 + 55$ **Commutative Property of Addition**
2. $6 \cdot 7 = 7 \cdot 6$ **Commutative Property of Multiplication**
3. $(x + 3) + y = x + (3 + y)$ **Associative Property of Addition**
4. $1 \cdot mp = mp$ **Multiplicative Identity**
5. $9 + (5 + 35) = (9 + 5) + 35$ **Associative Property of Addition**
6. $67 + 0 = 67$ **Additive Identity**
7. $7x \cdot 0 = 0$ **Multiplicative Property of Zero**
8. $4(3 \cdot z) = (4 \cdot 3)z$ **Associative Property of Multiplication**

ALGEBRA Simplify each expression.

9. $a(5 \cdot 7)$ **$35a$**
10. $(24 + s) + 16$ **$s + 40$**
11. $c + (17 + 8)$ **$c + 25$**
12. $72g(1)$ **$72g$**
13. $31 + (21 + p)$ **$p + 52$**
14. $(e \cdot 4) \cdot 12$ **$48e$**
15. $(m + 11) + 19$ **$m + 30$**
16. $(9 \cdot b) \cdot 10$ **$90b$**
17. $19 + (v + 8)$ **$27 + v$**
18. $(28 + 12) + x$ **$40 + x$**
19. $8a \cdot 0$ **0**
20. $4 \cdot (r \cdot 5)$ **$20r$**

21. GEOMETRY The volume of a box is given by $V = \ell \cdot w \cdot h$ where ℓ = length, w = width, and h = height. Find the volume of a box if the length is 25 cm, width is 13 cm, and height is 4 cm. **V = 25 cm · 13 cm · 4 cm = 25 cm · 4 cm · 13 cm = 1300 cm³**

22. SCHOOL In math class each assignment is worth 20 points. David got 17, 20, 19, and 13 points on his last four assignments. How many points did David score all together? **17 + 20 + 19 + 13 = 17 + 13 + 20 + 19 = 69 points**

23. State whether the following statement is true or false: Multiplying any number by one produces the original number. Explain. **True. The Multiplicative Identity states that any number times one is the original number.**

Chapter 1 21 Glencoe Pre-Algebra

Word Problem Practice
CRM p. 22 AL OL BL

NAME ________ DATE ________ PERIOD ________

1-3 Word Problem Practice

Properties

1. TRAVEL Mike and his family are driving from Dallas to Fort Worth, a distance of 30 miles, to visit a cousin. Then, they will drive from Fort Worth to San Antonio, a distance of 229 miles, to visit his grandparents. On the way back, Mike reverses his trip and travels from San Antonio to Dallas through Forth Worth. Write one equation to show the distance traveled from Dallas to San Antonio, and a second equation to show the distance traveled from San Antonio to Dallas. What do you notice about the distance traveled each way? **30 + 229 = 259 and 229 + 30 = 259 The distances are equal.**

2. SHOPPING Sara is buying some new clothes for school. She buys a pair of shoes for \$65, a blouse for \$42, jeans for \$58, and a skirt for \$35. Using the Associative and Commutative Properties of Addition, add the prices so that the total cost can be found easily with mental arithmetic. **(65 + 35) = 100 and (42 + 58) = 100 100 + 100 = \$200**

3. CLOTHES Most people wear both socks and shoes when they go to work. When getting dressed, is putting on socks and shoes a commutative process? Explain. **No; putting your socks on and then your shoes is different than putting your shoes on and then your socks.**

4. COMBINATIONS A special lock has a unique combination lock. A value is assigned that opens the lock, and any combination of single-digit numbers and operations, with or without parentheses, will open the lock. For example, if 40 is the value assigned to the lock, then 8×5 or $12 + 28$ will open the lock. Find 3 different ways to unlock the lock if the combination is 17. **Sample answer: 9 + 8; (2 + 4) × 3 − 1; or 5 × 2 + 7**

5. BASEBALL One statistic used in baseball is percent (PCT) or the number of games a team has won of all of the games played to date. Alfie plays for the Lions in his town league. The table below shows the standing at the end of the season.

Team	Wins	Losses	PCT
Lions	15	5	0.75
Bears	14	6	0.7
Bullhorns	8	12	6

a. Alfie used the Commutative Property and divided 20 by 8 to find the percent for the Bullhorns. What error did Alfie make? **He incorrectly used the Commutative Property by dividing 20 ÷ 8 instead of dividing 8 ÷ 20. The Commutative Property does not apply to division.**

b. Alfie knows that the Mavericks have won 11 out of 20 games. He subtracts to find that the Mavericks lost −9 games. What error did Alfie make? **He incorrectly used the Commutative Property by subtracting 11 − 20 instead of subtracting 20 − 11. The Commutative Property does not apply to subtraction.**

Chapter 1 22 Glencoe Pre-Algebra

ALGEBRA Translate each verbal expression into an algebraic expression. Then simplify the expression.

39. the sum of two times a number and five added to six times a number **$2n + 5 + 6n$; $8n + 5$**

40. the product of seven and four times a number multiplied by three **$7 \cdot 4n \cdot 3$; $84n$**

41. eight more than the sum of six times a number and nine times a number added to one **$8 + 6n + 9n + 1$; $15n + 9$**

42. the product of eleven and five times a number multiplied by four **$4(11 \cdot 5n)$; $220n$**

43. **FINANCIAL LITERACY** The Center of Wonders science center has the rates shown.

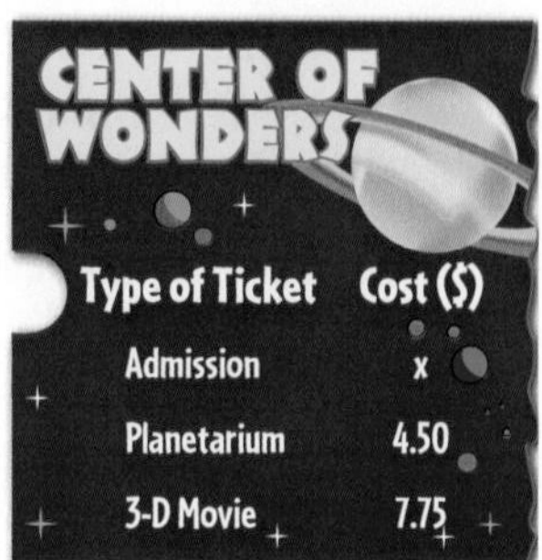

Type of Ticket	Cost (\$)
Admission	x
Planetarium	4.50
3-D Movie	7.75

a. Write an algebraic expression that could be used to find the total cost for five people to get into the center, visit the planetarium, and watch a 3-D movie. **$5x + \$61.25$**

b. If the cost of admission to the center is \$12, how much will it cost for four people to get into the center and watch a 3-D movie? **\$79**

Real-World Link

The Smithsonian Institute opened in 1846 as a national museum. It currently has 19 museums and 9 research centers. In 2006, 23.2 million people visited the museums. Admission to most of the museums is free.

H.O.T. Problems
Use **H**igher-**O**rder **T**hinking Skills

44. **OPEN ENDED** Write an algebraic expression that can be simplified using at least two different properties. Simplify the expression showing each step and justify for each step. **44–46. See Chapter 1 Answer Appendix.**

45. **WRITING IN MATH** Is the following statement *true* or *false*? Explain your reasoning.

$$15 + (4 \cdot 6) = (15 + 4) \cdot 6$$

46. **FIND THE ERROR** Meghan and Alejandro are simplifying the expression $8x \cdot 4 \cdot 2x \cdot 3$. Is either of them correct? Explain your reasoning.

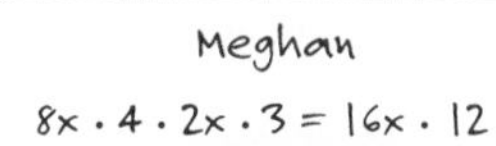

Alejandro
$8x \cdot 4 \cdot 2x \cdot 3 = 192x$

47. **CHALLENGE** If you take any two whole numbers and add them together, the sum is always a whole number. This is the Closure Property for Addition. The set of whole numbers is *closed* under addition.

a. Is the set of whole numbers closed under subtraction? If not, give a counterexample. **No; $2 - 3 = -1$ and -1 is not a whole number.**

b. Suppose you had a very small set of numbers that contained only 0 and 1. Would this set be closed under addition? If not, give a counterexample.

c. There is also a Closure Property for Multiplication of Whole Numbers. State this property using the addition property above as a guideline.

d. Is the set {0, 1} closed under multiplication? Explain.

48. **WRITING IN MATH** The number 1 is the identity for multiplication. Do you think that division has an identity? Explain your reasoning.

47b. No; $1 + 1 = 2$ and 2 is not a member of the set.

47c. The Closure Property for Multiplication states that because the product of two whole numbers is also a whole number, the set of whole numbers is closed under multiplication.

47d. Yes. $0 \cdot 0 = 0$, $0 \cdot 1 = 0$, $1 \cdot 0 = 0$, and $1 \cdot 1 = 1$.

48. Sample answer: While it seems that 1 would also be the identity for division because $a \div 1 = a$, it is not the identity because $1 \div a \neq a$. So, there is no identity for division.

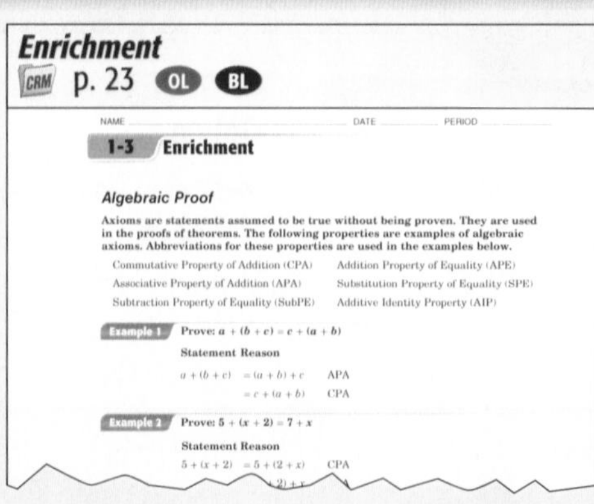

Enrichment
CRM p. 23 OL BL

NAME ________ DATE ________ PERIOD ________

1-3 Enrichment

Algebraic Proof

Axioms are statements assumed to be true without being proven. They are used in the proofs of theorems. The following properties are examples of algebraic axioms. Abbreviations for these properties are used in the examples below.

Commutative Property of Addition (CPA) Addition Property of Equality (APE)
Associative Property of Addition (APA) Substitution Property of Equality (SPE)
Subtraction Property of Equality (SubPE) Additive Identity Property (AIP)

Example 1 Prove: $a + (b + c) = c + (a + b)$

Statement Reason
$a + (b + c) = (a + b) + c$ APA
$= c + (a + b)$ CPA

Example 2 Prove: $5 + (x + 2) = 7 + x$

Statement Reason
$5 + (x + 2) = 5 + (2 + x)$ CPA

Standardized Test Practice

49. Which statement is an example of the Identity Property? **D**

A $3 \cdot x \cdot 0 = 0$
B $7(4x) = (4 \cdot 7)x$
C $5 + (4 + x) = (5 + 4) + x$
D $4x + 0 = 4x$

50. Which expression can be used to find the perimeter of the rectangle below? **G**

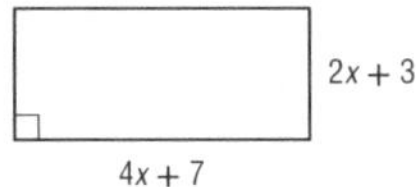

F $8x + 21$ H $6x + 10$
G $12x + 20$ J $8x + 10$

51. Which property is illustrated by the statement below? **B**

$$12 \cdot (n \cdot 5) = (12 \cdot n) \cdot 5$$

A Commutative Property
B Associative Property
C Identity Property
D Zero Property

52. SHORT RESPONSE Simplify the expression, show and justify each step.

$$10 \cdot (x \cdot 3)$$

$= 10 \cdot (3 \cdot x)$ Commutative Property of Multiplication
$= (10 \cdot 3) \cdot x$ Associative Property of Multiplication
$= 30x$

Spiral Review

ALGEBRA Translate each phrase into an algebraic expression. (Lesson 1-2)

53. Bianca's salary plus a \$200 bonus **$s + 200$**

54. three more than the number of cakes baked **$c + 3$**

55. six feet shorter than the mountain's height **$h - 6$**

56. eight less than the quotient of the number of quarters and four **$n \div 4 - 8$**

57. SCIENCE The number of times a cricket chirps can be used to estimate the temperature in degrees Fahrenheit. Use $c \div 4 + 37$, where c is the number of chirps in 1 minute. (Lesson 1-2)

a. Find the approximate temperature if a cricket chirps 136 times a minute. **71°F**
b. What is the temperature if a cricket chirps 100 times in a minute? **62°F**

Evaluate each expression. (Lesson 1-1)

58. $50 \div 2 \times 5$ **125** **59.** $6(8 - 4) + 3 \cdot 7$ **45** **60.** $16 - 2 \cdot 4$ **8**

61. $18 + 2 \cdot 3$ **24** **62.** $49 - 25 + 5$ **29** **63.** $3(7 \cdot 5) \cdot 2$ **210**

Skills Review

Find each product. (Previous Course)

64. 22×7 **154** **65.** 9×45 **405** **66.** 8×34 **272** **67.** 18×3 **54**

68. 15×13 **195** **69.** 8×42 **336** **70.** 109×21 **2289** **71.** 43×119 **5117**

4 ASSESS

Name the Math Have students name two properties and explain how the properties help them in mathematics. The explanations should include examples of the properties.

Formative Assessment

Check for student understanding of concepts in Lesson 1-3.

CRM Quiz 2, p. 46

The Four-step Teaching Plan shows you how to **Focus, Teach, Practice,** and **Assess** each lesson. Each lesson ends with a creative strategy for closing the lesson.

Differentiated Instruction

Extension Write the numbers 2, 3, 4, and 7 on the board. Tell students to make the number 7 by using each of the numbers one time, along with operations and grouping symbols.
Sample answer: $(7 + 2) \div 3 + 4$

CHAPTER 1 Mid-Chapter Quiz

Formative Assessment

Use the Mid-Chapter Quiz to assess students' progress in the first half of the chapter.

For problems answered incorrectly, have students review the lessons indicated in parentheses.

ExamView Assessment Suite Customize and create multiple versions of your Mid-Chapter Quiz and their answer keys.

FOLDABLES® Follow-Up

Before students complete the Mid-Chapter Quiz, encourage them to review the information for Lessons 1-1 through 1-3 in their Foldables.

Additional Answers

7. 35 + 5(6.95); $69.75;

Number of Hours	Expression	Cost ($)
5	35 + 5(6.95)	69.75
6	35 + 6(6.95)	76.70
7	35 + 7(6.95)	83.65
8	35 + 8(6.95)	90.60

25. Turning the player on and programming it are not commutative. You need to turn the MP3 player on first before you can program it.

CHAPTER 1 Mid-Chapter Quiz

Lessons 1-1 through 1-3

Write a numerical expression for each verbal phrase. (Lesson 1-1)

1. the total number of video games if Tonya has 26 and Mary has 38 **26 + 38**
2. the number of years until the Olympics if the Olympics are 36 months away **36 ÷ 12**

Evaluate each expression. (Lesson 1-1)

3. $3 \cdot 4 + 2$ **14**
4. $45 \div 15 \times 5$ **15**
5. $(18 - 6) \div 4$ **3**
6. $3[(4 + 6) \div 2]$ **15**

7. **POPCORN** To rent a popcorn machine, it costs $35 plus $6.95 for each hour. Write and evaluate an expression to find the total cost of renting the popcorn machine for 5 hours. Then make a table showing the cost for 5, 6, 7, and 8 hours. (Lesson 1-1) **See margin.**

8. **SWIMMING** The table shows the prices of admission to a pool.

Age	Cost
Adults (18–62)	$6
Children (3–17)	$4
Seniors (63+)	$3

Write an expression that can be used to find the total cost of admission for 2 adults, 3 children, and 2 seniors. Then find the total cost. (Lesson 1-1) **2(6) + 3(4) + 2(3); $30**

Evaluate each expression if $a = 5$, $b = 7$, and $c = 9$. (Lesson 1-2)

9. $a + 7$ **12**
10. ab **35**
11. $(c + 6) \times a$ **75**
12. $(a + c) \div b$ **2**

13. **MULTIPLE CHOICE** Carlos does lawn work on the weekends. He charges $12 per lawn and $5 per hour trimming bushes. Which expression represents the total amount of money Carlos charges to mow 2 lawns and trim bushes for h hours? (Lesson 1-2) **D**

A $12 + 2 + 5 + h$

B $2h + 5 \cdot 12$

C $2 \cdot 12 + h$

D $2 \cdot 12 + 5h$

14. **MEASUREMENT** There are 12 inches in 1 foot. Write an algebraic expression that represents the number of inches in f feet. Then complete the table. (Lesson 1-2) **12f**

Number of Feet	Number of Inches
2	24
4	■ **48**
6	■ **72**
8	96

15. **MULTIPLE CHOICE** Which of the following phrases represents the expression $3n - 4$? (Lesson 1-2) **G**

F The cost of a new DVD is $4 more than three times the price of a used DVD.

G The cost of a new DVD is $4 less than three times the price of a used DVD.

H The cost of a new DVD is $3 more than four times the price of a used DVD.

J The cost of a new DVD is $3 less than four times the price of a used DVD.

Name the property shown by each statement. (Lesson 1-3)

16. $35 + 0 = 35$ **Identity (+)**
17. $(3 + y) + 11 = 3 + (y + 11)$ **Associative (+)**
18. $9 \cdot 3 = 3 \cdot 9$ **Commutative (×)**

Simplify each expression. (Lesson 1-3)

19. $13 + (27 + a)$ **40 + a**
20. $x \cdot (6 \cdot 9)$ **54x**
21. $(z + 4) + 12$ **z + 16**
22. $10a(6)$ **60a**
23. $18 + (h + 15)$ **33 + h**

24. **REASONING** *True* or *False*? Is the difference of two whole numbers always a whole number? If false, give a counterexample. (Lesson 1-3) **False; Sample answer: 6 – 10 is not a whole number.**

25. **TECHNOLOGY** When you listen to music on an MP3 player, you turn it on and then program the player. Is programming the MP3 player and turning it on commutative? Explain. (Lesson 1-3) **See margin.**

Intervention Planner

Tier 1 On Level	Tier 2 Strategic Intervention approaching grade level	Tier 3 Intensive Intervention 2 or more grades below level
If students miss about 25% of the exercises or less,	**If** students miss about 50% of the exercises,	**If** students miss about 75% of the exercises,
Then choose a resource:	**Then** choose a resource:	**Then** use *Math Triumphs, Grade 8,* Ch. 2, 3, 9
SE Lessons 1-1, 1-2, and 1-3 **CRM** Skills Practice, pp. 7, 13, and 20 **TE** Chapter Project, p. 2	**CRM** Study Guide and Intervention, pp. 5, 11, and 18 *Quick Review Math Handbook*	
Math Online Self-Check Quiz	**Math Online** Extra Examples, Personal Tutor, Homework Help	**Math Online** Extra Examples, Personal Tutor, Homework Help, Review Vocabulary

1-4 Ordered Pairs and Relations

Then

You have already graphed numbers on number lines. (Previous Course)

Now

- Use ordered pairs to locate points.
- Use graphs to represent relations.

New Vocabulary

coordinate system
coordinate plane
y-axis
origin
x-axis
ordered pair
x-coordinate
y-coordinate
graph
relation
domain
range

Math Online

glencoe.com

- Extra Examples
- Personal Tutor
- Self-Check Quiz
- Homework Help
- Math in Motion

Why?

Brenna is planning a treasure hunt for her little brother in their yard. She has drawn an imaginary grid over the area for the hunt.

Clue 1 is located 2 units over (east) and 1 unit up (north) on the grid from the starting point named (0, 0). This location will be named (2, 1) on the list of clues. Use this information to answer the questions below.

a. Find Clue 2 on the grid. Name this location using the method used for Clue 1. **(3, 2)**

b. Clue 3 is located at (2, 4). Describe its location on the grid. **It is two units east and four units north of the starting point.**

c. Describe how to get from Clue 3 to Clue 4 using units and directions. Give the final location of Clue 4. **Go east two units and north one unit to get to (4, 5).**

d. To get to Clue 5, you can go 2 units south and 1 unit west from Clue 4. Name the location. **(3, 3)**

e. Clue 5 tells you that Clue 6 is 3 units west and 2 units south from Clue 5. Name the location. **(0, 1)**

f. Clue 6 says that the treasure is located halfway between Clue 1 and Clue 2. What is the location of the treasure? **(2.5, 1.5)**

Ordered Pairs In mathematics, a **coordinate system** or **coordinate plane** is used to locate points. The coordinate system is formed by the intersection of two number lines that meet at right angles at their zero points.

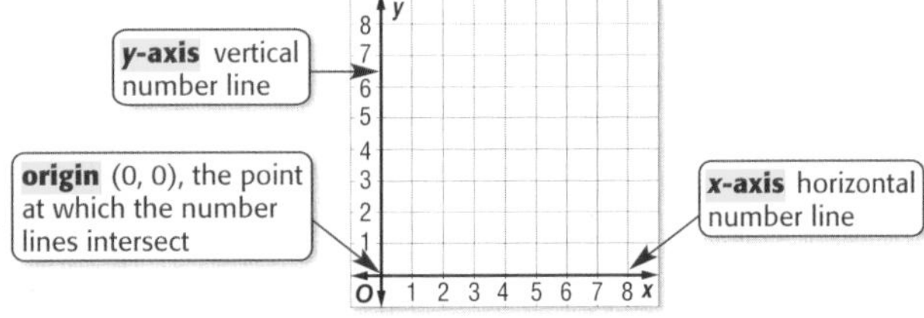

An **ordered pair** of numbers is used to locate any point on a coordinate plane. The first number is call the **x-coordinate** and the second number is called the **y-coordinate.**

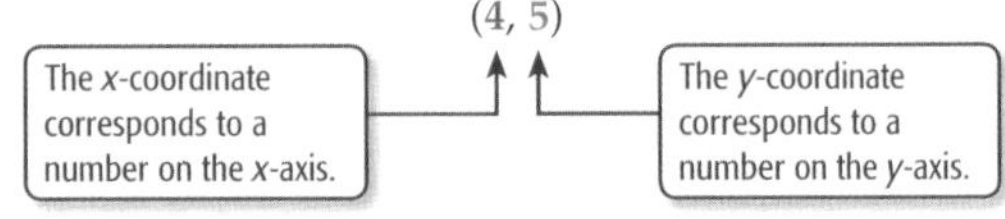

(4, 5)
The x-coordinate corresponds to a number on the x-axis.
The y-coordinate corresponds to a number on the y-axis.

1-4 Lesson Notes

1 FOCUS

Vertical Alignment

Before Lesson 1-4
Graph numbers on number lines.

Lesson 1-4
Use ordered pairs to locate points.
Use graphs to represent relations.

After Lesson 1-4
Represent relationships among quantities using concrete models, tables, graphs, diagrams, verbal descriptions, equations, and inequalities.

2 TEACH

Scaffolding Questions

Have students read the *Why?* section of the lesson and answer the questions.

Ask:

- From the starting point, in which two directions are all the clues located? east and north
- If clue 3 is located at (4, 2) rather than (2, 4), how is the location of the clue changed? The location is different because the number of units you move east and north has changed.

(continued on next page)

Lesson 1-4 Resources

Resource	Approaching-Level	On-Level	Beyond-Level	English Learners
Teacher Edition	• Differentiated Instruction, p. 26		• Differentiated Instruction, p. 30	
Chapter Resource Masters	• Study Guide and Intervention, pp. 24–25 • Skills Practice, p. 26 • Practice, p. 27 • Word Problem Practice, p. 28	• Study Guide and Intervention, pp. 24–25 • Skills Practice, p. 26 • Practice, p. 27 • Word Problem Practice, p. 28 • Enrichment, p. 29	• Practice, p. 27 • Word Problem Practice, p. 28 • Enrichment, p. 29	• Study Guide and Intervention, pp. 24–25 • Skills Practice, p. 26 • Practice, p. 27
Transparencies	• 5-Minute Check Transparency 1-4	• 5-Minute Check Transparency 1-4	• 5-Minute Check Transparency 1-4	• 5-Minute Check Transparency 1-4
Other	• Study Notebook • Teaching Pre-Algebra with Manipulatives	• Study Notebook • Teaching Pre-Algebra with Manipulatives	• Study Notebook	• Study Notebook • Teaching Pre-Algebra with Manipulatives

- What does the first number of the location tell you? the second number? how many units to move east or west from your starting location; how many units to move north or south of your starting location.

Ordered Pairs

Examples 1 and 2 show how to graph and identify ordered pairs.

Formative Assessment

Use the Check Your Progress exercises after each example to determine students' understanding of concepts.

Additional Examples

1 Graph each ordered pair on a coordinate plane.

a. (3, 4) **b.** (0, 2)

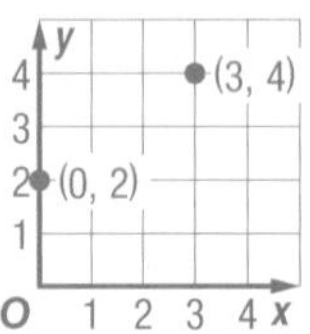

2 Write the ordered pair that names each point.

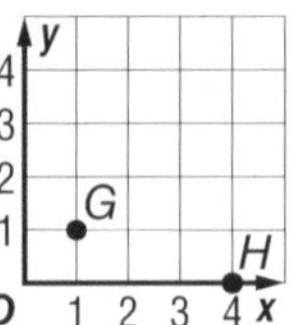

a. *G* (1, 1) **b.** *H* (4, 0)

Additional Examples also in Interactive Classroom PowerPoint® Presentations

IWB INTERACTIVE WHITEBOARD READY

Additional Answers

1A–D.

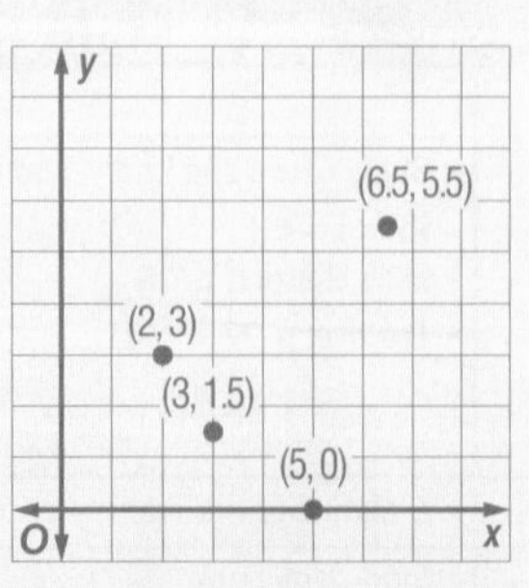

To **graph** an ordered pair, draw a dot at the point that corresponds to the ordered pair. The coordinates are your directions to locate the point.

StudyTip

Coordinate Planes Unless they are marked otherwise, you can assume that each unit on the x-axis and y-axis represents 1 unit.

EXAMPLE 1 Graph Ordered Pairs

Graph each ordered pair on a coordinate plane.

a. (5, 3)

Step 1 Start at the origin.

Step 2 Since the x-coordinate is 5, move 5 units to the right.

Step 3 Since the y-coordinate is 3, move 3 units up. Draw a dot.

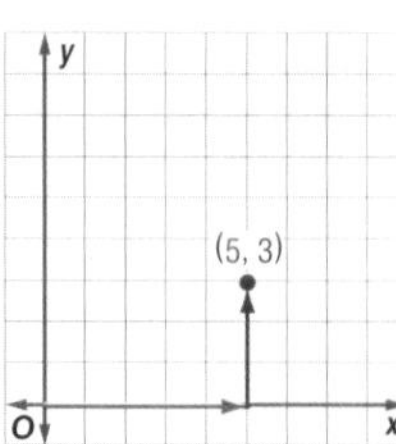

b. (0, 4)

Step 1 Start at the origin.

Step 2 Since the x-coordinate is 0, you do not need to move right.

Step 3 Since the y-coordinate is 4, move 4 units up. Place the dot on the axis.

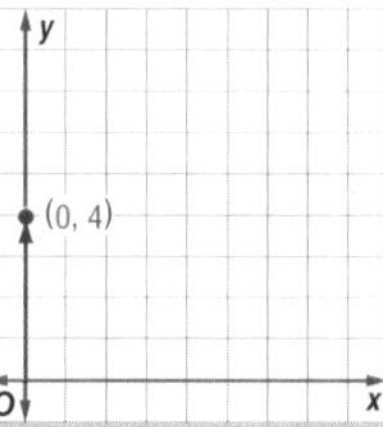

Check Your Progress 1A–1D. See margin.

1A. (2, 3) **1B.** (5, 0) **1C.** $\left(3, 1\frac{1}{2}\right)$ **1D.** $\left(6\frac{1}{2}, 5\frac{1}{2}\right)$

Personal Tutor glencoe.com

Sometimes a point on a graph is named by using a letter. To identify its location, you can write the ordered pair that represents the point.

EXAMPLE 2 Identify Ordered Pairs

Write the ordered pair that names each point.

a. *A*

Step 1 Start at the origin.

Step 2 Move right on the x-axis to find the x-coordinate of point A, which is 2.

Step 3 Move up the y-axis to find the y-coordinate, which is 6.

The ordered pair for point A is (2, 6).

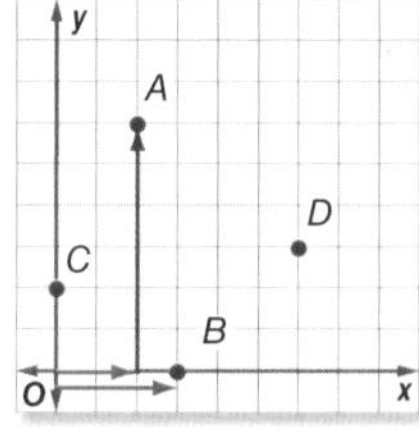

b. *B*

The x-coordinate of point B is 3, and the y-coordinate is 0.

The ordered pair for point B is (3, 0).

Check Your Progress

2A. C (0, 2) **2B.** D (6, 3)

Personal Tutor glencoe.com

Differentiated Instruction

AL

If students have difficulty graphing or locating points on a coordinate grid,

Then use masking tape to mark an x-axis and y-axis on the floor. Make up cards with ordered pairs. Give several students a card and ask them to start at the origin and walk to the location of their point. Make sure they move along the x-axis first and the y-axis second.

ReadingMath

Domain and Range The domain of a relation is also called the *input*. The range of a relation is also called the *output*.

Relations A set of ordered pairs such as {(2, 3), (3, 5), (4, 1), (5, 6)} is a **relation**. A relation can also be shown in a table or a graph. The **domain** of the relation is the set of x-coordinates. The **range** of the relation is the set of y-coordinates.

Ordered Pairs

(2, 3)
(3, 5)
(4, 1)
(5, 6)

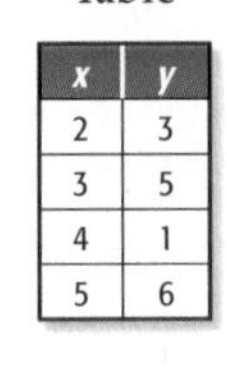

The domain is {2, 3, 4, 5}. The range is {3, 5, 1, 6}.

Table

x	y
2	3
3	5
4	1
5	6

Graph

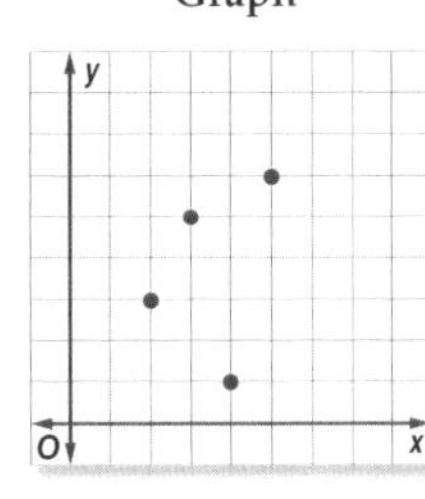

Math *in Motion*, Animation glencoe.com

EXAMPLE 3 Relations as Tables

Express the relation {(0, 2), (1, 4), (2, 5), (3, 8)} as a table. Then determine the domain and range.

x	0	1	2	3
y	2	4	5	8

The domain is {0, 1, 2, 3}, and the range is {2, 4, 5, 8}.

Check Your Progress

3. Express the relation {(2, 4), (0, 3), (1, 4), (1, 1)} as a table. Then determine the domain and range. **See Chapter 1 Answer Appendix.**

Personal Tutor glencoe.com

Real-World Link

Seahorses are the slowest swimming fish due to their unusual body shape. To move, they flutter their back fin up to 35 times per second.

Real-World EXAMPLE 4 Relations as Graphs

SEAHORSES A seahorse swims at a rate of about 5 feet per hour.

a. Make a table of ordered pairs in which the x-coordinate represents the hours and the y-coordinate represents the number of feet for 1, 2, and 4 hours.

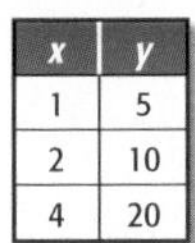

x	y
1	5
2	10
4	20

b. Graph the ordered pairs and describe the graph.

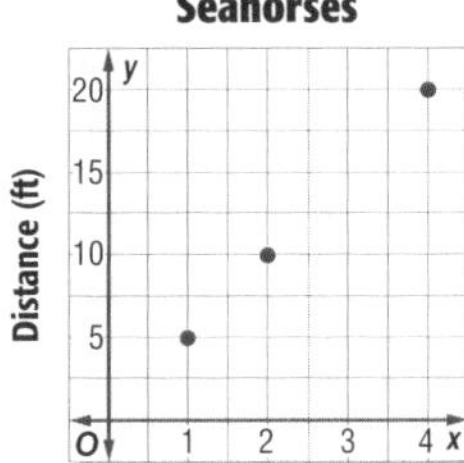

The points appear to lie in a line.

Check Your Progress **4. See Chapter 1 Answer Appendix.**

4. **MEASURMENT** One square mile is equal to six hundred forty acres.
   A. Make a table of ordered pairs in which the x-coordinate represents the number of square miles and the y-coordinate represents the number of acres in 1, 2, and 3 square miles.
   B. Graph the ordered pairs. Then describe the graph.

Personal Tutor glencoe.com

Focus on Mathematical Content

Coordinate Graphs The coordinate system is formed by two number lines that intersect at right angles. Both the x- and y-axes continue to infinity in both directions. In quadrants I and III, the coordinates are both the same sign. In quadrants II and IV, one of the coordinates is negative. Note that in this chapter, students graph in quadrant I only. In Lesson 2-6, students will graph in all four quadrants.

Relations

Example 3 shows how to express a relation as a table and how to use the table to determine the domain and range of the relation. **Example 4** shows how to make a table and a graph of ordered pairs to solve a real-world problem.

Additional Examples

3 Express the relation {(1, 4), (2, 2), (3, 0), (0, 2)} as a table. Then determine the domain and range.
D = {0, 1, 2, 3}, R = {0, 2, 4}

x	y
1	4
2	2
3	0
0	2

Graph points: (1, 4), (2, 2), (0, 2), (3, 0)

4 **EARNINGS** José earns \$5 an hour doing yard work.

a. Make a table of ordered pairs in which the x-coordinate represents the hours worked and the y-coordinate represents the amount of money José earns for 1, 2, 3, and 5 hours of work.

x	y
1	5
2	10
3	15
5	25

b. Graph the ordered pairs and describe the graph.

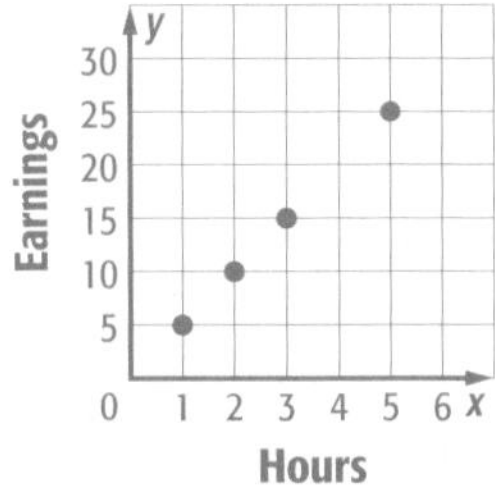

The points appear to lie on a line.

3 PRACTICE

Formative Assessment

Use Exercises 1–11 to check for understanding.

Use the chart at the bottom of this page to customize assignments for your students.

Exercise Alert!

Grid Paper Most of the exercises require graphing. Students who are new to graphing may prefer using grid paper. They may also need a straight edge or ruler.

Additional Answers

1–4.

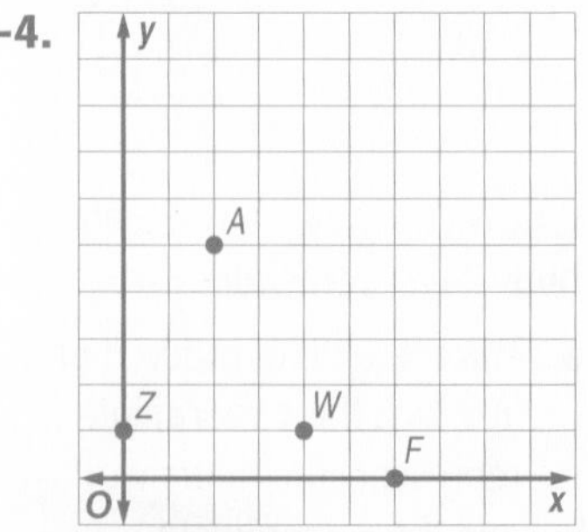

9.

x	y
3	4
1	5
4	2

D = {1, 3, 4}, R = {2, 4, 5}

10.

x	y
1	3
2	6
3	3
4	7

D = {1, 2, 3, 4}, R = {3, 6, 7}

11a.

x	y	(x, y)
1	2	(1, 2)
2	4	(2, 4)
3	6	(3, 6)
4	8	(4, 8)

Check Your Understanding

Example 1 p. 26

Graph each ordered pair on a coordinate plane. 1–4. See margin.

1. $F(6, 0)$ **2.** $A(2, 5)$ **3.** $W(4, 1)$ **4.** $Z(0, 1)$

Example 2 p. 26

Refer to the coordinate plane shown at the right. Write the ordered pair that names each point.

y
M
J
L
K
O
x

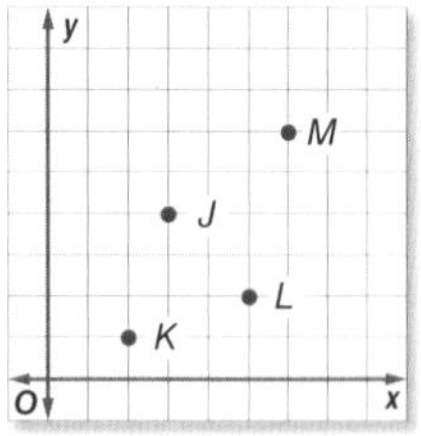

5. J (3, 4) **6.** K (2, 1)

7. L (5, 2) **8.** M (6, 6)

Example 3 p. 27

Express each relation as a table. Then determine the domain and range. 9–10. See margin.

9. {(3, 4), (1, 5), (4, 2)}

10. {(1, 3), (2, 6), (3, 3), (4, 7)}

Example 4 p. 27

11. CAPACITY One quart is the same as two pints.

a. Make a table of ordered pairs in which the x-coordinate represents the number of quarts and the y-coordinate represents the number of pints in 1, 2, 3, and 4 quarts. See margin.

b. Graph the ordered pairs. Then describe the data. The points appear to lie in a line. See Chapter 1 Answer Appendix for graph.

Practice and Problem Solving

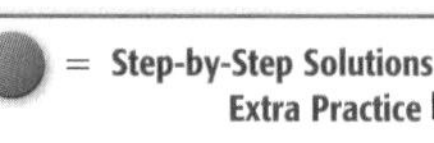
= **Step-by-Step Solutions** begin on page R11. **Extra Practice** begins on page 810.

Example 1 p. 26

Graph each ordered pair on a coordinate plane. 12–19. See Chapter 1 Answer Appendix.

12. $A(4, 7)$ **13.** $B(0, 4)$ **14.** $C(7, 3)$ **15.** $D(3, 4)$

16. $F(6, 1)$ **17.** $G(6, 5)$ **18.** $H(3, 0)$ **19.** $J(2, 2)$

Example 2 p. 26

Refer to the coordinate system shown at the right. Write the ordered pair that names each point.

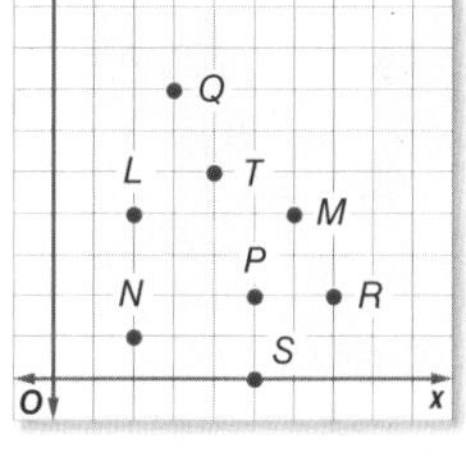

20. L (2, 4) **21.** M (6, 4)

22. N (2, 1) **23.** P (5, 2)

24. Q (3, 7) **25.** R (7, 2)

26. S (5, 0) **27.** T (4, 5)

Example 3 p. 27

Express each relation as a table. Then determine the domain and range. 28–32a. See Chapter 1 Answer Appendix.

28. {(4, 5), (2, 1), (5, 0), (3, 2)} **29** {(0, 2), (2, 2), (4, 1), (3, 5)}

30. {(6, 0), (4, 5), (2, 1), (3, 1)} **31.** {(5, 1), (3, 7), (4, 8), (5, 7)}

Example 4 p. 27

32. PIZZA The cost of a mini pizza is $7 at Pizza Pizza.

a. Make a table of ordered pairs in which the x-coordinate represents the number of mini pizzas and the y-coordinate represents the cost of 1, 3, 5, and 7 mini pizzas at Pizza Pizza.

b. Graph the ordered pairs. Then describe the graph. The points appear to lie in a line. See Chapter 1 Answer Appendix for graph.

Differentiated Homework Options

Level	Assignment	Two-Day Option	
AL Basic	12–33, 36, 37, 39–57	13–33 odd, 41–44	12–32 even, 36, 37, 39, 40, 45–57
OL Core	13–33 odd, 34–37, 39–57	12–33, 41–44	34–37, 39, 40, 45–57
BL Advanced	35–51, (optional: 52–57)		

28 Chapter 1 The Tools of Algebra

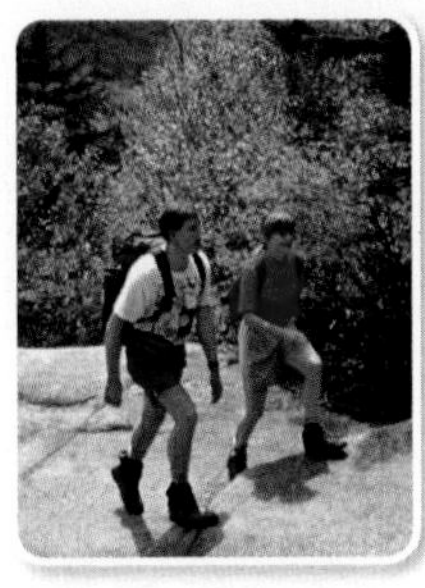

Real-World Link

The Appalachian Trail is one of the most hiked trails in the United States. It winds through 14 states with an estimated length of 2170 miles. Almost 10,000 people have hiked the entire trail.

Source: Appalachian Trail Conservancy

33. **HIKING** Aaron is hiking in a state park. He averages 3 miles per hour.

    a. Make a table of ordered pairs in which the x-coordinate represents the number hours and the y-coordinate represents the number of miles hiked in 1, 2, 4, and 6 hours.

    b. Graph the ordered pairs.

34. **MULTIPLE REPRESENTATIONS** In this problem, you will explore more about relations. Suppose Jamal has only 30 minutes to practice the piano and study for a science test.

    a. **TABULAR** Make a table of ordered pairs showing at least 6 ways Jamal can split the time between the two activities. Let the x-coordinate represent the number of minutes spent playing the piano and the y-coordinate represent the number of minutes spent studying.

    b. **GRAPHICAL** Graph the ordered pairs.

    c. **VERBAL** Describe the general pattern of points of your graph.

    d. **GRAPHICAL** Connect the points on your graph with line segments. Then choose a point on the graph that is *not* one of the points you plotted. Use the coordinates to predict a pair of values for the piano time and study time.

35. **SCHOOL** Six students in Mr. Maloney's class made a table of ordered pairs for their height in inches x and their shoe size y.

Height (in.)	58	56	62	60	59	61
Shoe Size	6	$5\frac{1}{2}$	$8\frac{1}{2}$	8	7	$7\frac{1}{2}$

    a. Graph the ordered pairs.

    b. Compare this graph to the graph in Example 4.
    Sample answer: The graph is not linear like the other graph.

33–35a. See Chapter 1 Answer Appendix

H.O.T. Problems

Use Higher-Order Thinking Skills

36. **OPEN ENDED** Write a set of four ordered pairs. Then create a table and graph of the pairs and state the domain and range. See Chapter 1 Answer Appendix.

37. **REASONING** The numbers 4, 7, 10, 13, … form an *arithmetic sequence* because each term can be found by adding the same number to the previous term.

Term Number	1	2	3	4
Term	4	7	10	13

    a. Write the set of ordered pairs (term number, term).
    {(1, 4), (2, 7), (3, 10), (4, 13)}

    b. Graph the ordered pairs. See Chapter 1 Answer Appendix.

    c. Describe the shape of the graph. The graph shows a positive, linear relationship.

    d. If possible, write a rule to find the twentieth term. Explain how you found the rule or why you cannot write a rule.
    3 times the x value plus 1 to get the y-value; 61

38. **CHALLENGE** Describe all of the possible locations for the graph of (x, y) if $x = 2$.
    the vertical line where $x = 2$

39. **WRITING IN MATH** Refer to Exercises 32 and 33. For which graph would it make more sense to connect the points with line segments? Explain.

40. **WRITING IN MATH** Explain why the point $M(4, 3)$ is different from the point $N(3, 4)$.

39. Exercise 33; Sample answer: By connecting the points on the graph in Exercise 33, you could determine how far he will have hiked at any time other than hours. In Exercise 32, the points do not need to be connected because you wouldn't need to know how much a portion of a pizza would cost.

40. Sample answer: Point M is 4 units to the right on the x-axis and 3 units up the y-axis. Point N is 3 units to the right on the x-axis and 4 units up the y-axis.

Multiple Representations In Exercise 34, students use a table of ordered pairs and a graph of plotted points to model a real-world situation involving two variables.

Enrichment
CRM p. 29 OL BL

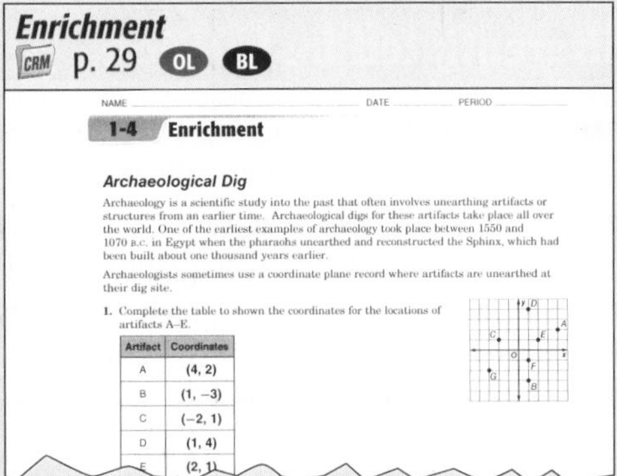

1-4 Enrichment

Archaeological Dig

Archaeology is a scientific study into the past that often involves unearthing artifacts or structures from an earlier time. Archaeological digs for these artifacts take place all over the world. One of the earliest examples of archaeology took place between 1550 and 1070 B.C. in Egypt when the pharaohs unearthed and reconstructed the Sphinx, which had been built about one thousand years earlier.

Archaeologists sometimes use a coordinate plane record where artifacts are unearthed at their dig site.

1. Complete the table to shown the coordinates for the locations of artifacts A–E.

Artifact	Coordinates
A	(4, 2)
B	(1, −3)
C	(−2, 1)
D	(1, 4)
E	(2, 1)

Study Guide and Intervention
CRM pp. 24–25 AL OL ELL

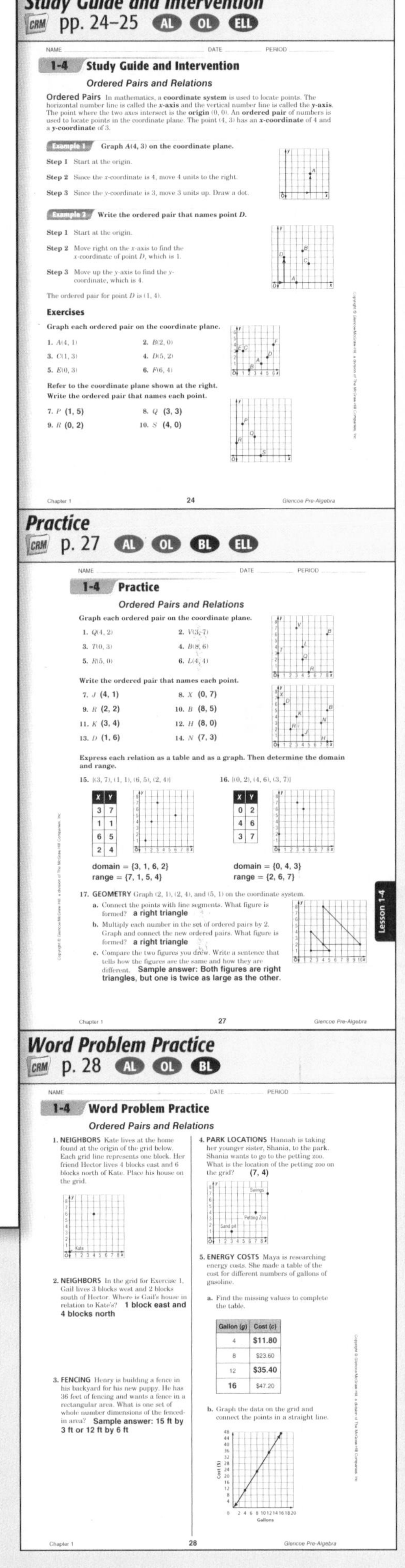

1-4 Study Guide and Intervention

Ordered Pairs and Relations

Ordered Pairs In mathematics, a **coordinate system** is used to locate points. The horizontal number line is called the **x-axis** and the vertical number line is called the **y-axis**. The point where the two axes intersect is the **origin** (0, 0). An **ordered pair** of numbers is used to locate points in the coordinate plane. The point (4, 3) has an **x-coordinate** of 4 and a **y-coordinate** of 3.

Example 1 Graph $A(4, 3)$ on the coordinate plane.

Step 1 Start at the origin.
Step 2 Since the x-coordinate is 4, move 4 units to the right.
Step 3 Since the y-coordinate is 3, move 3 units up. Draw a dot.

Example 2 Write the ordered pair that names point D.

Step 1 Start at the origin.
Step 2 Move right on the x-axis to find the x-coordinate of point D, which is 1.
Step 3 Move up the y-axis to find the y-coordinate, which is 4.

The ordered pair for point D is (1, 4).

Exercises

Graph each ordered pair on the coordinate plane.

1. $A(4, 1)$ 2. $B(2, 0)$
3. $C(1, 3)$ 4. $D(5, 2)$
5. $E(0, 3)$ 6. $F(6, 4)$

Refer to the coordinate plane shown at the right. Write the ordered pair that names each point.

7. P (1, 5) 8. Q (3, 3)
9. R (0, 2) 10. S (4, 0)

Chapter 1 24 Glencoe Pre-Algebra

Practice
CRM p. 27 AL OL BL ELL

1-4 Practice

Ordered Pairs and Relations

Graph each ordered pair on the coordinate plane.

1. $Q(4, 2)$ 2. $V(3, 7)$
3. $T(0, 3)$ 4. $B(8, 6)$
5. $R(5, 0)$ 6. $L(4, 4)$

Write the ordered pair that names each point.

7. J (4, 1) 8. X (0, 7)
9. R (2, 2) 10. B (8, 5)
11. K (3, 4) 12. H (8, 0)
13. D (1, 6) 14. N (7, 3)

Express each relation as a table and as a graph. Then determine the domain and range.

15. {(3, 7), (1, 1), (6, 5), (2, 4)}

x	y
3	7
1	1
6	5
2	4

domain = {3, 1, 6, 2}
range = {7, 1, 5, 4}

16. {(0, 2), (4, 6), (3, 7)}

x	y
0	2
4	6
3	7

domain = {0, 4, 3}
range = {2, 6, 7}

17. GEOMETRY Graph (2, 1), (2, 4), and (5, 1) on the coordinate system.
a. Connect the points with line segments. What figure is formed? **a right triangle**
b. Multiply each number in the set of ordered pairs by 2. Graph and connect the new ordered pairs. What figure is formed? **a right triangle**
c. Compare the two figures you drew. Write a sentence that tells how the figures are the same and how they are different. **Sample answer: Both figures are right triangles, but one is twice as large as the other.**

Chapter 1 27 Glencoe Pre-Algebra

Lesson 1-4

Word Problem Practice
CRM p. 28 AL OL BL

1-4 Word Problem Practice

Ordered Pairs and Relations

1. NEIGHBORS Kate lives at the home found at the origin of the grid below. Each grid line represents one block. Her friend Hector lives 4 blocks east and 6 blocks north of Kate. Place his house on the grid.

2. NEIGHBORS In the grid for Exercise 1, Gail lives 3 blocks west and 2 blocks south of Hector. Where is Gail's house in relation to Kate's? **1 block east and 4 blocks north**

3. FENCING Henry is building a fence in his backyard for his new puppy. He has 36 feet of fencing and wants a fence in a rectangular area. What is one set of whole number dimensions of the fenced-in area? **Sample answer: 15 ft by 3 ft or 12 ft by 6 ft**

4. PARK LOCATIONS Hannah is taking her younger sister, Shania, to the park. Shania wants to go to the petting zoo. What is the location of the petting zoo on the grid? **(7, 4)**

5. ENERGY COSTS Maya is researching energy costs. She made a table of the cost for different numbers of gallons of gasoline.

a. Find the missing values to complete the table.

Gallon (g)	Cost (c)
4	$11.80
8	$23.60
12	$35.40
16	$47.20

b. Graph the data on the grid and connect the points in a straight line.

Chapter 1 28 Glencoe Pre-Algebra

TEACH with TECH

INTERACTIVE WHITEBOARD Find a coordinate plane in the resources provided with your IWB software. Plot several points in the first quadrant and ask students to give the coordinates of the points. Invite students to drag the points to other locations in the first quadrant and identify the new coordinates.

Standardized Test Practice exercises help students solidify their knowledge of the standards using exercises in a multiple-choice format.

4 ASSESS

Crystal Ball Have students write about how today's lesson on graphing ordered pairs and relations might help them with tomorrow's lesson on making function tables. Encourage them to glance forward at the next section if they want to preview the lesson.

Additional Answer

Extension

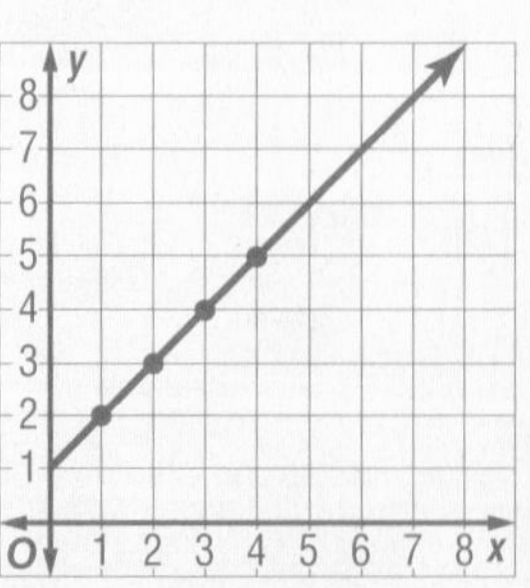

Standardized Test Practice

41. On the map of a campsite shown below, the tent is located at (3, 7). Which point represents the location of the tent? **C**

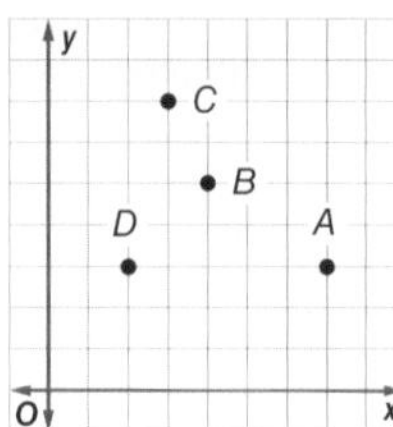

A point A C point C
B point B D point D

42. Rectangle $ABCD$ has vertices $A(1, 3)$, $B(1, 6)$, and $C(5, 6)$. What are the coordinates of point D? **H**

F (6, 5) H (5, 3)
G (5, 1) J (6, 1)

43. What is the domain of the relation below? **A**

x	y
1	3
2	4
4	8
6	1
7	4

A {1, 2, 4, 6, 7}
B {1, 3}
C {3, 4, 8, 1, 4}
D {(1, 3), (2, 4), (4, 8), (6, 1), (7, 4)}

44. GRIDDED RESPONSE Point Z is located at (4, 7) on a coordinate plane. Point T is located 3 units to the right and 4 units down from point Z. What is the x-coordinate of point T? **7**

Spiral Review

Name the property shown by each statement. (Lesson 1-3)

45. $5 \cdot 3 = 3 \cdot 5$ **Commutative (×)**

46. $6 \cdot 2 \cdot 0 = 0$ **Multiplicative (0)**

47. $0 + 13 = 13$ **Identity (+)**

48. $(5 + x) + 6 = 5 + (x + 6)$ **Associative (+)**

State whether each conjecture is true. If not, give a counterexample. (Lesson 1-3)

49. Division of whole numbers is associative. **no; $(100 \div 10) \div 2 \neq 100 \div (10 \div 2)$**

50. Subtraction of whole numbers is commutative. **no; $9 - 3 \neq 3 - 9$**

51. SHOPPING Melinda purchased the items shown in the table. (Lesson 1-2)

Item	Price ($)
sweater	s
purse	$s + 12$
belt	$s + 4$

a. Write an expression to show the total cost of the items. **$3s + 16$**

b. Suppose the cost of the sweater is $25. How much did she spend together? **$91**

Skills Review

Find the value of each expression. (Lesson 1-2)

52. $x + 7$ if $x = 8$ **15**

53. $d - 5$ if $d = 12$ **7**

54. $18 + m$ if $m = 4$ **22**

55. $f - 12$ if $f = 28$ **16**

56. $s + 14$ if $s = 32$ **46**

57. $19 - b$ if $b = 5$ **14**

Differentiated Instruction

Extension Explain to students that a function is a type of relation where each member of the domain is paired with exactly one member in the range. Functions are relations, so they can be represented with ordered pairs and graphed. Ask students to graph this function on graph paper: $y = x + 1$. Have them fill in the table to make ordered pairs and graph the points. Suggest that they use a straightedge to extend the line beyond the points.

x	y
1	2
2	3
3	4
4	5

EXPLORE 1-5

Algebra Lab: Relations and Functions

Math Online > glencoe.com
Math *in Motion*, Animation

A **relation** is any set of ordered pairs. A **function** is a special relation in which each member of the domain is paired with *exactly* one member in the range.

Here is an example to help you remember how to identify functions. Suppose three students are asked to choose their favorite pet. The mapping diagrams below show some possible results.

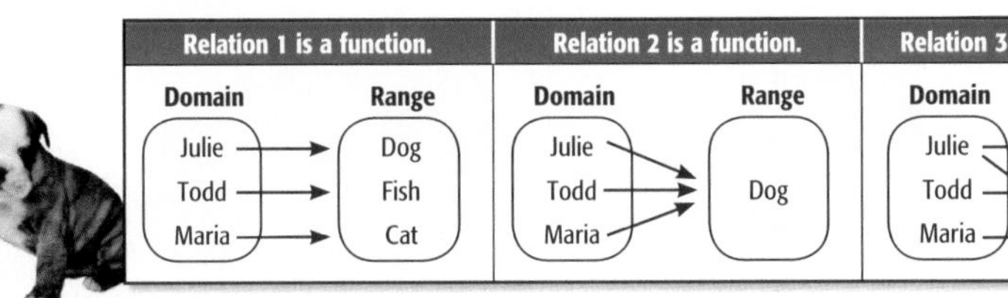

In the example above, the first two relations are functions, because each person chose only one favorite pet. The third relation is *not* a function, because Julie chose two favorite pets, a dog and a cat.

ACTIVITY 1

Step 1 Three students reported the number of cell phone minutes they had every month. Copy and complete the mapping diagram shown below.

Student	1	2	3
Number of Minutes	400	400	750

Domain: 1, 2, 3 — Range: 400, 750

Step 2 Student 1 added a phone in the middle of the month and reported two sets of times. Copy and complete the mapping diagram with the new information.

Student	1	1	2	3
Number of Minutes	600	400	400	750

Domain: 1, 2, 3 — Range: 400, 600, 750

Analyze the Results

1. A relation can be written as a set of ordered pairs, with the input as the x-coordinate and the output as the y-coordinate. For each relation diagram you drew in the Activity above, write the relation as a set of ordered pairs. Sample Answer: (1, 400), (2, 400), (3, 750); (1, 400), (1, 600), (2, 400), (3, 750)
2. Is each relation above a function? Explain your reasoning in terms of the ordered pairs. See margin.

Make a mapping diagram for each relation. Then determine whether each relation is a function. Explain. 3-6. See margin.

3. {(2, 5), (4, 5), (6, 6), (7, 8)}
4. {(12, 18), (16, 21), (16, 25), (20, 30)}
5. {(1, 3), (9, 15), (6, 10), (9, 8)}
6. {(5, 6), (10, 11), (8, 13), (0, 7)}

4. Domain: 12, 16, 20 — Range: 18, 21, 25, 30. No; 16 is assigned 2 y-values, 21 and 25.

5. Domain: 1, 6, 9 — Range: 3, 8, 10, 15. No; 9 is assigned two y-values, 15 and 8.

6. Domain: 0, 5, 8, 10 — Range: 7, 6, 13, 11. Yes; each x-value is assigned exactly one y-value.

EXPLORE 1-5

Lesson Notes

1 FOCUS

Objective Identify a function.

Materials for Each Group

- centimeter cubes
- grid paper

Teaching Tip

Before asking students to work through the Activities, have them examine the three relations shown in the mapping diagrams at the beginning of the lesson. Point out the difference between Relation 2 and Relation 3.

2 TEACH

Working in Cooperative Groups

Group students in pairs, mixing abilities. Have pairs work through Activity 1 and Activity 2.

Activity 1

Ask:

- In Steps 1 and 2, what do the values in the range represent? the number of cell phone minutes for each student

Practice Have students complete Exercises 1–6.

Additional Answers

2. Sample answer: The first relation is a function since each x-value is assigned exactly one y-value. The second relation is not a function since some x-values are assigned more than one y-value.
3. Domain: 2, 4, 6, 7 — Range: 5, 6, 8. Yes; each x-value is assigned exactly one y-value.

EXPLORE 1-5 Lesson Notes

Activity 2

Ask:

- In Step 3, how many cubes do you add to each existing figure to build the next? 3
- Is the rule simply to multiply the figure number by 3? Explain. No, the values in the range showing the number of cubes are all multiples of 3, but the first figure number does not begin with 3.

Practice Have students complete Exercises 7–11.

3 ASSESS

Formative Assessment

Use Exercises 3–6 to assess whether students know how to determine if a relation is a function.

From Concrete to Abstract

Ask students to explain how to determine if a relation is a function. Make a table of values for the domain and range. Then check to see if each value in the domain is assigned exactly one value in the range.

Additional Answers

7.

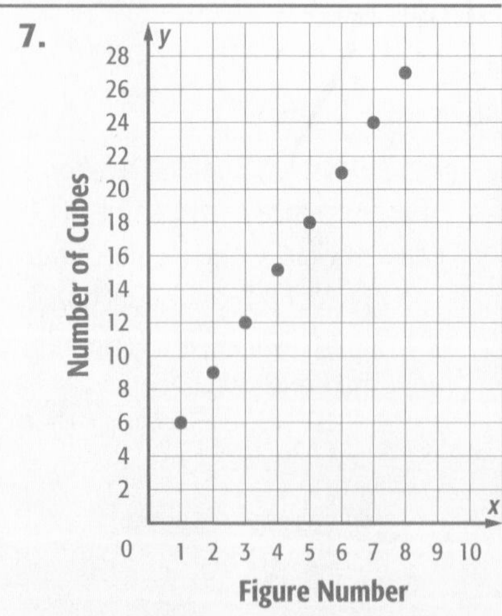

A *function rule* is the operation(s) performed on the domain value to get the range value.

ACTIVITY 2

Step 1 Use centimeter cubes to build the figures below.

Figure 1

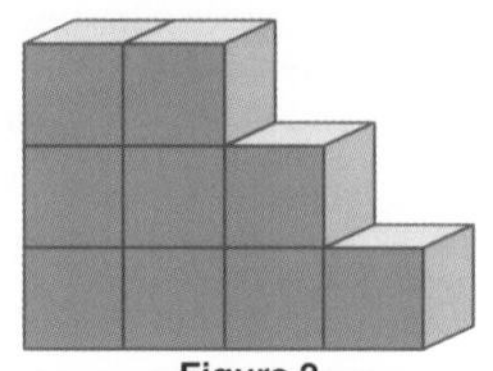

Figure 2

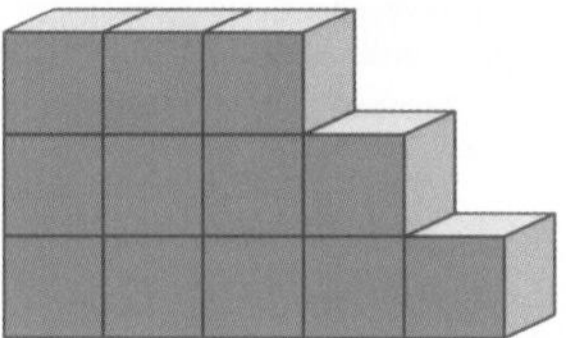

Figure 3

Step 2 Make a table like the one shown and record the figure number and number of cubes used in each figure.

Step 3 Construct the next figure in this pattern. Record your results.

Step 4 Repeat Step 3 until you have found the next four figures in the pattern shown above.

Figure Number	Number of Cubes
1	6
2	9
3	12
⋮	⋮

Analyze the Results

7. Suppose x represents the figure number and y represents the number of cubes. Graph the data from your table on a coordinate plane. **See margin.**
8. Look at the results in the table and graph. Does this data represent a function? Explain your reasoning. **Yes; each domain value is paired with exactly one range value.**
9. Write a rule to determine the number of cubes for any figure number. Use x for the figure number and y for the number of cubes. $y = 3x + 3$
10. *Perimeter* is the distance around a figure. Write a rule that describes the relationship between the figure number x and the perimeter y for the figures shown below. Then make a table and graph the data on a coordinate plane. **See margin.**

Figure 1

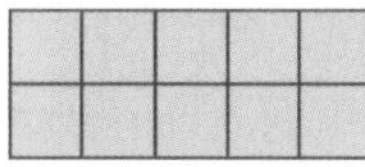

Figure 2

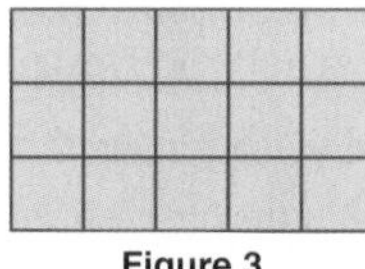

Figure 3

11. **WRITING IN MATH** Look at the results from Exercise 10. Does this data represent a function? Explain your reasoning. **See margin.**

10. $y = 2x + 10$

Figure Number	Perimeter (units)
1	12
2	14
3	16

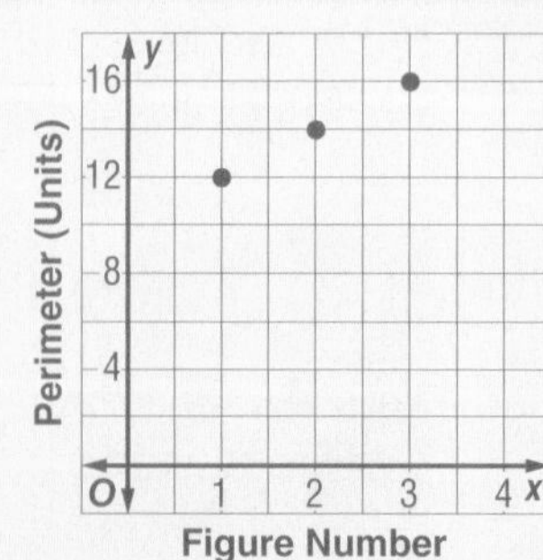

11. Yes; each domain value is paired with exactly one range value.

1-5 Words, Equations, Tables, and Graphs

Then
You have already learned how to represent relations as tables and graphs. (Lesson 1-4)

Now
- Use multiple representations to represent functions.
- Translate among different verbal, tabular, graphical, and algebraic representations of functions.

New Vocabulary
function
function rule
function table
equation

Math Online
glencoe.com
- Extra Examples
- Personal Tutor
- Self-Check Quiz
- Homework Help

Why? a–c. See Chapter 1 Answer Appendix.

The table shows the time it should take a scuba diver to ascend to the surface from several depths to prevent sickness.

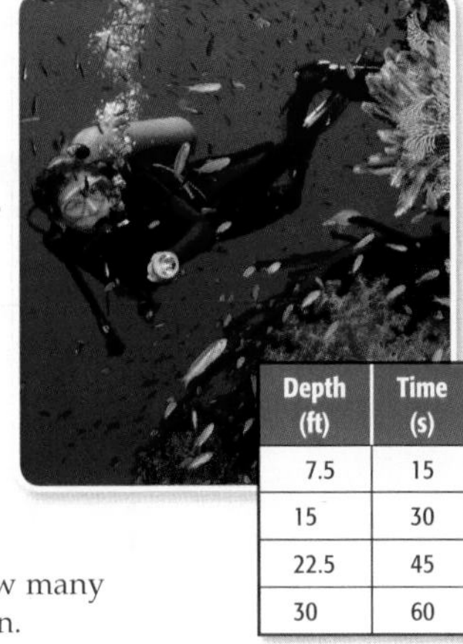

Depth (ft)	Time (s)
7.5	15
15	30
22.5	45
30	60

a. On grid paper, graph the data as ordered pairs (depth, time).

b. Write a rule to describe the relationship between the sets of numbers.

c. If a scuba diver is at a depth of 45 feet, how many seconds should she take to ascend? Explain.

Represent Functions A **function** is a relation in which each member of the domain is paired with *exactly* one member in the range. A **function rule** is the operation(s) performed on the domain value to get the range value. A **function table** is a table that lists the x-coordinates (input), rule, and y-coordinates (output).

EXAMPLE 1 Make a Function Table

In a game of *What's My Rule?* Kinna picked the card shown at the right. Make a function table for four different input values and write an algebraic expression for the rule. Then state the domain and range of the function.

What's My Rule?
double a number, then add three

Step 1 Create a function table showing the input, rule, and output. Enter four different input values.

Step 2 The rule "double a number, then add three" translates to $2x + 3$. Use the rule to complete the table.

Input (x)	Rule: $2x + 3$	Output (y)
1	2(1) + 3	5
2	2(2) + 3	7
3	2(3) + 3	9
4	2(4) + 3	11

Step 3 The domain is {1, 2, 3, 4}. The range is {5, 7, 9, 11}.

Check Your Progress

1. Jenna picked a game card with the function shown. Make a function table for four different input values and write an algebraic expression for the rule. Then state the domain and range of the function. See Chapter 1 Answer Appendix.

What's My Rule?
triple the number and subtract one

Personal Tutor glencoe.com

1-5 Lesson Notes

1 FOCUS

Vertical Alignment

Before Lesson 1-5
Represent relations as tables and graphs.

Lesson 1-5
Use multiple representations to represent functions.
Translate among different verbal, tabular, graphical, and algebraic representations of functions.

After Lesson 1-5
Gather and record data and use data sets to determine functional relationships between quantities.

2 TEACH

Scaffolding Questions

Have students read the *Why?* section of the lesson and answer the questions.

Ask:
- Write the relation shown in the table as a set of ordered pairs. (7.5, 15); (15, 30); (22.5, 45); (30, 60)
- Is the relation a function? Explain. Yes, each x-value is paired with exactly one y-value.
- When the diver goes 15 feet deeper, how much more time is needed for ascension? 30 s

Lesson 1-5 Resources

Resource	Approaching-Level	On-Level	Beyond-Level	English Learners
Teacher Edition			• Differentiated Instruction, pp. 34, 37	
Chapter Resource Masters	• Study Guide and Intervention, pp. 30–31 • Skills Practice, p. 32 • Practice, p. 33 • Word Problem Practice, p. 34 • Graphing Calculator, p. 36	• Study Guide and Intervention, pp. 30–31 • Skills Practice, p. 32 • Practice, p. 33 • Word Problem Practice, p. 34 • Enrichment, p. 35 • Graphing Calculator, p. 36	• Practice, p. 33 • Word Problem Practice, p. 34 • Enrichment, p. 35 • Graphing Calculator, p. 36	• Study Guide and Intervention, pp. 30–31 • Skills Practice, p. 32 • Practice, p. 33 • Graphing Calculator, p. 36
Transparencies	• 5-Minute Check Transparency 1-5	• 5-Minute Check Transparency 1-5	• 5-Minute Check Transparency 1-5	• 5-Minute Check Transparency 1-5
Other	• Study Notebook • Teaching Pre-Algebra with Manipulatives	• Study Notebook • Teaching Pre-Algebra with Manipulatives	• Study Notebook	• Study Notebook • Teaching Pre-Algebra with Manipulatives

Represent Functions

Example 1 shows how to use a rule to create a function table.

Formative Assessment

Use the Check Your Progress exercises after each example to determine students' understanding of concepts.

Additional Example

1 Make a function table for four different input values and write an algebraic expression for the rule. Then state the domain and range of the function.

Rule: double a number and subtract one.

Input (x)	$2x-1$	Output (y)
1	$2(1)-1$	1
2	$2(2)-1$	3
3	$2(3)-1$	5
4	$2(4)-1$	7

Domain {1, 2, 3, 4}

Range {1, 3, 5, 7}

Additional Examples also in Interactive Classroom PowerPoint® Presentations

IWB INTERACTIVE WHITEBOARD READY

Focus on Mathematical Content

Functions In a function, x is usually the input value and y is usually the output value.

Multiple Representations

Example 2 shows how to use equations, tables, and graphs to describe relationships in real-world applications.

Vocabulary Link

function

Everyday Use a relationship in which one quality or trait depends on another. Height is usually a function of age.

Math Use a relationship in which a range value depends on a domain value, y is a function of x.

Multiple Representations Words, equations, tables, and graphs can be used to represent functions. An **equation** is a mathematical sentence stating that two quantities are equal. Functions are often written as equations with two variables—one to represent the input and one to represent the output.

Concept Summary — Multiple Representations

For Your FOLDABLE

Words
Distance is equal to 60 miles per hour times the number of hours.

Equation
$d = 60t$

Table

Time (h)	Distance (mi)
1	60
2	120
3	180
4	240

Graph

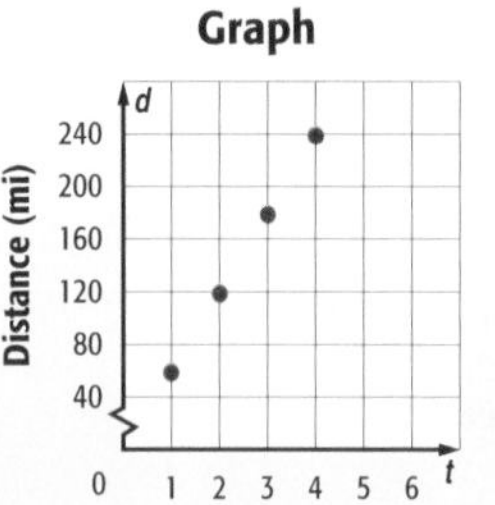

EXAMPLE 2 Use Multiple Representations

TECHNOLOGY The navigation message from a satellite to a GPS in an airplane is sent once every 12 minutes.

a. Write an equation to find the number of messages sent in any number of minutes.

Let t represent the time, and n represent the number of messages. The equation is $n = t \div 12$.

b. Make a function table to find the number of messages in 120, 180, 240, and 300 minutes. Then graph the ordered pairs.

Input (t)	$t \div 12$	Output (n)
120	$120 \div 12$	10
180	$180 \div 12$	15
240	$240 \div 12$	20
300	$300 \div 12$	25

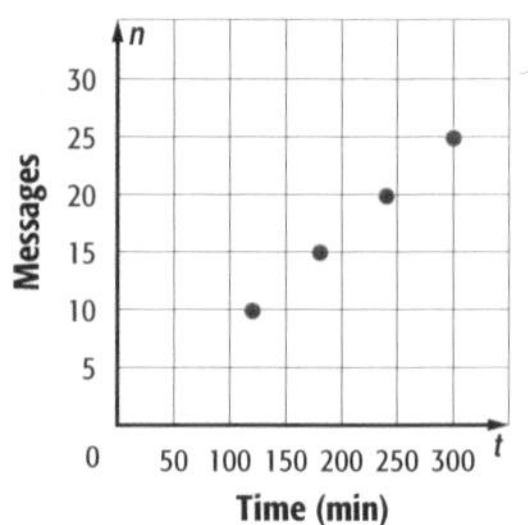

Real-World Career

Air Traffic Controller Air traffic controllers monitor the movement of objects in the air. They must have good spatial awareness and computational skills.

There are 14 schools that offer programs to become an air traffic controller. After graduation, students must then enroll in the FAA Air Traffic Controller Academy.

Check Your Progress

2. **MULTIPLE REPRESENTATIONS** The speed of sound is about 1088 feet per second at 32°F in dry air at sea level.

   A. ALGEBRAIC Write an equation to find the distance traveled by sound for any number of seconds. **1088x**

   B. TABULAR Make a function table to find the distance sound travels in 0, 1, 2, and 3 seconds. Then graph the ordered pairs for the function.

2B. See Chapter 1 Answer Appendix.

Personal Tutor glencoe.com

Differentiated Instruction BL

If students enjoy logical puzzles,

Then have them create a concealed rule with one operation and make an input/output table with inputs of 1, 2, 3, and 4. Students can then switch tables, determine the rule, and write an algebraic expression for the table.

Check Your Understanding

Example 1 p. 33

Copy and complete each function table. Then state the domain and range of the function.

1. The team scores 6 points for each touchdown.

Number of Touchdowns	Number of Points
Input (x)	Output (y)
1	■ 6
2	■ 12
5	■ 30
7	■ 42

D: {1, 2, 5, 7}; R: {6, 12, 30, 42}

2. Bob spent 5 more than 3 times what Anna spent.

Anna's Spending ($)	Bob's Spending ($)
Input (x)	Output (y)
2	■ 11
4	■ 17
6	■ 23
8	■ 29

D: {2, 4, 6, 8}; R: {11, 17, 23, 29}

Example 2 p. 34

3. **MULTIPLE REPRESENTATIONS** There are sixteen ounces in one pound.

a. **ALGEBRAIC** Write an equation that can be used to find the number of ounces in any number of pounds. $z = 16p$

b. **TABULAR** Make a function table to find the number of ounces in 5, 8, 11, and 13 pounds.

c. **GRAPHICAL** Graph the ordered pairs for the function.

3b–c. See Chapter 1 Answer Appendix.

Practice and Problem Solving

● = **Step-by-Step Solutions** begin on page R11. **Extra Practice** begins on page 810.

Example 1 p. 33

Copy and complete each function table. Then state the domain and range of the function.

4. Each ticket to the school musical costs $8.

Number of Tickets	Total Cost ($)
Input (x)	Output (y)
4	■ 32
7	■ 56
9	■ 72
12	■ 96

D: {4, 7, 9, 12}; R: {32, 56, 72, 96}

5. The dog weighs 4 pounds more than the cat.

Weight of Cat (lb)	Weight of Dog (lb)
Input (x)	Output (y)
3	■ 7
6	■ 10
9	■ 13
12	■ 16

D: {3, 6, 9, 12}; R: {7, 10, 13, 16}

6. Today's attendance is four less than half of yesterday's attendance.

Yesterday's Attendance	Today's Attendance
Input (x)	Output (y)
14	■ 3
18	■ 5
22	■ 7
26	■ 9

D: {14, 18, 22, 26}; R: {3, 5, 7, 9}

7. Casey has 5 less than 4 times as many baseball cards than Ben.

Ben's Cards	Casey's Cards
Input (x)	Output (y)
3	■ 7
7	■ 23
11	■ 39
15	■ 55

D: {3, 7, 11, 15}; R: {7, 23, 39, 55}

Additional Example

2 **BUSINESS** An assembly line produces 30 boxes per hour.

a. Write an equation to find the amount of boxes it can produce for any number of hours. $n = 30h$

b. Make a function table for 5, 10, 15, and 20 hours of production. Then graph the ordered pairs.

Input (h)	$30h$	Output (n)
5	30(5)	150
10	30(10)	300
15	30(15)	450
20	30(20)	600

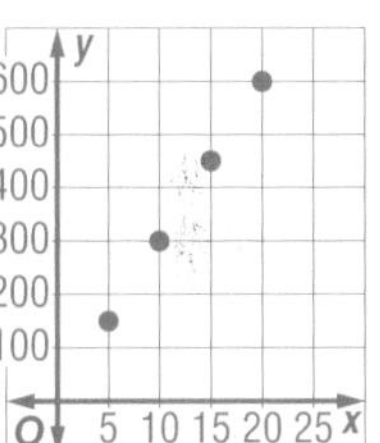

Watch Out!

Student Misconceptions Rules can be found to describe most of the functions in this lesson. Point out to students that this is not always the case—not all functions have rules. Refer students back to Explore 1-5 where they can see mappings and tables of functions that cannot be described by a rule.

Differentiated Homework Options

Level	Assignment	Two-Day Option	
AL Basic	4–9, 12, 14–39	5–9 odd, 15–18	4–8 even, 12, 14, 19–39
OL Core	5–9 odd, 10–12, 14–39	4–9, 15–18	10–12, 14, 19–39
BL Advanced	10–31, (optional: 32–39)		

3 PRACTICE

Formative Assessment

Use Exercises 1–3 to check for understanding.

Use the table at the left to customize assignments for your students.

Multiple Representations In exercises throughout this lesson, students learn to use words, tables, equations, and graphs in various combinations to model mathematical operations and real-world problems.

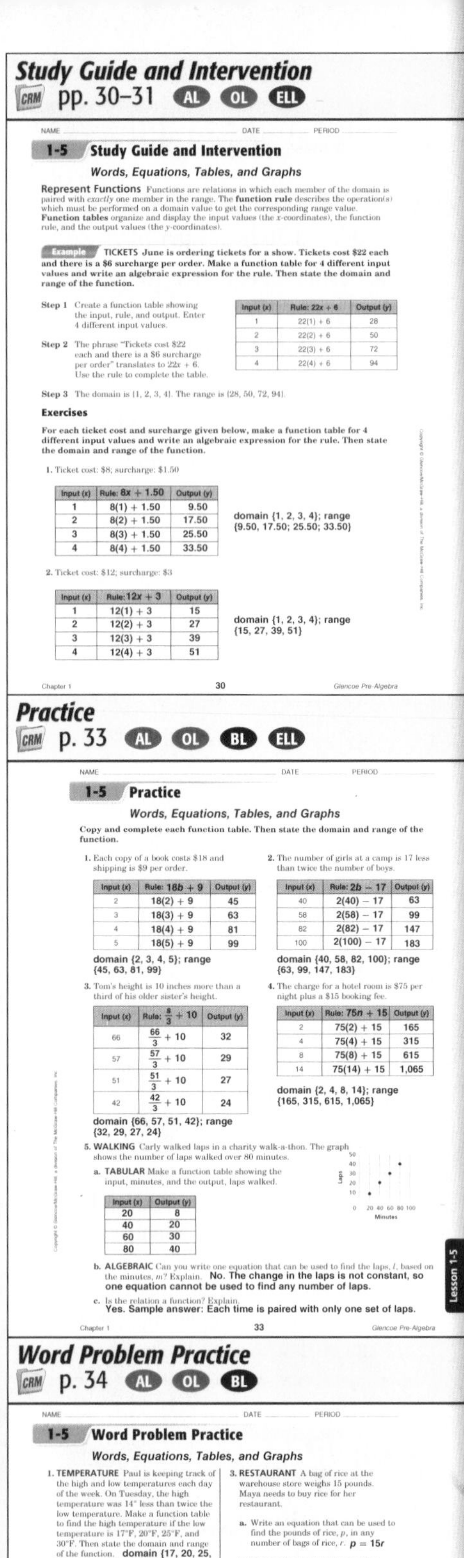

Study Guide and Intervention

CRM pp. 30–31 AL OL ELL

NAME ______ DATE ______ PERIOD ______

1-5 Study Guide and Intervention

Words, Equations, Tables, and Graphs

Represent Functions Functions are relations in which each member of the domain is paired with *exactly* one member in the range. The **function rule** describes the operation(s) which must be performed on a domain value to get the corresponding range value. **Function tables** organize and display the input values (the x-coordinates), the function rule, and the output values (the y-coordinates).

Example **TICKETS June is ordering tickets for a show. Tickets cost $22 each and there is a $6 surcharge per order. Make a function table for 4 different input values and write an algebraic expression for the rule. Then state the domain and range of the function.**

Step 1 Create a function table showing the input, rule, and output. Enter 4 different input values.

Step 2 The phrase "Tickets cost $22 each and there is a $6 surcharge per order" translates to $22x + 6$. Use the rule to complete the table.

Input (x)	Rule: 22x + 6	Output (y)
1	22(1) + 6	28
2	22(2) + 6	50
3	22(3) + 6	72
4	22(4) + 6	94

Step 3 The domain is {1, 2, 3, 4}. The range is {28, 50, 72, 94}.

Exercises

For each ticket cost and surcharge given below, make a function table for 4 different input values and write an algebraic expression for the rule. Then state the domain and range of the function.

1. Ticket cost: $8; surcharge: $1.50

Input (x)	Rule: 8x + 1.50	Output (y)
1	8(1) + 1.50	9.50
2	8(2) + 1.50	17.50
3	8(3) + 1.50	25.50
4	8(4) + 1.50	33.50

domain {1, 2, 3, 4}; range {9.50, 17.50; 25.50; 33.50}

2. Ticket cost: $12; surcharge: $3

Input (x)	Rule: 12x + 3	Output (y)
1	12(1) + 3	15
2	12(2) + 3	27
3	12(3) + 3	39
4	12(4) + 3	51

domain {1, 2, 3, 4}; range {15, 27, 39, 51}

Practice

CRM p. 33 AL OL BL ELL

NAME ______ DATE ______ PERIOD ______

1-5 Practice

Words, Equations, Tables, and Graphs

Copy and complete each function table. Then state the domain and range of the function.

1. Each copy of a book costs $18 and shipping is $9 per order.

Input (x)	Rule: 18b + 9	Output (y)
2	18(2) + 9	45
3	18(3) + 9	63
4	18(4) + 9	81
5	18(5) + 9	99

domain {2, 3, 4, 5}; range {45, 63, 81, 99}

2. The number of girls at a camp is 17 less than twice the number of boys.

Input (x)	Rule: 2b − 17	Output (y)
40	2(40) − 17	63
58	2(58) − 17	99
82	2(82) − 17	147
100	2(100) − 17	183

domain {40, 58, 82, 100}; range {63, 99, 147, 183}

3. Tom's height is 10 inches more than a third of his older sister's height.

Input (x)	Rule: $\frac{s}{3} + 10$	Output (y)
66	$\frac{66}{3} + 10$	32
57	$\frac{57}{3} + 10$	29
51	$\frac{51}{3} + 10$	27
42	$\frac{42}{3} + 10$	24

domain {66, 57, 51, 42}; range {32, 29, 27, 24}

4. The charge for a hotel room is $75 per night plus a $15 booking fee.

Input (x)	Rule: 75n + 15	Output (y)
2	75(2) + 15	165
4	75(4) + 15	315
8	75(8) + 15	615
14	75(14) + 15	1,065

domain {2, 4, 8, 14}; range {165, 315, 615, 1,065}

5. **WALKING** Carly walked laps in a charity walk-a-thon. The graph shows the number of laps walked over 80 minutes.

a. **TABULAR** Make a function table showing the input, minutes, and the output, laps walked.

Input (x)	Output (y)
20	8
40	20
60	30
80	40

b. **ALGEBRAIC** Can you write one equation that can be used to find the laps, l, based on the minutes, m? Explain. **No. The change in the laps is not constant, so one equation cannot be used to find any number of laps.**

c. Is the relation a function? Explain. **Yes. Sample answer: Each time is paired with only one set of laps.**

Lesson 1-5

Word Problem Practice

CRM p. 34 AL OL BL

NAME ______ DATE ______ PERIOD ______

1-5 Word Problem Practice

Words, Equations, Tables, and Graphs

1. **TEMPERATURE** Paul is keeping track of the high and low temperatures each day of the week. On Tuesday, the high temperature was 14° less than twice the low temperature. Make a function table to find the high temperature if the low temperature is 17°F, 20°F, 25°F, and 30°F. Then state the domain and range of the function. **domain {17, 20, 25, 30}; range {20, 26, 36, 46}**

Input (x)	Rule: h = 2l − 14	Output (y)
17	2(17) − 14	20
20	2(20) − 14	26
25	2(25) − 14	36
30	2(30) − 14	46

2. **READING COUNTS** The table below shows the total number of books read by Mrs. Benitez's class over a 5-week period. Graph the ordered pairs on a coordinate plane. Then explain whether or not the relation is a function. **The relationship is a function because each week is paired with only one number of books.**

Week	Number of Books
1	38
2	74
3	105
4	133
5	156

3. **RESTAURANT** A bag of rice at the warehouse store weighs 15 pounds. Maya needs to buy rice for her restaurant.

a. Write an equation that can be used to find the pounds of rice, p, in any number of bags of rice, r. $\mathbf{p = 15r}$

b. Make a function table to find the number of pounds in 2, 5, 8, and 12 bags of rice.

Input (x)	Rule: 15r	Output (y)
2	15(2)	30
5	15(5)	75
8	15(8)	120
12	15(12)	180

c. Graph the ordered pairs for the function.

Example 2 p. 34

8. **MULTIPLE REPRESENTATIONS** One roll of quarters contains 40 quarters.

a. **ALGEBRAIC** Write an equation that can be used to find the number of quarters q in any number of rolls of quarters r. $\mathbf{q = 40r}$

b. **TABULAR** Make a function table to find the number of quarters in 3, 4, 5, and 6 rolls. **b–c. See Chapter 1 Answer Appendix.**

c. **GRAPHICAL** Graph the ordered pairs for the function.

9. **MULTIPLE REPRESENTATIONS** Kevin's Flooring sells different sizes of square floor tiles. Carl wants to purchase 10 tiles. **b–c. See Chapter 1 Answer Appendix.**

a. **ALGEBRAIC** Write an equation that can be used to find the area of any ten square floor tiles. (*Hint:* area = side × side) $\mathbf{A = 10 \cdot s \cdot s}$

b. **TABULAR** Make a function table to find the area covered by ten tiles that measure 6, 12, 15, and 24 inches on one side.

c. **GRAPHICAL** Graph the ordered pairs for the function.

10a, c. See Chapter 1 Answer Appendix.

10. **MULTIPLE REPRESENTATIONS** Sales for a new video game offered by Technogames is shown at the right.

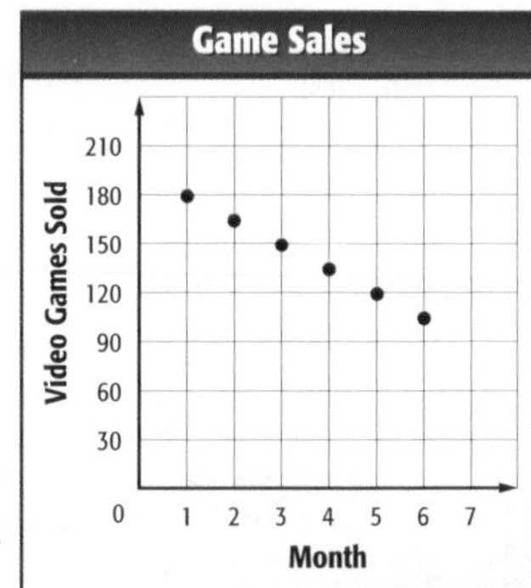

a. **TABULAR** Make a function table showing the input, month, and the output, video games sold.

b. **ALGEBRAIC** Write an equation that can be used to find the number of games sold g for any month m. $\mathbf{g = 195 - 15m}$

c. **ANALYTICAL** Is the set of ordered pairs (month, games sold) a function? Explain.

Real-World Link

In 2006, sales for computer and video games totaled about $7,400,000,000. The average age of game buyers was 38.

Source: Entertainment Software Association

11. **MULTIPLE REPRESENTATIONS** The table shows the temperatures at various depths in a lake.

Depth (ft)	Temperature (°F)
0	74
10	72
20	71
30	61
40	55
50	53

a. **GRAPHICAL** Graph the ordered pairs on a coordinate plane. **See Chapter 1 Answer Appendix.**

b. **ALGEBRAIC** Can you write one equation that can be used to find the temperature t based on the depth in the lake d? Explain.

c. **ANALYTICAL** Is the relation a function? Explain.

11b. No; the change in temperature is not constant so one equation cannot be used to find any temperature value.

11c. yes; Sample answer: Each depth is paired with only one temperature.

H.O.T. Problems

Use **H**igher-**O**rder **T**hinking Skills

12. **OPEN ENDED** Write about a real-world situation that can be represented by the equation $y = 4x$.

12. Sample answer: The cost of each used CD is $4 at an electronics store. In the equation $y = 4x$, x represents the number of CDs and y represents the total of the CDs.

13. **CHALLENGE** Write a rule for the function shown in the table. $\mathbf{2(x + 4)}$

Input (x)	1	2	3	4
Output (y)	10	12	14	16

14. **WRITING IN MATH** Give a set of data that does *not* represent a function. Explain your reasoning. **See Chapter 1 Answer Appendix.**

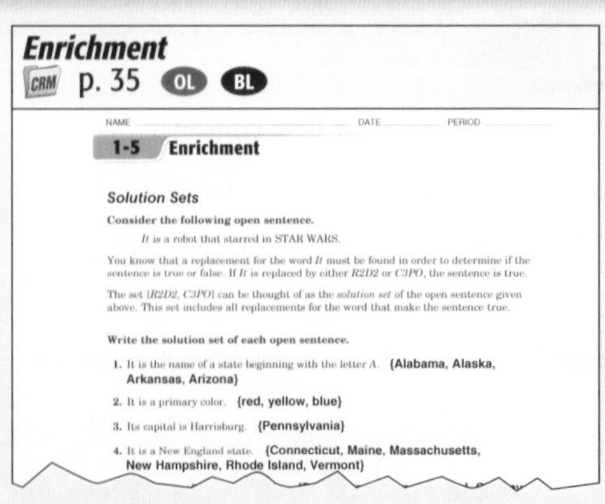

Enrichment

CRM p. 35 OL BL

NAME ______ DATE ______ PERIOD ______

1-5 Enrichment

Solution Sets

Consider the following open sentence.

It is a robot that starred in STAR WARS.

You know that a replacement for the word *It* must be found in order to determine if the sentence is true or false. If *It* is replaced by either *R2D2* or *C3PO*, the sentence is true.

The set {*R2D2*, *C3PO*} can be thought of as the *solution set* of the open sentence given above. This set includes all replacements for the word that make the sentence true.

Write the solution set of each open sentence.

1. It is the name of a state beginning with the letter *A*. **{Alabama, Alaska, Arkansas, Arizona}**
2. It is a primary color. **{red, yellow, blue}**
3. Its capital is Harrisburg. **{Pennsylvania}**
4. It is a New England state. **{Connecticut, Maine, Massachusetts, New Hampshire, Rhode Island, Vermont}**

36 Chapter 1 The Tools of Algebra

Standardized Test Practice

15. EXTENDED RESPONSE The function table below follows a function rule.

x	y
1	5
3	11
5	17
7	23
8	■ 26
10	■ 32

a. Complete the table by filling in the two missing numbers.

b. Based on the table, write a function rule that represents the relationship between x and y. **$3x + 2$**

16. Walik is buying CDs from an online store. Each CD costs $12.99. There is a flat shipping charge of $4.95. Which expression represents the cost of purchasing m CDs? **C**

A $m(12.99 + 4.95)$ C $12.99m + 4.95$
B $4.95m + 12.99$ D $(12.99 - 4.95)m$

17. Which of the following equations would describe the graph shown below? **J**

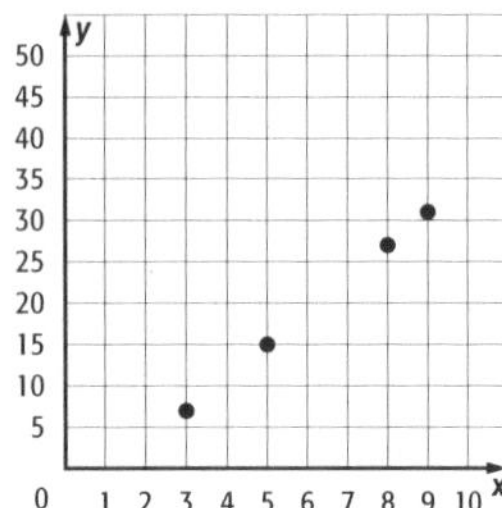

F $y = 2x + 1$ H $y = 5x - 10$
G $y = 3x - 2$ J $y = 4x - 5$

18. Which of the following sets of ordered pairs is a function? **B**

A {(0, 0), (1, 0), (0, 1), (1, 1)}
B {(0, 3), (1, 3), (2, 3), (3, 3)}
C {(0,1), (0, 2), (0, 3), (0, 4)}
D {(0,0), (0, 4), (4, 0), 4, 4)}

Spiral Review

Refer to the coordinate plane at the right. Write the ordered pair that names each point. (Lesson 1-4)

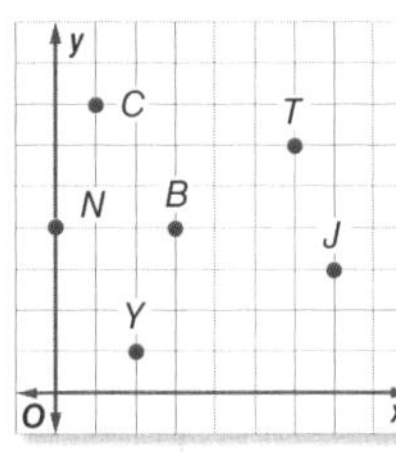

19. C **(1, 7)** **20.** J **(7, 3)** **21.** N **(0, 4)**
22. T **(6, 6)** **23.** Y **(2, 1)** **24.** B **(3, 4)**

ALGEBRA Simplify each expression (Lesson 1-3)

25. $(m + 8) + 4$ **$m + 12$** **26.** $(17 + p) + 9$ **$26 + p$** **27.** $21 + (k + 16)$ **$37 + k$**
28. $(6 \cdot c) \cdot 8$ **$48c$** **29.** $8 \cdot (y \cdot 2)$ **$16y$** **30.** $25s\,(3)$ **$75s$**

31. MONEY There are 20 nickels in one dollar.

a. Write an algebraic expression that can be used to find the number of nickels in any number of dollars n. **$20n$**

b. How many nickels are in $7.00? **140 nickels**

Skills Review

Find each quotient. (Previous Course)

32. $68 \div 4$ **17** **33.** $84 \div 6$ **14** **34.** $126 \div 9$ **14** **35.** $135 \div 9$ **15**

Differentiated Instruction

Extension In algebra, students graph functions in the form $y = ax^2 + bx + c$ (where $a \neq 0$). Have students use a graphing calculator to graph $y = x^2$ and $y = -x^2$. Have students compare the graphs and make conclusions about what they observe. The graph of $y = x^2$ opens upward and the graph of $y = -x^2$ opens downward. The graphs of functions in this form are U-shaped and open upward if the x^2 coefficient is positive and downward if it is negative.

Tips for New Teachers

Connections Show students how functions are like many everyday machines by choosing one or a few such items to bring to class. For example, a toaster receives bread as input and produces toast as output. Other machines include a label maker, a shredder, and a laminator.

4 ASSESS

Ticket Out the Door Have students write a paragraph comparing function tables and graphs. Have them describe which form of data they prefer and why. Students should hand in their paragraphs as they exit.

Formative Assessment

Check for student understanding of concepts in Lessons 1-4 and 1-5.

CRM Quiz 3, p. 47

EXTEND 1-5 Lesson Notes

1 FOCUS

Objective Use a graphing calculator to create function tables.

Materials for Each Student

- TI-Nspire graphing calculator

Teaching Tip

The graphing calculator opens on the same screen as when it was turned off. To begin a new document, have students press Home and then choose 6: New Document.

2 TEACH

Working in Cooperative Groups

Have students of mixed abilities work in pairs to complete the Activity and Exercise 1a.

- In Step 2: Add Function Table, students can press [menu] 2 8 to add a function table.
- In Step 2: Edit Function Table Settings, students change the setting for Independent from Auto to Ask so they can enter data in the function table. They should not change the setting for Dependent. Explain that Independent refers to domain values and Dependent to range values.
- For Step 3, ask students to give the cost for 8 batteries. $30

Practice Have students complete Exercises 1b–1e.

3 ASSESS

Formative Assessment

Use Exercise 1b to assess whether students know how to create a graph and function table to represent a given set of domain values.

EXTEND 1-5 Graphing Technology Lab: Function Tables

Math Online glencoe.com
- Other Calculator Keystrokes
- Graphing Technology Personal Tutor

You can use a TI-Nspire graphing calculator to create function tables. If you enter a function and the domain values, the calculator will give you the corresponding range values.

ACTIVITY

Packages of batteries cost $4 each at a store. Bridgett has a coupon for $2 off her total purchase. Find the total cost y of buying x packages of batteries. Use a function table to find the range of $y = 4x - 2$ if the domain is {2, 5, 6, 8, 10}.

Step 1 Enter the function.

- The graphing calculator uses x for the domain values and *f1(x)* for the range values. So, *f1(x)* $= 4x - 2$ represents $y = 4x - 2$.
- Access Graphs and Geometry.

  KEYSTROKES: [on] [home] 2
- Enter *f1(x)* $= 4x - 2$.

  KEYSTROKES: 4 [X] [−] 2 [enter]

Step 2 Format the table.

- Add Function Table.

  KEYSTROKES: [menu] 2 8
- Edit Function Table Settings.

  KEYSTROKES: [menu] 5 3 ▸▸▸▸ [click] ▾ [click] ▸▸ [click]
- You can use [ctrl] + [tab] to switch between the graph and the table.

Step 3 Find the range by entering the domain values.

- Enter the domain values given above. The range values will appear automatically.

  KEYSTROKES: ◂ 2 [enter] ▾ 5 [enter] ▾ 6 [enter] ▾ 8 [enter] ▾ 10 [enter]

- Note the graph is a different representation of the same data.
- The *trace* function could be used to find domain and range values that were not requested.

Analyze the Results

Use the Function Table option on a TI-Nspire to complete each exercise.

1. **MULTIPLE REPRESENTATIONS** Suppose you are using the formula $d = rt$ to find the distance d a car travels for the times t in hours given by {0, 1, 3.5, 10}.
   a. **ALGEBRAIC** If the rate is 60 miles per hour, what function should be entered in the *f(x)* = list? Y = 60X
   b. **GRAPHICAL** Make a graph and function table for the given domain. Make sure to use an appropriate window. See Chapter 1 Answer Appendix.
   c. **NUMERICAL** Between which two times in the domain does the car travel 150 miles? 1 h and 3.5 h
   d. **NUMERICAL** How many miles will the car have traveled after 12 hours? 720 mi
   e. **VERBAL** Describe how a function table and graph can be used to estimate the time it takes to drive 150 miles. See margin.

From Concrete to Abstract

Use Exercise 1e to assess whether students know how to manipulate data in a graph and a function table, and whether they understand the relationship between the x- and y-values in the function.

Additional Answer

1e. Sample answers: Input X values between 1 and 3.5 until you get a Y value closer to 150; use the Trace function to find an X value that coordinates with a Y value of 150.

Scatter Plots

Math Online glencoe.com
Math *in Motion*, Animation

Objective
Use a scatter plot to investigate the relationship between two sets of data.

Sometimes it is difficult to determine whether a relationship exists between two sets of data by simply looking at them. To determine whether a relationship exists, you can write the data as a set of ordered pairs and then graph the ordered pairs on a coordinate plane. This kind of graph is called a **scatter plot**.

ACTIVITY 1

Collect data to investigate whether a relationship exists between height and arm span.

Step 1 Have a classmate measure your height and the length of your arm span with a yardstick to the nearest half inch. Then write your height and arm span as an ordered pair.

Step 2 Combine your data with that of your classmates.

Step 3 Make a list of ordered pairs in which the x-coordinate represents height and the y-coordinate represents arm span.

Step 4 Draw a coordinate plane like the one shown and graph the ordered pairs (height, arm span).

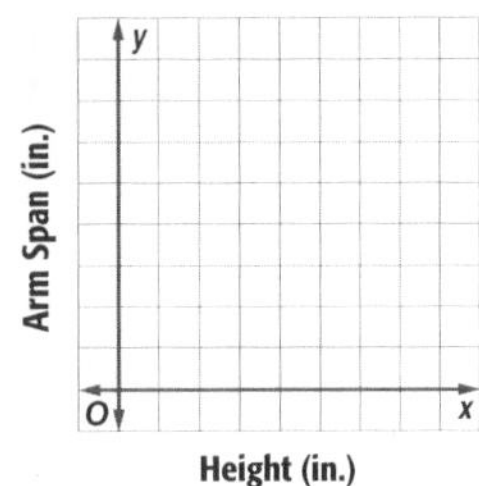

StudyTip
A scatter plot is a collection of points that may or may not show a relationship between sets of data.

Algebra Labs use manipulatives and models to help students learn key concepts. There are teacher notes for every Algebra Lab in the Student Edition.

Analyze the Results

1. Does there appear to be a trend in the data? If so, describe the trend. Yes; as height increases, arm span increases.
2. Using your graph, estimate the arm span of a person whose height is 60 inches. 72 inches. about 60 inches; about 72 inches
3. How does your arm span compare with your height? Sample answer: My arm span is about equal to my height.
4. **MAKE A CONJECTURE** Suppose the variable x represents height and the variable y represents arm span. Write an equation relating x to the arm span y. $y = x$
5. **COLLECT DATA** Collect and graph data to determine whether a relationship exists between height and foot length. Explain your results. See students' work; generally as height increases, foot length increases.

EXPLORE 1-6 Lesson Notes

1 FOCUS

Objective Use a scatter plot to investigate the relationship between two sets of data.

Materials for Each Group

- grid paper
- yardstick or tape measure

Easy-to-Make Manipulatives

Teaching Pre-Algebra with Manipulatives, templates for centimeter grid paper

Teaching Tip

Show students how to measure arm span. With arms outstretched, measure the distance from the tips of the middle fingers.

2 TEACH

Working in Pairs Arrange students in pairs, mixing abilities. Have pairs complete the Activity.

Ask:

- Describe the graph of ordered pairs from the Activity. Answers may vary: the points will generally show a positive relationship.
- Looking at the graph, what information does it give? As height increases, so does arm span.
- Suppose you have a friend who is about 5 feet tall. What would you expect her arm span to be? about 5 feet

Practice Have students complete Exercises 1–5.

From Concrete to Abstract

Show students three scatter plots: one with a positive relationship, one with a negative relationship, and one with no relationship or pattern. Ask students to brainstorm possible scenarios that those plots could represent.

Extending the Concept

Ask:

- What would you predict the trend is between height and month of birth? no trend or pattern

3 ASSESS

Formative Assessment

Use Exercise 5 to assess whether students comprehend how to determine whether a relationship exists between two sets of data.

1-6 Lesson Notes

1 FOCUS

Vertical Alignment

Before Lesson 1-6
Graph ordered pairs and relations on a coordinate system.

Lesson 1-6
Construct scatter plots.
Analyze trends in scatter plots.

After Lesson 1-6
Look for patterns and represent generalizations algebraically.

2 TEACH

Scaffolding Questions

Have students read the *Why?* section of the lesson and answer the questions.

Ask:

- About what percent of the population used the Internet in 1997? Sample answer: about 22%
- What are the coordinates of this point? (1997, 22); accept answers close to 22
- What does the first coordinate of the ordered pair indicate? the second coordinate? the year; percent of population

Construct Scatter Plots

Example 1 shows how to make a scatter plot from a data table.

1-6 Scatter Plots

Then
You have already graphed ordered pairs and relations on a coordinate system. (Lesson 1-4)

Now
- Construct scatter plots.
- Analyze trends in scatter plots.

New Vocabulary
scatter plot

Math Online
glencoe.com
- Extra Examples
- Personal Tutor
- Self-Check Quiz
- Homework Help

Why?

The graph shows the percent of the total population that are Internet users in the United States over the years.

a. Do you see a trend in the data?

b. Predict the percent of the total population that are internet users in the U. S. in 2012.
Sample answer: 90%

c. Do you think this trend will continue? Explain your reasoning.
a, c. See Chapter 1 Answer Appendix.

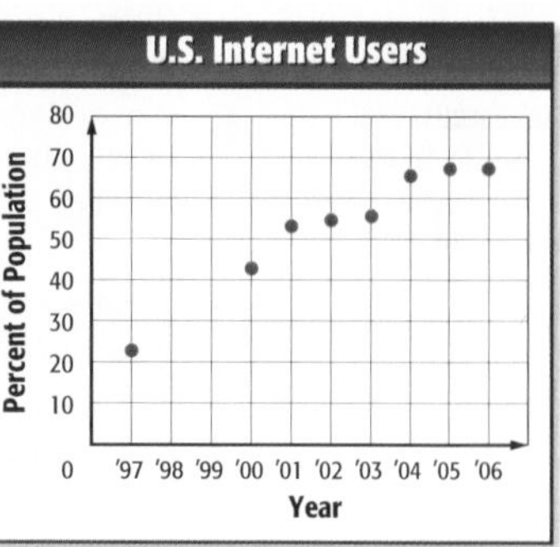

Source: NY Times Almanac

Construct Scatter Plots A **scatter plot** shows the relationship between a set of data with two variables, graphed as ordered pairs on a coordinate plane.

EXAMPLE 1 Construct a Scatter Plot

POPULATION Make a scatter plot of the approximate population of Tampa, Florida.

Year	Population (thousands)
1940	108
1950	125
1960	275
1970	278
1980	272
1990	280
2000	303

Source: U.S. Census Bureau

Let the horizontal axis, or x-axis, represent the year. Let the vertical axis, or y-axis, represent the population. Then graph ordered pairs (year, population).

Population of Tampa, Florida 1940–2000

Population (thousands): 0, 50, 100, 150, 200, 250, 300, 350
Year: '40 '50 '60 '70 '80 '90 '00

Check Your Progress

1. **BASKETBALL** Make a scatter plot of the number of field goals made by a WNBA player from 1997–2006. See Chapter 1 Answer Appendix.

Season	'00	'01	'02	'03	'04	'05	'06	'07	'08	'09
Number of Field Goals Made	160	202	182	197	221	189	165	223	204	257

Personal Tutor glencoe.com

Lesson 1-6 Resources

Resource	Approaching-Level	On-Level	Beyond-Level	English Learners
Teacher Edition		• Differentiated Instruction, p. 42	• Differentiated Instruction, p. 46	
Chapter Resource Masters	• Study Guide and Intervention, pp. 37–38 • Skills Practice, p. 39 • Practice, p. 40 • Word Problem Practice, p. 41 • Spreadsheet Activity, p. 43	• Study Guide and Intervention, pp. 37–38 • Skills Practice, p. 39 • Practice, p. 40 • Word Problem Practice, p. 41 • Enrichment, p. 42 • Spreadsheet Activity, p. 43	• Practice, p. 40 • Word Problem Practice, p. 41 • Enrichment, p. 42 • Spreadsheet Activity, p. 43	• Study Guide and Intervention, pp. 37–38 • Skills Practice, p. 39 • Practice, p. 40 • Spreadsheet Activity, p. 43
Transparencies	• 5-Minute Check Transparency 1-6	• 5-Minute Check Transparency 1-6	• 5-Minute Check Transparency 1-6	• 5-Minute Check Transparency 1-6
Other	• Study Notebook • Teaching Pre-Algebra with Manipulatives	• Study Notebook • Teaching Pre-Algebra with Manipulatives	• Study Notebook	• Study Notebook • Teaching Pre-Algebra with Manipulatives

StudyTip

Scatter Plots Data that appear to go uphill from left to right show a positive relationship. Data that appear to go downhill from left to right show a negative relationship.

Analyze Scatter Plots The following scatter plots show the types of relationships or patterns of two sets of data.

Key Concept Types of Relationships — For Your FOLDABLE

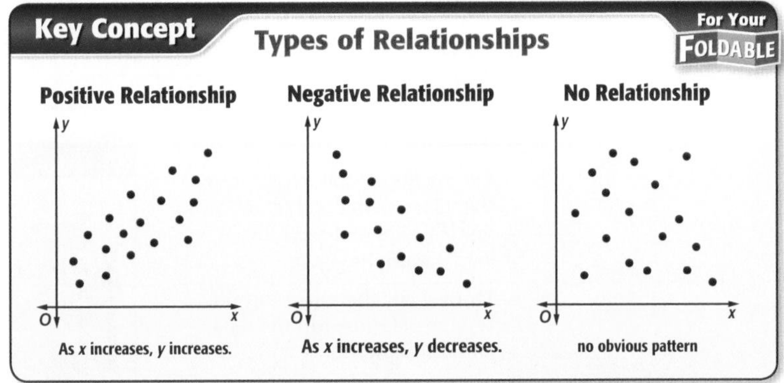

Real-World Link

Over 5 million people celebrate their birthday each week in the United States. On average, 700,000 people celebrate their birthday every day.

Source: Hallmark

EXAMPLE 2 Interpret Scatter Plots

PEOPLE Determine whether a scatter plot of the birth month and age of people in a park might show a *positive*, *negative*, or *no* relationship. Explain your answer.

A person's age is not affected by their birth month. Therefore, a scatter plot of the data would show no relationship.

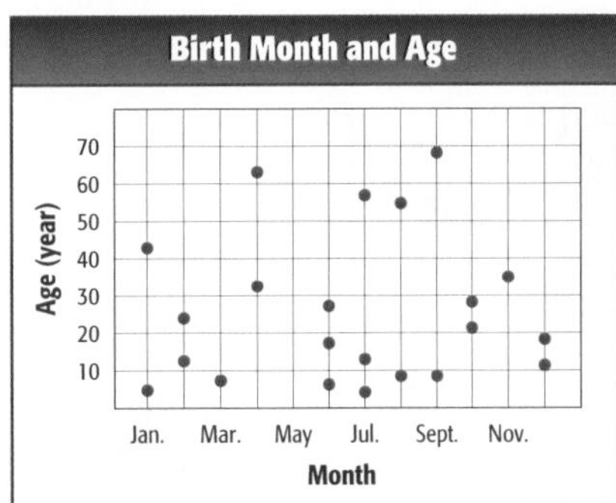

Check Your Progress

2. **TEST SCORES** Determine whether a scatter plot of the study time and resulting test score might show a *positive*, *negative*, or *no* relationship. Explain your answer.
   Sample answer: As the study time increases, the test score increases. So, the scatter plot shows a positive relationship.

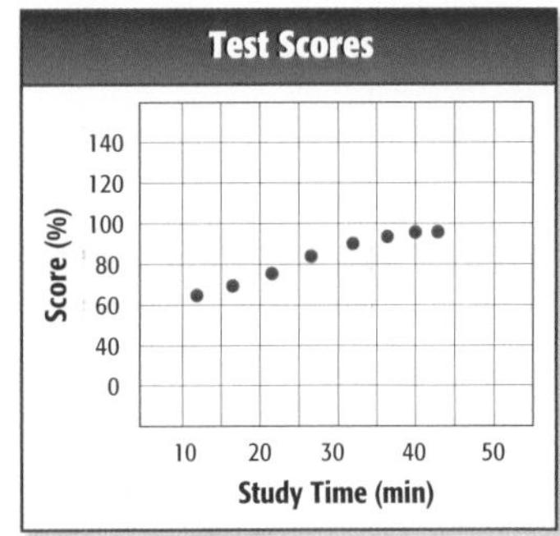

Personal Tutor glencoe.com

You can also use scatter plots to spot trends, draw conclusions, and make predictions about the data.

Formative Assessment

Use the Check Your Progress exercises after each example to determine students' understanding of concepts.

Additional Example

1 **BREAD** The table shows the average cost of a loaf of bread from 1920–2000. Make a scatter plot of the data.

Year	1920	1930	1940	1950	1960
Cents	12	9	8	14	20

Year	1970	1980	1990	2000
Cents	24	52	72	99

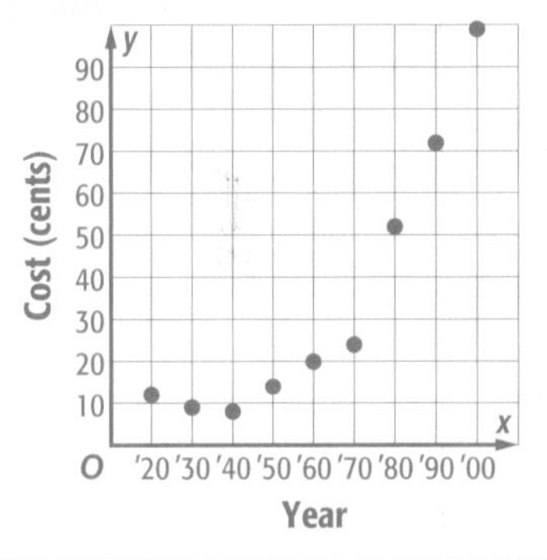

Additional Examples also in Interactive Classroom PowerPoint® Presentations

IWB INTERACTIVE WHITEBOARD READY

Analyze Scatter Plots

Example 2 shows how to analyze a scatter plot and determine whether there is a positive, negative, or no relationship between the data. **Example 3** shows how to create and analyze a scatter plot in a real-world problem.

Focus on Mathematical Content

Coordinate Graphs A scatter plot can be used to explore the relationship between two sets of data. A negative relationship is shown when the *x*-variable increases as the *y*-variable decreases. A positive relationship is shown when the *y*-variable increases as the *x*-variable increases. A scatter plot can also demonstrate that no relationship exists between the data and that the variables are independent of one another.

Additional Examples

2 Determine whether a scatter plot of the data for the following might show a *positive, negative,* or *no* relationship. Explain your answer.

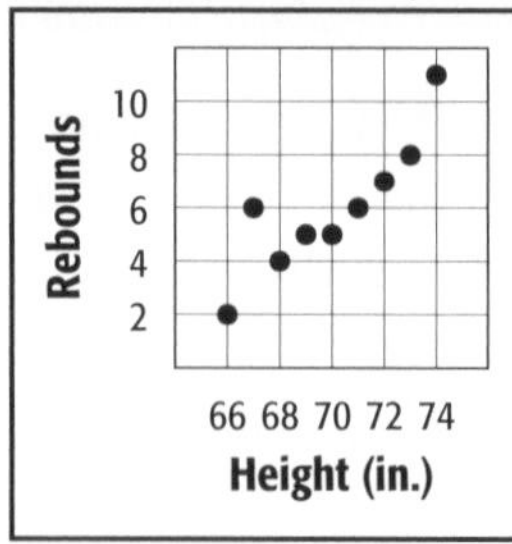

As height increases, number of rebounds increases; positive relationship.

3 **TEMPERATURE** The table shows temperatures in degrees Celsius and the corresponding temperatures in Fahrenheit.

°F	32	41	50	59	68	77	86
°C	0	5	10	15	20	25	30

a. Make a scatter plot of the data.

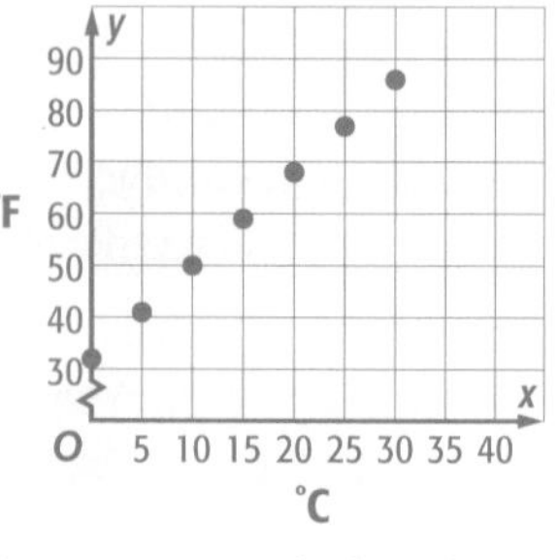

b. Draw a conclusion about the type of relationship the data shows. Explain. Positive; as °C increase, so do °F.

c. Predict the Fahrenheit temperature for 35° C. about 95°

3 PRACTICE

Formative Assessment

Use Exercise 1 to check for understanding.

Use the chart at the bottom of the next page to customize assignments for your students.

Real-World EXAMPLE 3 Analyze Scatter Plots

SALES **The table shows how many cups of coffee were sold during outdoor games at certain temperatures.**

Temperature (°F)	34	36	43	45	48	54	59	62	65	71	75
Number of Cups	42	39	34	33	37	18	18	13	12	9	8

a. Make a scatter plot of the data.

Let the horizontal axis represent the temperature and let the vertical axis represent the cups sold. Graph the data.

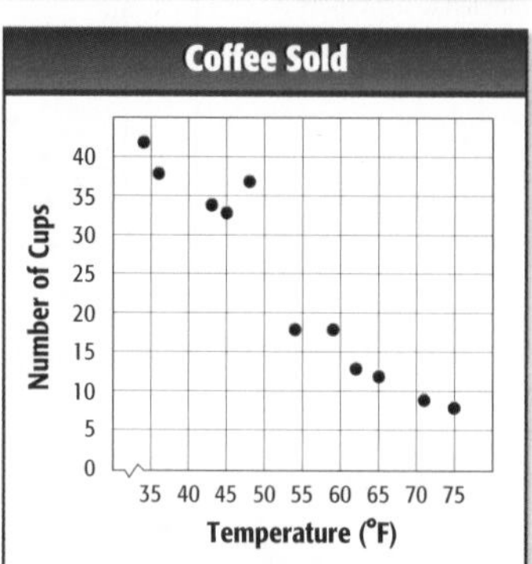

b. Draw a conclusion about the type of relationship the data shows. Explain.

As the temperature increases, the number of cups sold decreases. So, the scatter plot shows a negative relationship.

c. Predict the number of cups sold if the temperature is 30° Fahrenheit.

By looking at the pattern in the graph, you can predict that between 40 and 45 cups will be sold.

Real-World Link

Average typing speed is about 50 to 70 words per minute. The world's fastest typer can maintain a typing speed of 150 words per minute for 50 minutes using a simplified keyboard.

Check Your Progress

3. **KEYBOARDING** The table shows keyboarding speeds in words per minute (wpm) of 12 students. **3A–C. See Chapter 1 Answer Appendix.**

Experience (weeks)	4	7	8	1	6	3	5	2	9	6	7	10
Speed (wpm)	38	46	48	20	40	30	38	22	52	44	42	55

A. Make a scatter plot of the data.

B. Draw a conclusion about the type of relationship the data shows.

C. Predict the keyboarding speed of a student with 12 weeks of experience.

Personal Tutor glencoe.com

Check Your Understanding

1a–c. See Chapter 1 Answer Appendix.

Examples 1–3 p. 40–42

1 **TEXT MESSAGING** The table shows the number of friends per group in a cell phone network and the average number of text messages made per day.

Number of Friends	5	4	2	4	6	3	4	3	5	2
Number of Text Messages	131	86	39	98	234	43	100	85	190	55

a. Make a scatter plot of the data.

b. Draw a conclusion about the type of relationship the data shows. Explain.

c. If a relationship exists, predict the number of text messages made during the week for a group of 8.

Differentiated Instruction OL

Logical Have students research and analyze data of their own choice. Suggestion: level of education completed and average salaries. Students can graph their data and write a paragraph analyzing the relationship they identify.

Practice and Problem Solving

● = **Step-by-Step Solutions** begin on page R11.
Extra Practice begins on page 810.

Example 1 p. 40

2. **MUSIC** The table shows the number of songs and the total number of minutes on different CDs. Make a scatter plot of the data. **See margin.**

Number of Songs	15	20	13	12	15	16	17	18	20	19	11	14
Total Minutes	64	63	70	59	61	77	75	71	78	75	63	69

3. **OLYMPICS** The table shows the winning times for the women's Olympic 100-meter run. Make a scatter plot of the data. **See Chapter 1 Answer Appendix.**

Year	'28	'32	'36	'48	'52	'56	'60	'64	'68
Winning Time(s)	12.2	11.9	11.5	11.9	11.5	11.5	11.0	11.4	11.08
Year	'72	'76	'80	'84	'88	'92	'96	'00	'04
Winning Time(s)	11.07	11.08	11.06	10.97	10.54	10.82	10.94	10.75	10.93

Example 2 p. 41

Determine whether the data for the following might show a *positive*, *negative*, or *no* relationship. Explain your answer.

4. **Music**

Number of Songs on CD (vertical axis: 4, 8, 12, 16, 20, 24, 26); Cost of CD ($) (horizontal axis: 0, 8, 12, 16, 20, 24, 26, 28, 30)

5. 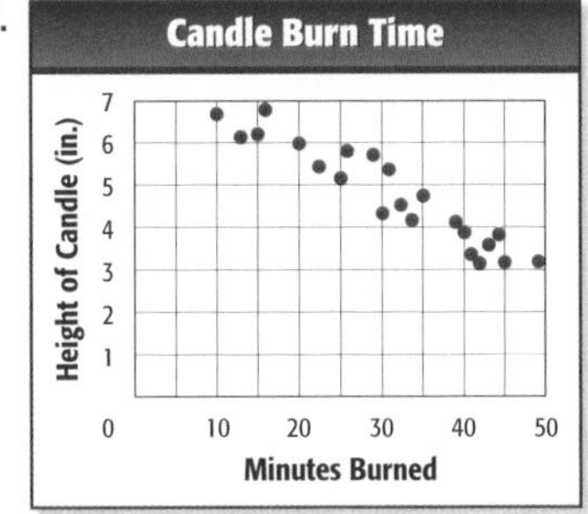

6. size of household and amount of water bill
7. distance driven and gallons of gasoline used
8. age of adults and number of pets currently owned
9. size of lawn and amount of water used to water the lawn

Example 3 p. 42

10. **MULTIPLE REPRESENTATIONS** The table shows the approximate number of students, in millions, that attended public schools in the U.S. in various years.

Year	1900	1920	1940	1960	1980	2000
Number of Students	16	22	25	35	42	47

a. **GRAPHICAL** Make a scatter plot of the data. **See margin.**

b. **VERBAL** Draw a conclusion about the type of relationship the data shows. Explain your reasoning.

c. **ANALYTICAL** If a relationship exists, predict the number of students in public school in the year 2020. **Sample answer: 55 million students**

4. No; The number of songs on a CD usually does not affect the cost of the CD.
5. Negative; candle burn time increases as the height of the candle decreases
6. Positive; as a household size increases, the amount of the water bill increases.
7. Positive; as the distance increases, the number of gallons increases.
8. No; the age does not generally affect the number of pets.
9. Positive; as the lawn size increases, the amount of water used increases.

10b. As the years increase, the number of students enrolled in public school increases. This shows a positive relationship.

Differentiated Homework Options

Level	Assignment	Two-Day Option	
AL Basic	2–10, 16–19, 21–39	3–9 odd, 23–26	2–10 even, 16–19, 21, 22, 27–39
OL Core	3–9 odd, 11–19, 21–39	2–10, 23–26	11–19, 21, 22, 27–39
BL Advanced	11–33, (optional: 34–39)		

Multiple Representations In Exercise 10, students use a table, a scatter plot, and verbal descriptions to analyze trends in a dataset and make predictions about future values.

TEACH with TECH

WEB SEARCH Have students search for examples of scatter plots on the Web and identify the type of relationship shown on each plot. Then have them find two occupations that use scatter plots to analyze data.

Additional Answers

2. 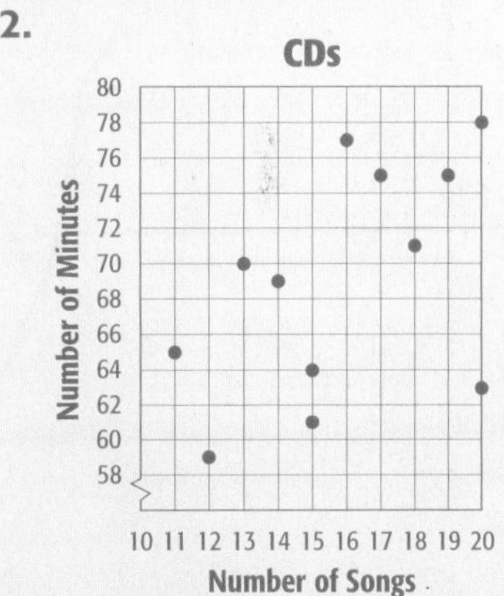

10a. 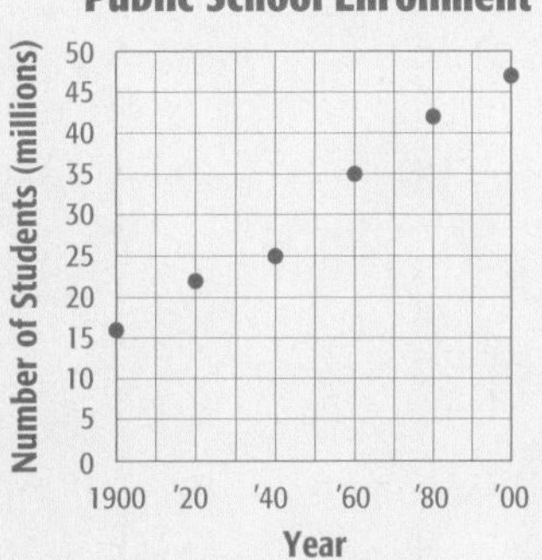

Watch Out!

Find the Error For Exercise 21, have students focus on the relationships shown between the x- and y- values in each table. Encourage them to make a mapping or graph of each table.

Multiple Representations In Exercise 11, students use a table, a scatter plot, and verbal analysis to draw a conclusion about the relationship between two statistical factors.

In Exercise 12, students use a table, a scatter plot, and algebra to show the relationship between two factors and predict data values not shown.

In Exercise 13, students use a table, a scatter plot, and a written description to describe the real-world situation modeled by the given data.

Real-World Link

The highest temperature recorded in the United States was 134°F on July 10, 1913, in Death Valley, California. This is just 2 degrees below the world temperature high.

Source: National Weather Service

11–13. See Chapter 1 Answer Appendix.

11. **MULTIPLE REPRESENTATIONS** The table shows the average high temperatures for Louisville, Kentucky.

Month	Temperature (°F)	Month	Temperature (°F)
January	41	July	87
February	47	August	86
March	57	September	79
April	67	October	68
May	75	November	56
June	83	December	45

a. **GRAPHICAL** Make a scatter plot of the data.

b. **ANALYTICAL** Draw a conclusion about the type of relationship the data shows. Explain.

12. **MULTIPLE REPRESENTATIONS** A person breathes about 20 times per minute.

a. **TABULAR** Let x represent minutes and y represent the number of times a person breathes. Make a table using the x-values of 1, 2, 4, 8, and 10.

b. **GRAPHICAL** Make a scatter plot of the data.

c. **ALGEBRAIC** Write an equation relating x and y. $y = 20x$

d. **ANALYTICAL** Predict how many times a person would breathe in 25 minutes. Explain how you arrived at your answer.

13. **MULTIPLE REPRESENTATIONS** The scatter plot at the right shows a relationship between two variables, x and y.

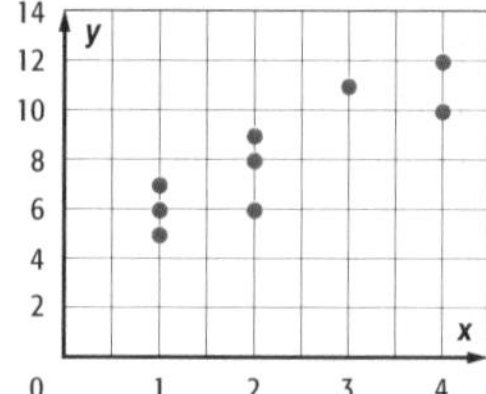

a. **TABULAR** Make a table showing the x-values and y-values.

b. **VERBAL** Write about a situation that could produce the data values shown.

c. **ANALYTICAL** Draw a conclusion about the type of relationship the data shows. Explain.

14. **DVDS** The scatter plot at the right shows the number of DVD players sold from 1996 to 2006.

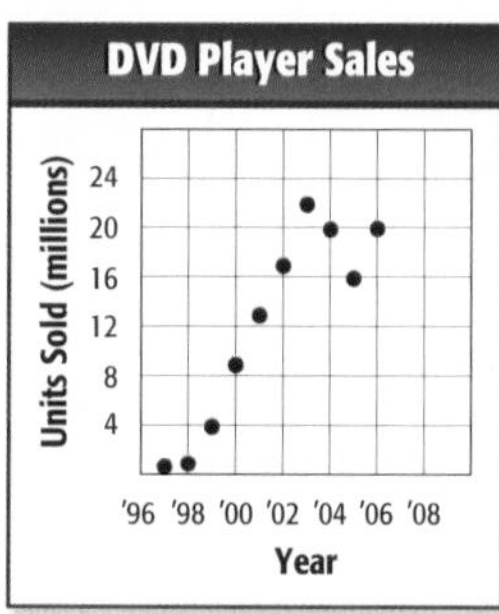

a. Do the data show a *positive*, *negative*, or *no* relationship between the year and the number of players sold?

b. What appears to be the trend between 1997 and 2003? 2003 and 2006?

c. What factors could contribute to the trend displayed in the scatter plot?

14a. Sample answer: Overall, the data shows a postive relationship between the year and the number of DVD players sold.

14b. Between 1997 and 2003, the number of players sold increases every year.; Between 2003 and 2006, the number of players sold decreases every year.

14c. Sample answers: New equipment being developed, people already have DVD players so not as many are being sold.

16. Sample answer: Speed and distance traveled would be a positive relationship. The faster you are traveling, the more distance you will cover in the same amount of time.

19. Sample answer: Because both are warm weather activities, the scatter plot would show a positive relationship. They are both independent events so they do not affect each other.

15. **AREA** The area of a rectangle can be found using the expression $\ell \cdot w$ where ℓ is the length and w is the width of the rectangle. **a–b. See Chapter 1 Answer Appendix.**

    a. Make a table of values showing possible lengths and widths of a rectangle with an area of 36 square inches.

    b. Graph the ordered pairs (length, width). Connect the points.

    c. Predict the width of a rectangle with a length of 7 inches. **about 5 in.**

H.O.T. Problems

Use Higher-Order Thinking Skills

16. **OPEN ENDED** Describe an example of two sets of data that would show a positive relationship.

NUMBER SENSE What type of relationship is shown on a graph that shows the following values.

17. As x increases, y decreases. **negative**

18. As x decreases, y decreases. **positive**

19. **WRITING IN MATH** Explain why a scatter plot of swimming pool attendance and ice cream sales might show a positive relationship. Does this mean that one factor caused the other?

Real-World Link

A recent survey showed that America's favorite ice cream flavors are vanilla, chocolate, neopolitan, strawberry, and cookies and cream.

Source: National Eating Trends Services

20. **CHALLENGE** The number 3 is considered the *principal square root* of 9 because 3×3 is equal to 9. Some numbers have whole number square roots and others, like 5, do not. **a–d. See Chapter 1 Answer Appendix.**

    a. **TABULAR** Let x represent numbers with whole number square roots and y represent the positive square root of x. Copy and complete the table. Is the data in the table a function? Explain.

x	y
1	1
4	■
9	■
16	■
■	5
36	■

    b. **GRAPHICAL** Make a scatter plot of the data. Describe the relationship shown in the graph.

    c. **TABULAR** Reverse the x- and y-coordinates and write the new set of ordered pairs in a table. Is the set of ordered pairs a function? Explain.

    d. **GRAPHICAL** Make a scatter plot of the data in part c. Describe the relationship shown in the graph.

21. No; Sample answer: The table does represent a function. Sonya is incorrect because even though it shows a negative relationship, it is still a function. Melisa is incorrect because each x-value can be paired with only 1 y-value, but y-values can be paired with any number of x-values.

21. **FIND THE ERROR** Sonya and Melisa were asked to determine if the table represents a function. Is either of them correct? Explain your reasoning.

x	y
4	1
3	3
1	5
2	5

Sonya	Melisa
It is not a function because it shows a negative relationship.	It is not a function becauses the y-value of 5 is paired with two x-values

22. **WRITING IN MATH** The relationship between variables can be strong or weak. Describe a situation that would have a *strong* positive relationship. What makes it a strong positive relationship? **See Chapter 1 Answer Appendix.**

Study Guide and Intervention

CRM pp. 37–38 AL OL ELL

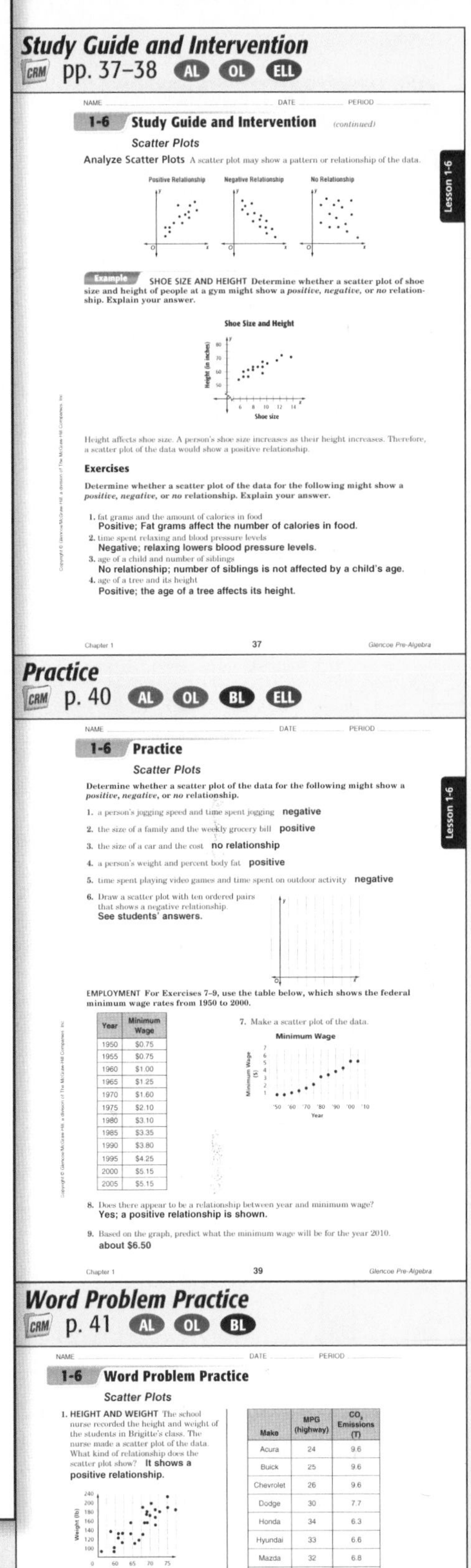

NAME ______ DATE ______ PERIOD ______

1-6 Study Guide and Intervention *(continued)*

Scatter Plots

Analyze Scatter Plots A scatter plot may show a pattern or relationship of the data.

Example SHOE SIZE AND HEIGHT **Determine whether a scatter plot of shoe size and height of people at a gym might show a *positive*, *negative*, or *no* relationship. Explain your answer.**

Height affects shoe size. A person's shoe size increases as their height increases. Therefore, a scatter plot of the data would show a positive relationship.

Exercises

Determine whether a scatter plot of the data for the following might show a *positive*, *negative*, or *no* relationship. Explain your answer.

1. fat grams and the amount of calories in food
   Positive; Fat grams affect the number of calories in food.
2. time spent relaxing and blood pressure levels
   Negative; relaxing lowers blood pressure levels.
3. age of a child and number of siblings
   No relationship; number of siblings is not affected by a child's age.
4. age of a tree and its height
   Positive; the age of a tree affects its height.

Chapter 1 37 Glencoe Pre-Algebra

Practice

CRM p. 40 AL OL BL ELL

NAME ______ DATE ______ PERIOD ______

1-6 Practice

Scatter Plots

Determine whether a scatter plot of the data for the following might show a *positive*, *negative*, or *no* relationship.

1. a person's jogging speed and time spent jogging **negative**
2. the size of a family and the weekly grocery bill **positive**
3. the size of a car and the cost **no relationship**
4. a person's weight and percent body fat **positive**
5. time spent playing video games and time spent on outdoor activity **negative**
6. Draw a scatter plot with ten ordered pairs that shows a negative relationship.
   See students' answers.

EMPLOYMENT **For Exercises 7–9, use the table below, which shows the federal minimum wage rates from 1950 to 2000.**

Year	Minimum Wage
1950	$0.75
1955	$0.75
1960	$1.00
1965	$1.25
1970	$1.60
1975	$2.10
1980	$3.10
1985	$3.35
1990	$3.80
1995	$4.25
2000	$5.15
2005	$5.15

7. Make a scatter plot of the data.

8. Does there appear to be a relationship between year and minimum wage?
   Yes; a positive relationship is shown.
9. Based on the graph, predict what the minimum wage will be for the year 2010.
   about $6.50

Chapter 1 39 Glencoe Pre-Algebra

Word Problem Practice

CRM p. 41 AL OL BL

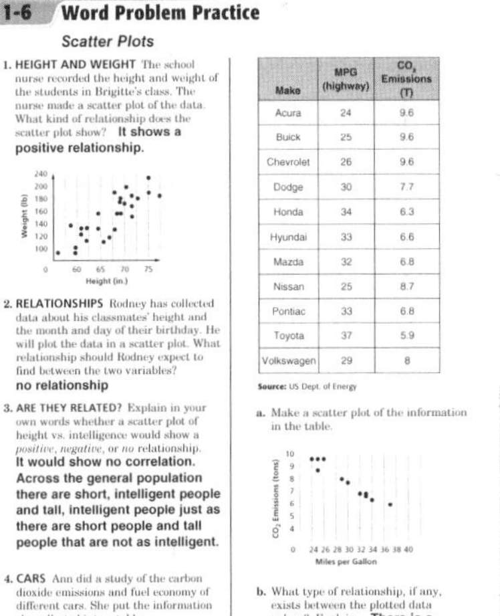

NAME ______ DATE ______ PERIOD ______

1-6 Word Problem Practice

Scatter Plots

1. **HEIGHT AND WEIGHT** The school nurse recorded the height and weight of the students in Brigitte's class. The nurse made a scatter plot of the data. What kind of relationship does the scatter plot show? **It shows a positive relationship.**

2. **RELATIONSHIPS** Rodney has collected data about his classmates' height and the month and day of their birthday. He will plot the data in a scatter plot. What relationship should Rodney expect to find between the two variables? **no relationship**

3. **ARE THEY RELATED?** Explain in your own words whether a scatter plot of height vs. intelligence would show a *positive*, *negative*, or *no* relationship. **It would show no correlation. Across the general population there are short, intelligent people and tall, intelligent people just as there are short people and tall people that are not as intelligent.**

4. **CARS** Ann did a study of the carbon dioxide emissions and fuel economy of different cars. She put the information she collected into a table.

Make	MPG (highway)	CO_2 Emissions (T)
Acura	24	9.6
Buick	25	9.6
Chevrolet	26	9.6
Dodge	30	7.7
Honda	34	6.3
Hyundai	33	6.6
Mazda	32	6.8
Nissan	25	8.7
Pontiac	33	6.8
Toyota	37	5.9
Volkswagen	29	8

Source: US Dept. of Energy

a. Make a scatter plot of the information in the table.

b. What type of relationship, if any, exists between the plotted data values? Explain. **There is a negative correlation. As the fuel economy of the car increases it would give off less CO_2, so carbon dioxide emissions would decrease.**

Chapter 1 40 Glencoe Pre-Algebra

Enrichment

CRM p. 42 OL BL

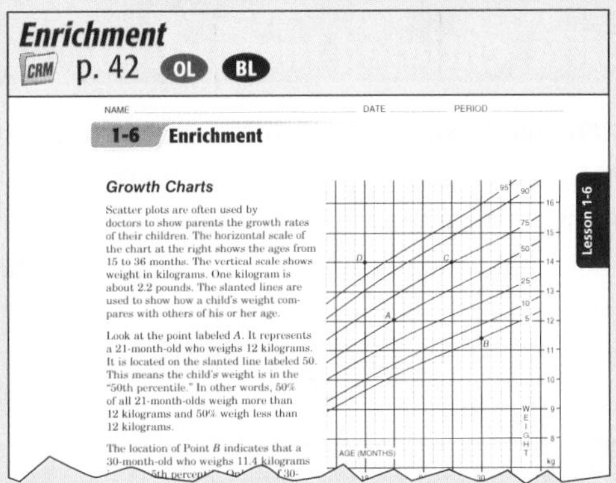

NAME ______ DATE ______ PERIOD ______

1-6 Enrichment

Growth Charts

Scatter plots are often used by doctors to show parents the growth rates of their children. The horizontal scale of the chart at the right shows the ages from 15 to 36 months. The vertical scale shows weight in kilograms. One kilogram is about 2.2 pounds. The slanted lines are used to show how a child's weight compares with others of his or her age.

Look at the point labeled *A*. It represents a 21-month-old who weighs 12 kilograms. It is located on the slanted line labeled 50. This means the child's weight is in the "50th percentile." In other words, 50% of all 21-month-olds weigh more than 12 kilograms and 50% weigh less than 12 kilograms.

The location of Point *B* indicates that a 30-month-old who weighs 11.4 kilograms

4 ASSESS

Yesterday's News Ask students to write about how yesterday's lesson on graphs helped them with today's lesson on scatter plots.

Formative Assessment

Check for student understanding of concepts in Lesson 1-6.

CRM Quiz 4, p. 47

Additional Answers

27a. $32.50 + 4.95c$

27b.

Number of Channels	Cost
0	32.50
1	37.45
2	42.40
3	47.35
4	52.30

27c.

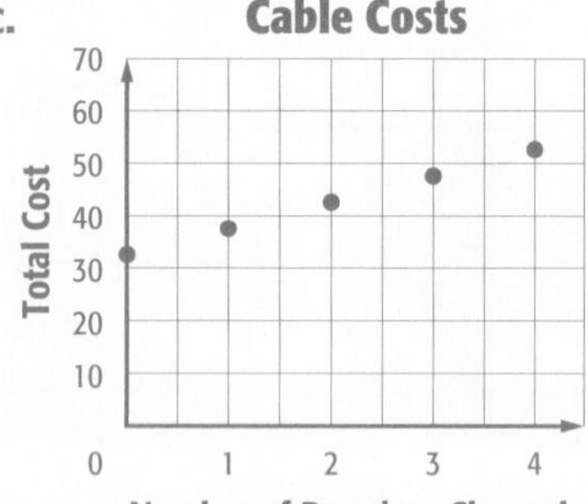

28–33.

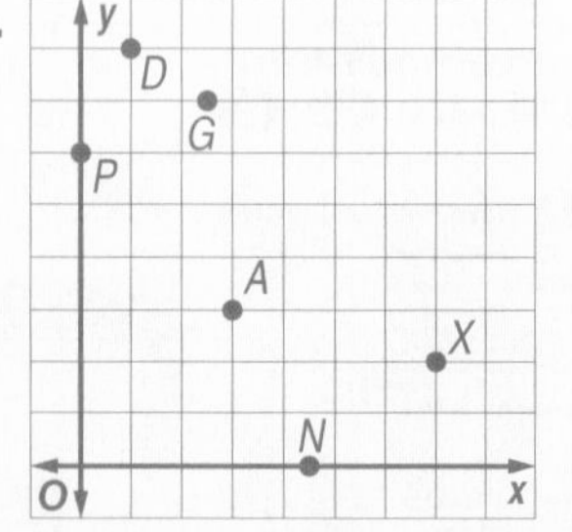

Standardized Test Practice

23. The scatter plot below shows the relationship between the age of a car and the average number of visits to a repair shop. **C**

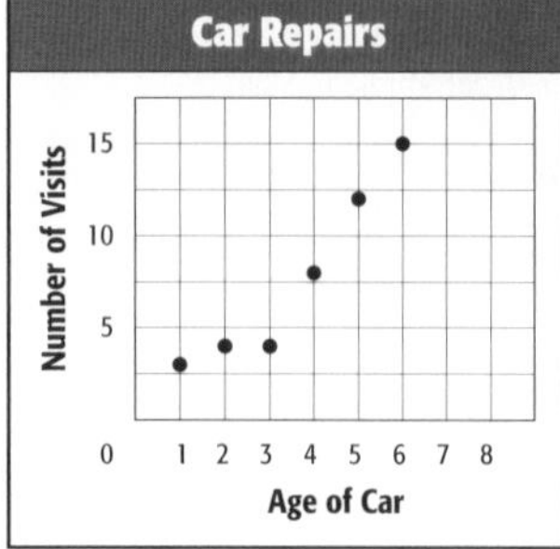

Which statement below is best supported by this scatter plot?

A As the age of the car increases, the number of visits doubles.

B As the age of the car increases, the number of visits decreases.

C As the age of the car increases, the number of visits increases.

D As the age of the car increases, the number of visits stays the same.

24. Refer to the graph in Exercise 23. Which kind of relationship exists between the age of the car and the number of visits to the repair shop? **F**

F positive H neutral

G negative J none

25. The table shows the number of people that attended a new movie over the course of a week.

Day	Attendance
1	13,400
3	13,000
5	12,600
7	12,200

Which answer choice below is the *best* prediction for attendance on the 8th day? **B**

A 11,800 C 12,100

B 12,000 D 11,700

26. SHORT RESPONSE Based on the table in Exercise 25, which kind of relationship exists between the length of time the movie is at the theatre and the number people that attend the movie? **negative**

Spiral Review

27. MULTIPLE REPRESENTATIONS Cornet Cable charges $32.50 a month for basic cable television. Each premium channel selected costs an additional $4.95 per month. (Lesson 1-5) **a–c. See margin.**

a. ALGEBRAIC Write an expression to find the cost of a month of cable service.

b. TABULAR Make a table to show the monthly cost for 0, 1, 2, 3, and 4 premium channels.

c. GRAPHICAL Graph the ordered pairs from the table.

Graph each ordered pair on a coordinate system. (Lesson 1-4) **28–33. See margin.**

28. $A(3, 3)$ **29.** $D(1, 8)$ **30.** $G(2.5, 7)$

31. $X(7, 2)$ **32.** $P(0, 6)$ **33.** $N(4\frac{1}{2}, 0)$

Skills Review

Replace each ● with <, >, or = to make a true sentence.

34. 6 ● 8 < **35.** 12 ● 9 > **36.** 14 ● 15 <

37. 3 ● 3 = **38.** 17 ● 15 > **39.** 29 ● 19 >

Differentiated Instruction

BL

Extension Have students work in groups to brainstorm two sets of data that could have a positive correlation, negative correlation, or no correlation. One of the sets of data should be the same for each type of correlation. For example, correlate the number of times you wash your hands with sets of data that would result in each type of correlation. Sample answer: Positive correlation: the number of times you wash your hands and the number of paper towels you use; negative: the number of times you wash your hands and the amount of soap left; no correlation: the number of times you wash your hands and the cost of paper towels.

46 Chapter 1 The Tools of Algebra

Graphing Technology Lab
Scatter Plots

Math Online glencoe.com
• Other Calculator Keystrokes

You have learned that graphing ordered pairs as a scatter plot on a coordinate plane is one way to make it easier to "see" if there is a relationship. You can use a graphing calculator to create scatter plots.

ACTIVITY 1

GEOGRAPHY The U.S. Census Bureau estimated the population and area of certain countries. Mr. Henderson's geography class wanted to see if there was a correlation between a country's size and population. Use the table of data below to make a scatter plot.

Country	Hemisphere	Area (million square miles)	Population (millions)
Australia	Eastern	2.97	20.3
Brazil	Western	3.29	188.1
Canada	Western	3.86	33.1
Chile	Western	0.29	16.1
Egypt	Eastern	0.39	78.9
India	Eastern	1.27	1095.4
Japan	Eastern	0.15	127.5
Mexico	Western	0.76	107.5
Russia	Eastern	6.60	142.9
United States	Western	3.72	298.4

Step 1 Enter the data.

- Clear any existing list.

KEYSTROKES: STAT ENTER ▲ CLEAR ENTER

- Enter the area as L1 and population as L2.

KEYSTROKES: STAT ENTER 2.97 ENTER 3.29 ENTER … 3.72 ENTER ▶ 20.3 ENTER 188.1 ENTER … 298.4 ENTER

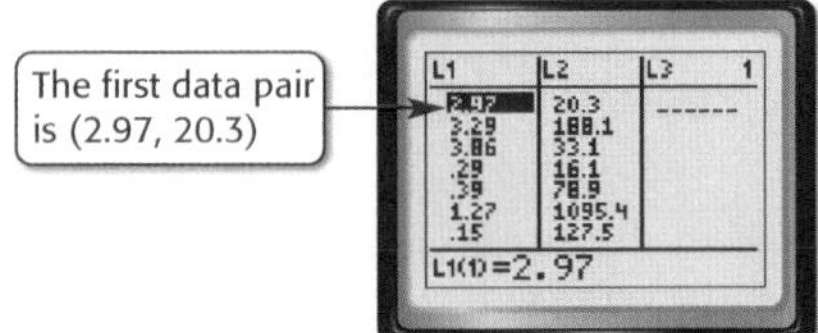

Step 2 Format the graph.

- Turn on the statistical plot.

KEYSTROKES: 2nd STAT PLOT ENTER ENTER

- Select the scatter plot, L1 as the Xlist and L2 as the Ylist.

KEYSTROKES: ▼ ENTER ▼ 2nd L1 ENTER

EXTEND 1-6 Lesson Notes

1 FOCUS

Objective Use a graphing calculator to graph scatter plots.

Materials for Each Student

- graphing calculator

Teaching Tip

Show students how to clear out all the equations in the Y= list before graphing the scatter plot.

2 TEACH

Working in Cooperative Groups

Arrange students in pairs, mixing abilities. Have pairs work through the Activity.

Students should double check that all data have been entered correctly and that each list contains the same number of entries. Only the ordered pairs from the data set should be in L1 and L2.

Ask:

- Looking at the data, is there a relationship between the size of a country and its population? hard to tell
- Using the trace key, which point has the greatest *x*-value? (6.60, 142.9)
- What does the *x*-value represent? area of the country
- Which point has the greatest *y*-value? (1.27, 1,095.4)
- What does the *y*-value represent? population

Practice Have students complete Exercises 1–7.

3 ASSESS

Formative Assessment

Use Exercise 6a to determine whether students understand how to create a scatter plot using the graphing calculator. Use 6b to assess if students can describe the relationship between two sets of data in a scatter plot.

From Concrete to Abstract

Working with partners, ask students to measure the length of their forearm and the length of their left foot. Draw a table on the board where students can post their data in inches. Have students create a scatter plot from the classroom data making the x-value represent forearm length, and the y-value represent foot length. Ask students to analyze the data by describing the scatter plot and any relationship that is evident.

Extending the Concept

Have students complete Exercise 8.

Additional Answers

5. 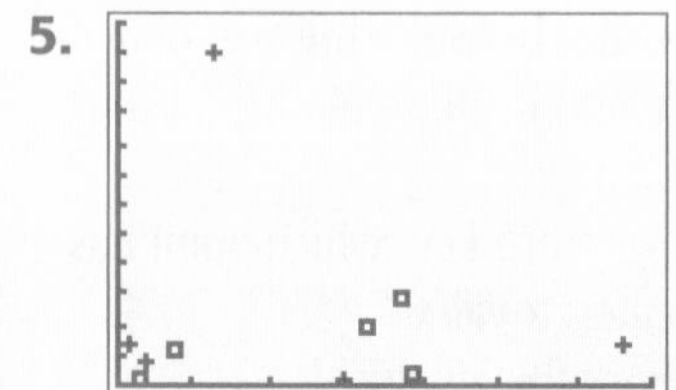

no; Sample answer: The data for the western hemisphere show a positive relationship while the data for the eastern hemisphere show no relationship.

6a. 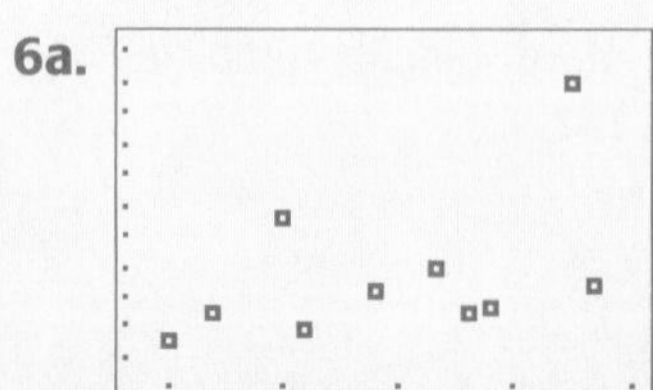

6b. Sample answer: The points seem to be slanting up from left to right. One point seems much higher than the others.

Step 3 Graph the data.

- Display the scatter plot.

KEYSTROKES: ZOOM 9

- Use the TRACE feature and the left and right arrow keys to move from one point to another.

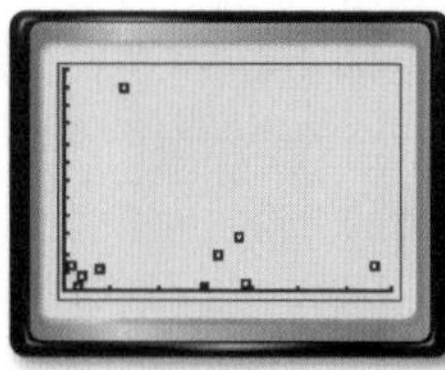

Analyze the Results

1. Press TRACE. Use the left and right arrow keys to move from one point to another. What do the coordinates of each data point represent? **The x-coordinate represents the area of the country and the y-coordinate represents the population of the country.**
2. Describe the scatter plot. **Sample answer: The points seem to be all over the place. One point is much higher than the others.**
3. Is there a relationship between the area of a country and its population? If so, write a sentence or two that describes the relationship. **There is no relationship.**
4. Based on the scatter plot, does the area of a country affect its population? **No.**
5. Separate the data by hemisphere. Enter the area and population for the western hemisphere as lists L1 and L2 and for the eastern hemisphere as lists L3 and L4. Use the graphing calculator to make a scatter plot with different marks for the western and eastern hemispheres. Do the different scatter plots agree with your answer in Exercise 3? Explain. **See margin.**
6. **SCIENCE** A zoologist studied the extinction times (in years) of island birds. The zoologist wanted to see if there was a relationship between the average number of nests and the time needed for each bird to become extinct on the islands. The results are shown in the table. **a–c. See margin.**

Bird Name	Bird Size	Average Number of Nests	Extinction Time
Buzzard	large	2.0	5.5
Quail	large	1.0	1.5
Curlew	large	2.8	3.1
Cuckoo	large	1.4	2.5
Magpie	large	4.5	10.0
Swallow	small	3.8	2.6
Robin	small	3.3	4.0
Stonechat	small	3.6	2.4
Blackbird	small	4.7	3.3
Tree-Sparrow	small	2.2	1.9

   a. Use your graphing calculator to make a scatter plot of the data.
   b. Is there a relationship between the average number of nests and extinction times? If so, write a sentence or two that describes the relationship.
   c. Are there any differences between the extinction times of large birds versus small birds?
7. Make a scatter plot of the data and describe the relationship, if any, between the x- and y-values. **See margin.**

x	3.2	3.8	4.3	4.7	5.5	5.9	7.2	7.8	8.2
y	15.7	13.2	13.9	11.1	12.8	11.4	10.7	11.3	10.4

8. **RESEARCH** Find two sets of data on your own. Then determine whether a relationship exists between the data. **See margin.**

6c. Sample answer: Large birds tend to have longer extinction times.

7. 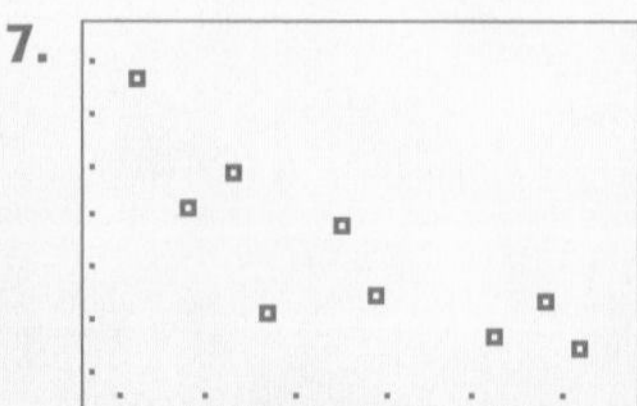

As x increases, y decreases. There is a negative relationship.

8. Sample answer: year vs. 100-meter dash times has a negative relationship; year vs. school enrollment has a positive relationship.

Math Online glencoe.com
• STUDY TO GO
• Vocabulary Review

CHAPTER 1 Study Guide and Review

Chapter Summary

Key Concepts

Order of Operations (Lesson 1-1)

Step 1 Evaluate the expressions inside grouping symbols.

Step 2 Multiply and/or divide in order from left to right.

Step 3 Add and/or subtract in order from left to right.

Expressions (Lessons 1-1 and 1-2)

- A numerical expression contains a combination of numbers and operations.
- An algebraic expression is a numerical expression that contains at least one variable.

Properties (Lesson 1-3)

- Commutative Property
  $4 + 5 = 5 + 4$
  $2 \cdot 7 = 7 \cdot 2$
- Identity Property
  $3 + 0 = 3$
  $3 \cdot 1 = 3$
- Associative Property
  $10 + (8 + 3) = (10 + 8) + 3$
  $6 \cdot (5 \cdot 9) = (6 \cdot 5) \cdot 9$

Coordinate Plane (Lesson 1-4)

- *x*- and *y*- coordinates are used to indicate a point's position in a coordinate system.
- The domain of a relation is the set of *x*-coordinates and the range of a relation is the set of *y*-coordinates.

Functions (Lesson 1-5)

- A function is a relation that assigns exactly one *domain* value for each *range* value.

FOLDABLES® Study Organizer

Be sure the Key Concepts are noted in your Foldable.

Key Vocabulary

algebra (p. 11)
algebraic expression (p. 11)
coordinate plane (p. 25)
coordinate system (p. 25)
counterexample (p. 19)
deductive reasoning (p. 20)
defining a variable (p. 11)
domain (p. 27)
equation (p. 34)
evaluate (p. 6)
function (p. 33)
function rule (p. 33)
function table (p. 33)
graph (p. 26)
numerical expression (p. 5)
order of operations (p. 6)
ordered pair (p. 25)
origin (p. 25)
properties (p. 18)
range (p. 27)
relation (p. 27)
scatter plot (p. 40)
simplify (p. 20)
variable (p. 11)
***x*-axis** (p. 25)
***x*-coordinate** (p. 25)
***y*-axis** (p. 25)
***y*-coordinate** (p. 25)

Vocabulary Check

State whether each sentence is *true* or *false*. If *false*, replace the underlined term to make a true sentence.

1. An example of a(n) algebraic expression is $a + 2c + 6$. true
2. The set of all y-coordinates is called the domain. false; range
3. A variable is a letter used to represent a value. true
4. The x-axis is formed by the intersection of two number lines at right angles at their zero points. false; coordinate plane
5. An ordered pair names a point on a coordinate system. true
6. To find the value of a numerical expression, you evaluate it. true
7. A numerical expression contains a combination of numbers and operations. true
8. The set of all x-values is called the domain. true
9. A coordinate plane is a graph that shows the relationship between a set of data with two variables. false; scatter plot

Formative Assessment

Key Vocabulary The page reference after each word denotes where that term was first introduced. If students have difficulty answering questions 1–9, remind them that they can use these page references to refresh their memories about the vocabulary terms.

Summative Assessment

CRM Vocabulary Test, p. 49

Math Online glencoe.com

Vocabulary PuzzleMaker improves students' mathematics vocabulary using four puzzle formats–crossword, scramble, word search using a word list, and word search using clues. Students can work online or from a printed worksheet.

FOLDABLES® Study Organizer

Dinah Zike's Foldables®

Have students look through the chapter to make sure they have included examples in their Foldables.

Suggest that students keep their Foldables handy while completing the Study Guide and Review pages. Point out that their Foldables can serve as a quick review tool when studying for the Chapter Test.

Lesson-by-Lesson Review

Intervention If the given examples are not sufficient to review the topics covered by the questions, remind students that the page references tell them where to review that topic in their textbook.

Two-Day Option Have students complete the Lesson-by-Lesson Review on pp. 50–52. Then you can use ExamView® Assessment Suite to customize another review worksheet that practices all the objectives of this chapter or only the objectives on which your students need more help.

Differentiated Instruction

Super DVD: Mindjogger Videoquizzes Use this DVD as an alternative format of review for the test.

CHAPTER 1 Study Guide and Review

Lesson-by-Lesson Review

1-1 Words and Expressions (pp. 5–9)

10. Write a numerical expression for the verbal phrase *the total number of students if there are nineteen in one class and thirteen in another.* **19 + 13**

Evaluate each expression.

11. $6(7) + 3$ **45**

12. $4[(12 - 4) + 2]$ **40**

13. PROFITS Yu, Collin, and Sydney spent $284 to make bracelets. They sold the bracelets for $674. If they split the profits evenly, how much did each person earn? **$130**

EXAMPLE 1

Write the phrase *the total number of post cards if eight people each buy five* as a numerical expression.

Phrase the product of 8 and 5

Expression 8×5

1-2 Variables and Expressions (pp. 11–16)

14. Translate into an algebraic expression *the quotient of the number of points and three.* $n \div 3$

ALGEBRA Evaluate each expression if $a = 4$, $b = 8$, and $c = 11$.

15. $3a + b$ **20**

16. $16 - c$ **5**

17. $3a + 4b - c$ **33**

18. $\frac{3b}{a} + ac$ **50**

19. MEASUREMENT There are 36 inches in a yard. Write an expression to find the number of yards in x inches. $\frac{x}{36}$

EXAMPLE 2

Evaluate $x - 5 + 2y$ if $x = 6$ and $y = 4$.

$x - 5 + 2y = 6 - 5 + 2(4)$ **Replace *x* with 6 and *y* with 4.**

$= 6 - 5 + 8$ **Multiply 2 and 4.**

$= 1 + 8$ **Subtract 5 from 6.**

$= 9$ **Add 1 and 8.**

1-3 Properties (pp. 18–23)

Name the property shown by each statement.

20. $12 \times 0 = 0$ **Multiplicative Property of Zero**

21. $(3 \cdot 5) \cdot 2 = 3 \cdot (5 \cdot 2)$ **Associative (×)**

ALGEBRA Simplify each expression.

22. $3 \cdot (2 \cdot x)$ **6x**

23. $(5 + v) + 7$ **12 + v**

24. TOYS Gloria has 58 dolls. If she does not add any dolls to her collection, write a number sentence that represents the situation. Then name the property that is illustrated. **58 + 0 = 58; Additive Identity**

EXAMPLE 3

Simplify $(4 + x) + 6$.

$(4 + x) + 6 = (x + 4) + 6$ **Commutative (+)**

$= x + (4 + 6)$ **Associative (+)**

$= x + 10$ **Simplify.**

MIXED PROBLEM SOLVING
For mixed problem-solving practice, see page 843.

1-4 Ordered Pairs and Relations (pp. 25–30)

Express each relation as a table. Then determine the domain and range.

25. {(2, 3), (2, 6), (2, 5)} **25–27. See margin.**

26. {(1, 4), (2, 8), (3, 12), (4, 16)}

27. FAIRS It costs $2 per person to ride the Ferris wheel.

a. Make a table of ordered pairs in which the x-coordinate represents the number of people and the y-coordinate represents the cost for 4, 8, 12, and 16 people.

b. Graph the ordered pairs and then describe the graph.

EXAMPLE 4

Express the relation {(2, 1), (5, 6), (2, 7), (6, 1)} as a table. Then determine the domain and range.

x	2	5	2	6
y	1	6	7	1

The domain is {2, 5, 6} and the range is {1, 6, 7}.

1-5 Word, Equations, Tables, and Graphs (pp. 33–37)

28. MULTIPLE REPRESENTATIONS Shanna downloaded 5 more songs than videos.

a. ALGEBRAIC Write an equation that can be used to find the number of songs downloaded given the number of videos downloaded. $s = v + 5$

b. TABULAR Complete the function table for the number of songs downloaded when the number of videos downloaded is 2, 4, 6, and 8.

Number of Videos Input (v)	Number of Songs Output (s)
2	■ 7
4	■ 9
6	■ 11
8	■ 13

c. GRAPHICAL Graph the ordered pairs for the function. **See margin.**

EXAMPLE 5

MULTIPLE REPRESENTATIONS There are 3 apples for each horse.

a. ALGEBRAIC Write an equation that can be used to find the number of apples needed for any number of horses.
$w = 3h$

b. TABULAR Make a function table for 3, 5, 7, and 11 horses.

Number of Horses Input (x)	Number of Apples Output (y)
3	9
5	15
7	21
11	33

c. GRAPHICAL Graph the ordered pairs for the function.

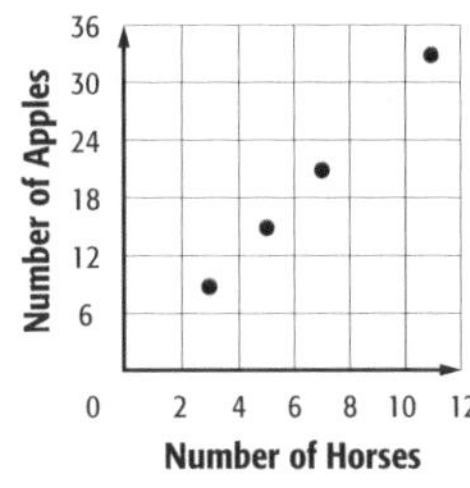

Additional Answers

25.

x	y
2	3
2	6
2	5

D = {2}; R = {3, 5, 6}

26.

x	y
1	4
2	8
3	12
4	16

D = {1, 2, 3, 4}; R = {4, 8, 12, 16}

27a.

x	y
4	8
8	16
12	24
16	32

27b.

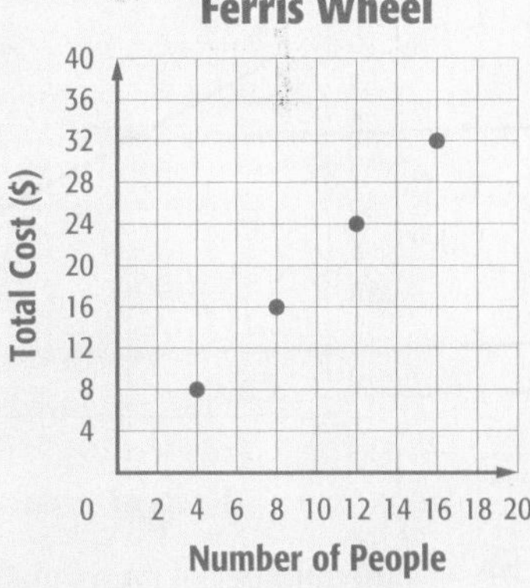

The points appear to fall in a line.

28c.

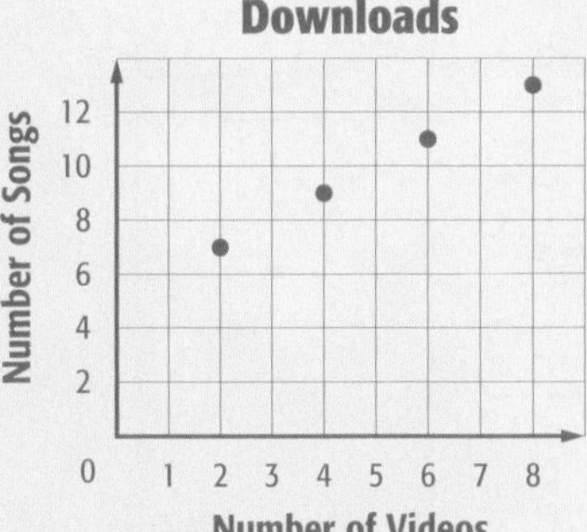

Problem Solving Review

For additional practice in problem solving for Chapter 1, see the Mixed Problem Solving Appendix, p. 843, in the Student Handbook section.

Anticipation Guide

Have students complete the Chapter 1 Anticipation Guide and discuss how their responses have changed now that they have completed Chapter 1.

Additional Answers

29.

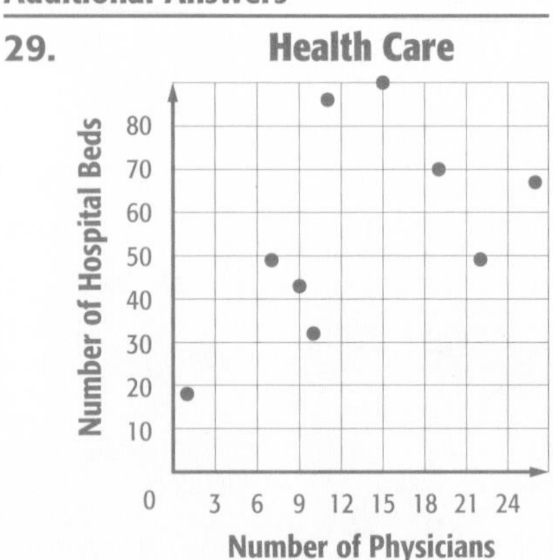

30a.

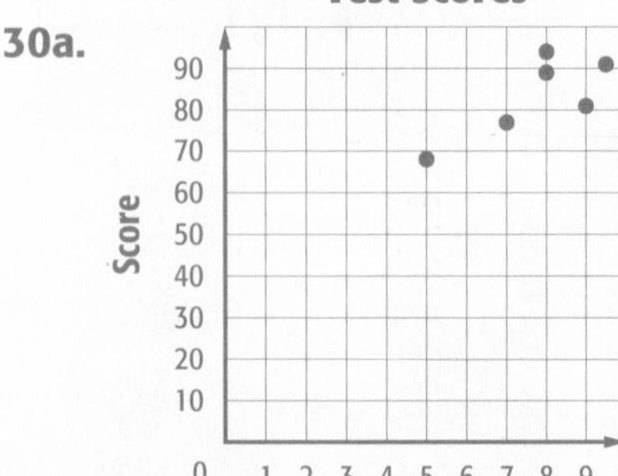

30b. As the number of hours of sleep increases, so does the score. So, there is a positive relationship.

CHAPTER 1 Study Guide and Review

1-6 Scatter Plots (pp. 40–46)

29. **HEALTH CARE** The table shows the number of physicians and hospital beds for nine rural counties. Make a scatter plot of the data.

Physicians	11	26	10	19	22	9	15	7	1
Hospital Beds	85	67	32	69	49	43	90	49	18

See margin.

30. **SLEEP** The table shows the amount of sleep students received the night before a standardized test and their score on the test.

Number of Sleep Hours	8	9.5	8	5	9	7
Score	89	91	94	68	81	77

a. Make a scatter plot of the data. See margin.

b. Draw a conclusion about the type of relationship the data shows. Explain. See margin.

c. Predict the score of a person who got 4 hours of sleep the night before the test. Sample answer: 60

EXAMPLE 6

The table shows the number of cups of lemonade two girls sold at their lemonade stand at certain temperatures.

Number of Cups	5	7	9	6	8
Temperature (F°)	75	85	90	86	88

a. Make a scatter plot of the data.

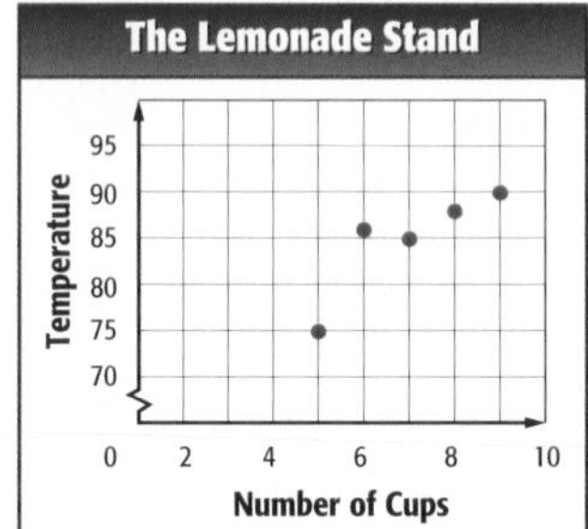

b. Draw a conclusion about the type of relationship the data shows. Explain.
The scatter plot shows a positive relationship since the number of cups sold increases as the temperature increases.

c. Predict the number of cups sold when the temperature is 95°.
By looking at the scatter plot of the data, it appears that the girls will sell about 10 cups of lemonade.

52 Chapter 1 The Tools of Algebra

Math Online glencoe.com
Chapter Test

Write a numerical expression for each verbal phrase.

1. two people share a lunch bill of \$10 $10 \div 2$
2. the new price if \$6 is taken off a \$15 item $15 - 6$

Evaluate each expression.

3. $8 \div 2 + 11$ 15
4. $(12 - 4) + 4$ 12
5. $15 + 7 \cdot 9$ 78
6. **ALGEBRA** Evaluate $3x - y$ if $x = 10$ and $y = 7$. 23
7. **MULTIPLE CHOICE** What is the value of $(a + b) \div c$ if $a = 17$, $b = 7$ and $c = 12$? D

A 24 C 10

B 19 D 2

8. **GOLF** The table below shows the cost to play miniature golf. Write and evaluate an expression that can be used to find the total cost for 2 adults, 4 children, and 1 senior. $2(5) + 4(3) + 1(4)$; \$26

Age	Cost (\$)
Adults (16–62)	\$5
Children (3–15)	\$3
Seniors (63+)	\$4

9. Translate the phrase *the number of books increased by thirteen* into an algebraic expression. $b + 13$
10. **SPORTS** The table shows the point values of different scoring plays in football.

Scoring Play	Points
touchdown	6
extra point	1
field goal	3

a. During the championship game, the winning team scored t touchdowns, e extra points, and f field goals. Write an algebraic expression to show the total points scored. $6t + e + 3f$

b. If the team scored 27 total points, give one possible combination for touchdowns, extra points, and field goals.

Sample answer: 3 touchdowns, 3 extra points, 2 field goals

Name the property shown by each statement.

11. $x + y = y + x$ Commutative (+)
12. $20 \cdot 1 = 20$ Identity (×)
13. $(2 \cdot 3) \cdot 5 = 2 \cdot (3 \cdot 5)$ Associative (×)
14. $12 + 0 = 12$ Identity (+)

Simplify each expression.

15. $23 + (z + 47)$ $70 + z$
16. $5a(3)$ $15a$
17. $(8 \cdot b) \cdot 4$ $32b$
18. $(17 + m) + 31$ $48 + m$

Refer to the coordinate system at the right. Write the ordered pair that names each point.

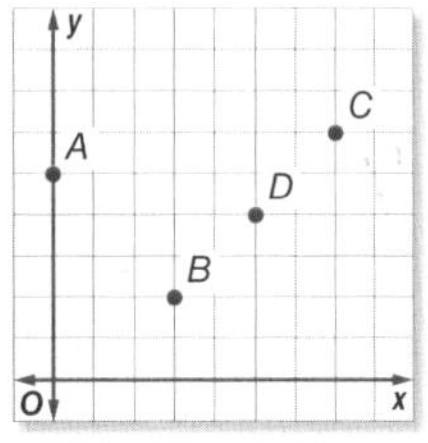

19. A (0, 5)
20. B (3, 2)
21. C (7, 6)
22. D (5, 4)

23. **MULTIPLE REPRESENTATIONS** Luz is three times as old as Malik.

a. **ALGEBRAIC** Write an equation that can be used to find Luz's age given Malik's age. $l = 3m$

b. **TABULAR** Make a function table to show Luz's age when Malik is 1, 2, 3, 4, and 5. See margin.

c. **GRAPHICAL** Graph the ordered pairs. See margin.

24. Express the relation {(1,3), (2, 7), (4, 13), and (5, 15) as a table. Then determine the domain and range. See Chapter 1 Answer Appendix.

25. **MULTIPLE CHOICE** The scatter plot shows semester grades and school days missed for the students in Mr. Hernandez's math class. Which of the following is a reasonable score for a student who missed three days? H

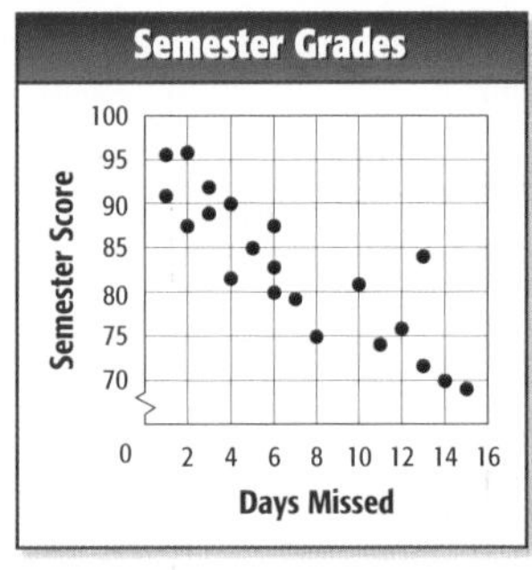

F 80 G 85 H 90 J 95

CHAPTER 1 Practice Test

ExamView Assessment Suite Customize and create multiple versions of your chapter test and their answer keys. All of the questions from the leveled chapter tests in the *Chapter 1 Resource Masters* are also available on ExamView® Assessment Suite.

Additional Answers

23b.

rule: $l = 3m$		
Input (x)		Output (y)
1	$l = 3(1)$	3
2	$l = 3(2)$	6
3	$l = 3(3)$	9
4	$l = 3(4)$	12
5	$l = 3(5)$	15

23c.

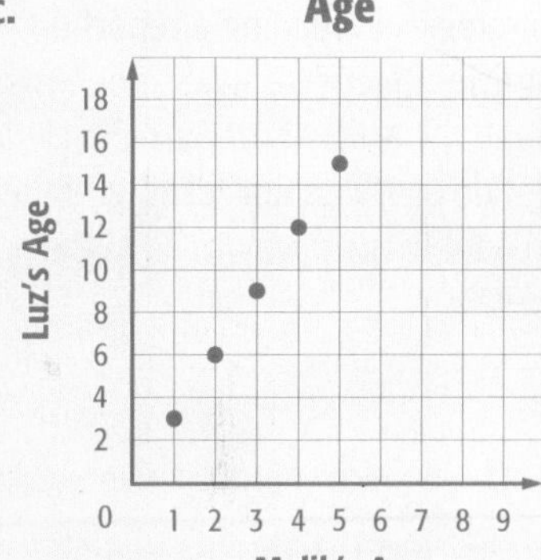

Intervention Planner

Tier 1 On Level	Tier 2 Strategic Intervention approaching grade level	Tier 3 Intensive Intervention 2 or more grades below level
If students miss about 25% of the exercises or less,	**If** students miss about 50% of the exercises,	**If** students miss about 75% of the exercises,
Then choose a resource:	**Then** choose a resource:	**Then** use *Math Triumphs, Grade 8,* Ch. 2, 3, 9
SE Lessons 1-1, 1-2, 1-3, 1-4, 1-5, and 1-6 **CRM** Skills Practice, pp. 7, 13, 20, 26, 32, and 39 **TE** Chapter Project, p. 2	**CRM** Study Guide and Intervention, Chapter 1, pp. 5, 11, 18, 24, 30, and 37 *Quick Review Math Handbook*	
Math Online Self-Check Quiz	**Math Online** Extra Examples, Personal Tutor, Homework Help	**Math Online** Extra Examples, Personal Tutor, Homework Help, Review Vocabulary

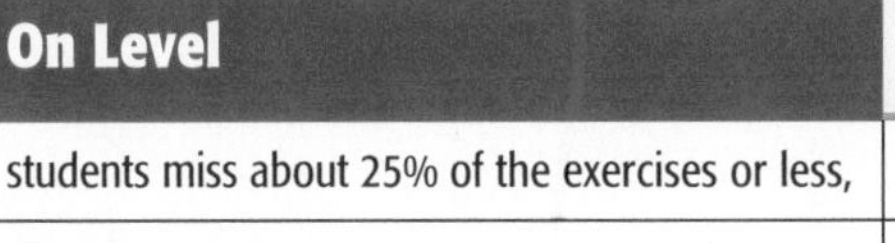

1 FOCUS

Objective Use the strategy of reading the problem to solve standardized test problems.

2 TEACH

Scaffolding Questions

Ask:

- Why would you skim or quickly read a report or article? Sample answer: To get an idea of what the report or article is about.
- Why would you read a report or article more slowly? Sample answer: To find the details.
- How would you combine these two strategies in reading a report or article? Sample answer: You might read the article or report quickly to jot down the major ideas, and then read it more slowly to fill in the details.

CHAPTER 1 Preparing for Standardized Tests

Reading to Solve Problems

The first step to solving any math problem is to read the problem. When reading a math problem to get the information you need to solve, it is helpful to use special reading strategies.

Strategies for Reading Math Problems

Step 1

Read the problem quickly to gain a general understanding of it.

- **Ask yourself:** "What do I know?" "What do I need to find out?"
- **Think:** "Is there enough information to solve the problem? Is there extra information?"
- **Highlight:** If you are allowed to write in your test booklet, underline or highlight important information. Cross out any information you don't need.

Step 2

Reread the problem to identify relevant facts.

- **Analyze:** Determine how the facts are related.
- **Key Words:** Look for keywords to solve the problem.
- **Vocabulary:** Identify mathematical terms. Think about the concepts and how they are related.
- **Plan:** Make a plan to solve the problem.
- **Estimate:** Quickly estimate the answer.

Step 3

Identify any obvious wrong answers.

- **Eliminate:** Eliminate any choices that are very different from your estimate.
- **Units of Measure:** Identify choices that are possible answers based on the units of measure in the question. For example, if the question asks for area, only answers in square units will work.

Step 4

Look back after solving the problem.

- **Check:** Make sure you have answered the question.

54 Chapter 1 The Tools of Algebra

EXAMPLE

Read the problem. Identify what you need to know. Then use the information in the problem to solve.

The 8th graders are going on a field trip. They will rent a bus that costs $40 plus $3 for each passenger. Each student must bring $6.50 for the field trip. How much will it cost to rent the bus if there will be 42 students, 4 teachers, and 5 parent volunteers going on the field trip?

A $40 C 42 people

B $193 D 51 people

Read the problem. Highlight important information. Cross out information you don't need.

~~The 8th graders are going on a field trip.~~ **They will rent a bus that costs $40 plus $3 for each passenger.** ~~Each student must bring $6.50 for the field trip.~~ **How much will it cost to rent the bus if there will be 42 students, 4 teachers, and 5 parent volunteers going on the field trip?**

Answer choices C and D are numbers of people, not dollar amounts. Since they do not have the correct units, they can be eliminated. You know the correct answer will be choice A or B.

Answer choice A gives only the base price for renting the bus, $40. It does not include the cost of the passengers, so it can be eliminated. The correct answer is B.

Exercises

Read each problem. Identify what you need to know. Then use the information in the problem to solve.

1. An electrician charges a fee of $35 plus $20 per hour to work on customers' homes. The electrician works 5 days per week. How much would it cost to hire the electrician for 4 hours? B

   A $80 B $115 C $145 D $160

2. Which algebraic expression represents sixteen stickers shared equally by some students? G

   F $s \div 16$ G $16 \div s$ H $16s$ J $s + 16$

3. A toy manufacturer can produce 500 toys in one hour. Each toy weighs 24 ounces. If the manufacturer operates for 8 hours per day, how many toys can be produced in one day? C

   A 96,000 ounces C 4000 toys

   B 12,000 ounces D 192 toys

4. Danika bought an MP3 player for $197.78. She paid $50 then made 6 equal monthly payments. What was her monthly payment amount? H

   F $39.55 H $24.63

   G $83.33 J $32.96

Additional Example

Some friends and their children are going horseback riding. At a horse ranch, the group rate for two hours of riding is $50 plus $70 for each rider. Individual riding lessons cost $85 per hour. How much will it cost if 3 adults, 2 boys, and 3 girls go for a group ride? C

A 5 people

B 8 people

C $610

D $680

3 ASSESS

Use Exercises 1–4 to assess students' understanding.

Diagnose Student Errors

Survey students' responses for each item. Class trends may indicate common errors and misconceptions.

1. A correct
B added instead of multiplied the number of tickets times the cost
C misunderstood the relationship between tickets and cost
D misunderstood the relationship between tickets and cost

2. F guess
G calculated children's tickets twice instead of senior tickets
H correct
J calculated adult tickets twice instead of children's tickets

3. A misunderstood relationship between *n* gallons and cups
B correct
C misunderstood relationship between *n* gallons and cups
D misunderstood relationship between *n* gallons and cups

4. F misunderstood that the word *twice* refers to the number of cards only
G transposed the numbers 2 and 5 in the expression
H misunderstood *more* to mean subtraction instead of addition
J correct

5. A misunderstood the words *total combined score* to mean multiplication instead of addition
B correct
C did not include one of the scores
D did not include one of the scores

6. F confused Quadrant III and Quadrant IV and switched *x*- and *y*-coordinates
G confused Quadrant II and Quadrant IV
H switched *x*- and *y*-coordinates
J correct

Multiple Choice

Read each question. Then fill in the correct answer on the answer document provided by your teacher or on a sheet of paper.

1. The table shows the prices of admission to an amusement park.

Amusement Park Admission	
Ticket	Cost ($)
Children (up to 12)	8
Adults (13–64)	20
Seniors (65+)	15

Which expression can be used to find the total cost of admission for 4 children, 2 adults, and 3 seniors? A

A $4(8) + 2(20) + 3(15)$

B $(4 + 8) + (2 + 20) + (3 + 15)$

C $(4 + 2 + 3) \times (8 + 20 + 15)$

D $9 \times (8 + 20 + 15)$

2. In Exercise 1, what is the total cost of admission for 4 children, 2 adults, and 3 seniors? H

F $88 H $117

G $104 J $125

3. One gallon is equivalent to 16 cups. Write an expression to find the number of cups in n gallons. B

A $n + 16$

B $16n$

C $n - 16$

D $\frac{n}{16}$

Test-Taking Tip

Question 3 You can check your answer by replacing *n* with 1 gallon. The result should be equal to 16 cups.

4. Jeremy has five more than twice the number of baseball cards that José has. If José has c cards, which expression represents the number of baseball cards that Jeremy has? J

F $2(c + 5)$

G $5c + 2$

H $2c - 5$

J $2c + 5$

5. Use the table to write an expression that shows Marie's total combined score from the three judges. B

Marie's Dance Routine	
Judge	Score
Smitherman	8
Rodriguez	*s*
Hampton	7

A $15s$

B $s + 15$

C $s + 8$

D $s + 7$

6. What are the coordinates of point K on the coordinate grid below? J

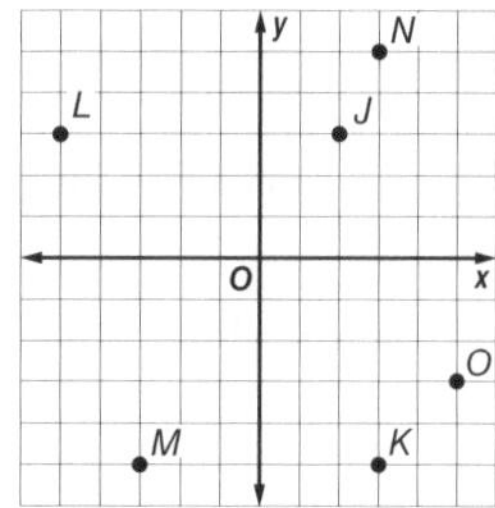

F $(-5, -3)$ H $(-5, 3)$

G $(-3, 5)$ J $(3, -5)$

Short Response/Gridded Response

Record your answers on the answer sheet provided by your teacher or on a sheet of paper.

7. What mathematical property is illustrated below?

$$5 + 3 = 3 + 5$$

Commutative Property of Addition

8. GRIDDED RESPONSE Rachel had $80 in a savings account before making several withdrawals and deposits as shown in the table. How much money in dollars did Rachel have in the account after the activity shown? **$70**

Rachel's Savings Account	
Activity	**Amount ($)**
Starting Balance	80
Deposit	10
Deposit	5
Withdrawal	20
Deposit	10
Withdrawal	15

9. State the domain and range of the relation graphed below.

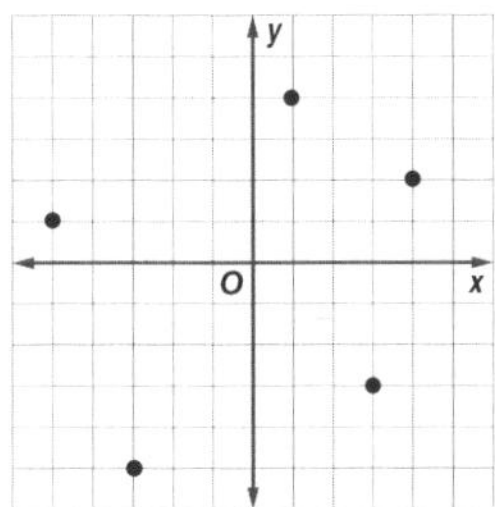

D: {−5, −3, 1, 3, 4};
R: {−5, −3, 1, 2, 4}

10. GRIDDED RESPONSE Evaluate the expression $\frac{2a + 4}{17 - 3b}$ for $a = 4$ and $b = 5$. **6**

Extended Response

Record your answers on a sheet of paper. Show your work.

11. The scatter plot below shows the relationship between the value of several cars and the ages of the cars, in years.

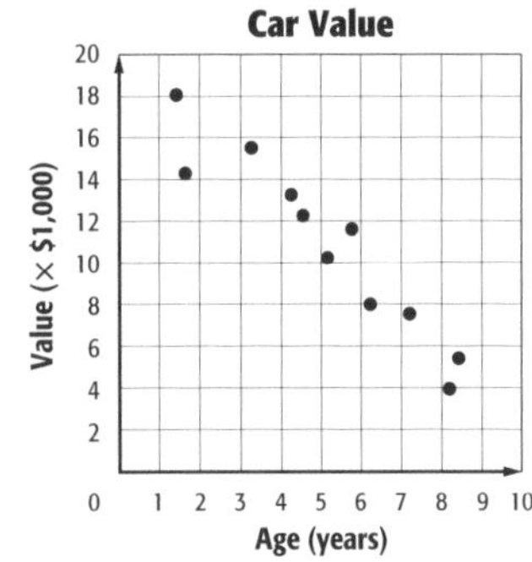

a. Does the scatter plot show a *positive, negative,* or *no* relationship? Explain.

b. Draw a conclusion about the relationship between the value of a car and the car's age.

c. About how much would you expect a car that is 5 years old to be worth? Explain.

11a. Negative; the values decrease from left to right.
11b. As the age of a car increases, its value decreases.
11c. Sample answer: about $10,000; if you draw a line through the points, it would be close to (5, 10).

Need Extra Help?											
If you missed Question...	1	2	3	4	5	6	7	8	9	10	11
Go to Lesson or Page...	1-1	1-1	1-2	1-2	1-3	1-4	1-3	1-5	1-4	1-2	1-6

CHAPTER 1 Standardized Test Practice

Formative Assessment

You can use these two pages to benchmark student progress.

CRM Standardized Test Practice, pp. 63–65

Answer Sheet Practice

Have students simulate taking a standardized test by recording their answers on practice recording sheets.

CRM Student Recording Sheet, p. 43

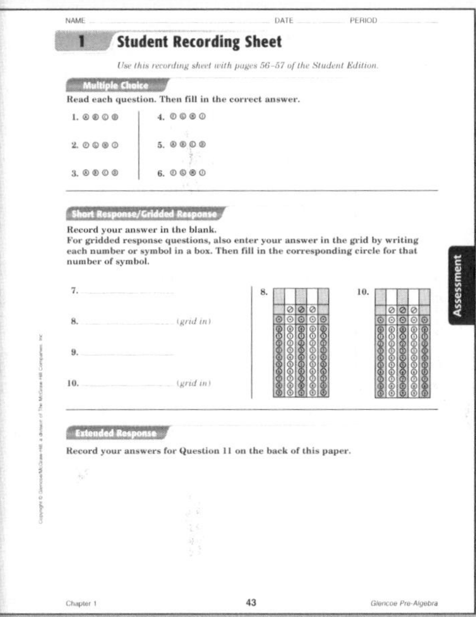

Create practice worksheets or tests that align to your state's standards as well as TIMSS and NAEP tests.

Homework Option

Get Ready for Chapter 2 Assign students the exercises on p. 59 as homework to assess whether they possess the prerequisite skills needed for the next chapter.

Page 7, Lesson 1-1 (Check Your Progress)

3. $15 + 0.25(40)$; \$25.00

Number of Calls	Expression	Cost (\$)
40	15 + 0.25(40)	25.00
50	15 + 0.25(50)	27.50
60	15 + 0.25(60)	30.00
70	15 + 0.25(70)	32.50

Pages 7–8, Lesson 1-1

11.

Number of Passengers	Expression	Cost (\$)
25	75 + 6(25)	225
30	75 + 6(30)	255
35	75 + 6(35)	285
40	75 + 6(40)	315

30.

Red Tiles	Expression	Total Number of Tiles
15	15 + 12(15)	195
20	20 + 12(20)	260
25	25 + 12(25)	325
30	30 + 12(30)	390

31.

Number of Lines	Expression	Cost (\$)
6	8 + 6(0.75)	12.50
10	8 + 10(0.75)	15.50
14	8 + 14(0.75)	18.50
18	8 + 18(0.75)	21.50

Page 11, Lesson 1-2 (Why?)

b. To find the cost of 20 songs, multiply 20 by \$0.88.

Page 17, Extend 1-2

8. Let x represent the number. When you double the number, the result is $2x$. When you add 4, the result is $2x + 4$. After dividing by 2, the result is $x + 2$. Finally after subtracting the original number, x, you are left with 2.

9. Sample answer: Think of a number. Double it, add 6. Divide by 2. Then subtract the original number. The result is always 3; When you double the number, the result is $2x$. When you add 6, the result is $2x + 6$. After dividing by 2, the result is $x + 3$. Finally after subtracting the original number, x, you are left with 3.

Page 18, Lesson 1-3 (Why?)

a. Sample answers: putting on your left shoe or right shoe first, putting on a shirt or pants first

b. Sample answers: typing a letter and turning on the computer, opening the car door and inserting the key into the ignition

Page 22, Lesson 1-3

44. $5 + b + 10$

$5 + b + 10 = 5 + 10 + b$ Commutative Property of Addition
$= (5 + 10) + b$ Associative Property of Addition
$= 15 + b$ Add 5 and 10 mentally.

45. false; $15 + (4 \cdot 6) = 39$ and $(15 + 4) \cdot 6 = 114$; Since $39 \neq 114$, the statement is false.

46. Neither of them is correct. Sample answer: Meghan did not simplify $16 \cdot 12$ or take $x \cdot x$ and get x^2. Alejandro did not square the x.

Page 27, Lesson 1-4 (Check Your Progress)

3.

x	y
2	4
0	3
1	4
1	1

D = {2, 0, 1}
R = {4, 3, 1}

4A.

x	y	(x, y)
1	640	(1, 640)
2	1280	(2, 1280)
3	1920	(3, 1920)

4B.

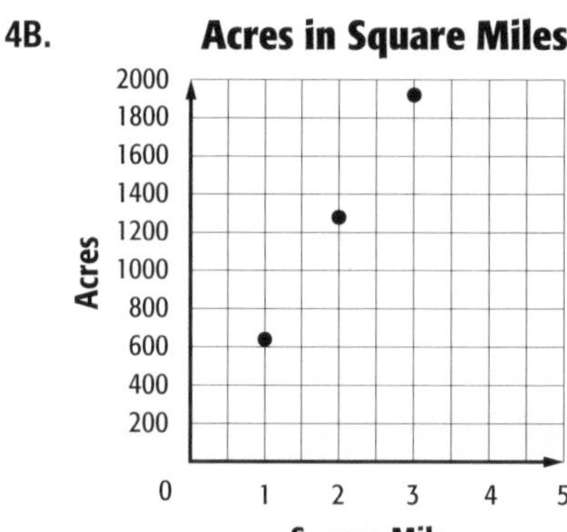

The points appear to lie in a line.

Pages 28–29, Lesson 1-4

11b.

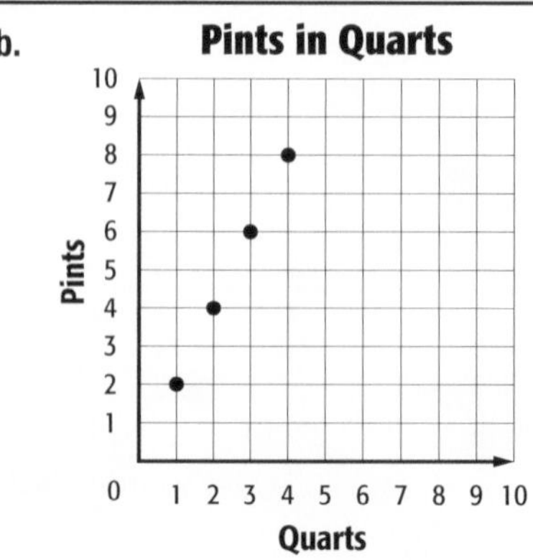

12–19.
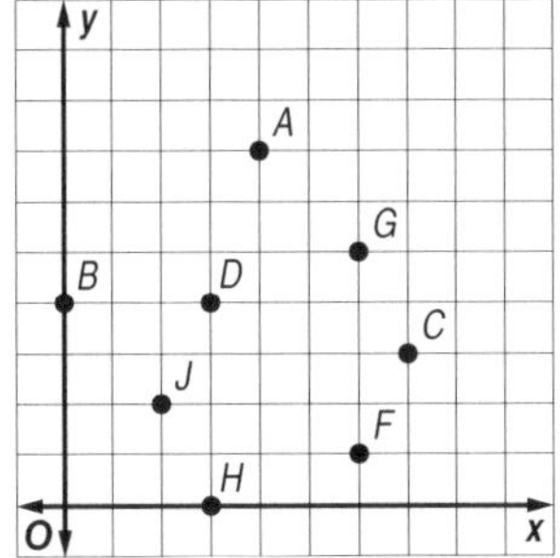

28.

x	y
4	5
2	1
5	0
3	2

D = {2, 3, 4, 5}, R = {0, 1, 2, 5}

29.

x	y
0	2
2	2
4	1
3	5

D = {0, 2, 3, 4}, R = {1, 2, 5}

30.

x	y
6	0
4	5
2	1
3	1

D = {2, 3, 4, 6}, R = {0, 1, 5}

31.

x	y
5	1
3	7
4	8
5	7

D = {3, 4, 5}, R = {1, 7, 8}

32a.

x	y	(x, y)
1	7	(1, 7)
3	21	(3, 21)
5	35	(5, 35)
7	49	(7, 49)

32b.
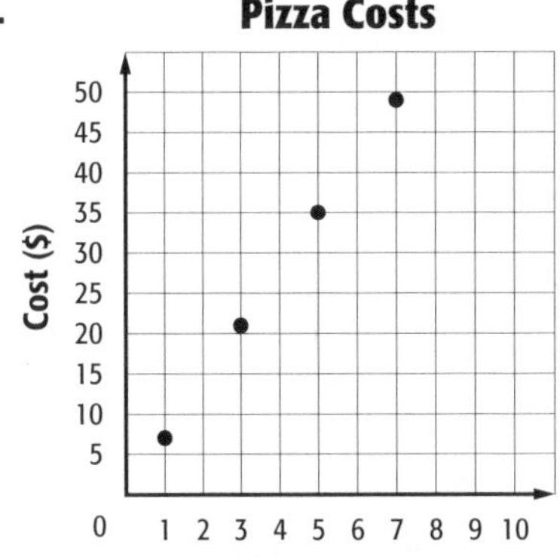

33a.

x	y	(x, y)
1	3	(1, 3)
2	6	(2, 6)
4	12	(4, 12)
6	18	(6, 18)

33b.
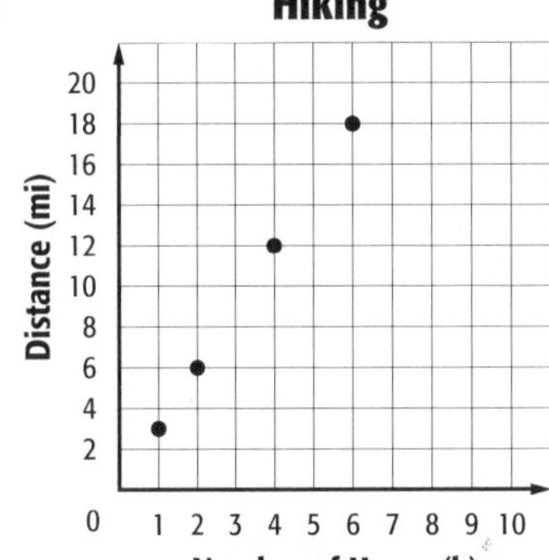

34a. Sample answer:

Piano Time (min)	5	10	15	20	25	30
Study Time (min)	25	20	15	10	5	0

34b.
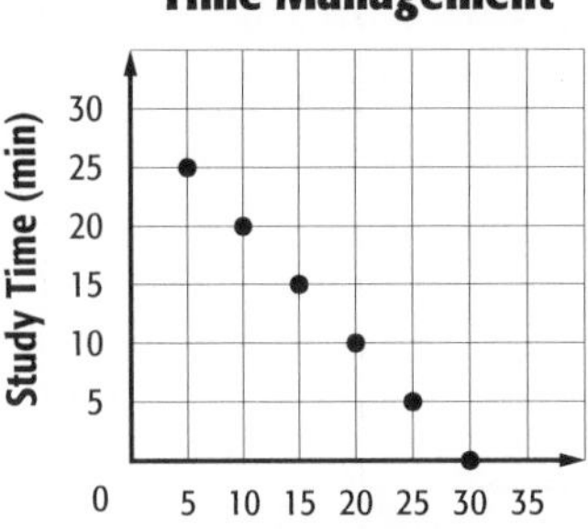

34c. The points appear to lie in a straight line that slants down from left to right.

Chapter 1 Answer Appendix

34d. **Time Management**

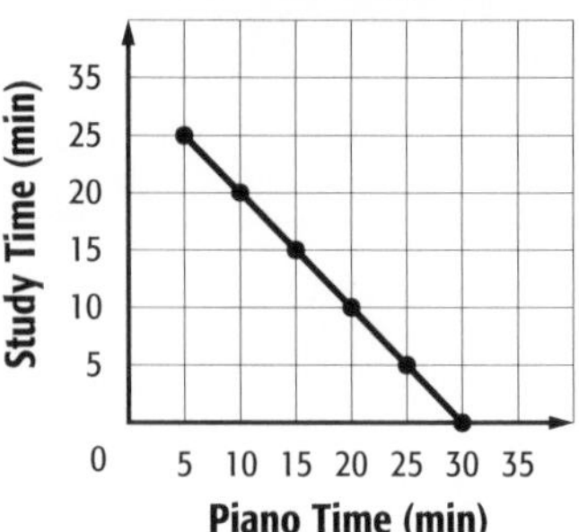

12 minutes spent playing the piano, 18 minutes spent studying for the test

35a. **Mr. Maloney's Students**

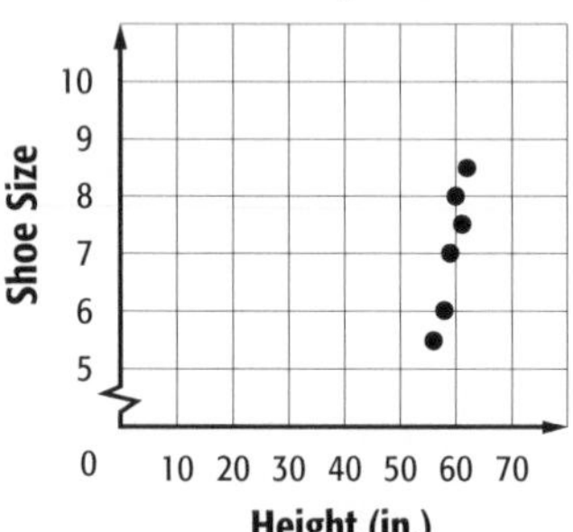

36. {(1, 4), (3, 8), (5, 2), (3, 7)}

x	y
1	4
3	8
5	2
3	7

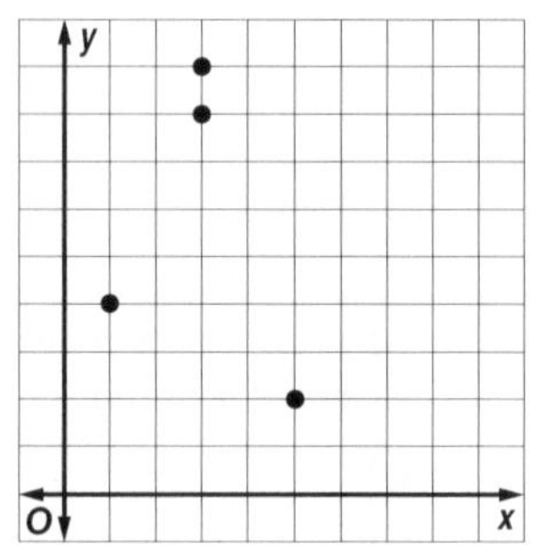

D = {1, 3, 5}, R = {2, 4, 7, 8}

37b. **Arithmetic Sequence**

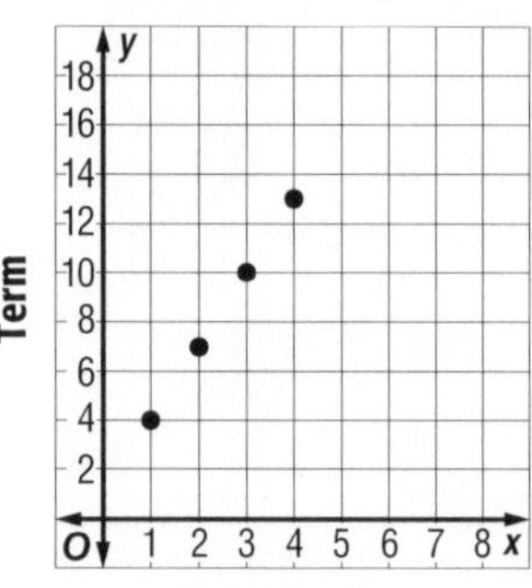

Page 33, Lesson 1-5 (Why?)

a. **Scuba Diving**

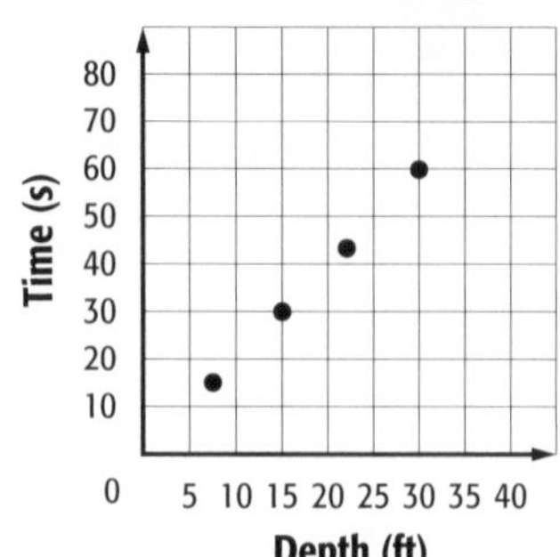

b. Sample answer: As the depth increases, the time to ascend increases.

c. 90 s; for every 15-feet increase in depth, the time increases by 30 seconds, 30 + 15 or 45 ft; 60 + 30 or 90 s

Pages 33–34, Lesson 1-5 (Check Your Progress)

1. Sample answer:

Input (x)	$3x - 1$	Output (y)
2	3(2) – 1	5
4	3(4) – 1	11
6	3(6) – 1	17
8	3(8) – 1	23

D: {2, 4, 6 , 8}; R: {5, 11, 17, 23}

2B.

Input (x)	$1088x$	Output (y)
0	1088(0)	0
1	1088(1)	1088
2	1088(2)	2176
3	1088(3)	3264

Speed of Sound

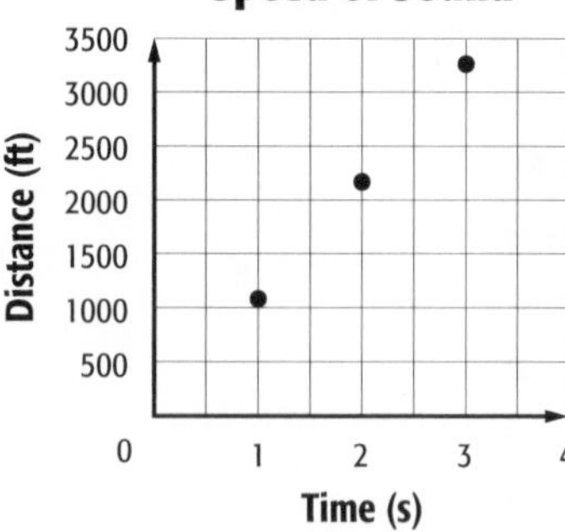

Pages 35–36, Lesson 1-5

3b.

Input (p)	$16p$	Output (z)
5	16(5)	80
8	16(8)	128
11	16(11)	176
13	16(13)	208

3c.

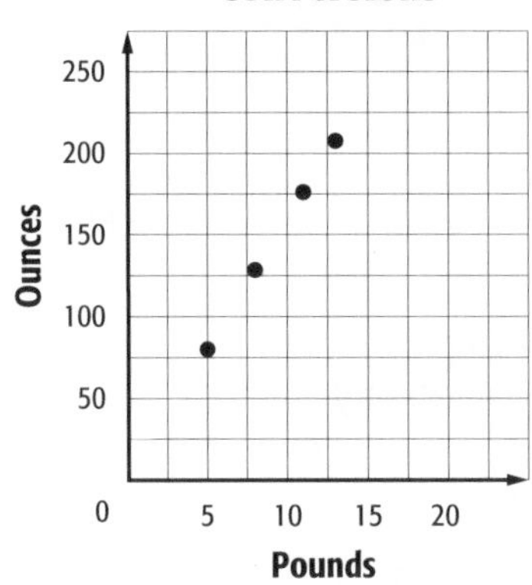

8b.

Input (r)	$40r$	Output (q)
3	40(3)	120
4	40(4)	160
5	40(5)	200
6	40(6)	240

8c.

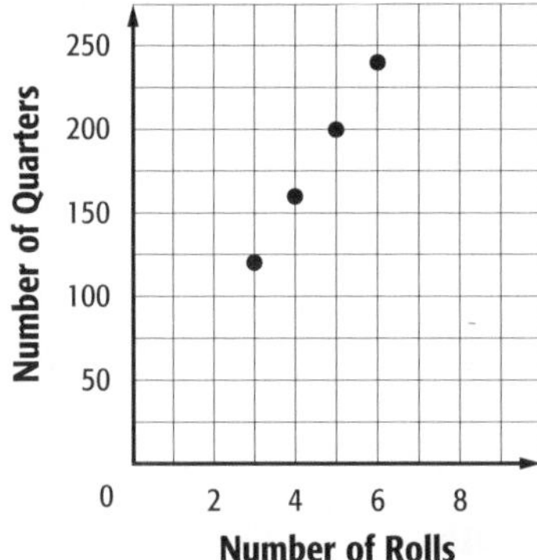

9b.

Input (s)	$10 \cdot s \cdot s$	Output (A)
6	$10 \cdot 6 \cdot 6$	360
12	$10 \cdot 12 \cdot 12$	1440
15	$10 \cdot 15 \cdot 15$	2250
24	$10 \cdot 24 \cdot 24$	5760

9c.

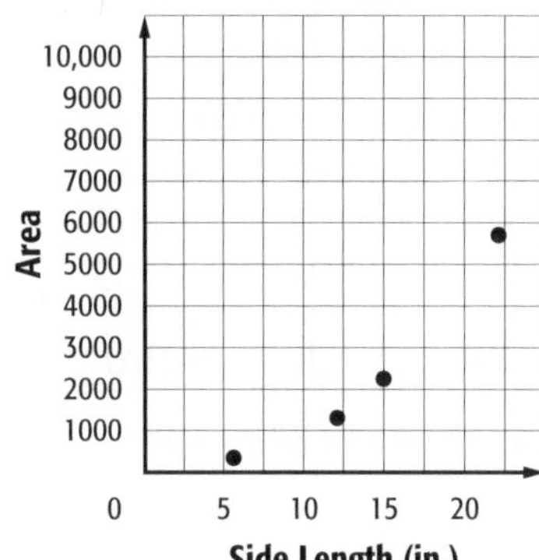

10a.

Input (m)	Output (g)
1	180
2	165
3	150
4	135
5	120
6	105

10c. yes; each member of the domain (month) is paired with only one member of the range (games sold)

11a.

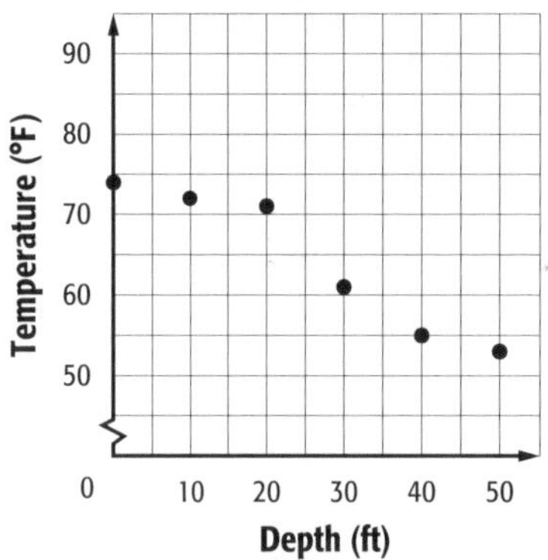

14. Sample answer: {(0, 0), (1, 1), (2, 2), (1, 3)}; A function is a special relation in which each member of the domain is paired with *exactly* one member in the range. The domain of 1 is paired with 1 and 3.

Page 38, Extend 1-5

1b.

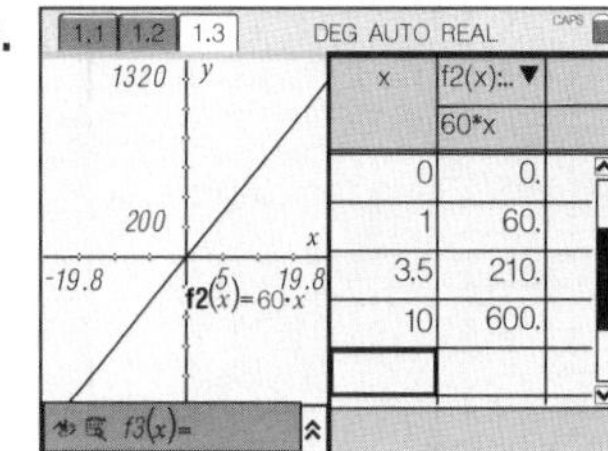

Page 40, Lesson 1-6 (Why?)

a. Yes, the enrollment is steadily increasing.

c. Sample answer: Yes; the number of Internet users will continue to increase as the population increases. However, as the percent gets closer to 100%, the percent will level off.

Pages 40–42, Lesson 1-6 (Check Your Progress)

1. **Field Goals Made 2000-2009**

3A. **Keyboarding Speeds**

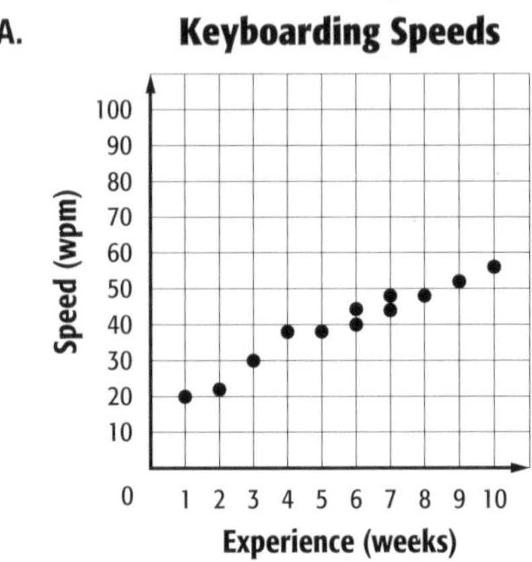

3B. As a student's experience increases, so does his or her keyboarding speed. So, the scatter plot shows a positive relationship.

3C. The keyboarding speed of a student with 12 weeks experience would be about 63 words per minute.

Pages 42–45, Lesson 1-6

1a. **Text Messages**

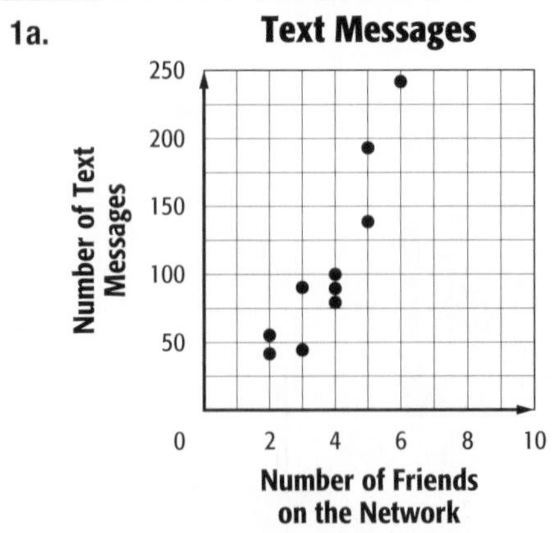

1b. As the number of friends increases, the number of messages increases. There is a positive relationship between the number of friends and the number of messages.

1c. By looking at the pattern in the graph, you can determine that a group of 8 friends will have around 300 messages.

3. **Women's Olympic 100-meter Run**

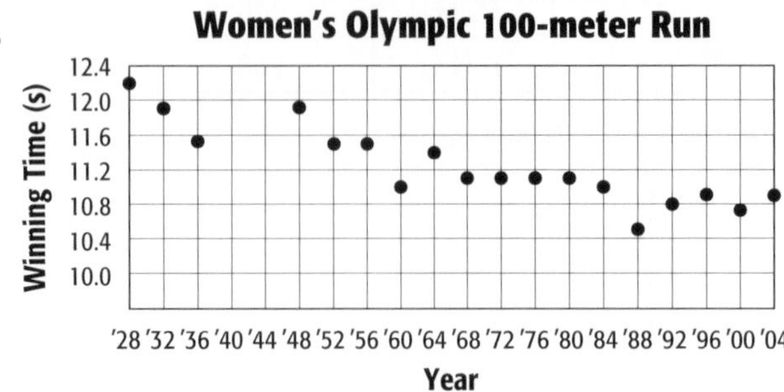

11a. **Average High Temperature for Louisville, Kentucky**

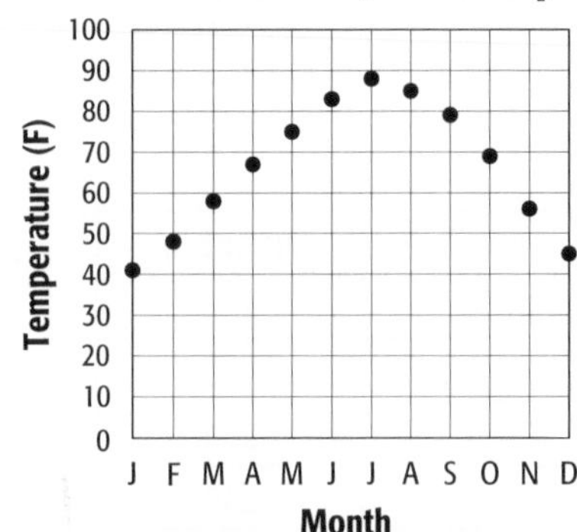

11b. Sample answer: There is a positive relationship from January through July then a negative relationship for the rest of the year.

12a.

x	y
1	20
2	40
4	80
8	160
10	200

12b. **Human Breaths per Minute**

12d. A person would breathe 500 times in 25 minutes. $y = 20(25)$; $y = 500$

13a.

x	y
1	5
1	6
1	7
2	6
2	8
2	9
3	11
4	10
4	12

13b. Sample answer: The *x*-value could represent the number of people that went out to lunch and the *y*-value could represent the total cost of lunch.

13c. Sample answer: Overall, the data shows a positive relationship between the *x* and *y* values.

15a. Sample answer:

length (in.)	width (in.)
2	18
4	9
6	6
12	3
18	2

15b.

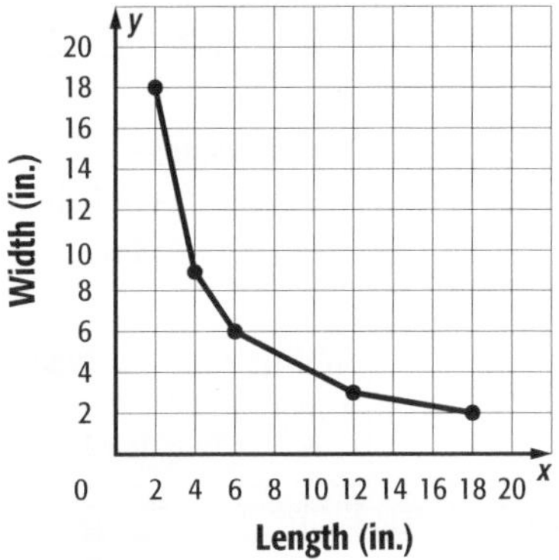

20a.

x	y
1	1
4	2
9	3
16	4
25	5
36	6

This does represent a function because there is only one *y*-value for each *x*-value.

20b.

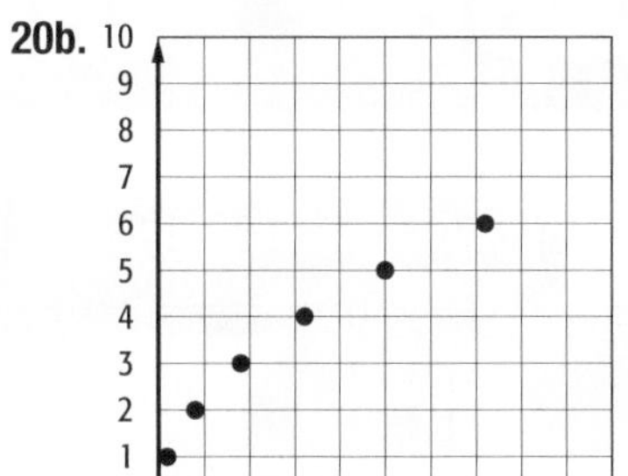

The graph appears to be a curve and shows a positive relationship.

20c.

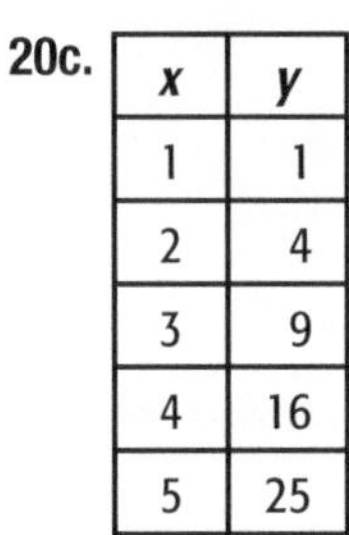

x	y
1	1
2	4
3	9
4	16
5	25
6	36

The set of ordered pairs is a function because each *x*-value has exactly one *y*-value.

20d.

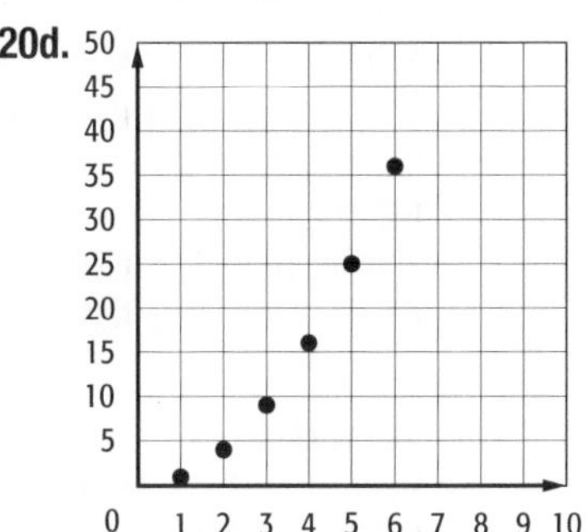

The graph appears to be a curve and shows a positive relationship, but is rising faster than the graph in part b.

22. Sample answer: The years and the number of DVD players sold shows a strong positive relationship because as the years increase, DVD player sales will increase.

Page 53, Practice Test

24.

x	y
1	3
2	7
4	13
5	15

D: {1, 2, 4, 5};
R: {3, 7, 13, 15}

CHAPTER 2

Chapter Planner

Diagnostic Assessment
Quick Check, p. 59

	Lesson 2-1 Pacing: 1 day	Explore 2-2 Pacing: 1 day	Lesson 2-2 Pacing: 1 day
Title	**Integers with Absolute Value**	**Algebra Lab: Adding Integers**	**Adding Integers**
Objectives	• Compare and order integers. • Find the absolute value of an expression.	• Add integers using algebra tiles.	• Add two integers. • Add more than two integers.
Key Vocabulary	negative number positive number integers coordinate inequality absolute value	zero pair	opposites additive inverse
NCTM Focal Points	G7-FP3 For the complete wording of the Focal Points for Grades 7 and 8, please see pages iv, v, FP0, and FP1.		
Multiple Representations	p. 66		
Lesson Resources	**Chapter 2 Resource Masters** • Study Guide and Intervention, pp. 5–6 AL OL ELL • Skills Practice, p. 7 AL OL ELL • Practice, p. 8 AL OL BL ELL • Word Problem Practice, p. 9 AL OL ELL • Enrichment, p. 10 OL BL • Quiz 1, p. 52 AL OL BL ELL **Transparencies** • 5-Minute Check Transparency 2-1 AL OL BL ELL **Additional Print Resources** • *Study Notebook* AL OL BL ELL	**Materials:** • algebra tiles • integer mats	**Chapter 2 Resource Masters** • Study Guide and Intervention, pp. 11–12 AL OL ELL • Skills Practice, p. 13 AL OL ELL • Practice, p. 14 AL OL BL ELL • Word Problem Practice, p. 15 AL OL ELL • Enrichment, p. 16 OL BL • Quiz 1, p. 52 AL OL BL ELL **Transparencies** • 5-Minute Check Transparency 2-2 AL OL BL ELL **Additional Print Resources** • *Study Notebook* AL OL BL ELL
Technology for Every Lesson	**Math Online** glencoe.com • Extra Examples • Self-Check Quizzes • Personal Tutor	**CD/DVD Resources** IWB INTERACTIVE WHITEBOARD READY IWB StudentWorks Plus IWB Interactive Classroom IWB Diagnostic and Assessment Planner	• TeacherWorks Plus • eSolutions Manual Plus • ExamView Assessment Suite
Math in Motion			
Differentiated Instruction	pp. 63, 66		pp. 71, 74

KEY: AL Approaching Level OL On Level BL Beyond Level ELL English Learners

Operations with Integers

Suggested Pacing			
Time Periods	Instruction	Review & Assessment	Total
45-minute	11	2	13
90-minute	5.5	1	6.5

Explore 2-3 Pacing: 1 day	Lesson 2-3 Pacing: 1 day	Explore 2-4 Pacing: 1 day	Lesson 2-4 Pacing: 1 day
Algebra Lab: Subtracting Integers	**Subtracting Integers**	**Algebra Lab: Multiplying Integers**	**Multiplying Integers**
• Use algebra tiles to model subtraction with integers.	• Subtract integers. • Evaluate expressions containing variables.	• Use algebra tiles to multiply integers.	• Multiply integers. • Simplify algebraic expressions.
	p. 79		p. 87
Materials: • algebra tiles • integer mats	**Chapter 2 Resource Masters** • Study Guide and Intervention, pp. 17–18 AL OL ELL • Skills Practice, p. 19 AL OL ELL • Practice, p. 20 AL OL BL ELL • Word Problem Practice, p. 21 AL OL ELL • Enrichment, p. 22 OL BL • Quiz 2, p. 52 AL OL BL ELL **Transparencies** • 5-Minute Check Transparency 2-3 AL OL BL ELL **Additional Print Resources** • *Study Notebook* AL OL BL ELL	**Materials:** • algebra tiles • integer mats	**Chapter 2 Resource Masters** • Study Guide and Intervention, pp. 23–24 AL OL ELL • Skills Practice, p. 25 AL OL ELL • Practice, p. 26 AL OL BL ELL • Word Problem Practice, p. 27 AL OL ELL • Enrichment, p. 28 OL BL • Quiz 2, p. 52 AL OL BL ELL **Transparencies** • 5-Minute Check Transparency 2-4 AL OL BL ELL **Additional Print Resources** • *Study Notebook* AL OL BL ELL
Math Online glencoe.com • Extra Examples • Self-Check Quizzes • Personal Tutor	**CD/DVD Resources** IWB INTERACTIVE WHITEBOARD READY IWB StudentWorks Plus IWB Interactive Classroom IWB Diagnostic and Assessment Planner	• TeacherWorks Plus • eSolutions Manual Plus • ExamView Assessment Suite	
	pp. 77, 80		pp. 84, 88

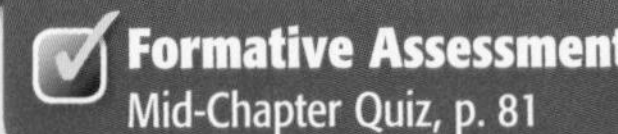

Formative Assessment
Mid-Chapter Quiz, p. 81

Chapter 2 Chapter Planner

	Explore 2-5 Pacing: 1 day	Lesson 2-5 Pacing: 1 day	Lesson 2-6 Pacing: 1 day	Lesson 2-7 Pacing: 1 day
Title	**Algebra Lab: Dividing Integers**	**Dividing Integers**	**Graphing in Four Quadrants**	**Translations and Reflections on the Coordinate Plane**
Objectives	• Divide integers using algebra tiles.	• Divide integers. • Find the mean (average) of a set of data.	• Graph points on a coordinate plane. • Graph algebraic relationships.	• Define and identify transformations. • Draw translations and reflections.
Key Vocabulary		mean	quadrants	translation reflection
NCTM Focal Points				
Multiple Representations		p. 95		
Lesson Resources	**Materials:** • Algebra tiles • Integer mats	**Chapter 2 Resource Masters** • Study Guide and Intervention, pp. 29–30 AL OL ELL • Skills Practice, p. 31 AL OL ELL • Practice, p. 32 AL OL BL ELL • Word Problem Practice, p. 33 AL OL ELL • Enrichment, p. 34 OL BL • Graphic Calculator, p. 35 AL OL BL ELL • Quiz 3, p. 53 AL OL BL ELL **Transparencies** • 5-Minute Check Transparency 2-5 AL OL BL ELL **Additional Print Resources** • *Study Notebook* AL OL BL ELL	**Chapter 2 Resource Masters** • Study Guide and Intervention, pp. 36–37 AL OL ELL • Skills Practice, p. 38 AL OL ELL • Practice, p. 39 AL OL BL ELL • Word Problem Practice, p. 40 AL OL ELL • Enrichment, p. 41 OL BL • Spreadsheet Activity, p. 42 AL OL BL ELL • Quiz 3, p. 53 AL OL BL ELL **Transparencies** • 5-Minute Check Transparency 2-6 AL OL BL ELL **Additional Print Resources** • *Study Notebook* AL OL BL ELL	**Chapter 2 Resource Masters** • Study Guide and Intervention, pp. 43–44 AL OL ELL • Skills Practice, p. 45 AL OL ELL • Practice, p. 46 AL OL BL ELL • Word Problem Practice, p. 47 AL OL ELL • Enrichment, p. 48 OL BL • Quiz 4, p. 53 AL OL BL ELL **Transparencies** • 5-Minute Check Transparency 2-7 AL OL BL ELL **Additional Print Resources** • *Study Notebook* AL OL BL ELL
Technology for Every Lesson	Math Online **glencoe.com** • Extra Examples • Self-Check Quizzes • Personal Tutor	**CD/DVD Resources** IWB INTERACTIVE WHITEBOARD READY IWB StudentWorks Plus IWB Interactive Classroom IWB Diagnostic and Assessment Planner		• TeacherWorks Plus • eSolutions Manual Plus • ExamView Assessment Suite
Math in Motion				
Differentiated Instruction		pp. 92, 95	pp. 97, 100	pp. 102, 106

Summative Assessment
- Study Guide and Review, pp. 107–110
- Practice Test, p. 111

KEY: 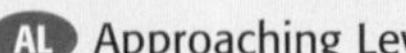 AL Approaching Level  OL On Level 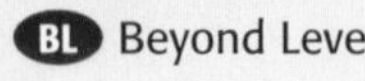 BL Beyond Level 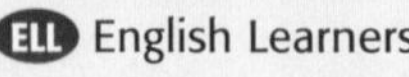 ELL English Learners

Quick Review Math Handbook*

is Glencoe's mathematical handbook for students and parents.

Hot Words includes a glossary of terms.

Hot Topics consists of two parts:

- explanations of key mathematical concepts
- exercises to check students' understanding

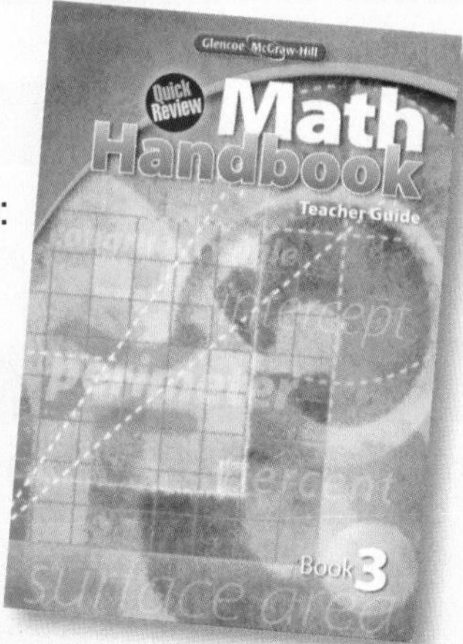

Lesson	Hot Topics Section	Lesson	Hot Topics Section
2-1	1.3	2-4	1.3, 6.3
2-2	1.3	2-5	1.3, 6.3
2-3	1.3, 6.3	2-6	6.7

** Also available in Spanish*

What the Research Says ...

Wenglinsky (2000) found that students whose teachers conduct hands-on learning activities outperform their peers by more than 70% of a grade level in math on the National Assessment of Educational Progress. A study of over 7,000 students was conducted. (Wenglinsky, 2000)

- Give students ample opportunity to use manipulatives, such as algebra tiles, to perform the operations with integers in Lessons 2-1 through 2-5.
- Students can use maps, globes, and grid paper to practice graphing techniques in Lesson 2-6.

Professional Development

Targeted professional development has been articulated throughout McGraw-Hill's mathematics program. The **McGraw-Hill Professional Development Video Library** provides short videos that support key topics. For more information, visit **glencoe.com.**

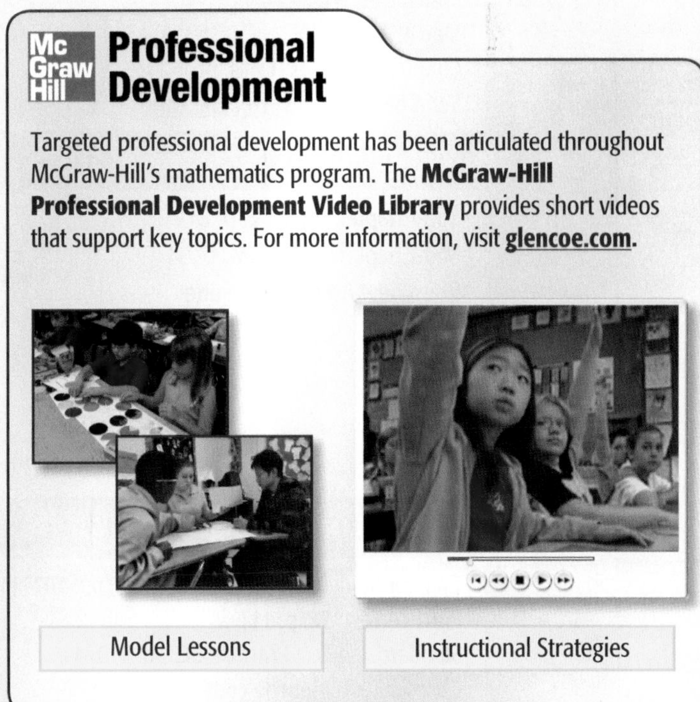

CHAPTER 2 Assessment and Intervention

SE = Student Edition, **TE** = Teacher Edition, **CRM** = Chapter Resource Masters

	Diagnosis	Prescription
Diagnostic Assessment	**Beginning Chapter 2**	
	Get Ready for Chapter 2 **SE,** p. 59	Response to Intervention **TE,** p. 59
	Beginning Every Lesson	
	Then, Now, Why? **SE** 5-Minute Check Transparencies	Chapter 2 **SE,** pp. P1–P22 Concepts and Skills Bank **SE,** pp. 856–887 *Quick Review Math Handbook*
Formative Assessment	**During/After Every Lesson**	
	Check Your Progress **SE,** every example Check Your Understanding **SE** Spiral Review **SE** Additional Examples **TE** Watch Out! **TE** Step 4, Assess **TE** Chapter 2 Quizzes **CRM,** pp. 52–53 Self-Check Quizzes **glencoe.com**	Tier 1 Intervention Concepts and Skills Bank **SE,** pp. 856–887 Skills Practice **CRM** **glencoe.com** Tier 2 Intervention Differentiated Instruction **TE** Study Guide and Intervention Masters **CRM** *Quick Review Math Handbook* Tier 3 Intervention *Math Triumphs, Grade 8,* Ch. 1–2
	Mid-Chapter	
	Mid-Chapter Quiz **SE,** p. 81 Mid-Chapter Test **CRM,** p. 54 ExamView Assessment Suite	Tier 1 Intervention Study Guide and Intervention Masters Concepts and Skills Bank **SE,** pp. 856–887 Skills Practice **CRM** **glencoe.com** Tier 2 Intervention *Math Triumphs* **CRM** *Quick Review Math Handbook* Tier 3 Intervention *Math Triumphs, Grade 8,* Ch. 1–2
	Before Chapter Test	
	Chapter Study Guide and Review **SE,** pp. 107–110 Practice Test **SE,** p. 111 Standardized Test Practice **SE,** pp. 112–115 Chapter Test **glencoe.com** Standardized Test Practice **glencoe.com** Vocabulary Review **glencoe.com** ExamView Assessment Suite	Tier 1 Intervention Concepts and Skills Bank **SE,** pp. 856–887 Skills Practice **CRM** **glencoe.com** Tier 2 Intervention Study Guide and Intervention Masters **CRM** *Quick Review Math Handbook* Tier 3 Intervention *Math Triumphs, Grade 8,* Ch. 1–2
Summative Assessment	**After Chapter 2**	
	Multiple-Choice Tests, Forms 1, 2A, 2B, **CRM,** pp. 56–61 Free-Response Tests, Forms 2C, 2D, 3, **CRM,** pp. 62–68 Vocabulary Test **CRM,** p. 55 Extended Response Test **CRM,** p. 68 Standardized Test Practice **CRM,** pp. 69–71 ExamView Assessment Suite	Study Guide and Intervention Masters **CRM** *Quick Review Math Handbook* **glencoe.com**

Differentiated Instruction

Option 1 Reaching All Learners AL OL BL ELL

VISUAL/SPATIAL Have students create a line design that extends to all four quadrants on a coordinate grid. Have them list each vertex of the design as an ordered pair and in sequence as they progress around the outline of the design. Then have them exchange their lists of ordered pairs with other students to plot on a coordinate grid. As students "connect the dots," they will see the designs take shape.

LOGICAL Ask students to write on separate index cards a statement that could be true or false for each of the following:

- The product of integers is negative.
- The quotient of integers is positive.

An example might be: *The quotient of an odd number of integers is negative.* Have students write on the back of the card whether the statement is true or false, and give an example. Place the cards in a box, and periodically choose a few for students to solve as a class.

Option 2 Approaching Level AL

Have students model "average." Write $-7 + 2 + 10 + (-6) + (-9) + (-8)$ on the board and then have students model the solution. One student holds a sign with "(+)" on one side and "(−)" on the other. Then 7 students come up and the sign bearer shows the negative sign. Two students sit down to show that $-7 + 2 = -5$. In order to add 10, 5 students sit down and 5 more come up. The sign then changes to positive. After all the terms are added, the students divide into 6 equal groups to find the average. -3

Option 3 English Learners ELL

As students learn about negative integers, have them note and explain the differences between the use of the symbol (−) for subtraction sentences and for identifying negative numbers.

- When (−) is used as an operation in mathematical sentences, use the word *minus sign* to show subtraction.
- When (−) is used in front of a number, use the word *negative* to show that the number is a negative integer.

REAL WORLD Help students make connections between everyday situations and the use of positive numbers, negative numbers, or zero by making posters depicting different scenarios, i.e. a lemonade stand, a bank account, or temperature change. Include illustrations and a paragraph explaining the situation. Show coins and paper money to help illustrate the problem. Represent a loss of $2 as -2 and a profit or gain of $5 as $+5$ or 5. Then have students solve problems about the scenario. They can also write problems for other students to solve. This can help with cultural understanding.

Option 4 Beyond Level BL

Have students perform transformations on the figure *ABCDEF* so that the final image lies in Quadrant II without passing through Quadrant I.

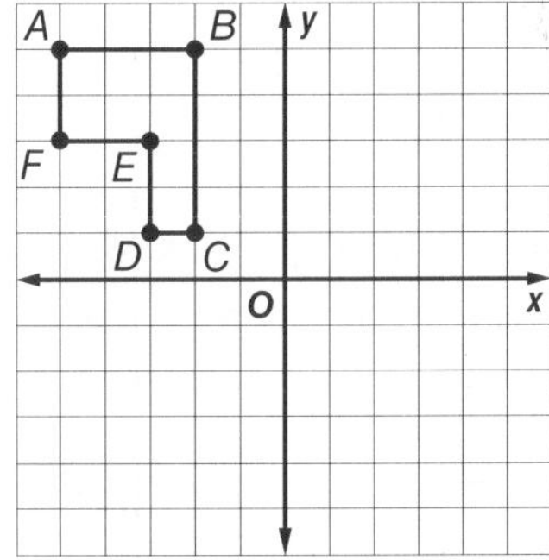

Ask students to draw and then describe each of the transformations. Have them compare their transformations and then write a comparison statement about the transformations.

CHAPTER 2

Focus on Mathematical Content

Vertical Alignment

Before Chapter 2

Related Topics before Pre-Algebra

- locate and name points on a coordinate plane using ordered pairs of integers
- use integers to represent real-life situations

Previous Topics from Pre-Algebra

- draw conclusions and make predictions by analyzing trends in scatter plots
- use appropriate operations

Chapter 2

Related Topics from Pre-Algebra

- compare and order integers
- select appropriate operations to solve problems involving integers
- locate and name points on a coordinate plane using ordered pairs of integers
- graph reflections and translations on a coordinate plane

After Chapter 2

Preparation for Algebra 1

- find and evaluate an algebraic expression to determine any term in an arithmetic sequence
- use appropriate operations to solve problems involving rational numbers in problem situations
- generate different representations of data given another representation of data

Lesson-by-Lesson Preview

2-1 Integers and Absolute Value

Negative and positive numbers, such as −8 and 6, are members of the set of integers, which includes whole numbers and their opposites. Integers can be represented as points on a number line.

- Graph integers by locating the points named by the integers on a number line. The number that corresponds to a point is called the *coordinate* of the point.
- The numbers on a number line increase from left to right, which can be used to compare inequalities and to order integers.

If two integers on a number line are on opposite sides of zero and are the same distance from zero, they have the same absolute value.

$$|3| = 3 \text{ and } |-3| = 3$$

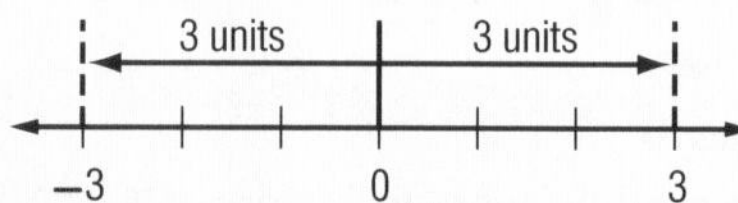

The symbol for absolute value is two vertical bars on either side of a number or expression, e.g., $|-5| = 5$. Because variables represent numbers, absolute value notation can be used in algebraic expressions involving variables.

2-2 Adding Integers

When adding two integers with the same sign:

- add their absolute values;
- the sum takes the same sign as the addends.

When adding integers with different signs:

- subtract their absolute values;
- the sum takes the same sign as the addend with the greater absolute value.

When adding more than two integers:

- Look for opposites, such as −2 and 2, and use the Additive Inverse Property (the sum of any number and its opposite is zero) to add the numbers;
- Use the Commutative and Associate Properties to group the positive and the negative addends and then add.

Subtracting Integers

The rules for adding integers are extended to the subtraction of integers. To subtract an integer, add its additive inverse. For example, to find the difference $2 - 5$, add the additive inverse of 5 to 2: $2 + (-5) = -3$.

You can use the same rule for evaluating expressions. For example, to evaluate $x - (-4)$ when $x = 3$, replace x with 3 and add the additive inverse of -4: $3 + 4 = 7$.

Multiplying Integers

Multiplication is repeated addition, so $3(-7)$ means that -7 is used as an addend 3 times: $3(-7) = -7 + (-7) + (-7) = -21$. This fact and the fact that the product of two positive integers is positive lead to these rules:

- The product of two integers with different signs is negative.
- The product of two integers with the same sign is positive.

Dividing Integers

The quotient of two integers can be found by using the related multiplication sentence. For example, the division sentence $-12 \div (-4) = 3$ is related to the multiplication sentence $-4 \times 3 = -12$. The following rules apply to the division of integers:

- The quotient of two integers with different signs is negative.
- The quotient of two integers with the same sign is positive.

Use division of integers to find the mean of a set of data: find the sum of the numbers in the data set, and then divide by the number of items in the set.

Graphing in Four Quadrants

In the Cartesian coordinate system, the y-axis extends above and below the origin and the x-axis extends to the right and left of the origin. The origin is the point at which the x- and y-axes intersect.

- A point graphed on the coordinate system has an x-coordinate and a y-coordinate. In the ordered pair $(1, -2)$, the x-coordinate is 1 and the y-coordinate is -2.
- $(1, -2)$ is located 1 unit to the right of the origin on the x-axis and 2 units below the origin on the y-axis.

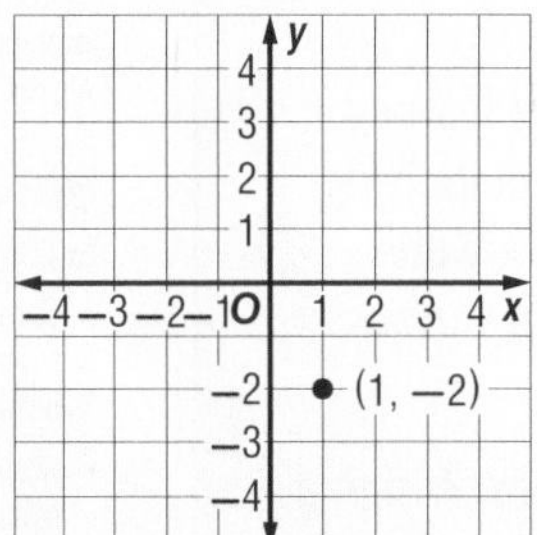

The x- and y-axes divide the coordinate plane into four regions, called *quadrants,* labeled I to IV, starting in the upper right quadrant and proceeding counterclockwise.

- In quadrant I, both coordinates are positive.
- In quadrant II, the x-coordinate is negative and the y-coordinate is positive.
- In quadrant III, both coordinates are negative.
- In quadrant IV, the x-coordinate is positive and the y-coordinate is negative.

Translations and Reflections on the Coordinate Plane

A transformation maps an original geometric figure onto a new figure called an *image.*

- A translation slides a figure from one position to another without turning it. Every point of the original figure is moved the same distance and in the same direction. The orientation of the image is the same as the original figure.
- A reflection flips a figure over a line of symmetry to form a mirror image of the figure. Every point of the original figure has a corresponding point on the other side of the line of symmetry. The orientation of the image is different from the original figure.

In translations and reflections, the original figure and the image have the same shape and the same size.

CHAPTER 2 Notes

Chapter Project

Highs and Lows

Students use what they have learned about adding, subtracting, multiplying, and dividing integers to work with weather statistics for cities in various states.

- Divide students into groups. Assign a northern state, such as Alaska, Maine, Michigan, Minnesota, or North Dakota to a group. Ask each group member to research and bring to class the monthly high and monthly low temperatures, in degrees Celsius, for a city in the state. Round temperatures to the nearest integer.
- Have groups find the monthly range of temperatures in a city. For each group, which city, in which month, has the greatest range in temperature? the least?
- Ask groups to find the *yearly* mean high and mean low for each city, rounded to the nearest integer. Have them order the cities from least to greatest mean highs and mean lows. Which cities have the greatest and least highs and lows?
- Ask groups to find the means of the highs and lows for each month for each city in their group. Have them assign a number to each month (1, 2, 3,. . .,12) and plot the monthly mean temperatures for all of the cities on a coordinate plane, using different colors of points for each city. Ask them to analyze the results in terms of monthly and seasonal mean temperatures.

CHAPTER 2 Operations with Integers

Then

In Chapter 1, you solved problems using the tools of algebra.

Now

In Chapter 2, you will:

- Compare, order, add, subtract, multiply, and divide integers.
- Graph points and algebraic relationships on a coordinate plane.
- Define, identify, and draw transformations.

Why?

WEATHER Rapid temperature changes, ice fog, and summer thunderstorms with hail, lightning, and snow are normal for Fairbanks, Alaska. Fairbanks experiences some of the most extreme weather in the world. Winter spans eight months and the temperature is often below zero for entire months.

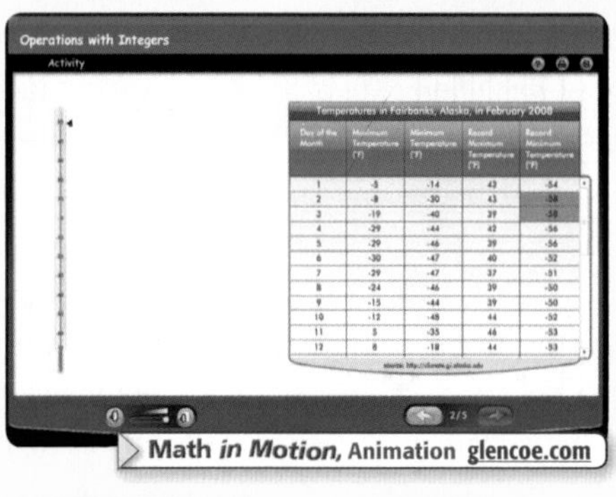

Key Vocabulary Introduce the key vocabulary in the chapter using the routine below.

Define: The quadrants are the four regions into which the *x*-axis and *y*-axis separate the coordinate plane.

Example: The ordered pair $(-2, 4)$ represents a point in quadrant II.

Ask: If the coordinates of a point are both negative numbers, in which quadrant is the point? quadrant III

Get Ready for Chapter 2

Diagnose Readiness You have two options for checking Prerequisite Skills.

Text Option Take the Quick Check below. Refer to the Quick Review for help.

*Quick*Check

(Used in Lessons 2-2 through 2-5)

Evaluate each expression if $x = 2$, $y = 11$, and $z = 5$. (Lesson 1-2)

1. $x + y + z$ 18
2. $yz - xy$ 33
3. $y + xz$ 21
4. $4z + 3y$ 53
5. **SALES** Flora sold three times as many bottles of water on Sunday than on Saturday. How many bottles of water did she sell Saturday if she sold 120 bottles on Sunday? 40

(Used in Lessons 2-2 through 2-4)

Find the next term in each list. (Previous Course)

6. 28, 34, 40, 46, 52, ... 58
7. 135, 120, 105, 90, 75, ... 60
8. **PHONE** The telephone company charges \$0.30 for the first minute and \$0.15 for each additional minute. How much would it cost to talk for 10 minutes? \$1.65

(Used in Lessons 2-6 and 2-7)

Use the graph to name the coordinates of each point. (Lesson 1-4)

9. D (1, 6)
10. B (0, 3)
11. A (2, 4)
12. J (6, 1)
13. C (3, 0)
14. G (4, 3)
15. F (5, 2)
16. H (2, 2)

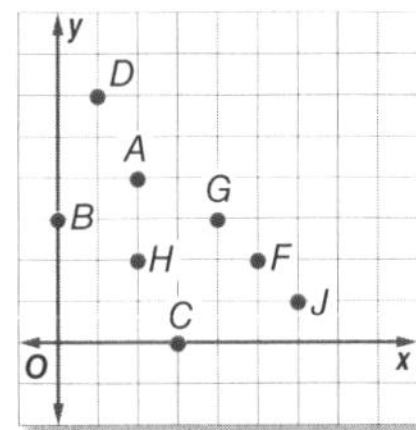

*Quick*Review

EXAMPLE 1

Evaluate $2b + 3c$ if $b = 2$ and $c = 3$.

$2b + 3c = 2(2) + 3(3)$	**Replace b with 2 and c with 3.**
$= 4 + 9$	**Multiply.**
$= 13$	**Add.**

EXAMPLE 2

Find the next term in the list.

6, 11, 16, 21, ...

6, 11, 16, 21, ■

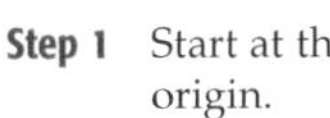

The next term is 21 + 5 or 26.

EXAMPLE 3

Use the coordinate plane to write the ordered pair that names point A.

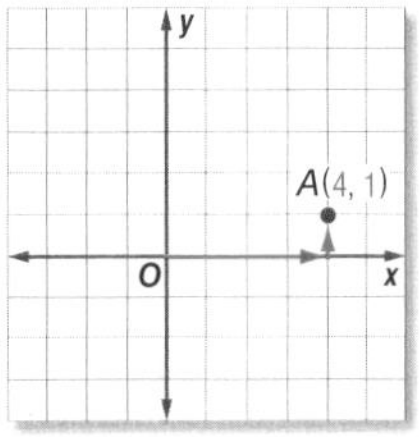

Step 1 Start at the origin.

Step 2 Move right on the x-axis to find the x-coordinate of point A, which is 4.

Step 3 Move up the y-axis to find the y-coordinate, which is 1.

The ordered pair for point A is (4, 1).

Online Option Math Online Take a self-check Chapter Readiness Quiz at glencoe.com.

Chapter 2 Operations with Integers 59

Get Ready for Chapter 2

Response to Intervention (RtI)

Use the *Quick Check* results and the Intervention Planner to help you determine your Response to Intervention. The If-Then statements in the chart below help you decide the appropriate tier of RtI and suggest intervention resources for each tier.

Intervention Planner

Tier 1 On Level

If students miss about 25% of the exercises or less,

Then choose a resource:

- **SE** Lessons 1-2 and 1-4
- **CRM** Skills Practice, Chapter 1, pp. 13, 26
- **TE** Chapter Project, p. 58
- Math Online Self-Check Quiz

Tier 2 Strategic Intervention approaching grade level

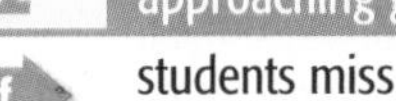
If students miss about 50% of the exercises,

Then choose a resource:

- **CRM** Study Guide and Intervention, Chapter 1, pp. 11, 24
- *Quick Review Math Handbook*
- Math Online Extra Examples, Personal Tutor, Homework Help

Tier 3 Intensive Intervention 2 or more grades below level

If students miss about 75% of the exercises,

Then use *Math Triumphs, Grade 8*, Ch. 1–2

Math Online Extra Examples, Personal Tutor, Homework Help, Review Vocabulary

CHAPTER 2 Notes

FOLDABLES® Study Organizer

Dinah Zike's Foldables®

Focus Students write notes under each tab. As they work through each lesson, remind them to show examples of each operation with integers under the appropriate tab.

Teach Have students make and label the tabs for each lesson of their Foldables as illustrated.

Have students use the appropriate tabs as they cover each lesson in this chapter.

When to Use It Encourage students to add to their Foldable as they work through the chapter, and use them to review for the chapter test.

Differentiated Instruction

CRM Student-Built Glossary, pp. 1–2 Students should complete the chart by providing a definition of each term and an example as they progress through Chapter 2. This study tool can also be used to review for the chapter test.

Get Started on Chapter 2

You will learn several new concepts, skills, and vocabulary terms as you study Chapter 2. To get ready, identify important terms and organize your resources. You may wish to refer to **Chapter 0** to review prerequisite skills.

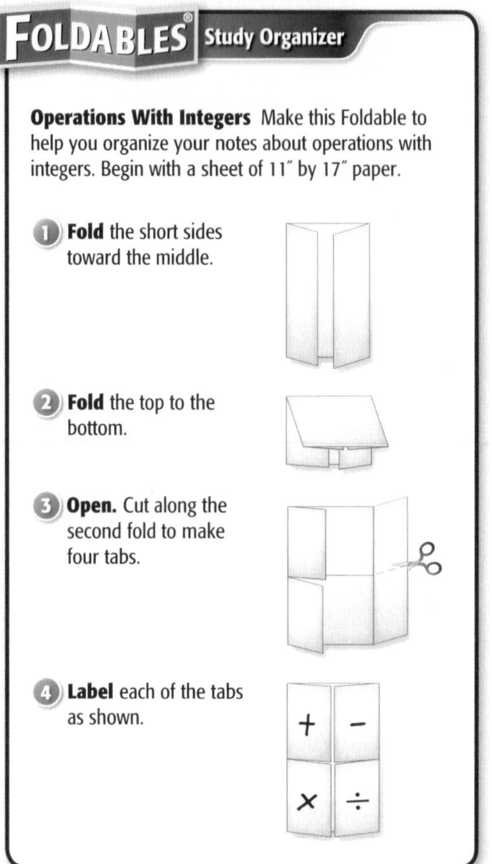

FOLDABLES® Study Organizer

Operations With Integers Make this Foldable to help you organize your notes about operations with integers. Begin with a sheet of 11″ by 17″ paper.

1. **Fold** the short sides toward the middle.
2. **Fold** the top to the bottom.
3. **Open.** Cut along the second fold to make four tabs.
4. **Label** each of the tabs as shown.

New Vocabulary

English		Español
integer	p. 61	entero
coordinate	p. 62	coordine
zero pair	p. 67	par nulo
additive inverse	p. 71	inverso de añadidura
quadrants	p. 97	cuadrantes
reflection	p. 101	reflejo
transformation	p. 101	transformación
translation	p. 101	traducción

Review Vocabulary

addends • p. 69 • sumandos numbers that are added together

coordinate plane • p. 96 • plano de coordenadas a coordinate plane is formed by the intersection of two number lines that meet at right angles at their zero points

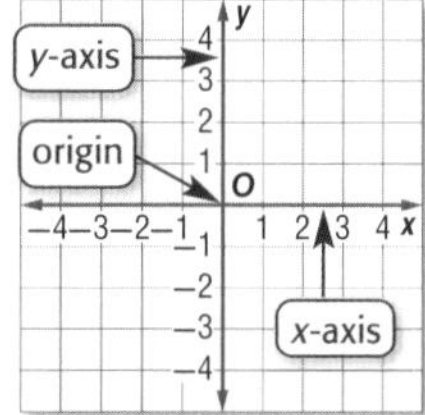

expression • p. 63 • expresión a combination of numbers, variables, and at least one operation

factors • p. 85 • factors numbers that are multiplied together

product • p. 83 • producto the result when two or more numbers are multiplied together

sum • p. 69 • suma the result when two or more numbers are added together

Multilingual eGlossary glencoe.com

Math Online glencoe.com

- Study the chapter online
- Explore **Math in Motion**
- Get extra help from your own **Personal Tutor**
- Use **Extra Examples** for additional help
- Take a **Self-Check Quiz**
- **Review Vocabulary** in fun ways

2-1

Integers and Absolute Value

Why?

In miniature golf, *par* is the number of strokes a golfer should take to complete a hole. In the graph, a score of −3 represents 3 strokes under par.

a. What does a value of −2 represent? 2 strokes under par

b. Which golfer's score was farthest from par? Lin

c. How would you represent 2 strokes above par? +2 or 2

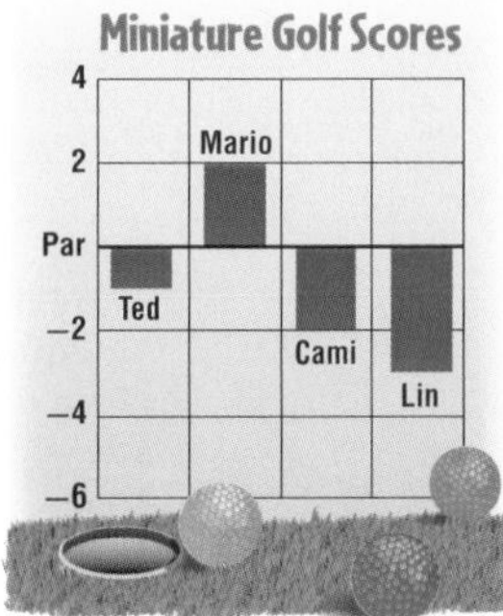

Then
You have already compared and ordered whole numbers. (Previous Course)

Now
- Compare and order integers.
- Find the absolute value of an expression.

New Vocabulary
negative number
positive number
integers
coordinate
inequality
absolute value

Math Online
glencoe.com
- Extra Examples
- Personal Tutor
- Self-Check Quiz
- Homework Help

Compare and Order Integers A **negative number** is a number less than zero. A **positive number** is a number greater than zero.

Negative numbers like −3 and positive numbers like +3, are members of the set of integers. An **integer** is any number from the set {…, −3, −2, −1, 0, 1, 2, 3, …}, where … means continues indefinitely.

Integers can be represented as points on a number line.

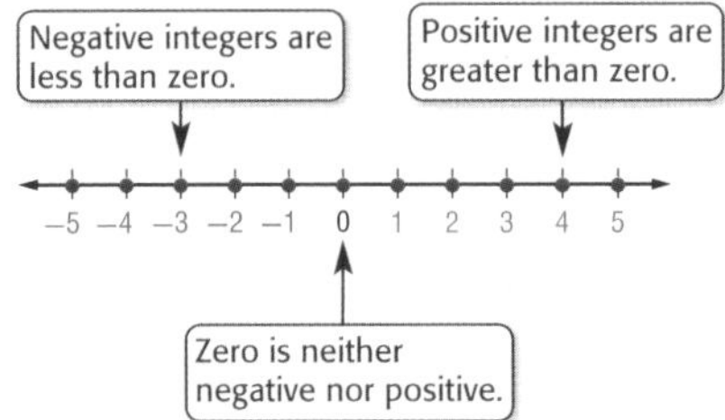

You can write integers to represent real-world situations.

EXAMPLE 1 Write Integers for Real-World Situations

Write an integer for each situation.

a. 23°F *below* zero

Because it is below zero, the integer is −23.

b. 11 inches more than normal

Because it is *more than* normal, the integer is +11 or 11.

Check Your Progress

1A. a loss of 8 yards −8

1B. a deposit of $15 +15 or 15

Personal Tutor glencoe.com

2-1 Lesson Notes

1 FOCUS

Vertical Alignment

Before Lesson 2-1
Compare and order whole numbers.

Lesson 2-1
Compare and order integers. Find the absolute value of an expression.

After Lesson 2-1
Use integers to graph in four quadrants and to add, subtract, multiply, and divide.

2 TEACH

Scaffolding Questions

Have students read the *Why?* section of the lesson and answer the questions.

Ask:

- What represents a score of 0 on the graph? Par, the number of strokes a golfer should take to complete a hole.
- What score did Cami receive? 2 under par, or −2
- How do you know whether to represent a score as positive or negative? If the score is over par, it is positive. If it is under par, it is negative.

Lesson 2-1 Resources

Resource	Approaching-Level	On-Level	Beyond-Level	English Learners
Teacher Edition		• Differentiated Instruction, pp. 63, 66	• Differentiated Instruction, p. 66	
Chapter Resource Masters	• Study Guide and Intervention, pp. 5–6 • Skills Practice, p. 7 • Practice, p. 8 • Word Problem Practice, p. 9	• Study Guide and Intervention, pp. 5–6 • Skills Practice, p. 7 • Practice, p. 8 • Word Problem Practice, p. 9 • Enrichment, p. 10	• Practice, p. 8 • Word Problem Practice, p. 9 • Enrichment, p. 10	• Study Guide and Intervention, pp. 5–6 • Skills Practice, p. 7 • Practice, p. 8
Transparencies	• 5-Minute Check Transparency 2-1	• 5-Minute Check Transparency 2-1	• 5-Minute Check Transparency 2-1	• 5-Minute Check Transparency 2-1
Other	• Study Notebook • Teaching Pre-Algebra with Manipulatives	• Study Notebook • Teaching Pre-Algebra with Manipulatives	• Study Notebook	• Study Notebook • Teaching Pre-Algebra with Manipulatives

Compare and Order Integers

Examples 1–3 show how to write, compare, and order integers. Students should compare and order integers with and without the use of a number line.

Formative Assessment

Use the Check Your Progress exercises after each example to determine students' understanding of concepts.

Additional Examples

1 Write an integer for each situation.

a. 32 feet under ground -32

b. 8 weeks after birth $+8$ or 8

2 Use the integers graphed on the number line below.

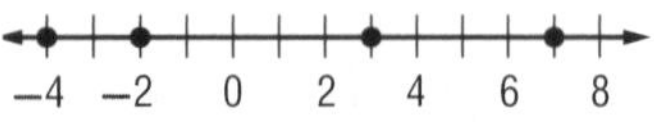

a. Write two inequalities involving 7 and -4. $7 > -4$; $-4 < 7$

b. Replace the ● with <, >, or = in -2 ● 3 to make a true sentence. <

3 **WEATHER** The high temperatures for the first seven days of January were -8°F, 10°F, 2°F, -3°F, -11°F, 0°F, and 1°F. Order the integers from least to greatest. -11, -8, -3, 0, 1, 2, 10

Additional Examples also in Interactive Classroom PowerPoint® Presentations

IWB INTERACTIVE WHITEBOARD READY

To graph an integer, locate the point named by the integer on a number line. The **coordinate** is the number that corresponds to the point on a number line.

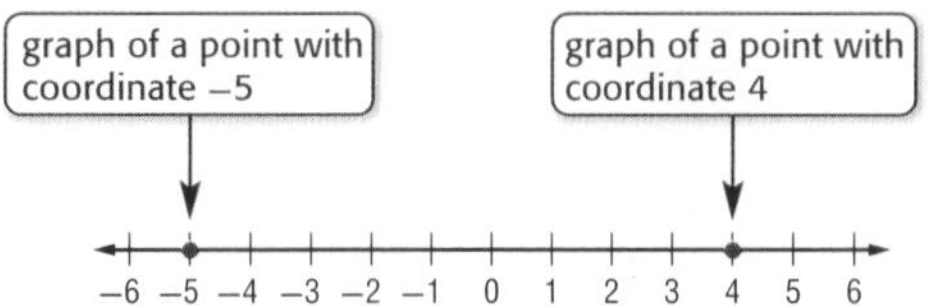

Any mathematical sentence containing < or > is called an inequality. An **inequality** compares numbers or quantities. When two numbers are graphed on a number line, the number to the left is always less than the number to the right.

ReadingMath

Inequalities The inequality symbol always points to the lesser number.

EXAMPLE 2 Compare Two Integers

Use the integers graphed on the number line below.

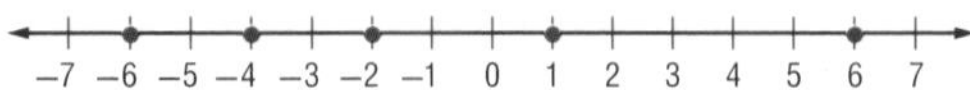

a. Write two inequalities involving 1 and -2.

Since 1 is to the right of -2, 1 is greater than -2. So, $1 > -2$.

Since -2 is to the left of 1, -2 is less than 1. So, $-2 < 1$.

b. Replace the ● with <, >, or = in -4 ● -6 to make a true sentence.

Since -4 is to the right of -6, -4 is greater. So, $-4 > -6$.

Check Your Progress

2A. Write two inequalities involving -7 and -3. $-3 > -7$; $-7 < -3$

2B. Replace the ● with <, >, or = in -1 ● 2 to make a true sentence. <

Personal Tutor glencoe.com

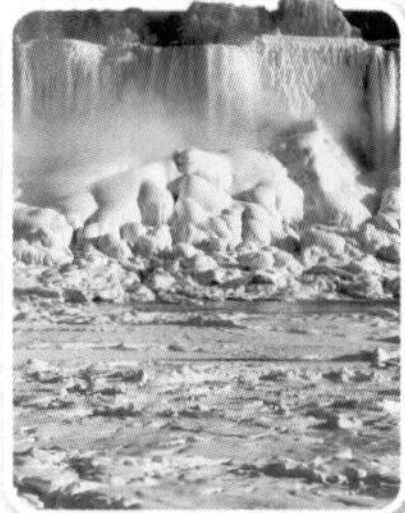

Real-World Link

The American Falls, one of the falls that makes up the Niagara Falls, has frozen six times since recorded history. In February 1936, the American Falls was frozen for 15 days.

Source: Niagara Parks

Real-World EXAMPLE 3 Order Integers

VIDEO GAMES Bethany and her friends played a question and answer video game. Their scores at the end of the game were 1, -5, 0, -1, 2, and 4. Order the scores from least to greatest.

Graph each integer on a number line.

–7 –6 –5 –4 –3 –2 –1 0 1 2 3 4 5 6 7

Write the numbers as they appear from left to right. The scores -5, -1, 0, 1, 2, and 4 are in order from least to greatest.

Check Your Progress

3. WEATHER The recorded highs in degrees Celsius in Niagara Falls from February 21–28 of a recent year are 4, 2, 3, -6, -5, -1, 0, and 1. Order the temperatures from greatest to least. **4, 3, 2, 1, 0, -1, -5, and -6**

Personal Tutor glencoe.com

Tips for New Teachers

Read -3 as *negative* 3. A positive integer like 3 can be written as $+3$ or 3. It is usually written without the + sign, as 3.

TEACH with TECH

INTERACTIVE WHITEBOARD Draw a number line on the interactive whiteboard and lock in place. Use 2 different colors to highlight the number of units from 0 in either direction to demonstrate absolute value. Have students come to the board and work several sample problems.

Absolute Value Notice on the number line that −6 and 6 are each 6 units from 0, even though they are on opposite sides of 0. The **absolute value** of a number is the distance the number is from zero on a number line. So, −6 and 6 have the same absolute value.

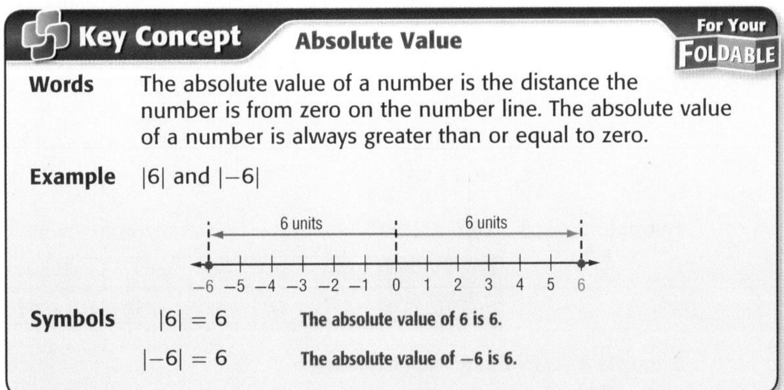

Key Concept — Absolute Value

For Your FOLDABLE

Words The absolute value of a number is the distance the number is from zero on the number line. The absolute value of a number is always greater than or equal to zero.

Example $|6|$ and $|-6|$

Symbols $|6| = 6$ **The absolute value of 6 is 6.**

$|-6| = 6$ **The absolute value of −6 is 6.**

EXAMPLE 4 Expressions with Absolute Value

Evaluate each expression.

a. $|-4|$

On the number line, the graph of −4 is 4 units from 0.

$|-4| = 4$

b. $|-8| - |5|$

$|-8| - |5| = 8 - 5$ **The absolute value of −8 is 8. The absolute value of 5 is 5.**

$= 3$ **Simplify.**

Vocabulary Review

expression A combination of numbers, variables, and a least one operation. (Lesson 1-2)

Check Your Progress

4A. $|-3|$ 3 **4B.** $|-4| - |3|$ 1

Personal Tutor glencoe.com

You can use absolute value notation with algebraic expressions involving variables since variables represent numbers.

EXAMPLE 5 Algebraic Expressions with Absolute Value

ALGEBRA Evaluate $6 + |x|$ if $x = -2$.

$6 + |x| = 6 + |-2|$ **Replace x with −2.**

$= 6 + 2$ **The absolute value of −2 is 2.**

$= 8$ **Simplify.**

Check Your Progress

5. Evaluate $|y| + 8$ if $y = -7$. 15

Personal Tutor glencoe.com

Absolute Value

Examples 4 and 5 show how to evaluate expressions that contain absolute value notation.

Tips for New Teachers

Absolute Value Absolute value is the distance a number is from 0 on a number line. Point out to students that distance is measured in nonnegative numbers.

Additional Examples

4 Evaluate each expression.

a. $|5|$ 5

b. $|-8| + |-1|$ 9

5 **ALGEBRA** Evaluate $|x| + 8$ if $x = -2$. 10

Focus on Mathematical Content

Evaluating Algebraic Expressions with Absolute Value For some expressions, two different input values for x may produce the same value for the expression. Ask students to compare the values of $|x| - 8$ when x is 15 and its value when x is −15. The value is 7 regardless of whether x is 15 or −15.

Watch Out!

Student Misconceptions Remind students that it is not always true that the absolute value of a number is the opposite of the number. Absolute value is always positive or 0.

Differentiated Instruction

OL

Auditory Bring to class several bars of music in the key of C to distribute to small groups or to individual students. Let middle C correspond to 0 on the number line. Have students plot the notes in the bar of music onto a number line. Let each whole step count as 1; the first F above middle C would equal 3 and the first A below middle C would equal −2. Have students play or sing the music, and then play the notes ordered from least to greatest on the number line.

3 PRACTICE

Formative Assessment

Use Exercises 1–15 to check for understanding.

Use the chart at the bottom of this page to customize assignments for your students.

Additional Answers

1. −500

2. +4 or 4

16. +5 or 5

−6 −4 −2 0 2 4 6

17. −200

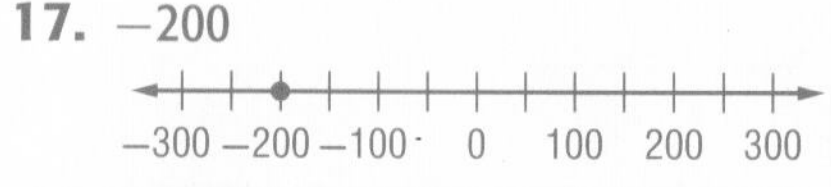

18. −18

19. 0

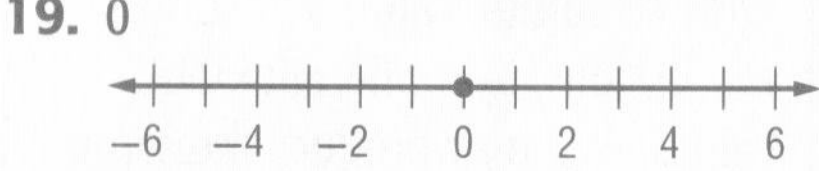

20. $5 > -11; -11 < 5$
21. $14 > -8; -8 < 14$
22. $-1 > -6; -6 < -1$
23. $-11 > -12; -12 < -11$
24. $0 > -4; -4 < 0$
25. $4 > 0; 0 < 4$
26. $55 > 50; 50 < 55$
27. $30 > 27; 27 < 30$

Check Your Understanding

Example 1 p. 61

Write an integer for each situation. Then graph on a number line.

1. a bank withdrawal of \$500
2. a gain of 4 pounds

1–2. See margin.

Example 2 p. 62

Write two inequalities using the number pairs. Use the symbols < or >.

3. 2 and −5 **$2 > -5; -5 < 2$**
4. −4 and −8 **$-4 > -8; -8 < -4$**
5. −1 and 1 **$1 > -1; -1 < 1$**

Replace each ● with <, >, or = to make a true sentence.

6. −9 ● −16 **>**
7. −7 ● 7 **<**
8. −6 ● 0 **<**

Example 3 p. 62

9. **TEMPERATURES** Order the state temperatures from least to greatest.

State	AL	AK	CA	FL	HI	ME	NJ	OH	TX
Temperature	−27	−80	−45	−2	12	−48	−34	−39	−23

−80, −48, −45, −39, −34, −27, −23, −2, 12

Example 4 p. 63

Evaluate each expression.

10. $|-12|$ **12**
11. $|-14| + |3|$ **17**
12. $|18| - |-5|$ **13**

Example 5 p. 63

ALGEBRA Evaluate each expression if $x = 7$ and $y = -6$.

13. $15 - |y|$ **9**
14. $|y| + x$ **13**
15. $3|y|$ **18**

Practice and Problem Solving

● = **Step-by-Step Solutions** begin on page R11. **Extra Practice** begins on page 810.

Example 1 p. 61

Write an integer for each situation. Then graph on a number line.

16. 5 strokes above par
17. 200 feet below sea level
18. an elevator descends 18 floors
19. no gain on fourth down

16–27. See margin.

Example 2 p. 62

Write two inequalities using the number pairs. Use the symbols < or >.

20. 5 and −11
21. −8 and 14
22. −6 and −1
23. −12 and −11
24. 0 and −4
25. 4 and 0
26. $|55|$ and $|50|$
27. $|-27|$ and $|-30|$

Replace each ● with <, >, or = to make a true sentence.

28. −11 ● −9 **<**
29. −14 ● −17 **>**
30. 15 ● −6 **>**
31. −2 ● 16 **<**
32. 21 ● 0 **>**
33. 0 ● −35 **>**
34. $|13|$ ● $|-13|$ **=**
35. $|-27|$ ● $|-27|$ **=**

Example 3 p. 62

36. **CAR RACING** In a recent year, Jimmy Johnson was the point leader in NASCAR's Chase to the Cup. Other drivers' standings are shown.

   a. Write an integer to describe each driver's standing with respect to the leader.

   b. Order the integers from least to greatest.

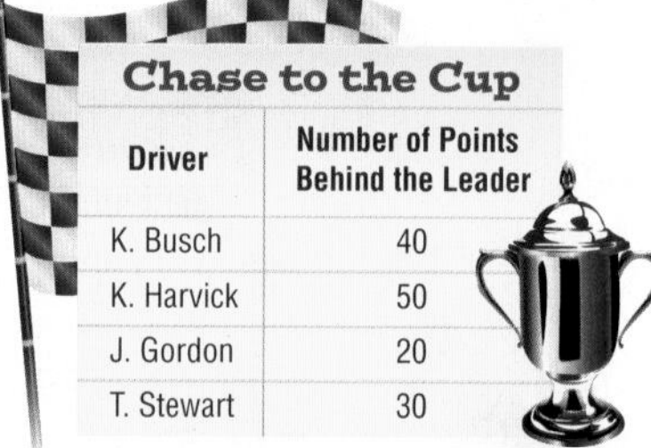

Chase to the Cup

Driver	Number of Points Behind the Leader
K. Busch	40
K. Harvick	50
J. Gordon	20
T. Stewart	30

36a. K. Busch: −40; K. Harvick: −50; J. Gordon: −20; T. Stewart: −30

36b. −50, −40, −30, −20

37. **GOLF** The top fourth round scores of a recent PGA Championship were +4, −2, +6, +1, −4, −3, +5, −1, +2, and +3. Order the scores from least to greatest.

37. −4, −3, −2, −1, 1, 2, 3, 4, 5, 6

Differentiated Homework Options

Level	Assignment	Two-Day Option	
AL Basic	16–52, 64, 68, 70–83	17–51 odd, 71–74	16–52 even, 64, 68, 70, 75–83
OL Core	17–51 odd, 53–57, 59–63 odd, 64, 68, 70–83	16–52, 71–74	53–64, 68, 70, 75–83
BL Advanced	53–77 (optional: 78–83)		

Example 4 p. 63

Evaluate each expression.

38. $|8|$ **8**
39. $|-17|$ **17**
40. $|-21|$ **21**
41. $-|15|$ **−15**
42. $|0| + -|4|$ **−4**
43. $-|-7| + |12|$ **5**
44. $|12| - |-2|$ **10**
45. $|-32| - |-6|$ **26**
46. $|18 - 4| - |9 - 4|$ **9**

Example 5 p. 63

ALGEBRA Evaluate each expression if $x = -3$, $y = 4$, and $z = 2$.

47. $10 - |x|$ **7**
48. $2y - |x|$ **5**
49. $|z| + 19$ **21**
50. $3y + 3z + |x|$ **21**
51. $|4yz| - 3|x|$ **23**
52. $2(z + y) - |x|$ **9**

B

53. **MOVIES** Each week, movies are ranked based on ticket sales. The top movies for one week are listed in the table showing the change in position from the previous week. Which movie had the greatest absolute change? Explain. **See margin.**

Movie	A	B	C	D	E	F	G	H
Change in Position	−2	−7	+1	−3	+2	−8	−4	0

Real-World Link

In 2006, 1.4 billion people attended movie theatres. This was more than theme park and sporting event attendance combined.

Source: Motion Picture Association

SCIENCE The table below shows the freezing point of various elements.

Element	Freezing Point (°C)
chlorine	−101
helium	−272
krypton	−157
neon	−249
nitrogen	−201

54. Write two inequalities using the freezing point of neon and helium. **−272 < −249; −249 > −272**
55. Order the temperatures from least to greatest using a number line. **−272, −249, −201, −157, −101**
56. Is the absolute value of the freezing point of chlorine greater than or less than the absolute value of the freezing point of nitrogen? **less than**
57. **SOLAR SYSTEM** The average temperature of Saturn is −218°F while the average temperature of Jupiter is −162°F. Which planet has the lower average temperature? Explain. **Saturn; −218 < −162**

Order the integers in each set from greatest to least.

58. $\{4, -2, -10, 3\}$ **4, 3, −2, −10**
59. $\{-13, 5, 0, -5\}$ **5, 0, −5, −13**
60. $\{7, -26, -15, 32, -19\}$ **32, 7, −15, −19, −26**
61. $\{-28, 62, -35, 20, -59\}$ **62, 20, −28, −35, −59**
62. $\{-42, 1, -6, 74, 0, -11\}$ **74, 1, 0, −6, −11, −42**
63. $\{88, -72, -83, 232, -165, -94\}$ **232, 88, −72, −83, −94, −165**

H.O.T. Problems

Use Higher-Order Thinking Skills

64. **OPEN ENDED** Write a real-world situation in which you compare two negative integers. **Sample answer: A temperature of −2°F is greater than a temperature of −5°F.**

C

CHALLENGE Determine whether each statement is *always*, *sometimes*, or *never* true. Explain your reasoning.

65. $|x| = |-x|$
66. $|x| = -|x|$
67. $|-x| = -|x|$
68. **REASONING** Find all the values of x that make the statement $|x| = 7$ true. **7, −7**
69. **CHALLENGE** What is the least integer value of n such that $n > 0$? **1**
70. **WRITING IN MATH** Order the integers −12, −5, −15, −10, −3 from least to greatest without using a number line. Explain your method. **See margin.**

65. Always; the absolute value of a non-zero number is always positive.

66. Sometimes; when $x = 0$, $|0| = -|0|$, but when $x = 1$, $|1| \neq -|1|$.

67. Sometimes; when $x = 0$, $|-0| = -0$, but when $x = 1$, $|-1| \neq -1$.

Additional Answers

53. Movie F; the absolute value of −8 is 8 and 8 is greater than any other value in the table.

70. −15, −12, −10, −5, −3; Sample answer: Order the integers from greatest to least according to their absolute values. Then, order these absolute values from greatest to least. Replacing these absolute values with their original integers orders the original set integers from least to greatest.

Enrichment CRM p. 10 OL BL

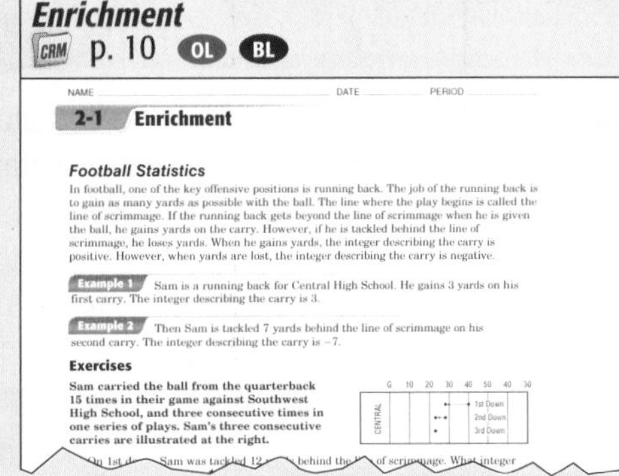
2-1 Enrichment

Football Statistics

In football, one of the key offensive positions is running back. The job of the running back is to gain as many yards as possible with the ball. The line where the play begins is called the line of scrimmage. If the running back gets beyond the line of scrimmage when he is given the ball, he gains yards on the carry. However, if he is tackled behind the line of scrimmage, he loses yards. When he gains yards, the integer describing the carry is positive. However, when yards are lost, the integer describing the carry is negative.

Example 1 Sam is a running back for Central High School. He gains 3 yards on his first carry. The integer describing the carry is 3.

Example 2 Then Sam is tackled 7 yards behind the line of scrimmage on his second carry. The integer describing the carry is −7.

Exercises

Sam carried the ball from the quarterback 15 times in their game against Southwest High School, and three consecutive times in one series of plays. Sam's three consecutive carries are illustrated at the right.

Study Guide and Intervention CRM pp. 5–6 AL OL ELL

2-1 Study Guide and Intervention

Integers and Absolute Value

Compare and Order Integers The set of integers can be written {..., −3, −2, −1, 0, 1, 2, 3, ...} where ... means continues indefinitely. Two integers can be compared using an inequality, which is a mathematical sentence containing < or >.

Example 1 Write an integer for each situation.

a. 16 feet below the surface — The integer is −16.
b. 5 strokes over par — The integer is +5 or 5.

Example 2 Use the integers graphed on the number line below.

Replace each ● with < or > to make a true sentence.

a. −6 ● −2 — −2 is greater since it lies to the right of −6. So write −6 < −2.
b. 3 ● −4 — 3 is greater since it lies to the right of −4. So write 3 > −4.

Exercises

Write an integer for each situation.

1. 2 inches less than normal **−2**
2. 13°F above average **+13 or 13**
3. a deposit of $50 **+50 or 50**
4. a loss of 8 yards **−8**

Replace each ● with <, >, or = to make a true sentence.

5. 4 ● −4 **>** 6. 8 ● 12 **<** 7. −7 ● −5 **<** 8. 2 ● 5 **<**
9. −1 ● 1 **<** 10. 4 ● −3 **>** 11. 6 ● 8 **<** 12. −2 ● 12 **<**
13. 9 ● −1 **>** 14. −6 ● −6 **=** 15. 5 ● −3 **>** 16. −10 ● 2 **<**

Chapter 2 5 Glencoe Pre-Algebra

Practice CRM p. 8 AL OL BL ELL

2-1 Practice

Integers and Absolute Value

Write an integer for each situation. Then graph on a number line.

1. an elevator ascends 4 floors **+4 or 4**
2. to be at par **0**
3. 11°F below zero **−11**
4. a profit of $52 on a sale **+52 or 52**

Replace each ● with <, >, or = to make a true sentence.

5. 0 ● −5 **>** 6. 10 ● −10 **>** 7. −8 ● 3 **<** 8. 11 ● 11 **=**
9. −18 ● −18 **=** 10. −18 ● 18 **<** 11. 18 ● −18 **>** 12. 18 ● 18 **=**
13. −120 ● −95 **<** 14. 35 ● −12 **>** 15. −35 ● 12 **<** 16. 41 ● 17 **>**

Evaluate each expression.

17. $|-7|$ **7** 18. $|14|$ **14** 19. $|-11|$ **11**
20. $|-9| - |6|$ **3** 21. $|-18| - |-8|$ **10** 22. $|-12| + |1|$ **13**
23. $|8 - 4|$ **4** 24. $|23| - |18|$ **5** 25. $|-16| + |-22|$ **38**

ALGEBRA Evaluate each expression if $a = -3$, $b = 0$, and $c = 1$.

26. $|a| - |c|$ **2** 27. $|a| + |c|$ **4** 28. $|ab| + c$ **1**
29. $5 - |ac|$ **2** 30. $c + |-5|$ **6** 31. $c + |5|$ **6**

32. WEATHER At 6:15 A.M. the temperature was −8°F. At 12:15 P.M. the temperature was −12°F. At 6:16 P.M. the temperature was −10°F. Order the temperatures from least to greatest. **−12°F, −10°F, −8°F**

Chapter 2 8 Glencoe Pre-Algebra

Word Problem Practice CRM p. 9 AL OL BL

2-1 Word Problem Practice

Integers and Absolute Value

1. ELEVATION The surface of the Dead Sea is 1312 feet below sea level. Use an integer to express the surface of the Dead Sea in relation to sea level. **−1312**

2. FOOTBALL During a football game between the Eagles and the Bears, the quarterback of the Eagles was tackled for a loss of six yards. Use an integer to express the Eagles' new location on the football field in relation to their previous location. **−6**

3. WINDCHILL The windchill factor, shown in the table below, indicates how much colder the wind feels than the actual outdoor temperature. How much colder does it feel when the outdoor temperature is 10°F and the wind is blowing at 10 miles per hour? **14°F colder**

4. BANKING One page in Joe's check register looks like the following table. How do the total deposits compare with the total withdrawals?

Description	Deposit	Withdrawal	Balance
Movies		$15	$360
Paycheck	$300		$660
Gas		$25	$635
Groceries		$50	$585
Car		$150	$435

The value of Joe's deposit equals $300; the value of his withdrawals equals $240. His deposits are greater than his withdrawals.

5. GOLF Joe is a golfer. He keeps track of his scores by noting the difference between his score and par, the number of swings it should take the ball to descend into the hole. The scorecard below shows Joe's scores from a recent round of golf.

a. Compare Joe's scores on the 7th and 13th holes. **1 > −1**
b. Compare Joe's scores on the 6th and 18th holes. **−2 < −1**
c. Write the scores for the 1st, 3rd, 4th, and 8th holes in the order from least to greatest. **−1, 0, 1, 2**

Chapter 2 9 Glencoe Pre-Algebra

4 Assess

Crystal Ball Have students write about how today's lesson on integers and absolute value will help with tomorrow's lesson on adding integers.

Multiple Representations In Exercise 77, students use an equation to generate a function table and then graph the ordered pairs to show cost relations.

Additional Answers

73. –10, –9, –4, 0, 5, 7; Sample answer: Graph each integer on a number line. Then write the numbers as they appear from left to right. The integers –10, –9, –4, 0, 5, and 7 are in order from least to greatest.

75. Positive; as the number of hours increases, the number of homeruns increases. Thus, the scatter plot shows a positive relationship.

76. No relationship; Sample answer: the data appears random on a scatter plot.

77a. $y = 3x$

77b.

x	y
3	9
4	12
5	15
6	18

77c.

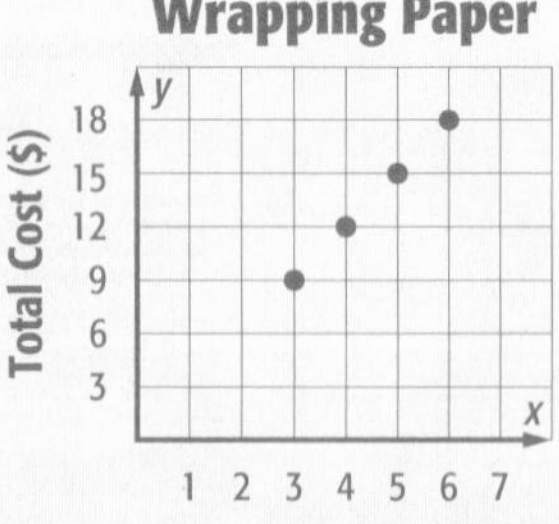

Standardized Test Practice

71. Which of the following statements is false if $a = 3$ and $b = -3$? **D**

A $|b| = a$ C $|b| = |a|$
B $|b| > 0$ D $|b| < 0$

72. If $|x| = 1$, what is the value of x? **J**

F 1 and 2 H -1 and 0
G 1 and 0 J 1 and -1

73. **EXTENDED RESPONSE** Order the integers $|-5|$, $-|9|$, -4, 0, $-|10|$, 7 from least to greatest. Explain how you determined the order. **See margin.**

74. The table shows the number of points selected players have at the end of a game.

Player	Points
A	−10
B	−50
C	−5
D	0
E	−15

Which list shows the finishing order of the players from first to fifth? **A**

A D, C, A, E, B
B B, E, A, C, D
C D, C, A, B, E
D B, C, A, D, E

Spiral Review

Determine whether a scatter plot of the data for the following might show a *positive, negative,* or *no* relationship. Explain your answer. (Lesson 1-6) **75–77. See margin.**

75.

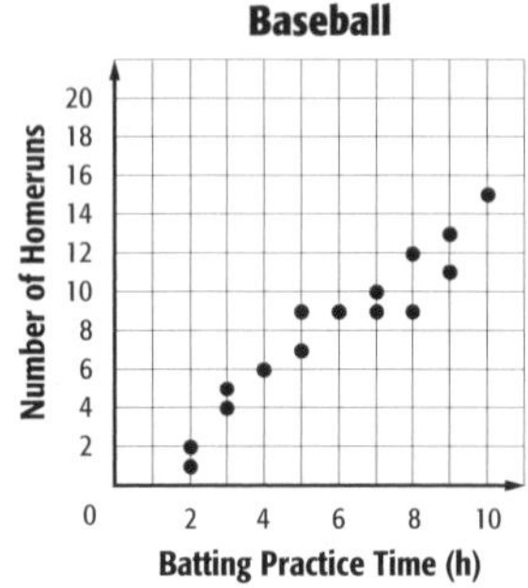

76.

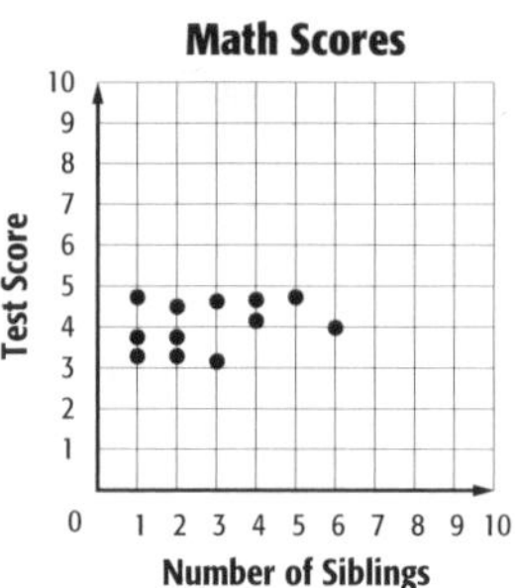

77. **MULTIPLE REPRESENTATIONS** A roll of wrapping paper costs $3. (Lesson 1-5)

a. **ALGEBRAIC** Write an equation that can be used to find the cost y of buying x number of rolls of wrapping paper.

b. **TABULAR** Make a function table to find the cost of 3, 4, 5, and 6 rolls.

c. **GRAPHICAL** Graph the ordered pairs.

Skills Review

Find each sum or difference. (Previous Course)

78. 121 − 56 **65** **79.** 381 + 57 **438** **80.** 743 − 259 **484**

81. 427 + 598 **1025** **82.** 892 − 645 **247** **83.** 63 + 97 + 21 **181**

Differentiated Instruction OL BL

Extension Have students provide a real-world situation in which they would use positive numbers and another in which they would use negative numbers. In each situation, they should explain what the positive and negative numbers represent. Sample answer: 50 feet above sea level is a positive number since sea level represents 0 and numbers above sea level or 0 are positive numbers. The second floor of an underground parking garage is a negative number since ground level represents 0 and numbers below ground level or 0 are negative numbers.

EXPLORE 2-2

Algebra Lab: Adding Integers

Math Online glencoe.com
Math *in Motion*, Animation

You can use algebra tiles and an integer mat to model operations with integers. In a set of algebra tiles, [1] represents the integer 1, and [−1] represents the integer −1.

ACTIVITY 1

Find the sum −2 + (−4) using algebra tiles.

Recall that addition means *to combine*. The expression, −2 + (−4) tells you to combine a set of 2 negative tiles with a set of 4 negative tiles.

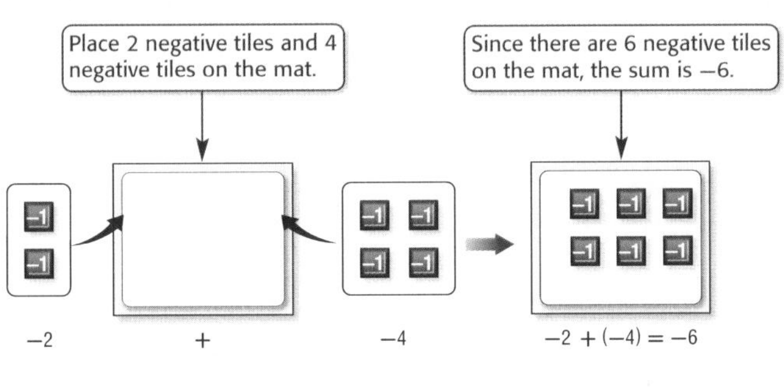
Place 2 negative tiles and 4 negative tiles on the mat.
Since there are 6 negative tiles on the mat, the sum is −6.
−2
+
−4
−2 + (−4) = −6

So, −2 + (−4) = −6.

One positive tile paired with one negative tile is called a **zero pair.** You can add or remove zero pairs from a mat because removing or adding zero does not change the value of the tiles on the mat.

ACTIVITY 2

Find the sum −3 + 2 using algebra tiles.

Place 3 negative tiles and 2 positive tiles on the mat.

Remove 2 zero pairs.

Since there is one negative tile remaining, the sum is −1.

−3 | + | 2 | −3 + 2 | −3 + 2 = −1

So, −3 + 2 = −1.

EXPLORE 2-2

Lesson Notes

1 FOCUS

Objective Add integers using algebra tiles.

Materials for Each Group

- algebra tiles
- integer mats

Easy to Make Manipulatives

Teaching Pre-Algebra with Manipulatives, templates for:

- algebra tiles, pp. 7–8
- integer mat, p. 12

2 TEACH

Working in Cooperative Groups

Arrange students in pairs or small groups, mixing abilities. Then have them complete Activities 1–3.

Ask:

- What makes a zero pair? one positive tile and one negative tile
- How does adding zero to a number change it? It does not change the number. The number's value remains the same.
- In Activity 3, what is the sum of 1 and −2 as shown in the table? −1 What addition sentence represents the sum? 1 + (−2) = −1

Explore 2-2 Algebra Lab: Adding Integers 67

Practice Have students complete Exercises 1–15.

3 ASSESS

Formative Assessment

Use Exercises 1–8 to assess whether students understand how to model a sum using algebra tiles.

Use Exercises 9–11 to assess whether students see patterns in the addition of integers.

From Concrete to Abstract

Use Exercise 15 to determine whether students understand how to add integers without the use of manipulatives.

Additional Answers

9. The addends are both +, or one is + and one – with the + addend having the greater absolute value.

10. The addends are both –, or one is + and one – with the – addend having the greater absolute value.

13. Yes; Sample answer: $-1 + 3 = 2$ and $3 + (-1) = 2$; $-2 + (-1) = -3$; $-1 + (-2) = -3$

14. Yes; Sample answer:

$$[3 + (-2)] + (-1) = 3 + [(-2) + (-1)]$$
$$1 + (-1) = 3 + (-3)$$
$$0 = 0$$

$$[1 + (-2)] + 2 = 1 + [(-2) + 2]$$
$$-1 + 2 = 1 + 0$$
$$1 = 1$$

15. Sample answer: If two integers have the same sign, add and keep the sign. If two integers have different signs, subtract and keep the sign of the integer with the greater absolute value.

ACTIVITY 3

Complete the Addition Table below using algebra tiles.

In the highlighted portion of the table, the addends are −4 and 3, and the sum is −1. So, $-4 + 3 = -1$.

Addition Table

+	4	3	2	1	0	−1	−2	−3	−4
4	8	7	6	5	4	3	2	1	0
3	7	6	5	4	3	2	1	0	−1
2	6	5	4	3	2	1	0	−1	−2
1	5	4	3	2	1	0	−1	−2	−3
0	4	3	2	1	0	−1	−2	−3	−4
−1	3	2	1	0	−1	−2	−3	−4	−5
−2	2	1	0	−1	−2	−3	−4	−5	−6
−3	1	0	−1	−2	−3	−4	−5	−6	−7
−4	0	−1	−2	−3	−4	−5	−6	−7	−8

addends (top row) · sums (body) · addends (left column)

Analyze the Results

Model and find each sum using algebra tiles. 1–8. See Chapter 2 Answer Appendix for models.

1. $-2 + (-1)$ **−3** **2.** $-4 + (-4)$ **−8** **3.** $-3 + (-4)$ **−7** **4.** $-6 + (-3)$ **−9**

5. $1 + (-2)$ **−1** **6.** $(-5) + 3$ **−2** **7.** $(-2) + 2$ **0** **8.** $2 + (-6)$ **−4**

For Exercises 9–11, use the Addition Table above. 9–10. See margin.

9. MAKE A CONJECTURE Look at all of the positive sums in the table. What is true about the addends that result in a positive sum?

10. MAKE A CONJECTURE Look at all of the negative sums in the table. What is true about the addends that result in a negative sum?

11. MAKE A CONJECTURE Look at all of the sums that are zero. What is true about the addends that result in a sum of zero? **They are additive inverses.**

For Exercises 12–14, does it appear that the property is true for addition of integers? If so, write two examples that illustrate the property. If not, give a counterexample. 13–15. See margin.

12. Identity Property **Yes; Sample answer: $-1 + 0 = -1$; $0 + (-2) = -2$**

13. Commutative Property

14. Associative Property

15. WRITING IN MATH Write a rule to help you determine the sum of any two integers.

2-2 Adding Integers

Why?

An increase in temperature is represented by a positive integer. A decrease in temperature is represented by a negative integer. In one hour, the temperature dropped 2 degrees. In the next hour, the temperature dropped an additional 3 degrees.

a. What integer represents the total temperature change over these two hours? −5

b. Write an addition expression that describes this situation. −2 + (−3)

c. Suppose the temperature rose 4 degrees in the third hour and dropped 1 degree in the fourth hour. Write an addition expression to represent the temperature change over all four hours. What integer represents that change? −2 + (−3) + 4 + (−1); −2

Then
You added integers using algebra tiles. (Explore 2-2)

Now
- Add two integers.
- Add more than two integers.

New Vocabulary
opposites
additive inverse

Math Online
glencoe.com
- Extra Examples
- Personal Tutor
- Self-Check Quiz
- Homework Help

Add Integers The equation −2 + (−3) = −5 is an example of adding two integers with the same sign. Notice the sign of the sum is the same as the sign of the addends.

EXAMPLE 1 Add Integers Using a Number Line

Find −1 + (−5).

Use a number line.

Step 1 Start at zero.

Step 2 Move 1 unit to the left.

Step 3 From there, move 5 more units to the left.

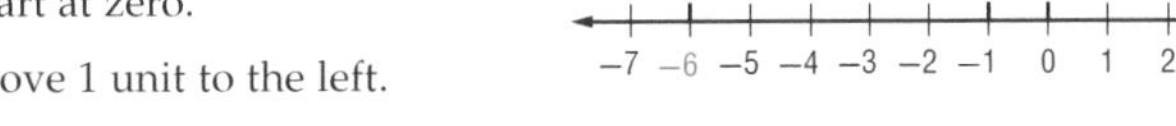

So, −1 + (−5) = −6.

Check Your Progress

Find each sum.

1A. −3 + (−4) −7 **1B.** −6 + (−14) −20 **1C.** −7 + (−2) −9

Personal Tutor glencoe.com

These and other similar examples suggest a rule for adding integers with the same sign.

Key Concept — Adding Integers with the Same Sign (For Your FOLDABLE)

Words To add integers with the same sign, add their absolute values. The sum is:
- positive if both integers are positive.
- negative if both integers are negative.

Examples −2 + (−4) = −6 8 + 1 = 9

2-2 Lesson Notes

1 FOCUS

Vertical Alignment

Before Lesson 2-2
Add integers using algebra tiles.

Lesson 2-2
Add two integers and add more than two integers.

After Lesson 2-2
Use appropriate operations to solve problems involving integers.

2 TEACH

Scaffolding Questions

Have students read the *Why?* section of the lesson and answer the questions.

Ask:
- Where on the thermometer is the starting temperature? 0°
- Suppose the temperature started at 3°. What expression would represent a drop in two degrees followed by another drop in three degrees? 3 + (−2) + (−3) What integer represents this change? −2°
- Suppose the temperature started at −6° and rose 8 degrees. Write an addition expression describing the situation. −6 + 8 What integer represents this change? 2°

Lesson 2-2 Resources

Resource	Approaching-Level	On-Level	Beyond-Level	English Learners
Teacher Edition	• Differentiated Instruction, p. 71	• Differentiated Instruction, p. 74	• Differentiated Instruction, p. 74	• Differentiated Instruction, p. 71
Chapter Resource Masters	• Study Guide and Intervention, pp. 11–12 • Skills Practice, p. 13 • Practice, p. 14 • Word Problem Practice, p. 15	• Study Guide and Intervention, pp. 11–12 • Skills Practice, p. 13 • Practice, p. 14 • Word Problem Practice, p. 15 • Enrichment, p. 16	• Practice, p. 14 • Word Problem Practice, p. 15 • Enrichment, p. 16	• Study Guide and Intervention, pp. 11–12 • Skills Practice, p. 13 • Practice, p. 14
Transparencies	• 5-Minute Check Transparency 2-2	• 5-Minute Check Transparency 2-2	• 5-Minute Check Transparency 2-2	• 5-Minute Check Transparency 2-2
Other	• Study Notebook • Teaching Pre-Algebra with Manipulatives	• Study Notebook • Teaching Pre-Algebra with Manipulatives	• Study Notebook	• Study Notebook • Teaching Pre-Algebra with Manipulatives

Add Integers

Examples 1–5 show how to add integers with the same signs and different signs by adding and subtracting their absolute values. Students will add integers with and without a number line.

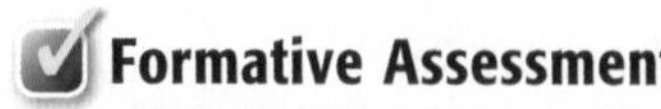

Formative Assessment

Use the Check Your Progress exercises after each example to determine students' understanding of concepts.

Additional Examples

 Find $-2 + (-4)$. -6

 Find $-5 + (-4)$. -9

 Find each sum.

a. $7 + (-11)$ -4

b. $-2 + 9$ 7

Additional Examples also in Interactive Classroom PowerPoint® Presentations

IWB INTERACTIVE WHITEBOARD READY

Focus on Mathematical Content

Adding Integers When adding two integers, it is probably easier to envision a number line. When adding integers with the same sign, move along the number line in the same direction as the sign. When the signs are different, moving from one number in the opposite direction toward the other number on a number line will yield the sum as well as the sign. The sign will be the same sign as the addend with the greatest absolute value.

EXAMPLE 2 Add Integers with the Same Sign

Find $-3 + (-6)$.

$-3 + (-6) = -9$ Add $|-3|$ and $|-6|$. Both numbers are negative, so the sum is negative.

Check Your Progress

Find each sum.

2A. $-8 + (-2)$ -10 **2B.** $-1 + (-12)$ -13

Personal Tutor glencoe.com

To add integers with different signs you can also use a number line.

StudyTip

Adding Integers on a Number Line Always start at zero. Move right to model a positive integer. Move left to model a negative integer.

EXAMPLE 3 Add Integers Using a Number Line

Find each sum.

a. $6 + (-3)$

Use a number line.

Step 1 Start at zero.

Step 2 Move 6 units to the right.

Step 3 From there, move 3 units to the left.

So, $6 + (-3) = 3$.

b. $1 + (-4)$

Use a number line.

Step 1 Start at zero.

Step 2 Move 1 unit to the right.

Step 3 From there, move 4 units to the left.

So, $1 + (-4) = -3$.

Check Your Progress

3A. $5 + (-2)$ 3 **3B.** $4 + (-8)$ -4

Personal Tutor glencoe.com

These examples suggest a rule for adding integers with different signs.

Key Concept Adding Integers with Different Signs

For Your FOLDABLE

Words To add integers with different signs, subtract their absolute values. The sum is:

- positive if the positive integer's absolute value is greater.
- negative if the negative integer's absolute value is greater.

Examples $9 + (-4) = 5$ $-9 + 4 = -5$

Tips for New Teachers

Direction on a Number Line Tell students that positive indicates a movement right and negative a movement left. When adding a positive integer to a positive or negative integer, move right on the number line. When adding a negative integer to a positive or negative integer, move left on the number line.

EXAMPLE 4 Add Integers with Different Signs

Find each sum.

a. $12 + (-6)$

$12 + (-6) = 6$ — **To find $12 + (-6)$, subtract $|-6|$ from $|12|$. The sum is positive because $|12| > |-6|$.**

b. $-7 + 5$

$-7 + 5 = -2$ — **To find $-7 + 5$, subtract $|5|$ from $|-7|$. The sum is negative because $|-7| > |2|$.**

Check Your Progress

4A. $-20 + 4$ -16 **4B.** $16 + (-5)$ 11

Personal Tutor glencoe.com

Real-World EXAMPLE 5 Solve Equations

WHALES **A blue whale was at a depth of 275 feet below the surface of the water. After 10 minutes, it rose 194 feet. What is the current depth of the blue whale? Write an addition equation and then solve.**

Words	Beginning depth	plus	increase after 10 minutes	equals	current depth
Variable	Let d = the current depth.				
Equation	-275	$+$	194	$=$	d

Solve the equation. **Estimate $-275 + 200 = -75$.**

$-275 + 194 = d$ **To find the sum, subtract 194 from $|-275|$.**

$-81 = d$ **The sum is negative because $|-275| > |194|$.**

The current depth is -81 feet. **Check for Reasonableness $-81 \approx -75$ ✓**

Real-World Link

The blue whale is the largest mammal on Earth. It can grow up to 100 feet long and can weigh as much as 300,000 pounds. There's enough room on its tongue for 50 people!

Source: National Geographic

Check Your Progress

5. SCUBA DIVING A scuba diver is 120 feet below the water's surface. She then ascends 83 feet. What is her current depth? Write an addition equation and then solve. $-120 + 83 = x$; -37 ft

Personal Tutor glencoe.com

Add More Than Two Integers The integers -4 and 4 are an example of opposites. **Opposites** are two numbers with the same absolute value but different signs. An integer and its opposite are also called **additive inverses**.

Key Concept Additive Inverse Property

Words The sum of any number and its additive inverse is zero.

Examples $2 + (-2) = 0$ **Symbols** $a + (-a) = 0$

This property will be useful when adding 2 or more integers.

Additional Examples

4 Find each sum.

a. $-9 + 10$ 1

b. $8 + (-15)$ -7

5 **WEATHER** On February 1, the temperature at dawn was -22°F. By noon it had risen 19 degrees. Write an addition equation and solve. $-22 + 19 = t$; -3°F

Tips for New Teachers

You can create a game for two or more students that involves operations with integers. Make two spinners showing the numbers -6 to $+6$. Each player should have a blank addition table. Player one will spin both spinners and create an addition problem containing the numbers shown and writing the correct answer in the table. Player two repeats this procedure. The first player to fill their table wins. This game can be repeated with subtraction and multiplication as well.

+	−6	−5	−4	...	4	5	6
−6							
−5							
−4							
...							
4							
5							
6							

Differentiated Instruction

If students are having difficulty adding integers,

Then write an addition sentence on the board such as $8 + (-5)$ and have students act out adding the integers. For example, have 8 students come to the front of the class and hand each a sheet of yellow construction paper with a (+) sign on it. Then have 5 students come to the front of the class and hand each a sheet of red construction paper with a (–) sign on it. Ask a student volunteer to pair students with a positive and a negative sign, and have each pair sit down. Ask questions like these: How many students remain standing? What is the sign on the number?

Additional Example

6 Find each sum.

a. –8 + (–4) + 8 –4

b. 6 + (–3) + (–9) + 2 –4

Add More Than Two Integers

Example 6 shows how to add more than two integers using the Commutative, Associative, Additive Inverse, and Identity Properties.

Tips for New Teachers

Properties Remember to emphasize the Additive Inverse Property throughout the year.

3 PRACTICE

Formative Assessment

Use Exercises 1–8 to check for understanding.

Use the chart at the bottom of this page to customize assignments for your students.

StudyTip

Adding Mentally
- One way to add a group of integers mentally is to look for addends that are opposites.
- Another way is to group the positive addends together and the negative addends together. Then add.

EXAMPLE 6 Add More Than Two Integers

Find each sum.

a. $-6 + (-15) + 6$

$-6 + (-15) + 6 = -6 + 6 + (-15)$	**Commutative Property**
$= 0 + (-15)$	**Additive Inverse Property**
$= -15$	**Identity Property of Addition**

b. $7 + (-1) + 26 + (-13)$

$7 + (-1) + 26 + (-13) = 7 + 26 + (-1) + (-13)$	**Commutative Property**
$= (7 + 26) + [-1 + (-13)]$	**Associative Property**
$= 33 + (-14)$ or 19	**Simplify.**

Check Your Progress

6A. $4 + (-2) + (-7)$ **–5**

6B. $-10 + 3 + (-7) + 12$ **–2**

Personal Tutor glencoe.com

Check Your Understanding

Examples 1–4 pp. 69–71

Find each sum.

1. $-5 + (-6)$ **–11**
2. $14 + (-5)$ **9**
3. $-18 + 11$ **–7**
4. $16 + (-13)$ **3**

Example 5 p. 71

5. GAME SHOWS A contestant has –1500 points. He loses another 1250 points. What is his new score? Write an addition equation and then solve. **$-1500 + (-1250) = p$; –2750**

Example 6 p. 72

Find each sum.

6. $-7 + 14 + 7$ **14**
7. $11 + (-2) + (-10)$ **–1**
8. $-5 + 4 + (-5) + 3$ **–3**

Practice and Problem Solving

= **Step-by-Step Solutions** begin on page R11.
Extra Practice begins on page 810.

Examples 1–4 pp. 69–71

Find each sum.

9. $-7 + (-3)$ **–10**
10. $-6 + (-14)$ **–20**
11. $17 + (-8)$ **9**
12. $21 + (-11)$ **10**
13. $8 + (-13)$ **–5**
14. $12 + (-16)$ **–4**
15. $11 + (-5)$ **6**
16. $13 + (-2)$ **11**

Example 5 p. 71

For Exercises 17 and 18, write an addition equation. Then solve.

17. FOOTBALL A football team gained 6 yards on a play. It then lost 10 yards on the next play. What was the total change of yardage for the team? **$6 + (-10) = x$; –4 yards**

18. TEMPERATURE The temperature in Rockford, Illinois, was –3°F. The temperature rose 7 degrees. What is the current temperature? **$-3 + 7 = t$; 4°F**

Example 6 p. 72

Find each sum.

19. $10 + (-3) + 3$ **10**
20. $-7 + (-1) + 7$ **–1**
21. $-15 + 8 + (-9)$ **–16**
22. $-6 + (-2) + 14$ **6**
23. $8 + (-11) + (-19) + 11$ **–11**
24. $13 + 20 + (-17) + (-13)$ **3**

Differentiated Homework Options

Level	Assignment	Two-Day Option	
AL Basic	9–24, 36, 37, 41, 44–64	9–23 odd, 45–48	10–24 even, 36, 37, 41, 44, 49–64
OL Core	9–23 odd, 25–26, 27–31 odd, 33–37, 41, 44–64	9–24, 45–48	25–26, 27–31 odd, 33, 35, 36, 37, 41, 44, 49–64
BL Advanced	25–60 (optional: 61–64)		

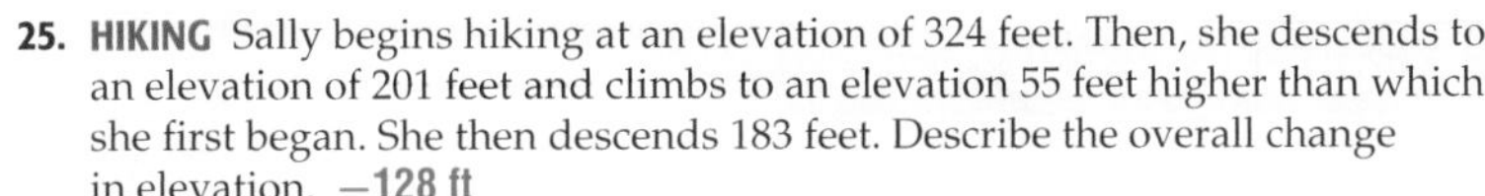

25. **HIKING** Sally begins hiking at an elevation of 324 feet. Then, she descends to an elevation of 201 feet and climbs to an elevation 55 feet higher than which she first began. She then descends 183 feet. Describe the overall change in elevation. **−128 ft**

Problem-SolvingTip

Draw a Diagram To find the overall change in elevation, draw a diagram.

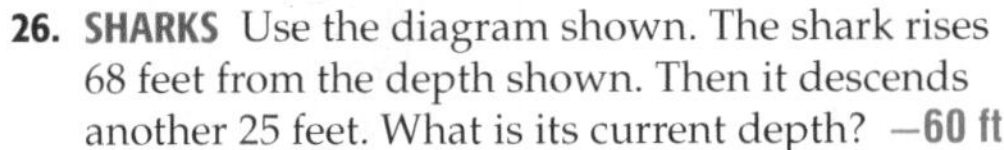

26. **SHARKS** Use the diagram shown. The shark rises 68 feet from the depth shown. Then it descends another 25 feet. What is its current depth? **−60 ft**

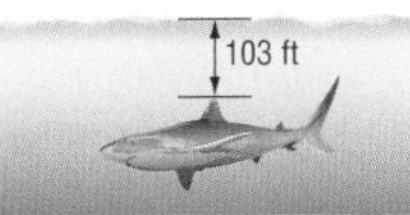

Find each sum.

27. $|-4 + 15|$ **11**
28. $|-2 + 11|$ **9**
29. $|17 - 25|$ **8**
30. $|21 - 42|$ **21**
31. $|-13 + (-22)|$ **35**
32. $|-17 + (-39)|$ **56**

33. **MUSIC TRENDS** **The table below shows the change in music sales to the nearest percent from 1997 to 2006.**

Style of Music	Percent of Music Sold in 1997	Percent Change as of 2006
Rock	33	+1
Rap/Hip Hop	10	+2
Pop	9	−2
Country	14	−1

a. What is the percent of music sold in 2006 for each of these music categories? **Rock: 34%, Rap/Hip Hop: 12%, Pop: 7%, Country: 13%**

b. What was the total percent change in the sale of these types of music? **0%**

ALGEBRA **Evaluate each sum if $x = -6$ and $y = -4$.**

34. $-35 + x + y + (-15)$ **−60**
35. $x + y + x + y$ **−20**

Real-World Link

With 38%, the United States is the leader of album sales. Japan is second with 10%.

Source: Nation Master

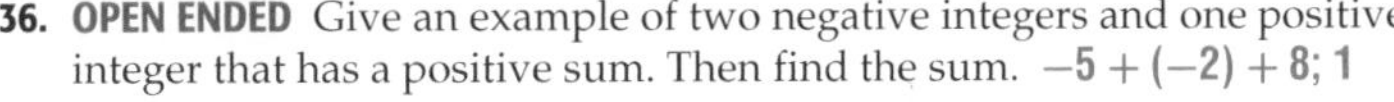

H.O.T. Problems
Use Higher-Order Thinking Skills

36. **OPEN ENDED** Give an example of two negative integers and one positive integer that has a positive sum. Then find the sum. **$-5 + (-2) + 8$; 1**

37. **WRITING IN MATH** Write a real-world problem that can be solved by using the number line shown at the right. **See margin.**

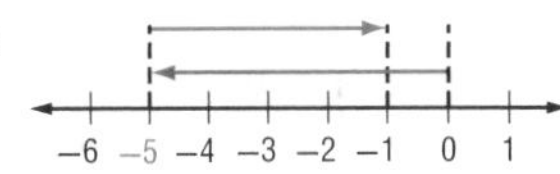

38. **CHALLENGE** *True* or *false?* $-n$ always names a negative number. If false, give a counterexample. **False; sample counterexample: If $n = -2$ then $-(-2)$ is positive.**

CHALLENGE Name the property illustrated by each of the following.

39. $a(b + (-b)) = (b + (-b))a$ **Commutative Property of Multiplication**
40. $a(b + (-b)) = 0$ **Multiplicative Property of 0**

41. **WHICH ONE DOESN'T BELONG?** Identify the expression that does not belong with the other three. Explain your reasoning.

$7 + (-13)$	$-35 + 29$	$-22 + (28)$	$-2 + (-19) + 15$

CHALLENGE **Simplify each expression.**

42. $-5x + (-2) + 3x + 9$ **$-2x + 7$**
43. $7 + (-4y) + y + (-3)$ **$4 - 3y$**

44. **WRITING IN MATH** Explain how you know the sum of 5, 4, and −5 is positive without actually adding.

41. $-22 + (28)$ equals positive 6, while the sum of the other expressions is negative 6

44. Sample answer: 5 and −5 are additive inverses and the sum of any number and its additive inverse is zero. So, the integer 4 is positive so the sum will be positive

Additional Answer

37. At midnight the temperature was 0°F. From midnight to 3:00 A.M. the temperature dropped 5°. From 3:00 A.M. to 6:00 A.M. the temperature raised 4°. What was the temperature at 6:00 A.M.?

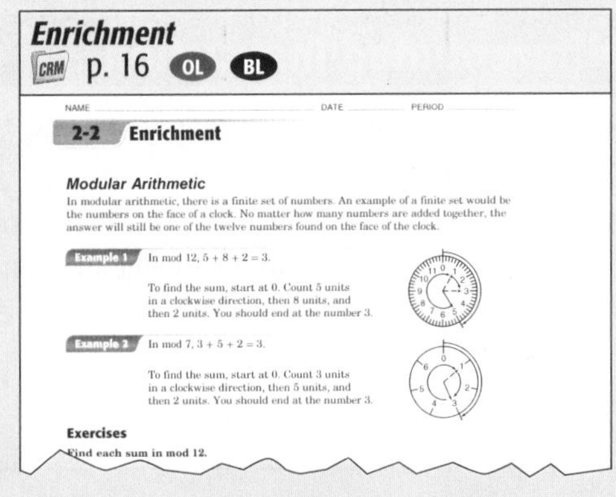

Enrichment
CRM p. 16 OL BL

NAME ______ DATE ______ PERIOD ______

2-2 Enrichment

Modular Arithmetic

In modular arithmetic, there is a finite set of numbers. An example of a finite set would be the numbers on the face of a clock. No matter how many numbers are added together, the answer will still be one of the twelve numbers found on the face of the clock.

Example 1 In mod 12, $5 + 8 + 2 = 3$.

To find the sum, start at 0. Count 5 units in a clockwise direction, then 8 units, and then 2 units. You should end at the number 3.

Example 2 In mod 7, $3 + 5 + 2 = 3$.

To find the sum, start at 0. Count 3 units in a clockwise direction, then 5 units, and then 2 units. You should end at the number 3.

Exercises

Find each sum in mod 12.

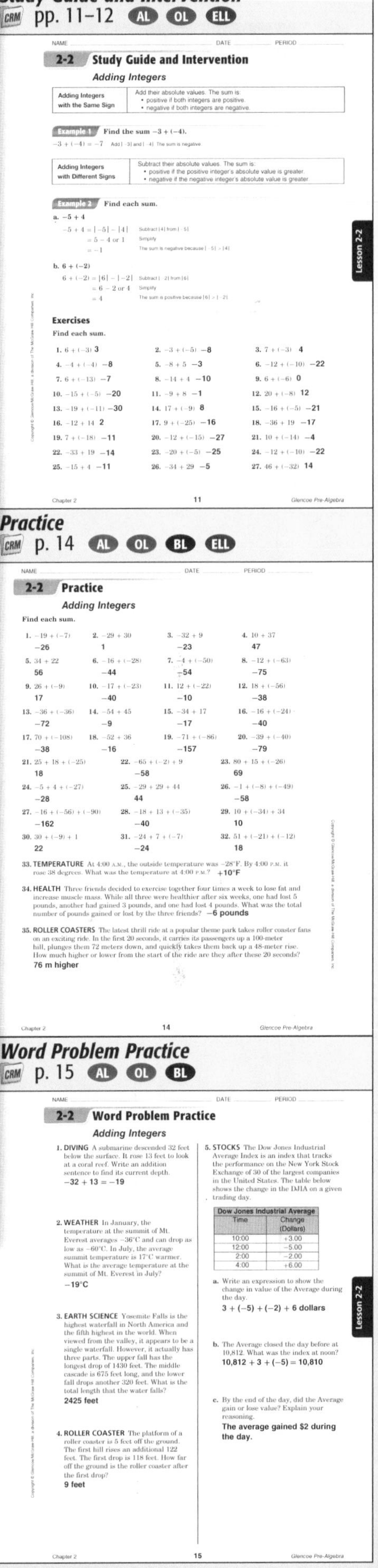

Study Guide and Intervention
CRM pp. 11–12 AL OL ELL

NAME ______ DATE ______ PERIOD ______

2-2 Study Guide and Intervention

Adding Integers

Adding Integers with the Same Sign	Add their absolute values. The sum is: • positive if both integers are positive. • negative if both integers are negative.

Example 1 Find the sum $-3 + (-4)$.

$-3 + (-4) = -7$ Add $|-3|$ and $|-4|$. The sum is negative.

Adding Integers with Different Signs	Subtract their absolute values. The sum is: • positive if the positive integer's absolute value is greater. • negative if the negative integer's absolute value is greater.

Example 2 Find each sum.

a. $-5 + 4$

$-5 + 4 = |-5| - |4|$ Subtract $|4|$ from $|-5|$.
$= 5 - 4$ or 1 Simplify.
$= -1$ The sum is negative because $|-5| > |4|$.

b. $6 + (-2)$

$6 + (-2) = |6| - |-2|$ Subtract $|-2|$ from $|6|$.
$= 6 - 2$ or 4 Simplify.
$= 4$ The sum is positive because $|6| > |-2|$.

Exercises

Find each sum.

1. $6 + (-3)$ **3**
2. $-3 + (-5)$ **−8**
3. $7 + (-3)$ **4**
4. $-4 + (-4)$ **−8**
5. $-8 + 5$ **−3**
6. $-12 + (-10)$ **−22**
7. $6 + (-13)$ **−7**
8. $-14 + 4$ **−10**
9. $6 + (-6)$ **0**
10. $-15 + (-5)$ **−20**
11. $-9 + 8$ **−1**
12. $20 + (-8)$ **12**
13. $-19 + (-11)$ **−30**
14. $17 + (-9)$ **8**
15. $-16 + (-5)$ **−21**
16. $-12 + 14$ **2**
17. $9 + (-25)$ **−16**
18. $-36 + 19$ **−17**
19. $7 + (-18)$ **−11**
20. $-12 + (-15)$ **−27**
21. $10 + (-14)$ **−4**
22. $-33 + 19$ **−14**
23. $-20 + (-5)$ **−25**
24. $-12 + (-10)$ **−22**
25. $-15 + 4$ **−11**
26. $-34 + 29$ **−5**
27. $46 + (-32)$ **14**

Chapter 2 11 *Glencoe Pre-Algebra*

Lesson 2-2

Practice
CRM p. 14 AL OL BL ELL

NAME ______ DATE ______ PERIOD ______

2-2 Practice

Adding Integers

Find each sum.

1. $-19 + (-7)$ **−26**
2. $-29 + 30$ **1**
3. $-32 + 9$ **−23**
4. $10 + 37$ **47**
5. $34 + 22$ **56**
6. $-16 + (-28)$ **−44**
7. $-4 + (-50)$ **−54**
8. $-12 + (-63)$ **−75**
9. $26 + (-9)$ **17**
10. $-17 + (-23)$ **−40**
11. $12 + (-22)$ **−10**
12. $18 + (-56)$ **−38**
13. $-36 + (-36)$ **−72**
14. $-54 + 45$ **−9**
15. $-34 + 17$ **−17**
16. $-16 + (-24)$ **−40**
17. $70 + (-108)$ **−38**
18. $-52 + 36$ **−16**
19. $-71 + (-86)$ **−157**
20. $-39 + (-40)$ **−79**
21. $25 + 18 + (-25)$ **18**
22. $-65 + (-2) + 9$ **−58**
23. $80 + 15 + (-26)$ **69**
24. $-5 + 4 + (-27)$ **−28**
25. $-29 + 29 + 44$ **44**
26. $-1 + (-8) + (-49)$ **−58**
27. $-16 + (-56) + (-90)$ **−162**
28. $-18 + 13 + (-35)$ **−40**
29. $10 + (-34) + 34$ **10**
30. $30 + (-9) + 1$ **22**
31. $-24 + 7 + (-7)$ **−24**
32. $51 + (-21) + (-12)$ **18**

33. **TEMPERATURE** At 4:00 A.M., the outside temperature was −28°F. By 4:00 P.M. it rose 38 degrees. What was the temperature at 4:00 P.M.? **+10°F**

34. **HEALTH** Three friends decided to exercise together four times a week to lose fat and increase muscle mass. While all three were healthier after six weeks, one had lost 5 pounds, another had gained 3 pounds, and one had lost 4 pounds. What was the total number of pounds gained or lost by the three friends? **−6 pounds**

35. **ROLLER COASTERS** The latest thrill ride at a popular theme park takes roller coaster fans on an exciting ride. In the first 20 seconds, it carries its passengers up a 100-meter hill, plunges them 72 meters down, and quickly takes them back up a 48-meter rise. How much higher or lower from the start of the ride are they after these 20 seconds? **76 m higher**

Chapter 2 14 *Glencoe Pre-Algebra*

Word Problem Practice
CRM p. 15 AL OL BL

NAME ______ DATE ______ PERIOD ______

2-2 Word Problem Practice

Adding Integers

1. **DIVING** A submarine descended 32 feet below the surface. It rose 13 feet to look at a coral reef. Write an addition sentence to find its current depth. **$-32 + 13 = -19$**

2. **WEATHER** In January, the temperature at the summit of Mt. Everest averages −36°C and can drop as low as −60°C. In July, the average summit temperature is 17°C warmer. What is the average temperature at the summit of Mt. Everest in July? **−19°C**

3. **EARTH SCIENCE** Yosemite Falls is the highest waterfall in North America and the fifth highest in the world. When viewed from the valley, it appears to be a single waterfall. However, it actually has three parts. The upper fall has the longest drop of 1430 feet. The middle cascade is 675 feet long, and the lower fall drops another 320 feet. What is the total length that the water falls? **2425 feet**

4. **ROLLER COASTER** The platform of a roller coaster is 5 feet off the ground. The first hill rises an additional 122 feet. The first drop is 118 feet. How far off the ground is the roller coaster after the first drop? **9 feet**

5. **STOCKS** The Dow Jones Industrial Average Index is an index that tracks the performance on the New York Stock Exchange of 30 of the largest companies in the United States. The table below shows the change in the DJIA on a given trading day.

Dow Jones Industrial Average	
Time	Change (Dollars)
10:00	+3.00
12:00	−5.00
2:00	−2.00
4:00	+6.00

a. Write an expression to show the change in value of the Average during the day. **$3 + (-5) + (-2) + 6$ dollars**

b. The Average closed the day before at 10,812. What was the index at noon? **$10{,}812 + 3 + (-5) = 10{,}810$**

c. By the end of the day, did the Average gain or lose value? Explain your reasoning. **The average gained $2 during the day.**

Lesson 2-2

Chapter 2 15 *Glencoe Pre-Algebra*

4 ASSESS

Name the Math Have students write how to find the sum $-3 + (-4) + 6$. Tell them to include the names of the properties that they used to group or add the integers.

Formative Assessment

Check for student understanding of concepts in Lessons 2-1 and 2-2.

CRM Quiz 1, p. 52

Standardized Test Practice

45. The table shows the low temperature and the high temperature on Monday for a certain city.

High Temperature	4°F
Low Temperature	−10°F

How much did the temperature rise? **A**

A 14°F
B 10°F
C 6°F
D 4°F

46. SHORT RESPONSE On a drive, a football team gained 3 yards, lost 11 yards, and gained 15 yards. What was their total yardage for that drive? **+7 yd**

47. A bird is flying at an altitude of 100 feet. It descends 30 feet then ascends 50 feet. Which of the following expressions best represents this situation? **H**

F $100 + 30 + (-50)$
G $100 + (-30) + (-50)$
H $100 + (-30) + 50$
J $100 + 30 + 50$

48. EXTENDED RESPONSE A team started with 4 points. They gained 3 points, lost 6 points, and gained 2 points. **a.** $4 + 3 + (-6) + 2$

a. Write an expression to find how many points the team has now.
b. How many points does the team have now? **3**

Spiral Review

49. WEATHER The record low temperature for Wisconsin is 54°F below zero. Write an integer to represent this situation. (Lesson 2-1) **−54**

Determine whether a scatter plot of the data for the following might show a *positive, negative,* or *no* relationship. (Lesson 1-6)

50. speed of a car and miles traveled in four hours **positive**

51. eye color and weight **no relationship**

52. car value and age of car **negative**

Name the property shown by each statement. (Lesson 1-3)

53. $12 \cdot 7 = 7 \cdot 12$ **Commutative Property (×)**

54. $1 \cdot 4 \cdot 0 = 0$ **Multiplicative Property of 0**

55. $4xy \cdot 1 = 4xy$ **Identity Property (×)**

56. SOCCER A soccer league ranks each team in their league using points. A team gets three points for a win, one point for a tie, and zero points for a loss. Write an expression that can be used to find the total number of points a team receives. (Lesson 1-2) $3w + 1t$

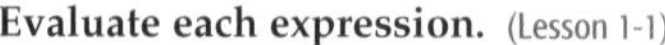

Evaluate each expression. (Lesson 1-1)

57. $9 \div 3 \cdot 6$ **18**

58. $25 - 12 \div 4$ **22**

59. $(7 \cdot 5) + (8 \cdot 2)$ **51**

60. $(34 \div 2) - (8 \cdot 2)$ **1**

Skills Review

ALGEBRA Evaluate each expression if $a = 5$, $b = 12$, and $c = 7$. (Lesson 1-2)

61. $2c - 11$ **3**

62. $4a - 16$ **4**

63. $bc - ac$ **49**

64. $(3b - c) - 4c$ **1**

Differentiated Instruction

OL BL

Extension In the table are the profits and losses for two companies, A and B, for the last 5 years. Without a calculator, scan the figures and predict which company is more profitable. Find the sum of the figures for each company. Which is more profitable? Estimates will vary; Company A is more profitable.

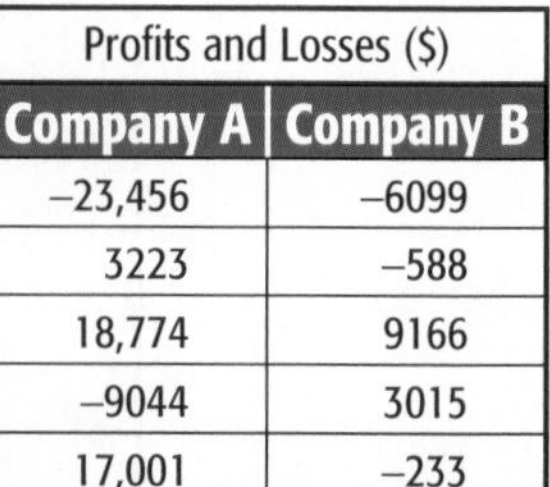

Profits and Losses ($)	
Company A	**Company B**
−23,456	−6099
3223	−588
18,774	9166
−9044	3015
17,001	−233

Subtracting Integers

Math Online glencoe.com
Math *in Motion,* Animation

You can also use algebra tiles to model subtraction of integers. Remember, one meaning of subtraction is to *take away*.

ACTIVITY 1 Find 7 − 4.

Place 7 positive tiles on the mat. Remove 4 positive tiles.

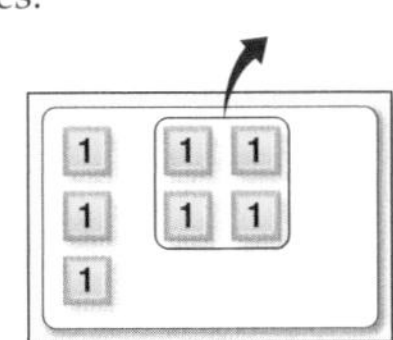

So, 7 − 4 = 3.

ACTIVITY 2 Find − 8 − (− 3).

Place 8 negative tiles on the mat. Remove 3 negative tiles.

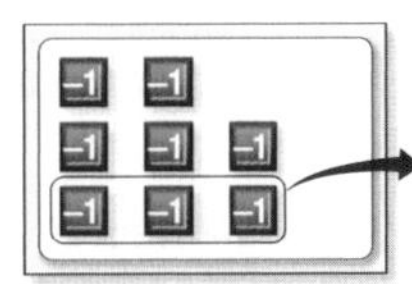

So, −8 − (−3) = −5.

ACTIVITY 3 Find 5 − (− 2).

Place 5 positive tiles on the mat. There are no negative tiles to remove. Add 2 zero pairs to the set.

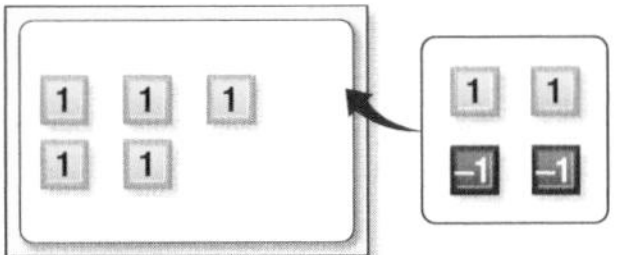

Then remove the 2 negative tiles.

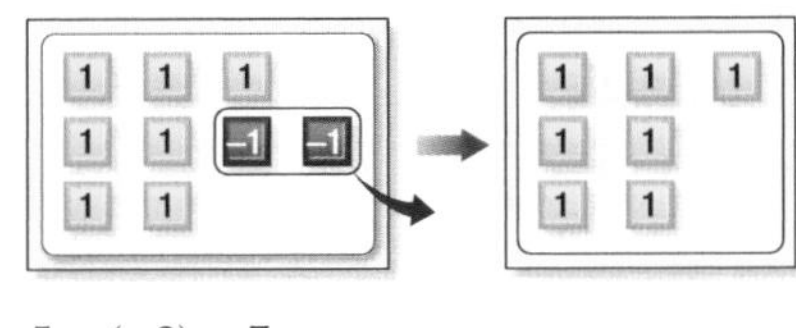

So, 5 − (−2) = 7.

ACTIVITY 4 Find − 6 − 2.

Place 6 negative tiles on the mat. Since there are no positive tiles, add 2 zero pairs to the mat.

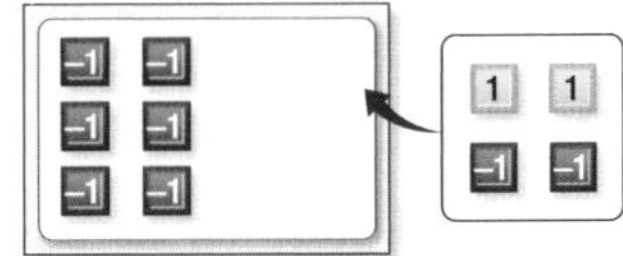

Then remove the 2 positive tiles.

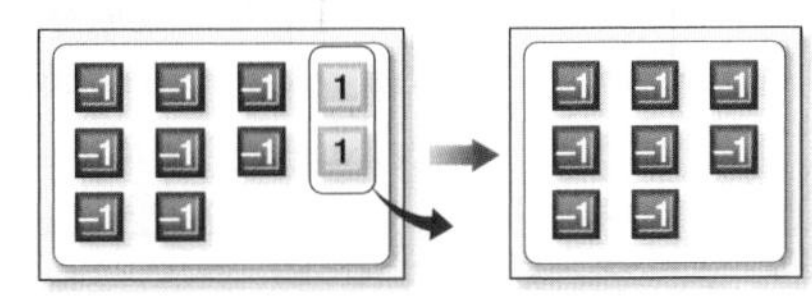

So, −6 − 2 = −8.

Analyze the Results

Model and find each difference using algebra tiles. 1–8. See Chapter 2 Answer Appendix for models.

1. 9 − 7 2
2. 5 − (−3) 8
3. 6 − (−3) 9
4. 1 − (−5) 6
5. 3 − (−9) 12
6. −8 − 3 −11
7. −8 − (−1) −7
8. −1 − 4 −5

9. MAKE A CONJECTURE Write a rule that will help you determine the sign of the difference of two integers. See margin.

Extending the Concept

Ask:

- When a negative integer is subtracted from a positive integer, is the sum always positive or negative? positive Why? Subtracting a negative integer is the same as adding a positive integer.

Additional Answer

9. Sample answer: The difference of two integers is positive when the starting number, the minuend, is greater than the number to be subtracted, the subtrahend. The difference of two integers is negative when the minuend is less than the subtrahend.

1 FOCUS

Objective Use algebra tiles to model subtraction with integers.

Materials for Each Student

- algebra tiles
- integer mats

Easy to Make Manipulatives

Teaching Pre-Algebra with Manipulatives, templates for:

- algebra tiles, pp. 7–8
- integer mat, p. 12

2 TEACH

Working in Cooperative Groups

Have students work in groups of mixed abilities to complete Activities 1–4.

Ask:

- Suppose in Activity 3 the expression was 5 − (−4). What would you do differently? Add 4 zero pairs and then remove 4 negative tiles.
- Why? There needs to be enough negative tiles to remove 4. Since there are none, add 4 zero pairs and remove 4 negative tiles, leaving the 4 positive tiles.

Practice Have students complete Exercises 1–9.

3 ASSESS

Formative Assessment

Use Exercises 1–8 to assess whether students comprehend how to subtract integers.

From Concrete to Abstract

Use Exercise 9 to assess whether students can formulate a rule for subtracting integers.

2-3 Lesson Notes

1 FOCUS

Vertical Alignment

Before Lesson 2-3
Learn to subtract integers using algebra tiles.

Lesson 2-3
Subtract integers and evaluate expressions containing variables.

After Lesson 2-3
Find and evaluate an algebraic expression to determine any term in an arithmetic sequence.

2 TEACH

Scaffolding Questions

Have students read the *Why?* section of the lesson and answer the questions.

Ask:

- What does a positive balance mean? The child has not spent all of his/her allowance.
- If Elizabeth spent another $6, how much will she owe her parents at the end of the month? Write this amount as an integer. $11; -11
- Suppose Ginny spends $11. Will she still have a positive balance? Explain. Yes; $12 - 11 = 1$, so her balance is still positive.
  What if she spends $13? No; $12 - 13 = -1$, so the balance is now negative.

2-3 Subtracting Integers

Then
You have already learned to subtract integers using algebra tiles. (Explore 2-3)

Now
- Subtract integers.
- Evaluate expressions containing variables.

Math Online
glencoe.com
- Extra Examples
- Personal Tutor
- Self-Check Quiz
- Homework Help
- Math in Motion

Why?

The table shows the amount of money remaining in the monthly allowance of the Coughlin children at the middle of the month. A negative amount means the child overspent the monthly allowance and owes his or her parents.

Children	Monthly Allowance Balance ($)
Elizabeth	−5
Ginny	12
James	4

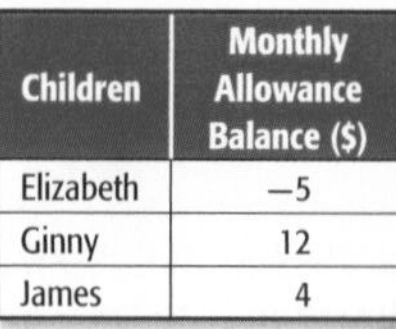

a. Suppose James spends $9 between the middle of the month and the end of the month. Write an expression to find his allowance balance at the end of the month. $4 - 9$

b. How much does James owe his parents at the end of the month? Write this amount as an integer. $5; -5

Subtract Integers The number line shows $4 - 9 = -5$.

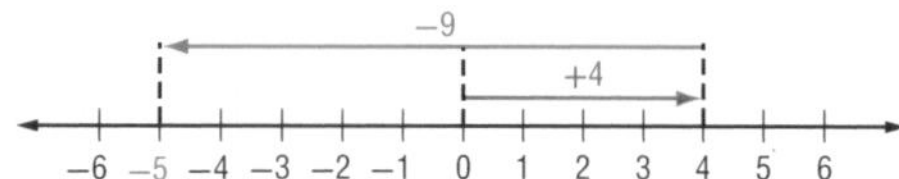

When you subtract 9 on the number line, the result is the same as adding −9.

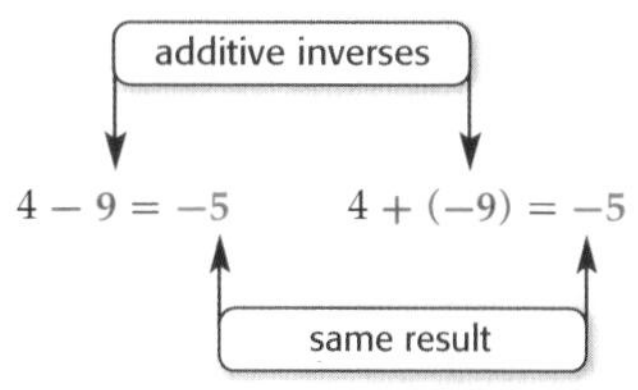

Key Concept Subtracting Integers — For Your FOLDABLE

Words To subtract an integer, add its additive inverse.

Examples $2 - 7 = 2 + (-7)$ **Symbols** $a - b = a + (-b)$

Math *in Motion*, BrainPOP® glencoe.com

EXAMPLE 1 Subtract a Positive Integer

Find each difference.

a. $6 - 15$

$6 - 15 = 6 + (-15)$ **To subtract 15, add −15.**

$= -9$ **Simplify.**

b. $-7 - 8$

$-7 - 8 = -7 + (-8)$ **To subtract 8 add −8.**

$= -15$ **Simplify.**

Check Your Progress

1A. $4 - 15$ -11

1B. $-3 - 12$ -15

Personal Tutor glencoe.com

Lesson 2-3 Resources

Resource	Approaching-Level	On-Level	Beyond-Level	English Learners
Teacher Edition	• Differentiated Instruction, p. 77	• Differentiated Instruction, pp. 77, 80	• Differentiated Instruction, p. 80	
Chapter Resource Masters	• Study Guide and Intervention, pp. 17–18 • Skills Practice, p. 19 • Practice, p. 20 • Word Problem Practice, p. 21	• Study Guide and Intervention, pp. 17–18 • Skills Practice, p. 19 • Practice, p. 20 • Word Problem Practice, p. 21 • Enrichment, p. 22	• Practice, p. 20 • Word Problem Practice, p. 21 • Enrichment, p. 22	• Study Guide and Intervention, pp. 17–18 • Skills Practice, p. 19 • Practice, p. 20
Transparencies	• 5-Minute Check Transparency 2-3	• 5-Minute Check Transparency 2-3	• 5-Minute Check Transparency 2-3	• 5-Minute Check Transparency 2-3
Other	• Study Notebook • Teaching Pre-Algebra with Manipulatives	• Study Notebook • Teaching Pre-Algebra with Manipulatives	• Study Notebook	• Study Notebook • Teaching Pre-Algebra with Manipulatives

StudyTip

Inductive Reasoning Making a conjecture based on a pattern of examples or past events

In Example 1, you subtracted a positive integer by adding its additive inverse. Use inductive reasoning to see if the method also applies to subtracting a negative integer.

Adding the Additive Inverse		
Input	rule: $4 + (-x)$	Output
2	$4 + (-2)$	2
1	$4 + (-1)$	3
0	$4 + 0$	4
−1	$4 + 1$	5

Subtracting an Integer		
Input	rule: $4 - x$	Output
2	$4 - 2$	2
1	$4 - 1$	3
0	$4 - 0$	4
−1	$4 - (-1)$	■

Continuing the pattern in the first column, $4 - (-1) = 5$. The result is the same as when you add the additive inverse.

EXAMPLE 2 **Subtract a Negative Integer**

Find each difference.

a. $9 - (-2)$

$9 - (-2) = 9 + 2$ — To subtract −2, add 2.
$= 11$

b. $3 - (-5)$

$3 - (-5) = 3 + 5$ — To subtract −5, add 5.
$= 8$

Check Your Progress

2A. $18 - (-2)$ 20

2B. $-5 - (-11)$ 6

Personal Tutor glencoe.com

Real-World Career

Climatologist
A climatologist studies the long term trends in the climate, collects climate data, investigates climate indicators, and makes predictions regarding climate patterns.

To be a climatologist, you need a bachelor's degree in meteorology or atmospheric sciences.

Source: NASA

Real-World EXAMPLE 3 **Subtract a Negative Integer**

WIND CHILL **The wind makes the outside temperature feel colder than the actual temperature. How much colder does a temperature of 10°F with a 30-mile-per-hour wind feel than the same temperature with a 20-mile-per-hour wind?**

Wind Chill Temperature				
Temperature (°F)	Wind Speed (miles per hour)			
Calm	10	20	30	
20°	9	4	1	
10°	−4	−9	−12	
0°	−16	−22	−26	
−10°	−28	−35	−39	

Understand You need to find how much colder 10°F feels with a 30-mile-per-hour wind than with a 20-mile-per-hour wind.

Plan Subtract the wind chill temperature at 20 miles per hour from the temperature at 30 miles per hour.

Solve $-12 - (-9) = -12 + 9$ — To subtract −9, add 9.
$= -3$ — Add −12 and 9.

It feels 3°F colder.

Check Since $-12 < -9$, it makes sense that the temperature is colder.

Check Your Progress

3. SPACE On Mars, the temperature ranges from 68°F during the day to −220°F at night. Find the change from the day temperature to the night temperature. −288°F

Personal Tutor glencoe.com

Differentiated Instruction 

 students are having difficulty subtracting integers,

 have them make cards: four with different positive integers and four with different negative integers. Then have them ask another student to draw two cards randomly and subtract the number on the second card from the number on the first card. Students can work in pairs, small groups, or circulate around the room.

Subtract Integers

Examples 1–3 show how to subtract a positive or negative integer by adding its additive inverse. Students will subtract negative and positive integers.

Formative Assessment

Use the Check Your Progress exercises after each example to determine students' understanding of concepts.

Additional Examples

 Find each difference.

a. $9 - 14$ −5

b. $-10 - 8$ −18

 Find each difference.

a. $15 - (-4)$ 19

b. $-11 - (-7)$ −4

 **WEATHER** Refer to the table in Example 3. How much colder does a temperature of 0°F with a 20-mile-per-hour wind feel than the same temperature with a 10-mile-per-hour wind? $-22 - (-16) = 6$°F colder

Additional Example also in Interactive Classroom PowerPoint® Presentations

IWB INTERACTIVE WHITEBOARD READY

Tips for New Teachers

Study Tip To subtract a positive integer, tell students to think about moving left on a number line from the starting integer. In Example 1a, for instance, they should start at 6 and move left 15 to end at −9. In Example 1b, they should start at −7, then move left 8 to end at −15.

Focus on Mathematical Content

Additive Inverses To *subtract* a positive or negative integer, *add* its additive inverse. When adding the additive inverse, the sum will have the same sign as the integer with the greatest absolute value. This works because subtraction and addition are inverse operations. One operation will undo the other.

Evaluate Expressions

Example 4 shows how to evaluate algebraic expressions using the rule for subtracting integers. Students will subtract integers in algebraic expressions by adding their additive inverses.

Additional Example

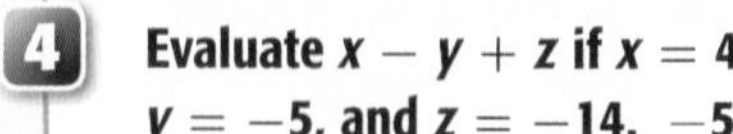

4 Evaluate $x - y + z$ if $x = 4$, $y = -5$, and $z = -14$. -5

3 PRACTICE

Formative Assessment

Use Exercises 1–12 to check for understanding.

Use the chart at the bottom of this page to customize assignments for your students.

Additional Answers

13. −1
14. −4
15. −7
16. −12
17. 15
18. 19
19. −1
20. −1
21. 10
22. 2
23. −60
24. −81

Evaluate Expressions Use the rule for subtracting integers to evaluate expressions.

EXAMPLE 4 **Evaluate Algebraic Expressions**

Evaluate.

$a - b - c$ if $a = 4$, $b = 3$, and $c = -10$.

$a - b - c = 4 - 3 - (-10)$	Replace a with 4, b with 3, and c with −10.
$= 1 - (-10)$	Use order of operations.
$= 1 + 10$	To subtract −10, add its additive inverse, 10.
$= 11$	Add 1 and 10.

Check Your Progress

Evaluate each expression if $\ell = 7$, $m = -3$, and $n = -10$.

4A. $n - \ell$ −17 **4B.** $\ell - m + n$ 0

Personal Tutor glencoe.com

Check Your Understanding

Examples 1 and 2 pp. 76–77

Find each difference.

1. $3 - 5$ −2
2. $10 - 15$ −5
3. $-10 - 14$ −24
4. $-8 - 9$ −17
5. $17 - (-14)$ 31
6. $16 - (-12)$ 28
7. $-7 - (-11)$ 4
8. $-4 - (-3)$ −1

Example 3 p. 77

9. **ANIMALS** A gopher begins at 7 inches below the surface of a garden and digs another 9 inches. Find an integer that represents the gopher's position in relation to the surface of the garden. −16 in.

Example 4 p. 78

ALGEBRA Evaluate each expression if $a = 5$, $b = -7$, and $c = -16$.

10. $2a - (-11)$ 21
11. $c - b$ −9
12. $a + b - c$ 14

Practice and Problem Solving

● = Step-by-Step Solutions begin on page R11. Extra Practice begins on page 810.

Examples 1 and 2 pp. 76–77

Find each difference. 13–24. See margin.

13. $6 - 7$
14. $4 - 8$
15. $-5 - 2$
16. $-9 - 3$
17. $5 - (-10)$
18. $1 - (-18)$
19. $-12 - (-11)$
20. $-15 - (-14)$
21. $-20 - (-30)$
22. $-38 - (-40)$
23. $-32 - 28$
24. $-47 - 34$

Example 3 p. 77

25. **FINANCIAL LITERACY** Suppose you deposited \$25 into your checking account and wrote a check for \$38. What was the change in your account balance? −\$13

26. **SCORES** At the end of the first round of a game show, Jillian had a score of 40 points and Marty had a score of −50 points. Find the difference between their two scores. 90 points

Example 4 p. 78

ALGEBRA Evaluate each expression if $a = -3$, $b = 8$, and $c = -12$.

27. $7 - b$ −1
28. $10 - c$ 22
29. $a - 9$ −12
30. $b - 5$ 3
31. $c - b$ −20
32. $c - a$ −9
33. $a + b - c$ 17
34. $a - b - c$ 1

Differentiated Homework Options

Level	Assignment	Two-Day Option	
AL Basic	13–34, 41, 42, 44–61	13–33 odd, 45–48	14–34 even, 41, 42, 44, 49–61
OL Core	13–33 odd, 35–39 odd, 40–42, 44–61	13–34, 45–48	35, 37, 39–42, 44, 49–61
BL Advanced	35–57 (optional: 58–61)		

B

35. **SPORTS** The table shows the approximate participation numbers for different high school sports.

a. Write an integer to represent the change in the participation related to each sport from 2005 to 2006.

b. What was the total change in participation related to these sports from 2005 to 2006? **44,000**

U.S. High School Sports Participation (thousands)

Sport	2005	2006
Baseball	461	472
Basketball	1002	999
Softball	366	370
Football	1047	1073
Gymnastics	21	19
Hockey	44	43
Tennis	318	327

Source: National Federation of State High School Associations

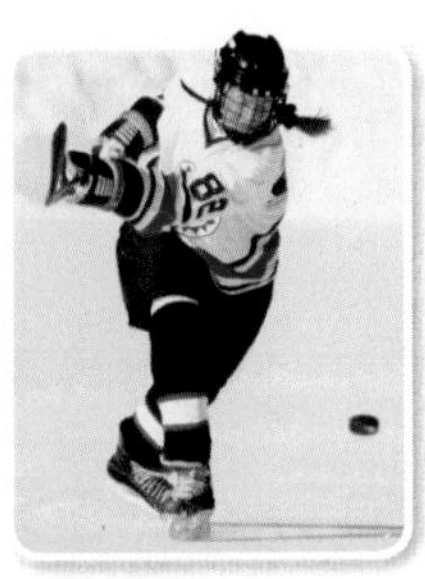

 **Real-World Link**

In 2006, the number of girls playing high school sports hit an all-time high of 2,953,355 participants.

Source: NFHS

Find each difference.

36. $125 - (-114)$ **239** 37. $-320 - (-106)$ **−214** 38. $-2200 - (-3500)$ **1300**

39. **STOCKS** The daily closing prices for a company's stock are shown.

Date	May 3	May 4	May 5	May 6	May 7
Closing Price	\$33.30	\$30.59	\$31.04	\$31.97	\$30.15
Change	—	■ **−\$2.71**	■ **\$0.45**	■ **\$0.93**	■ **−\$1.82**

a. Find the change in the closing price since the previous day. **See table.**

b. What is the difference between the highest and lowest changes? **\$3.64**

C

40. **MULTIPLE REPRESENTATIONS** In this problem, you will apply subtraction of integers to a real-world situation. An underwater video camera is 7 feet below the surface. It will be lowered an additional f feet.

a. **ALGEBRAIC** Write a function rule to show how many total feet below the surface the camera will be after it is lowered. **$-7 - f$**

b. **TABULAR** Make a function table to show the depth of the camera if it is lowered 5, 8, 10, or 12 feet. **See Chapter 2 Answer Appendix.**

35a. $+11{,}000$; -3000; $+4000$; $+26{,}000$; -2000; -1000; $+9000$

41. Sample answer: $4 - (-7)$; 11

42. No; Sample answer: Rick incorrectly made -6 $+6$ and Michael did not add the opposite.

44. Sample answer: $-4 - (-2) = -2$; $-4 + 2 = -2$; The results are the same because to subtract an integer is to add its additive inverse.

H.O.T. Problems

Use Higher-Order Thinking Skills

41. **OPEN ENDED** Write a subtraction expression with a positive integer and a negative integer whose difference is positive. Then find the difference.

C

42. **FIND THE ERROR** Rick and Michael are finding $-6 - (-2)$. Is either of them correct? Explain your reasoning.

Rick	Michael
$-6 - (-2) = 6 - 2$ $= 4$	$-6 - (-2) = -6 - 2$ $= -8$

43. **CHALLENGE** *True* or *false*? A subtraction expression with a positive integer and a negative can have a difference of zero. If *false*, give a counterexample. **False; $2 - (-2) = 4$ and $(-2) - 2 = -4$**

44. **WRITING IN MATH** Write an expression involving the subtraction of a negative integer. Then write an equivalent addition expression. Explain why the result is the same.

Multiple Representations In Exercise 40, students use a function rule and a function table to model a real-world situation involving integers.

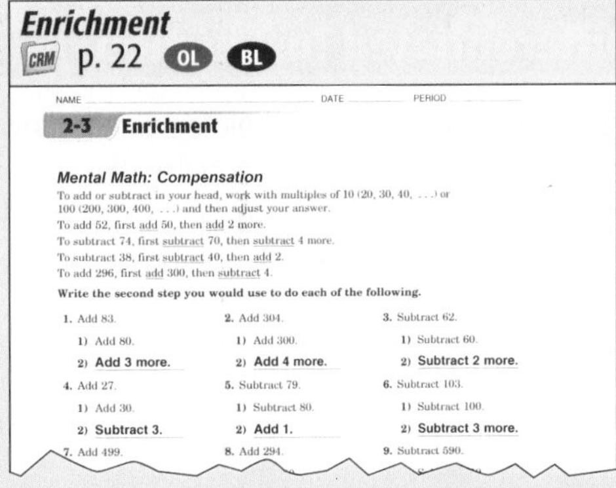

Enrichment
CRM p. 22 OL BL

NAME ______ DATE ______ PERIOD ______

2-3 Enrichment

Mental Math: Compensation

To add or subtract in your head, work with multiples of 10 (20, 30, 40, . . .) or 100 (200, 300, 400, . . .) and then adjust your answer.

To add 52, first add 50, then add 2 more.

To subtract 74, first subtract 70, then subtract 4 more.

To subtract 38, first subtract 40, then add 2.

To add 296, first add 300, then subtract 4.

Write the second step you would use to do each of the following.

1. Add 83.
 1) Add 80.
 2) **Add 3 more.**
2. Add 304.
 1) Add 300.
 2) **Add 4 more.**
3. Subtract 62.
 1) Subtract 60.
 2) **Subtract 2 more.**
4. Add 27.
 1) Add 30.
 2) **Subtract 3.**
5. Subtract 79.
 1) Subtract 80.
 2) **Add 1.**
6. Subtract 103.
 1) Subtract 100.
 2) **Subtract 3 more.**
7. Add 499.
8. Add 294.
9. Subtract 590.

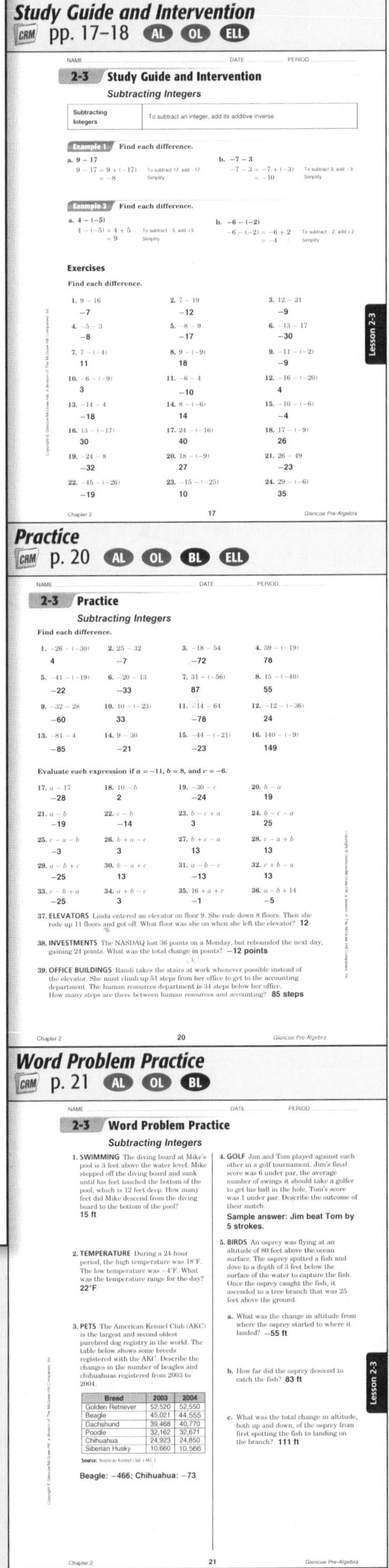

Study Guide and Intervention
CRM pp. 17–18 AL OL ELL

NAME ______ DATE ______ PERIOD ______

2-3 Study Guide and Intervention

Subtracting Integers

Subtracting Integers	To subtract an integer, add its additive inverse.

Example 1 Find each difference.

a. $9 - 17$
$9 - 17 = 9 + (-17)$ To subtract 17, add −17.
$= -8$ Simplify.

b. $-7 - 3$
$-7 - 3 = -7 + (-3)$ To subtract 3, add −3.
$= -10$ Simplify.

Example 2 Find each difference.

a. $4 - (-5)$
$4 - (-5) = 4 + 5$ To subtract −5, add +5.
$= 9$ Simplify.

b. $-6 - (-2)$
$-6 - (-2) = -6 + 2$ To subtract −2, add +2.
$= -4$ Simplify.

Exercises

Find each difference.

1. $9 - 16$ **−7**
2. $7 - 19$ **−12**
3. $12 - 21$ **−9**
4. $-5 - 3$ **−8**
5. $-8 - 9$ **−17**
6. $-13 - 17$ **−30**
7. $7 - (-4)$ **11**
8. $9 - (-9)$ **18**
9. $-11 - (-2)$ **−9**
10. $-6 - (-9)$ **3**
11. $-6 - 4$ **−10**
12. $-16 - (-20)$ **4**
13. $-14 - 4$ **−18**
14. $8 - (-6)$ **14**
15. $-10 - (-6)$ **−4**
16. $13 - (-17)$ **30**
17. $24 - (-16)$ **40**
18. $17 - (-9)$ **26**
19. $-24 - 8$ **−32**
20. $18 - (-9)$ **27**
21. $26 - 49$ **−23**
22. $-45 - (-26)$ **−19**
23. $-15 - (-25)$ **10**
24. $29 - (-6)$ **35**

Chapter 2 17 Glencoe Pre-Algebra

Practice
CRM p. 20 AL OL BL ELL

NAME ______ DATE ______ PERIOD ______

2-3 Practice

Subtracting Integers

Find each difference.

1. $-26 - (-30)$ **4**
2. $25 - 32$ **−7**
3. $-18 - 54$ **−72**
4. $59 - (-19)$ **78**
5. $-41 - (-19)$ **−22**
6. $-20 - 13$ **−33**
7. $31 - (-56)$ **87**
8. $15 - (-40)$ **55**
9. $-32 - 28$ **−60**
10. $10 - (-23)$ **33**
11. $-14 - 64$ **−78**
12. $-12 - (-36)$ **24**
13. $-81 - 4$ **−85**
14. $9 - 30$ **−21**
15. $-44 - (-21)$ **−23**
16. $140 - (-9)$ **149**

Evaluate each expression if $a = -11$, $b = 8$, and $c = -6$.

17. $a - 17$ **−28**
18. $10 - b$ **2**
19. $-30 - c$ **−24**
20. $b - a$ **19**
21. $a - b$ **−19**
22. $c - b$ **−14**
23. $b - c + a$ **3**
24. $b - c - a$ **25**
25. $c - a - b$ **−3**
26. $b + a - c$ **3**
27. $b + c - a$ **13**
28. $c - a + b$ **13**
29. $a - b + c$ **−25**
30. $b - a + c$ **13**
31. $a - b - c$ **−13**
32. $c + b - a$ **13**
33. $c - b + a$ **−25**
34. $a + b - c$ **3**
35. $16 + a + c$ **−1**
36. $a - b + 14$ **−5**

37. **ELEVATORS** Linda entered an elevator on floor 9. She rode down 8 floors. Then she rode up 11 floors and got off. What floor was she on when she left the elevator? **12**

38. **INVESTMENTS** The NASDAQ lost 36 points on a Monday, but rebounded the next day, gaining 24 points. What was the total change in points? **−12 points**

39. **OFFICE BUILDINGS** Randi takes the stairs at work whenever possible instead of the elevator. She must climb up 51 steps from her office to get to the accounting department. The human resources department is 34 steps below her office. How many steps are there between human resources and accounting? **85 steps**

Chapter 2 20 Glencoe Pre-Algebra

Word Problem Practice
CRM p. 21 AL OL BL

NAME ______ DATE ______ PERIOD ______

2-3 Word Problem Practice

Subtracting Integers

1. **SWIMMING** The diving board at Mike's pool is 3 feet above the water level. Mike stepped off the diving board and sank until his feet touched the bottom of the pool, which is 12 feet deep. How many feet did Mike descend from the diving board to the bottom of the pool? **15 ft**

2. **TEMPERATURE** During a 24-hour period, the high temperature was 18°F. The low temperature was −4°F. What was the temperature range for the day? **22°F**

3. **PETS** The American Kennel Club (AKC) is the largest and second oldest purebred dog registry in the world. The table below shows some breeds registered with the AKC. Describe the changes in the number of beagles and chihuahuas registered from 2003 to 2004.

Breed	2003	2004
Golden Retriever	52,520	52,550
Beagle	45,021	44,555
Dachshund	39,468	40,770
Poodle	32,162	32,671
Chihuahua	24,923	24,850
Siberian Husky	10,660	10,566

Source: American Kennel Club (AKC)

Beagle: −466; Chihuahua: −73

4. **GOLF** Jim and Tom played against each other in a golf tournament. Jim's final score was 6 under par, the average number of swings it should take a golfer to get his ball in the hole. Tom's score was 1 under par. Describe the outcome of their match. **Sample answer: Jim beat Tom by 5 strokes.**

5. **BIRDS** An osprey was flying at an altitude of 80 feet above the ocean surface. The osprey spotted a fish and dove to a depth of 3 feet below the surface of the water to capture the fish. Once the osprey caught the fish, it ascended to a tree branch that was 25 feet above the ground.

a. What was the change in altitude from where the osprey started to where it landed? **−55 ft**

b. How far did the osprey descend to catch the fish? **83 ft**

c. What was the total change in altitude, both up and down, of the osprey from first spotting the fish to landing on the branch? **111 ft**

Chapter 2 21 Glencoe Pre-Algebra

Lesson 2-3

TEACH with TECH

AUDIO RECORDING Have each student work with a partner. Explain out loud and record how to subtract a negative number from another number. Post the audio files on the class Web site.

ASSESS

Ticket Out the Door Have students draw a number line on paper and use it to show how to find the differences of 8 − (−3) and −8 − (−3). As students leave, have them turn in their number lines.

Multiple Representations In Exercise 53, students use an equation to generate a function table and then graph the ordered pairs to show cost relations.

Additional Answers

53b.

Input (*x*)	6*x*	Output (*y*)
2	6(2)	12
4	6(4)	24
5	6(5)	30
7	6(7)	42

53c.

Movie Tickets

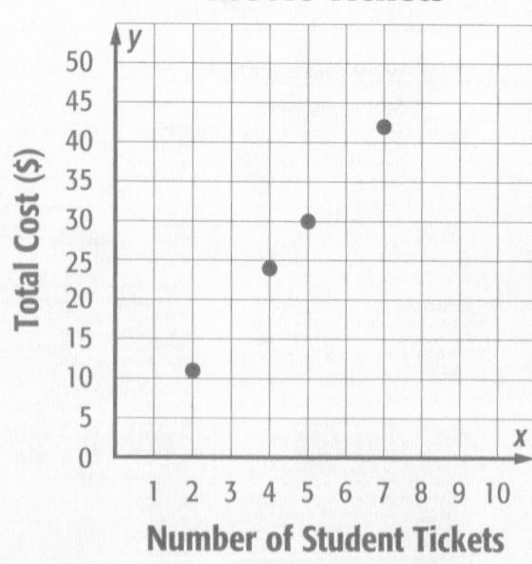

Standardized Test Practice

45. The melting point of mercury is −39°C. The freezing point of alcohol is −114°C. How much warmer is the melting point of mercury than the freezing point of alcohol? **C**

A −153°C   C 75°C
B −75°C   D 153°C

46. Which expression is modeled below? **F**

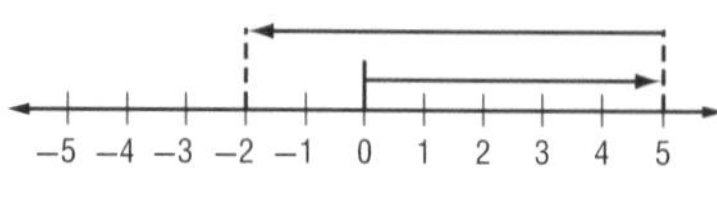

F 5 − 7   H 0 − 2
G 5 − 2   J 5 + 2

47. GRIDDED RESPONSE The crest of a mountain is 5740 feet above sea level. The base of the mountain is 25 feet below sea level. What is the difference in feet between the crest and base of the mountain? **5765**

48. Which statement about subtracting integers is always true? **A**

A positive − negative = positive
B negative − positive = positive
C negative − negative = positive
D positive − positive = positive

Spiral Review

49. FOOTBALL A team gained 4 yards on one play. On the next play, they lost 5 yards. Write an addition sentence to find the change in yardage. (Lesson 2-2) **4 + (−5) = −1**

Replace each ● with <, >, or = to make a true sentence. (Lesson 2-1)

50. −18 ● −8 **<**   **51.** 0 ● −3 **>**   **52.** 9 ● −9 **>**

53. MULTIPLE REPRESENTATIONS In this problem, you will work with functions. It costs $6 to buy a student ticket to the movies. (Lesson 1-5) **b–c. See margin.**

a. **ALGEBRAIC** Write an equation that can be used to find the cost of any number of student tickets. $y = 6x$

b. **TABULAR** Make a function table to find the cost of 2, 4, 5, and 7 tickets.

c. **GRAPHICAL** Graph the ordered pairs for the function.

ALGEBRA Translate each phrase into an algebraic expression. (Lesson 1-2)

54. eight more than the amount Kira saved $s + 8$

55. five runs fewer than the Pirates scored $r - 5$

56. the quotient of a number and four, minus five $k \div 4 - 5$

57. seven increased by the quotient of a number and eight $7 + n \div 8$

Skills Review

Find each product. (Previous Course)

58. 9 × 8 **72**   **59.** 14 × 4 **56**   **60.** 3 × 2 × 8 **48**   **61.** 6 × 7 × 10 **420**

Differentiated Instruction

Extension Have students complete the following problem:
A submarine descends 8500 feet below the surface of the ocean. It then descends 3200 feet, 480 feet, and 254 feet, where it rests on the ocean's floor. Find the depth at each resting point from the surface to the bottom. How far will the submarine need to ascend to reach a depth of 8500 feet?
−11,700 ft; −12,180 ft; −12,434 ft; 3934 ft

CHAPTER 2 Mid-Chapter Quiz

Lessons 2-1 through 2-3

Write an integer for each situation. Then graph on a number line. (Lesson 2-1) 1–2. See margin.

1. 300 feet below sea level
2. a profit of $90

Replace each ● with <, >, or = to make a true sentence. (Lesson 2-1)

3. 9 ● −5 >
4. −3 ● 0 <
5. −8 ● −6 <
6. 2 ● −4 >

7. **MULTIPLE CHOICE** Refer to the number line. Which statement is true? (Lesson 2-1) D

D B C A
−5 −4 −3 −2 −1 0 1 2 3

A $|B| < |C|$
C $C > A$
B $B > C$
D $|D| > |A|$

8. **GEOGRAPHY** The table shows the elevations of geographic areas in relation to sea level. Order the elevations from least to greatest. (Lesson 2-1) −418, −86, −66, −15

Area	Elevation (m)
Dead Sea	−418
Death Valley	−86
Lake Eyre	−15
Salton Sea	−66

Find each sum. (Lesson 2-2)

9. −6 + (−15) −21
10. −4 + 12 8
11. −7 + 9 + (−8) −6
12. 12 + (−6) + (−15) −9
13. |−33 + 19| 14
14. |−23 + −20| 43

15. **MULTIPLE CHOICE** Which day had the greatest change in stock price? (Lesson 2-2) H

Day	Open Price	Close Price
Monday	$43.29	$48.55
Tuesday	$48.55	$46.65
Wednesday	$46.65	$41.30
Thursday	$41.30	$45.99

F Monday
H Wednesday
G Tuesday
J Thursday

16. **WEATHER** The highest recorded temperature on Earth was 136°F in Libya. The lowest recorded temperature on Earth was −128.6°F in Antarctica. What is the average of the two temperatures? (Lesson 2-2) 3.7°F

17. **ACCOUNTING** A company showed the following earnings for a three-month period. How much did the company earn during this time period? (Lesson 2-2) −$1390

Month	Earnings ($)
January	−$3674
February	$4013
March	−$1729

Find each difference. (Lesson 2-3)

18. 15 − 21 −6
19. −16 − 9 −25
20. 35 − (−7) 42
21. −16 − (−11) −5

ALGEBRA Evaluate each expression if $x = 3$, $y = -2$, **and** $z = 6$. (Lesson 2-3)

22. $x - y$ 5
23. $x - z - y$ −1

24. **WEATHER** If the temperature is −1°F and it drops 5°F overnight, what is the new temperature? (Lesson 2-3) −6°F

25. **ASTRONOMY** Use the graph below to find the difference between the highest and lowest points on each planet. Which planet has the greatest difference? (Lesson 2-3) Earth: 19,883 m; Venus: 13,564 m; Mars: 29,261 m; Mars

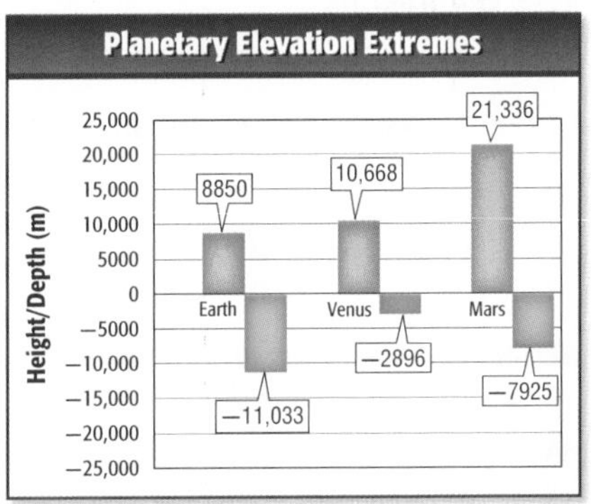

CHAPTER 2 Mid-Chapter Quiz

Formative Assessment

Use the Mid-Chapter Quiz to assess students' progress in the first half of the chapter.

For problems answered incorrectly, have students review the lessons indicated in parentheses.

Customize and create multiple versions of your Mid-Chapter Quiz and their answer keys.

FOLDABLES Follow-Up

Before students complete the Mid-Chapter Quiz, encourage them to review the information for Lessons 2-1 through 2-3 in their Foldables.

Additional Answers

1. −300

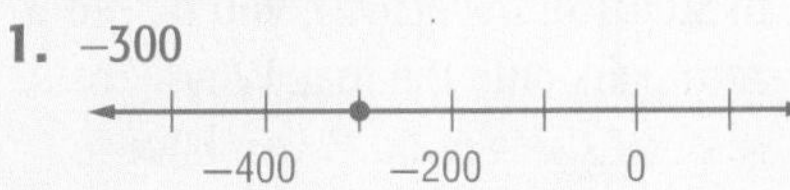

2. +90 or 90

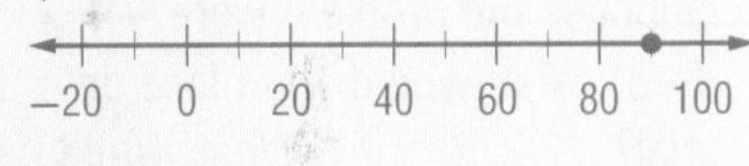

Intervention Planner

Tier 1 On Level	Tier 2 Strategic Intervention approaching grade level	Tier 3 Intensive Intervention 2 or more grades below level
If students miss about 25% of the exercises or less,	**If**  students miss about 50% of the exercises,	**If** students miss about 75% of the exercises,
Then choose a resource: **SE** Lessons 2-1, 2-2, and 2-3 **CRM** Skills Practice, pp. 7, 13, and 19 **TE** Chapter Project, p. 58 **Math Online** Self-Check Quiz	**Then**  choose a resource: **CRM** Study Guide and Intervention, Chapter 2, pp. 5, 11, and 17 *Quick Review Math Handbook* **Math Online** Extra Examples, Personal Tutor, Homework Help	**Then** use *Math Triumphs, Grade 8,* Ch. 1–2 **Math Online** Extra Examples, Personal Tutor, Homework Help, Review Vocabulary

FOCUS

Objective Use algebra tiles to multiply integers.

Materials for Each Student

- algebra tiles
- integer mats

Easy to Make Manipulatives

Teaching Pre-Algebra with Manipulatives, templates for:

- algebra tiles, pp. 7–8
- integer mat, p. 12

TEACH

Working in Cooperative Groups

Have students work in pairs or small groups of mixed abilities.

Ask:

- In Step 1 of the activity, you placed 6 zero pairs onto the mat. Why? To remove 2 sets of (−3) you have to have 6 negative tiles on the mat.
- Suppose the problem were −4 × (−3); what would you place onto the mat? 12 zero pairs What would be the product? Explain. 12; after removing 4 sets of (−3) tiles, 12 positive tiles would remain.

Practice Have students complete Exercises 1–15.

ASSESS

Formative Assessment

Use Exercises 2–13 to assess whether students comprehend how to multiply integers.

From Concrete to Abstract

Use Exercise 15 to assess whether students can formulate a rule to determine the sign of the product when multiplying integers.

Multiplying Integers

Math Online glencoe.com
Math *in Motion,* Animation

You can also use algebra tiles to model multiplication of integers. Remember that 2 × 3 means *two sets of three items.* So, you can show 2 × 3 by placing 2 sets of 3 positive tiles on a mat.

Similarly, you can model 2 × (−3) by placing 2 sets of 3 negative tiles on the mat, as shown at the right.

If the first factor is negative, you will need to *remove* tiles from the mat.

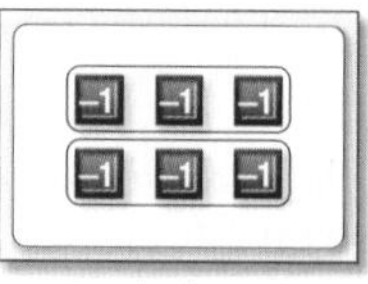

2 × (−3) = −6

ACTIVITY

Find −2 × (−3) using algebra tiles.

Step 1 The expression −2 × (−3) means to *remove* 2 sets of 3 negative tiles. To do this, first place 2 × 3 or 6 zero pairs on the mat.

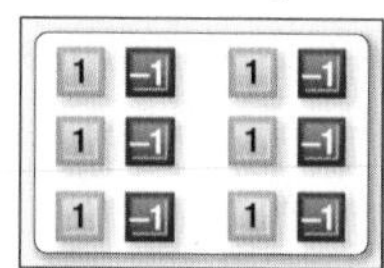

Step 2 Then remove 2 sets of 3 negative tiles from the mat. There are 6 positive tiles remaining.

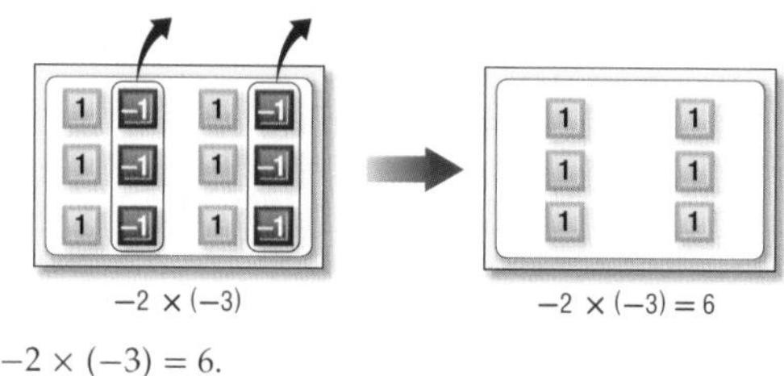

−2 × (−3)   −2 × (−3) = 6

So, −2 × (−3) = 6.

Analyze the Results

1. Explain the meaning of −2 × 3. Then find the product using algebra tiles. See margin.

Model and find each product using algebra tiles. 2–13. See Chapter 2 Answer Appendix for models.

2. 6 × (−2) −12	3. 3 × (−5) −15	4. 3 × (−4) −12	5. 1 × (−8) −8
6. −4 × (−2) 8	7. −5 × (−2) 10	8. −7 × (−1) 7	9. −2 × (−2) 4
10. −4 × 2 −8	11. −3 × 5 −15	12. −2 × 6 −12	13. −1 × 3 −3

14. **WRITING IN MATH** How are the operations −3 × 4 and 4 × (−3) the same? How do they differ? 14–15. See Chapter 2 Answer Appendix.

15. **MAKE A CONJECTURE** Find a rule you can use to find the sign of the product of two integers given the sign of both factors.

Extending the Concept

Have students write a word problem that each model could represent. For example, a model for Exercise 1 could be six sets of two baseball cards given away. The word problem could be Trey gave six friends each a set of two baseball cards from his collection. By what number has Trey's collection changed?

Additional Answer

1. Sample answer: −2 × 3 means to remove 2 sets of 3 positive tiles. See students' work for the model. −6

Multiplying Integers

Then
You multiplied integers using algebra tiles. (Explore 2-4)

Now
- Multiply integers.
- Simplify algebraic expressions.

Math Online
glencoe.com
- Extra Examples
- Personal Tutor
- Self-Check Quiz
- Homework Help

Why?

A one passenger submersible descends at a rate of 40 feet per minute. The table shows the submersible's depth after various minutes.

Time (min)	Depth (ft)
1	−40
2	−80
⋮	⋮

a. Write two different addition expressions that could be used to find the submersible's depth after 3 minutes. Then find their sum.

a. $-80 + (-40)$; $(-40) + (-40) + (-40)$; -120

b. Write a multiplication expression that could be used to find this same depth. Explain your reasoning.
$3(-40)$; you are adding -40 three times

Multiply Integers Multiplication is repeated addition. So, $3(-40)$ means that -40 is used as an addend 3 times.

$$3(-40) = (-40) + (-40) + (-40)$$
$$= -120$$

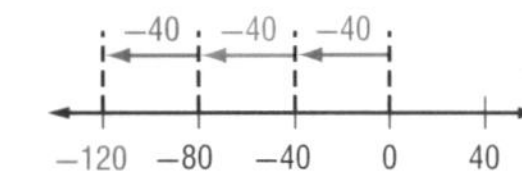

By the Commutative Property of Multiplication, $3(-40) = -40(3)$. This and other similar examples suggests the following rule for multiplying integers.

Key Concept Multiplying Two Integers with Different Signs

Words The product of two integers with different signs is negative.

Examples $2(-6) = -12$ $-2(6) = -12$

EXAMPLE 1 Multiply Integers with Different Signs

Find each product.

a. $-3 \cdot 12$

$-3(12) = -36$ The factors have different signs. The product is negative.

b. $4(-7)$

$4(-7) = -28$ The factors have different signs. The product is negative.

Check Your Progress

1A. $7(-8)$ -56 **1B.** $-6 \cdot 12$ -72

Personal Tutor glencoe.com

2-4 Lesson Notes

1 FOCUS

Vertical Alignment

Before Lesson 2-4
Multiply integers using algebra tiles.

Lesson 2-4
Multiply integers and simplify algebraic expressions.

After Lesson 2-4
Use appropriate operations to solve problems involving rational numbers.

2 TEACH

Scaffolding Questions

Have students read the *Why?* section of the lesson and answer the questions.

Ask:
- At what depth was the submersible at 0 minutes? 0 ft or sea level
- What multiplication sentence could be used to find the depth after 4 minutes? 4 (−40)
- How could you find the depth of the submersible after 10 minutes? Multiply 10 by −40.

Lesson 2-4 Resources

Resource	Approaching-Level	On-Level	Beyond-Level	English Learners
Teacher Edition		• Differentiated Instruction, p. 84	• Differentiated Instruction, pp. 84, 88	
Chapter Resource Masters	• Study Guide and Intervention, pp. 23–24 • Skills Practice, p. 25 • Practice, p. 26 • Word Problem Practice, p. 27	• Study Guide and Intervention, pp. 23–24 • Skills Practice, p. 25 • Practice, p. 26 • Word Problem Practice, p. 27 • Enrichment, p. 28	• Practice, p. 26 • Word Problem Practice, p. 27 • Enrichment, p. 28	• Study Guide and Intervention, pp. 23–24 • Skills Practice, p. 25 • Practice, p. 26
Transparencies	• 5-Minute Check Transparency 2-4	• 5-Minute Check Transparency 2-4	• 5-Minute Check Transparency 2-4	• 5-Minute Check Transparency 2-4
Other	• Study Notebook • Teaching Pre-Algebra with Manipulatives	• Study Notebook • Teaching Pre-Algebra with Manipulatives	• Study Notebook	• Study Notebook • Teaching Pre-Algebra with Manipulatives

Multiply Integers

Examples 1–3 show how to multiply positive and negative integers.

Example 4 shows how to use the Commutative and Associative Properties of Multiplication to multiply more than two integers.

Formative Assessment

Use the Check Your Progress exercises after each example to determine students' understanding of concepts.

Additional Examples

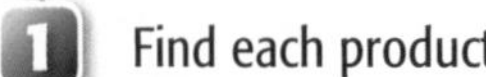

1 Find each product.

a. $8(-9)$ -72

b. $-9(11)$ -99

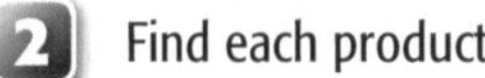

2 Find each product.

a. Find $-4(-16)$. 64

b. Find $-9(-6)$. 54

3 **SKI LIFTS** A ski lift descends the side of a mountain at the rate of 450 feet per minute. What is the lift's change in altitude after 7 minutes? -3150 feet

Additional Examples also in Interactive Classroom PowerPoint® Presentations

IWB INTERACTIVE WHITEBOARD READY

Tips for New Teachers

Vocabulary Remind students that a product is the result when two or more numbers are multiplied together.

The product of two positive integers is positive. What is the sign of the product of two negative integers? Look at the pattern below.

Input	Rule: Times −5	Output
2	−5(2)	−10
1	−5(1)	−5
0	−5(0)	0
−1	−5(−1)	5
−2	−5(−2)	−10

One positive and one negative factor: Negative product

Two negative factors: Positive product

+5 +5 +5 +5

Each product is 5 more than the previous product.

Key Concept — Multiplying Two Integers with Same Signs

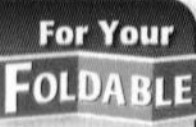

For Your FOLDABLE

Words The product of two integers with the same sign is positive.

Example $4 \cdot 6 = 24$ $-4(-6) = 24$

EXAMPLE 2 Multiply Integers with the Same Sign

Find each product.

a. $-5(-7)$

$-5(-7) = 35$ **The product is positive.**

b. $-8(-14)$

$-8(-14) = 112$ **The product is positive.**

Check Your Progress

2A. $-5(-11)$ **55**

2B. $-13(-4)$ **52**

Personal Tutor glencoe.com

Real-World EXAMPLE 3 Multiply Integers with Different Signs

AIRPLANES An airplane descends at a rate of 175 feet per minute. What is the airplane's change in altitude after 5 minutes?

Understand You need to find how many feet the airplane descended.

Plan The word *descends* means *downward*, so the rate per minute is represented by -175. You could make a function table like the one at the right. You could also multiply 5 and -175 to find the change in altitude after 5 minutes.

x	y
1	−175
2	−350
3	−525
⋮	⋮

Solve $5(-175) = -875$ **The product is negative.**

So, the change in altitude is -875 feet.

Check $5(-200)$ is -1000 and -875 is close to -1000. ✓

Real-World Link

The fastest airplane is the Lockheed SR-71 Blackbird. It is capable of speeds over 2200 miles per hour, which is more than 3 times the speed of sound.

Check Your Progress

3. DEPTH A scuba diver descends from the surface at a rate of 7 feet per minute. What was the scuba diver's depth at 15 minutes? **-105 ft**

Personal Tutor glencoe.com

Differentiated Instruction

OL BL

Logical On a blank transparency, draw a multiplication table. Factors should head each column and row. The product of those factors would be where the two factors intersect. Beginning with positive factors, have students find a pattern for the values in the table. Extend the pattern to complete the table to include negative integers.

Use the Commutative and Associative Properties of Multiplication to multiply more than two integers.

EXAMPLE 4 **Multiply More than Two Integers**

Find $-4(12)(-5)$.

Method 1 Use the Associative Property

$-4(12)(-5) = [-4(12)](-5)$ **Associative Property**

$= -48(-5)$ $-4(12) = -48$

$= 240$ $-48(-5) = 240$

Method 2 Use the Commutative Property

$-4(12)(-5) = -4(-5)(12)$ **Commutative Property**

$= 20(12)$ $-4(-5) = 20$

$= 240$ $20(12) = 240$

StudyTip

Mental Math Look for products that are multiples of ten to make the multiplication simpler.

Check Your Progress

4A. Find $-7(9)(-6)$. 378 **4B.** Find $-3(-4)(-5)$. -60

Personal Tutor glencoe.com

Algebraic Expressions You can use the rules for multiplying integers to simplify and evaluate algebraic expressions.

EXAMPLE 5 **Simplify Algebraic Expressions**

Simplify $-7a(4b)$.

$-7a(4b) = (-7)(a)(4)(b)$ $-7a = (-7)(a),\ 4b = (4)(b)$

$= (-7 \cdot 4)(a \cdot b)$ **Commutative Property of Multiplication**

$= -28ab$ $-7 \cdot 4 = -28,\ a \cdot b = ab$

Check Your Progress

5A. Simplify $-3(6y)$. $-18y$ **5B.** Simplify $-9x(3y)$. $-27xy$

Personal Tutor glencoe.com

EXAMPLE 6 **Evaluate Algebraic Expressions**

Evaluate $3xy$ if $x = 2$ and $y = -6$.

$3xy = 3(2)(-6)$ **Replace x with 2 and y with -6.**

$= [3(2)](-6)$ **Associative Property of Multiplication**

$= 6(-6)$ **The product of 3 and 2 is positive.**

$= -36$ **The product of 6 and -6 is negative.**

Check Your Progress

6A. Evaluate $2rs$ if $r = 5$ and $s -10$. -100

6B. Evaluate $4ab$ if $a = -8$ and $b = -4$. 128

Personal Tutor glencoe.com

Additional Examples

4 Find $7(-11)(4)$. -308

5 Simplify $8a(-5b)$. $-40ab$

6 Evaluate $-3xy$ if $x = -4$ and $y = 9$. 108

Algebraic Expressions

Example 5 shows how to simplify algebraic expressions.

Example 6 shows how to evaluate algebraic expressions.

Focus on Mathematical Content

Multiplying Integers When multiplying more than two integers with different signs, the number of negative factors determines the sign of the product. If there is an even number of negative factors, the product is positive. Another negative factor turns that positive product to a negative one. Ask students if the product would be negative or positive if there were 200 factors and 21 of them were negative. The product would be negative because there are an odd number of negative factors.

TEACH with TECH

BLOG Have students write a blog entry on your secure class blog to describe how to determine the sign of the product of two integers. Ask them to include examples of both cases.

3 PRACTICE

Formative Assessment

Use Exercises 1–10 to check for understanding.

Use the chart at the bottom of the next page to customize assignments for your students.

Tips for New Teachers

Multiplying Integers When multiplying integers, have students complete the multiplication first. Next, have students determine the appropriate sign. Remind students that an even number of negative signs has a positive result and an odd number of negative signs has a negative result.

Additional Answer

41. Team 1 answered 12 questions correctly, 3 questions incorrectly, and passed on 1 question, so Team 1 earned 12(5) + 3(−8) + 1(−2) or 34 points. Team 2 answered 13 questions correctly, 2 questions incorrectly, and passed on 7 questions, so Team 2 earned 13(5) + 2(−8) + 7(−2) or 35 points. Since 34 < 35, Team 2 won.

Check Your Understanding

Examples 1, 2, and 4 (pp. 83–85)

Find each product.

1. $-6 \cdot 7$ **−42**
2. $-5(-8)$ **40**
3. $8(-3)(-5)$ **120**
4. $-2(-9)(-5)$ **−90**

Example 3 (p. 84)

5. **MONEY** Mr. Heppner bought lunch with his debit card every day for 5 days. Each day he spent $8. If these were his only transactions this week, what was the change in his account balance? **−$40**

Example 5 (p. 85)

ALGEBRA Simplify each expression.

6. $-2 \cdot 9m$ **−18*m***
7. $-3a(7b)$ **−21*ab***
8. $-6e(-4f)$ **24*ef***

Example 6 (p. 85)

ALGEBRA Evaluate each expression.

9. $8j$, if $j = -11$ **−88**
10. $-9cd$, if $c = -3$ and $d = -7$ **−189**

Practice and Problem Solving

● = **Step-by-Step Solutions** begin on page R11. **Extra Practice** begins on page 810.

Examples 1, 2, and 4 (pp. 83–85)

Find each product.

11. $3(-9)$ **−27**
12. $8 \cdot -9$ **−72**
13. $25 \cdot 3$ **75**
14. $-4(-8)$ **32**
15. $-7 \cdot -7$ **49**
16. $2(-11)(5)$ **−110**
17. $-8(-7)(-6)$ **−336**
18. $-8(-20)(5)$ **800**

Example 3 (p. 84)

19. **TEMPERATURE** The temperature dropped 2°F every hour for the last 6 hours. What is the total change in temperature? **−12°F**

20. **ELEVATORS** An elevator takes passengers from the ground floor down to an underground parking garage. Where will the elevator be in relation to the ground floor after 5 seconds if it travels at a rate of 3 feet per second? **−15 ft**

Example 5 (p. 85)

ALGEBRA Simplify each expression.

21. $5(-6m)$ **−30*m***
22. $-5 \cdot 10s$ **−50*s***
23. $-9m(-9n)$ **81*mn***
24. $11a(7c)$ **77*ac***
25. $4a(b)(-9)$ **−36*ab***
26. $-12(-j)(-3k)$ **−36*jk***
27. $3e(-2f)(9g)$ **−54*efg***
28. $3r(7s)(5t)$ **105*rst***

Example 6 (p. 85)

ALGEBRA Evaluate each expression.

29. $10n$, if $n = -10$ **−100**
30. $8m$, if $m = -5$ **−40**
31. $4xy$ if $x = -6$ and $y = 3$ **−72**
32. $-15st$, if $s = 4$ and $t = -9$ **540**

FUNCTION TABLES Identify the function rule for each table.

33. $y = -2x$

x	y
1	−2
2	−4
3	−6

34. $y = -5x$

x	y
2	−10
0	0
−2	10

35. $y = -4x$

x	y
−3	12
−6	24
−9	36

36. **FITNESS** The table shows the number of Calories burned per minute for a 120-pound person during different activities. What is the change in the number of Calories in a 120-pound person's body if he runs for 20 minutes and swims for 25 minutes? **−560 Calories**

Activity	Calories per Minute
Ballet Dancing	6
Bicycling	12
Running	18
Swimming	8

Differentiated Homework Options

Level	Assignment	Two-Day Option	
AL Basic	11–32, 43, 44, 46, 49–63	11–31 odd, 50–53	12–32 even, 43, 44, 46, 49, 54–63
OL Core	11–35 odd, 36, 37, 39, 40–44, 46, 49–63	11–32, 50–53	33–44, 46, 49, 54–63
BL Advanced	33–59 (optional: 60–63)		

Replace each ● with <, >, or = to make a true sentence.

37. $-4(6) ● 3(8)$ **<**

38. $(-5)(-2)(9) ● (4)(10)(-9)$ **>**

39. $(-11)(-3)(6)(-2) ● -24(18)$ **>**

40. INVESTMENTS The price of stock fell $2 each day for 14 consecutive days. The original price of the stock was $41. Write an expression that you could use to find the price of the stock on any day. **$-2d + 41$**

41. TRIVIA Two groups were playing a trivia game. Each team earned 5 points for every correct answer, lost 8 points for every incorrect answer, and lost 2 points for every passed question. For each team, write an expression to determine the number of points they earned. Which team won? **See margin.**

Team	Correct	Incorrect	Passed
1	12	3	1
2	13	2	7

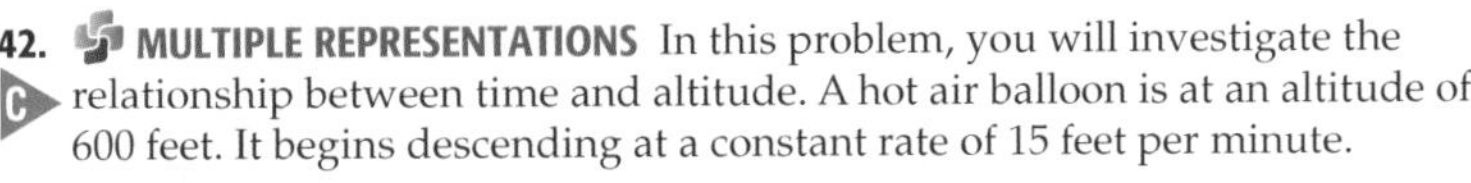

42. MULTIPLE REPRESENTATIONS In this problem, you will investigate the relationship between time and altitude. A hot air balloon is at an altitude of 600 feet. It begins descending at a constant rate of 15 feet per minute.

a. TABULAR Complete the table below that shows the altitude of the balloon every 5 minutes.

Input x (minutes)	$y = -15x + 600$	Output y (altitude)
0	$-15(0) + 600$	600
5	■	■
10	■	■
15	■	■

b. VERBAL What does the input value of 0 represent? **The time the balloon began descending.**

c. GRAPHICAL Graph the ordered pairs.

d. ALGEBRAIC Determine the time it will take for the balloon to reach the ground. Explain how you solved. **40 minutes; Sample answer: If you continue the pattern in the table, for every 10 minutes, the balloon drops 150 feet. $150 \times 4 = 600$ so $10 \cdot 4 = 40$ minutes.**

Real-World Link

Hot-air balloons can lift off when the air inside the balloon is heated. This makes the air inside the balloon less dense than the air outside the balloon. It takes about 65,000 cubic feet of air to lift 1000 pounds.

Source: How Stuff Works

42a,c. See Chapter 2 Answer Appendix.

H.O.T. Problems

Use Higher-Order Thinking Skills

43. OPEN ENDED Name two integers that have a product between -10 and -15. **Sample answer: 2 and -7**

44. REASONING Name all of the values of x if $7|x| = 63$. **-9 and 9**

45. CHALLENGE Positive integers A and C satisfy $A(A - C) = 23$. What is the value of C? **22**

46. REASONING Calculate $(-10)(5)(18)[7 + (-7)]$ mentally. Justify your answer. **0; Multiplicative Property of Zero**

CHALLENGE Determine whether each of the following is *true* or *false*. If *false*, give a counterexample.

47. The product of three negative integers is positive. **false; Sample answer: $-3(-2)(-2) = -12$**

48. The product of four negative integers is positive. **true**

49. WRITING IN MATH When multiplying more than two integers, how can you determine the sign of the product?

49. Sample answer: The sign of the product will be negative if there is an odd number of negative integers; otherwise the sign will be positive.

Multiple Representations In Exercise 42, students use a function table, a graph of ordered pairs, verbal analysis, and algebra to model time, rate, and altitude relationships.

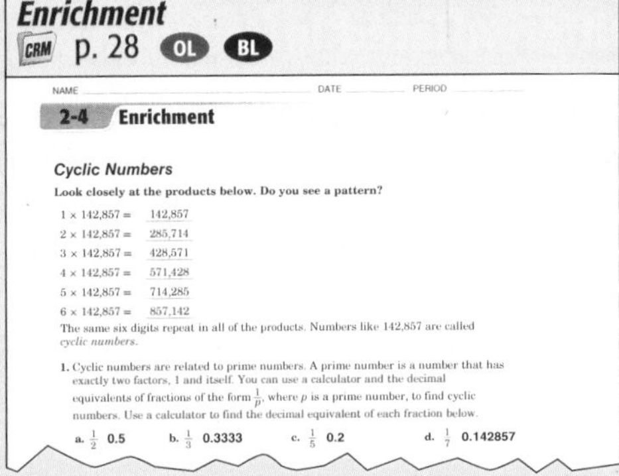

Enrichment
CRM p. 28 OL BL

NAME ______ DATE ______ PERIOD ______

2-4 Enrichment

Cyclic Numbers

Look closely at the products below. Do you see a pattern?

1 × 142,857 = 142,857
2 × 142,857 = 285,714
3 × 142,857 = 428,571
4 × 142,857 = 571,428
5 × 142,857 = 714,285
6 × 142,857 = 857,142

The same six digits repeat in all of the products. Numbers like 142,857 are called *cyclic numbers*.

1. Cyclic numbers are related to prime numbers. A prime number is a number that has exactly two factors, 1 and itself. You can use a calculator and the decimal equivalents of fractions of the form $\frac{1}{p}$, where p is a prime number, to find cyclic numbers. Use a calculator to find the decimal equivalent of each fraction below.

a. $\frac{1}{2}$ **0.5** b. $\frac{1}{3}$ **0.3333** c. $\frac{1}{5}$ **0.2** d. $\frac{1}{7}$ **0.142857**

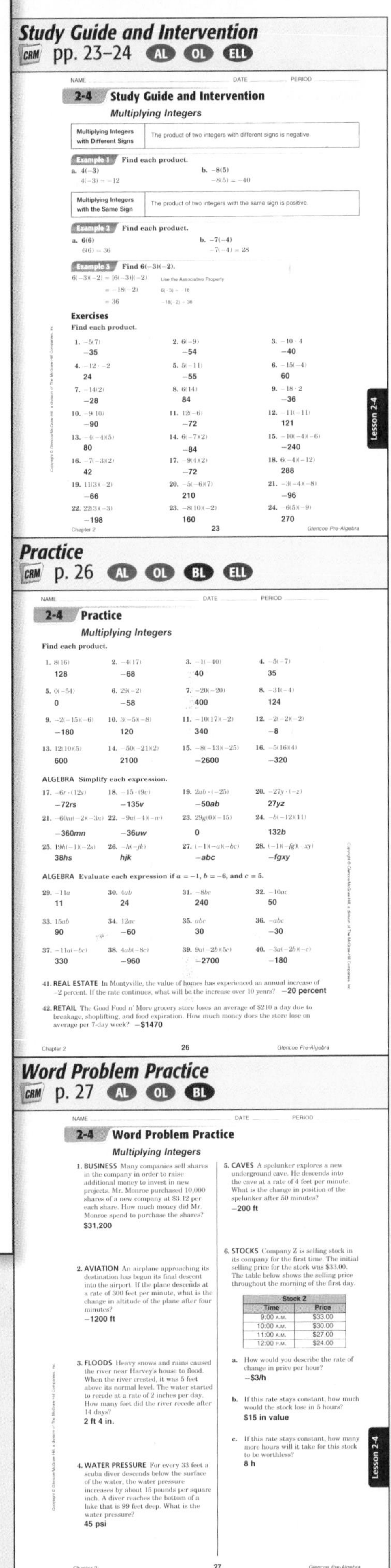

Study Guide and Intervention
CRM pp. 23–24 AL OL ELL

NAME ______ DATE ______ PERIOD ______

2-4 Study Guide and Intervention

Multiplying Integers

Multiplying Integers with Different Signs	The product of two integers with different signs is negative.

Example 1 Find each product.

a. $4(-3)$: $4(-3) = -12$
b. $-8(5)$: $-8(5) = -40$

Multiplying Integers with the Same Sign	The product of two integers with the same sign is positive.

Example 2 Find each product.

a. $6(6)$: $6(6) = 36$
b. $-7(-4)$: $-7(-4) = 28$

Example 3 Find $6(-3)(-2)$.

$6(-3)(-2) = [6(-3)](-2)$ Use the Associative Property
$= -18(-2)$ $6(-3) = -18$
$= 36$ $-18(-2) = 36$

Exercises

Find each product.

1. $-5(7)$ **−35** 2. $6(-9)$ **−54** 3. $-10 \cdot 4$ **−40**
4. $-12 \cdot -2$ **24** 5. $5(-11)$ **−55** 6. $-15(-4)$ **60**
7. $-14(2)$ **−28** 8. $6(14)$ **84** 9. $-18 \cdot 2$ **−36**
10. $-9(10)$ **−90** 11. $12(-6)$ **−72** 12. $-11(-11)$ **121**
13. $-4(-4)(5)$ **80** 14. $6(-7)(2)$ **−84** 15. $-10(-4)(-6)$ **−240**
16. $-7(-3)(2)$ **42** 17. $-9(4)(2)$ **−72** 18. $6(-4)(-12)$ **288**
19. $11(3)(-2)$ **−66** 20. $-5(-6)(7)$ **210** 21. $-3(-4)(-8)$ **−96**
22. $22(3)(-3)$ **−198** 23. $-8(10)(-2)$ **160** 24. $-6(5)(-9)$ **270**

Chapter 2 23 Glencoe Pre-Algebra

Practice
CRM p. 26 AL OL BL ELL

NAME ______ DATE ______ PERIOD ______

2-4 Practice

Multiplying Integers

Find each product.

1. $8(16)$ **128** 2. $-4(17)$ **−68** 3. $-1(-40)$ **40** 4. $-5(-7)$ **35**
5. $0(-54)$ **0** 6. $29(-2)$ **−58** 7. $-20(-20)$ **400** 8. $-31(-4)$ **124**
9. $-2(-15)(-6)$ **−180** 10. $3(-5)(-8)$ **120** 11. $-10(17)(-2)$ **340** 12. $-2(-2)(-2)$ **−8**
13. $12(10)(5)$ **600** 14. $-50(-21)(2)$ **2100** 15. $-8(-13)(-25)$ **−2600** 16. $-5(16)(4)$ **−320**

ALGEBRA Simplify each expression.

17. $-6r \cdot (12s)$ **−72rs** 18. $-15 \cdot (9v)$ **−135v** 19. $2ab \cdot (-25)$ **−50ab** 20. $-27y \cdot (-z)$ **27yz**
21. $-60m(-2)(-3n)$ **−360mn** 22. $-9u(-4)(-w)$ **−36uw** 23. $29g(0)(-15)$ **0** 24. $-b(-12)(11)$ **132b**
25. $19h(-1)(-2s)$ **38hs** 26. $-h(-jk)$ **hjk** 27. $(-1)(-a)(-bc)$ **−abc** 28. $(-1)(-fg)(-xy)$ **−fgxy**

ALGEBRA Evaluate each expression if $a = -1$, $b = -6$, and $c = 5$.

29. $-11a$ **11** 30. $4ab$ **24** 31. $-8bc$ **240** 32. $-10ac$ **50**
33. $15ab$ **90** 34. $12ac$ **−60** 35. abc **30** 36. $-abc$ **−30**
37. $-11a(-bc)$ **330** 38. $4ab(-8c)$ **−960** 39. $9a(-2b)(5c)$ **−2700** 40. $-3a(-2b)(-c)$ **−180**

41. **REAL ESTATE** In Montyville, the value of homes has experienced an annual increase of −2 percent. If the rate continues, what will be the increase over 10 years? **−20 percent**

42. **RETAIL** The Good Food n' More grocery store loses an average of $210 a day due to breakage, shoplifting, and food expiration. How much money does the store lose on average per 7-day week? **−$1470**

Chapter 2 26 Glencoe Pre-Algebra

Word Problem Practice
CRM p. 27 AL OL BL

NAME ______ DATE ______ PERIOD ______

2-4 Word Problem Practice

Multiplying Integers

1. **BUSINESS** Many companies sell shares in the company in order to raise additional money to invest in new projects. Mr. Monroe purchased 10,000 shares of a new company at $3.12 per each share. How much money did Mr. Monroe spend to purchase the shares? **$31,200**

2. **AVIATION** An airplane approaching its destination has begun its final descent into the airport. If the plane descends at a rate of 300 feet per minute, what is the change in altitude of the plane after four minutes? **−1200 ft**

3. **FLOODS** Heavy snows and rains caused the river near Harvey's house to flood. When the river crested, it was 5 feet above its normal level. The water started to recede at a rate of 2 inches per day. How many feet did the river recede after 14 days? **2 ft 4 in.**

4. **WATER PRESSURE** For every 33 feet a scuba diver descends below the surface of the water, the water pressure increases by about 15 pounds per square inch. A diver reaches the bottom of a lake that is 99 feet deep. What is the water pressure? **45 psi**

5. **CAVES** A spelunker explores a new underground cave. He descends into the cave at a rate of 4 feet per minute. What is the change in position of the spelunker after 50 minutes? **−200 ft**

6. **STOCKS** Company Z is selling stock in its company for the first time. The initial selling price for the stock was $33.00. The table below shows the selling price throughout the morning of the first day.

Stock Z	
Time	Price
9:00 A.M.	$33.00
10:00 A.M.	$30.00
11:00 A.M.	$27.00
12:00 P.M.	$24.00

a. How would you describe the rate of change in price per hour? **−$3/h**

b. If this rate stays constant, how much would the stock lose in 5 hours? **$15 in value**

c. If this rate stays constant, how many more hours will it take for this stock to be worthless? **8 h**

Chapter 2 27 Glencoe Pre-Algebra

Lesson 2-4

Lesson 2-4 Multiplying Integers 87

4 ASSESS

Crystal Ball Ask students to write how they think multiplying integers will connect with tomorrow's lesson about dividing integers.

Formative Assessment

Check for student understanding of concepts in Lessons 2-3 and 2-4.

CRM Quiz 2, p. 52

Standardized Test Practice

50. A submarine descends at a constant rate of 300 feet per minute. Which of the following equations could be used to find the altitude of the submarine after 5 minutes? **A**

A $5(-300) = -1500$
B $5(300) = 1500$
C $-5(300) = -1500$
D $-5(-300) = 1500$

51. Which of the following equations is modeled by the number line below? **J**

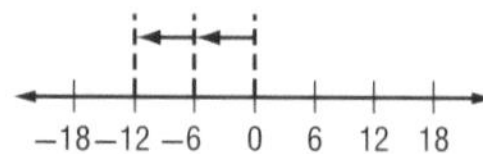

F $-2(-6) = -12$
G $-2(6) = -12$
H $2(6) = -12$
J $2(-6) = -12$

52. Simplify $-14(-2)(-12)$. **A**

A -336
B -168
C 168
D 288

53. GRIDDED RESPONSE The distance from the water line to the bottom of a cargo ship changes based on the weight of the cargo.

Weight of Cargo (tons)	Depth of Ship (feet)
35	30
25	25
15	20

If the pattern in the table continues, find the depth of the ship, in feet, if the ship is carrying 100 tons of cargo. **62.5**

Spiral Review

54. GEOGRAPHY The highest point in California is Mount Whitney, with an elevation of 14,494 feet. The lowest point is Death Valley, with an elevation of −282 feet. How much greater is the elevation of Mount Whitney than Death Valley? (Lesson 2-3) **14,776 ft**

Find each sum. (Lesson 2-2)

55. $6 + (-9) + 9$ **6**
56. $-7 + (-13) + 4$ **−16**
57. $-9 + 16 + (-10)$ **−3**
58. $-12 + 18 + (-12)$ **−6**

59. WEATHER The table shows the lowest recorded temperatures for certain states.

Record Lowest Temperatures by State

State	Station	Date	Temperature (°F)
Alaska	Prospect Creek Camp	Jan. 23, 1971	−80
Montana	Rogers Pass	Jan. 20, 1954	−70
Wisconsin	Danbury	Jan. 24, 1922	−54

a. Compare the lowest temperature in Montana and the lowest temperature in Wisconsin using an inequality. **$-54 > -70$**

b. Write the temperatures in order from greatest to least. **−54°, −70°, −80°**

Skills Review

Find each quotient. (Previous Course)

60. $72 \div 9$ **8**
61. $108 \div 12$ **9**
62. $84 \div 7$ **12**
63. $52 \div 4$ **13**

Differentiated Instruction

BL

Extension Explain to students that distance, or displacement, is the velocity, or speed, multiplied by time. Then pose the following problem. A bird dives from his perch towards a mouse sleeping on the ground. The bird's velocity is −2.5 feet per second. What is the bird's change of position in 4 seconds? −10 feet Suppose the mouse is 75 feet below the bird's perch. How long will it take the bird to reach the mouse? 30 seconds

Dividing Integers

Math Online glencoe.com
Math *in Motion,* Animation

You can model division by separating algebra tiles into equal-sized groups.

ACTIVITY 1

Find 10 ÷ 2.

Place 10 positive tiles on the mat to represent 10.

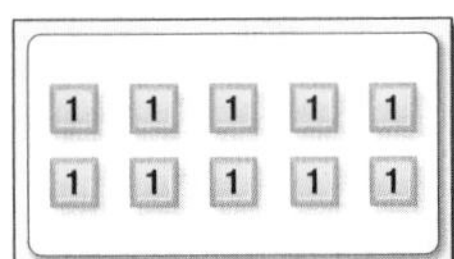

Separate the tiles into 2 equal-sized groups.

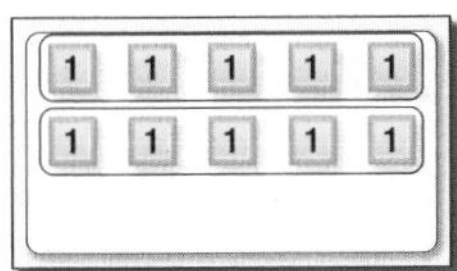

10 ÷ 2 = 5

There are 5 positive tiles in each of the 2 groups.

So, 10 ÷ 2 = 5.

ACTIVITY 2

Find −12 ÷ 2.

Place 12 negative tiles on the mat to represent −12.

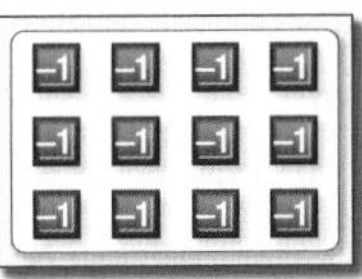

Separate the tiles into 2 equal-sized groups.

−12 ÷ 2 = −6

There are 6 negative tiles in each of the 2 groups.

So, −12 ÷ 2 = −6.

Analyze the Results

Model each quotient using algebra tiles. 1–9. See Chapter 2 Answer Appendix for models.

1. 12 ÷ 6 2
2. 16 ÷ 2 8
3. 14 ÷ 7 2
4. −8 ÷ 2 −4
5. −9 ÷ 3 −3
6. −6 ÷ 2 −3
7. −16 ÷ 4 −4
8. −5 ÷ 5 −1
9. −10 ÷ 2 −5

For Exercises 10–12, study the quotients in Exercises 1–9.

10. When the dividend and the divisor are both positive, is the quotient positive or negative? How does this compare to the sign of a product when both factors are positive? positive; It is the same.

11. When the dividend is negative and the divisor is positive, is the quotient positive or negative? How does this compare to the sign of a product when one factor is positive and one is negative? negative; It is the same.

12. **MAKE A CONJECTURE** Write a rule that will help you determine the sign of the quotient of two integers. See margin.

Extending the Concept

Ask:

- How can you check to make certain the sign of the quotient is correct? Multiply the divisor and the dividend.

Additional Answer

12. Sample answer: The quotient of two integers with the same sign is positive. The quotient of two integers with different signs is negative.

EXPLORE 2-5 Lesson Notes

1 FOCUS

Objective Divide integers using algebra tiles.

Materials for Each Student

- algebra tiles
- integer mats

Easy to Make Manipulatives

Teaching Pre-Algebra with Manipulatives, templates for:

- algebra tiles, pp. 7–8
- integer mat, p. 12

2 TEACH

Working in Cooperative Groups

Have students work in small groups of mixed abilities to complete Activities 1 and 2.

Ask:

- In Activity 2, you grouped 12 negative tiles into 2 groups to get a quotient of −6. Suppose the problem were 12 ÷ 2. Would you expect the answer to be the same or different? Why? Different; if you divide 12 into 2 groups, you will get 6, not −6.

Practice Have students complete Exercises 1–12.

3 ASSESS

Formative Assessment

Use Exercises 1–9 to assess whether students comprehend how to divide integers.

From Concrete to Abstract

Use Exercise 12 to assess whether students can formulate a rule to determine the sign of the quotient when dividing integers.

2-5 Lesson Notes

FOCUS

Vertical Alignment

Before Lesson 2-5
Divide integers using algebra tiles.

Lesson 2-5
Divide integers and find the mean (average) of a set of data.

After Lesson 2-5
Determine the appropriate operation to solve problems involving integers.

2 TEACH

Scaffolding Questions

Have students read the *Why?* section of the lesson and answer the questions.

Ask:

- What will be the change of elevation when the climber reaches the ground? −800 feet
- Suppose the climber descends to the ground at a rate of −20 feet per minute. Write an expression to determine the number of minutes it takes to reach the ground. −800 ÷ (−20)
- How many minutes will it take the climber to reach the ground? 40 minutes

2-5 Dividing Integers

Then
You divided integers using algebra tiles. (Explore 2-5)

Now
- Divide integers.
- Find the mean (average) of a set of data.

New Vocabulary
mean

Math Online
glencoe.com
- Extra Examples
- Personal Tutor
- Self-Check Quiz
- Homework Help

Why?

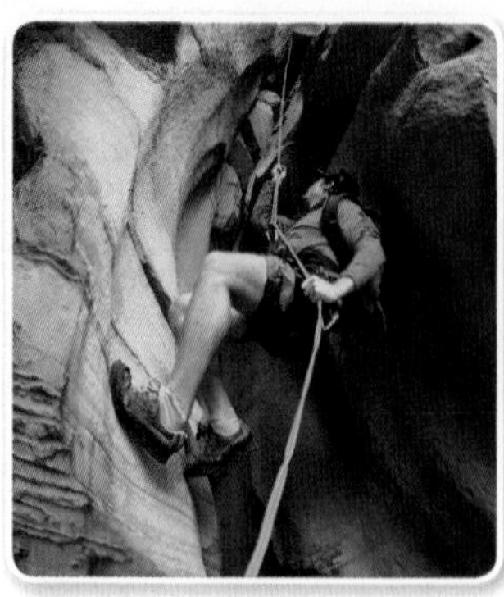

Rappelling is one way climbers descend rocks and mountains. A climber was at an elevation of 800 feet above sea level. Five minutes later, the climber was at an elevation of 755 feet above sea level.

a. What was the climber's change in altitude? −45 ft

b. Suppose the climber descended the same number of feet each minute. Write an expression to determine the number of feet the climber descended each minute. $-45 \div 5$

Divide Integers The expression $-45 \div 5$ is an example of dividing integers. Division of integers is related to multiplication of integers. So, one way to find the quotient is by using related multiplication sentences.

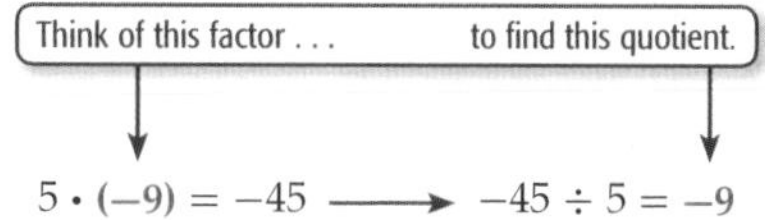
Think of this factor . . .
to find this quotient.

$$5 \cdot (-9) = -45 \longrightarrow -45 \div 5 = -9$$

In the division sentence $-45 \div 5 = -9$, notice that the dividend and the divisor have different signs. So, the quotient is negative. This suggests a rule for dividing integers with different signs.

Key Concept — Dividing Integers with Different Signs — For Your FOLDABLE

Words The quotient of two integers with different signs is negative.

Example $-10 \div 5 = -2$ $\quad 10 \div (-5) = -2$

EXAMPLE 1 Divide Integers with Different Signs

Find each quotient.

a. $-35 \div (7)$

$-35 \div (7) = -5$ **The quotient is negative.**

b. $\frac{64}{-8}$

$\frac{64}{-8} = -8$ **The quotient is negative.**

Check Your Progress

1A. $-63 \div 7$ −9

1B. $\frac{110}{-10}$ −11

Personal Tutor glencoe.com

Lesson 2-5 Resources

Resource	Approaching-Level	On-Level	Beyond-Level	English Learners
Teacher Edition	• Differentiated Instruction, p. 92	• Differentiated Instruction, pp. 92, 95	• Differentiated Instruction, p. 95	• Differentiated Instruction, p. 92
Chapter Resource Masters	• Study Guide and Intervention, pp. 29–30 • Skills Practice, p. 31 • Practice, p. 32 • Word Problem Practice, p. 33 • Graphing Calculator, p. 35	• Study Guide and Intervention, pp. 29–30 • Skills Practice, p. 31 • Practice, p. 32 • Word Problem Practice, p. 33 • Enrichment, p. 34 • Graphing Calculator, p. 35	• Practice, p. 32 • Word Problem Practice, p. 33 • Enrichment, p. 34 • Graphing Calculator, p. 35	• Study Guide and Intervention, pp. 29–30 • Skills Practice, p. 31 • Practice, p. 32 • Graphing Calculator, p. 35
Transparencies	• 5-Minute Check Transparency 2-5	• 5-Minute Check Transparency 2-5	• 5-Minute Check Transparency 2-5	• 5-Minute Check Transparency 2-5
Other	• Study Notebook • Teaching Pre-Algebra with Manipulatives	• Study Notebook • Teaching Pre-Algebra with Manipulatives	• Study Notebook	• Study Notebook • Teaching Pre-Algebra with Manipulatives

You can also use multiplication and division sentences to find the quotient of integers with the same sign.

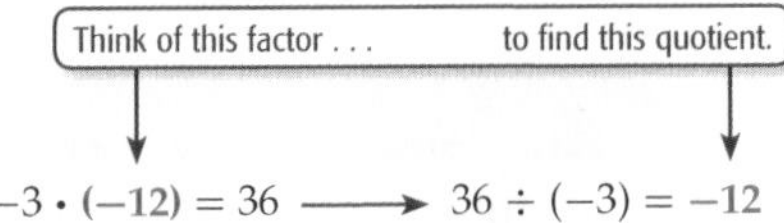

$-3 \cdot (-12) = 36 \longrightarrow 36 \div (-3) = -12$

This suggests a rule for dividing integers with the same sign.

Key Concept — Dividing Integers with the Same Signs

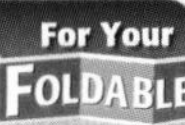

Words The quotient of two integers with the same sign is positive.

Example $-10 \div (-5) = 2$ $10 \div 5 = 2$

EXAMPLE 2 Divide Integers with the Same Signs

Find each quotient.

a. $48 \div 12$

$48 \div 12 = 4$ **The quotient is positive.**

b. $\frac{-56}{-8}$

$\frac{-56}{-8} = 7$ **The quotient is positive.**

StudyTip

Check Your Work Always check your work after finding an answer. Does $-8 \times 7 = -56$?

Check Your Progress

2A. $-35 \div (-5)$ 7

2B. $\frac{39}{3}$ 13

Personal Tutor glencoe.com

You can use the rules for dividing integers to evaluate algebraic expressions.

EXAMPLE 3 Evaluate Algebraic Expressions

Evaluate each expression if $x = -6$ and $y = -3$.

a. $12y \div x$

$12y \div (x) = 12(-3) \div (-6)$ **Replace y with -3 and x with -6.**

$= -36 \div (-6)$ **The product of 12 and -3 is negative.**

$= 6$ **The quotient of -36 and -6 is positive.**

b. $\frac{-5x}{y}$

$\frac{-5x}{y} = \frac{-5(-6)}{-3}$ **Replace x with -6 and y with -3.**

$= \frac{30}{-3}$ **The product of -5 and -6 is positive.**

$= -10$ **The quotient of 30 and -3 is negative.**

Check Your Progress

3A. $4b \div a$ if $a = -2$ and $b = -5$ 10

3B. $4y \div 2x$ if $x = 14$ and $y = -7$ -1

Personal Tutor glencoe.com

Divide Integers

Examples 1 and 2 show how to divide positive and negative integers. **Example 3** shows how to evaluate algebraic expressions using the rules for dividing integers.

Formative Assessment

Use the Check Your Progress exercises after each example to determine students' understanding of concepts.

Additional Examples

Find each quotient.

a. $28 \div (-4)$ -7

b. $\frac{96}{-8}$ -12

Find each quotient.

a. $-54 \div (-3)$ 18

b. $\frac{-42}{-6}$ 7

Evaluate each expression if $x = -4$ and $y = -8$.

a. $6x \div y$ 3

b. $\frac{-4x}{y}$ -2

Additional Examples also in Interactive Classroom PowerPoint® Presentations

TEACH with TECH

DOCUMENT CAMERA Have students work through a division problem using the document camera. Students should explain their work as they find the quotient and determine its sign. Take a picture of the completed work to print or post on the class Web site.

Focus on Mathematical Content

Dividing Integers When dividing integers, follow the rules for multiplication of integers because division and multiplication are related operations. The dividend and the divisor in a division problem become the product and a factor in a related multiplication problem. Ask students how they can verify $-56 \div 7 = -8$ using multiplication. $-8 \times 7 = -56$

Mean (Average)

Example 4 shows how to find the mean of a set of numbers by dividing the sum of the numbers by the number of values in the set.

Additional Example

4 **GAMES** Ramón has scores of 12, –18, 3, –7, 1, and –3 in six rounds of a word game. Find the mean of his scores. –2

3 PRACTICE

Formative Assessment

Use Exercises 1–12 to check for understanding.

Use the chart at the bottom of the next page to customize assignments for your students.

Mean (Average) Division is used in statistics to find the average, or mean, of a set of data. To find the **mean** of a set of numbers, find the sum of the numbers and then divide by the number of items in the set.

Real-World EXAMPLE 4 Find the Mean

WEATHER The wind chill temperatures in degrees Fahrenheit for 7 days were –6, –5, 2, –10, 1, –9 and 6. Find the mean temperature.

$$\frac{-6 + (-5) + 2 + (-10) + 1 + (-9) + 6}{7} = \frac{-21}{7}$$ **Find the sum of the temperatures. Divide by the number of days.**

$$= -3$$ **Simplify.**

The mean wind chill temperature is –3°F.

Check Your Progress

4. **GOLF** Linda has scores of –3, –2, 1, and 0 during 4 rounds of golf. Find the mean of her golf scores. **–1**

Personal Tutor glencoe.com

Concept Summary: Operations with Integers

For Your FOLDABLE

Words	Examples
Adding Integers **Same Signs:** Add absolute values. The sum has the same sign as the integers. **Different Signs:** Subtract absolute values. The sum has the same sign as the integer with the greater absolute value.	3 + 2 = 5 –3 + (–2) = –5 –3 + 2 = –1 3 + (–2) = 1
Subtracting Integers To subtract an integer, add its additive inverse.	3 – 5 = 3 + (–5) or –2 3 – (–5) = 3 + 5 or 8
Multiplying and Dividing Two Integers **Same Signs:** The product or quotient is positive. **Different Signs:** The product or quotient is negative.	3 · 2 = 6 6 ÷ 3 = 2 –3(–2) = 6 –6 ÷ (–3) = 2 –3 · 2 = –6 –6 ÷ 3 = –2 3(–2) = –6 6 ÷ (–3) = –2

Check Your Understanding

Examples 1 and 2 (pp. 90–91) Find each quotient.

1. 40 ÷ –10 **–4**
2. $\frac{39}{13}$ **3**
3. –26 ÷ (–3) **$8.\overline{6}$**
4. $\frac{-54}{6}$ **–9**
5. –48 ÷ 3 **–16**
6. $\frac{72}{-18}$ **–4**
7. 36 ÷ (–4) **–9**
8. $\frac{-72}{-9}$ **8**

Example 3 (p. 91) **ALGEBRA** Evaluate each expression if $s = -2$ and $t = 7$.

9. $14s \div t$ **–4**
10. $\frac{-10t}{s}$ **35**
11. $4t \div (2s)$ **–7**

Example 4 (p. 92)

12. **MONEY** The following are the changes of a value of a certain stock over the last 5 days: –\$7, +\$3, +\$6, –\$2, –\$5. Find the mean change. **–\$1**

Differentiated Instruction

Extension To help students see the connection between the rules for multiplication and division of integers, have them write two division statements for the following multiplication problems: –12 • 6 = –72, 10 • –5 = –50, and –8 • –6 = 48. This also reinforces the inverse relationship between the operations of multiplication and division. –72 ÷ 6 = –12, –72 ÷ –12 = 6; –50 ÷ –5 = 10, –50 ÷ 10 = –5; 48 ÷ –6 = –8; 48 ÷ –8 = –6

Practice and Problem Solving

= **Step-by-Step Solutions** begin on page R11.
Extra Practice begins on page 810.

Examples 1 and 2 pp. 90–91

Find each quotient.

13. $-33 \div 11$ **−3** **14.** $28 \div -14$ **−2** **15.** $-36 \div (-2)$ **18** **16.** $-60 \div (-5)$ **12**

17. $\frac{-150}{10}$ **−15** **18.** $\frac{600}{-20}$ **−30** **19.** $126 \div 9$ **14** **20.** $750 \div 15$ **50**

21. $-770 \div 7$ **−110** **22.** $-560 \div 8$ **−70** **23.** $\frac{-350}{-70}$ **5** **24.** $\frac{-480}{-16}$ **30**

Example 3 p. 91

ALGEBRA Evaluate each expression.

25. $\frac{n}{-13}$, if $n = -182$ **14** **26.** $252 \div k$, if $k = 9$ **28**

27. $\frac{-6a}{b}$, if $a = -24$ and $b = -4$ **−36** **28.** $\frac{9y}{x}$, if $x = -21$ and $y = -35$ **15**

29. $-2st \div (-3t)$, if $s = 18$ and $t = -14$ **12** **30.** $4qr \div (2r)$ if $q = -16$ and $r = -8$ **−32**

Example 4 p. 92

31. **FINANCIAL LITERACY** The last 5 transactions at Mr. Brigham's ATM were $250, −$60, −$94, $300, and −$186. Find the mean transaction amount. **$42**

32. **GAMES** The final scores of contestants on a game show were −14, 0, 78, −12, 46, and 64. What is the mean score? **27**

TEMPERATURE The expression $\frac{5(F - 32)}{9}$, where F represents the temperature in degrees Fahrenheit, can be used to convert temperatures from degrees Fahrenheit to degrees Celsius.

33. The surface temperature on Mercury at night can fall to −300°F. Convert this temperature to degrees Celsius. Round to the nearest tenth. **−184.4°C**

34. The extreme high and low temperatures for different states are shown in the table.

a. Find the extreme high and low temperatures for each state in degrees Celsius. Round to the nearest tenth.

b. The difference between the extreme high and low temperatures is called the range. Find the range of the temperatures in degrees Celsius for each state.

c. List the states in order from least to greatest ranges. **Florida, Kentucky, Michigan, New York, Arizona**

Extreme Temperature

State	Extreme Low (°F)	Extreme High (°F)
Arizona	−40	128
Florida	−2	109
Kentucky	−34	114
Michigan	−51	112
New York	−57	108

34a. Arizona: low: −40°C, high: 53.3°C; Florida: low: −18.9°C, high: 42.8°C; Kentucky: low: −36.7°C, high: 45.6°C; Michigan: low: −46.1°C, high: 44.4°C; New York: low: −49.4°C, high: 42.2°C

34b. Arizona: 93.3°C; Florida: 61.7°C; Kentucky: 82.3°C; Michigan: 90.5°C; New York: 91.6°C

35. **MONEY** Last year, a small clothing company's total income was $64,000, while its total expenses were $67,600. Use the expression $\frac{I - E}{12}$, where I represents total income and E represents total expenses, to find the average difference between the company's income and expenses each month. Explain what the answer means. **−$300; Sample answer: Every month, the company spends $300 more than they earn.**

Replace each ● with <, >, or = to make a true sentence.

36. $-80 \div (-2)$ ● $120 \div 3$ **=** **37.** $-1750 \div 70$ ● $-1008 \div 48$ **<**

38. $\frac{240}{-80}$ ● $\frac{-150}{-50}$ **<** **39.** $\frac{675}{-45}$ ● $\frac{867}{-51}$ **>**

Watch Out!

Common Error If students have difficulty finding the mean in Exercises 31 and 32, remind them to pay attention to the sign of each number when finding the sum.

Differentiated Homework Options

Level	Assignment	Two-Day Option	
AL Basic	13–32, 49, 51, 53–69	13–31 odd, 54–57	14–32 even, 49, 51, 53, 58–69
OL Core	13–31 odd, 33–35, 37–43 odd, 44–49, 51, 53–69	13–32, 54–57	33–49, 51, 53, 58–69
BL Advanced	33–65 (optional: 66–69)		

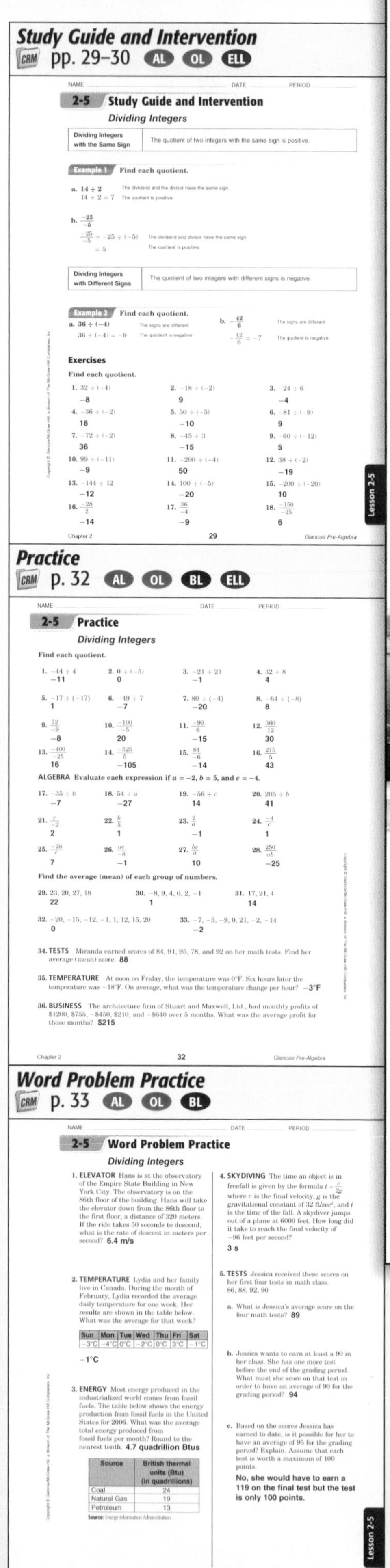

Study Guide and Intervention
CRM pp. 29–30 AL OL ELL

NAME ______ DATE ______ PERIOD ______

2-5 Study Guide and Intervention
Dividing Integers

Dividing Integers with the Same Sign	The quotient of two integers with the same sign is positive.

Example 1 Find each quotient.

a. $14 \div 2$
$14 \div 2 = 7$ — The dividend and the divisor have the same sign. The quotient is positive.

b. $\frac{-25}{-5}$
$\frac{-25}{-5} = -25 \div (-5)$ — The dividend and divisor have the same sign.
$= 5$ — The quotient is positive.

Dividing Integers with Different Signs	The quotient of two integers with different signs is negative.

Example 2 Find each quotient.

a. $36 \div (-4)$ — The signs are different.
$36 \div (-4) = -9$ — The quotient is negative.

b. $-\frac{42}{6}$ — The signs are different.
$-\frac{42}{6} = -7$ — The quotient is negative.

Exercises
Find each quotient.

1. $32 \div (-4)$ **−8**
2. $-18 \div (-2)$ **9**
3. $-24 \div 6$ **−4**
4. $-36 \div (-2)$ **18**
5. $50 \div (-5)$ **−10**
6. $-81 \div (-9)$ **9**
7. $-72 \div (-2)$ **36**
8. $-45 \div 3$ **−15**
9. $-60 \div (-12)$ **5**
10. $99 \div (-11)$ **−9**
11. $-200 \div (-4)$ **50**
12. $38 \div (-2)$ **−19**
13. $-144 \div 12$ **−12**
14. $100 \div (-5)$ **−20**
15. $-200 \div (-20)$ **10**
16. $\frac{-28}{2}$ **−14**
17. $\frac{36}{-4}$ **−9**
18. $\frac{-150}{-25}$ **6**

Chapter 2 29 Glencoe Pre-Algebra

Lesson 2-5

Practice
CRM p. 32 AL OL BL ELL

NAME ______ DATE ______ PERIOD ______

2-5 Practice
Dividing Integers

Find each quotient.

1. $-44 \div 4$ **−11**
2. $0 \div (-5)$ **0**
3. $-21 \div 21$ **−1**
4. $32 \div 8$ **4**
5. $-17 \div (-17)$ **1**
6. $-49 \div 7$ **−7**
7. $80 \div (-4)$ **−20**
8. $-64 \div (-8)$ **8**
9. $\frac{72}{-9}$ **−8**
10. $\frac{-100}{-5}$ **20**
11. $\frac{-90}{6}$ **−15**
12. $\frac{360}{12}$ **30**
13. $\frac{-400}{-25}$ **16**
14. $\frac{-525}{5}$ **−105**
15. $\frac{84}{-6}$ **−14**
16. $\frac{215}{5}$ **43**

ALGEBRA Evaluate each expression if $a = -2$, $b = 5$, and $c = -4$.

17. $-35 \div b$ **−7**
18. $54 \div a$ **−27**
19. $-56 \div c$ **14**
20. $205 \div b$ **41**
21. $\frac{c}{-2}$ **2**
22. $\frac{b}{5}$ **1**
23. $\frac{2}{a}$ **−1**
24. $\frac{-4}{c}$ **1**
25. $\frac{-28}{c}$ **7**
26. $\frac{ac}{-8}$ **−1**
27. $\frac{bc}{a}$ **10**
28. $\frac{250}{ab}$ **−25**

Find the average (mean) of each group of numbers.

29. 23, 20, 27, 18 **22**
30. −8, 9, 4, 0, 2, −1 **1**
31. 17, 21, 4 **14**
32. −20, −15, −12, −1, 1, 12, 15, 20 **0**
33. −7, −3, −9, 0, 21, −2, −14 **−2**

34. TESTS Miranda earned scores of 84, 91, 95, 78, and 92 on her math tests. Find her average (mean) score. **88**

35. TEMPERATURE At noon on Friday, the temperature was 0°F. Six hours later the temperature was −18°F. On average, what was the temperature change per hour? **−3°F**

36. BUSINESS The architecture firm of Stuart and Maxwell, Ltd., had monthly profits of \$1200, \$755, −\$450, \$210, and −\$640 over 5 months. What was the average profit for those months? **\$215**

Chapter 2 32 Glencoe Pre-Algebra

Word Problem Practice
CRM p. 33 AL OL BL

NAME ______ DATE ______ PERIOD ______

2-5 Word Problem Practice
Dividing Integers

1. ELEVATOR Hans is at the observatory of the Empire State Building in New York City. The observatory is on the 86th floor of the building. Hans will take the elevator down from the 86th floor to the first floor, a distance of 320 meters. If the ride takes 50 seconds to descend, what is the rate of descent in meters per second? **6.4 m/s**

2. TEMPERATURE Lydia and her family live in Canada. During the month of February, Lydia recorded the average daily temperature for one week. Her results are shown in the table below. What was the average for that week?

Sun	Mon	Tue	Wed	Thu	Fri	Sat
−3°C	−4°C	0°C	−2°C	0°C	3°C	−1°C

−1°C

3. ENERGY Most energy produced in the industrialized world comes from fossil fuels. The table below shows the energy production from fossil fuels in the United States for 2006. What was the average total energy produced from fossil fuels per month? Round to the nearest tenth. **4.7 quadrillion Btus**

Source	British thermal units (Btu) (in quadrillions)
Coal	24
Natural Gas	19
Petroleum	13

Source: Energy Information Administration

4. SKYDIVING The time an object is in freefall is given by the formula $t = \frac{v}{32}$ where v is the final velocity, g is the gravitational constant of 32 ft/sec², and t is the time of the fall. A skydiver jumps out of a plane at 6000 feet. How long did it take to reach the final velocity of −96 feet per second? **3 s**

5. TESTS Jessica received these scores on her first four tests in math class. 86, 88, 92, 90

a. What is Jessica's average score on the four math tests? **89**

b. Jessica wants to earn at least a 90 in her class. She has one more test before the end of the grading period. What must she score on that test in order to have an average of 90 for the grading period? **94**

c. Based on the scores Jessica has earned to date, is it possible for her to have an average of 95 for the grading period? Explain. Assume that each test is worth a maximum of 100 points. **No, she would have to earn a 119 on the final test but the test is only 100 points.**

Chapter 2 33 Glencoe Pre-Algebra

Lesson 2-5

Problem-Solving Tip

Guess and Check To find the value of x, try different values until you find the one that makes each sentence true.

ALGEBRA Find the value of x that makes each statement true.

40. $-375 \div x = -15$ **25**
41. $22 = x \div (-34)$ **−748**
42. $x \div (-17) = -35$ **595**
43. $-689 \div x = 53$ **−13**

For Exercises 44–46, write an expression to represent each real-world situation. Then evaluate the expression and interpret the meaning of the solution.

44. Jean owes her parents \$90, to be paid in 5 equal installments. How much is each installment?

45. The temperature dropped a total of 40°F over an 8 hour period. What was the mean hourly temperature drop?

46. In October, the full price of a television is \$695. Over the next seven months, the price of the television drops a total of \$140. How much did the price of the television drop each month on average?

47. **GEOGRAPHY** The table shows the deepest point of each of the Great Lakes.

Great Lake	Deepest Point (m)
Erie	−64
Huron	−229
Michigan	−281
Ontario	−244
Superior	−406

a. What is the mean of the deepest points of the Great Lakes?

b. Suppose each of the deepest points were 10 meters higher. Find the mean. Compare the new mean to the original.

Real-World Link

There is enough water in the five Great Lakes to cover the entire continental United States with 9.5 feet of water.

Source: Alliance for the Great Lakes

48. **MULTIPLE REPRESENTATIONS** In this problem, you will investigate the relationships between distance and time. Suppose Joseph was tracking a submarine. The submarine descended 480 feet in 20 minutes.

a. **NUMERICAL** How many feet did the submarine descend per minute? **24 ft**

b. **ALGEBRAIC** Write a function rule to determine how many feet the submarine will descend after any number of minutes. **24*m***

c. **TABULAR** Create a function table to show how far the submarine descended after 5, 10, 15, and 18 minutes. **See margin.**

H.O.T. Problems
Use **H**igher-**O**rder **T**hinking Skills

49. **OPEN ENDED** Write a division expression with a quotient between −20 and −25.

50. **CHALLENGE** The mean temperature during 5 days was −10°F. Give a sample set of what the temperatures might have been for the 5 days.

51. **REASONING** Find the next two numbers in the pattern 1024, −256, 64, −16,. . . . Explain your reasoning.

52. **CHALLENGE** Addition and multiplication are said to be *closed* for whole numbers, but subtraction and division are not. That is, when you add or multiply any two whole numbers, the result is a whole number. Which operations are closed for integers?

53. **WRITING IN MATH** Explain whether the Associative Property and Commutative Property are true for division of integers. Support your reasoning with an example. **See margin.**

Answers:

44. −\$90 ÷ 5; −\$18; She will pay her parents \$18 each time to repay the debt.
45. −40 ÷ 8; −5°F; Each hour the temperature dropped 5°F.
46. −\$140 ÷ 7; −\$20; The price dropped \$20 every month.
47a. −244.8 m
47b. −234.8 m; The mean would be 10 meters higher.
49. Sample answer: −110 ÷ 5 = −22
50. Sample answer: −4°, −8°, −11°, −12°, −15°
51. 4, −1; Divide the previous term by −4
52. addition, subtraction, and multiplication

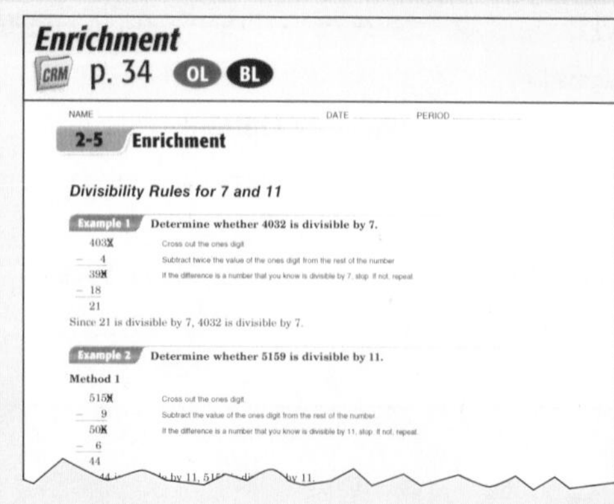

Enrichment
CRM p. 34 OL BL

NAME ______ DATE ______ PERIOD ______

2-5 Enrichment

Divisibility Rules for 7 and 11

Example 1 Determine whether 4032 is divisible by 7.

403~~2~~ — Cross out the ones digit.
− 4 — Subtract twice the value of the ones digit from the rest of the number.
39~~9~~ — If the difference is a number that you know is divisible by 7, stop. If not, repeat.
− 18
21

Since 21 is divisible by 7, 4032 is divisible by 7.

Example 2 Determine whether 5159 is divisible by 11.

Method 1

515~~9~~ — Cross out the ones digit.
− 9 — Subtract the value of the ones digit from the rest of the number.
50~~6~~ — If the difference is a number that you know is divisible by 11, stop. If not, repeat.
− 6
44

Additional Answer

48c.

Input (m)	$24m$	Output (f)
5	24(5)	120
10	24(10)	240
15	24(15)	360
18	24(18)	432

Standardized Test Practice

54. Yesterday's low temperature was 24 degrees Fahrenheit. Use the expression $\frac{5(F - 32)}{9}$, where F represents the temperature in degrees Fahrenheit, to find the approximate low temperature in degrees Celsius. **B**

A −9.8°C C 4.4°C
B −4.4°C D 9.8°C

55. Miss Washer recorded the low temperature each day for a week. What is the mean low temperature? **J**

Day	M	T	W	Th	F
Temperature (°F)	−18	12	−7	9	−2

F 9.6°F H −9.6°F
G 1.2°F J −1.2°F

56. The depth of a reservoir decreased 84 inches in two weeks. If the water depth changed by the same amount each day, how much did the depth of the water change per day? **B**

A −7 inches C 6 inches
B −6 inches D 7 inches

57. EXTENDED RESPONSE The temperature dropped 30°F in a 6 hour period.

a. What was the mean hourly temperature change? **−5°F**
b. Write a function rule to represent the situation. **$-5h$**
c. Create a function table to show how much the temperature changed in 1, 3, and 5 hours. **See margin.**

Spiral Review

58. TIDES During low tide, in Wrightsville, North Carolina, the beachfront in some places is about 350 feet from the ocean to the homes. High tide can change the width of a beach at a rate of −17 feet an hour. It takes 6 hours for the ocean to move from low to high tide. (Lesson 2-4)

a. What is the change in the width of the beachfront from low to high tide? **−102 ft**
b. What is the distance from the ocean to the homes at high tide? **248 ft**

Find each difference. (Lesson 2-3)

59. 3 − 8 **−5**
60. 4 − 5 **−1**
61. 2 − 9 **−7**
62. −9 − (−7) **−2**
63. −7 − (−10) **3**
64. −11 − (−12) **1**

65. MONEY The starting balance in a checking account was $50. What was the balance after checks were written for $25 and for $32? (Lesson 2-2) **−$7**

Skills Review

Use the coordinate plane to name the ordered pairs for each point. (Lesson 1-6)

66. Point A **(0, 3)**
67. Point G **(5, 1)**
68. Point C **(2, 7)**
69. Point E **(5, 4)**

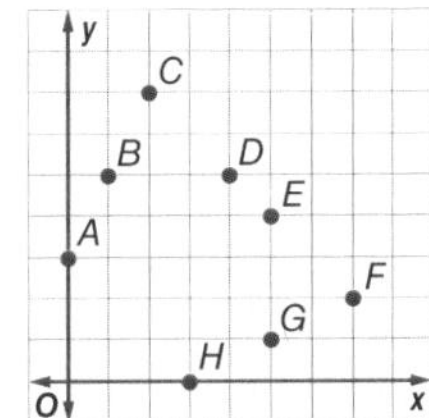

Differentiated Instruction

Extension Tell students that in algebra, quotients can be calculated in expressions that contain variables. Ask them to find the quotient of $\frac{7b - c}{b}$ when $b = -3$ and $c = 6$. 9

Multiple Representations In Exercise 48, students use numbers, a function rule, and a function table to model time, speed, and distance relations.

Exercise Alert!

Open Ended Exercise 49 can have a rational number as the solution.

4 ASSESS

Ticket Out the Door Have students write a paragraph explaining how they know whether a quotient should be positive or negative. As they leave the class, have them turn in their paragraphs.

Additional Answers

53. Sample answer: The Associative Property is not true for the division of integers because how the integers are grouped affects the solution. $[24 \div (-6)] \div 2 = -2$; $24 \div [(-6 \div 2)] = -8$; The Commutative Property is not true for the division of integers because the order of the integers affects the solution. $-2 \div 10 = -0.2$; $10 \div -2 = -5$

57c.

Input (h)	$-5h$	Output (t)
1	−5(1)	−5
3	−5(3)	−15
5	−5(5)	−25

2-6 Lesson Notes

1 FOCUS

Vertical Alignment

Before Lesson 2-6
Use ordered pairs to name and locate points.

Lesson 2-6
Graph points on a coordinate plane and graph algebraic relationships.

After Lesson 2-6
Draw conclusions and make predictions by analyzing trends in scatter plots.

2 TEACH

Scaffolding Questions

Have students read the *Why?* section of the lesson and answer the questions.

Ask:

- What are the coordinates of the swimming pool? (0, 0)
- Who has farther to walk to the swimming pool, Staci or Kacy? Explain. Staci; Staci walks 6 blocks and Kacy walks 5 blocks.
- Describe two routes Marcus could walk to the pool. Is the distance the same? Explain. He could walk 2 blocks east and 3 blocks south or 3 blocks south and 2 blocks east; yes, he walks the same number of blocks east and south for both routes.

2-6 Graphing in Four Quadrants

Then
You have already used ordered pairs to name and locate points. (Lesson 1-4)

Now
- Graph points on a coordinate plane.
- Graph algebraic relationships.

New Vocabulary
quadrants

Math Online
glencoe.com
- Extra Examples
- Personal Tutor
- Self-Check Quiz
- Homework Help
- Math in Motion

Why?

Duncan and his friends have agreed to meet at the community swimming pool. The map shows where each person lives in relationship to the swimming pool.

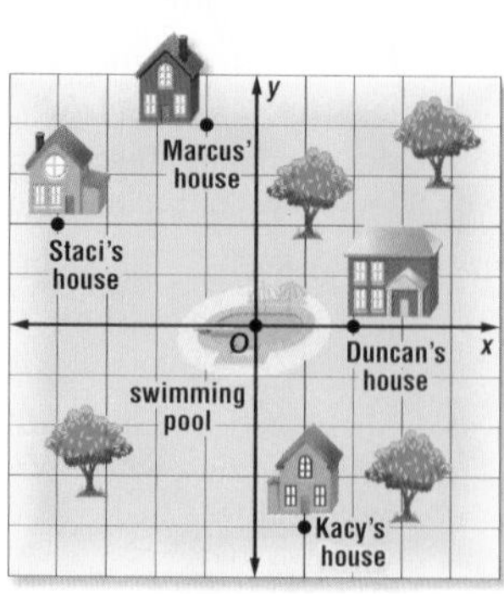

a. Explain how Kacy would go to the swimming pool. walk 4 blocks north and 1 block west

b. Which two friends live the same distance from the swimming pool? Why are they in different locations? Marcus and Kacy; Marcus lives north of the pool and Kacy lives south of the pool.

Graph Points Street maps use a coordinate system. The coordinate system you used in Lesson 1-4 can be extended to include points below and to the left of the origin.

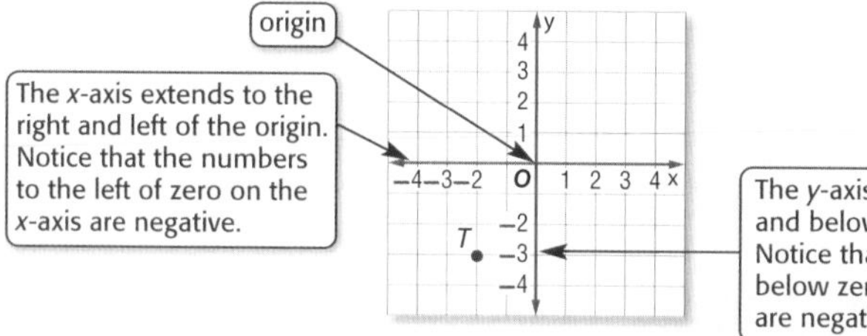

Recall that a point graphed on the coordinate system has an x-coordinate and a y-coordinate. The dot at the ordered pair $(-2, -3)$ is the graph of point T.

x-coordinate → $(-2, -3)$ ← y-coordinate

EXAMPLE 1 Write Ordered Pairs

Write the ordered pair that names each point.

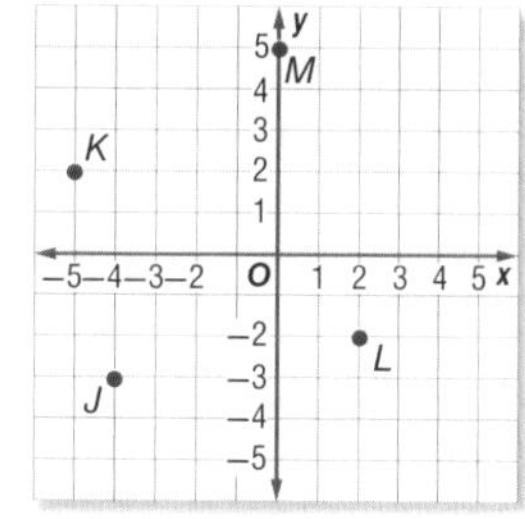

a. J

The x-coordinate is -4.
The y-coordinate is -3.
The ordered pair is $(-4, -3)$.

b. L

The x-coordinate is 2.
The y-coordinate is -2.
The ordered pair is $(2, -2)$.

Check Your Progress

1A. M (0, 5) **1B.** K (−5, 2)

Personal Tutor glencoe.com

Lesson 2-6 Resources

Resource	Approaching-Level	On-Level	Beyond-Level	English Learners
Teacher Edition	• Differentiated Instruction, p. 97		• Differentiated Instruction, p. 100	
Chapter Resource Masters	• Study Guide and Intervention, pp. 36–37 • Skills Practice, p. 38 • Practice, p. 39 • Word Problem Practice, p. 40 • Spreadsheet Activity, p. 42	• Study Guide and Intervention, pp. 36–37 • Skills Practice, p. 38 • Practice, p. 39 • Word Problem Practice, p. 40 • Enrichment, p. 41 • Spreadsheet Activity, p. 42	• Practice, p. 39 • Word Problem Practice, p. 40 • Enrichment, p. 41 • Spreadsheet Activity, p. 42	• Study Guide and Intervention, pp. 36–37 • Skills Practice, p. 38 • Practice, p. 39 • Spreadsheet Activity, p. 42
Transparencies	• 5-Minute Check Transparency 2-6	• 5-Minute Check Transparency 2-6	• 5-Minute Check Transparency 2-6	• 5-Minute Check Transparency 2-6
Other	• Study Notebook • Teaching Pre-Algebra with Manipulatives	• Study Notebook • Teaching Pre-Algebra with Manipulatives	• Study Notebook	• Study Notebook • Teaching Pre-Algebra with Manipulatives

The x-axis and the y-axis separate the coordinate plane into four regions, called **quadrants**. The quadrants are named I, II, III, and IV.

The axes and points on the axes are not located in any of the quadrants.

Math *in Motion*, Interactive Lab glencoe.com

Math History Link

René Descartes (1596–1650) The coordinate plane can also be called the *Cartesian* plane. The word *Cartesian* comes from the name Descartes. René Descartes was a French mathematician who is credited with developing the coordinate plane.

EXAMPLE 2 Graph Points and Name the Quadrant

Graph and label each point on a coordinate plane. Name the quadrant in which each point lies.

a. $A(-2, -4)$

Start at the origin. Move 2 units left. Then move 4 units down and draw a dot. Point $A(-2, -4)$ is in quadrant III.

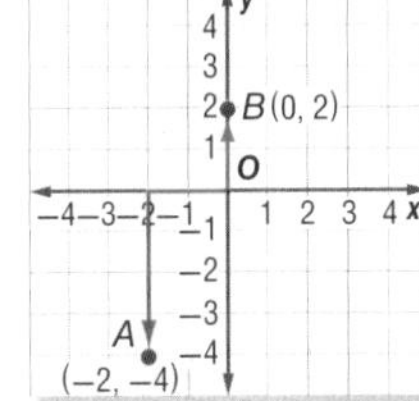

b. $B(0, 2)$

Start at the origin. Since the x-coordinate is 0, the point will lie on the y-axis. So, move 2 units up. Point $B(0, 2)$ is not in a quadrant.

Check Your Progress 2A–C. See Chapter 2 Answer Appendix for graph.

2A. $H(4, -3)$ IV **2B.** $I(-1, 4)$ II **2C.** $J(0, -2)$ None

Personal Tutor glencoe.com

Graph Algebraic Relationships You can use a coordinate graph to show relationships between two numbers.

Real-World EXAMPLE 3 Graph an Algebraic Relationship

GOLF The difference between John and Tarie's golf score is 2. If x represents John's score and y represents Tarie's score, make a function table of possible values for x and y. Graph the ordered pairs and describe the graph.

Choose values for x and y that have a difference of 2. Then graph the ordered pairs.

The points are along a diagonal line that crosses the x-axis at $x = 2$.

$x - y = 2$		
x	y	(x, y)
2	0	(2, 0)
1	−1	(1, −1)
0	−2	(0, −2)
−1	−3	(−1, −3)
−2	−4	(−2, −4)

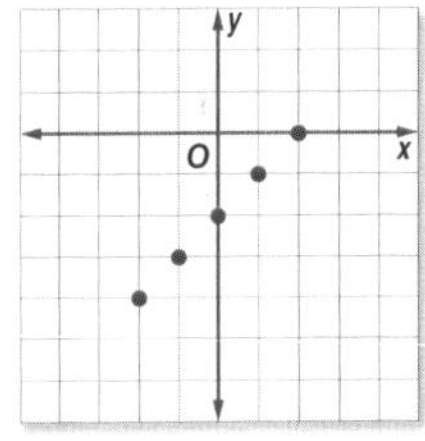

StudyTip

Scale When no numbers are shown on the x- or y-axis, you can assume that each square is one unit long on each side.

Check Your Progress

3. GOLF The sum of two golf scores is 3. If x represents one score and y represents the other score, make a function table of possible values for x and y. Graph the ordered pairs and describe the graph.

3. See Chapter 2 Answer Appendix.

Personal Tutor glencoe.com

Graph Points

Examples 1 and 2 show how to write ordered pairs, graph points, and name quadrants on a coordinate graph.

Formative Assessment

Use the Check Your Progress exercises after each example to determine students' understanding of concepts.

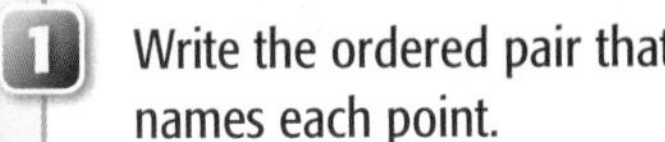

Additional Examples

1 Write the ordered pair that names each point.

a. P (4, −2) **b.** Q (−3, −1)

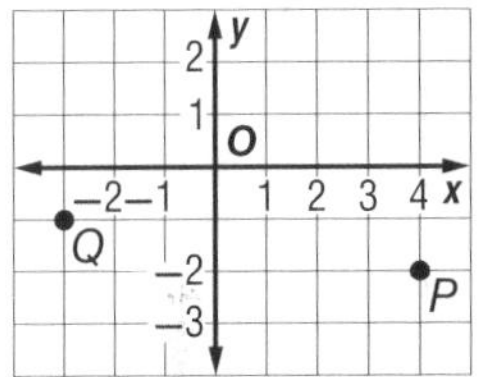

2 Graph and label each point on a coordinate plane. Name the quadrant in which each point lies.

a. $S(-1, -5)$ Quadrant III

b. $U(-2, 3)$ Quadrant II

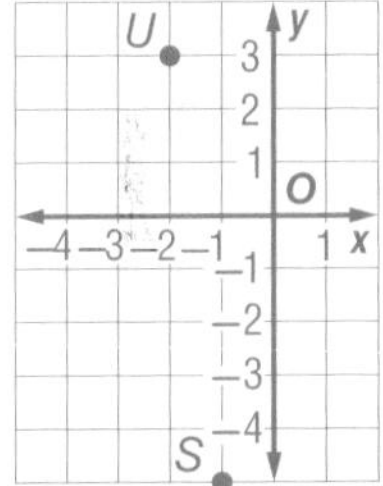

Additional Examples also in Interactive Classroom PowerPoint® Presentations

IWB INTERACTIVE WHITEBOARD READY

Differentiated Instruction

If students are having trouble locating coordinates on the plane,

Then have them place one finger on the horizontal number and one finger on the vertical number. Students should trace the lines until they intersect. The point of intersection names the coordinates.

Graph Algebraic Relationships

Example 3 uses a real-world example to show how an algebraic relationship is represented in a coordinate graph.

Additional Example

3 **GAMES** Mrs. Gossell's class is playing a classroom quiz game. The difference between Ali's and Joachim's scores is 3 points. If x represents Ali's score and y represnts Joachim's scores, make a table of possible values for x and y. Then graph the ordered pairs and describe the graph. The points in the graph are on a line that slants upward to the right. The line crosses the y-axis at $y = -3$.

$x - y = 3$		
x	y	(x, y)
2	−1	(2, −1)
1	−2	(1, −2)
0	−3	(0, −3)
−1	−4	(−1, −4)
−2	−5	(−2, −5)

TEACH with TECH

INTERACTIVE WHITEBOARD Find a coordinate plane in the resources provided with your IWB software. Ask a student to randomly plot points on the plane. For each point, ask students to name the quadrant in which the point lies.

3 PRACTICE

Formative Assessment

Use Exercises 1–9 to check for understanding.

Use the chart at the bottom of this page to customize assignments for your students.

Check Your Understanding

Example 1 p. 96

Name the ordered pair for each point graphed at the right.

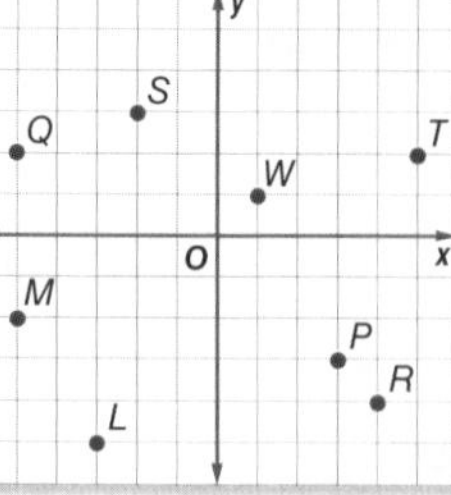

1. Q (−5, 2)
2. P (3, −3)
3. T (5, 2)
4. M (−5, −2)

Example 2 p. 97

5–8. See Chapter 2 Answer Appendix for graph.

Graph and label each point on a coordinate plane. Name the quadrant in which each point is located.

5. $A(-2, 3)$ II
6. $B(4, -1)$ IV
7. $C(-3, -2)$ III
8. $D(0, -5)$ None

Example 3 p. 97

9. **TEMPERATURE** The difference of two temperatures is 4°F. If x represents the first temperature and y represents the second temperature, make a function table of possible values for x and y. Graph the ordered pairs and describe the graph. See Chapter 2 Answer Appendix.

Practice and Problem Solving

● = **Step-by-Step Solutions** begin on page R11. **Extra Practice** begins on page 810.

Example 1 p. 96

Name the ordered pair for each point graphed at the right.

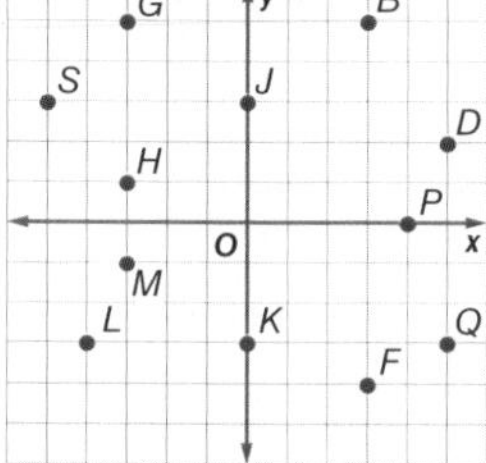

10. S (−5, 3)
11. H (−3, 1)
12. D (5, 2)
13. B (3, 5)
14. M (−3, −1)
15. L (−4, −3)
16. F (3, −4)
17. Q (5, −3)
18. K (0, −3)
19. J (0, 3)

Example 2 p. 97

20–31. See Chapter 2 Answer Appendix for graph.

Graph and label each point on a coordinate plane. Name the quadrant in which each point is located.

20. $Z(-1, 1)$ II
21. $Y(-2, 3)$ II
22. $X(5, 6)$ I
23. $W(6, 2)$ I
24. $V(-1, -6)$ III
25. $S(2, -1)$ IV
26. $T(-5, 0)$ None
27. $R(0, -4)$ None
28. $P(-4, 5)$ II
29. $Q(-3, 3)$ II
30. $N(1, -1)$ IV
31. $K(5, -3)$ IV

Example 3 p. 97

32–33. See Chapter 2 Answer Appendix.

32. **FOOTBALL** After two plays, the Wildcats gained a total of 16 yards. If x represents the number of yards for play one, and y represents the number of yards for play two, make a function table of possible values for x and y. Graph the ordered pairs and describe the graph.

33. **SCUBA DIVING** The difference in depth between two scuba divers is 10 feet. If x represents the depth of one scuba diver and y represents the depth of the second scuba diver, make a function table of possible values for x and y. Graph the ordered pairs and describe the graph.

Name the quadrant in which each point lies.

34. $A(5, |-6|)$ I
35. $E(|-5|, -3)$ IV
36. $I(x, y)$ if $x < 0, y > 0$ II
37. $U(x, y)$ if $x > 0, y < 0$ IV

Differentiated Homework Options

Level	Assignment	Two-Day Option	
AL Basic	10–33, 47, 50–68	11–33 odd, 51–54	10–32 even, 47, 50, 55–68
OL Core	11–37 odd, 38–40, 41–47 odd, 50–68	10–33, 51–54	34–47, 50, 55–68
BL Advanced	34–62 (optional: 63–68)		

38–46. See Chapter 2 Answer Appendix.

38. GEOMETRY Graph points $A(-4, 3)$, $B(1, 3)$, $C(1, 2)$, and $D(-4, 2)$ on a coordinate plane and connect them to form a rectangle.

a. Add 4 to the x-coordinate of each ordered pair and re-draw the figure.

b. Compare the two rectangles.

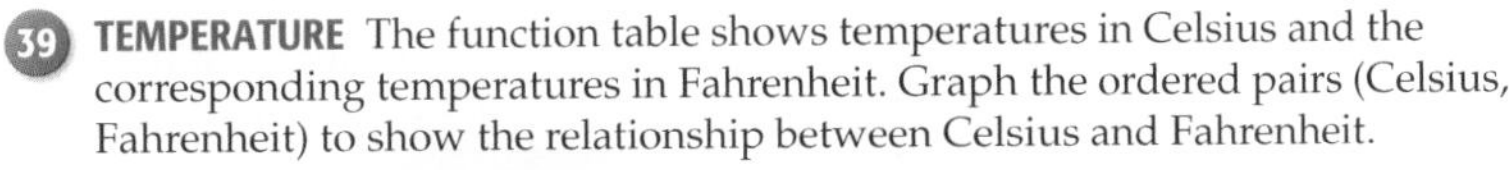

39. TEMPERATURE The function table shows temperatures in Celsius and the corresponding temperatures in Fahrenheit. Graph the ordered pairs (Celsius, Fahrenheit) to show the relationship between Celsius and Fahrenheit.

Celsius	−10	−5	0	5	10
Fahrenheit	14	23	32	41	50

40. FINANCIAL LITERACY The function table shows the balance on a $50 music card after a certain number of songs have been downloaded. Make a graph to show how the number of songs downloaded and the remaining balance are related.

Songs Downloaded	Balance ($)
0	50
5	45
10	40
15	35

Real-World Link

The first MP3 player to become widely available was released in 1999 and cost around $200. It weighed about 2 ounces and held 32 minutes of music. In contrast, an MP3 player that holds 8 hours of music costs less than $50 in 2007.

For each graph, create a function table showing the input, rule, and output.

41. C

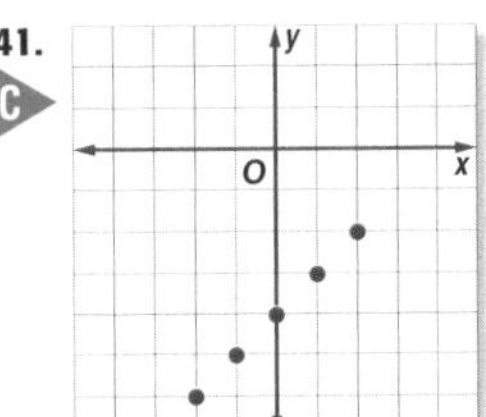

42.

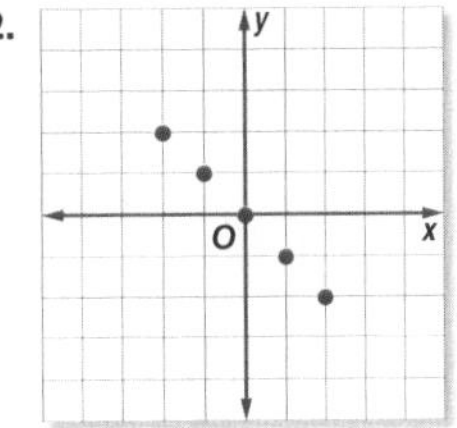

Graph and label each point on a coordinate plane.

43. $A(-6.5, 3)$ **44.** $B(-2, -5.75)$ **45.** $C(4.1, -1)$ **46.** $D(-3.4, 1.5)$

H.O.T. Problems
Use Higher-Order Thinking Skills

47. OPEN ENDED Write the coordinates of a point located in quadrant II. Sample answer: (−3, 1)

48. CHALLENGE The product of two numbers is 12. a–b. See Chapter 2 Answer Appendix.

a. Make a function table using −3, −2, −1, 1, 2, and 3 as input values.

b. Graph the ordered pairs. Compare and contrast your graph with the graph in Example 3.

49. CHALLENGE Determine whether each statement is *always*, *sometimes*, or *never* true. Explain or give a counterexample to support your answer.

a. Both x- and y-coordinates of a point in quadrant I are negative.

b. The x-coordinate of a point that lies on the x-axis is negative.

50. WRITING IN MATH Are the points at (−7, 8) and (8,−7) in the same location? Explain your reasoning.

49a. Sample answer: Never; both coordinates are positive.

b. Sample answer: Sometimes; both (−2, 0) and (2, 0) lie on the x-axis.

50. No; Sample answer: the point (−7, 8) lies in quadrant II and the point (8, −7) lies in quadrant IV

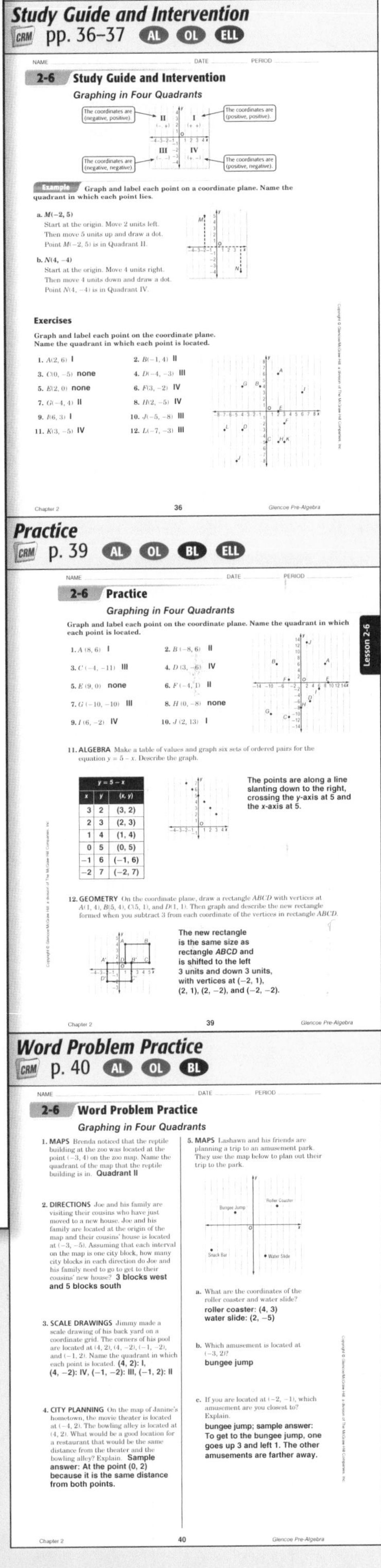

Study Guide and Intervention CRM pp. 36–37 AL OL ELL

2-6 Study Guide and Intervention

Graphing in Four Quadrants

Example: Graph and label each point on a coordinate plane. Name the quadrant in which each point lies.

a. $M(-2, 5)$ Start at the origin. Move 2 units left. Then move 5 units up and draw a dot. Point $M(-2, 5)$ is in Quadrant II.

b. $N(4, -4)$ Start at the origin. Move 4 units right. Then move 4 units down and draw a dot. Point $N(4, -4)$ is in Quadrant IV.

Exercises

Graph and label each point on the coordinate plane. Name the quadrant in which each point is located.

1. $A(2, 6)$ I 2. $B(-1, 4)$ II 3. $C(0, -5)$ none 4. $D(-4, -3)$ III 5. $E(2, 0)$ none 6. $F(3, -2)$ IV 7. $G(-4, 4)$ II 8. $H(2, -5)$ IV 9. $I(6, 3)$ I 10. $J(-5, -8)$ III 11. $K(3, -5)$ IV 12. $L(-7, -3)$ III

Practice CRM p. 39 AL OL BL ELL

2-6 Practice

Graphing in Four Quadrants

Graph and label each point on the coordinate plane. Name the quadrant in which each point is located.

1. $A(8, 6)$ I 2. $B(-8, 6)$ II 3. $C(-4, -11)$ III 4. $D(3, -6)$ IV 5. $E(9, 0)$ none 6. $F(-4, 1)$ II 7. $G(-10, -10)$ III 8. $H(0, -8)$ none 9. $I(6, -2)$ IV 10. $J(2, 13)$ I

11. ALGEBRA Make a table of values and graph six sets of ordered pairs for the equation $y = 5 - x$. Describe the graph.

x	y	(x, y)
3	2	(3, 2)
2	3	(2, 3)
1	4	(1, 4)
0	5	(0, 5)
−1	6	(−1, 6)
−2	7	(−2, 7)

The points are along a line slanting down to the right, crossing the y-axis at 5 and the x-axis at 5.

12. GEOMETRY On the coordinate plane, draw a rectangle ABCD with vertices at A(1, 4), B(5, 4), C(5, 1), and D(1, 1). Then graph and describe the new rectangle formed when you subtract 3 from each coordinate of the vertices in rectangle ABCD.

The new rectangle is the same size as rectangle ABCD and is shifted to the left 3 units and down 3 units, with vertices at (−2, 1), (2, 1), (2, −2), and (−2, −2).

Word Problem Practice CRM p. 40 AL OL BL

2-6 Word Problem Practice

Graphing in Four Quadrants

1. MAPS Brenda noticed that the reptile building at the zoo was located at the point (−3, 4) on the zoo map. Name the quadrant of the map that the reptile building is in. Quadrant II

2. DIRECTIONS Joe and his family are visiting their cousins who have just moved to a new house. Joe and his family are located at the origin of the map and their cousins' house is located at (−3, −5). Assuming that each interval on the map is one city block, how many city blocks in each direction do Joe and his family need to go to get to their cousins' new house? 3 blocks west and 5 blocks south

3. SCALE DRAWINGS Jimmy made a scale drawing of his back yard on a coordinate grid. The corners of his pool are located at (4, 2), (4, −2), (−1, −2), and (−1, 2). Name the quadrant in which each point is located. (4, 2): I, (4, −2): IV, (−1, −2): III, (−1, 2): II

4. CITY PLANNING On the map of Janine's hometown, the movie theater is located at (−4, 2). The bowling alley is located at (4, 2). What would be a good location for a restaurant that would be the same distance from the theater and the bowling alley? Explain. Sample answer: At the point (0, 2) because it is the same distance from both points.

5. MAPS Lashawn and his friends are planning a trip to an amusement park. They use the map below to plan out their trip to the park.

a. What are the coordinates of the roller coaster and water slide? roller coaster: (4, 3) water slide: (2, −5)

b. Which amusement is located at (−3, 2)? bungee jump

c. If you are located at (−2, −1), which amusement are you closest to? Explain. bungee jump; sample answer: To get to the bungee jump, one goes up 3 and left 1. The other amusements are farther away.

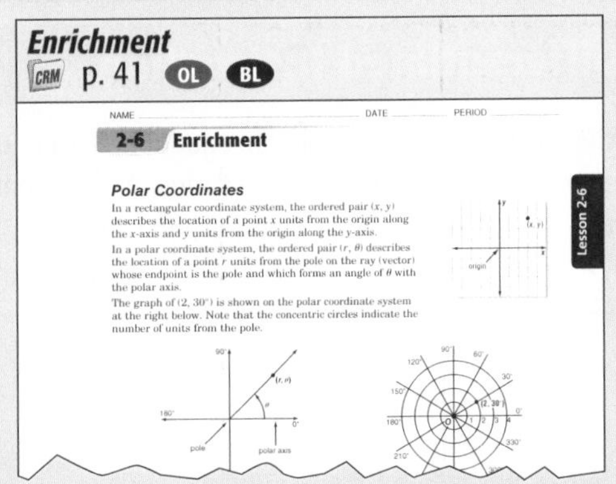

Enrichment CRM p. 41 OL BL

2-6 Enrichment

Polar Coordinates

In a rectangular coordinate system, the ordered pair (x, y) describes the location of a point x units from the origin along the x-axis and y units from the origin along the y-axis.

In a polar coordinate system, the ordered pair (r, θ) describes the location of a point r units from the pole on the ray (vector) whose endpoint is the pole and which forms an angle of θ with the polar axis.

The graph of (2, 30°) is shown on the polar coordinate system at the right below. Note that the concentric circles indicate the number of units from the pole.

Tips for New Teachers

Comparisons Students have already plotted points in Quadrant I, where the coordinates in the ordered pairs were both positive. In the other quadrants, at least one coordinate in the pair will be negative. Equate the axes with a number line. All coordinates to the left of the zero on the *x*-axis and below the zero on the *y*-axis will be negative coordinates. Have students place the sign pairs (+, +), (−, +), (−, −), and (+, −) into their proper quadrants. Ask them what patterns they observe and what opposite quadrants, such as I and III, have in common.

4 ASSESS

Name the Math Hand out a coordinate graph and a list of 4–6 ordered pairs that the students can graph. Have them name and label each point and name the quadrants in which each point lies. Make certain to include points that are in each quadrant.

Formative Assessment

Check for student understanding of concepts in Lessons 2-5 and 2-6.

 Quiz 3, p. 53

Standardized Test Practice

51. Which point on the graph best represents the location of the library? **C**

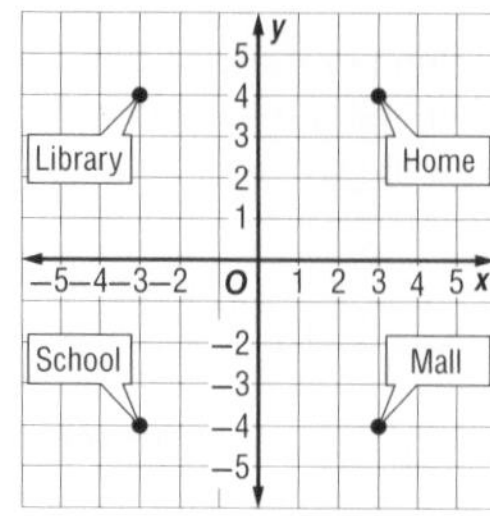

A (3, 4) C (−3, 4)
B (−3, −4) D (3, −4)

52. What building is located at point (−3, −4) on the graph above? **F**

F School H Library
G Mall J Home

53. In which quadrant on the coordinate plane is point (2, −3)? **D**

A quadrant I
B quadrant II
C quadrant III
D quadrant IV

54. EXTENDED RESPONSE Juan wants to rent 4 DVDs. Each DVD costs $3 for 2 days.

a. Complete the table to show his total cost for the number of days given.

Number of Days	Total Cost
2	■ 12
4	■ 24
6	■ 36

b. How much will Juan have to pay if he wants to keep the DVDs for 10 days? **$60**

Spiral Review

Find each quotient (Lesson 2-5)

55. −27 ÷ (−9) **3** **56.** −77 ÷ 7 **−11** **57.** −300 ÷ 6 **−50**

58. GLACIERS A glacier was receding at a rate of 300 feet per day. What is the glacier's movement in 5 days? (*Hint:* The word *receding* means moving backward.) (Lesson 2-4) **−1500 ft**

59. SWIMMING Lincoln High School's swim team finished the 4 × 100-meter freestyle relay in 5 minutes 18 seconds. Prospect High School's swim team finished the race in 5 minutes 7 seconds. Write an integer that represents Lincoln's finish compared to Prospect's finish. (Lesson 2-3) **−11 s**

Evaluate each expression. (Lessons 2-1 through 2-3)

60. |−10| **10** **61.** |10| − |−4| **6** **62.** |16| + |−5| **21**

Skills Review

Use the grid to name the point for each ordered pair. (Lesson 1-4)

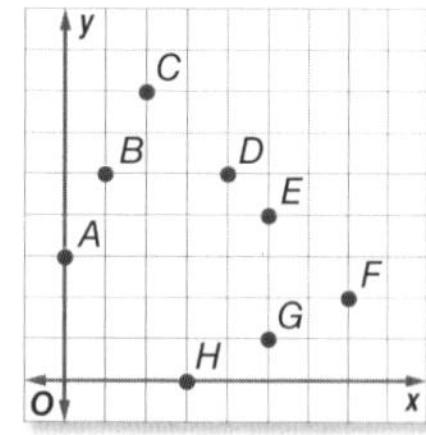

63. (1, 5) *B* **64.** (7, 2) *F*
65. (4, 5) *D* **66.** (0, 3) *A*
67. (2, 7) *C* **68.** (5, 4) *E*

Differentiated Instruction

BL

Extension Explain that a linear equation is an equation with two different variables (both first degree) that appear in separate terms. Ask students to find three solutions (ordered pairs) for the linear equation $y = 3x + 4$ and graph the line. Ordered pairs will vary; sample pairs: (−2, −2), (2, 10), (0, 4). Check students' graphs. Using your graph, predict the value of y when $x = 1$. $y = 7$

2-7 Translations and Reflections on the Coordinate Plane

Then

You have already graphed points on a coordinate plane. (Lesson 2-6)

Now

- Define and identify transformations.
- Draw translations and reflections on a coordinate plane.

New Vocabulary

transformation
image
translation
reflection
line of symmetry

Math Online

glencoe.com

- Extra Examples
- Personal Tutor
- Self-Check Quiz
- Homework Help

Why?

Suppose a line of tuba players marched across the field for 20 yards, then turned left and marched another 5 yards. a–b. See Chapter 2 Answer Appendix.

a. Compare and contrast the original position and resulting position of the tubas.

b. Suppose that a line of bass drums is on the 50-yard line. One half of the drummers turned around and marched 10 yards back, while the other half kept marching 10 yards forward. Compare and contrast these motions.

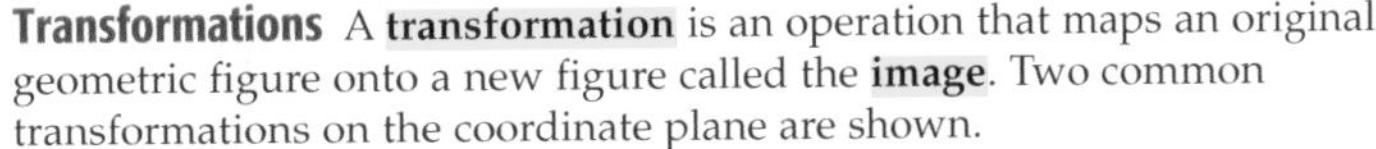

Transformations A **transformation** is an operation that maps an original geometric figure onto a new figure called the **image**. Two common transformations on the coordinate plane are shown.

A **translation** is when you slide a figure from one position to another without turning it.

Translation

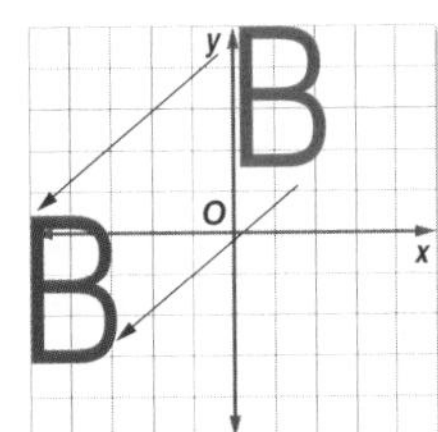

A **reflection** is when you flip a figure over a line. This line is called the **line of symmetry**.

Reflection

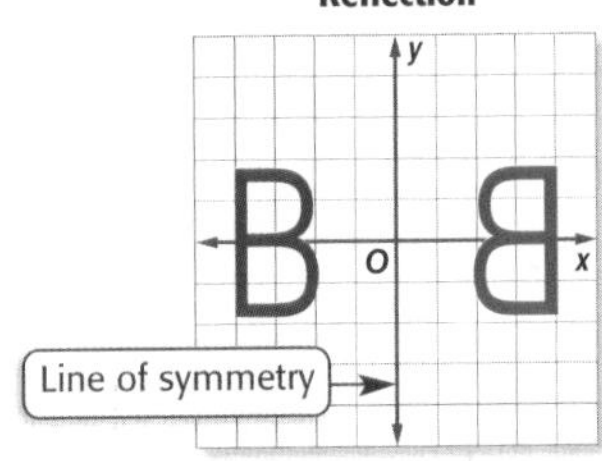

Key Concept Translations and Reflections — For Your FOLDABLE

Translation

- called a *slide*
- image is the same shape and the same size as original figure
- orientation is the *same* as the original figure

Reflection

- called a *flip*
- figures are mirror images of each other
- image is the same shape and same size as original figure
- orientation is *different* from the original figure

2-7 Lesson Notes

1 FOCUS

Vertical Alignment

Before Lesson 2-7
Graph points on a coordinate plane.

Lesson 2-7
Define and identify transformations. Draw translations and reflections on a coordinate plane.

After Lesson 2-7
Use congruence and transformations to make conjectures about geometric figures.

2 Teach

Scaffolding Questions

Have students read the *Why?* section of the lesson and answer the questions.

Ask:

- How could you describe the position of the tubas as coordinates, assuming their starting position to be (0, 0)? (20, 5)
- Compare the orientation of the two lines of base drums. One drum line is turned 180° from the other drum line.
- Suppose the drum major starts at the center of the field and walks forward 5 yards, then turns left and walks 5 yards, then turns left again and walks another 5 yards. How far is the drum major from her original position? 5 yards

Lesson 2-7 Resources

Resource	Approaching-Level	On-Level	Beyond-Level	English Learners
Teacher Edition		• Differentiated Instruction, p. 102	• Differentiated Instruction, p. 106	
Chapter 2 Resource Masters	• Study Guide and Intervention, pp. 43–44 • Skills Practice, p. 45 • Practice, p. 46 • Word Problem Practice, p. 47	• Study Guide and Intervention, pp. 43–44 • Skills Practice, p. 45 • Practice, p. 46 • Word Problem Practice, p. 47 • Enrichment, p. 48	• Practice, p. 46 • Word Problem Practice, p. 47 • Enrichment, p. 48	• Study Guide and Intervention, pp. 43–44 • Skills Practice, p. 45 • Practice, p. 46
Transparencies	• 5-Minute Check Transparency 2-7	• 5-Minute Check Transparency 2-7	• 5-Minute Check Transparency 2-7	• 5-Minute Check Transparency 2-7
Other	• Study Notebook • Teaching Pre-Algebra with Manipulatives	• Study Notebook • Teaching Pre-Algebra with Manipulatives	• Study Notebook	• Study Notebook • Teaching Pre-Algebra with Manipulatives

Translations

Example 1 shows how to draw a translation on a coordinate plane.

Formative Assessment

Use the Check Your Progress exercises after each example to determine students' understanding of concepts.

Additional Example

STANDARDIZED TEST PRACTICE Triangle *ABC* is shown on the coordinate plane. Find the coordinates of the vertices of the image if the triangle is translated 4 units right and 5 units down. D

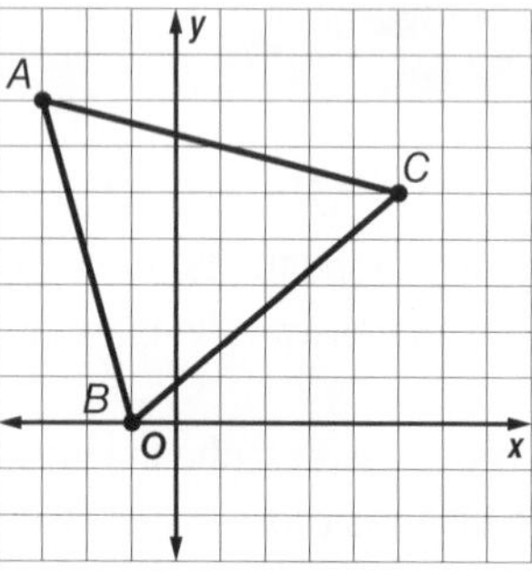

A $A'(-7, 2)$, $B'(-5, -5)$, $C'(1, 0)$

B $A'(1, 12)$, $B'(3, 5)$, $C'(9, 10)$

C $A'(-7, 12)$, $B'(-5, 5)$, $C'(1, 10)$

D $A'(1, 2)$, $B'(3, -5)$, $C'(9, 0)$

Additional Examples also in Interactive Classroom PowerPoint® Presentations

IWB INTERACTIVE WHITEBOARD READY

StudyTip

Notation The notation *M'* is read *M prime*. It corresponds to point *M*.

Translations When translating a figure, every point of the original figure is moved the same distance and in the same direction.

Translation 5 units right

Translation 4 units up

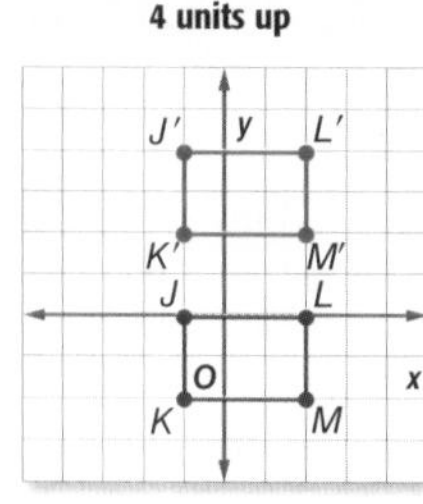

Translation 3 units left, 5 units down

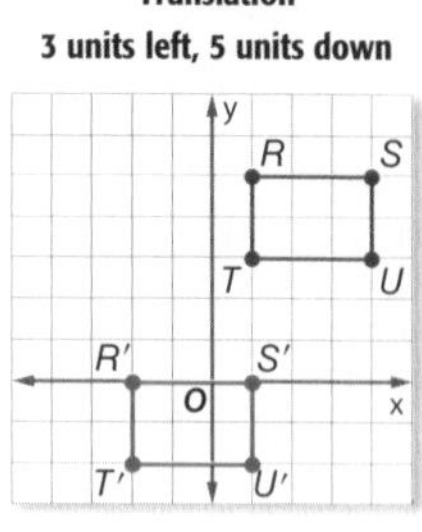

You can describe the translation using an ordered pair (a, b). For example, a translation of 3 units left and 5 units down corresponds to $(-3, -5)$. A translation moves every point $P(x, y)$ to an image $P'(x + a, y + b)$.

ReadingMath

Vertex, Vertices A *vertex* of a figure is a point where two sides of the figure meet. *Vertices* is the plural of *vertex*.

STANDARDIZED TEST EXAMPLE 1

Rectangle *JKLM* is shown. If it is translated 6 units to the right and 4 units down, find the coordinates of the vertices of the image.

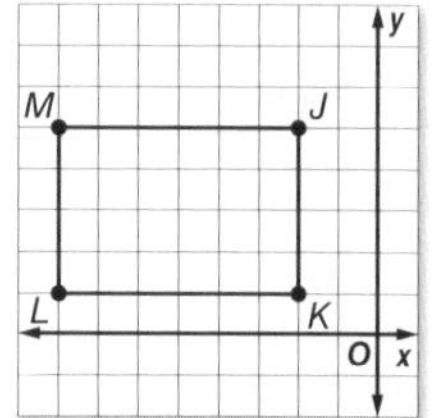

A $J'(-8, 1)$, $K'(-8, -3)$, $L'(-14, -3)$, $M'(-14, -3)$

B $J'(4, 1)$, $K'(4, 0)$, $L'(-2, -3)$, $M'(-2, -1)$

C $J'(4, 1)$, $K'(4, -3)$, $L'(-2, -3)$, $M'(-2, 1)$

D $J'(-2, -1)$, $K'(-2, -3)$, $L'(4, -3)$, $M'(4, -1)$

Read the Test Item

This translation can be written as $(6, -4)$. To find the coordinates of the translated image, add 6 to each *x*-coordinate and add -4 to each *y*-coordinate.

Solve the Test Item

original		translation		image
$J(-2, 5)$	+	$(6, -4)$	→	$J'(4, 1)$
$K(-2, 1)$	+	$(6, -4)$	→	$K'(4, -3)$
$L(-8, 1)$	+	$(6, -4)$	→	$L'(-2, -3)$
$M(-8, 5)$	+	$(6, -4)$	→	$M'(-2, 1)$

The coordinates of the vertices of rectangle $J'K'L'M'$ are $(4, 1)$, $(4, -3)$, $(-2, -3)$, and $(-2, 1)$. So the answer is C.

Check Your Progress

1. Triangle *ABC* is translated so that *B* is mapped to *B'*. Which coordinate pair represents *C'*? G

   F $(-4, 1)$ **H** $(-1, 1)$

   G $(0, 3)$ **J** $(1, 3)$

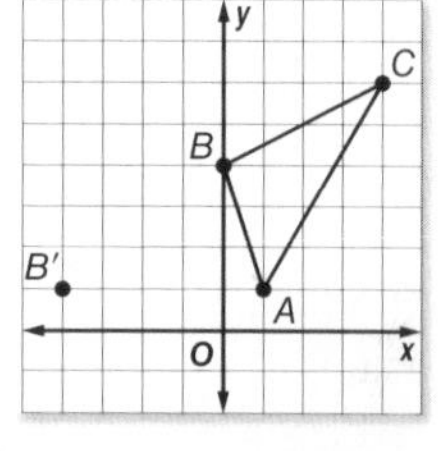

Personal Tutor glencoe.com

Differentiated Instruction OL

Verbal/Linguistic Have students write descriptions of transformations in real-world situations. Look around the classroom and have them point out and discuss transformations they see. Encourage them to bring in pictures, drawings, or models of what they are describing.

TEACH with TECH

INTERACTIVE WHITEBOARD Draw a triangle on a coordinate plane. Then demonstrate a translation by dragging the triangle to another location on the coordinate plane. Have students find the vertices of the image of the triangle and use these to describe the translation.

Reflections When reflecting a figure, every point of the original figure has a corresponding point on the other side of the line of symmetry. Corresponding points are the same distance from the line of symmetry.

Vocabulary Review

Opposites
Opposites are two numbers with the same absolute value but different signs.
(Lesson 2-2)

Reflection over x-axis

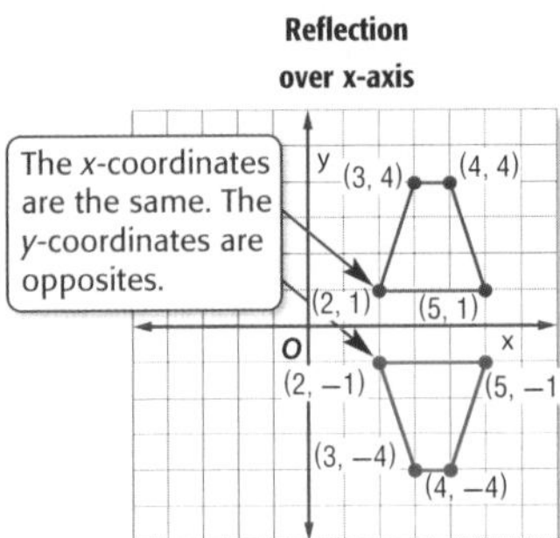

Reflection over y-axis

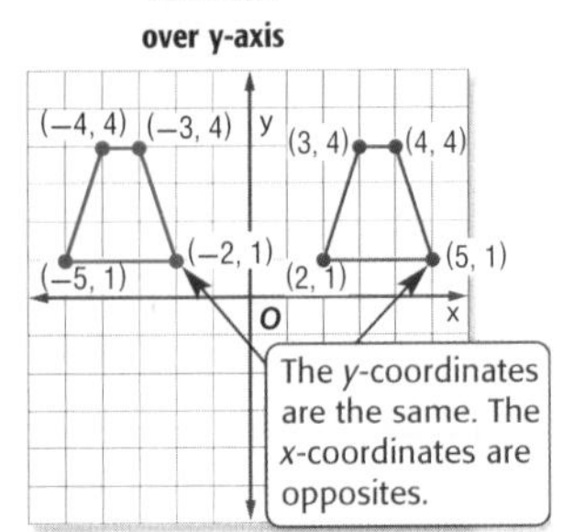

To reflect a point over the x-axis, use the same x-coordinate and multiply the y-coordinate by -1. To reflect a point over the y-axis, use the same y-coordinate and multiply the x-coordinate by -1.

EXAMPLE 2 **Reflections on a Coordinate Plane**

The vertices of figure *DEFG* are $D(4, -2)$, $E(5, -5)$, $F(2, -4)$, and $G(1, -1)$. Graph the figure and its image after a reflection over the y-axis.

To find the coordinates of the vertices of the image after a reflection over the y-axis, use the same y-coordinate. Replace the x-coordinate with its opposite.

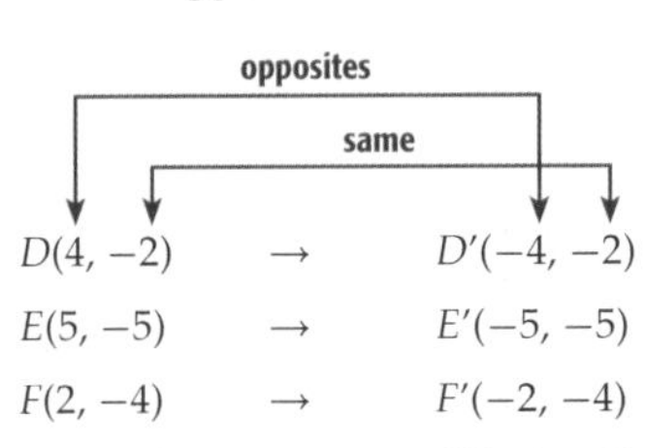

$D(4, -2) \rightarrow D'(-4, -2)$

$E(5, -5) \rightarrow E'(-5, -5)$

$F(2, -4) \rightarrow F'(-2, -4)$

$G(1, -1) \rightarrow G'(-1, -1)$

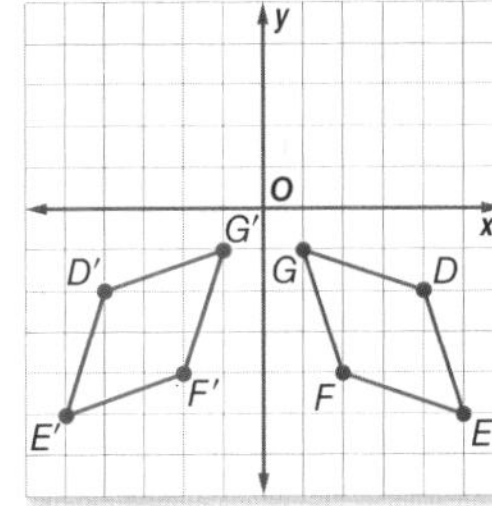

The coordinates of the vertices of the image are $D'(-4, -2)$, $E'(-5, -5)$, $F'(-2, -4)$, and $G'(-1, -1)$.

Check Your Progress **2A–2B. See margin.**

2A. The vertices of $\triangle ABC$ are $A(4, -2)$, $B(0, 2)$, and $C(5, 2)$. Graph the triangle and its image after a reflection over the x-axis.

2B. The vertices of rectangle $WXYZ$ are $W(-3,-3)$, $X(-3, 4)$, $Y(2, 4)$ and $Z(2, -3)$. Graph the rectangle and its image after a reflection over the y-axis.

Personal Tutor glencoe.com

Reflections

Example 2 shows how to graph a figure and its image after a reflection.

Additional Example

2 The vertices of figure *MNOP* are $M(-8, 6)$, $N(5, 9)$, $O(2, 1)$, and $P(-10, 3)$. Graph the figure and the image of the figure after a reflection over the y-axis.

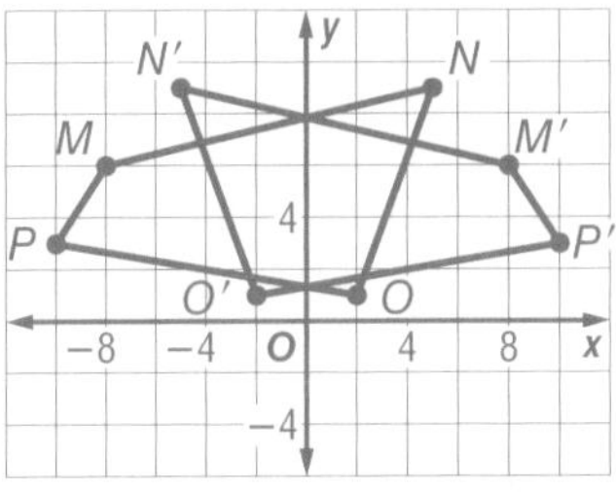

Focus on Mathematical Content

Transformation When a figure undergoes a translation or reflection, the shape and size of the image are the same. Therefore, the image is congruent to the original figure.

Tips for New Teachers

Study Tip Point out to students that an image and reflection are mirror images of each other with respect to the x-axis or the y-axis.

Additional Answers

2A.

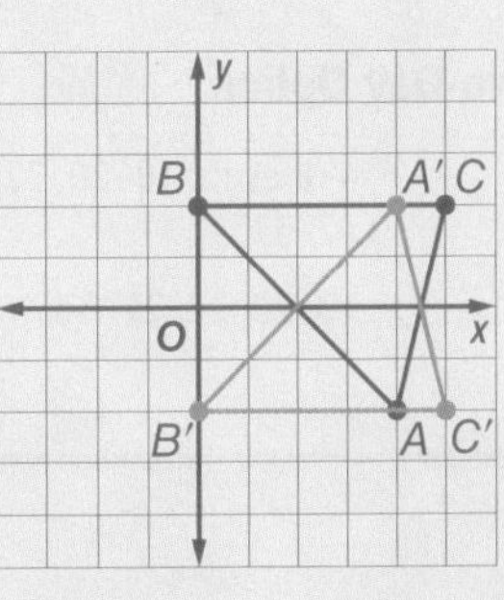

2B.

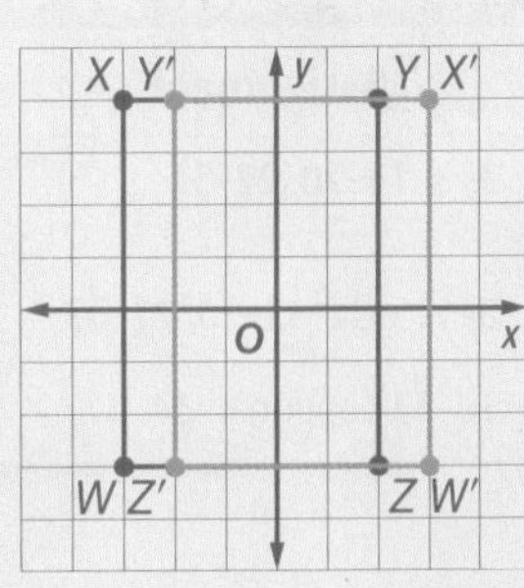

Lesson 2-7 Translations and Reflections on the Coordinate Plane 103

3 PRACTICE

Formative Assessment

Use Exercises 1–2 to check for understanding.

Use the chart at the bottom of this page to customize assignments for your students.

Additional Answers

2\.

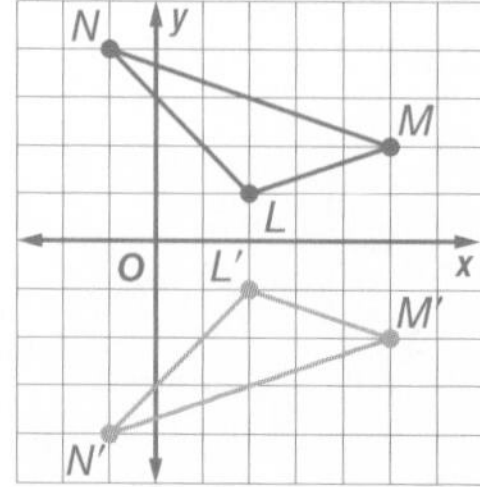

5\.

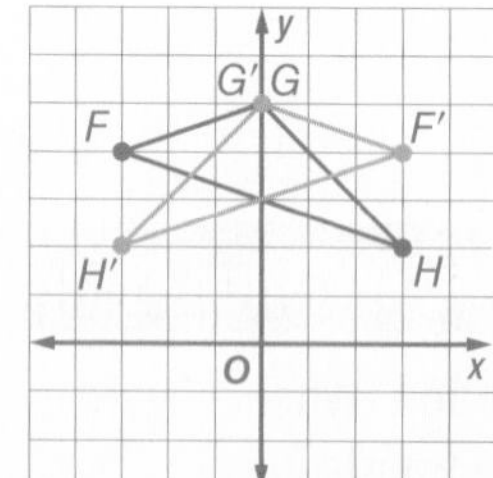

6\.

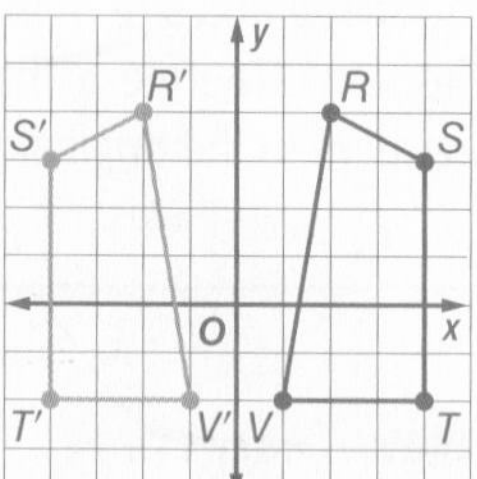

7\.

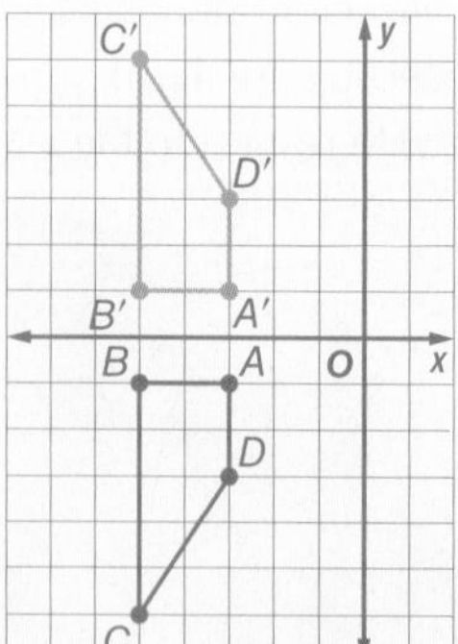

8\.

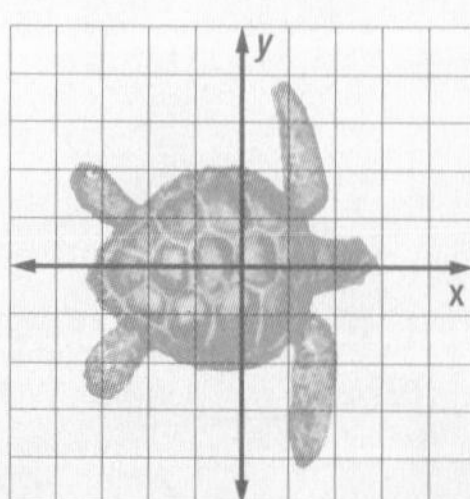

turtle

Check Your Understanding

Example 1 p. 102

1. **MULTIPLE CHOICE** Triangle MNP is shown on the coordinate plane. Find the coordinates of the vertices of the image of the triangle MNP translated 5 units to the right and 3 units up. **A**

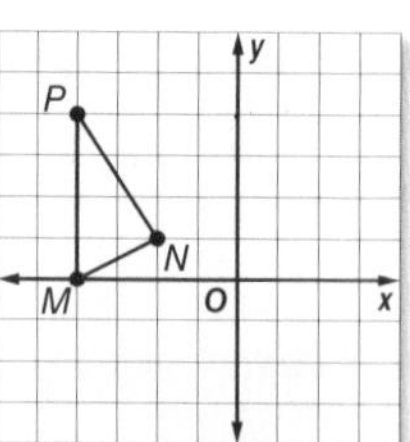

   A $M'(1, 3)$, $N'(3, 4)$, $P'(1, 7)$

   B $M'(3, 1)$, $N'(3, 4)$, $P'(1, 7)$

   C $M'(1, 3)$, $N'(4, 3)$, $P'(7, 1)$

   D $M'(1, 3)$, $N'(3, -4)$, $P'(1, 7)$

Example 2 p. 103

2. The vertices of $\triangle LMN$ are $L(2, 1)$, $M(5, 2)$, and $N(-1, 4)$. Graph the triangle and its image after a reflection over the x-axis. **See margin.**

Practice and Problem Solving

● = **Step-by-Step Solutions** begin on page R11. **Extra Practice** begins on page 810.

Example 1 p. 102

For Exercises 3 and 4, use the coordinate plane at the right. Triangle XYZ is shown.

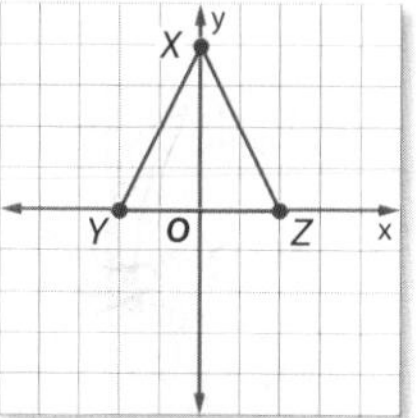

3. Find the coordinates of the vertices of the image of $\triangle XYZ$ translated 4 units to the right and 5 units down. **$X'(4, -1)$, $Y'(2, -5)$, $Z'(6, -5)$**

4. Find the coordinates of the vertices of the image of $\triangle XYZ$ translated 2 units to the left and 3 units up. **$X'(-2, 7)$, $Y'(-4, 3)$, $Z'(0, 3)$**

Example 2 p. 103

5. The vertices of $\triangle FGH$ are $F(-3, 4)$, $G(0, 5)$, and $H(3, 2)$. Graph the triangle and its image after a reflection over the y-axis.

5–8. See margin.

6. The vertices of figure $RSTV$ are $R(2, 4)$, $S(4, 3)$, $T(4, -2)$, and $V(1, -2)$. Graph the figure and its image after a reflection over the y-axis.

7. The vertices of figure $ABCD$ are $A(-3, -1)$, $B(-5, -1)$, $C(-5, -6)$, and $D(-3, -3)$. Graph the figure and its image after a reflection over the x-axis.

8. **ART** Reflect the figure below over the x-axis. Sketch the figure and its image on grid paper. What is the animal?

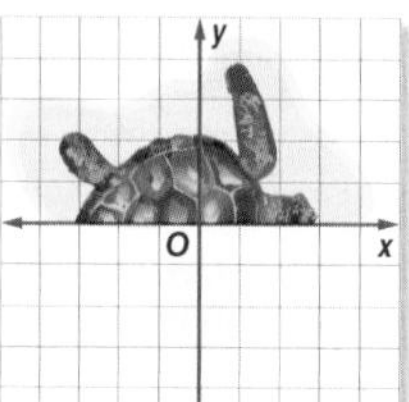

9. **CHESS** In chess, the rook can only move vertically or horizontally across the board. The chessboard below shows the movement of a rook after two turns. Describe this translation in words.

9. 5 units left and 3 units up

Differentiated Homework Options

Level	Assignment	Two-Day Option	
AL Basic	3–9, 18–20, 22–37	3–9 odd, 23–26	4–8 even, 18–20, 22, 27–37
OL Core	3–11 odd, 13–20, 22–37	3–11, 23–26	10–20, 22, 27–37
BL Advanced	10–33 (optional: 34–37)		

For Exercises 10–14, identify each transformation as a *translation* or a *reflection*. If the green image is the original, describe each transformation.

10. translation; 5 units to the right.
11. reflection over the x-axis

10.

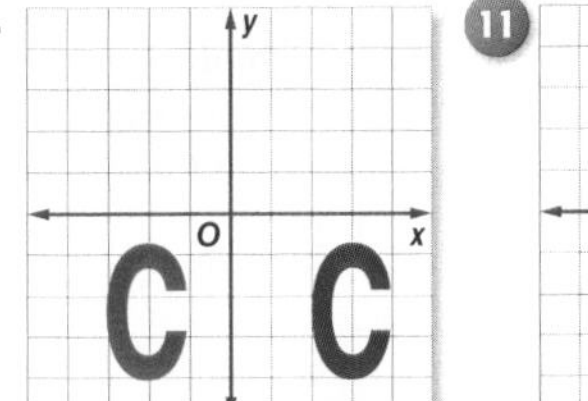

11

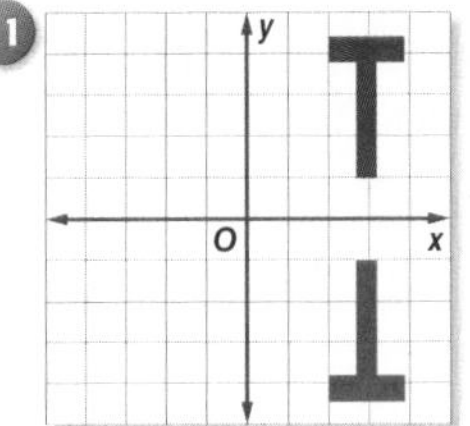

12.

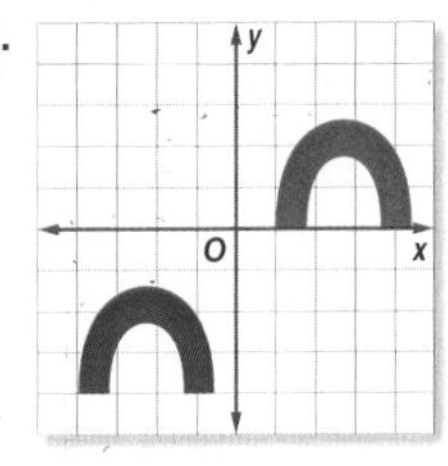

13. A figure has vertices $H(1, -1)$, $J(1, 5)$, $K(3, -1)$, and $L(3, 5)$. The image's vertices are $H'(-4, -5)$, $J'(-4, 1)$, $K'(-2, -5)$, and $L'(-2, 1)$.

14. Triangle QRS has vertices $Q(1, -1)$, $R(5, -3)$, and $S(3, 2)$. The vertices of the image are $Q'(1, 1)$, $R'(5, 3)$, and $S'(3, -2)$.

15. **GEOMETRY** Triangle RST has vertices $R(4, 2)$, $S(-8, 0)$, and $T(6, 7)$. When translated, R' has coordinates $(-2, 4)$. Find the coordinates of S' and T'. Then describe the translation of triangle RST onto triangle $R'S'T'$.

Real-World Link

The world's largest rubber stamp, located in Cleveland, Ohio has the word "FREE" on it. The stamp, is 28 feet tall and 48 feet long.

Source: Roadside America

16. **ART** A mosaic is a type of art created using glass, stone, tile, or other materials. Describe the transformation that maps the red outlined tile to the purple outlined tile.

17. **STAMPS** The image the ink makes on a page is a reflection of the rubber stamp. Suppose you create a rubber stamp that would print the word MATH. Draw the rubber stamp. Is the image a reflection over the x-axis or y-axis? **See margin.**

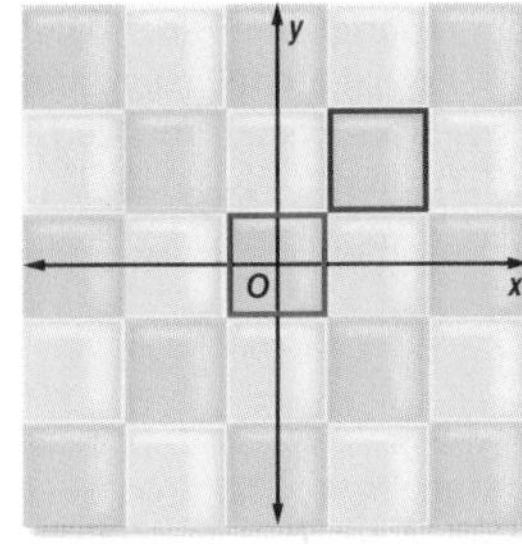

H.O.T. Problems

Use **H**igher-**O**rder **T**hinking Skills

18–22. See Chapter 2 Answer Appendix.

12. Translation; 5 units to the left and 4 units down
13. The translation is to the left 5 units and down 4 units.
14. The transformation is a reflection over the x-axis
15. $S'(-14, 2)$, $T'(0, 9)$; The translation is to the left 6 units and up 2 units.
16. 1 unit right and 1 unit up

18. **OPEN ENDED** Draw a figure on the coordinate plane. Then reflect the figure over the y-axis.

19. **WRITING IN MATH** Suppose you reflect a figure over the x-axis and then you reflect the figure over the y-axis. Is there a single transformation using reflections or translations that maps the original figure to its image? If so, name it. Explain your reasoning.

20. **WHICH ONE DOESN'T BELONG?** Without graphing, identify the pair of points that does not represent a reflection over the y-axis. Justify your reasoning.

$E(0, 1)$ $E'(0, 1)$	$F(-2, 5)$ $F'(2, 5)$	$G(-3, -4)$ $G'(-3, 4)$	$H(5, 0)$ $H'(-5, 0)$

21. **CHALLENGE** Discuss how an image compares to the original figure if you reflect a triangle in Quadrant I over the x-axis, then translate the image 4 units right and 3 units up. Determine if a single transformation can map the original figure to the final image.

22. **WRITING IN MATH** A figure is translated by $(2, -3)$ and then the image is translated by $(-2, 3)$. Without graphing, describe the final position of the figure. Explain your reasoning.

Additional Answer

17. HTAM ; y-axis

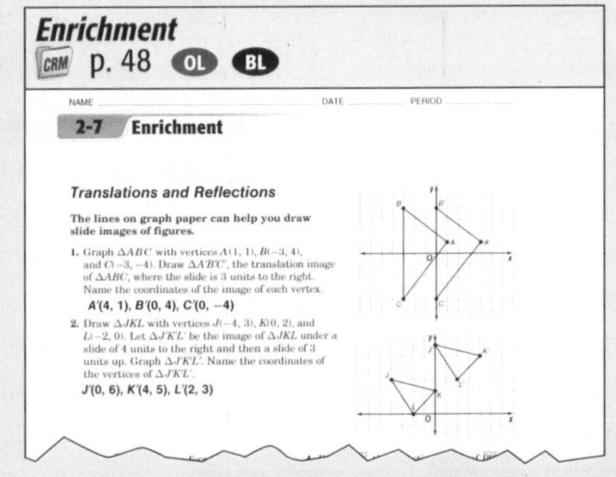

Enrichment

CRM p. 48 OL BL

NAME ______ DATE ______ PERIOD ______

2-7 Enrichment

Translations and Reflections

The lines on graph paper can help you draw slide images of figures.

1. Graph $\triangle ABC$ with vertices $A(1, 1)$, $B(-3, 4)$, and $C(-3, -4)$. Draw $\triangle A'B'C'$, the translation image of $\triangle ABC$, where the slide is 3 units to the right. Name the coordinates of the image of each vertex.
$A'(4, 1)$, $B'(0, 4)$, $C'(0, -4)$
2. Draw $\triangle JKL$ with vertices $J(-4, 3)$, $K(0, 2)$, and $L(-2, 0)$. Let $\triangle J'K'L'$ be the image of $\triangle JKL$ under a slide of 4 units to the right and then a slide of 3 units up. Graph $\triangle J'K'L'$. Name the coordinates of the vertices of $\triangle J'K'L'$.
$J'(0, 6)$, $K'(4, 5)$, $L'(2, 3)$

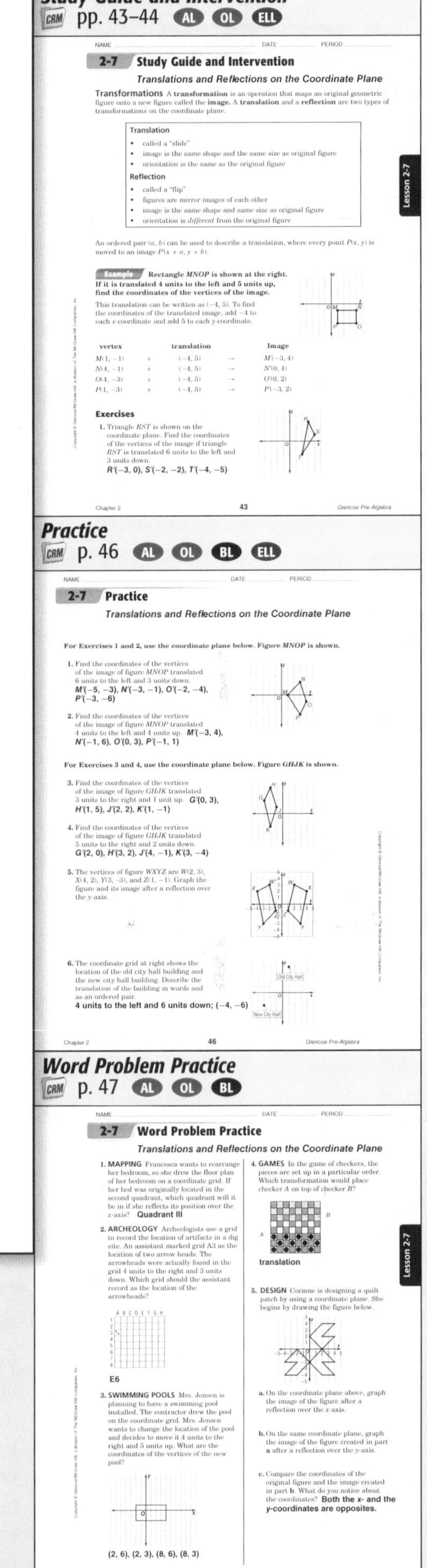

Study Guide and Intervention

CRM pp. 43–44 AL OL ELL

NAME ______ DATE ______ PERIOD ______

2-7 Study Guide and Intervention

Translations and Reflections on the Coordinate Plane

Transformations A **transformation** is an operation that maps an original geometric figure onto a new figure called the **image.** A **translation** and a **reflection** are two types of transformations on the coordinate plane.

Translation
- called a "slide"
- image is the same shape and the same size as original figure
- orientation is the same as the original figure

Reflection
- called a "flip"
- figures are mirror images of each other
- image is the same shape and same size as original figure
- orientation is *different* from the original figure

An ordered pair (a, b) can be used to describe a translation, where every point $P(x, y)$ is moved to an image $P'(x + a, y + b)$.

Example **Rectangle $MNOP$ is shown at the right. If it is translated 4 units to the left and 5 units up, find the coordinates of the vertices of the image.**

This translation can be written as $(-4, 5)$. To find the coordinates of the translated image, add -4 to each x-coordinate and add 5 to each y-coordinate.

vertex		translation		Image
$M(1, -1)$	+	$(-4, 5)$	→	$M'(-3, 4)$
$N(4, -1)$	+	$(-4, 5)$	→	$N'(0, 4)$
$O(4, -3)$	+	$(-4, 5)$	→	$O'(0, 2)$
$P(1, -3)$	+	$(-4, 5)$	→	$P'(-3, 2)$

Exercises

1. Triangle RST is shown on the coordinate plane. Find the coordinates of the vertices of the image if triangle RST is translated 6 units to the left and 3 units down.
$R'(-3, 0)$, $S'(-2, -2)$, $T'(-4, -5)$

Chapter 2 43 *Glencoe Pre-Algebra*

Practice

CRM p. 46 AL OL BL ELL

NAME ______ DATE ______ PERIOD ______

2-7 Practice

Translations and Reflections on the Coordinate Plane

For Exercises 1 and 2, use the coordinate plane below. Figure $MNOP$ is shown.

1. Find the coordinates of the vertices of the image of figure $MNOP$ translated 6 units to the left and 3 units down.
$M'(-5, -3)$, $N'(-3, -1)$, $O'(-2, -4)$, $P'(-3, -6)$
2. Find the coordinates of the vertices of the image of figure $MNOP$ translated 4 units to the left and 4 units up. **$M'(-3, 4)$, $N'(-1, 6)$, $O'(0, 3)$, $P'(-1, 1)$**

For Exercises 3 and 4, use the coordinate plane below. Figure $GHJK$ is shown.

3. Find the coordinates of the vertices of the image of figure $GHJK$ translated 3 units to the right and 1 unit up. **$G'(0, 3)$, $H'(1, 5)$, $J'(2, 2)$, $K'(1, -1)$**
4. Find the coordinates of the vertices of the image of figure $GHJK$ translated 5 units to the right and 2 units down.
$G'(2, 0)$, $H'(3, 2)$, $J'(4, -1)$, $K'(3, -4)$
5. The vertices of figure $WXYZ$ are $W(2, 3)$, $X(4, 2)$, $Y(3, -3)$, and $Z(1, -1)$. Graph the figure and its image after a reflection over the y-axis.
6. The coordinate grid at right shows the location of the old city hall building and the new city hall building. Describe the translation of the building in words and as an ordered pair.
4 units to the left and 6 units down; $(-4, -6)$

Old City Hall
New City Hall

Chapter 2 46 *Glencoe Pre-Algebra*

Word Problem Practice

CRM p. 47 AL OL BL

NAME ______ DATE ______ PERIOD ______

2-7 Word Problem Practice

Translations and Reflections on the Coordinate Plane

1. **MAPPING** Francesca wants to rearrange her bedroom, so she drew the floor plan of her bedroom on a coordinate grid. If her bed was originally located in the second quadrant, which quadrant will it be in if she reflects its position over the x-axis? **Quadrant III**
2. **ARCHEOLOGY** Archeologists use a grid to record the location of artifacts in a dig site. An assistant marked grid A3 as the location of two arrow heads. The arrowheads were actually found in the grid 4 units to the right and 3 units down. Which grid should the assistant record as the location of the arrowheads?
E6
3. **SWIMMING POOLS** Mrs. Jensen is planning to have a swimming pool installed. The contractor drew the pool on the coordinate grid. Mrs. Jensen wants to change the location of the pool and decides to move it 4 units to the right and 5 units up. What are the coordinates of the vertices of the new pool?
(2, 6), (2, 3), (8, 6), (8, 3)
4. **GAMES** In the game of checkers, the pieces are set up in a particular order. Which transformation would place checker A on top of checker B?
translation
5. **DESIGN** Corinne is designing a quilt patch by using a coordinate plane. She begins by drawing the figure below.
a. On the coordinate plane above, graph the image of the figure after a reflection over the x-axis.
b. On the same coordinate plane, graph the image of the figure created in part **a** after a reflection over the y-axis.
c. Compare the coordinates of the original figure and the image created in part **b**. What do you notice about the coordinates? **Both the x- and the y-coordinates are opposites.**

Chapter 2 47 *Glencoe Pre-Algebra*

4 ASSESS

Yesterday's News Ask students to write a brief statement on how yesterday's lesson on the coordinate system helped them with today's lesson on translations and reflections on the coordinate plane.

Formative Assessment

Check for student understanding of concepts in Lesson 2-7.

CRM Quiz 4, p. 53

Standardized Test Practice

23. Which of the following is a vertex of the figure shown below after a translation of 2 units right and 2 units up? **D**

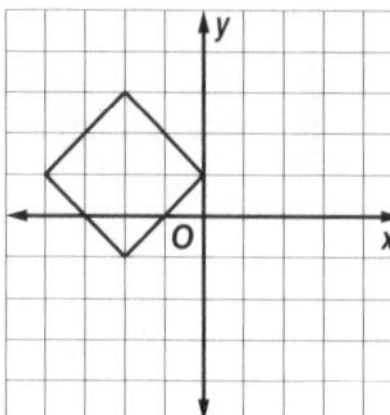

A (5, 0)
B (0, 2)
C (2, 0)
D (0, 5)

24. SHORT RESPONSE The coordinates of a triangle are $A(0, -1)$, $B(-2, -1)$, and $C(3, 5)$. What are the coordinates of the triangle after it has been translated 3 units left and 4 units down? **$A'(-3, -5)$ $B'(-5, -5)$ $C'(0, 1)$**

25. Which of the following *best* represents a reflection over the vertical line segment in the center of the rectangle? **H**

F
G

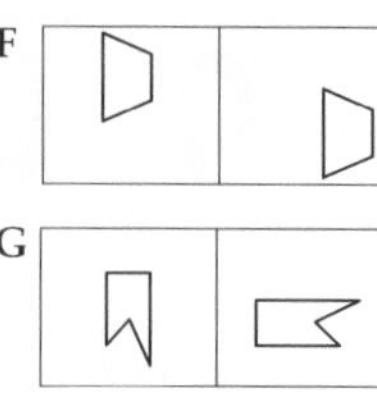

H

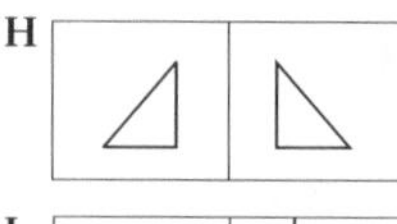

J

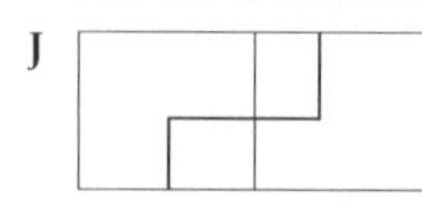

26. SHORT RESPONSE What are the coordinates of the point $(-3, 5)$ after it has been reflected over the y-axis? **(3, 5)**

Spiral Review

Name the ordered pair for each point graphed at the right. (Lesson 2-6)

27. A **(−4, 4)**
28. C **(1, 3)**
29. G **(−3, −2)**
30. K **(3, −4)**

31. BASKETBALL In their first five games, the Jefferson Middle School basketball team scored 46, 52, 49, 53, and 45 points. What was their average number of points per game? (Lesson 2-5) **49 points**

32. MONEY The starting balance in a checking account was −\$50. What was the balance after a \$100 deposit was made and checks were written for \$25 and for \$32? (Lesson 2-2) **−\$7; $-50 + 100 - 25 - 32 = -7$**

33. Translate the phrase *three times as many cards as Neville has* into an algebraic expression. (Lesson 1-2) **$3n$**

Skills Practice

Divide. (Previous Course)

34. $4\overline{)2.0}$ **0.5**
35. $5\overline{)1.0}$ **0.2**
36. $12\overline{)6.0}$ **0.5**
37. $8\overline{)5.000}$ **0.625**

Differentiated Instruction

BL

Extension Tell students a tessellation is an arrangement of shapes that cover a plane without gaps or overlaps. Ask them to use pattern blocks, or shapes made from stiff paper and create tessellations using available polygons. Create a tessellation by translation and/or reflection by tracing the shape, then moving the polygon to an adjacent location, again tracing its shape, and so on. As students work on their tessellations, point out that some shapes and polygons will not tessellate. Have students exchange their tessellations and try to describe the transformations used to create them. Ask: Is it possible to create the same tessellation using a different set of transformations? Answers will vary.

106 Chapter 2 Operations with Integers

Study Guide and Review

Math Online glencoe.com
- STUDY TO GO
- Vocabulary Review

Chapter Summary

Key Concepts

Integers and Absolute Value (Lesson 2-1)

- Numbers on a number line increase as you move from left to right.
- The absolute value of a number is the distance the number is from zero on the number line.

Adding and Subtracting Integers (Lessons 2-2 and 2-3)

- To add integers with the same sign, add their absolute values. Give the result the same sign as the integers.
- To add integers with different signs subtract their absolute values. Give the result the same sign as the integer with the greater absolute value.
- To subtract an integer, add its additive inverse.

Multiplying and Dividing Integers (Lessons 2-4 and 2-5)

- The product or quotient of two integers with the same sign is positive.
- The product or quotient of two integers with different signs is negative.

The Coordinate Plane (Lesson 2-6)

- The x-axis and the y-axis separate the coordinate plane into four quadrants.
- The axes and points on the axes are not located in any of the quadrants.

Transformations (Lesson 2-7)

- Sliding a figure from one position to another without turning it is called a translation.
- Flipping a figure over a line is called a reflection.

FOLDABLES® Study Organizer

Be sure the Key Concepts are noted in your Foldable.

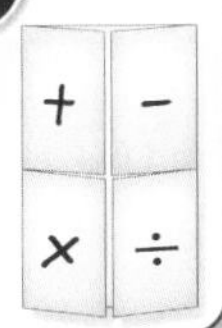

Key Vocabulary

absolute value (p. 63)
additive inverse (p. 71)
coordinate (p. 62)
inequality (p. 62)
integer (p. 61)
mean (p. 92)
negative number (p. 61)
opposites (p. 71)
positive number (p. 61)
quadrant (p. 97)
reflection (p. 101)
transformation (p. 101)
translation (p. 101)

Vocabulary Check

Determine whether each statement is *true* or *false*. If *false*, replace the underlined word or number to make a true statement.

1. Two numbers with the same absolute values but different signs are <u>opposites</u>. **true**
2. A positive number is a number <u>less</u> than zero. **false; greater**
3. A reflection occurs when you <u>turn</u> a figure over a line. **false, flip**
4. The number that corresponds to a point on the number line is called a(n) <u>integer</u>. **false; coordinate**
5. An integer and its <u>opposite</u> are also called additive inverses of each other. **true**
6. The set of <u>quadrants</u> includes positive whole numbers, their opposites, and zero. **false; integers**
7. The <u>absolute value</u> of a number is the distance the number is from zero on the number line. **true**
8. A point located in quadrant <u>IV</u> has an x-coordinate that is positive and a y-coordinate that is negative. **true**
9. To find the <u>additive inverse</u> of a set of numbers, find the sum of the numbers and then divide by the number of items in the set. **false; mean**
10. Numbers like $\underline{-6}$ and $-\frac{3}{5}$ are examples of integers. **false; sample answer: −6 and 5**
11. You can write an inequality when two quantities are <u>not equal</u>. **true**

Formative Assessment

Key Vocabulary The page references after each word denote where that term was first introduced. If students have difficulty answering questions 1–11, remind them that they can use these page references to refresh their memories about the vocabulary.

Summative Assessment

CRM Vocabulary Test, p. 55

Math Online glencoe.com

Vocabulary PuzzleMaker improves students' mathematics vocabulary using four puzzle formats–crossword, scramble, word search using a word list, and word search using clues. Students can work online or from a printed worksheet.

FOLDABLES® Study Organizer

Dinah Zike's Foldables®

Have students look through the chapter to make sure they have included examples in their Foldables. Suggest that students keep their Foldables handy while completing the Study Guide and Review pages. Point out that their Foldables can serve as a quick review tool when studying for the Chapter Test.

CHAPTER 2

Study Guide and Review

Lesson-by-Lesson Review

Intervention If the given examples are not sufficient to review the topics covered by the questions, remind students that the page references tell them where to review that topic in their textbook.

Two-Day Option Have students complete the Lesson-by-Lesson Review on pp. 108–110. Then you can use ExamView® Assessment Suite to customize another review worksheet that practices all the objectives of this chapter or only the objectives on which your students need more help.

Differentiated Instruction

Super DVD: MindJogger Videoquizzes Use this DVD as an alternative format of review for the test.

CHAPTER 2

Study Guide and Review

Lesson-by-Lesson Review

2-1 Integers and Absolute Value (pp. 61–66)

Write two inequalities using the number pairs. Use the symbols < or >.

12. −20 and −18 **−18 > −20; −20 < −18**

13. 0 and −5 **0 > −5; −5 < 0**

Replace each ● with <, >, or = to make a true sentence.

14. 5 ● −5 >

15. 7 ● 7 =

16. −3 ● 1 <

17. −14 ● −22 >

Evaluate each expression.

18. |−16| **16**

19. |4| **4**

20. −|34| **−34**

21. |−2| + |−11| **13**

22. BASEBALL CARDS Jamal traded away 7 shortstop cards for 5 pitcher cards. Find an integer that represents the change in the number of cards Jamal had after the trade. **−2**

EXAMPLE 1

Write two inequalities comparing −5 and −4. Use the symbols < or >.

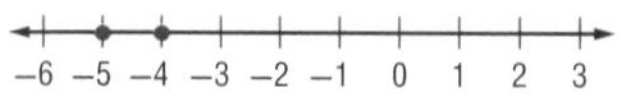

Since −4 is to the right of −5, −4 > −5.

Since −5 is to the left of −4, −5 < −4.

EXAMPLE 2

Evaluate |−5|.

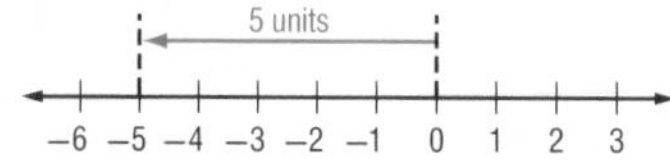

The graph of −5 is 5 units from 0.

So, |−5| = 5.

2-2 Adding Integers (pp. 69–74)

Find each sum.

23. −5 + (−1) **−6**

24. −3 + (−7) **−10**

25. −6 + 10 **4**

26. 4 + (−9) **−5**

27. 7 + (−2) **5**

28. 2 + 8 + (−3) **7**

29. −12 + 5 + (−6) **−13**

30. −7 + 5 + (−4) **−6**

31. GAME SHOWS A contestant on a quiz game show has −25 points. If she loses an additional 50 points, what is her score? Write an addition equation and then solve. **−25 + (−50); −75 points**

32. GOLF A golfer's scores for the last five weeks are −3, +5, −1, −2, and +4. What is the sum of his scores? **+3**

EXAMPLE 3

Find −2 + (−3).

Use a number line.

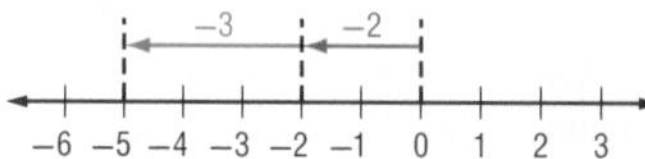

Start at zero. Move 2 units to the left. From there, move 3 more units to the left.

So, −2 + (−3) = −5.

EXAMPLE 4

Find 9 + (−4).

9 + (−4) = 5 **Subtract |−4| from |9|. The sum is positive.**

MIXED PROBLEM SOLVING
For mixed problem-solving practice, see page 844.

2-3 Subtracting Integers (pp. 76–80)

Find each difference.

33. 13 − 7 6
34. −2 − 5 −7
35. 8 − (−3) 11
36. −1 − (−4) 3
37. −4 − 6 −10
38. 3 − 5 −2

39. **ELEVATION** The table shows the highest and lowest elevations for North America. Find the difference between the highest and lowest elevations. 20,602 ft

Lowest Elevation (feet)	Highest Elevation (feet)
−282	20,320

EXAMPLE 5

Find −13 − 4.

−13 − 4 = −13 + (−4)
= −17

To subtract 4, add −4.

So, −13 − 4 = −17.

EXAMPLE 6

Find 10 − (−2).

10 − (−2) = 10 + 2
= 12

To subtract −2, add 2.

So, 10 − (−2) = 12.

2-4 Multiplying Integers (pp. 83–88)

Find each product.

40. −2(3) −6
41. −5(6) −30
42. −7(−9) 63
43. −12(−4) 48
44. 11(−7) −77
45. −10(14) −140

46. **ICE SKATING** For each jump she completes incorrectly in the competition, Dawn receives −2 points. If Dawn completes six jumps incorrectly, what is her score? −12

EXAMPLE 7

Find 3(−7).

3(−7) = −21

The factors have different signs. The product is negative.

EXAMPLE 8

Find −5(−4).

−5(−4) = 20

The factors have the same sign. The product is positive.

2-5 Dividing Integers (pp. 90–95)

Find each quotient.

47. −16 ÷ (−4) 4
48. −56 ÷ (−8) 7
49. −30 ÷ 5 −6
50. 15 ÷ (−3) −5
51. −88 ÷ −11 8
52. 170 ÷ (−10) −17

53. **RACING** For the first five legs of a bicycle race, Elena was +32 seconds, +5 seconds, +10 seconds, +8 seconds, and +12 seconds behind the leader. What was the average time she was behind the leader? 13.4 s

EXAMPLE 9

Find −24 ÷ (−6).

−24 ÷ (−6) = 4

The quotient is positive.

EXAMPLE 10

Find 15 ÷ (−3).

15 ÷ (−3) = −5

The quotient is negative.

Chapter 2 Study Guide and Review 109

Problem Solving Review

For additional practice in problem solving for Chapter 2, see the Mixed Problem Solving Appendix, pp. 843–855, in the Student Handbook section.

Anticipation Guide

Have students complete the Chapter 2 Anticipation Guide and discuss how their responses have changed now that they have completed Chapter 2.

Additional Answers

54–57.

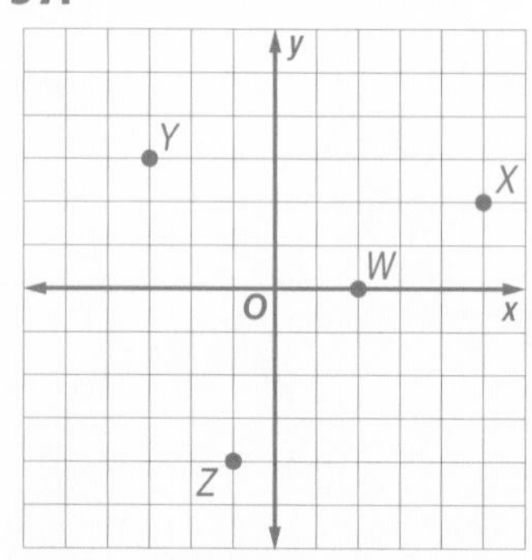

59. $A'(1, 3)$, $B'(4, 3)$, $C'(1, 1)$, and $D'(-2, 1)$

60.

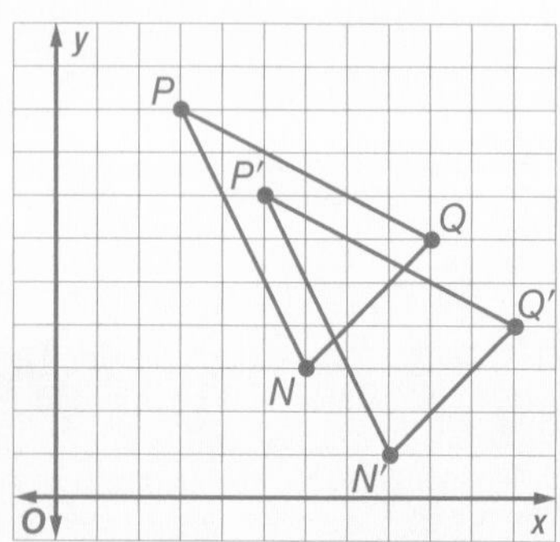

2-6 Graphing in Four Quadrants (pp. 96–100)

Graph and label each point on a coordinate plane. Name the quadrant in which each point is located. See margin for graph.

54. $X(5, 2)$ I

55. $Y(-3, 3)$ II

56. $W(2, 0)$ none

57. $Z(-1, -4)$ III

58. **GAMES** The coordinate plane shown represents a board game. Name the quadrant in which each player's game piece is located.

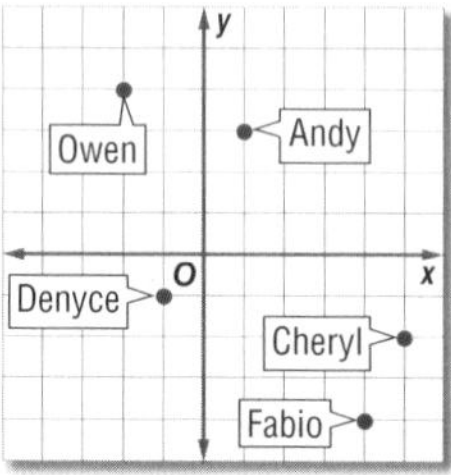

Andy: I, Owen: II, Cheryl: IV, Denyce: III, and Fabio: IV.

EXAMPLE 11

Graph and label $J(-3, 5)$ point on a coordinate plane. Name the quadrant in which the point is located

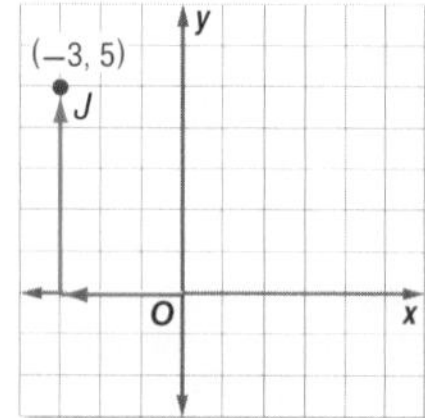

Point $J(-3, 5)$ is in quadrant II.

2-7 Translations and Reflections on the Coordinate Plane (pp. 101–106)

59. The vertices of figure $ABCD$ are $A(1, -3)$, $B(4, -3)$, $C(1, -1)$, and $D(-2, -1)$. Find the vertices after a reflection over the x-axis. See margin.

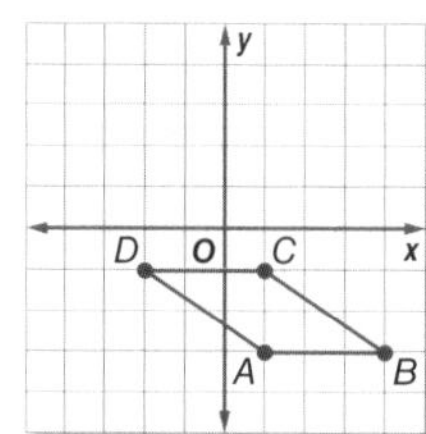

60. A triangle has vertices $N(6, 3)$, $P(3, 9)$, and $Q(9, 6)$. The triangle is translated 2 units right and two units down. Graph the figure and its image. See margin.

61. **ESCALATORS** What type of transformation is used when moving up an escalator? translation

EXAMPLE 12

The vertices of $\triangle JKL$ are $J(1, 2)$, $K(3, 2)$, and $L(1, -1)$. Find the vertices of the image after a translation 3 units left and 2 units up. Then find the vertices of the image after $\triangle JKL$ is reflected over the x-axis.

Translation This translation can be written as $(-3, 2)$.

original		translation		image
$J(1, 2)$	+	$(-3, 2)$	→	$J'(-2, 4)$
$K(3, 2)$	+	$(-3, 2)$	→	$K'(0, 4)$
$L(1, -1)$	+	$(-3, 2)$	→	$L'(-2, 1)$

Reflection Use the same x-coordinate and replace the y-coordinate with its opposite.

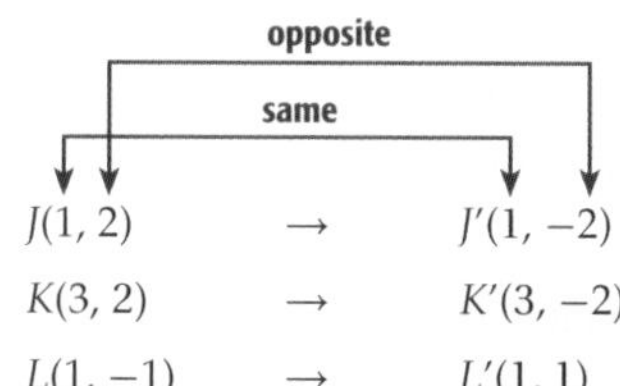

110 Chapter 2 Operations with Integers

CHAPTER 2

Practice Test

Math Online glencoe.com
Chapter Test

Write two inequalities using each pair of numbers. Use the symbols < and >.

1. 7 and −5 $7 > -5$; $-5 < 7$
2. −1 and 0 $-1 < 0$; $0 > -1$
3. −21 and −22 $-21 > -22$; $-22 < -21$

4. **MULTIPLE CHOICE** A scuba diver records her depth in the lake every minute. Choose the group of depths that is listed in order from least to greatest. D

   A −13 ft, −12 ft, −9 ft, −3 ft, −1 ft, −5 ft

   B −5 ft, −3 ft, −1 ft, −9 ft, −12 ft, −13 ft

   C −12 ft, −13 ft, −3 ft, −1 ft, −9 ft, −5 ft

   D −13 ft, −12 ft, −9 ft, −5 ft, −3 ft, −1 ft

Find each sum or difference.

5. $(-3) + (-7)$ −10
6. $7-(-5)$ 12
7. $-4 + 11$ 7
8. $11 + (-13)$ −2
9. $3 - 11$ −8
10. $-21 - (-6)$ −15
11. $13 + (-2) + (-9)$ 2
12. $-4 - (-8)$ 4

13. **GOLF** Jack played in a 4-day golf tournament. His score at the end of each day is shown in the table. What was his final score at the end of the tournament? +1

Day	Score
Monday	−3
Tuesday	+1
Wednesday	+4
Thursday	−1

Find each product or quotient.

14. $7(-6)$ −42
15. $-36 \div (-6)$ 6
16. $54 \div (-6)$ −9
17. $-5(-9)$ 45
18. $-4(7)$ −28
19. $-95 \div 5$ −19
20. $2(-3)10$ −60
21. $-132 \div 11$ −12

22. **SWIMMING POOL** The water in the swimming pool drains at a rate of 24 gallons per minute. Describe the change in the amount of water in the swimming pool after 1 hour. −1440 gal

ALGEBRA Evaluate each expression if $a = -3$, $b = 6$, and $c = -9$.

23. $ca - b$ 21
24. $|bc| \div (-|a|)$ −18
25. $4b + |a|$ 27
26. $\frac{ab}{c} - 6$ −4

27. **AIRPLANES** An airplane descends 500 feet each minute when beginning to land.

   a. **VERBAL** Write an expression to find how many minutes an airplane has been descending if it has descended x feet. $\frac{x}{500}$

   b. **ALGEBRAIC** Find the total number of minutes an airplane has been descending if the plane has descended 9000 feet. 18

Graph and label each point on a coordinate plane. Name the quadrant in which each point is located. 28–31. See margin for graph.

28. $A(-4, 3)$ II
29. $B(1, -3)$ IV
30. $C(-2, -4)$ III
31. $D(5, 6)$ I

32. **MULTIPLE CHOICE** Suppose Elan's home represents the origin on a coordinate plane. If Elan leaves his home and walks two miles west and then four miles north, what is the location of his destination as an ordered pair? F

   F (−2, 4) H (−2, −4)

   G (2, 4) J (4, −2)

33. Triangle ABC is graphed on the coordinate plane shown below. Find the coordinates of the vertices of the image of ΔABC translated 3 units to the left and 2 units up. $A'(-4, 1)$, $B'(-2, 4)$, $C'(-1, -1)$

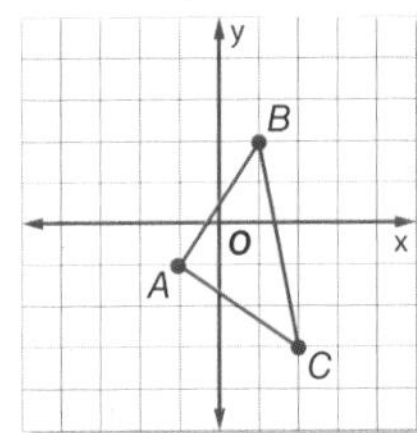

CHAPTER 2 Practice Test

ExamView Assessment Suite Customize and create multiple versions of your chapter test and their answer keys. All of the questions from the leveled chapter tests in the *Chapter 2 Resource Masters* are also available on ExamView® Assessment Suite.

Additional Answers

28–31.

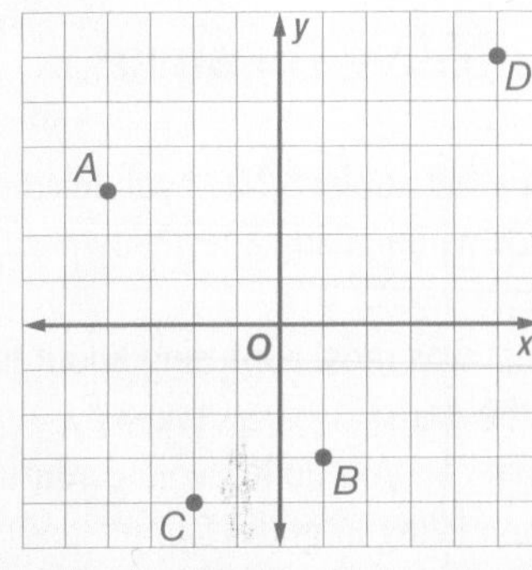

Intervention Planner

Tier 1 On Level	Tier 2 Strategic Intervention approaching grade level	Tier 3 Intensive Intervention 2 or more grades below level
If students miss about 25% of the exercises or less,	**If** students miss about 50% of the exercises,	**If** students miss about 75% of the exercises,
Then choose a resource:  SE Lessons 2-1 through 2-7  CRM Skills Practice, pp. 7, 13, 19, 25, 31, 38, 45  TE Chapter Project, p. 58  Math Online Self-Check Quiz	**Then** choose a resource:   CRM Study Guide and Intervention, Chapter 2, pp. 5, 11, 17, 23, 29, 36, 43  *Quick Review Math Handbook* 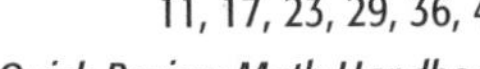 Math Online Extra Examples, Personal Tutor, Homework Help	  **Then** use *Math Triumphs, Grade 8,* Ch. 1–2  Math Online Extra Examples, Personal Tutor, Homework Help, Review Vocabulary

1 FOCUS

Objective Use strategies for solving questions and learn how to fill in grids for gridded response standardized test problems.

2 TEACH

Scaffolding Questions

Ask:

- For what subjects have you filled in grids when taking a test? Answers will vary.
- What was most confusing about filling in the grids? Answers will vary.
- What can you do to avoid confusion when filling in grids? Sample answer: Make sure you understand the directions before filling in the grids.

CHAPTER 2 Preparing for Standardized Tests

Gridded Response Questions

In addition to multiple choice, short answer, and extended response questions, you will likely encounter gridded response questions on standardized tests. For gridded response questions, print your answer on an answer sheet and mark in the correct circles on the grid to match your answer.

Strategies for Solving Gridded Response Questions

Step 1

Read the problem carefully.

- **Ask yourself:** "What information is given?" "What do I need to find?" "How do I solve this type of problem?"
- **Solve the Problem:** Use the information given in the problem to solve.
- **Check your answer:** If time permits, check your answer to make sure you have solved the problem correctly.

Step 2

Print your answer in the answer boxes.

- Print only one digit or symbol in each answer box.
- Do not write any digits or symbols outside the answer boxes.
- You may print your answer with the first digit in the left answer box, or with the last digit in the right answer box. You may leave blank any boxes you do not need on the right or the left side of your answer.

Step 3

Fill in the grid.

- Fill in only one bubble for every answer box that you have written in. Be sure not to fill in a bubble under a blank answer box.
- Fill in each bubble completely and clearly.

112 Chapter 2 Operations with Integers

EXAMPLE

Read the problem. Identify what you need to know. Then use the information in the problem to solve.

> **GRIDDED RESPONSE** Manuel rode his bike for 15 miles. The trip took him 2 hours. Find Manuel's rate of speed.

Read the problem carefully. You are given the distance and time that Manuel rode his bike. You are asked to find his rate of speed.

Use the formula $d = rt$. Replace d with 15 and t with 2. Solve for r.

Solve the Problem	Fill in the Grid
$d = rt$ $15 = r \cdot 2$ $\frac{15}{2} = \frac{r \cdot 2}{2}$ $7\frac{1}{2} = r$ You cannot grid in the mixed number $7\frac{1}{2}$. Either grid the fraction $\frac{15}{2}$ or the decimal 7.5.	1 5 / 2 7 . 5 7 . 5

Exercises

Read each problem. Identify what you need to know. Then use the information in the problem to solve. Copy and complete an answer grid on your paper.

1. **GRIDDED RESPONSE** Last year, Michael was 61 inches tall. During the past year, he grew a total of 4 inches. How tall is Michael now? Express your answer in inches. **65**

2. **GRIDDED RESPONSE** Jamal scored 14, 12, 9, 17, 15, and 11 points in his last 6 basketball games. What is the mean number of points per game that he scored? **13**

3. **GRIDDED RESPONSE** Find the sum of the integers below. **27**

   $14 + (-19) + (-3) + 35$

4. **GRIDDED RESPONSE** The table shows the number of Calories burned per minute for a 130-pound person during different activities.

Activity	Calories Per Minute
Basketball	11
Bicycling (10 mph)	8
Jogging (6 mph)	9
Swimming	6
Walking (3 mph)	4

   How many Calories would Colleen burn if she rides her bicycle for 15 minutes and jogs for 30 minutes? **390**

5. **GRIDDED RESPONSE** Point D has coordinates $D(8, -2)$. What will the y-coordinate of the image be after a reflection over the x-axis? **2**

Additional Example

GRIDDED RESPONSE Jena bought 4 handmade marbles for \$38. If she paid the same for each marble, what was the cost in dollars of one marble? 9.50

9 . 5 0

3 ASSESS

Use Exercises 1–5 to assess students' understanding.

Diagnose Student Errors

Survey students' responses for each item. Class trends may indicate common errors and misconceptions.

1. A chose greatest instead of least temperature
B correct
C misunderstood concept of ordering integers from least to greatest
D misunderstood concept of ordering integers from least to greatest

2. F added 35 to 52 instead of subtracted 52 from 35
G subtracted 17 from 52 instead of 52 from 17
H correct
J added –35 and –52

3. A used positive sign instead of negative sign
B multiplication error and used positive sign instead of negative sign
C multiplication error
D correct

4. F correct
G division error
H division error and used positive sign instead of negative sign
J used positive sign instead of negative sign

5. A guess based on number of months
B division error
C correct
D division error

6. F used rule for first *x*- and *y*-values only
G confused multiplication and addition
H correct
J misunderstood relationship between *x* and *y*

7. A guess
B correct
C confused slide (translation) and reflection
D confused translation and reflection

8. F transposed the numbers 3 and 2 in the expression
G transposed the numbers 3 and 2 in the expression and interpreted *older* to mean subtraction instead of addition
H correct
J interpreted *older* to mean subtraction instead of addition

Standardized Test Practice

Cumulative, Chapters 1 through 2

Multiple Choice

Read each question. Then fill in the correct answer on the answer document provided by your teacher or on a sheet of paper.

1. The record low temperatures of four U.S. cities are shown in the table.

Record Low Temperatures	
City	Temperature (°F)
Denver, CO	–30
Hartford, CT	–26
Atlanta, GA	–8
Indianapolis, IN	–27

Which city has the coldest record low temperature? B

A Atlanta
B Denver
C Hartford
D Indianapolis

2. Lucinda received $35 for her birthday and deposited it into her checking account. Later in the week, she wrote a check for $52 to pay for a DVD player. Which of the following represents the change in Lucinda's checking account balance? H

F $87
G $17
H –$17
J –$87

3. Write a function rule for the input and output values shown in the table below. D

x	–4	–2	0	3
y	12	6	0	–9

A $y = 3x$
B $y = 2x$
C $y = -2x$
D $y = -3x$

Test-TakingTip

Question 2 After the deposit and check, would Lucinda's balance increase or decrease? This will tell you what sign the correct answer should be.

4. Find the quotient of the expression shown below. F

$$\frac{-360}{30}$$

F –12
G –8
H 8
J 12

5. The total cost of Jason's guitar is $180. If he pays for the guitar in 12 equal payments, how much is each payment? C

A $12
B $14
C $15
D $16

6. Which of the following equations describes the rule shown in the table? H

x	1	2	3	4
y	5	6	7	8

F $y = 5x$
G $y = 4x$
H $y = x + 4$
J $y = x + 5$

7. Which term *best* describes flipping an object to create a mirror image? B

A movement
B reflection
C slide
D translation

8. Sholanda is 3 years older than twice her sister Lakita's age. If Lakita is *a* years old, which expression represents Sholanda's age? H

F $3a + 2$
G $3a - 2$
H $2a + 3$
J $2a - 3$

CHAPTER 2 Standardized Test Practice

Short Response/Gridded Response

Record your answers on the answer sheet provided by your teacher or on a sheet of paper.

9. GRIDDED RESPONSE A scuba diver is 83 feet below the surface of the water when she dives to a depth of 114 feet below the surface. How many feet did she dive from her previous depth to arrive at her current depth? Express your answer in feet. 31

10. GRIDDED RESPONSE Marco and Monica are playing a board game. At the end of the first round, Marco had a score of 30 points and Monica had a score of −20 points. Find the difference between the two scores. 50

11. Suppose triangle ABC is reflected over the y-axis. $A'(-1, 2)$, $B'(-5, 5)$, $C'(-4, -5)$

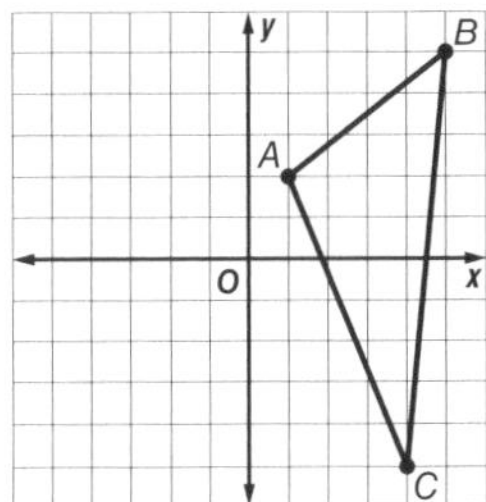

What are the coordinates of the vertices of the image?

12. Suppose the mean low temperature over a 5-day period in Chicago was −12°F. Give a sample set of what the low temperatures might have been for the 5 days.
Sample answer: −15°F, −13°F, −12°F, −11°F, −9°F

13. Alexandria recently had a birthday. Her age is now four less than twice her younger sister Sara's age. Let s represent Sara's age in years.

a. Write an expression that represents Alexandria's age in terms of Sara's age. $2s - 4$

b. Suppose Sara is 6 years old. Use the expression from part **a** to find Alexandria's age. $2(6) - 4$; 8 years old

Extended Response

Record your answers on a sheet of paper. Show your work.

14. After three rounds of a 4-round tournament, Reggie is the leader. Other players' standings in relation to Reggie are shown in the table.

Golf Standings	
Player	**Number of Strokes Behind the Leader**
Reggie	0
Benjamin	3
Alejandro	7
Christopher	4
Thomas	1

a. Write an integer to describe each golfer's standing with respect to the leader after 3 rounds.

b. Order the integers from least to greatest. −7, −4, −3, −1, 0

c. Which player is currently in second place? Benjamin

14a. Benjamin, −3; Alejandro, −7; Christopher, −4; Thomas, −1

Need Extra Help?														
If you missed Question...	1	2	3	4	5	6	7	8	9	10	11	12	13	14
Go to Lesson or Page...	2-1	2-3	2-4	2-5	2-5	1-5	2-7	1-2	2-2	2-3	2-7	2-5	1-3	2-1

Formative Assessment

You can use these two pages to benchmark student progress.

Answer Sheet Practice

Have students simulate taking a standardized test by recording their answers on practice recording sheets.

CRM Student Recording Sheet, p. 50

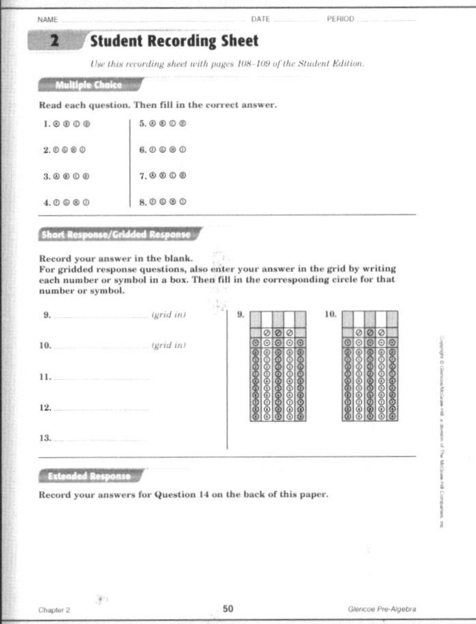
NAME ______ DATE ______ PERIOD ______

2 **Student Recording Sheet**

Use this recording sheet with pages 108–109 of the Student Edition.

Multiple Choice

Read each question. Then fill in the correct answer.

1. Ⓐ Ⓑ Ⓒ Ⓓ
2. Ⓕ Ⓖ Ⓗ Ⓘ
3. Ⓐ Ⓑ Ⓒ Ⓓ
4. Ⓕ Ⓖ Ⓗ Ⓘ
5. Ⓐ Ⓑ Ⓒ Ⓓ
6. Ⓕ Ⓖ Ⓗ Ⓘ
7. Ⓐ Ⓑ Ⓒ Ⓓ
8. Ⓕ Ⓖ Ⓗ Ⓘ

Short Response/Gridded Response

Record your answer in the blank.
For gridded response questions, also enter your answer in the grid by writing each number or symbol in a box. Then fill in the corresponding circle for that number or symbol.

9. ______ (grid in)
10. ______ (grid in)
11. ______
12. ______
13. ______

Extended Response

Record your answers for Question 14 on the back of this paper.

Chapter 2 50 Glencoe Pre-Algebra

Create practice worksheets or tests that align to your state's standards as well as TIMSS and NAEP tests.

Homework Option

Get Ready for Chapter 3 Assign students the exercises on p. 117 as homework to assess whether they possess the prerequisite skills needed for the next chapter.

Page 68, Explore 2-2

1.

−2 + (−1)

2.

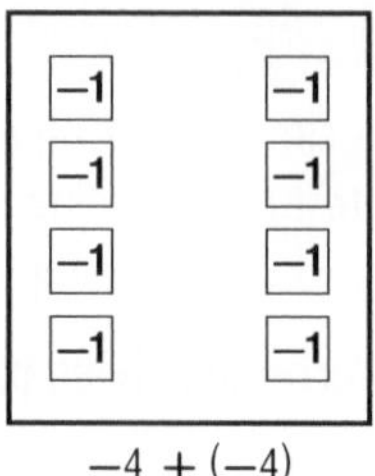

−4 + (−4)

3.

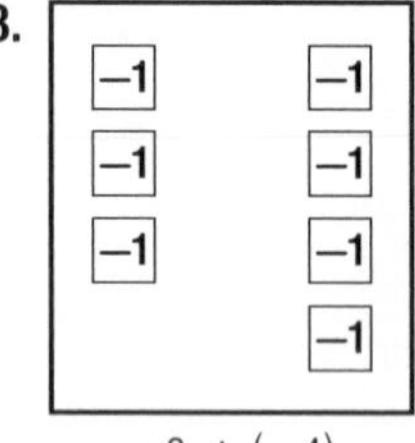

−3 + (−4)

4.

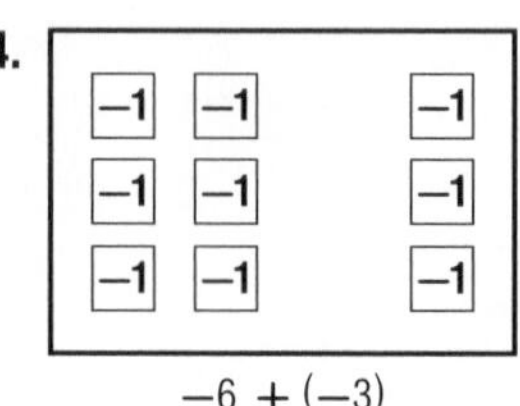

−6 + (−3)

5.

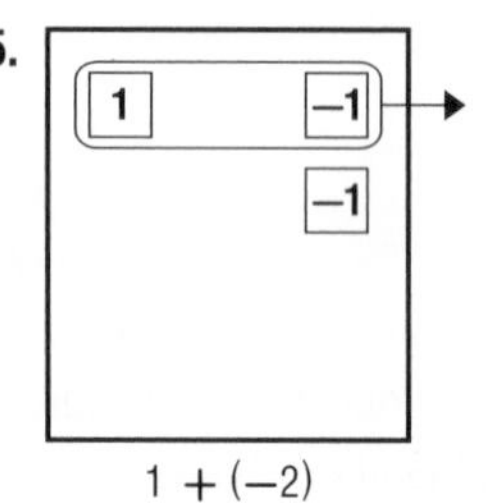

1 + (−2)

6.

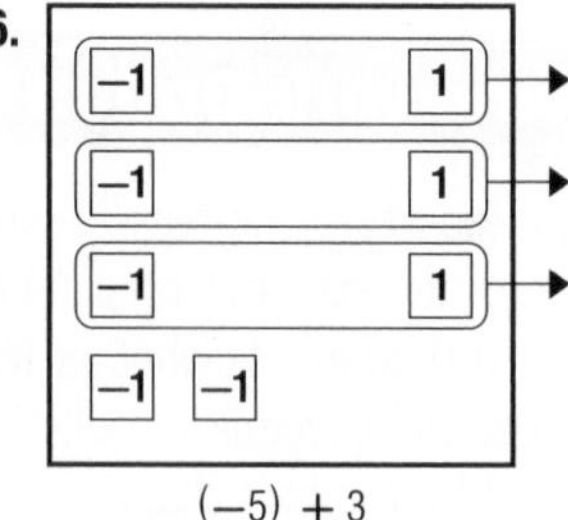

(−5) + 3

7.

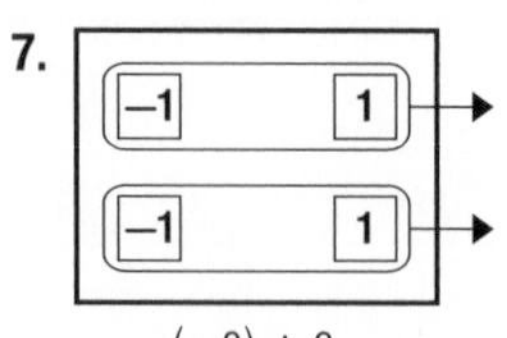

(−2) + 2

8.

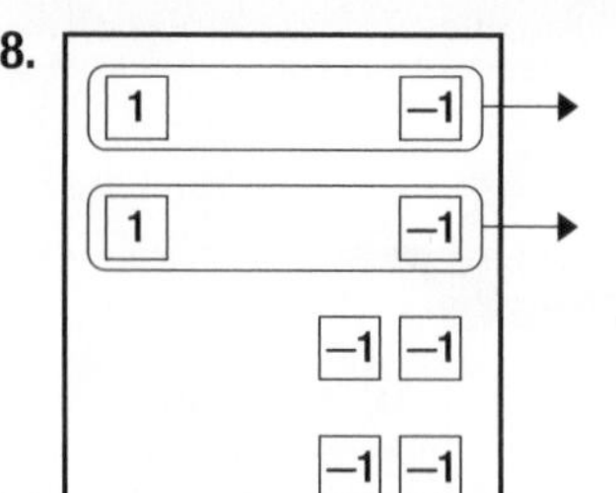

2 + (−6)

Page 75, Explore 2-3

1.

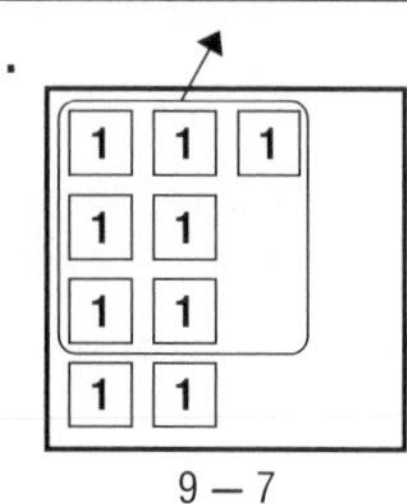

9 − 7

2.

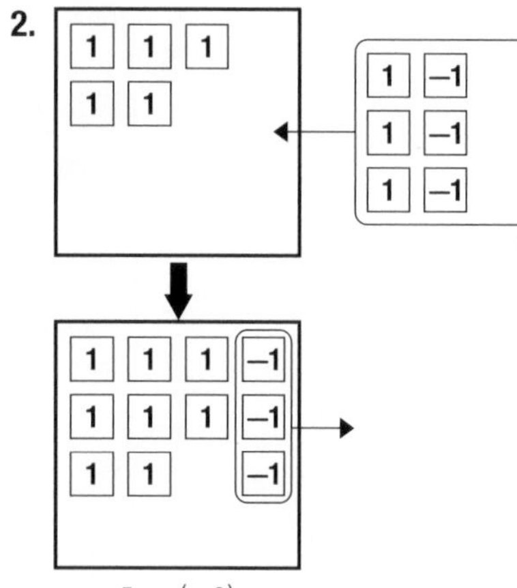

5 − (−3)

3.

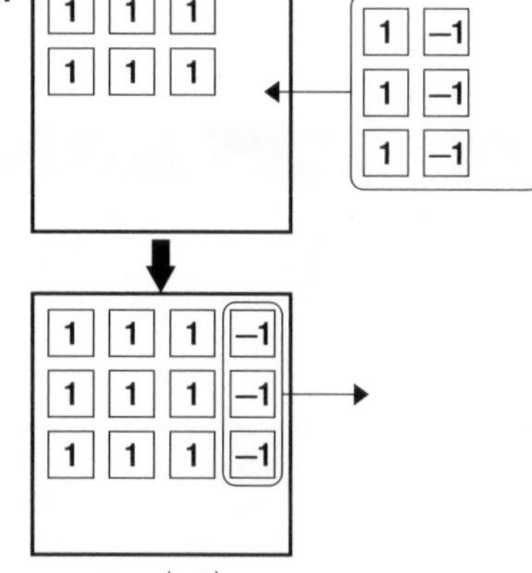

6 − (−3)

4.

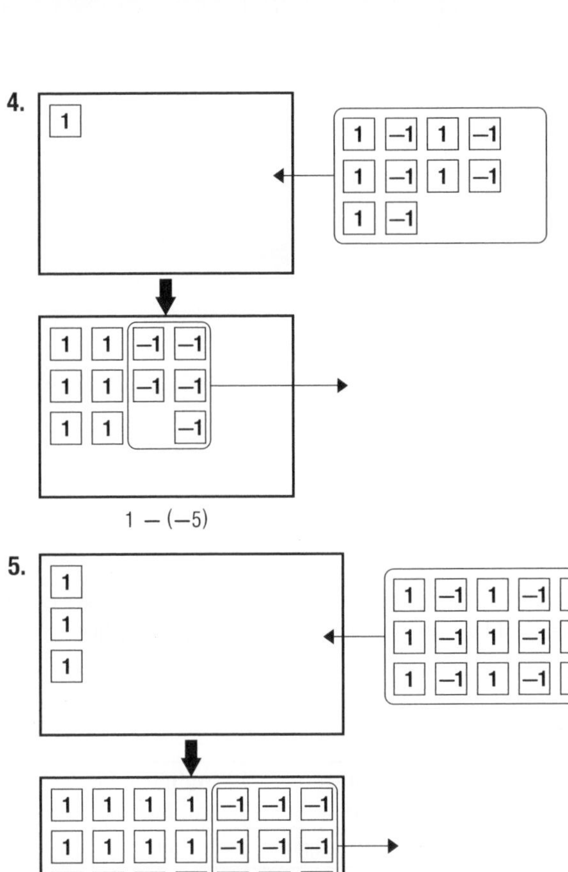

1 − (−5)

5.

3 − (−9)

6.

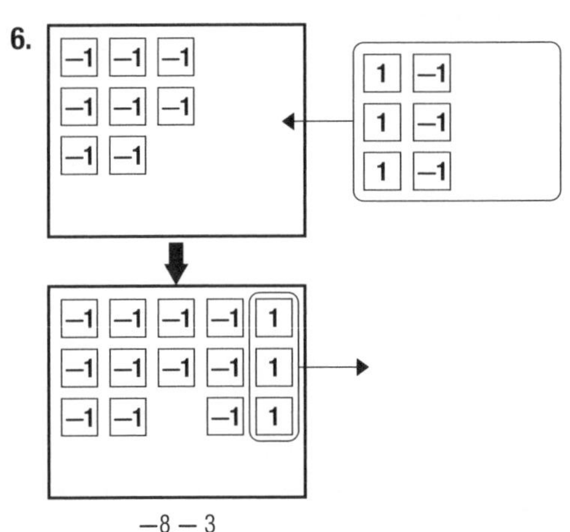

−8 − 3

7.

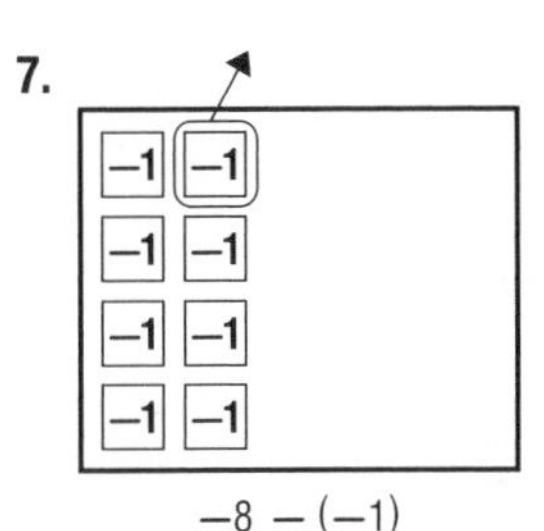

−8 − (−1)

8.

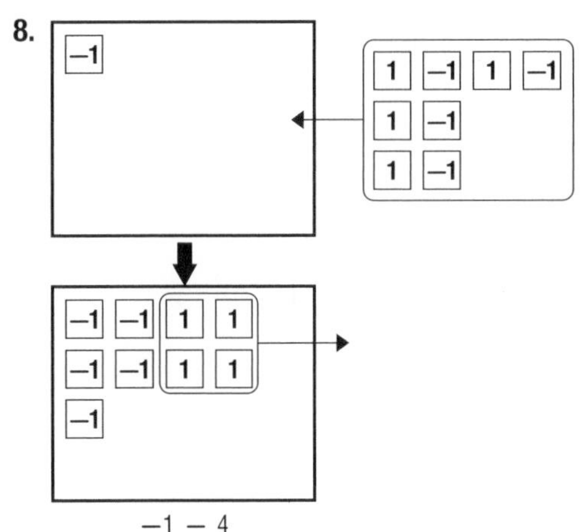

−1 − 4

Page 79, Lesson 2-3

40b.

Input	Rule: −7 − *f*	Output
5	−7 − 5	−12
8	−7 − 8	−15
10	−7 − 10	−17
12	−7 − 12	−19

Page 82, Explore 2-4

2.

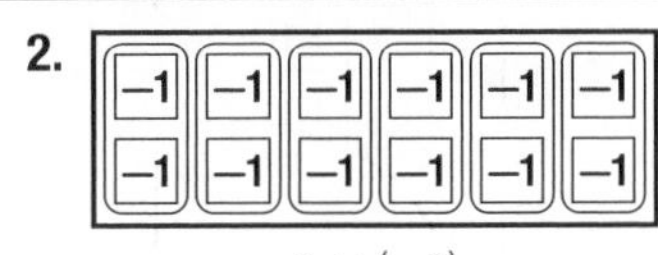

6 × (−2)

3.

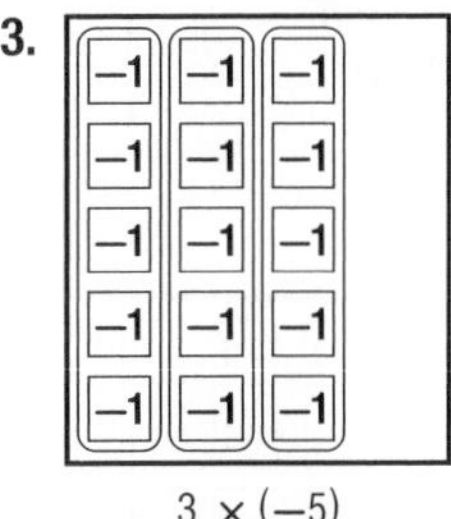

3 × (−5)

4.

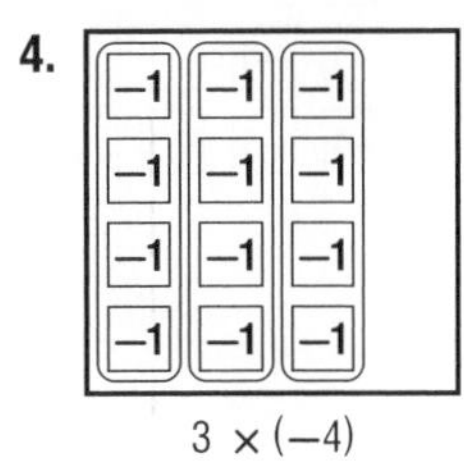

3 × (−4)

5.

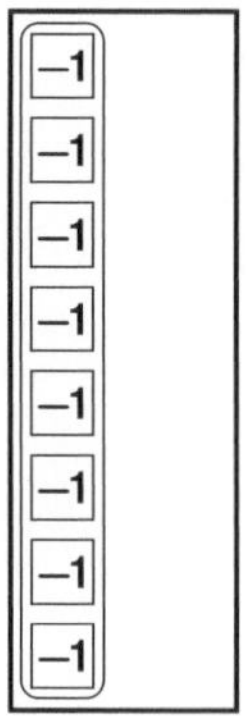

1 × (−8)

6.

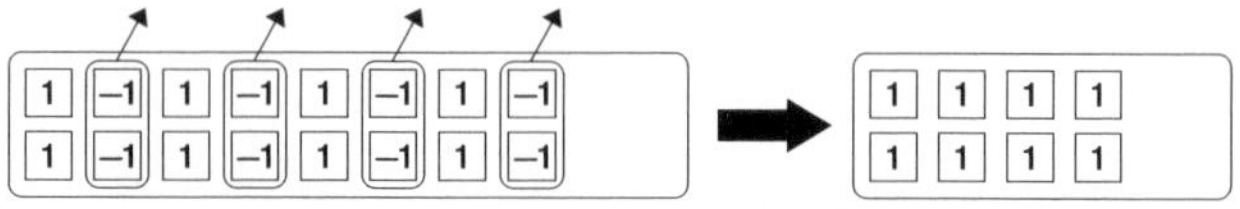

−4 × (−2)

7.

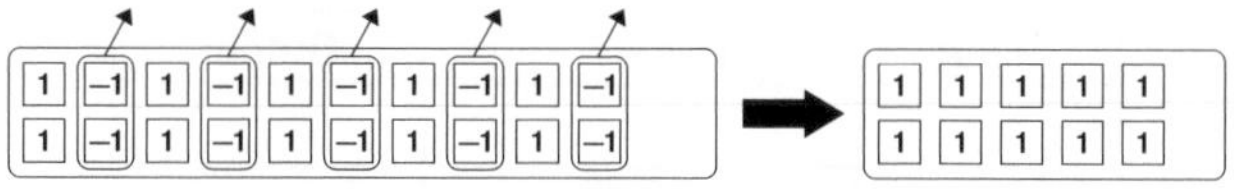

−5 × (−2)

8.

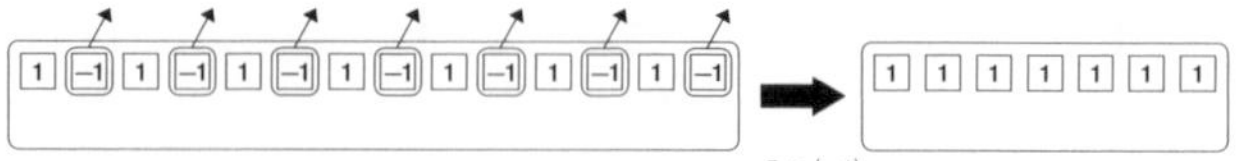

−7 × (−1)

9.

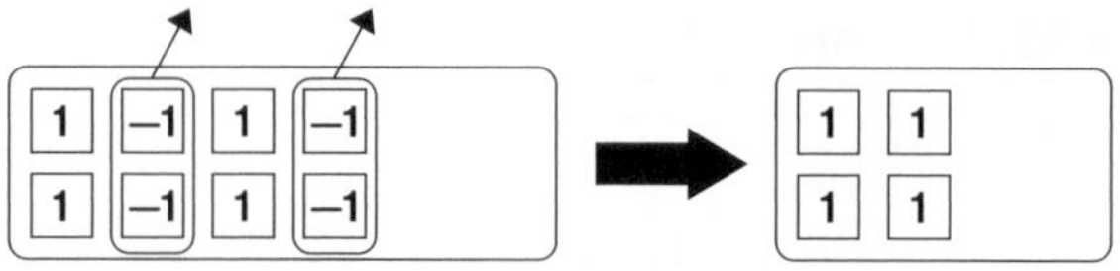

−2 × (−2)

10.

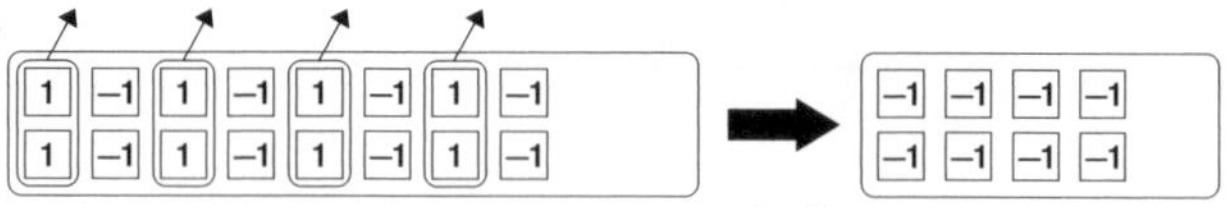

−4 × 2

11.

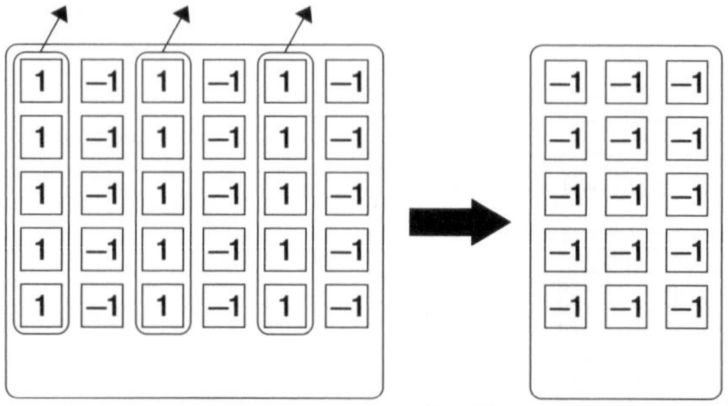

−3 × 5

12.

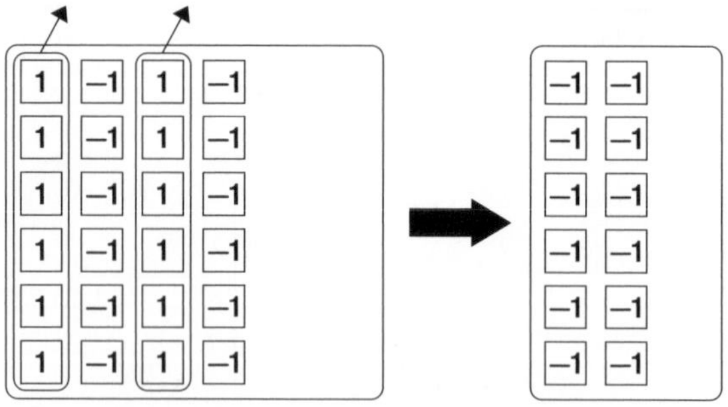

−2 × 6

13.

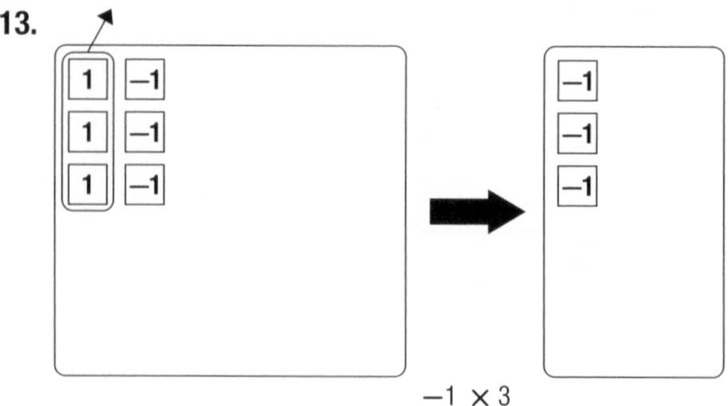

−1 × 3

14. Sample answer: Both operations produce a product of –12. The operation –3 × 4 means to remove 3 sets of 4 positive tiles, and the operation 4 × (–3) means to place four sets of 3 negative tiles.

15. The product of two integers with the same sign is positive. The product of two integers with different signs is negative.

Page 87, Lesson 2-4

42a.

input *x* (minutes)	rule: $y = -15x + 600$	output *y* (altitude)
0	−15(0) + 600	600
5	−15(5) + 600	525
10	−15(10) + 600	450
15	−15(15) + 600	375

42c.

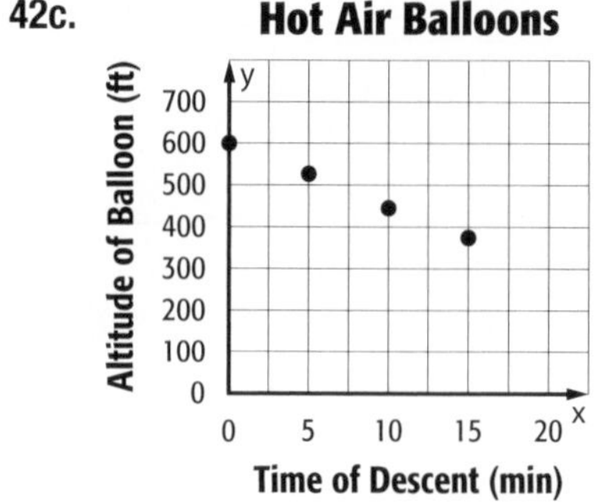

Page 89, Explore 2-5

1.

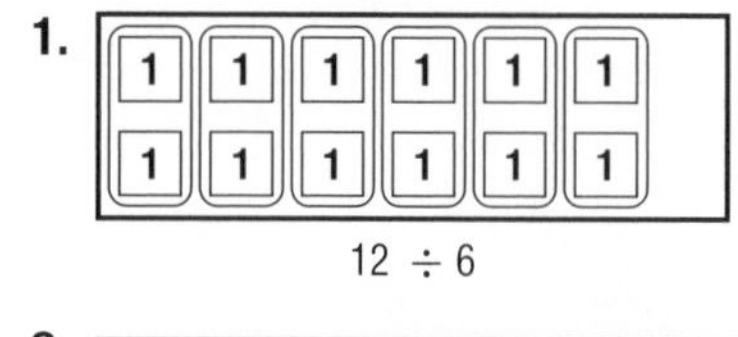

12 ÷ 6

2.

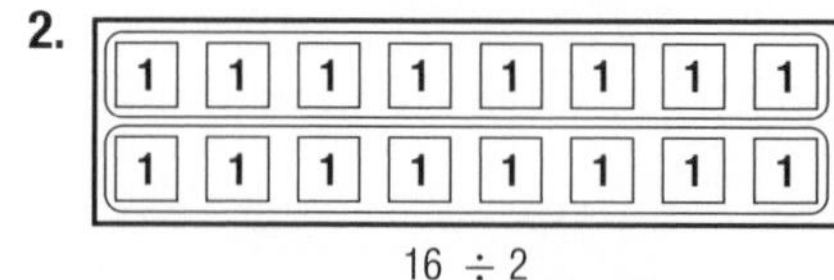

16 ÷ 2

3.

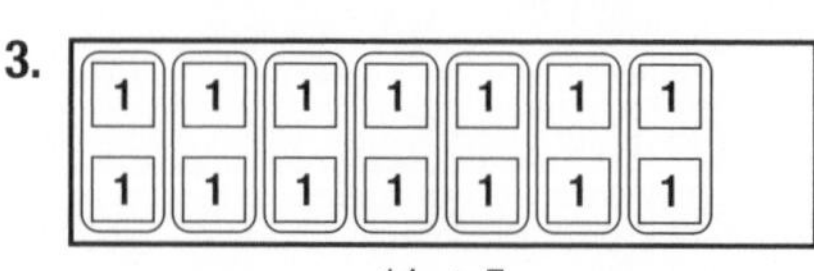

14 ÷ 7

4. 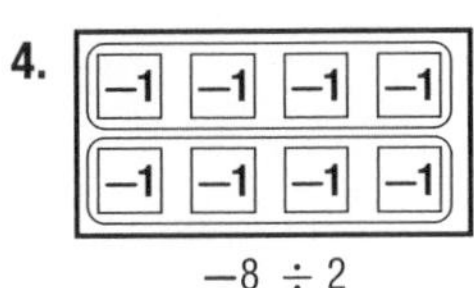

−8 ÷ 2

5. 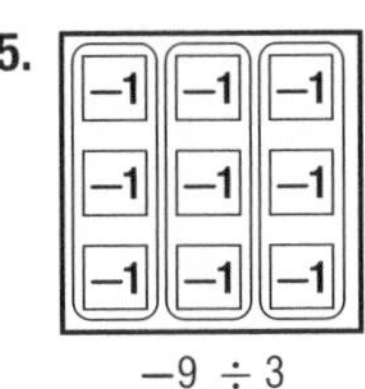

−9 ÷ 3

6. 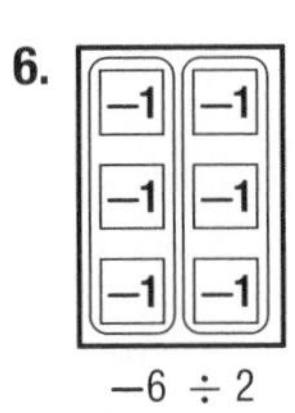

−6 ÷ 2

7. 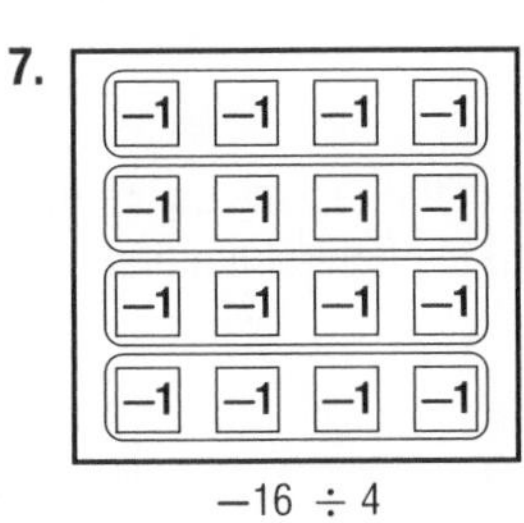

−16 ÷ 4

8. 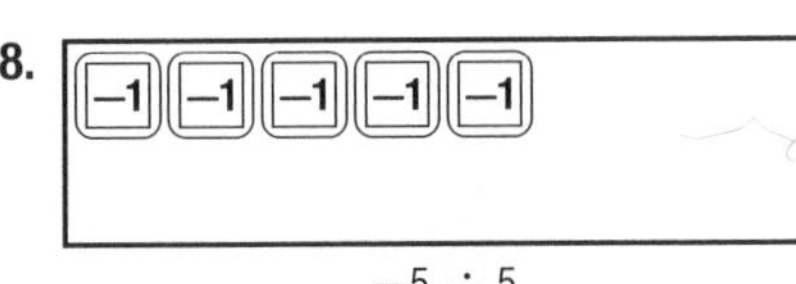

−5 ÷ 5

9. 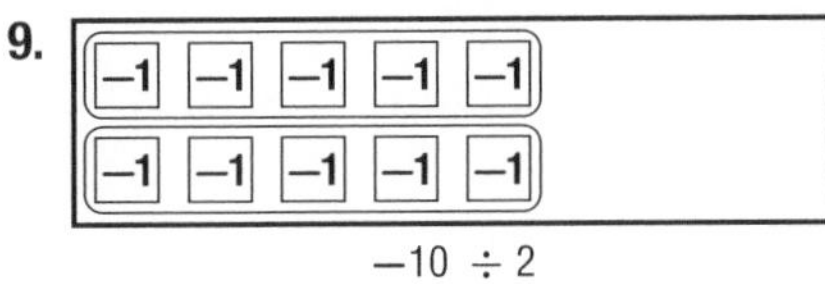

−10 ÷ 2

Page 97, Lesson 2-6 (Check Your Progress)

2A–C. 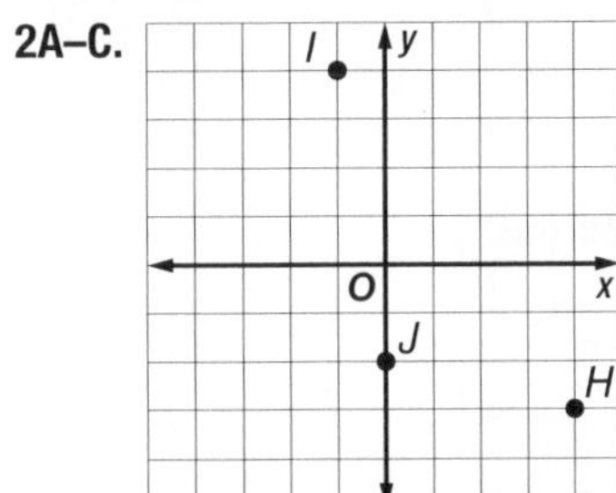

3.

$x + y = 3$		
x	y	(x, y)
1	2	(1, 1)
0	3	(0, 3)
3	0	(3, 0)
−1	4	(−1, 4)
2	1	(2, 1)

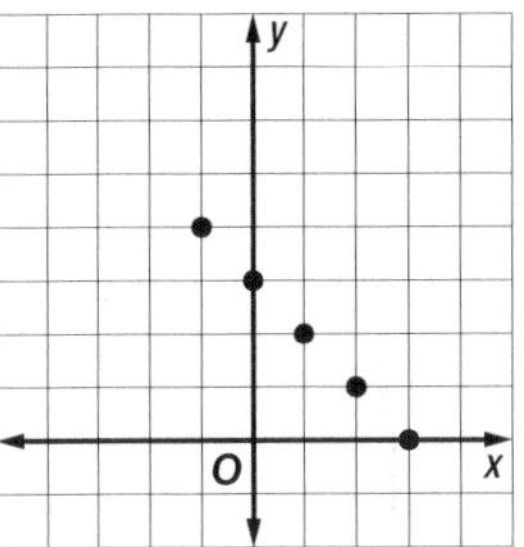

The points on the graph are in a line. The line crosses the y-axis at $y = 3$ and the x-axis at $x = 3$.

Pages 98–99, Lesson 2-6

5–8. 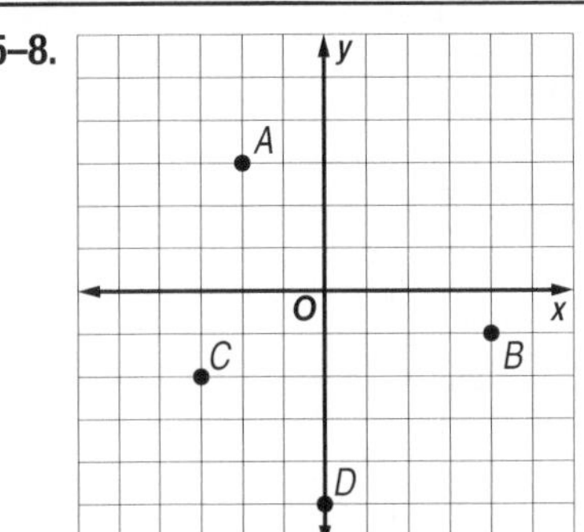

9.

$x - y = 4$		
x	y	(x, y)
6	2	(6, 2)
5	1	(5, 1)
4	0	(4, 0)
−1	−5	(−1, −5)
−2	−6	(−2, −6)

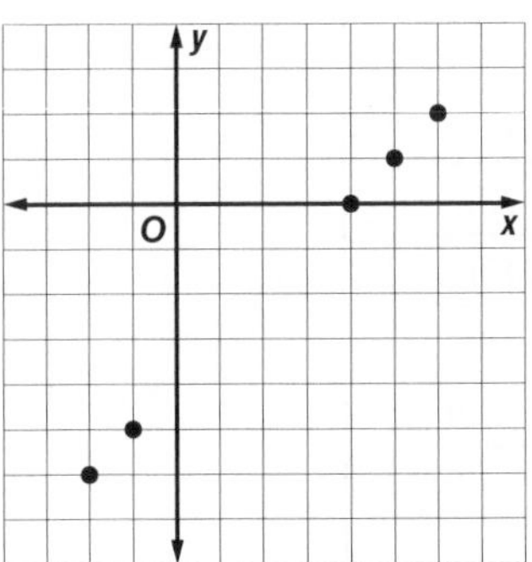

The points are along a diagonal line that crosses the y-axis at $y = -4$ and the x-axis at $x = 4$.

20–31.

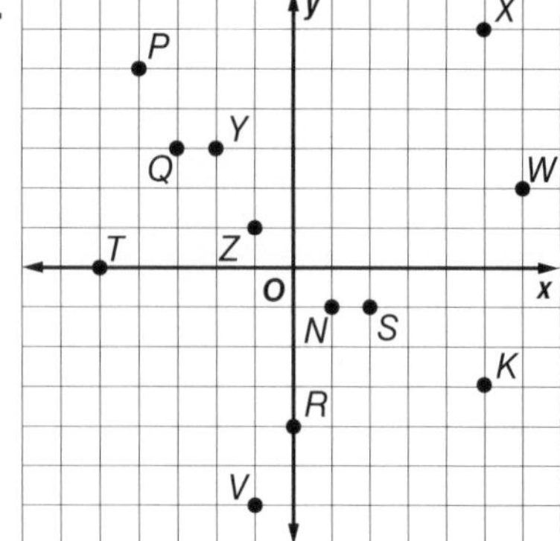

32.

$x + y = 16$		
x	y	(x, y)
0	16	(0, 16)
4	12	(4, 12)
8	8	(8, 8)
12	4	(12, 4)
16	0	(16, 0)

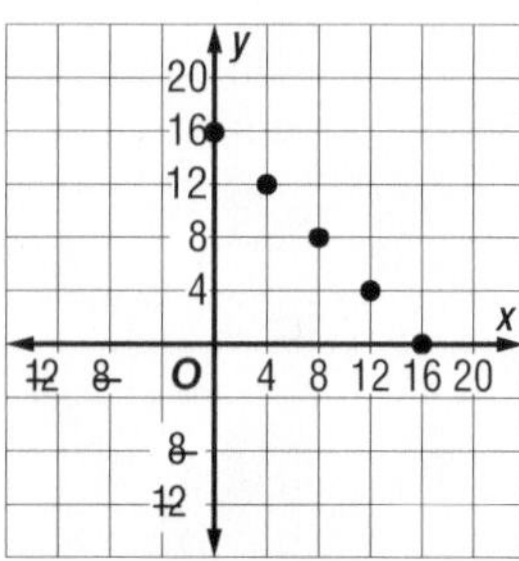

The points on the graph are in a line. The line crosses the y-axis at $y = 16$ and the x-axis at $x = 16$.

33.

$x - y = 10$		
x	y	(x, y)
30	20	(30, 20)
20	10	(20, 10)
10	0	(10, 0)
–20	–30	(–20, –30)
–30	–40	(–30, –40)

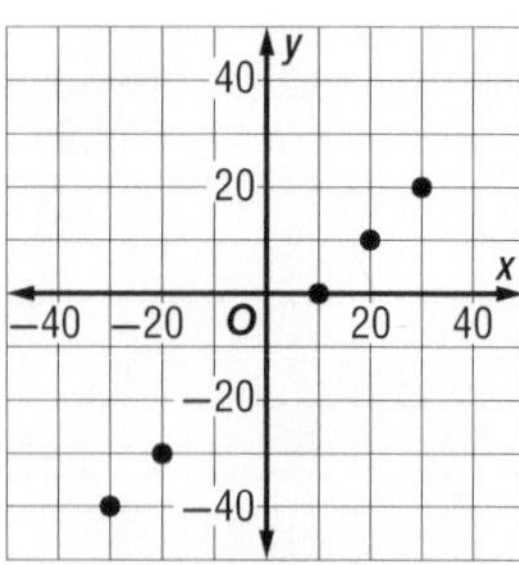

The points on the graph are in a line that slants downward to the left. The line crosses the x-axis at $x = 10$.

38.

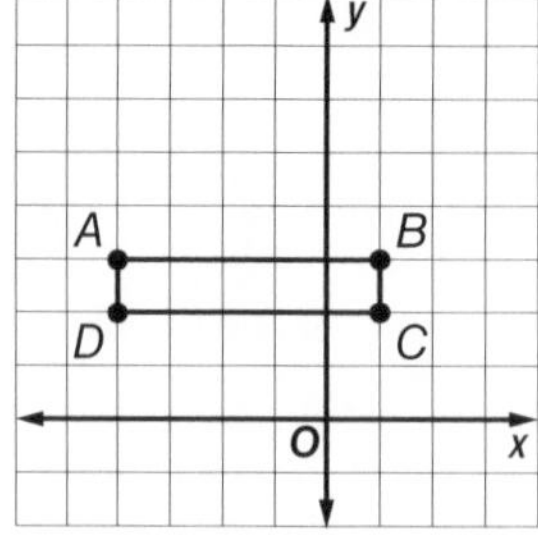

a. $A(0,3)$, $B(5,3)$, $C(5,2)$, $D(0,2)$

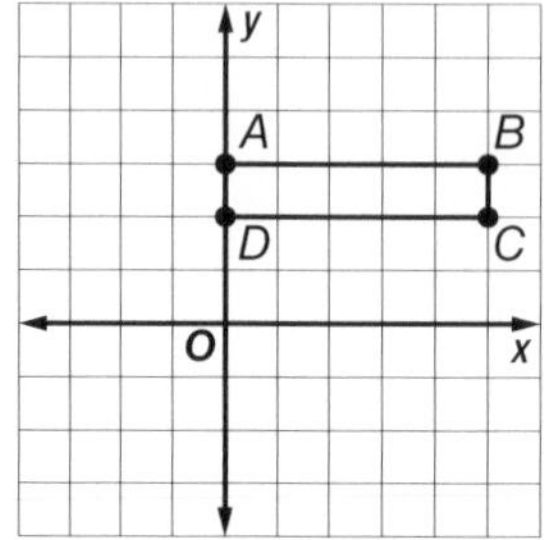

b. Sample answer: The shape and size of the rectangles are the same. The 2nd rectangle is 4 units to the right of the first rectangle.

39.

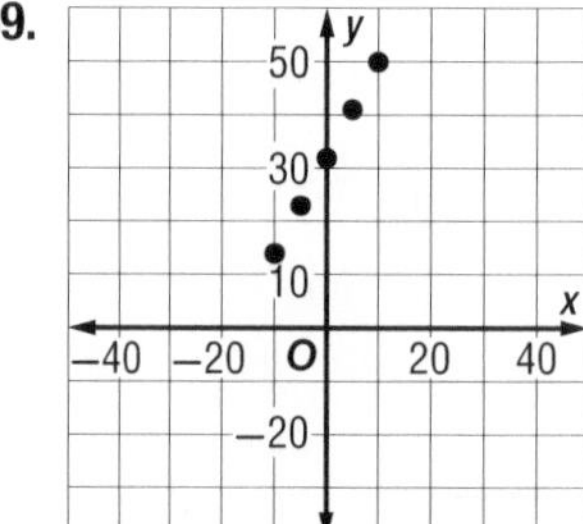

40.

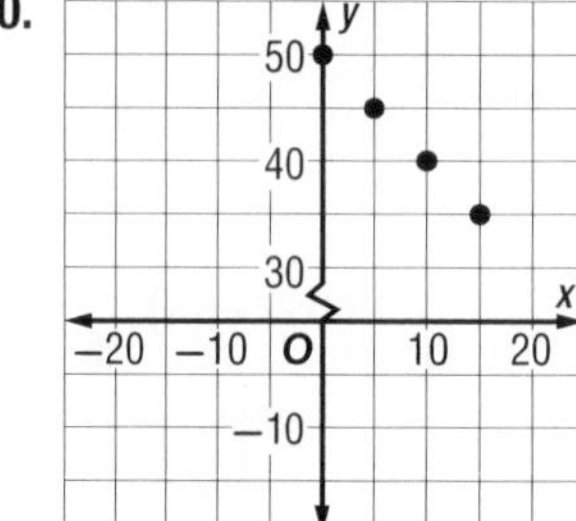

41.

Input	rule: $x - 4$	Output
−2	−2 − 4	−6
−1	−1 − 4	−5
0	0 − 4	−4
1	1 − 4	−3
2	2 − 4	−2

42.

Input	rule: $-x$	Output
−2	−(−2)	2
−1	−(−1)	1
0	−(0)	0
1	−(1)	−1
2	−(2)	−2

43–46. 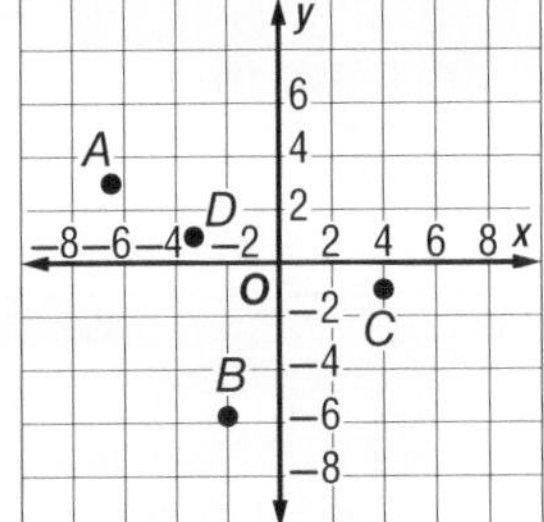

48a.

input	output
−3	−4
−2	−6
−1	−12
1	12
2	6
3	4

b. 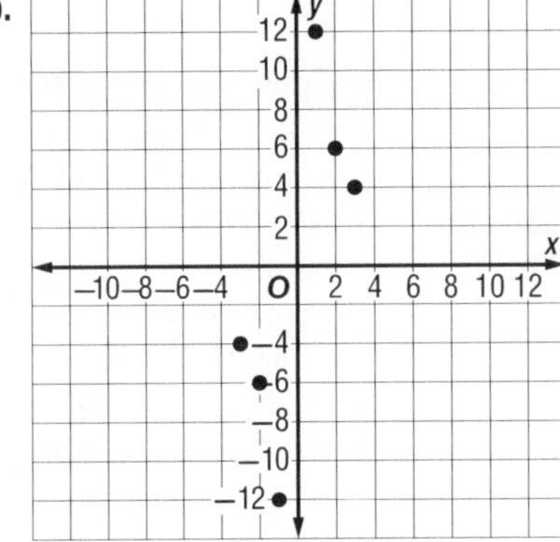

Sample answer: The graph is curved and only in the first and third quadrants. There is no output value for an input of 0.

Page 101, Lesson 2-7 (Why?)

a. Sample answer: They are still in a line, but they have moved diagonally from the original position.

b. Sample answer: They are both the same distance away from the 50-yard line, but in opposite directions.

Page 105, Lesson 2-7

18. Sample answer:

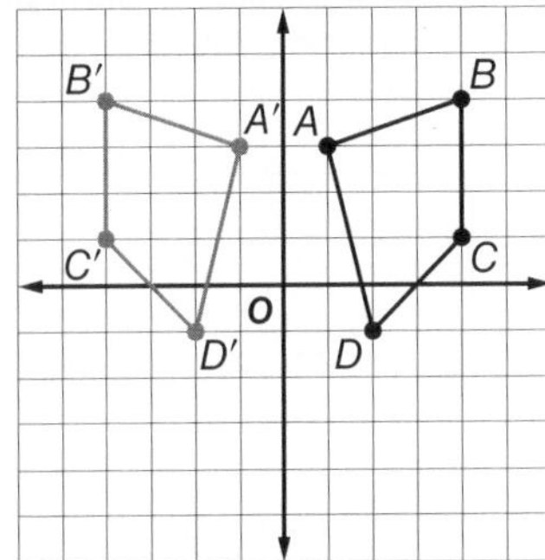

19. No; For example, the vertices of ΔABC are $A(1,3)$, $B(7, 3)$, and $C(1, 6)$. The image's vertices reflected over the x-axis and y-axis would be $A'(-1,-3)$, $B'(-7, -3)$, and $C'(-1, -6)$.

20. $G(-3, -4)$ $G'(-3, 4)$ is a reflection over the x-axis; to reflect over the y-axis, multiply the x-coordinate by −1.

21. No single transformation is equivalent to the original two. The new figure is a reflection of the original but moved up and over to the right.

22. The final position of the figure will be the original position. Translating a figure by (2, 3) and then by (−2, 3) is the same as translating it by (0, 0).

CHAPTER 3

Chapter Planner

Diagnostic Assessment
Quick Check, p. 117

	Explore 3-1 Pacing: 1 day	**Lesson 3-1** Pacing: 1 day	**Lesson 3-2** Pacing: 1 day
Title	**Algebra Lab: Fractions and Decimals on the Number Line**	**Fractions and Decimals**	**Rational Numbers**
Objectives	• Represent positive and negative fractions and decimals on a number line.	• Write fractions as terminating or repeating decimals. • Compare fractions and decimals.	• Write rational numbers as fractions. • Identify and classify rational numbers.
Key Vocabulary		terminating decimal repeating decimal bar notation	rational numbers
NCTM Focal Points	G7–FP3, G7–FP5C For the complete wording of the Focal Points for Grades 7 and 8, please see pages iv, v, FP0, and FP1.		
Multiple Representations		p. 126	p. 132
Lesson Resources	**Materials:** • rulers	**Chapter 3 Resource Masters** • Study Guide and Intervention, pp. 5–6 AL OL ELL • Skills Practice, p. 7 AL OL ELL • Practice, p. 8 AL OL BL ELL • Word Problem Practice, p. 9 AL OL BL • Enrichment, p. 10 OL BL • Spreadsheet Activity, p. 11 AL OL BL ELL **Transparencies** • 5-Minute Check Transparency 3-1 AL OL BL ELL **Additional Print Resources** • *Study Notebook* AL OL BL ELL	**Chapter 3 Resource Masters** • Study Guide and Intervention, pp. 12–13 AL OL ELL • Skills Practice, p. 14 AL OL ELL • Practice, p. 15 AL OL BL ELL • Word Problem Practice, p. 16 AL OL BL • Enrichment, p. 17 OL BL • Quiz 1, p. 46 AL OL BL ELL **Transparencies** • 5-Minute Check Transparency 3-2 AL OL BL ELL **Additional Print Resources** • *Study Notebook* AL OL BL ELL
Technology for Every Lesson	Math Online glencoe.com • Extra Examples • Self-Check Quizzes • Personal Tutor	**CD/DVD Resources** IWB INTERACTIVE WHITEBOARD READY IWB StudentWorks Plus IWB Interactive Classroom IWB Diagnostic and Assessment Planner	• TeacherWorks Plus • eSolutions Manual Plus • ExamView Assessment Suite
Math in Motion	p. 119	p. 122	
Differentiated Instruction		pp. 122, 127	pp. 129, 133

KEY:  Approaching Level  On Level BL Beyond Level ELL English Learners

Rational Numbers

Suggested Pacing			
Time Periods	Instruction	Review & Assessment	Total
45-minute	7	2	9
90-minute	3.5	1	4.5

Lesson 3-3 Pacing: 1 day	Lesson 3-4 Pacing: 1 day	Lesson 3-5 Pacing: 1 day	Lesson 3-6 Pacing: 1 day
Multiplying Rational Numbers	**Dividing Rational Numbers**	**Adding and Subtracting Like Fractions**	**Adding and Subtracting Unlike Fractions**
• Multiply positive and negative fractions. • Evaluate algebraic expressions with fractions.	• Divide positive and negative fractions using multiplicative inverses. • Divide algebraic fractions.	• Add rational numbers with common denominators. • Subtract rational numbers with common denominators.	• Add unlike fractions. • Subtract unlike fractions.
	multiplicative inverse reciprocal	like fractions	unlike fractions
			p. 156
Chapter 3 Resource Masters • Study Guide and Intervention, pp. 18–19 AL OL ELL • Skills Practice, p. 20 AL OL ELL • Practice, p. 21 AL OL BL ELL • Word Problem Practice, p. 22 AL OL BL • Enrichment, p. 23 OL BL • Quiz 2, p. 46 AL OL BL ELL	**Chapter 3 Resource Masters** • Study Guide and Intervention, pp. 24–25 AL OL ELL • Skills Practice, p. 26 AL OL ELL • Practice, p. 27 AL OL BL ELL • Word Problem Practice, p. 28 AL OL BL • Enrichment, p. 29 OL BL	**Chapter 3 Resource Masters** • Study Guide and Intervention, pp. 30–31 AL OL ELL • Skills Practice, p. 32 AL OL ELL • Practice, p. 33 AL OL BL ELL • Word Problem Practice, p. 34 AL OL BL • Enrichment, p. 35 OL BL • Quiz 3, p. 47 AL OL BL ELL	**Chapter 3 Resource Masters** • Study Guide and Intervention, pp. 36–37 AL OL ELL • Skills Practice, p. 38 AL OL ELL • Practice, p. 39 AL OL BL ELL • Word Problem Practice, p. 40 AL OL BL • Enrichment, p. 41 OL BL • Graphing Calculator, p. 42 AL OL BL ELL • Quiz 4, p. 47 AL OL BL ELL
Transparencies • 5-Minute Check Transparency 3-3 AL OL BL ELL	**Transparencies** • 5-Minute Check Transparency 3-4 AL OL BL ELL	**Transparencies** • 5-Minute Check Transparency 3-5 AL OL BL ELL	**Transparencies** • 5-Minute Check Transparency 3-6 AL OL BL ELL
Additional Print Resources • *Study Notebook* AL OL BL ELL	**Additional Print Resources** • *Study Notebook* AL OL BL ELL	**Additional Print Resources** • *Study Notebook* AL OL BL ELL	**Additional Print Resources** • *Study Notebook* AL OL BL ELL

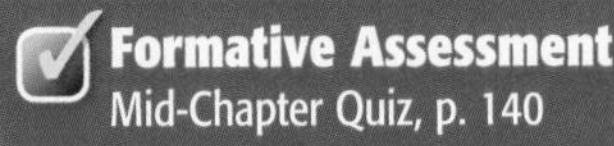

- Extra Examples
- Self-Check Quizzes
- Personal Tutor

CD/DVD Resources IWB INTERACTIVE WHITEBOARD READY

- IWB StudentWorks Plus
- IWB Interactive Classroom
- IWB Diagnostic and Assessment Planner
- TeacherWorks Plus
- eSolutions Manual Plus
- ExamView Assessment Suite

pp. 136, 139	pp. 142, 146	pp. 148, 152	pp. 154, 158

Formative Assessment
Mid-Chapter Quiz, p. 140

Summative Assessment
- Study Guide and Review, pp. 159–162
- Practice Test, p. 163

CHAPTER 3

Assessment and Intervention

SE = Student Edition, **TE** = Teacher Edition, **CRM** = Chapter Resource Masters

	Diagnosis	Prescription
Diagnostic Assessment	**Beginning Chapter 3**	
	Get Ready for Chapter 3 **SE,** p. 117	Response to Intervention **TE,** p. 117
	Beginning Every Lesson	
	Then, Now, Why? **SE** 5-Minute Check Transparencies	Chapter 0 **SE,** pp. P1 through P22 Concepts and Skills Bank **SE** pp. 856–887 *Quick Review Math Handbook*
Formative Assessment	**During/After Every Lesson**	
	Check Your Progress **SE,** every example Check Your Understanding **SE** Spiral Review **SE** Additional Examples **TE** Watch Out! **TE** Step 4, Assess **TE** Chapter 3 Quizzes **CRM,** pp. 46–47 Self-Check Quizzes glencoe.com	**Tier 1 Intervention** Concepts and Skills Bank **SE,** pp. 856–887 Skills Practice **CRM,** Ch. 1–3 glencoe.com **Tier 2 Intervention** Differentiated Instruction **TE** Study Guide and Intervention Masters **CRM,** Ch. 1–3 *Quick Review Math Handbook* **Tier 3 Intervention** *Math Triumphs, Grade 8,* Ch. 1, 3, 7
	Mid-Chapter	
	Mid-Chapter Quiz **SE,** p. 140 Mid-Chapter Test **CRM,** p. 48 ExamView Assessment Suite	**Tier 1 Intervention** Concepts and Skills Bank **SE,** pp. 856–887 Skills Practice **CRM,** Ch. 1–3 glencoe.com **Tier 2 Intervention** Study Guide and Intervention Masters **CRM,** Ch. 1–3 *Quick Review Math Handbook* **Tier 3 Intervention** *Math Triumphs, Grade 8,* Ch. 1, 3, 7
	Before Chapter Test	
	Chapter Study Guide and Review **SE,** pp. 159–162 Practice Test **SE,** p. 163 Standardized Test Practice **SE,** pp. 164–167 Chapter Test glencoe.com Standardized Test Practice glencoe.com Vocabulary Review glencoe.com ExamView Assessment Suite	**Tier 1 Intervention** Concepts and Skills Bank **SE,** pp. 856–887 Skills Practice **CRM,** Ch. 1–3 glencoe.com **Tier 2 Intervention** Study Guide and Intervention Masters **CRM,** Ch. 1–3 *Quick Review Math Handbook* **Tier 3 Intervention** *Math Triumphs, Grade 8,* Ch. 1, 3, 7
Summative Assessment	**After Chapter 3**	
	Multiple-Choice Tests, Forms 1, 2A, 2B, **CRM,** pp. 50–55 Free-Response Tests, Forms 2C, 2D, 3, **CRM,** pp. 56–61 Vocabulary Test **CRM,** p. 49 Extended Response Test **CRM,** p. 62 Standardized Test Practice **CRM,** pp. 63–65 ExamView Assessment Suite	Study Guide and Intervention Masters **CRM,** Ch. 1–3 *Quick Review Math Handbook* glencoe.com

CHAPTER 3

Differentiated Instruction

Option 1 Reaching All Learners AL OL BL ELL

LOGICAL Write the following numbers on the board: $-2\frac{4}{7}$, $\frac{5}{8}$, $1\frac{4}{5}$, $-3\frac{1}{4}$.

Without calculating, have students determine the following:

- the two numbers with the least product $1\frac{4}{5}$, $-3\frac{1}{4}$
- the two numbers with the greatest product $-2\frac{4}{7}$, $-3\frac{1}{4}$

Have students explain their reasoning.

KINESTHETIC Make a number line on the floor, from −2 to 2, using masking tape for the line and tick marks. Use cards to show −2, −1, 0, 1, and 2 and divide the line into fourths. Call out a variety of rational numbers and then invite students to write the number on a card, name the set(s) of numbers to which it belongs, and then stand on the number line to show the number's location. Continue until the number line is filled.

Option 2 Approaching Level AL

Give students a 5 × 5 geoboard with two colors of rubber bands and geodot paper. Demonstrate how to use the geoboard to find $\frac{2}{3} \times \frac{3}{4}$.

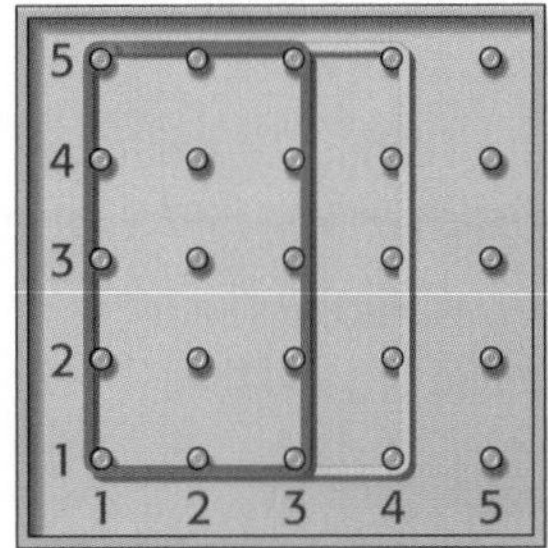

- Show how to place one band around $\frac{3}{4}$ of the whole board.
- Show how to place the other band around $\frac{2}{3}$ of $\frac{3}{4}$.

Lead students to see that the second rubber band is wrapped around 2 columns out of 4 columns, or $\frac{1}{2}$ of the whole board, so $\frac{2}{3} \times \frac{3}{4} = \frac{1}{2}$.

Next, show students how to use geodot paper to model the problem. Challenge students to write additional problems that can be solved using various sizes of geoboards or geodot paper.

Option 3 English Learners ELL

MEASUREMENT Some exercises in the chapter use the customary system of measurement. You can use this opportunity to teach ELL students about the customary system. Create posters showing the tools used to measure in both systems and the equivalent measurements. For example, post a liquid measuring cup that shows both customary and metric measures. Under the picture, write $\frac{1}{2}$ cup is about 120 mL.

VOCABULARY Have students look up the words *terminate, terminating, repeat,* and *repeating* in a dictionary and thesaurus. Ask them to select one definition and two synonyms for each word and then discuss in small groups how the definitions and synonyms contribute to an understanding of the meaning of terminating and repeating decimals.

After the discussion, have students write a definition of terminating and repeating decimals in their own words. Ask them to include examples with their definitions.

Option 4 Beyond Level BL

Explain to students that algebraic fractions with unlike denominators, like their numerical counterparts, must have a common denominator before they can be added or subtracted. They can use the LCM to rename algebraic fractions with the LCD, just as they do for numerical fractions.

Challenge students to add or subtract the following algebraic fractions:

- $\frac{7}{a} + \frac{3b}{c}$, $a, c \neq 0$ $\frac{7c + 3ab}{ac}$
- $\frac{5}{xy} - \frac{2}{yz}$ $x, y, z \neq 0$ $\frac{5z - 2x}{xyz}$

CHAPTER 3

Focus on Mathematical Content

Vertical Alignment

Before Chapter 3

Related Topics before Pre-Algebra

- convert between fractions, decimals, whole numbers, and percents
- solve problems involving fractions and decimals

Previous Topics from Pre-Algebra

- evaluate the effectiveness of different representations to communicate ideas
- add, subtract, multiply, and divide integers

Chapter 3

Related Topics from Pre-Algebra

- explore rational numbers
- multiply and divide fractions
- add and subtract like fractions and unlike fractions
- convert fractions to decimals
- factor numbers
- determine least common multiple

After Chapter 3

Preparation for Algebra 1

- identify and apply mathematics to everyday experiences, to activities in and outside school, with other disciplines, and with other mathematical topics
- simplify rational expressions
- add and subtract rational expressions
- multiply and divide rational expressions

Lesson-by-Lesson Preview

3-1 Fractions and Decimals

Any fraction $\frac{a}{b}$, where $b \neq 0$, can be written as a decimal by dividing the numerator by the denominator.

- If the division ends, or terminates, when the remainder is zero, the decimal is a terminating decimal. For example, $\frac{3}{8} = 3 \div 8 = 0.375$.
- If the division does not terminate, and the remainder is not zero, the decimal is a repeating decimal. For example, $\frac{4}{9} = 4 \div 9 = 0.444444\ldots$ or $0.\overline{4}$. A bar placed over a digit or digits indicates that the digit(s) repeat(s).
- When comparing fractions with unlike denominators, write the fractions as decimals and place them on a number line.

$\frac{7}{8} \bullet \frac{6}{7}$

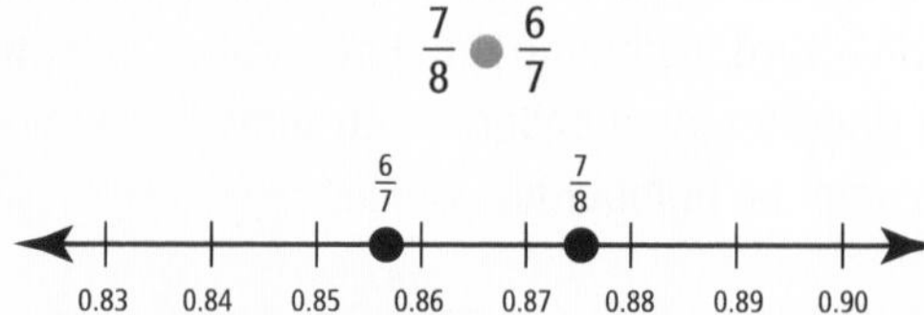

The number line shows that $\frac{7}{8} > \frac{6}{7}$.

3-2 Rational Numbers

A rational number is any number that can be written as a fraction, including terminating and repeating decimals, integers, fractions, and mixed numbers.

Decimals that do not terminate or repeat cannot be written as fractions, and are irrational numbers, such as 3.141592… or π.

- Terminating decimals can be written as fractions with denominators of 10, 100, 1,000, and so on, and then simplified. For example, $0.32 = \frac{32}{100} = \frac{8}{25}$.
- Repeating decimals can also be written as fractions. Let N equal the number, multiply each side by 10, 100, and so on depending on how many numbers repeat, subtract N from $10N$ and so on to eliminate the repeating part, and then divide and simplify. For example, since $0.\overline{45}$ has two repeating numbers, multiply by 100 and subtract N from $100N$ to give $0.\overline{45} = \frac{45}{99} = \frac{5}{11}$.

Multiplying Rational Numbers

Use the following rules to multiply fractions:

- Multiply the numerators and multiply the denominators, and write the product in simplest form.
- If the fractions have common factors in the numerators and denominators, simplify first and then multiply.
- If one of the fractions is negative, then the product will be negative.
- Multiply mixed numbers in the same way as fractions after first renaming the mixed numbers as improper fractions.

Algebraic expressions can contain variables that represent fractions. Replace the variable with the fraction, and then use the rules for multiplying with fractions.

Dividing Rational Numbers

Rational numbers have all of the properties of whole numbers and integers. Another property, shown by $\frac{7}{4} \cdot \frac{4}{7} = 1$, is the Inverse Property of Multiplication, which states that the product of a number and its reciprocal, or multiplicative inverse, is 1.

Use the following rules to divide fractions:

- When dividing by a fraction, multiply by its multiplicative inverse.
- When dividing by a mixed number, first rename the number as an improper fraction, and then multiply by its multiplicative inverse.
- When dividing by a whole number, write the whole number as a fraction, and then divide by its multiplicative inverse.

A fraction that contains one or more variables in the numerator or the denominator is an algebraic fraction. Use the same rules for dividing algebraic fractions as for dividing numeric fractions.

Adding and Subtracting Like Fractions

Fractions with the same denominator are called like fractions.

- To add like fractions, add the numerators and write the sum over the denominator.
- To add mixed numbers with the same denominators, add the whole numbers and fractions separately, and then simplify.
- To subtract like fractions, subtract the numerators and write the difference over the denominator.
- To subtract mixed numbers, rename the mixed numbers as improper fractions, and then subtract the numerators and simplify.
- Use the same rules for adding and subtracting like fractions to add and subtract like algebraic fractions.

Adding and Subtracting Unlike Fractions

Fractions with different denominators are called unlike fractions.

- To add and subtract unlike fractions, rename the fractions with a common denominator, and then add or subtract as with like fractions.
- Use the LCD for the common denominator to make simplifying easier.
- To add and subtract mixed numbers with unlike fractions, rename the mixed numbers as improper fractions, find a common denominator, and then add or subtract as with like mixed numbers.

Targeted professional development has been articulated throughout McGraw-Hill's mathematics program. The **McGraw-Hill Professional Development Video Library** provides short videos that support key topics. For more information, visit glencoe.com.

Model Lessons

Instructional Strategies

CHAPTER 3

Notes

Chapter Project

Measure for Measure

Students use what they have learned about adding, subtracting, multiplying, and dividing fractions to work with recipes and compile shopping lists.

- Ask each student to bring a favorite recipe to class. Alternatively, you could have students vote on a theme and have them research or bring in recipes that relate to the chosen theme.
- Divide students into groups. Ask them to identify each measure in their recipes as a fraction, mixed number, or an integer. Then ask them to order the measures from least to greatest. For which ingredients do they need the greatest amounts? The least?
- Ask each group to compile a shopping list that includes all of the ingredients they would need to make all of the recipes in their group. For example, if one student's recipe calls for $\frac{1}{2}$ cup of milk, and another's calls for $\frac{3}{4}$ cup, the group shopping list should call for $\frac{5}{4}$ or $1\frac{1}{4}$ cup of milk.
- Have each group choose one of the recipes from their group and determine how much of each ingredient they would need if they were making the recipe for one person. Then after they have calculated those amounts, have them determine how much they would need to make the recipe for the whole class.
- Remind students that each recipe should indicate the number of servings it makes, and that they should multiply or divide as necessary to adjust amounts.

CHAPTER 3

Operations With Rational Numbers

Then

In Chapter 2, you learned to add, subtract, multiply, and divide integers.

Now

In Chapter 3, you will:

- Write fractions as terminating or repeating decimals.
- Identify, add, subtract, multiply, and divide rational numbers.
- Evaluate algebraic expressions with fractions.

Why?

COOKING

Cookbooks are among the top selling books each year. Recipes in the books give a set of instructions to make a dish. In most recipes, fractions and mixed numbers appear. Being able to understand and use rational numbers will help make a more delicious meal.

Math *in Motion*, Animation glencoe.com

116 Chapter 3 Operations with Rational Numbers

Key Vocabulary Introduce the key vocabulary in the chapter using the routine below.

Define: The multiplicative inverse of a number is the number that, when multiplied by a given number, results in a product of one.

Example: The multiplicative inverse of $\frac{4}{9}$ is $\frac{9}{4}$.

Ask: What is the multiplicative inverse of $6\frac{2}{5}$? $\frac{5}{32}$

Get Ready for Chapter 3

Diagnose Readiness You have two options for checking Prerequisite Skills.

Text Option Take the Quick Check below. Refer to the Quick Review for help.

*Quick*Check

(Used in Lessons 3-1 through 3-4)

Find each quotient. Round to the nearest tenth, if necessary. (Previous Course)

1. $4 \div 7$ **0.6**
2. $-1 \div 6$ **−0.2**
3. $3 \div 15$ **0.2**
4. $-18 \div 3$ **−6**
5. $-5 \div (-11)$ **0.5**
6. $6 \div (-19)$ **−0.3**
7. $-28 \div 16$ **−1.8**
8. $-63 \div (-7)$ **9**

9. **LANDSCAPING** How many bricks, each 0.25 meter long, are needed to make a row that is 7.25 meters long? **29 bricks**

*Quick*Review

EXAMPLE 1

Find 5 ÷ 9. Round to the nearest tenth.

$5 \div 9 = 0.555...$ **Find the quotient.**
≈ 0.6 **Round to the nearest tenth.**

(Used in Lessons 3-2 through 3-6)

Write each fraction in simplest form. If the fraction is already in simplest form, write *simplified*. (Previous Course)

10. $\frac{6}{30}$ **$\frac{1}{5}$**
11. $\frac{40}{50}$ **$\frac{4}{5}$**
12. $\frac{17}{36}$ **simplified**
13. $\frac{12}{80}$ **$\frac{3}{20}$**
14. $\frac{32}{64}$ **$\frac{1}{2}$**
15. $\frac{56}{71}$ **simplified**

16. **SURVEY** Twelve of the 28 students in math class have blonde hair. In simplest form, what fraction of the students in math class do *not* have blonde hair? **$\frac{4}{7}$**

EXAMPLE 2

Write $\frac{12}{36}$ in simplest form.

Factors of 12: 1, 2, 3, 4, 6, 12
Factors of 36: 1, 2, 3, 4, 6, 9, 12, 18, 36
The GCF of 12 and 36 is 12.

$\frac{12}{36} = \frac{12 \div 12}{36 \div 12}$ **Divide the numerator and the denominator by the GCF.**

$= \frac{1}{3}$ **Simplest form**

(Used in Lessons 3-5 and 3-6)

Find each sum or difference. (Lessons 2-2 and 2-3)

17. $3 + (-7)$ **−4**
18. $-11 + 19$ **8**
19. $(-2) + (-5)$ **−7**
20. $-6 - (-12)$ **6**

21. **TRAVEL** A family drives 26 miles east from their house. Then they drive 17 miles west. Find an integer that represents the family's position in relation to their house. **+9 miles**

EXAMPLE 3

Find 10 − 16.

$10 - 16 = 10 + (-16)$ **To subtract 16, add −16.**
$= -6$ **Simplify.**

Online Option Math Online Take a self-check Chapter Readiness Quiz at glencoe.com.

Get Ready for Chapter 3

Response to Intervention (RtI)

Use the *Quick Check* results and the Intervention Planner to help you determine your Response to Intervention. The If-Then statements in the chart below help you decide the appropriate tier of RtI and suggest intervention resources for each tier.

Intervention Planner

Tier 1 On Level

If students miss about 25% of the exercises or less,

Then choose a resource:

SE Lessons 2-2 through 2-3
CRM Skills Practice, Chapter 2, pp. 13 and 19
TE Chapter Project p. 116
Math Online Self-Check Quiz

Tier 2 Strategic Intervention approaching grade level

If students miss about 50% of the exercises,

Then choose a resource:

SE Lessons 2-2 through 2-3
CRM Study Guide and Intervention, Chapter 2, pp. 11, 12, 17 and 18
Quick Review Math Handbook
Math Online Extra Examples, Personal Tutor, Homework Help

Tier 3 Intensive Intervention 2 or more grades below level

If students miss about 75% of the exercises,

Then use *Math Triumphs, Grade 8*, Ch. 1, 3, 7

Math Online Extra Examples, Personal Tutor, Homework Help, Review Vocabulary

Chapter 3 Operations with Rational Numbers 117

CHAPTER 3 Notes

FOLDABLES® Study Organizer

Dinah Zike's Foldables™

Focus Students write notes about the algebraic processes involved in solving equations.

Teach Have students make and label the tabs for each lesson of their Foldables as illustrated. Have students use the appropriate tabs as they cover each lesson in this chapter. Ask students to write a short descriptive paragraph about each method for solving an equation and encourage them to make connections between the various methods.

When to Use It Encourage students to add to their Foldable as they work through the chapter, and use them to review for the chapter test.

Differentiated Instruction

CRM Student-Built Glossary, pp. 1–2 Students should complete the chart by providing a definition of each term and an example as they progress through Chapter 3. This study tool can also be used to review for the chapter test.

Get Started on Chapter 3

You will learn several new concepts, skills, and vocabulary terms as you study Chapter 3. To get ready, identify important terms and organize your resources. You may wish to refer to **Chapter 0** to review prerequisite skills.

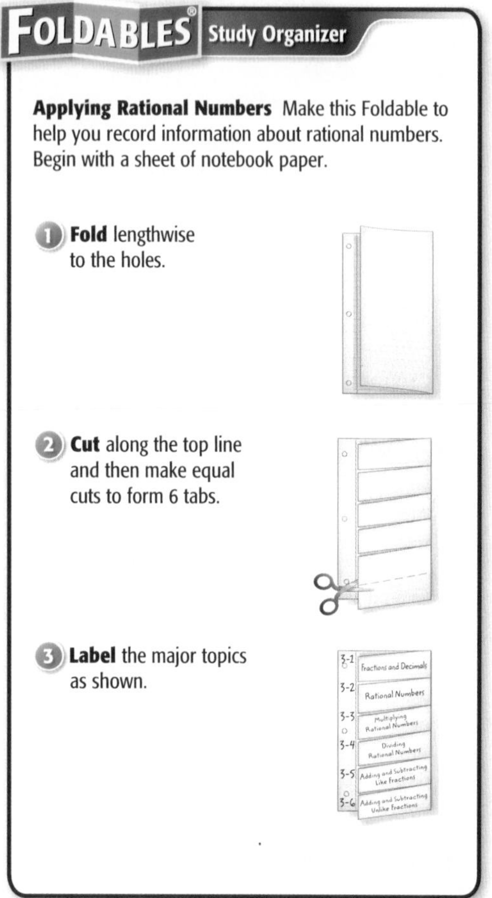

FOLDABLES® Study Organizer
Applying Rational Numbers Make this Foldable to help you record information about rational numbers. Begin with a sheet of notebook paper.
1 **Fold** lengthwise to the holes.
2 **Cut** along the top line and then make equal cuts to form 6 tabs.
3 **Label** the major topics as shown.
3-1 Fractions and Decimals
3-2 Rational Numbers
3-3 Multiplying Rational Numbers
3-4 Dividing Rational Numbers
3-5 Adding and Subtracting Like Fractions
3-6 Adding and Subtracting Unlike Fractions

Math Online glencoe.com

- Study the chapter online
- Explore **Math in Motion**
- Get extra help from your own **Personal Tutor**
- Use **Extra Examples** for additional help
- Take a **Self-Check Quiz**
- **Review Vocabulary** in fun ways

New Vocabulary

English		Español
terminating decimal	p. 121	decimal terminal
repeating decimal	p. 122	decimal periódico
bar notation	p. 122	notación de barra
rational number	p. 128	número racional
multiplicative inverse	p. 141	inversos multiplicativos
reciprocal	p. 141	recíproco
like fractions	p. 147	fracciones semejantes
unlike fractions	p. 153	fracciones con distintos denominadores

Review Vocabulary

GCF (greatest common factor) • p. 858 • máximo común divisor (MCD) the greatest number that is a factor of two or more numbers; Example: the GCF of 14 and 35 is 7

LCM (least common multiple) • p. 860 • mínimo común múltiplo (MCM) the least of the nonzero common multiples of two or more numbers; Example: the LCM of 4 and 6 is 12

opposites • p. 71 • opuestos two numbers with the same absolute value but different signs

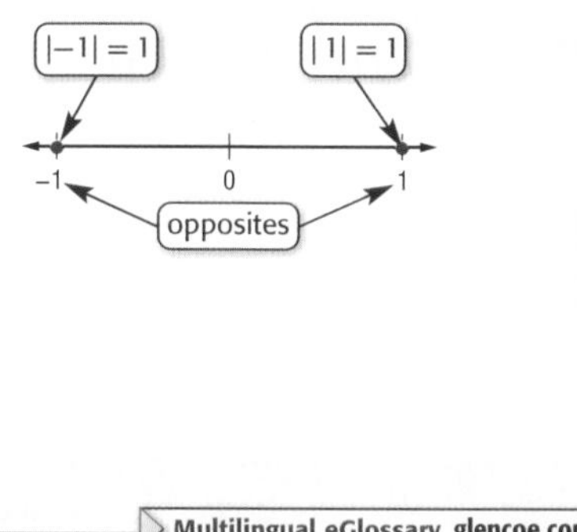

Multilingual eGlossary glencoe.com

118 Chapter 3 Operations with Rational Numbers

Algebra Lab: Fractions and Decimals on the Number Line

Math Online glencoe.com
Math *in Motion*, Animation

Objective
Represent positive and negative fractions and decimals on a number line.

You have already used a number line to graph integers. The number line below shows the graph of the integers 1 and −1.

In this lab, you will graph positive and negative fractions and decimals on a number line.

ACTIVITY 1

Use a number line to graph $\frac{5}{8}$.

Step 1 Draw a number line showing 0 and 1.

Step 2 Since the denominator is eighths, divide the number line between 0 and 1 into 8 equal parts.
Label the number line with $\frac{1}{8}$, $\frac{2}{8}$, $\frac{3}{8}$, and so on.

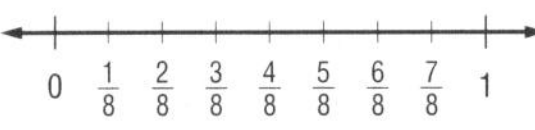

Step 3 Draw a dot on the number line above the $\frac{5}{8}$ mark.

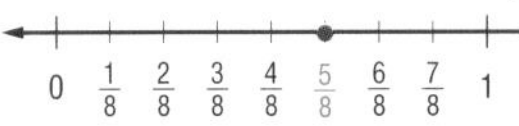

ACTIVITY 2

Use a number line to graph $-2\frac{4}{5}$.

Step 1 Draw a number line showing −2 and −3.

Step 2 Since the denominator is fifths, divide the number line between −2 and −3 into 5 equal parts.
On the number line, $-2\frac{1}{5}$ lies just to the left of −2. Continue in this manner until you reach −3.

$-3 \quad -2\frac{4}{5} \quad -2\frac{3}{5} \quad -2\frac{2}{5} \quad -2\frac{1}{5} \quad -2$

Step 3 Draw a dot on the number line above the $-2\frac{4}{5}$ mark.

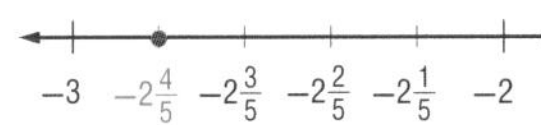

Exercises

Graph each fraction on a number line. a–d. See margin.

a. $\frac{2}{3}$ **b.** $-\frac{3}{4}$ **c.** $-2\frac{5}{6}$ **d.** $3\frac{1}{5}$

Additional Answers

a.

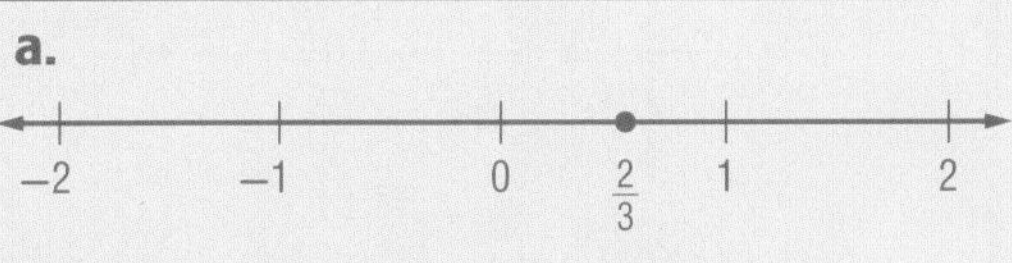

b.

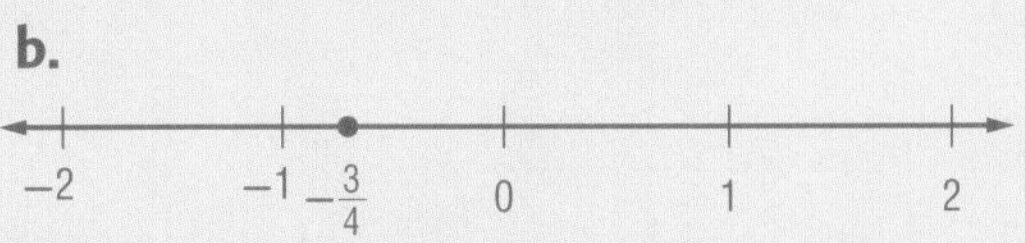

c.

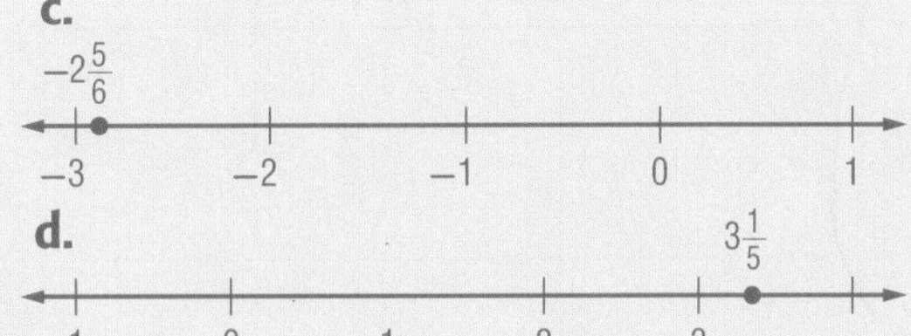

d.

$3\frac{1}{5}$

−1 0 1 2 3

1 FOCUS

Objective Represent positive and negative fractions and decimals on a number line.

Materials for Each Group

- rulers

Teaching Tip

To save time and eliminate some distraction while working through the activities, prepare a page of number lines ahead of time. Leave some blank so students can practice determining the appropriate scale.

2 TEACH

Working in Cooperative Groups

Students can work in pairs or small groups, mixing abilities, to complete Activities 1–3 and Exercises a–h. It is important for all students to determine a scale, label a number line, and graph the numbers on it. Encourage students to ask for and offer help within their groups.

Ask:

- For Activity 1, why do we choose the interval 0 to 1? 0 and 1 are the closest integers: $0 < \frac{5}{8} < 1$.
- Notice there are 7 lines marked between 0 and 1 in the first number line. Why doesn't labeling eighths require eight lines in this interval? $\frac{8}{8} = 1$, so its mark is already on the number line.
- After finishing Activity 1 as a class, continue working through Activities 2 and 3 in small groups.
- Discuss how to graph decimals expressed in hundredths. Point out that since it is not practical to divide a unit into a hundred sections, they could divide it into tenths and estimate the location of the decimal between the nearest tenths.

- For Activity 3 discuss how to graph decimals expressed in hundredths. Point out that since it is not practical to divide a unit into a hundred sections, they could divide it into tenths and estimate the location of the decimal between the nearest tenths.

Practice Have students complete Exercises 1–6.

ASSESS

Formative Assessment

Use Exercise 2 to assess whether students understand how to represent positive and negative fractions and decimals on a number line.

From Concrete to Abstract

Ask students to determine without graphing which is greater, -0.75 or $-\frac{4}{5}$. Then have them use a number line to check their solutions.

Extending the Concept

Have students explain how a number line might be used to help them change a decimal to a fraction. Sample answer: Label the number line with both decimals and fractions.

Additional Answers

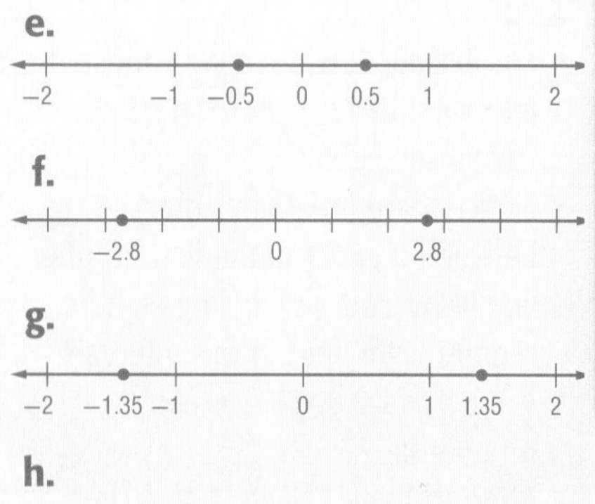

StudyTip

Scale When deciding on the scale for the number line, use the first integer less than -1.3 and the first integer greater than 1.3. So, the number line should range from -2 to 2.

ACTIVITY 3

Use a number line to graph 1.3 and −1.3.

Step 1 The decimals are expressed in tenths. So, divide the number line between -2 and 2 so there are 10 sections between each integer.

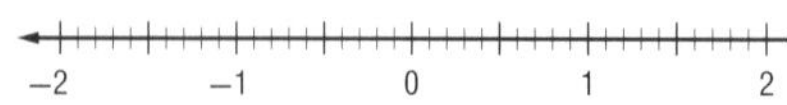

Step 2 Locate 1.3 on the number line. Draw a dot on the number line above the 1.3 mark. Draw another dot on the number line above the -1.3 mark.

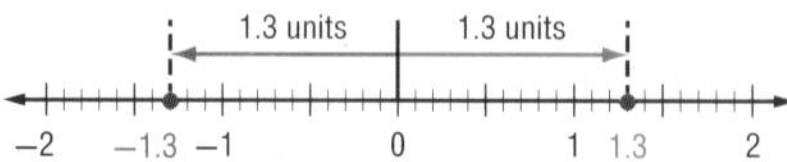

The two points graphed on the number line are the same distance away from zero. The numbers 1.3 and -1.3 are opposites. Recall that opposites are two numbers with the same absolute value but different signs.

Exercises

Graph each decimal and its opposite on a number line. e–h. See margin.

e. 0.5 **f.** -2.8 **g.** 1.35 **h.** -2.24

Analyze the Results

1. In Activity 2, you graphed $-2\frac{4}{5}$ on a number line. From that point, in what direction on the number line would you move if you wanted to graph $-3\frac{1}{5}$?
2. Equivalent numbers are graphed in the same place on a number line. Use a number line to determine if the following pairs of numbers are equivalent.
   a. -1.6 and $-1\frac{3}{5}$ **b.** $\frac{2}{3}$ and 0.8 **c.** -1.75 and $-1\frac{3}{4}$
   a–c. See margin.
3. Use a number line to determine which number is greater in each pair of numbers. Justify your reasoning.
   a. $-2\frac{5}{8}$ or -2.75 **b.** -1.4 or -1.7 **c.** $\frac{1}{5}$ or $-1\frac{1}{5}$
4. When graphing fractions on a number line, explain how to divide the number line into equal parts. Sample answer: The denominator tells you how many equal parts.
5. **OPEN ENDED** Name a fraction and its opposite. Then graph the fractions on a number line. See margin.
6. **WRITING IN MATH** Explain why $\frac{3}{4}$ is graphed to the right of $\frac{1}{4}$ but $-\frac{3}{4}$ is graphed to the left of $-\frac{1}{4}$.

1. to the left of $-2\frac{4}{5}$

3a. $-2\frac{5}{8}$; it is farther to the right on the number line.

3b. -1.4; it is farther to the right on the number line.

3c. $\frac{1}{5}$; positive numbers are greater than negative numbers.

6. Sample answer: Since $\frac{1}{4} < \frac{3}{4}$, $\frac{3}{4}$ is graphed to the right of $\frac{1}{4}$. Since $-\frac{3}{4} < -\frac{1}{4}$, $-\frac{3}{4}$ is graphed to the left of $-\frac{1}{4}$.

2a. equivalent

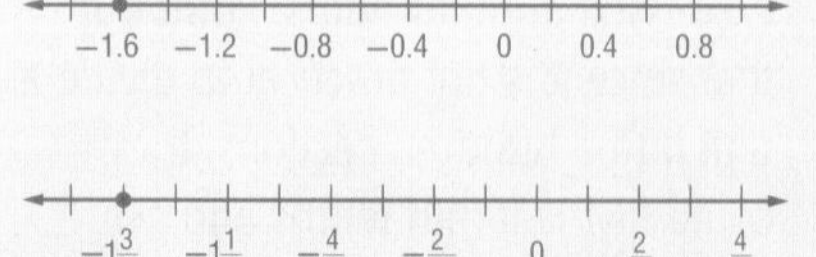

2b. not equivalent

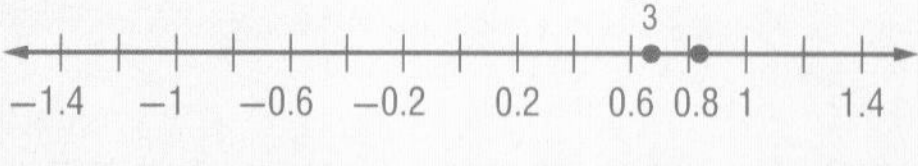

2c. equivalent

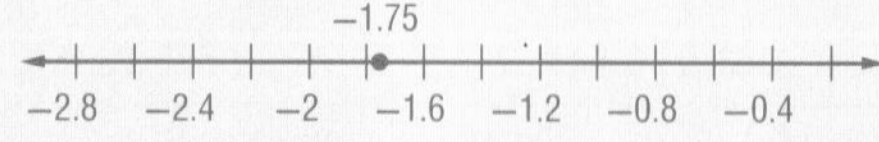

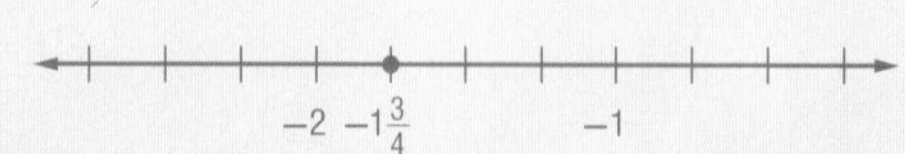

5. Sample Answer: $+\frac{1}{3}, -\frac{1}{3}$

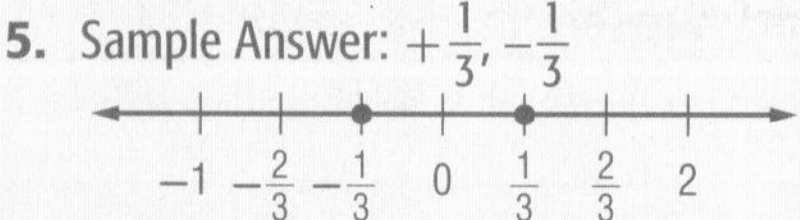

3-1 Fractions and Decimals

Why?

Tara was making tacos for her friends. She bought $\frac{1}{2}$ pound of chicken. The scale showed 0.5 pound.

a. Explain why $\frac{1}{2}$ is the same as 0.5.

b. She needed $\frac{3}{4}$ pound of cheese. What decimal is equivalent to $\frac{3}{4}$? Explain.

a–b. See Chapter 3 Answer Appendix.

Then

You have used a number line to graph integers. (Lesson 2-1)

Now

- Write fractions as terminating or repeating decimals.
- Compare fractions and decimals.

New Vocabulary

terminating decimal
repeating decimal
bar notation

Math Online

glencoe.com

- Extra Examples
- Personal Tutor
- Self-Check Quiz
- Homework Help
- Math in Motion

Write Fractions as Decimals Some fractions like $\frac{1}{2}$ and $\frac{3}{4}$ can be written as a decimal by making equivalent fractions with denominators of 10, 100, or 1000. However, any fraction $\frac{a}{b}$, where $b \neq 0$, can be written as a decimal by dividing the numerator by the denominator. So, $\frac{a}{b} = a \div b$.

If the division ends, or terminates, when the remainder is zero, the decimal is a **terminating decimal**.

EXAMPLE 1 Write a Fraction as a Terminating Decimal

Write $\frac{7}{8}$ as a decimal.

Method 1 Use paper and pencil.

$$\begin{array}{r} 0.875 \\ 8\overline{)7.000} \\ -6\,4 \\ 60 \\ -56 \\ 40 \\ -40 \\ 0 \end{array}$$

Place the decimal point.
Annex zeros and divide as with whole numbers.

Division ends when the remainder is 0.

So, $\frac{7}{8} = 0.875$.

Method 2 Use a calculator.

7 [÷] 8 [ENTER] 0.875

Using either method, $\frac{7}{8} = 0.875$.

Check Your Progress

Write each fraction as a decimal.

1A. $\frac{4}{5}$ **0.8** **1B.** $\frac{3}{16}$ **0.1875**

Personal Tutor glencoe.com

3-1 Lesson Notes

1 FOCUS

Vertical Alignment

Before Lesson 3-1
Use a number line to graph integers.

Lesson 3-1
Write fractions as terminating or repeating decimals.
Compare fractions and decimals.

After Lesson 3-1
Use positive and negative fractions and decimals to evaluate expressions and solve equations.

2 TEACH

Scaffolding Questions

Have students read the *Why?* section of the lesson and answer the questions.

Ask:

- Why can't $\frac{3}{4}$ be written as tenths? 4 is not a factor of 10.
- Suppose Tara needs $\frac{5}{8}$ pound of tomatoes. Graph $\frac{1}{2}$, $\frac{3}{4}$, and $\frac{5}{8}$ on a number line divided into eighths. Check students' work.
- Will the decimal equivalent for tomatoes be less than or greater than the decimal equivalent for cheese? Less than; $\frac{5}{8}$ is less than $\frac{3}{4}$, so the decimal equivalent for tomatoes is less than that for cheese.

Lesson 3-1 Resources

Resource	Approaching-Level	On-Level	Beyond-Level	English Learners
Teacher Edition	• Differentiated Instruction, p. 122		• Differentiated Instruction, p. 127	• Differentiated Instruction, p. 122
Chapter Resource Masters	• Study Guide and Intervention, pp. 5–6 • Skills Practice, p. 7 • Practice, p. 8 • Word Problem Practice, p. 9 • Spreadsheet Activity, p. 11	• Study Guide and Intervention, pp. 5–6 • Skills Practice, p. 7 • Practice, p. 8 • Word Problem Practice, p. 9 • Enrichment, p. 10 • Spreadsheet Activity, p. 11	• Practice, p. 8 • Word Problem Practice, p. 9 • Enrichment, p. 10 • Spreadsheet Activity, p. 11	• Study Guide and Intervention, pp. 5–6 • Skills Practice, p. 7 • Practice, p. 8 • Spreadsheet Activity, p. 11
Transparencies	• 5-Minute Check Transparency 3-1	• 5-Minute Check Transparency 3-1	• 5-Minute Check Transparency 3-1	• 5-Minute Check Transparency 3-1
Other	• Study Notebook • Teaching Pre-Algebra with Manipulatives	• Study Notebook • Teaching Pre-Algebra with Manipulatives	• Study Notebook	• Study Notebook • Teaching Pre-Algebra with Manipulatives

Write Fractions as Decimals

Examples 1–3 show how to write fractions as terminating decimals or repeating decimals.

 **Formative Assessment**

Use the Check Your Progress exercises after each example to determine students' understanding of concepts.

Additional Examples

 Write $\frac{1}{16}$ as a decimal. 0.0625

 Write each fraction as a decimal. Use a bar to show a repeating decimal.

a. $\frac{6}{11}$ $0.\overline{54}$

b. $-\frac{4}{33}$ $-0.\overline{12}$

Additional Examples also in Interactive Classroom PowerPoint® Presentations

Tips for New Teachers

Terminating Decimals Fractions that have twos, fives, and tens in the denominators always represent terminating decimals.

Vocabulary Link

Terminating
Everyday Use bringing to an end
Math Use a decimal whose digits end

Not all fractions can be written as terminating decimals. Sometimes a digit or group of digits repeats without end in the quotient.

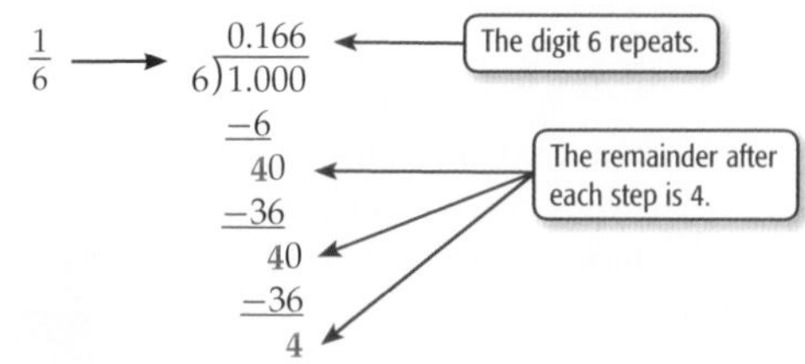

$\frac{1}{6}$ → 6)1.000 = 0.166
−6
40
−36
40
−36
4
The digit 6 repeats.
The remainder after each step is 4.

Check 1 [÷] 6 [ENTER] 0.1666666667 ✓ **The last digit is rounded.**

You can indicate that the digit 6 repeats by annexing dots. So, $\frac{1}{6} = 0.1666666666...$. This decimal is called a repeating decimal.

Repeating decimals have a pattern in their digits that repeats without end. **Bar notation** is a bar or line placed over the digit(s) that repeats. The table shows some examples of repeating decimals and their bar notations.

Decimal	Bar Notation
0.166666...	$0.1\overline{6}$
0.353535...	$0.\overline{35}$
12.6888888...	$12.6\overline{8}$
5.71428571...	$5.\overline{714285}$

Write Fractions as Repeating Decimals

Write each fraction as a decimal. Use a bar to show a repeating decimal.

a. $\frac{5}{12}$

$\frac{5}{12} \rightarrow 12\overline{)5.0000...}$ = 0.4166... **The digit 6 repeats.**

So, $\frac{5}{12} = 0.41\overline{6}$.

b. $-\frac{2}{11}$

$-\frac{2}{11} \rightarrow 11\overline{)2.0000...}$ = 0.1818... **The digits 18 repeat.**

So, $-\frac{2}{11} = -0.\overline{18}$.

Check Your Progress

2A. $-\frac{5}{6}$ **$-0.8\overline{3}$**

2B. $\frac{7}{9}$ **$0.\overline{7}$**

Personal Tutor glencoe.com

It is helpful to memorize these fraction-decimal equivalents.

Concept Summary — **Fraction-Decimal Equivalents** — For Your FOLDABLE

$\frac{1}{2} = 0.5$ $\frac{1}{3} = 0.\overline{3}$ $\frac{1}{4} = 0.25$ $\frac{1}{5} = 0.2$ $\frac{1}{10} = 0.1$ $\frac{1}{100} = 0.01$

$\frac{2}{3} = 0.\overline{6}$ $\frac{3}{4} = 0.75$ $\frac{2}{5} = 0.4$ $\frac{3}{5} = 0.6$ $\frac{4}{5} = 0.8$ $\frac{5}{6} = 0.8\overline{3}$

Differentiated Instruction

AL ELL

 students have difficulty writing fractions as decimals,

 give each student a large index card with a fraction or mixed number on one side. Each student should rewrite the number as a decimal on the back side of the card. Then have students line up in the front of the classroom in order from least value to greatest value.

Real-World Link

The new food pyramid was released in 2005 by the United States Department of Agriculture (USDA). It provides guidelines for a balanced diet by recommending amounts of different foods based on percents of total Calorie intake. Male and female teens should consume 1300 grams of Calcium each day.

Source: USDA

Real-World EXAMPLE 3 Write a Fraction as a Decimal

FOOD According to the USDA, teenage boys should consume an average of 2700 Calories per day. About 360 Calories should come from milk. To the nearest hundredth, what part of a teenage boy's total Calories should come from milk?

Divide the number of Calories that should come from milk, 360, by the number of total Calories, 2700.

360 [÷] 2700 [ENTER] 0.133... or $0.1\overline{3}$

Look at the digit to the right of the thousandths place. Round down since $3 < 5$.

Milk should be 0.13 of the daily Calories consumed by a teenage boy.

Check Your Progress

3. **GOLF** In a recent Masters Tournament, Zach Johnson's first shot landed on the fairway 45 out of 56 times. To the nearest thousandth, what part of the time did his shot land on the fairway? **0.804**

Personal Tutor glencoe.com

Compare Fractions and Decimals It may be easier to compare numbers when they are written as decimals.

EXAMPLE 4 Compare Fractions and Decimals

Replace each ● with <, >, or = to make a true sentence.

a. $\frac{1}{4}$ ● **0.2**

$\frac{1}{4}$ ● 0.2	**Write the sentence.**
0.25 ● 0.20	**Write $\frac{1}{4}$ as a decimal. Annex a zero to 0.2.**
$0.25 > 0.20$	**In the hundredths place, $5 > 0$.**

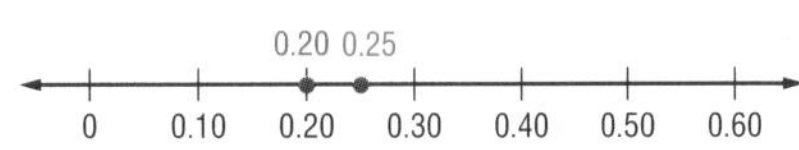

Check Since 0.20 is to the left of 0.25 on the number line, $\frac{1}{4} > 0.2$.

b. $-\frac{5}{8}$ ● $-\frac{6}{9}$

Write the fractions as decimals and then compare the decimals.

$-\frac{5}{8} = -0.625$ $\quad -\frac{6}{9} = -0.666\ldots$ or $-0.\overline{6}$

−0.666... −0.625

−0.68 −0.67 −0.66 −0.65 −0.64 −0.63 −0.62 −0.61

Since −0.625 is to the right of $-0.\overline{6}$ on the number line, $-\frac{5}{8} > -\frac{6}{9}$.

Check Your Progress

4A. $\frac{7}{8}$ ● 0.87 $>$ **4B.** $-\frac{7}{15}$ ● $-\frac{5}{12}$ $<$

Personal Tutor glencoe.com

Additional Example

SOCCER Camille's soccer team won 32 out of 44 games to make it to the championships. To the nearest thousandth, find the team's rate of winning. 0.727

Tips for New Teachers

Dividing To write a mixed number as a decimal, you can express the mixed number as an improper fraction and divide. For example, $3\frac{1}{2} = \frac{7}{2} = 3.5$.

Focus on Mathematical Content

Fractions into Decimals When reading and writing a fraction as a division problem, the problem is read from the numerator to the denominator. The numerator is written as the dividend and the denominator is written as the divisor.

Compare Fractions and Decimals

Examples 4 and 5 show how to compare fractions and decimals. To compare fractions, students can first write each as a decimal.

Additional Example

Replace ● with <, >, or = to make a true sentence.

a. $\frac{13}{20}$ ● 0.7 $<$

b. $-\frac{11}{15}$ ● $-\frac{13}{25}$ $<$

TEACH with TECH

STUDENT RESPONSE SYSTEM Using your SRS software, develop several slides that compare two fractions. For each question, have students respond 1 for <, 2 for >, and 3 for =. Use results to gauge student understanding.

Additional Example

5 **GRADES** Jeremy got a score of $\frac{16}{20}$ on his first quiz and $\frac{20}{25}$ on his second quiz. Which quiz has the higher score? Both quizzes have the same score of 0.80.

3 PRACTICE

Formative Assessment

Use Exercises 1–15 to check for understanding.

Use the table at the bottom of the next page to customize assignments for your students.

Problem-SolvingTip

Use a Graph You can use a graph to visualize data, analyze trends, and make predictions. In this example, you can compare the decimals on a number line.

Real-World EXAMPLE 5 Compare Fractions Using Decimals

FUNDRAISING Thirty out of 36 freshmen and 34 out of 40 sophomores participated in a marathon for charity. Which class had a greater fraction participating in the marathon?

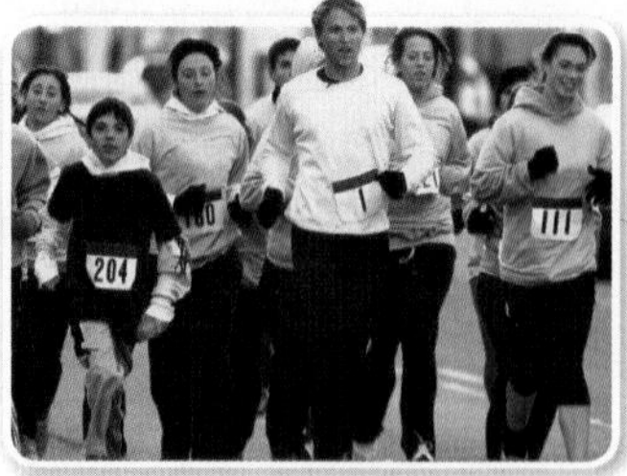

Write each fraction as a decimal. Then compare the decimals.

freshmen: $\frac{30}{36} = 0.8\overline{3}$

sophomores: $\frac{34}{40} = 0.85$

On a number line, $0.8\overline{3}$ is to the left of 0.85. Since $0.8\overline{3} < 0.85$, $\frac{30}{36} < \frac{34}{40}$. So, a greater fraction of sophomores participated in the marathon.

Check Your Progress

5. MOVIES Over the weekend, $\frac{16}{28}$ of the 8th-grade girls and $\frac{19}{30}$ of the 8th-grade boys went to see a new comedy movie. Did a greater fraction of girls or boys see the movie? **boys**

Personal Tutor glencoe.com

Check Your Understanding

Examples 1 and 2 pp. 121–122

Write each fraction as a decimal. Use a bar to show a repeating decimal.

1. $\frac{3}{5}$ **0.6**
2. $\frac{5}{16}$ **0.3125**
3. $-\frac{3}{20}$ **−0.15**
4. $\frac{5}{8}$ **0.625**
5. $-\frac{2}{3}$ $-0.\overline{6}$
6. $-\frac{7}{9}$ $-0.\overline{7}$

Example 3 p. 123

7. **FOOTBALL** In one season, the New England Patriots converted 16 of 20 fourth downs. What part of the time did the Patriots convert on fourth down? **0.8**

Example 4 p. 123

Replace each ● with <, >, or = to make a true sentence.

8. $0.89 ● \frac{11}{13}$ $>$
9. $-\frac{2}{3} ● -\frac{3}{5}$ $<$
10. $-0.21 ● \frac{1}{5}$ $<$
11. $\frac{5}{9} ● \frac{6}{11}$ $>$
12. $-\frac{9}{15} ● -0.61$ $>$
13. $\frac{3}{4} ● \frac{7}{9}$ $<$

Example 5 p. 124

14. **WATER USAGE** Of Nikki's home water usage, $\frac{7}{50}$ comes from lawn watering, and $\frac{3}{20}$ comes from cooking. Does a greater fraction of water usage come from lawn watering or from cooking? **cooking**

15. **SCHOOL** On his first reading test, Tre answered $\frac{26}{30}$ questions correctly. On his second reading test, he answered $\frac{34}{40}$ questions correctly. On which test did Tre have the better score? **test 1**

Practice and Problem Solving

● = **Step-by-Step Solutions** begin on page R11.
Extra Practice begins on page 810.

Examples 1 and 2 pp. 121–122

Write each fraction as a decimal. Use a bar to show a repeating decimal.

16. $\frac{3}{8}$ **0.375**
17. $\frac{7}{20}$ **0.35**
18. $-\frac{8}{25}$ **−0.32**
19. $-\frac{3}{16}$ **−0.1875**
20. $\frac{4}{5}$ **0.8**
21. $\frac{9}{25}$ **0.36**
22. $-\frac{1}{8}$ **−0.125**
23. $-\frac{7}{16}$ **−0.4375**
24. $\frac{3}{11}$ $0.\overline{27}$
25. $\frac{33}{45}$ $0.7\overline{3}$
26. $-\frac{5}{11}$ $-0.\overline{45}$
27. $-\frac{2}{9}$ $-0.\overline{2}$

Example 3 p. 123

28. **BUSINESS** The customer service department resolved 106 of 120 customer complaints in a one-hour time span. To the nearest thousandth, find the resolve rate of the customer service department. **0.883**

29. **HOCKEY** In a recent season, Niklas Backstrom of the Minnesota Wild saved 955 out of 1028 shots on goal. To the nearest thousandth, what part of the time did Backstrom save shots on goal? **0.929**

Example 4 p. 123

Replace each ● with <, >, or = to make a true sentence.

30. $\frac{6}{15}$ ● 0.4 **=**
31. 0.7 ● $\frac{17}{20}$ **<**
32. $\frac{5}{6}$ ● $\frac{7}{8}$ **<**
33. $\frac{5}{7}$ ● $\frac{10}{14}$ **=**
34. $-\frac{2}{9}$ ● $-\frac{1}{4}$ **>**
35. $-\frac{1}{8}$ ● $-\frac{1}{10}$ **<**
36. $0.\overline{6}$ ● $\frac{5}{9}$ **>**
37. $\frac{1}{2}$ ● 0.67 **<**

Example 5 p. 124

WEATHER The graph at the right shows the amount of rain, in inches, that fell in a 5-day period.

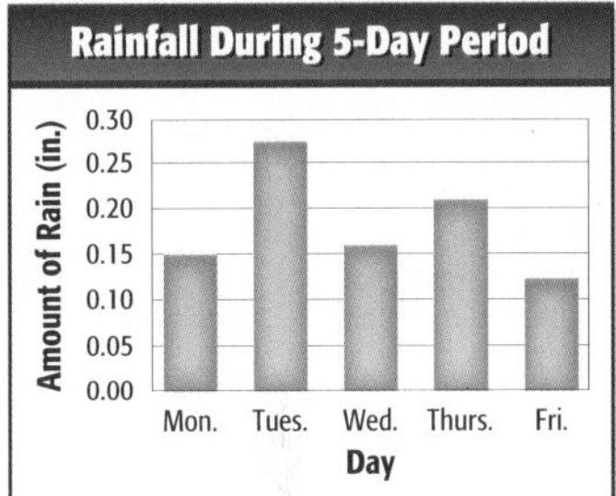

38. On which days did it rain less than one fifth of an inch? **Monday, Wednesday, Friday**
39. Did more or less than one-fourth inch of rain fall on Tuesday? Explain.
40. Suppose it rained $\frac{9}{10}$ inch on Saturday. How does this compare to the previous five days?

39. more than; $\frac{1}{4} = 0.25$ and $0.28 > 0.25$

40. This is less than the amount that fell during the previous 5 days because $\frac{9}{10} = 0.90$ and $0.9 < 0.93$.

B **Replace each ● with <, >, or = to make a true sentence.**

41. $-\frac{5}{13}$ ● $-0.\overline{36}$ **<**
42. $0.\overline{54}$ ● $\frac{6}{11}$ **=**
43. $-5.\overline{42}$ ● $-5\frac{3}{7}$ **>**
44. $-\frac{5}{16}$ ● $-\frac{8}{25}$ **>**
45. −2.2 ● $-2\frac{2}{7}$ **>**
46. $-5\frac{1}{3}$ ● $-5\frac{3}{10}$ **<**

47. **CARPENTRY** A carpenter has some bolts that are marked $\frac{1}{2}$, $\frac{5}{16}$, $\frac{3}{32}$, $\frac{3}{4}$, and $\frac{3}{8}$. If all measurements are in inches, how should these bolts be arranged from least to greatest? $\frac{3}{32}, \frac{5}{16}, \frac{3}{8}, \frac{1}{2}, \frac{3}{4}$

Order each group of numbers from least to greatest.

48. $-0.29, -\frac{3}{11}, -\frac{2}{7}$ $-0.29, -\frac{2}{7}, -\frac{3}{11}$
49. $2\frac{3}{5}, 2.67, 2\frac{2}{3}$ $2\frac{3}{5}, 2\frac{2}{3}, 2.67$
50. $-1.\overline{1}, -1\frac{1}{8}, -1\frac{1}{10}$
51. $\frac{2}{25}, \frac{1}{13}, 0.089$ $\frac{1}{13}, \frac{2}{25}, 0.089$

50. $-1\frac{1}{8}, -1.\overline{1}, -1\frac{1}{10}$

Focus on Mathematical Content

Comparing Fractions to Decimals It is easier to compare fractions and decimals when they are in like formats. Fractions can be written as decimals or as fractions with the same denominator. With practice, students will become familiar with common fractions and decimals and will be able to approximately judge their size. Ask students whether 0.80 or $\frac{3}{4}$ is greater. Students will probably recognize $\frac{3}{4}$ as 0.75, and therefore be able to tell that 0.80 is greater than $\frac{3}{4}$.

Differentiated Homework Options

Level	Assignment	Two-Day Option	
AL Basic	16–40, 59, 62, 64–82	17–39 odd, 65–68	16–40 even, 59, 62, 64, 69–82
OL Core	17–39 odd, 41–51 odd, 52, 53–57 odd, 58–59, 62, 64–82	16–40, 65–68	41–59, 62, 64, 69–82
BL Advanced	41–78 (optional: 79–82)		

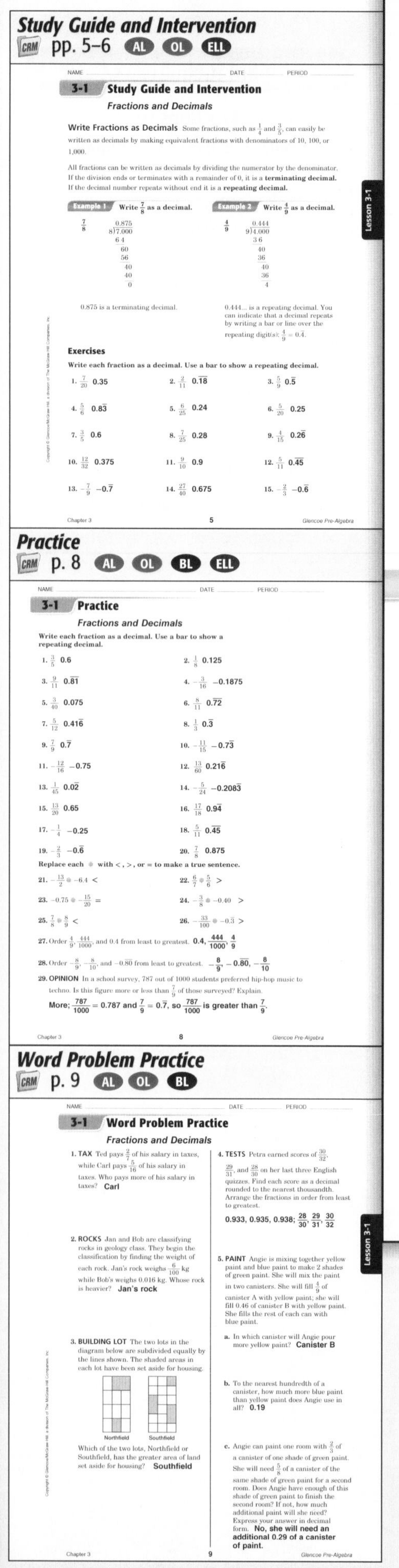

Study Guide and Intervention
CRM pp. 5–6 AL OL ELL

NAME ______ DATE ______ PERIOD ______

3-1 Study Guide and Intervention
Fractions and Decimals

Write Fractions as Decimals Some fractions, such as $\frac{1}{4}$ and $\frac{3}{5}$, can easily be written as decimals by making equivalent fractions with denominators of 10, 100, or 1,000.

All fractions can be written as decimals by dividing the numerator by the denominator. If the division ends or terminates with a remainder of 0, it is a **terminating decimal.** If the decimal number repeats without end it is a **repeating decimal.**

Example 1 Write $\frac{7}{8}$ as a decimal.

$\frac{7}{8}$ → $8\overline{)7.000}$ = 0.875

0.875 is a terminating decimal.

Example 2 Write $\frac{4}{9}$ as a decimal.

$\frac{4}{9}$ → $9\overline{)4.000}$ = 0.444

0.444… is a repeating decimal. You can indicate that a decimal repeats by writing a bar or line over the repeating digit(s): $\frac{4}{9} = 0.\overline{4}$.

Exercises

Write each fraction as a decimal. Use a bar to show a repeating decimal.

1. $\frac{7}{20}$ 0.35
2. $\frac{2}{11}$ $0.\overline{18}$
3. $\frac{5}{9}$ $0.\overline{5}$
4. $\frac{5}{6}$ $0.8\overline{3}$
5. $\frac{6}{25}$ 0.24
6. $\frac{5}{20}$ 0.25
7. $\frac{3}{5}$ 0.6
8. $\frac{7}{25}$ 0.28
9. $\frac{4}{15}$ $0.2\overline{6}$
10. $\frac{12}{32}$ 0.375
11. $\frac{9}{10}$ 0.9
12. $\frac{5}{11}$ $0.\overline{45}$
13. $-\frac{7}{9}$ $-0.\overline{7}$
14. $\frac{27}{40}$ 0.675
15. $-\frac{2}{3}$ $-0.\overline{6}$

Chapter 3 5 Glencoe Pre-Algebra

Practice
CRM p. 8 AL OL BL ELL

NAME ______ DATE ______ PERIOD ______

3-1 Practice
Fractions and Decimals

Write each fraction as a decimal. Use a bar to show a repeating decimal.

1. $\frac{3}{5}$ 0.6
2. $\frac{1}{8}$ 0.125
3. $\frac{9}{11}$ $0.\overline{81}$
4. $-\frac{3}{16}$ −0.1875
5. $\frac{3}{40}$ 0.075
6. $\frac{8}{11}$ $0.\overline{72}$
7. $\frac{5}{12}$ $0.41\overline{6}$
8. $\frac{1}{3}$ $0.\overline{3}$
9. $\frac{7}{9}$ $0.\overline{7}$
10. $-\frac{11}{15}$ $-0.7\overline{3}$
11. $-\frac{12}{16}$ −0.75
12. $\frac{13}{60}$ $0.21\overline{6}$
13. $\frac{1}{45}$ $0.0\overline{2}$
14. $-\frac{5}{24}$ $-0.208\overline{3}$
15. $\frac{13}{20}$ 0.65
16. $\frac{17}{18}$ $0.9\overline{4}$
17. $-\frac{1}{4}$ −0.25
18. $\frac{5}{11}$ $0.\overline{45}$
19. $-\frac{2}{3}$ $-0.\overline{6}$
20. $\frac{7}{8}$ 0.875

Replace each ● with <, >, or = to make a true sentence.

21. $-\frac{13}{2}$ ● −6.4 <
22. $\frac{6}{7}$ ● $\frac{5}{6}$ >
23. −0.75 ● $-\frac{15}{20}$ =
24. $-\frac{3}{8}$ ● −0.40 >
25. $\frac{7}{8}$ ● $\frac{8}{9}$ <
26. $-\frac{33}{100}$ ● $-0.\overline{3}$ >
27. Order $\frac{4}{9}$, $\frac{444}{1000}$, and 0.4 from least to greatest. 0.4, $\frac{444}{1000}$, $\frac{4}{9}$
28. Order $-\frac{8}{9}$, $-\frac{8}{10}$, and −0.80 from least to greatest. $-\frac{8}{9}$, −0.80, $-\frac{8}{10}$
29. **OPINION** In a school survey, 787 out of 1000 students preferred hip-hop music to techno. Is this figure more or less than $\frac{7}{9}$ of those surveyed? Explain. More; $\frac{787}{1000}$ = 0.787 and $\frac{7}{9} = 0.\overline{7}$, so $\frac{787}{1000}$ is greater than $\frac{7}{9}$.

Chapter 3 8 Glencoe Pre-Algebra

Word Problem Practice
CRM p. 9 AL OL BL

NAME ______ DATE ______ PERIOD ______

3-1 Word Problem Practice
Fractions and Decimals

1. **TAX** Ted pays $\frac{2}{9}$ of his salary in taxes, while Carl pays $\frac{5}{16}$ of his salary in taxes. Who pays more of his salary in taxes? Carl

2. **ROCKS** Jan and Bob are classifying rocks in geology class. They begin the classification by finding the weight of each rock. Jan's rock weighs $\frac{6}{100}$ kg while Bob's weighs 0.016 kg. Whose rock is heavier? Jan's rock

3. **BUILDING LOT** The two lots in the diagram below are subdivided equally by the lines shown. The shaded areas in each lot have been set aside for housing.

Northfield Southfield

Which of the two lots, Northfield or Southfield, has the greater area of land set aside for housing? Southfield

4. **TESTS** Petra earned scores of $\frac{30}{32}$, $\frac{29}{31}$, and $\frac{28}{30}$ on her last three English quizzes. Find each score as a decimal rounded to the nearest thousandth. Arrange the fractions in order from least to greatest. 0.933, 0.935, 0.938; $\frac{28}{30}$, $\frac{29}{31}$, $\frac{30}{32}$

5. **PAINT** Angie is mixing together yellow paint and blue paint to make 2 shades of green paint. She will mix the paint in two canisters. She will fill $\frac{4}{9}$ of canister A with yellow paint; she will fill 0.46 of canister B with yellow paint. She fills the rest of each can with blue paint.

a. In which canister will Angie pour more yellow paint? Canister B

b. To the nearest hundredth of a canister, how much more blue paint than yellow paint does Angie use in all? 0.19

c. Angie can paint one room with $\frac{2}{3}$ of a canister of one shade of green paint. She will need $\frac{5}{8}$ of a canister of the same shade of green paint for a second room. Does Angie have enough of this shade of green paint to finish the second room? If not, how much additional paint will she need? Express your answer in decimal form. No, she will need an additional 0.29 of a canister of paint.

Chapter 3 9 Glencoe Pre-Algebra

57. Sample answers:

a. $A: \frac{7}{9}$; $B: \frac{9}{10}$; $C: 1\frac{1}{5}$; $D: 1\frac{3}{10}$; $E: 1\frac{3}{5}$

b. $\frac{7}{9} < \frac{9}{10}$

52. **SOFTBALL** The table shows the number of times at bat and hits that players on Rawson Middle School team had last season. Order the players based on their batting averages from greatest to least. (*Hint:* Divide the number of hits by the number of at bats.) **Jessica, Alma, Kristen, Brooke, Cho**

Player	Hits	At Bats
Kristen	35	47
Cho	51	73
Brooke	36	50
Alma	49	65
Jessica	46	60

Write each decimal using bar notation.

53. 0.99999… $0.\overline{9}$
54. 4.636363… $4.\overline{63}$
55. −10.3444… $-10.3\overline{4}$
56. −22.8151515… $-22.8\overline{15}$

57. **MULTIPLE REPRESENTATIONS** Use the number line shown.

A B C D E; 0.5, 1, 1.5

a. **NUMERICAL** Find a fraction or mixed number that might represent each point on the graph.

b. **ALGEBRAIC** Write an inequality using two of your values.

Real-World Link

Glass beads are one of the most popular forms of jewelry. But, did you know that glass beads have been made for about 9,000 years? They come in all shapes, colors, and finishes.

58. **JEWELRY** The table shows the number of each type of bead on 3 bracelets that Mrs. Fraser made for a craft show. Which bracelet has the greatest fraction of glass beads? the least? **bracelet 1; bracelet 2**

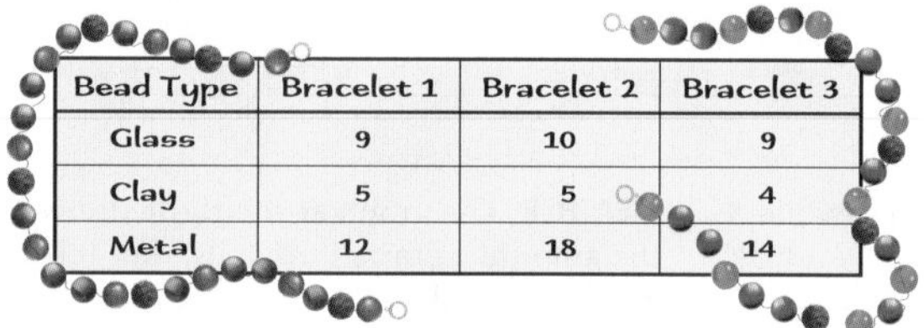

Bead Type	Bracelet 1	Bracelet 2	Bracelet 3
Glass	9	10	9
Clay	5	5	4
Metal	12	18	14

H.O.T. Problems

Use Higher-Order Thinking Skills

59. **OPEN ENDED** Give one example each of real-world situations where it is most appropriate to give a response in fractional form and in decimal form. **See margin.**

60. **CHALLENGE** Are there any rational numbers between $0.\overline{4}$ and $\frac{4}{9}$? Explain.

60. No; $0.\overline{4} = \frac{4}{9}$

61. **CHALLENGE** A *unit fraction* is a fraction that has 1 as its numerator. Write the four greatest unit fractions that are repeating decimals. Write each fraction as a decimal. $\frac{1}{3} = 0.\overline{3}$, $\frac{1}{6} = 0.1\overline{6}$, $\frac{1}{7} = 0.\overline{142857}$, $\frac{1}{9} = 0.\overline{1}$

62–64. See margin.

62. **WRITING IN MATH** Luke is making lasagna that calls for $\frac{4}{5}$ pound of mozzarella cheese. The store only has packages that contain 0.75- and 0.85-pound of mozzarella cheese. Which of the following techniques might Luke use to determine which package to buy? Justify your selection(s). Then use the technique(s) to solve the problem.

mental math	number sense	estimation

63. **CHALLENGE** Write the following fractions as decimals: $\frac{1}{9}$, $\frac{23}{99}$, and $\frac{75}{99}$. Make a conjecture about how to express these kinds of fractions as decimals.

64. **WRITING IN MATH** Explain how 0.5 and $0.\overline{5}$ are different. Which is greater?

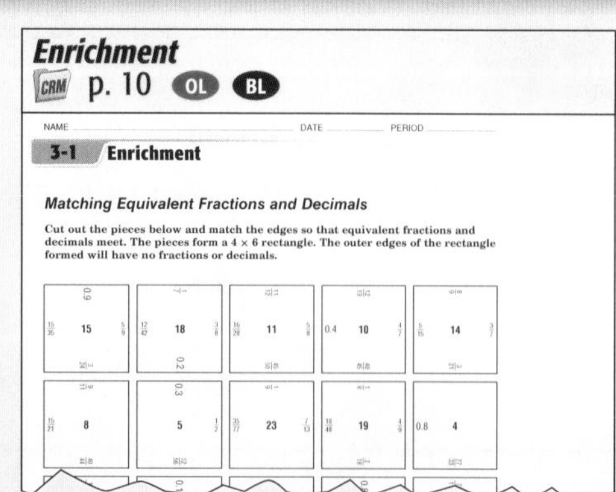

Enrichment
CRM p. 10 OL BL

NAME ______ DATE ______ PERIOD ______

3-1 Enrichment

Matching Equivalent Fractions and Decimals

Cut out the pieces below and match the edges so that equivalent fractions and decimals meet. The pieces form a 4 × 6 rectangle. The outer edges of the rectangle formed will have no fractions or decimals.

Multiple Representations In Exercise 57, students use a number line and an algebraic inequality to compare and order fractions, mixed numbers, and decimals.

Standardized Test Practice

65. Sherman answered $\frac{4}{5}$ of the multiple-choice questions on his science test correctly. Write this fraction as a decimal. **C**

A 0.4

B 0.45

C 0.8

D 4.5

66. Which of the following show the fractions $\frac{2}{5}, \frac{3}{8}, \frac{1}{3}, \frac{1}{2}$, and $\frac{5}{12}$ in order from least to greatest? **H**

F $\frac{1}{3}, \frac{3}{8}, \frac{2}{5}, \frac{1}{2}, \frac{5}{12}$

G $\frac{1}{2}, \frac{1}{3}, \frac{2}{5}, \frac{3}{8}, \frac{5}{12}$

H $\frac{1}{3}, \frac{3}{8}, \frac{2}{5}, \frac{5}{12}, \frac{1}{2}$

J $\frac{1}{2}, \frac{5}{12}, \frac{2}{5}, \frac{3}{8}, \frac{1}{3}$

67. The fraction $\frac{7}{9}$ is found between which pair of fractions on a number line? **B**

A $\frac{3}{5}$ and $\frac{3}{4}$

C $\frac{7}{10}$ and $\frac{3}{4}$

B $\frac{7}{10}$ and $\frac{4}{5}$

D $\frac{3}{5}$ and $\frac{2}{3}$

68. SHORT RESPONSE Which items shown in the table have a recycle rate less than one half? **paper, glass**

Material	Fraction Recycled
Paper	$\frac{5}{11}$
Aluminum Cans	$\frac{5}{8}$
Glass	$\frac{2}{5}$

Spiral Review

Find each product or quotient. (Lessons 2-4 and 2-5)

69. 4(−12)(−5) **240**

70. −2(42)(3) **−252**

71. −54 ÷ (−6) **9**

72. 72 ÷ (−9) **−8**

73. SCUBA DIVING A scuba diver descends from the surface of the lake at a rate of 6 meters per minute. Where will the diver be in relation to the lake's surface after 4 minutes? (Lesson 2-4) **24 m below the surface**

74. EMPLOYMENT The scatter plot shows the years of experience and salaries of twenty people. Does the data show a *positive*, *negative*, or *no* relationship? Explain. (Lesson 1-6) **Positive; as experience increases, salaries increase.**

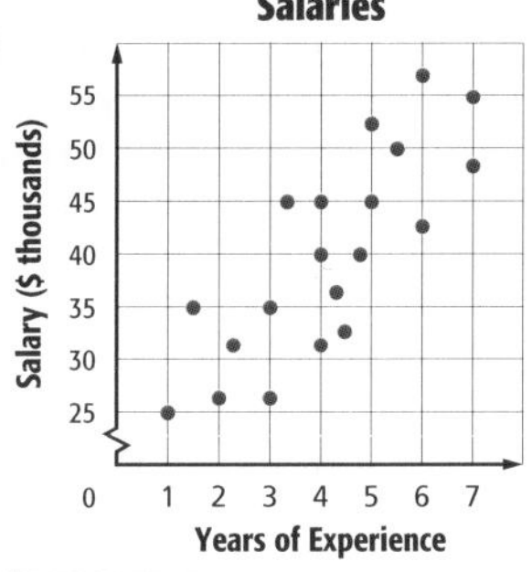

Evaluate each expression if $x = 7$, $y = 3$, and $z = 5$. (Lesson 1-2)

75. $x + y + z$ **15**

76. $4x - z$ **23**

77. $6y - z$ **13**

78. $9x + 8y$ **87**

Skills Review

Write each decimal in word form. (Previous Course)

79. 0.34 **thirty-four hundredths**

80. 5.836 **five and eight hundred, thirty-six thousandths**

81. 0.3 **three-tenths**

82. 2.875 **two and eight hundred seventy-five thousandths**

4 ASSESS

Crystal Ball Have students write a brief statement on how they think today's lesson on writing fractions as decimals will help them with tomorrow's lesson on writing decimals as fractions.

Additional Answers

59. Sample answer: fractional form: customary measurement; decimal form: stock price

62. Mental math: Since $\frac{4}{5} = 0.8$, he should buy the 0.85 = pound package so he'll have enough.

63. $0.\overline{1}$, $0.\overline{23}$, and $0.\overline{75}$. Sample answer: When the denominator is a 9 or 99, the numerator repeats.

64. $0.5 = 0.50$ and $0.\overline{5} = 0.55...$; $0.\overline{5}$ is greater because in the hundredths place, $5 > 0$.

Differentiated Instruction

BL

Extension Students usually find it easier to perform operations on decimals rather than fractions. Ask students to simplify the following expressions first by changing fractions to decimals and round if necessary. Then simplify the same expressions by changing decimals to fractions. Compare the results a. $\frac{1}{3}(1.5 + 5\frac{8}{9})$ b. $3.6(\frac{3}{8} + \frac{1}{6})$ **a.** 2.22; $2\frac{25}{54}$ The mixed number is greater by about 0.24. **b.** 1.95; $1\frac{19}{20}$ They are equal. Discuss the results. What are the advantages and disadvantages of changing fractions to decimals before performing operations? Sample answer: It is easier to do on a calculator, but you do not always get an exact answer. When would you *not* want to change fractions to decimals before performing an operation? Sample answer: when an exact answer is needed

3-2 Lesson Notes

1 FOCUS

Vertical Alignment

Before Lesson 3-2
Identify natural numbers, whole numbers, and integers.

Lesson 3-2
Write rational numbers as fractions.
Identify and classify rational numbers.

After Lesson 3-2
Identify and classify irrational and complex numbers.

2 TEACH

Scaffolding Questions

Have students read the *Why?* section of the lesson and answer the questions.

Ask:

- Is there a way to write an integer, such as 1 tsp. cinnamon, as a fraction? Give an example. Yes; $\frac{3}{3}$ or $\frac{2}{2}$
- Is there a way to write a fraction, such as $\frac{3}{4}$ cup bananas, as an integer? No
- Is there a way to write fractions such as $\frac{-6}{3}$ as an integer? Explain. Yes, $\frac{-6}{3}$ can be divided, or simplified; $\frac{-6}{3} = -2$.

3-2 Rational Numbers

Then
You have already studied natural numbers, whole numbers, and integers. (Lesson 2-1)

Now
- Write rational numbers as fractions.
- Identify and classify rational numbers.

New Vocabulary
rational numbers

Math Online
glencoe.com
- Extra Examples
- Personal Tutor
- Self-Check Quiz
- Homework Help
- Math in Motion

Why?

Mr. Marsh's banana waffle recipe is shown at the right.

a. What measures are written as whole numbers? 2, 1

b. What measures are written as fractions or mixed numbers?

c. Which measures are written as integers? 1, 2

b. $1\frac{3}{4}, \frac{3}{4}, 1\frac{1}{2}, \frac{1}{2}, \frac{1}{4}$

Banana Waffles
2 Servings

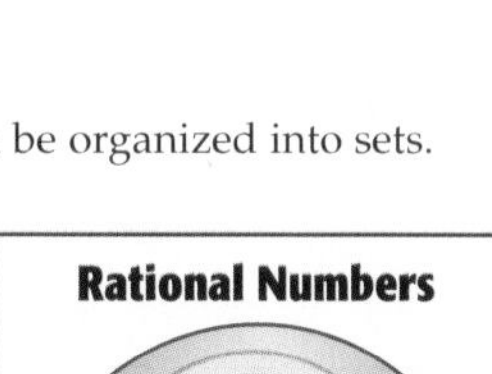

- $1\frac{3}{4}$ cups flour
- $\frac{3}{4}$ cup mashed banana
- 2 egg whites, whipped
- $1\frac{1}{2}$ cups skim milk
- $\frac{1}{2}$ cup applesauce
- 1 teaspoon cinnamon
- 1 teaspoon baking powder
- $\frac{1}{4}$ teaspoon salt

Rational Numbers Numbers like 1, 0, −3, and $1\frac{1}{2}$ can be organized into sets.

When you first learned to count using the numbers 1, 2, 3, ..., you were using members of the set of *natural numbers*, N = {1, 2, 3, ...}.

If you add zero to the set of natural numbers, the result is the set of *whole numbers*, W = {0, 1, 2, 3, ...}.

Whole numbers and their opposites make up the set of *integers*, Z = {..., −3, −2, −1, 0, 1, 2, 3, ...}.

Any number that can be written as a fraction is part of the set of **rational numbers**, Q. Some examples of rational numbers are shown below.

$0.87 \quad -23 \quad \frac{2}{3} \quad -2.\overline{56} \quad 1\frac{1}{2}$

Rational Numbers

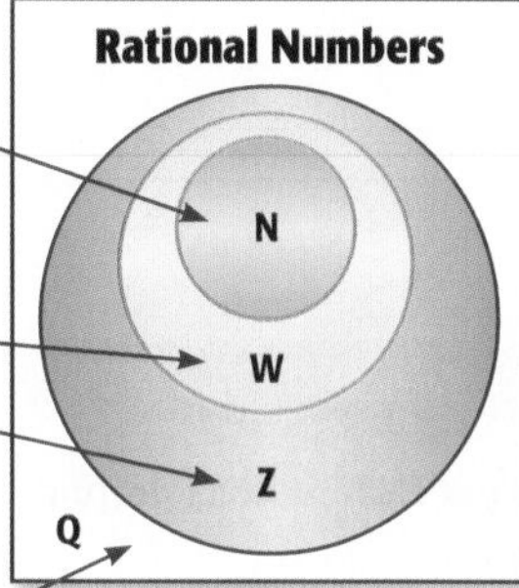

EXAMPLE 1 Write Mixed Numbers and Integers as Fractions

Write each rational number as a fraction.

a. $6\frac{1}{6}$

$6\frac{1}{6} = \frac{37}{6}$ **Write $6\frac{1}{6}$ as an improper fraction.**

b. −23

$-23 = \frac{-23}{1}$ or $-\frac{23}{1}$

Check Your Progress

1A. $4\frac{2}{3}$ $\frac{14}{3}$

1B. 7 $\frac{7}{1}$

Personal Tutor glencoe.com

Fractions, mixed numbers, and integers are all rational numbers. Terminating decimals are also rational numbers because they can be written as a fraction with a denominator of 10, 100, 1000, and so on.

Lesson 3-2 Resources

Resource	Approaching-Level	On-Level	Beyond-Level	English Learners
Teacher Edition		• Differentiated Instruction, p. 129	• Differentiated Instruction, p. 133	
Chapter Resource Masters	• Study Guide and Intervention, pp. 12–13 • Skills Practice, p. 14 • Practice, p. 15 • Word Problem Practice, p. 16	• Study Guide and Intervention, pp. 12–13 • Skills Practice, p. 14 • Practice, p. 15 • Word Problem Practice, p. 16 • Enrichment, p. 17	• Practice, p. 15 • Word Problem Practice, p. 16 • Enrichment, p. 17	• Study Guide and Intervention, pp. 12–13 • Skills Practice, p. 14 • Practice, p. 15
Transparencies	• 5-Minute Check Transparency 3-2	• 5-Minute Check Transparency 3-2	• 5-Minute Check Transparency 3-2	• 5-Minute Check Transparency 3-2
Other	• Study Notebook • Teaching Pre-Algebra with Manipulatives	• Study Notebook • Teaching Pre-Algebra with Manipulatives	• Study Notebook	• Study Notebook • Teaching Pre-Algebra with Manipulatives

ReadingMath

Decimal Point Use the word *and* to represent the decimal point.

- Read 0.625 as *six hundred twenty-five thousandths.*
- Read 20.005 as *twenty and five thousandths.*

Real-World EXAMPLE 2 Write Terminating Decimals as Fractions

a. Write 0.64 as a fraction in simplest form.

$0.64 = \frac{64}{100}$ **0.64 is 64 hundredths.**

$= \frac{16}{25}$ **The GCF of 64 and 100 is 4.**

thousands	hundreds	tens	ones	tenths	hundredths	thousandths	ten-thousandths
0	0	0	0.	6	4	0	0

b. GAMES A handheld video game system weighs 9.675 ounces. Write this decimal as a mixed number in simplest form.

$9.675 = 9\frac{675}{1000}$ **0.675 is 675 thousandths.**

$= 9\frac{27}{40}$ **The GCF of 675 and 1000 is 25.**

thousands	hundreds	tens	ones	tenths	hundredths	thousandths	ten-thousandths
0	0	0	9.	6	7	5	0

Check Your Progress

Write each decimal as a fraction or mixed number in simplest form.

2A. 0.84 $\frac{21}{25}$

2B. 5.875 $5\frac{7}{8}$

2C. MUSIC Rock music accounted for 0.35 of the total music sales in a recent year. Write this decimal as a fraction in simplest form. $\frac{7}{20}$

Personal Tutor glencoe.com

Any repeating decimal can be written as a fraction, so repeating decimals are also rational numbers.

EXAMPLE 3 Write Repeating Decimals as Fractions

Write $0.\overline{6}$ as a fraction in simplest form.

$N = 0.6666...$ **Let N represent the number.**

$10N = 10(0.6666...)$ **Multiply each side by 10 because one digit repeats.**

$10N = 6.666...$

Subtract N from $10N$ to eliminate the repeating part, 0.666...

$10N = 6.666...$

$-N = 0.666...$

$9N = 6$ **$10N - N = 10N - 1N$ or $9N$**

$\frac{9N}{9} = \frac{6}{9}$ **Divide each side by 9.**

$N = \frac{6}{9}$ or $\frac{2}{3}$

Check 6 [÷] 9 [ENTER] 0.666666667 ✓

Check Your Progress

3. Write $0.\overline{42}$ as a fraction in simplest form. $\frac{14}{33}$

Personal Tutor glencoe.com

StudyTip

Repeating Decimals When *two* digits repeat, multiply each side by 100. Then subtract *N* from 100*N* to eliminate the repeating part.

Lesson 3-2 Rational Numbers 129

Rational Numbers

Examples 1–3 show how to write rational numbers as fractions and mixed numbers in simplest form.

Formative Assessment

Use the Check Your Progress exercises after each example to determine students' understanding of concepts.

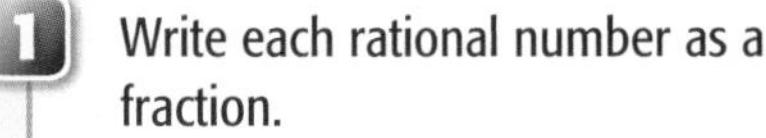

Additional Examples

1 Write each rational number as a fraction.

a. $-4\frac{3}{8}$ $-\frac{35}{8}$

b. 10 $\frac{10}{1}$

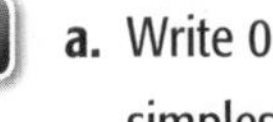

2 **a.** Write 0.26 as a fraction in simplest form. $\frac{13}{50}$

b. SHIPPING The shipping weight of a package is 2.875 pounds. Write this decimal as a mixed number in simplest form. $2\frac{7}{8}$

3 Write $0.\overline{39}$ as a fraction in simplest form. $\frac{13}{33}$

Additional Examples also in Interactive Classroom PowerPoint® Presentations

IWB INTERACTIVE WHITEBOARD READY

Differentiated Instruction

students need additional practice in identifying rational numbers,

display the Venn diagram shown on the first page of this lesson. Invite a student to come forward to place a number on the diagram. The class can assist in identifying all the sets to which the number belongs. Continue inviting students forward until each section has at least two examples.

Identify and Classify Rational Numbers

Example 4 shows how to classify numbers as rational numbers, integers, and/or whole numbers.

Additional Example

Identify all sets to which each number belongs.

a. $7\frac{1}{8}$ rational

b. 1.414213562... irrational

c. 15 whole number, integer, and rational

Focus on Mathematical Content

Complex Number System The complex number system is made up of real and imaginary numbers. Real numbers are then classified as rational or irrational.

TEACH with TECH

WIKI On a secure class wiki, have a student post a repeating decimal. All other students should add examples and comments about repeating decimals.

3 PRACTICE

Formative Assessment

Use Exercises 1–10 to check for understanding.

Use the chart at the bottom of the next page to customize assignments for your students.

ReadingMath

Ratios Rational comes from the word ratio. A *ratio* is the comparison of two quantities by division.
Recall that $\frac{a}{b} = a \div b$, where $b \neq 0$.

Identify and Classify Rational Numbers All rational numbers can be written as terminating or repeating decimals. Decimals that neither terminate nor repeat, such as the numbers below, are called *irrational numbers*. ***You will learn more about irrational numbers in Chapter 10.***

$\pi = 3.141592...$ → **The digits do not repeat.**

$8.787787778...$ → **The same block of digits does not repeat.**

Concept Summary — Rational Numbers

For Your FOLDABLE

A rational number is any number that can be expressed as the quotient $\frac{a}{b}$, where a and b are integers and $b \neq 0$.

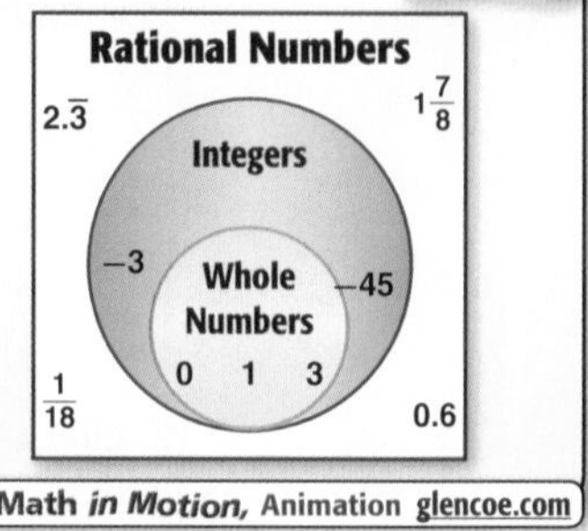

Math *in Motion*, Animation glencoe.com

EXAMPLE 4 Classify Numbers

Identify all sets to which each number belongs.

a. $-2\frac{6}{11}$

Since $-2\frac{6}{11}$ can be written as $-\frac{28}{11}$, it is rational.

b. 1.313313331...

This is a nonterminating and nonrepeating decimal. So, it is irrational.

c. 45

45 is a whole number, an integer, and a rational number.

Check Your Progress

5A. 0 whole, integers, rational **5B.** $1\frac{4}{5}$ rational **5C.** 1.414213562... irrational

Personal Tutor glencoe.com

Check Your Understanding

Example 1 p. 128 — **Write each number as a fraction.**

1. $3\frac{3}{4}$ $\frac{15}{4}$ **2.** -9 $-\frac{9}{1}$ **3.** $-1\frac{3}{4}$ $-\frac{7}{4}$

Examples 2 and 3 p. 129 — **Write each decimal as a fraction or mixed number in simplest form.**

4. 0.07 $\frac{7}{100}$ **5.** $-3.\overline{85}$ $-3\frac{85}{99}$ **6.** $0.\overline{78}$ $\frac{26}{33}$

7. MEASUREMENT There are approximately 2.54 centimeters in 1 inch. Express 2.54 as a mixed number. 7. $2\frac{27}{50}$

Example 4 p. 130 — **Identify all sets to which each number belongs.**

8. −632 integer, rational **9.** $0.\overline{56}$ rational **10.** 21 whole, integer, rational

Practice and Problem Solving

● = Step-by-Step Solutions begin on page R11.
Extra Practice begins on page 810.

Example 1 p. 128

Write each number as a fraction.

11. $1\frac{5}{6}$ $\frac{11}{6}$ **12.** -12 $-\frac{12}{1}$ **13.** $-10\frac{7}{8}$ $-\frac{87}{8}$ **14.** 49 $\frac{49}{1}$

Example 2 p. 129

Write each decimal as a fraction or mixed number in simplest form.

15. 3.625 $3\frac{5}{8}$ **16.** 0.55 $\frac{11}{20}$ **17.** -5.36 $-5\frac{9}{25}$

18. -0.265 $-\frac{53}{200}$ **19.** -1.3 $-1\frac{3}{10}$ **20.** 0.9 $\frac{9}{10}$

Example 2 p. 129

21. **FINANCIAL LITERACY** Recently, one U.S. dollar was equal to 0.506 British pounds. Express 0.506 as a fraction. $\frac{253}{500}$

22. **POPULATION** The estimated portions for various age groups of the population for 2010 are shown in the table.

a. Find the fraction of the population that is 19 years of age or younger. $\frac{27}{100}$

b. Find the fraction of the population that is 20 to 64 years of age. $\frac{3}{5}$

Age Group	Portion of Population
19 years and under	0.27
20 to 64 years	0.60
65 years and over	0.13

Source: United States Census Bureau

Example 3 p. 129

Write each decimal as a fraction or mixed number in simplest form.

23. $-2.\overline{5}$ $-2\frac{5}{9}$ **24.** $0.\overline{36}$ $\frac{4}{11}$ **25.** 0.161616... $\frac{16}{99}$

26. $9.\overline{27}$ $9\frac{3}{11}$ **27.** $-0.\overline{09}$ $-\frac{1}{11}$ **28.** $-10.\overline{74}$ $-10\frac{74}{99}$

Example 4 p. 130

Identify all sets to which each number belongs.

29. -8 integer, rational **30.** 14 whole, integer, rational **31.** 9.23 rational

32. $1\frac{5}{9}$ rational **33.** 0.323322333... irrational **34.** 3.141516... irrational

35. Yes; $\frac{5}{8} = 0.625$ and $0.625 > 0.6$, so the bead will fit.

35. **JEWELRY** Maria has a bead that is 0.6 inch long. She wants to use the bead to fill a space that is $\frac{5}{8}$ inch long. Will the bead fit? Explain.

36. **FOOD** All of the Calories in one cup of milk come from fat, protein, and carbohydrates. Use the table to find the fraction of Calories that comes from protein. Write the fraction in simplest form. $\frac{11}{25}$

Nutrient	Decimal Part of Calories
Fat	0.03
Protein	■
Carbohydrates	0.53

Source: *Nutrition Data*

Replace each ● with <, >, or = to make a true sentence.

37. -0.23 ● -0.3 $>$ **38.** $\frac{8}{9}$ ● 0.888... $=$ **39.** 0.714 ● $\frac{5}{7}$ $<$

40. $-1\frac{1}{11}$ ● -0.9 $<$ **41.** $4.\overline{63}$ ● $4\frac{5}{8}$ $>$ **42.** $-5.\overline{3}$ ● 5.333... $<$

Write each decimal as a fraction or mixed number in simplest form.

43. $0.\overline{652}$ $\frac{652}{999}$ **44.** $0.1\overline{8}$ $\frac{17}{90}$ **45.** $0.72\overline{4}$ $\frac{163}{225}$

46. $3.5\overline{96}$ $3\frac{197}{330}$ **47.** $9.2\overline{43}$ $9\frac{241}{990}$ **48.** $0.24\overline{67}$ $\frac{2443}{9900}$

Focus on Mathematical Content

Rational Numbers Rational numbers include all real numbers except for those that are non-terminating and non-repeating decimals, because these cannot be written as fractions. The sum of a rational number, such as $-0.\overline{3}$, plus an irrational number, such as 4.232232223…, is an irrational number.

Differentiated Homework Options

Level	Assignment	Two-Day Option	
AL Basic	11–34, 56–57, 59–79	11–33 odd, 61–64	12–34 even, 56–57, 59–60, 65–79
OL Core	11–33 odd, 35–36, 37–49 odd, 50, 51–55 odd, 56–57, 59–79	11–34, 61–64	35–57, 60, 65–79
BL Advanced	35–75 (optional: 76–79)		

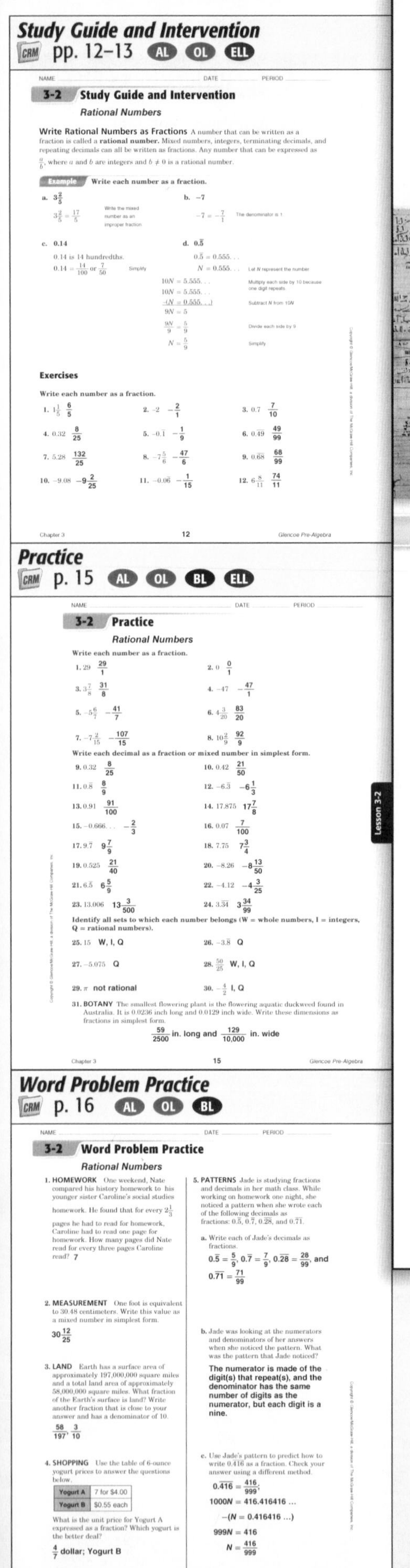

Study Guide and Intervention
CRM pp. 12–13 AL OL ELL

NAME ______ DATE ______ PERIOD ______

3-2 Study Guide and Intervention

Rational Numbers

Write Rational Numbers as Fractions A number that can be written as a fraction is called a **rational number**. Mixed numbers, integers, terminating decimals, and repeating decimals can all be written as fractions. Any number that can be expressed as $\frac{a}{b}$, where a and b are integers and $b \neq 0$ is a rational number.

Example Write each number as a fraction.

a. $3\frac{2}{5}$ — $3\frac{2}{5} = \frac{17}{5}$ Write the mixed number as an improper fraction.

b. -7 — $-7 = -\frac{7}{1}$ The denominator is 1.

c. 0.14 — 0.14 is 14 hundredths. $0.14 = \frac{14}{100}$ or $\frac{7}{50}$ Simplify.

d. $0.\overline{5}$ — $0.\overline{5} = 0.555\ldots$; $N = 0.555\ldots$ Let N represent the number. $10N = 5.555\ldots$ Multiply each side by 10 because one digit repeats. $10N = 5.555\ldots$; $-(N = 0.555\ldots)$ Subtract N from $10N$. $9N = 5$; $\frac{9N}{9} = \frac{5}{9}$ Divide each side by 9. $N = \frac{5}{9}$ Simplify.

Exercises

Write each number as a fraction.

1. $1\frac{1}{5}$ $\frac{6}{5}$
2. -2 $-\frac{2}{1}$
3. 0.7 $\frac{7}{10}$
4. 0.32 $\frac{8}{25}$
5. $-0.\overline{1}$ $-\frac{1}{9}$
6. $0.\overline{49}$ $\frac{49}{99}$
7. 5.28 $\frac{132}{25}$
8. $-7\frac{5}{6}$ $-\frac{47}{6}$
9. $0.\overline{68}$ $\frac{68}{99}$
10. -9.08 $-9\frac{2}{25}$
11. $-0.0\overline{6}$ $-\frac{1}{15}$
12. $6\frac{8}{11}$ $\frac{74}{11}$

Chapter 3 — 12 — Glencoe Pre-Algebra

Practice
CRM p. 15 AL OL BL ELL

NAME ______ DATE ______ PERIOD ______

3-2 Practice

Rational Numbers

Write each number as a fraction.

1. 29 $\frac{29}{1}$
2. 0 $\frac{0}{1}$
3. $3\frac{7}{8}$ $\frac{31}{8}$
4. -47 $-\frac{47}{1}$
5. $-5\frac{6}{7}$ $-\frac{41}{7}$
6. $4\frac{3}{20}$ $\frac{83}{20}$
7. $-7\frac{2}{15}$ $-\frac{107}{15}$
8. $10\frac{2}{9}$ $\frac{92}{9}$

Write each decimal as a fraction or mixed number in simplest form.

9. 0.32 $\frac{8}{25}$
10. 0.42 $\frac{21}{50}$
11. $0.\overline{8}$ $\frac{8}{9}$
12. $-6.\overline{3}$ $-6\frac{1}{3}$
13. 0.91 $\frac{91}{100}$
14. 17.875 $17\frac{7}{8}$
15. $-0.666\ldots$ $-\frac{2}{3}$
16. 0.07 $\frac{7}{100}$
17. $9.\overline{7}$ $9\frac{7}{9}$
18. 7.75 $7\frac{3}{4}$
19. 0.525 $\frac{21}{40}$
20. -8.26 $-8\frac{13}{50}$
21. $6.\overline{5}$ $6\frac{5}{9}$
22. -4.12 $-4\frac{3}{25}$
23. 13.006 $13\frac{3}{500}$
24. $3.\overline{34}$ $3\frac{34}{99}$

Identify all sets to which each number belongs (W = whole numbers, I = integers, Q = rational numbers).

25. 15 W, I, Q
26. $-3.\overline{8}$ Q
27. -5.075 Q
28. $\frac{50}{25}$ W, I, Q
29. π not rational
30. $-\frac{4}{2}$ I, Q

31. **BOTANY** The smallest flowering plant is the flowering aquatic duckweed found in Australia. It is 0.0236 inch long and 0.0129 inch wide. Write these dimensions as fractions in simplest form. $\frac{59}{2500}$ in. long and $\frac{129}{10{,}000}$ in. wide

Chapter 3 — 15 — Glencoe Pre-Algebra

Word Problem Practice
CRM p. 16 AL OL BL

NAME ______ DATE ______ PERIOD ______

3-2 Word Problem Practice

Rational Numbers

1. **HOMEWORK** One weekend, Nate compared his history homework to his younger sister Caroline's social studies homework. He found that for every $2\frac{1}{3}$ pages he had to read for homework, Caroline had to read one page for homework. How many pages did Nate read for every three pages Caroline read? 7

2. **MEASUREMENT** One foot is equivalent to 30.48 centimeters. Write this value as a mixed number in simplest form. $30\frac{12}{25}$

3. **LAND** Earth has a surface area of approximately 197,000,000 square miles and a total land area of approximately 58,000,000 square miles. What fraction of the Earth's surface is land? Write another fraction that is close to your answer and has a denominator of 10. $\frac{58}{197}$; $\frac{3}{10}$

4. **SHOPPING** Use the table of 6-ounce yogurt prices to answer the questions below.

Yogurt A	7 for $4.00
Yogurt B	$0.55 each

What is the unit price for Yogurt A expressed as a fraction? Which yogurt is the better deal? $\frac{4}{7}$ dollar; Yogurt B

5. **PATTERNS** Jade is studying fractions and decimals in her math class. While working on homework one night, she noticed a pattern when she wrote each of the following decimals as fractions: $0.\overline{5}$, $0.\overline{7}$, $0.\overline{28}$, and $0.\overline{71}$.

a. Write each of Jade's decimals as fractions. $0.\overline{5} = \frac{5}{9}$, $0.\overline{7} = \frac{7}{9}$, $0.\overline{28} = \frac{28}{99}$, and $0.\overline{71} = \frac{71}{99}$

b. Jade was looking at the numerators and denominators of her answers when she noticed the pattern. What was the pattern that Jade noticed? The numerator is made of the digit(s) that repeat(s), and the denominator has the same number of digits as the numerator, but each digit is a nine.

c. Use Jade's pattern to predict how to write $0.\overline{416}$ as a fraction. Check your answer using a different method. $0.\overline{416} = \frac{416}{999}$; $1000N = 416.416416\ldots$; $-(N = 0.416416\ldots)$; $999N = 416$; $N = \frac{416}{999}$

Chapter 3 — 16 — Glencoe Pre-Algebra

49c. Sample answer: If the diameter is a multiple of 7, use $\frac{22}{7}$. Otherwise, use 3.14.

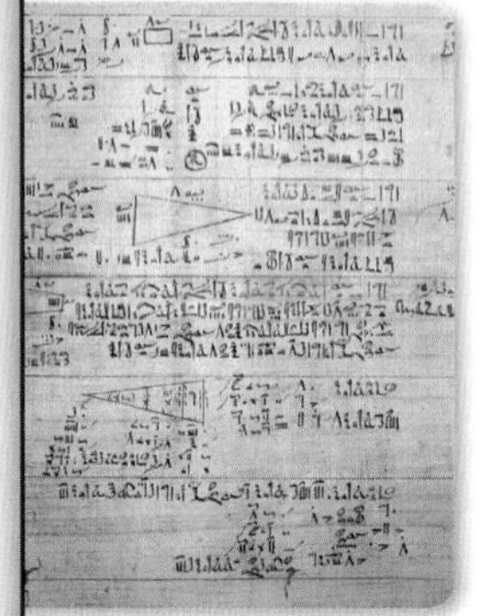

Math History Link

Rhind or Ahmes Papyrus (c1600 B.C.)
The Rhind Papyrus is the chief source of information on Egyptian mathematics. It was originally written by the Egyptian, Ahmes, around 1600 B.C. and contains 15 problems that show the first references to Egyptians using fractions.

C

51. $-3.4\overline{2}$, -3.4, $3\frac{4}{11}$, 3.38

53. -1.95, $-1\frac{13}{14}$, -1.9, $-1\frac{9}{11}$

60. Sample answer: In the real world, repeating decimals are usually rounded to the nearest tenth or hundredth. For example, money is rounded to the nearest hundredth.

49. **MULTIPLE REPRESENTATIONS** Pi (π) is a nonrepeating, nonterminating decimal. Two common estimates for pi are 3.14 and $\frac{22}{7}$.
    a. **GRAPHICAL** Use a calculator to find the value of π to seven decimal places. Then graph the three values on a number line. **See margin.**
    b. **SYMBOLIC** Write an inequality comparing the values. $3.14 < \pi < \frac{22}{7}$
    c. **VERBAL** To find the circumference of a circle, you multiply pi by the diameter d of the circle. Explain when you might use 3.14 to find the circumference and when you might use $\frac{22}{7}$ to find the circumference.

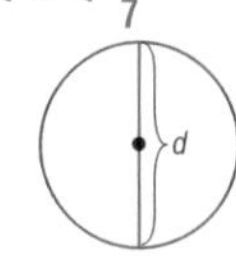

50. **HISTORY** The mathematician Archimedes believed that π was between $3\frac{1}{7}$ and $3\frac{10}{71}$. **a–b. See margin.**
    a. Express each mixed number as a decimal rounded to the nearest thousandth. Was Archimedes' theory correct? Explain.
    b. The Rhind Papyrus records that the Egyptians used $\frac{256}{81}$ for π. Express the fraction as a decimal rounded to the nearest thousandth. Which value is closer to the actual value of π, Arcihimedes' or the Egyptians' value?

Order each set of rational numbers from least to greatest.

51. -3.4, $3\frac{4}{11}$, $-3.4\overline{2}$, 3.38

52. $\frac{1}{3}$, $0.1\overline{3}$, $\frac{5}{13}$, 0.32 **$0.\overline{13}$, 0.32, $\frac{1}{3}$, $\frac{5}{13}$**

53. $-1\frac{13}{14}$, -1.9, $-1\frac{9}{11}$, -1.95

54. $9\frac{4}{5}$, $9.\overline{79}$, $9\frac{11}{13}$, 9.82 **$9.\overline{79}$, $9\frac{4}{5}$, 9.82, $9\frac{11}{13}$**

55. **ANIMALS** A lion's speed is $\frac{5}{7}$ the speed of a cheetah. Find the least rational number with a denominator of 9 that is greater than $\frac{5}{7}$. Find the greatest rational number with a denominator of 8 that is less than $\frac{5}{7}$. Write an inequality comparing the three numbers. **$\frac{7}{9}$; $\frac{5}{8}$; $\frac{5}{8} < \frac{5}{7} < \frac{7}{9}$**

H.O.T. Problems
Use Higher-Order Thinking Skills **56–58. See margin.**

56. **OPEN ENDED** Choose a repeating decimal in which three digits repeat. Write the number as a fraction or mixed number in simplest form.

57. **WRITING IN MATH** Explain why $0.\overline{76}$ is greater than 0.76.

58. **CHALLENGE** Antonio stated that $0.\overline{9} = 1$. Show that he is correct.

59. **REASONING** Determine whether the following statements are *true* or *false*. If true, explain your reasoning. If false, give a counterexample. **See Chapter 3 Answer Appendix.**
    a. All integers are rational numbers.
    b. All whole numbers are integers.
    c. A rational number is always an integer.
    d. All natural numbers are rational.

60. **WRITING IN MATH** How are repeating decimals usually represented in real-world situations? Give an example to explain your reasoning.

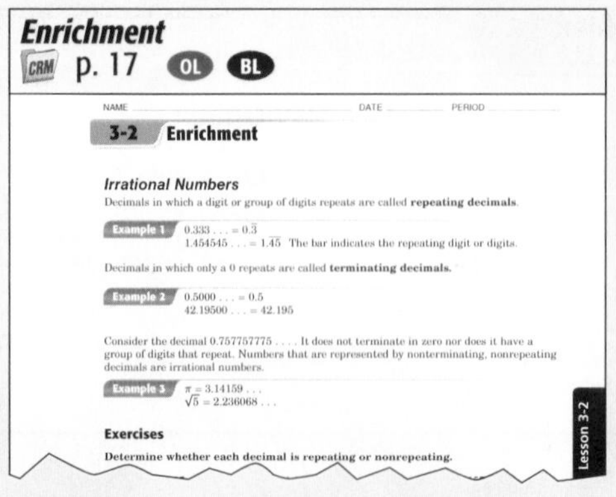

Enrichment
CRM p. 17 OL BL

NAME ______ DATE ______ PERIOD ______

3-2 Enrichment

Irrational Numbers

Decimals in which a digit or group of digits repeats are called **repeating decimals**.

Example 1 $0.333\ldots = 0.\overline{3}$; $1.454545\ldots = 1.\overline{45}$ The bar indicates the repeating digit or digits.

Decimals in which only a 0 repeats are called **terminating decimals**.

Example 2 $0.5000\ldots = 0.5$; $42.19500\ldots = 42.195$

Consider the decimal 0.757757775… It does not terminate in zero nor does it have a group of digits that repeat. Numbers that are represented by nonterminating, nonrepeating decimals are irrational numbers.

Example 3 $\pi = 3.14159\ldots$; $\sqrt{5} = 2.236068\ldots$

Exercises

Determine whether each decimal is repeating or nonrepeating.

Multiple Representations In Exercise 49, students use a calculator, a graph, an inequality, and verbal explanations to estimate the value of pi to different levels of precision.

Standardized Test Practice

61. Which fraction is between 0.12 and 0.15? **B**

A $\frac{3}{25}$ C $\frac{3}{20}$

B $\frac{1}{8}$ D $\frac{1}{5}$

62. Which of the following is *not* a rational number? **J**

F $\frac{4}{9}$ H $0.\overline{62}$

G −4.27 J −3.131131113...

63. Last football season, Jason made 0.85 of his field goal attempts. Write this decimal as a fraction in simplest form. **C**

A $\frac{85}{100}$ C $\frac{17}{20}$

B $\frac{20}{17}$ D $\frac{100}{85}$

64. EXTENDED RESPONSE The table shows the results of a survey about how students get to school.

Method of Transportation	Portion of Students
bus	0.40
walk	0.18
car	0.36
bicycle	0.04
other	0.02

a. Write each decimal in the table as a fraction in simplest form. **See margin.**

b. List the methods of transportation in order from least to greatest.

c. Which method of transportation do most students use to get to school? **bus**

64b. other, bicycle, walk, car, bus

Spiral Review

Write each fraction as a decimal. Use a bar to show a repeating decimal. (Lesson 3-1)

65. $-\frac{5}{8}$ **−0.625** **66.** $\frac{1}{6}$ **$0.1\overline{6}$** **67.** $-\frac{2}{10}$ **−0.2** **68.** $\frac{4}{7}$ **$0.\overline{571428}$**

Graph the figure at the right and its image after the transformation indicated. (Lesson 2-7) **69–72. See Chapter 3 Answer Appendix.**

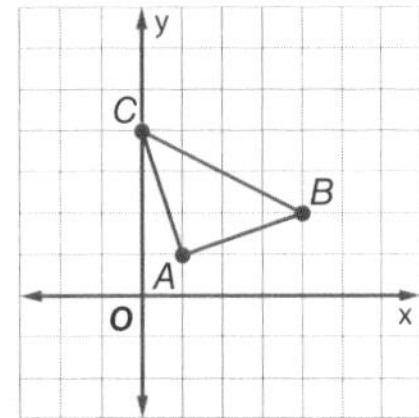

69. translation 3 units down and 2 units left

70. translation 4 units up and 1 unit right

71. reflection across the x-axis

72. reflection across the y-axis

State the domain and range for each relation.

73. {(0, 0), (3, 2), (4, 6), (8, 12)}. (Lesson 1-4)
D = {0, 3, 4, 8}; R = {0, 2, 6, 12}

74. {(1, 2), (3, 4), (5, 6), (7, 8)}.
D = {1, 3, 5, 7}; R = {2, 4, 6, 8}

75. Mount Kilimanjaro's altitude is 5895 meters. Lake Assal's altitude is −155 meters. Find the difference between these altitudes. (Lesson 2-3) **6050 m**

Skills Review

Find each product. (Lesson 2-4)

76. −6(−12) **72** **77.** 15(−3)(−4)(0) **0** **78.** −3(5)(−9) **135** **79.** 14(−20) **−280**

Differentiated Instruction

Extension Write $0.\overline{35}$ and $0.\overline{125}$ as fractions. What can you conclude? Students should conclude that the fraction for a repeating decimal has the repeating digits in the numerator and 9s in the denominator. The number of 9s in the denominator is the same as the number of repeating digits.

4 ASSESS

Name the Math Instruct students to write an explanation about what they have learned about rational numbers today. Tell them to use mathematical terminology to describe how to classify rational numbers.

Formative Assessment

Check for student understanding of concepts in Lessons 3-1 and 3-2.

CRM Quiz 1, p. 46

Additional Answers

49a. 3.1415927

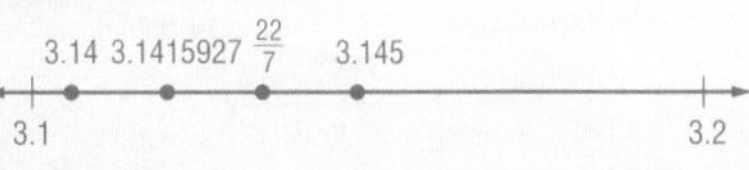

50a. $3\frac{1}{7} \approx 3.143$, $3\frac{10}{71} \approx 3.141$; yes; Sample answer: Since 3.143 > 3.1415927... > 3.141, pi is between the two values and his theory was correct.

50b. $\frac{256}{81} \approx 3.160$;

Archimedes' value is closer than the Egyptians.

56. Sample answer: $0.\overline{231}$

$$1000N = 231.231...$$
$$-N = 0.231$$
$$999N = 231$$
$$\frac{999N}{999} = \frac{231}{999}$$
$$N = \frac{231}{999}$$

57. Sample answer: Since $0.\overline{76} = 0.76767676...$ and $0.76 = 0.76000000...$, $0.\overline{76}$ is greater than 0.76.

58. Let $N = 0.999...$ and let

$$10N = 10(0.999...)$$
$$-(N = 0.999...)$$
$$9N = 9$$
$$\frac{9N}{9} = \frac{9}{9}$$
$$N = 1$$

64a. bus: $\frac{2}{5}$; walk: $\frac{9}{50}$; car: $\frac{9}{25}$; bicycle: $\frac{1}{25}$; other: $\frac{1}{50}$

3-3 Lesson Notes

1 FOCUS

Vertical Alignment

Before Lesson 3-3
Multiply positive fractions.

Lesson 3-3
Multiply positive and negative fractions.
Evaluate algebraic expressions with fractions.

After Lesson 3-3
Solve equations involving fractions.

2 TEACH

Scaffolding Questions

Have students read the *Why?* section of the lesson and answer the questions.

Ask:

- What is the product of **c** in simplest form? $\frac{3}{10}$
- When using area models to find the product of two fractions, does it matter which fraction is shaded first? No
- When multiplying fractions, does it matter which fraction you multiply first? No, the result is the same regardless of which fraction is multiplied first.

3-3 Multiplying Rational Numbers

Then
You have already multiplied positive fractions.
(Previous Course)

Now
- Multiply positive and negative fractions.
- Evaluate algebraic expressions with fractions.

Math Online
glencoe.com
- Extra Examples
- Personal Tutor
- Self-Check Quiz
- Homework Help

Why?

The students in Genoa Middle School were surveyed about their favorite school lunch. One half of the students chose pizza. Of those students, one third chose plain cheese. What part of the students in the school chose plain cheese pizza as their favorite?

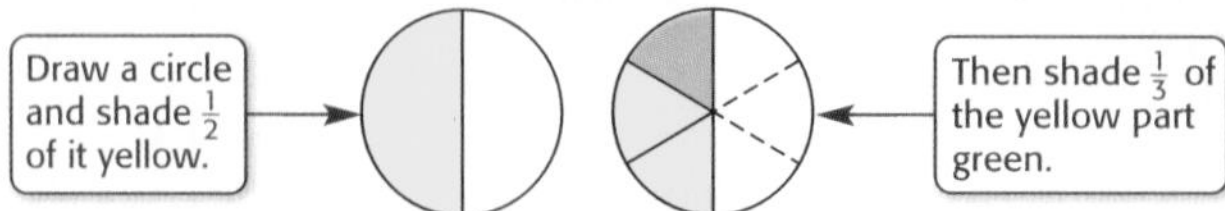

Draw a circle and shade $\frac{1}{2}$ of it yellow.
Then shade $\frac{1}{3}$ of the yellow part green.

The green area represents the product of $\frac{1}{3}$ and $\frac{1}{2}$. One sixth of the circle is shaded green. So $\frac{1}{3} \times \frac{1}{2} = \frac{1}{6}$. One sixth of the students chose plain cheese.

Use an area model to find each product. a–c. See margin for models.

a. $\frac{1}{2} \cdot \frac{1}{4}$ $\frac{1}{8}$ b. $\frac{1}{3} \cdot \frac{1}{3}$ $\frac{1}{9}$ c. $\frac{2}{5} \cdot \frac{3}{4}$ $\frac{6}{20}$

d. **MAKE A CONJECTURE** What is the relationship between the numerators and denominators of the factors and the numerator and denominator of the product?

d. The numerator of the product equals the product of the factors' numerators. The denominator of the product equals the product of the factors' denominator.

Multiply Fractions These models suggest a rule for multiplying fractions.

Key Concept Multiplying Fractions

For Your FOLDABLE 

Words To multiply fractions, multiply the numerators and multiply the denominators.

Symbols $\frac{a}{b} \cdot \frac{c}{d} = \frac{a \cdot c}{b \cdot d}$, where $b, d \neq 0$

Example $\frac{3}{4} \cdot \frac{1}{2} = \frac{3 \cdot 1}{4 \cdot 2}$ or $\frac{3}{8}$

EXAMPLE 1 Multiply Fractions

Find $\frac{1}{6} \cdot \frac{2}{3}$. Write the product in simplest form.

$\frac{1}{6} \cdot \frac{2}{3} = \frac{1 \cdot 2}{6 \cdot 3}$ ← Multiply the numerators. ← Multiply the denominators.

$= \frac{2}{18}$ or $\frac{1}{9}$ Simplify. The GCF of 2 and 18 is 2.

Check Your Progress

Find each product. Write in simplest form.

1A. $\frac{1}{2} \cdot \frac{4}{10}$ $\frac{1}{5}$ 1B. $\frac{5}{12} \cdot \frac{6}{10}$ $\frac{1}{4}$

Personal Tutor glencoe.com

Lesson 3-3 Resources

Resource	Approaching-Level	On-Level	Beyond-Level	English Learners
Teacher Edition	• Differentiated Instruction, p. 136	• Differentiated Instruction, p. 136	• Differentiated Instruction, p. 139	• Differentiated Instruction, p. 136
Chapter 3 Resource Masters	• Study Guide and Intervention, pp. 18–19 • Skills Practice, p. 20 • Practice, p. 21 • Word Problem Practice, p. 22	• Study Guide and Intervention, pp. 18–19 • Skills Practice, p. 20 • Practice, p. 21 • Word Problem Practice, p. 22 • Enrichment, p. 23	• Practice, p. 21 • Word Problem Practice, p. 22 • Enrichment, p. 23	• Study Guide and Intervention, pp. 18–19 • Skills Practice, p. 20 • Practice, p. 21
Transparencies	• 5-Minute Check Transparency 3-3	• 5-Minute Check Transparency 3-3	• 5-Minute Check Transparency 3-3	• 5-Minute Check Transparency 3-3
Other	• Study Notebook • Teaching Pre-Algebra with Manipulatives	• Study Notebook • Teaching Pre-Algebra with Manipulatives	• Study Notebook	• Study Notebook • Teaching Pre-Algebra with Manipulatives

If the fractions have common factors in the numerators and denominators, you can simplify before you multiply.

StudyTip

Negative Signs When working with negative fractions, assign the negative sign to the numerator. Example: Write $-\frac{7}{9}$ as $\frac{-7}{9}$.

EXAMPLE 2 Multiply Negative Fractions and Mixed Numbers

Find each product. Write in simplest form.

a. $\frac{3}{4}\left(-\frac{7}{9}\right)$

$\frac{3}{4}\left(-\frac{7}{9}\right) = \frac{\overset{1}{\cancel{3}}}{4}\left(\frac{-7}{\underset{3}{\cancel{9}}}\right)$ **Divide 3 and 9 by their GCF, 3.**

$= \frac{1 \cdot -7}{4 \cdot 3}$ **Multiply the numerators and multiply the denominators.**

$= -\frac{7}{12}$ **Simplify.**

b. $2\frac{1}{3} \cdot 2\frac{5}{7}$

Estimate $2 \cdot 3 = 6$

$2\frac{1}{3} \cdot 2\frac{5}{7} = \frac{7}{3} \cdot \frac{19}{7}$ **Rename $2\frac{1}{3}$ as $\frac{7}{3}$ and $2\frac{5}{7}$ as $\frac{19}{7}$.**

$= \frac{\overset{1}{\cancel{7}}}{3} \cdot \frac{19}{\underset{1}{\cancel{7}}}$ **Divide by the GCF, 7.**

$= \frac{1 \cdot 19}{3 \cdot 1}$ **Multiply.**

$= \frac{19}{3}$ or $6\frac{1}{3}$ **Simplify.**

Check **The solution is close to the estimate.** ✓

Check Your Progress

2A. $-\frac{9}{12} \cdot -\frac{2}{3}$ $\frac{1}{2}$

2B. $\frac{6}{9} \cdot -\frac{3}{11}$ $-\frac{2}{11}$

2C. $3\frac{3}{8} \cdot 2\frac{1}{3}$ $\frac{63}{8}$ or $7\frac{7}{8}$

2D. $-1\frac{5}{6} \cdot 5\frac{1}{7}$ $-\frac{66}{7}$ or $-9\frac{3}{7}$

Personal Tutor glencoe.com

Evaluate Expressions with Fractions Variables can represent fractions in algebraic expressions.

EXAMPLE 3 Evaluate Rational Expressions Using Multiplication

Evaluate $\frac{1}{2}ab$ if $a = \frac{6}{7}$ and $b = -\frac{4}{9}$. Write in simplest form.

$\frac{1}{2}ab = \frac{1}{2}\left(\frac{6}{7}\right)\left(-\frac{4}{9}\right)$ **Replace a with $\frac{6}{7}$ and b with $-\frac{4}{9}$.**

$= \frac{1}{\underset{1}{\cancel{2}}}\left(\frac{\overset{2}{\cancel{6}}}{7}\right)\left(-\frac{\overset{2}{\cancel{4}}}{\underset{3}{\cancel{9}}}\right)$ **The GCF of 6 and 9 is 3. The GCF of 2 and 4 is 2.**

$= -\frac{4}{21}$ **Simplify.**

Check Your Progress

Evaluate each expression if $x = \frac{3}{8}$, $y = -2\frac{2}{9}$, and $z = -\frac{7}{10}$. Write in simplest form.

3A. xy $-\frac{5}{6}$

3B. $5x$ $\frac{15}{8}$ or $1\frac{7}{8}$

3C. yz $\frac{14}{9}$ or $1\frac{5}{9}$

Personal Tutor glencoe.com

Multiply Fractions

Examples 1 and 2 show how to multiply and simplify positive and negative fractions and mixed numbers.

Formative Assessment

Use the Check Your Progress exercises after each example to determine students' understanding of concepts.

Additional Examples

1 Find $\frac{2}{5} \cdot \frac{5}{8}$. Write in simplest form. $\frac{1}{4}$

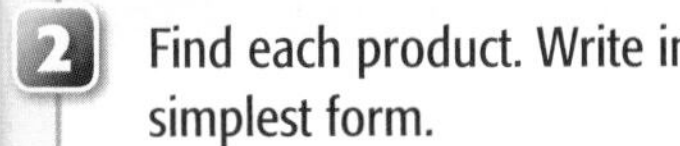

2 Find each product. Write in simplest form.

a. $-\frac{1}{4} \cdot \frac{2}{7}$ $-\frac{1}{14}$

b. $1\frac{1}{2} \cdot 3\frac{2}{3}$ $\frac{11}{2}$ or $5\frac{1}{2}$

Additional Examples also in Interactive Classroom PowerPoint® Presentations

IWB INTERACTIVE WHITEBOARD READY

Additional Example

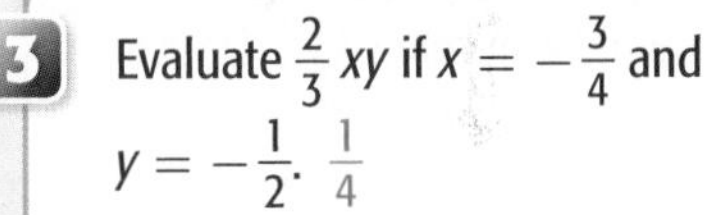

3 Evaluate $\frac{2}{3}xy$ if $x = -\frac{3}{4}$ and $y = -\frac{1}{2}$. $\frac{1}{4}$

Evaluate Expressions with Fractions

Example 3 shows how to evaluate an algebraic expression that has fractions as variables. **Example 4** shows how to solve a real-world problem that involves multiplying a fraction and a whole number.

Watch Out!

Student Misconceptions From Example 2, students may think that the negative sign in a fraction always goes with the numerator. Point out that $-\frac{5}{12} = \frac{-5}{12} = \frac{5}{-12}$, but NOT $\frac{-5}{-12}$.

Additional Answers (Why)

a.

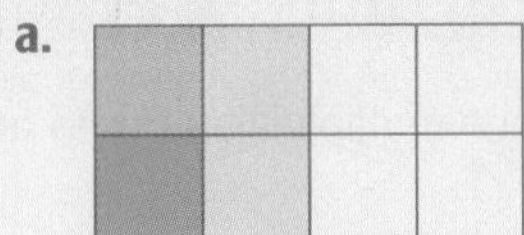

c.

b.

TEACH with TECH

WEB ACTIVITY/INTERACTIVE WHITEBOARD Find a Web site with an applet that gives an area model of multiplying fractions, and show it using your interactive whiteboard. Provide additional examples to students. Save it in the interactive whiteboard software and post it on the class Web site.

Additional Example

4 **DONATIONS** Rasheed collects cash donations for underprivileged children every October. This October he collected \$784. Last year he collected $\frac{5}{8}$ as much. How much did Rasheed collect last October? \$490

Focus on Mathematical Content

Multiplying Fractions When multiplying a number by a fraction less than 1, the product will be a number less than the original factor. Students can think of multiplying by a fraction less than 1 as taking part "of" a number.

3 PRACTICE

Formative Assessment

Use Exercises 1–14 to check for understanding.

Use the chart at the bottom of the next page to customize assignments for your students.

Real-World Link

The world's tallest structure is the KVLY-TV Tower located in Fargo, North Dakota. The 2063-foot tower is supported by 7.5 miles of steel wires.

Real-World EXAMPLE 4 Multiply Fractions by Whole Numbers

ROLLER COASTERS The first drop on a certain roller coaster at a theme park is 255 feet. The first drop on another roller coaster is about $\frac{11}{20}$ as high. Find the height of the drop on the second roller coaster.

To find the height of the drop on the second roller coaster, multiply $\frac{11}{20}$ by 255.

$$\frac{11}{20} \cdot 255 = \frac{11}{20} \cdot \frac{255}{1}$$ **Rename 255 as $\frac{255}{1}$.**

$$= \frac{11}{\cancel{20}_{4}} \cdot \frac{\cancel{255}^{51}}{1}$$ **Divide by the GCF, 5.**

$$= \frac{11 \cdot 51}{4 \cdot 1}$$ **Multiply.**

$$= \frac{561}{4} \text{ or } 140\frac{1}{4}$$ **Simplify.**

So, the height of the drop is about 140 feet.

Check Your Progress

4. **SKYSCRAPERS** The Sears Tower in Chicago is about 1450 feet. The Empire State Building in New York City is about $\frac{4}{5}$ as tall. About how tall is the Empire State Building? **1160 ft**

Personal Tutor glencoe.com

Check Your Understanding

Examples 1 and 2 pp. 134–135

Find each product. Write in simplest form.

1. $\frac{7}{8} \cdot \frac{1}{2}$ **$\frac{7}{16}$**
2. $\frac{1}{3} \cdot \frac{2}{5}$ **$\frac{2}{15}$**
3. $-\frac{2}{3} \cdot \frac{3}{16}$ **$-\frac{1}{8}$**
4. $-\frac{3}{5} \cdot -\frac{10}{21}$ **$\frac{2}{7}$**
5. $-4\frac{1}{2} \cdot -1\frac{1}{9}$ **5**
6. $-2\frac{1}{2} \cdot 5\frac{2}{3}$ **$-\frac{85}{6}$ or $-14\frac{1}{6}$**

Example 3 p. 135

ALGEBRA Evaluate each expression if $x = \frac{14}{15}$, $y = -1\frac{2}{5}$, and $z = -\frac{3}{7}$. Write the product in simplest form.

7. xy **$-\frac{98}{75}$ or $-1\frac{23}{75}$**
8. $z \cdot z$ **$\frac{9}{49}$**
9. xz **$-\frac{2}{5}$**
10. $\frac{3}{4}xz$ **$-\frac{3}{10}$**
11. $4y$ **$-\frac{28}{5}$ or $-5\frac{3}{5}$**
12. $2\frac{1}{3}z$ **-1**

Example 4 p. 136

13. **GEOGRAPHY** "Midway" is the name of 252 towns in the United States. "Pleasant Hill" occurs $\frac{5}{9}$ as many times. How many towns named "Pleasant Hill" are there in the United States? **140 towns**

14. **SCHOOL SPORTS** Of the 480 students at Pleasantview Middle School, $\frac{13}{20}$ play a school sport. How many students play a sport? **312 students**

Differentiated Instruction

AL OL ELL

If students have trouble when multiplying a mixed number and a proper fraction,

Then have them use a manipulative to model multiplying a mixed number by a proper fraction such as $4\frac{3}{5} \cdot \frac{2}{3}$. Instruct students to draw 5 rectangles, divide each into fifths horizontally, and shade $4\frac{3}{5}$. Then divide each rectangle into thirds vertically and shade two-thirds of each. They should state what the overlapping areas represent.

Practice and Problem Solving

● = **Step-by-Step Solutions** begin on page R11.
Extra Practice begins on page 810.

Examples 1 and 2 pp. 134–135

Find each product. Write in simplest form.

15. $\frac{3}{4} \cdot \frac{1}{8}$ $\frac{3}{32}$
16. $\frac{3}{7} \cdot \frac{1}{6}$ $\frac{1}{14}$
17. $\frac{2}{3} \cdot \frac{4}{9}$ $\frac{8}{27}$
18. $\frac{1}{12} \cdot \frac{3}{8}$ $\frac{1}{32}$
19. $\frac{5}{10} \cdot \frac{2}{9}$ $\frac{1}{9}$
20. $\frac{4}{5} \cdot \frac{5}{8}$ $\frac{1}{2}$
21. $-\frac{1}{15} \cdot -\frac{10}{13}$ $\frac{2}{39}$
22. $-\frac{6}{10} \cdot -\frac{1}{8}$ $\frac{3}{40}$
23. $3\frac{1}{3} \cdot -\frac{1}{5}$ $-\frac{2}{3}$
24. $\frac{12}{45} \cdot -\frac{9}{16}$ $-\frac{3}{20}$
25. $-1\frac{1}{2} \cdot \frac{2}{3}$ -1
26. $4\frac{3}{8} \cdot -3\frac{3}{7}$ -15

Example 3 p. 135

ALGEBRA Evaluate each expression if $a = \frac{10}{24}$, $b = -3\frac{1}{8}$, and $c = -\frac{4}{5}$. Write the product in simplest form.

27. bc $\frac{5}{2}$ or $2\frac{1}{2}$
28. ab $-\frac{125}{96}$ or $-1\frac{29}{96}$
29. $2c$ $-\frac{8}{5}$ or $-1\frac{3}{5}$
30. $\frac{2}{3}abc$ $\frac{25}{36}$
31. $-4bc$ -10
32. $-3\frac{4}{5}ac$ $\frac{19}{15}$ or $1\frac{4}{15}$

Example 4 p. 136

33. **BEEF** The average person living in Argentina consumes about 145 pounds of beef per year. The average person living in the United States consumes about $\frac{3}{5}$ as much. How many pounds of beef does the average American consume every year? **87 lb**

34. **BRIDGES** The Golden Gate Bridge in San Francisco is 4200 feet long. The Brooklyn Bridge in New York City is $\frac{19}{50}$ as long. How long is the Brooklyn Bridge? **1596 ft**

Find each product. Write in simplest form.

35. $\frac{3}{5} \cdot \frac{10}{28} \cdot \frac{2}{9}$ $\frac{1}{21}$
36. $\frac{2}{3} \cdot \frac{1}{4} \cdot \frac{6}{13}$ $\frac{1}{13}$
37. $3\frac{1}{2} \cdot \left(-1\frac{1}{14}\right) \cdot \frac{4}{5}$ -3
38. $4\frac{1}{5} \cdot -1\frac{3}{7} \cdot \frac{6}{11}$
39. $-\frac{6}{11} \cdot -4 \cdot -2\frac{3}{4} \cdot \frac{1}{3}$ -2
40. $-\frac{9}{10} \cdot 7 \cdot 2\frac{1}{3} \cdot \frac{1}{21}$ $-\frac{7}{10}$

38. $-\frac{36}{11}$ or $-3\frac{3}{11}$

41. **LAWN CARE** Dexter's lawn is $\frac{2}{3}$ of an acre. If $7\frac{1}{2}$ bags of fertilizer are needed for 1 acre, how much will he need to fertilize his lawn? **5 bags**

42. **HYBRID CARS** A certain hybrid car can travel $1\frac{4}{11}$ times as far as a similar nonhybrid car with one gallon of gasoline. If the nonhybrid car can travel 33 miles per gallon of gasoline, how far can the hybrid travel on $\frac{4}{5}$ gallon of gasoline? **36 mi**

Real-World Link

On April 1, 2004, the first American-made hybrid SUV was released. The hybrid averaged 40 miles to the gallon and saved the consumer an average of $4000 in gasoline costs.

MEASUREMENT Complete.

43. ■ ounces = $\frac{3}{4}$ pound **12**
(*Hint:* 1 pound = 16 ounces)
44. ■ feet = $\frac{2}{3}$ mile **3520**
(*Hint:* 1 mile = 5280 feet)
45. $\frac{5}{6}$ foot = ■ inches **10**
46. $\frac{1}{4}$ minute = ■ seconds **15**
47. ■ cups = $\frac{1}{4}$ gallon **4**
(*Hint:* 1 gallon = 16 cups)
48. $\frac{3}{4}$ year = ■ weeks **39**

49. **RESEARCH** Use a cookbook to find a recipe for guacamole. Change the recipe to make $2\frac{1}{4}$ times the original amount. **See students' work.**

Exercise Alert

Research Exercise 49 requires students to look up a recipe for guacamole. Offer ideas of Web sites they can reference or provide a recipe for students who cannot find a cookbook recipe.

Tips for New Teachers

If students have difficulty completing Exercises 43–48, show them how to draw visuals to help. For example, in Exercise 45, they can draw a ruler, 1 foot, and show it as 12 inches. They can then divide the twelve inches into 6 parts and count 5 of the 6 or 10 inches.

Differentiated Homework Options

Level	Assignment	Two-Day Option	
AL Basic	15–34, 52–53, 57–83	15–33 odd, 59–62	16–34 even, 52–53, 57–58, 63–83
OL Core	15–51 odd, 52–53, 57–83	15–34, 59–62	35–53, 57–58, 63–83
BL Advanced	35–79 (optional: 80–83)		

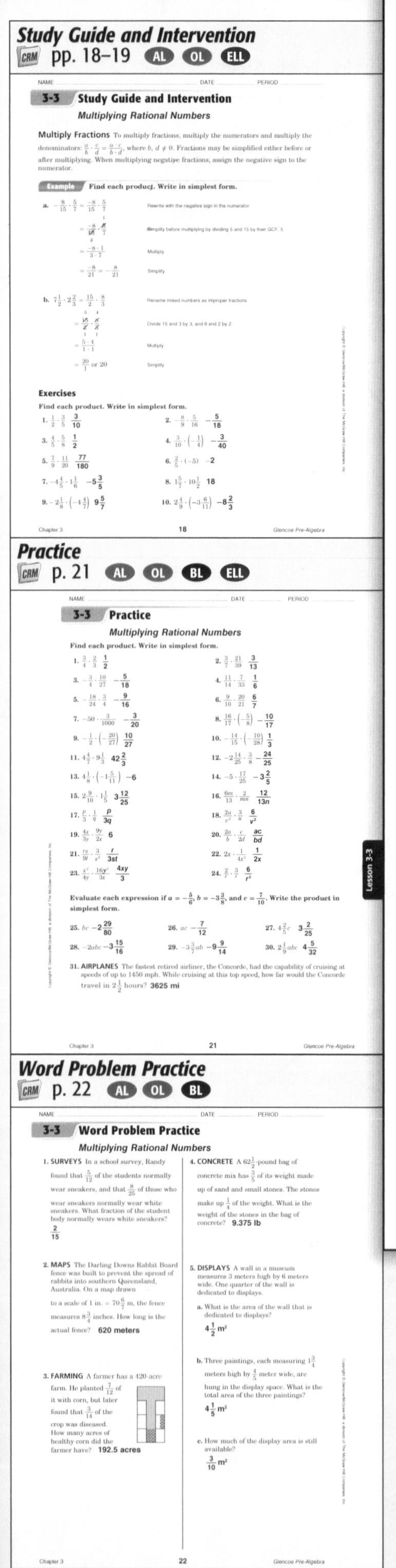

Study Guide and Intervention CRM pp. 18–19 AL OL ELL

3-3 Study Guide and Intervention
Multiplying Rational Numbers

Practice CRM p. 21 AL OL BL ELL

3-3 Practice
Multiplying Rational Numbers

Word Problem Practice CRM p. 22 AL OL BL

3-3 Word Problem Practice
Multiplying Rational Numbers

50. ANALYZE TABLES Use the table that shows statistics from the last election for 8th grade class president. There are 540 students in the 8th grade.

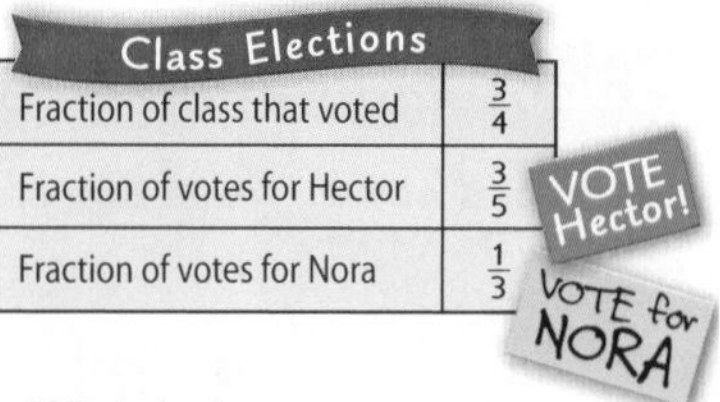

Class Elections	
Fraction of class that voted	$\frac{3}{4}$
Fraction of votes for Hector	$\frac{3}{5}$
Fraction of votes for Nora	$\frac{1}{3}$

a. How many students voted for Hector? **243 students**

b. How many students voted for Nora? **135 students**

c. Were there other candidates for class president? How do you know? Explain your reasoning. If there were other candidates, what fraction of the student body voted for them? **See margin.**

StudyTip

Area Models To find each product, you could draw an area model.

51 C **NUMBER SENSE** The expression $\frac{1}{2} \times 4$ means $\frac{1}{2}$ of 4. The number line shows that the product of $\frac{1}{2}$ and 4 is 2.

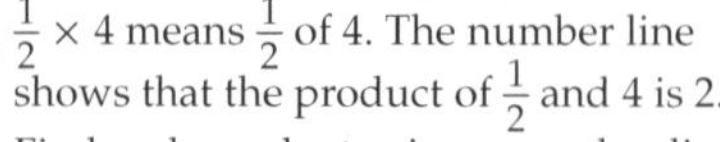

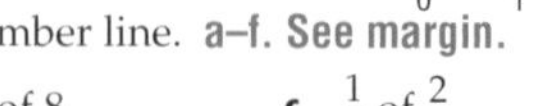

Find each product using a number line. **a–f. See margin.**

a. $\frac{2}{3}$ of 6 b. $\frac{3}{4}$ of 8 c. $\frac{1}{2}$ of $\frac{2}{3}$

d. $\frac{1}{2}$ of 2 e. $\frac{2}{3}$ of $\frac{3}{2}$ f. $\frac{3}{7}$ of $\frac{7}{3}$

g. Look back at the solutions for Exercises d–f. What pattern do you notice? **Each product is 1.**

h. What is the product of $\frac{a}{b} \cdot \frac{b}{a}$ where $a, b \neq 0$? **1**

H.O.T. Problems Use Higher-Order Thinking Skills

52. OPEN ENDED Find two rational numbers greater than $\frac{1}{3}$ whose product is less than $\frac{1}{3}$. **Sample answer: $\frac{1}{2} \cdot \frac{5}{12} = \frac{5}{24}$**

53. FIND THE ERROR Kelly and Marina are finding $-4\frac{1}{6} \cdot 2\frac{2}{9}$. Is either of them correct? Explain your reasoning.

53. Marina; Kelly did not write the mixed numbers as improper fractions before multiplying.

Kelly

$-4\frac{1}{6} \cdot 2\frac{2}{9} = -4\frac{1}{6} \cdot 2\frac{2}{9}$

$= -8\frac{1}{27}$

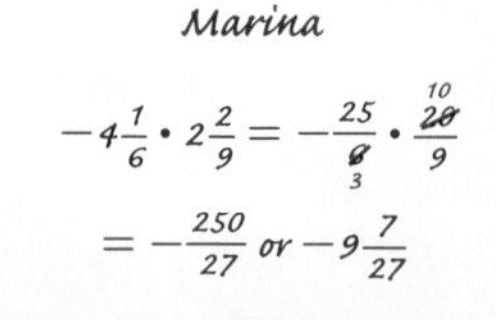

Marina

$-4\frac{1}{6} \cdot 2\frac{2}{9} = -\frac{25}{6} \cdot \frac{20}{9}$

$= -\frac{250}{27}$ or $-9\frac{7}{27}$

CHALLENGE Find each missing fraction.

54. $\frac{2}{3} \cdot \frac{x}{y} = -\frac{3}{8}$ $-\frac{9}{16}$ **55.** $\frac{a}{b} \cdot -\frac{3}{4} = \frac{5}{8}$ $-\frac{5}{6}$ **56.** $\frac{8}{9} \cdot \frac{m}{n} = \frac{14}{27}$ $\frac{7}{12}$

57–58. See Chapter 3 Answer Appendix.

57. REASONING Investigate the product of a fraction between 0 and 1 and a whole number or mixed number. Is the product *always*, *sometimes*, or *never* less than the whole number or mixed number? Explain.

58. WRITING IN MATH Estimate $3\frac{3}{5} \cdot 4\frac{2}{3}$. Then find the actual product. Explain why the estimate and the product are different. What could you do to make your estimate closer to the actual product?

Enrichment CRM p. 23 OL BL

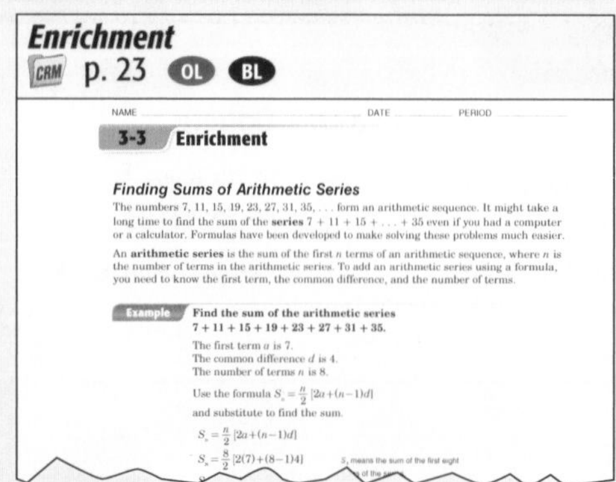

3-3 Enrichment

Finding Sums of Arithmetic Series

Watch Out!

Find the Error If students have difficulty with Exercise 53, remind them that mixed numbers should be renamed as improper fractions before multiplying.

Standardized Test Practice

59. Of the students in Mr. Boggs' class, $\frac{3}{5}$ participate in an after school sport. Of these, $\frac{1}{3}$ participate in track and field. What fraction of the students participates in track and field? **A**

A $\frac{1}{5}$ C $\frac{3}{5}$

B $\frac{1}{3}$ D $\frac{14}{15}$

60. Which statement is shown on the number line below? **G**

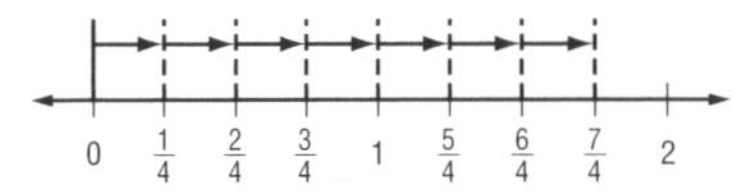

F $\frac{1}{4} + 7 = \frac{7}{4}$ H $\frac{7}{4} \cdot 7 = \frac{1}{4}$

G $\frac{1}{4} \cdot 7 = \frac{7}{4}$ J $\frac{7}{4} + 7 = \frac{1}{4}$

61. What is the value of the expression $2ab$ if $a = \frac{5}{7}$ and $b = -\frac{3}{8}$? **B**

A $-2\frac{15}{56}$

B $-\frac{15}{28}$

C $\frac{15}{28}$

D $2\frac{15}{56}$

62. EXTENDED RESPONSE The length of one side of a square garden tile is $1\frac{2}{3}$ feet.

a. Write a mixed number to represent the perimeter of the tile. **$6\frac{2}{3}$ ft**

b. Write a mixed number to represent the area of the tile. **$2\frac{7}{9}$ ft^2**

c. What is the perimeter of the tile in inches? **80 in.**

d. What is the area of the tile in square inches? **400 in^2**

Spiral Review

Write each decimal as a fraction or mixed number in simplest form. (Lesson 3-2)

63. 4.02 **$4\frac{1}{50}$** **64.** 0.215 **$\frac{43}{200}$** **65.** -5.125 **$-5\frac{1}{8}$**

66. $-0.\overline{3}$ **$-\frac{1}{3}$** **67.** $4.\overline{5}$ **$4\frac{5}{9}$** **68.** $-2.\overline{05}$ **$-2\frac{5}{99}$**

Replace each ● with <, >, or = to make a true sentence. (Lesson 3-1)

69. $0.3 \bullet \frac{1}{4}$ **>** **70.** $\frac{5}{8} \bullet 0.65$ **<** **71.** $\frac{2}{5} \bullet 0.4$ **=**

72. $\frac{7}{8} \bullet \frac{8}{9}$ **<** **73.** $\frac{1}{5} \bullet 0.\overline{5}$ **<** **74.** $3\frac{4}{9} \bullet 3.\overline{4}$ **=**

75. SLEEP In an online survey, about $\frac{1}{4}$ of teenagers go to sleep between 9 and 10 P.M., while $\frac{13}{50}$ of teenagers go to sleep at 12 A.M. or later. Which group is larger? (Lesson 3-1) **The group that goes to sleep at 12 A.M. or later.**

Find each product. (Lesson 2-4)

76. $14(-5)$ **-70** **77.** $-8(-11)$ **88** **78.** $-7(-8)(-3)$ **-168** **79.** $2(-8)(-9)(10)$ **1440**

Skills Review

Multiply. (Lesson 2-5)

80. $-50(-5)$ **250** **81.** $(12)(-2)(8)$ **-192** **82.** $(-1)(16)(-2)$ **32** **83.** $14(-2)(-3)$ **84**

Differentiated Instruction BL

Extension What rational numbers can $\frac{12}{17}$, $\frac{8}{9}$, and $\frac{27}{46}$ be multiplied by to give a product of 1? $\frac{17}{12}$, $\frac{9}{8}$, and $\frac{46}{27}$, respectively. What conclusions can you draw about other rational numbers? All rational numbers, when multiplied by their inverse, give a product of 1. What might be the usefulness of this property? Sample answer: if there is a number in an equation that you want to remove, you can multiply both sides by the inverse of the number.

4 ASSESS

Crystal Ball Ask students to write about how they believe today's lesson on multiplying rational numbers will connect with tomorrow's lesson on dividing rational numbers.

Formative Assessment

Check for student understanding of concepts in Lesson 3-3.

CRM Quiz 2, p. 46

Additional Answers

50c. Yes; a third candidate, or a combination of other candidates, received votes because 243 + 135 students voted for Hector and Nora. $\frac{3}{4}$ of the class voted, so $\frac{3}{4} \cdot 540 = 405$ students voted. So, 405 − 378 or 27 students voted for the other candidate(s). $\frac{27}{540} = \frac{1}{20}$

51a.

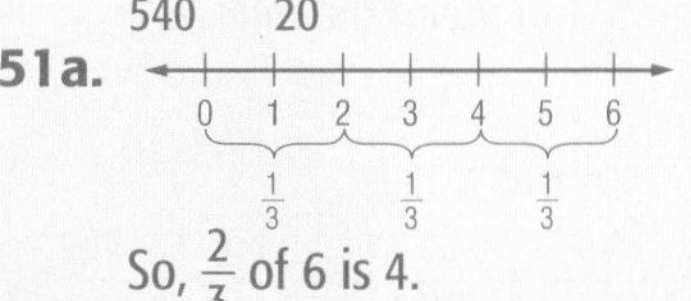

So, $\frac{2}{3}$ of 6 is 4.

51b.

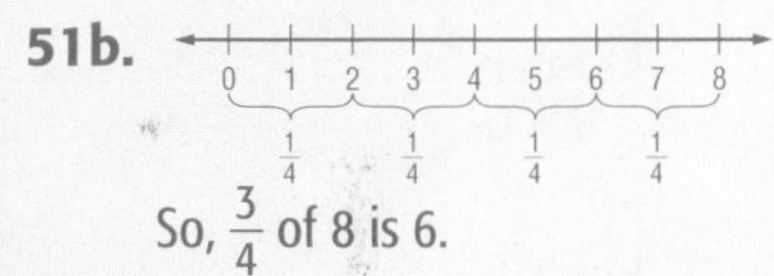

So, $\frac{3}{4}$ of 8 is 6.

51c.

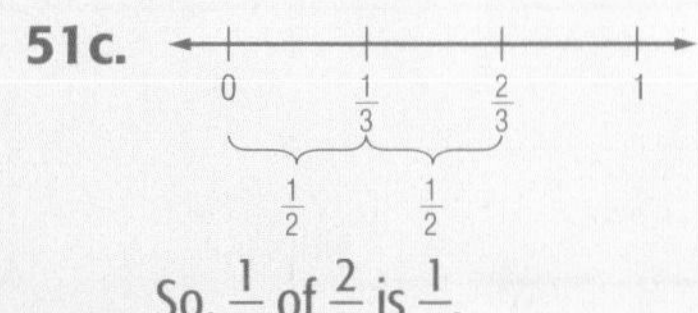

So, $\frac{1}{2}$ of $\frac{2}{3}$ is $\frac{1}{3}$.

51d.

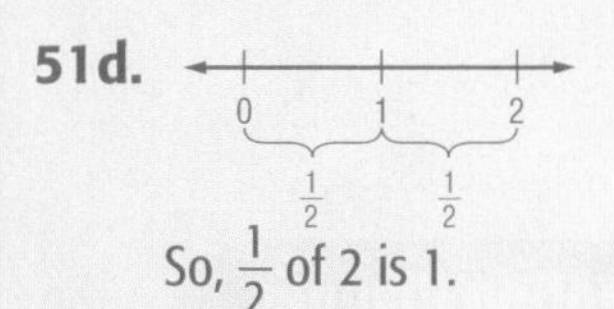

So, $\frac{1}{2}$ of 2 is 1.

51e.

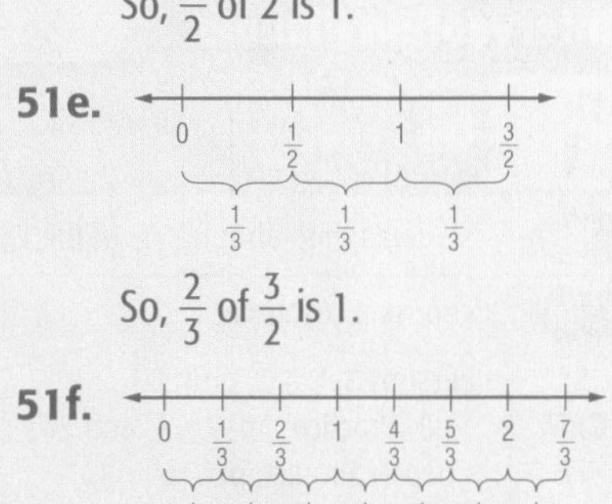

So, $\frac{2}{3}$ of $\frac{3}{2}$ is 1.

51f.

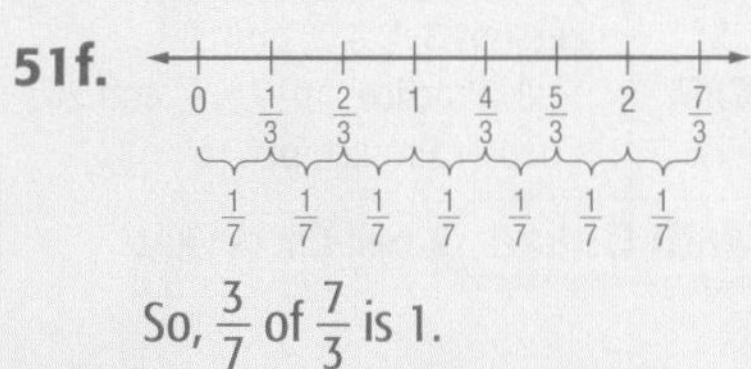

So, $\frac{3}{7}$ of $\frac{7}{3}$ is 1.

CHAPTER 3 Mid-Chapter Quiz

Formative Assessment

Use the Mid-Chapter Quiz to assess students' progress in the first half of the chapter.

For problems answered incorrectly, have students review the lessons indicated in parentheses.

ExamView Assessment Suite — Customize and create multiple versions of your Mid-Chapter Quiz and their answer keys.

FOLDABLES Follow-Up

Before students complete the Mid-Chapter Quiz, encourage them to review the information for Lessons 3-1 through 3-3 in their Foldables.

Additional Answer

16. Antarctica: $\frac{19}{200}$; Asia: $\frac{59}{200}$; Europe: $\frac{7}{100}$; North America: $\frac{4}{25}$

CHAPTER 3 Mid-Chapter Quiz

Lessons 3-1 through 3-3

Write each fraction as a decimal. Use a bar to show a repeating decimal. (Lesson 3-1)

1. $\frac{9}{20}$ **0.45**
2. $-\frac{3}{11}$ **$-0.\overline{27}$**
3. $\frac{3}{4}$ **0.75**
4. $-\frac{4}{7}$ **$-0.\overline{571428}$**

5. **MULTIPLE CHOICE** In a recent year, a baseball team won 36 of their 42 games. Which of the following shows the part of games they won to the nearest thousandth? (Lesson 3-1) **A**

   A 0.857 C 1.17

   B 0.86 D 1.167

6. **SHOPPING** A store estimates that 14 out of 120 people return items to the store. To the nearest thousandth, find the rate of customer returns. (Lesson 3-1) **0.117**

Replace each ● with <, >, or = to make a true sentence. (Lesson 3-1)

7. $\frac{3}{9}$ ● $0.\overline{3}$ =
8. $-\frac{3}{8}$ ● -0.5 >
9. $1\frac{5}{6}$ ● 1.8 >
10. $4.\overline{25}$ ● $\frac{17}{4}$ >

11. **MANUFACTURING** A garbage bag has a thickness of 0.8 mil, which is equal to 0.0008 inch. What fraction of an inch is this? (Lesson 3-2) **$\frac{1}{1250}$ in.**

Write each decimal as a fraction or mixed number in simplest form. (Lesson 3-2)

12. -4.075 **$-4\frac{3}{40}$**
13. $-1.3636...$ **$-1\frac{4}{11}$**
14. 0.42 **$\frac{21}{50}$**
15. $3.08\overline{3}$ **$3\frac{1}{12}$**

16. **GEOGRAPHY** Africa makes up $\frac{1}{5}$ of Earth's entire land surface. Use the table to find the fraction of Earth's land surface that is made up by each of the other continents. Write each fraction in simplest form. (Lesson 3-2) **See margin.**

Continent	Decimal Portion of Earth's Land
Antarctica	0.095
Asia	0.295
Europe	0.07
North America	0.16

Source: *Incredible Comparisons*

17. **TRAVEL** One of the fastest commuter trains is the Japanese Nozomi, which averages 162 miles per hour. About how many minutes would it take to travel 119 miles from Hiroshima to Kokura on the train? (Lesson 3-3) **44 min**

Find each product. Write in simplest form. (Lesson 3-3)

18. $\frac{5}{18} \cdot \frac{4}{15}$ **$\frac{2}{27}$**
19. $-2\frac{1}{3} \cdot 2\frac{1}{7}$ **-5**
20. $-1\frac{1}{2} \cdot \frac{2}{3}$ **-1**
21. $-\frac{3}{16} \cdot (-3\frac{5}{9})$ **$\frac{2}{3}$**

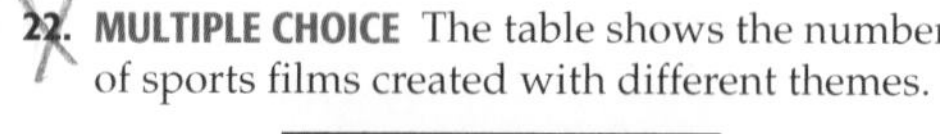

22. **MULTIPLE CHOICE** The table shows the number of sports films created with different themes.

Sport Theme	Films
boxing	204
horse racing	139
football	123
baseball	85

Which theme occurs $\frac{5}{12}$ as many times as boxing? (Lesson 3-3) **H**

F horse racing

G football

H baseball

J none of the above

ALGEBRA Evaluate each expression if $w = -3$, $x = \frac{3}{4}$, $y = -\frac{4}{5}$, and $z = -2\frac{2}{9}$. (Lesson 3-3)

23. $-wyz$ **$\frac{16}{3}$ or $5\frac{1}{3}$**
24. $\frac{2}{3}xy$ **$-\frac{2}{5}$**
25. $5wxyz$ **-20**
26. $xy \cdot xy$ **$\frac{9}{25}$**
27. $-\frac{1}{2}wx$ **$1\frac{1}{8}$**
28. $-\frac{3}{2}yz$ **$-2\frac{2}{3}$**

29. **RIVERS** The Nile River is 4160 miles long. The Amazon River is $\frac{25}{26}$ as long. How long is the Amazon River? (Lesson 3-3) **4000 mi**

30. **JEWELRY** Magda is making five necklaces. She uses $20\frac{3}{4}$ inches of wire for each necklace. How much wire will Magda use? (Lesson 3-3) **$103\frac{3}{4}$ in.**

Intervention Planner

Tier 1 — On Level

If students miss about 25% of the exercises or less,

Then choose a resource:

- **SE** Lessons 3-1, 3-2, and 3-3
- **CRM** Skills Practice, pp. 7, 14, and 20
- **TE** Chapter Project, p. 116

Math Online Self-Check Quiz

Tier 2 — Strategic Intervention Approaching grade level

If students miss about 50% of the exercises,

Then choose a resource:

- **CRM** Study Guide and Intervention, Chapter 3, pp. 5, 12, and 18

Quick Review Math Handbook

Math Online Extra Examples, Personal Tutor, Homework Help

Tier 3 — Intensive Intervention 2 or more grades below level

If students miss about 75% of the exercises,

Then use *Math Triumphs, Grade 8*, Ch. 1, 3, 7

Math Online Extra Examples, Personal Tutor, Homework Help, Review Vocabulary

3-4 Dividing Rational Numbers

Why?

Mrs. Hollern had 3 apples. She cut each of them in half.

There are six half-pieces in 3 apples, so $3 \div \frac{1}{2} = 6$.

Another way to find the number of sections is to multiply $3 \times 2 = 6$.

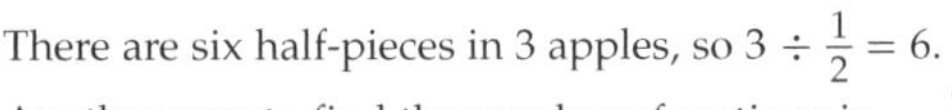

Use an area model or another model to find each quotient. Explain how the model shows the quotient. a–d. See Chapter 3 Answer Appendix.

a. $5 \div \frac{1}{2}$

b. $2 \div \frac{1}{4}$

c. $3 \div \frac{1}{3}$

d. **MAKE A CONJECTURE** Write about how dividing by a fraction is related to multiplying.

Then

You have already divided positive fractions and multiplied rational numbers. (Lesson 3-3)

Now

- Divide positive and negative fractions using multiplicative inverses.
- Divide algebraic fractions.

New Vocabulary

multiplicative inverse
reciprocal

Math Online

glencoe.com

- Extra Examples
- Personal Tutor
- Self-Check Quiz
- Homework Help

Divide Fractions All of the properties of integers also apply to rational numbers. The statement $\frac{1}{4} \cdot 4 = 1$ demonstrates another property. Two numbers whose product is 1 are called **multiplicative inverses** or **reciprocals**.

Key Concept — Inverse Property of Multiplication (For Your FOLDABLE)

Words The product of a number and its multiplicative inverse is 1.

Symbols For every number $\frac{a}{b}$, where $a, b \neq 0$, there is exactly one number $\frac{b}{a}$ such that $\frac{a}{b} \cdot \frac{b}{a} = 1$.

Example $\frac{2}{3} \cdot \frac{3}{2} = 1$

EXAMPLE 1 Find Multiplicative Inverses

Find the multiplicative inverse of each number.

a. $\frac{7}{16}$

$\frac{7}{16}\left(\frac{16}{7}\right) = 1$ **The product is 1.**

The multiplicative inverse or reciprocal of $\frac{7}{16}$ is $\frac{16}{7}$.

b. $-6\frac{1}{3}$

$-6\frac{1}{3} = -\frac{19}{3}$ **Write $-6\frac{1}{3}$ as an improper fraction.**

$-\frac{19}{3}\left(-\frac{3}{19}\right) = 1$ **The product is 1.**

The multiplicative inverse or reciprocal of $-6\frac{1}{3}$ is $-\frac{3}{19}$.

Check Your Progress

1A. $-\frac{7}{9}$ $-\frac{9}{7}$

1B. $2\frac{1}{12}$ $\frac{12}{25}$

Personal Tutor glencoe.com

3-4 Lesson Notes

1 FOCUS

Vertical Alignment

Before Lesson 3-4
Divide positive fractions and multiply rational numbers.

Lesson 3-4
Divide positive and negative fractions using multiplicative inverses.
Divide algebraic fractions.

After Lesson 3-4
Use multiplicative inverses to solve equations.

2 TEACH

Scaffolding Questions

Have students read the *Why?* section of the lesson and answer the questions.

Ask:

- What is another way to phrase $3 \div \frac{1}{2}$? How many halves are in 3 wholes?
- Suppose each apple was cut into fourths. How many apple sections would there be? 12
- What are two number sentences that show the number of fourths in 3 apples? $3 \div \frac{1}{4} = 12$ and $3 \cdot 4 = 12$

Lesson 3-4 Resources

Resource	Approaching-Level	On-Level	Beyond-Level	English Learners
Teacher Edition	• Differentiated Instruction, p. 142	• Differentiated Instruction, p. 142	• Differentiated Instruction, p. 146	
Chapter Resource Masters	• Study Guide and Intervention, pp. 24–25 • Skills Practice, p. 26 • Practice, p. 27 • Word Problem Practice, p. 28	• Study Guide and Intervention, pp. 24–25 • Skills Practice, p. 26 • Practice, p. 27 • Word Problem Practice, p. 28 • Enrichment, p. 29	• Practice, p. 27 • Word Problem Practice, p. 28 • Enrichment, p. 29	• Study Guide and Intervention, pp. 24–25 • Skills Practice, p. 26 • Practice, p. 27
Transparencies	• 5-Minute Check Transparency 3-4	• 5-Minute Check Transparency 3-4	• 5-Minute Check Transparency 3-4	• 5-Minute Check Transparency 3-4
Other	• Study Notebook • Teaching Pre-Algebra with Manipulatives	• Study Notebook • Teaching Pre-Algebra with Manipulatives	• Study Notebook	• Study Notebook • Teaching Pre-Algebra with Manipulatives

Divide Fractions

Example 1 shows how to find the multiplicative inverse of a number. **Example 2** shows how to divide a fraction by a fraction or a whole number. **Example 3** shows how to divide a mixed number by a mixed number. **Example 4** shows how to solve a real-world problem that involves division of rational numbers.

Formative Assessment

Use the Check Your Progress exercises after each example to determine students' understanding of concepts.

Additional Examples

1 Find the multiplicative inverse of each number.

a. $\frac{6}{7}$ $\frac{7}{6}$

b. $-3\frac{2}{5}$ $-\frac{5}{17}$

2 Find each quotient. Write in simplest form.

a. $\frac{4}{5} \div \frac{3}{10}$ $\frac{8}{3}$ or $2\frac{2}{3}$

b. $\frac{5}{6} \div 3$ $\frac{5}{18}$

3 Find $9\frac{1}{3} \div -3\frac{1}{9}$. -3

Additional Examples also in Interactive Classroom PowerPoint® Presentations

IWB INTERACTIVE WHITEBOARD READY

Focus on Mathematical Content

Multiplicative Inverse Every rational number has a multiplicative inverse except 0, because the product of 0 and any number is 0.

Multiplicative inverses are used in division. Consider $\frac{4}{9} \div \frac{3}{5}$ and $\frac{a}{b} \div \frac{c}{d}$.

$$\frac{\frac{4}{9}}{\frac{3}{5}} = \frac{\frac{4}{9} \cdot \frac{5}{3}}{\frac{3}{5} \cdot \frac{5}{3}}$$ **Multiply the numerator and denominator by $\frac{5}{3}$, the multiplicative inverse of $\frac{3}{5}$.**

$$= \frac{\frac{4}{9} \cdot \frac{5}{3}}{1}$$ **$\frac{3}{5} \cdot \frac{5}{3} = 1$**

$$= \frac{4}{9} \cdot \frac{5}{3}$$

$$\frac{\frac{a}{b}}{\frac{c}{d}} = \frac{\frac{a}{b} \cdot \frac{d}{c}}{\frac{c}{d} \cdot \frac{d}{c}}$$ **Multiply the numerator and denominator by $\frac{d}{c}$, the multiplicative inverse of $\frac{c}{d}$.**

$$= \frac{\frac{a}{b} \cdot \frac{d}{c}}{1}$$ **$\frac{c}{d} \cdot \frac{d}{c} = 1$**

$$= \frac{a}{b} \cdot \frac{d}{c}$$

These examples suggest the following rule for dividing fractions.

Key Concept — Dividing Fractions

For Your FOLDABLE

Words To divide by a fraction, multiply by its multiplicative inverse.

Examples $\frac{4}{9} \div \frac{3}{5} = \frac{4}{9} \cdot \frac{5}{3}$ $\quad \frac{a}{b} \div \frac{c}{d} = \frac{a}{b} \cdot \frac{d}{c}$, where b, c, and $d \neq 0$

StudyTip

Dividing By a Whole Number When dividing by a whole number, always rename it as an improper fraction first. Then multiply by its reciprocal.

EXAMPLE 2 Divide by a Fraction or Whole Number

Find each quotient. Write in simplest form.

a. $\frac{1}{9} \div \frac{5}{12}$

$\frac{1}{9} \div \frac{5}{12} = \frac{1}{9} \cdot \frac{12}{5}$ **Multiply by the reciprocal of $\frac{5}{12}$, $\frac{12}{5}$.**

$= \frac{1}{\cancel{9}_3} \cdot \frac{\cancel{12}^4}{5}$ **Divide by the GCF, 3.**

$= \frac{4}{15}$ **Simplify.**

b. $\frac{3}{7} \div 8$

$\frac{3}{7} \div 8 = \frac{3}{7} \div \frac{8}{1}$ **Write 8 as $\frac{8}{1}$.**

$= \frac{3}{7} \cdot \frac{1}{8}$ **Multiply by the reciprocal of $\frac{8}{1}$, $\frac{1}{8}$.**

$= \frac{3}{56}$ **Simplify.**

Check Your Progress

2A. $\frac{1}{3} \div \frac{7}{15}$ $\frac{5}{7}$ **2B.** $\frac{5}{8} \div \left(-\frac{3}{4}\right)$ $-\frac{5}{6}$ **2C.** $\frac{3}{4} \div 11$ $\frac{3}{44}$ **2D.** $-\frac{6}{7} \div 12$ $-\frac{1}{14}$

Personal Tutor glencoe.com

EXAMPLE 3 Divide by a Mixed Number

Find $-4\frac{2}{3} \div 3\frac{1}{9}$.

$-4\frac{2}{3} \div 3\frac{1}{9} = -\frac{14}{3} \div \frac{28}{9}$ **Rename the mixed numbers as improper fractions.**

$= -\frac{14}{3} \cdot \frac{9}{28}$ **Multiply by the reciprocal, $\frac{9}{28}$.**

$= -\frac{\cancel{14}^1}{\cancel{3}_1} \cdot \frac{\cancel{9}^3}{\cancel{28}_2}$ **Divide out common factors.**

$= -\frac{3}{2}$ or $-1\frac{1}{2}$ **Simplify.**

Check Your Progress

3A. Find $6\frac{3}{8} \div \left(-4\frac{1}{4}\right)$. $-\frac{3}{2}$ or $-1\frac{1}{2}$ **3B.** Find $-6\frac{4}{5} \div \left(-2\frac{2}{5}\right)$. $\frac{17}{6}$ or $2\frac{5}{6}$

Personal Tutor glencoe.com

Differentiated Instruction

Visual/Spatial To reinforce the *Why?* section at the beginning of the lesson, have students cut two circle models into three equal pieces each to show $2 \div \frac{2}{3}$. Ask students to explain how many groups of $\frac{2}{3}$ are in 2. The model shows that there are 3 groups of $\frac{2}{3}$, so $2 \div \frac{2}{3}$ is 3. Have students make similar models to solve the following division problems:

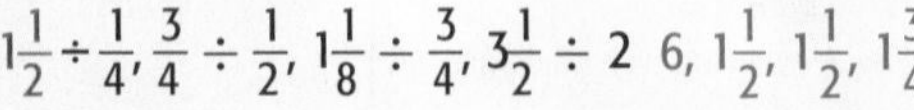

$1\frac{1}{2} \div \frac{1}{4}, \frac{3}{4} \div \frac{1}{2}, 1\frac{1}{8} \div \frac{3}{4}, 3\frac{1}{2} \div 2$ $\quad 6, 1\frac{1}{2}, 1\frac{1}{2}, 1\frac{3}{4}$

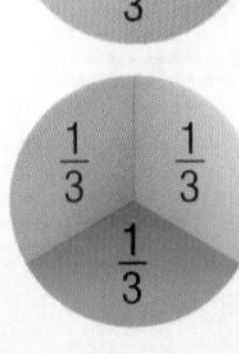

Division can be used to find the number of equal size groups in a real-world situation.

Test-Taking Tip

Underlining Underline key words and identify what you are being asked to do in the problem.

STANDARDIZED TEST EXAMPLE 4

Tessa feeds her dog Roscoe $3\frac{3}{4}$ cups of dog food per day. If she buys a bag of food that contains 165 cups, how many days will the bag of food last?

A 600 days B 480 days C 90 days D 44 days

Read the Test Item

You need to find how many days the bag of food will last.

Solve the Test Item

To find how many days, divide. $165 \div 3\frac{3}{4}$ **Think** **How many $3\frac{3}{4}$s are in 165?**

$165 \div 3\frac{3}{4} = \frac{165}{1} \div \frac{15}{4}$ **Rewrite 165 and $3\frac{3}{4}$ as improper fractions.**

$= \frac{165}{1} \cdot \frac{4}{15}$ **Multiply by the reciprocal of $\frac{15}{4}$, $\frac{4}{15}$.**

$= \frac{\overset{11}{\cancel{165}}}{\cancel{1}} \cdot \frac{\cancel{4}}{\underset{1}{\cancel{15}}}$ **Divide out common factors.**

$= 44$ **Simplify.**

So, the correct choice is D.

Check Your Progress

4. A box of cereal contains $15\frac{3}{5}$ ounces. If one bowl holds $2\frac{2}{5}$ ounces of cereal, how many bowls of cereal are in one box? F

F $6\frac{1}{2}$ G $13\frac{1}{5}$ H 18 J $37\frac{11}{25}$

Personal Tutor glencoe.com

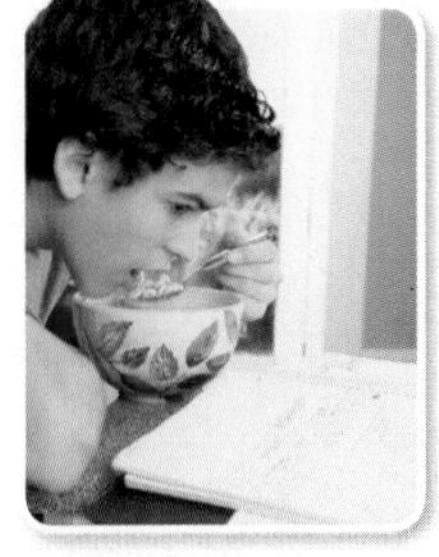

Real-World Link

About 50% of Americans start their day with a bowl of cereal. So, it is not surprising that 2.7 billion packages of cereal are sold each year. That is enough cardboard to wrap around Earth 13 times.

Source: American Cereal Council

Divide Algebraic Expressions You can divide algebraic fractions in the same way that you divide numerical fractions.

EXAMPLE 5 Divide Algebraic Fractions

Find $\frac{5}{3ab} \div \frac{15}{abc}$. Write the quotient in simplest form.

$\frac{5}{3ab} \div \frac{15}{abc} = \frac{5}{3ab} \cdot \frac{abc}{15}$ **Multiply by the reciprocal of $\frac{15}{abc}$, $\frac{abc}{15}$.**

$= \frac{\overset{1}{\cancel{5}}}{\underset{1}{\cancel{3ab}}} \cdot \frac{\overset{1}{\cancel{abc}}}{\underset{3}{\cancel{15}}}$ **Divide out common factors.**

$= \frac{c}{9}$ **Simplify.**

Check Your Progress

Find each quotient. Write in simplest form.

5A. $\frac{5ab}{6} \div \frac{10b}{7}$ $\frac{7a}{12}$ **5B.** $\frac{mn}{4} \div \frac{m}{8}$ $2n$

Personal Tutor glencoe.com

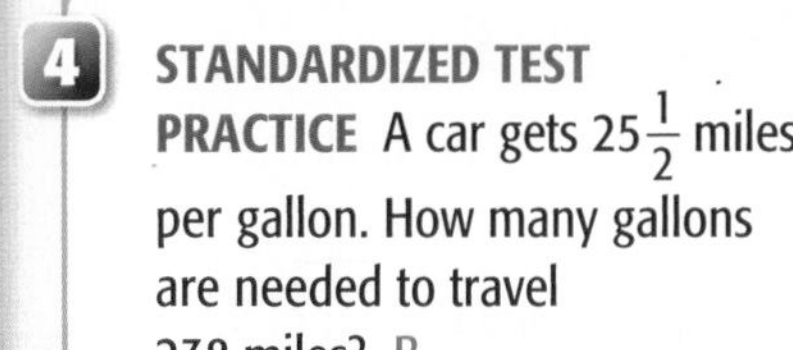

Additional Example

4 STANDARDIZED TEST PRACTICE A car gets $25\frac{1}{2}$ miles per gallon. How many gallons are needed to travel 238 miles? B

A. $\frac{3}{28}$ gal

B. $9\frac{1}{3}$ gal

C. $9\frac{2}{13}$ gal

D. $19\frac{1}{25}$ gal

Divide Algebraic Fractions

Example 5 shows how to divide algebraic fractions.

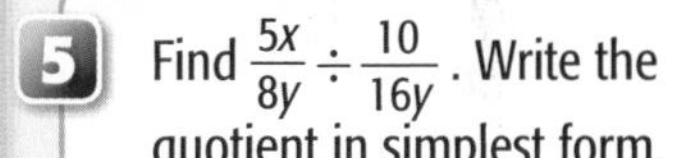

Additional Example

5 Find $\frac{5x}{8y} \div \frac{10}{16y}$. Write the quotient in simplest form. x

TEACH with TECH

PORTABLE MEDIA PLAYER Create a recording explaining how to divide fractions and why you multiply by the reciprocal. Send this to your students so they can use it as a reference outside of class.

Lesson 3-4 Dividing Rational Numbers 143

3 PRACTICE

Formative Assessment

Use Exercises 1–13 to check for understanding.

Use the chart at the bottom of this page to customize assignments for your students.

Tips for New Teachers

Multiplicative Inverses Mixed numbers must be renamed as improper fractions in order to find their multiplicative inverse.

Additional Answers

42. Sample answer:

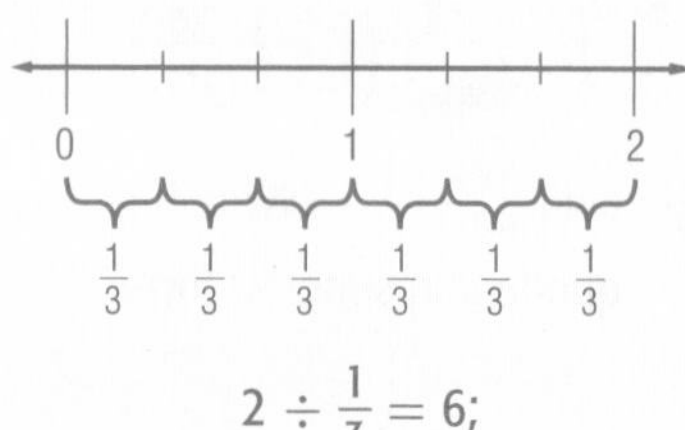

$2 \div \frac{1}{3} = 6$;

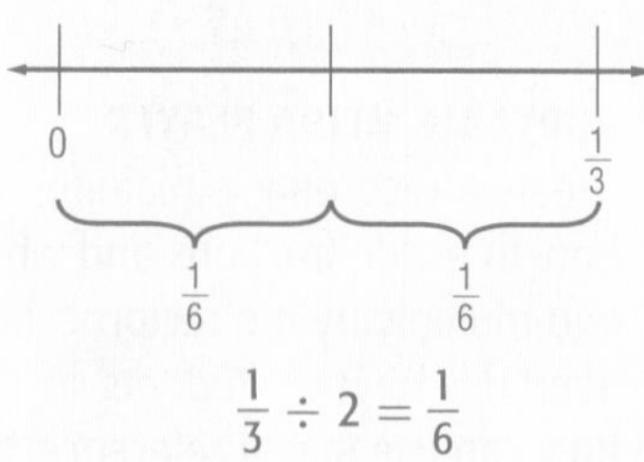

$\frac{1}{3} \div 2 = \frac{1}{6}$

43. The quotient of $\frac{1}{2} \div \frac{3}{4}$ is $\frac{2}{3}$. The fraction $\frac{2}{3}$ is not a whole number.

44. $40 \div \frac{1}{4}$; 40 multiplied by a number less than 1 will be a number less than 40. However, 40 divided by a number less than 1 will be a number greater than 40.

Check Your Understanding

Example 1 (p. 141) Find the multiplicative inverse of each number.

1. $\frac{6}{7}$ **$\frac{7}{6}$**
2. $-5\frac{1}{2}$ **$-\frac{2}{11}$**
3. -63 **$-\frac{1}{63}$**

Examples 2 and 3 (p. 142) Find each quotient. Write in simplest form.

4. $-\frac{4}{5} \div \frac{8}{9}$ **$-\frac{9}{10}$**
5. $-\frac{5}{7} \div \frac{2}{35}$ **$-\frac{25}{2}$ or $-12\frac{1}{2}$**
6. $\frac{4}{9} \div (-2)$ **$-\frac{2}{9}$**
7. $\frac{7}{9} \div (-14)$ **$-\frac{1}{18}$**
8. $-2\frac{1}{5} \div \left(-3\frac{2}{3}\right)$ **$\frac{3}{5}$**
9. $7\frac{1}{9} \div \left(-1\frac{1}{3}\right)$ **$-\frac{16}{3}$ or $-5\frac{1}{3}$**

Example 4 (p. 143)

10. **MULTIPLE CHOICE** Sonia is making a quilted wall hanging that is 38 inches wide. If each quilt square is $4\frac{3}{4}$ inches wide, how many squares will she need to complete one row of the wall hanging? **B**

A $6\frac{1}{2}$
B 8
C $42\frac{3}{4}$
D 190

Example 5 (p. 143) **ALGEBRA** Find each quotient. Write in simplest form.

11. $\frac{4ab}{c} \div \frac{3a}{2c}$ **$\frac{8b}{3}$**
12. $\frac{mn}{6} \div \frac{3m}{p}$ **$\frac{np}{18}$**
13. $\frac{3xy}{yz} \div \frac{6y}{5}$ **$\frac{5x}{2yz}$**

Practice and Problem Solving

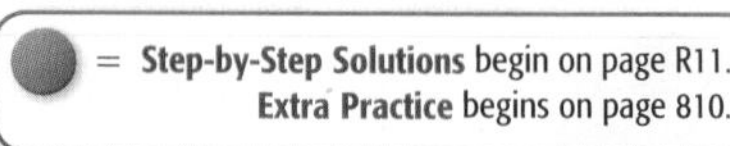
= **Step-by-Step Solutions** begin on page R11.
Extra Practice begins on page 810.

Example 1 (p. 141) Find the multiplicative inverse of each number.

14. $-\frac{4}{5}$ **$-\frac{5}{4}$**
15. $\frac{10}{19}$ **$\frac{19}{10}$ or $1\frac{9}{10}$**
16. $6\frac{1}{8}$ **$\frac{8}{49}$**
17. $-4\frac{2}{7}$ **$-\frac{7}{30}$**
18. 19 **$\frac{1}{19}$**
19. -54 **$-\frac{1}{54}$**

Examples 2 and 3 (p. 142) Find each quotient. Write in simplest form.

20. $-\frac{1}{8} \div \frac{2}{5}$ **$-\frac{5}{16}$**
21. $-\frac{5}{12} \div \frac{2}{3}$ **$-\frac{5}{8}$**
22. $-\frac{6}{7} \div \left(-\frac{16}{21}\right)$ **22. $\frac{9}{8}$ or $1\frac{1}{8}$**
23. $-\frac{4}{9} \div (-24)$ **$\frac{1}{54}$**
24. $-\frac{9}{10} \div (-21)$ **$\frac{3}{70}$**
25. $-6\frac{1}{9} \div 3\frac{2}{3}$ **$-\frac{5}{3}$ or $-1\frac{2}{3}$**
26. $-10\frac{3}{5} \div \left(-2\frac{2}{5}\right)$ **$\frac{53}{12}$ or $4\frac{5}{12}$**
27. $2\frac{3}{8} \div 1\frac{1}{6}$ **$\frac{57}{28}$ or $2\frac{1}{28}$**

Example 4 (p. 143)

28. **COOKING** Hannah is making chocolate chip cookies. How many batches of cookies can she make if she has $7\frac{1}{2}$ cups of brown sugar? Use the recipe card. **5 batches**

29. **DRAMA CLUB** How many play costumes can be made with $49\frac{1}{2}$ yards of fabric if each costume requires $4\frac{1}{8}$ yards? **12 costumes**

Chocolate Chip Cookies

- 1 cup softened butter (2 sticks)
- $\frac{1}{2}$ cup granulated sugar
- $1\frac{1}{2}$ cups packed brown sugar
- 2 eggs
- $2\frac{1}{2}$ cups all-purpose flour
- $\frac{3}{4}$ teaspoon salt
- 1 teaspoon baking powder
- 1 teaspoon baking soda
- 18 ounces chocolate chips

Example 5 (p. 143) **ALGEBRA** Find each quotient. Write in simplest form.

30. $\frac{x}{20} \div \frac{x}{5}$ **$\frac{1}{4}$**
31. $\frac{m}{6n} \div \frac{7m}{3n}$ **$\frac{1}{14}$**
32. $\frac{m}{np} \div \frac{3m}{2p}$ **$\frac{2}{3n}$**
33. $\frac{5a}{3bc} \div \frac{2a}{9bc}$ **$\frac{15}{2}$ or $7\frac{1}{2}$**

Differentiated Homework Options

Level	Assignment	Two-Day Option	
AL Basic	14–33, 42, 44–67	15–33 odd, 47–50	14–32 even, 42, 44–46, 51–67
OL Core	15–33 odd, 34–37, 39–42, 44–67	14–33, 47–50	34–42, 44–46, 51–67
BL Advanced	34–61 (optional: 62–67)		

34. **BABYSITTING** Barbara babysat for $3\frac{1}{4}$ hours and earned \$19.50. What was her hourly rate? **\$6/hour**

35. **TRAINS** A train traveled 405 miles in $4\frac{1}{2}$ hours. How fast was the train traveling on average? (*Hint:* distance equals the rate multiplied by the time.) **90 mph**

36. **PHOTOS** Sydney reduced her favorite photograph to put in a scrapbook. How many times as wide is the actual photo than the reduced photo? **$1\frac{1}{3}$**

4 in.

3 in.

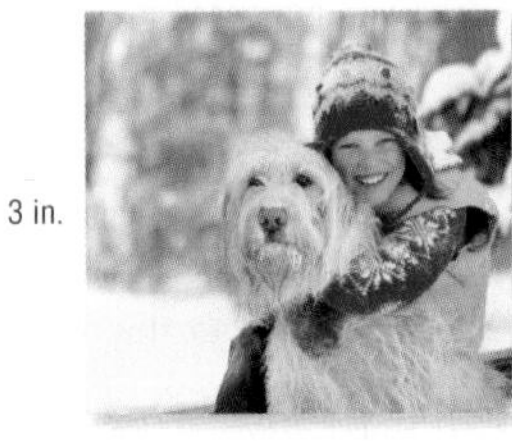

ALGEBRA **Evaluate each expression if $m = 2\frac{2}{5}$, $n = -\frac{3}{10}$, and $p = 6$.**

37. $mn \div p$ **$-\frac{3}{25}$**

38. $\frac{m}{n}$ **-8**

39. $np \div m$ **$-\frac{3}{4}$**

40. **TIE DYE** Ms. Augello is making tie dye shirts with her students. Each gallon of hot water needs $\frac{2}{3}$ cup of tie dye. If Ms. Augello has $5\frac{1}{4}$ cups of tie dye, how many batches of solution will she be able to make? **7 batches**

41. The model at the left shows $\frac{3}{4} \div \frac{1}{2}$. The model at the right shows $\frac{3}{4} \div \frac{1}{4}$.

How many $\frac{1}{2}$s are in $\frac{3}{4}$?

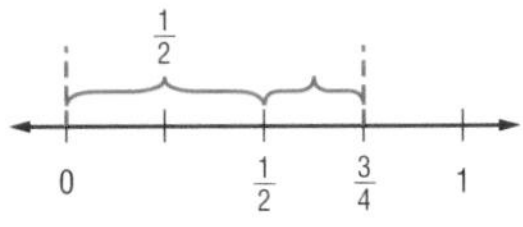

There are $1\frac{1}{2}$ $\frac{1}{2}$s in $\frac{3}{4}$.

How many $\frac{1}{4}$s are in $\frac{3}{4}$?

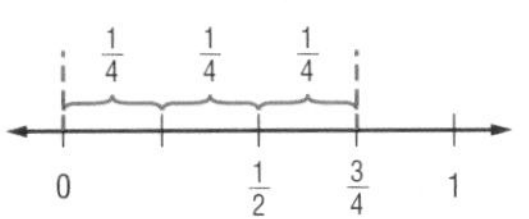

There are three $\frac{1}{4}$s in $\frac{3}{4}$.

Make a conjecture about what happens to the quotient as the value of the divisor increases. Test your conjecture. **The quotient decreases; $\frac{3}{4} \div \frac{1}{8} = 6$.**

Real-World Link

One of the more common tie dyeing techniques is the swirl. To produce the swirl effect on a T-shirt, pinch the center of the shirt and twist into a spiral. Then tie the shape with 2 rubberbands to form 4 sections.

H.O.T. Problems

Use **H**igher-**O**rder **T**hinking Skills **42–44. See margin.**

42. **OPEN ENDED** Choose two fractions and use an area model or number line to show that division of rational numbers is not commutative.

43. **CHALLENGE** Give a counterexample to this statement. *The quotient of two fractions between 0 and 1 is always a whole number.*

44. **WRITING IN MATH** Which is greater $40 \cdot \frac{1}{4}$ or $40 \div \frac{1}{4}$? Explain.

45. **REASONING** Is a whole number divided by a proper fraction *always*, *sometimes*, or *never* greater than the whole number? **always**

46. **WRITING IN MATH** Explain why, for a positive number n, $n \div \frac{1}{2} > n$.

46. Sample answer: $n \div \frac{1}{2} = 2n$, so if n is positive, $2n > n$.

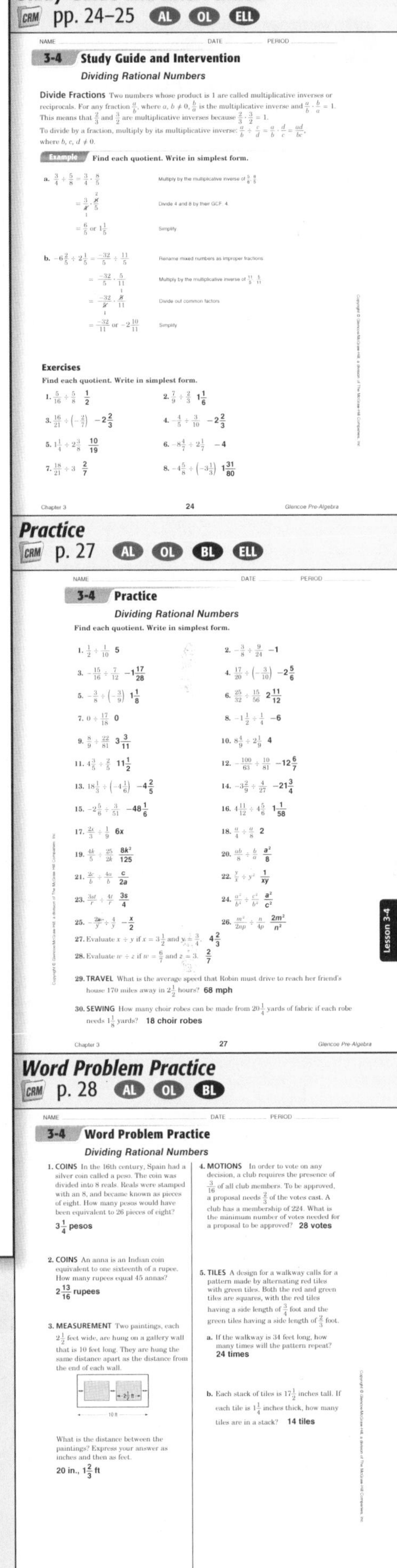

Study Guide and Intervention
CRM pp. 24–25 AL OL ELL

NAME ______ DATE ______ PERIOD ______

3-4 Study Guide and Intervention

Dividing Rational Numbers

Divide Fractions Two numbers whose product is 1 are called multiplicative inverses or reciprocals. For any fraction $\frac{a}{b}$, where $a, b \neq 0$, $\frac{b}{a}$ is the multiplicative inverse and $\frac{a}{b} \cdot \frac{b}{a} = 1$. This means that $\frac{2}{3}$ and $\frac{3}{2}$ are multiplicative inverses because $\frac{2}{3} \cdot \frac{3}{2} = 1$.

To divide by a fraction, multiply by its multiplicative inverse: $\frac{a}{b} \div \frac{c}{d} = \frac{a}{b} \cdot \frac{d}{c} = \frac{ad}{bc}$, where $b, c, d \neq 0$.

Example Find each quotient. Write in simplest form.

a. $\frac{3}{4} \div \frac{5}{8} = \frac{3}{4} \cdot \frac{8}{5}$ Multiply by the multiplicative inverse of $\frac{5}{8}$, $\frac{8}{5}$

$= \frac{3}{\cancel{4}_1} \cdot \frac{\cancel{8}^2}{5}$ Divide 4 and 8 by their GCF, 4.

$= \frac{6}{5}$ or $1\frac{1}{5}$ Simplify

b. $-6\frac{2}{5} \div 2\frac{1}{5} = \frac{-32}{5} \div \frac{11}{5}$ Rename mixed numbers as improper fractions

$= \frac{-32}{5} \cdot \frac{5}{11}$ Multiply by the multiplicative inverse of $\frac{11}{5}$, $\frac{5}{11}$

$= \frac{-32}{\cancel{5}_1} \cdot \frac{\cancel{5}^1}{11}$ Divide out common factors

$= \frac{-32}{11}$ or $-2\frac{10}{11}$ Simplify

Exercises

Find each quotient. Write in simplest form.

1. $\frac{5}{16} \div \frac{5}{8}$ **$\frac{1}{2}$**
2. $\frac{7}{9} \div \frac{2}{3}$ **$1\frac{1}{6}$**
3. $\frac{16}{21} \div \left(-\frac{2}{7}\right)$ **$-2\frac{2}{3}$**
4. $-\frac{4}{5} \div \frac{3}{10}$ **$-2\frac{2}{3}$**
5. $1\frac{1}{4} \div 2\frac{3}{8}$ **$\frac{10}{19}$**
6. $-8\frac{4}{7} \div 2\frac{1}{7}$ **-4**
7. $\frac{18}{21} \div 3$ **$\frac{2}{7}$**
8. $-4\frac{5}{8} \div \left(-3\frac{1}{3}\right)$ **$1\frac{31}{80}$**

Chapter 3 24 Glencoe Pre-Algebra

Practice
CRM p. 27 AL OL BL ELL

NAME ______ DATE ______ PERIOD ______

3-4 Practice

Dividing Rational Numbers

Find each quotient. Write in simplest form.

1. $\frac{1}{2} \div \frac{1}{10}$ **5**
2. $-\frac{3}{8} \div \frac{9}{24}$ **-1**
3. $-\frac{15}{16} \div \frac{7}{12}$ **$-1\frac{17}{28}$**
4. $\frac{17}{20} \div \left(-\frac{3}{10}\right)$ **$-2\frac{5}{6}$**
5. $-\frac{3}{8} \div \left(-\frac{3}{9}\right)$ **$1\frac{1}{8}$**
6. $\frac{25}{32} \div \frac{15}{56}$ **$2\frac{11}{12}$**
7. $0 \div \frac{17}{18}$ **0**
8. $-1\frac{1}{2} \div \frac{1}{4}$ **-6**
9. $\frac{8}{9} \div \frac{22}{81}$ **$3\frac{3}{11}$**
10. $8\frac{4}{9} \div 2\frac{1}{9}$ **4**
11. $4\frac{3}{5} \div \frac{2}{5}$ **$11\frac{1}{2}$**
12. $-\frac{100}{63} \div \frac{10}{81}$ **$-12\frac{6}{7}$**
13. $18\frac{1}{3} \div \left(-4\frac{1}{6}\right)$ **$-4\frac{2}{5}$**
14. $-3\frac{2}{9} \div \frac{4}{27}$ **$-21\frac{3}{4}$**
15. $-2\frac{5}{6} \div \frac{3}{51}$ **$-48\frac{1}{6}$**
16. $4\frac{11}{12} \div 4\frac{5}{6}$ **$1\frac{1}{58}$**
17. $\frac{2x}{3} \div \frac{1}{9}$ **$6x$**
18. $\frac{a}{4} \div \frac{a}{8}$ **2**
19. $\frac{4k}{5} \div \frac{25}{2k}$ **$\frac{8k^2}{125}$**
20. $\frac{ab}{8} \div \frac{b}{a}$ **$\frac{a^2}{8}$**
21. $\frac{2c}{b} \div \frac{4a}{b}$ **$\frac{c}{2a}$**
22. $\frac{y}{x} \div y^2$ **$\frac{1}{xy}$**
23. $\frac{3st}{r} \div \frac{4t}{r}$ **$\frac{3s}{4}$**
24. $\frac{a^2}{b^2} \div \frac{c^2}{b^2}$ **$\frac{a^2}{c^2}$**
25. $-\frac{2x}{y} \div \frac{4}{y}$ **$-\frac{x}{2}$**
26. $\frac{m^2}{2np} \div \frac{n}{4p}$ **$\frac{2m^2}{n^2}$**

27. Evaluate $x \div y$ if $x = 3\frac{1}{2}$ and $y = \frac{3}{4}$. **$4\frac{2}{3}$**

28. Evaluate $w \div z$ if $w = \frac{6}{7}$ and $z = 3$. **$\frac{2}{7}$**

29. **TRAVEL** What is the average speed that Robin must drive to reach her friend's house 170 miles away in $2\frac{1}{2}$ hours? **68 mph**

30. **SEWING** How many choir robes can be made from $20\frac{1}{4}$ yards of fabric if each robe needs $1\frac{1}{8}$ yards? **18 choir robes**

Chapter 3 27 Glencoe Pre-Algebra

Lesson 3-4

Word Problem Practice
CRM p. 28 AL OL BL

NAME ______ DATE ______ PERIOD ______

3-4 Word Problem Practice

Dividing Rational Numbers

1. **COINS** In the 16th century, Spain had a silver coin called a peso. The coin was divided into 8 reals. Reals were stamped with an 8, and became known as pieces of eight. How many pesos would have been equivalent to 26 pieces of eight? **$3\frac{1}{4}$ pesos**

2. **COINS** An anna is an Indian coin equivalent to one sixteenth of a rupee. How many rupees equal 45 annas? **$2\frac{13}{16}$ rupees**

3. **MEASUREMENT** Two paintings, each $2\frac{1}{2}$ feet wide, are hung on a gallery wall that is 10 feet long. They are hung the same distance apart as the distance from the end of each wall.

$2\frac{1}{2}$ ft
10 ft

What is the distance between the paintings? Express your answer as inches and then as feet. **20 in., $1\frac{2}{3}$ ft**

4. **MOTIONS** In order to vote on any decision, a club requires the presence of $\frac{3}{16}$ of all club members. To be approved, a proposal needs $\frac{2}{3}$ of the votes cast. A club has a membership of 224. What is the minimum number of votes needed for a proposal to be approved? **28 votes**

5. **TILES** A design for a walkway calls for a pattern made by alternating red tiles with green tiles. Both the red and green tiles are squares, with the red tiles having a side length of $\frac{3}{4}$ foot and the green tiles having a side length of $\frac{2}{3}$ foot.

a. If the walkway is 34 feet long, how many times will the pattern repeat? **24 times**

b. Each stack of tiles is $17\frac{1}{2}$ inches tall. If each tile is $1\frac{1}{4}$ inches thick, how many tiles are in a stack? **14 tiles**

Chapter 3 28 Glencoe Pre-Algebra

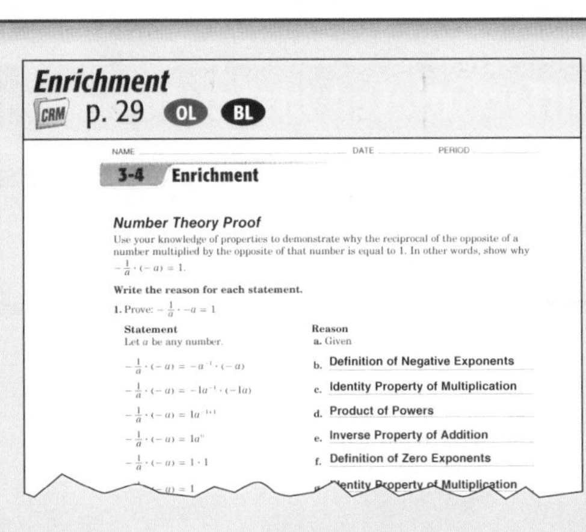

Enrichment
CRM p. 29 OL BL

NAME ______ DATE ______ PERIOD ______

3-4 Enrichment

Number Theory Proof

Use your knowledge of properties to demonstrate why the reciprocal of the opposite of a number multiplied by the opposite of that number is equal to 1. In other words, show why $-\frac{1}{a} \cdot (-a) = 1$.

Write the reason for each statement.

1. Prove: $-\frac{1}{a} \cdot -a = 1$

Statement	Reason
Let a be any number.	a. Given
$-\frac{1}{a} \cdot (-a) = -a^{-1} \cdot (-a)$	b. **Definition of Negative Exponents**
$-\frac{1}{a} \cdot (-a) = -1a^{-1} \cdot (-1a)$	c. **Identity Property of Multiplication**
$-\frac{1}{a} \cdot (-a) = 1a^{-1+1}$	d. **Product of Powers**
$-\frac{1}{a} \cdot (-a) = 1a^{0}$	e. **Inverse Property of Addition**
$-\frac{1}{a} \cdot (-a) = 1 \cdot 1$	f. **Definition of Zero Exponents**
$-\frac{1}{a} \cdot (-a) = 1$	g. **Identity Property of Multiplication**

ASSESS

Ticket Out the Door Give students two problems with division of rational numbers, including whole numbers and mixed numbers. Ask them to write a word problem that fits each problem. Have them turn in the paper as they exit the room.

Standardized Test Practice

47. Heidi is having a party. She is planning that each of her 16 guests will have $\frac{3}{4}$ cup of snack mix. She has made 12 cups of snack mix. Which expression could Heidi use to determine if she has made enough snack mix for each of her guests? **C**

A $16 \div \frac{3}{4}$ C $12 \div \frac{3}{4}$

B $12 \div 16$ D $\frac{3}{4}(12)$

48. A bag of potting soil contains $4\frac{1}{4}$ pounds of soil. Each flower that Mr. Henderson plants will need $\frac{1}{8}$ pound of soil. How many flowers will he be able to plant? **J**

F 16 H 32

G 28 J 34

49. A recipe for one batch of soft pretzels calls for $\frac{1}{4}$ cup of salt and $\frac{2}{3}$ cup of sugar. If Mrs. Valdez used $\frac{7}{8}$ cup of salt and $2\frac{1}{3}$ cups of sugar, how many batches of pretzels has she made? **A**

A $3\frac{1}{2}$ C $2\frac{1}{4}$

B 3 D 2

50. **SHORT RESPONSE** Popcorn is sold in a variety of sizes. Use the table to find how many times as large the regular bag of popcorn is than the snack bag. $2\frac{1}{2}$

Size	Amount (cups)
Snack	$3\frac{1}{2}$
Regular	$8\frac{3}{4}$
Large	12

Spiral Review

Find each product. Write in simplest form. (Lesson 3-3)

51. $2 \cdot \frac{9}{16}$ $\frac{9}{8}$ or $1\frac{1}{8}$

52. $-4\frac{4}{7} \cdot 2\frac{5}{8}$ -12

53. $\frac{3}{20} \cdot \left(-\frac{10}{11}\right)$ $-\frac{3}{22}$

54. $-6\frac{1}{2} \cdot \left(-3\frac{1}{4}\right)$ $\frac{169}{8}$ or $21\frac{1}{8}$

55. $-\frac{5}{6} \cdot \left(-1\frac{7}{35}\right)$ 1

56. $1\frac{1}{8} \cdot 1\frac{1}{3}$ $\frac{3}{2}$ or $1\frac{1}{2}$

57. **WHITE HOUSE** The White House covers an area of 0.028 square mile. What fraction of a square mile is this? (Lesson 3-2) $\frac{7}{250}$ mi^2

58. **SPORTS** The Wildcat football team was penalized the same amount four times during the third quarter. The total of the four penalties was 60 yards. If –60 represents a loss of 60 yards, write a division sentence to represent this situation. Then express the number of yards of each penalty as an integer. (Lesson 2-5) $-60 \div 4 = y$; -15

Find each product. (Lesson 2-4)

59. $12(-6)$ -72

60. $-12(-11)$ 132

61. $4(-2)(-6)$ 48

Skills Review

Find each sum or difference. (Lessons 2-2 and 2-3)

62. $23 - (-13)$ 36

63. $-42 + (-26)$ -68

64. $-80 - (-80)$ 0

65. $n + 2n$ $3n$

66. $-4x - (-3x)$ $-1x$ or $-x$

67. $5n - 10n$ $-5n$

Differentiated Instruction

BL

Extension A fraction is a division problem. Have students find the solution to $\frac{-\frac{1}{3}}{4}$.

$-\frac{1}{3} \div 4 = -\frac{1}{3} \cdot \frac{1}{4} = -\frac{1}{12}$

3-5

Adding and Subtracting Like Fractions

Then

You have already added and subtracted positive fractions with like denominators. (Previous Course)

Now

- Add rational numbers with common denominators.
- Subtract rational numbers with common denominators.

New Vocabulary

like fractions

Math Online

glencoe.com

- Extra Examples
- Personal Tutor
- Self-Check Quiz
- Homework Help

Why?

Javier is making a smoothie that uses $\frac{1}{8}$ cup of milk and $\frac{3}{8}$ cup of pineapple juice. Javier will use $\frac{4}{8}$ cup of liquid in his smoothie. Use the measuring cup to find each of the following measures.

a. $\frac{1}{8}c + \frac{1}{8}c$ $\frac{2}{8}$ c

b. $\frac{3}{8}c + \frac{2}{8}c$ $\frac{5}{8}$ c

c. $\frac{5}{8}c + \frac{2}{8}c$ $\frac{7}{8}$ c

d. $\frac{8}{8}c - \frac{4}{8}c$ $\frac{4}{8}$ c

Add Like Fractions **Like fractions** are fractions with the same denominator.

Key Concept — Adding Like Fractions

For Your FOLDABLE

Words To add fractions with like denominators, add the numerators and write the sum over the denominator.

Symbols $\frac{a}{c} + \frac{b}{c} = \frac{a+b}{c}$, where $c \neq 0$

Example $\frac{2}{8} + \frac{3}{8} = \frac{2+3}{8}$ or $\frac{5}{8}$

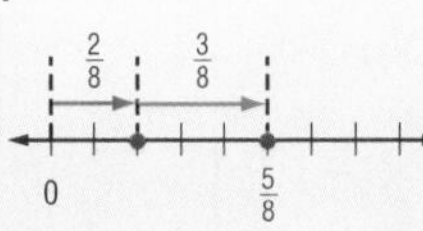

EXAMPLE 1 Add Fractions

Find each sum. Write in simplest form.

a. $\frac{7}{10} + \frac{6}{10}$ Estimate $1 + \frac{1}{2} = 1\frac{1}{2}$

$\frac{7}{10} + \frac{6}{10} = \frac{7+6}{10}$ The denominators are the same. Add the numerators.

$= \frac{13}{10}$ or $1\frac{3}{10}$ Simplify and rename as a mixed number. Is the answer reasonable?

b. $\frac{5}{8} + \left(-\frac{7}{8}\right)$ Estimate $\frac{1}{2} + (-1) = -\frac{1}{2}$

$\frac{5}{8} + \left(-\frac{7}{8}\right) = \frac{5+(-7)}{8}$ The denominators are the same. Add the numerators.

$= \frac{-2}{8}$ or $-\frac{1}{4}$ Simplify. Compare to the estimate. Is it reasonable?

Check Your Progress

1A. $\frac{5}{6} + \frac{4}{6}$ $1\frac{1}{2}$

1B. $\frac{4}{7} + (-\frac{6}{7})$ $-\frac{2}{7}$

Personal Tutor glencoe.com

3-5 Lesson Notes

1 FOCUS

Vertical Alignment

Before Lesson 3-5
Add and subtract positive fractions with like denominators.

Lesson 3-5
Add rational numbers with common denominators.
Subtract rational numbers with common denominators.

After Lesson 3-5
Solve equations involving the addition and subtraction of rational numbers with like denominators.

2 TEACH

Scaffolding Questions

Have students read the *Why?* section of the lesson and answer the questions.

Ask:

- If Javier used $\frac{1}{8}$ cup strawberries and $\frac{2}{8}$ cup blueberries, how much fruit would he have used? $\frac{3}{8}$ cup
- Write the amount of liquid Javier uses in one smoothie in simplest form. $\frac{1}{2}$ cup
- When adding or subtracting fractions with like denominators, does the denominator change? no

Lesson 3-5 Resources

Resource	Approaching-Level	On-Level	Beyond-Level	English Learners
Teacher Edition	• Differentiated Instruction, p. 148		• Differentiated Instruction, p. 152	• Differentiated Instruction, p. 148
Chapter Resource Masters	• Study Guide and Intervention, pp. 30–31 • Skills Practice, p. 32 • Practice, p. 33 • Word Problem Practice, p. 34	• Study Guide and Intervention, pp. 30–31 • Skills Practice, p. 32 • Practice, p. 33 • Word Problem Practice, p. 34 • Enrichment, p. 35	• Practice, p. 33 • Word Problem Practice, p. 34 • Enrichment, p. 35	• Study Guide and Intervention, pp. 30–31 • Skills Practice, p. 32 • Practice, p. 33
Transparencies	• 5-Minute Check Transparency 3-5	• 5-Minute Check Transparency 3-5	• 5-Minute Check Transparency 3-5	• 5-Minute Check Transparency 3-5
Other	• Study Notebook • Teaching Pre-Algebra with Manipulatives	• Study Notebook • Teaching Pre-Algebra with Manipulatives	• Study Notebook	• Study Notebook • Teaching Pre-Algebra with Manipulatives

Add Like Fractions

Example 1 shows how to add fractions that have the same denominators. **Example 2** shows how to add mixed numbers with the same denominator.

Formative Assessment

Use the Check Your Progress exercises after each example to determine students' understanding of concepts.

Additional Examples

1 Find each sum. Write in simplest form.

a. $\frac{3}{4}+\frac{3}{4}$ $1\frac{1}{2}$

b. $\frac{5}{9}+\left(-\frac{7}{9}\right)$ $-\frac{2}{9}$

2 Find $3\frac{4}{9}+8\frac{2}{9}$. Write in simplest form. $11\frac{2}{3}$

Additional Examples also in Interactive Classroom PowerPoint® Presentations

IWB INTERACTIVE WHITEBOARD READY

Subtract Like Fractions

Example 3 shows how to subtract fractions that have the same denominators. **Example 4** shows how to subtract mixed numbers with regrouping. **Example 5** shows how to subtract mixed numbers to solve a real-world problem. **Example 6** shows how to add and subtract algebraic fractions.

Additional Example

3 Find $\frac{11}{12}-\frac{5}{12}$. Write in simplest form. $\frac{1}{2}$

StudyTip

Alternative Method When adding or subtracting mixed numbers, you can write them as improper fractions before adding or subtracting. If any of the numbers are negative, it is easier to use this method.

$$2\frac{3}{8}+3\frac{7}{8}=\frac{19}{8}+\frac{31}{8}$$
$$=\frac{50}{8}\text{ or }6\frac{1}{4}$$

EXAMPLE 2 Add Mixed Numbers

Find $2\frac{3}{8}+3\frac{7}{8}$. Write in simplest form.

Estimate $2+4=6$

$2\frac{3}{8}+3\frac{7}{8}=(2+3)+\left(\frac{3}{8}+\frac{7}{8}\right)$ **Add the whole numbers and fractions separately.**

$=5+\frac{10}{8}$ **Add the numerators.**

$=5\frac{10}{8}\text{ or }6\frac{1}{4}$ **Simplify. Rename $5\frac{10}{8}$ as $6\frac{2}{8}$ or $6\frac{1}{4}$.**

Check for Reasonableness $6\frac{1}{4}\approx 6$ ✓

Check Your Progress

Find each sum. Write in simplest form.

2A. $1\frac{3}{4}+4\frac{3}{4}$ $6\frac{1}{2}$ **2B.** $3\frac{2}{5}+8\frac{1}{5}$ $11\frac{3}{5}$ **2C.** $-2\frac{3}{7}+\left(-4\frac{5}{7}\right)$ $-7\frac{1}{7}$

Personal Tutor glencoe.com

Subtract Like Fractions The rule for subtracting fractions with like denominators is similar to the rule for addition.

Key Concept Subtracting Like Fractions

For Your FOLDABLE

Words To subtract fractions with like denominators, subtract the numerators and write the difference over the denominator.

Symbols $\frac{a}{c}-\frac{b}{c}=\frac{a-b}{c}$, where $c\neq 0$

Example $\frac{4}{9}-\frac{3}{9}=\frac{4-3}{9}$ or $\frac{1}{9}$

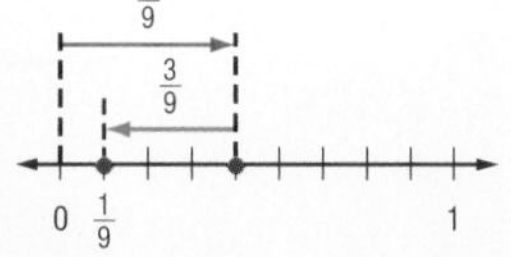

EXAMPLE 3 Subtract Fractions

Find $\frac{3}{10}-\frac{9}{10}$. Write in simplest form.

Estimate $\frac{1}{2}-1=-\frac{1}{2}$

$\frac{3}{10}-\frac{9}{10}=\frac{3-9}{10}$ **The denominators are the same. Subtract the numerators.**

$=\frac{-6}{10}\text{ or }-\frac{3}{5}$ **Simplify.**

Check for Reasonableness $-\frac{3}{5}\approx-\frac{1}{2}$ ✓

Check Your Progress

Find each difference. Write in simplest form.

3A. $\frac{5}{15}-\frac{10}{15}$ $-\frac{1}{3}$ **3B.** $\frac{3}{9}-\frac{4}{9}$ $-\frac{1}{9}$ **3C.** $\frac{7}{8}-\frac{3}{8}$ $\frac{1}{2}$

Personal Tutor glencoe.com

Differentiated Instruction

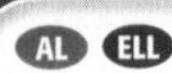

If students struggle with adding and subtracting fractions with like denominators,

Then have them use rectangles divided into parts to model addition and subtraction of fractions. Students can also draw rectangles on paper (or grid paper), and then shade in the fractions to be added or subtracted.

148 Chapter 3 Operations with Rational Numbers

EXAMPLE 4 Subtract Mixed Numbers with Regrouping

Evaluate $x - y$ when $x = 3\frac{1}{4}$ and $y = 1\frac{3}{4}$.

$x - y = 3\frac{1}{4} - 1\frac{3}{4}$ **Replace x with $3\frac{1}{4}$ and y with $1\frac{3}{4}$.**

Since $\frac{1}{4}$ is less than $\frac{3}{4}$, rename $3\frac{1}{4}$ before subtracting.

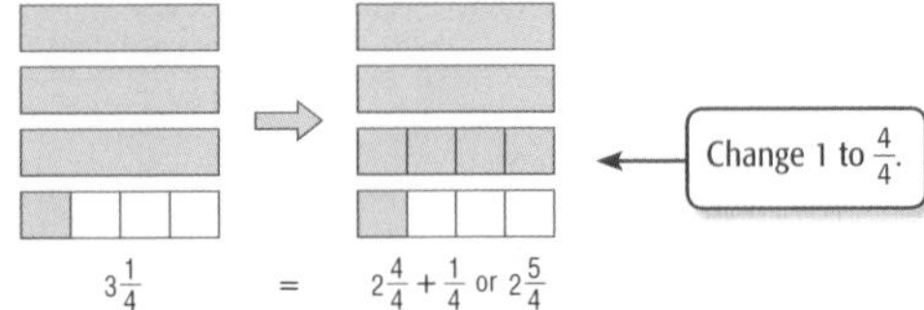

Change 1 to $\frac{4}{4}$.
$3\frac{1}{4}$ = $2\frac{4}{4} + \frac{1}{4}$ or $2\frac{5}{4}$

$3\frac{1}{4} - 1\frac{3}{4} = 2\frac{5}{4} - 1\frac{3}{4}$ **Rename $3\frac{1}{4}$ as $2\frac{5}{4}$.**

$= 1\frac{2}{4}$ **Subtract the whole numbers and then the fractions.**

$= 1\frac{1}{2}$ **Simplify.**

Check Your Progress

4. Evaluate $x - y$ when $x = 9\frac{3}{8}$ and $y = 5\frac{5}{8}$. $3\frac{3}{4}$

Personal Tutor glencoe.com

Real-World EXAMPLE 5 Subtract Mixed Numbers

CRAFTS LaShaun has $5\frac{1}{8}$ yards of ribbon to border scrapbook pages. If she uses $1\frac{7}{8}$ yards on one page, how much ribbon is left?

Understand You know how much ribbon she has and how much ribbon she will use.

Plan Subtract the amount of ribbon she will use from the total amount of ribbon.

Estimate $5\frac{1}{8} - 1\frac{7}{8} \approx 5 - 2$ **or 3 yards**

Solve $5\frac{1}{8} - 1\frac{7}{8} = 4\frac{9}{8} - 1\frac{7}{8}$ **Rename**

$= 3\frac{2}{8}$ **Subtract the whole numbers and then the fractions.**

$= 3\frac{2}{8}$ or $3\frac{1}{4}$ **Simplify.**

LaShaun has $3\frac{1}{4}$ yards of ribbon remaining.

Check Since $3\frac{1}{2}$ is close to 3, the answer is reasonable. ✔

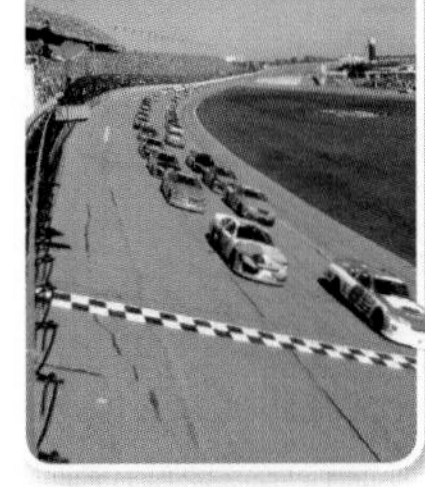

Real-World Link

The Daytona 500 is the first Nextel Cup Race of the annual NASCAR season. In 2008, the race celebrated its 50th anniversary.

Check Your Progress

5. **CAR RACING** The Daytona International Speedway is one of the longest tracks used in NASCAR races. It is $2\frac{2}{4}$ miles long. Richmond International Speedway is $\frac{3}{4}$ mile long. How much longer is the Daytona Speedway than the Richmond Speedway? $1\frac{3}{4}$ miles

Personal Tutor glencoe.com

Additional Examples

4 Evaluate $q - r$ if $r = 7\frac{3}{5}$ and $q = 9\frac{1}{5}$. $1\frac{3}{5}$

5 **COOKING** Keora bought $3\frac{3}{8}$ pounds of apples. If she uses $1\frac{7}{8}$ pounds for a pie, how many pounds of apples does she have left? $1\frac{1}{2}$

Focus on Mathematical Content

Algebraic Fractions The same steps used for numerical fractions are followed when adding or subtracting algebraic fractions with unlike variables in the numerators. The fractions may not reduce. For example, $\frac{x}{7} + \frac{2y}{7} = \frac{x+2y}{7}$.

TEACH with TECH

INTERACTIVE WHITEBOARD Create a template that you can use to show addition of fractions, such as:

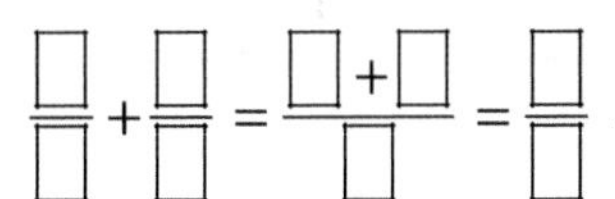

Use the template and write on the whiteboard as you work through examples.

Additional Example

Find $\frac{5}{2b} + \frac{3}{2b}$. Write in the simplest form. $\frac{4}{b}$

3 PRACTICE

Formative Assessment

Use Exercises 1–13 to check for understanding.

Use the chart at the bottom of this page to customize assignments for your students.

Watch Out!

Find the Error Remind students that they can use a number line to check Xavier's solution to the addition problem in Exercise 45.

Additional Answers

46. Sample answer: Group the fractions that have the same denominator; they all add up to one each. Add the whole numbers: $1 + 2 + 3 + 4 + 5 + 6 = 21$ plus the fraction groups $+ 3 = 24$.

47. Sample answer: A recipe requires $\frac{3}{4}$ cup of milk and $1\frac{1}{4}$ cups of water. How much liquid is in the recipe?; 2 cups

You can use the same rules for adding or subtracting like algebraic fractions as you did for adding or subtracting like numerical fractions.

EXAMPLE 6 Add or Subtract Algebraic Fractions

Find $\frac{2a}{10} + \frac{4a}{10}$. Write in simplest form.

$\frac{2a}{10} + \frac{4a}{10} = \frac{2a + 4a}{10}$ **The denominators are the same. Add the numerators.**

$= \frac{6a}{10}$ or $\frac{3a}{5}$ **Simplify.**

Check Your Progress

Find each sum or difference. Write in simplest form.

6A. $\frac{y}{8} + \frac{5y}{8}$ $\frac{3y}{4}$ **6B.** $\frac{3x}{7} - \frac{5x}{7}$ $-\frac{2x}{7}$ **6C.** $\frac{x}{5} + \frac{4x}{5}$ $1x$ or x

Personal Tutor glencoe.com

Check Your Understanding

Examples 1–3 pp. 147–148

Find each sum or difference. Write in simplest form.

1. $\frac{3}{6} + \frac{5}{6}$ $1\frac{1}{3}$
2. $\frac{2}{9} + \left(-\frac{4}{9}\right)$ $-\frac{2}{9}$
3. $\frac{4}{12} - \frac{10}{12}$ $-\frac{1}{2}$
4. $\frac{8}{15} - \frac{11}{15}$ $-\frac{1}{5}$
5. $3\frac{3}{8} + 6\frac{5}{8}$ 10
6. $2\frac{1}{6} + 8\frac{3}{6}$ $10\frac{2}{3}$

Example 4 p. 149

ALGEBRA Evaluate each expression if $s = 7\frac{1}{7}$ and $t = 6\frac{3}{7}$.

7. $s - t$ $\frac{5}{7}$
8. $t - s$ $-\frac{5}{7}$
9. $2s - t$ $7\frac{6}{7}$

Example 5 p. 149

10. **WOODWORKING** Mia is making a bookcase and has $92\frac{5}{8}$ inches of wood. If she uses $30\frac{7}{8}$ inches of wood for the top and bottom, find the amount of wood she has left for the sides. $61\frac{3}{4}$

Example 6 p. 150

ALGEBRA Find each sum or difference. Write in simplest form.

11. $\frac{5x}{y} - \frac{7x}{y}, y \neq 0$ $-\frac{2x}{y}$
12. $\frac{3a}{13} + (-\frac{8a}{13})$ $-\frac{5a}{13}$
13. $-\frac{4c}{ab} - \frac{8c}{ab}, a, b \neq 0$ $-\frac{12c}{ab}$

Practice and Problem Solving

● = **Step-by-Step Solutions** begin on page R11. **Extra Practice** begins on page 810.

Examples 1–3 pp. 147–148

Find each sum or difference. Write in simplest form.

14. $\frac{5}{6} + \left(-\frac{4}{6}\right)$ $\frac{1}{6}$
15. $-\frac{11}{12} + \frac{7}{12}$ $-\frac{1}{3}$
16. $\frac{3}{14} + \left(-\frac{5}{14}\right)$ $-\frac{1}{7}$
17. $-\frac{3}{7} + \frac{6}{7}$ $\frac{3}{7}$
18. $5\frac{1}{4} + \left(5\frac{1}{4}\right)$ $10\frac{1}{2}$
19. $12\frac{5}{9} + 1\frac{1}{9}$ $13\frac{2}{3}$
20. $2\frac{12}{13} + -7\frac{10}{13}$ $-\frac{63}{13}$ or $-4\frac{11}{13}$
21. $-8\frac{3}{10} + 4\frac{9}{10}$ 21. $-\frac{17}{5}$ or $-3\frac{2}{5}$
22. $\frac{2}{15} - \frac{7}{15}$ $-\frac{1}{3}$
23. $\frac{5}{11} - \frac{7}{11}$ $-\frac{2}{11}$
24. $-\frac{1}{5} - \frac{4}{5}$ -1
25. ● $-\frac{7}{20} - \frac{7}{20}$ $-\frac{7}{10}$

Example 4 p. 149

ALGEBRA Evaluate each expression if $a = 4\frac{4}{9}$, $b = 6\frac{5}{9}$, and $c = \frac{1}{9}$.

26. $b - a$ $2\frac{1}{9}$
27. $a - b$ $-2\frac{1}{9}$
28. $c - a$ $-4\frac{1}{3}$
29. $c - b$ $-6\frac{4}{9}$

Differentiated Homework Options

Level	Assignment	Two-Day Option	
AL Basic	14–35, 43, 45, 47–65	15–35 odd, 48–51	14–28 even, 43, 45, 47, 52–65
OL Core	15–37 odd, 38–41, 43, 45, 47–65	14–34, 48–51	36–43, 45, 47, 52–65
BL Advanced	36–59 (optional: 60–65)		

Example 5 p. 149

30. **MEASUREMENT** Nan was $59\frac{7}{8}$ inches tall at the end of the summer. She was $62\frac{1}{8}$ inches by her birthday in March. How much did she grow during that time? $2\frac{1}{4}$ **inches**

31. **FOOD** Yahto needs $3\frac{3}{4}$ cups of sugar to make cookies. He needs an additional $\frac{3}{4}$ cup for bread. Find the total amount of sugar that Yahto needs. $4\frac{1}{2}$ **c**

Example 6 p. 150

ALGEBRA Find each sum or difference. Write in simplest form.

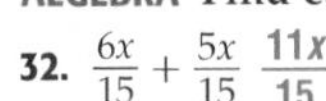

32. $\frac{6x}{15}+\frac{5x}{15}$ $\frac{11x}{15}$ 33. $\frac{2m}{5}+\frac{7m}{5}$ $\frac{9m}{5}$ 34. $\frac{7a}{10}+\frac{4a}{10}$ $\frac{11a}{10}$ 35. $-\frac{p}{14}+\frac{6p}{14}$ $\frac{5p}{14}$

Find each sum or difference. Write in simplest form.

B 36. $-2\frac{9}{10}+\left(-9\frac{9}{10}\right)+\left(-6\frac{9}{10}\right)$ $-19\frac{7}{10}$ 37. $\frac{1}{9}-2\frac{4}{9}-\frac{5}{9}$ $-2\frac{8}{9}$

38. **SPORTS** A triathlon consists of three races: swimming, biking and hiking. If an athlete swims for $18\frac{2}{4}$ minutes, runs for $37\frac{3}{4}$ minutes, and bikes for $59\frac{1}{4}$ minutes, what was his total time? $115\frac{2}{4}$ **or** $115\frac{1}{2}$ **minutes**

39. **PETS** The table shows the weight of Leon's dog during its first 5 years.

Age (years)	1	2	3	4	5
Weight (pounds)	$17\frac{2}{8}$	$18\frac{5}{8}$	$19\frac{4}{8}$	$18\frac{3}{8}$	$20\frac{7}{8}$

a. How much weight did Leon's dog gain or lose between ages 3 and 4? between years 1 and 5? $1\frac{1}{8}$ **lb;** $3\frac{5}{8}$ **lb**

b. If Leon's dog gains $1\frac{3}{8}$ pounds each year between years 5 and 7, how much will his dog weigh? $23\frac{5}{8}$ **lb**

40. **COOKING** Chad is making lasagna for a party. The recipe uses $1\frac{2}{4}$-teaspoons of basil, $\frac{2}{4}$ teaspoon of salt, $\frac{1}{4}$ teaspoon of pepper, and 4 teaspoons of parsley. If he needs to double the recipe, how many teaspoons will he use? $12\frac{1}{2}$ **teaspoons**

Real-World Career

Chef

Chefs frequently work with fractional measurements when preparing dishes and when creating their own recipes.

Education and training for chefs range from on the job training to obtaining a 4-year degree. Many cities have culinary institutes which offer associate degree programs with restaurant experience.

C **ALGEBRA Find each sum or difference. Write in simplest form.**

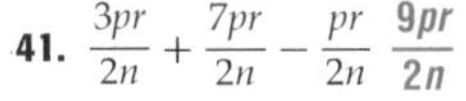

41. $\frac{3pr}{2n}+\frac{7pr}{2n}-\frac{pr}{2n}$ $\frac{9pr}{2n}$ 42. $-\frac{8x}{y}+\frac{6x}{y}+\left(-\frac{3x}{y}\right)$ $-\frac{5x}{y}$

H.O.T. Problems

Use Higher-Order Thinking Skills

43. **OPEN ENDED** Write a subtraction problem with a difference of $-\frac{2}{3}$.

44. **CHALLENGE** Lopez Construction is replacing a window in a house. The window is currently 3 feet wide by 4 feet tall. The homeowner wants to add 9 inches to each side of the window. What is the new perimeter of the window in feet? Support your answer with a model.

45. **FIND THE ERROR** Xavier said the sum of $-4\frac{1}{9}$ and $1\frac{7}{9}$ is $-3\frac{8}{9}$. Is he correct? Explain your reasoning.

46. **CHALLENGE** Explain how you could use mental math to find the following sum. Then find the sum. Support your answer with a model.

46–47. See margin. $1\frac{1}{4}+2\frac{1}{3}+3\frac{2}{3}+4\frac{1}{2}+5\frac{1}{2}+6\frac{3}{4}$

47. **WRITING IN MATH** Write a real-world problem about cooking that can be solved by adding or subtracting fractions. Then solve the problem.

43. Sample answer: $\frac{1}{3}-1=-\frac{2}{3}$

44. 17 feet $3\frac{9}{12}+3\frac{9}{12}+4\frac{9}{12}+4\frac{9}{12}=14\frac{36}{12}$ or 17 feet.

45. No; he did not add the fraction part of the mixed numbers correctly.

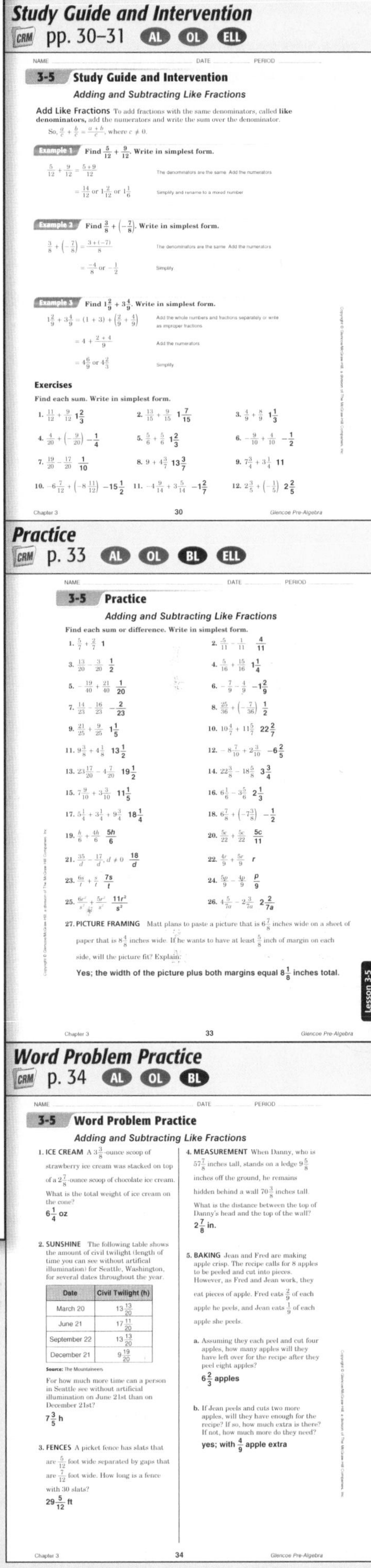

Study Guide and Intervention CRM pp. 30–31 AL OL ELL

3-5 Study Guide and Intervention

Adding and Subtracting Like Fractions

Add Like Fractions To add fractions with the same denominators, called like denominators, add the numerators and write the sum over the denominator.

So, $\frac{a}{c}+\frac{b}{c}=\frac{a+b}{c}$, where $c \neq 0$.

Example 1 Find $\frac{5}{12}+\frac{9}{12}$. Write in simplest form.

$\frac{5}{12}+\frac{9}{12}=\frac{5+9}{12}$ The denominators are the same. Add the numerators.

$=\frac{14}{12}$ or $1\frac{2}{12}$ or $1\frac{1}{6}$ Simplify and rename to a mixed number.

Example 2 Find $\frac{3}{8}+\left(-\frac{7}{8}\right)$. Write in simplest form.

$\frac{3}{8}+\left(-\frac{7}{8}\right)=\frac{3+(-7)}{8}$ The denominators are the same. Add the numerators.

$=\frac{-4}{8}$ or $-\frac{1}{2}$ Simplify.

Example 3 Find $1\frac{2}{9}+3\frac{4}{9}$. Write in simplest form.

$1\frac{2}{9}+3\frac{4}{9}=(1+3)+\left(\frac{2}{9}+\frac{4}{9}\right)$ Add the whole numbers and fractions separately or write as improper fractions.

$=4+\frac{2+4}{9}$ Add the numerators.

$=4\frac{6}{9}$ or $4\frac{2}{3}$ Simplify.

Exercises

Find each sum. Write in simplest form.

1. $\frac{11}{12}+\frac{9}{12}$ $1\frac{2}{3}$ 2. $\frac{13}{15}+\frac{9}{15}$ $1\frac{7}{15}$ 3. $\frac{4}{9}+\frac{8}{9}$ $1\frac{1}{3}$
4. $\frac{4}{20}+\left(-\frac{9}{20}\right)$ $-\frac{1}{4}$ 5. $\frac{5}{6}+\frac{5}{6}$ $1\frac{2}{3}$ 6. $-\frac{9}{10}+\frac{4}{10}$ $-\frac{1}{2}$
7. $\frac{19}{20}-\frac{17}{20}$ $\frac{1}{10}$ 8. $9+4\frac{3}{7}$ $13\frac{3}{7}$ 9. $7\frac{3}{4}+3\frac{1}{4}$ 11
10. $-6\frac{7}{12}+\left(-8\frac{11}{12}\right)$ $-15\frac{1}{2}$ 11. $-4\frac{9}{14}+3\frac{5}{14}$ $-1\frac{2}{7}$ 12. $2\frac{3}{5}+\left(-\frac{1}{5}\right)$ $2\frac{2}{5}$

Chapter 3 30 Glencoe Pre-Algebra

Practice CRM p. 33 AL OL BL ELL

3-5 Practice

Adding and Subtracting Like Fractions

Find each sum or difference. Write in simplest form.

1. $\frac{5}{7}+\frac{2}{7}$ 1 2. $\frac{5}{11}-\frac{1}{11}$ $\frac{4}{11}$
3. $\frac{13}{20}-\frac{3}{20}$ $\frac{1}{2}$ 4. $\frac{5}{16}+\frac{15}{16}$ $1\frac{1}{4}$
5. $-\frac{19}{40}+\frac{21}{40}$ $\frac{1}{20}$ 6. $-\frac{7}{9}-\frac{4}{9}$ $-1\frac{2}{9}$
7. $\frac{14}{23}-\frac{16}{23}$ $-\frac{2}{23}$ 8. $\frac{25}{36}+\left(-\frac{7}{36}\right)$ $\frac{1}{2}$
9. $\frac{21}{25}+\frac{9}{25}$ $1\frac{1}{5}$ 10. $10\frac{4}{7}+11\frac{5}{7}$ $22\frac{2}{7}$
11. $9\frac{3}{8}+4\frac{1}{8}$ $13\frac{1}{2}$ 12. $-8\frac{7}{10}+2\frac{3}{10}$ $-6\frac{2}{5}$
13. $23\frac{17}{20}-4\frac{7}{20}$ $19\frac{1}{2}$ 14. $22\frac{3}{8}-18\frac{5}{8}$ $3\frac{3}{4}$
15. $7\frac{9}{10}+3\frac{3}{10}$ $11\frac{1}{5}$ 16. $6\frac{1}{6}-3\frac{5}{6}$ $2\frac{1}{3}$
17. $5\frac{1}{4}+3\frac{1}{4}+9\frac{3}{4}$ $18\frac{1}{4}$ 18. $6\frac{7}{8}+\left(-7\frac{3}{8}\right)$ $-\frac{1}{2}$
19. $\frac{h}{6}+\frac{4h}{6}$ $\frac{5h}{6}$ 20. $\frac{5c}{22}+\frac{5c}{22}$ $\frac{5c}{11}$
21. $\frac{35}{d}-\frac{17}{d}$, $d \neq 0$ $\frac{18}{d}$ 22. $\frac{4r}{9}+\frac{5r}{9}$ r
23. $\frac{6t}{t}+\frac{t}{t}$ $\frac{7s}{t}$ 24. $\frac{5p}{9}-\frac{4p}{9}$ $\frac{p}{9}$
25. $\frac{6r^2}{s^2}+\frac{5r^2}{s^2}$ $\frac{11r^2}{s^2}$ 26. $4\frac{5}{7a}-2\frac{3}{7a}$ $2\frac{2}{7a}$

27. PICTURE FRAMING Matt plans to paste a picture that is $6\frac{7}{8}$ inches wide on a sheet of paper that is $8\frac{4}{8}$ inches wide. If he wants to have at least $\frac{5}{8}$ inch of margin on each side, will the picture fit? Explain.

Yes; the width of the picture plus both margins equal $8\frac{1}{8}$ inches total.

Chapter 3 33 Glencoe Pre-Algebra

Word Problem Practice CRM p. 34 AL OL BL

3-5 Word Problem Practice

Adding and Subtracting Like Fractions

1. ICE CREAM A $3\frac{3}{8}$-ounce scoop of strawberry ice cream was stacked on top of a $2\frac{7}{8}$-ounce scoop of chocolate ice cream. What is the total weight of ice cream on the cone? $6\frac{1}{4}$ oz

2. SUNSHINE The following table shows the amount of civil twilight (length of time you can see without artifical illumination) for Seattle, Washington, for several dates throughout the year.

Date	Civil Twilight (h)
March 20	$13\frac{13}{20}$
June 21	$17\frac{11}{20}$
September 22	$13\frac{13}{20}$
December 21	$9\frac{19}{20}$

Source: The Mountaineers

For how much more time can a person in Seattle see without artificial illumination on June 21st than on December 21st? $7\frac{3}{5}$ h

3. FENCES A picket fence has slats that are $\frac{5}{12}$ foot wide separated by gaps that are $\frac{7}{12}$ foot wide. How long is a fence with 30 slats? $29\frac{5}{12}$ ft

4. MEASUREMENT When Danny, who is $57\frac{7}{8}$ inches tall, stands on a ledge $9\frac{5}{8}$ inches off the ground, he remains hidden behind a wall $70\frac{3}{8}$ inches tall. What is the distance between the top of Danny's head and the top of the wall? $2\frac{7}{8}$ in.

5. BAKING Jean and Fred are making apple crisp. The recipe calls for 8 apples to be peeled and cut into pieces. However, as Fred and Jean work, they eat pieces of apple. Fred eats $\frac{2}{9}$ of each apple he peels, and Jean eats $\frac{1}{9}$ of each apple she peels.

a. Assuming they each peel and cut four apples, how many apples will they have left over for the recipe after they peel eight apples? $6\frac{2}{3}$ apples

b. If Jean peels and cuts two more apples, will they have enough for the recipe? If so, how much extra is there? If not, how much more do they need? yes; with $\frac{4}{9}$ apple extra

Chapter 3 34 Glencoe Pre-Algebra

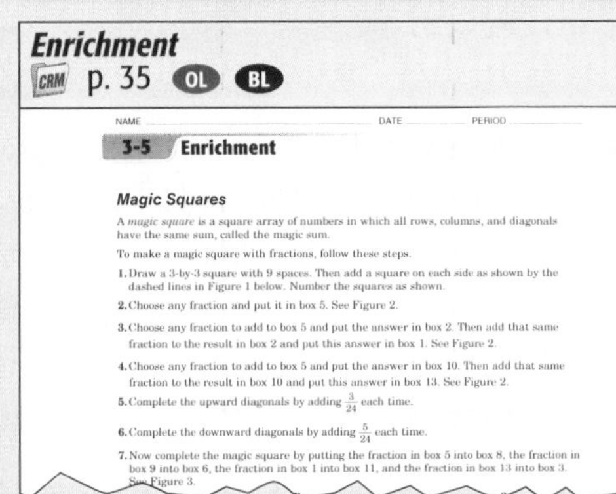

Enrichment CRM p. 35 OL BL

3-5 Enrichment

Magic Squares

A *magic square* is a square array of numbers in which all rows, columns, and diagonals have the same sum, called the magic sum.

To make a magic square with fractions, follow these steps.

1. Draw a 3-by-3 square with 9 spaces. Then add a square on each side as shown by the dashed lines in Figure 1 below. Number the squares as shown.
2. Choose any fraction and put it in box 5. See Figure 2.
3. Choose any fraction to add to box 5 and put the answer in box 2. Then add that same fraction to the result in box 2 and put this answer in box 1. See Figure 2.
4. Choose any fraction to add to box 5 and put the answer in box 10. Then add that same fraction to the result in box 10 and put this answer in box 13. See Figure 2.
5. Complete the upward diagonals by adding $\frac{3}{24}$ each time.
6. Complete the downward diagonals by adding $\frac{5}{24}$ each time.
7. Now complete the magic square by putting the fraction in box 5 into box 8, the fraction in box 9 into box 6, the fraction in box 1 into box 11, and the fraction in box 13 into box 3. See Figure 3.

4 ASSESS

Name the Math Tell students to draw a rectangular area model representing $\frac{3}{8} + 2\frac{5}{8}$. Have them explain how to use their model to find the sum.

Formative Assessment

Check for student understanding of concepts in Lessons 3-4 and 3-5.

CRM Quiz 3, p. 47

Standardized Test Practice

48. The average times it takes Miguel to cut his lawn and his neighbor's lawn are given in the table.

Lawn	Time to Cut (h)
Miguel's	$\frac{3}{4}$
Neighbor's	$1\frac{1}{4}$

Last summer, he cut his lawn 10 times and his neighbor's 6 times. How many hours did he spend cutting both lawns? **D**

A $13\frac{1}{2}$ h **C** $14\frac{1}{2}$ h

B 14 h **D** 15 h

49. A piece of wood is $1\frac{9}{16}$ inches thick. A layer of padding $\frac{15}{16}$ inch thick is placed on top of the wood. What is the total thickness of the wood and the padding? **J**

F $1\frac{3}{8}$ in. **H** $1\frac{15}{16}$ in.

G $1\frac{1}{2}$ in. **J** $2\frac{1}{2}$ in.

50. Ronata is putting lace around the tablecloth shown below. How much lace will she need to cover all 4 sides? **D**

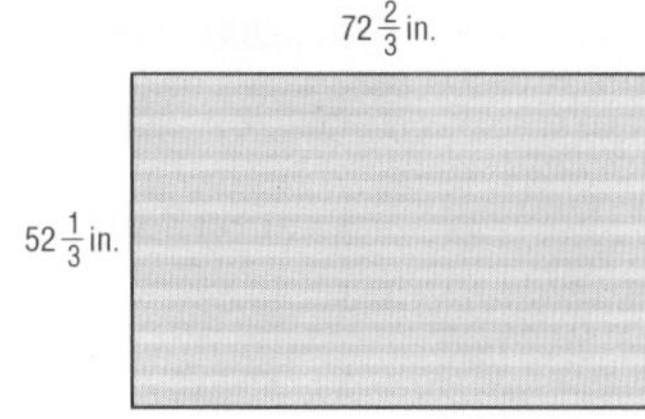

A $20\frac{1}{2}$ in. **C** 125 in.

B 41 in. **D** 250 in.

51. SHORT RESPONSE Simplify the expression below. **$-6\frac{1}{3}$**

$$-5\frac{7}{9} - 2\frac{4}{9} + 1\frac{8}{9}$$

Spiral Review

Find each quotient. Write in simplest form. (Lesson 3-4)

52. $\frac{2}{7} \div \frac{5}{14}$ **$\frac{4}{5}$**

53. $-3\frac{1}{8} \div \frac{5}{16}$ **-10**

54. $4\frac{2}{3} \div \left(-3\frac{1}{9}\right)$ **$-\frac{3}{2}$ or $-1\frac{1}{2}$**

Find each product. Write in simplest form. (Lesson 3-3)

55. $\frac{3}{10} \cdot \frac{4}{21}$ **$\frac{2}{35}$**

56. $\frac{3}{8}(-6)$ **$-2\frac{1}{4}$**

57. $\frac{5}{19} \cdot 2\frac{2}{18}$ **$\frac{5}{9}$**

58. FURNITURE A shelf $16\frac{5}{8}$ inches wide is to be placed in a space that is $16\frac{3}{4}$ inches wide. Will the shelf fit in the space? Explain. (Lesson 3-1) **Yes; $16\frac{5}{8} < 16\frac{3}{4}$**

59. FOOTBALL The Hawks started a play on their own 31-yard line. They lost 9 yards on one play and another 5 yards on the next play. Find the team's field location after the two plays. (Lesson 2-3) **17 yard line**

Skills Review

Find the LCM of each pair of numbers or monomials.
(Concepts and Skills Bank pp. 860–861)

60. 6, 8 **24**

61. 12, 15 **60**

62. 3, 7 **21**

63. 15, 45 **45**

64. $2a$, $2b$ **$2ab$**

65. x, x^2y **x^2y**

Differentiated Instruction

Extension Present students with the following problem. Ian's mom bought 7 yards of fabric to make a costume for a play. She used $2\frac{5}{8}$ yards for a shirt, $\frac{7}{8}$ yard for a vest, and $3\frac{3}{8}$ yards for a pair of pants. Does she have enough fabric left over to make a sash that requires $\frac{3}{8}$ yard of fabric? Explain. No; Sample Answer: The shirt, vest, and pants require $6\frac{7}{8}$ yards of fabric, which leaves only $\frac{1}{8}$ yard, and that is not enough to make the sash.

3-6 Adding and Subtracting Unlike Fractions

Then
You have already added and subtracted rational numbers with like denominators. (Lesson 3-5)

Now
- Add unlike fractions.
- Subtract unlike fractions.

New Vocabulary
unlike fractions

Math Online
glencoe.com
- Extra Examples
- Personal Tutor
- Self-Check Quiz
- Homework Help

Why?

Tasha feeds her cats $\frac{2}{3}$ cup of cat food in the morning and $\frac{1}{2}$ cup in the evening. You can use the least common multiple, or LCM, to find how much food her cats eat each day.

a. What is the LCM of the denominators? 6

b. Each model is divided into six parts. What parts of each model are shaded? $\frac{3}{6}$ and $\frac{4}{6}$

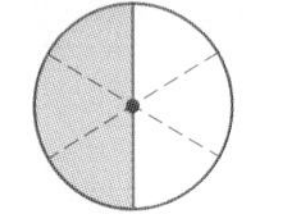
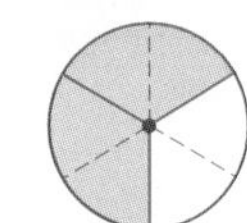

c. How many parts are in the sum $\frac{2}{3} + \frac{1}{2}$? $\frac{7}{6}$ or $1\frac{1}{6}$

Add Unlike Fractions **Unlike fractions** are fractions with different denominators. Use the least common multiple of the denominators to rename the fractions before adding them.

Key Concept Adding Unlike Fractions — For Your FOLDABLE

Words To add fractions with unlike denominators, rename the fractions with a common denominator. Then add and simplify as with like fractions.

Example

$$\frac{2}{3} + \frac{1}{2} = \frac{2}{3} \cdot \frac{2}{2} + \frac{1}{2} \cdot \frac{3}{3}$$
$$= \frac{4}{6} + \frac{3}{6}$$
$$= \frac{7}{6} \text{ or } 1\frac{1}{6}$$

EXAMPLE 1 Adding Unlike Fractions

Find $\frac{3}{5} + \frac{1}{3}$. Write in simplest form. Estimate $1 + 0 = 1$

$\frac{3}{5} + \frac{1}{3} = \frac{3}{5} \cdot \frac{3}{3} + \frac{1}{3} \cdot \frac{5}{5}$ — Use $3 \cdot 5$ or 15 as the common denominator.

$= \frac{9}{15} + \frac{5}{15}$ — Rename each fraction with the common denominator.

$= \frac{14}{15}$ — Add the numerators.

Check for Reasonableness $\frac{14}{15} \approx 1$ ✓

Check Your Progress

Find each sum. Write in simplest form.

1A. $\frac{1}{6} + \frac{3}{4}$ $\frac{11}{12}$

1B. $\frac{2}{7} + \frac{3}{14}$ $\frac{1}{2}$

Personal Tutor glencoe.com

3-6 Lesson Notes

1 FOCUS

Vertical Alignment

Before Lesson 3-6
Add and subtract rational numbers with like denominators.

Lesson 3-6
Add unlike fractions.
Subtract unlike fractions.

After Lesson 3-6
Solve equations containing rational numbers.

2 TEACH

Scaffolding Questions

Have students read the *Why?* section of the lesson and answer the questions.

Ask:
- How many sixths make up $\frac{2}{3}$ of a circle? 4
- How many sixths are equal to $\frac{1}{2}$ of a circle? 3
- What number sentence can you use to represent the total number of sixths in $\frac{2}{3}$ and $\frac{1}{2}$ of a circle? $\frac{4}{6} + \frac{3}{6} = \frac{7}{6}$ or $1\frac{1}{6}$

Lesson 3-6 Resources

Resource	Approaching-Level	On-Level	Beyond-Level	English Learners
Teacher Edition			• Differentiated Instruction, pp. 154, 158	
Chapter 3 Resource Masters	• Study Guide and Intervention, pp. 36–37 • Skills Practice, p. 38 • Practice, p. 39 • Word Problem Practice, p. 40 • Graphing Calculator, p. 42	• Study Guide and Intervention, pp. 36–37 • Skills Practice, p. 38 • Practice, p. 39 • Word Problem Practice, p. 40 • Enrichment, p. 41 • Graphing Calculator, p. 42	• Practice, p. 39 • Word Problem Practice, p. 40 • Enrichment, p. 41 • Graphing Calculator, p. 42	• Study Guide and Intervention, pp. 36–37 • Skills Practice, p. 38 • Practice, p. 39 • Graphing Calculator, p. 42
Transparencies	• 5-Minute Check Transparency 3-6	• 5-Minute Check Transparency 3-6	• 5-Minute Check Transparency 3-6	• 5-Minute Check Transparency 3-6
Other	• Study Notebook • Teaching Pre-Algebra with Manipulatives	• Study Notebook • Teaching Pre-Algebra with Manipulatives	• Study Notebook	• Study Notebook • Teaching Pre-Algebra with Manipulatives

Add Unlike Fractions

Examples 1 and 2 show how to add fractions and mixed numbers with unlike denominators.

Formative Assessment

Use the Check Your Progress exercises after each example to determine students' understanding of concepts.

Additional Examples

1 Find $\frac{3}{4} + \frac{1}{7}$. Write in simplest form. $\frac{25}{28}$

2 Find each sum. Write in simplest form.

a. $\frac{5}{6} + (-\frac{3}{10})$ $\frac{8}{15}$

b. $2\frac{1}{8} + \left(-3\frac{2}{3}\right)$ $-1\frac{13}{24}$

Additional Examples also in Interactive Classroom PowerPoint® Presentations

IWB INTERACTIVE WHITEBOARD READY

Subtract Unlike Fractions

Example 3 shows how to subtract fractions and mixed numbers with unlike denominators. **Example 4** shows how to use mixed numbers to solve a real-world problem.

Additional Example

3 Find each difference. Write in simplest form.

a. $\frac{9}{16} - \frac{5}{8}$ $-\frac{1}{16}$

b. $4\frac{2}{3} - 3\frac{6}{7}$ $\frac{17}{21}$

StudyTip

LCD You can rename fractions using any common denominator. However, using the least common denominator will make simplifying the solution easier.

EXAMPLE 2 Add Fractions and Mixed Numbers

Find each sum. Write in simplest form.

a. $-\frac{5}{6} + \frac{1}{8}$ **Estimate** $-1 + 0 = -1$

$-\frac{5}{6} + \frac{1}{8} = \frac{-5}{6} \cdot \frac{4}{4} + \frac{1}{8} \cdot \frac{3}{3}$ **The LCD of 6 and 8 is 24.**

$= \frac{-20}{24} + \frac{3}{24}$ **Rename each fraction using the LCD, 24.**

$= \frac{-17}{24}$ **Simplify.**

b. $-\frac{3}{10} + \left(-5\frac{3}{4}\right)$ **Estimate** $-\frac{1}{2} + -6 = -6\frac{1}{2}$

$-\frac{3}{10} + \left(-5\frac{3}{4}\right) = \frac{-3}{10} + \frac{-23}{4}$ **Write $-5\frac{3}{4}$ as an improper fraction.**

$= \frac{-3}{10} \cdot \frac{2}{2} + \frac{-23}{4} \cdot \frac{5}{5}$ **The LCD of 10 and 4 is 20.**

$= \frac{-6}{20} + \frac{-115}{20}$ **Rename each fraction using the LCD, 20.**

$= \frac{-121}{20}$ or $-6\frac{1}{20}$ **Simplify.**

Check Your Progress

2A. $3\frac{3}{4} + \frac{5}{14}$ $4\frac{3}{28}$ **2B.** $-6\frac{8}{9} + 7\frac{5}{12}$ $\frac{19}{36}$ **2C.** $3\frac{3}{5} + \left(-4\frac{5}{6}\right)$ $-1\frac{7}{30}$

Personal Tutor glencoe.com

Subtract Unlike Fractions The rule for subtracting fractions with unlike denominators is similar to the rule for addition.

Key Concept **Subtracting Unlike Fractions** For Your FOLDABLE

To subtract fractions with unlike denominators, rename the fractions with a common denominator. Then subtract and simplify as with like fractions.

StudyTip

Reasonableness Use estimation to check whether your answer is reasonable.

$\frac{3}{8} - \frac{3}{4} \approx \frac{1}{2} - 1$

$\approx -\frac{1}{2}$

$-\frac{3}{8}$ is close to $-\frac{1}{2}$.

EXAMPLE 3 Subtract Fractions and Mixed Numbers

Find each difference. Write in simplest form.

a. $\frac{3}{8} - \frac{3}{4}$

$\frac{3}{8} - \frac{3}{4} = \frac{3}{8} - \frac{3}{4} \cdot \frac{2}{2}$ **The LCD is 8.**

$= \frac{3}{8} - \frac{6}{8}$ **Rename using the LCD.**

$= -\frac{3}{8}$ **Simplify.**

b. $9\frac{3}{5} - 7\frac{2}{3}$

$9\frac{3}{5} - 7\frac{2}{3} = \frac{48}{5} - \frac{23}{3}$

$= \frac{48}{5} \cdot \frac{3}{3} - \frac{23}{3} \cdot \frac{5}{5}$ **The LCD is 15.**

$= \frac{144}{15} - \frac{115}{15}$ **Rename using the LCD.**

$= \frac{29}{15}$ or $1\frac{14}{15}$ **Simplify.**

Check Your Progress

3A. $\frac{3}{4} - \frac{8}{9}$ $-\frac{5}{36}$ **3B.** $7\frac{1}{6} - 6\frac{5}{8}$ $\frac{13}{24}$ **3C.** $5\frac{1}{3} - \left(-4\frac{5}{9}\right)$ $\frac{89}{9}$ or $9\frac{8}{9}$

Personal Tutor glencoe.com

Differentiated Instruction BL

Linguistic Ask students to write a paragraph explaining why common denominators are needed to add and subtract fractions. They should include an example and a drawing of the example.

Real-World Link

Computers can connect to networks without cables by using wireless cards. Wireless networks, or WiFi, use radio waves to transmit the information. A typical indoor range for a wireless connection is 150–300 feet from the access point.

Source: How Stuff Works

Real-World EXAMPLE 4 Add and Subtract Mixed Numbers

COMPUTERS To set up a computer network in an office, a 100-foot cable is cut and used to connect three computers to the server as shown. How much cable is left to connect the third computer?

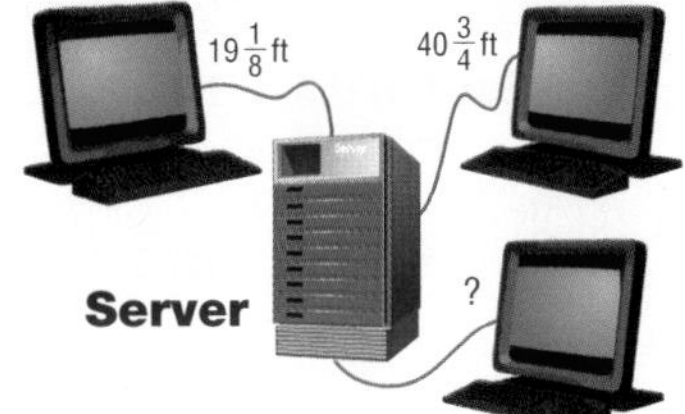

Understand You know that the 100-foot cable was used to connect two computers to the server.

Plan Add the measures of the cables that were already used and subtract that sum from 100.

Estimate $100 - (19 + 41) \approx 100 - 60$ or 40 feet

Solve

$19\frac{1}{8} + 40\frac{3}{4} = 19\frac{1}{8} + 40\frac{6}{8}$ Rename $40\frac{3}{4}$ using the LCD, 8.

$= 59\frac{7}{8}$ Simplify.

$100 - 59\frac{7}{8} = 99\frac{8}{8} - 59\frac{7}{8}$ Rename 100 as $99\frac{8}{8}$.

$= 40\frac{1}{8}$ Simplify.

There is $40\frac{1}{8}$ feet of cable left to connect the third computer.

Check Since $40\frac{1}{8}$ is close to 40, the answer is reasonable. ✓

Check Your Progress

4. **FROGS** At a recent frog jumping contest, the winning frog jumped $21\frac{1}{3}$ feet. The second place frog jumped $20\frac{1}{2}$ feet. How much farther did the first place frog jump? $\frac{5}{6}$ feet

Personal Tutor glencoe.com

Check Your Understanding

Examples 1 and 2 pp. 153–154

Find each sum. Write in simplest form.

1. $\frac{1}{15} + \frac{3}{5}$ $\frac{2}{3}$
2. $-\frac{5}{9} + \frac{1}{6}$ $-\frac{7}{18}$
3. $\frac{7}{8} + \left(-\frac{2}{7}\right)$ $\frac{33}{56}$
4. $8\frac{5}{12} + 11\frac{1}{4}$ $19\frac{2}{3}$
5. $-2\frac{1}{3} + \left(-7\frac{1}{2}\right)$ $-9\frac{5}{6}$
6. $4\frac{3}{8} + 10\frac{5}{12}$ $14\frac{19}{24}$

Example 3 p. 154

Find each difference. Write in simplest form.

7. $-\frac{1}{4} - \frac{7}{9}$ $-1\frac{1}{36}$
8. $\frac{3}{5} - \frac{9}{10}$ $-\frac{3}{10}$
9. $\frac{5}{8} - \frac{7}{12}$ $\frac{1}{24}$
10. $-1\frac{1}{3} - 4\frac{2}{7}$ $-5\frac{13}{21}$
11. $5\frac{5}{6} - \left(-2\frac{1}{4}\right)$ $8\frac{1}{12}$
12. $12\frac{1}{2} - 6\frac{3}{8}$ $6\frac{1}{8}$

Example 4 p. 155

13. **COOKING** Dwayne needs $1\frac{2}{3}$ cups of shredded cheese to put in his enchilada casserole and $\frac{3}{4}$ cup of cheese for the top. If he has 3 cups of cheese in all, how much cheese will he have left? $\frac{7}{12}$ c

Focus on Mathematical Content

Common Denominator To add or subtract unlike fractions, the denominators have to be the same number. Using the LCD eliminates steps in simplifying later, but any common denominator can be used. The easiest common denominator to find is the product of the two denominators.

Additional Example

4. **JOGGING** Juyong jogged three days this week for a total of $11\frac{17}{20}$ miles. If she jogged $3\frac{1}{2}$ miles one day and $4\frac{1}{4}$ miles another, how many miles did she jog on the third day? $4\frac{1}{10}$ miles

3 PRACTICE

Formative Assessment

Use Exercises 1–13 to check for understanding.

Use the chart at the bottom of the next page to customize assignments for your students.

Tips for New Teachers

Adding a Step Encourage students to write mixed numbers as improper fractions before adding or subtracting. This method produces fewer errors than adding or subtracting the whole numbers and fractions separately.

Multiple Representations
In Exercise 37, students use a table, ordered pairs, and a graph to relate the length and width of a rectangle with constant perimeter.

Watch Out!

Internet Exercise 39 requires the use of the Internet or other reference material to find rainfall totals.

Watch Out!

Find the Error If students are having difficulty with Exercise 50, point out that both Cooper and Yu are incorrect. Have students find the least common denominator of the three numbers, and then compare their answer to those of Cooper and Yu to find their errors.

Additional Answers

37b. (8, 2), (7, 3), (6, 4), (5, 5)

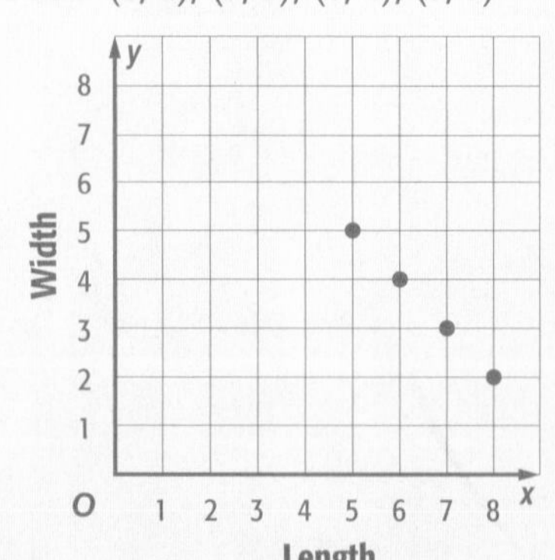

37c. $4\frac{1}{2}$ in.

Practice and Problem Solving

● = **Step-by-Step Solutions** begin on page R11.
Extra Practice begins on page 810.

Examples 1 and 3 pp. 153–154

Find each sum or difference. Write in simplest form.

14. $-\frac{8}{35}+\frac{2}{5}$ **$\frac{6}{35}$**
15. $\frac{5}{7}+\left(-\frac{10}{21}\right)$ **$\frac{5}{21}$**
16. $-\frac{5}{8}+\left(-\frac{8}{9}\right)$ **$-1\frac{37}{72}$**
17. $-\frac{1}{3}+\left(-\frac{10}{11}\right)$ **$-1\frac{8}{33}$**
18. $\frac{7}{8}-\frac{2}{5}$ **$\frac{19}{40}$**
19. $\frac{1}{6}-\frac{5}{7}$ **$-\frac{23}{42}$**
20. $-\frac{2}{5}-\frac{1}{3}$ **$-\frac{11}{15}$**
21. $-\frac{3}{10}-\frac{1}{15}$ **$-\frac{11}{30}$**
22. $-\frac{3}{4}-\frac{5}{6}$ **$-1\frac{7}{12}$**

23. **BASEBALL** During spring training, the Detroit Tigers won about $\frac{2}{3}$ of the games they played while the Cleveland Indians won $\frac{7}{15}$ of the games they played. What fraction more of the games did Detroit win than Cleveland? **$\frac{1}{5}$**

24. **COLLEGE** In a college dormitory, $\frac{1}{10}$ of the residents are juniors and $\frac{2}{5}$ of the residents are sophomores. What fraction of the students at the dormitory are juniors and sophomores? **$\frac{1}{2}$**

Examples 2 and 3 p. 154

Find each sum or difference. Write in simplest form.

25. $8\frac{1}{2}+3\frac{4}{5}$ **$12\frac{3}{10}$**
26. $-10\frac{2}{3}+9\frac{7}{12}$ **$-1\frac{1}{12}$**
27. $16\frac{5}{6}-12\frac{1}{3}$ **$4\frac{1}{2}$**
28. $6\frac{6}{7}-11\frac{7}{8}$ **$-5\frac{1}{56}$**
29. $-4\frac{1}{9}-7\frac{2}{3}$ **$-11\frac{7}{9}$**
30. $-\frac{5}{6}+8\frac{1}{4}$ **$7\frac{5}{12}$**
31. $\frac{9}{16}+3\frac{5}{6}$ **$4\frac{19}{48}$**
32. $-5\frac{3}{5}+\left(-7\frac{1}{6}\right)$ **$-12\frac{23}{30}$**
33. $-10\frac{1}{2}-6\frac{5}{7}$ **$-17\frac{3}{14}$**

Example 4 p. 155

34. **JEWELRY** Sybrina wants to make a 17-inch necklace with a $\frac{3}{4}$-inch bead, a $1\frac{1}{2}$-inch bead and another $\frac{3}{4}$-inch bead on it. What is the length of the remaining part of the necklace? **14 inches**

35. **BAKING** Kenzie is making three desserts for a party. The recipes call for $\frac{2}{3}$ cup of sugar, $1\frac{5}{6}$ cups of sugar, and $2\frac{3}{4}$ cups of sugar. If she has 6 cups of sugar, how much sugar will she have left over? **$\frac{3}{4}$ c**

36. **YEARBOOKS** The length of a page in a yearbook is 10 inches. The top margin is $\frac{1}{2}$ inch, and the bottom margin is $\frac{3}{4}$ inch. What is the length of the page inside the margins? **$8\frac{3}{4}$ in.**

37. **MULTIPLE REPRESENTATIONS** The perimeter of a geometric figure is the distance around the figure. You can find the perimeter of a rectangle by adding the measures of all four sides.

a. **TABULAR** Copy and complete the table at the right by listing the lengths and widths of three additional rectangles that have a perimeter of 20.

Perimeter of 20	
Length	Width
8	2
■ 7	■ 3
■ 6	■ 4
■ 5	■ 5

b. **GRAPHICAL** Write the values from the table as ordered pairs (ℓ, w). Graph the ordered pairs on the coordinate plane. **See margin.**

c. **NUMERICAL** Use the graph to predict the length of a rectangle with a perimeter of 20 inches and a width of $5\frac{1}{2}$ inches. Check the prediction by finding the actual length of the rectangle. **See margin.**

Differentiated Homework Options

Level	Assignment	Two-Day Option	
AL Basic	14–36, 47–50, 52–68	15–35 odd, 53–56	14–36 even, 47–50, 52, 57–68
OL Core	15–35 odd, 36–39, 41–45 odd, 46–50, 52–68	14–36, 53–56	37–50, 52, 57–68
BL Advanced	37–65 (optional: 66–68)		

Real-World Link

A shortage of rainfall can cause major problems in forestry, agriculture, tourism, and city water supplies. The U.S. Federal Emergency Management Agency estimates that droughts cost the country \$6–\$8 billion each year.

38. ANALYZE TABLES Use the table to find the total average precipitation that falls in August, September, and October. $6\frac{8}{25}$ **in.**

Average Precipitation	
Month	**Amount (in.)**
Aug.	$2\frac{47}{50}$
Sept.	$1\frac{22}{25}$
Oct.	$1\frac{1}{2}$

39. RESEARCH Use the Internet or another source to find out the monthly rainfall totals in your community during the past year. How much rain fell in August, September, and October? **See students' work.**

Find each difference. Write in simplest form.

40. $-3\frac{2}{5} - \left(-2\frac{4}{7}\right)$ $-\frac{29}{35}$ **41.** $-19\frac{3}{8} - \left(-4\frac{3}{4}\right)$ $-14\frac{5}{8}$ **42.** $8\frac{5}{12} - \left(-12\frac{13}{18}\right)$ $21\frac{5}{36}$

43. $-35\frac{5}{6} - 23.\overline{3}$ $-59\frac{1}{6}$ **44.** $-17\frac{7}{8} - (-17.\overline{9})$ $\frac{1}{8}$ **45.** $24.\overline{56} - (-12.\overline{1})$ $36\frac{67}{99}$

46. GEOMETRY The length of a rectangle is $3\frac{1}{3}$ inches. The width is $\frac{1}{5}$ of the length. Find the width and the perimeter of the rectangle. Support your answer with a drawing. $\frac{2}{3}$ **inch; 8 inches**

H.O.T. Problems Use Higher-Order Thinking Skills

47. OPEN ENDED Write a subtraction problem using unlike fractions with a least common denominator of 24. Find the difference. **Sample answer:** $\frac{2}{3} - \frac{5}{8} = \frac{1}{24}$

48. REASONING Is the difference between a positive mixed number and a negative mixed number *always*, *sometimes*, or *never* positive? Justify your answer with an example.

49. WRITING IN MATH Explain why you cannot add or subtract fractions with unlike denominators without renaming the fractions. You may use a diagram to illustrate your answer.

50. FIND THE ERROR Cooper and Yu are adding the fractions $\frac{1}{3}$, $\frac{7}{9}$, and $\frac{4}{15}$. Their first step is to find the least common denominator of 3, 9, and 15. Is either of them correct? Explain your reasoning.

Cooper	Yu
The least common denominator of 3, 9, and 15 is 3 because 3 divides into all these numbers evenly.	The least common denominator of 5, 9, and 15 is 90 because you can divide 90 by all of those numbers without getting a remainder.

51. CHALLENGE A set of measuring cups has measures of 1 cup, $\frac{3}{4}$ cup, $\frac{1}{2}$ cup, $\frac{1}{3}$ cup, and $\frac{1}{4}$ cup. How could you measure $\frac{1}{6}$ cup of milk by using these measuring cups?

52. WRITING IN MATH Suppose you use 24 instead of 12 as a common denominator when finding $2\frac{3}{4} - 5\frac{5}{6}$. Will you get the correct answer? Explain. **See Chapter 3 Answer Appendix.**

48. always; $4\frac{3}{4} - \left(-1\frac{1}{4}\right) = 4\frac{3}{4} + 1\frac{1}{4} = 6$

49. Sample answer: One way to respond is to use a diagram similar to the one given in the lesson opener to show that the fractions have to have the same "unit" (parts of a whole) to be added or subtracted.

50. No; Cooper found the GCF of 3, 9 and 15. Yu found a common denominator but not the least.

51. Sample answer: Fill the $\frac{1}{2}$-cup. From the $\frac{1}{2}$-cup, fill the $\frac{1}{3}$-cup. $\frac{1}{6}$-cup will be left in the $\frac{1}{2}$-cup because $\frac{1}{2} - \frac{1}{3} = \frac{1}{6}$.

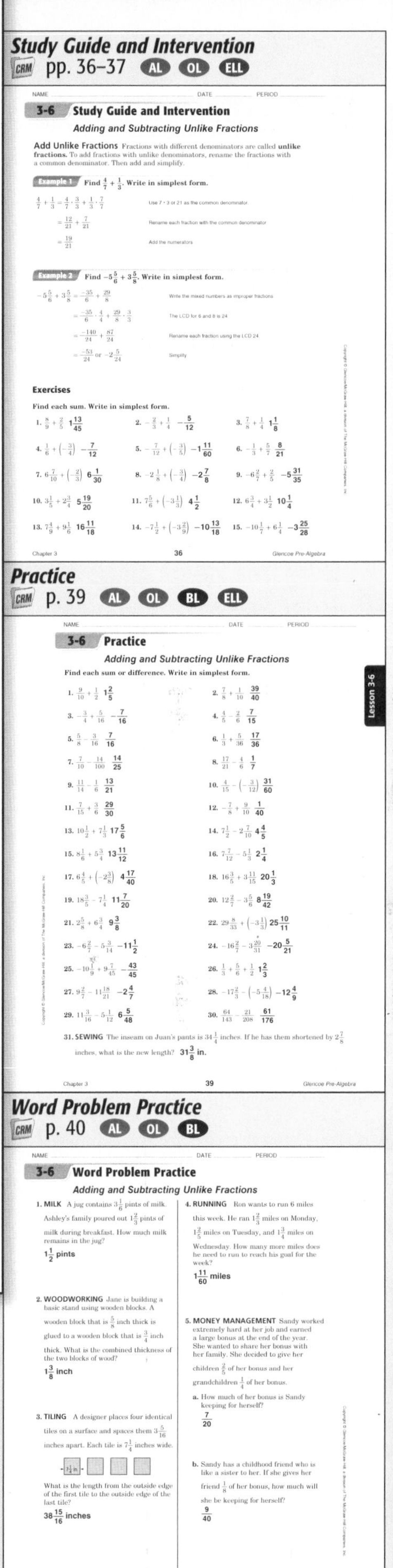

Study Guide and Intervention CRM pp. 36–37 AL OL ELL

Practice CRM p. 39 AL OL BL ELL

Word Problem Practice CRM p. 40 AL OL BL

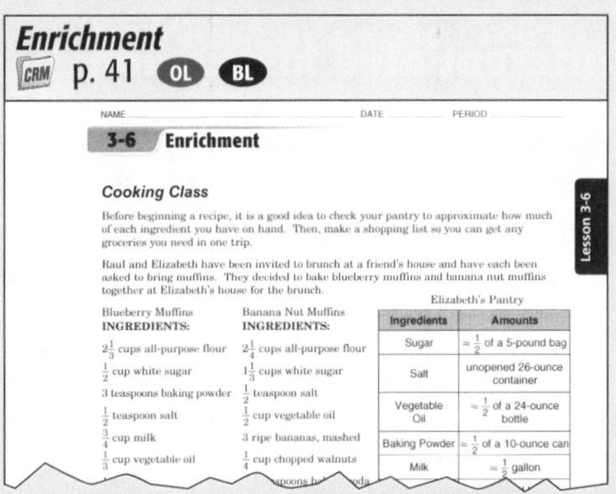

Enrichment CRM p. 41 OL BL

4 ASSESS

Yesterday's News Have students explain how yesterday's lesson on adding and subtracting like fractions helped them with today's lesson on adding and subtracting unlike fractions.

Formative Assessment

Check for student understanding of concepts in Lesson 3-6.

CRM Quiz 4, p. 47

Standardized Test Practice

53. A recipe for snack mix contains $2\frac{1}{3}$ cups of mixed nuts, $3\frac{1}{2}$ cups of granola, and $\frac{3}{4}$ cup raisins. What is the total amount of snack mix? **D**

A $5\frac{2}{3}$ c C $6\frac{2}{3}$ c

B $5\frac{7}{12}$ c D $6\frac{7}{12}$ c

54. SHORT RESPONSE The graph shows the results of an election for class president. What fraction of the votes did Michaela receive? $\frac{1}{6}$

Class Election Results

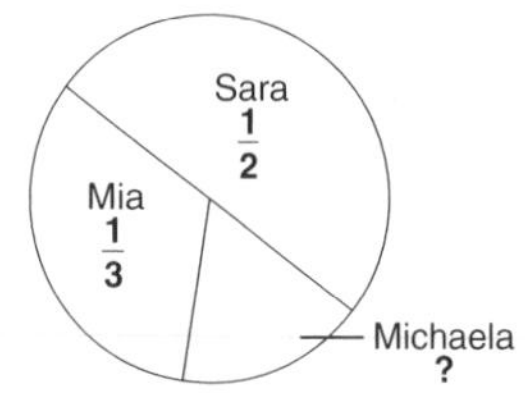

55. The results of a grocery store survey are listed in the table. Find the fraction of families who grill out 2, 3, or 4 or more times per month. **H**

F $\frac{2}{25}$ H $\frac{7}{10}$

G $\frac{23}{100}$ J $\frac{39}{50}$

How Often Do You Grill Out?

Times per Month	Fraction of People
Less than 1	$\frac{11}{50}$
1	$\frac{2}{25}$
2–3	$\frac{4}{25}$
4 or more	$\frac{27}{50}$

56. Marco spent $\frac{4}{5}$ hour doing homework on Monday. On Tuesday, he spent $1\frac{1}{3}$ hours doing homework. How long did he spend working on homework for those two days? **D**

A $\frac{8}{15}$ h C $1\frac{16}{15}$ h

B $1\frac{5}{8}$ h D $2\frac{2}{15}$ h

Spiral Review

Find each sum or difference. Write in simplest form. (Lesson 3-5)

57. $6\frac{1}{12} - (-8\frac{5}{12})$ **$14\frac{1}{2}$**

58. $2\frac{5}{12} + (2\frac{7}{12})$ **5**

59. $2\frac{3}{8} - 1\frac{5}{8}$ **$\frac{3}{4}$**

60. CARPENTRY A 3-foot-long shelf is to be installed between two walls that are $32\frac{5}{8}$ inches apart. How much of the shelf must be cut off so that it fits between the walls? (Lesson 3-5) **$3\frac{3}{8}$ in.**

Find each quotient. Write in simplest form. (Lesson 3-4)

61. $\frac{8}{9} \div \frac{4}{3}$ **$\frac{2}{3}$**

62. $12 \div \frac{4}{9}$ **27**

63. $\frac{a}{7} \div \frac{a}{42}$ **6**

64. FOOD How many $\frac{1}{4}$-pound hamburgers can be made from $2\frac{3}{4}$ pounds of ground beef? (Lesson 3-4) **11 hamburgers**

65. MEASUREMENT A *micron* is a unit of measure that is approximately 0.000039 inch. Express this decimal as a fraction. (Lesson 3-2) **$\frac{39}{1{,}000{,}000}$**

Skills Review

Multiply. (Previous Course)

66. $2 \cdot (5 \cdot 10)$ **100**

67. $(1 \cdot 5) \cdot 10$ **50**

68. $(15 + 7) \cdot 11$ **242**

158 Chapter 3 Operations with Rational Numbers

Differentiated Instruction

Extension Students may encounter algebraic fractions with variables in the denominator. The process of combining the fractions is the same. First, the LCD is found, and then the fractions are combined. Have students show the steps to add $\frac{2}{x} + \frac{1}{3}$ using the LCD. Then have them evaluate the expression for $x = 4$.

$\frac{2}{x}\left(\frac{3}{3}\right) + \frac{1}{3}\left(\frac{x}{x}\right)$

$\frac{6}{3x} + \frac{x}{3x}$

$\frac{6 + x}{3x}; \frac{5}{6}$

Math Online glencoe.com
• STUDY TO GO
• Vocabulary Review

Chapter Summary

Key Concepts

Comparing Rational Numbers (Lesson 3-1)

- To compare fractions with unlike denominators, write the fractions as decimals and compare.

Fractions and Decimals (Lessons 3-1 and 3-2)

- Any number that can be written as a fraction is a rational number.
- Decimals that are terminating or repeating are rational numbers.

Multiplying and Dividing Rational Numbers (Lessons 3-3 and 3-4)

- To multiply fractions, multiply the numerators and then multiply the denominators.
- The product of a number and its multiplicative inverse, or reciprocal, is 1.
- To divide by a fraction, multiply by its multiplicative inverse.

Adding and Subtracting Rational Numbers (Lessons 3-5 and 3-6)

- To add like fractions, add the numerators and write the sum over the denominator.
- To subtract like fractions, subtract the numerators and write the difference over the denominator.
- To add or subtract fractions with unlike denominators, rename the fractions with the LCD. Then add or subtract.

FOLDABLES® Study Organizer

Be sure the Key Concepts are noted in your Foldable.

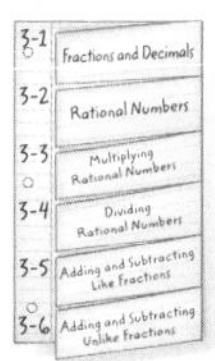

Key Vocabulary

bar notation (p. 122)
like fractions (p. 147)
multiplicative inverse (p. 141)
rational number (p. 128)
reciprocal (p. 141)
repeating decimal (p. 122)
terminating decimal (p. 121)
unlike fractions (p. 153)

Vocabulary Check

State whether each sentence is *true* or *false*. If *false*, replace the underlined term to make a true sentence.

1. Numbers that can be written as fractions are called reciprocals. **false; rational**
2. The decimal 4.7 is a terminating decimal. **true**
3. The fractions $\frac{4}{6}$ and $\frac{1}{3}$ are like fractions. **false; unlike**
4. To add unlike fractions, rename the fractions using the GCF. **false; LCD**
5. The product of a number and its multiplicative inverse is 1. **true**
6. A mixed number is another name for the multiplicative inverse. **false; reciprocal**
7. Like fractions are fractions that have the same numerator. **false; denominator**
8. Terminating decimals use bar notation to show which digits terminate. **false; repeating decimals, repeat**
9. You need a common denominator to divide fractions. **false; add or subtract**
10. Decimals that repeat or terminate are rational numbers. **true**

CHAPTER 3 Study Guide and Review

Formative Assessment

Key Vocabulary The page references after each word denote where that term was first introduced. If students have difficulty answering questions 1–10, remind them that they can use these page references to refresh their memories about the vocabulary.

Summative Assessment

CRM Vocabulary Test, p. 49

Vocabulary PuzzleMaker improves students' mathematics vocabulary using four puzzle formats–crossword, scramble, word search using a word list, and word search using clues. Students can work online or from a printed worksheet.

FOLDABLES® Study Organizer

Dinah Zike's Foldables®
Have students look through the chapter to make sure they have included examples in their Foldables. Suggest that students keep their Foldables handy while completing the Study Guide and Review pages. Point out that their Foldables can serve as a quick review tool when studying for the Chapter Test.

Lesson-by-Lesson Review

Intervention If the given examples are not sufficient to review the topics covered by the questions, remind students that the page references tell them where to review that topic in their textbook.

Two-Day Option Have students complete the Lesson-by-Lesson Review on pp. 160–162. Then you can use ExamView® Assessment Suite to customize another review worksheet that practices all the objectives of this chapter or only the objectives on which your students need more help.

Differentiated Instruction

Super DVD: Mindjogger Videoquizzes
Use this DVD as an alternative format of review for the test.

CHAPTER 3 Study Guide and Review

Lesson-by-Lesson Review

3-1 Writing Fractions as Decimals (pp. 121–127)

Write each fraction or mixed number as a decimal. Use a bar to show a repeating decimal.

11. $\frac{3}{10}$ **0.3**
12. $\frac{2}{5}$ **0.4**
13. $-\frac{5}{6}$ **$-0.8\overline{3}$**
14. $-7\frac{4}{9}$ **$-7.\overline{4}$**
15. $\frac{5}{8}$ **0.625**
16. $1\frac{4}{15}$ **$1.2\overline{6}$**

Replace each ● with <, >, or = to make a true sentence.

17. $2\frac{1}{2} \bullet 2\frac{5}{12}$ **>**
18. $\frac{5}{8} \bullet 0.625$ **=**
19. $10.74 \bullet 10\frac{7}{10}$ **>**
20. $-\frac{5}{6} \bullet -0.83$ **<**
21. $4.\overline{37} \bullet 4\frac{19}{50}$ **<**
22. $-2.54 \bullet -2\frac{27}{50}$ **=**
23. **CARPENTRY** Antoine is cutting a $5\frac{5}{16}$-inch board for a project. Write $5\frac{5}{16}$ as a decimal. **5.3125**

EXAMPLE 1

Write $\frac{3}{4}$ as a decimal.

$$4\overline{)3.00} = 0.75$$

28
20
−20
0

Divide 3 by 4.

Divide until the remainder is zero or until a sequence of numbers repeats.

EXAMPLE 2

Replace the ● with <, >, or = to make $\frac{4}{5} \bullet 0.75$ a true sentence.

$\frac{4}{5} \bullet 0.75$ Write the sentence.

$0.8 \bullet 0.75$ Write $\frac{4}{5}$ as a decimal.

$0.8 > 0.75$ In the tenths place, 8 > 7.

3-2 Rational Numbers (pp. 128–133)

Write each decimal as a fraction or mixed number in simplest form.

24. 2.08 **$2\frac{2}{25}$**
25. −0.45 **$-\frac{9}{20}$**
26. 0.875 **$\frac{7}{8}$**
27. −0.56 **$-\frac{14}{25}$**
28. $0.\overline{1}$ **$\frac{1}{9}$**
29. $-2.\overline{03}$ **$-2\frac{1}{33}$**
30. $0.\overline{5}$ **$\frac{5}{9}$**
31. $10.\overline{27}$ **$10\frac{3}{11}$**

Identify all sets to which each number belongs.

32. −4 **integer, rational**
33. $3\frac{1}{3}$ **rational**
34. 1.151551555… **irrational**
35. $-0.\overline{67}$ **rational**
36. **MUSIC** Suzanne practiced playing the piano for $1.\overline{6}$ hours after school. Write $1.\overline{6}$ as a mixed number. **$1\frac{2}{3}$ h**

EXAMPLE 3

Write 1.25 as a fraction in simplest form.

$1.25 = 1\frac{25}{100}$ 1.25 is *1 and 25 hundredths.*

$= 1\frac{1}{4}$ Simplify. The GCF of 25 and 100 is 25.

EXAMPLE 4

Write $0.\overline{7}$ as a fraction in simplest form.

$N = 0.777\ldots$

$10N = 10(0.777\ldots)$ Multiply each side by 10.

$10N = 7.777\ldots$

$-N = 0.777\ldots$ Subtract N from $10N$.

$9N = 7$ Simplify.

$N = \frac{7}{9}$ Divide each side by 9.

160 Chapter 3 Operations with Rational Numbers

MIXED PROBLEM SOLVING
For mixed problem-solving practice, see page 845.

3-3 Multiplying Rational Numbers (pp. 134–139)

Find each product. Write in simplest form.

37. $\frac{1}{5} \cdot \frac{3}{4}$ $\frac{3}{20}$

38. $-\frac{3}{7} \cdot \frac{4}{9}$ $-\frac{4}{21}$

39. $-\frac{2}{3} \cdot (-5)$ $3\frac{1}{3}$

40. $-3\frac{1}{2} \cdot (-5\frac{1}{5})$ $18\frac{1}{5}$

41. CRAFTS Mireille has a piece of ribbon that is 10 inches long. Abi's ribbon is $\frac{5}{8}$ as long. How long is Abi's ribbon? $6\frac{1}{4}$ in.

42. BACKPACKING A liter of water weighs approximately $2\frac{1}{5}$ pounds. While backpacking, Enrique wants to carry $3\frac{1}{2}$ liters of water with him. Find the weight of the water that Enrique is taking with him. $7\frac{7}{10}$ lb

EXAMPLE 5

Find $\frac{3}{8} \cdot \frac{20}{27}$. Write in simplest form.

$\frac{3}{8} \cdot \frac{20}{27} = \frac{3 \cdot 20}{8 \cdot 27}$ Multiply the numerators. Multiply the denominators.

$= \frac{60}{216}$ or $\frac{5}{18}$ Simplify. The GCF of 60 and 216 is 12.

EXAMPLE 6

Find $-4\frac{1}{6} \cdot \frac{3}{5}$. Write in simplest form.

$-4\frac{1}{6} \cdot \frac{3}{5} = -\frac{25}{6} \cdot \frac{3}{5}$ Rename $-4\frac{1}{6}$ as an improper fraction.

$= -\frac{\overset{5}{\cancel{25}}}{\underset{2}{\cancel{6}}} \cdot \frac{\overset{1}{\cancel{3}}}{\underset{1}{\cancel{5}}}$ Divide by the GCFs, 5 and 3.

$= -\frac{5}{2}$ or $-2\frac{1}{2}$ Multiply. Then simplify.

3-4 Dividing Rational Numbers (pp. 141–146)

Find the multiplicative inverse of each number.

43. -16 $-\frac{1}{16}$

44. $\frac{7}{9}$ $\frac{9}{7}$

45. $3\frac{4}{5}$ $\frac{5}{19}$

46. $-4\frac{1}{3}$ $-\frac{3}{13}$

Find each quotient. Write in simplest form.

47. $\frac{7}{9} \div (-\frac{4}{15})$ $-2\frac{11}{12}$

48. $-2\frac{2}{3} \div 2\frac{2}{7}$ $-1\frac{1}{6}$

49. $\frac{3}{5} \div \frac{9}{10}$ $\frac{2}{3}$

50. $3\frac{1}{9} \div (-1\frac{1}{6})$ $-2\frac{2}{3}$

51. FOOD Pilar drinks $1\frac{3}{4}$ glasses of milk each day. At this rate, how many days will it take her to drink a total of 14 glasses? 8 days

EXAMPLE 7

Find the multiplicative inverse of $2\frac{3}{4}$.

$2\frac{3}{4} = \frac{11}{4}$ Rename $2\frac{3}{4}$ as an improper fraction.

$\frac{11}{4} \cdot \frac{4}{11} = 1$ The product is 1.

The multiplicative inverse of $2\frac{3}{4}$ is $\frac{4}{11}$.

EXAMPLE 8

Find $\frac{4}{9} \div \frac{2}{15}$. Write in simplest form.

$\frac{4}{9} \div \frac{2}{15} = \frac{4}{9} \cdot \frac{15}{2}$ Multiply by the reciprocal of $\frac{2}{15}$, $\frac{15}{2}$.

$= \frac{\overset{2}{\cancel{4}}}{\underset{3}{\cancel{9}}} \cdot \frac{\overset{5}{\cancel{15}}}{\underset{1}{\cancel{2}}}$ Divide out common factors.

$= \frac{10}{3}$ or $3\frac{1}{3}$ Simplify.

Chapter 3 Study Guide and Review 161

Problem Solving Review

For additional practice in problem solving for Chapter 3, see the Mixed Problem Solving Appendix, p. 845, in the Student Handbook section.

Anticipation Guide

Have students complete the Chapter 3 Anticipation Guide and discuss how their responses have changed now that they have completed Chapter 3.

CHAPTER 3 Study Guide and Review

3-5 Adding and Subtracting Like Fractions (pp. 147–152)

Find each sum or difference. Write in simplest form.

52. $\frac{8}{15} + \left(-\frac{2}{15}\right)$ $\frac{2}{5}$

53. $\frac{6}{12} - \frac{11}{12}$ $-\frac{5}{12}$

54. $2\frac{5}{12} - \left(-8\frac{7}{12}\right)$ 11

55. $5\frac{3}{7} + 2\frac{6}{7}$ $8\frac{2}{7}$

56. EXERCISE Samantha is going to walk $3\frac{5}{16}$ miles today and $2\frac{3}{16}$ miles tomorrow. What is the total distance she will walk? $5\frac{1}{2}$ mi

57. PETS Last week, Douglas fed his puppy $10\frac{1}{4}$ cups of food. This week the puppy will be fed an additional $1\frac{1}{4}$ cups of food. Find the total amount of food the puppy will be fed this week. $11\frac{1}{2}$ c

EXAMPLE 9

Find $\frac{3}{4} - \left(-\frac{3}{4}\right)$. Write in simplest form.

$\frac{3}{4} - \left(-\frac{3}{4}\right) = \frac{3}{4} + \frac{3}{4}$ — To subtract $-\frac{3}{4}$, add $\frac{3}{4}$.

$= \frac{3+3}{4}$ — The denominators are the same. Add the numerators.

$= \frac{6}{4}$ — Simplify.

$= 1\frac{1}{2}$ — Simplify.

3-6 Adding and Subtracting Unlike Fractions (pp. 153–158)

Find each sum or difference. Write in simplest form.

58. $\frac{2}{5} + \frac{1}{15}$ $\frac{7}{15}$

59. $-3\frac{5}{6} - 2\frac{1}{2}$ $-6\frac{1}{3}$

60. $\frac{4}{7} + \left(-1\frac{1}{3}\right)$ $-\frac{16}{21}$

61. $\frac{3}{10} - \left(-\frac{1}{8}\right)$ $\frac{17}{40}$

62. $25\frac{1}{3} - 14\frac{2}{5}$ $10\frac{14}{15}$

63. $7\frac{3}{4} + 1\frac{3}{8}$ $9\frac{1}{8}$

64. $-\frac{5}{9} - 3\frac{2}{3}$ $-4\frac{2}{9}$

65. $-4\frac{1}{6} + \frac{3}{4}$ $-3\frac{5}{12}$

66. COOKING Monica needs $2\frac{3}{4}$ cups of flour for a batch of cookies and $3\frac{1}{3}$ cups of flour for a dozen muffins. How many cups of flour does Monica need altogether? $6\frac{1}{12}$ c

67. TRAVEL Dane and his family drove 357.9 miles in one day. If their trip is a total of $524\frac{3}{4}$ miles, how much farther do they need to drive? $166\frac{17}{20}$ miles or 166.85 miles

EXAMPLE 10

Find $-\frac{3}{8} + \frac{5}{6}$. Write in simplest form.

$-\frac{3}{8} + \frac{5}{6} = -\frac{3}{8} \cdot \frac{3}{3} + \frac{5}{6} \cdot \frac{4}{4}$ — The LCD is 24. Rename the fractions using the LCD.

$= -\frac{9}{24} + \frac{20}{24}$ — Simplify.

$= \frac{-9+20}{24}$ — Add the numerators.

$= \frac{11}{24}$ — Simplify.

EXAMPLE 11

Find $6\frac{5}{9} - 4\frac{11}{12}$. Write in simplest form.

$6\frac{5}{9} - 4\frac{11}{12} = 6\frac{20}{36} - 4\frac{33}{36}$ — The LCD is 36. Rename the fractions using the LCD.

$= 5\frac{56}{36} - 4\frac{33}{36}$ — Since $\frac{20}{36}$ is less than $\frac{33}{36}$, rename $6\frac{20}{36}$.

$= 1\frac{23}{36}$ — Subtract the whole numbers and then the fractions.

162 Chapter 3 Operations with Rational Numbers

Math Online glencoe.com
Chapter Test

Write each fraction as a decimal. Use a bar to show a repeating decimal.

1. $\frac{3}{9}$ $0.\overline{3}$
2. $-\frac{3}{25}$ -0.12
3. $\frac{1}{8}$ 0.125
4. $\frac{2}{7}$ $0.\overline{285714}$

Write each decimal as a fraction or mixed number in simplest form.

5. 0.38 $\frac{19}{50}$
6. 10.17 $10\frac{17}{100}$
7. $-5.\overline{5}$ $-5\frac{5}{9}$
8. -1.44 $-1\frac{11}{25}$

Replace each ● with <, >, or = to make a true sentence.

9. $\frac{3}{10}$ ● $0.\overline{3}$ $<$
10. -0.58 ● $-\frac{1}{4}$ $<$
11. $-6\frac{7}{8}$ ● -6.8 $<$
12. $1\frac{2}{3}$ ● $1\frac{5}{7}$ $<$

13. **FOOTBALL** The table shows the average number of points scored per game for four NFL teams. Denver scored $\frac{3}{4}$ as many points as Dallas scored. How many points per game did Denver score? $19\frac{19}{20}$

Team	Average Points per Game
San Diego	$30\frac{4}{5}$
Indianapolis	$26\frac{7}{10}$
Chicago	$26\frac{7}{10}$
Dallas	$26\frac{3}{5}$

Find each product or quotient. Write in simplest form.

14. $-\frac{2}{9} \cdot \frac{3}{14}$ $-\frac{1}{21}$
15. $4\frac{4}{7} \cdot 9\frac{1}{3}$ $42\frac{2}{3}$
16. $\frac{5}{6} \div \left(-\frac{7}{18}\right)$ $-2\frac{1}{7}$
17. $-8\frac{4}{9} \div 2\frac{1}{9}$ -4

18. **MONEY** A dollar bill remains in circulation about $1\frac{1}{4}$ years. A coin lasts about $22\frac{1}{2}$ times longer. How long is a coin in circulation? $28\frac{1}{8}$ yr

19. **FOOD** If each guest at a party eats two-thirds of a small pizza, how many guests would finish 12 small pizzas? 18 guests

Find each sum or difference. Write in simplest form.

20. $-\frac{3}{7} + \frac{5}{14}$ $-\frac{1}{14}$
21. $1\frac{1}{5} - \left(-\frac{7}{15}\right)$ $1\frac{2}{3}$
22. $6\frac{3}{4} - 2\frac{1}{6}$ $4\frac{7}{12}$
23. $9\frac{1}{3} + \left(-7\frac{5}{6}\right)$ $1\frac{1}{2}$

24. **MULTIPLE CHOICE** Use the table to find the fraction of people who voted for Collins, Johnson, and Shaw in the election for freshman class president. C

Candidate	Fraction of People
Collins	$\frac{3}{20}$
Johnson	$\frac{21}{50}$
Juarez	$\frac{3}{10}$
Shaw	$\frac{3}{100}$

A $\frac{3}{10}$
B $\frac{2}{5}$
C $\frac{3}{5}$
D $\frac{7}{10}$

Evaluate each expression if $p = \frac{1}{3}$, $r = \frac{5}{8}$, $a = 2\frac{1}{2}$, and $c = 6$.

25. pr $\frac{5}{24}$
26. $r \div a$ $\frac{1}{4}$
27. $c - p$ $5\frac{2}{3}$
28. $ac + p$ $15\frac{1}{3}$

29. **MULTIPLE CHOICE** A pipe that is $12\frac{3}{4}$ feet long is cut into pieces that are each $2\frac{2}{3}$ feet long. Which step below would give the number of pieces into which the pipe is cut? G

F Subtract $2\frac{2}{3}$ from $12\frac{3}{4}$.

G Divide $12\frac{3}{4}$ by $2\frac{2}{3}$.

H Multiply $12\frac{3}{4}$ by $2\frac{2}{3}$.

J Add $2\frac{2}{3}$ to $12\frac{3}{4}$.

30. **COOKING** Reena is making $2\frac{1}{2}$ times a recipe. If the recipe calls for $1\frac{2}{3}$ cups of milk, how much milk will Reena need? $4\frac{1}{6}$ cups

CHAPTER 3 Practice Test

Customize and create multiple versions of your chapter tests and their answer keys. All of the questions from the leveled chapter tests in the *Chapter 3 Resource Masters* are also available on ExamView® Assessment Suite.

Intervention Planner

Tier 1 On Level

If students miss about 25% of the exercises or less,

Then choose a resource:

- SE Lessons 3-1 through 3-6
- CRM Skills Practice, pp. 7, 14, 20, 26, 32, and 38
- TE Chapter Project, p.116

Math Online Self-Check Quiz

Tier 2 Strategic Intervention Approaching grade level

If students miss about 50% of the exercises,

Then choose a resource:

- CRM Study Guide and Intervention, Chapter 3, pp. 5, 12, 18, 24, 30, and 36

Quick Review Math Handbook

Math Online Extra Examples, Personal Tutor, Homework Help

Tier 3 Intensive Intervention 2 or more grades below level

If students miss about 75% of the exercises,

Then use *Math Triumphs, Grade 8*, Ch. 1, 3, 7

Math Online Extra Examples, Personal Tutor, Homework Help, Review Vocabulary

1 FOCUS

Objective Use a combination of strategies and steps for solving short answer standardized test problems.

TEACH

Scaffolding Questions

Ask:

- How do you think a short answer question is different from a multiple choice question? Sample answer: In a multiple choice question, you choose from several answers, but in a short answer question, your answer is the only answer.
- Why do you think math tests include short answer questions? Sample answer: To assess whether you understand a concept and know how to solve a problem.
- How can you show in a short answer response that you know how to solve a problem? Sample answer: Show the steps you used to solve the problem and/or explain how you solved it.

CHAPTER 3 Preparing for Standardized Tests

Short-Response Questions

Short-response questions require you to provide a solution to the problem, as well as any method, explanation, and/or justification you used to arrive at the solution.

These questions are sometimes called *constructed-response, open-response, open-ended, free-response,* or *student-produced* questions.

The following is sample rubric, or scoring guide.

Credit	Score	Criteria
Full	2	The answer is correct and a full explanation is provided that shows each step in arriving at the final answer.
Partial	1	There are two different ways to receive partial credit. • The answer is correct, but the explanation is incomplete. • The answer is incorrect, but the explanation is correct.
None	0	Either an answer is not provided or the answer does not make sense.

On some standardized tests, no credit is given for a correct answer if your work is not shown.

In solving short-response questions, remember to...

- explain your reasoning or state your approach to solving the problem.
- show all of your work or steps.
- check your answer if time permits.

EXAMPLE

Read the problem. Identify what you need to know. Then use the information in the problem to solve. Show your work.

The table shows the number of at-bats and hits of three teammates. Which player had the greatest fraction of at-bats that were hits? Show your work.

Softball Statistics

Player	At-Bats	Hits
Umeko	84	35
Melanie	75	30
Olivia	64	28

Read the problem statement carefully. You are given the number of at-bats for 3 players and the number of hits they each had. You need to find the player with the greatest fraction of at-bats that were hits.

164 Chapter 3 Operations with Rational Numbers

Full Credit Solution

In this sample solution, the student gave a clear explanation of the process, showed work, and arrived at the correct answer.

In order for me to compare the fractions, I need to write them in the same form. I'll use a calculator to divide the number of hits by the number of at-bats for each player to write the fractions as decimals.

Umeko	Melanie	Olivia
35 hits out of 84 at-bats	30 hits out of 75 at-bats	28 hits out of 64 at-bats
35 [÷] 84 [ENTER] .41666667	30 [÷] 75 [ENTER] 0.4	28 [÷] 64 [ENTER] .4375
35 out of 84 = $0.41\overline{6}$	30 out of 75 = 0.4	28 out of 84 = 0.4375

The steps, calculations, and reasoning are clearly stated.

Since $0.4 < 0.41\overline{6} < 0.4375$, Olivia had the greatest fraction of at-bats that were hits.

Be sure to complete this final step to answer the question asked.

Partial Credit Solution

In this sample solution, there are no explanations for finding the calculations.

Umeko	Melanie	Olivia
35 hits out of 84 at-bats = $0.41\overline{6}$	30 hits out of 75 at-bats = 0.4	28 hits out of 64 at-bats = 0.4375

Since $0.4 < 0.41\overline{6} < 0.4375$, Olivia had the greatest fraction of at-bats that were hits.

No Credit Solution

In this sample solution, there are no explanations for finding the calculations, and the calculations are wrong.

Umeko	Melanie	Olivia
35 hits out of 84 at-bats = 2.4	30 hits out of 75 at-bats = 2.5	28 hits out of 64 at-bats = 2.2

Melanie had the greatest fraction of at-bats that were hits.

Exercises

Read each problem. Identify what you need to know. Then use the information in the problem to solve. Show your work.

1. A customer service department satisfactorily resolved 55 out of 60 customer complaints over the weekend. To the nearest thousandth, find the satisfaction rate of the customer service department. **0.917**

2. A zebra's top running speed is $\frac{5}{4}$ the top running speed of a giraffe. If a zebra can run up to 40 miles per hour, how fast can a giraffe run? **32 mph**

3. Find the sum of the expression shown below. **$5\frac{13}{28}$**

$$-3\frac{2}{7} + 8\frac{3}{4}$$

Additional Example

The table shows the number of free-throw shots and number of baskets for three players on a school team. Which player had the greatest success rate?

Player	Free Throws	Baskets
Brett	32	28
Marcus	25	20
Tony	42	35

Sample 2-point response: Show the number of baskets to free throws as fractions with baskets as the numerator and free throws as the denominator. Write the fractions as decimals. Then compare.

Brett

$$\begin{array}{r} 0.875 \\ 32\overline{)28.000} \\ -25.6 \\ 2.40 \\ -2.24 \\ 0.160 \\ -0.160 \\ 0 \end{array}$$

$\frac{28}{32} = 0.875$

Marcus

$\frac{20}{25} = 0.8$

Tony

$$\begin{array}{r} 0.833 \\ 42\overline{)35.000} \\ -33.6 \\ 1.40 \\ -1.26 \\ 0.140 \\ -0.126 \\ 0.014 \end{array}$$

$\frac{35}{42} = 0.8\overline{3}$

$0.8 < 0.8\overline{3} < 0.875$

Since 0.875 or 28 out of 32 is the greatest number, Brett has the greatest success rate.

3 ASSESS

Use Exercises 1–3 to assess students' understanding.

CHAPTER 3 Standardized Test Practice

Diagnose Student Errors

Survey student responses for each item. Class trends may indicate common errors and misconceptions.

1. A chose lowest instead of highest success rate
B correct
C comparison error or guess
D comparison error or guess

2. F guess
G denominator correct, but numerator incorrect
H correct
J guess or mistakenly wrote fraction for 0.32 instead of 0.62

3. A multiplied by $\frac{4}{3}$ instead of $\frac{5}{3}$
B guess
C multiplied by $\frac{14}{9}$ instead of $\frac{5}{3}$
D correct

4. F correct
G misunderstood concept of reflection
H misunderstood concept of reflection
J chose reflection over x-axis instead of y-axis

5. A switched x- and y-coordinates
B identified correct quadrant, but confused coordinates
C confused Quadrant II and Quadrant IV
D correct

6. F confused Commutative and Identity Properties
G confused Associative and Identity Properties
H correct
J confused Zero and Identity Properties

7. A calculated numerators incorrectly
B correct
C calculated numerators incorrectly and chose the sign of the numerator with the lesser absolute value instead of the greater absolute value
D incorrectly chose the sign of the numerator with the lesser absolute value instead of the greater absolute value

CHAPTER 3 Standardized Test Practice

Cumulative, Chapters 1 through 3

Multiple Choice

Read each question. Then fill in the correct answer on the answer document provided by your teacher or on a sheet of paper.

1. The table shows the number of field goal attempts and successes for four place kickers this season.

Kicker	Attempts	Success
Roland	39	30
Michael	45	36
Cameron	32	25
Jorge	48	41

Which kicker had the highest success rate? **B**

A Cameron
B Jorge
C Michael
D Roland

2. The portion of fish caught at East Fork Lake yesterday that were large mouth bass was 0.62. Which of the following represents the number of large mouth bass caught as a fraction? **H**

F $\frac{15}{26}$
G $\frac{29}{50}$
H $\frac{31}{50}$
J $\frac{8}{25}$

3. Rachael's new printer can print $1\frac{2}{3}$ times as many pages per minute as her old printer. Her old printer could print 9 pages per minute. How many pages per minute does Rachael's new printer print? **D**

A 12 pages per minute
B 13 pages per minute
C 14 pages per minute
D 15 pages per minute

4. What are the coordinates of point A (4, −1) after it has been reflected over the y-axis? **F**

F (−4, −1)
G (−4, 1)
H (4, −1)
J (4, 1)

5. What are the coordinates of point Z on the coordinate plane? **D**

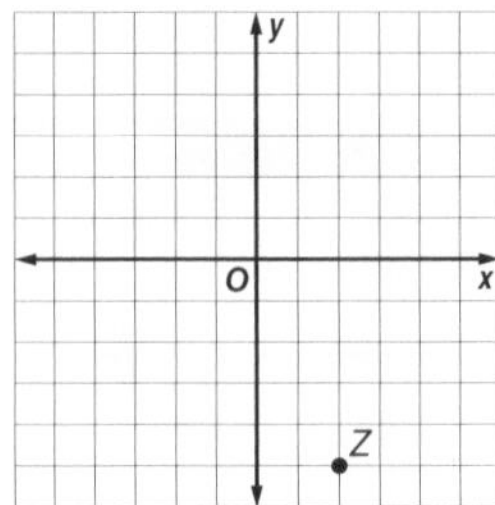

A (−5, 2)
B (5, −2)
C (−2, 5)
D (2, −5)

6. Which property is illustrated in the statement shown below? **H**

$$23 \cdot 1 = 23$$

F Commutative Property
G Associative Property
H Identity Property
J Zero Property

7. Find the sum of the expression shown below. **B**

$$-\frac{8}{15} + \frac{12}{15}$$

A $\frac{3}{15}$
B $\frac{4}{15}$
C $-\frac{5}{15}$
D $-\frac{4}{15}$

Test-TakingTip

Question 7 The fractions have the same denominator, so the sign of the answer will match the numerator with the greater absolute value.

CHAPTER 3 Standardized Test Practice

Short Response/Gridded Response

Record your answers on the answer sheet provided by your teacher or on a sheet of paper.

8. Use the number line below to answer each of the following.

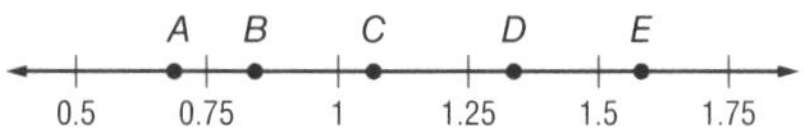

a. Write a fraction or mixed number that could represent each point on the graph. **See margin.**

b. Write an inequality comparing two of the points. **Sample answer:** $\frac{7}{10} < \frac{4}{5}$

9. GRIDDED RESPONSE Mario made 27 out of 40 penalty kicks last season. Write the fraction of penalty kicks that he did not make as a decimal. **0.325**

10. Jamie claims that in order for the sum of two integers to be positive, both of the addends must be positive. Do you agree or disagree with this claim? Justify your answer. **See margin.**

11. GRIDDED RESPONSE Nicole drove 156 miles to her grandmother's house last week for a family reunion. Her sister drove $\frac{5}{4}$ of this distance to get to the reunion. How many more miles did Nicole's sister drive than Nicole? **39**

12. There are 60 minutes in 1 hour.

a. Write an equation to find the number of hours h in any number of minutes m. $h = \frac{m}{60}$

b. How many hours are in 210 minutes? **3.5 h**

13. The area model shows the product of two rational numbers. Write an expression that represents the model. Then state the product. $\frac{1}{3} \cdot \frac{1}{4}; \frac{1}{12}$

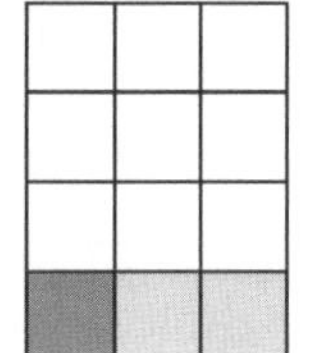

Extended Response

Record your answers on a sheet of paper. Show your work.

14. Mr. Lombardo has five wrenches in his toolbox that are labeled $\frac{3}{8}$ in., $\frac{1}{4}$ in., $\frac{5}{16}$ in., $\frac{7}{8}$ in., and $\frac{9}{32}$ in.

a. Write each fraction as a decimal. Use a bar to show a repeating decimal. **0.375, 0.25, 0.3125, 0.875, 0.28125**

b. Order the sizes of the wrenches from smallest to largest. $\frac{1}{4}, \frac{9}{32}, \frac{5}{16}, \frac{3}{8}, \frac{7}{8}$

c. How else could you order the wrenches from smallest to largest? Explain your reasoning. **Write them with the common denominator 32.**

Need Extra Help?														
If you missed Question...	1	2	3	4	5	6	7	8	9	10	11	12	13	14
Go to Lesson or Page...	3-1	3-2	3-3	2-7	1-4	1-3	3-5	3-1	3-2	2-2	3-3	1-5	3-3	3-1

Formative Assessment

You can use these two pages to benchmark student progress.

CRM Standardized Test Practice, pp. 63–65

Answer Sheet Practice

Have students simulate taking a standardized test by recording their answers on practice recording sheets.

CRM Student Recording Sheet, p. 44

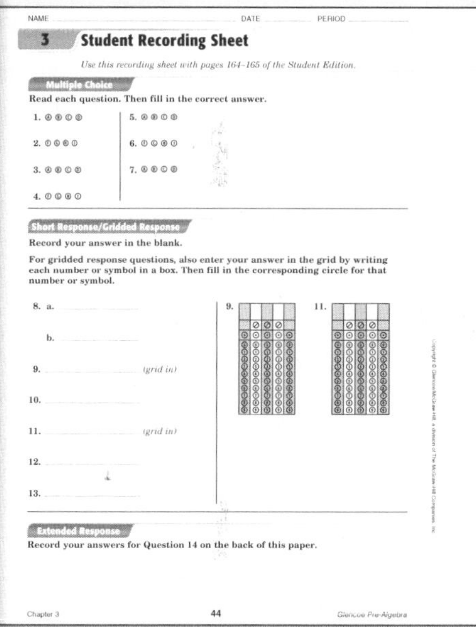
NAME DATE PERIOD

3 Student Recording Sheet

Use this recording sheet with pages 164–165 of the Student Edition.

Multiple Choice

Read each question. Then fill in the correct answer.

1. 2. 3. 4. 5. 6. 7.

Short Response/Gridded Response

Record your answer in the blank.

For gridded response questions, also enter your answer in the grid by writing each number or symbol in a box. Then fill in the corresponding circle for that number or symbol.

8. a. b.
9. (grid in)
10.
11. (grid in)
12.
13.

Extended Response

Record your answers for Question 14 on the back of this paper.

Chapter 3 44 Glencoe Pre-Algebra

Create practice worksheets or tests that align to your state's standards as well as TIMSS and NAEP tests.

Additional Answers

8a. A $\frac{7}{10}$, B $\frac{4}{5}$, C $1\frac{1}{10}$, D $1\frac{4}{10}$, E $1\frac{3}{5}$

10. Answers will vary. Sample Answer: Disagree; One addend can be negative and one positive if the positive integer has a larger absolute value. For example, $5 + (-3) = 2$.

Homework Option

Get Ready for Chapter 4 Assign students the exercises on p. 169 as homework to assess whether they possess the prerequisite skills needed for the next chapter.

Page 121, Lesson 3-1 (Why?)

a. Since 2 is a factor of 10, write an equivalent fraction with a denominator of 10. Multiply the numerator and denominator by 5. So, $\frac{1}{2} = \frac{5}{10}$ and $\frac{5}{10}$ written as a decimal is 0.5.

b. 0.75; Since 4 is a factor of 100, write an equivalent fraction with a denominator of 100. Multiply the numerator and denominator by 25. So, $\frac{3}{4} = \frac{75}{100}$ and $\frac{75}{100}$ written as a decimal is 0.75.

Pages 132–133, Lesson 3-2

59a. true; Sample answer: Integers include all whole numbers and their opposites. Therefore, they belong to the set of rational numbers.

59b. true; Sample answer: All whole numbers and their opposites belong to the set of integers.

59c. false: Sample answer: $\frac{1}{2}$ is not an integer

59d. true: Sample answer: All natural numbers are rational because they can be expressed as fractions.

69.

70.

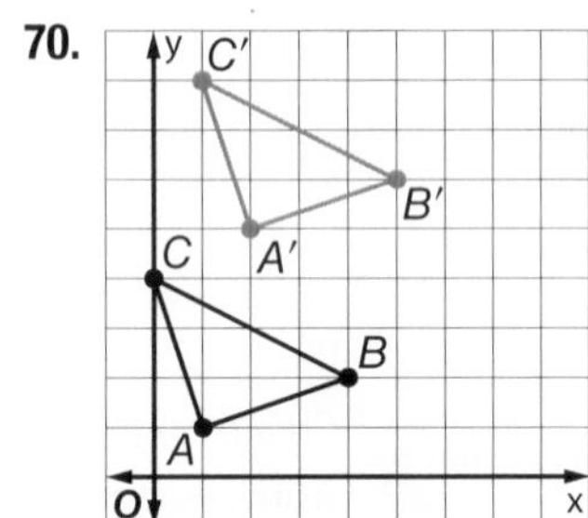

71.

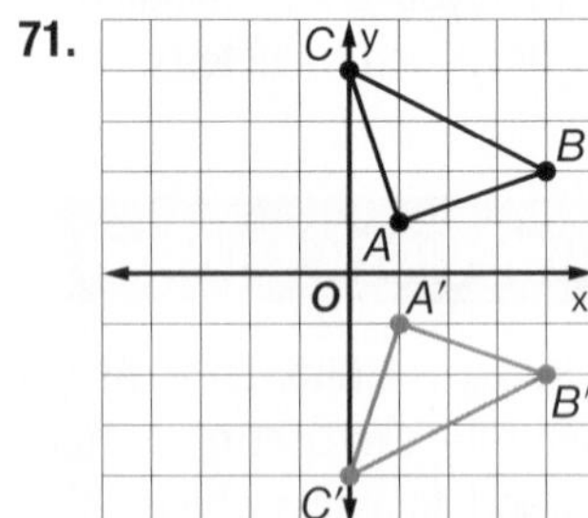

72.

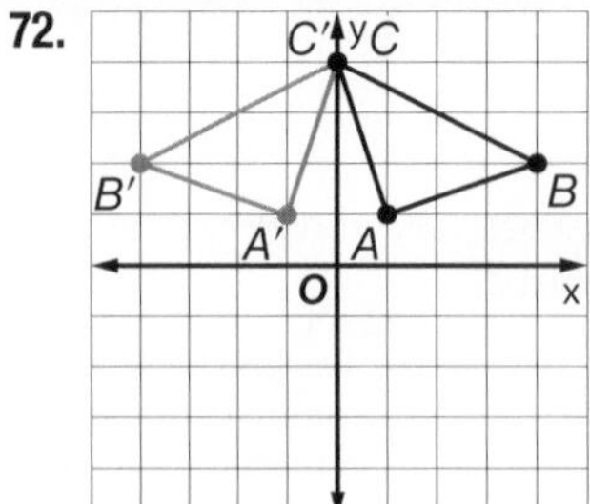

Page 138, Lesson 3-3

57. always; Sample answer: When you multiply a fraction by a whole number or mixed number, you are finding a part of that whole number or mixed number. Since you are finding a part, the product will always be less than the whole number or mixed number.

58. 20; $16\frac{4}{5}$; If you have mixed numbers and both are rounded up, your estimate may be closer to the actual product if you round one mixed number up and the other one down.

Page 141, Lesson 3-4 (Why?)

a. Draw five circles each divided into $\frac{1}{2}$-sections. There are ten $\frac{1}{2}$-sections, so $5 \div \frac{1}{2} = 10$.

b. Draw two circles each divided into $\frac{1}{4}$-sections. There are eight $\frac{1}{4}$-sections, so $2 \div \frac{1}{4} = 8$.

c. Draw three circles each divided into $\frac{1}{3}$-sections. There are nine $\frac{1}{3}$-sections, so $3 \div \frac{1}{3} = 9$.

d. Dividing by a fraction with 1 in the numerator is the same as multiplying by the number that is in the denominator.

Page 157, Lesson 3-6

52. yes; Sample answer: there is an additional step involved at the end, reducing $-\frac{74}{24}$.

$$\begin{aligned} 2\tfrac{3}{4} - 5\tfrac{5}{6} &= \frac{11}{4} - \frac{35}{6} \\ &= \frac{66}{24} - \frac{140}{24} \\ &= -\frac{74}{24} \\ &= -\frac{37}{12} \text{ or } -3\tfrac{1}{12} \end{aligned}$$

$$\begin{aligned} 2\tfrac{3}{4} - 5\tfrac{5}{6} &= \frac{11}{4} - \frac{35}{6} \\ &= \frac{33}{12} - \frac{70}{12} \\ &= -\frac{37}{12} \text{ or } -3\tfrac{1}{12} \end{aligned}$$

Notes

CHAPTER 4

Chapter Planner

Diagnostic Assessment
Quick Check, p. 169

	Lesson 4-1 Pacing: 1 day	Explore 4-2 Pacing: 1 day	Lesson 4-2 Pacing: 1 day	Lesson 4-3 Pacing: 1 day
Title	**The Distributive Property**	**Algebra Lab: Simplifying Algebraic Expressions**	**Simplifying Algebraic Expressions**	**Solving Equations by Adding or Subtracting**
Objectives	• Use the Distributive Property to write equivalent numerical expressions. • Use the Distributive Property to write equivalent algebraic expressions.	• Use algebra tiles to represent and simplify algebraic expressions.	• Identify parts of an algebraic expression.	• Solve equations by using the Addition and Subtraction Properties of Equality. • Translate verbal sentences into equations.
Key Vocabulary	equivalent expressions Distributive Property		term coefficient constant	equation solution inverse operation
NCTM Focal Points	G7-FP3, G7-FP5C For the complete wording of the Focal Points for Grades 7 and 8, please see pages iv, v, FP0, and FP1.			
Multiple Representations	p. 175		p. 182	p. 188
Lesson Resources	**Chapter 4 Resource Masters** • Study Guide and Intervention, pp. 5–6 AL OL ELL • Skills Practice, p. 7 AL OL ELL • Practice, p. 8 AL OL BL ELL • Word Problem Practice, p. 9 AL OL ELL • Enrichment, p. 10 OL BL **Transparencies** • 5-Minute Check Transparency 4-1 AL OL BL ELL **Additional Print Resources** • *Study Notebook* AL OL BL ELL	**Materials:** • algebra tiles	**Chapter 4 Resource Masters** • Study Guide and Intervention, pp. 11–12 AL OL ELL • Skills Practice, p. 13 AL OL ELL • Practice, p. 14 AL OL BL ELL • Word Problem Practice, p. 15 AL OL BL • Enrichment, p. 16 OL BL • Quiz 1, p. 44 AL OL BL ELL **Transparencies** • 5-Minute Check Transparency 4-2 AL OL BL ELL **Additional Print Resources** • *Study Notebook* AL OL BL ELL	**Chapter 4 Resource Masters** • Study Guide and Intervention, pp. 17–18 AL OL ELL • Skills Practice, p. 19 AL OL ELL • Practice, p. 20 AL OL BL ELL • Word Problem Practice, p. 21 AL OL BL • Enrichment, p. 22 OL BL • Quiz 2, p. 44 AL OL BL ELL **Transparencies** • 5-Minute Check Transparency 4-3 AL OL BL ELL **Additional Print Resources** • *Study Notebook* AL OL BL ELL
Technology for Every Lesson	Math Online **glencoe.com** • Extra Examples • Self-Check Quizzes • Personal Tutor	**CD/DVD Resources** IWB INTERACTIVE WHITEBOARD READY IWB StudentWorks Plus IWB Interactive Classroom IWB Diagnostic and Assessment Planner		• TeacherWorks Plus • eSolutions Manual Plus • ExamView Assessment Suite
Math in Motion		p. 177		p. 185
Differentiated Instruction	pp. 172, 176		pp. 179, 183	pp. 185, 189

KEY: AL Approaching Level OL On Level BL Beyond Level ELL English Learners

Suggested Pacing			
Time Periods	Instruction	Review & Assessment	Total
45-minute	8	2	10
90-minute	4	1	5

Expressions and Equations

Lesson 4-4 Pacing: 1 day	Explore 4-5 Pacing: 1 day	Lesson 4-5 Pacing: 1 day	Lesson 4-6 Pacing: 1 day
Solving Equations by Multiplying or Dividing	**Algebra Lab: Solving Two-Step Equations Using Algebra Tiles**	**Solving Two-Step Equations**	**Writing Equations**
• Solve equations by using the Division Property of Equality. • Solve equations by using the Multiplication Property of Equality.	• Use algebra tiles to solve two-step equations.	• Solve two-step equations. • Solve real-world problems involving two-step equations.	• Write two-step equations. • Solve verbal problems by writing and solving two-step equations.
		two-step equation	
p. 195		p. 203	p. 208
Chapter 4 Resource Masters • Study Guide and Intervention, pp. 23–24 AL OL ELL • Skills Practice, p. 25 AL OL ELL • Practice, p. 26 AL OL BL ELL • Word Problem Practice, p. 27 AL OL BL • Enrichment, p. 28 OL BL **Transparencies** • 5-Minute Check Transparency 4-4 AL OL BL ELL **Additional Print Resources** • *Study Notebook* AL OL BL ELL	**Materials:** • algebra tiles • equation mat	**Chapter 4 Resource Masters** • Study Guide and Intervention, pp. 29–30 AL OL ELL • Skills Practice, p. 31 AL OL ELL • Practice, p. 32 AL OL BL ELL • Word Problem Practice, p. 33 AL OL BL • Enrichment, p. 34 OL BL • Graphing Calculator, p. 35 AL OL BL ELL • Quiz 3, p. 45 AL OL BL ELL **Transparencies** • 5-Minute Check Transparency 4-5 AL OL BL ELL **Additional Print Resources** • *Study Notebook* AL OL BL ELL	**Chapter 4 Resource Masters** • Study Guide and Intervention, pp. 36–37 AL OL ELL • Skills Practice, p. 38 AL OL ELL • Practice, p. 39 AL OL BL ELL • Word Problem Practice, p. 40 AL OL BL • Enrichment, p. 41 OL BL • Quiz 4, p. 45 AL OL BL ELL **Transparencies** • 5-Minute Check Transparency 4-6 AL OL BL ELL **Additional Print Resources** • *Study Notebook* AL OL BL ELL
p. 193	p. 197	p. 200	
pp. 193, 196		pp. 201, 204	pp. 206, 209

Math Online glencoe.com
- Extra Examples
- Self-Check Quizzes
- Personal Tutor

CD/DVD Resources IWB INTERACTIVE WHITEBOARD READY
- IWB StudentWorks Plus
- IWB Interactive Classroom
- IWB Diagnostic and Assessment Planner
- TeacherWorks Plus
- eSolutions Manual Plus
- ExamView Assessment Suite

Summative Assessment
- Study Guide and Review, pp. 210–212
- Practice Test, p. 213

CHAPTER 4

Assessment and Intervention

SE = Student Edition, **TE** = Teacher Edition, **CRM** = Chapter Resource Masters

	Diagnosis	Prescription
Diagnostic Assessment	**Beginning Chapter 4**	
	Get Ready for Chapter 4 **SE,** p. 169	Intervention **TE,** p. 169
	Beginning Every Lesson	
	Then, Now, Why? **SE** 5-Minute Check Transparencies	Chapter 0 **SE,** p. P1 through p. P22 Concepts and Skills Bank **SE,** pp. 856–887 *Quick Review Math Handbook*
Formative Assessment	**During/After Every Lesson**	
	Check Your Progress **SE,** every example Check Your Understanding **SE** H.O.T. Problems **SE** Spiral Review **SE** Additional Examples **TE** Watch Out! **TE** Step 4, Assess **TE** Chapter 4 Quizzes **CRM,** pp. 44–45 Self-Check Quizzes glencoe.com	**Tier 1 Intervention** Concepts and Skills Bank **SE,** pp. 856–887 Skills Practice **CRM,** Ch. 1–4 glencoe.com **Tier 2 Intervention** Differentiated Instruction **TE** Differentiated Homework Options **TE** Study Guide and Intervention Masters **CRM,** Ch. 1–4 *Quick Review Math Handbook* **Tier 3 Intervention** *Math Triumphs, Grade 8,* Ch. 3
	Mid-Chapter	
	Mid-Chapter Quiz **SE,** p. 190 Mid-Chapter Test **CRM,** p. 46 ExamView Assessment Suite	**Tier 1 Intervention** Concepts and Skills Bank **SE,** pp. 856–887 Skills Practice **CRM,** Ch. 1–4 glencoe.com **Tier 2 Intervention** Study Guide and Intervention Masters **CRM,** Ch. 1–4 *Quick Review Math Handbook* **Tier 3 Intervention** *Math Triumphs, Grade 8,* Ch. 3
	Before Chapter Test	
	Chapter Study Guide and Review **SE,** pp. 210–212 Practice Test **SE,** p. 213 Standardized Test Practice **SE,** pp. 214–217 Chapter Test glencoe.com Standardized Test Practice glencoe.com Vocabulary Review glencoe.com ExamView Assessment Suite	**Tier 1 Intervention** Concepts and Skills Bank **SE,** pp. 856–887 Skills Practice **CRM,** Ch. 1–4 glencoe.com **Tier 2 Intervention** Study Guide and Intervention Masters **CRM,** Ch. 1–4 *Quick Review Math Handbook* **Tier 3 Intervention** *Math Triumphs, Grade 8,* Ch. 3
Summative Assessment	**After Chapter 4**	
	Multiple-Choice Tests, Forms 1, 2A, 2B **CRM,** pp. 48–59 Free-Response Tests, Forms 2C, 2D, 3 **CRM,** pp. 48–59 Vocabulary Test **CRM,** p. 47 Extended Response Test **CRM,** p. 60 Standardized Test Practice **CRM,** pp. 61–63 ExamView Assessment Suite	Study Guide and Intervention Masters **CRM,** Ch. 1–4 *Quick Review Math Handbook* glencoe.com

CHAPTER 4

Differentiated Instruction

Option 1 Reaching All Learners AL OL BL ELL

Visual/Spatial Have students work with a partner. First, one student writes an equation such as $x + 6 = -2$ or $x - 5 = 8$. The other student then solves the equation using algebra tiles. After solving the equation, partners switch roles and repeat the activity. Next, have one student pose a problem by using algebra tiles to make an equation. The other student writes the equation that the tiles represent and then solves the equation using tiles.

Intrapersonal Have students work in groups to model combining like terms. Call out an everyday school item, such as "pencil." Each student in the group then places the pencils in his or her possession in a pile on the table or desk. Then the group writes an expression to show, for example, that each person in turn had 4, 3, 1, and 0 pencils: $4p + 3p + 1p + 0$. Finally, the group simplifies the expression: $8p$.

Option 2 Approaching Level AL

Have students write in their journals a number of equations using each of the four operations. For each equation, have them write a question that will help them solve it mentally, such as "What number times 2 is 10?" for the equation $2x = 10$. Ask students which operation is the most difficult for them to do mentally, and then have them describe in their journals a strategy that will help them solve such problems more quickly.

Option 3 English Learners ELL

Give students a group of ten algebraic expressions and then have them use the following key to identify *terms, like terms, coefficients,* and *constants.*

Key	
Terms:	Circle in blue.
Like terms:	Underline the first set in red, and the second set in green.
Coefficients:	Shade in blue.
Constants:	Shade in yellow.

For example, $7x + 4 - 3x + 8$ would be coded as follows:

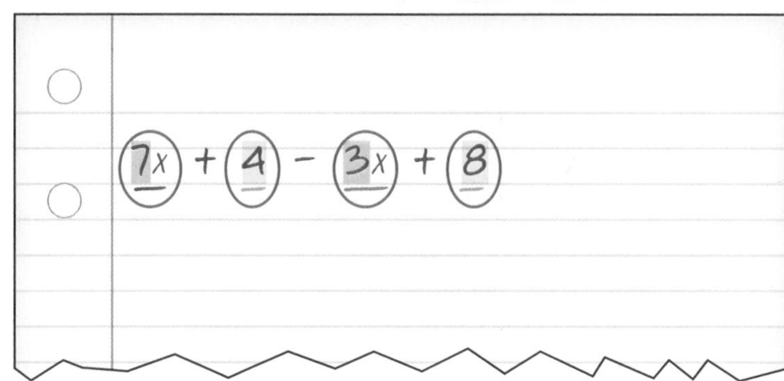

To enhance their understanding of the vocabulary, suggest that students first find the terms in each of the ten expressions, then the like terms, and so on.

Option 4 Beyond Level BL

Students can create "What Number Am I" cards.

As students become more comfortable with the game, impose restrictions like the following:

If you multiply me by 5,
then add 4, you get 39.
What number am I?

- Create a card with an answer is negative.
- Create a card with an answer is 4432.
- Create a card with an answer of $-3\frac{3}{4}$.
- Create a card with at least 3 operations.

CHAPTER 4 Focus on Mathematical Content

Vertical Alignment

Before Chapter 4

Related Topics before Pre-Algebra
- use models to connect to algorithms
- select and use appropriate operations

Previous Topics from Pre-Algebra
- select appropriate operations
- predict, find, and justify solutions

Chapter 4

Related Topics from Pre-Algebra
- communicate mathematical ideas using algebraic mathematical models
- use inverse operations to solve equations
- predict, find, and justify solutions to application problems using algebraic equations

After Chapter 4

Preparation for Algebra 1
- simplify polynomial expressions
- investigate methods for solving linear equations
- analyze situations involving linear equations

Lesson-by-Lesson Preview

4-1 The Distributive Property

The equation $3(x + 2) = 3x + 6$ is an example of the Distributive Property, which states that to multiply a sum or difference by a number, multiply each number inside the parentheses by the factor outside the parentheses.

Algebra tiles can be used to demonstrate the Distributive Property by showing that two equivalent algebraic expressions have the same value, no matter the value of the variable.

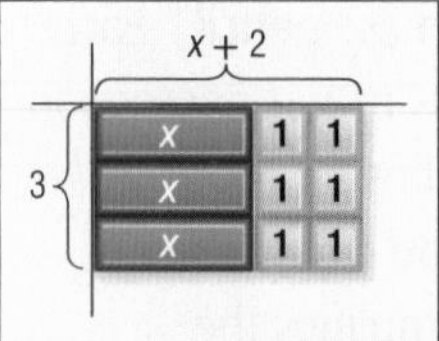

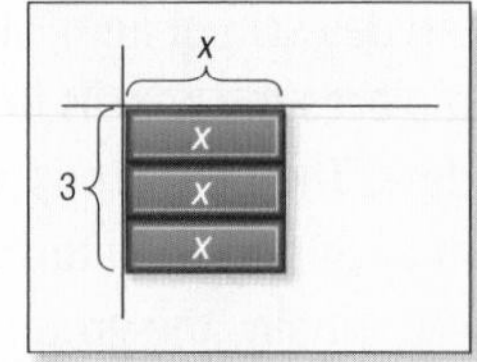

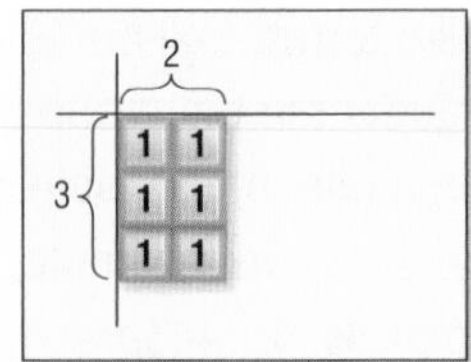

The Distributive Property can be used to write equivalent algebraic expressions, evaluate numerical and algebraic expressions, and find products mentally.

4-2 Simplifying Algebraic Expressions

Plus or minus signs separate an algebraic expression into parts.

- Each part is a *term.* For example, the expression $4x - 6 + x + 3$ has four terms. *Like terms* contain the same variable, such as $4x$ and x.
- The numerical part of a term that contains a variable is the *coefficient* of the variable. The coefficient of $4x$ is 4 and the coefficient of x is 1.
- A term without a variable is a *constant,* such as -6 or 3 in the expression $4x - 6 + x + 3$. -6 and 3 are also like terms.

An algebraic expression in simplest form has no like terms and no parentheses. Simplify algebraic expressions by using properties to combine like terms and remove parentheses.

Solving Equations by Adding or Subtracting

Inverse operations "undo" each other and can be used to solve equations. To undo the addition of 4 in the equation $x + 4 = 9$, subtract 4 from each side of the equation.

The following applies when solving equations by adding or subtracting:

- The Addition and Subtraction Properties of Equality state that if you add or subtract the same number from each side of an equation, the two sides remain equal.
- Two equations are equivalent if they have the same solution. For example, $x + 4 = 9$ is equivalent to $x = 5$ because they both have the same solution of 5.
- Check a solution by using it to replace the variable in the original equation, and then check to see whether the sentence is true.

Solving Equations by Multiplying or Dividing

Multiplication and division are inverse operations, so undo multiplication by dividing and undo division by multiplying.

- The Division Property of Equality states that when you divide each side of an equation by the same nonzero number, the two sides remain equal. The equation $4x = 20$ involves multiplication, so use division to solve:

$$4x = 20, \frac{4x}{4} = \frac{20}{4}, x = 5$$

- The Multiplication Property of Equality states that when you multiply each side of an equation by the same number, the two sides remain equal. For example, the equation $\frac{x}{3} = 5$ involves division, so use multiplication to solve:

$$\frac{x}{3} = 5, 3\left(\frac{x}{3}\right) = 3(5), x = 15$$

Solving Two-Step Equations

A two-step equation contains two operations, such as multiplication and addition in the equation $2x + 1 = 7$. When solving two-step equations, use inverse operations to undo each operation in reverse order.

For example, to solve the equation $2x + 1 = 7$:

- Undo addition by subtracting 1 from each side to give $2x = 6$.
- Undo multiplication by dividing each side by 2 to give $x = 3$.

Writing Equations

Verbal sentences can be written as equations. An equation is a statement that two expressions are equal. The expressions are joined with an equals sign (=). Words such as *equals* and *is* can be used to translate verbal sentences into equations.

Translate the verbal sentence *−33 is 24 more than 3 times a number* as follows:

Words:	−33 is 24 more than 3 times a number
Variable:	Let n = a number
Equation:	$-33 = 24 + 3n$

Many real-world situations can be represented by equations.

Nina deposited \$100 in her savings account and plans to deposit \$25 each month. How many months will it take to save \$500?

Words:	A deposit of \$100 plus \$25 per month equals \$500.
Variable:	Let m = the number of months
Equation:	$100 + 25m = 500$

Professional Development

Targeted professional development has been articulated throughout McGraw-Hill's mathematics program. The **McGraw-Hill Professional Development Video Library** provides short videos that support key topics. For more information, visit glencoe.com.

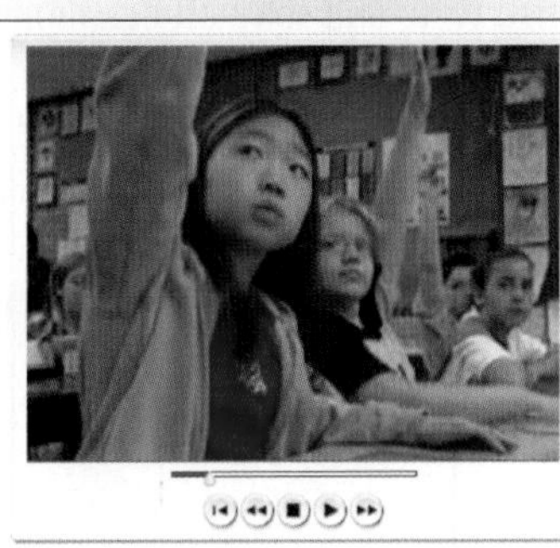

Model Lessons

Instructional Strategies

CHAPTER 4 Notes

Chapter Project

Play-Making

Students use what they have learned about algebraic expressions and equations to determine the costs and profits of producing a play with a $15,000 budget.

- Divide students into groups. Ask each group to write expressions to represent reasonable costs in four areas: cast and crew salaries; rent for a theater; technical production, including props, lighting, and costumes; and advertising, including flyers and ads.
- Have students represent the costs for each area using a variable with a coefficient and a constant. Suppose a theater charges a rental fee of $500 plus an additional fee each day. Students could represent the cost of renting the theater for 10 days as $10t + 500$, where t is the daily cost to rent the theater.
- Have each group allocate a reasonable portion of the budget to the four areas, and then write and solve equations to project the costs of each area. For example, the solution of $10t + 500 = 2500$ shows that they can pay $200 per day to rent the theater for 10 days.
- Ask each group to decide on how much profit they want to make, and then write and solve an equation to show what they must charge per ticket to make the profit. Remind students that ticket sales depend on seating in the theater and the number of performances each day that the play runs.

CHAPTER 4 Expressions and Equations

Then
In Chapters 2 and 3, you worked with integers and rational numbers.

Now
In Chapter 4, you will:
- Use the Distributive Property.
- Solve equations by using properties of equality.
- Write equations to solve problems.

Why?
ENTERTAINMENT
The entertainment field uses equations to balance the costs and profits of a project. These situations can be represented using variables, coefficients, and constants. The variable represents something that changes, such as the cost of costumes.

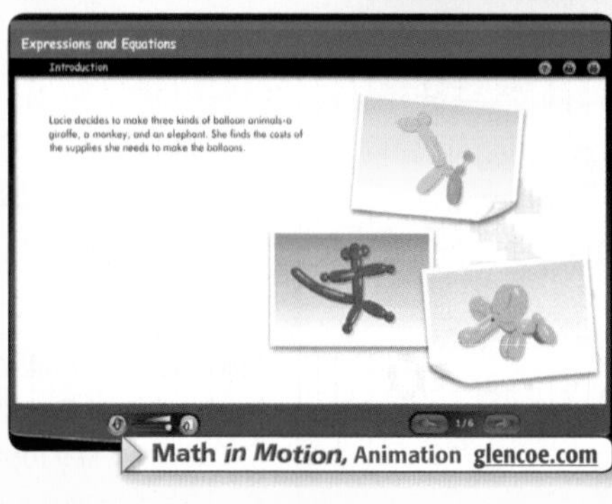

Key Vocabulary Introduce the key vocabulary in the chapter using the routine below.

Define: An algebraic expression is in simplest form when it has no like terms and no parentheses.

Example: The expression $4w - 7q + 3$ is in simplest form.

Ask: Is the expression $5x - 2 + 3x - 7$ in simplest form? No Simplify it. $8x - 9$

Get Ready for Chapter 4

Diagnose Readiness You have two options for checking Prerequisite Skills.

Text Option Take the Quick Check below. Refer to the Quick Review for help.

*Quick*Check

(Used in Lessons 4-1 through 4-6)
Find each product. (Lesson 2-4)

1. $3(-3)$ -9
2. $-4(2)$ -8
3. $-7(-4)$ 28
4. $-4 \cdot 5$ -20
5. $-11(-8)$ 88
6. $9(-4)$ -36

(Used in Lessons 4-1 through 4-6)

7. **STOCK MARKET** The price of a stock decreased \$2.05 each day for five consecutive days. What was the total change in value of the stock over the five day period? (Lesson 2-4) \$10.25 decrease

(Used in Lessons 4-3 through 4-6)
Write each subtraction expression as an addition expression. (Lesson 2-3)

8. $5 - 9$ $5 + (-9)$
9. $4 - 10$ $4 + (-10)$
10. $-11 - 9$ $-11 + (-9)$
11. $-19 - 10$ $-19 + (-10)$
12. **MONEY** Student Council spent \$178 on decorations and \$110 on snacks for the dance. Write an addition expression for the amount remaining in the dance budget if Student Council initially had \$593. $593 + (-178) + (-110)$

(Used in Lessons 4-3 and 4-5)
Find each sum. (Lesson 2-2)

13. $6 + (-7)$ -1
14. $-8 + 6$ -2
15. $3 + (-3)$ 0
16. $4 + (-10)$ -6
17. $-13 + (-8)$ -21
18. $-11 + 12$ 1
19. **CAVERNS** A tour group began 26 feet underground. During their tour, they went down 15 feet more and then went up 19 feet. Express their current depth as an integer. -22 ft

*Quick*Review

EXAMPLE 1

Find 7(−2).

$7(-2) = -14$ — The factors have different signs, so the product is negative.

EXAMPLE 2

Find −5(−9).

$-5(-9) = 45$ — The factors have the same sign, so the product is positive.

EXAMPLE 3

Write 8 − 12 as an addition expression.

$8 - 12 = 8 + (-12)$ — To subtract 12, add −12.

EXAMPLE 4

Find −5 + 7.

$-5 + 7 = 2$ — Subtract $|-5|$ from $|7|$. The sum is positive because $|7| > |-5|$.

Online Option Math Online Take a self-check Chapter Readiness Quiz at glencoe.com.

Response to Intervention (RtI)

Use the *Quick Check* results and the Intervention Planner to help you determine your Response to Intervention. The If-Then statements in the chart help you decide the appropriate tier of RtI and suggest intervention resources for each tier.

Intervention Planner

Tier 1 On Level

 students miss about 25% of the exercises or less,

 choose a resource:

- **SE** Lessons 2-2 through 2-4
- **CRM** Skills Practice, Chapter 2, pp. 13, 19, and 25
- **TE** Chapter Project, p. 168

Math Online Self-Check Quiz

Tier 2 Strategic Intervention approaching grade level

 students miss about 50% of the exercises,

 choose a resource:

- **CRM** Study Guide and Intervention, pp. 4, 11, 12, 17, 18, 22, and 23

Quick Review Math Handbook

Math Online Extra Examples, Personal Tutor, Homework Help

Tier 3 Intensive Intervention 2 or more years below grade level

 students miss about 75% of the exercises,

 use *Math Triumphs, Grade 8,* Ch. 3

Math Online Extra Examples, Personal Tutor, Homework Help, Review Vocabulary

CHAPTER 4 Notes

FOLDABLES® Study Organizer

Dinah Zike's Foldables®

Focus Students write notes about expressions and equations as they work through this chapter.

Teach Have students make and label their Foldables as illustrated. After each lesson, have students write a summary of the lesson including any new vocabulary. Encourage them to include examples of important concepts.

When to Use It Encourage students to add to their Foldable as they work through the chapter, and use them to review for the Chapter Test.

Differentiated Instruction

CRM Student-Built Glossary, pp. 1–2 Students should complete the chart by providing a definition of each term and an example as they progress through Chapter 4. This study tool can also be used to review for the Chapter Test.

Get Started on Chapter 4

You will learn several new concepts, skills, and vocabulary terms as you study Chapter 4. To get ready, identify important terms and organize your resources. You may wish to refer to **Chapter 0** to review prerequisite skills.

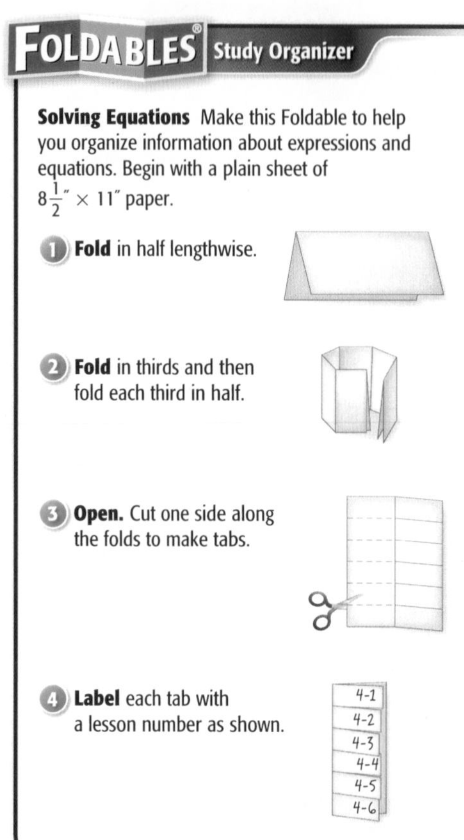

FOLDABLES Study Organizer
Solving Equations Make this Foldable to help you organize information about expressions and equations. Begin with a plain sheet of $8\frac{1}{2}'' \times 11''$ paper.
1 **Fold** in half lengthwise.
2 **Fold** in thirds and then fold each third in half.
3 **Open.** Cut one side along the folds to make tabs.
4 **Label** each tab with a lesson number as shown.
4-1
4-2
4-3
4-4
4-5
4-6

Math Online glencoe.com

- Study the chapter online
- Explore **Math in Motion**
- Get extra help from your own **Personal Tutor**
- Use **Extra Examples** for additional help
- Take a **Self-Check Quiz**
- **Review Vocabulary** in fun ways

New Vocabulary

English		Español
Distributive Property	p. 171	Propiedad distributiva
equivalent expressions	p. 171	expresiones equivalentes
coefficient	p. 178	coeficiente
constant	p. 178	constante
like terms	p. 178	terminos semejantes
term	p. 178	término
simplest form	p. 179	forma reducida
simplifying the expression	p. 179	reducir la expresión
equation	p. 184	ecuación
equivalent equations	p. 184	ecuaciones equivalentes
inverse operations	p. 184	operaciones inversas
solution	p. 184	solución
solving the equation	p. 184	resolver la ecuación
two-step equation	p. 199	ecuación de dos pasos

Review Vocabulary

algebraic expression • p. 11 • expresión algebraica any combination of terms and operations

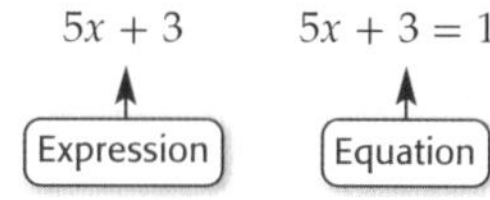

equation • p. 34 • ecuación a mathematical sentence stating that two quantities are equal

Multilingual eGlossary glencoe.com

The Distributive Property

Why?

Lita's mother is paying for her and two friends to go to the movies. She will buy each of them a snack and a drink.

a. Find the total amount that Lita's mother will need to pay. $37.50

b. Describe the method you used to find the total cost. Sample answer: Find the cost for 1 person then multiply by 3.

Here are two ways to find the total cost.

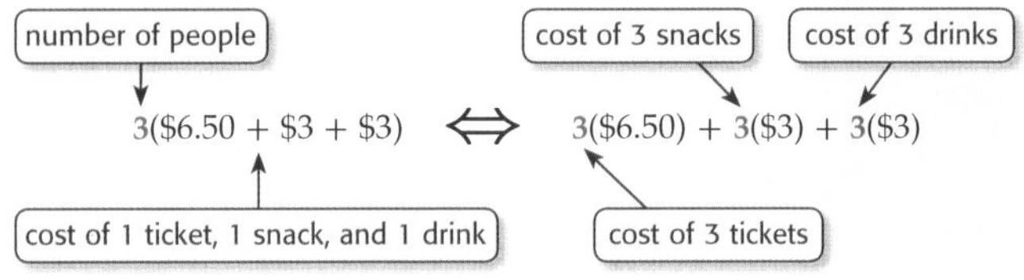

Then
You have already evaluated numerical expressions using addition and multiplication.

Now
- Use the Distributive Property to write equivalent numerical expressions.
- Use the Distributive Property to write equivalent algebraic expressions.

New Vocabulary
equivalent expressions
Distributive Property

Math Online
glencoe.com
- Extra Examples
- Personal Tutor
- Self-Check Quiz
- Homework Help

Numerical Expressions The expressions above are **equivalent expressions** because they have the same value, $37.50. This example also shows the **Distributive Property**.

Key Concept — Distributive Property (For Your FOLDABLE)

Words To multiply a sum or difference by a number, multiply each term inside the parentheses by the number outside the parentheses.

Symbols $a(b + c) = ab + ac$ $a(b - c) = ab - ac$

Example $5(6 + 7) = 5 \cdot 6 + 5 \cdot 7$ $(9 - 3)8 = 9 \cdot 8 - 3 \cdot 8$

Math *in Motion*, BrainPOP® glencoe.com

EXAMPLE 1 Evaluate Numerical Expressions

Use the Distributive Property to write each expression as an equivalent expression. Then evaluate the expression.

a. $5(12 + 4)$

$5(12 + 4) = 5 \cdot 12 + 5 \cdot 4$
$= 60 + 20$ **Multiply.**
$= 80$ **Add.**

b. $(20 - 3)8$

$(20 - 3)8 = 20 \cdot 8 - 3 \cdot 8$
$= 160 - 24$ **Multiply.**
$= 136$ **Subtract.**

Check Your Progress

1A. $(6 + 3)4$ 36

1B. $4(9 - 2)$ 28

Personal Tutor glencoe.com

4-1 Lesson Notes

1 FOCUS

Vertical Alignment

Before Lesson 4-1
Evaluate numerical expressions using addition and multiplication.

Lesson 4-1
Use the Distributive Property to write equivalent numerical and algebraic expressions.

After Lesson 4-1
Use the Distributive Property to simplify algebraic expressions.

2 TEACH

Scaffolding Questions

Have students read the *Why?* section of the lesson and answer the questions.

Ask:
- How many tickets will be purchased? three
- What is the cost of each item that will be purchased? tickets: $6.50, snacks: $3, drinks: $3
- What operation(s) can you use to find the total cost? Sample answers: addition or addition and multiplication

Lesson 4-1 Resources

Resource	Approaching-Level	On-Level	Beyond-Level	English Learners
Teacher Edition	• Differentiated Instruction, p. 172	• Differentiated Instruction, p. 172	• Differentiated Instruction, p. 176	
Chapter Resource Masters	• Study Guide and Intervention, pp. 5–6 • Skills Practice, p. 7 • Practice, p. 8 • Word Problem Practice, p. 9	• Study Guide and Intervention, pp. 5–6 • Skills Practice, p. 7 • Practice, p. 8 • Word Problem Practice, p. 9 • Enrichment, p. 10	• Practice, p. 8 • Word Problem Practice, p. 9 • Enrichment, p. 10	• Study Guide and Intervention, pp. 5–6 • Skills Practice, p. 7 • Practice, p. 8
Transparencies	• 5-Minute Check Transparency 4-1	• 5-Minute Check Transparency 4-1	• 5-Minute Check Transparency 4-1	• 5-Minute Check Transparency 4-1
Other	• Study Notebook • Teaching Pre-Algebra with Manipulatives	• Study Notebook • Teaching Pre-Algebra with Manipulatives	• Study Notebook	• Study Notebook • Teaching Pre-Algebra with Manipulatives

Numerical Expressions

Examples 1 and 2 show how to write equivalent numerical expressions and find their values using the Distributive Property. Students will multiply each value inside the parentheses by the value outside the parentheses and then add or subtract to find the value of the expression.

Formative Assessment

Use the Check Your Progress exercises after each example to determine students' understanding of concepts.

Additional Examples

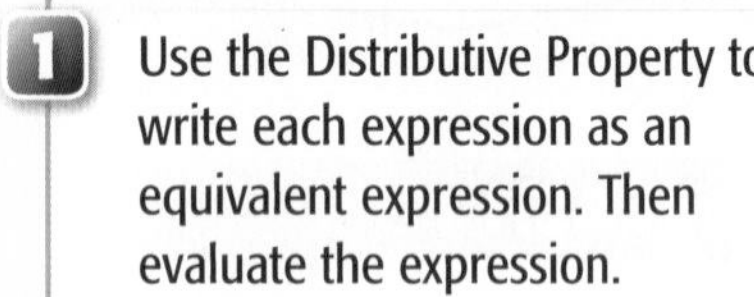

1 Use the Distributive Property to write each expression as an equivalent expression. Then evaluate the expression.

a. $4(5 + 8)$ $4 \cdot 5 + 4 \cdot 8$; 52

b. $(6 - 9)2$ $6 \cdot 2 - 9 \cdot 2$; -6

2 **RECREATION** A community center offers a canoeing day trip. The canoeing fee is \$80 per person. The cost of food is an additional \$39 per person. Find the total cost for a family of four. $4(80 + 39)$; $4 \cdot 80 + 4 \cdot 39$ \$476

Additional Examples also in Interactive Classroom PowerPoint® Presentations

IWB INTERACTIVE WHITEBOARD READY

The Distributive Property allows you to find some products mentally. For example, you can find $7 \cdot 34$ mentally by evaluating $7 \cdot (30 + 4)$.

$$7 \cdot (30 + 4) = 7 \cdot 30 + 7 \cdot 4$$

$$= 210 + 28 \quad \textbf{Think } 7 \cdot 30 = 210$$

$$= 238 \quad \textbf{Think } 210 + 28 = 238$$

Real-World EXAMPLE 2 Use the Distributive Property

FINANCIAL LITERACY On a school visit to Washington, D.C., Dichali and his class visited the Smithsonian Air and Space Museum. Tickets to the IMAX movie cost \$8.99. Find the total cost for 20 students to see the IMAX movie.

Understand You know how many students will be attending the movie and how much the movie costs. You need to find the total cost for the group to see the IMAX movie.

Plan You can use the Distributive Property and mental math to find the total cost for the movie. To find the total cost mentally, find 20(\$9.00 − \$0.01).

Solve 20(\$9.00 − \$0.01) = 20(\$9.00) − 20(\$0.01) **Distributive Property**

= \$180 − \$0.20 **Multiply.**

= \$179.80 **Subtract.**

The total cost is \$179.80.

Check You can check your result by multiplying 20 • \$9 to get \$180. The answer seems reasonable. ✓

Real-World Link

The National Air and Space Museum opened in Washington, D.C., in 1976. It contains the world's largest collection of aircraft and spacecraft, including the 1903 Wright brothers' *Kitty Hawk Flyer*.

Source: Smithsonian Museum

Check Your Progress

2. **FOOD** A spaghetti dinner at the Italian Village restaurant costs \$10.25. Use the Distributive Property and mental math to find the total cost of the dinner for Sherita, her brother, and her parents.
4(\$10 + 0.25); 4 • 10 + 4 • 0.25; \$41

Personal Tutor glencoe.com

Algebraic Expressions You can model the Distributive Property by using algebra tiles and variables.

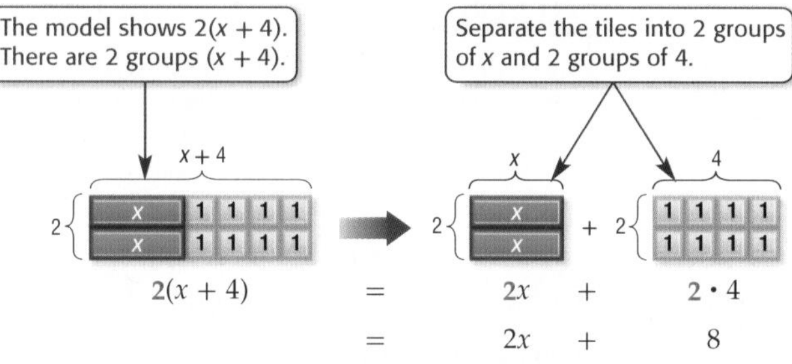

The model shows 2(x + 4). There are 2 groups (x + 4).
Separate the tiles into 2 groups of x and 2 groups of 4.
x + 4
x
4
2

$$2(x + 4) = 2x + 2 \cdot 4$$

$$= 2x + 8$$

The expressions $2(x + 4)$ and $2x + 8$ are equivalent expressions because no matter what the value of x is, these expressions have the same value.

Vocabulary Link

Distribute
Everyday Use to deliver to each member of a group

Distributive
Math Use a property that allows you to multiply each member of a sum by a number

Differentiated Instruction

AL OL

If students are having difficulty using the Distributive Property,

Then have them write the equations shown in the definition of the Distributive Property in the Key Concept box. Then have them use colored pencils or markers to color each number or variable in an equation using the same unique color each time it appears. Have students describe the pattern shown by the colors and use the Distributive Property to explain the pattern.

EXAMPLE 3 Simplify Algebraic Expressions

Use the Distributive Property to write each expression as an equivalent algebraic expression.

a. $4(x + 5)$

$4(x + 5) = 4x + 4 \cdot 5$

$= 4x + 20$ **Simplify.**

b. $(y + 10)6$

$(y + 10)6 = y \cdot 6 + 10 \cdot 6$

$= 6y + 60$ **Simplify.**

Watch Out!

Distributive Property In Example 3a, remember to distribute the 4 to both values inside the parentheses.

Check Your Progress

3A. $2(a + 5)$ **$2a + 10$**

3B. $(b + 6)3$ **$3b + 18$**

Personal Tutor glencoe.com

EXAMPLE 4 Simplify Expressions with Subtraction

Use the Distributive Property to write each expression as an equivalent algebraic expression.

a. $3(m - 4)$

$3(m - 4) = 3[m + (-4)]$	Rewrite $m - 4$ as $m + (-4)$.
$= 3 \cdot m + 3 \cdot (-4)$	Distributive Property
$= 3m + (-12)$	Simplify.
$= 3m - 12$	Definition of subtraction

b. $-9(n - 7)$

$-9(n - 7) = -9[n + (-7)]$	Rewrite $n - 7$ as $n + (-7)$.
$= -9 \cdot n + (-9)(-7)$	Distributive Property
$= -9n + 63$	Simplify.

Check Your Progress

4A. $4(d - 3)$ **$4d - 12$**

4B. $-7(e - 4)$ **$-7e + 28$**

Personal Tutor glencoe.com

Check Your Understanding

Example 1 p. 171

Use the Distributive Property to write each expression as an equivalent expression. Then evaluate the expression.

1. $7(9 + 3)$ **$7 \cdot 9 + 7 \cdot 3$; 84**
2. $4(3 + 5)$ **$4 \cdot 3 + 4 \cdot 5$; 32**
3. $(7 + 8)2$ **$7 \cdot 2 + 8 \cdot 2$; 30**
4. $(5 + 6)8$ **$5 \cdot 8 + 6 \cdot 8$; 88**

Example 2 p. 172

5. **SCHOOL SUPPLIES** You purchase 3 blue notebooks and 2 red notebooks. Each notebook costs \$1.30. Use mental math to find the total cost of the notebooks. Justify your answer by using the Distributive Property. **\$6.50; $5(\$1 + \$0.30) = 5 \cdot 1 + 5 \cdot 0.30$**

Examples 3 and 4 p. 173

Use the Distributive Property to write each expression as an equivalent algebraic expression.

6. $8(m + 4)$ **$8m + 32$**
7. $(p + 4)5$ **$5p + 20$**
8. $-6(b - 5)$ **$-6b + 30$**
9. $9(a - 10)$ **$9a - 90$**

Algebraic Expressions

Examples 3 and 4 show how to write and simplify equivalent algebraic expressions using the Distributive Property.

Additional Examples

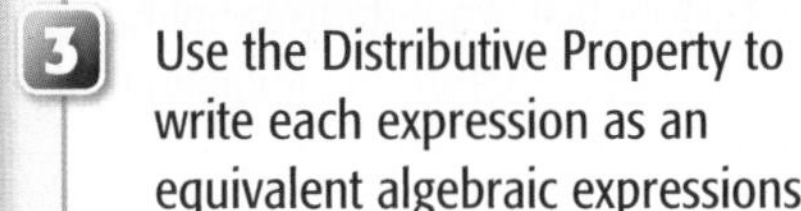

3 Use the Distributive Property to write each expression as an equivalent algebraic expressions.

a. $2(x + 4)$ $2x + 8$

b. $(y + 3)6$ $6y + 18$

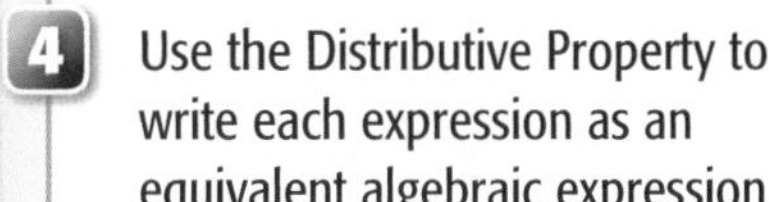

4 Use the Distributive Property to write each expression as an equivalent algebraic expression.

a. $4(x - 2)$ $4x - 8$

b. $-2(n - 3)$ $-2n + 6$

Tips for New Teachers

Study Tip Remind students that to subtract an integer, they should add its additive inverse.

3 PRACTICE

Formative Assessment

Use Exercises 1–9 to check for understanding.

Use the chart at the bottom of the next page to customize assignments for your students.

TEACH with TECH

INTERACTIVE WHITEBOARD On the board, work through several examples using the Distributive Property. Save the examples and the work to a file and print it or e-mail it to your students so they can use it for reference.

Focus on Mathematical Content

Writing Equivalent Expressions Using the Distributive Property When solving equations that have variables inside parentheses, students should use the Distributive Property to simplify the expression before manipulating the equation.

Tips for New Teachers

Refer to Exercise 30. Double bar graphs are good sources for data. Have students find examples of double bar graphs and then write problems similar to Exercise 30.

Additional Answers

42a. **Volume (in³)**

h (in.)	V (in³)
1	276
2	264
3	252
4	240

42b. **Volume of the Bird Feeder**

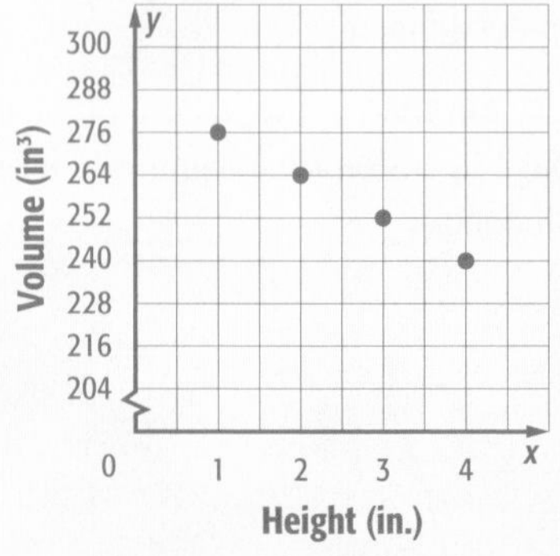

58. Sample answer: You can break up $2\frac{1}{2}$ to be $2 + \frac{1}{2}$ and $4\frac{1}{2}$ to be $4 + \frac{1}{2}$. Then set up the multiplication expression $2(4 + \frac{1}{2}) + \frac{1}{2}(4 + \frac{1}{2})$. Distribute $2 \cdot 4 + 2 \cdot \frac{1}{2} + \frac{1}{2} \cdot 4 + \frac{1}{2} \cdot \frac{1}{2}$. Add $8 + 1 + 2 + \frac{1}{4} = 11\frac{1}{4}$.

Practice and Problem Solving

= **Step-by-Step Solutions** begins on page R11. **Extra Practice** begins on page 810.

Example 1 p. 171

Use the Distributive Property to write each expression as an equivalent expression. Then evaluate the expression.

10. $6(3 + 9)$ **$6 \cdot 3 + 6 \cdot 9$; 72**
11. $8(8 + 5)$ **$8 \cdot 8 + 8 \cdot 5$; 104**
12. $(10 + 9)3$ **$3 \cdot 10 + 3 \cdot 9$; 57**
13. $(12 + 7)5$ **$5 \cdot 12 + 5 \cdot 7$; 95**
14. $9(12 - 3)$ **$9 \cdot 12 - 9 \cdot 3$; 81**
15. $3(15 - 5)$ **$3 \cdot 15 - 3 \cdot 5$; 30**
16. $-4(8 - 5)$ **$-4 \cdot 8 - (-4)5$; −12**
17. $-7(16 - 8)$ **$-7 \cdot 16 - (-7)8$; −56**
18. $14(20 - 4)$ **$14 \cdot 20 - 14 \cdot 4$; 224**

Example 2 p. 172

19. **SHOPPING** Martine bought two pairs of jeans that are on sale for $32.85 each. Use mental math to find the total cost of the jeans. Justify your answer by using the Distributive Property. **$65.70; 2($32.85) = 2($33 − $0.15)**

20. **EXERCISE** Tionne can ride 6 miles on her bike in one hour. If she rode for 1.5 hours on Saturday and 2 hours on Sunday, use mental math to find the total distance she rode that weekend. Justify your answer by using the Distributive Property. **21 miles; $6(1.5 + 2) = 6 \cdot 1.5 + 6 \cdot 2$**

Examples 3 and 4 p. 173

Use the Distributive Property to write each expression as an equivalent algebraic expression.

21. $4(y + 7)$ **$4y + 28$**
22. $8(x + 2)$ **$8x + 16$**
23. $(a + 9)6$ **$6a + 54$**
24. $(b + 4)12$ **$12b + 48$**
25. $5(t - 6)$ **$5t - 30$**
26. $3(r - 1)$ **$3r - 3$**
27. $-1(d - 10)$ **$-d + 10$**
28. $-5(f - 5)$ **$-5f + 25$**
29. $(x - 3)(-7)$ **$-7x + 21$**

30. **CELL PHONE The double bar graph shows average monthly cell phone usage by age.**

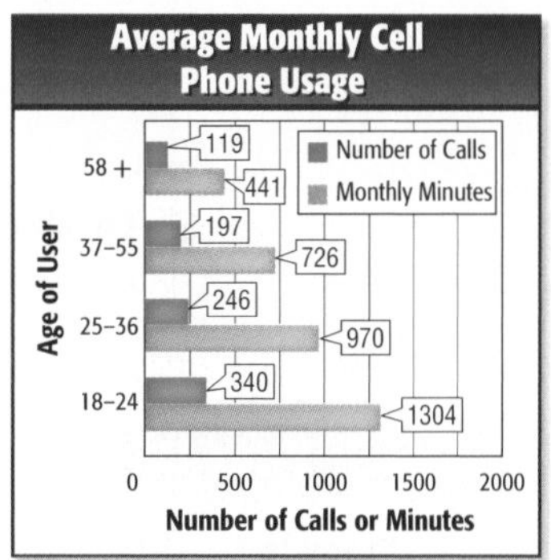

a. Find the total number of minutes used in a month by a family with an 18-year old, a 19-year old, and two 37–55-year old members. **4060 minutes**

b. Find the total number of calls made in 3 months by two 20-year olds and two 30-year olds. **3516 calls**

c. Which group placed the most monthly calls? How do you know?

c. 18–24-year-olds; The bar for that age group is the longest.

MENTAL MATH **Find each product mentally. Justify your answer.** **31–39. See students' work for justifications.**

31. $8 \cdot 22$ **176**
32. $13 \cdot 39$ **507**
33. $19 \cdot 41$ **779**
34. $29 \cdot 13$ **377**
35. $75 \cdot 40$ **3000**
36. $95 \cdot 38$ **3610**
37. $9 \cdot 49$ **441**
38. $31 \cdot 11$ **341**
39. $121 \cdot 15$ **1815**

40. **MONEY** Sarah charges $6.50 per hour to babysit. She babysat for 3 hours on Friday, and 5 hours on Saturday. Write two equivalent expressions for her total wages. Then find her total wage. **$6.50(3 + 5), $6.50(3) + $6.50(5); $52**

41. **ENTERTAINMENT** Admission to the state fair is $8 for adults and $7 for students. Write two equivalent expressions if two adults and two students go to the fair. Then find the total admission cost. **2($8 + $7), 2($8) + 2($7); $30**

Differentiated Homework Options

Level	Assignment	Two-Day Option	
AL Basic	10–29, 55, 56, 58–76	11–29 odd, 59–62	10–28 even, 55, 56, 58, 63–76
OL Core	11–29 odd, 30, 31–39 odd, 40–42, 43, 45, 47, 49–53 odd, 54–56, 58–76	10–29, 59–62	30–56, 58, 63–76
BL Advanced	30–72, (optional: 73–76)		

42. **MULTIPLE REPRESENTATIONS** In this problem, you will use the Distributive Property. The volume of seed in a bird feeder is represented by the equation $V = 12(24 - h)$. **a–b. See margin.**

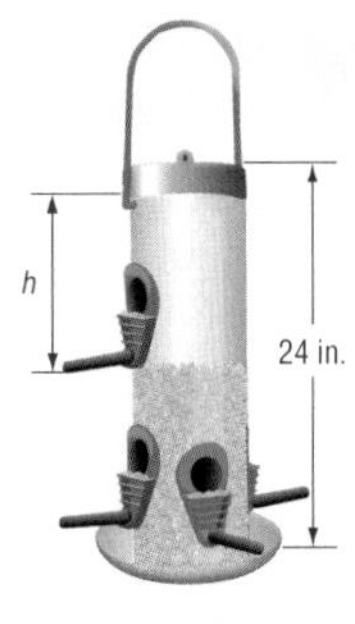

a. **TABULAR** Make a table of ordered pairs (h, V).

b. **GRAPHICAL** Graph the ordered pairs on the coordinate plane.

c. **VERBAL** Explain what happens to the volume as the height increases. **The volume decreases.**

Use the Distributive Property to write each expression as an equivalent expression. Then evaluate the expression. $\left(\textit{Hint}: 3\frac{1}{4} \text{ can be written as the sum of } 3 + \frac{1}{4}.\right)$

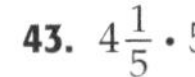

43. $4\frac{1}{5} \cdot 5$　　44. $10 \cdot 5\frac{1}{2}$　　45. $6 \cdot 4\frac{2}{3}$　　46. $2\frac{2}{7} \cdot 14$

43. $5 \cdot 4 + 5 \cdot \frac{1}{5}$; 21
44. $10 \cdot 5 + 10 \cdot \frac{1}{2}$; 55
45. $6 \cdot 4 + 6 \cdot \frac{2}{3}$; 28
46. $14 \cdot 2 + 14 \cdot \frac{2}{7}$; 32

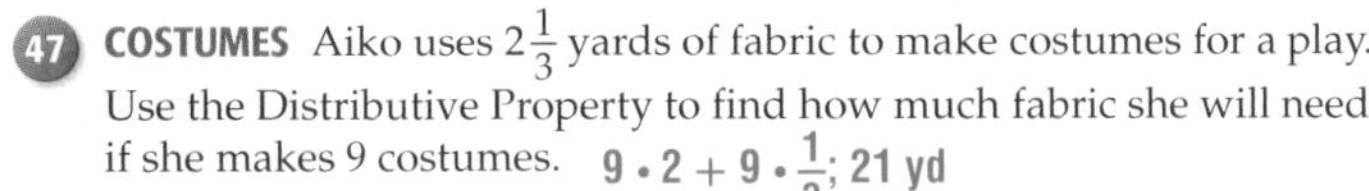

47. **COSTUMES** Aiko uses $2\frac{1}{3}$ yards of fabric to make costumes for a play. Use the Distributive Property to find how much fabric she will need if she makes 9 costumes. **$9 \cdot 2 + 9 \cdot \frac{1}{3}$; 21 yd**

Use the Distributive Property to write each expression as an equivalent algebraic expression.

48. $3(a + b)$ **$3a + 3b$**　　49. $(e + f)(-5)$ **$-5e - 5f$**　　50. $-6(x - y)$ **$-6x + 6y$**

51. $-4(j - k)$ **$-4j + 4k$**　　52. $10(r - s)$ **$10r - 10s$**　　53. $(u - w)(8)$ **$8u - 8w$**

54. **ENTERTAINMENT** Admission to Hersheypark Theme Park in Hershey, Pennsylvania, is \$45.95 for an adult and \$26.95 for children. The Diego family has a coupon for \$10 off each admission ticket. Write an expression to find the cost for x adults and y children. **$x(\$45.95 - \$10) + y(\$26.95 - \$10)$**

Real-World Link

HersheyPark in Hershey, PA, began as a park for people who worked in Milton Hershey's chocolate company. In the 1970s, it became one the country's top theme parks. Today, the park contains 11 roller coasters and 13 water rides.

H.O.T. Problems

Use Higher-Order Thinking Skills

55. **OPEN ENDED** Write an equation using three integers that is an example of the Distributive Property. **Sample answer: $2(3 + 4) = 2 \cdot 3 + 2 \cdot 4$**

56. **FIND THE ERROR** Julia and Catelyn are using the Distributive Property to simplify $3(x + 2)$. Is either of them correct? Explain your reasoning. **Catelyn; each number inside the parentheses should be multiplied by 3.**

Julia	Catelyn
$3(x + 2) = 3x + 2$	$3(x + 2) = 3x + 6$

57. **CHALLENGE** Is $3 + (x \cdot y) = (3 + x) \cdot (3 + y)$ a true statement? If so, explain your reasoning. If not, give a counterexample. **No; $3 + (4 \cdot 5) = 23$, $(3 + 4)(3 + 5) = 56$**

58. **WRITING IN MATH** Explain how you can use the Distributive Property and mental math to simplify $2\frac{1}{2} \cdot 4\frac{1}{2}$. **See margin.**

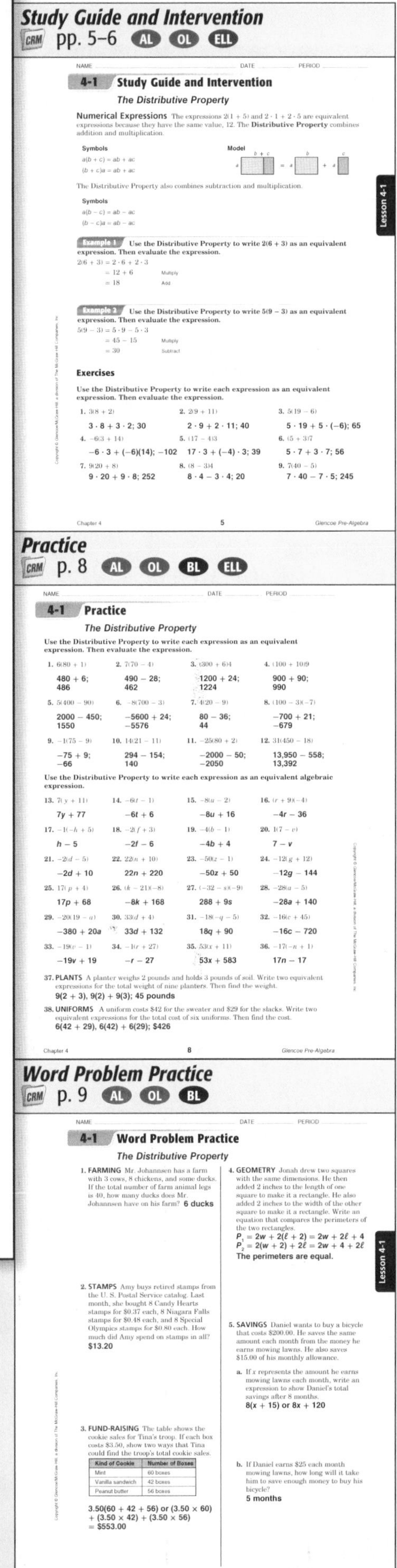

Study Guide and Intervention
CRM pp. 5–6 AL OL ELL

NAME ______ DATE ______ PERIOD ______

4-1 Study Guide and Intervention

The Distributive Property

Numerical Expressions The expressions $2(1 + 5)$ and $2 \cdot 1 + 2 \cdot 5$ are equivalent expressions because they have the same value, 12. The **Distributive Property** combines addition and multiplication.

Symbols
$a(b + c) = ab + ac$
$(b + c)a = ab + ac$

Model

The Distributive Property also combines subtraction and multiplication.

Symbols
$a(b - c) = ab - ac$
$(b - c)a = ab - ac$

Example 1 Use the Distributive Property to write $2(6 + 3)$ as an equivalent expression. Then evaluate the expression.

$2(6 + 3) = 2 \cdot 6 + 2 \cdot 3$
$= 12 + 6$　Multiply
$= 18$　Add

Example 2 Use the Distributive Property to write $5(9 - 3)$ as an equivalent expression. Then evaluate the expression.

$5(9 - 3) = 5 \cdot 9 - 5 \cdot 3$
$= 45 - 15$　Multiply
$= 30$　Subtract

Exercises

Use the Distributive Property to write each expression as an equivalent expression. Then evaluate the expression.

1. $3(8 + 2)$ **$3 \cdot 8 + 3 \cdot 2$; 30**
2. $2(9 + 11)$ **$2 \cdot 9 + 2 \cdot 11$; 40**
3. $5(19 - 6)$ **$5 \cdot 19 + 5 \cdot (-6)$; 65**
4. $-6(3 + 14)$ **$-6 \cdot 3 + (-6)(14)$; -102**
5. $(17 - 4)3$ **$17 \cdot 3 + (-4) \cdot 3$; 39**
6. $(5 + 3)7$ **$5 \cdot 7 + 3 \cdot 7$; 56**
7. $9(20 + 8)$ **$9 \cdot 20 + 9 \cdot 8$; 252**
8. $(8 - 3)4$ **$8 \cdot 4 - 3 \cdot 4$; 20**
9. $7(40 - 5)$ **$7 \cdot 40 - 7 \cdot 5$; 245**

Chapter 4　5　Glencoe Pre-Algebra

Practice
CRM p. 8 AL OL BL ELL

NAME ______ DATE ______ PERIOD ______

4-1 Practice

The Distributive Property

Use the Distributive Property to write each expression as an equivalent expression. Then evaluate the expression.

1. $6(80 + 1)$ **$480 + 6$; 486**
2. $7(70 - 4)$ **$490 - 28$; 462**
3. $(300 + 6)4$ **$1200 + 24$; 1224**
4. $(100 + 10)9$ **$900 + 90$; 990**
5. $5(400 - 90)$ **$2000 - 450$; 1550**
6. $-8(700 - 3)$ **$-5600 + 24$; -5576**
7. $4(20 - 9)$ **$80 - 36$; 44**
8. $(100 - 3)(-7)$ **$-700 + 21$; -679**
9. $-1(75 - 9)$ **$-75 + 9$; -66**
10. $14(21 - 11)$ **$294 - 154$; 140**
11. $-25(80 + 2)$ **$-2000 - 50$; -2050**
12. $31(450 - 18)$ **$13{,}950 - 558$; 13,392**

Use the Distributive Property to write each expression as an equivalent algebraic expression.

13. $7(y + 11)$ **$7y + 77$**
14. $-6(t - 1)$ **$-6t + 6$**
15. $-8(u - 2)$ **$-8u + 16$**
16. $(r + 9)(-4)$ **$-4r - 36$**
17. $-1(-h + 5)$ **$h - 5$**
18. $-2(f + 3)$ **$-2f - 6$**
19. $-4(b - 1)$ **$-4b + 4$**
20. $1(7 - v)$ **$7 - v$**
21. $-2(d - 5)$ **$-2d + 10$**
22. $22(n + 10)$ **$22n + 220$**
23. $-50(z - 1)$ **$-50z + 50$**
24. $-12(g + 12)$ **$-12g - 144$**
25. $17(p + 4)$ **$17p + 68$**
26. $(k - 21)(-8)$ **$-8k + 168$**
27. $(-32 - s)(-9)$ **$288 + 9s$**
28. $-28(a - 5)$ **$-28a + 140$**
29. $-20(19 - a)$ **$-380 + 20a$**
30. $33(d + 4)$ **$33d + 132$**
31. $-18(-q - 5)$ **$18q + 90$**
32. $-16(c + 45)$ **$-16c - 720$**
33. $-19(v - 1)$ **$-19v + 19$**
34. $-1(r + 27)$ **$-r - 27$**
35. $53(x + 11)$ **$53x + 583$**
36. $-17(-n + 1)$ **$17n - 17$**

37. **PLANTS** A planter weighs 2 pounds and holds 3 pounds of soil. Write two equivalent expressions for the total weight of nine planters. Then find the weight. **$9(2 + 3)$, $9(2) + 9(3)$; 45 pounds**

38. **UNIFORMS** A uniform costs \$42 for the sweater and \$29 for the slacks. Write two equivalent expressions for the total cost of six uniforms. Then find the cost. **$6(42 + 29)$, $6(42) + 6(29)$; \$426**

Chapter 4　8　Glencoe Pre-Algebra

Word Problem Practice
CRM p. 9 AL OL BL

NAME ______ DATE ______ PERIOD ______

4-1 Word Problem Practice

The Distributive Property

1. **FARMING** Mr. Johannsen has a farm with 3 cows, 8 chickens, and some ducks. If the total number of farm animal legs is 40, how many ducks does Mr. Johannsen have on his farm? **6 ducks**

2. **STAMPS** Amy buys retired stamps from the U. S. Postal Service catalog. Last month, she bought 8 Candy Hearts stamps for \$0.37 each, 8 Niagara Falls stamps for \$0.48 each, and 8 Special Olympics stamps for \$0.80 each. How much did Amy spend on stamps in all? **\$13.20**

3. **FUND-RAISING** The table shows the cookie sales for Tina's troop. If each box costs \$3.50, show two ways that Tina could find the troop's total cookie sales.

Kind of Cookie	Number of Boxes
Mint	60 boxes
Vanilla sandwich	42 boxes
Peanut butter	56 boxes

$3.50(60 + 42 + 56)$ or $(3.50 \times 60) + (3.50 \times 42) + (3.50 \times 56) = \$553.00$

4. **GEOMETRY** Jonah drew two squares with the same dimensions. He then added 2 inches to the length of one square to make it a rectangle. He also added 2 inches to the width of the other square to make it a rectangle. Write an equation that compares the perimeters of the two rectangles.
$P_1 = 2w + 2(\ell + 2) = 2w + 2\ell + 4$
$P_2 = 2(w + 2) + 2\ell = 2w + 4 + 2\ell$
The perimeters are equal.

5. **SAVINGS** Daniel wants to buy a bicycle that costs \$200.00. He saves the same amount each month from the money he earns mowing lawns. He also saves \$15.00 of his monthly allowance.

a. If x represents the amount he earns mowing lawns each month, write an expression to show Daniel's total savings after 8 months. **$8(x + 15)$ or $8x + 120$**

b. If Daniel earns \$25 each month mowing lawns, how long will it take him to save enough money to buy his bicycle? **5 months**

Chapter 4　9　Glencoe Pre-Algebra

Lesson 4-1

Multiple Representations In Exercise 42, students use an algebraic formula, a table of ordered pairs, a graph of the ordered pairs, and a verbal explanation to relate dimensions and volume in a figure.

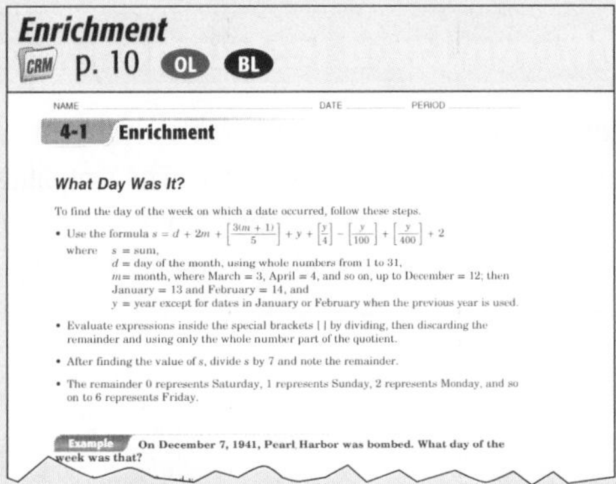

Enrichment
CRM p. 10 OL BL

NAME ______ DATE ______ PERIOD ______

4-1 Enrichment

What Day Was It?

To find the day of the week on which a date occurred, follow these steps.

- Use the formula $s = d + 2m + \left[\frac{3(m + 1)}{5}\right] + y + \left[\frac{y}{4}\right] - \left[\frac{y}{100}\right] + \left[\frac{y}{400}\right] + 2$
  where s = sum,
  d = day of the month, using whole numbers from 1 to 31,
  m = month, where March = 3, April = 4, and so on, up to December = 12; then January = 13 and February = 14, and
  y = year except for dates in January or February when the previous year is used.
- Evaluate expressions inside the special brackets [ ] by dividing, then discarding the remainder and using only the whole number part of the quotient.
- After finding the value of s, divide s by 7 and note the remainder.
- The remainder 0 represents Saturday, 1 represents Sunday, 2 represents Monday, and so on to 6 represents Friday.

Example On December 7, 1941, Pearl Harbor was bombed. What day of the week was that?

Watch Out!

Find the Error If students are having difficulty finding the error in Exercise 56, have them replace x with 8 in $3(x + 2)$, $3x + 2$, and $3x + 6$ to determine which expression is correct. Then ask who is correct and why.

4 ASSESS

Name the Math Ask students to draw a model to explain the Distributive Property. Students should label their drawings and make certain to use the correct names of the mathematical procedures.

Standardized Test Practice

59. Admission to a science museum is d dollars and a ticket for the 3-D movie is t dollars. Which expression represents the total cost of admission and a movie for p people? **C**

A dtp
B $p + (dt)$
C $p(d + t)$
D $d(p + t)$

60. Which expression represents the total areas of the rectangles? **G**

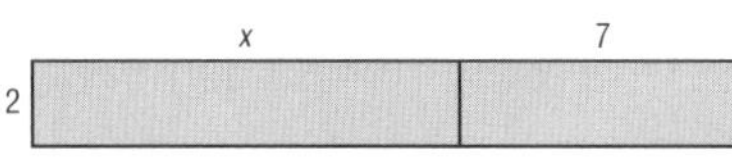

F $2 + x + 7 + 2 + x + 7$
G $2x + 14$
H $2x + 7$
J $14x$

61. Which expression can be written as $7(c + d)$? **C**

A $7c \cdot 7d$
B $(7 + c) \cdot (7 + d)$
C $7c + 7d$
D $(7 + c) + (7 + d)$

62. EXTENDED RESPONSE A car rental company charges $45 per day to rent a car.

a. Write an equation to show the total cost c of renting a car for d days. **$c = 45d$**

b. If you rent the car for more than seven days, the cost will be reduced by $10 per day. Write an equation to show the total cost c of renting a car for d days if you rent the car for more than seven days. **b. $c = d(45 - 10)$**

c. How much will it cost to rent the car for 4 days? 9 days? **$180; $315**

d. If you have $300, for how many days can you rent the car? **6 days or 8 days**

Spiral Review

Find each sum or difference. Write in simplest form. (Lesson 3-6)

63. $-\frac{5}{8} + \frac{3}{4}$ **$\frac{1}{8}$**

64. $-2\frac{1}{2} - \frac{2}{3}$ **$-3\frac{1}{6}$**

65. $\frac{2}{5} + \frac{1}{6}$ **$\frac{17}{30}$**

66. $-5\frac{6}{7} + \frac{1}{9}$ **$-\frac{362}{63}$ or $-5\frac{47}{63}$**

67. SEWING Jessica needs $5\frac{5}{8}$ yards of fabric to make a skirt and $14\frac{1}{2}$ yards to make a coat. How much fabric does she need in all? (Lesson 3-6) **$20\frac{1}{8}$ yd**

68. GARDENING Tate's flower garden has a perimeter of 25 feet. He plans to add 2 feet 9 inches to the width and 3 feet 9 inches to the length. What is the new perimeter in feet? (Lesson 3-6) **38 ft**

ALGEBRA Evaluate each expression. (Lessons 2-4 and 2-5)

69. $-6h$, if $h = -20$ **120**

70. $-4st$, if $s = -9$ and $t = 3$ **108**

71. $\frac{x}{-5}$, if $x = -85$ **17**

72. $\frac{108}{m}$, if $m = -9$ **−12**

Skills Review

Write each subtraction expression as an addition expression. (Lesson 2-3)

73. $9 - 12$ **$9 + -12$**

74. $-2 - 6$ **$-2 + -6$**

75. $-10 - (-3)$ **$-10 + 3$**

76. $-12 - 14$ **$-12 + -14$**

Differentiated Instruction

BL

Extension In algebra, students will learn to use a form of the Distributive Property to multiply expressions such as $(x + 4)(x + 5)$. The simplification process uses the Distributive Property twice. In this example, the simplification is $x(x + 5) + 4(x + 5)$, or $x^2 + 5x + 4x + 20$, which simplifies to $x^2 + 9x + 20$. Have students simplify $(x + 2)(x + 7)$. $x^2 + 9x + 14$

EXPLORE 4-2

Algebra Lab: Simplifying Algebraic Expressions

Math Online glencoe.com
Math *in Motion*, Animation

In a set of algebra tiles, [x-tile] represents the variable x, [1] represents the integer 1, and [−1] represents the integer −1. You can use algebra tiles to represent and simplify algebraic expressions.

ACTIVITY 1

Simplify $2x + 4 + 4x + 1$.

Step 1 $2x + 4 + 4x + 1$ — **Model the expression.**

Step 2 $6x + 5$ — **Group like tiles together. There are 6 *x*-tiles and 5 1-tiles.**

So, $2x + 4 + 4x + 1 = 6x + 5$.

ACTIVITY 2

Simplify $x + 6 + 3x - 3$.

Step 1 $x + 6 + 3x + (-3)$ — **Model the expression.**

Step 2 $4x + 3$ — **Group like tiles together. Remove zero pairs.**

So, $x + 6 + 3x - 3 = 4x + 3$.

Analyze the Results 1. $4x + 7$ 2. $4x + 6$

Model and simplify each expression using algebra tiles. 1–6. See Chapter 4 Answer Appendix for models.

1. $3x + 4 + x + 3$
2. $2x + 3 + 2x + 3$
3. $x + 7 + 5x$ $6x + 7$
4. $4x - 1 + 2x + 5$ $6x + 4$
5. $3x + 2x - 4$ $5x - 4$
6. $2x + 2 + 2x - 2$ $4x$
7. What mathematical properties allow you to sort the algebra tiles by their shapes? Commutative and Associative Properties of Addition
8. What mathematical property allows you to remove zero pairs? Additive Inverse Property

From Concrete to Abstract

Show a model like the one below.

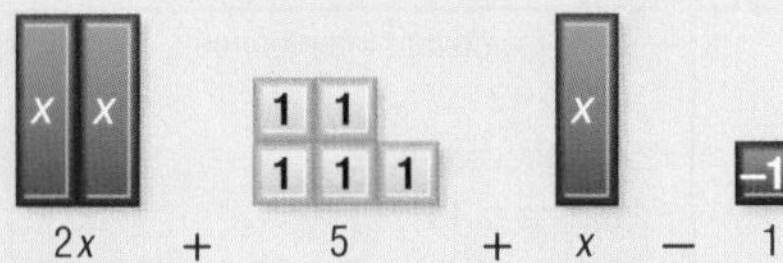

Then have students write and simplify the algebraic expression. $2x + 5 + x + -1 = 3x + 4$

EXPLORE 4-2

Lesson Notes

1 FOCUS

Objective Use algebra tiles to represent and simplify algebraic expressions.

Materials for Each Student

- algebra tiles

Teaching Tip

Put sets of tiles in individual bags so that they are ready to distribute as students are grouped in pairs.

2 TEACH

Working in Cooperative Groups

Put students in groups of two or more, mixing abilities. Have each pair work through the Activities and Exercises 1–3. Have one student represent the expression. Have the second student group like tiles.

Ask:

- Which tile represents a variable? a green rectangular tile
- Which tile represents a positive integer? a yellow tile
- Which tile represents a negative integer? a red tile
- Which tiles make a zero pair? a positive and negative tile

Practice Have students complete Exercises 4–8.

3 ASSESS

Formative Assessment

Use Exercise 4 to assess whether students can use algebra tiles to represent and simplify algebraic expressions.

Lesson Notes

1 FOCUS

Vertical Alignment

Before Lesson 4-2
Write algebraic expressions.

Lesson 4-2
Identify the parts of an algebraic expression and use the Distributive Property to simplify algebraic expressions.

After Lesson 4-2
Simplify polynomial expressions.

2 TEACH

Scaffolding Questions

Have students read the *Why?* section of the lesson and answer the questions.

Ask:

- Which color socks cost more? red
- Write a numerical expression to find the cost of one pair of shoes, one pair of white socks, and two pairs of red socks. $45 + 5 + 2(7.50)$
- What is the total cost of the above purchase? $65

Focus on Mathematical Content

Terms A term can be a number, a variable, or a product of numbers and variables. Like terms will be revisited in Chapter 9.

4-2 Simplifying Algebraic Expressions

Then
You already know how to write algebraic expressions. (Lesson 1-2)

Now
- Identify parts of an algebraic expression.
- Use the Distributive Property to simplify algebraic expressions.

New Vocabulary
term
coefficient
like terms
constant
simplest form
simplifying the expression

Math Online
glencoe.com
- Extra Examples
- Personal Tutor
- Self-Check Quiz
- Homework Help

Why?

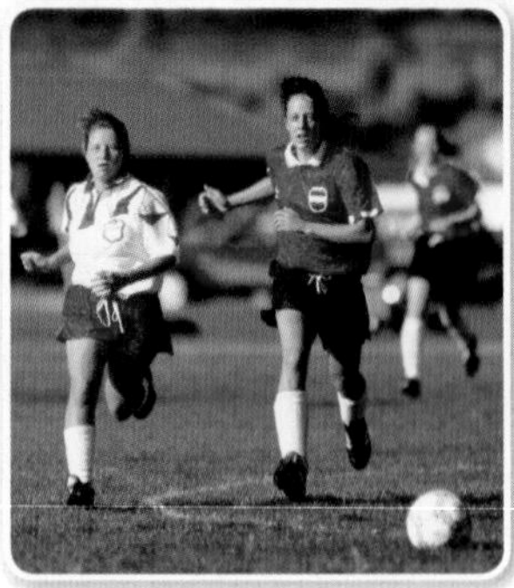

Sandra needs soccer shoes and socks. Shoes cost \$45, a pair of white socks costs \$5, and a pair of red socks costs \$7.50.

a. Find the total cost of one pair of shoes and 2 pairs of white socks. **\$55**

b. If she buys 2 pairs of white socks and 2 pairs of red socks, what is the total cost? **\$25**

c. Let x represent the number of pairs of socks she buys. Write an expression to represent the cost of one pair of shoes, x pairs of white socks, and x pairs of red socks. $\mathbf{45 + 5x + 7.5x}$

Parts of Algebraic Expressions When addition or subtraction signs separate an algebraic expression into parts, each part is a **term**. The numerical part of a term that contains a variable is called the **coefficient** of the variable.

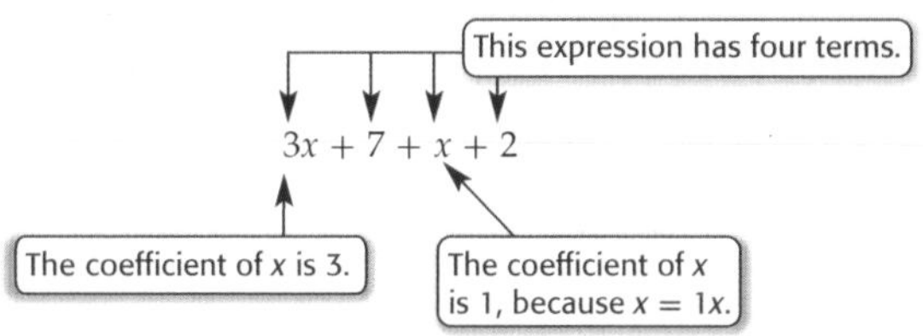
This expression has four terms.
$3x + 7 + x + 2$
The coefficient of x is 3.
The coefficient of x is 1, because $x = 1x$.

In this chapter, we will work only with terms with an exponent of 1. In this case, **like terms** are terms that contain the same variables, such as $2n$ and $5n$ or $6xy$ and $4xy$. A term without a variable is called a **constant**.

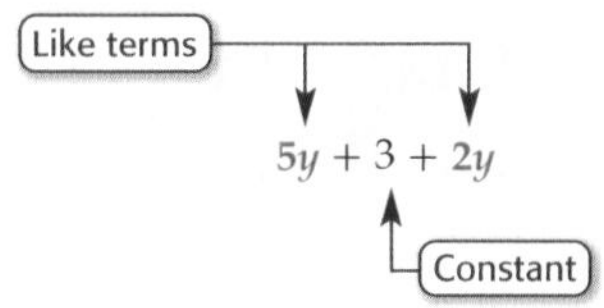
Like terms
$5y + 3 + 2y$
Constant

EXAMPLE 1 Identify Like Terms

Identify the like terms in the following expressions.

a. $3x + 4y + 4x$

$3x$ and $4x$ are like terms since the variables are the same.

b. $5x + 3 + 7x + 4$

$5x$ and $7x$ are like terms since the variables are the same. Constant terms 3 and 4 are also like terms.

Check Your Progress

1. Identify the like terms in the expression $-4x + 2y + 3y + 2x$. $\mathbf{-4x}$ **and** $\mathbf{2x}$, $\mathbf{2y}$ **and** $\mathbf{3y}$

Personal Tutor glencoe.com

Lesson 4-2 Resources

Resource	Approaching-Level	On-Level	Beyond-Level	English Learners
Teacher Edition	• Differentiated Instruction, p. 179	• Differentiated Instruction, p. 179	• Differentiated Instruction, p. 183	
Chapter Resource Masters	• Study Guide and Intervention, pp. 11–12 • Skills Practice, p. 13 • Practice, p. 14 • Word Problem Practice, p. 15	• Study Guide and Intervention, pp. 11–12 • Skills Practice, p. 13 • Practice, p. 14 • Word Problem Practice, p. 15 • Enrichment, p. 16	• Practice, p. 14 • Word Problem Practice, p. 15 • Enrichment, p. 16	• Study Guide and Intervention, pp. 11–12 • Skills Practice, p. 13 • Practice, p. 14
Transparencies	• 5-Minute Check Transparency 4-2	• 5-Minute Check Transparency 4-2	• 5-Minute Check Transparency 4-2	• 5-Minute Check Transparency 4-2
Other	• Study Notebook • Teaching Pre-Algebra with Manipulatives	• Study Notebook • Teaching Pre-Algebra with Manipulatives	• Study Notebook	• Study Notebook • Teaching Pre-Algebra with Manipulatives

2. $3n$, $5m$, $-6m$, and 2 are the terms. $5m$ and $-6m$ are like terms. The coefficients are 3, 5, and -6. The constant is 2.

Rewriting a subtraction expression using addition will help you identify the terms of an expression.

EXAMPLE 2 Identify Parts of an Expression

Identify the terms, like terms, coefficients, and constants in the expression $6x - 2y + x - 5$.

$6x - 2y + x - 5 = 6x + (-2y) + x + (-5)$ **Definition of subtraction**

$= 6x + (-2y) + 1x + (-5)$ **Identity Property**

The terms are $6x$, $-2y$, x, and -5. The like terms are $6x$ and x. The coefficients are 6, -2, and 1. The constant is -5.

Check Your Progress

2. Identify the terms, like terms, coefficients, and constants in the expression $3n + 5m - 6m + 2$.

Personal Tutor glencoe.com

Math History Link

Emmy Noether (1882–1935) Emmy Noether was known as the "mother of modern abstract algebra." Her later works focused on noncommutative algebra, which is where the order in which elements are multiplied *does* affect the solution.

Source: *Encyclopaedia Britannica*

Simplify Algebraic Expressions An algebraic expression is in **simplest form** if it has no like terms and no parentheses. When you use the Distributive Property to combine like terms, you are **simplifying the expression**.

EXAMPLE 3 Simplify Algebraic Expressions

Simplify each expression.

a. $4x + 6 + 2x$

$4x + 6 + 2x = 4x + 2x + 6$ **Commutative Property**

$= (4 + 2)x + 6$ **Distributive Property**

$= 6x + 6$ **Simplify.**

b. $5n + 2 - n - 6$

$5n + 2 - n - 6 = 5n + 2 + (-n) + (-6)$ **Definition of Subtraction**

$= 5n + 2 + (-1n) + (-6)$ **Identity Property**

$= 5n + (-1n) + 2 + (-6)$ **Commutative Property**

$= [5 + (-1)]n + 2 + (-6)$ **Distributive Property**

$= 4n + (-4)$ or $4n - 4$ **Simplify.**

c. $6y - 3(x - 2y)$

$6y - 3(x - 2y) = 6y + (-3)[x + (-2y)]$ **Definition of Subtraction**

$= 6y + (-3x) + (-3 \cdot -2)y$ **Distributive Property**

$= 6y + (-3x) + 6y$ **Simplify.**

$= 6y + 6y + (-3x)$ **Commutative Property**

$= (6 + 6)y + (-3x)$ **Distributive Property**

$= 12y + (-3x)$ or $12y - 3x$ **Simplify.**

Watch Out!

Distributive Property In Example 3c, remember to distribute -3, not $+3$, to the terms in the parentheses.

Check Your Progress

3A. $4x + 6 - 3x$ $x + 6$ **3B.** $2m + 3 - 7m - 4$ $-5m - 1$ **3C.** $4(q + 8p) + p$ $33p + 4q$

Personal Tutor glencoe.com

Parts of Algebraic Expressions

Examples 1 and 2 show how to identify the parts of an expression.

TEACH with TECH

INTERACTIVE WHITEBOARD Write an algebraic expression on the board. Ask students to name the like terms and physically drag these terms to different parts of the board to group them. Then discuss how to use the like terms to simplify the expression.

Formative Assessment

Use the Check Your Progress exercises after each example to determine students' understanding of concepts.

Additional Examples

1. Identify the like terms in the following expressions.
   a. $4x + y + 7x$ $4x$ and $7x$
   b. $3x + 8 + 2x + 1$ $3x$ and $2x$; 8 and 1

2. Identify the terms, like terms, coefficients, and constants in the expression $4x - x + 2y - 3$. terms: $4x$, $-x$, $2y$, -3; coefficients: 4, -1, 2; like terms: $4x$, $-x$; constant: -3

Simplify Algebraic Expressions

Examples 3 and 4 show how to write and simplify expressions.

Additional Example

3. Simplify each expression.
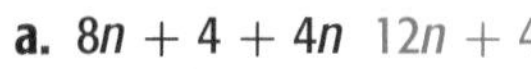
   a. $8n + 4 + 4n$ $12n + 4$
   b. $6x + 4 - 5x - 7$ $x - 3$
   c. $y - 2(x - 3y)$ $-2x + 7y$

Differentiated Instruction

AL OL

If students forget to combine all of the terms when expressions contain coefficients of 1,

Then have them first rewrite the expression before combining like terms. For example, if they mistakenly simplify $5n + n$ as $5n$, have them rewrite the expression as $5n + 1n$ before combining.

Watch Out!

Preventing Errors To check whether $x + x + 25$ and $2x + 25$ are equivalent expressions, tell students to substitute any value for x in both expressions and see if the expressions have the same value.

Additional Example

4 **WORK** Suppose you and a friend worked in the school store last week. You worked 4 hours more than your friend. Write an expression in simplest form that represents the total number of hours you both worked. $2h + 4$, where h is the number of hours your friend worked

Additional Examples also in Interactive Classroom PowerPoint® Presentations

IWB INTERACTIVE WHITEBOARD READY

3 PRACTICE

Formative Assessment

Use Exercises 1–14 to check for understanding.

Use the chart at the bottom of the next page to customize assignments for your students.

Additional Answers

1. terms: $-2a$, $3a$, $5b$; like terms: $-2a$, $3a$; coefficients: -2, 3, 5; constant: none
2. terms: $2x$, $3x$, 4, $4x$; like terms: $2x$, $3x$, $4x$; coefficients: 2, 3, 4; constant: 4
3. terms: mn, $4m$, $6n$, $2mn$; like terms: mn, $2mn$; coefficients: 1, 4, 6, 2; constant: none
4. terms: $3a$, $5b$, 4, $6a$; like terms: $3a$, $6a$; coefficients: 3, 5, 6; constant: 4
5. terms: $3x$, $4x$, $5y$; like terms: $3x$, $4x$; coefficients: 3, 4, 5; constant: none
6. terms: $-4p$, $-6q$, -5; like terms: none; coefficients: -4, -6; constant: -5

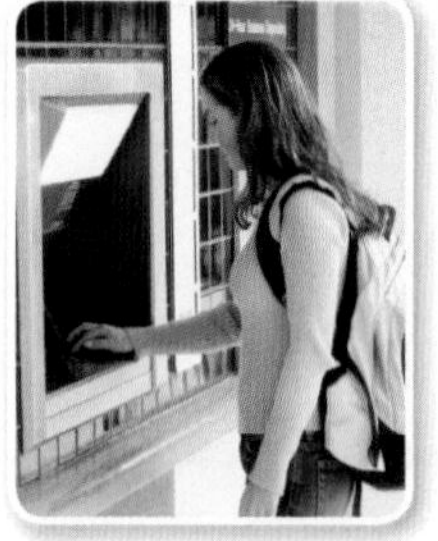

Real-World Link

According to FDIC, there are three main goals for teens to save money. First, set goals for how much you want to save/spend each month. Second, have a plan for saving money. Third, cut back on spending but don't stop spending.

Source: Federal Deposit Insurance Corporation

Real-World EXAMPLE 4 Write and Simplify Algebraic Expressions

MONEY You have some money in a savings account. Your sister has $25 more than you have in her account. Write an expression in simplest form that represents the total amount of money in both accounts.

Words	amount of your money	plus	amount of your sister's money
Variables	Let x = amount of your money. Let $x + 25$ = amount of your sister's money.		
Expression	x	$+$	$(x + 25)$

$x + (x + 25) = (x + x) + 25$	**Associative Property**
$= (1x + 1x) + 25$	**Identity Property**
$= (1 + 1)x + 25$	**Distributive Property**
$= 2x + 25$	**Simplify.**

The expression $2x + 25$ represents the total amount of money you and your sister have in your accounts.

Check Your Progress

4. **STAMPS** Mato and Lola both collect stamps. Lola has 16 more stamps in her collection than Mato has. Write an expression in simplest form that represents the total number of stamps in both collections. $2x + 16$

Personal Tutor glencoe.com

Check Your Understanding

1–6. See margin.

Examples 1 and 2 pp. 178–179

Identify the terms, like terms, coefficients, and constants in each expression.

1. $-2a + 3a + 5b$
2. $2x + 3x + 4 + 4x$
3. $mn + 4m + 6n + 2mn$
4. $3a + 5b + 4 + 6a$
5. $3x + 4x + 5y$
6. $-4p - 6q - 5$

Example 3 p. 179

Simplify each expression.

7. $6x + 2x + 3$ $8x + 3$
8. $-2a + 3a + 6$ $a + 6$
9. $7x + 4 - 5x - 8$ $2x - 4$
10. $5a - 2 - 3a + 7$ $2a + 5$
11. $-3(m - 1) + 4m + 2$ $m + 5$
12. $4a - 6 - 2(a - 1)$ $2a - 4$

Example 4 p. 180

13. **JEWELRY** Marena is using a certain number of blue beads in a bracelet design. She will use 7 more red beads than blue beads. Write an expression in simplest form that represents the total number of beads in her bracelet design. $2x + 7$
14. **ENTERTAINMENT** Kyung bought 3 CDs that cost x dollars each, 2 DVDs that cost $10 each; and a book that costs $15. Write an expression in simplest form that represents the total amount that Kyung spent. $3x + 35$

Practice and Problem Solving

 = **Step-by-Step Solutions** begin on page R11. **Extra Practice** begins on page 810.

Examples 1 and 2 pp. 178–179

Identify the terms, like terms, coefficients, and constants in each expression.

15. $3a + 2 + 3a + 7$ **15–18. See margin.**
16. $4m + 3 + m + 1$
17. $3c + 4d + 5c + 8$
18. $7j + 11jk + k + 9$
19. $4x + 4y + 4z + 4$ terms: $4x$, $4y$, $4z$, 4; like terms: none; coefficients: 4, 4, 4; constants: 4
20. $3m + 3n + 2p + 4r$ terms: $3m$, $3n$, $2p$, $4r$; like terms: none; coefficients: 3, 3, 2, 4; constants: none

Example 3 p. 179

Simplify each expression.

21. $4a + 3a$ $7a$
22. $9x + 2x$ $11x$
23. $-5m + m + 5$ $-4m + 5$
24. $6x - x + 3$ $5x + 3$
25. $7p + 3 + 4p + 5$ $11p + 8$
26. $2a + 4 + 2a + 9$ $4a + 13$
27. $4a - 3b - 7a - 3b$ $-3a - 6b$
28. $-x - 2y - 8x - 2y$ $-9x - 4y$
29. $x + 5(6 + x)$ $6x + 30$
30. $2a + 3(2 + a)$ $5a + 6$
31. $-3(6 - 2r) - 3r$ $-18 + 3r$
32. $-2(2x - 5) - 4x$ $-8x + 10$

Example 4 p. 180

For each situation write an expression in simplest form that represents the total amount.

33. **FASHION** Mateo has y pairs of shoes. His brother has 5 fewer pairs. $2y - 5$
34. **CELL PHONES** You used p minutes one month on your cell phone. The next month you used 75 fewer minutes. $2p - 75$
35. **SPORTS** Nathan scored x points in his first basketball game. He scored three times as many points in his second game. In his third game, he scored 6 more than the second game. $x + 3x + (3x + 6) = 7x + 6$
36. **MONEY** On Monday, Rebekah spent d dollars on lunch. She spent \$0.50 more on Tuesday than she did on Monday. On Wednesday, she spent twice as much as she did on Tuesday. $4d + \$1.50$

B **Simplify each expression.**

37. $2(x - y) + 3x$ $5x - 2y$
38. $-3(a - 2b) - 4b$ $-3a + 2b$
39. $-4(3m + 2n) - 5m + y$
40. $\frac{2}{3}(6a + 3b) - \frac{1}{2}(a - 2b)$ $\frac{7}{2}a + 3b$
41. $\frac{1}{4}(m + 2n) - \frac{1}{3}(3m - 3n)$
42. $2(x - y) - (x + y)$ $x - 3y$
43. $\frac{2}{5}(2a - b) + \frac{2}{3}(a + 2b)$ $\frac{22}{15}a + \frac{14}{15}b$
44. $-\frac{3}{4}(3x + 2y) - \frac{3}{8}(x - 3y)$ $-\frac{21}{8}x - \frac{3}{8}y$

39. $-17m - 8n + y$

41. $-\frac{3}{4}m + \frac{3}{2}n$

45. **ALGEBRA** **Write an expression to represent each model. Then simplify the expression using algebra tiles.** **a–b. See margin.**

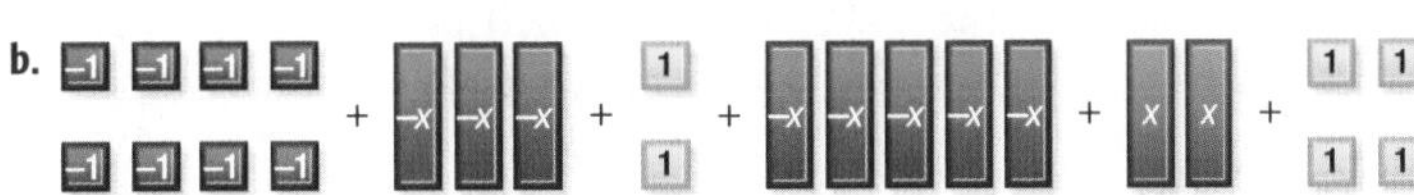

c. Use algebra tiles to write and simplify your own expression. **See students' work.**

Focus on Mathematical Content

Simplifying Algebraic Expressions When simplifying an algebraic expression, students are actually using the Distributive Property. For example, simplifying $4x + 9x$ is the same as $x(4 + 9)$, or $13x$.

Additional Answers

15. terms: $3a$, 2, $3a$, 7; like terms: $3a$, $3a$; coefficients: 3, 3; constants: 2, 7
16. terms: $4m$, 3, m, 1; like terms: $4m$, m; coefficients: 4, 1; constants: 3, 1
17. terms: $3c$, $4d$, $5c$, 8; like terms: $3c$, $5c$; coefficients: 3, 4, 5; constant: 8
18. terms: $7j$, $11jk$, k, 9; like terms: none; coefficients: 7, 11, 1; constant: 9

45a. $7 + 4x + (-4) + (-2x) + 3$;

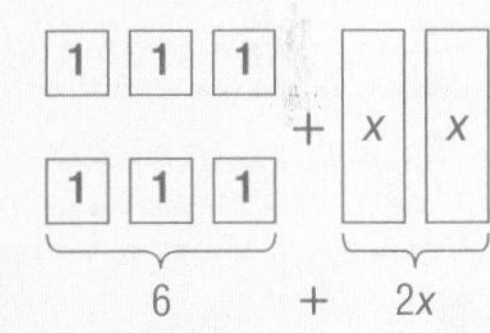

45b. $-8 + (-3x) + 2 + (-5x) + 2x + 4$;

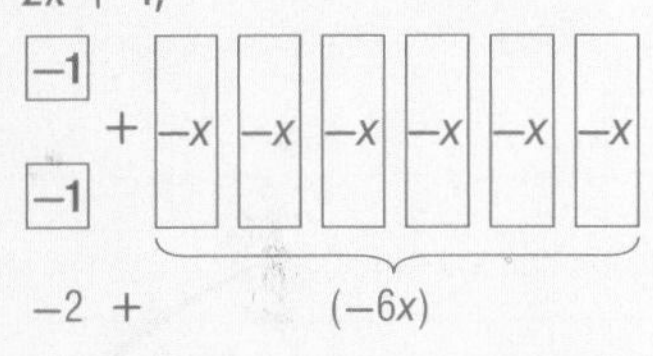

Differentiated Homework Options

Level	Assignment	Two-Day Option	
AL Basic	15–36, 54, 56, 57, 59–80	15–35 odd, 60–63	16–36 even, 54, 56, 57, 59, 64–80
OL Core	15–45 odd, 46, 47–51 odd, 53, 54, 56, 57, 59–80	15–36, 60–63	37–54, 56, 57, 59, 64–80
BL Advanced	37–77, (optional: 78–80)		

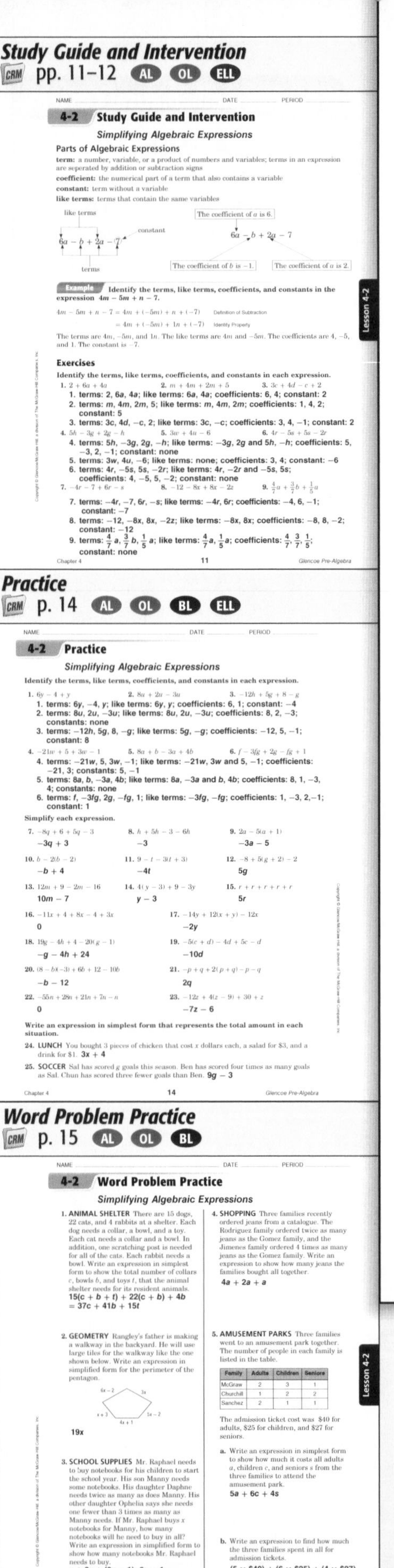

StudyTip

Perimeter The perimeter of a figure is the distance around the figure. You can find the perimeter of a rectangle using the expression $2\ell + 2w$ where ℓ is the length and w is the width of the rectangle.

46. MULTIPLE REPRESENTATIONS In this problem, you will investigate the perimeter of a rectangle. Consider a rectangle that has a length that is twice its width.

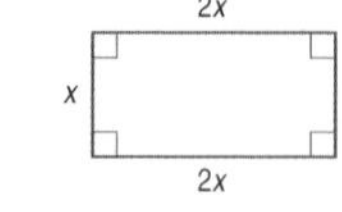

a. **TABULAR** Make a table that shows the width of a rectangle and its perimeter for widths of 1, 2, 3, 4, 5, and 6 units.

b. **GRAPHICAL** Graph the ordered pairs (width, perimeter). **a–b. See margin.**

c. **ALGEBRAIC** Write an expression in simplest form for the perimeter of a rectangle if the width is w units. **6w**

d. **VERBAL** If you double the width, what happens to the perimeter? Justify your reasoning. **See margin.**

GEOMETRY Write an expression in simplest form for the perimeter of each rectangle.

47. 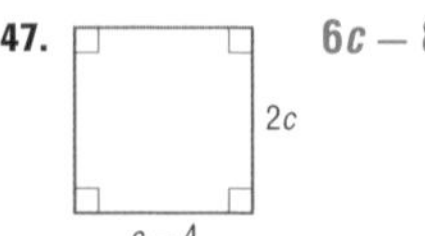

6c − 8

48. 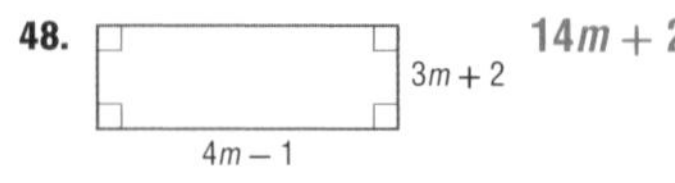

14m + 2

49–52. See Chapter 4 Answer Appendix.

Simplify. Identify the properties you used in each step of your calculation.

49. $16 \cdot (-31) + 16 \cdot 32$

50. $72(38) + (-72)(18)$

51. $24 \cdot (-15) + 36 \cdot 15$

52. $22(-18) - 22(24)$

53. AGE This year Ana's mother is 2 years more than 3 times Ana's age. Write an expression in simplest form for the total of their ages. **4x + 2**

H.O.T. Problems
Use Higher-Order Thinking Skills

54. OPEN ENDED Write an expression containing at least 2 unlike terms. Then simplify the expression. **Sample answer: $x + 2x + 4$; $3x + 4$**

55. CHALLENGE Simplify $(2 + x)(y + 5)$. **$5x + xy + 2y + 10$**

56. REASONING Classify the following statement as *sometimes*, *always*, or *never* true. Explain your reasoning.

When using the Distributive Property, if the term outside the parentheses is negative, then the sign of each term inside the parentheses will change.

56. Always; Sample answer: If the term outside the parentheses is negative and is multiplied by a term with a positive coefficient, the product will be negative. If the coefficient of the term in the parentheses is negative, then the product will be positive.

57. WHICH ONE DOESN'T BELONG? Identify the algebraic expression that does not belong with the other three. Explain your reasoning.

$-6(x - 2)$	$x + 12 - 7x$	$-x - 5x + 12$	$-6x - 12$

$-6x - 12$; the other expressions are equivalent to $-6x + 12$.

58. CHALLENGE In a three-digit number, the second and third digits are the same. The first digit is 4 more than the sum of the second and third digits. Write an expression in simplest form for the total sum of all three digits. **4 + 4a**

59. WRITING IN MATH Suppose your friend simplifies $4x - 2(x + 5)$ as $2x + 10$. Identify the error and correct it. **See Chapter 4 Answer Appendix.**

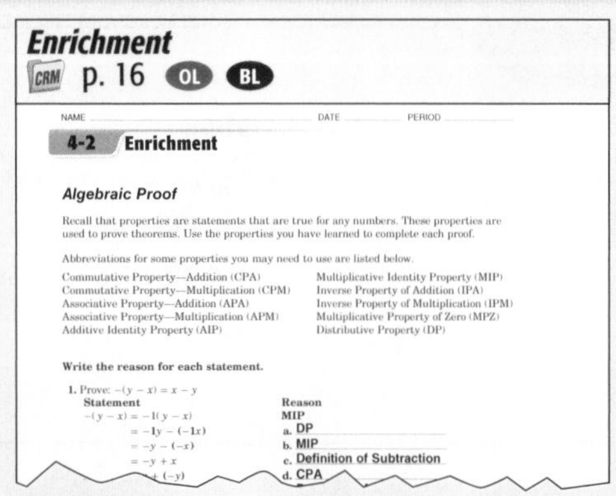

Multiple Representations In Exercise 46, students use a table of values, a graph, a formula, an algebraic expression, and a verbal description to relate the length, width, and perimeter of a rectangle.

Standardized Test Practice

60. The perimeter of $\triangle DEF$ is $4x + 3y$. What is the measure of the third side of the triangle? **A**

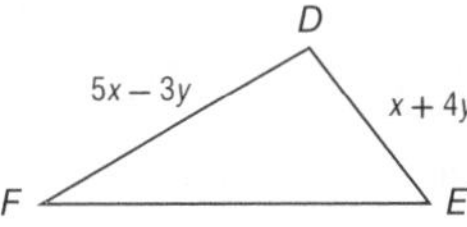

A $-2x + 2y$ C $x - y$
B $2x + 2y$ D $-x + 2y$

61. Which of the following expressions is equivalent to $4x + 4y$? **G**

F $4xy$ H $4x + y$
G $4(x + y)$ J $x + 4y$

62. Adriana spent m minutes on her homework on Monday. She spent 45 more minutes doing her homework on Tuesday than on Monday. Which expression represents the total amount of time she spent on her homework on Monday and Tuesday? **C**

A $m + 45$
B $m - 45$
C $2m + 45$
D $2m - 45$

63. **SHORT RESPONSE** Simplify the following expression. **$9a - 9b - 6$**

$$7(3a - 2b) + 5b - 3(4a + 2)$$

Spiral Review

Use the Distributive Property to write each expression as an equivalent expression. (Lesson 4-1)

64. $8(z - 3)$ **$8z - 24$**
65. $(a - 6)(-5)$ **$-5a + 30$**
66. $15(s + 2)$ **$15s + 30$**

67. **ENTERTAINMENT** The table shows the cost of different items at a movie theater. Write two equivalent expressions for the total cost of four movie tickets and four bags of popcorn. Then find the total cost. (Lesson 4-1) **See margin.**

Item	Cost ($)
ticket	7.00
small popcorn	3.00
small drink	2.50
candy bar	1.75

68. **COOKING** Simon has $1\frac{1}{4}$ cups of margarine. He needs $\frac{1}{2}$ cup for a cake and another $\frac{1}{3}$ cup for the icing. How much margarine will he have left? (Lesson 3-6) **$\frac{5}{12}$ c**

Write two inequalities using the number pairs. Use the symbols $<$ or $>$. (Lesson 2-1)

69. -6 and -2 **$-6 < -2$; $-2 > -6$**
70. -10 and -13 **See margin.**
71. 0 and -9 **$0 > -9$; $-9 < 0$**
72. $|-11|$ and $|-7|$ **$|-11| > |-7|$; $|-7| < |-11|$**
73. $|15|$ and $|18|$ **$|15| < |18|$; $|18| > |15|$**
74. $|-12|$ and $|14|$ **$|-12| < |14|$; $|14| > |-12|$**

ALGEBRA Find the value of each expression if $a = 6$ and $b = 7$. (Lesson 1-2)

75. $\frac{4b + 3a}{b - 5}$ **23**
76. $\frac{6a - 2ab}{a + 2}$ **-6**
77. $\frac{3(4a - 3b)}{b - 4}$ **3**

Skills Review

Find each sum or difference. (Lessons 2-2 and 2-3)

78. $-21 - 6$ **-27**
79. $62 - (-12)$ **74**
80. $-32 + 26$ **-6**

Differentiated Instruction

Extension Explain to students that a term that has an exponent of 2 or more may be combined with other terms that have the same variable raised to the same exponent. For example, $4x^7 + 2x^7 = 6x^7$. Have students simplify $9y^3 + 4m^2 + 3m^2 + 15y^3$. **$24y^3 + 7m^2$**

4 ASSESS

Crystal Ball Have students tell how they think simplifying algebraic expressions might connect with tomorrow's lesson on solving equations by adding or subtracting. Ask them to include *why* they think that simplifying expressions could be important.

Formative Assessment

Check for student understanding of concepts in Lessons 4-1 and 4-2.

CRM Quiz 1, p. 44

Additional Answers

46a.

Width	Perimeter
1	6
2	12
3	18
4	24
5	30
6	36

46b.

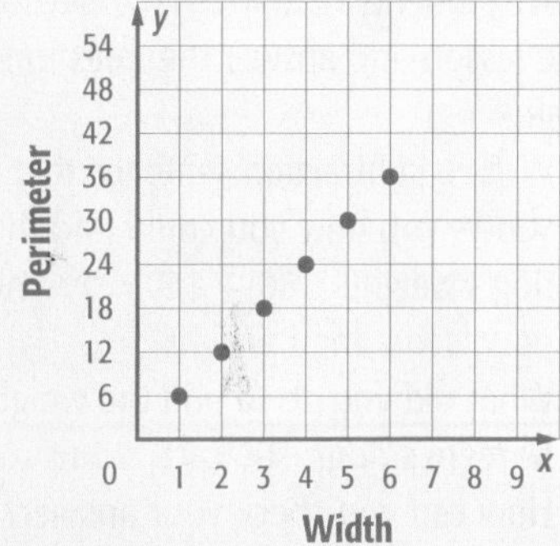

46d. Sample answer: The perimeter also doubles. If the width is $2w$, then the length is $2(2w)$ or $4w$. So
$$P = 2(2w) + 2(4w) = 4w + 8w = (4 + 8)w = 12w$$

67. $4(\$7 + \$3)$, $4(\$7) + 4(\$3)$; $40

70. $-10 > -13$; $-13 < -10$

4-3 Lesson Notes

1 FOCUS

Vertical Alignment

Before Lesson 4-3
Work with the additive inverse of a number when subtracting integers.

Lesson 4-3
Solve equations by using the Addition and Subtraction Properties of Equality. Translate verbal sentences into equations.

After Lesson 4-3
Solve equations using the Multiplication and Division Properties of Equality.

2 TEACH

Scaffolding Questions

Have students read the *Why?* section of the lesson and answer the questions.

Ask:

- Write a subtraction sentence that shows you how you could find the dog's weight. $168 - 120 = x$, where x equals the dog's weight
- What did you do to find the weight of Kareem's dog? subtract 120 from 168
- How can you check your answer? Substitute the weight, 48, for x in the equation and see if the equation is true.

4-3 Solving Equations by Adding or Subtracting

Then
You have already worked with the additive inverse of a number when you subtracted integers. (Lesson 2-2)

Now
- Solve equations by using the Addition and Subtraction Properties of Equality.
- Translate verbal sentences into equations.

New Vocabulary
equation
solution
solving the equation
inverse operation
equivalent equation

Math Online
glencoe.com
- Extra Examples
- Personal Tutor
- Self-Check Quiz
- Homework Help
- Math in Motion

Why?

Kareem wants to determine how much his dog weighs. When he weighs himself, he weighs 120 pounds. When he and his dog are both on the scale, they weigh 168 pounds.

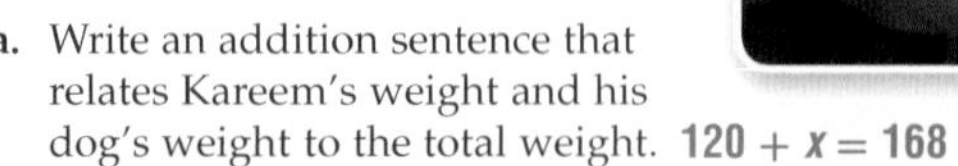

a. Write an addition sentence that relates Kareem's weight and his dog's weight to the total weight. $120 + x = 168$

b. How much does Kareem's dog weigh? 48 lb

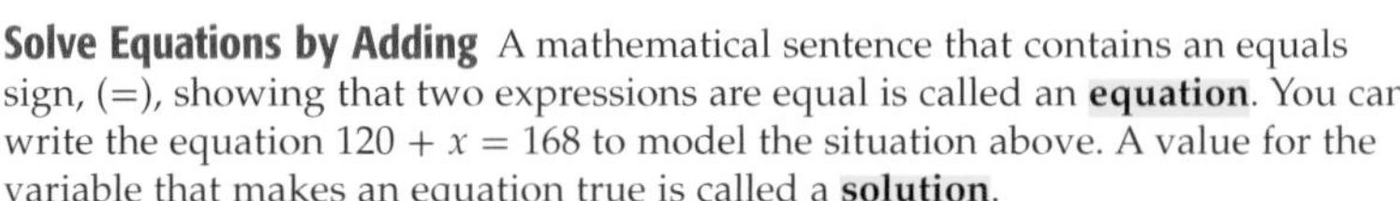

Solve Equations by Adding A mathematical sentence that contains an equals sign, (=), showing that two expressions are equal is called an **equation**. You can write the equation $120 + x = 168$ to model the situation above. A value for the variable that makes an equation true is called a **solution**.

$120 + x = 168$		$120 + x = 168$	
$120 + 40 \stackrel{?}{=} 168$	**Replace x with 40.**	$120 + 48 \stackrel{?}{=} 168$	**Replace x with 48.**
$160 \neq 168$	**False**	$168 = 168$	**True ✓**

For $120 + x = 168$, the solution is 48. The process of finding a solution is called **solving the equation**.

You can use inverse operations to solve an equation. **Inverse operations** "undo" each other. For example, to undo the subtraction of 5 in the equation $y - 5 = 10$, you could add 5 to each side of the equation.

Key Concept — Addition Property of Equality (For Your FOLDABLE)

Words If you add the same number to each side of an equation, the two sides remain equal.

Symbols For any numbers a, b, and c, if $a = b$, then $a + c = b + c$.

Examples

$$4 = 4 \qquad 4 + 9 = 4 + 9 \qquad 13 = 13$$

$$\begin{aligned} y - 5 &= 10 \\ +5 &= +5 \\ \hline y &= 15 \end{aligned}$$

Equivalent equations are equations that have the same solution. Because the equations $y - 5 = 10$ and $y = 15$ have the same solution, 15, they are equivalent equations.

Lesson 4-3 Resources

Resource	Approaching-Level	On-Level	Beyond-Level	English Learners
Teacher Edition		• Differentiated Instruction, p. 185	• Differentiated Instruction, pp. 185, 189	
Chapter Resource Masters	• Study Guide and Intervention, pp. 17–18 • Skills Practice, p. 19 • Practice, p. 20 • Word Problem Practice, p. 21	• Study Guide and Intervention, pp. 17–18 • Skills Practice, p. 19 • Practice, p. 20 • Word Problem Practice, p. 21 • Enrichment, p. 22	• Practice, p. 20 • Word Problem Practice, p. 21 • Enrichment, p. 22	• Study Guide and Intervention, pp. 17–18 • Skills Practice, p. 19 • Practice, p. 20
Transparencies	• 5-Minute Check Transparency 4-3	• 5-Minute Check Transparency 4-3	• 5-Minute Check Transparency 4-3	• 5-Minute Check Transparency 4-3
Other	• Study Notebook • Teaching Pre-Algebra with Manipulatives	• Study Notebook • Teaching Pre-Algebra with Manipulatives	• Study Notebook	• Study Notebook • Teaching Pre-Algebra with Manipulatives

StudyTip

Solving Equations When you solve an equation, you should always check to be sure that the first and last equations are equivalent.

EXAMPLE 1 Solve Equations by Adding

Solve each equation. Check your solution and graph it on a number line.

a. $x - 7 = -4$

$x - 7 = -4$ **Write the equation.**

$+7 = +7$ **Addition Property of Equality**

$x + 0 = 3$ **Additive Inverse Property; $-7 + 7 = 0$**

$x = 3$ **Identity Property; $x + 0 = x$**

To check that 3 is the solution, replace x with 3 in the original equation.

Check $x - 7 = -4$ **Write the equation.**

$3 - 7 \stackrel{?}{=} -4$ **Check to see whether this sentence is true.**

$-4 = -4$ ✓ **The sentence is true.**

The solution is 3. To graph 3, draw a dot at 3 on a number line.

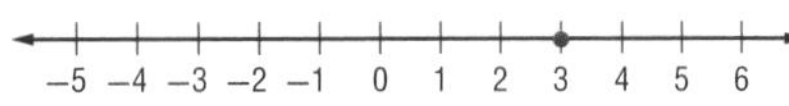

StudyTip

Position of the Variable You could begin solving Example 1b by rewriting the equation so that the expression containing the variable is to the left of the equals sign.
$-13.9 = n - 9.7$
↓
$n - 9.7 = -13.9$

b. $-13.9 = n - 9.7$

$-13.9 = n - 9.7$ **Write the equation.**

$+ 9.7 = +9.7$ **Addition Property of Equality**

$-4.2 = n + 0$ **Additive Inverse Property; $-9.7 + 9.7 = 0$**

$-4.2 = n$ **Identity Property; $n + 0 = n$**

The solution is -4.2. **Check your solution.**

To graph -4.2, draw a dot at -4.2 on a number line.

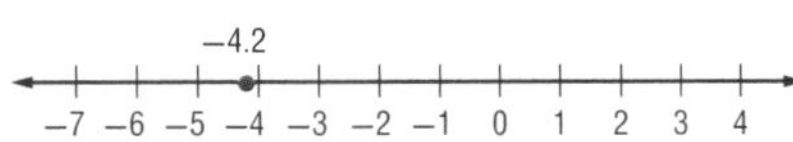

Check Your Progress

1A. $x - 5 = 20$ **See margin.** **1B.** $y - 6.4 = 10.7$ **See margin.**

Personal Tutor glencoe.com

Solve Equations by Subtracting Some equations can be solved by subtracting the same number from each side.

Key Concept **Subtraction Property of Equality** *For Your FOLDABLE*

Words If you subtract the same number from each side of an equation, the two sides remain equal.

Symbols For any numbers a, b, and c, if $a = b$, then $a - c = b - c$.

Examples

$7 = 7$ $\quad$ $n + 4 = 9$

$7 - 3 = 7 - 3$ $\quad$ $-4 = -4$

$4 = 4$ $\quad$ $n = 5$

Math *in Motion,* Animation glencoe.com

Solve Equations by Adding

Example 1 shows how to solve an equation using the Addition Property of Equality and how to graph the solution on a number line.

Formative Assessment

Use the Check Your Progress exercises after each example to determine students' understanding of concepts.

Additional Example

1 Solve each equation. Check your solution and graph it on a number line.

a. $x - 4 = -3$ $x = 1$

b. $-8.4 = n - 6.1$ -2.3

−5 −4 −3 −2 −1 0 1 2 3 4 5

Additional Examples also in Interactive Classroom PowerPoint® Presentations

IWB INTERACTIVE WHITEBOARD READY

Focus on Mathematical Content

Solving Equations by Adding or Subtracting Solving equations involves undoing an operation by using the inverse operation. The inverse operation of addition is subtraction and the inverse operation of subtraction is addition. When a value is subtracted or added to both sides of the equation, the two sides remain equal.

Differentiated Instruction OL BL

Interpersonal Have students prepare a quiz of five questions covering expressions, equations, and translating verbal sentences. Each question must include instructions with complete solutions. The questions can then be exchanged among students. Any discrepancies can be discussed and corrected as needed.

Additional Answers

1A. 25

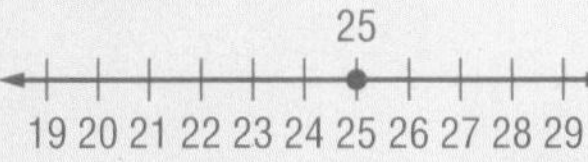

1B. 17.1

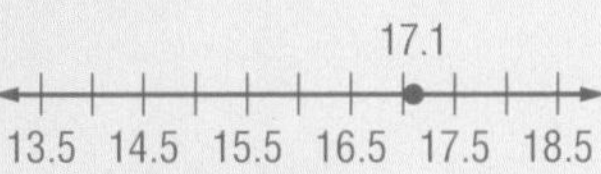

Solve Equations by Subtracting

Example 2 shows how to solve an equation using the Subtraction Property of Equality. **Example 3** shows how to write equations from verbal sentences and write and solve the equations using the Subtraction Property of Equality.

Additional Examples

2 Solve each equation. Check your solution.

a. $32 = y + 12$ 20

b. $x + 6.9 = 4.2$ −2.7

3 **MOUNTAINS** Driskill Mountain, with a height of 535 feet, is the highest point in Louisiana. It is 8214 feet lower than Guadalupe Peak, which is the highest point in Texas. Write and solve a subtraction equation to find the height of Guadalupe Peak.

$535 = h - 8214$; 8749 feet

Tips for New Teachers

Alternative Assessment Some alternative assessments for students that may suffer from test anxiety include:

- Demonstration of mastery by completing problems on the board.
- Working with a partner to complete problems.
- Oral presentations of Exercise solutions.
- Checking students' notebooks or learning logs.

While these will not completely take the place of tests and quizzes, they may give you a clearer idea of student progress.

StudyTip

Isolating the Variable When trying to decide which value to subtract from each side of an equation, remember that your goal is to get the variable by itself on one side of the equal sign. This is called *isolating the variable.*

EXAMPLE 2 Solve by Subtracting

Solve each equation. Check your solution.

a. $23 = y + 10$

$$\begin{aligned} 23 &= y + 10 && \textbf{Write the equation.} \\ -10 &= -10 && \textbf{Subtraction Property of Equality} \\ \hline 13 &= y && \textbf{Additive Inverse and Identity Properties} \end{aligned}$$

To check that 13 is the solution, replace y with 13 in the original equation.

Check

$$\begin{aligned} 23 &= y + 10 && \textbf{Write the equation.} \\ 23 &\stackrel{?}{=} 13 + 10 && \textbf{Check to see whether this sentence is true.} \\ 23 &= 23 \checkmark && \textbf{The sentence is true.} \end{aligned}$$

b. $m + 6.7 = 3.4$

$$\begin{aligned} m + 6.7 &= 3.4 && \textbf{Write the equation.} \\ -6.7 &= -6.7 && \textbf{Subtraction Property of Equality} \\ \hline m &= -3.3 && \textbf{Additive Inverse and Identity Properties} \end{aligned}$$

The solution is −3.3. **Check your solution.**

Check Your Progress

2A. $16 + z = 14$ **−2**

2B. $0.7 + a = 0.4$ **−0.3**

Personal Tutor glencoe.com

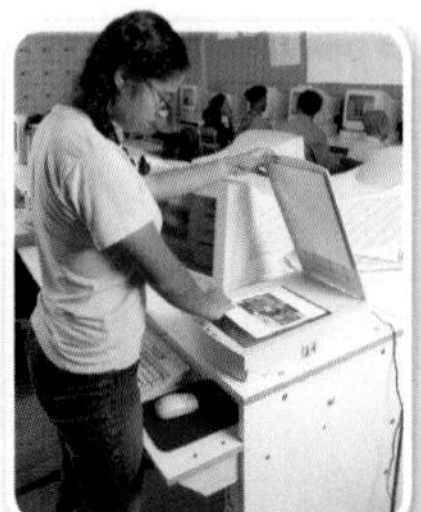

Real-World Link

Digital scrapbooking is becoming more and more popular. The advantages to digital scrapbooking include being able to enhance your photos, printing multiple copies of pages, and being able to undo mistakes.

Source: Kaboose Scrapbook LLC

Real-World EXAMPLE 3 Solve by Subtracting

PHOTO Pilar is making digital scrapbooks as gifts for her family. After saving her current work onto a CD, the CD is $\frac{5}{6}$ full. If the CD was $\frac{1}{3}$ full before she started saving, what fraction of the space on the CD do the new pages occupy?

Words	Starting amount	+	amount for new pages	is	new amount.
Variable	Let x = amount for the new pages.				
Equation	$\frac{1}{3}$	+	x	=	$\frac{5}{6}$

$$\begin{aligned} \frac{1}{3} + x &= \frac{5}{6} && \textbf{Write the equation.} \\ \frac{1}{3} - \frac{1}{3} + x &= \frac{5}{6} - \frac{1}{3} && \textbf{Subtraction Property of Equality} \\ x &= \frac{1}{2} && \textbf{Additive Inverse and Identity Properties} \end{aligned}$$

The new scrapbook pages take up $\frac{1}{2}$ of the space on the CD.

Check Your Progress

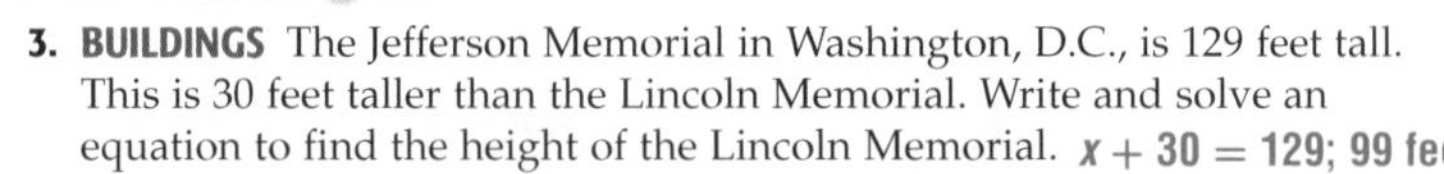

3. BUILDINGS The Jefferson Memorial in Washington, D.C., is 129 feet tall. This is 30 feet taller than the Lincoln Memorial. Write and solve an equation to find the height of the Lincoln Memorial. **$x + 30 = 129$; 99 feet**

Personal Tutor glencoe.com

Check Your Understanding

Examples 1 and 2 pp. 185–186

ALGEBRA **Solve each equation. Check your solution and graph it on a number line.**

1. $25 = y - 14$ **39**
2. $67 = m - 29$ **96**
3. $d - \frac{1}{3} = \frac{1}{6}$ **$\frac{1}{2}$**
4. $x + 24 = 72$ **48**
5. $p - 13 = -45$ **−32**
6. $x - 36 = -2$ **34**
7. $0.53 + a = 1.97$ **1.44**
8. $1\frac{3}{4} = b + \frac{5}{8}$ **$1\frac{1}{8}$**
9. $a + 5.7 = 9.2$ **3.5**

Example 3 p. 186

10. **FUNDRAISING** Joaquim sold 43 magazine subscriptions to raise money for a class trip. This is 15 less than the number Den sold. Write and solve a subtraction equation to find the number of subscriptions Den sold. **$43 = n - 15$; 58 subscriptions**

11. **WEATHER** The air pressure before a storm was 29.15 inches. After the storm, the pressure was 28.79 inches. Write and solve an addition equation to find how much the pressure changed during the storm.

11. **$29.15 + x = 28.79$; −0.36 in.**

Practice and Problem Solving

 = **Step-by-Step Solutions** begins on page R11. **Extra Practice** begins on page 810.

Examples 1 and 2 pp. 185–186

ALGEBRA **Solve each equation. Check your solution and graph it on a number line.** **See students' work for number lines.**

12. $p - 12 = 20$ **32**
13. $x - 24 = 73$ **97**
14. $-14 = y - 16$ **2**
15. $-31 = r - 36$ **5**
16. $y + 14 = 72$ **58**
17. $m + 21 = 60$ **39**
18. $m + 1\frac{3}{8} = 5$ **$3\frac{5}{8}$**
19. $y + \frac{3}{4} = -\frac{1}{2}$ **$-1\frac{1}{4}$**
20. $-6.5 = x - 0.54$ **−5.96**
21. $56 = -78.9 + p$ **134.9**
22. $1.4 + t = 3.6$ **2.2**
23. $2.9 + z = -1.2$ **−4.1**
24. $0.97 + a = 2.6$ **1.63**
25. $-1\frac{3}{8} = x - \frac{1}{2}$ **$-\frac{7}{8}$**
26. $8\frac{3}{8} = r - 2\frac{1}{3}$ **$10\frac{17}{24}$**

Example 3 p. 186

27. **FINANCIAL LITERACY** Amado budgets \$65 for his monthly cell phone bill. This is \$25 less than his monthly savings deposit. Write and solve a subtraction equation to find how much money Amado saves each month. **$65 = m - 25$; \$90**

28. **PETS** Keisha feeds her dog $\frac{2}{3}$ cup of food in the morning. She feeds the dog a total of $1\frac{1}{2}$ cups of food every day. Write an addition equation to find how much food she gives the dog the rest of the day. **$\frac{2}{3} + x = 1\frac{1}{2}$; $\frac{5}{6}$ c**

ALGEBRA **Solve each equation. Check your solution.**

29. $e - (-36) = -5$ **−41**
30. $f - (-40) = -12$ **−52**
31. $-2.5 + g = -1.3 + -1.1$ **0.1**
32. $-1.7 + h = -2.2 - 3.4$ **−3.9**
33. $j + 17 - 23 = -7$ **−1**
34. $k - 32 - (-16) = -9$ **7**
35. $1\frac{1}{4} + b = 1.6$ **$\frac{7}{20}$ or 0.35**
36. $y + 5.8 = \frac{3}{20}$ **$-5\frac{13}{20}$ or −5.65**

37. **SPORTS** Damon scored 13 points more than Wes and 9 points less than Ross. Ross scored 97. Write and solve equations to find the scores of Damon and Wes.

37. **$97 - 9 = d$, $d - 13 = w$; Damon scored 88 points and Wes scored 75 points.**

38. **GEOMETRY** The perimeter of a triangle is 27.1 feet. The sides of the triangle measure 9.8 feet, 10.9 feet, and x feet. Write and solve an equation to find the length of the missing side. **$9.8 + 10.9 + x = 27.1$; 6.4 feet**

3 PRACTICE

Formative Assessment

Use Exercises 1–11 to check for understanding.

Use the chart at the bottom of this page to customize assignments for your students.

TEACH with TECH

BLOG On your secure classroom blog, have students create entries describing what they learned about solving equations using addition and subtraction. Allow students to use language they are comfortable with, and check for their understanding of the concept.

Differentiated Homework Options

Level	Assignment	Two-Day Option	
AL Basic	12–28, 43–45, 47–65	13–27 odd, 48–51	12–28 even, 43–45, 47, 52–65
OL Core	13–27 odd, 29–35 odd, 37–45, 47–65	12–28, 48–51	29–45, 47, 52–65
BL Advanced	29–59, (optional: 60–65)		

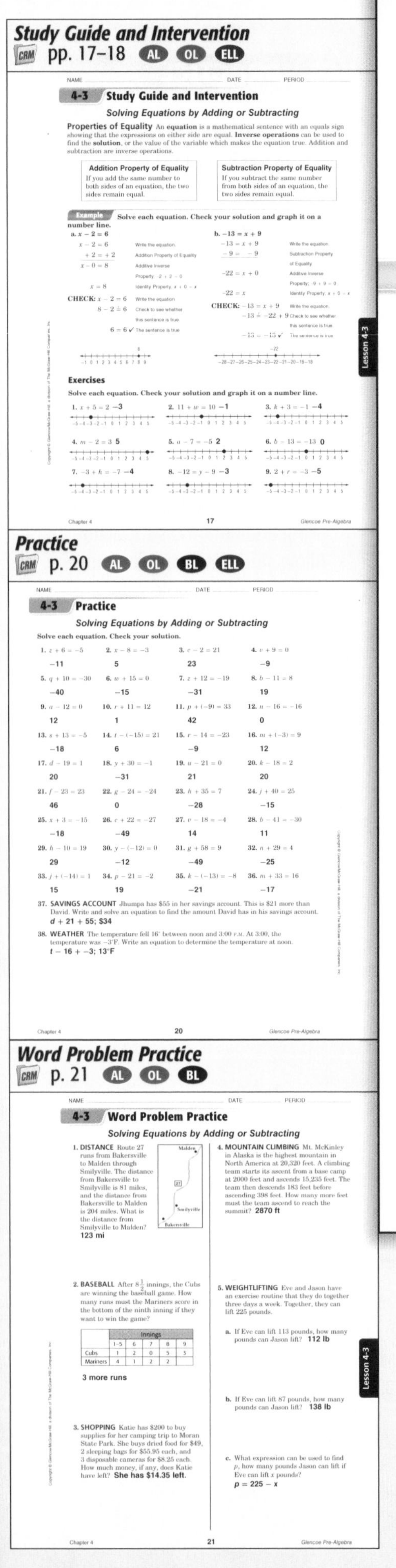
Study Guide and Intervention CRM pp. 17–18 AL OL ELL

4-3 Study Guide and Intervention

Solving Equations by Adding or Subtracting

Properties of Equality An **equation** is a mathematical sentence with an equals sign showing that the expressions on either side are equal. **Inverse operations** can be used to find the **solution**, or the value of the variable which makes the equation true. Addition and subtraction are inverse operations.

Addition Property of Equality	Subtraction Property of Equality
If you add the same number to both sides of an equation, the two sides remain equal.	If you subtract the same number from both sides of an equation, the two sides remain equal.

Exercises

Solve each equation. Check your solution and graph it on a number line.

1. $x + 5 = 2$ **−3** 2. $11 + w = 10$ **−1** 3. $k + 3 = -1$ **−4**
4. $m - 2 = 3$ **5** 5. $a - 7 = -5$ **2** 6. $b - 13 = -13$ **0**
7. $-3 + h = -7$ **−4** 8. $-12 = y - 9$ **−3** 9. $2 + r = -3$ **−5**

Chapter 4 17 Glencoe Pre-Algebra

Practice CRM p. 20 AL OL BL ELL

4-3 Practice

Solving Equations by Adding or Subtracting

Solve each equation. Check your solution.

1. −11	2. 5	3. 23	4. −9
5. −40	6. −15	7. −31	8. 19
9. 12	10. 1	11. 42	12. 0
13. −18	14. 6	15. −9	16. 12
17. 20	18. −31	19. 21	20. 20
21. 46	22. 0	23. −28	24. −15
25. −18	26. −49	27. 14	28. 11
29. 29	30. −12	31. −49	32. −25
33. 15	34. 19	35. −21	36. −17

37. SAVINGS ACCOUNT Jhumpa has \$55 in her savings account. This is \$21 more than David. Write and solve an equation to find the amount David has in his savings account. **d + 21 = 55; \$34**

38. WEATHER The temperature fell 16° between noon and 3:00 P.M. At 3:00, the temperature was −3°F. Write an equation to determine the temperature at noon. **t − 16 = −3; 13°F**

Chapter 4 20 Glencoe Pre-Algebra

Word Problem Practice CRM p. 21 AL OL BL

4-3 Word Problem Practice

Solving Equations by Adding or Subtracting

1. DISTANCE Route 27 runs from Bakersville to Malden through Smilyville. The distance from Bakersville to Smilyville is 81 miles, and the distance from Bakersville to Malden is 204 miles. What is the distance from Smilyville to Malden? **123 mi**

2. BASEBALL After $8\frac{1}{2}$ innings, the Cubs are winning the baseball game. How many runs must the Mariners score in the bottom of the ninth inning if they want to win the game? **3 more runs**

3. SHOPPING Katie has \$200 to buy supplies for her camping trip to Moran State Park. She buys dried food for \$49, 2 sleeping bags for \$55.95 each, and 3 disposable cameras for \$8.25 each. How much money, if any, does Katie have left? **She has \$14.35 left.**

4. MOUNTAIN CLIMBING Mt. McKinley in Alaska is the highest mountain in North America at 20,320 feet. A climbing team starts its ascent from a base camp at 2000 feet and ascends 15,235 feet. The team then descends 183 feet before ascending 398 feet. How many more feet must the team ascend to reach the summit? **2870 ft**

5. WEIGHTLIFTING Eve and Jason have an exercise routine that they do together three days a week. Together, they can lift 225 pounds.

a. If Eve can lift 113 pounds, how many pounds can Jason lift? **112 lb**

b. If Eve can lift 87 pounds, how many pounds can Jason lift? **138 lb**

c. What expression can be used to find p, how many pounds Jason can lift if Eve can lift x pounds? **p = 225 − x**

Chapter 4 21 Glencoe Pre-Algebra

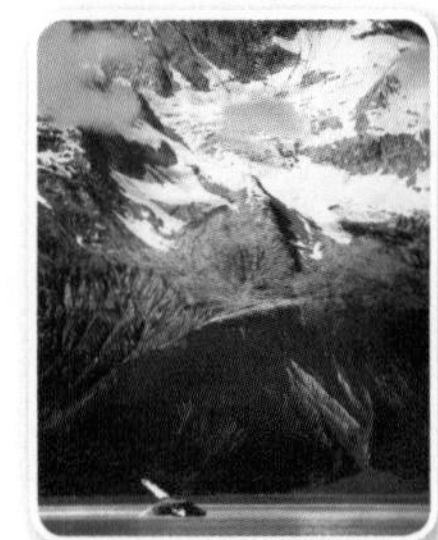

Real-World Link

In a recent year, annual visitation to the national parks reached an all-time high of 438,392,184 visitors.

Source: NPS

NATIONAL PARKS The graph shows the areas of the six largest national parks in the United States.

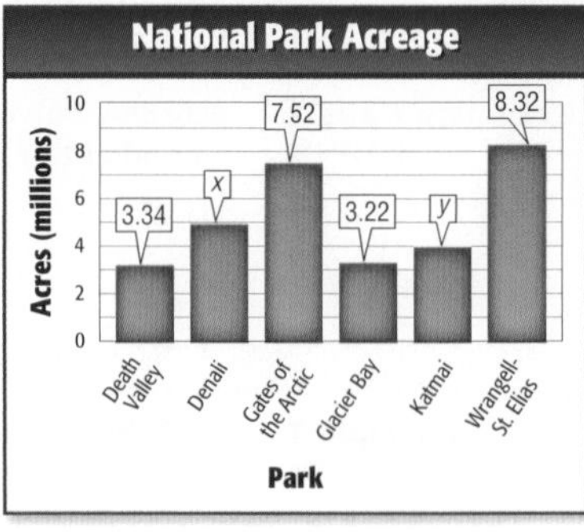

39. The Gates of the Arctic National Park is 2.78 million acres larger than Denali National Park. Write and solve an equation to find the size of Denali National Park. **$7.52 = x + 2.78$; 4.74 million acres**

40. Death Valley National Park is 0.75 million acres smaller than Katmai National Park. Write and solve an equation to find the size of Katmai National Park. **$y - 0.75 = 3.34$; 4.09 million acres**

41. **MULTIPLE REPRESENTATIONS** In this problem, you will investigate more about functions. **b–d. See margin.**

x	y
5	3
4	4
0	8
−1	9

a. **ALGEBRAIC** Find the function rule. **$y = 8 - x$ or $x + y = 8$**

b. **GRAPHICAL** Graph the ordered pairs.

c. **VERBAL** Write a real-world situation for the rule.

d. **VERBAL** How many solutions does $x + y = 8$ have? If $y = 3$, how many solutions does $x + 3 = 8$ have?

42. **PUBLISHING** A newspaper is $12\frac{1}{4}$ inches wide and 22 inches long. This is $1\frac{1}{4}$ inches narrower and half an inch longer than the old edition. What were the dimensions of the old edition? **See margin.**

H.O.T. Problems Use Higher-Order Thinking Skills

43. **OPEN ENDED** As shown in Example 2, $23 = y + 10$ is equivalent to the equation $y = 13$. Write an equation that is equivalent to $x = -2.4$. **Sample answer: $x - (-1.2) = -1.2$**

44. **FIND THE ERROR** Liam and Marcus are solving the equation $x - (-2) = 4$. Is either of them correct? Explain your reasoning.

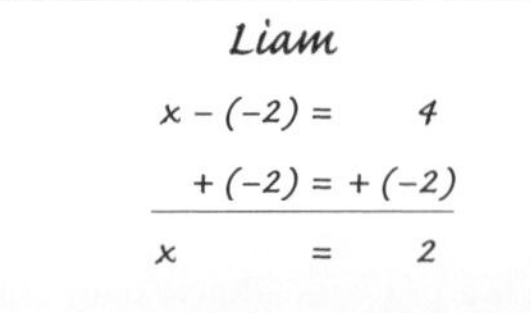

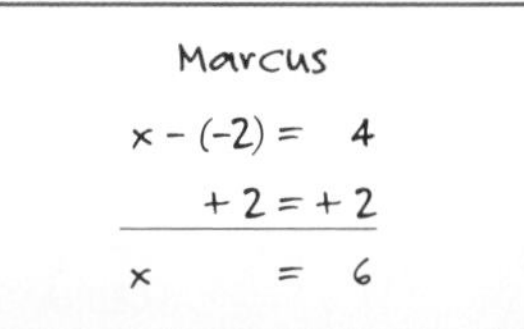

45. **WRITING IN MATH** Jaime's golf score after a round of golf was −9. She had decreased her score by 5 strokes from the day before. Explain how you could use a model to determine her golf score on the previous day. Then use the model to solve the problem. **See margin.**

46. **CHALLENGE** Is the following statement *always*, *sometimes*, or *never* true? Explain your reasoning.

If $a + x = 100$, then x is less than 100.

47. **WRITING IN MATH** Write a real-word problem that can be modeled by the equation $p - 2.70 = 3.25$.

44. Liam; Sample answer: Marcus did not use the correct additive inverse. $x - (-2) = 4$ can be rewritten as $x + 2 = 4$. So, −2 needs to be added to each side of the equation, not +2.

46. Sometimes; Sample answer: If a is a positive number, then x will have to be less than 100 in order for the sum of a and x to be 100. If a is negative, then x will be greater than 100.

47. Sample answer: Peggy paid \$3.25 for a new notebook that was on sale. The sale price was \$2.70 less than the original price. Find the original price of the notebook.

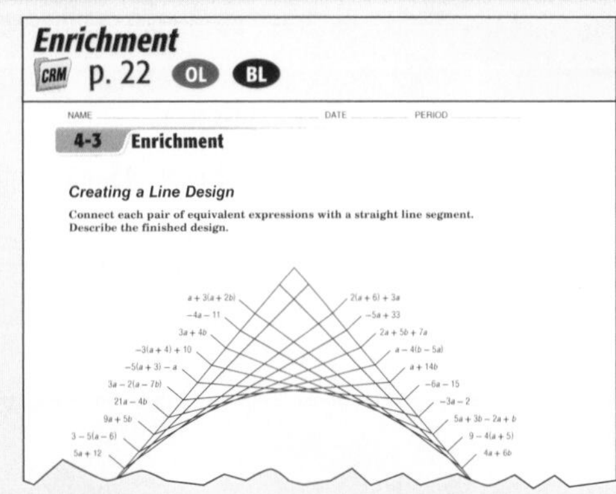
Enrichment CRM p. 22 OL BL

4-3 Enrichment

Creating a Line Design

Connect each pair of equivalent expressions with a straight line segment. Describe the finished design.

Watch Out!

Find the Error For Exercise 44, students should see that Liam and Marcus solved the equation differently in the second line. Students need to understand how to subtract a negative number.

Standardized Test Practice

48. What situation can be represented by the equation $p = c + 12$? **B**

A The Cardinals scored 12 more runs last season than the Panthers.

B The Panthers scored 12 more runs last season than the Cardinals.

C Together, the Panthers and the Cardinals scored 12 runs last season.

D The Panthers scored 12 runs last season.

49. What value of x makes the equation true? **H**

$$5.47 - (-x) = 9.24$$

F -14.71 H 3.77

G -3.77 J 14.71

50. GRIDDED RESPONSE Refer to the table in Exercise 51. How many light years closer is Alpha Centauri B to Earth than Wolf 359? **3.39**

51. The table shows the five nearest stars to Earth, excluding the Sun.

Star	Distance (light-years)
Proxima Centauri	4.22
Alpha Centauri A	4.40
Alpha Centauri B	4.40
Barnard's Star	5.94
Wolf 359	7.79

Which equation will best help you find how much closer Proxima Centauri is to Earth than Barnard's Star? **B**

A $x - 5.94 = 4.22$

B $x + 4.22 = 5.94$

C $5.94 + x = 4.22$

D $5.94 + 4.22 = x$

Spiral Review

Simplify each expression. (Lessons 4-1 and 4-2)

52. $-2(z - 4)$ **$-2z + 8$**

53. $(r - 5)6$ **$6r - 30$**

54. $8e - 4(2f + 5e)$ **$-12e - 8f$**

55. $4 + 3(c - 12)$ **$3c - 32$**

56. $-3(a + 2) - a$ **$-4a - 6$**

57. $8 + x - 5x$ **$8 - 4x$**

58. MONEY Suppose you work in a grocery store 4 hours on Friday and 5 hours on Saturday. You earn $7.25 an hour. Write two different expressions to find your wages. Then find the total wages for that weekend. (Lesson 4-1) **7.25(4) + 7.25(5), 7.25(4 + 5); $65.25**

59. POPULATION The city of Heath makes up $\frac{1}{10}$ of the population in Rockwall County. Use the table to find the fraction of Rockwall County's population that lives in other cities. Write each fraction in simplest form. (Lesson 3-2) **Fate: $\frac{9}{500}$; McLendon-Chisholm: $\frac{1}{50}$; Rockwall: $\frac{21}{50}$; Royse City: $\frac{7}{100}$**

City	Decimal Part of Rockwall County's Population
Fate	0.018
McLendon-Chisholm	0.02
Rockwall	0.42
Royse City	0.07

Skills Review

Find each product or quotient. (Lessons 2-4 and 2-5)

60. $-3(-15)$ **45**

61. $42 \div (-6)$ **-7**

62. $-4 \cdot 8$ **-32**

63. $\frac{-12}{-3}$ **4**

64. $\frac{-27}{9}$ **-3**

65. $(-25)(-5)$ **125**

Differentiated Instruction

Extension Explain to students that if there is a variable on both sides of an equation, the variables need to be moved to the same side of the equals sign to solve the equation. In the equation $x + 4 = 2x - 1$, variable x is subtracted from both sides of the equation and 1 is added to both sides for a solution of $x = 5$. Challenge students to solve $2x + 4 = x + 7$. 3

4 ASSESS

Name the Math Have students tell what mathematical procedure they would use to solve the equation $x - 5 = -3$. Use the Addition Property of Equality to add 5 to each side of the equation, which gives $x = 2$.

Formative Assessment

Check for student understanding of concepts in Lesson 4-3.

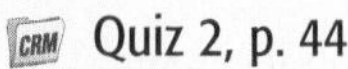

Quiz 2, p. 44

Additional Answers

41b.

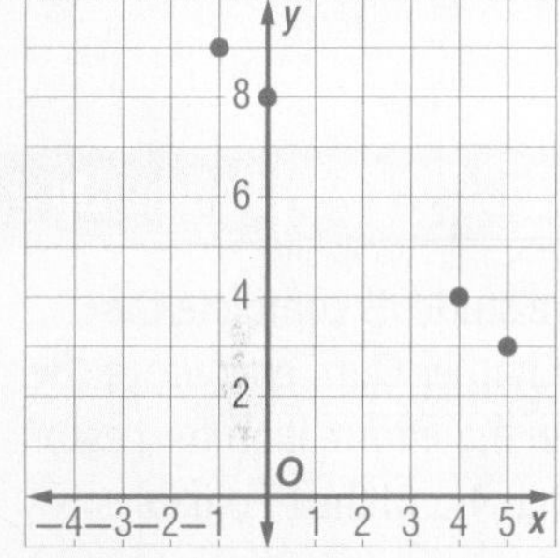

41c. Sample answer: Together, Melinda and Ariana sold 8 t-shirts for the school fundraiser.

41d. The equation $x + y = 8$ has an infinite number of solutions. If $y = 3$, there is only one solution, 5.

42. $x - 1\frac{1}{4} = 12\frac{1}{4}$; $13\frac{1}{2}$ in.; $y + \frac{1}{2} = 22$; $21\frac{1}{2}$ in.; $13\frac{1}{2}$ in. by $21\frac{1}{2}$ in.

45. Sample answer: The small numbers allow you to use algebra tiles to solve the problem. $x - 5 = -9$; place an x-tile and 5 negative tiles on the left side of the mat and 9 negative tiles on the right side of the mat. Then remove 5 negative tiles from each side. The x-tile remains on the left side and four negative tiles remain on the right side. So, Jaime shot a -4 on the previous day.

CHAPTER 4 Mid-Chapter Quiz

Formative Assessment

Use the Mid-Chapter Quiz to assess students' progress in the first half of the chapter.

For problems answered incorrectly, have students review the lessons indicated in parentheses.

ExamView Assessment Suite Customize and create multiple versions of your Mid-Chapter Quiz and their answer keys.

FOLDABLES Follow-Up

Before students complete the Mid-Chapter Quiz, encourage them to review the information for Lessons 4-1 through 4-3 in their Foldables.

CHAPTER 4 Mid-Chapter Quiz

Lessons 4-1 through 4-3

1. **MULTIPLE CHOICE** Lucita works at a bookstore and earns \$5.50 per hour. She works 3 hours on Friday and 7 hours on Saturday. Which expression does *not* represent her wages for those days? (Lesson 4-1) **D**

   A $5.50(3 + 7)$ C $5.50(3) + 5.50(7)$

   B $10(5.50)$ D $7(5.50 + 3)$

2. **BUSINESS** A local newspaper can be ordered for delivery on weekdays or Sundays. A weekday paper is 35¢ and the Sunday Edition is \$1.50. The Stadlers ordered delivery of the weekday papers. The month of March had 23 weekdays and April had 20. How much should the carrier charge the Stadlers for those two months? (Lesson 4-1) **\$15.05**

Simplify each expression. (Lessons 4-1 and 4-2)

3. $8(x + 3)$ $\mathbf{8x + 24}$
4. $4(x - 5)$ $\mathbf{4x - 20}$
5. $9y + 3 - y$ $\mathbf{8y + 3}$
6. $6(m + 2) - 2m$ $\mathbf{4m + 12}$
7. $5 - 4(12 - 3y)$ $\mathbf{-43 + 12y}$
8. $2p - 7 - 6p - 8$ $\mathbf{-4p - 15}$
9. $8 - 12r - 5r - 3$ $\mathbf{-17r + 5}$
10. $-5t + 12 + 8 - 7t$ $\mathbf{-12t + 20}$

11. **CONSTRUCTION** A paving brick is shown. Find the perimeter of five bricks. (Lesson 4-2) $\mathbf{60x + 5}$

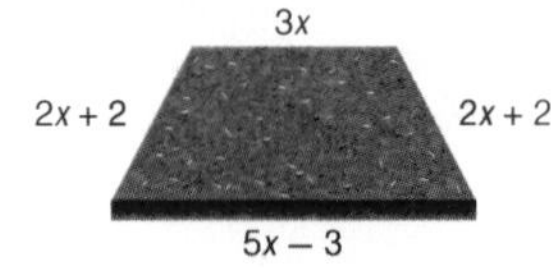

12. **SHOPPING** You buy x pairs of shoes that each cost \$24.95, the same number of socks that each cost \$4.75, and a pair of pants that costs \$29.99. Write an expression in simplest form that represents the total amount of money spent. (Lesson 4-2) $\mathbf{29.70x + 29.99}$

13. **GEOMETRY** Write an expression in simplest form that represents the total distance around the figure below. (Lesson 4-2) $\mathbf{4x + 2}$

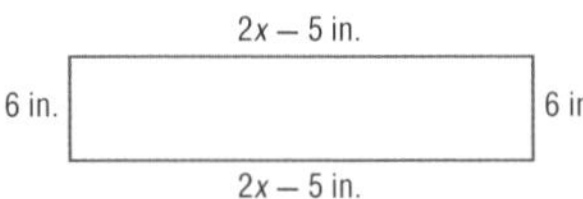

14. **AVIATION** On December 17, 1903, the Wright brothers made the first flights in a power-driven airplane. Orville's flight covered 120 feet, which was 732 feet shorter than Wilbur's. Write and solve a subtraction equation to find the length of Wilbur Wright's flight. (Lesson 4-3) $\mathbf{x - 732 = 120}$**; 852 ft**

ALGEBRA Solve each equation. (Lesson 4-3)

15. $p + 15 = 34$ **19**
16. $\frac{2}{3} + y = 2\frac{1}{2}$ $\mathbf{1\frac{5}{6}}$
17. $a + 12 = -7$ **−19**
18. $45 = b + 18$ **27**
19. $-33 = x - 14$ **−19**
20. $-3.6 = t - 6.8$ **3.2**
21. $-\frac{3}{8} = \frac{1}{5} + r$ $\mathbf{-\frac{23}{40}}$
22. $w - 0.87 = -2.4$ **−1.53**

23. **MULTIPLE CHOICE** The table shows the five nearest train stops along the route from Main Street to Peach Court. Which equation will best help you find how much farther Peach Court is from Main Street than it is from City Center? (Lesson 4-3) **J**

Train Stop	Distance to Main Street (mi)
City Center	4
14th Street	6
Grand Hotel	7
Stadium	12
Peach Court	17

   F $x - 17 = 4$ H $x - 4 = 17$

   G $x + 17 = 4$ J $x + 4 = 17$

24. **MONEY** Ricardo spent \$37 for a jacket, which included \$2.38 in sales tax. Write and solve an addition equation to find the price of the jacket before tax. (Lesson 4-3) $\mathbf{x + 2.38 = 37}$**; \$34.62**

25. **DRAMA** Last school year, the fall play sold 45 more tickets than the spring play. Write and solve an equation to find the number of tickets sold at the spring play. (Lesson 4-3) $\mathbf{x + 45 = 214}$**; 169 tickets**

Play	Number of Tickets
Fall	214
Spring	■

Intervention Planner

Tier 1 On Level	Tier 2 Strategic Intervention approaching grade level	Tier 3 Intensive Intervention 2 or more grades below level
If students miss about 25% of the exercises or less,	**If** students miss about 50% of the exercises,	**If** students miss about 75% of the exercises,
Then choose a resource:	**Then** choose a resource:	**Then** use *Math Triumphs, Grade 8*, Ch. 3
SE Lessons 4-1, 4-2, and 4-3 **CRM** Skills Practice, pp. 7, 13, and 19 **TE** Chapter Project, p. 168	**CRM** Study Guide and Intervention, Chapter 4, pp. 5, 11, and 17 *Quick Review Math Handbook*	
Math Online Self-Check Quiz	**Math Online** Extra Examples, Personal Tutor, Homework Help	**Math Online** Extra Examples, Personal Tutor, Homework Help, Review Vocabulary

4-4 Solving Equations by Multiplying or Dividing

Then

You have already solved equations using addition and subtraction. (Lesson 4-3)

Now

- Solve equations by using the Division Property of Equality.
- Solve equations by using the Multiplication Property of Equality.

Math Online

glencoe.com

- Extra Examples
- Personal Tutor
- Self-Check Quiz
- Homework Help
- Math in Motion

Why?

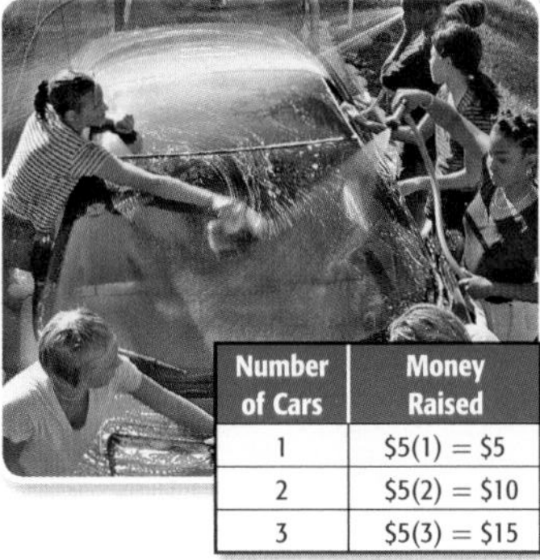

Number of Cars	Money Raised
1	$5(1) = $5
2	$5(2) = $10
3	$5(3) = $15

The Spirit Club at Westown Middle School is sponsoring a car wash. They charge $5 to wash each car.

Let c represent the number of cars the club washes and m represent the money the club raises. Then $5c = m$.

a. Suppose the Spirit Club wants to raise $120. Write an equation to find the number of cars they need to wash. $5c = 120$

b. How can you find the number of cars? Divide the amount of money you want to raise by $5.

Solve Equations by Dividing The equation $5c = 120$ represents the relationship described above. The operation involved in the equation is multiplication. To undo multiplication, use division.

Key Concept — Division Property of Equality (For Your FOLDABLE)

Words When you divide each side of an equation by the same nonzero number, the two sides remain equal.

Symbols For numbers a, b, and c, where $c \neq 0$, if $a = b$, then $\frac{a}{c} = \frac{b}{c}$.

Examples

$1.8 = 1.8$ | $4x = 24$

$\frac{1.8}{2} = \frac{1.8}{2}$ | $\frac{4x}{4} = \frac{24}{4}$

$0.9 = 0.9$ | $x = 6$

EXAMPLE 1 Solve Equations by Dividing

Solve $5c = 120$.

$5c = 120$ — Write the equation.

$\frac{5c}{5} = \frac{120}{5}$ — Division Property of Equality

$1c = 24$ — $5 \div 5 = 1$, $120 \div 5 = 24$

$c = 24$ — Identity Property; $1c = c$

The solution is 24.

Check Your Progress

Solve each equation.

1A. $-54 = 6x$ -9

1B. $7a = 63$ 9

Personal Tutor glencoe.com

4-4 Lesson Notes

1 FOCUS

Vertical Alignment

Before Lesson 4-4
Solve equations using addition and subtraction.

Lesson 4-4
Solve equations using the Division and Multiplication Properties of Equality.

After Lesson 4-4
Solve two-step equations using properties of equality.

2 TEACH

Scaffolding Questions

Have students read the *Why?* section of the lesson and answer the questions.

Ask:

- Suppose the Spirit Club decided to charge $8 per car instead of $5. What equation would represent the number of cars they would need to wash to raise the same amount of money? $8c = 120$
- To solve the equation, what operation would you use to "undo" multiplication? division
- How many cars would the Spirit Club need to wash if they charged $8 per car? Explain. 15; if you undo multiplication by dividing each side of the equation by 8

Lesson 4-4 Resources

Resource	Approaching-Level	On-Level	Beyond-Level	English Learners
Teacher Edition		• Differentiated Instruction, p. 193	• Differentiated Instruction, pp. 193, 196	
Chapter Resource Masters	• Study Guide and Intervention, pp. 23–24 • Skills Practice p. 25 • Practice, p. 26 • Word Problem Practice, p. 27	• Study Guide and Intervention, pp. 23–24 • Skills Practice p. 25 • Practice, p. 26 • Word Problem Practice, p. 27 • Enrichment, p. 28	• Practice, p. 26 • Word Problem Practice, p. 27 • Enrichment, p. 28	• Study Guide and Intervention, pp. 23–24 • Skills Practice p. 25 • Practice, p. 26
Transparencies	• 5-Minute Check Transparency 4-4	• 5-Minute Check Transparency 4-4	• 5-Minute Check Transparency 4-4	• 5-Minute Check Transparency 4-4
Other	• Study Notebook • Teaching Pre-Algebra with Manipulatives	• Study Notebook • Teaching Pre-Algebra with Manipulatives	• Study Notebook	• Study Notebook • Teaching Pre-Algebra with Manipulatives

Solve Equations by Dividing

Examples 1–3 show how to use the Division Property of Equality to solve equations.

Formative Assessment

Use the Check Your Progress exercises after each example to determine students' understanding of concepts.

Additional Examples

1 Solve $7w = 161$. 23

2 Solve $7x = -56$. Check your solution and graph it on a number line. -8

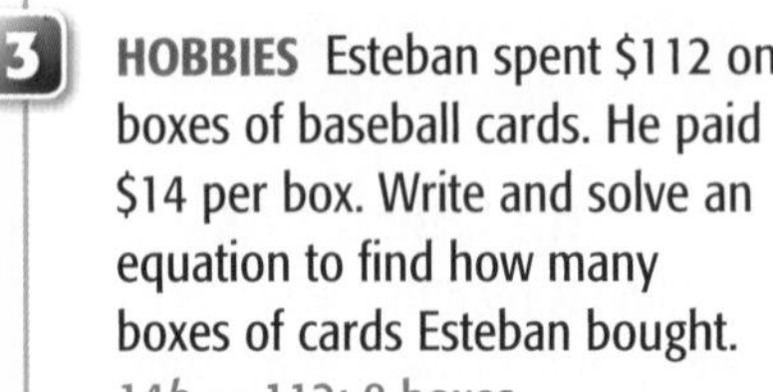

3 **HOBBIES** Esteban spent $112 on boxes of baseball cards. He paid $14 per box. Write and solve an equation to find how many boxes of cards Esteban bought. $14b = 112$; 8 boxes

Additional Examples also in Interactive Classroom PowerPoint® Presentations

IWB INTERACTIVE WHITEBOARD READY

Additional Answers

2A.

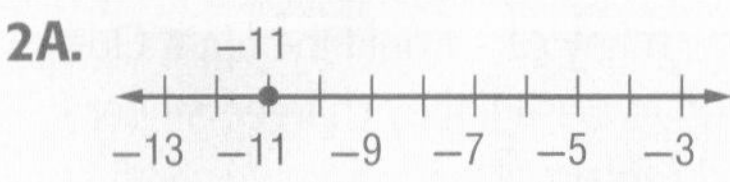

2B.

EXAMPLE 2 Solve Equations by Dividing

Solve $4x = -48$. Check your solution and graph it on a number line.

$4x = -48$	**Write the equation.**
$\frac{4x}{4} = \frac{-48}{4}$	**Division Property of Equality**
$1x = -12$	**$4 \div 4 = 1$, $-48 \div 4 = -12$**
$x = -12$	**Identity Property; $1x = x$**

To check your solution, replace x with -12 in the original equation.

Check $4x = -48$	**Write the equation.**
$4(-12) \stackrel{?}{=} -48$	**Replace x with -12.**
$-48 = -48$ ✓	**The sentence is true.**

The solution is -12. To graph it, draw a dot at -12 on the number line.

−12

−14 −12 −10 −8 −6 −4

2A. −11; See margin.
2B. 7; See margin.

Check Your Progress

2A. Solve $-121 = 11x$.

2B. Solve $-15x = -105$.

Personal Tutor glencoe.com

Real-World Link

Safari zoos allow animals the chance to roam while visitors tour in their cars. The first one in the United States opened in Florida in 1967.

Source: Lion Country Safari

Real-World EXAMPLE 3 Solve an Equation by Dividing

ZOOS **A drive-through safari zoo charges $12.50 per person for admission. In one hour, the park raised $675 in admission fees. Write and solve an equation to find how many people visited that hour.**

Words	Admission fee	times	the number of visitors	equals	the total money raised.
Variable	Let v = the number of zoo visitors.				
Equation	12.50	·	v	=	675

$12.5v = 675$	**Write the equation.**
$\frac{12.5v}{12.5} = \frac{675}{12.5}$	**Division Property of Equality**
$v = 54$	**Simplify. Check this solution.**

The zoo admitted 54 people in one hour.

Check Your Progress

3. **PARKS** An in-state one year camping permit for New Mexico State Parks costs $180. If the total income from the camping permits is $8280 during the first day of sales, how many permits were purchased? **46 permits**

Personal Tutor glencoe.com

Solve Equations by Multiplying Equations in which a variable is divided can be solved by multiplying each side by the same number.

Key Concept — Multiplication Property of Equality

For Your FOLDABLE

Words When you multiply each side of an equation by the same nonzero number, the two sides remain equivalent.

Symbols For any numbers a, b, and c, if $a = b$, then $ca = cb$.

Examples

$-3 = -3$ | $\frac{1}{5}x = -3$
$4(-3) = 4(-3)$ | $5\left(\frac{1}{5}x\right) = 5(-3)$
$-12 = -12$ | $x = -15$

Math *in Motion*, Interactive Lab glencoe.com

EXAMPLE 4 Solve Equations by Multiplying

Solve $\frac{y}{4} = -8$. Check your solution.

$\frac{y}{4} = -8.$	Write the equation.
$4 \cdot \frac{y}{4} = 4 \cdot (-8)$	Multiplication Property of Equality
$1y = -32$	Multiplicative Inverse Property; $4 \cdot \frac{1}{4} = 1$
$y = -32$	Identity Property. Check your solution.

StudyTip

Division In Example 4, $\frac{y}{4}$ means y divided by 4.

Check Your Progress

Solve each equation. Check your solution.

4A. $7 = \frac{x}{-2}$ -14

4B. $\frac{a}{6} = 12$ 72

Personal Tutor glencoe.com

To solve an equation such as $-\frac{3}{5}x = -6$, you can divide each side by $-\frac{3}{5}$ or multiply each side by $-\frac{5}{3}$.

EXAMPLE 5 Solve Equations by Multiplying by the Reciprocal

Solve $-\frac{3}{5}x = -6$. Check your solution.

$-\frac{3}{5}x = -6$	Write the equation.
$-\frac{5}{3}\left(-\frac{3}{5}\right)x = -\frac{5}{3}\left(-\frac{6}{1}\right)$	Multiply each side by $-\frac{5}{3}$.
$1x = 10$	Multiplicative Inverse Property; $-\frac{5}{3}\left(-\frac{3}{5}\right) = 1$
$x = 10$	Identity Property. Check your solution.

StudyTip

Multiplicative Inverse Remember that the product of a number and its multiplicative inverse is 1. Use this property when the coefficient of x is a fraction.

Check Your Progress

Solve each equation. Check your solution.

5A. $\frac{6}{7}m = -24$ -28

5B. $5 = -\frac{5}{9}x$ -9

Personal Tutor glencoe.com

Solve Equations by Multiplying

Examples 4 and 5 show how to write and solve an equation by multiplying both sides by the same value.

Additional Examples

4 Solve $\frac{y}{-5} = -12$. Check your solution. 60

5 Solve $-\frac{3}{4}x = -9$. Check your solution. 12

Focus on Mathematical Content

Solving Equations by Multiplying or Dividing It is helpful to think of an equation as two sides of a scale. Each side has to have the same operations performed to keep the scale balanced.

TEACH with TECH

STUDENT RESPONSE SYSTEM Create a set of multiple-choice questions on equations. Have students form two teams to answer questions with the clickers. The team with the most correct answers wins.

Differentiated Instruction

OL BL

Verbal/Linguistic Have students think of ways they encounter multiplication and division in their lives. Then have them express each situation as a multiplication or division equation. Examples: "You can read 20 pages of a book in an hour. How long will it take you to read a 280-page book of the same difficulty?" $20h = 280$; 14 h "You want to serve 8 ounces of apple cider to each of 12 people. How much cider do you need?" $\frac{c}{12} = 8$; 96 oz

Watch Out!

Checking Answers Many students mistakenly switch dividends and divisors when solving equations by multiplying. Have them check their answers by substituting the found value into the equation.

3 PRACTICE

Formative Assessment

Use Exercises 1–11 to check for understanding.

Use the chart at the bottom of this page to customize assignments for your students.

Additional Answers

42.

Area (A)	15	15	15	15	15
base (b)	1	2	3	4	5
height (h)	30	15	10	7.5	6

43b. Multiply each input value by 50 to get the output value.

Time (d)	1	2	3	4	5	6
Distance (mi)	50	100	150	200	250	300

43c.

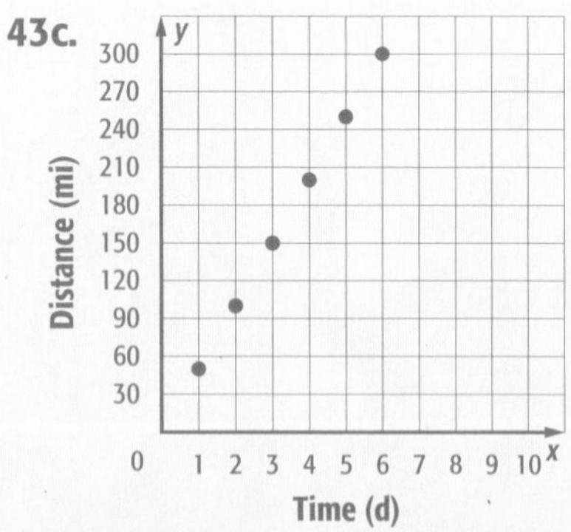

49. Sample answer: Yes; he can multiply each side of the equation by $\frac{1}{3}$ instead of dividing by 3.

Check Your Understanding

Examples 1, 2, 4 and 5 pp. 191–193

Solve each equation. Check your solution.

1. $5c = -65$ **−13**
2. $-42 = -7m$ **6**
3. $8p = 96$ **12**
4. $\frac{n}{12} = 12$ **144**
5. $18 = \frac{t}{-2}$ **−36**
6. $0.6h = 1.8$ **3**
7. $-3.4 = 0.4j$ **−8.5**
8. $-\frac{3}{4}k = 12$ **−16**
9. $36 = \frac{3}{5}m$ **60**

Example 3 p. 192

10. **BOATING** A forest preserve rents canoes for \$18 per hour. Corey has \$90 to spend. Write and solve a multiplication equation to find how many hours he can rent a canoe. **$18h = 90$; 5 h**

11. **SPACE** The weight of an object on the Moon is one-sixth its weight on Earth. If an object weighs 54 pounds on the Moon, write and solve a division equation to find how much it weighs on Earth. **$\frac{x}{6} = 54$; 324 lb**

Practice and Problem Solving

● = **Step-by-Step Solutions** begin on page R11. **Extra Practice** begins on page 810.

Examples 1, 2, 4 and 5 pp. 191–193

Solve each equation. Check your solution.

12. $9x = 54$ **6**
13. $5s = -60$ **−12**
14. $64 = -4r$ **−16**
15. $-72 = 3y$ **−24**
16. $0.3x = -4.5$ **−15**
17. $4.95 = 0.3t$ **16.5**
18. $-8.4 = -6g$ **1.4**
19. $-28 = \frac{d}{-14}$ **392**
20. $\frac{b}{9} = -108$ **−972**
21. $16 = -\frac{b}{4}$ **−64**
22. $\frac{x}{-8} = -4$ **32**
23. $-32 = -\frac{4}{3}s$ **24**
24. $-25 = -\frac{5}{6}r$ **30**
25. $-\frac{9}{10}k = 72$ **−80**
26. $\frac{2}{3}n = -22$ **−33**

Example 3 p. 192

27. **FRUIT** Rashid picked a total of 420 strawberries in $\frac{5}{6}$ hour. Write and solve a multiplication equation to find how many strawberries Rashid could pick in 1 hour. **$\frac{5}{6}x = 420$; 504 strawberries**

28. **ATHLETICS** Marcus ran every day for 14 weeks to train for a marathon. Write and solve a division equation to find how many days he trained. **$\frac{d}{7} = 14$; 98 days**

Solve each equation. Check your solution.

29. $5p - 2p = -12$ **−4**
30. $42 = 4x + 3x$ **6**
31. $-2(6y) = 144$ **−12**
32. $72 = -12(-3x)$ **2**
33. $\frac{r}{4} = -25 + 9$ **−64**
34. $\frac{m}{-3} = -5 - 18$ **69**
35. $\frac{1}{3}n = \frac{2}{9}$ **$\frac{2}{3}$**
36. $\frac{5}{8} = -\frac{1}{2}x$ **$-1\frac{1}{4}$**
37. $-0.7 = -\frac{7}{9}z$ **0.9 or $\frac{9}{10}$**
38. $1\frac{7}{8}y = 4\frac{1}{2}$ **$2\frac{2}{5}$**
39. $2\frac{1}{3} = -9m$ **$-\frac{7}{27}$**
40. $-\frac{7}{9}t = -\frac{28}{36}$ **1**

41. **ANIMALS** The sleeping heart rate of a black bear during hibernation is about $\frac{2}{5}$ of its summer rate. If the sleeping heart rate of a bear is 28 beats per minute during hibernation, find the summer sleeping heart rate. **70 bpm**

Differentiated Homework Options

Level	Assignment	Two-Day Option	
AL Basic	12–28, 44–47, 49–76	13–27 odd, 50–53	12–28 even, 44–47, 49, 54–76
OL Core	13–39 odd, 41–47, 49–76	12–28, 50–53	29–47, 49, 54–76
BL Advanced	29–70, (optional: 71–76)		

42. GEOMETRY The formula for finding the area of a triangle is $A = \frac{1}{2}bh$, where A represents the area, b represents the length of the base of the triangle, and h represents the height of the triangle. Write and solve equations to complete the table of values. **See margin.**

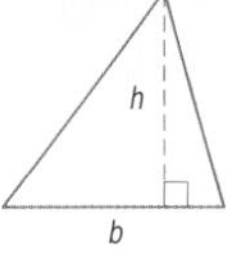

Area (*A*)	15	15	15	15	15
base (*b*)	1	2	3	4	5
height (*h*)	■	■	■	■	■

Real-World Link

Monarchs east of the Rocky Mountains migrate to small forest groves in Mexico's mountains. As many as 500 million butterflies have migrated in a given year.

Source: Monarch Watch

43. MULTIPLE REPRESENTATIONS Every autumn, the North American Monarch butterfly migrates up to 3000 miles to California and Mexico where it hibernates until early spring. The butterfly travels on average 50 miles per day.

a. ALGEBRAIC Write an equation that represents the distance d a butterfly will travel in t days. $d = 50t$

b. TABULAR Use the equation to complete the table at the right. **See margin.**

Time (days)	1	2	3	4	5	6
Distance (miles)	■	■	■	■	■	■

c. GRAPHICAL Graph the points from the table on the coordinate plane. Graph time on the x-axis and distance on the y-axis. **See margin.**

d. GRAPHICAL Using the graph, estimate the number of days it will take the butterfly to travel 450 miles. **9 days**

e. VERBAL How many days will it take a butterfly to travel 2500 miles? Which method did you use to solve the problem? **50 days; See students' work.**

H.O.T. Problems

Use Higher-Order Thinking Skills

44. OPEN ENDED Write a multiplication equation and a division equation which has a solution of −5. **Sample answer: $5x = -25$; $\frac{-25}{x} = 5$**

45. WRITING IN MATH Write a real-world example that uses an equation containing a decimal and a fraction. Then find the solution.

46. REASONING *True* or *false*: $\frac{x}{4}$ is equivalent to $\frac{1}{4}x$. Explain your reasoning.

47. FIND THE ERROR Sam and Rachel are solving $\frac{x}{4} = -20$. Is either of them correct? Explain your reasoning. **Rachel; to undo division, you multiply.**

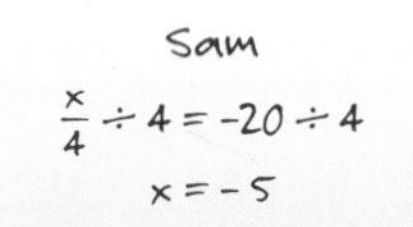

48. CHALLENGE If $\frac{3}{10}x = 3$, what is the value of $7x + 13$? **83**

49. WRITING IN MATH Suppose your friend says he can solve $3x = 15$ by using the Multiplication Property of Equality. Is he correct? Justify your response. **See margin.**

45. Sample answer: A shirt was on sale for half off. If the sale price was \$15.60, find the original price; \$31.20

46. Sample answer: The statement is always true. If you have an equation involving division, then you can write the numerator with a coefficient of 1. The coefficient of 1 and the divisor form a fraction that can be used as the coefficient of the variable.

Multiple Representations In Exercise 43, students use an equation, a table of values, a graph of ordered pairs, and mental math to relate time, distance, and speed to predict the duration of a trip.

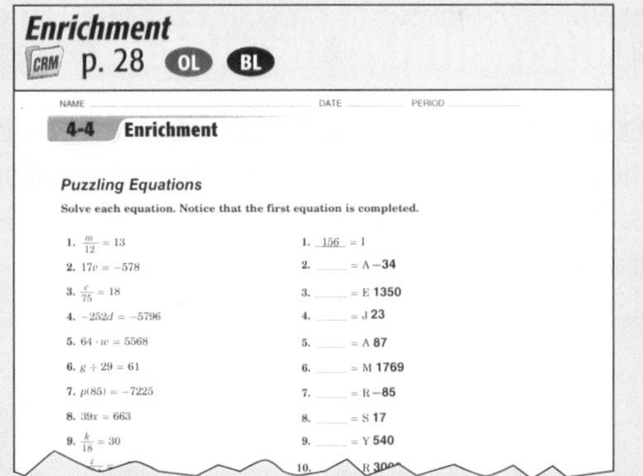

Enrichment CRM p. 28 OL BL

NAME ______ DATE ______ PERIOD ______

4-4 Enrichment

Puzzling Equations

Solve each equation. Notice that the first equation is completed.

1. $\frac{m}{12} = 13$		1. 156 = I	
2. $17v = -578$		2. ____ = A −34	
3. $\frac{c}{75} = 18$		3. ____ = E 1350	
4. $-252d = -5796$		4. ____ = J 23	
5. $64 \cdot w = 5568$		5. ____ = A 87	
6. $g + 29 = 61$		6. ____ = M 1769	
7. $p(85) = -7225$		7. ____ = R −85	
8. $39x = 663$		8. ____ = S 17	
9. $\frac{k}{18} = 30$		9. ____ = Y 540	

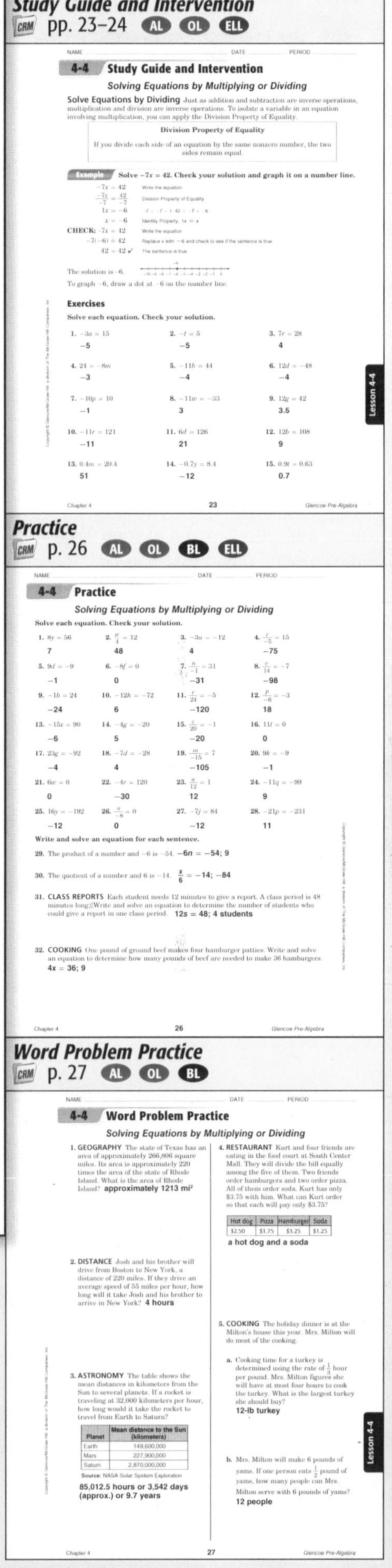

Study Guide and Intervention CRM pp. 23–24 AL OL ELL

NAME ______ DATE ______ PERIOD ______

4-4 Study Guide and Intervention

Solving Equations by Multiplying or Dividing

Solve Equations by Dividing Just as addition and subtraction are inverse operations, multiplication and division are inverse operations. To isolate a variable in an equation involving multiplication, you can apply the Division Property of Equality.

Division Property of Equality

If you divide each side of an equation by the same nonzero number, the two sides remain equal.

Example Solve $-7x = 42$. Check your solution and graph it on a number line.

$-7x = 42$ Write the equation.
$\frac{-7x}{-7} = \frac{42}{-7}$ Division Property of Equality
$1x = -6$
$x = -6$ Identity Property, $1x = x$
CHECK: $-7x = 42$ Write the equation.
$-7(-6) = 42$ Replace x with −6 and check to see if the sentence is true.
$42 = 42$ ✓ The sentence is true.

The solution is −6.
To graph −6, draw a dot at −6 on the number line.

Exercises

Solve each equation. Check your solution.

1. $-3a = 15$ **−5**	2. $-t = 5$ **−5**	3. $7r = 28$ **4**
4. $24 = -8m$ **−3**	5. $-11b = 44$ **−4**	6. $12d = -48$ **−4**
7. $-10p = 10$ **−1**	8. $-11w = -33$ **3**	9. $12g = 42$ **3.5**
10. $-11r = 121$ **−11**	11. $6d = 126$ **21**	12. $12b = 108$ **9**
13. $0.4m = 20.4$ **51**	14. $-0.7y = 8.4$ **−12**	15. $0.9t = 0.63$ **0.7**

Chapter 4 23 Glencoe Pre-Algebra

Practice CRM p. 26 AL OL BL ELL

NAME ______ DATE ______ PERIOD ______

4-4 Practice

Solving Equations by Multiplying or Dividing

Solve each equation. Check your solution.

1. $8y = 56$ **7**	2. $\frac{w}{4} = 12$ **48**	3. $-3u = -12$ **4**	4. $\frac{r}{-5} = 15$ **−75**
5. $9d = -9$ **−1**	6. $-8f = 0$ **0**	7. $\frac{n}{-1} = 31$ **−31**	8. $\frac{c}{14} = -7$ **−98**
9. $-1b = 24$ **−24**	10. $-12h = -72$ **6**	11. $\frac{t}{24} = -5$ **−120**	12. $\frac{p}{-6} = -3$ **18**
13. $-15x = 90$ **−6**	14. $-4g = -20$ **5**	15. $\frac{z}{20} = -1$ **−20**	16. $11t = 0$ **0**
17. $23g = -92$ **−4**	18. $-7d = -28$ **4**	19. $\frac{m}{-15} = 7$ **−105**	20. $9k = -9$ **−1**
21. $6r = 0$ **0**	22. $-4r = 120$ **−30**	23. $\frac{a}{12} = 1$ **12**	24. $-11q = -99$ **9**
25. $16y = -192$ **−12**	26. $\frac{a}{-8} = 0$ **0**	27. $-7j = 84$ **−12**	28. $-21p = -231$ **11**

Write and solve an equation for each sentence.

29. The product of a number and −6 is −54. **$-6n = -54$; 9**

30. The quotient of a number and 6 is −14. **$\frac{x}{6} = -14$; −84**

31. CLASS REPORTS Each student needs 12 minutes to give a report. A class period is 48 minutes long. Write and solve an equation to determine the number of students who could give a report in one class period. **$12s = 48$; 4 students**

32. COOKING One pound of ground beef makes four hamburger patties. Write and solve an equation to determine how many pounds of beef are needed to make 36 hamburgers. **$4x = 36$; 9**

Chapter 4 26 Glencoe Pre-Algebra

Word Problem Practice CRM p. 27 AL OL BL

NAME ______ DATE ______ PERIOD ______

4-4 Word Problem Practice

Solving Equations by Multiplying or Dividing

1. GEOGRAPHY The state of Texas has an area of approximately 266,806 square miles. Its area is approximately 220 times the area of the state of Rhode Island. What is the area of Rhode Island? **approximately 1213 mi²**

2. DISTANCE Josh and his brother will drive from Boston to New York, a distance of 220 miles. If they drive an average speed of 55 miles per hour, how long will it take Josh and his brother to arrive in New York? **4 hours**

3. ASTRONOMY The table shows the mean distances in kilometers from the Sun to several planets. If a rocket is traveling at 32,000 kilometers per hour, how long would it take the rocket to travel from Earth to Saturn?

Planet	Mean distance to the Sun (kilometers)
Earth	149,600,000
Mars	227,900,000
Saturn	2,870,000,000

Source: NASA Solar System Exploration

85,012.5 hours or 3,542 days (approx.) or 9.7 years

4. RESTAURANT Kurt and four friends are eating in the food court at South Center Mall. They will divide the bill equally among the five of them. Two friends order hamburgers and two order pizza. All of them order soda. Kurt has only \$3.75 with him. What can Kurt order so that each will pay only \$3.75?

Hot dog	Pizza	Hamburger	Soda
\$2.50	\$1.75	\$3.25	\$1.25

a hot dog and a soda

5. COOKING The holiday dinner is at the Milton's house this year. Mrs. Milton will do most of the cooking.

a. Cooking time for a turkey is determined using the rate of $\frac{1}{3}$ hour per pound. Mrs. Milton figures she will have at most four hours to cook the turkey. What is the largest turkey she should buy? **12-lb turkey**

b. Mrs. Milton will make 6 pounds of yams. If one person eats $\frac{1}{2}$ pound of yams, how many people can Mrs. Milton serve with 6 pounds of yams? **12 people**

Chapter 4 27 Glencoe Pre-Algebra

Watch Out!

Find the Error For Exercise 47, students should see that Rachel and Sam solved the equation differently. Tell students to think of the operation that must be used to undo the operation in the equation. They should also check their answer in the original equation.

4 ASSESS

Yesterday's News Have students write how yesterday's lesson on solving equations using addition and subtraction helped them in learning today's lesson on solving equations using multiplication and division. What ideas are the same? Which are different?

Standardized Test Practice

50. During a vacation, the Morales family drove 63 miles in 1 hour. If they averaged the same speed during their trip, which equation can be used to find how far the Morales family drove in 6 hours? **B**

A $\frac{63}{x} = 6$

B $\frac{x}{6} = 63$

C $6x = 63$

D $63x = 6$

51. The solution of which equation is *not* graphed on the number line below? **J**

(number line from −4 to 6 with a point at −2)

F $12 = -6x$

G $8x = -16$

H $-14 = 7x$

J $-18x = -36$

52. Ella paid \$11.85 for 3 magazines. If each magazine was the same price, how much did each magazine cost? **C**

A \$4.59

B \$4.00

C \$3.95

D \$3.59

53. EXTENDED RESPONSE Stanley paid half of what Royce paid for his baseball glove. Royce paid \$64 for his glove.

a. Write an equation to find how much Stanley paid for his glove. $c = \frac{64}{2}$

b. How much did Stanley pay for his glove? **\$32**

Spiral Review

Solve each equation. Check your solution. (Lesson 4-3)

54. $x - 5 = -22$ **−17**

55. $4 = 7 + p$ **−3**

56. $-40 = y - 9$ **−31**

57. $2.3 + r = 1.6$ **−0.7**

58. $d - 2.7 = -1.4$ **1.3**

59. $t + (-16) = -24$ **−8**

60. $p + \frac{1}{10} = -\frac{3}{4}$ $\mathbf{\frac{-17}{20}}$

61. $\frac{2}{3} + k = \frac{1}{6}$ $\mathbf{-\frac{1}{2}}$

62. $d - \frac{4}{9} = -\frac{1}{12}$ $\mathbf{\frac{13}{36}}$

Simplify each expression. (Lesson 4-2)

63. $5(t + 3)$ **5*t* + 15**

64. $7x - 12x$ **−5*x***

65. $9p + 4 + 3p$ **12*p* + 4**

66. $3w + 4s - w + 5s$ **2*w* + 9*s***

67. $7 - 4(x + 3)$ **−4*x* − 5**

68. $3(2 + 3x) + 21x$ **6 + 30*x***

69. ALGEBRA Find the values that complete the table at the right for $y = -4x$. (Lesson 2-4)

x	−2	−1	0	1
y	■	■	■	■
	8	**4**	**0**	**−4**

70. AGE Gabriel is 12 years old, and his younger brother Elias is 2 years old. How old will each of them be when Gabriel is twice as old as Elias? (Lesson 1-1) **Gabriel: 20; Elias: 10**

Skills Review

Find the value of each expression. (Lesson 1-1)

71. $-3 + 7(4)$ **25**

72. $\frac{6-9}{8+4}$ $\mathbf{-\frac{1}{4}}$

73. $5 - 3(6 + 2)$ **−19**

74. $14 - 24 + 6 \cdot 8$ **38**

75. $9 \cdot 7 - 4 \cdot 5$ **43**

76. $3[15 - (-9)]$ **72**

Differentiated Instruction

Extension Some equations have rational coefficients, such as $\frac{3}{5}x = 150$. There are multiple methods you can use to solve this type of equation. In one method, you can multiply both sides by 5. The resulting equation is $3x = 750$. Then, divide both sides by 3 to get $x = 250$. Have students use this method to solve the equation $\frac{2}{3}x = 60$. 90

EXPLORE 4-5

Algebra Lab Solving Two-Step Equations Using Algebra Tiles

Math Online glencoe.com
Math *in Motion,* Interactive Lab

Like one-step equations, two-step equations can be solved using algebra tiles. I'm thinking of a number. If you multiply it by 3 and add 2, the result is 8. To solve the problem, you can use the *work backward strategy*. Undo each operation in reverse order.

ACTIVITY 1

Model and solve $3x + 2 = 8$ using algebra tiles.

Step 1

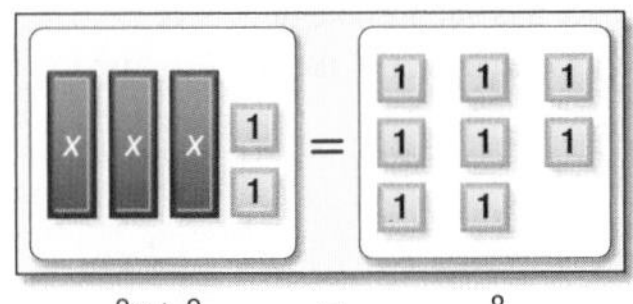

Model the equation.

Step 2

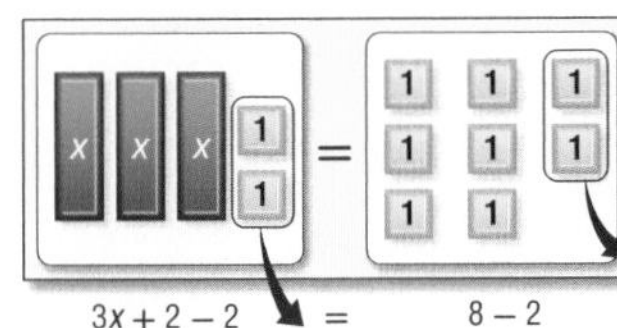

Remove two 1-tiles from each side of the mat.

Step 3

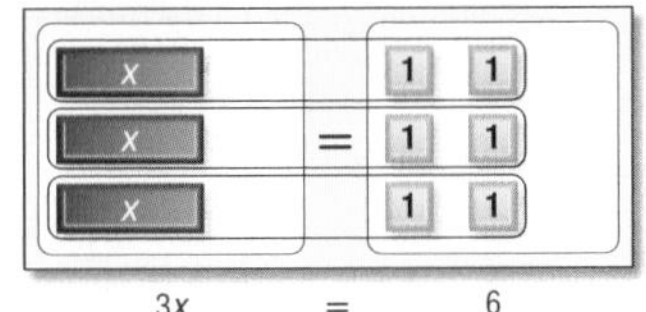

Separate the remaining tiles into three equal groups.

So, $x = 2$.

Step 4 Check your solution by replacing x with 2 in the original equation.

$3x + 2 = 8$ **Write the equation.**

$3(2) + 2 = 8$ **Replace x with 2**

$6 + 2 = 8$ **Multiply.**

$8 = 8$ ✓ **The statement is true.**

Analyze the Results

Model and solve each equation using algebra tiles. 1–3. See Chapter 4 Answer Appendix for models.

1. $2x + 2 = 12$ 5
2. $9 = 4 + 5x$ 1
3. $3x + 6 = 15$ 3

EXPLORE 4-5

Lesson Notes

1 FOCUS

Objective Use algebra tiles to solve two-step equations.

Materials for Each Group

- equation mat
- algebra tiles

Teaching Tip

Review how to form zero pairs.

2 TEACH

Working in Cooperative Groups

Put students in groups of two or three, mixing abilities. Have students work through Activities 1 and 2.

Activity 1:

Ask:

- In Step 1, if you remove two 1-tiles from one side of the equation, what must you do to the other? Remove two 1-tiles.
- What operation is being performed in Step 3? division

Make sure students understand that addition and subtraction need to be performed before multiplication or division to isolate the variable. Encourage students to always check their solutions in the original equation.

Activity 2:

Ask:

- In Step 2, why were the zero pairs added? so that you can remove four 1-tiles from the right side of the equation
- Why does this not change the value of the equation? Adding zero to a number does not change the value of the number.

Practice Have students complete Exercises 1–8.

3 ASSESS

Formative Assessment

Use Exercise 6 to assess whether students can solve two-step equations using algebra tiles.

From Concrete to Abstract

Have students select a problem from Exercises 4 or 5. Have them explain in two steps how they would use inverse operations to solve the equation.

Extending the Concept

Have students write a word problem that Activity 1 or Activity 2 could represent. For example, a word problem for Activity 1 could be the following: Three equal-numbered groups of students are going to the movies. When they arrive, two additional students join them. There were eight students all together. How many students were in each of the original three groups?

Some equations are solved by using zero pairs. One +1 tile and one −1 tile make a zero pair. Since $1 + (-1) = 0$, you can add or subtract a zero pair from either side of an equation mat without changing its value.

ACTIVITY 2

Model and solve $2x + 4 = 2$ using algebra tiles.

Step 1

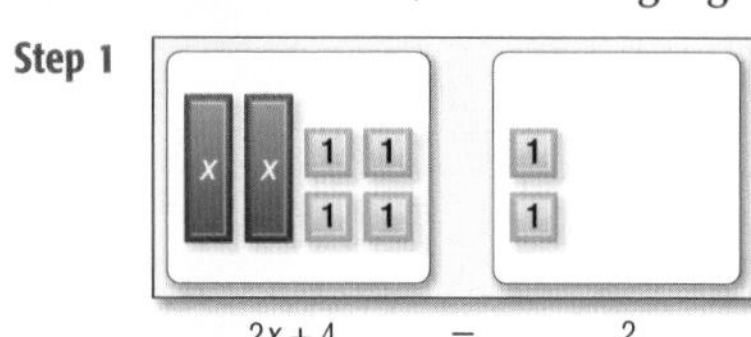

Model the equation. Notice it is not possible to remove four positive 1-tiles from the right side of the equation mat.

Step 2

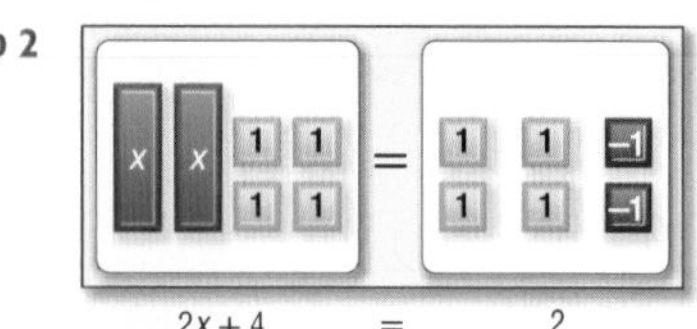

Add 2 zero pairs to the right side of the mat so you have enough positive 1-tiles.

Step 3

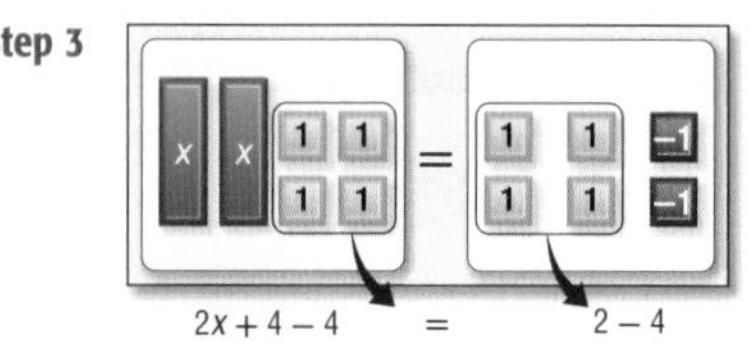

Remove the same number of 1-tiles from each side of the mat until the x-tile is alone on one side.

Step 4

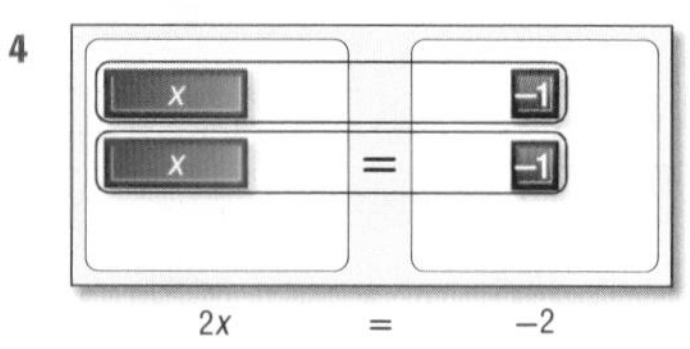

Separate the remaining tiles into two equal groups.

So, $x = -1$.

Analyze the Results

Model and solve each equation using algebra tiles. 4–6. See Chapter 4 Answer Appendix for models.

4. $4x + 3 = -9$ −3 **5.** $3x - 3 = 6$ 3 **6.** $-6 = 2x + 4$ −5

7. What property is shown by removing tiles from each side? Subtraction Property of Equality

8. What property is shown by separating the tiles into groups? Division Property of Equality

198 Chapter 4 Expressions and Equations

4-5 Solving Two-Step Equations

Why?

Santos is planning a hot air balloon ride. The cost of the ride is \$125 plus \$50 for each hour in the air. The equation $c = 50h + 125$ represents the total cost c to ride a hot air balloon for h hours.

a. Find the total cost if Santos rides for 2 hours. **\$225**

b. How long could Santos ride if he had \$325? **4 hours**

Then
You have already solved one-step equations. (Lessons 4-3 and 4-4)

Now
- Solve two-step equations.
- Solve real-world problems involving two-step equations.

New Vocabulary
two-step equation

Math Online
glencoe.com
- Extra Examples
- Personal Tutor
- Self-Check Quiz
- Homework Help
- Math in Motion

Solve Two-Step Equations A **two-step equation** like the one above contains two operations. To solve a two-step equation, use inverse operations to undo each operation in reverse order of the order of operations.

EXAMPLE 1 Solve a Two-Step Equation

Solve $3a + 9 = 33$. Check your solution.

Method 1 The Vertical Method

$3a + 9 = 33$ — Write the equation.

$3a + 9 = 33$
$\quad -9 = -9$ — Subtraction Property of Equality

$3a = 24$ — Simplify.

$\frac{3a}{3} = \frac{24}{3}$ — Division Property of Equality

$a = 8$ — Simplify.

Method 2 The Horizontal Method

$3a + 9 = 33$ — Write the equation.

$3a + 9 - 9 = 33 - 9$ — Subtraction Property of Equality

$3a = 24$ — Simplify.

$\frac{3a}{3} = \frac{24}{3}$ — Division Property of Equality

$a = 8$ — Simplify.

Using either method, the solution is 8.

Check
$3a + 9 = 33$ — Write the equation.
$3(8) + 9 \stackrel{?}{=} 33$ — Replace a with 8.
$24 + 9 \stackrel{?}{=} 33$ — Multiply.
$33 = 33$ ✓ — The sentence is true.

Check Your Progress

Solve each equation. Check your solution.

1A. $6x + 1 = 25$ 4 **1B.** $4x - 5 = -33$ -7

Personal Tutor glencoe.com

4-5 Lesson Notes

1 FOCUS

Vertical Alignment

Before Lesson 4-5
Solve one-step equations.

Lesson 4-5
Solve two-step equations. Solve real-world problems involving two-step equations.

After Lesson 4-5
Write verbal sentences as two-step equations.

2 TEACH

Scaffolding Questions

Have students read the *Why?* section of the lesson and answer the questions.

Ask:
- What is the constant in the equation $c = 50h + 125$? 125
- Will your cost ever be less than \$125 to ride in a balloon? Why? No, the base price is \$125 plus \$50 for each hour.
- Describe the steps you used to find the total cost for Santos to ride for 2 hours. Substitute 2 for h in the equation, multiply 50(2), and add the result, 100, to 125 to get 225.

Lesson 4-5 Resources

Resource	Approaching-Level	On-Level	Beyond-Level	English Learners
Teacher Edition	• Differentiated Instruction, p. 201	• Differentiated Instruction, p. 201	• Differentiated Instruction, p. 204	
Chapter Resource Masters	• Study Guide and Intervention, pp. 29–30 • Skills Practice, p. 31 • Practice, p. 32 • Word Problem Practice, p. 33 • Graphing Calculator, p. 35	• Study Guide and Intervention, pp. 29–30 • Skills Practice, p. 31 • Practice, p. 32 • Word Problem Practice, p. 33 • Enrichment, p. 34 • Graphing Calculator, p. 35	• Practice, p. 32 • Word Problem Practice, p. 33 • Enrichment, p. 34 • Graphing Calculator, p. 35	• Study Guide and Intervention, pp. 29–30 • Skills Practice, p. 31 • Practice, p. 32 • Graphing Calculator, p. 35
Transparencies	• 5-Minute Check Transparency 4-5	• 5-Minute Check Transparency 4-5	• 5-Minute Check Transparency 4-5	• 5-Minute Check Transparency 4-5
Other	• Study Notebook • Teaching Pre-Algebra with Manipulatives	• Study Notebook • Teaching Pre-Algebra with Manipulatives	• Study Notebook	• Study Notebook • Teaching Pre-Algebra with Manipulatives

Solve Two-Step Equations

Examples 1–4 show how to use inverse operations to solve equations that have more than one operation. Students will solve two-step equations, including those with negative coefficients, by undoing the operations in the reverse order of operations.

Formative Assessment

Use the Check Your Progress exercises after each example to determine students' understanding of concepts.

Additional Examples

 Solve $2m + 8 = 32$. Check your solution. 12

 Solve $\frac{w}{4} + 6 = 9$. 12

 Solve $5 - x = 7$. -2

 Solve $b - 3b + 8 = 18$. Check your solution. -5

Additional Examples also in Interactive Classroom PowerPoint® Presentations

IWB INTERACTIVE WHITEBOARD READY

Tips for New Teachers

Reinforce that $\frac{1}{5}p$ and $\frac{p}{5}$ in Example 2 are equivalent.

StudyTip

Vertical Method You can also use the vertical method when solving equations.

EXAMPLE 2 Solve a Two-Step Equation

Solve $\frac{p}{5} - 12 = 20$.

$\frac{p}{5} - 12 = 20$	Write the equation.
$\frac{p}{5} - 12 + 12 = 20 + 12$	Addition Property of Equality
$\frac{p}{5} = 32$	Simplify.
$5 \cdot \frac{p}{5} = 5 \cdot 32$	Multiplication Property of Equality
$p = 160$	Simplify. Check your solution.

Check Your Progress

2A. $8 = 15 + \frac{n}{3}$ **−21**

2B. $-\frac{1}{6}x - 3 = 2$ **−30**

Personal Tutor glencoe.com

Math *in Motion*, BrainPOP® glencoe.com

EXAMPLE 3 Equations with Negative Coefficients

Solve $9 - t = -34$.

$9 - t = -34$	Write the equation.
$9 - 1t = -34$	Identity Property: $t = 1t$
$9 + (-1t) = -34$	Definition of Subtraction
$-9 + 9 + (-1t) = -9 + (-34)$	Addition Property of Equality
$-1t = -43$	Simplify.
$\frac{-1t}{-1} = \frac{-43}{-1}$	Division Property of Equality
$t = 43$	Simplify. Check your solution.

Check Your Progress

3A. $-15 - b = 44$ **−59**

3B. $-6.5 = -4.3 - n$ **2.2**

Personal Tutor glencoe.com

StudyTip

Distributive Property You use the Distributive Property to mentally simplify $2x + x$.

$2x + 1x = (2 + 1)x$
$= 3x$

EXAMPLE 4 Combine Like Terms Before Solving

Solve $2x + x - 27 = 3$. Check your solution.

$2x + x - 27 = 3$	Write the equation.
$2x + 1x - 27 = 3$	Identity Property; $x = 1x$
$3x - 27 = 3$	Distributive Property; $2x + x = 3x$
$3x - 27 + 27 = 3 + 27$	Addition Property of Equality
$3x = 30$	Simplify.
$\frac{3x}{3} = \frac{30}{3}$	Division Property of Equality
$x = 10$	Simplify. Check your solution.

Check Your Progress

4A. $4 - 9c + 3c = 58$ **−9**

4B. $3.4 = 0.4m - 2 + 0.2m$ **9**

Personal Tutor glencoe.com

Tips for New Teachers

Multiplicative Inverse To solve an equation, the variable must be alone on one side with a coefficient of 1. The same action must be taken to both sides of the equation to keep them equal. When the variable in an equation has a fractional coefficient, multiplying both sides of an equation by the multiplicative inverse isolates the variable because the fraction, when multiplied by its reciprocal, equals 1.

Solve Real-World Problems

Solve Real-World Problems You can write and solve two-step equations to solve many real-world problems.

STANDARDIZED TEST EXAMPLE 5

Deon wants to go on a camping trip with his hiking club. The trip costs \$199. He paid a deposit of \$55 and will save an additional \$18 per week to pay for the trip. The equation $55 + 18w = 199$ can be used to find how many weeks Deon will need to save. Which series of steps can be used to solve the equation?

A Divide 199 by 18. Then subtract 55.

B Subtract 55 from 199. Then divide by 18.

C Subtract 199 from 55. Then multiply by 18.

D Subtract 18 from 199. Then divide by 55.

Problem-Solving Tip

Eliminating Choices Sometimes, you can save time by looking at the possible answers and eliminating choices. In this case, you can eliminate answer choice D. You would not undo multiplying 18 by subtracting 18.

Read the Test Item

Solve the equation so you can write the steps in the correct order that are necessary to solve the problem.

Solve the Test Item

$55 + 18w = 199$	**Write the equation.**
$55 - 55 + 18w = 199 - 55$	**Subtraction Property of Equality**
$18w = 144$	**Simplify.**
$\frac{18w}{18} = \frac{144}{18}$	**Division Property of Equality**
$w = 8$	**Simplify.**

To solve the equation, you first subtract 55 and then divide by 18. Choice B is the correct answer.

Check

When you solve an equation, you undo the steps in evaluating an expression in *reverse* order of the order of operations. In this equation, you would first undo adding 55 by subtracting 55 then undo multiplying by 18 by dividing by 18.

Check Your Progress

5. Salvatore purchased a computer for \$650. He paid \$105 initially and will pay \$20 per month until the computer is paid off. The equation $105 + 20x = 650$ can be used to find how many months he will make payments. Which series of steps can be used to solve the equation? H

F Add 105 to 650. Then divide by 20.

G Multiply 650 by 20. Then subtract 105.

H Subtract 105 from 650. Then divide by 20.

J Subtract 20 from 650. Then divide by 105.

Personal Tutor glencoe.com

Real-World Link

The average price of a popular computer in 2005 was \$963. This is about half the cost of a computer in 1995.

Source: CNET Networks

Differentiated Instruction

 students have difficulty solving two-step equations,

 use students to model the equation $3x + 2 = 8$ in front of the classroom. Use a chair to represent the equals sign. Have three students stand together holding signs labeled with an x. Two other students should stand to the left of the equals sign. Eight students should stand to the right of the chair. Then have them act out solving the equation.

Solve Real-World Problems

Example 5 shows how to solve a real-world problem on a standardized test.

Additional Example

STANDARDIZED TEST PRACTICE Marissa wants to go to summer camp. The camp costs \$229. She paid a deposit of \$75, and she will need to save \$14 per week to pay for the trip. The equation $75 + 14w = 229$ can be used to find how many weeks Marissa will need to save. Which series of steps can be used to solve the equation? C

A Divide 229 by 14. Then subtract 75.

B Subtract 14 from 229. Then divide by 75.

C Subtract 75 from 229. Then divide by 14.

D Subtract 229 from 75. Then divide by 75.

Focus on Mathematical Content

Solving Two-Step Equations A two-step equation contains two operations that are undone using inverse operations. Subtraction and addition are undone first, and then division and multiplication.

TEACH with TECH

DOCUMENT CAMERA Have students work in teams to solve several two-step equations. Choose three groups to share their work with the class. Take a picture of the work and distribute it to the class.

3 PRACTICE

Formative Assessment

Use Exercises 1–13 to check for understanding.

Use the chart at the bottom of this page to customize assignments for your students.

Multiple Representations In Exercise 42, students use a function table and an algebraic formula to relate length, width, and perimeter to find missing dimensions.

Additional Answers

42a.

w	f
12	48
15	54
18	60

45. Sample answer: When solving equations, you may have to combine like terms as a first step. Combining like terms is one way to simplify expressions. Also, after you use the Addition Property or the Multiplication Property, you will need to combine terms again. Throughout the entire equation solving process, you have to know how to simplify expressions.

Check Your Understanding

Examples 1 and 2 pp. 199–200

Solve each equation. Check your solution.

1. $4p + 9 = 25$ **4**
2. $-2x + 1 = 7$ **−3**
3. $5y - 3 = -23$ **−4**
4. $\frac{p}{4} - 6 = -8$ **−8**
5. $\frac{t}{-6} + 1 = 3$ **−12**
6. $\frac{r}{-2} - 12 = -27$ **30**

Examples 3 and 4 p. 200

Solve each equation. Check your solution.

7. $-7 - 8d = 17$ **−3**
8. $23 - 2c = 41$ **−9**
9. $1 - 2k = -9$ **5**
10. $-4 = 8y - 9y + 6$ **10**
11. $-1.3j + 0.4 = -1.16$ **1.2**
12. $1.1 - t + 2.2t = 5.9$ **4**

Example 5 p. 201

13. **MULTIPLE CHOICE** Kaleigh has \$25. She plans to save \$5 each week. The equation $\$25 + \$5w = \$150$ represents how long it will take her to save \$150. Which series of steps could be used to solve the equation? **C**

A Add 25 to 150. Then divide by 5.

B Divide 150 by 5. Then add 25.

C Subtract 25 from 150. Then divide by 5.

D Divide 150 by 5. Then subtract 25.

Practice and Problem Solving

● = **Step-by-Step Solutions** begin on page R11.
Extra Practice begins on page 810.

Examples 1 and 2 pp. 199–200

Solve each equation. Check your solution.

14. $5a + 3 = 28$ **5**
15. $3b + 15 = 27$ **4**
16. $25 = 2c - 9$ **17**
17. $4d - 18 = -34$ **−4**
18. $\frac{g}{3} + 4 = 2$ **−6**
19. $\frac{h}{9} - 3 = 2$ **45**
20. $-16 = \frac{k}{2} - 7$ **−18**
21. $20 = \frac{m}{5} + 12$ **40**
22. $\frac{n}{4} - 20 = -1$ **76**

Examples 3 and 4 p. 200

Solve each equation. Check your solution.

23. $46 - 8x = -18$ **8**
24. $y - 7y + 6 = 30$ **−4**
25. $-7 = \frac{p}{-5} - 1$ **30**
26. $14 = \frac{s}{-3} - 8$ **−66**
27. $x + 7 - 2x = 18$ **−11**
28. $46 - 3n = -23$ **23**

Example 5 p. 201

29. **FINANCIAL LITERACY** The cost of a family membership at a health club is shown at the right. The Johnson family budgets \$800 to use the health club. Solve $125 + 45f = 800$ to find the number of months the family can use the club. **15 months**

HEALTH CLUB
FAMILY MEMBERSHIP
Only $125 to join and $45 per month!

30. **ENTERTAINMENT** The second book in a fantasy series is 112 pages longer than the first book. The total number of pages in both books is 524. Solve the equation $b + b + 112 = 524$ to find the number of pages b in the first book. **206 pages**

Solve each equation. Check your solution.

31. $6.1e + 1.07 = 9$ **1.3**
32. $-2.5c + 6.7 = -1.3$ **3.2**
33. $\frac{2}{3} - 6y = -1\frac{5}{6}$ **$\frac{5}{12}$**
34. $\frac{3}{4}x + 1.5 = 2.7$ **1.6**
35. $\frac{f}{-4} + 20.5 = 12.9$ **30.4**
36. $54.8 - \frac{d}{5} = 60.1$ **−26.5**

Differentiated Homework Options

Level	Assignment	Two-Day Option	
AL Basic	14–30, 43, 45–65	15–29 odd, 48–51	14–30 even, 43, 45–47, 52–65
OL Core	15–29 odd, 30, 31–39 odd, 41–43, 45–65	14–30, 48–51	31–43, 45–47, 52–65
BL Advanced	31–59, (optional: 60–65)		

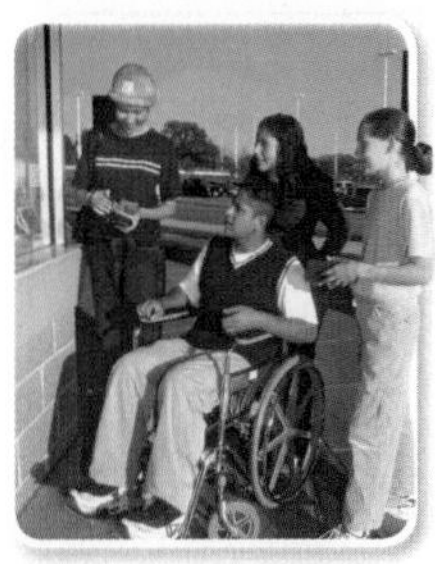

Real-World Link

In 2006, about 1.45 billion movie tickets were sold at an average cost of \$6.55. This generated a revenue of \$9.49 billion which was up 5.5% from the previous year.

Source: Variety Weekly

37. ENTERTAINMENT Janelle and some of her friends went to the movies. Tickets cost \$6 per person, and they each received a \$1.50 student discount. Each girl also purchased a snack for \$2.25. The total cost was \$40.50. Solve the equation $6s - 1.5s + 2.25s = 40.50$ to find how many girls went to the movies. **6**

Solve each equation. Check your solution.

38. $\frac{3x}{2} + 4x = 22$ **4**

39. $40.77 = \frac{y}{5} + 2.4y + \frac{y}{10}$ **15.1**

40. $\frac{x}{2} + \frac{5x}{6} + \frac{x}{4} = 380$ **240**

41. $\frac{-2x + 5}{2} = 17$ **−14.5**

42. MULTIPLE REPRESENTATIONS In this problem, you will investigate a function. Tia's family is installing a fence around three sides of her backyard as shown at the right. The equation $2w + 24 = f$ represents the relationship between the width of the fenced area and the total amount of fencing needed.

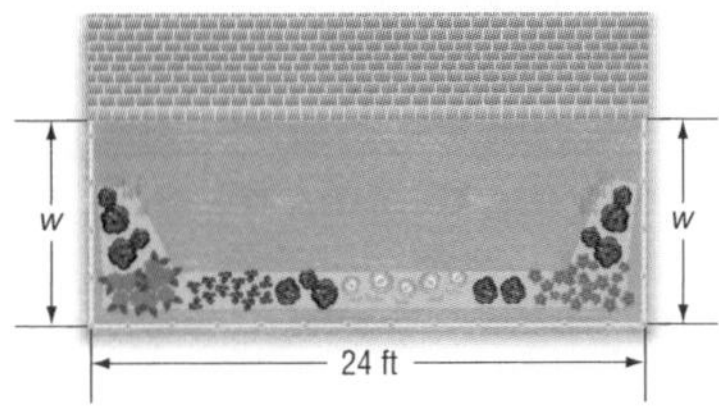

a. **TABULAR** Make a function table to show the amount of fencing needed for widths of 12, 15, and 18 feet. **See margin.**

b. **ALGEBRAIC** Find the width of the fenced area if Tia has 92 feet of fencing. **34 feet**

H.O.T. Problems
Use Higher-Order Thinking

43. OPEN ENDED Write a real-world example that could be solved by using the equation $2x + 7 = 15$. Then solve the equation.

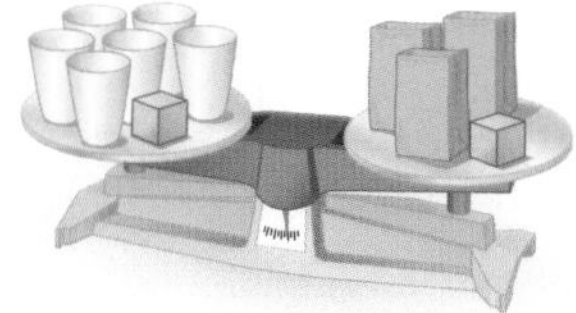

44. CHALLENGE The model at the right represents the equation $6y + 1 = 3x + 1$. What is the value of x? **2y**

45. WRITING IN MATH Describe why knowing how to simplify expressions is important when solving equations. **See margin.**

46. FIND THE ERROR Toshiro and Evelina are solving the equation $7 - 2x = -51$. Is either of them correct? Explain your reasoning.

Toshiro	Evelina
$7 - 2x = -51$	$7 - 2x = -51$
$7 + 7 - 2x = -51 + 7$	$-7 + 7 - 2x = -51 + (-7)$
$2x = -44$	$-2x = -58$
$\frac{2x}{2} = \frac{-44}{2}$	$\frac{-2x}{-2} = \frac{-58}{-2}$
$x = -22$	$x = -29$

47. WRITING IN MATH Evaluate $3(2) + 5$. Then solve the equation $3x + 5 = 11$. How are the problems and solutions similar? How are they different?

43. Sample answer: You spent \$7 at the bookstore and bought lunch for 2 days. You spent a total of \$15. How much was lunch? \$4

46. No; Toshiro did not subtract 7 from both sides and Evelina's answer has the wrong sign.

47. Sample answer: The problems both involve multiplying by 3 and adding 5. They are different because $3(2) + 5$ is an expression while $3x + 5 = 11$ is an equation in which you solve by subtracting 5 then dividing by 3.

Watch Out!

Find the Error For Exercise 46, students should see that Toshiro and Evelina solved the equation differently. Both Toshiro and Evelina solved the problem incorrectly. They should also check their answer in the original equation.

Enrichment
CRM p. 34 OL BL

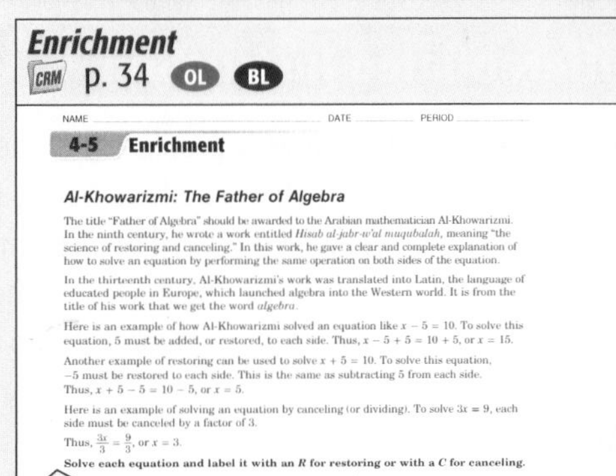

4-5 Enrichment

Al-Khowarizmi: The Father of Algebra

The title "Father of Algebra" should be awarded to the Arabian mathematician Al-Khowarizmi. In the ninth century, he wrote a work entitled *Hisab al-jabr w'al muqabalah*, meaning "the science of restoring and canceling." In this work, he gave a clear and complete explanation of how to solve an equation by performing the same operation on both sides of the equation.

In the thirteenth century, Al-Khowarizmi's work was translated into Latin, the language of educated people in Europe, which launched algebra into the Western world. It is from the title of his work that we get the word *algebra*.

Here is an example of how Al-Khowarizmi solved an equation like $x - 5 = 10$. To solve this equation, 5 must be added, or restored, to each side. Thus, $x - 5 + 5 = 10 + 5$, or $x = 15$.

Another example of restoring can be used to solve $x + 5 = 10$. To solve this equation, −5 must be restored to each side. This is the same as subtracting 5 from each side. Thus, $x + 5 - 5 = 10 - 5$, or $x = 5$.

Here is an example of solving an equation by canceling (or dividing). To solve $3x = 9$, each side must be canceled by a factor of 3. Thus, $\frac{3x}{3} = \frac{9}{3}$, or $x = 3$.

Solve each equation and label it with an *R* for restoring or with a *C* for canceling.

Study Guide and Intervention
CRM pp. 29–30 AL OL ELL

Practice
CRM p. 32 AL OL BL ELL

Word Problem Practice
CRM p. 33 AL OL BL

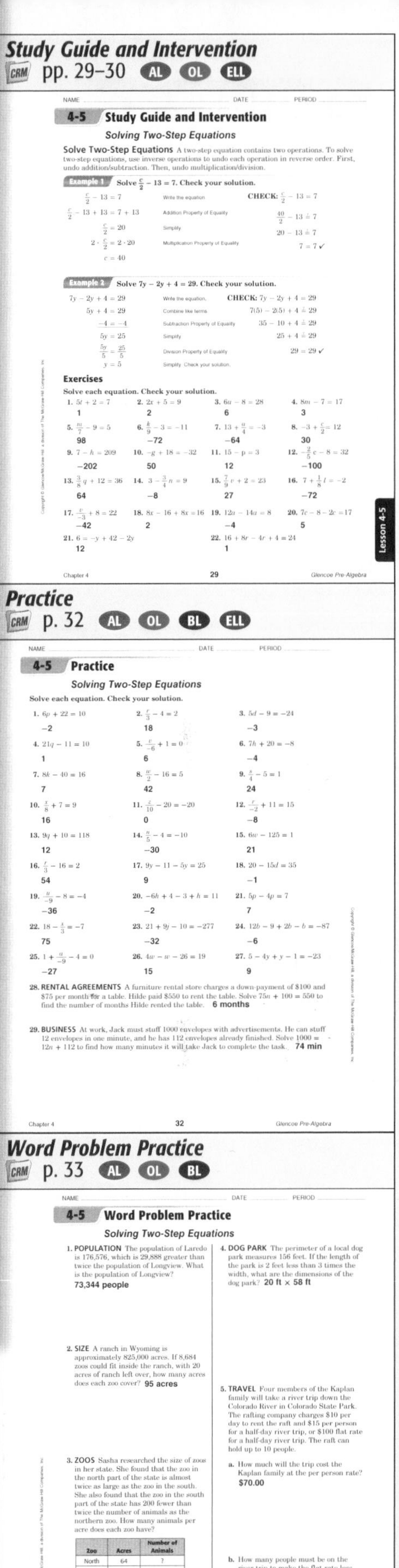

4-5 Study Guide and Intervention

Solving Two-Step Equations

Solve Two-Step Equations A two-step equation contains two operations. To solve two-step equations, use inverse operations to undo each operation in reverse order. First, undo addition/subtraction. Then, undo multiplication/division.

Example 1 Solve $\frac{c}{2} - 13 = 7$. Check your solution.

Example 2 Solve $7y - 2y + 4 = 29$. Check your solution.

Exercises

Solve each equation. Check your solution.

4-5 Practice

Solving Two-Step Equations

28. RENTAL AGREEMENTS A furniture rental store charges a down payment of \$100 and \$75 per month for a table. Hilde paid \$550 to rent the table. Solve $75n + 100 = 550$ to find the number of months Hilde rented the table. **6 months**

29. BUSINESS At work, Jack must stuff 1000 envelopes with advertisements. He can stuff 12 envelopes in one minute, and he has 112 envelopes already finished. Solve $1000 = 12n + 112$ to find how many minutes it will take Jack to complete the task. **74 min**

4-5 Word Problem Practice

Solving Two-Step Equations

1. POPULATION The population of Laredo is 176,576, which is 29,888 greater than twice the population of Longview. What is the population of Longview? **73,344 people**

2. SIZE A ranch in Wyoming is approximately 825,000 acres. If 8,684 zoos could fit inside the ranch, with 20 acres of ranch left over, how many acres does each zoo cover? **95 acres**

3. ZOOS Sasha researched the size of zoos in her state. She found that the zoo in the north part of the state is almost twice as large as the zoo in the south. She also found that the zoo in the south part of the state has 200 fewer than twice the number of animals as the northern zoo. How many animals per acre does each zoo have?

Zoo	Acres	Number of Animals
North	64	?
South	35	3800

Northern Zoo: about 31 animals per acre; Southern Zoo: about 109 animals per acre

4. DOG PARK The perimeter of a local dog park measures 156 feet. If the length of the park is 2 feet less than 3 times the width, what are the dimensions of the dog park? **20 ft × 58 ft**

5. TRAVEL Four members of the Kaplan family will take a river trip down the Colorado River in Colorado State Park. The rafting company charges \$10 per day to rent the raft and \$15 per person for a half-day river trip, or \$100 flat rate for a half-day river trip. The raft can hold up to 10 people.

a. How much will the trip cost the Kaplan family at the per person rate? **\$70.00**

b. How many people must be on the river trip to make the flat rate less expensive than the per person rate? **6 people would be the break-even point, so 7 people must go**

4 ASSESS

Ticket Out the Door Have students solve the following equations, writing out each step. Have them also write the name of the property that is shown next to each step. As students leave the classroom, have them turn in their solutions.

$2x + 6 = 14$

$2x + 6 = 14$
$2x + 6 - 6 = 14 - 6$ Subtr. Prop.
$\frac{2x}{2} = \frac{8}{2}$ Division Prop.
$x = 4$

$3x - 5 = -2$

$3x - 5 = -2$
$3x - 5 + 5 = -2 + 5$ Addition Prop.
$\frac{3x}{3} = \frac{3}{3}$ Division Prop.
$x = 1$

$9 = -4x - 3$

$9 = -4x - 3$
$9 + 3 = -4x - 3 + 3$ Addition Prop.
$\frac{12}{-4} = \frac{-4x}{-4}$ Division Prop.
$-3 = x$

Formative Assessment

Check for student understanding of concepts in Lessons 4-4 and 4-5.

CRM Quiz 3, p. 45

Standardized Test Practice

48. The results of a student council fundraiser are shown in the table.

Purchase Price for 144 Pens	Profit for 144 Pens
\$309.60	\$50.40

Use the equation below to find the selling price p of one pen. **C**

$$144p - 309.60 = 50.40$$

A \$1.80 C \$2.50
B \$2.15 D \$2.72

49. Ms. Fraser's total monthly cell phone bill b can be found using the equation $b = 45.60 + 0.10t$, where t represents the number of text messages she made. Find the number of text messages she made in a month in which the total charge was \$56.70. **G**

F 101
G 111
H 125
J 131

50. The distance d that Maxie can run in her first training run is represented by the equation $d = \frac{1}{2}m - 2$. What is the maximum distance m that she can run if her first training run is 3 miles? **A**

A 10 miles
B 8 miles
C 6 miles
D 4 miles

51. GRIDDED RESPONSE Jody bought two pairs of jeans. The first pair costs \$12 less than 3 times the cost c of the second pair. The first pair of jeans costs \$45. The equation below can be used to find the cost in dollars of the second pair of jeans. **19**

$$3c - 12 = 45$$

Solve the equation to find the cost of the second pair of jeans.

Spiral Review

Solve each equation. (Lessons 4-3 and 4-4)

52. $36 = -12y$ **−3**
53. $4 = \frac{x}{14}$ **56**
54. $5y = \frac{3}{2}$ **$\frac{3}{10}$**
55. $x - 13 = -45$ **−32**
56. $\frac{2}{3} + p = 1$ **$\frac{1}{3}$**
57. $t + 12.4 = 16.23$ **3.83**

58. WEATHER The difference between the record high and low temperatures in Columbus, Ohio, is 128° F. The record high temperature is 106° F. Write and solve an equation to find the record low temperature. (Lesson 4-3) **$106 - x = 128$; $x = -22$°F**

59. MONEY You have saved some money. Your friend has saved \$40 more than you. Write an expression in simplest form that represents the total amount of money you and your friend have saved. (Lesson 2-5) **$2x + 40$**

Skills Review

Evaluate each expression if $x = 4$, $y = -10$, and $z = 14$. (Lessons 2-2, 2-3, and 2-4)

60. xy **−40**
61. $y + z$ **4**
62. $2x - y$ **18**
63. $2z + 2y$ **8**
64. xyz **−560**
65. $z - 3x + y$ **−8**

Differentiated Instruction

Extension Present the following problem to students: Alone, you can paint a doghouse in five hours. Your older sister can finish in three hours. The expression $\frac{1}{5}t$ represents the fraction of the doghouse you can paint in one hour; $\frac{1}{3}t$ represents the fraction of the doghouse your sister can paint in one hour. So, $\frac{1}{5}t + \frac{1}{3}t$ is the fraction of the doghouse you and your sister can complete together in one hour. Solve for t, the time you and your sister would spend painting the doghouse together, with this equation: $\frac{1}{5}t + \frac{1}{3}t = 1$. Multiply each term in the equation by the LCD of 15, so $3t + 5t = 15$. $t = \frac{15}{8}$ or $1\frac{7}{8}$ h

4-6 Writing Equations

Why?

Marisol and Ivy spent a total of $22 for lunch. Ivy's lunch cost $5 more than Marisol's. How much did each girl spend for lunch?

a. Whose lunch cost more? **Ivy's**

b. How much more? **$5**

c. If m represents the cost of Marisol's lunch, how much did Ivy's lunch cost? $5 + m$

d. Write an expression that represents *the sum of Marisol's and Ivy's lunches.* $m + m + 5$

Then
You have already translated verbal phrases into algebraic expressions.
(Lessons 1-2)

Now
- Write two-step equations.
- Solve verbal problems by writing and solving two-step equations.

Math Online
glencoe.com
- Extra Examples
- Personal Tutor
- Self-Check Quiz
- Homework Help

Write Two-Step Equations You can summarize this information by writing an equation. Suppose the total cost of the lunches is $22.

Words	Marisol's lunch	plus	Ivy's lunch	costs	$22.
Symbols	Let m = the cost of Marisol's lunch. Let $m + 5$ = the cost of Ivy's lunch.				
Equation	m	$+$	$m + 5$	$=$	22

EXAMPLE 1 Translate Sentences into Equations

Translate each sentence into an equation.

a. Zack has 6 shirts. This is 4 less than twice the number of shirts n that Xavier has.

$6 = 2n - 4$

b. Eight more than the quotient of a number y and −3 is −24.

$8 + \frac{y}{-3} = -24$

c. Jeremy has 13 baseball cards, which is 7 more than 3 times the number m Michael has.

$13 = 7 + 3m$

Check Your Progress

1A. Four more than three times a number x is −26. $3x + 4 = -26$

1B. Hannah has 24 stickers. This is 6 less than twice the number of stickers n Molly has. $24 = 2n - 6$

1C. The quotient of a number n and 7, increased by 6, is equal to 12. $\frac{n}{7} + 6 = 12$

Personal Tutor glencoe.com

4-6 Lesson Notes

1 FOCUS

Vertical Alignment

Before Lesson 4-6
Translate verbal phrases into algebraic expressions.

Lesson 4-6
Write verbal sentences as two-step equations. Solve verbal problems by writing and solving two-step equations.

After Lesson 4-6
Analyze situations involving linear functions and formulate linear equations to solve problems.

2 TEACH

Scaffolding Questions

Have students read the *Why?* section of the lesson and answer the questions.

Ask:

- How could you simplify the expression that represents the cost of the lunches? $2m + 5$
- What is the above expression equal to? $22
- What equation could you write to represent the cost of the two lunches? $2m + 5 = 22$

Lesson 4-6 Resources

Resource	Approaching-Level	On-Level	Beyond-Level	English Learners
Teacher Edition			• Differentiated Instruction, p. 209	• Differentiated Instruction, p. 206
Chapter Resource Masters	• Study Guide and Intervention, pp. 36–37 • Skills Practice, p. 38 • Practice, p. 39 • Word Problem Practice, p. 40	• Study Guide and Intervention, pp. 36–37 • Skills Practice, p. 38 • Practice, p. 39 • Word Problem Practice, p. 40 • Enrichment, p. 41	• Practice, p. 39 • Word Problem Practice, p. 40 • Enrichment, p. 41	• Study Guide and Intervention, pp. 36–37 • Skills Practice, p. 38 • Practice, p. 39
Transparencies	• 5-Minute Check Transparency 4-6	• 5-Minute Check Transparency 4-6	• 5-Minute Check Transparency 4-6	• 5-Minute Check Transparency 4-6
Other	• Study Notebook • Teaching Pre-Algebra with Manipulatives	• Study Notebook • Teaching Pre-Algebra with Manipulatives	• Study Notebook	• Study Notebook • Teaching Pre-Algebra with Manipulatives

Write Two-Step Equations

Example 1 shows how to write two-step equations. **Example 2** shows how to write and solve a two-step equation.

Formative Assessment

Use the Check Your Progress exercises after each example to determine students' understanding of concepts.

Additional Examples

1 Translate each sentence into an equation.

a. Jackie's mother is 28 years old, which is four times Jackie's age a minus eight years. $28 = 4a - 8$

b. Five more than twice a number n is –25. $2n + 5 = -25$

c. Rafiq threw a baseball 84 miles per hour, which is 21 miles per hour less than twice the speed s that Jonah threw it. $84 = 2s - 21$

2 A baseball bat costs \$41, which is \$9 more than four times the wholesale cost of the bat. Find the bat's wholesale cost. $9 + 4c = 41$; \$8

Additional Examples also in Interactive Classroom PowerPoint® Presentations

IWB INTERACTIVE WHITEBOARD READY

Two-Step Verbal Problems

Example 3 shows how to write and solve a two-step real-world problem.

Additional Example

3 **MONEY** Ms. Parsons earns \$200 each week plus \$25 for each pair of shoes that she sells. How many pairs of shoes does she need to sell to earn \$1000 per week? $200 + 25s = 1000$; 32 pairs

---

EXAMPLE 2 Write and Solve an Equation

Juan's father was 29 years old when Juan was born. This year, the sum of their ages is 53. Find their ages.

Let x = Juan's age. Then, $x + 29$ = Juan's father's age.

$x + (x + 29) = 53$	**Write the equation.**
$2x + 29 = 53$	**Distributive Property**
$2x + 29 - 29 = 53 - 29$	**Subtraction Property of Equality**
$2x = 24$	**Simplify.**
$x = 12$	**Mentally divide each side by 2.**

Juan is 12 years old. His father is 12 + 29 or 41 years old.

Check Your Progress

2. Deisha saved d dollars last month. This month she saved \$8 more than 3 times the amount she saved last month. She saved a total of \$141. Write and solve an equation to find how much she saved last month. **See margin.**

Personal Tutor glencoe.com

StudyTip

Equations Look for the words *is, total, equals,* or *is equal to* when you translate sentences into equations.

Two-Step Verbal Problems In some real-world situations, you start with a given amount and then increase it at a certain rate.

Real-World EXAMPLE 3 Solve a Two-Step Verbal Problem

FUNDRAISING Logan collected pledges for the charity walk-a-thon. He will receive total contributions of \$68 plus \$20 for every mile that he walks. How many miles will he need to walk to raise \$348?

Understand He has already raised \$68. He can raise another \$20 per mile until he reaches \$348. You need to find how many miles he needs to walk.

Plan Organize the data for the first few miles in a table. Notice the pattern. Then write an equation to represent the situation.

Number of Miles	Total Amount Raised
0	$20(0) + 68 = \$68$
1	$20(1) + 68 = \$88$
2	$20(2) + 68 = \$108$

Solve Let m = the number of miles.

Then, $20m + 68 = 348$.

$20m + 68 = 348$	**Write the equation.**
$20m + 68 - 68 = 348 - 68$	**Subtraction Property of Equality**
$20m = 280$	**Simplify.**
$m = 14$	**Mentally divide each side by 20.**

Logan needs to walk 14 miles to raise \$348.

Check If he walks 14 miles he will have \$20 • 14 or an additional \$280. The answer seems reasonable. ✓

Check Your Progress

3. **SHOPPING** Jasmine bought 6 CDs, all at the same price. The tax on her purchase was \$5.04, and the total was \$85.74. What was the price of each CD? **\$13.45**

Personal Tutor glencoe.com

Differentiated Instruction

Vocabulary Writing equations from word problems can provide opportunities for students to use written and oral language. Prior to reading the problem, examine everyday vocabulary with students to help clarify the problem. For example, in Example 3, review the words *pledges, charity, walk-a-thon, contributions, miles*, and *raise*.

Check Your Understanding

Example 1 p. 205 — **Translate each sentence into an equation.**

1. The quotient of a number and 3, less 8, is 16. $\frac{n}{3} - 8 = 16$
2. Tiffani spent $95 for clothes. This is $15 more than 4 times the amount her sister spent for school supplies. $4s + 15 = 95$
3. Morgan has 98 baseball cards in his collection, which is twelve less than the product of 5 and the number of cards Tyler has. $5t - 12 = 98$

Example 2 p. 206 — **Solve each problem by writing and solving an equation.**

4. **SHOPPING** Kendra pays $132 for shoes and clothes. The clothes cost $54 more than the shoes. How much do the shoes cost? $2s + 54 = 132$; $39
5. **CAR WASH** During the spring car wash, the Activities Club washed 14 fewer cars than during the summer car wash. They washed a total of 96 cars during both car washes. How many cars did they wash during the spring car wash? $2x - 14 = 96$; 41 cars

Example 3 p. 206

6. **FITNESS** A gym charges a $50 activation fee and $17 per month for a membership. If you spend $356, for how many months do you have a gym membership? $356 = 50 + 17m$; 18 months

Practice and Problem Solving

 = **Step-by-Step Solutions** begin on page R11. **Extra Practice** begins on page 810.

Example 1 p. 205 — **Translate each sentence into an equation.**

7. Eighteen more than twice a number is 8. $2x + 18 = 8$
8. The product of a number and 9, less 20 is 7. $9n - 20 = 7$
9. There are 48 soccer teams in the Springtown Association. This is three less than three times the number of teams in the Lyon Association. $3x - 3 = 48$
10. Eileen swam for 85 minutes. This is 21 more minutes than 4 times the number of minutes Ethan swam. $4n + 21 = 85$

Examples 2 and 3 p. 206 — **Solve each problem by writing and solving an equation.**

11. **BASKETBALL** In 2007, Candace Parker, from the University of Tennessee, made 37 more field goals than she did in 2006. She had a total of 497 field goals for those years. How many field goals did she make in 2006? $2g + 37 = 497$; 230 field goals
12. **CARS** The Marsh family took a vacation that covered a total distance of 1356 miles. The return trip was 284 miles shorter than the first part of the trip. How long was the return trip? $2m - 284 = 1356$; 536 mi
13. **VIDEO GAMES** Three friends share the cost of renting a game system. Each person also rents one game for $8.50. If each person pays $13.25, what is the cost of renting the system?

13. $\frac{x}{3} + 8.50 = 13.25$; $14.25

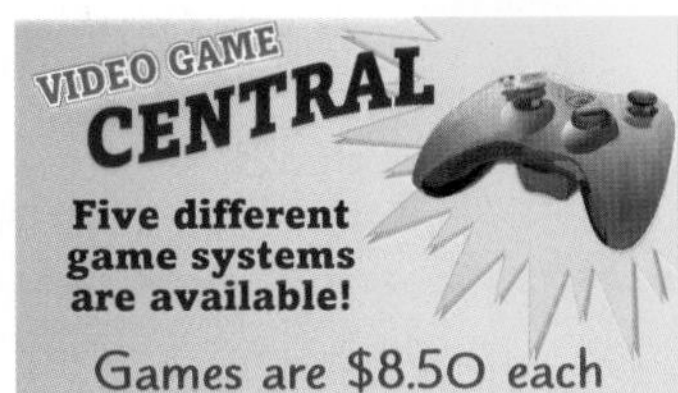

14. **VACATION** Suppose you purchase 3 identical T-shirts and a hat. The hat cost $21 and you spend $60 in all. How much does each T-shirt cost? $3t + 21 = 60$; $13

Focus on Mathematical Content

Solving Two-Step Equations In a verbal problem, written sentences are translated into an equation where an expression with an unknown value is on one side of the equals sign and a known value is on the other side. In a two-step equation, two basic operations, either addition, subtraction, division, or multiplication, are required to undo the operations and solve the equation.

TEACH with TECH

WIKI Encourage students to talk about math with each other on a secure class wiki. Start a discussion by describing a situation that can be solved algebraically to students. Students can then reply on the wiki with an algebraic equation and solution to the problem. All members of the class should contribute to the discussion.

3 PRACTICE

Formative Assessment

Use Exercises 1–6 to check for understanding.

Use the chart at the bottom of this page to customize assignments for your students.

Differentiated Homework Options

Level	Assignment	Two-Day Option	
AL Basic	7–14, 20–22, 24–41	8–13 odd, 25–28	7–14 even, 20–22, 24, 29–41
OL Core	7–13 odd, 15–22, 24–41	7–14, 25–28	15–22, 24, 29–41
BL Advanced	15–37, (optional: 38–41)		

Additional Answer (Check Your Progress)

2. $d + 3d + 8 = 141$; $33.25

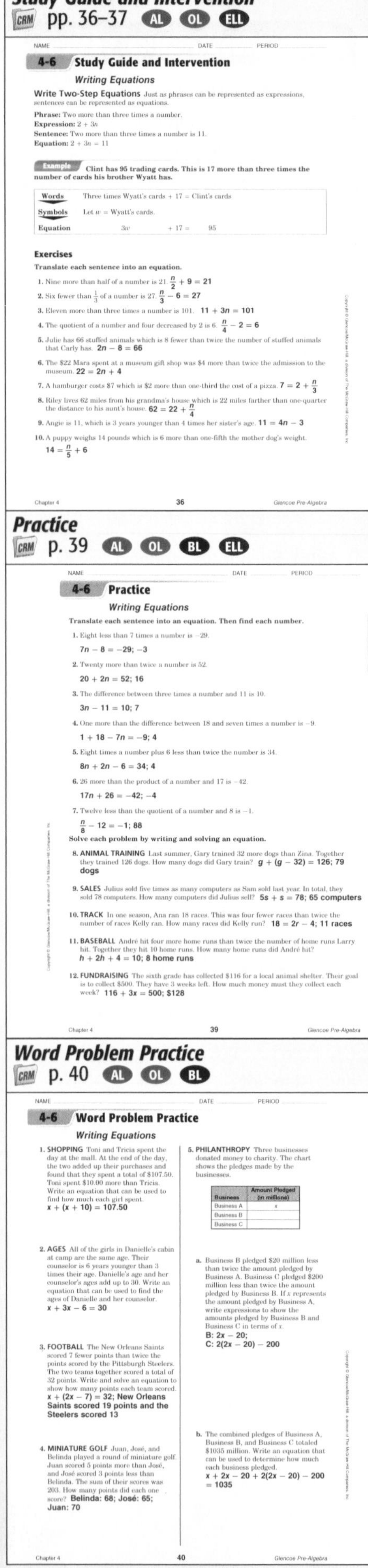

Study Guide and Intervention
CRM pp. 36–37 AL OL ELL

NAME ______ DATE ______ PERIOD ______

4-6 Study Guide and Intervention

Writing Equations

Write Two-Step Equations Just as phrases can be represented as expressions, sentences can be represented as equations.

Phrase: Two more than three times a number.
Expression: $2 + 3n$
Sentence: Two more than three times a number is 11.
Equation: $2 + 3n = 11$

Example **Clint has 95 trading cards. This is 17 more than three times the number of cards his brother Wyatt has.**

Words	Three times Wyatt's cards + 17 = Clint's cards		
Symbols	Let w = Wyatt's cards.		
Equation	$3w$	$+ 17 =$	95

Exercises

Translate each sentence into an equation.

1. Nine more than half of a number is 21. $\frac{n}{2} + 9 = 21$
2. Six fewer than $\frac{1}{3}$ of a number is 27. $\frac{n}{3} - 6 = 27$
3. Eleven more than three times a number is 101. $11 + 3n = 101$
4. The quotient of a number and four decreased by 2 is 6. $\frac{n}{4} - 2 = 6$
5. Julie has 66 stuffed animals which is 8 fewer than twice the number of stuffed animals that Carly has. $2n - 8 = 66$
6. The $22 Mara spent at a museum gift shop was $4 more than twice the admission to the museum. $22 = 2n + 4$
7. A hamburger costs $7 which is $2 more than one-third the cost of a pizza. $7 = 2 + \frac{n}{3}$
8. Riley lives 62 miles from his grandma's house which is 22 miles farther than one-quarter the distance to his aunt's house. $62 = 22 + \frac{n}{4}$
9. Angie is 11, which is 3 years younger than 4 times her sister's age. $11 = 4n - 3$
10. A puppy weighs 14 pounds which is 6 more than one-fifth the mother dog's weight. $14 = \frac{n}{5} + 6$

Chapter 4 36 Glencoe Pre-Algebra

Practice
CRM p. 39 AL OL BL ELL

NAME ______ DATE ______ PERIOD ______

4-6 Practice

Writing Equations

Translate each sentence into an equation. Then find each number.

1. Eight less than 7 times a number is −29.
   $7n - 8 = -29; -3$
2. Twenty more than twice a number is 52.
   $20 + 2n = 52; 16$
3. The difference between three times a number and 11 is 10.
   $3n - 11 = 10; 7$
4. One more than the difference between 18 and seven times a number is −9.
   $1 + 18 - 7n = -9; 4$
5. Eight times a number plus 6 less than twice the number is 34.
   $8n + 2n - 6 = 34; 4$
6. 26 more than the product of a number and 17 is −42.
   $17n + 26 = -42; -4$
7. Twelve less than the quotient of a number and 8 is −1.
   $\frac{n}{8} - 12 = -1; 88$

Solve each problem by writing and solving an equation.

8. **ANIMAL TRAINING** Last summer, Gary trained 32 more dogs than Zina. Together they trained 126 dogs. How many dogs did Gary train? $g + (g - 32) = 126$; **79 dogs**
9. **SALES** Julius sold five times as many computers as Sam sold last year. In total, they sold 78 computers. How many computers did Julius sell? $5s + s = 78$; **65 computers**
10. **TRACK** In one season, Ana ran 18 races. This was four fewer races than twice the number of races Kelly ran. How many races did Kelly run? $18 = 2r - 4$; **11 races**
11. **BASEBALL** André hit four more home runs than twice the number of home runs Larry hit. Together they hit 10 home runs. How many home runs did André hit? $h + 2h + 4 = 10$; **8 home runs**
12. **FUNDRAISING** The sixth grade has collected $116 for a local animal shelter. Their goal is to collect $500. They have 3 weeks left. How much money must they collect each week? $116 + 3x = 500$; **$128**

Lesson 4-6

Chapter 4 39 Glencoe Pre-Algebra

Word Problem Practice
CRM p. 40 AL OL BL

NAME ______ DATE ______ PERIOD ______

4-6 Word Problem Practice

Writing Equations

1. **SHOPPING** Toni and Tricia spent the day at the mall. At the end of the day, the two added up their purchases and found that they spent a total of $107.50. Toni spent $10.00 more than Tricia. Write an equation that can be used to find how much each girl spent.
   $x + (x + 10) = 107.50$
2. **AGES** All of the girls in Danielle's cabin at camp are the same age. Their counselor is 6 years younger than 3 times their age. Danielle's age and her counselor's ages add up to 30. Write an equation that can be used to find the ages of Danielle and her counselor.
   $x + 3x - 6 = 30$
3. **FOOTBALL** The New Orleans Saints scored 7 fewer points than twice the points scored by the Pittsburgh Steelers. The two teams together scored a total of 32 points. Write and solve an equation to show how many points each team scored.
   $x + (2x - 7) = 32$; **New Orleans Saints scored 19 points and the Steelers scored 13**
4. **MINIATURE GOLF** Juan, José, and Belinda played a round of miniature golf. Juan scored 5 points more than José, and José scored 3 points less than Belinda. The sum of their scores was 203. How many points did each one score? **Belinda: 68; José: 65; Juan: 70**
5. **PHILANTHROPY** Three businesses donated money to charity. The chart shows the pledges made by the businesses.

Business	Amount Pledged (in millions)
Business A	x
Business B	
Business C	

   a. Business B pledged $20 million less than twice the amount pledged by Business A. Business C pledged $200 million less than twice the amount pledged by Business B. If x represents the amount pledged by Business A, write expressions to show the amounts pledged by Business B and Business C in terms of x.
   B: $2x - 20$;
   C: $2(2x - 20) - 200$

   b. The combined pledges of Business A, Business B, and Business C totaled $1035 million. Write an equation that can be used to determine how much each business pledged.
   $x + 2x - 20 + 2(2x - 20) - 200 = 1035$

Chapter 4 40 Glencoe Pre-Algebra

Real-World Career

Computer animation involves changing still images to create the illusion of movement. Animators created 2D and 3D digital images that are found in movies, commercials, and on television.

Excellent drawing skills and formal training in graphic art and a degree in multimedia technology are strong requirements.

Source: WestOne Services

19d. The scatter plot is less accurate and will take a longer time to find because the plot will be large. Solving an equation is quick and ends with an exact answer.

24. Sample answer: You can use two-step equations to solve real world situations that involve multiplying an unknown by a number, then adding or subtracting another number. An example is if you deposit $100 into a bank account, then deposit $25 a week for x weeks. How long would it take you to have $250?

15. BOOK FINES You return a book that was 6 days overdue. Including a previous unpaid balance of $0.90, your new balance is $2.40. How much is the daily fine for an overdue book? $6d + 0.90 = 2.40$; **$0.25**

16. CONSTRUCTION Tao is building a door. The height of the door is 1 foot more than twice its width. If the door is 7 feet high, what is its width? $1 + 2w = 7$; **3 ft**

17. ENTERTAINMENT In his DVD collection, Domingo has eight more than twice as many animated movies as action movies. If he has 24 animated movies, write and solve an equation to find how many action movies are in his collection. $24 = 2n + 8$; $n = 8$

18. TRAVEL At the start of the school trip to Washington D.C., the tour bus has 40 gallons of gasoline in the fuel tank. Each hour, the bus uses 7 gallons of gasoline. The bus will stop for gas when there are 10 gallons left.

a. Make a table to show how many gallons of gasoline are remaining in the tank after each hour. **See margin.**

b. Write and solve an equation to find how many hours will pass before the bus will have to stop for gasoline. $40 - 7h = 10$; **about 4 hours**

19. MULTIPLE REPRESENTATIONS In this problem, you will use tables, graphs, and equations to solve a problem. Misty is saving money to buy an MP3 player that costs $212. She has already saved $47 and plans to save an additional $15 per week.

Number of Weeks	Amount of Savings ($)
1	62
2	77
3	92
4	107

a. **ALGEBRAIC** Write a variable expression to represent the amount of money saved after w weeks. Then use the expression to complete the table at the right. $47 + 15w$

b. **GRAPHICAL** Make a scatter plot of the data in the table. How can you use the graph to find the number of weeks it will take her to save enough money for the MP3 player? **See margin.**

c. **ALGEBRAIC** Write and solve an equation to find the number of weeks it will take her to save the money. $47 + 15w = 212$; **11 weeks**

d. **VERBAL** Compare the methods for finding the solution that you used in parts **b** and **c.**

H.O.T. Problems
Use Higher-Order Thinking Skills

20. OPEN ENDED Write a two-step equation with a solution of 6. Write the equation using both words and symbols. **Sample answer: Eight less than twice a number is 4;** $2n - 8 = 4$

21. NUMBER SENSE An example of two consecutive even numbers is 4 and 6. They can be represented by n and $n + 2$. Find 3 consecutive even numbers whose sum is 30. **8, 10, 12**

22. REASONING The equations $\frac{x + 4}{5} = 20$ and $\frac{x}{5} + 4 = 20$ are both two-step equations. Compare and contrast how to solve them. **See margin.**

23. CHALLENGE Emelia discovered that if she takes three-fourths of her age and adds 9, it produces the same result as when she takes one-fourth of her age and adds 21. How old is Emelia? **24 years old**

24. WRITING IN MATH Explain how two-step equations are used to represent real-world problems.

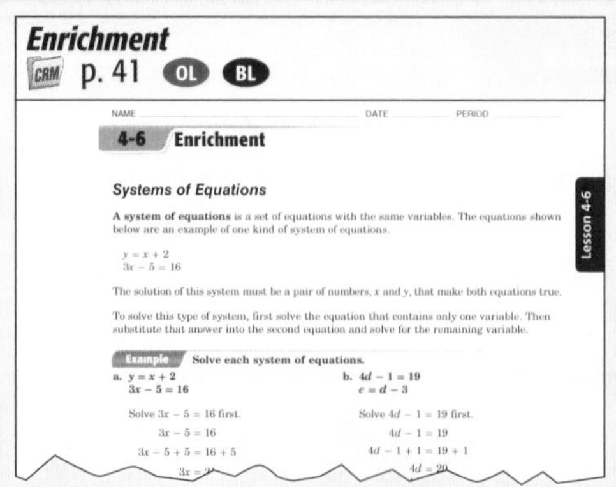

Enrichment
CRM p. 41 OL BL

NAME ______ DATE ______ PERIOD ______

4-6 Enrichment

Systems of Equations

A system of equations is a set of equations with the same variables. The equations shown below are an example of one kind of system of equations.

$y = x + 2$
$3x - 5 = 16$

The solution of this system must be a pair of numbers, x and y, that make both equations true.

To solve this type of system, first solve the equation that contains only one variable. Then substitute that answer into the second equation and solve for the remaining variable.

Example **Solve each system of equations.**

a. $y = x + 2$
   $3x - 5 = 16$

   Solve $3x - 5 = 16$ first.
   $3x - 5 = 16$
   $3x - 5 + 5 = 16 + 5$

b. $4d - 1 = 19$
   $c = d - 3$

   Solve $4d - 1 = 19$ first.
   $4d - 1 = 19$
   $4d - 1 + 1 = 19 + 1$
   $4d = 20$

Lesson 4-6

Multiple Representations In Exercise 19, students use a variable expression, a scatter plot, an equation, and a verbal explanation to track money savings over time.

Standardized Test Practice

25. An electrician charges \$35 for a house call and \$80 per hour for each hour worked. If the total charge was \$915, which equation would you use to find the number of hours n that the electrician worked? **D**

A $35n + 2n(80) = 915$

B $80 + 35n = 915$

C $35 + (80 - n) = 915$

D $35 + 80n = 915$

26. Belinda scored 16 goals this season. This is 4 more than three times the number she scored last season. Which equation could you use to find how many goals she scored last season? **G**

F $4n + 3 = 16$ H $4n - 3 = 16$

G $3n + 4 = 16$ J $3n - 4 = 16$

27. EXTENDED RESPONSE Sheila wants to buy a mountain bike for \$180. She has already saved \$60. For the next six months, she wants to save an equal amount each month in order to save the total amount.

a. Write an equation to represent the situation. $60 + 6d = 180$

b. How much money will Sheila need to save each month? **\$20 per month**

28. You and your friend spent a total of \$15 for lunch. Your friend's lunch cost \$3 more than yours did. How much did you spend for lunch? **A**

A \$6 C \$8

B \$7 D \$9

Spiral Review

Solve each equation. Check your solution. (Lessons 4-3, 4-4, and 4-5)

29. $x + 12 = -10$ -22

30. $-\frac{y}{6} = -2$ 12

31. $2p + 13 = -7$ -10

32. $7y + 3 = -11$ -2

33. $-8t - 9 = -41$ 4

34. $8z = 14$ $1\frac{3}{4}$

35. CONCERTS A concert ticket costs t dollars, a hamburger costs h dollars, and soda costs s dollars. Write an expression that represents the total cost of a ticket, hamburger, and soda for n people. (Lesson 4-1) $n(t + h + s)$

36. AIR PRESSURE The air pressure decreases as the distance from Earth increases. The table shows the air pressure for certain distances. (Lesson 2-6)

Air Pressure

Height (mi)	Pressure (lb/in^2)
0 (sea level)	14.7
1	10.2
2	6.4
3	4.3
4	2.7
5	1.6

a. Write a set of ordered pairs for the data. (0, 14.7), (1, 10.2), (2, 6.4),(3, 4.3), (4, 2.7), (5, 1.6)

b. Graph the data. **See Chapter 4 Answer Appendix.**

c. State the domain and the range of the relationship shown. domain = {0, 1, 2, 3, 4, 5}; range = {14.7, 10.2, 6.4, 4.3, 2.7, 1.6}

37. FOOD The SubShop had 36, 45, 41, and 38 customers during the lunch hour the last four days. Find the mean of the number of customers. (Lesson 2-5) **40**

Skills Review

Use the Distributive Property to write each expression as an equivalent algebraic expression. (Lesson 4-1)

38. $4(x + 3)$ $4x + 12$

39. $8(y - 2)$ $8y - 16$

40. $-6(z - 7)$ $-6z + 42$

41. $-2(-9 - p)$ $18 + 2p$

Differentiated Instruction

Extension Have students form a list of five occupations that interest them. Have them write a sentence describing people in these occupations. Have them write sample equations for each of their sentences. Check students' work.

4 ASSESS

Crystal Ball Ask students to write about how they think writing two-step equations might be helpful with the next chapter on multi-step equations.

Formative Assessment

Check for student understanding of concepts in Lesson 4-6.

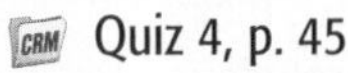

Quiz 4, p. 45

Additional Answers

18a.

Number of Hours	Gallons Left
1	33
2	26
3	19
4	12

19b.

Draw a straight line through the plotted points. Then go to the point that has 212 as its y-value, then find the corresponding x-value.

22. Sample answer: The equation $\frac{x + 4}{5} = 20$ is solved by multiplying both sides by 5 and then subtracting 4 from both sides. So, $x = 96$. The equation $\frac{x}{5} + 4 = 20$ is solved by subtracting 4 from both sides and then multiplying both sides by 5. So, $x = 80$. In both, you use the Subtraction Property of Equality and the Division Property of Equality but in a different order.

Formative Assessment

Key Vocabulary The page references after each word denote where that term was first introduced. If students have difficulty answering questions 1–10, remind them that they can use these page references to refresh their memories about the vocabulary.

Summative Assessment

CRM Vocabulary Test, p. 47

Math Online glencoe.com

Vocabulary PuzzleMaker improves students' mathematics vocabulary using four puzzle formats–crossword, scramble, word search using a word list, and word search using clues. Students can work online or from a printed worksheet.

CHAPTER 4 Study Guide and Review

Math Online glencoe.com
- STUDY TO GO
- Vocabulary Review

Chapter Summary

Key Concepts

Distributive Property (Lesson 4-1)

- For any numbers a, b, and c, $a(b + c) = ab + ac$.

Properties of Equality (Lessons 4-3 through 4-4)

Addition Property of Equality
- For any numbers a, b, and c, if $a = b$, then $a + c = b + c$.

Subtraction Property of Equality
- For any numbers a, b, and c, if $a = b$, then $a - c = b - c$.

Division Property of Equality
- For any numbers a, b, and c, where $c \neq 0$, if $a = b$, then $\frac{a}{c} = \frac{b}{c}$.

Multiplication Property of Equality
- For any nonzero numbers a, b, and c, if $a = b$, then $ca = cb$.

Solving Equations (Lessons 4-3 through 4-5)

- To solve a single-step equation, use the Properties of Equality and inverse operations.
- To solve a two-step equation, undo operations in reverse order of the order of operations.

Writing Equations (Lesson 4–6)

- You can write verbal sentences as equations.
- Some real-world situations start with a given amount and then increase it at a certain rate. These situations can be represented by two-step equations.

FOLDABLES® Study Organizer

Be sure the Key Concepts are noted in your Foldable.

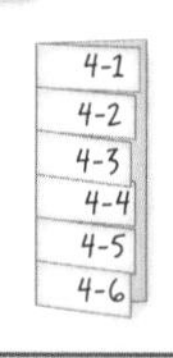

Key Vocabulary

coefficient (p. 178)
constant (p. 178)
Distributive Property (p. 171)
equation (p. 184)
equivalent equation (p. 184)
equivalent expressions (p. 171)
inverse operation (p. 184)
like terms (p. 178)
simplest form (p. 179)
simplifying the expression (p. 179)
solution (p. 184)
solving the equation (p. 184)
term (p. 178)
two-step equation (p. 199)

Vocabulary Check

Complete each sentence with the correct term. Choose from the list above.

1. Expressions that have the same value are called ______. equivalent expressions
2. An algebraic expression is in simplest form if it has no like terms and no parentheses.
3. A term without a variable is called a(n) constant.
4. The numerical part of a term that contains a variable is called the coefficient.
5. A value for the variable that makes an equation true is called a(n) solution.
6. Two ______ have the same solution. equivalent equations
7. The ______ allows you to multiply a sum or difference by a number. Distributive Property
8. An equation that contains two steps is called a(n) ______. two-step equation
9. Addition and subtraction are examples of ______. inverse operations
10. Like terms contain the same variable.

FOLDABLES® Study Organizer

Dinah Zike's Foldables®

Have students look through the chapter to make sure they have included examples in their Foldables.

Suggest that students keep their Foldables handy while completing the Study Guide and Review pages. Point out that their Foldables can serve as a quick review tool when studying for the Chapter Test.

MIXED PROBLEM SOLVING
For mixed problem-solving practice, see page 846.

CHAPTER 4 **Study Guide and Review**

Lesson-by-Lesson Review

4-1 The Distributive Property (pp. 171–176)

Use the Distributive Property to write each expression as an equivalent algebraic expression.

11. $(y+3)7$ $7y+21$

12. $-2(a-7)$ $-2a+14$

13. $-1(b-9)$ $-b+9$

14. $(8m-4)(-5)$ $-40m+20$

15. **FOOD** The Stuart family has 5 members. They each purchase a soda at $2.50 each and a hotdog at $3.50 each. Use mental math to find the total cost of the food. Justify your answer by using the Distributive Property.
$30; 5(2.50 + 3.50); 5 · 2.50 + 5 · 3.50

EXAMPLE 1

Use the Distributive Property to write $3(x-6)$ as an equivalent algebraic expression.

$3(x-6) = 3x - 3 \cdot 6$

$= 3x - 18$ Simplify.

4-2 Simplifying Algebraic Expressions (pp. 178–183)

Simplify each expression.

16. $6a+5a$ $11a$

17. $3x+6x$ $9x$

18. $7m-2m+3$ $5m+3$

19. $6x-3+2x+5$ $8x+2$

20. $a+6(a+3)$ $7a+18$

21. $2(b+3)+3b$ $5b+6$

22. **BASKETBALL** Karen made 5 less than 4 times the number of free throws that Kimi made. Write an expression in simplest form that represents the total number of free throws. $4x-5$

EXAMPLE 2

Simplify $-6x+5+x$.

$-6x+5+x$

$= -6x+x+5$ Commutative Property

$= [(-6)+1]x+5$ Distributive Property

$= -5x+5$ Simplify.

4-3 Solving Equations by Adding or Subtracting (pp. 184–189)

Solve each equation. Check your solution.

23. $x+4=10$ $x=6$

24. $a-9.45=-10.6$ $a=-1.15$

25. $x+3\frac{1}{4}=2\frac{1}{5}$

26. $-5.3=m+4.1$ $m=-9.4$

27. $p-6=12$ $p=18$

28. $s-\frac{2}{9}=\frac{2}{3}$ $s=\frac{8}{9}$

29. **REPORTS** Sonia needs to add 13 more pages to complete an assignment that is supposed to be 37 pages long. Write and solve an addition equation to find how many pages she has already completed.
$x+13=37$; 24 pages

25. $x=-1\frac{1}{20}$

EXAMPLE 3

Solve $x+6=11$.

$x+6=11$ Write the equation.

$x+6-6=11-6$ Subtraction Property of Equality

$x=5$ Simplify.

EXAMPLE 4

Solve $a-4=-3$.

$a-4=-3$ Write the equation.

$a-4+4=-3+4$ Addition Property of Equality

$a=1$ Simplify.

Lesson-by-Lesson Review

Intervention If the given examples are not sufficient to review the topics covered by the questions, remind students that the page references tell them where to review that topic in their textbook.

Two-Day Option Have students complete the Lesson-by-Lesson Review on pp. 211–212. Then you can use ExamView® Assessment Suite to customize another review worksheet that practices all the objectives of this chapter or only the objectives on which your students need more help.

Differentiated Instruction

Super DVD: MindJogger Videoquizzes Use this DVD as an alternative format of review for the test.

Problem Solving Review

For additional practice in problem solving for Chapter 4, see the Mixed Problem Solving Appendix, p. 846, in the Student Handbook section.

Anticipation Guide

Have students complete the Chapter 4 Anticipation Guide and discuss how their responses have changed now that they have completed Chapter 4.

CHAPTER 4 Study Guide and Review

4-4 Solving Equations by Multiplying or Dividing (pp. 191–196)

Solve each equation. Check your solution.

30. $12m = 24$ **$m = 2$**
31. $\frac{x}{5} = 4$ **$x = 20$**
32. $-2x = 22$ **$x = -11$**
33. $5x = 25$ **$x = 5$**
34. $\frac{x}{-4} = 16$ **$x = -64$**
35. $\frac{1}{6}x = -4$ **$x = -24$**
36. **FASHION** Rosa is making scarves for her friends. Each scarf requires 48 inches of material. Write and solve a multiplication equation to find how many scarves Rosa can make if she has 336 inches of material. **$48x = 336$; 7 scarves**

EXAMPLE 5

Solve $-4x = -32$.

$-4x = -32$ — **Write the equation.**

$\frac{-4x}{-4} = \frac{-32}{-4}$ — **Division Property of Equality**

$x = 8$ — **Simplify.**

EXAMPLE 6

Solve $\frac{a}{-2} = 5$.

$\frac{a}{-2} = 5$ — **Write the equation.**

$-2\left(\frac{a}{-2}\right) = -2(5)$ — **Multiplication Property of Equality**

$a = -10$ — **Simplify.**

4-5 Solving Two-Step Equations (pp. 199–204)

37. $3 + 4c = 15$ **3**
38. $2.1n - 5.31 = 18$ **11.1**
39. $\frac{a}{3} + 2 = 5$ **9**
40. $\frac{x}{5} - 3 = 7$ **50**
41. $\frac{4}{7} + 2p = \frac{2}{7}$ **$-\frac{1}{7}$**
42. $0.12t - 0.6 = -0.06$ **4.5**
43. **BOOKS** Nate read 10 more books than Maren for the summer reading program. The total number of books they read is 60. Solve $x + x + 10 = 60$ to find the number of books Nate read. **25 books**

EXAMPLE 7

Solve $3x + 5 = 29$.

$3x + 5 = 29$ — **Write the equation.**

$3x + 5 - 5 = 29 - 5$ — **Subtraction Property of Equality**

$3x = 24$ — **Simplify.**

$\frac{3x}{3} = \frac{24}{3}$ — **Division Property of Equality**

$x = 8$ — **Simplify.**

4-6 Writing Equations (pp. 205–209)

Translate each sentence into an equation. Then find each number.

44. Toya bought some fruit for $5 and 3 boxes of cereal and spent a total of $17. **$3n + 5 = 17$; $4 per box**
45. Six less than twice a number is -22. **$2n - 6 = -22$; -8**
46. **MONEY** Noelle spent $36 on books and pens. She spent $12 more on books than she did on pens. How much did she spend on books? **$24**

EXAMPLE 8

The product of a number and 6 is -36. Write and solve an equation to find the number.

$6n = -36$ — **Write the equation.**

$\frac{6n}{6} = \frac{-36}{6}$ — **Division Property of Equality**

$n = -6$ — **Simplify.**

Practice Test

Math Online glencoe.com
Chapter Test

Use the Distributive Property to write each expression as an equivalent algebraic expression.

1. $6(s + 10)$ $6s + 60$

2. $9(a - 4)$ $9a - 36$

3. $-5(3 - b)$ $-15 + 5b$

4. $11(m + 7)$ $11m + 77$

5. **ENTERTAINMENT** Suppose you pay \$15 per hour to go horseback riding. You ride 2 hours today and plan to ride 4 more hours this weekend.

a. Write two different expressions to find the total cost of horseback riding. $15(2 + 4)$, $15(2) + 15(4)$

b. Find the total cost. \$90

Simplify each expression.

6. $x + 3x$ $4x$

7. $10 + 6x - 11 + 7x$ $13x - 1$

8. $14n - 3(n + 8)$ $11n - 24$

9. $-7b - 5(b - 4)$ $-12b + 20$

10. **MUSIC** Omar and Deb each have a digital music player. Deb has 37 more songs on her player than Omar has on his player. Write an expression in simplest form that represents the total number of songs on both players. $2x + 37$

11. **MULTIPLE CHOICE** The table shows the prices of different items at a snack bar. D

Item	Cost (\$)
hot dog	2.50
drink	1.75
fries	2.00
hamburger	3.00
chips	0.75

After buying some items, you receive \$3.75 in change. If you paid with a \$10 bill, which equation could *not* be used to determine the amount of money you spent?

A $3.75 + n = 10$

B $10 - n = 3.75$

C $10 - 3.75 = n$

D $10 + n = 3.75$

Solve each equation. Check your solution.

12. $a - (-12) = 6$ -6

13. $16 + t = -9$ -25

14. $g + (-18) = -36$ -18

15. $-b - 15 = -21$ 6

16. $m + 3.75 = -4.15$ -7.9

17. $\frac{7}{9} - d = \frac{1}{3}$ $\frac{4}{9}$

Solve each equation. Check your solution.

18. $\frac{r}{13} = -4$ -52

19. $-75t = 300$ -4

20. $-8t = -72$ 9

21. $\frac{c}{3} = -42$ -126

22. $-\frac{m}{12} = \frac{3}{5}$ $-7\frac{1}{5}$

23. $0.4d = 3.6$ 9

24. **GENETICS** Approximately one-seventh of the people in the United States are left-handed. The population of the United States is about 300 million. Write and solve an equation to estimate how many people in the United States are left-handed. $\ell = \frac{1}{7}p$; 43 million

MEASUREMENT **Use the table to write and solve an equation to find each quantity.**

Customary System (capacity)
1 cup = 8 fluid ounces
1 pint = 2 cups
1 quart = 2 pints
1 gallon = 4 quarts

25. the number of cups in 7 pints $\frac{c}{2} = 7$; 14 cups

26. the number of quarts in 16 pints $2q = 16$; 8 quarts

27. the number of cups in 2 gallons $2 = \frac{c}{16}$; 32 cups

Solve each equation. Check your solution.

28. $16 + 5w = 31$ 3

29. $28 = 4g - 4$ 8

30. $211 - \frac{k}{3} = 111$ 300

31. $7.2j - 1.9 = 3.5$ 0.75

32. **TRAVEL** Mr. Carter is renting a car from an agency that charges \$20 per day plus \$0.15 per mile. He has a budget of \$80 per day. Write and solve an equation to find the maximum number of miles he can drive each day. $80 = 20 + 0.15m$; 400 mi

33. **MULTIPLE CHOICE** Kenneth signed up to receive Internet service for \$13 per month plus a \$30 start-up fee. Which equation could be used to find the number of months he can receive Internet service for \$134? J

F $\$134 + 30 = \$13m$

G $\$30 - \$13m = \$134$

H $\$13 + 30m = \$134$

J $\$30 + \$13m = \$134$

CHAPTER 4 Practice Test

ExamView Assessment Suite Customize and create multiple versions of your chapter test and their answer keys. All of the questions from the leveled chapter tests in the *Chapter 4 Resource Masters* are also available on ExamView® Assessment Suite.

Intervention Planner

Tier 1 On Level

If students miss about 25% of the exercises or less,

Then choose a resource:

SE Lessons 4-1, 4-2, 4-3, 4-4, 4-5, and 4-6
CRM Skills Practice, pp. 7, 13, 19, 25, 31, and 38
TE Chapter Project, p. 168

Math Online Self-Check Quiz

Tier 2 Strategic Intervention approaching grade level

If students miss about 50% of the exercises,

Then choose a resource:

CRM Study Guide and Intervention, Chapter 4, pp. 5, 11, 17, 23, 29, and 36

Quick Review Math Handbook

Math Online Extra Examples, Personal Tutor, Homework Help

Tier 3 Intensive Intervention 2 or more grades below level

students miss about 75% of the exercises,

use *Math Triumphs, Grade 8,* Ch. 3

Math Online Extra Examples, Personal Tutor, Homework Help, Review Vocabulary

1 FOCUS

Objective Use the strategy of writing and solving an equation to solve standardized test problems.

2 TEACH

Scaffolding Questions

Ask:

- What is an equation? Sample answer: Two statements that are equal to each other.
- How can you tell that a word problem can be solved by writing and solving an equation? Sample answer: The word problem will contain words such as *is* or *is equal to,* an unknown quantity that represents one side of the equation, and a known quantity that represents the other side of the equation.

CHAPTER 4 Preparing for Standardized Tests

Write and Solve an Equation

Many standardized test questions can be solved by writing and solving an equation. Follow the steps below to help you successfully solve these types of problems.

Strategies for Writing and Solving Equations

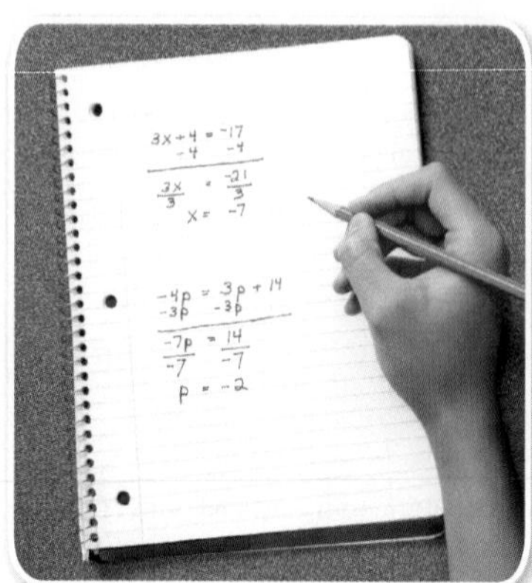

Step 1

Read the problem statement carefully.

Ask yourself:

- What am I being asked to solve?
- What information is given in the problem?
- What is the unknown quantity that I need to find?

Step 2

Translate the problem statement into an equation.

- Assign a variable to the unknown quantity.
- Write the word sentence as a mathematical number sentence.
- Look for keywords such as *is, is the same as, is equal to,* or *is identical to* that indicate where to place the equal sign.

Step 3

Solve the equation.

- Solve for the unknown in the equation.
- Check your answer to be sure it makes sense.

EXAMPLE

Read the problem. Identify what you need to know. Then use the information in the problem to solve.

Lisa baked 48 cookies for the school bake sale. This is three times the number of cookies that Kyle baked. How many cookies did Kyle bake for the sale?

A 16 cookies
B 21 cookies
C 24 cookies
D 28 cookies

214 Chapter 4 Expressions and Equations

Read the problem carefully. You know how many cookies Lisa baked. You also know that this is three times the number of cookies Kyle baked.

The unknown quantity that you need to find is the number of cookies that Kyle baked.

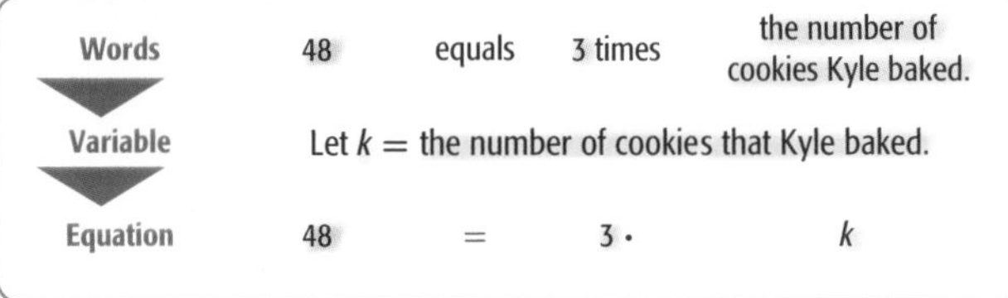

Words
48
equals
3 times
the number of cookies Kyle baked.
Variable
Let k = the number of cookies that Kyle baked.
Equation
48
=
3 ·
k

Solve the equation for k.

$48 = 3k$ **Write the equation.**

$\frac{48}{3} = \frac{3k}{3}$ **Divide each side by 3.**

$16 = k$ **Simplify.**

So, Kyle baked 16 cookies for the bake sale. The correct answer is A.

Additional Example

Tomas scored 18 touchdowns this season for his school team. This is 4 more than twice as many touchdowns as Jamal scored. How many touchdowns did Jamal score this season? A

A 7

B 11

C 13

D 14

3 ASSESS

Use Exercises 1–3 to assess students' understanding.

Exercises

Read each problem. Identify what you need to know. Then use the information in the problem to solve.

1. Angelica is 4 years older than her sister, Suzie. Angelica is 26 years old. How old is Suzie? D

   A 19 years old C 21 years old

   B 20 years old D 22 years old

2. The quotient of a number and 5 is equal to 19. What is the number? J

   F 60 H 80

   G 75 J 95

3. Mr. Lombardi is installing rectangular tiles like the one shown in his bathroom shower. The perimeter of one tile is 38 inches.

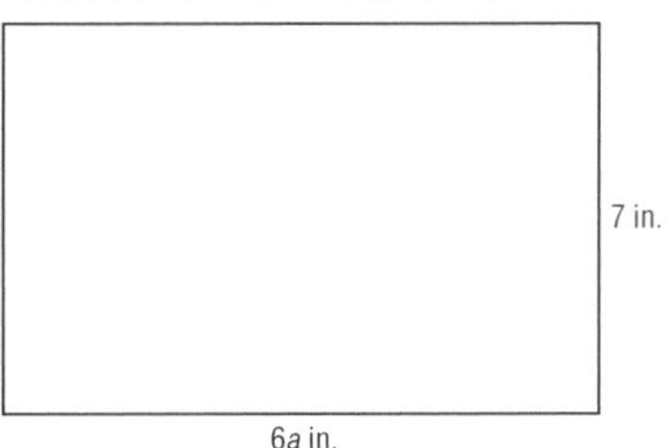

   What is the length of the tile? B

   A 11 in. C 13 in.

   B 12 in. D 14 in.

Chapter 4 Preparing for Standardized Tests 215

Diagnose Student Errors

Survey student responses for each item. Class trends may indicate common errors and misconceptions.

1. A correct
   B misinterpreted *less than* to mean addition
   C confused total cans collected by 7th graders with the number of fewer cans collected
   D confused total cans collected by 7th graders with the number of fewer cans collected and misinterpreted *less than* to mean addition
2. F subtracted instead of added to find *n*
   G calculation error and/or used wrong equation to solve the problem
   H correct
   J calculation error
3. A guess
   B guess
   C guess or calculation error arising from incorrectly converting mixed numbers to improper fractions
   D correct
4. F overlooked –2 when simplifying
   G correct
   H added $8b + 10b$ incorrectly
   J added two sides instead of four sides
5. A misunderstood concept of common denominator
   B misunderstood concept of common denominator
   C correct
   D chose common denominator but not *least* common denominator
6. F correct
   G guess
   H calculation error
   J guess
7. A correctly recognized that point *Z* consists of *x*- and *y*-coordinates of points *W* and *Y*, but used the *x*-coordinate of *Y* instead of *y*-coordinate
   B same error as answer choice A and switched *x*- and *y*-coordinates
   C correct
   D confused *x*- and *y*-coordinates

CHAPTER 4 Standardized Test Practice

Cumulative, Chapters 1 through 4

Multiple Choice

Read each question. Then fill in the correct answer on the answer document provided by your teacher or on a sheet of paper.

1. The 7th graders have collected 86 cans for a food drive so far. This is fifteen less than the number of cans collected by the 8th graders. Which of the following equations could be used to find the number of cans collected by the 8th graders? **A**

   A $n - 15 = 86$ C $n - 86 = 15$

   B $n + 15 = 86$ D $n + 86 = 15$

2. Refer to Exercise 1. How many cans have the 8th graders collected so far? **H**

   F 71 H 101

   G 91 J 105

3. The recipe shown makes one batch of chocolate chip cookies. How many batches can you make if you have $12\frac{1}{2}$ cups of flour? **D**

Recipe
1 cup softened butter (2 sticks)
$\frac{1}{2}$ cup granulated sugar
$1\frac{1}{2}$ cups packed brown sugar
2 eggs
$2\frac{1}{2}$ cups all-purpose flour
$\frac{3}{4}$ teaspoon salt
1 teaspoon baking powder
1 teaspoon baking soda
18 ounces chocolate chips

   A 8 C 6

   B 7 D 5

4. Write an expression in simplest form for the perimeter of the rectangle shown. **G**

   F $18b + 4$ H $16b + 2$

   G $18b + 2$ J $9b + 1$

5. What is the least common denominator of $\frac{7}{12}$ and $\frac{5}{8}$? **C**

   A 12 C 24

   B 16 D 48

6. Myriah's long distance telephone plan is shown. If she only wants to spend $10 per month on long distance, how many minutes can she use? **F**

Long Distance Charges
• $3.95 per month
• $0.05 per minute

   F 121 minutes H 135 minutes

   G 126 minutes J 142 minutes

7. Rectangle *WXYZ* has vertices *W*(0, –5), *X*(5, –5), and *Y*(5, 3). What are the coordinates of point *Z*? **C**

   A (0, 5) C (0, 3)

   B (5, 0) D (3, 0)

Test-Taking Tip

Question 6 To find how much money she can spend on minutes, find $10 – $3.95. Then write a multiplication equation to find the total number of minutes.

CHAPTER 4 Standardized Test Practice

Short Response/Gridded Response

Record your answers on the answer sheet provided by your teacher or on a sheet of paper.

8. **GRIDDED RESPONSE** Josiah put \$45 in a savings account. If he saves an additional \$10 per week, the equation $\$10w = \$175 - \$45$ represents how long it will take him to save \$175. Find the number of weeks Josiah will need to save in order to reach \$175. 13

9. Douglas charges \$18 per yard to mow lawns in his neighborhood. Yesterday he mowed 3 lawns. Today he mowed 4 lawns.
   a. Write two equivalent expressions for the total amount of money Douglas earned mowing lawns over the two days. $\$18(3 + 4)$, $\$18(3) + \$18(4)$
   b. How much did he earn altogether? \$126

10. **GRIDDED RESPONSE** What is the least common denominator of $\frac{3}{16}$ and $\frac{1}{3}$? 48

11. At the start of a long trip, Jasmine has 19 gallons of gasoline in her car. Every 30 minutes, her car uses a gallon of gasoline. Jasmine plans to stop and refuel when there are 3 gallons of gasoline left in her tank.
    a. Write an equation to represent the amount of gasoline in her car's tank after h half-hours. $19 - h = 3$
    b. Solve the equation from part **a** to find how long Jasmine will be able to drive before she needs to refuel. 16 half-hours or 8 hours

12. Evaluate $x \cdot y \div 4$ when $x = 10$ and $y = -3$. $-7\frac{1}{2}$ or -7.5

13. **GRIDDED RESPONSE** Evaluate abc if $a = -\frac{2}{5}$, $b = \frac{20}{32}$, and $c = -\frac{4}{10}$. 1/10

14. What mathematical property is illustrated below?

$$(p + 5) + 13 = p + (5 + 13)$$

Associative Property of Addition

Extended Response

Record your answers on a sheet of paper. Show your work.

15. On Wednesday, Carlos spent d dollars for lunch. He spent \$0.80 less than this amount for lunch on Thursday. Friday, he spent twice as much as he did on Thursday.
    a. Write an expression for the amount of money Carlos spent for lunch on Thursday. $d - 0.80$
    b. Write an expression for the amount Carlos spent for lunch on Friday. $2d - 1.60$
    c. Write an expression for the total amount of money Carlos spent for lunch on all three days. $4d - 2.40$
    d. If Carlos spent \$8 for lunch on Wednesday, how much money did he spend all three days? \$29.60

Need Extra Help?

If you missed Question...	1	2	3	4	5	6	7	8	9	10	11	12	13	14	15
Go to Lesson or Page...	4-3	4-3	3-4	4-2	3-6	4-5	1-4	4-5	4-1	3-6	4-6	2-5	3-3	1-3	4-2

Formative Assessment

You can use these two pages to benchmark student progress.

Standardized Test Practice, pp. 61–63

Answer Sheet Practice

Have students simulate taking a standardized test by recording their answers on practice recording sheets.

CRM Student Recording Sheet, p. 42

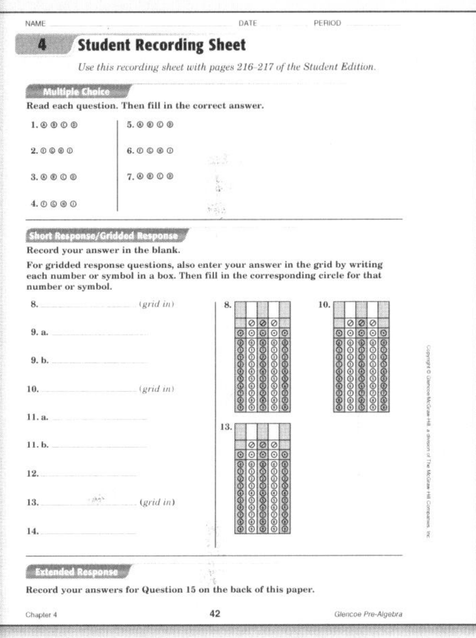

Create practice worksheets or tests that align to your state's standards as well as TIMSS and NAEP tests.

Homework Option

Get Ready for Chapter 5 Assign students the exercises on p. 219 as homework to assess whether they possess the prerequisite skills needed for the next chapter.

Page 177, Explore 4-2

1.

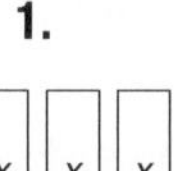
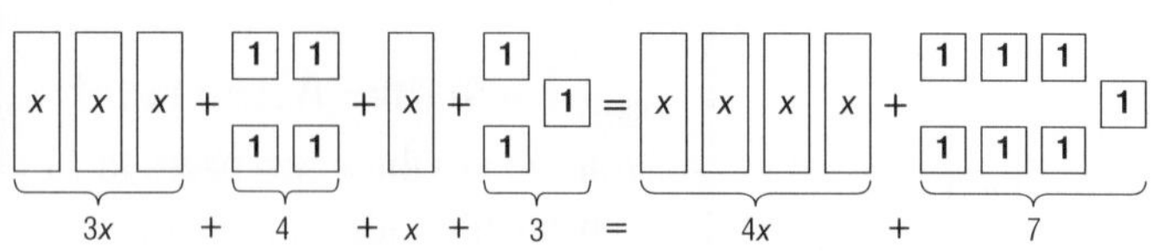

2.

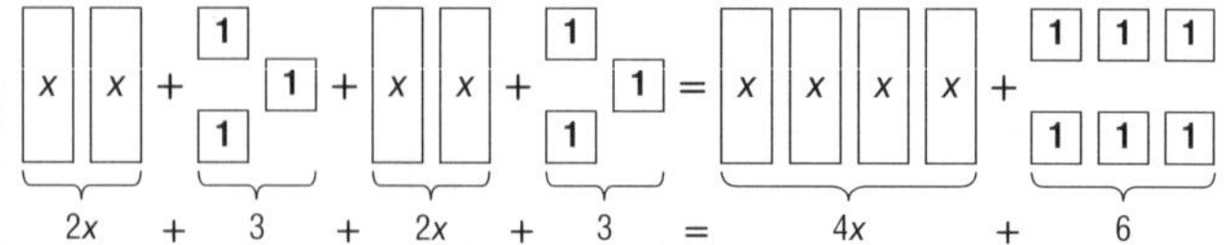

3.

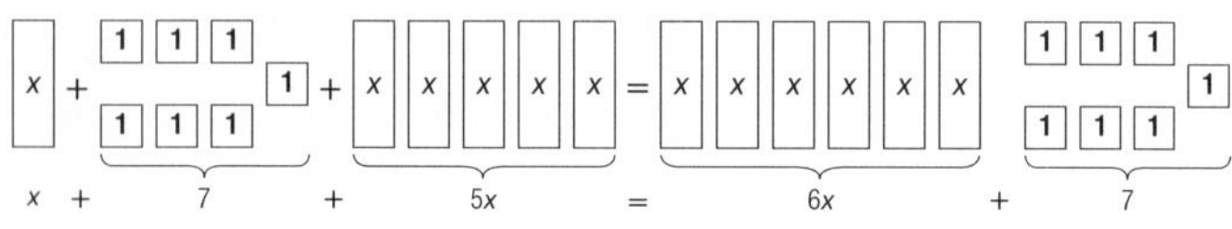

4.

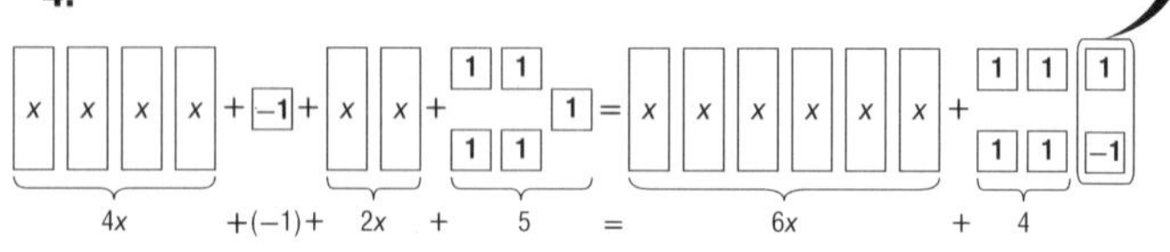

5.

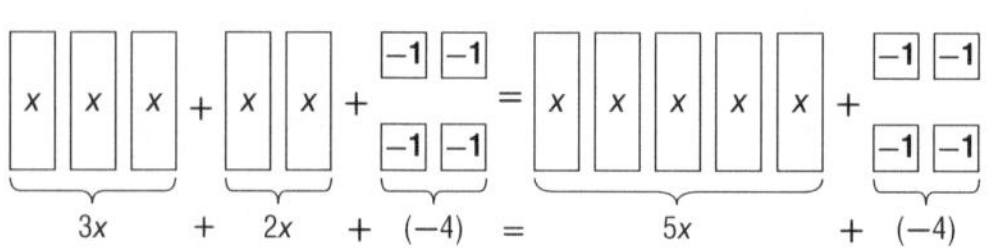

6.

2x + 2 + 2x +(−2) = 4x

Page 182, Lesson 4-2

49. $16 \cdot (-31) + 16 \cdot 32 = 16(-31 + 32)$ Distributive Property
$= 16(1)$ Add −31 and 32.
$= 16$ Multiplicative Identity

50. $72(38) + (-72)(18) = 72(38 - 18)$ Distributive Property
$= 72(20)$ Simplify.
$= (70 + 2)20$ Distributive Property
$= 1400 + 40$ or 1440 Simplify.

51. $24 \cdot (-15) + 36 \cdot 15 = (-24 + 36)15$ Distributive Property
$= (12)15$ Simplify.
$= (10 + 2)15$ Distributive Property
$= 150 + 30$ or 180 Simplify.

52. $22(-18) - 22(24) = 22(-18 - 24)$ Distributive Property
$= 22(-42)$ Simplify.
$= 22(-40 - 2)$ Distributive Property
$= -880 - 44$ or -924 Simplify.

59. Sample answer: The friend multiplied 5 by +2 instead of −2.
$4x - 2(x + 5) = 4x - 2x - 10$
$= 2x - 10$

Page 197, Explore 4-5

1. 5

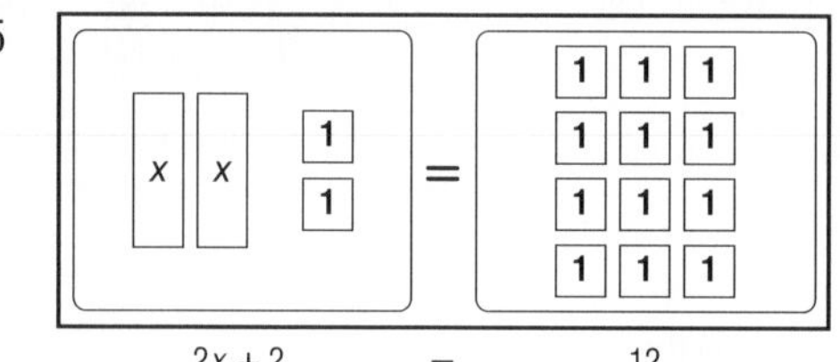

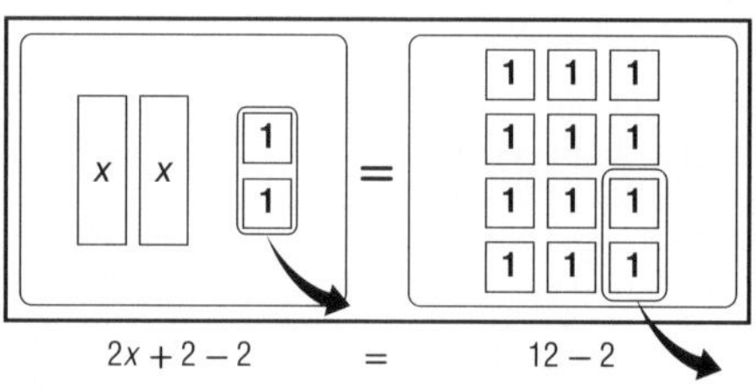

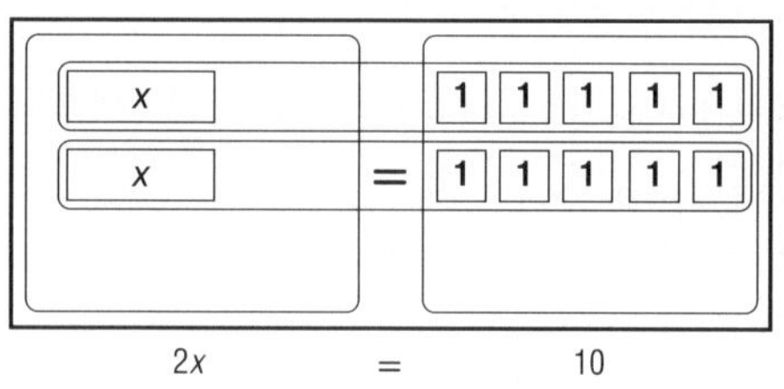

2. 1 

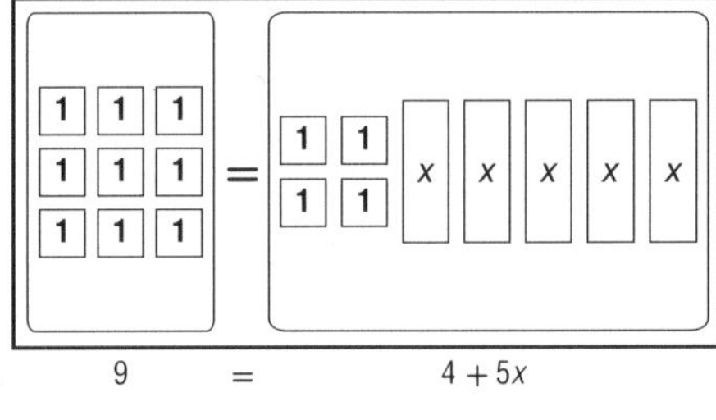

$9 = 4 + 5x$

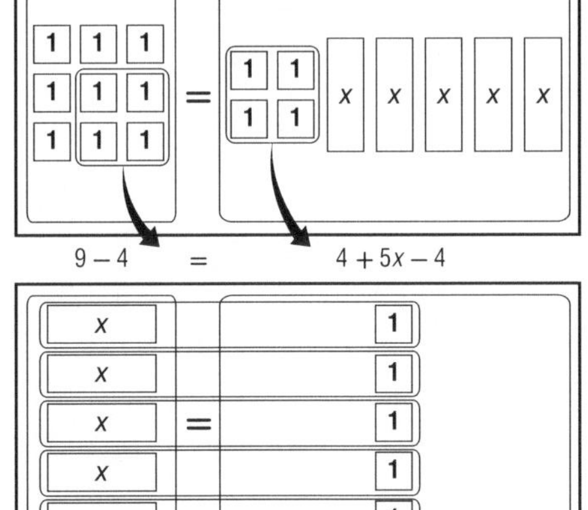

$9 - 4 = 4 + 5x - 4$

$5x = 5$

3. 3

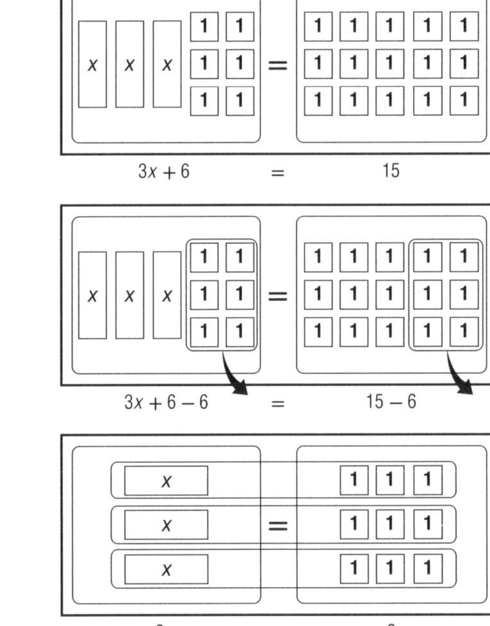

$3x + 6 = 15$

$3x + 6 - 6 = 15 - 6$

$3x = 9$

4. −3

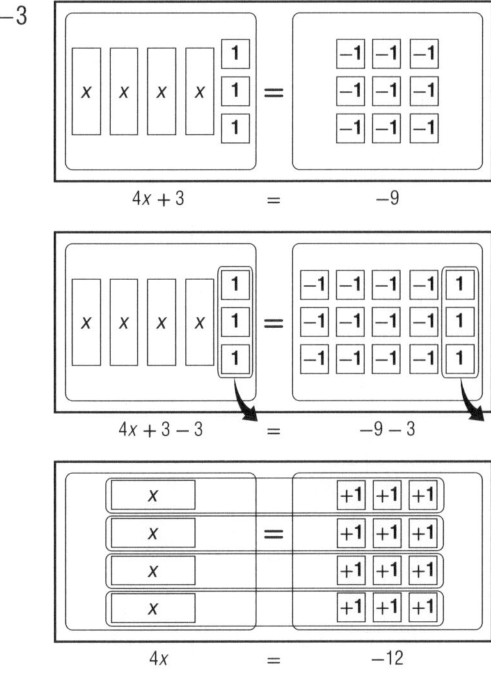

$4x + 3 = -9$

$4x + 3 - 3 = -9 - 3$

$4x = -12$

5. 3

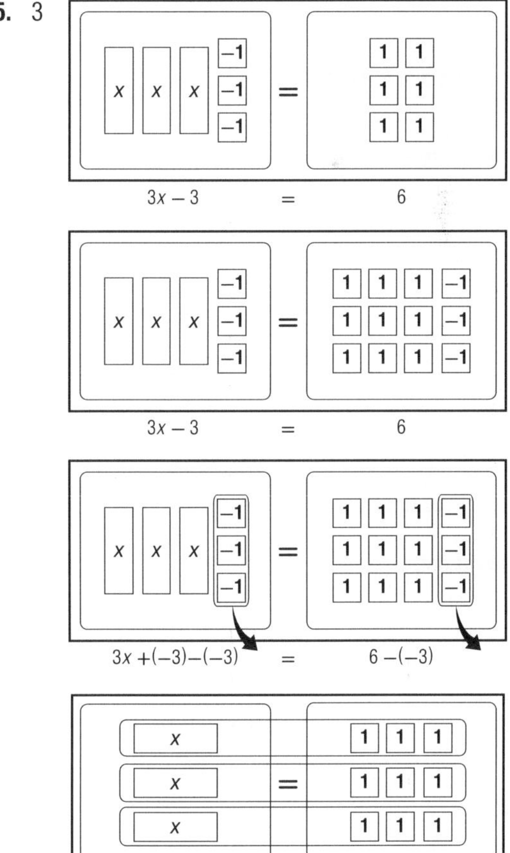

$3x - 3 = 6$

$3x - 3 = 6$

$3x + (-3) - (-3) = 6 - (-3)$

$3x = 9$

6. –5

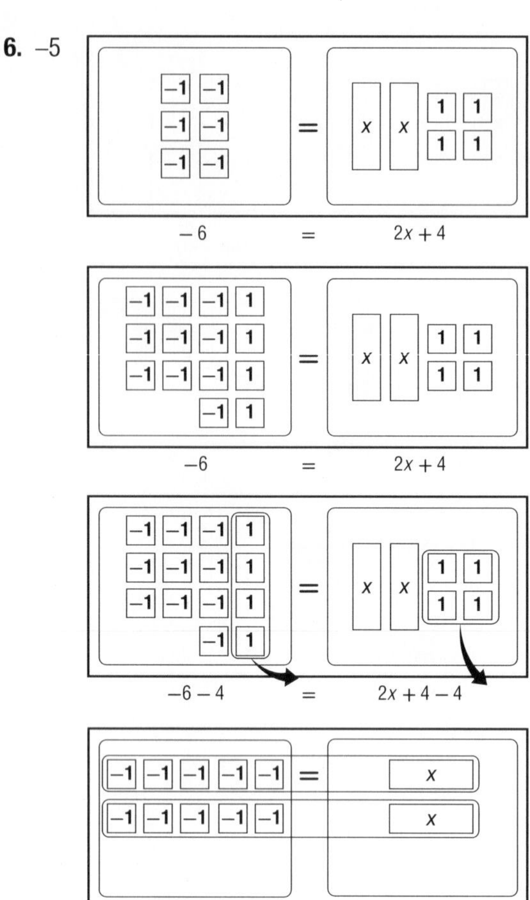

Page 209, Lesson 4-6

36b.

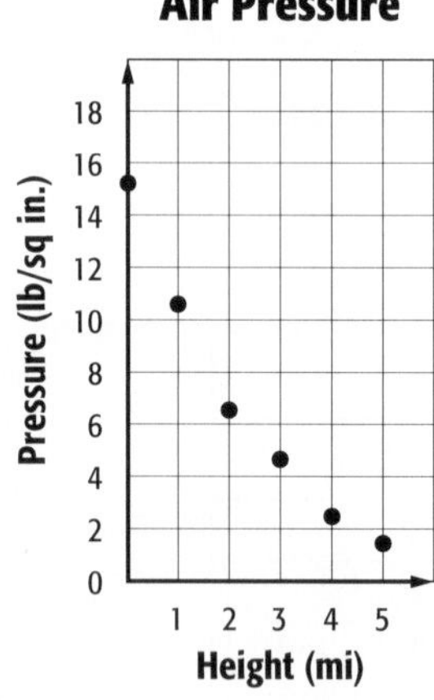

Notes

CHAPTER 5

Chapter Planner

Diagnostic Assessment
Quick Check, p. 219

	Lesson 5-1 Pacing: 1 day	Extend 5-1 Pacing: 1 day	Explore 5-2 Pacing: 1 day
Title	**Perimeter and Area**	**Spreadsheet Lab: Perimeter and Area**	**Algebra Lab: Equations with Variables on Each Side**
Objectives	• Solve problems involving the perimeters of triangles. • Solve problems involving the areas of triangles and rectangles.	• Use a spreadsheet to solve real-world problems involving perimeter and area.	• Use algebra tiles to solve equations with variables on each side.
Key Vocabulary	formula perimeter area		
NCTM Focal Points	G8–FP1 For the complete wording of the Focal Points for Grades 7 and 8, please see page iv, v, FP0, and FP1.		
Multiple Representations	p. 225		
Lesson Resources	**Chapter 5 Resource Masters** • Study Guide and Intervention, pp. 5–6 AL OL ELL • Skills Practice, p. 7 AL OL ELL • Practice, p. 8 AL OL BL ELL • Word Problem Practice, p. 9 AL OL ELL • Enrichment, p. 10 OL BL • Spreadsheet, p. 11 AL OL BL ELL **Transparencies** • 5-Minute Check Transparency 5-1 AL OL BL ELL **Additional Print Resources** • *Study Notebook* AL OL BL ELL	**Materials:** • computer with spreadsheet software	**Materials:** • algebra tiles • equation mat
Technology for Every Lesson	Math Online glencoe.com • Extra Examples • Self-Check Quizzes • Personal Tutor	**CD/DVD Resources** IWB INTERACTIVE WHITEBOARD READY IWB StudentWorks Plus IWB Interactive Classroom IWB Diagnostic and Assessment Planner	• TeacherWorks Plus • eSolutions Manual Plus • ExamView Assessment Suite
Math in Motion			p. 228
Differentiated Instruction	pp. 223, 226		

KEY: AL Approaching Level OL On Level BL Beyond Level ELL English Learners

Multi-Step Equations and Inequalities

Suggested Pacing			
Time Periods	Instruction	Review & Assessment	Total
45-minute	7	2	9
90-minute	3.5	1	4.5

Lesson 5-2 Pacing: 1 day	Lesson 5-3 Pacing: 1 day	Lesson 5-4 Pacing: 1 day	Lesson 5-5 Pacing: 1 day
Solving Equations with Variables on Each Side	**Inequalities**	**Solving Inequalities**	**Solving Multi-Step Equations and Inequalities**
• Solve equations with variables on each side. • Solve equations that involve grouping symbols.	• Write inequalities. • Graph inequalities on a number line.	• Solve inequalities by using the Addition and Subtraction Properties of Inequality. • Solve inequalities by multiplying or dividing by a positive or negative number.	• Solve multi-step equations. • Solve multi-step inequalities.
	inequality		null or empty set identify
		p. 246	
Chapter 5 Resource Masters • Study Guide and Intervention, pp. 12–13 AL OL ELL • Skills Practice, p. 14 AL OL ELL • Practice, p. 15 AL OL BL ELL • Word Problem Practice, p. 16 AL OL ELL • Enrichment, p. 17 OL BL • Quiz 1, p. 40 AL OL BL ELL **Transparencies** • 5-Minute Check Transparency 5-2 AL OL BL ELL **Additional Print Resources** • *Study Notebook* AL OL BL ELL	**Chapter 5 Resource Masters** • Study Guide and Intervention, pp. 18–19 AL OL ELL • Skills Practice, p. 20 AL OL ELL • Practice, p. 21 AL OL BL ELL • Word Problem Practice, p. 22 AL OL ELL • Enrichment, p. 23 OL BL • Spreadsheet, p. 24 AL OL BL ELL • Quiz 2, p. 40 AL OL BL ELL **Transparencies** • 5-Minute Check Transparency 5-3 AL OL BL ELL **Additional Print Resources** • *Study Notebook* AL OL BL ELL	**Chapter 5 Resource Masters** • Study Guide and Intervention, pp. 25–26 AL OL ELL • Skills Practice, p. 27 AL OL ELL • Practice, p. 28 AL OL BL ELL • Word Problem Practice, p. 29 AL OL ELL • Enrichment, p. 30 OL BL • Quiz 3, p. 41 AL OL BL ELL **Transparencies** • 5-Minute Check Transparency 5-4 AL OL BL ELL **Additional Print Resources** • *Study Notebook* AL OL BL ELL	**Chapter 5 Resource Masters** • Study Guide and Intervention, pp. 31–32 AL OL ELL • Skills Practice, p. 33 AL OL ELL • Practice, p. 34 AL OL BL ELL • Word Problem Practice, p. 35 AL OL ELL • Enrichment, p. 36 OL BL • Graphing Calculator, p. 37 AL OL BL ELL • Quiz 4, p. 41 AL OL BL ELL **Transparencies** • 5-Minute Check Transparency 5-5 AL OL BL ELL **Additional Print Resources** • *Study Notebook* AL OL BL ELL
Math Online glencoe.com • Extra Examples • Self-Check Quizzes • Personal Tutor	**CD/DVD Resources** IWB INTERACTIVE WHITEBOARD READY IWB StudentWorks Plus IWB Interactive Classroom IWB Diagnostic and Assessment Planner	• TeacherWorks Plus • eSolutions Manual Plus • ExamView Assessment Suite	
		p. 244	
pp. 230, 233	pp. 235, 239	pp. 242, 247	pp. 250, 253

Formative Assessment
Mid-Chapter Quiz, p. 240

Summative Assessment
- Study Guide and Review, p. 256
- Practice Test, p. 257

CHAPTER 5

Assessment and Intervention

SE = Student Edition, **TE** = Teacher Edition, **CRM** = Chapter Resource Masters

	Diagnosis	Prescription
Diagnostic Assessment	**Beginning Chapter 5**	
	Get Ready for Chapter 5 **SE**, p. 219	Response to Intervention **TE,** p. 219
	Beginning Every Lesson	
	Then, Now, Why? **SE** 5-Minute Check Transparencies	Chapter 0 **SE,** pp. P1–P22 Concepts and Skills Bank **SE,** pp. 856–887 *Quick Review Math Handbook*
Formative Assessment	**During/After Every Lesson**	
	Check Your Progress **SE,** every example Check Your Understanding **SE** H.O.T. Problems **SE** Spiral Review **SE** Additional Examples **TE** Watch Out! **TE** Step 4, Assess **TE** Chapter 5 Quizzes **CRM,** pp. 40–41 Self-Check Quizzes **glencoe.com**	**Tier 1 Intervention** Concepts and Skills Bank **SE,** pp. 856–887 Skills Practice **CRM,** Ch. 1–5 **glencoe.com** **Tier 2 Intervention** Differentiated Instruction **TE** Study Guide and Intervention Masters **CRM,** Ch. 1–5 *Quick Review Math Handbook* **Tier 3 Intervention** *Math Triumphs, Grade 8,* Ch. 3
	Mid-Chapter	
	Mid-Chapter Quiz **SE,** p. 240 Mid-Chapter Test **CRM,** p. 42 ExamView Assessment Suite	**Tier 1 Intervention** Concepts and Skills Bank **SE,** pp. 856–887 Skills Practice **CRM,** Ch. 1–5 **glencoe.com** **Tier 2 Intervention** Study Guide and Intervention Masters **CRM,** Ch. 1–5 *Quick Review Math Handbook* **Tier 3 Intervention** *Math Triumphs, Grade 8,* Ch. 3
	Before Chapter Test	
	Chapter Study Guide and Review **SE,** pp. 254–256 Practice Test **SE,** p. 257 Standardized Test Practice **SE,** pp. 258–261 Chapter Test **glencoe.com** Standardized Test Practice **glencoe.com** Vocabulary Review **glencoe.com** ExamView Assessment Suite	**Tier 1 Intervention** Concepts and Skills Bank **SE,** pp. 856–887 Skills Practice **CRM,** Ch. 1–5 **glencoe.com** **Tier 2 Intervention** Study Guide and Intervention Masters **CRM,** Ch. 1–5 *Quick Review Math Handbook* **Tier 3 Intervention** *Math Triumphs, Grade 8,* Ch. 3
Summative Assessment	**After Chapter 5**	
	Multiple-Choice Tests, Forms 1, 2A, 2B, **CRM,** pp. 44–49 Free-Response Tests, Forms 2C, 2D, 3, **CRM,** pp. 50–55 Vocabulary Test **CRM,** p. 43 Extended Response Test **CRM,** p. 56 Standardized Test Practice **CRM,** pp. 57–59 ExamView Assessment Suite	Study Guide and Intervention Masters **CRM,** Ch. 1–5 *Quick Review Math Handbook* **glencoe.com**

CHAPTER 5 Differentiated Instruction

Option 1 Reaching All Learners AL OL BL ELL

VERBAL/LINGUISTIC Show students how to solve the formula $A = \ell w$ for the variable w. Ask them to consider why it might be helpful to solve the formula for w if they know the area of a rectangle and its length.

Then have students write a problem in which they could solve one of the following formulas for a variable on the right side of the equation.

- $A = \frac{1}{2}bh$
- $P = 2(\ell + w)$
- $P = a + b + c$

Ask students to show how to solve for the variable, and then have them solve the problem. Have students discuss whether it was useful or not to solve for the variable first.

VISUAL/SPATIAL Have students work in pairs. One graphs a solution to an inequality on a number line. The other writes the inequality in words and symbols. For example,

- One student graphs an inequality:

−3 −2 −1 0 1 2 3

- The second student writes *a number less than 1* and $n < 1$.

Students then switch roles. As an alternative, have one student write an inequality and the other student graph it on a number line.

Option 2 Approaching Level AL

Have students create two checklists:

- steps needed to solve multi-step equations
- steps needed to solve multi-step inequalities

Have students exchange and review the lists for possible missing steps and then return the lists and make any corrections.

Next, ask students to write a multi-step equation and inequality, and then trade problems with another student. Have them solve the problems using their checklists.

Option 3 English Learners ELL

Some of the verbal phrases associated with inequalities can be difficult to understand. Have students discuss the meaning of the following phrases:

- is no more than
- is at most
- is no less than
- is at least

Then have students write a real-world example for each phrase and explain what the phrase means in the context of the example.

Option 4 Beyond Level BL

Give students the inequality $y \geq -2$ and have them graph the solution using the draw function of their graphing calculators.

- Press [Y =] [CLEAR], and then [2nd] 1 [ENTER] to clear the calculator.
- Then press [2nd] 7 [(−)] 2 [,] 10 [)] and [ENTER].

Ask students to discuss the graph. Guide them to realize that any value for y in the shaded area makes the inequality true.

After clearing the calculator, have students solve and graph the solution of $y \leq -2$.

- Have them switch the places of -2 and 10 in the previous sequence on the calculator.
- Have them replace 10 with -10.

Ask students to compare the two graphs. Allow them to experiment with the calculator and graph different inequalities, such as $y \geq 2x + 4$, to see how the calculator gives the solution to the inequality.

Focus on Mathematical Content

Vertical Alignment

Before Chapter 5

Related Topics before Pre-Algebra

- use models to solve equations

Previous Topics from Pre-Algebra

- select and solve problems with rational numbers
- select and use appropriate operations to solve problems

Chapter 5

Related Topics from Pre-Algebra

- predict, find, and justify solutions to application problems using appropriate tables, graphs, and algebraic equations
- use formulas to solve problems
- translate verbal phrases into inequalities

After Chapter 5

Preparation for Algebra 1

- investigate methods for solving linear equations using concrete models, graphs, and the properties of equality, select a method, and solve equations
- investigate methods for solving linear inequalities using concrete models, graphs, and the properties of equality, select a method, and solve inequalities

Lesson-by-Lesson Preview

5-1 Perimeter and Area

A formula is an equation that shows a relationship among certain quantities. It usually contains two or more variables. When using a formula, replace any variables with known values, and then solve the resulting equation.

Formulas for perimeter (the distance around a geometric figure) include:

- $P = 2(\ell + w)$ for a rectangle, where ℓ is length and w is width.
- $P = a + b + c$ for a triangle, where a, b, and c are the sides of the triangle.

Formulas for area (the measure of the surface enclosed by a figure) include:

- $A = \ell w$ for a rectangle
- $A = \frac{1}{2}bh$ for a triangle, where b is the base and h is the height of the triangle.

5-2 Solving Equations with Variables on Each Side

Use the Addition or Subtraction Property of Equality, introduced in Lesson 4-3, to solve equations with variables on each side. Add or subtract to write an equivalent equation with the variables on one side of the equation. Then solve the equation.

For example, to solve $3x - 8 = 5x$:

- Subtract $3x$ from each side to get $-8 = 2x$.
- Then divide each side by 2 to get $x = -4$.

5-3 Inequalities

A mathematical sentence that contains the symbols $<$ (less than), $>$ (greater than), $\leq$ (less than or equal to), or $\geq$ (greater than or equal to) is called an inequality. For example, the statement that it is legal to drive 55 miles per hour or slower can be shown by the sentence $s \leq 55$.

Inequalities with variables are open sentences. When a variable in an open sentence is replaced with a number, the inequality may be true or false.

The solutions of inequalities can be graphed on a number line.

- Use an open dot to show the solution to an inequality that contains a $<$ or $>$ symbol. The open dot is used to show that a number is not included in the graph.

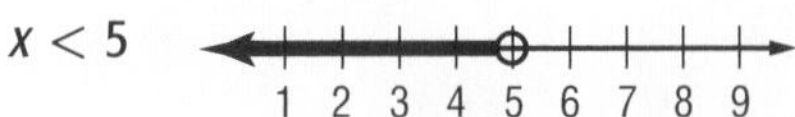

- Use a closed dot to show the solution to an inequality that contains a $\leq$ or $\geq$ symbol. The closed dot is used to show that a number is included in the graph.

$x \leq 5$

1 2 3 4 5 6 7 8 9

5-4 Solving Inequalities

Solving an inequality means finding values for the variable that make the inequality true.

Some inequalities can be solved by adding or subtracting:

- The Addition and Subtraction Properties of Inequalities state that when you add or subtract the same number from each side of an inequality, the inequality remains true. For example, if you add 5 to each side of the inequality $3 < 6$, the resulting inequality $8 < 11$ is also true.
- Adding or subtracting the same number from each side of an inequality does not affect the inequality sign.
- Since the solutions to an inequality include all real numbers satisfying it, inequalities have an infinite number of solutions.

Some inequalities can be solved by multiplying or dividing.

- The Multiplication and Division Properties of Inequalities state that when multiplying or dividing each side of an inequality by the same *positive* number, the inequality remains true. In such cases, the inequality symbol does not change.
- When multiplying or dividing each side of an inequality by a *negative* number, the inequality symbol must be reversed. For example, if you divide each side of the inequality $-4x \geq -8$ by -4, the inequality sign must be changed to $\leq$ for the resulting inequality, $x \leq 2$, to be true.

5-5 Solving Multi-Step Equations and Inequalities

Multi-step equations and inequalities often contain grouping symbols such as parentheses or brackets. The first step in solving equations and inequalities with grouping symbols is to use the Distributive Property to remove the grouping symbols.

To solve an inequality that involves more than one operation, undo each operation as with solving equations with more than one operation. Remember to reverse the inequality symbol if you multiply or divide by a negative number.

Some equations have no solution, i.e., there is no value of the variable that results in a true sentence. For such an equation, the solution set is called the null or empty set, and is represented by the symbol $\varnothing$. Other equations may have every number as the solution. An equation that is true for every value of the variable is called an identity.

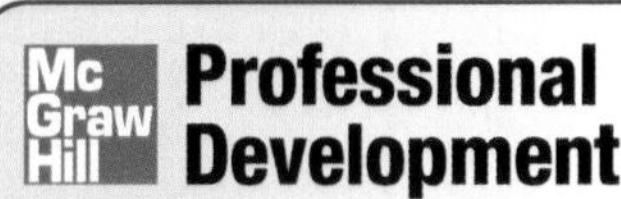

Targeted professional development has been articulated throughout McGraw-Hill's mathematics program. The **McGraw-Hill Professional Development Video Library** provides short videos that support key topics. For more information, visit glencoe.com.

Model Lessons

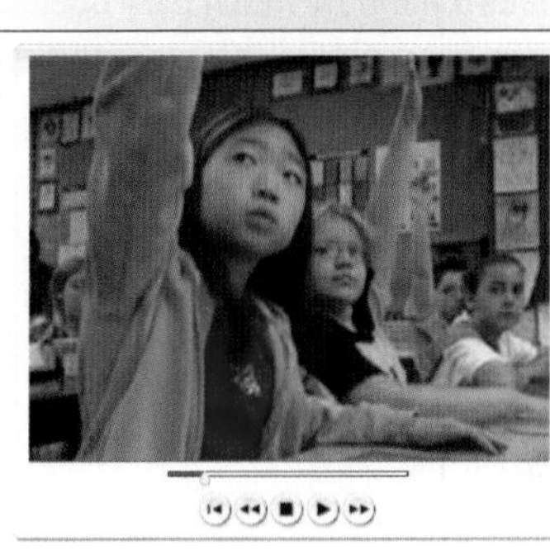

Instructional Strategies

CHAPTER 5 Notes

Chapter Project

Budgeting Sense

Students use what they have learned about writing and solving equations and inequalities to develop a budget and financial plan for a class party. Remind students to describe in words all equations and inequalities that they write and solve.

- Divide students into groups. Have each group decide on a theme for a class party. Ask them to make a list of what they will need for each of these categories: decorations, refreshments, supplies, and entertainment. Have them decide how much they will spend overall and how much they will budget for each category.
- Have groups write and solve equations to determine the numbers of items and/or how much to spend on items for each category. For example, the equation $10(b + 2.50) + 20 = 55$ might be used to model the decorations budget, and solving for b would give how much to spend per balloon. The numbers that students use for refreshments and supplies should be for the whole class.
- Next, have groups make a plan for financing the party that includes at least two sources. Then have them write and solve an inequality to determine how much they need to earn from one of the sources. For example, $30c + 75 \geq 225$ might be used to determine the least contribution c that students need to make to the party fund.

CHAPTER 5 Multi-Step Equations and Inequalities

Then

In Chapter 4, you learned how to solve simple equations.

Now

In Chapter 5, you will:

- Use the Distributive Property to solve equations and inequalities.
- Select and use appropriate operations to solve problems and justify solutions.

Why?

BUDGETS Many students receive a monthly allowance. A budget can help you determine how much of your allowance you can spend or save every month. You can use an inequality to calculate the number of months that it will take to save enough money to purchase an item.

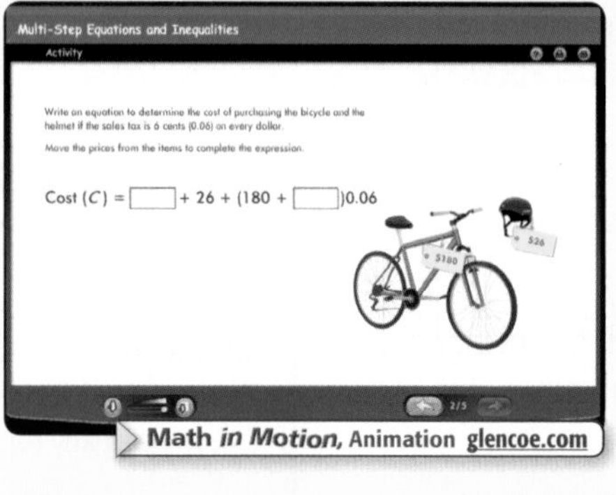

Key Vocabulary Introduce the key vocabulary in the chapter using the routine below.

Define: An identity is an equation that is true for every value of the variable.

Example: The equation $4(k - 3) = 4k + 8 - 20$ is an identity. Solving the equation results in $-12 = -12$, which is always true.

Ask: Is the equation $5t + 13 = 2(t - 9) + 3t$ an identity? Explain. No; solving the equation results in $13 = -18$, which is never true.

Get Ready for Chapter 5

Diagnose Readiness You have two options for checking Prerequisite Skills.

Text Option Take the Quick Check below. Refer to the Quick Review for help.

*Quick*Check

Solve each equation. Check your solution. (Lesson 4-5) (Used in Lesson 5-2)

1. $-3m - 8 = 10$ -6
2. $5n - 9 = 6$ 3
3. $\frac{d}{9} + 5 = 15$ 90
4. $-3 = 7 + \frac{f}{-2}$ 20
5. $-18 = 4b + 10$ -7
6. $-9 - \frac{h}{4} = 5$ -56
7. **SALES** Suppose a computer costs $600. Tony pays a down payment of $150 and plans to pay the balance in 6 equal installments. How much will each installment be? $75

(Used in Lesson 5-4)
Find each sum or difference. (Lessons 2-2 and 2-3)

8. $-42 + (-23)$ -65
9. $42 + (-79)$ -37
10. $-27 + 5$ -22
11. $15 + (-88)$ -73
12. $12 - 60$ -48
13. $-35 - (-35)$ 0
14. **STOCKS** The stock market fell 507.99 points on October 19, 1987. If the stock market was 2246.73 points at the beginning of the day, what was its value at the end of the day? 1738.74 points

(Used in Lesson 5-4)
Find each product or quotient. (Lessons 2-4 and 2-5)

15. $5(-8)$ -40
16. $-10(-12)$ 120
17. $-3(5)(-8)$ 120
18. $54 \div (-2)$ -27
19. $-20 \div 5$ -4
20. $-27 \div (-3)$ 9
21. **CHEMISTRY** A solution cooled at a rate of 6°F every 5 minutes. What integer represents the change in the solution's temperature in $\frac{1}{2}$ hour? −36°F

*Quick*Review

EXAMPLE 1

Solve $\frac{r}{4} + 6 = 5$.

$\frac{r}{4} + 6 = 5$	Write the equation.
$\frac{r}{4} + 6 - 6 = 5 - 6$	Subtract 6 from each side.
$\frac{r}{4} = -1$	Simplify.
$4\left(\frac{r}{4}\right) = 4(-1)$	Undo division. Multiply each side by 4.
$r = -4$	Simplify.

EXAMPLE 2

Find $-30 - (-42)$.

$-30 - (-42) = -30 + 42$	To subtract −42, add 42.
$= 12$	Simplify.

EXAMPLE 3

Find $6(-15)$.

$6(-15) = -90$	The factors have different signs so the product is negative.

Online Option Math Online Take a self-check Chapter Readiness Quiz at glencoe.com.

Get Ready for Chapter 5

Response to Intervention (RtI)

Use the *Quick Check* results and the Intervention Planner to help you determine your Response to Intervention. The If-Then statements in the chart help you decide the appropriate tier of RtI and suggest intervention resources for each tier.

Intervention Planner

Tier 1 On Level

 **If** students miss about 25% of the exercises or less,

 **Then** choose a resource:

SE	Lessons 2-2 through 2-5, 4-5
CRM	Skills Practice, Chapter 2, pp. 13, 19, 25, 31; Chapter 4, p. 31
TE	Chapter Project, p. 218

Math Online Self-Check Quiz

Tier 2 Strategic Intervention approaching grade level

 **If** students miss about 50% of the exercises,

Then choose a resource:

CRM	Study Guide and Intervention, Chapter 2, pp. 11, 17, 23, 29; Chapter 4, p. 29

Quick Review Math Handbook

Math Online Extra Examples, Personal Tutor, Homework Help

Tier 3 Intensive Intervention 2 or more grades below level

 **If** students miss about 75% of the exercises,

 **Then** use *Math Triumphs, Grade 8*, Ch. 3

Math Online Extra Examples, Personal Tutor, Homework Help, Review Vocabulary

CHAPTER 5 Notes

FOLDABLES® Study Organizer

Dinah Zike's Foldables®

Focus Students write notes about rational numbers as they work through each lesson in this chapter.

Teach Have students make and label the tabs for each lesson of their Foldables as illustrated. Have students make notes under the appropriate tabs as they cover each lesson in this chapter. Ask students to write about equations and inequalities. For example, they might choose to compare how to graph the solution to different kinds of inequalities ($<$, $>$, $\leq$, $\geq$) or discuss the differences between solving equations and inequalities.

When to Use It Encourage students to add to their Foldable as they work through the chapter, and include vocabulary, examples, and everyday uses of the topics in their notes.

Differentiated Instruction

CRM Student-Built Glossary, pp. 1–2 Students should complete the chart by providing a definition of each term and an example as they progress through Chapter 5. This study tool can also be used to review for the chapter test.

Get Started on Chapter 5

You will learn several new concepts, skills, and vocabulary terms as you study Chapter 5. To get ready, identify important terms and organize your resources. You may wish to refer to **Chapter 0** to review prerequisite skills.

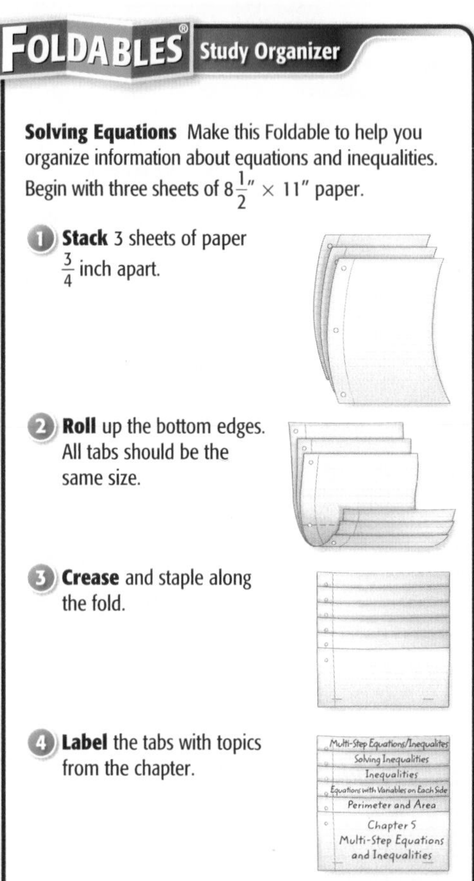

FOLDABLES® Study Organizer

Solving Equations Make this Foldable to help you organize information about equations and inequalities. Begin with three sheets of $8\frac{1}{2}'' \times 11''$ paper.

1. **Stack** 3 sheets of paper $\frac{3}{4}$ inch apart.
2. **Roll** up the bottom edges. All tabs should be the same size.
3. **Crease** and staple along the fold.
4. **Label** the tabs with topics from the chapter.

Math Online glencoe.com

- Study the chapter online
- Explore **Math in Motion**
- Get extra help from your own **Personal Tutor**
- Use **Extra Examples** for additional help
- Take a **Self-Check Quiz**
- **Review Vocabulary** in fun ways

New Vocabulary

English		Español
formula	p. 221	fórmula
perimeter	p. 221	perímetro
area	p. 222	área
inequality	p. 234	desigualdad
null Set or empty Set	p. 250	conjunto vacío
identity	p. 250	identidad

Review Vocabulary

Distributive Property • p. 171 • Propiedad distributíva
To multiply a sum by a number, multiply each number in parenthesis by the number outside the parenthesis

Properties of Equality • Propiedad de igualdad	
Addition (p. 184)	For any numbers a, b, and c, if a $= b$, then $a + c = b + c$.
Subtraction (p. 185)	For any numbers a, b, and c, if $a = b$, then $a - c = b - c$.
Multiplication (p. 193)	For any numbers a, b, and c, if $a = b$, then $ca = cb$.
Division (p. 191)	For any numbers a, b, and c, where $c \neq 0$, if $a = b$, then $\frac{a}{c} = \frac{b}{c}$.

Multilingual eGlossary glencoe.com

5-1 Perimeter and Area

Then
You have already found values of algebraic expressions by substituting values for the variables. (Lesson 1-2)

Now
- Solve problems involving the perimeters of triangles and rectangles.
- Solve problems involving the areas of triangles and rectangles.

New Vocabulary
formula
perimeter
area

Math Online
glencoe.com
- Extra Examples
- Personal Tutor
- Self-Check Quiz
- Homework Help

Why?

In professional baseball, the infield diamond is actually a square that measures 90 feet on each side.

a. How far does a player run if he runs from home plate to second base? 180 ft

b. How far does a player run if he hits a home run? 360 ft

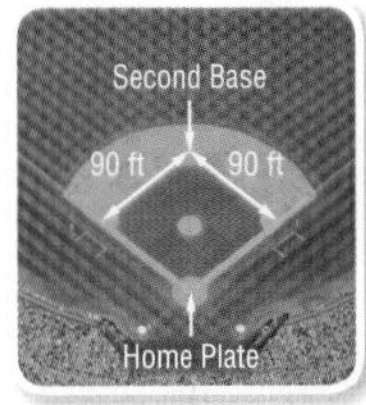

Perimeter A **formula** is an equation that shows a relationship among certain quantities. Formulas are commonly used in measurement. For example, the distance around a geometric figure is called the **perimeter**.

The formula $P = 4s$, where s represents the distance from home plate to first base, can be used to find the perimeter of the infield.

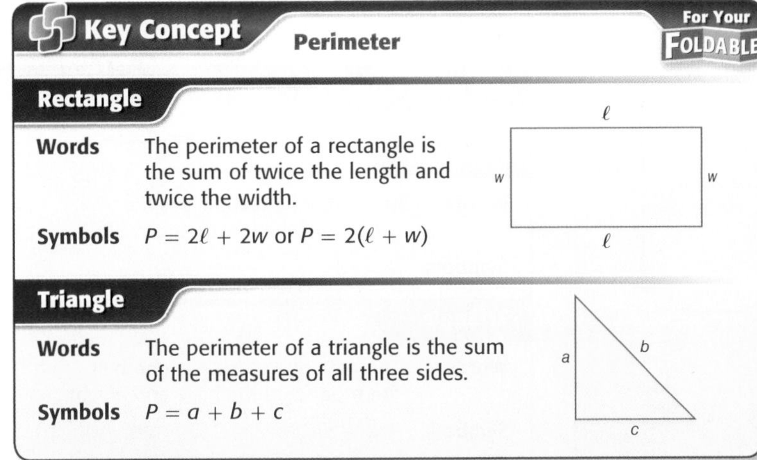

Key Concept Perimeter — For Your FOLDABLE

Rectangle

Words The perimeter of a rectangle is the sum of twice the length and twice the width.

Symbols $P = 2\ell + 2w$ or $P = 2(\ell + w)$

Triangle

Words The perimeter of a triangle is the sum of the measures of all three sides.

Symbols $P = a + b + c$

EXAMPLE 1 Find the Perimeter

Find the perimeter of the triangle.

28.5 cm, 12.8 cm, 17 cm

$P = a + b + c$ — Write the formula for perimeter.

$P = 12.8 + 28.5 + 17$ — Replace a with 12.8, b with 28.5, and c with 17.

$P = 58.3$ cm — Simplify.

The perimeter is 58.3 centimeters.

Check Your Progress

1. Find the perimeter of a rectangle with length 15.2 meters and width 10.5 meters. 51.4 m

Personal Tutor glencoe.com

5-1 Lesson Notes

1 FOCUS

Vertical Alignment

Before Lesson 5-1
Find values of algebraic expressions by substituting values for the variables.

Lesson 5-1
Solve problems involving the perimeters of triangles and rectangles.
Solve problems involving the areas of triangles and rectangles.

After Lesson 5-1
Represent relationships among quantities using concrete models, descriptions, and equations.

2 TEACH

Scaffolding Questions

Have students read the *Why?* section of the lesson and answer the questions.

Ask:

- Write an expression to represent the feet a player would run depending on which base he reaches. $90b$
- What does the variable in the expression represent? the number of bases run
- How can you use the expression to find the number of feet the player runs from home plate to third base? Substitute 3 for b and multiply to give 270 feet.

Lesson 5-1 Resources

Resource	Approaching-Level	On-Level	Beyond-Level	English Learners
Teacher Edition		• Differentiated Instruction, p. 223	• Differentiated Instruction, p. 226	
Chapter Resource Masters	• Study Guide and Intervention, pp. 5–6 • Skills Practice, p. 7 • Practice, p. 8 • Word Problem Practice, p. 9 • Spreadsheet Activity, p. 11	• Study Guide and Intervention, pp. 5–6 • Skills Practice, p. 7 • Practice, p. 8 • Word Problem Practice, p. 9 • Enrichment, p. 10 • Spreadsheet Activity, p. 11	• Practice, p. 8 • Word Problem Practice, p. 9 • Enrichment, p. 10 • Spreadsheet Activity, p. 11	• Study Guide and Intervention, pp. 5–6 • Skills Practice, p. 7 • Practice, p. 8 • Spreadsheet Activity, p. 11
Transparencies	• 5-Minute Check Transparency 5-1	• 5-Minute Check Transparency 5-1	• 5-Minute Check Transparency 5-1	• 5-Minute Check Transparency 5-1
Other	• Study Notebook • Teaching Pre-Algebra with Manipulatives	• Study Notebook • Teaching Pre-Algebra with Manipulatives	• Study Notebook	• Study Notebook • Teaching Pre-Algebra with Manipulatives

Perimeter

Example 1 shows how to find the perimeter of a triangle. **Example 2** shows how to use the formula for finding the perimeter of a rectangle to find the length of a missing side.

Formative Assessment

Use the Check Your Progress exercises after each example to determine students' understanding of concepts.

Additional Examples

1 Find the perimeter of the triangle. 76 cm

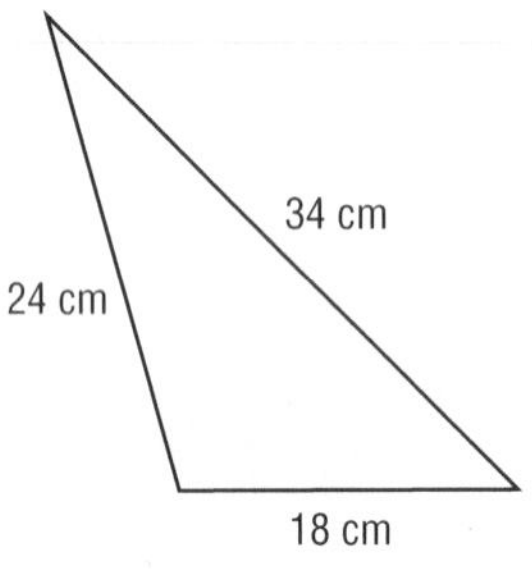

2 The perimeter of a rectangle is 60 feet. Its width is 9 feet. Find its length. 21 ft

Additional Examples also in Interactive Classroom PowerPoint® Presentations

IWB INTERACTIVE WHITEBOARD READY

Area

Example 3 shows how to use a formula to find the area of a triangle. **Example 4** shows how to use a formula to solve a real-world problem involving the area of a rectangle.

Additional Example

3 The base of a triangle is 10 inches and the height is 7 inches. Find the area. 35 square inches

---

EXAMPLE 2 Find the Length

The perimeter of a rectangle is 42 feet. Its width is 10 feet. Find the length.

$P = 2\ell + 2w$	Write the formula for perimeter.
$42 = 2\ell + 2(10)$	Replace *P* with 42 and *w* with 10.
$42 = 2\ell + 20$	Simplify.
$42 - 20 = 2\ell + 20 - 20$	Subtraction Property of Equality
$22 = 2\ell$	Simplify.
$\frac{22}{2} = \frac{2\ell}{2}$	Division Property of Equality
$11 = \ell$	Simplify.

The length of the rectangle is 11 feet.

Check Your Progress

2. The perimeter of a rectangle is 26 yards. Its length is 8 yards. Find the width. 5 yd

Personal Tutor glencoe.com

StudyTip

Units of Measure When finding perimeter, use linear units such as feet, inches, or centimeters. When finding area, use square units such as square feet, square inches, or square centimeters.

Area The measure of the surface enclosed by a figure is its **area**.

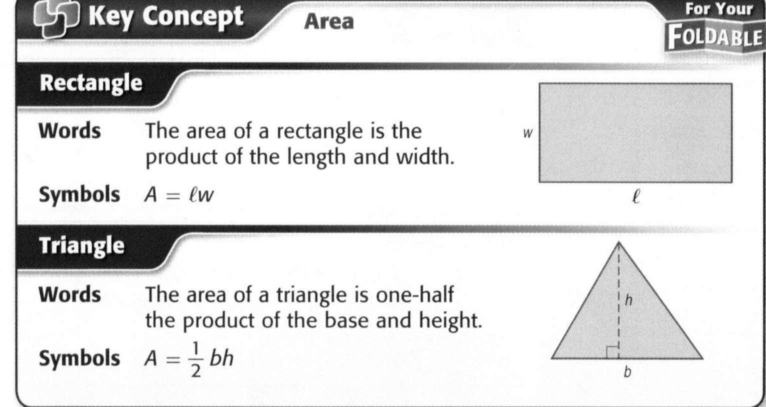

Key Concept Area — For Your FOLDABLE

Rectangle

Words The area of a rectangle is the product of the length and width.

Symbols $A = \ell w$

Triangle

Words The area of a triangle is one-half the product of the base and height.

Symbols $A = \frac{1}{2}bh$

Math History Link

Jiuzhang Suanshu (c. 100 B.C.) The Jiuzhang Suanshu or Nine Chapters on the Mathematical Art is a Chinese handbook of mathematics. The first chapter deals with areas of shapes.

Source: Clark University

EXAMPLE 3 Find the Area

The base of a triangle is 12 inches, and its height is $5\frac{1}{4}$ inches. Find the area.

$A = \frac{1}{2}bh$	Write the formula for area.
$A = \frac{1}{2} \cdot 12 \cdot 5\frac{1}{4}$	Replace *b* with 12 and *h* with $5\frac{1}{4}$.
$A = 31\frac{1}{2}$	Simplify. This can also be written as 31.5 square inches.

The area is 31.5 square inches.

Check Your Progress

3. The width of a rectangle is 11.4 meters and its length is 18.9 meters. Find the area. 215.46 m^2

Personal Tutor glencoe.com

Tips for New Teachers

Using Units Point out that area is measured in square units. Students can internalize this by remembering that a line, such as the side of a rectangle or its perimeter, has one dimension, but a plane has two dimensions.

Real-World EXAMPLE 4 Find the Width

DECORATING **Tyler has enough blue paint to cover 800 square inches. He wants to paint a rectangular stripe on his bedroom wall that is 120 inches long. Find the width of the section he can paint.**

Understand You know Tyler wants to paint a rectangle that is 120 inches long. He has enough paint to cover 800 square inches. You need to find the width of the rectangle.

Plan Use the formula $A = \ell w$ to find the width.

Solve Solve for w. Then substitute.

$A = \ell w$	**Write the formula for area.**
$\frac{A}{\ell} = \frac{\ell w}{\ell}$	**Divide each side by ℓ.**
$\frac{A}{\ell} = w$	**Simplify.**
$\frac{800}{120} = w$	**Replace A with 800 and ℓ with 120.**
$6\frac{2}{3} = w$	**Simplify.**

The stripe should be $6\frac{2}{3}$ inches wide.

Check Check by multiplying. $120 \cdot 6\frac{2}{3} = 800$ ✓

StudyTip

Literal Equations In Example 4, the area formula contains 3 variables. When an equation or formula has more than one variable, it is called a *literal equation.* You can apply the properties of equality to solve for any of the variables.

Check Your Progress

4. **FLAGS** The area of the triangular flag case shown is 69 square inches. Find the height of the case. 6 in.

Personal Tutor glencoe.com

Check Your Understanding

Examples 1 and 3 pp. 221–222

1. Find the perimeter and area of the rectangle. 28 cm, 24 cm^2

2 cm
12 cm

Example 2 p. 222

2. The perimeter of a rectangle is 45 meters. Its width is 6 meters. What is the length of the rectangle? 16.5 m

Example 4 p. 223

3. **CRAFTS** Dena's mother is making a rectangular quilt. She has 117 squares and wants the quilt to be nine squares wide. How many squares will make up the length of the quilt? 13 squares

Differentiated Instruction OL

Logical Have students determine all possible whole number widths and lengths of a rectangle with an area of 72 square inches. Which combination of length and width gives the smallest perimeter? 1 and 72, 2 and 36, 3 and 24, 4 and 18, 6 and 12, 8 and 9; smallest perimeter: 8 and 9

Focus on Mathematical Content

Using Formulas A formula is an equation that shows a relationship between quantities. Two ways to solve a verbal problem using a formula are to substitute the values from the verbal problem and then isolate the unknown variable and solve, *or* isolate the unknown variable first and then substitute the values from the problem and solve. Students should recognize which values in a verbal problem represent each variable in a formula.

Additional Example

4 **SEEDING** Mrs. Winston has a small bag of grass seed that will seed 750 square feet. If the area she wants to reseed is 30 feet long, how wide can the area be? 25 feet

3 PRACTICE

Formative Assessment

Use Exercises 1–3 to check for understanding.

Use the chart at the bottom of the next page to customize assignments for your students.

Tips for New Teachers

Area Other area formulas will be discussed in Chapter 11. Preview them by giving students graph paper and having them draw a rectangle on it. They can cut and move parts of the rectangle around to make a triangle and parallelogram. They can then use the formula for the area of a rectangle to find the area of those figures.

Tips for New Teachers

Drawing When solving geometry problems, have students sketch the figure and label it with both known and unknown values.

Additional Answers

24a.

Perimeter = 20 inches		
Length ℓ (in.)	Width w (in.)	Area A (in^2)
9	1	9
8	2	16
7	3	21
6	4	24
5	5	25
4	6	24
3	7	21
2	8	16
1	9	9

24b. **Area of a Rectangle**

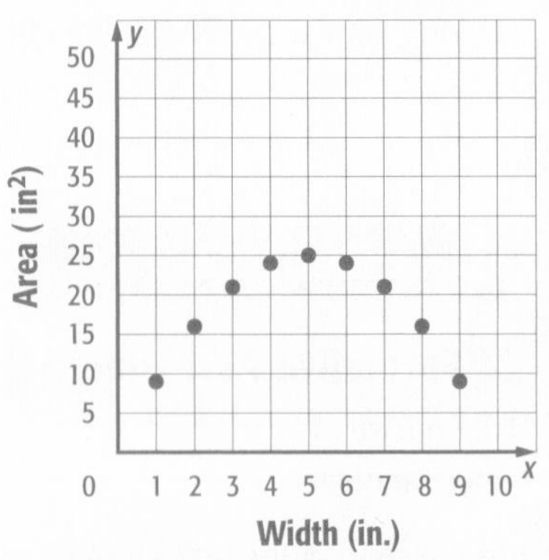

Sample answer: The graph is a curve that starts at (1, 9) and ends at (9, 9). The peak of the curve happens at (5, 25).

Practice and Problem Solving

● = **Step-by-Step Solutions** begin on page R11.
Extra Practice begins on page 810.

Examples 1 and 3 pp. 221–222

Find the perimeter and area for each figure.

4.

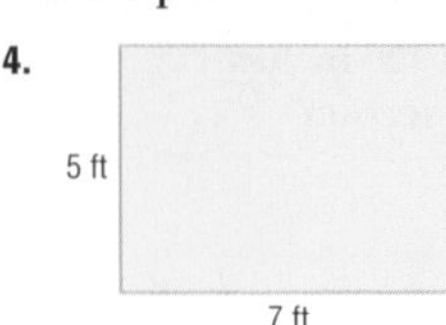

24 ft, 35 ft²

5.

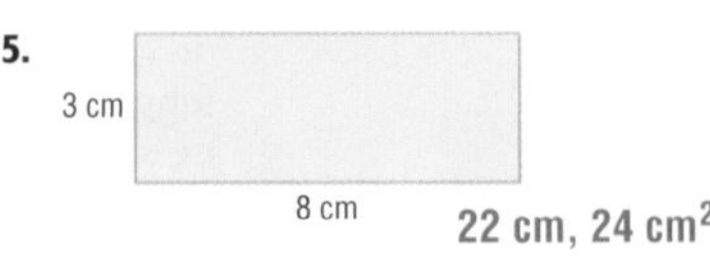

22 cm, 24 cm²

6.

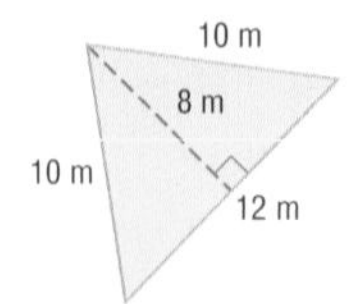

32 m, 48 m²

7.

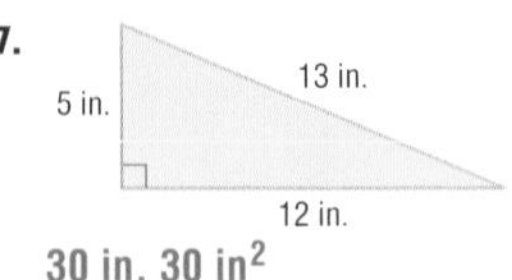

30 in, 30 in²

Example 2 p. 222

8. A rectangle has a length of 16.3 meters and a perimeter of 80.6 meters. What is the width of the rectangle? **24 m**

9. Find the third side of a triangle if the perimeter is $124\frac{1}{4}$ feet and two of the sides each measure $36\frac{3}{4}$ feet. **$50\frac{3}{4}$ ft**

Example 4 p. 223

10. **PARKS** The city park shown at the right has an area of 6889 square meters. The park's length along Front Street is 83 meters. Find the length of the park along Second Avenue. **166 m**

Find the missing dimension for each figure.

11. **12 cm** **12.** **19 ft**

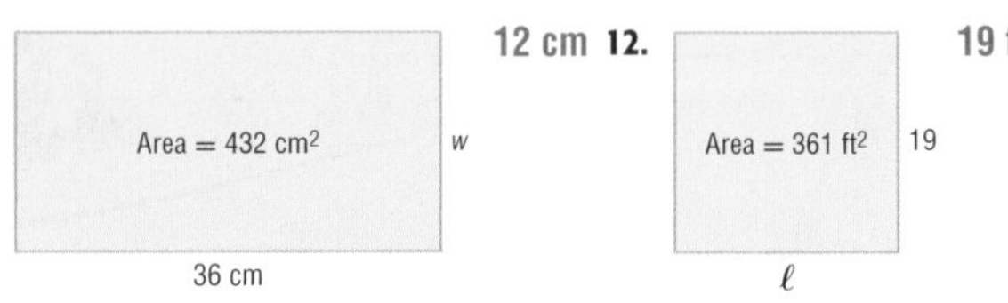

Real-World Link

A pumpkin pie with a 14-foot diameter holds the record for the world's largest pumpkin pie. It took over 10 hours to bake.

Source: American City and Country

13. **FOOD** The circumference of a circle is the distance around the circle. It can be found by using the formula $C \approx 3.14\,d$, where d represents the diameter. Find the circumference of the pie described at the left in inches. **527.52 in.**

14. **GEOMETRY** A *trapezoid* is a four-sided figure with exactly one set of parallel sides.

a. The area of a trapezoid is one half the product of the height h and the sum of the two bases b_1 and b_2. Translate this relationship into a formula. Use the formula to find the area of each trapezoid shown below. $A = \frac{1}{2}h(b_1 + b_2)$

b.

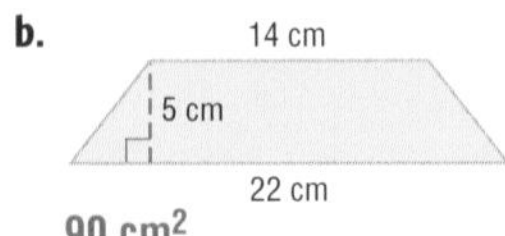

90 cm²

c.

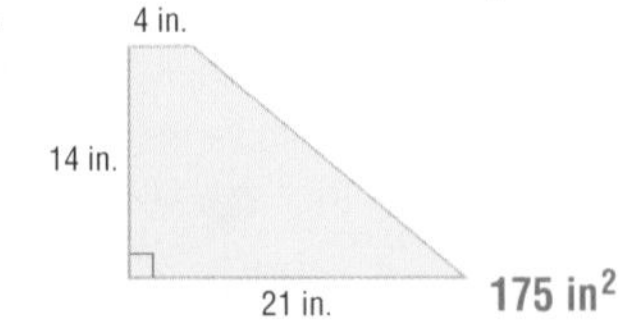

175 in²

Differentiated Homework Options

Level	Assignment	Two-Day Option	
AL Basic	4–10, 25–26, 28–44	5–9 odd, 29–32	4–10 even, 25–26, 28, 33–44
OL Core	5–9 odd, 13–15, 17–23 odd, 24–26, 28–44	4–10, 29–32	11–26, 28, 33–44
BL Advanced	11–41 (optional: 42–44)		

224 Chapter 5 Multi-Step Equations and Inequalities

Problem-Solving Tip

Solve a Simpler Problem Sometimes it is easier to break a problem into parts, solve each part, then combine the solutions of the parts. In Exercise 15b, you know one bag covers 150 square feet. The width of the garden is 15 feet so you will use one bag for every 10 feet of length.

25. Sample answer: The dimensions of a lacrosse field are 330 feet by 180 feet. What is the perimeter and area of the field? $P = 1020$ ft, $A = 59{,}400$ ft^2

26a. true. You can divide a 4×6 rectangle with a total area of 24 square units into four 1×6 rectangles with areas of 6 square units each. The sum of those equals 24 square units.

26b. false. The perimeter of a 4×6 rectangle is 20 units. The perimeter of 4 1×6 rectangles is $4 \cdot 14$ or 56 units.

28. Sample answer: If you double the dimensions of a rectangle, the perimeter will double and the area is multiplied by 4.

15. **GARDENING** Use the diagram of a vegetable garden.

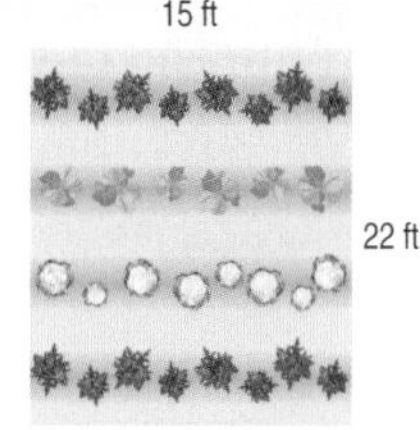

a. You want to put fencing around the garden to keep animals out. How much fencing will you need? **74 ft**

b. If one bag of fertilizer covers 150 square feet, how many bags would you need for the garden? **3**

Find the area of each rectangle.

16. 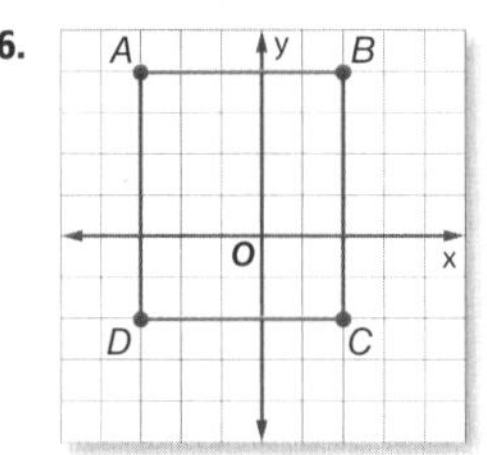

30 units^2

17. 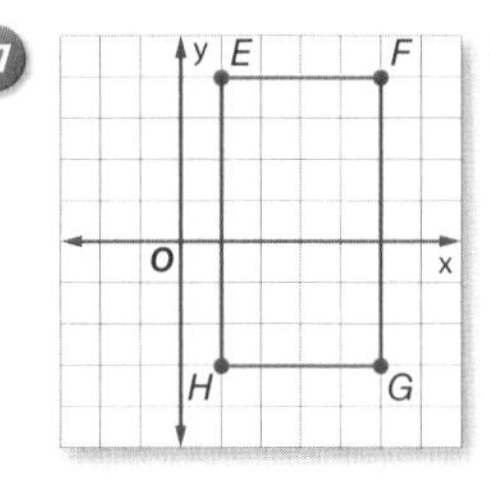

28 units^2

Solve for the indicated variable.

18. $d = rt$ **$\frac{d}{t} = r$**

19. $V = Ah$ **$\frac{V}{A} = h$**

20. $2p = s - t$ **$2p + t = s$**

21. $r = st + p$ **$r - st = p$**

22. $P = 2(\ell + w)$ **$\frac{P}{2} - \ell = w$ or $\frac{P - 2\ell}{2} = w$**

23. $A = \frac{1}{2}bh$ **$\frac{2A}{h} = b$**

24. **MULTIPLE REPRESENTATIONS** In this problem, you will explore a rectangle that has a perimeter of 20 inches. **a–b. See margin.**

a. **TABULAR** Copy and complete the table at the right using only whole number values for the length and the width.

b. **GRAPHICAL** Graph the points (w, A) on a coordinate plane. Describe the graph.

Perimeter = 20 inches		
Length ℓ	Width w	Area A
9	1	9
8	2	16
7	■	■
⋮	■	■
1	■	■

H.O.T. Problems
Use Higher-Order Thinking Skills

25. **OPEN ENDED** Write and solve a real-world problem in which you would use the perimeter or area formula.

26. **REASONING** Classify the following statements as *true* or *false*. Explain your reasoning and provide examples.

a. The area of a larger rectangle that can be divided into smaller rectangles is the sum of the areas of the smaller rectangles.

b. The perimeter of a larger rectangle that can be divided into smaller rectangles is the sum of the perimeters of the smaller rectangles.

27. **CHALLENGE** Find the dimensions of a rectangle with the largest area if the perimeter of the rectangle is 40 feet. **$\ell = 10$ ft, $w = 10$ ft**

28. **WRITING IN MATH** Describe the effect on the perimeter and area of a rectangle if its length and width are doubled.

Multiple Representations In Exercise 24, students use a table of values and a graph to relate the length, width, and area of a rectangle with constant perimeter.

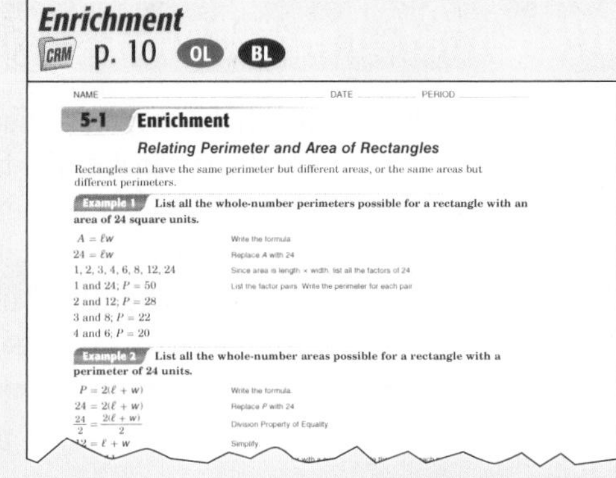
Enrichment CRM p. 10 OL BL

NAME ______ DATE ______ PERIOD ______

5-1 Enrichment

Relating Perimeter and Area of Rectangles

Rectangles can have the same perimeter but different areas, or the same areas but different perimeters.

Example 1 List all the whole-number perimeters possible for a rectangle with an area of 24 square units.

$A = \ell w$ Write the formula
$24 = \ell w$ Replace A with 24
1, 2, 3, 4, 6, 8, 12, 24 Since area is length × width, list all the factors of 24
1 and 24; $P = 50$ List the factor pairs. Write the perimeter for each pair
2 and 12; $P = 28$
3 and 8; $P = 22$
4 and 6; $P = 20$

Example 2 List all the whole-number areas possible for a rectangle with a perimeter of 24 units.

$P = 2(\ell + w)$ Write the formula
$24 = 2(\ell + w)$ Replace P with 24
$\frac{24}{2} = \frac{2(\ell + w)}{2}$ Division Property of Equality
$12 = \ell + w$ Simplify

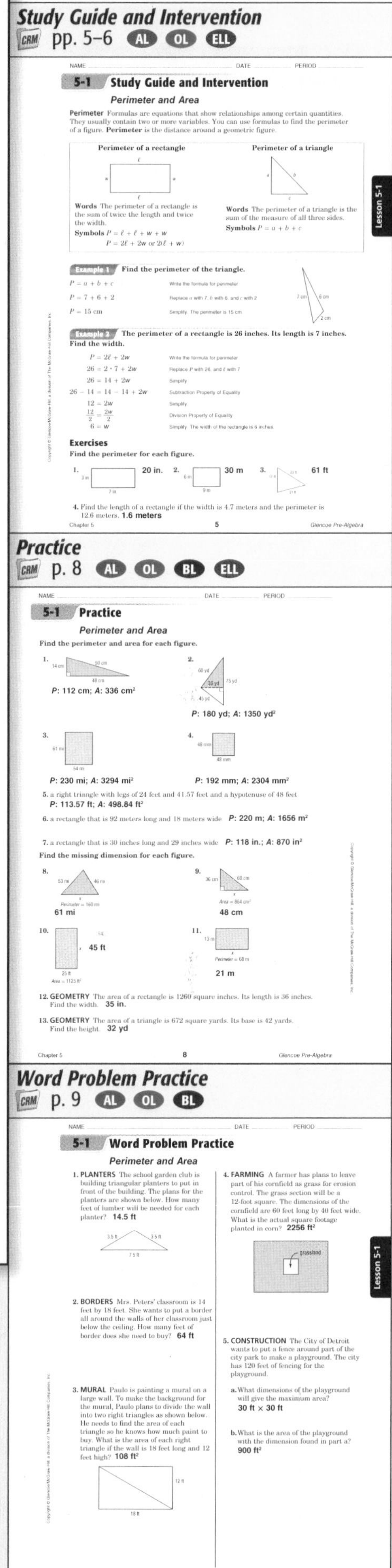
Study Guide and Intervention CRM pp. 5–6 AL OL ELL

NAME ______ DATE ______ PERIOD ______

5-1 Study Guide and Intervention

Perimeter and Area

Perimeter Formulas are equations that show relationships among certain quantities. They usually contain two or more variables. You can use formulas to find the perimeter of a figure. **Perimeter** is the distance around a geometric figure.

Perimeter of a rectangle
Words The perimeter of a rectangle is the sum of twice the length and twice the width.
Symbols $P = \ell + \ell + w + w$
$P = 2\ell + 2w$ or $2(\ell + w)$

Perimeter of a triangle
Words The perimeter of a triangle is the sum of the measure of all three sides.
Symbols $P = a + b + c$

Example 1 Find the perimeter of the triangle.

$P = a + b + c$ Write the formula for perimeter
$P = 7 + 6 + 2$ Replace a with 7, b with 6, and c with 2
$P = 15$ cm Simplify. The perimeter is 15 cm.

Example 2 The perimeter of a rectangle is 26 inches. Its length is 7 inches. Find the width.

$P = 2\ell + 2w$ Write the formula for perimeter
$26 = 2 \cdot 7 + 2w$ Replace P with 26, and ℓ with 7
$26 = 14 + 2w$ Simplify
$26 - 14 = 14 - 14 + 2w$ Subtraction Property of Equality
$12 = 2w$ Simplify
$\frac{12}{2} = \frac{2w}{2}$ Division Property of Equality
$6 = w$ Simplify. The width of the rectangle is 6 inches.

Exercises
Find the perimeter for each figure.

1. **20 in.** 2. **30 m** 3. **61 ft**

4. Find the length of a rectangle if the width is 4.7 meters and the perimeter is 12.6 meters. **1.6 meters**

Chapter 5 5 Glencoe Pre-Algebra

Practice CRM p. 8 AL OL BL ELL

NAME ______ DATE ______ PERIOD ______

5-1 Practice

Perimeter and Area

Find the perimeter and area for each figure.

1. **P: 112 cm; A: 336 cm²**
2. **P: 180 yd; A: 1350 yd²**
3. **P: 230 mi; A: 3294 mi²**
4. **P: 192 mm; A: 2304 mm²**

5. a right triangle with legs of 24 feet and 41.57 feet and a hypotenuse of 48 feet **P: 113.57 ft; A: 498.84 ft²**

6. a rectangle that is 92 meters long and 18 meters wide **P: 220 m; A: 1656 m²**

7. a rectangle that is 30 inches long and 29 inches wide **P: 118 in.; A: 870 in²**

Find the missing dimension for each figure.

8. Perimeter = 160 mi **61 mi**
9. Area = 864 cm² **48 cm**
10. Area = 1125 ft² **45 ft**
11. Perimeter = 68 m **21 m**

12. **GEOMETRY** The area of a rectangle is 1260 square inches. Its length is 36 inches. Find the width. **35 in.**

13. **GEOMETRY** The area of a triangle is 672 square yards. Its base is 42 yards. Find the height. **32 yd**

Chapter 5 8 Glencoe Pre-Algebra

Word Problem Practice CRM p. 9 AL OL BL

NAME ______ DATE ______ PERIOD ______

5-1 Word Problem Practice

Perimeter and Area

1. **PLANTERS** The school garden club is building triangular planters to put in front of the building. The plans for the planters are shown below. How many feet of lumber will be needed for each planter? **14.5 ft**

2. **BORDERS** Mrs. Peters' classroom is 14 feet by 18 feet. She wants to put a border all around the walls of her classroom just below the ceiling. How many feet of border does she need to buy? **64 ft**

3. **MURAL** Paulo is painting a mural on a large wall. To make the background for the mural, Paulo plans to divide the wall into two right triangles as shown below. He needs to find the area of each triangle so he knows how much paint to buy. What is the area of each right triangle if the wall is 18 feet long and 12 feet high? **108 ft²**

4. **FARMING** A farmer has plans to leave part of his cornfield as grass for erosion control. The grass section will be a 12-foot square. The dimensions of the cornfield are 60 feet long by 40 feet wide. What is the actual square footage planted in corn? **2256 ft²**

5. **CONSTRUCTION** The City of Detroit wants to put a fence around part of the city park to make a playground. The city has 120 feet of fencing for the playground.

a. What dimensions of the playground will give the maximum area? **30 ft × 30 ft**

b. What is the area of the playground with the dimension found in part a? **900 ft²**

Chapter 5 9 Glencoe Pre-Algebra

4 ASSESS

Ticket Out the Door Cut out rectangles of various sizes and give one to each student. Have students find the perimeter and area of their rectangles by measuring the sides with a ruler and applying the correct formulas. As students leave the classroom, have them turn in their solutions.

Standardized Test Practice

29. The rectangle below has a perimeter of P yards. **C**

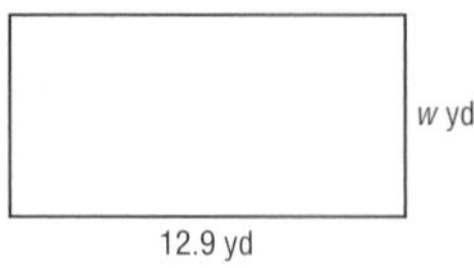

Which of the following could be used to find the width of the rectangle?

A $w = P - 12.9$

B $w = P - 25.8$

C $w = \frac{P}{2} - 12.9$

D $w = \frac{P}{2} - 25.8$

30. If the width of a rectangle is doubled but its length remains the same, what will happen to its area? **G**

F The area will be four times as large.

G The area will be twice as large.

H The area will not change.

J The area will be three times as large.

31. An architect designed a great room for the Martes family. The small carpeted areas are 8 foot squares. The rest of the floor is wood.

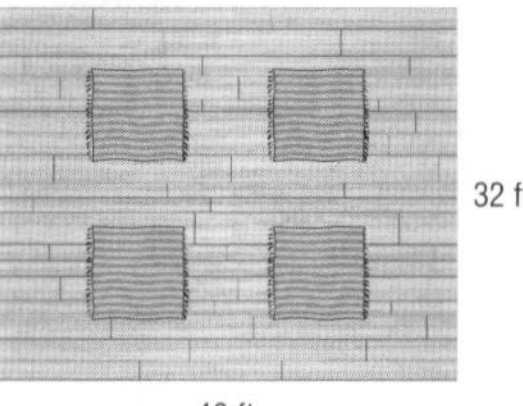

What is the area in square feet of the floor that is *not* carpeted? **C**

A 64

B 256

C 1024

D 1280

32. **GRIDDED RESPONSE** A rectangular desk in a classroom is 6 inches longer than it is wide. The perimeter of the desk is 84 inches. What is its length in inches? **24**

Spiral Review

33. **TEMPERATURE** Suppose the current temperature is 17°F. It is expected to rise 3°F each hour for the next several hours. Write and solve an equation to find in how many hours the temperature will be 32°F. (Lesson 4-6) **$17 + 3x = 32$, 5 h**

Solve each equation. Check your solution. (Lesson 4-5)

34. $22 = 8k - 18$ **5**

35. $8 = \frac{c}{-3} + 15$ **21**

36. $5r + 3r - 6 = 10$ **2**

MEASUREMENT **The table shows several conversions in the customary system. Write and solve an equation to find each quantity.** (Lesson 4-4)

Customary System (length)		
1 mile	=	5280 feet
1 mile	=	1760 yards
1 yard	=	3 feet
1 foot	=	12 inches
1 yard	=	36 inches

37. the number of feet in 132 inches **$12f = 132$; 11 ft**

38. the number of yards in 15 feet **$3y = 15$; 5 yd**

39. the number of miles in 10,560 feet **$5280m = 10{,}560$; 2 mi**

Find each quotient. (Lesson 2-5)

40. $-64 \div (-8)$ **8**

41. $72 \div (-9)$ **−8**

Skills Review

Evaluate each expression. (Lesson 1-2)

42. $6w - 4$ if $w = 9$ **50**

43. $45 - 4x$ if $x = 12$ **−3**

44. $-7b - 9$ if $b = -6$ **33**

Differentiated Instruction

Extension Have students sketch the shape described and find the missing values: One large rectangle is divided into 3 smaller rectangles. The largest rectangle of these is 12 meters wide and 6 meters long. Underneath it, side-by-side, lie the other two rectangles. One of these measures 8 meters long and has an area of 32 square meters. Its width is x meters. Find x, as well as the area A of the last smaller rectangle, and the perimeter P of the large rectangle, comprised of the three smaller rectangles. Check students' sketches. Possible answers: $x = 4$, $A = 16\text{ m}^2$, $P = 52$ m

Perimeter and Area

Math Online glencoe.com
- Other Calculator Keystrokes
- Graphing Technology Personal Tutor

A spreadsheet allows you to use formulas to investigate problems. When you change a numerical value in a cell, the spreadsheet recalculates the formula and automatically updates the results.

ACTIVITY

Kina wants to build a kennel for her dog using 50 feet of fencing. She wants the dog to have the largest possible play area. Find the whole number dimensions of the kennel.

Dog Kennel

	A	B	C
1	Length of Fencing Material	50	
2	Length of Kennel	Width of Kennel	Area
3	1	24	24
4	2	23	46
5	3	22	66
6	4	21	84
7	5	20	100
8	6	19	114
9	7	18	126
10	8	17	136
11	9	16	144
12	10	15	150
13	11	14	154
14	12	13	156
15	13	12	156
16	14	11	154

Sheet 1 | Sheet 2 | Sheet 3

If ℓ represents the length, then $25 - \ell$ represents the width. The spreadsheet evaluates the formula 25 − A3.

The spreadsheet evaluates the formula A9 • B9.

The largest area is 156 square feet. It occurs when the length is 12 feet and the width is 13 feet or the length is 13 feet and the width is 12 feet.

Analyze the Results

1. What happens to the area as the length of the kennel increases beyond 14 feet? **It begins to decrease again.**
2. Suppose you want to find the largest area you can enclose with 70 feet of fencing. Which cell should you modify to solve this problem? **Cell B1**
3. Use a spreadsheet to find the whole number dimensions of the greatest area you can enclose with 60 feet, 70 feet, and 80 feet. **See margin.**
4. **MAKE A CONJECTURE** Use any pattern you may have observed in your answers to find the dimensions of the greatest area you can enclose with 100 feet of fencing. **A square with sides of 25 feet.**

From Concrete to Abstract

Use Exercise 4 to assess whether students can apply what they have learned using spreadsheets to find the dimensions of the greatest area for a given perimeter.

Extending the Concept

Ask:

- What is the greatest area that can be enclosed with 1200 feet of fencing if a wall is used as one side? 180,000 ft^2

Additional Answer

3. 60 ft: 15 ft by 15 ft with an area of 225 ft^2.
   70 ft: 17 ft by 18 ft with an area of 306 ft^2.
   80 ft: 20 ft by 20 ft with an area of 400 ft^2.

EXTEND 5-1 Lesson Notes

1 FOCUS

Objective Use a spreadsheet to solve real-world problems involving perimeter and area.

Materials for Each Group

- computer with spreadsheet software

Teaching Tip

In a spreadsheet, columns are labeled A, B, C and rows are labeled 1, 2, 3. To name a cell, you need to indicate the column and row. For example, A7 specifies column A, row 7.

2 TEACH

Working in Cooperative Groups

Arrange students in groups of two or three, mixing abilities. Then have groups complete the Activity.

Ask:

- Which row on the spreadsheet provides the kennel with the least area? row 3
- Which rows on the spreadsheet provide the kennel with the greatest area? rows 14 and 15
- Explain each term in the formula 25 – A3. 25 is half the perimeter and A3 is the length of the kennel.
- What happens between $\ell = 12$ and $\ell = 13$? When $\ell = 12.5$, the area is the largest.

Practice Have students complete Exercises 1–4.

3 ASSESS

Formative Assessment

Use Exercise 3 to assess whether students comprehend how to find the maximum area using a spreadsheet.

EXPLORE 5-2

Lesson Notes

1 FOCUS

Objective Use algebra tiles to solve equations with variables on each side of the equation.

Materials for Each Group

- algebra tiles
- equation mat

Easy to Make Manipulatives

Teaching Pre-Algebra with Manipulatives, templates for:

- algebra tiles, pp. 7–8
- equation mat, p. 13

Teaching Tip

Remind students that even though the x-tiles are slightly larger than the numerical tiles, the x-tiles could represent values much larger or smaller than 1.

2 TEACH

Working in Cooperative Groups

Arrange students in groups of two or three, mixing abilities. Have groups work through the Activity.

Ask:

- Why does adding and removing tiles to solve the equation work in this Activity? Adding and removing tiles maintains balance on both sides of the equation and gets the variable alone to solve the equation.

Practice Have students complete Exercises 1–6.

3 ASSESS

Formative Assessment

Use Exercise 5 to assess whether students comprehend using algebra tiles to solve equations with variables on each side.

EXPLORE 5-2

Algebra Lab: Equations with Variables on Each Side

Math Online  glencoe.com
Math *in Motion,* Animation

Use algebra tiles to solve equations with variables on each side of the equation.

ACTIVITY

Solve $2x - 5 = 3x + 3$ using algebra tiles.

Step 1

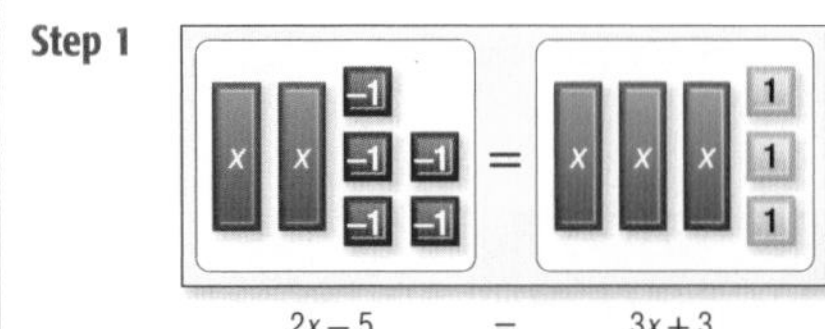

Model the equation.

Step 2

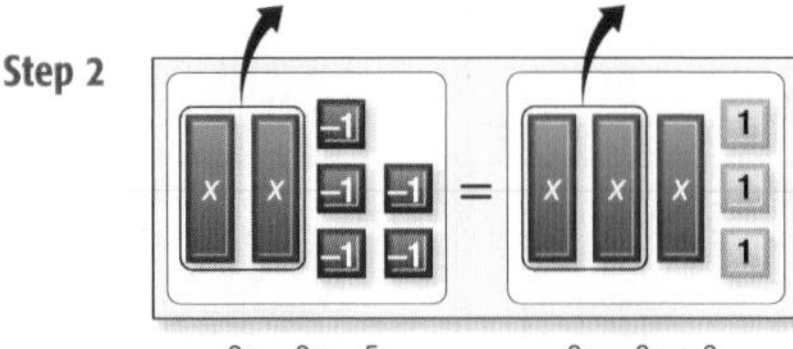

Remove two x-tiles from each side of the mat. All of the x-tiles are on one side of the mat.

Step 3

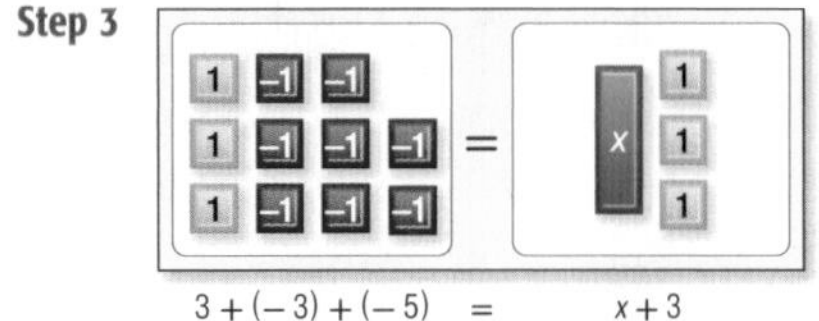

It is not possible to remove three 1-tiles from each side of the mat. So, add 3 zero pairs to the left side of the mat.

Step 4

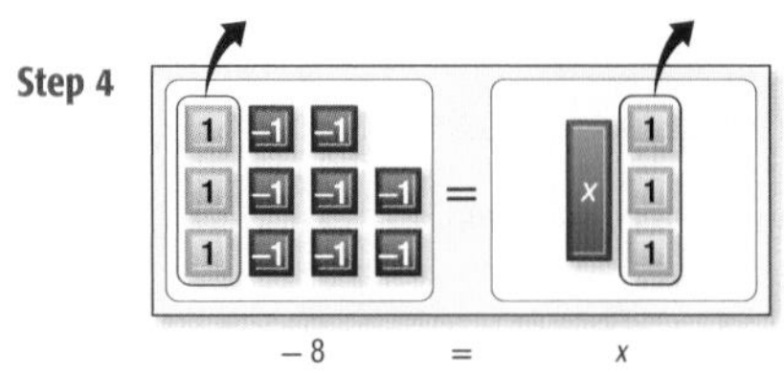

Now you can remove three 1-tiles from each side. There are 8 negative tiles on the left side of the mat.

The solution is –8.

Analyze the Results

Use algebra tiles to model and solve each equation. 1–4. See Chapter 5 Answer Appendix.

1. $4x - 3 = 3x + 1$
2. $2x + 6 = 5x - 3$
3. $x + 8 = 3x - 4$
4. $2x - 5 = 5x + 4$
5. Does it matter whether you remove x-tiles or 1-tiles first? Explain. See margin.
6. What property of equality allows you to remove an x-tile from each side of the mat? Subtraction Property of Equality

From Concrete to Abstract

Show with algebra tiles how to solve the equation $6x + 3 = 2x + 1$. After solving it on the equation mat, tell students to write the equation and the steps involved in solving it on paper.

Additional Answer

5. no; Sample answer: You can remove either tile first. But it is a good idea to remove the 1-tile first because you are using the work backward strategy.

5-2

Solving Equations with Variables on Each Side

Then

You have already solved two-step equations. (Lesson 4-5)

Now

- Solve equations with variables on each side.
- Solve equations that involve grouping symbols.

Math Online

glencoe.com

- Extra Examples
- Personal Tutor
- Self-Check Quiz
- Homework Help

Why?

Antelopes and zebras are racing to a watering hole. The antelope can travel 90 feet per second while the zebra travels 60 feet per second. The zebra has a 120-foot head start.

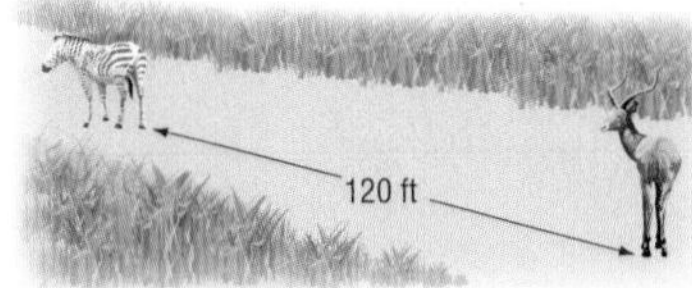

a. Write an expression for the distance covered by the antelope in t seconds. $90t$

b. Write an expression for the total distance covered by the zebra in t seconds. $60t$

c. Are the two expressions equal? How could you show they are equal? No; Sample answer: Add 120 to the shorter distance. So, $60t + 120 = 90t$.

Equations with Variables on Each Side The equation $90t = 60t + 120$ represents the point in the race when the antelope catches up to the zebra. To solve equations with variables on each side, use the Addition or Subtraction Property of Equality to write an equivalent equation with the variables on one side. Then solve the equation.

EXAMPLE 1 Equations with Variables on Each Side

Solve $3x = x + 8$.

$3x = x + 8$ Write the equation.

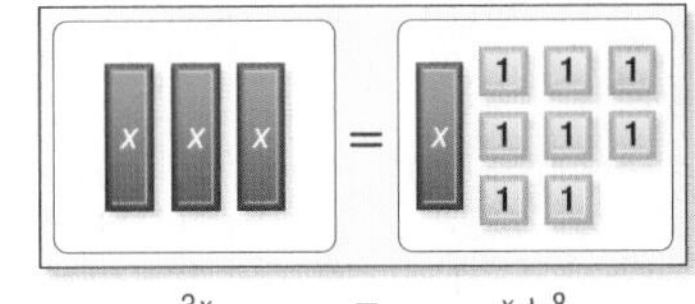

$3x = x + 8$ Subtact x from each side.
$\underline{-x = -x}$
$2x = 8$ Simplify.

$3x - x \quad = \quad x - x + 8$

$\frac{2x}{2} = \frac{8}{2}$ Divide each side by 2.

$x = 4$ Simplify.

$2x \quad = \quad 8$

The solution is 4.

Check Your Progress

Solve each equation.

1A. $7x = 5x + 4$ 2

1B. $3x - 2 = x + 4$ 3

Personal Tutor glencoe.com

5-2 Lesson Notes

1 FOCUS

Vertical Alignment

Before Lesson 5-2
Solve two-step equations.

Lesson 5-2
Solve equations with variables on each side.
Solve equations that involve grouping symbols.

After Lesson 5-2
Use the methods learned in solving equations to solve inequalities.

2 TEACH

Scaffolding Questions

Have students read the *Why?* section of the lesson and answer the questions.

Ask:

- What does the variable in the expression represent? time in seconds
- What does the 120 represent in the equation? the 120-foot head start that the zebra had
- What equation could you write to represent the situation? $90t = 60t + 120$

Lesson 5-2 Resources

Resource	Approaching-Level	On-Level	Beyond-Level	English Learners
Teacher Edition	• Differentiated Instruction, p. 230	• Differentiated Instruction, p. 230	• Differentiated Instruction, p. 233	• Differentiated Instruction, p. 230
Chapter Resource Masters	• Study Guide and Intervention, pp. 12–13 • Skills Practice, p. 14 • Practice, p. 15 • Word Problem Practice, p. 16	• Study Guide and Intervention, pp. 12–13 • Skills Practice, p. 14 • Practice, p. 15 • Word Problem Practice, p. 16 • Enrichment, p. 17	• Practice, p. 15 • Word Problem Practice, p. 16 • Enrichment, p. 17	• Study Guide and Intervention, pp. 12–13 • Skills Practice, p. 14 • Practice, p. 15
Transparencies	• 5-Minute Check Transparency 5-2	• 5-Minute Check Transparency 5-2	• 5-Minute Check Transparency 5-2	• 5-Minute Check Transparency 5-2
Other	• Study Notebook • Teaching Pre-Algebra with Manipulatives	• Study Notebook • Teaching Pre-Algebra with Manipulatives	• Study Notebook	• Study Notebook • Teaching Pre-Algebra with Manipulatives

Equations with Variables on Each Side

Examples 1–3 show how to isolate the variable to one side of an equation that has variables on both sides.

Formative Assessment

Use the Check Your Progress exercises after each example to determine students' understanding of concepts.

Additional Examples

1 Solve $5x + 12 = 2x$. -4

2 Solve $7x + 3 = 2x + 23$. Check your solution. 4

3 **CAR RENTAL** A car rental agency has two plans. Under Plan A, a car rents for \$80 plus \$20 each day. Under Plan B, a car rents for \$120 plus \$15 a day. Write and solve an equation to determine for what number of days the costs of the two plans will be equal. $80 + 20d = 120 + 15d$; 8 days

Additional Examples also in Interactive Classroom PowerPoint® Presentations

IWB INTERACTIVE WHITEBOARD READY

Focus on Mathematical Content

Equations The main objective in solving two-step equations is similar to solving any equation: Use inverse operations to isolate the variable on one side of the equation.

StudyTip

Solve a Simpler Equation Notice that the equations in the third step of each solution are similar to the equations that you solved in Lesson 4-5.

EXAMPLE 2 Equations with Variables on Each Side

Solve $7y + 8 = 4y - 10$. Check your solution.

$7y + 8 = 4y - 10$	Write the equation.
$7y - 4y + 8 = 4y - 4y - 10$	Subtract 4*y* from each side.
$3y + 8 = -10$	Simplify.
$3y + 8 - 8 = -10 - 8$	Subtract 8 from each side.
$3y = -18$	Simplify.
$y = -6$	Mentally divide each side by 3.
Check $7y + 8 = 4y - 10$	Write the equation.
$7(-6) + 8 \stackrel{?}{=} 4(-6) - 10$	Substitute –6 for *y*.
$-42 + 8 \stackrel{?}{=} -24 - 10$	Check to see whether this sentence is true.
$-34 = -34$ ✓	The sentence is true.

Check Your Progress

Solve each equation. Check your solution.

2A. $2x + 3 = 3x - 2$ **5** **2B.** $5p + 15 = p - 49$ **−16**

Personal Tutor glencoe.com

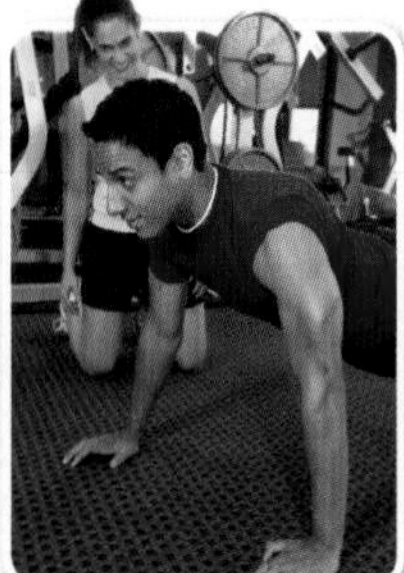

Real-World Link

Personal trainers can help teens build strength in order to avoid injuries in sports. Trainers for teenagers should be certified by a nationally recognized organization.

Source: IDEA Health & Fitness Association

Real-World EXAMPLE 3 Solve Equations with Variables on Each Side

EXERCISE A personal trainer charges a one time fee of \$60 plus \$25 for each individual session. A new fitness club charges a yearly fee of \$450 plus \$10 for each session with a personal trainer. Write and solve an equation to determine for what number of sessions will the costs be equal.

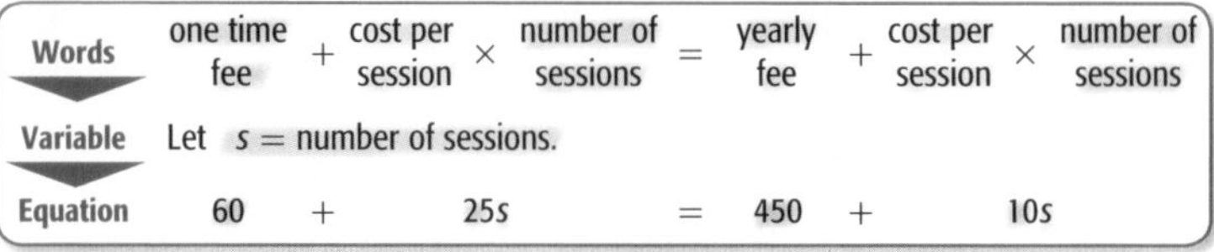

Words	one time fee	+	cost per session	×	number of sessions	=	yearly fee	+	cost per session	×	number of sessions
Variable	Let s = number of sessions.										
Equation	60	+		$25s$		=	450	+		$10s$	

$60 + 25s = 450 + 10s$	Write the equation.
$60 + 25s - 10s = 450 + 10s - 10s$	Subtract 10*s* from each side.
$60 + 15s = 450$	Simplify.
$60 - 60 + 15s = 450 - 60$	Subtract 60 from each side.
$15s = 390$	Simplify.
$\frac{15s}{15} = \frac{390}{15}$	Divide each side by 15.
$26 = s$	Simplify.

You would need to have 26 trainer sessions in order for the costs to be equal.

Check Your Progress

3. CRUISES Red Bird Cruises charges \$85 per day plus a one-time fee of \$75 for taxes and gratuities. King Cruises charges \$100 per day plus a fee of \$30. Write and solve an equation to determine for what number of days the charge for the cruises will be the same. $75 + 85d = 30 + 100d$; **3 days**

Personal Tutor glencoe.com

Differentiated Instruction

AL OL ELL

If students have trouble solving multi-step equations,

Then on index cards, have students write an equation that requires several steps to solve, such as $8c + 16 = 4c - 4$. Then, on separate cards, have them write out in words each step necessary to solve the equation, such as, "Subtract 4*c* from each side." Students should shuffle the cards, exchange sets with a partner, and place the cards in the correct order. They can then find a solution.

Check Your Understanding

Examples 1 and 2 pp. 229–230

Solve each equation. Check your solution.

1. $x + 6 = 3x$ **3**
2. $4y = 2y - 10$ **−5**
3. $7z - 4 = 12 + 3z$ **4**
4. $10t - 3 = t + 15$ **2**
5. $28 - x = 3x - 84$ **28**
6. $2p - 7 = 13 - 8p$ **2**

Example 3 p. 230

7. **MONEY** An Internet movie rental company charges a yearly membership fee of $50 plus $1.99 per DVD rental. Your neighborhood rental store has no membership fee and charges $3.99 per DVD rental. Write and solve an equation to find the number of DVDs so the cost for each will be the same. **$50 + 1.99m = 3.99m$; 25 DVDs**

Practice and Problem Solving

● = **Step-by-Step Solutions** begin on page R11. **Extra Practice** begins on page 810.

Examples 1 and 2 pp. 229–230

Solve each equation. Check your solution.

8. $2x + 3 = x$ **−3**
9. $8 - v = 7v$ **1**
10. $8 - 2c = 2c$ **2**
11. $q - 2 = -q + 1$ **$\frac{3}{2}$**
12. $-2 + x = -2 + 2x$ **0**
13. $14 + 3a = -2a - 1$ **−3**
14. $12p = p + 14 + p$ **1.4**
15. $5b - 4b = 6b - 2$ **$\frac{2}{5}$**

Example 3 p. 230

16. **CAR RENTALS** Use the table at the right to write and solve an equation to find the number of miles a rental car must be driven for each option to cost the same for one day. **$25 + 0.45m = 40 + 0.25m$; 75 mi**

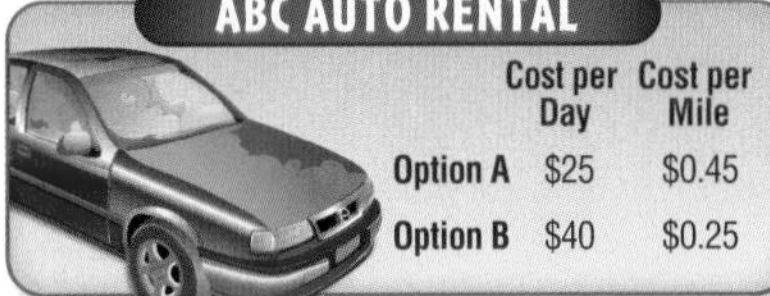

ABC AUTO RENTAL

	Cost per Day	Cost per Mile
Option A	$25	$0.45
Option B	$40	$0.25

17. **MUSIC DOWNLOADS** Denzel is comparing websites for downloading music. One charges a $5 membership fee plus $0.50 per song. Another charges $1.00 per song, but has no membership fee. Write and solve an equation to find how many songs Denzel would have to buy to spend the same amount at both websites. **$5 + 0.5s = s$; 10 songs**

Solve each equation. Check your solution.

18. $3.2 + 0.3x = 0.2x + 1.4$ **−18**
19. $0.4x = 2x + 1.2$ **−0.75**
20. $7.2 - 3c = 2c - 2$ **1.84**
21. $3 - 3.7b = 10.3b + 10$ **−0.5**
22. $-\frac{1}{4}x + 6 = \frac{2}{3}x + 28$ **−24**
23. $\frac{2}{5}x - 8 = 20 + \frac{3}{4}x$ **−80**

24. **SHOPPING** Gabriella bought some school supplies for $48 and then bought 3 CDs. Min did not buy any school supplies but bought 7 CDs. All the CDs cost the same amount and they both spent the same amount of money. Write and solve an equation to find the cost of one CD. **$48 + 3c = 7c$; $12**

25. **FINANCIAL LITERACY** One cell phone company charges $19.95 a month plus $0.21 per text message, and a second company charges $24.95 per month plus $0.16 per text message. For how many text messages is the cost of the plans the same? **100 text messages**

3 PRACTICE

Formative Assessment

Use Exercises 1–7 to check for understanding.

Use the chart at the bottom of this page to customize assignments for your students.

Tips for New Teachers

Graphing Calculator You can show solutions for the example problems using a graphing calculator. Enter each side of the equation as separate equations in y_1 and y_2. The x-coordinate of their intersection point is the solution to the equation because this number makes both sides of the equation equal.

Tips for New Teachers

H.O.T. Problems Cooperative groups can discuss and complete many of the H.O.T. problems. Provide forms so students can take the role of group leader, recorder, and presenter. Then, after they have completed the problem, they can present their solution to the class.

TEACH with TECH

VIDEO SHARING WEB SITE Create a video of yourself solving equations with variables on each side. Post the video so that your students have an additional reference outside of class.

Differentiated Homework Options

Level	Assignment	Two-Day Option	
AL Basic	8–17, 30–31, 33–49	9–17 odd, 35–38	8–16 even, 30–31, 33–34, 39–49
OL Core	9–23 odd, 24–31, 33–49	8–17, 35–38	18–31, 33–34, 39–49
BL Advanced	18–46 (optional: 47–49)		

Study Guide and Intervention
CRM pp. 12–13 AL OL ELL

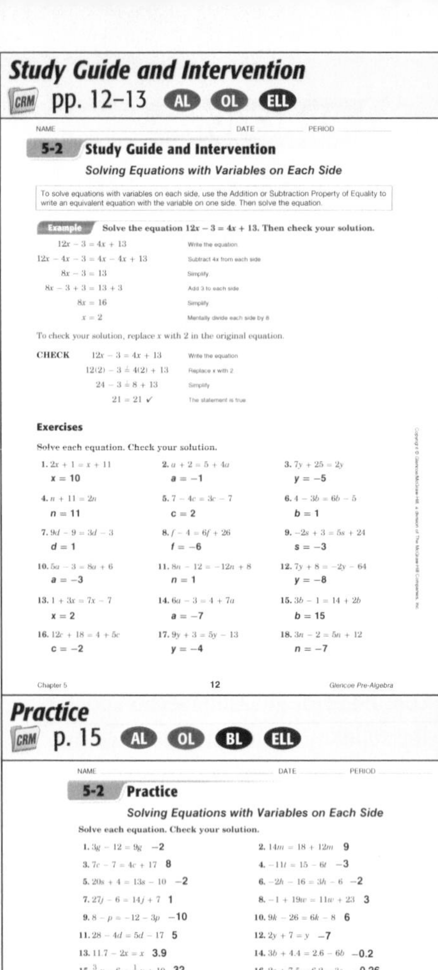
NAME ______ DATE ______ PERIOD ______

5-2 Study Guide and Intervention

Solving Equations with Variables on Each Side

To solve equations with variables on each side, use the Addition or Subtraction Property of Equality to write an equivalent equation with the variable on one side. Then solve the equation.

Example Solve the equation $12x - 3 = 4x + 13$. Then check your solution.

$12x - 3 = 4x + 13$ Write the equation.
$12x - 4x - 3 = 4x - 4x + 13$ Subtract 4x from each side.
$8x - 3 = 13$ Simplify.
$8x - 3 + 3 = 13 + 3$ Add 3 to each side.
$8x = 16$ Simplify.
$x = 2$ Mentally divide each side by 8.

To check your solution, replace x with 2 in the original equation.

CHECK $12x - 3 = 4x + 13$ Write the equation.
$12(2) - 3 \stackrel{?}{=} 4(2) + 13$ Replace x with 2.
$24 - 3 \stackrel{?}{=} 8 + 13$ Simplify.
$21 = 21$ ✓ The statement is true.

Exercises

Solve each equation. Check your solution.

1. $2x + 1 = x + 11$ $x = 10$
2. $a + 2 = 5 + 4a$ $a = -1$
3. $7y + 25 = 2y$ $y = -5$
4. $n + 11 = 2n$ $n = 11$
5. $7 - 4c = 3c - 7$ $c = 2$
6. $4 - 3b = 6b - 5$ $b = 1$
7. $9d - 9 = 3d - 3$ $d = 1$
8. $f - 4 = 6f + 26$ $f = -6$
9. $-2s + 3 = 5s + 24$ $s = -3$
10. $5a - 3 = 8a + 6$ $a = -3$
11. $8n - 12 = -12n + 8$ $n = 1$
12. $7y + 8 = -2y - 64$ $y = -8$
13. $1 + 3x = 7x - 7$ $x = 2$
14. $6a - 3 = 4 + 7a$ $a = -7$
15. $3b - 1 = 14 + 2b$ $b = 15$
16. $12c + 18 = 4 + 5c$ $c = -2$
17. $9y + 3 = 5y - 13$ $y = -4$
18. $3n - 2 = 5n + 12$ $n = -7$

Chapter 5 12 Glencoe Pre-Algebra

Practice
CRM p. 15 AL OL BL ELL

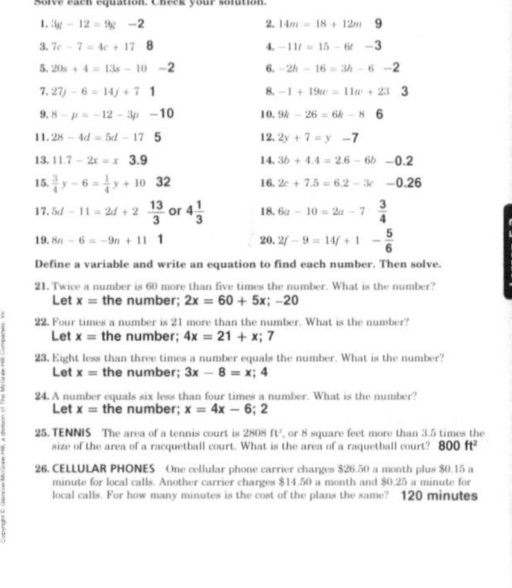
NAME ______ DATE ______ PERIOD ______

5-2 Practice

Solving Equations with Variables on Each Side

Solve each equation. Check your solution.

1. $3g - 12 = 9g$ -2
2. $14m = 18 + 12m$ 9
3. $7c - 7 = 4c + 17$ 8
4. $-11t = 15 - 6t$ -3
5. $20k + 4 = 13k - 10$ -2
6. $-2h - 16 = 3h - 6$ -2
7. $27j - 6 = 14j + 7$ 1
8. $-1 + 19w = 11w + 23$ 3
9. $8 - p = -12 - 3p$ -10
10. $9k - 26 = 6k - 8$ 6
11. $28 - 4d = 5d - 17$ 5
12. $2y + 7 = y$ -7
13. $11.7 - 2x = x$ 3.9
14. $3b + 4.4 = 2.6 - 6b$ -0.2
15. $\frac{3}{4}y - 6 = \frac{1}{4}y + 10$ 32
16. $2c + 7.5 = 6.2 - 3c$ -0.26
17. $5d - 11 = 2d + 2$ $\frac{13}{3}$ or $4\frac{1}{3}$
18. $6a - 10 = 2a - 7$ $\frac{3}{4}$
19. $8n - 6 = -9n + 11$ 1
20. $2f - 9 = 14f + 1$ $-\frac{5}{6}$

Define a variable and write an equation to find each number. Then solve.

21. Twice a number is 60 more than five times the number. What is the number? Let x = the number; $2x = 60 + 5x$; -20
22. Four times a number is 21 more than the number. What is the number? Let x = the number; $4x = 21 + x$; 7
23. Eight less than three times a number equals the number. What is the number? Let x = the number; $3x - 8 = x$; 4
24. A number equals six less than four times a number. What is the number? Let x = the number; $x = 4x - 6$; 2
25. **TENNIS** The area of a tennis court is 2808 ft², or 8 square feet more than 3.5 times the size of the area of a racquetball court. What is the area of a racquetball court? 800 ft²
26. **CELLULAR PHONES** One cellular phone carrier charges \$26.50 a month plus \$0.15 a minute for local calls. Another carrier charges \$14.50 a month and \$0.25 a minute for local calls. For how many minutes is the cost of the plans the same? 120 minutes

Chapter 5 15 Glencoe Pre-Algebra

Word Problem Practice
CRM p. 16 AL OL BL

NAME ______ DATE ______ PERIOD ______

5-2 Word Problem Practice

Solving Equations with Variables on Each Side

1. **BALLOONING** One hot air balloon is 15 meters above the ground, and is rising at a rate of 20 meters per minute. A second balloon is 195 meters above the ground, and is descending at a rate of 16 meters per minute. In how many minutes will the two balloons be at the same height? **5 minutes**

2. **TRANSPORTATION** A commuter train pulling 8 cars had room for another 84 passengers. Halfway through the commute, the train had to be taken out of service. All of the passengers were transferred to another commuter train that had 6 cars with the same capacity as those in the first train. After all of the passengers transferred to the replacement train, there was room for only 10 more people. What is the maximum number of passengers that each car can transport? **37 passengers**

3. **CAR RENTALS** The table below shows what two rental companies charge for an intermediate 4-door sedan. How many miles must a driver drive in one day to make First Choice a less expensive option? **more than 425 miles**

	First Choice Car	Best Rent-A-Car
Daily charge	\$65	\$48
Cost per mile	\$0.06	\$0.10

4. **TRAVEL** Cindy is saving for a trip to Hawaii. Each week, she puts aside the same amount of money for her airfare. After 9 weeks of saving, she needs \$390 more for her airfare. After 14 weeks, she still needs \$240. How much is the airfare to Hawaii? How much does Cindy put aside each week for her airfare? **\$660; \$30**

5. **PLUMBING** Josh has two leaking pipes in his basement. While waiting for the plumber to come, Josh puts a bucket under each leak. The two buckets have the same capacity. The bucket under the first leak fills in 20 minutes. The bucket under the second leak fills in 35 minutes.

a. Josh's brother takes away one of the buckets and places the one bucket under the two leaks. About how long will it take for the one bucket to fill completely? **approximately 12.7 minutes**

b. Josh wraps a cloth around the first leak, which cuts the rate of that leak in half. At the same time, it doubles the rate of the second leak. How will this affect the time it takes to fill the bucket? **It will now take approximately 12.2 minutes.**

Chapter 5 16 Glencoe Pre-Algebra

Real-World Link

Twenty-two states have borders on at least one of three oceans for a total of 12,383 miles of ocean coastline. Alaska alone accounts for 6640 miles of coast.

29. Sample answer: Use the information in the figure to write and solve an equation; $w = 55$ ft, $w + 40 = 95$ ft, $w + 45 = 100$ ft

26. **AGES** Five years ago Ang was $\frac{1}{2}$ as old as Paula. Now he is $\frac{3}{5}$ as old as Paula. Complete the table shown below. Then use the table to write and solve an equation to find their current ages. $\frac{1}{2}a + 5 = \frac{3}{5}(a + 5)$ **Paula: 25 years old, Ang: 15 years old**

Student	5 years ago	Now
Ang	$\frac{1}{2}a$	■
Paula	a	$a + 5$

27. **COASTLINE** Florida's coastline is 118 miles shorter than four times the coastline of Texas. It is also 983 miles longer than the coastline of Texas. Find the lengths of the coastlines of Florida and Texas. **FL: 1350 mi; TX 367 mi**

28. **GEOMETRY** Use the square shown at the right.

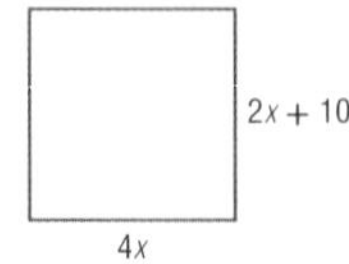

a. What is the value of x? **5**

b. Find the length of each side of the square. **20 units**

29. **LANDSCAPE** Jamie is going to fence the rectangular and triangular sections of grass shown below. The perimeters of the two sections are now equal. If w represents the width of the rectangle, how could you find the lengths of the sides of the rectangle and of the triangle? Justify your response and use your method to solve the problem.

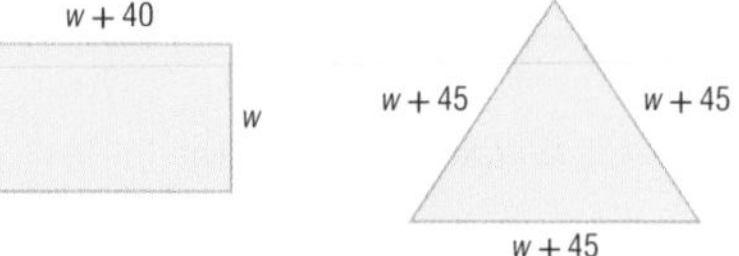

H.O.T. Problems
Use **H**igher-**O**rder **T**hinking Skills

30. **OPEN ENDED** Write an equation that has variables on each side and has a solution of -2. **Sample answer $3x + 2 = 2x$**

31. **NUMBER SENSE** Three times the sum of three consecutive integers x, $x + 1$, and $x + 2$, is 72. What are the integers? **7, 8, 9**

32. **CHALLENGE** The formula $F = 1.8C + 32$ can be used to find the temperature in degrees Fahrenheit F when the temperature is given in degrees Celsius C. For what value is the temperature in degrees Fahrenheit equal to the temperature in degrees Celsius? Justify your reasoning by writing and solving an equation. (*Hint:* If Fahrenheit and Celsius are equal, they can be assigned the same variable.)

33. **FIND THE ERROR** Mykia solved the equation $10x + 6 = 8x - 4$. Her steps are shown at the right. Is Mykia correct? If not, what error did she make? Then correct Mykia's error.

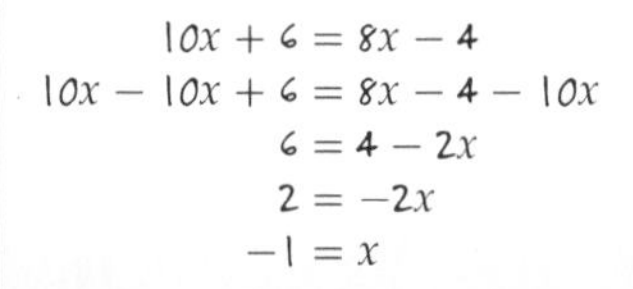

34. **WRITING IN MATH** Write a real-world problem that could be solved by using the equation $54 + 3.5x = 8x$. Then solve the equation and interpret your solution. **See margin.**

32. $t = 1.8t + 32$
$-32 = 0.8t$
$-40 = t$
At $-40°$, the temperatures are the same.

33. She is incorrect. In the third step, the 4 should be negative, not positive; $x = -5$

Enrichment
CRM p. 17 OL BL

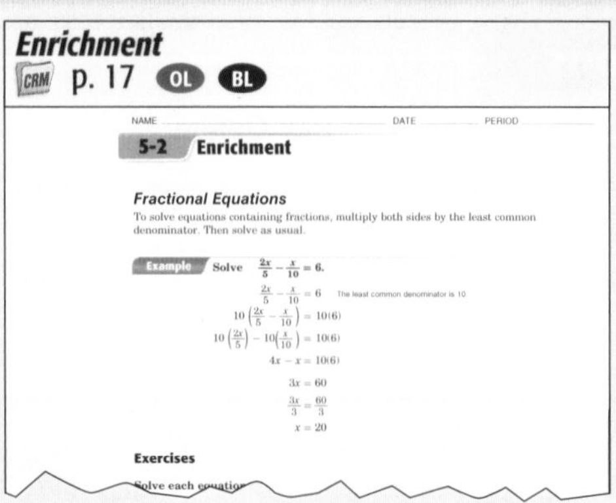
NAME ______ DATE ______ PERIOD ______

5-2 Enrichment

Fractional Equations

To solve equations containing fractions, multiply both sides by the least common denominator. Then solve as usual.

Example Solve $\frac{2x}{5} - \frac{x}{10} = 6$.

$\frac{2x}{5} - \frac{x}{10} = 6$ The least common denominator is 10
$10\left(\frac{2x}{5} - \frac{x}{10}\right) = 10(6)$
$10\left(\frac{2x}{5}\right) - 10\left(\frac{x}{10}\right) = 10(6)$
$4x - x = 10(6)$
$3x = 60$
$\frac{3x}{3} = \frac{60}{3}$
$x = 20$

Exercises

Solve each equatio

Standardized Test Practice

35. Yesterday, the math club had 1 less than 3 times their average attendance. Last week they had 3 more than their average attendance. If the attendance for both weeks were equal, what is the average attendance? **B**

A 1   C 3
B 2   D 4

36. For which of the following is -8 a solution? **G**

F $-2c + 18 = 10c + 12$
G $6m - 15 = 9m + 9$
H $4 + 7s = 5s + 20$
J $5d - 13 = 19 - 3d$

37. GRIDDED RESPONSE What is the solution of the equation $12x + 4 = 2x - 16$? **−2**

38. A cellular company has the following options for text messaging plans.

Text Plans	Monthly Fee	Cost per Message
Plan A	\$10	\$0.15
Plan B	\$20	\$0.05

Which equation shows how many text messages would need to be sent in order for the costs for one month to be the same? **C**

A $10 + 0.05m = 20 + 0.15m$
B $10m + 0.15 = 20m + 0.05$
C $10 + 0.15m = 20 + 0.05m$
D $10(m + 0.15) = 20(m + 0.05)$

Spiral Review

Find the perimeter and area of each figure (Lesson 5-1)

39. 

16 m, 12 m²

40. 5 ft, 4 ft **18 ft, 20 ft²**

41. SPORTS Carla paid \$45 to join a golf camp for the summer. She will also pay \$15 for every private lesson that she takes. If she has budgeted \$225 for the camp, how many private lessons can she take? (Lesson 4-6) **12 lessons**

Simplify each expression. (Lesson 4-2)

42. $2x + 5x$ **7x**   **43.** $7b + 2b$ **9b**   **44.** $y + 10y$ **11y**

45. WEATHER The table shows the number of tornadoes that occurred in Nebraska in May and the total number of tornadoes for selected years. What decimal part, rounded to the nearest hundredth, of the annual tornadoes occurred in May for each year? (Lesson 3-1) **2006: 0.36; 2003: 0.53; 2000: 0.34; 1997: 0.37**

Annual Nebraska Tornadoes

Year	May	Total
2006	8	22
2003	43	81
2000	21	61
1997	11	30

Source: Nebraska Severe Weather

46. WEATHER The low temperatures for 7 days in January were −2, 0, 5, −1, −4, 2, and 0. Find the average for the 7-day period. (Lesson 2-5) **0° F**

Skills Review

Evaluate each expression. (Lesson 1-2)

47. $8c + 5$, if $c = 6$ **53**   **48.** $22 - 3h$, if $h = 4$ **10**   **49.** $36 - (-6g)$, if $g = -2$ **24**

Differentiated Instruction 

Extension Write $\frac{x}{10} + 2.6 = 8.2$ on the board. Ask students by what number they could multiply each side of the equation to eliminate the fraction and decimals. 10 Ask students to solve the equation by multiplying both sides by that number. Then have them solve the equation in a different way. Have them explain which way was easier. 56; answers will vary, but students should note that it was easier to multiply by 10 first to eliminate the fraction and decimals.

Watch Out!

Find the Error For Exercise 33, remind students to pay close attention to the signs of the numbers.

 ASSESS

Name the Math Have students write an equation that has a variable on both sides and addition or subtraction on both sides. Write $7x + 5 = x - 2$ on the board as an example. Have them trade with another student. Ask them to solve the equation and to write the properties they used to find the solution.

Formative Assessment

Check for student understanding of concepts in Lessons 5-1 and 5-2.

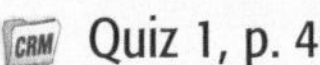 Quiz 1, p. 40

Additional Answer

34. Sample answer: The annual membership fee for a movie club is \$54; that allows you to buy tickets for \$3.50 each. If the local movie theatre charges \$8.00 for tickets, determine how many movie tickets you would need to buy through the club for the cost to equal that of buying tickets at the regular price. 12; You would have to buy 12 tickets for the costs to be equal.

Lesson Notes

1 FOCUS

Vertical Alignment

Before Lesson 5-3
Solve an equation and graph the solution on a number line.

Lesson 5-3
Write inequalities.
Graph inequalities on a number line.

After Lesson 5-3
Use the methods learned to solve multi-step equations and inequalities.

2 TEACH

Scaffolding Questions

Have students read the *Why?* section of the lesson and answer the questions.

Ask:

- What do the discounted prices represent? admission after 3 P.M.
- Name three ages of children under 12 who cannot attend the water park for free. Student answers should be between 2–11.
- A family of four (two adults and two children between 2–11) spend $34 to enter the water park. Do they go before or after 3 P.M.? after

5-3 Inequalities

Then
You have already solved equations and graphed the solution on a number line. (Lessons 4-3 and 4-4)

Now
- Write inequalities.
- Graph inequalities on a number line.

New Vocabulary
inequality

Math Online
glencoe.com
- Extra Examples
- Personal Tutor
- Self-Check Quiz
- Homework Help

Why?

The table shows the admission prices at a water park.

Water Park Tickets

Ticket	Price	Price after 3 P.M.
Children under 2	Free	Free
Children ages 2 - 11	$12	$8
Adults ages 12 - 59	$14	$9
Seniors ages 60 & up	$10	$7

a. Would a 2-year-old child be able to attend the water park free? **No**

b. When would an adult age 34 pay less than $14 for admission? **after 3 P.M.**

c. Find the difference between the admission prices before 3 P.M. for a person age 59 and a person age 60. **$4**

Write Inequalities An **inequality** is a mathematical sentence that compares quantities that are not equal. Inequalities contain the symbols <, >, ≤, or ≥.

EXAMPLE 1 Write an Inequality

Write an inequality for each sentence.

a. The DVD costs more than $15.

Words	The DVD	costs more than	$15.
Symbols	Let d = the cost of the DVD.		
Inequality	d	>	15

b. A dog weighs less than 50 pounds.

Words	A dog	weighs less than	50 pounds.
Symbols	Let d = the weight of the dog.		
Inequality	d	<	50

Check Your Progress

1A. The height requirement is greater than or equal to 40 inches. $h \geq 40$

1B. The speed limit is less than or equal to 35 miles per hour. $s \leq 35$

Personal Tutor glencoe.com

Lesson 5-3 Resources

Resource	Approaching-Level	On-Level	Beyond-Level	English Learners
Teacher Edition	• Differentiated Instruction, p. 235	• Differentiated Instruction, p. 235	• Differentiated Instruction, pp. 235, 239	• Differentiated Instruction, p. 235
Chapter Resource Masters	• Study Guide and Intervention, pp. 18–19 • Skills Practice, p. 20 • Practice, p. 21 • Word Problem Practice, p. 22 • Spreadsheet Activity, p. 24	• Study Guide and Intervention, pp. 18–19 • Skills Practice, p. 20 • Practice, p. 21 • Word Problem Practice, p. 22 • Enrichment, p. 23 • Spreadsheet Activity, p. 24	• Practice, p. 21 • Word Problem Practice, p. 22 • Enrichment, p. 23 • Spreadsheet Activity, p. 24	• Study Guide and Intervention, pp. 18–19 • Skills Practice, p. 20 • Practice, p. 21 • Spreadsheet Activity, p. 24
Transparencies	• 5-Minute Check Transparency 5-3	• 5-Minute Check Transparency 5-3	• 5-Minute Check Transparency 5-3	• 5-Minute Check Transparency 5-3
Other	• Study Notebook • Teaching Pre-Algebra with Manipulatives	• Study Notebook • Teaching Pre-Algebra with Manipulatives	• Study Notebook	• Study Notebook • Teaching Pre-Algebra with Manipulatives

ReadingMath

Inequalities Notice that $\leq$ and $\geq$ are a combination of the $<$ or $>$ symbol with part of the symbol for equals, $=$.

The table below shows some common verbal phrases and the corresponding mathematical inequalities.

Concept Summary — **Inequalities** (For Your FOLDABLE)

$<$	$>$	$\leq$	$\geq$
• is less than • is fewer than	• is greater than • is more than • exceeds	• is less than or equal to • is no more than • is at most	• is greater than or equal to • is no less than • is at least

Real-World EXAMPLE 2 **Write an Inequality**

CIVICS You must be at least 18 years old to vote. Write an inequality to describe this situation.

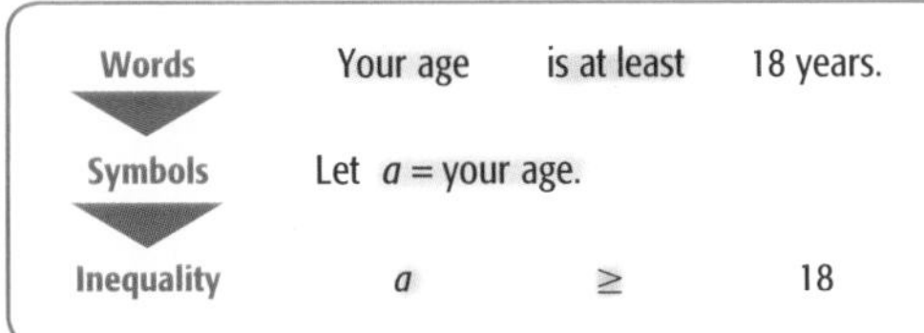

Words
Your age
is at least
18 years.
Symbols
Let a = your age.
Inequality
a
≥
18

The inequality is $a \geq 18$.

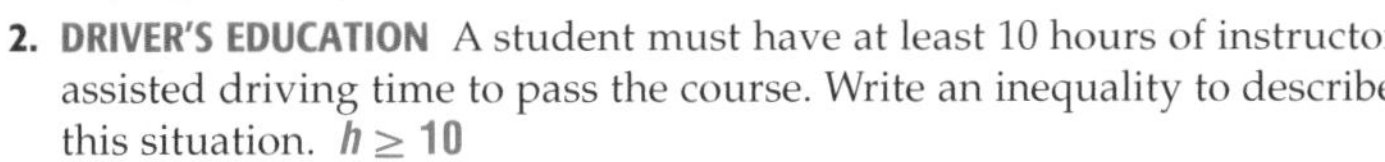

Check Your Progress

2. **DRIVER'S EDUCATION** A student must have at least 10 hours of instructor assisted driving time to pass the course. Write an inequality to describe this situation. $h \geq 10$

Personal Tutor glencoe.com

Real-World Link

The right to vote has changed since the Constitution was written.

1870–The 15th Amendment included men of color.

1920–The 19th Amendment gave women the right to vote.

1971–The 26th Amendment lowered the voting age from 21 years to 18 years.

Inequalities with variables are open sentences. When the variable in an open sentence is replaced with a number, the inequality may be true or false.

EXAMPLE 3 **Determine Truth of an Inequality**

For the given value, state whether each inequality is *true* or *false*.

a. $2t + 8 > 7; t = -1$

$2t + 8 > 7$	**Write the inequality.**
$2(-1) + 8 \overset{?}{>} 7$	**Replace *t* with −1.**
$6 \not> 7$	**Simplify.**

This sentence is false.

b. $p - 42 \leq -2; p = 40$

$p - 42 \leq -2$	**Write the inequality.**
$40 - 42 \overset{?}{\leq} -2$	**Replace *p* with 40.**
$-2 \leq -2$	**Simplify.**

Although the inequality $-2 < -2$ is false, the equation $-2 = -2$ is true. So, this sentence is true.

Check Your Progress

3A. $3 + x \leq 12, x = 6$ true

3B. $y - 7 < 10, y = 17$ false

Personal Tutor glencoe.com

Write Inequalities

Examples 1–3 show how to write an inequality and how to determine if an inequality is true or false when given a value for a variable.

Formative Assessment

Use the Check Your Progress exercises after each example to determine students' understanding of concepts.

Additional Examples

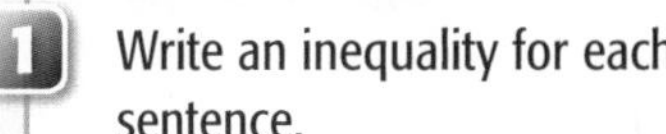

1 Write an inequality for each sentence.

a. Your height is greater than 52 inches. $h > 52$

b. Your speed is less than or equal to 62 mph. $s \leq 62$

2 **ENVIRONMENT** To meet a certain air quality standard, an automobile must have a fuel efficiency of at least 27.5 miles per gallon. Write an inequality to describe this situation. $f \geq 27.5$

3 For the given value, state whether each inequality is *true* or *false*.

a. $s - 9 < 4; s = 6$ true

b. $14 \leq \frac{a}{3} + 1; a = 36$ false

Additional Examples also in Interactive Classroom PowerPoint® Presentations

IWB INTERACTIVE WHITEBOARD READY

Differentiated Instruction

Naturalist Have students take nature walks to record examples of relationships among natural elements that can be described using inequalities. For example, students may note that the size of a crow is greater than the size of a sparrow. They might also compare leaves from different tree species. Encourage students to research the organisms they observe.

Focus on Mathematical Content

Graphing Inequalities and Writing Inequalities from a Graph If the symbols $\leq$ or $\geq$ are in an inequality, the starting point on the line graph is a closed circle. This shows the number *is* part of the solution. In inequalities with the symbols $<$ and $>$, an open circle is used on the line graph to show that the number is *not* part of the solution.

Graph Inequalities

Example 4 shows how to graph inequalities on a number line. **Example 5** shows how to write an inequality from a graph.

Additional Examples

4 Graph each inequality on a number line.

a. $x > 10$

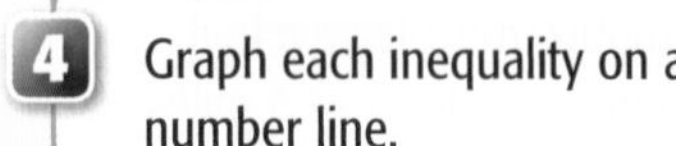

b. $x \leq 10$

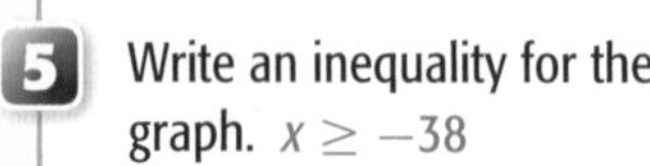

5 Write an inequality for the graph. $x \geq -38$

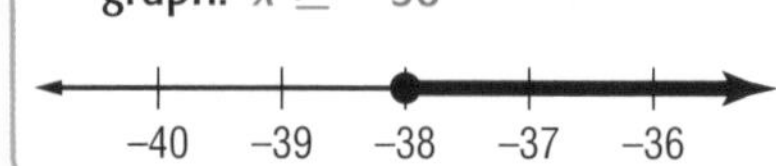

Tips for New Teachers

Signs Students might still confuse the $>$ and $<$ symbols. You may want to suggest that the $>$ and $<$ symbols "point to the lesser value and open to the greater value."

Graph Inequalities Inequalities can be graphed on a number line. The graph helps you visualize the values that make the inequality true.

StudyTip

Graphing Inequalities When inequalities are graphed, an open dot means the number is *not* included ($<$ or $>$) and a closed dot means it is included ($\leq$ or $\geq$).

EXAMPLE 4 Graph an Inequality

Graph each inequality on a number line.

a. $a > 6$

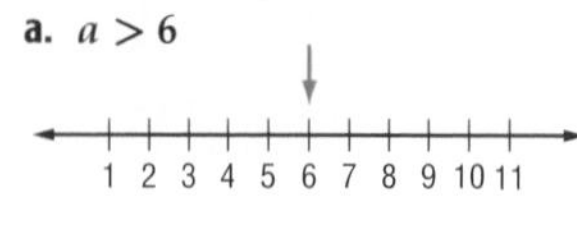

Locate 6 on the number line. It is a key point in the inequality.

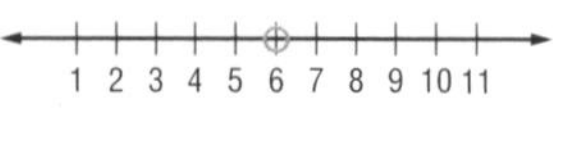

Draw an *open* dot on 6 because 6 is *not* included.

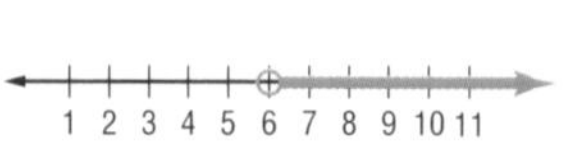

The inequality $a > 6$ means that all numbers *greater than* 6 will make the sentence true. Draw an arrow from the dot pointing to the right.

b. $x \leq -1$

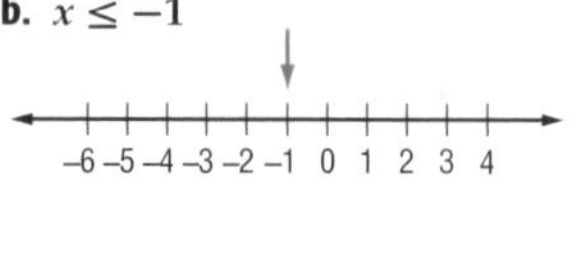

Locate -1 on the number line. It is a key point in the inequality.

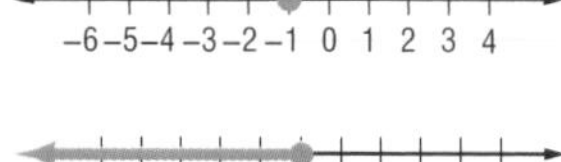

Draw a *closed* dot on -1 because -1 *is* included.

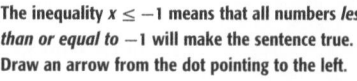

The inequality $x \leq -1$ means that all numbers *less than or equal to* -1 will make the sentence true. Draw an arrow from the dot pointing to the left.

Check Your Progress 4A–4C. See margin.

4A. $x < 5$ **4B.** $x \geq -2$ **4C.** $x > 0$

Personal Tutor glencoe.com

EXAMPLE 5 Write an Inequality

Write an inequality for the graph.

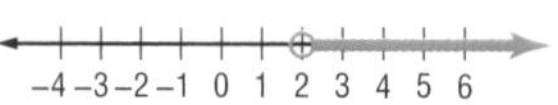

An open circle is on 2, so the point 2 is *not* included in the graph. The arrow points to the right, so the graph includes all numbers greater than 2. The inequality is $x > 2$.

Check Your Progress

Write an inequality for each graph. 5A. $x \geq -3$ 5B. $x < -2$

5A.

5B.

Personal Tutor glencoe.com

TEACH with TECH

STUDENT RESPONSE SYSTEM Develop a sequence of inequalities with the SRS software. For each inequality, have students respond with 1 if the graph of the inequality will contain a closed circle and 2 if the graph will contain an open circle.

Additional Answers

4A.

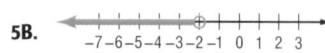

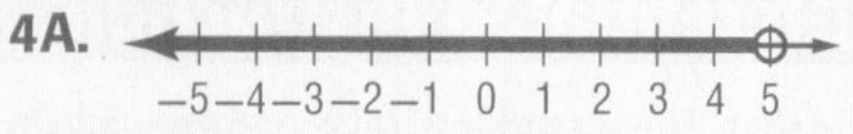

4B.

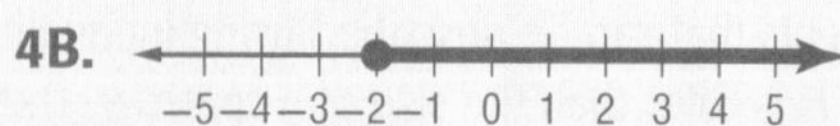

4C.

236 Chapter 5 Multi-Step Equations and Inequalities

Check Your Understanding

Example 1 p. 234 — **Write an inequality for each sentence.**

1. Lacrosse practice will be no more than 45 minutes. $x \leq 45$
2. Mario is more than 60 inches tall. $t > 60$

Example 2 p. 235

3. **SOCCER** More than 8000 fans attended the Wizards' opening soccer game at Arrowhead Stadium in Kansas City, Missouri. Write an inequality to describe the attendance. $f > 8000$

Example 3 p. 235 — **For the given value, state whether the inequality is *true* or *false*.**

4. $13 - x < 4; x = 9$ false
5. $45 > 2x - 5; x = 20$ true

Example 4 p. 236 — **Graph each inequality on a number line.** 6–9. See margin.

6. $x < -1$
7. $y \geq 5$
8. $w > 9$
9. $z \leq 2$

Example 5 p. 236 — **Write an inequality for each graph.**

10. 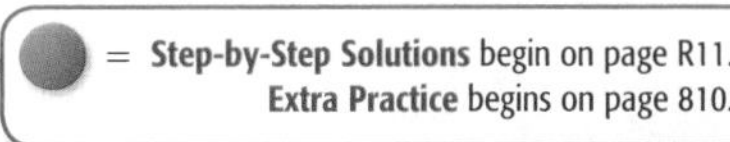

$x \leq -2$

11. 
−1 0 1 2 3 4 5 6 7 8 9
$y > 5$

Practice and Problem Solving

● = **Step-by-Step Solutions** begin on page R11. **Extra Practice** begins on page 810.

Example 1 p. 234 — **Write an inequality for each sentence.**

12. The elevators in an office building have been approved for a maximum load of 3600 pounds. $m \leq 3600$
13. Children under the age of 2 fly free. $c < 2$
14. An assignment requires at least 45 minutes. $a \geq 45$
15. While shopping, Abby spent no more than $50. $s \leq 50$

Example 2 p. 235 — **ANALYZE GRAPHS The graph shows the average life span of various animals.**

16. The average lifespan of a Galapagos tortoise is at least 4 times that of a chimpanzee. Write an inequality for the lifespan of a tortoise. $t \geq 200$
17. The average lifespan of a lobster is at most the lifespan of a cat. Write an inequality for the lifespan of a lobster. $l \leq 15$

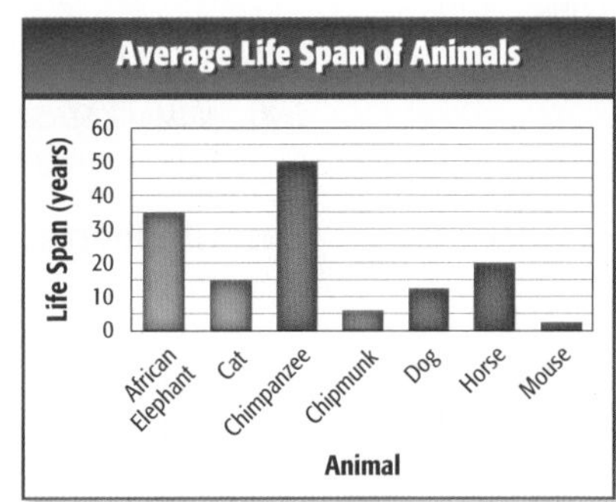

Source: *World Almanac for Kids*

18. false
19. false
20. true

Example 3 p. 235 — **For the given value, state whether the inequality is *true* or *false*.**

18. $13 - a < 29; a = -30$
19. $4b \geq -12; b = -4$
20. $2c + 18 \leq 50; c = 15$
21. $\frac{120}{d} > 40; d = 3$ false
22. $\frac{55}{f} > -22; f = -5$ true
23. $c + 19 < 2c; c = 20$ true

3 PRACTICE

Formative Assessment

Use Exercises 1–11 to check for understanding.

Use the chart at the bottom of this page to customize assignments for your students.

Exercise Alert

Internet In Exercise 38, students are required to use the Internet or some other reference material to find governmental spending limits.

Additional Answers

6. 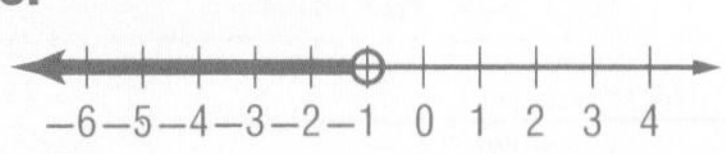

7. 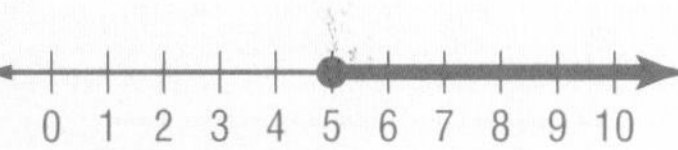

8. 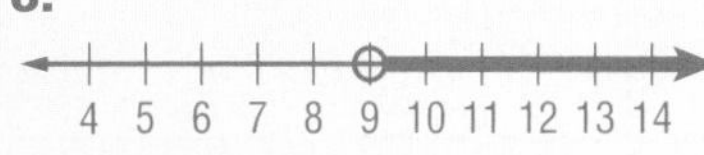

9. 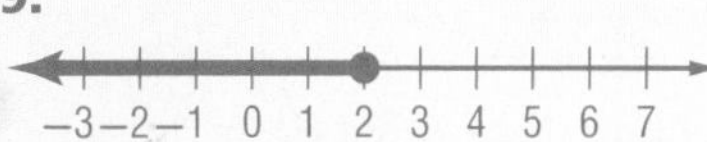

Differentiated Homework Options

Level	Assignment	Two-Day Option	
AL Basic	12–35, 39–66	13–35 odd, 44–47	12–34 even, 39–43, 48–66
OL Core	13–35 odd, 36–66	12–35, 44–47	36–43, 48–66
BL Advanced	36–60 (optional: 61–66)		

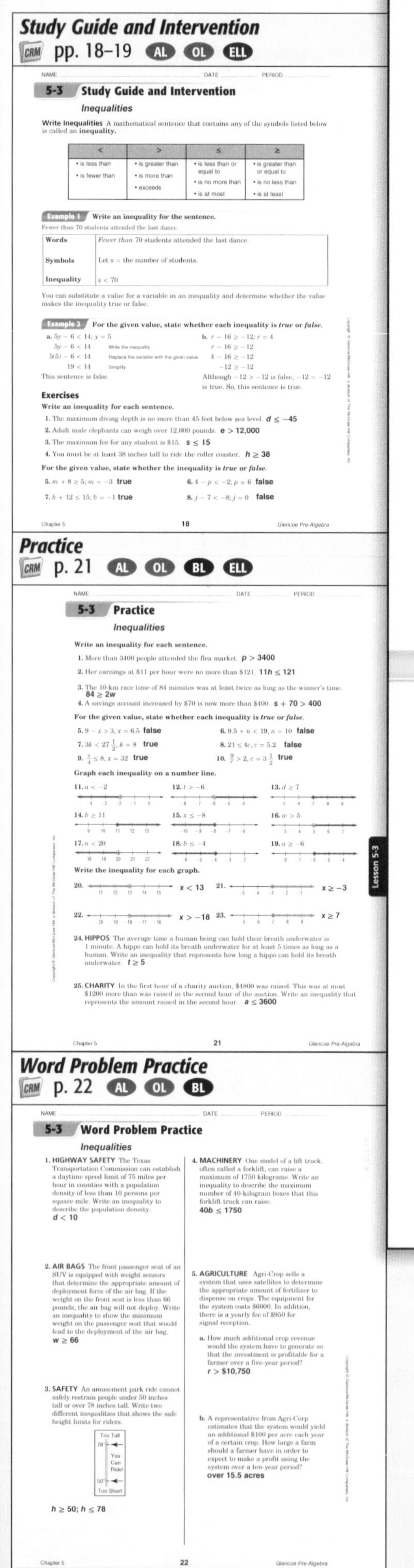

Study Guide and Intervention
CRM pp. 18–19 AL OL ELL

NAME ______ DATE ______ PERIOD ______

5-3 Study Guide and Intervention

Inequalities

Write Inequalities A mathematical sentence that contains any of the symbols listed below is called an **inequality.**

<	>	≤	≥
• is less than • is fewer than	• is greater than • is more than • exceeds	• is less than or equal to • is no more than • is at most	• is greater than or equal to • is no less than • is at least

Example 1 **Write an inequality for the sentence.**

Fewer than 70 students attended the last dance.

Words	*Fewer than* 70 students attended the last dance.
Symbols	Let s = the number of students.
Inequality	$s < 70$

You can substitute a value for a variable in an inequality and determine whether the value makes the inequality true or false.

Example 2 **For the given value, state whether each inequality is *true* or *false*.**

a. $5y - 6 < 14$; $y = 5$
$5y - 6 < 14$ Write the inequality
$5(5) - 6 < 14$ Replace the variable with the given value
$19 < 14$ Simplify
This sentence is false.

b. $r - 16 \geq -12$; $r = 4$
$r - 16 \geq -12$
$4 - 16 \geq -12$
$-12 \geq -12$
Although $-12 > -12$ is false, $-12 = -12$ is true. So, this sentence is true.

Exercises

Write an inequality for each sentence.

1. The maximum diving depth is no more than 45 feet below sea level. **$d \leq -45$**
2. Adult male elephants can weigh over 12,000 pounds. **$e > 12{,}000$**
3. The maximum fee for any student is $15. **$s \leq 15$**
4. You must be at least 38 inches tall to ride the roller coaster. **$h \geq 38$**

For the given value, state whether the inequality is *true* or *false*.

5. $m + 8 \geq 5$; $m = -3$ **true**
6. $4 - p < -2$; $p = 6$ **false**
7. $b + 12 \leq 15$; $b = -1$ **true**
8. $j - 7 < -8$; $j = 0$ **false**

Chapter 5 18 Glencoe Pre-Algebra

Practice
CRM p. 21 AL OL BL ELL

NAME ______ DATE ______ PERIOD ______

5-3 Practice

Inequalities

Write an inequality for each sentence.

1. More than 3400 people attended the flea market. **$p > 3400$**
2. Her earnings at $11 per hour were no more than $121. **$11h \leq 121$**
3. The 10-km race time of 84 minutes was at least twice as long as the winner's time. **$84 \geq 2w$**
4. A savings account increased by $70 is now more than $400. **$s + 70 > 400$**

For the given value, state whether each inequality is *true* or *false*.

5. $9 - x > 3$, $x = 6.5$ **false**
6. $9.5 + n < 19$, $n = 10$ **false**
7. $3k < 27\frac{1}{2}$, $k = 8$ **true**
8. $21 \leq 4c$, $c = 5.2$ **false**
9. $\frac{x}{4} \leq 8$, $x = 32$ **true**
10. $\frac{9}{c} > 2$, $c = 3\frac{1}{2}$ **true**

Graph each inequality on a number line.

11. $a < -2$
12. $t > -6$
13. $d \geq 7$
14. $b \geq 11$
15. $x \leq -8$
16. $w > 5$
17. $n < 20$
18. $b \leq -4$
19. $a \geq -6$

Write the inequality for each graph.

20. **$x < 13$**
21. **$x \geq -3$**
22. **$x > -18$**
23. **$x \geq 7$**

24. **HIPPOS** The average time a human being can hold their breath underwater is 1 minute. A hippo can hold its breath underwater for at least 5 times as long as a human. Write an inequality that represents how long a hippo can hold its breath underwater. **$t \geq 5$**

25. **CHARITY** In the first hour of a charity auction, $4800 was raised. This was at most $1200 more than was raised in the second hour of the auction. Write an inequality that represents the amount raised in the second hour. **$a \leq 3600$**

Chapter 5 21 Glencoe Pre-Algebra

Lesson 5-3

Word Problem Practice
CRM p. 22 AL OL BL

NAME ______ DATE ______ PERIOD ______

5-3 Word Problem Practice

Inequalities

1. **HIGHWAY SAFETY** The Texas Transportation Commission can establish a daytime speed limit of 75 miles per hour in counties with a population density of less than 10 persons per square mile. Write an inequality to describe the population density. **$d < 10$**

2. **AIR BAGS** The front passenger seat of an SUV is equipped with weight sensors that determine the appropriate amount of deployment force of the air bag. If the weight on the front seat is less than 66 pounds, the air bag will not deploy. Write an inequality to show the minimum weight on the passenger seat that would lead to the deployment of the air bag. **$w \geq 66$**

3. **SAFETY** An amusement park ride cannot safely restrain people under 50 inches tall or over 78 inches tall. Write two different inequalities that shows the safe height limits for riders.

Too Tall
78"
You Can Ride!
50"
Too Short

$h \geq 50$; $h \leq 78$

4. **MACHINERY** One model of a lift truck, often called a forklift, can raise a maximum of 1750 kilograms. Write an inequality to describe the maximum number of 40-kilogram boxes that this forklift truck can raise. **$40b \leq 1750$**

5. **AGRICULTURE** Agri-Crop sells a system that uses satellites to determine the appropriate amount of fertilizer to dispense on crops. The equipment for the system costs $6000. In addition, there is a yearly fee of $950 for signal reception.

a. How much additional crop revenue would the system have to generate so that the investment is profitable for a farmer over a five-year period? **$r > \$10{,}750$**

b. A representative from Agri-Corp estimates that the system would yield an additional $100 per acre each year of a certain crop. How large a farm should a farmer have in order to expect to make a profit using the system over a ten-year period? **over 15.5 acres**

Chapter 5 22 Glencoe Pre-Algebra

Example 4 p. 236

Graph each inequality on a number line. **24–29. See margin.**

24. $x < 0$
25. $y \geq 3$
26. $p > -4$
27. $t > 6$
28. $s \geq -2$
29. $r \leq -4$

Example 5 p. 236

Write an inequality for each graph.

30. (number line: −5, −3, −1, 1, 3, 5)
31. (number line: −2, 0, 2, 4, 6)
32. (number line: −14, −12, −10, −8, −6)
33. (number line: −4, −2, 0, 2, 4)
34. 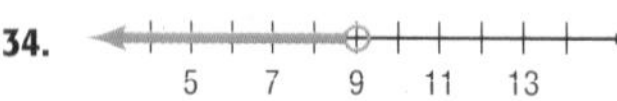

35. (number line: −8, −6, −4, −2, 0)

30. $x \leq -1$
31. $x > 2$
32. $x \geq -10$
33. $x \leq 0$
34. $x < 9$
35. $x > -4$

36. **BUDGET** Madison Middle School spends $750 per year on club activities. They spend at least twice that amount on after-school activities. Write an inequality that represents how much they spend on after-school activities. **$s \geq 1500$**

37. **FOOTBALL** In a recent year, Drew Brees threw for 4418 yards. This is at most 500 yards more than Brett Favre's passing yards. Write an inequality that represents Brett Favre's passing yards. **$f \geq 3918$**

Real-World Link

In 2007, Brett Favre broke an NFL record for the number of career completed passes. He has also won the Most Valuable Player award three times, the most in NFL history.

Source: National Football League

38. **RESEARCH** Use the Internet or another source to find the state or national spending limits on certain government branches, organizations, or projects. Write an inequality to express one or more of these limits. **See students' work.**

H.O.T. Problems
Use **H**igher-**O**rder **T**hinking Skills

39. **OPEN ENDED** State three numbers that could be solutions of the inequality $h \leq -12$. Then justify your response by using a number line. **39–40. See Chapter 5 Answer Appendix.**

40. **WRITING IN MATH** Write an email to a friend who missed class today explaining how to tell the difference between graphing an inequality with a closed dot and one with an open dot. Use examples to clarify your explanation.

41. **NUMBER SENSE** Provide a counterexample to the statement *All numbers less than 0 are negative integers.* **Sample answer: $-\frac{1}{2}$**

42. **FIND THE ERROR** Alex and Carlos are graphing the inequality $p < 14$. Is either of them correct? Explain.

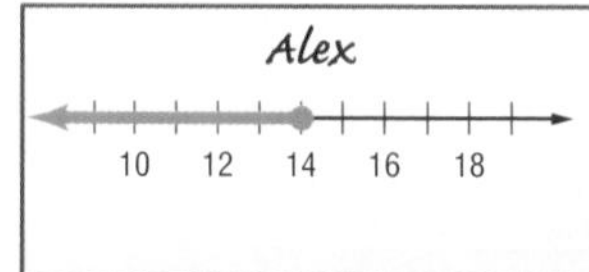

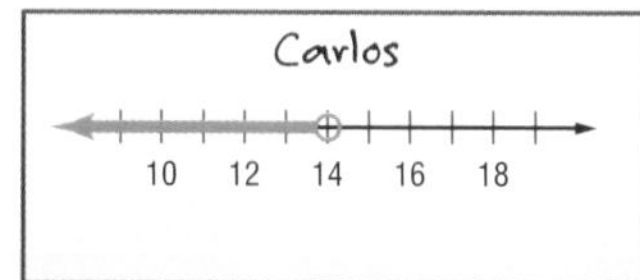

42. Carlos: Since the symbol is <, the dot should be open.

43. **WRITING IN MATH** Write a real-world example for the inequality below.

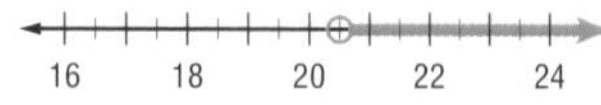

43. The Wilson family spent more than $20.50 on groceries.

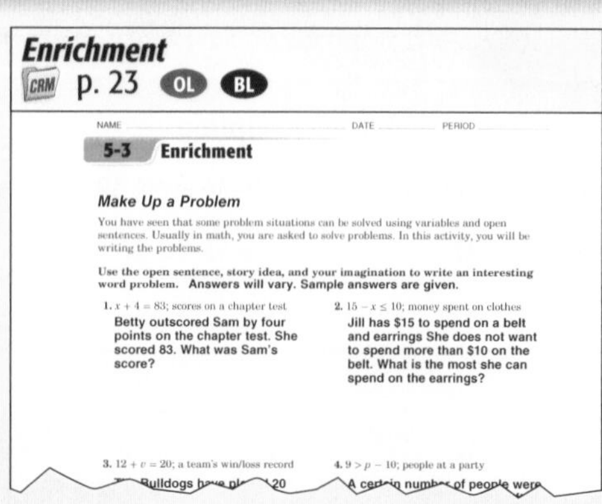

Enrichment
CRM p. 23 OL BL

NAME ______ DATE ______ PERIOD ______

5-3 Enrichment

Make Up a Problem

You have seen that some problem situations can be solved using variables and open sentences. Usually in math, you are asked to solve problems. In this activity, you will be writing the problems.

Use the open sentence, story idea, and your imagination to write an interesting word problem. **Answers will vary. Sample answers are given.**

1. $x + 4 = 83$; scores on a chapter test
Betty outscored Sam by four points on the chapter test. She scored 83. What was Sam's score?

2. $15 - x \leq 10$; money spent on clothes
Jill has $15 to spend on a belt and earrings She does not want to spend more than $10 on the belt. What is the most she can spend on the earrings?

3. $12 + v = 20$; a team's win/loss record

4. $9 > p - 10$; people at a party

Standardized Test Practice

44. Which of the following best represents the sign shown? **A**

A $t > 48$ C $t \geq 48$
B $t < 48$ D $t \leq 48$

45. SHORT RESPONSE Graph the following inequality on a number line. **See margin.**

$p < 3$

46. An elevator's maximum load is 3400 pounds. Which of the following best represents that sentence? **J**

F $\ell > 3400$ H $\ell \geq 3400$
G $\ell < 3400$ J $\ell \leq 3400$

47. The Chess Club is having a bake sale to raise money for a tournament. The club must raise at least three times what they raised at the last bake sale. What is the minimum amount they must raise if the last bake sale raised $45? **D**

A $15 C $90
B $45 D $135

Spiral Review

Solve each equation. (Lesson 5-2)

48. $3t - 6 = 6t + 30$ **−12**

49. $2y + 14 = 42 - 5y$ **4**

50. $3x = 12 - 3x$ **2**

51. $4p = -p - 20$ **−4**

52. LANDSCAPING Jordan is paving a rectangular patio with 308 bricks. If there are 22 bricks running along the length of the patio, how many bricks run along the width of the patio? (Lesson 5-1) **14 bricks**

53. CELLULAR PHONE A cell phone plan charges $7 per month and $0.10 per minute. If the monthly cost is $25, solve $10m + 700 = 2500$ to find the number of minutes you can talk that month. (Lesson 4-5) **180 min**

Find each sum or difference. (Lesson 3-5)

54. $\frac{2}{5} + \frac{1}{5}$ $\frac{3}{5}$

55. $\frac{3}{10} + \frac{7}{10}$ **1**

56. $-\frac{3}{4} + \left(-\frac{3}{4}\right)$ $-1\frac{1}{2}$

57. $-\frac{13}{16} + \left(-\frac{9}{16}\right)$ $-1\frac{3}{8}$

58. $7\frac{2}{5} + 4\frac{2}{5}$ $11\frac{4}{5}$

59. $5\frac{17}{20} + 5\frac{9}{20}$ $11\frac{3}{10}$

60. TEMPERATURE The low temperatures in degrees Fahrenheit for each day last week are −3°, 9°, 4°, −7°, 5°, 0°, and −1°. Find the average low temperature. (Lesson 2-5) **1°F**

Skills Review

Solve each equation. (Lessons 4-3 and 4-4)

61. $2y = -42$ **−21**

62. $b + 5 = -10$ **−15**

63. $90 = -6t$ **−15**

64. $56 = c + 24$ **32**

65. $f - 4.2 = -6$ **−1.8**

66. $-2.1m = 8.4$ **−4**

Watch Out!

Find the Error For Exercise 42, remind students that an open circle indicates that the number is *not* included in the solution and a closed circle indicates that the number *is* included in the solution.

4 ASSESS

Ticket Out the Door Give students statements from newspapers and magazines that include the words "at most" and "at least." Have students graph the inequality associated with one statement on a number line. Students will turn in their graphs as they leave the classroom.

Formative Assessment

Check for student understanding of concepts in Lesson 5-3.

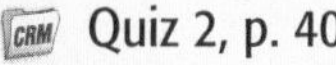

Quiz 2, p. 40

Additional Answers

24.

25.

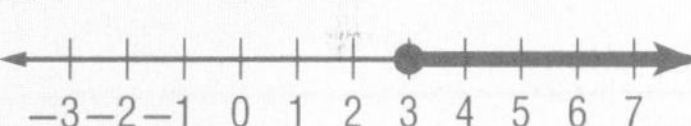

26.

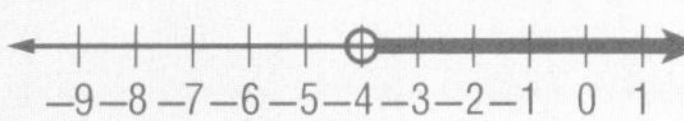

27.

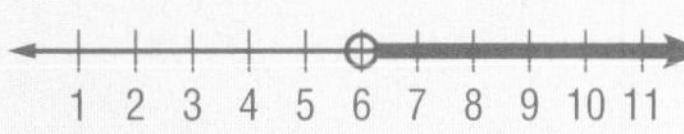

28.

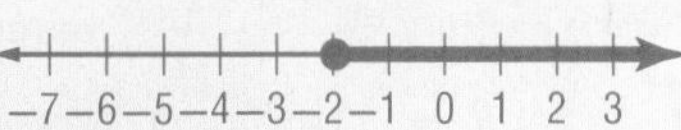

29.

45.

Differentiated Instruction

Extension Have the students graph the following compound inequalities.

a. $3 < x \leq 6$
b. $x < 4$ or $x \geq 7$

a. 0 2 4 6 8 10

b. 0 2 4 6 8 10

CHAPTER 5 Mid-Chapter Quiz

Formative Assessment

Use the Mid-Chapter Quiz to assess students' progress in the first half of the chapter.

For problems answered incorrectly, have students review the lessons indicated in parentheses.

ExamView Assessment Suite — Customize and create multiple versions of your Mid-Chapter Quiz and their answer keys.

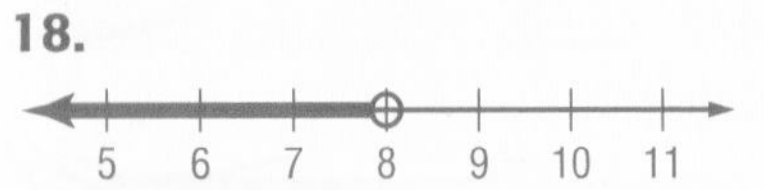

FOLDABLES Follow-Up

Before students complete the Mid-Chapter Quiz, encourage them to review the information for Lessons 5-1 through 5-3 in their Foldables.

Additional Answers

18. (number line from 5 to 11, open circle at 8, shaded to the left)

19. (number line from 6 to 12, open circle at 11, shaded to the left)

CHAPTER 5 Mid-Chapter Quiz

Lessons 5-1 through 5-3

Find the perimeter and area of each figure. (Lesson 5-1)

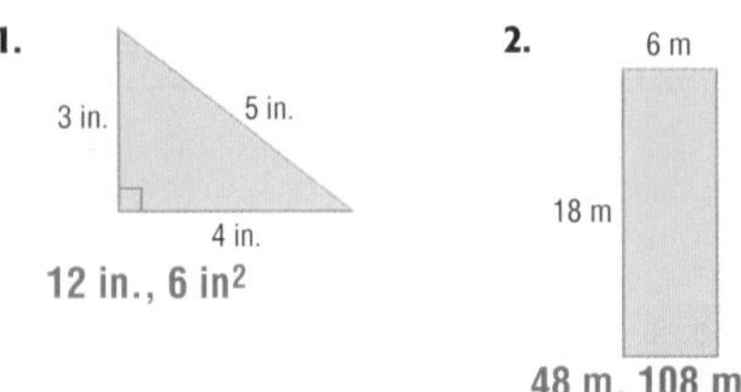

1. 12 in., 6 in²

2. 6 m, 18 m — 48 m, 108 m²

3. MEASUREMENT Find the base of a triangle if the height is 9.75 feet and its area is 58.5 square feet. (Lesson 5-1) **12 ft**

4. MEASUREMENT The perimeter of a rectangle is 28 inches. If the width is 5 inches, what is the length of the rectangle? (Lesson 5-1) **9 in.**

5. CAKES Mrs. Barsch had a cake made for her daughter's graduation party. The shaded area is where a photo will be placed and the rest of the cake will be covered with frosting.

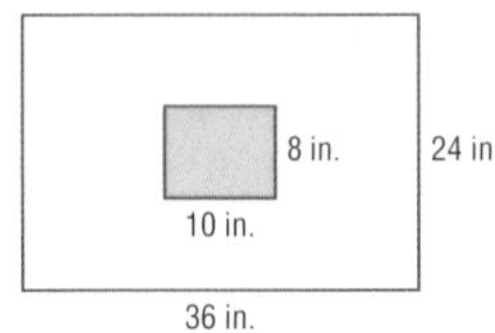

a. What is the perimeter of the entire cake? **120 in.**

b. What is the area of the photograph? (Lesson 5-1) **80 in²**

Solve each equation. Check your solution. (Lesson 5-2)

6. $-2w + 5 = 26 + w$ **−7**

7. $6z + 2 = 4z - 6$ **−4**

8. $12x - 19 = 3x + 8$ **3**

9. MULTIPLE CHOICE An online game site has two membership plans. The first plan gives you unlimited play for $40 a month. The second plan charges a monthly access fee of $4.25 plus $2.75 for each hour you play. After how many hours do the two plans cost the same? (Lesson 5-2) **D**

A 6.6 h
B 9.0 h
C 11.2 h
D 13.0 h

10. TESTS Carolina's score is 5 less than twice Aiko's score. It is also 45 points greater than Aiko's score. What score did the two girls receive? (Lesson 5-2) **95; 50**

Write an inequality for each sentence. (Lesson 5-3)

11. More than 35,000 people attended a college football game. $a > 35{,}000$

12. Toby wants to spend no more than 3 hours working on his model car. $t \leq 3$

13. Jameson's new guitar will cost at least $450. $g \geq 450$

14. MULTIPLE CHOICE Which of the following represents the inequality $-\frac{17}{5} \leq y$? (Lesson 5-3) **H**

F 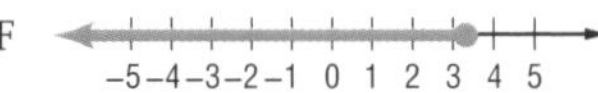

G 

H (number line −5 to 5)

J (number line −5 to 5)

For the given value, state whether each inequality is *true* or *false*. (Lesson 5-3)

15. $4a + 5 \geq 16$; $a = 4$ **true**

16. $3m - 12 < -40$; $m = 9$ **false**

17. $5s + 8 > -10$; $s = -3$ **true**

Graph each inequality on a number line. (Lesson 5-3) **18–19. See margin.**

18. $8 > d$

19. $f < 11$

20. FITNESS The table shows a gym class's average results for boys and girls participating in the long jump. $j \leq$ **18 ft 5 in.**

Gender	Distance
Male	17 feet 5 inches
Female	14 feet 3 inches

Ching-Li could jump no farther than 12 inches more than the average distance for males. Write an inequality that gives the possible distances that Ching-Li could jump. (Lesson 5-3)

Intervention Planner

Tier 1 On Level	Tier 2 Strategic Intervention approaching grade level	Tier 3 Intensive Intervention 2 or more grades below level
If students miss about 25% of the exercises or less,	**If** students miss about 50% of the exercises,	**If** students miss about 75% of the exercises,
Then choose a resource: SE Lessons 5-1, 5-2, and 5-3; CRM Skills Practice, pp. 7, 14, and 20; TE Chapter Project, p. 218; **Math Online** Self-Check Quiz	**Then** choose a resource: CRM Study Guide and Intervention, Chapter 5, pp. 5, 12, and 18; *Quick Review Math Handbook*; **Math Online** Extra Examples, Personal Tutor, Homework Help	**Then** use *Math Triumphs, Grade 8,* Ch. 3; **Math Online** Extra Examples, Personal Tutor, Homework Help, Review Vocabulary

5-4 Solving Inequalities

Then
You have already used the Properties of Equality to solve equations.
(Lessons 4-3 and 4-4)

Now
- Solve inequalities by using the Addition and Subtraction Properties of Inequality.
- Solve inequalities by multiplying or dividing by a positive or negative number.

Math Online
glencoe.com
- Extra Examples
- Personal Tutor
- Self-Check Quiz
- Homework Help
- Math in Motion

Why?

The bar graph shows the number of touchdowns the starting quarterbacks for different high school football teams threw last season.

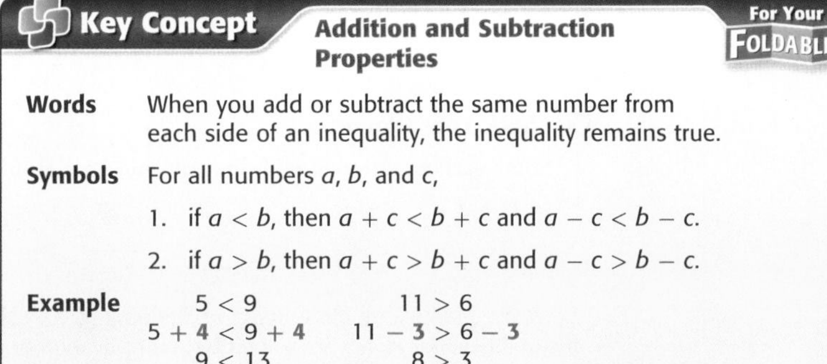

a. Write an inequality that compares the number of touchdowns thrown by Anthony and Malik. $18 > 12$

b. Suppose each quarterback threw 3 more touchdowns. Write a new inequality that compares the number thrown by Anthony and Malik. $21 > 15$

Solve Inequalities by Adding or Subtracting In this situation you added 3 to each side of the inequality. The inequality was still true. This and other similar examples suggest the following properties.

Key Concept — Addition and Subtraction Properties (For Your FOLDABLE)

Words When you add or subtract the same number from each side of an inequality, the inequality remains true.

Symbols For all numbers a, b, and c,

1. if $a < b$, then $a + c < b + c$ and $a - c < b - c$.
2. if $a > b$, then $a + c > b + c$ and $a - c > b - c$.

Example

$$5 < 9 \qquad 11 > 6$$
$$5 + 4 < 9 + 4 \qquad 11 - 3 > 6 - 3$$
$$9 < 13 \qquad 8 > 3$$

These properties are also true for $a \leq b$ and $a \geq b$.

EXAMPLE 1 Solve an Inequality

Solve $x + 5 > 12$. Check your solution.

$x + 5 > 12$	Write the inequality.
$-5 \quad -5$	Subtraction Property of Inequality
$x > 7$	Simplify.

Check	$x + 5 > 12$	Write the inequality.
	$9 + 5 \overset{?}{>} 12$	Replace x with any number greater than 7.
	$14 > 12$ ✓	The statement is true.

Check Your Progress

1A. $y + 10 < 3$ $y < -7$

1B. $x + 7 \geq 10$ $x \geq 3$

Personal Tutor glencoe.com

5-4 Lesson Notes

1 FOCUS

Vertical Alignment

Before Lesson 5-4
Use the Properties of Equality to solve equations.

Lesson 5-4
Solve inequalities by using the Addition and Subtraction Properties of Inequality.
Solve inequalities by multiplying or dividing by a positive or negative number.

After Lesson 5-4
Use the Properties of Equality to solve multi-step equations and inequalities.

2 TEACH

Scaffolding Questions

Have students read the *Why?* section of the lesson and answer the questions.

Ask:

- What does each mark on the vertical scale represent? 2 touchdowns
- How many more touchdowns did Anthony throw compared to Malik? 6
- Write an equation to find how many more touchdowns DeShaun threw compared to Preston. $t + 13 = 15$; 2 more touchdowns

Lesson 5-4 Resources

Resource	Approaching-Level	On-Level	Beyond-Level	English Learners
Teacher Edition		• Differentiated Instruction, p. 242	• Differentiated Instruction, pp. 242, 247	
Chapter Resource Masters	• Study Guide and Intervention, pp. 25–26 • Skills Practice, p. 27 • Practice, p. 28 • Word Problem Practice, p. 29	• Study Guide and Intervention, pp. 25–26 • Skills Practice, p. 27 • Practice, p. 28 • Word Problem Practice, p. 29 • Enrichment, p. 30	• Practice, p. 28 • Word Problem Practice, p. 29 • Enrichment, p. 30	• Study Guide and Intervention, pp. 25–26 • Skills Practice, p. 27 • Practice, p. 28
Transparencies	• 5-Minute Check Transparency 5-4	• 5-Minute Check Transparency 5-4	• 5-Minute Check Transparency 5-4	• 5-Minute Check Transparency 5-4
Other	• Study Notebook • Teaching Pre-Algebra with Manipulatives	• Study Notebook • Teaching Pre-Algebra with Manipulatives	• Study Notebook	• Study Notebook • Teaching Pre-Algebra with Manipulatives

Solve Inequalities by Adding or Subtracting

Example 1 shows how to isolate a variable to solve an inequality. **Example 2** shows how to solve an inequality and graph the solution on a number line.

Formative Assessment

Use the Check Your Progress exercises after each example to determine students' understanding of concepts.

Additional Examples

1 Solve $y + 5 > 11$. Check your solution. $y > 6$

2 Solve $h - 1\frac{1}{2} < 5$. Graph the solution on a number line.
$h < 6\frac{1}{2}$

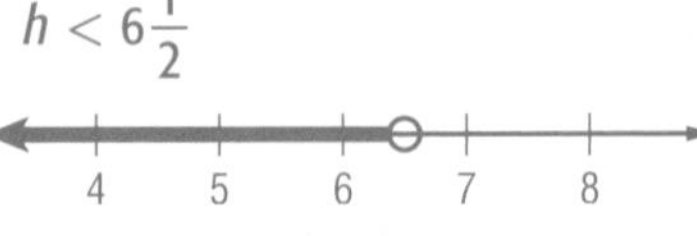

Additional Examples also in Interactive Classroom PowerPoint® Presentations

IWB INTERACTIVE WHITEBOARD READY

Tips for New Teachers

Infinity As students graph solutions on a number line, remind them that an inequality does not have just one solution, but an infinite number of solutions.

Additional Answers

2A.

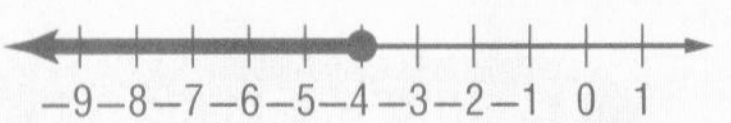

2B.

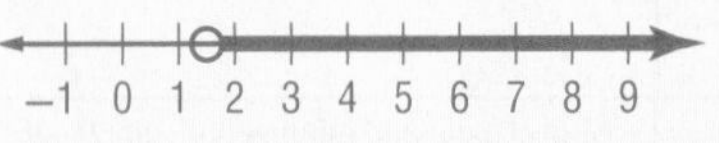

StudyTip

Equations and Inequalities In an equation, if $a = b$, then $b = a$. In an inequality, if $a < b$, then $b > a$.

Example: $7 = 2 + 5$ and $2 + 5 = 7$
$2 + 8 > 7$
but $7 < 2 + 8$

When graphing inequalities, it is often easier to visualize the solution when the variable is on the left side of the inequality symbol.

EXAMPLE 2 Graph the Solution of an Inequality

Solve $3 \le b - 1\frac{1}{3}$. Graph the solution on a number line.

$3 \le b - 1\frac{1}{3}$	**Write the inequality.**
$3 + 1\frac{1}{3} \le b - 1\frac{1}{3} + 1\frac{1}{3}$	**Addition Property of Inequality**
$4\frac{1}{3} \le b$ or $b \ge 4\frac{1}{3}$	**Simplify.**

The solution is $b \ge 4\frac{1}{3}$.

Check	$3 \le b - \frac{1}{3}$	**Write the inequality.**
	$3 \overset{?}{\le} 4\frac{1}{3} - 1\frac{1}{3}$	**Replace b with $4\frac{1}{3}$.**
	$3 \le 3$ ✓	**The statement is true.**

Graph the solution.

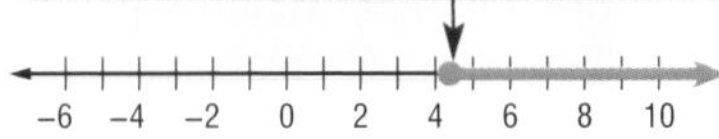

Check Your Progress 2A–2B. See margin for number lines.

Solve each equation. Graph the solution on a number line.

2A. $3 \ge g + 7$ $g \le -4$ **2B.** $b + \frac{5}{7} > 2$ $b > 1\frac{2}{7}$

Personal Tutor glencoe.com

Solve Inequalities by Multiplying or Dividing by a Positive Number Some inequalities like $4x > 8$ are solved by multiplication or division. You can multiply or divide each side of an inequality by a positive number and the inequality is still true.

StudyTip

Positive Number The statement $c > 0$ means that c is a positive number.

Key Concept Multiplication and Division Properties

For Your FOLDABLE

Words When you multiply or divide each side of an inequality by the same *positive* number, the inequality remains true.

Symbols For all numbers a, b, and c, where $c > 0$,
1. if $a < b$, then $ac < bc$ and $\frac{a}{c} < \frac{b}{c}$.
2. if $a > b$, then $ac > bc$ and $\frac{a}{c} > \frac{b}{c}$.

Example

$-6 < 10$	$20 > 16$
$-6 \cdot 2 < 10 \cdot 2$	$\frac{20}{4} > \frac{16}{4}$
$-12 < 20$	$5 > 4$

These properties are also true for $a \le b$ and $a \ge b$.

Differentiated Instruction

Intrapersonal Have students work together to create game-show questions that relate to the lesson. Questions should belong to different categories, such as "First Step" (in which the answer is simply the first step needed to solve an inequality); "Read the Inequality Number Line"; and "Solve" (in which contestants solve the inequality). Host the game if time allows.

StudyTip

Words to Symbols Remember, *at most* translates to $\leq$, while *at least* translates to $\geq$.

Real-World EXAMPLE 3 Divide by a Positive Number

JEWELRY Macy is making each of her 7 friends a bracelet. She does not want to spend more than \$40 on the bracelets. Find the maximum cost for each bracelet.

Understand You know that Macy wants to make 7 bracelets and does not want to spend more than \$40. You need to determine the most she can spend per bracelet.

Plan Since Macy wants to spend at most \$40, write and solve an inequality using the symbol $\leq$.

Words	Number of friends	times	cost of each bracelet	must be less than or equal to	\$40.
Variables	Let c = the cost of each bracelet.				
Inequality		$7c$		$\leq$	\$40

Solve $7c \leq 40$ **Write the inequality.**

$\frac{7c}{7} \leq \frac{40}{7}$ **Division Property of Inequality**

$c \leq 5\frac{5}{7}$ or $5.\overline{714285}$ **Simplify.**

Macy can spend no more than \$5.71 per bracelet.

Check If she spends \$5.71 per bracelet, then the total cost is \$5.71 × 7 or \$39.97. If she spends \$5.72 per bracelet then the total cost is \$5.72 × 7 or \$40.04. So, the answer is correct. ✓

Real-World Link

Jewelry and other artifacts made of gold have been discovered in archaeological sites that date back to 3000 B.C.

Source: Smithsonian

Check Your Progress

3. **WORK** It takes Alfonzo $\frac{3}{4}$ hour to mow a lawn. Write and solve an inequality to find the number of lawns he can mow if he works at least 15 hours. $\frac{3}{4}n \geq 15$; $n \geq 20$ lawns

Personal Tutor glencoe.com

Multiply or Divide an Inequality by a Negative Number What happens when each side of an inequality is multiplied or divided by a negative number?

Graph 2 and 4 on a number line.

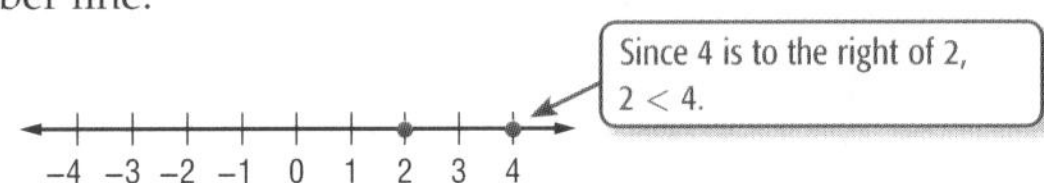

Since 4 is to the right of 2, $2 < 4$.

Now, multiply each number by −1.

Since −2 is to the right of −4, $-2 > -4$.

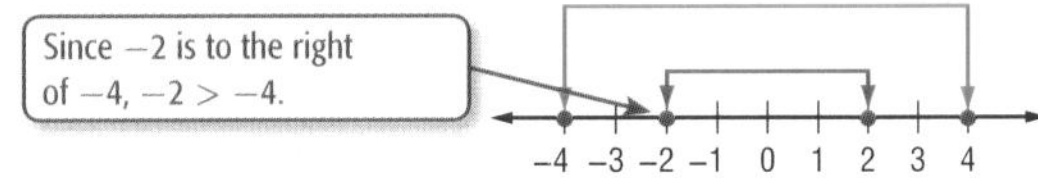

Notice that the numbers being compared switched positions as a result of being multiplied by a negative number. In other words, their order reversed. This suggests the properties shown on the next page.

Solve Inequalities by Multiplying or Dividing by a Positive Number

Example 3 shows how to write and solve inequalities using the Multiplication and Division Properties of Inequality.

Additional Example

3 **BOWLING** Juanita is going bowling and has \$25 to spend. If each game costs \$4, find the maximum number of games she can bowl. 6 games

Tips for New Teachers

Common Phrases Point out to students that *at least* and *at most* are common phrases on standardized tests. *At least* means "greater than or equal to," while *at most* means "less than or equal to."

Focus on Mathematical Content

Balance When you multiply or divide each side of an inequality by the same positive number, the inequality remains true.

Multiply or Divide an Inequality by a Negative Number

Example 4 shows how to multiply or divide by a negative number to solve an inequality and how to graph the solution on a number line.

TEACH with TECH

INTERACTIVE WHITEBOARD Project a number line on the board and lock it in place. Give the class several inequalities to solve, making sure to include some that require multiplying or dividing by a negative number. Select students to come to the board to graph their solutions on the number line.

Additional Example

4 Solve each inequality. Then graph the solution on a number line.

a. $-9x < -27$ $x > 3$

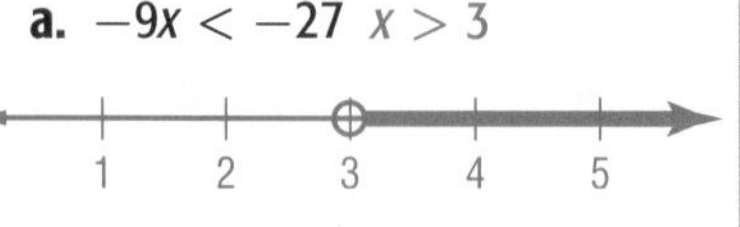

b. $\frac{x}{-5} \geq 7$ $x \leq -35$

−37 −36 −35 −34 −33

Focus on Mathematical Content

Properties When you multiply or divide both sides of an inequality by a negative number, the direction of the inequality symbol must be reversed in order for the inequality to remain true. Ask students if the inequality sign should be reversed in this example: $-42 \leq 6x$. No, because to solve it, you divide by a positive number; therefore the direction of the sign stays the same.

3 PRACTICE

Formative Assessment

Use Exercises 1–10 to check for understanding.

Use the chart at the bottom of the next page to customize assignments for your students.

StudyTip

Negative Number The statement $c < 0$ means that c is a negative number.

Key Concept — Multiplication and Division Properties

For Your FOLDABLE

Words When you multiply or divide each side of an inequality by the same *negative* number, the inequality symbol must be reversed for the inequality to remain true.

Symbols For all numbers a, b, and c, where $c < 0$,

1. if $a < b$, then $ac > bc$ and $\frac{a}{c} > \frac{b}{c}$.
2. if $a > b$, then $ac < bc$ and $\frac{a}{c} < \frac{b}{c}$.

Examples

$-4 < 5$	$18 > -12$
$-4 \cdot -3 > 5 \cdot -3$	$\frac{18}{-3} < \frac{-12}{-3}$
$12 > -15$	$-6 < 4$

Math *in Motion*, BrainPOP® glencoe.com

These properties are also true for $a \leq b$ and $a \geq b$.

EXAMPLE 4 Multiply or Divide by a Negative Number

Solve each inequality. Then graph the solution on a number line.

a. $-5x < 45$

$-5x < 45$	Write the inequality.
$\frac{-5x}{-5} > \frac{45}{-5}$	Division Property of Inequality
$x > -9$	Simplify.

−13 −11 −9 −7 −5 −3

b. $\frac{b}{-8} \geq -6$

$\frac{b}{-8} \geq -6$	Write the inequality.
$(-8)\,\frac{b}{-8} \leq -6\,(-8)$	Multiplication Property of Inequality
$b \leq 48$	Simplify.

42 44 46 48 50 52

StudyTip

Checking Solutions For Example 4a, try a number that is less than −9 to show it is *not* a solution.

$-5x < 45$
$-5(-10) \overset{?}{<} 45$
$50 \not< 45$

Check Your Progress 4A–4B. See margin for number lines.

4A. $-\frac{y}{4} < 3$. $y > -12$

4B. $7 \geq -2f$ $f \geq -3.5$

Personal Tutor glencoe.com

Check Your Understanding

Example 1 p. 241 Solve each inequality. Check your solution.

1. $y + 7 \leq 12$ $y \leq 5$
2. $b + 20 > -13$ $b > -33$
3. $-7 < x + (-3)$ $x > -4$

Example 2 p. 242 Solve each inequality. Graph the solution on a number line. See margin for number lines.

4. $d - 9.3 \geq 12.5$ $d \geq 21.8$
5. $3\frac{1}{5} > f - \frac{4}{5}$ $f < 4$
6. $g - 22 \leq -40$ $g \leq -18$

Example 3 p. 243

7. **JOBS** Isabel earns $7.50 per hour on the weekends. Write and solve an inequality to find how many hours she needs to work to earn at least $120. $7.5t \geq 120$; at least 16 hours

Example 4 p. 244 Solve each inequality. Graph the solution on a number line. 8–10. See margin for number lines.

8. $-20 < -4t$ $t < 5$
9. $-8z \leq -24$ $z \geq 3$
10. $18 > -\frac{2}{3}g$ $g > -27$

Additional Answers

4A.

−18 −16 −14 −12 −10 −8

4B.

−7 −6 −5 −4 −3 −2 −1 0 1 2

4.

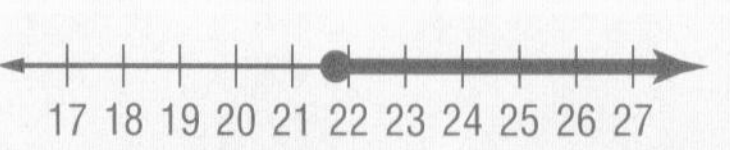

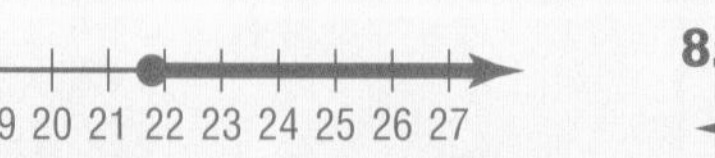

5.

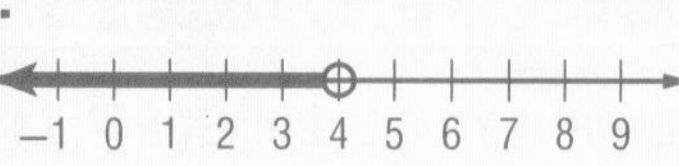

6.

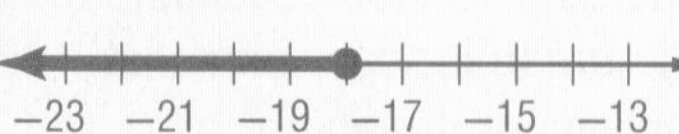

8.

9.

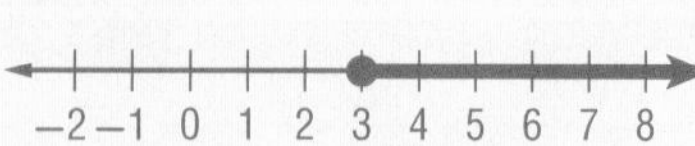

10.

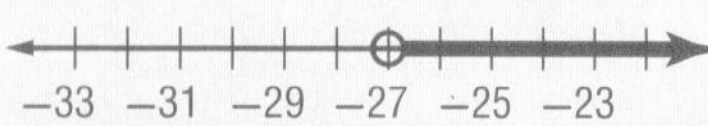

Practice and Problem Solving

● = **Step-by-Step Solutions** begin on page R11. **Extra Practice** begins on page 810.

Examples 1 and 2 pp. 241–242

Solve each inequality. Check your solution.

11. $a + 18 < 40$ $a < 22$ **12.** $h - 12 > 52$ $h > 64$ **13.** $y - 4.2 \leq 6.5$ $y \leq 10.7$

14. $g + 5.9 \geq 10$ $g \geq 4.1$ **15.** $p - 14 > 12$ $p > 26$ **16.** $x + 3.75 < 5$ $x < 1.25$

17. $n - 0.1 \leq 1.4$ $n \leq 1.5$ **18.** $7 > z + \frac{2}{3}$ $z < 6\frac{1}{3}$ **19.** $22 \geq c - 2.1$ $c \leq 24.1$

20. $13 \geq 9 + b$ $b \leq 4$ **21.** $14\frac{1}{2} < b - 1\frac{1}{4}$ $b > 15\frac{3}{4}$ **22.** $t + \frac{1}{5} < 2\frac{7}{10}$ $t < 2\frac{1}{2}$

Example 3 p. 243

23. ARCADES Montel spends $0.75 every time he plays his favorite video game. If he has $10, write and solve an inequality to find how many video games he can play. $0.75y \leq 10$; at most 13 games

24. ANIMALS Write and solve an inequality to find the swimming rate of a manatee that swims at least 15 miles in 3 hours. $3m \geq 15$; at least 5 miles per hour

Example 4 p. 244

Solve each inequality. Graph the solution on a number line. 25–36. See margin for number lines.

25. $4x > -36$ $x > -9$ **26.** $7y \leq -49$ $y \leq -7$ **27.** $-5m \geq 15$ $m \leq -3$

28. $-2p < -3$ $p > 1.5$ **29.** $45 \leq -10r$ $r \leq -4.5$ **30.** $-66 \geq -11t$ $t \geq 6$

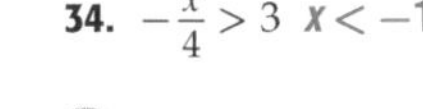

31. $\frac{7}{2}y > 63$ $y > 18$ **32.** $\frac{3}{4} \leq -\frac{5}{7}m$ **33.** $-\frac{3}{24}b \geq -\frac{1}{4}$ $b \leq 2$

32. $m \leq -\frac{21}{20}$ or $-1\frac{1}{20}$

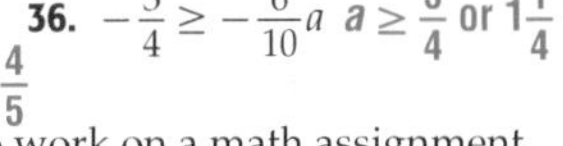

34. $-\frac{x}{4} > 3$ $x < -12$ **35.** $\frac{4}{9}c \leq -\frac{4}{5}$ $c \leq -\frac{9}{5}$ or $-1\frac{4}{5}$ **36.** $-\frac{3}{4} \geq -\frac{6}{10}a$ $a \geq \frac{5}{4}$ or $1\frac{1}{4}$

B

37. HOMEWORK Khadijah has at most three hours to work on a math assignment and a history project. If the math assignment will take $\frac{3}{4}$ hour, how much time can Khadijah spend working on her history project? at most $2\frac{1}{4}$ h or 2 h 15 min

38. STATE FAIRS The 2007 attendance at the Ohio State Fair was at least 8200 less than the attendance in 2006. If the attendance in 2007 was 806,300, write and solve an inequality to find the 2006 attendance. $806{,}300 \geq x - 8200$; $x \leq 814{,}500$

Real-World Link

The Ohio State Fair began in 1850. One of its most popular attractions is a butter cow, which is sculpted from 2000 pounds of real butter.

Source: Ohio State Fair

Solve each inequality. Check your solution.

39. $a - 3.5 < \frac{2}{5}$ $a < 3.9$ **40.** $b + 4\frac{1}{2} \geq 0.4$ $b \geq -4.1$ **41.** $26 \leq 5 - c$ $c \leq -21$

42. $12 - d > 40$ $d < -28$ **43.** $4.5 \geq \frac{3}{2}r$ $r \leq 3$ **44.** $f - 8 < -1.1$ $f < 6.9$

45. $t - 6 \leq 2.5$ $t \leq 8.5$ **46.** $-9.6 \geq \frac{1}{3}y$ $y \leq -28.8$ **47.** $-\frac{7}{11} \geq -\frac{14}{33}g$ $g \geq \frac{3}{2}$

Write an inequality to represent each situation. Then solve the inequality.

48. Seven more than a number is at most 24. $7 + n \leq 24$; $n \leq 17$

49. The quotient of a number and −3 is greater than the quotient of 5 and 6.

49. $\frac{n}{-3} > \frac{5}{6}$; $n < -\frac{5}{2}$

50. 18 is at least the product of −6 and a number. $18 \geq -6n$; $n \geq -3$

51. The difference of a number and 15 is no more than −8. $n - 15 \leq -8$; $n \leq 7$

52. FINANCIAL LITERACY Brian is saving money to buy a new mountain bike. The bike that he likes costs $375.95, and he has already saved $285.50. Write and solve an inequality to find the amount he must still save. $x + 285.50 \geq 375.95$; at least $90.45

Differentiated Homework Options

Level	Assignment	Two-Day Option	
AL Basic	11–36, 67–68, 70–92	11–35 odd, 73–76	12–36 even, 67–68, 70–72, 77–92
OL Core	11–35 odd, 37–38, 39–51 odd, 52–68, 70–92	11–36, 73–76	37–68, 70–72, 77–92
BL Advanced	37–86 (optional: 87–92)		

Tips for New Teachers

Line Direction Tell students that when graphing a solution on a number line, if the variable is on the left of the inequality symbol, the line of the graph will extend in the direction that the inequality symbol points. In the inequality $x > 3$, the line extends to the right. For $x < 3$, the line extends to the left.

Additional Answers

25.

26.

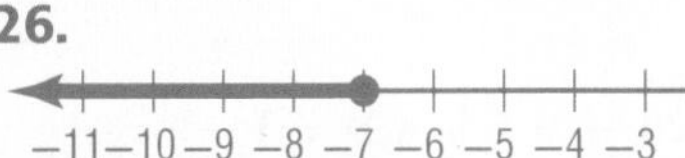

27.

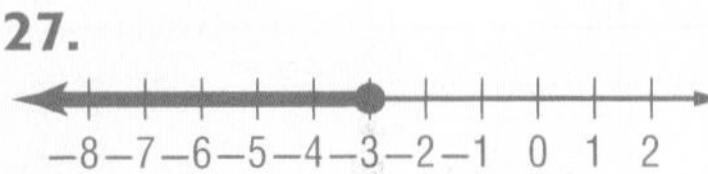

28.

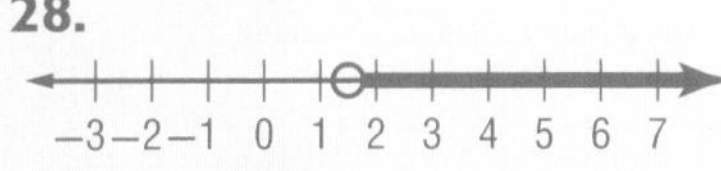

29.

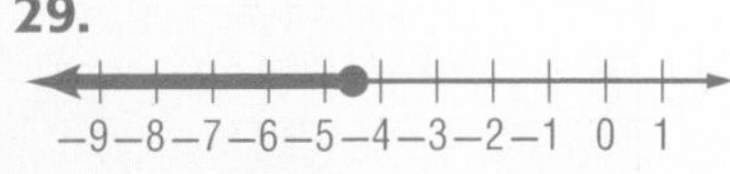

30.

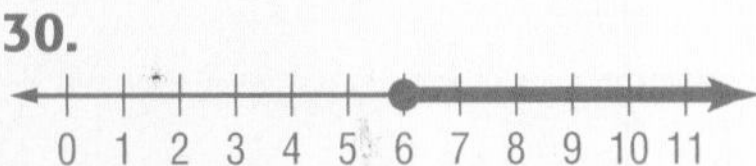

31.

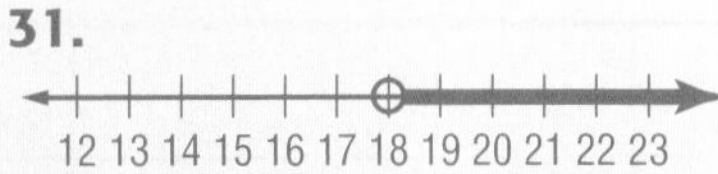

32.

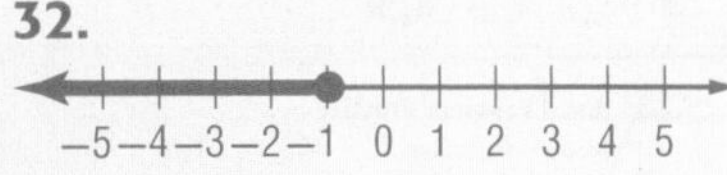

33.

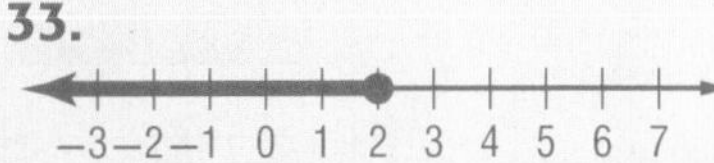

34.

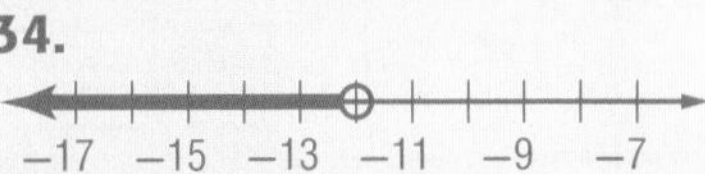

35.

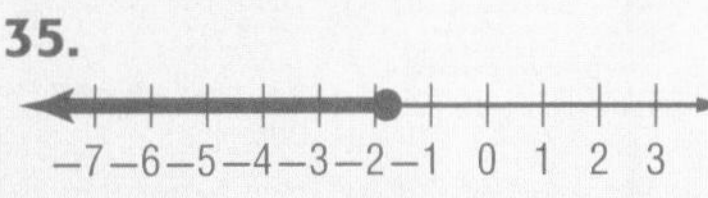

36.

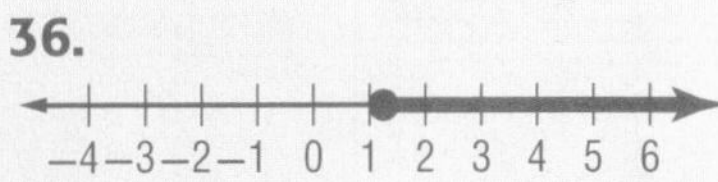

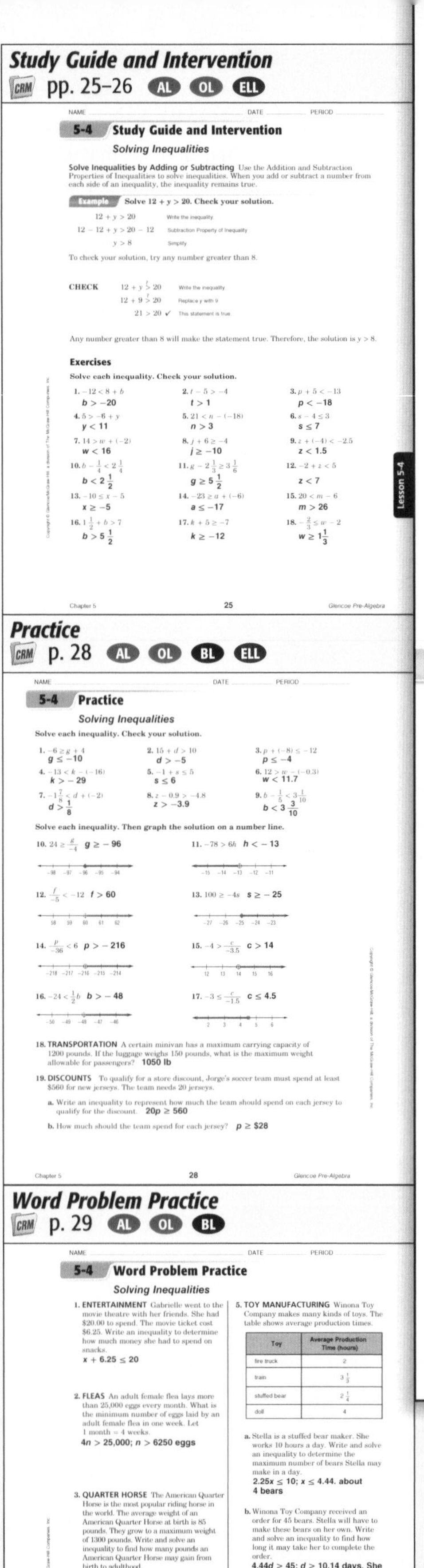

Study Guide and Intervention CRM pp. 25–26 AL OL ELL

Practice CRM p. 28 AL OL BL ELL

Word Problem Practice CRM p. 29 AL OL BL

62b. Yes it represents the solutions that satisfy both inequalities.

66a. $99.2 + t > 101$; $t > 1.8$; more than 1.8°F higher

Real-World Link

Throughout the day, the body temperature of a healthy person can fluctuate by 1°F or more depending on their physical activity. A person's body temperature is usually lowest just after waking up.

Source: WebMD

Solve each inequality. Check your solution.

53. $4a - 7 \geq 21$ $a \geq 7$
54. $8 < -\frac{m}{6} - 2$ $m < -60$
55. $3b + 15 \leq 8b - 5$ $b \geq 4$
56. $\frac{m}{5} - 12 > -18$ $m > -30$
57. $-\frac{3}{4}d - 6 \geq 9$ $d \leq -20$
58. $13 - 3n < -8$ $n > 7$
59. $11 - 2g > -7 - 8g$ $g > -3$
60. $15 \leq -\frac{k}{4} - 9$ $k \leq -96$
61. $-12 \geq -3q - 18$ $q \geq -2$

62. **MULTIPLE REPRESENTATIONS** Consider the inequalities $b \geq 4$ and $b \leq 13$.

a. **GRAPHICAL** Graph each inequality on the same number line. **See margin.**

b. **VERBAL** Do the solution sets of the two inequalities overlap? If so, what does this overlapping area represent?

c. **ALGEBRAIC** A *compound inequality* is an inequality that combines two inequalities. Write a compound inequality for the situation. $4 \leq b \leq 13$

d. **GRAPHICAL** Look back at the graph of the solutions for both inequalities. Make another graph that shows only the solution of the compound inequality. **See margin.**

Graph each compound inequality on a number line. 63–65. See margin.

63. $-3 < n < 5$
64. $4 \geq m > -2$
65. $8 \leq g < 14$

66. **SCIENCE** Use the body temperature scale shown.

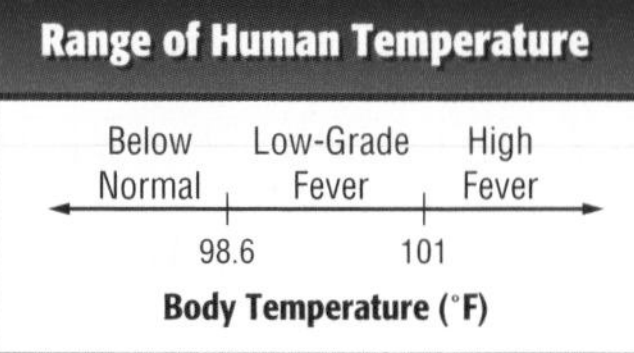

a. Suppose Malia has a temperature of 99.2°. Write and solve an inequality to find how much her temperature must increase before she is considered to have a high fever.

b. Hypothermia occurs when a person's body temperature falls below 95°F. Write and solve an inequality that describes how much lower the body temperature of a person with hypothermia will be than a person with a normal body temperature of 98.6°F. **$98.6 - t < 95$; $t > 3.6$; more than 3.6°F lower**

H.O.T. Problems

Use Higher-Order Thinking Skills

67. **OPEN ENDED** Write an inequality for the following sentence.

The quotient of a number and −5 increased by 4 is at most 8.

Name three numbers that are possible solutions. Explain.

68. **WRITING IN MATH** Write a real-world problem involving an inequality and negative numbers where the inequality symbol would *not* be reversed when finding the solution.

69. **CHALLENGE** Twenty more than half a number is at least 45. Find the least number that meets this condition. **50**

70. **REASONING** Is the following statement *true* or *false*? If false, provide a counterexample. **false; If $x = -2$, then $2x = -4$, $-2 > -4$.**

For all values of x, two times x is greater than x.

71. **REASONING** Is it *always*, *sometimes*, or *never* true that if $x \leq y$, then $y > x$? Explain your reasoning. **Sometimes; if $x = 21$ and $y = 21$ then $x \leq y$ is true but $y > x$ is not true.**

72. **WRITING IN MATH** Explain to a friend who was not in class today how to solve inequalities that involve multiplication and division. **See students' work.**

67. $\frac{x}{-5} + 4 \leq 8$; $x \geq -20$; Sample answers: −18, 0, 18 because they are greater than −20.

68. Sample answer: $x + (-3.60) \leq 15.00$; $x \leq 18.60$. After a discount of \$3.60 was applied to an item, the new price was at most \$15. Find the original price of the item.

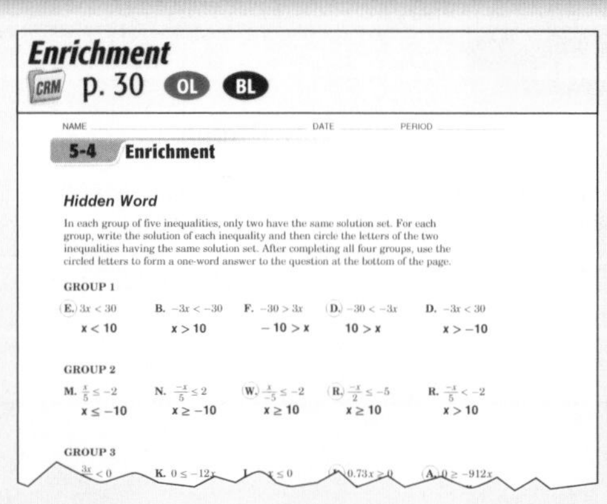

Enrichment CRM p. 30 OL BL

Multiple Representations In Exercise 62, students use a number line, an algebraic inequality, and verbal analysis to relate the parts of a compound inequality.

Standardized Test Practice

73. The length of the rectangle is greater than its width. Which inequality represents the possible values of x? **B**

A $x \leq 17$ C $x \geq 17$

B $x < 17$ D $x > 17$

74. If $n + 15 > 4$, then n could be which of the following values? **J**

F −13 H −11

G −12 J −10

75. The solutions for which inequality are represented by the following graph? **D**

−20 −18 −16 −14 −12 −10

A $\frac{x}{-3} < 5$ C $\frac{x}{3} > -5$

B $\frac{x}{-3} \leq 5$ D $\frac{x}{-3} \geq 5$

76. EXTENDED RESPONSE The product of a number and four is at most thirty.

a. Write an inequality for the sentence. $4n \leq 30$

b. Solve the inequality. $n \leq 7\frac{1}{2}$

c. Graph the solution on a number line. See margin.

Spiral Review

Write an inequality for each sentence. (Lesson 5-3)

77. Leticia made at least $45 babysitting last weekend. $l \geq 45$

78. Marc could pay no more than $8500 for his car. $c \leq 8500$

79. Adrienne needs an 86% or better to get a B in the class. $b \geq 86$

Solve each equation. Check your solution. (Lesson 5-2)

80. $4h + 5 = -6h - 19$ −2.4

81. $7d - 13 = 17 + 3d$ 7.5

82. $n - 14 = 3n$ −7

83. $2g + 12 = 3g - 1$ 13

84. $8y + 5 = 5y - 5 + 2y$ −10

85. $4t = 2t - 26$ −13

86. PLUMBING A standard showerhead uses about 6 gallons of water per minute. The table shows the relationship between time in minutes and the number of gallons of water used. (Lesson 1-5)

a. Given m, the number of minutes, write an equation that can be used to find g, the number of gallons used. $g = 6m$

b. How many minutes elapsed if 72 gallons of water were used? 12

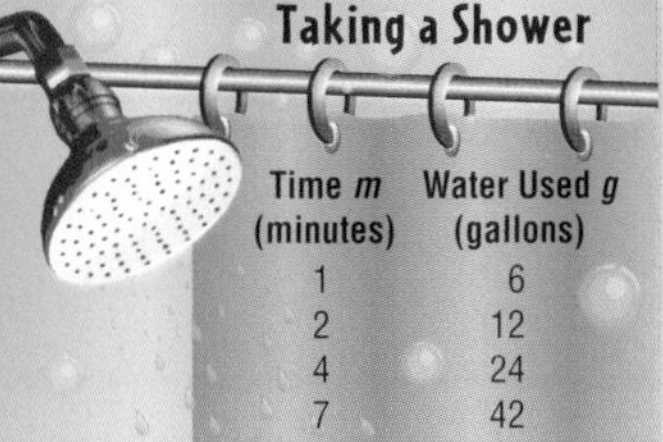

Taking a Shower

Time m (minutes)	Water Used g (gallons)
1	6
2	12
4	24
7	42

Skills Review

Solve each equation. (Lesson 4-5)

87. $3x + 1 = 7$ 2

88. $5x - 4 = 11$ 3

89. $4h + 6 = 22$ 4

90. $8n + 3 = -5$ −1

91. $37 = 4d + 5$ 8

92. $9 = 15 + 2p$ −3

4 ASSESS

Crystal Ball Ask students to write a brief statement on how they think today's lesson on solving inequalities will help them with the next lesson on solving multi-step equations and inequalities.

Formative Assessment

Check for student understanding of concepts in Lesson 5-4.

CRM Quiz 3, p. 41

Additional Answers

62a.

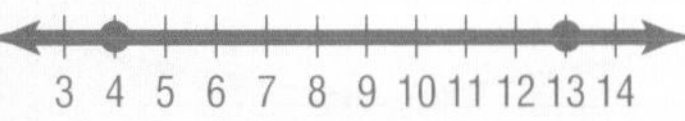

62d.

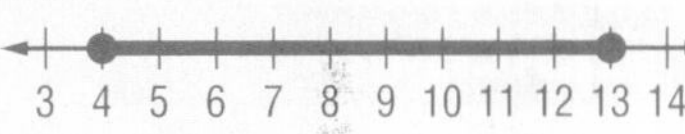

63.

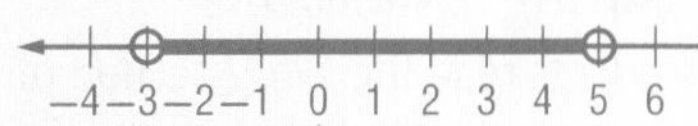

64.

65.

76c.

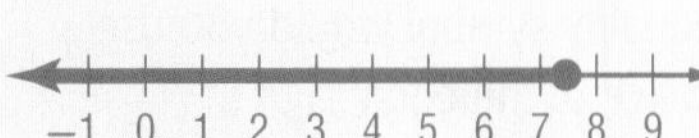

Differentiated Instruction 

Extension Present the following problem to students: Nina wants to rent a DVD. One store charges a $3 fee plus $0.50 per day per DVD. A second store has no fees and charges $2 per day per DVD. For how many days would the cost of the rentals be the same? 2 days At which store would it be less expensive to rent a DVD for 3 days? Explain. The first store would cost $4.50 for 3 days and the second store would cost $6 for 3 days, so the first store would be less expensive.

5-5 Lesson Notes

1 FOCUS

Vertical Alignment

Before Lesson 5-5
Solve two-step equations and inequalities.

Lesson 5-5
Solve multi-step equations.
Solve multi-step inequalities.

After Lesson 5-5
Use the Properties of Equality to solve real world applications involving multi-step equations and inequalities.

2 TEACH

Scaffolding Questions

Have students read the *Why?* section of the lesson and answer the questions.

Ask:

- If your average daily distance is 2 kilometers, you should have enough endurance to finish a race of how many kilometers? 6 km
- Suppose you want to increase your endurance so that you can run *at least* a 12-kilometer race. What inequality symbol would you use in place of the equal sign in $3(2 + d) = 12$? $\geq$
- What must you do first to solve the equation or inequality? Remove the parentheses

5-5 Solving Multi-Step Equations and Inequalities

Then
You have already solved two-step equations and inequalities.

Now
- Solve multi-step equations.
- Solve multi-step inequalities.

New Vocabulary
null or empty set
identity

Math Online
glencoe.com
- Extra Examples
- Personal Tutor
- Self-Check Quiz
- Homework Help

Why?

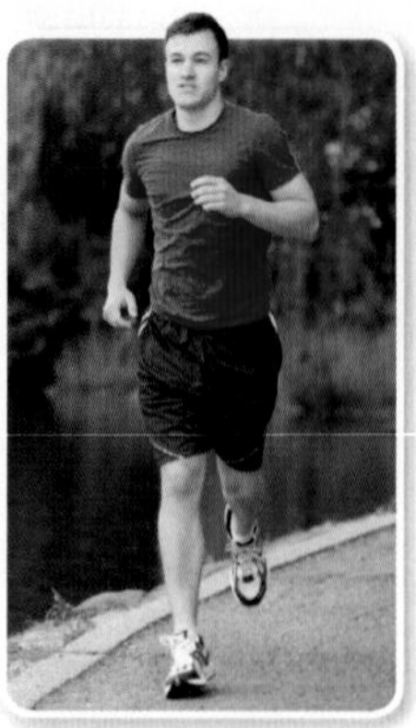

A good rule to know when training for a marathon is you will generally have enough endurance to finish a race that is 3 times your average daily distance.

a. Write an equation that represents the relationship between daily average distance d and possible race lengths l. $l = 3d$

b. Suppose your average daily run is 2 kilometers. Write an equation that represents the amount that you need to increase your daily run by d to have enough endurance for a 12-kilometer race. $3(2 + d) = 12$

Solve Equations and Inequalities with Grouping Symbols To find the minimum number of kilometers you need to increase your daily run, you can solve the equation $3(d + 2) = 12$. First, use the Distributive Property to remove the grouping symbols.

EXAMPLE 1 Solve Equations and Inequalities with Parentheses

a. Solve $3(d + 2) = 12$. Check your solution.

$3(d + 2) = 12$	Write the equation.
$3d + 6 = 12$	Distributive Property
$-6 \quad -6$	Subtraction Property of Equality
$3d = 6$	Simplify.
$\frac{3d}{3} = \frac{6}{3}$	Division Property of Equality
$d = 2$	Simplify.

b. Solve $4(x - 3) > 6$.

$4(x - 3) > 6$	Write the inequality.
$4x - 12 > 6$	Distributive Property
$+12 \quad +12$	Subtraction Property of Inequality
$4x > 18$	Simplify.
$\frac{4x}{4} > \frac{18}{4}$	Division Property of Inequality
$x > 4.5$	Simplify.

Check Your Progress

Solve. Check your solution.

1A. $3 = 4(x + 2)$ -1.25

1B. $4(b - 3) \leq 72$ $b \leq 21$

Personal Tutor glencoe.com

Lesson 5-5 Resources

Resource	Approaching-Level	On-Level	Beyond-Level	English Learners
Teacher Edition	• Differentiated Instruction, p. 250		• Differentiated Instruction, p. 253	
Chapter Resource Masters	• Study Guide and Intervention, pp. 31–32 • Skills Practice, p. 33 • Practice, p. 34 • Word Problem Practice, p. 35	• Study Guide and Intervention, pp. 31–32 • Skills Practice, p. 33 • Practice, p. 34 • Word Problem Practice, p. 35 • Enrichment, p. 36	• Practice, p. 34 • Word Problem Practice, p. 35 • Enrichment, p. 36	• Study Guide and Intervention, pp. 31–32 • Skills Practice, p. 33 • Practice, p. 34
Transparencies	• 5-Minute Check Transparency 5-5	• 5-Minute Check Transparency 5-5	• 5-Minute Check Transparency 5-5	• 5-Minute Check Transparency 5-5
Other	• Study Notebook • Teaching Pre-Algebra with Manipulatives	• Study Notebook • Teaching Pre-Algebra with Manipulatives	• Study Notebook	• Study Notebook • Teaching Pre-Algebra with Manipulatives

StudyTip

Alternative Method You can also solve the equation using the vertical method shown on p. 248.

EXAMPLE 2 Solve Multi-Step Equations

Solve $4(x + 5) = 3(2x + 4)$. Check your solution.

$4(x + 5) = 3(2x + 4)$	Write the equation.
$4x + 20 = 6x + 12$	Distributive Property
$4x - 4x + 20 = 6x - 4x + 12$	Subtraction Property of Equality
$20 = 2x + 12$	Simplify.
$20 - 12 = 2x + 12 - 12$	Subtraction Property of Equality
$8 = 2x$	Simplify.
$4 = x$	Division Property of Equality

Check Your Progress

Solve each equation. Check your solution.

2A. $12m + 12 = 6(3m + 3)$ -1

2B. $5(n - 3) = 3(n + 7)$ 18

Personal Tutor glencoe.com

STANDARDIZED TEST EXAMPLE 3

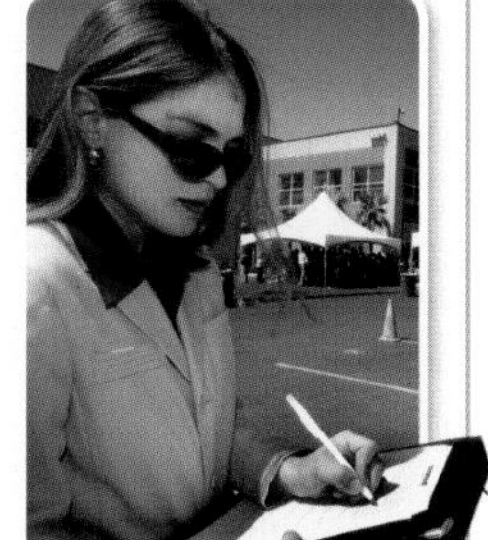

Real-World Career

Event Planner
Event planners plan, budget, and organize events including parties, weddings, and business conferences.

Education and training for event planners can include a college degree in hospitality at either a two-year or a four-year program.

Mariella's parents have budgeted \$575 for her quinceañera. The cost of the party room is \$75. How much can the family spend per guest on food if each of the 40 guests receives a \$5 favor?

A \$5.00 **B** \$7.50 **C** \$8.00 **D** \$9.50

Read the Test Item

You need to find the amount of money the family can spend per guest on food.

Solve the Test Item

Words	Party cost = room cost + the number of guests × the cost per guest.
Symbols	Let c = the food cost per guest so $c + 5$ = the total cost per guest.
Equation	$575 \quad = \quad 75 \quad + \quad 40(c + 5)$

$575 = 75 + 40(c + 5)$	Write the equation.
$575 = 75 + 40c + 200$	Distributive Property
$575 = 40c + 275$	Simplify.
$575 - 275 = 40c + 275 - 275$	Subtraction Property of Equality
$300 = 40c$	Simplify.
$7.5 = c$	Division Property of Equality

The answer is B.

Check Your Progress

3. Sofia recycled 3 pounds less than the amount that James recycled. Hannah recycled 3 times the amount that Sofia recycled. If they recycled a total of 53 pounds, how many pounds did Sofia recycle? F

F 10 pounds **G** 13 pounds **H** 30 pounds **J** 35 pounds

Personal Tutor glencoe.com

Solve Equations and Inequalities with Grouping Symbols

Examples 1–4 show how to solve equations and inequalities that contain parentheses by using the Distributive Property.

Formative Assessment

Use the Check Your Progress exercises after each example to determine students' understanding of concepts.

Additional Examples

1 a. Solve $5(h - 2) = 15$. $h = 5$

b. Solve $2(x - 4) > 11$. $x > 9.5$

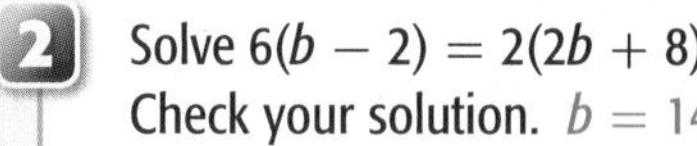

2 Solve $6(b - 2) = 2(2b + 8)$. Check your solution. $b = 14$

3 **STANDARDIZED TEST PRACTICE** The Carleton Company budgeted \$1,825 for a banquet. The cost of the facility is \$225. How much can the company spend per guest on food if there is a \$3 charge per guest for linens and there are 80 guests coming to the banquet? B

A \$15
B \$17
C \$20
D \$25

Additional Examples also in Interactive Classroom PowerPoint® Presentations

IWB INTERACTIVE WHITEBOARD READY

TEACH with TECH

WIKI On your class wiki, have students create a page explaining how they worked through solving a specific multi-step inequality. Instruct students to explain how they decided whether or not to reverse the inequality sign.

Additional Example

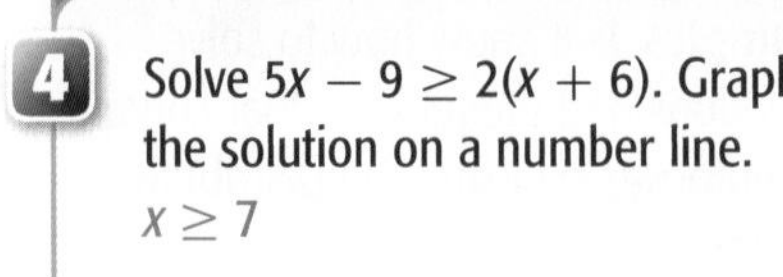

4 Solve $5x - 9 \geq 2(x + 6)$. Graph the solution on a number line.

$x \geq 7$

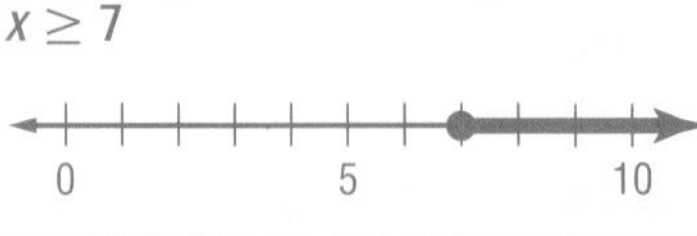

No Solution or All Numbers as Solutions

Example 5 shows how to determine whether the solution set is all numbers or an empty set.

Additional Example

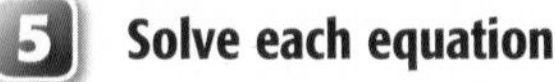

5 **Solve each equation.**

a. $3(4x - 2) + 15 = 12x + 9$
Identity; all numbers.

b. $7y - 8 = 3(2y + 4) + y$
Null Set; no solution.

Focus on Mathematical Content

Identities When solving some equations, the variables are eliminated and what remains is either true or false. If false, then the equation has no solution, or the solution set is the empty set. If true, then the equation is an identity, and the solution is the set of all numbers.

Additional Answers

4A.

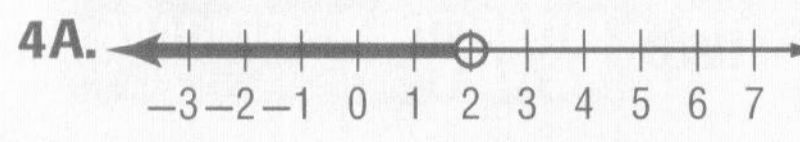

4B. 17 18 19 20 21 22 23 24 25 26 27

Watch Out!

Do not reverse the inequality sign just because there is a negative sign in the inequality. Only reverse the sign when you multiply or divide by a negative number.

EXAMPLE 4 Solve Multi-Step Inequalities

Solve $5a - 8 \geq 4(a - 3)$. Graph the solution on a number line.

$5a - 8 \geq 4(a - 3)$	**Write the inequality.**
$5a - 8 \geq 4a - 12$	**Distributive Property.**
$5a - 8 - 4a \geq 4a - 12 - 4a$	**Subtraction Property of Inequality**
$a - 8 \geq -12$	**Simplify.**
$a - 8 + 8 \geq -12 + 8$	**Addition Property of Inequality**
$a \geq -4$	**Simplify.**
−5 −4 −3 −2 −1 0 1 2 3 4 5	**Graph the solution on a number line.**

Check Your Progress

Solve each inequality. Graph the solution on a number line.
4A–B. See margin for number lines.

4A. $-2(k + 1) < -16 + 5k$ $k > 2$ **4B.** $2p + 5 \geq 3(p - 6)$ $p \leq 23$

Personal Tutor glencoe.com

No Solution or All Numbers as Solutions Some equations have *no* solution. When this occurs, the solution is the **null or empty set**, shown by the symbol ∅ or { }. Other equations may have every number as their solution. An equation that is true for every value of the variable is called an **identity**.

Review Vocabulary

Identities An identity is an equation that shows that a number or expression is equivalent to itself.

Additive Identity
$a + 0 = a$

Multiplicative Identity
$a \cdot 1 = a$

EXAMPLE 5 Null Set and Identities

Solve each equation.

a. $3(y - 5) + 25 = 3y + 10$

$3(y - 5) + 25 = 3y + 10$	**Write the equation.**
$3y - 15 + 25 = 3y + 10$	**Use the Distributive Property.**
$3y + 10 = 3y + 10$	**Simplify.**
$3y + 10 - 3y = 3y + 10 - 3y$	**Subtraction Property of Equality**
$10 = 10$	**Simplify.**

The statement $10 = 10$ is *always* true. The equation is an identity and the solution set is all numbers.

b. $-5s - 14 = 2(2s + 3) - 9s$

$-5s - 14 = 2(2s + 3) - 9s$	**Write the equation.**
$-5s - 14 = 4s + 6 - 9s$	**Use the Distributive Property.**
$-5s - 14 = 6 - 5s$	**Simplify.**
$-5s - 14 + 5s = 6 - 5s + 5s$	**Addition Property of Equality**
$-14 = 6$	**Simplify.**

The statement $-14 = 6$ is *never* true. The equation has no solutions and the solution set is ∅.

Check Your Progress 5A. Identity; All numbers 5B. Null set; No solution

5A. $-2(3r + 4) = -5r - 8 - r$ **5B.** $14 + 8w = 4(8 + 2w)$

Personal Tutor glencoe.com

Differentiated Instruction AL

If students are comfortable with solving multi-step equations,

Then have students write equations that are identities by working in reverse order. Students should begin with $x = x$, then multiply or divide the variable by a number, followed by several more operations until a complete equation is achieved. A grouping symbol (parentheses) that requires the use of the Distributive Property should be included.

Check Your Understanding

Examples 1, 2, and 5 pp. 248–250

Solve. Check your solution.

1. $4(x + 1) = 28$ **6**
2. $35 = 7(2p - 1)$ **3**
3. $2(a - 2) = 3(a - 5)$ **11**
4. $16(z + 3) = 4(z + 9)$ **−1**
5. $7(x + 2) = 2(x + 2)$ **−2**
6. $3(d - 2) = 5(d + 8)$ **−23**
7. $6x + 4 = 2(3x - 5)$ **Null set; No solution**
8. $20f + (-8f - 15) = 3(4f - 5)$ **Identity; All numbers**
9. $3(1 + 2f) - 5 = 6f - 2$ **Identity; All numbers**
10. $7x + 5 = 10(x - 7) - 3x$ **Null set; No solution**

Example 3 p. 249

11. **MULTIPLE CHOICE** You and three friends are going to the fair. The cost for parking is \$5 per car and admission to the fair is \$19 per person. If you have a total of \$113, how much can each person spend on food? **B**

A \$4 C \$12

B \$8 D \$24

Examples 1 and 4 pp. 248 and 250

Solve. Graph the solution on a number line. **12–17. See margin for number lines.**

12. $-2(k - 2) \geq -20$ **$k \leq 12$**
13. $(3r + 7)2 \leq -34$ **$r \leq -8$**
14. $-2(g - 1) > g - 4$ **$g < 2$**
15. $5p + 8 \geq 3(p + 6)$ **$p \geq 5$**
16. $6(-2z + 5) < -19z + 16$ **$z < -2$**
17. $10p \leq 7(2p - 4)$ **$p \geq 7$**

Practice and Problem Solving

 = **Step-by-Step Solutions** begin on page R11. **Extra Practice** begins on page 810.

Examples 1, 2, and 5 pp. 248–250

Solve. Check your solution.

18. $6n - 18 = 4(n + 2)$ **13**
19. $12y + 5(y - 6) = 4$ **2**
20. $12z + 4 = 2(5z + 8) - 12$ **0**
21. $d - 12 = 4(d - 6)$ **4**
22. $3x + 2 = 2(2x - 7)$ **16**
23. $6(y - 5) = 2(10 + 3y)$ **23. Null set; No solution**
24. $4(2c + 8) = 5(c + 4)$ **−4**
25. $10 + 12p = 3(3 + 4p)$ **Null set; No solution**
26. $3x + 2 + 5(x - 1) = 8x + 17$ **Null set; No solution**
27. $10z + 4 = 2(5z + 8) - 12$ **Identity; All numbers**

Example 3 p. 249

28. **GEOMETRY** The perimeter of a rectangle is 50 centimeters. The length of the rectangle is one more than 3 times the width of the rectangle. What are the dimensions of the rectangle? **6 cm and 19 cm**

29. **FINANCIAL LITERACY** Tim is taking the train to Seattle to visit his grandparents. He was given \$15 to spend on snacks and reading material. Granola bars cost \$1.15 each, and magazines cost \$1.25. If Tim buys the same number of granola bars and magazines, how many can he buy? **6 granola bars and 6 magazines**

Examples 1 and 4 pp. 248 and 250

Solve. Graph the solution on a number line. **30–37. See Chapter 5 Answer Appendix for number lines.**

30. $20 > 5(w + 3)$ **$w < 1$**
31. $-32 \leq 9(3h + 2) + 4$ **$h \geq -2$**
32. $3(6m - 4) \geq 24$ **$m \geq 2$**
33. $10(3 + s) < 4s$ **$s < -5$**
34. $3y - 6 > 4(y - 3)$ **$y < 6$**
35. $8(2h + 6) \leq 12h + 20$ **$h \leq -7$**
36. $3(3r + 5) \geq 24 + 10r$ **$r \leq -9$**
37. $14t - 28 < 7(t + 6)$ **$t < 10$**

Differentiated Homework Options

Level	Assignment	Two-Day Option	
AL Basic	18–37, 51–53, 55–78	19–37 odd, 56–59	18–36 even, 51–53, 55, 60–78
OL Core	19–37 odd, 38, 39–43 odd, 45–47, 49, 51–53, 55–78	18–37, 56–59	38–53, 55, 60–78
BL Advanced	38–74 (optional: 75–78)		

3 PRACTICE

Formative Assessment

Use Exercises 1–17 to check for understanding.

Use the chart at the bottom of this page to customize assignments for your students.

Watch Out!

Find the Error If students are having problems solving inequalities that contain grouping symbols, as in Exercise 53, review the Distributive Property and when the inequality sign is reversed.

Tips for New Teachers

Inequalities with More than One Operation An inequality that has more than one operation can be solved by using inverse operations to undo the operations. Students should realize that the order of operations must be followed, just as in solving multi-step equations. Subtraction and addition are undone first, before division and multiplication.

Additional Answers

12.

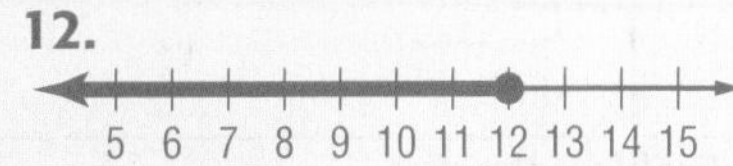

13.

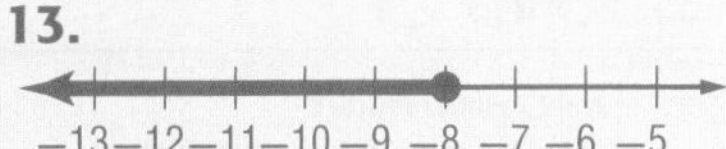

14.

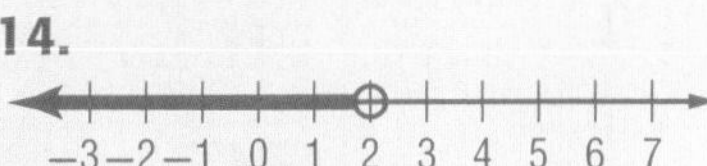

15.

16.

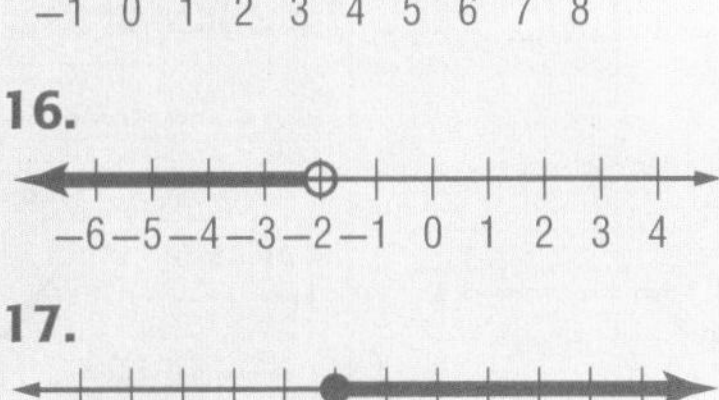

17.

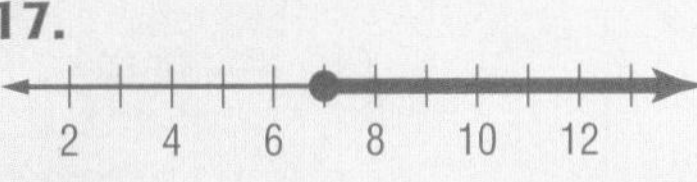

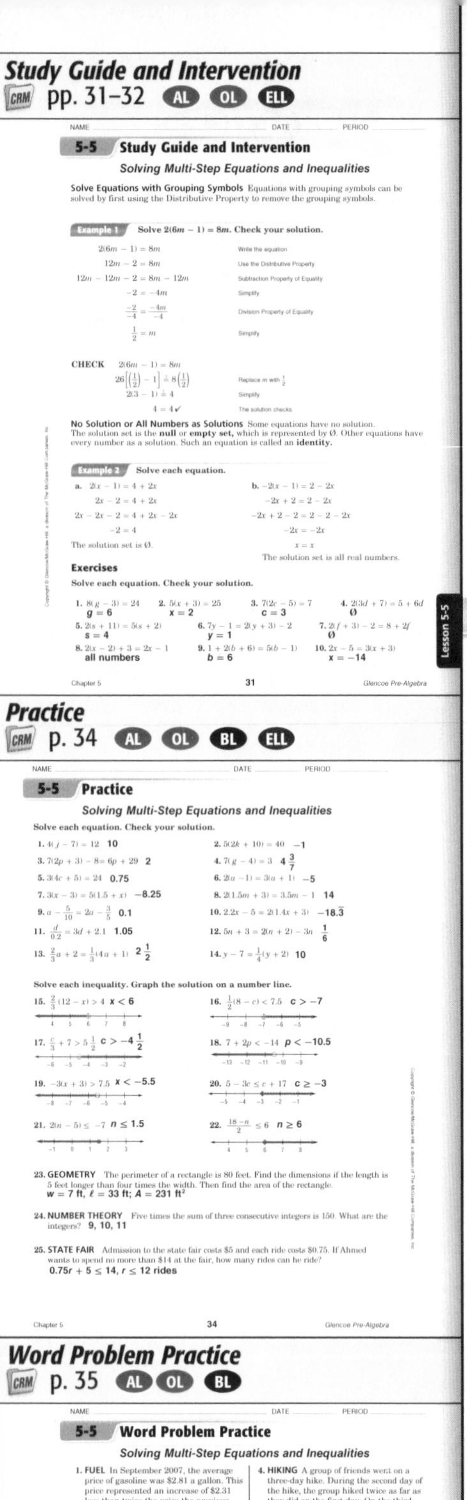
Study Guide and Intervention
CRM pp. 31–32 AL OL ELL

5-5 Study Guide and Intervention
Solving Multi-Step Equations and Inequalities

Solve Equations with Grouping Symbols Equations with grouping symbols can be solved by first using the Distributive Property to remove the grouping symbols.

Example 1 Solve $2(6m - 1) = 8m$. Check your solution.

No Solution or All Numbers as Solutions Some equations have no solution. The solution set is the **null** or **empty set**, which is represented by Ø. Other equations have every number as a solution. Such an equation is called an **identity**.

Example 2 Solve each equation.

Exercises
Solve each equation. Check your solution.

Practice
CRM p. 34 AL OL BL ELL

5-5 Practice
Solving Multi-Step Equations and Inequalities

Word Problem Practice
CRM p. 35 AL OL BL

5-5 Word Problem Practice
Solving Multi-Step Equations and Inequalities

B **38. SCHOOL** Nomar has earned scores of 73, 85, 91, and 82 on the first four of five math tests for the grading period. He would like to finish the grading period with a test average of at least 82. What is the minimum score Nomar needs to earn on the fifth test in order to achieve his goal? **$s \geq 79$**

Solve.

39. $-0.2(3c + 15) = 3(0.8c - 8)$ **7**

40. $2(t + 12) - 6(2t - 3) = 14$ **2.8**

41. $5 - \frac{1}{2}(x - 6) < 4$ **$x > 8$**

42. $6n - 18 \geq 4(n + 2.1)$ **$n \geq 13.2$**

43. $2.01c - 6 = -0.15c + 6.96$ **6**

44. $\frac{1}{4}x + 13 > 0.25(2x - 32)$ **$x < 84$**

45. RUNNING Refer to the application at the beginning of the lesson. Tammy wants to be able to run *at least* the standard marathon distance of 26.2 miles. The length of her current daily run is about 4 miles. By how many miles should she increase her daily run to meet her goal? **4.73 mi**

Real-World Link

One of the most popular races in America is the Chicago marathon. Usually about 36,000 people participate in the 26.2 mile race.

Source: Chicago Marathon

46. REPAIRS Cole is having his car repaired. The mechanic said it would cost at least $375 for parts and labor. If the cost of the parts was $150, and the mechanic charges $60 an hour, how many hours is the mechanic planning to work on the car? **at least 3 hours and 45 minutes**

Solve. Justify each step in the solution. Use a Property of Equality or Inequality when necessary. 47–50. See Chapter 5 Answer Appendix.

C **47.** $4(y - 3) = 2(3y + 10)$

48. $5(2f - 1) = 3(f + 3)$

49. $-1.2(w + 1.1) \leq 6.18$

50. $p > \frac{2}{3}(p - \frac{1}{2})$

H.O.T. Problems
Use Higher-Order Thinking Skills

51. OPEN ENDED Write a multi-step inequality that can be solved by first adding 3 to each side. **Sample answer: $10y - 3 \leq -12$**

52. WRITING IN MATH Explain how you can solve $45 > -6x + 3$ without multiplying or dividing each side by a negative number.

53. FIND THE ERROR Jada and Liu are solving $3x - 9 \leq 5(x + 10)$. Is either of them correct? Explain your reasoning.

Jada

$3x - 9 \leq 5(x + 10)$

$3x - 9 \leq 5x + 10$

$-2x \leq 19$

$x \geq -9.5$

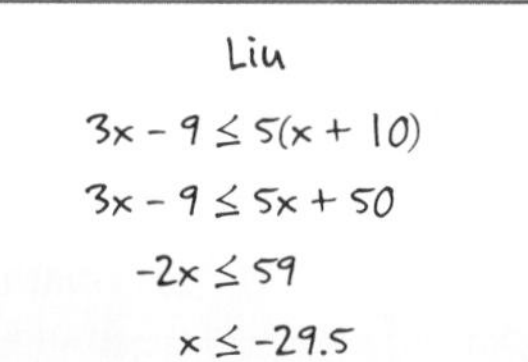

54. CHALLENGE Use the information in Example 5 about equations that have no solutions or those that are identities to solve the following inequalities. Justify each step in the solution. **See Chapter 5 Answer Appendix.**

a. $5x - 6 > 3(x - 2) + 2x$

b. $12p + 17 \leq 3(4p - 8)$

55. WRITING IN MATH Explain how to determine if an equation has no solution, one solution, or if all numbers are solutions. Use examples with your explanation. **See margin.**

52. Sample answer: You can add $6x$ to each side of the inequality before you solve.

53. Neither girl is correct. Jada did not distibute the 5 in the second step. Liu did not switch the inequality sign when she divided by -2 in the last step.

Enrichment
CRM p. 36 OL BL

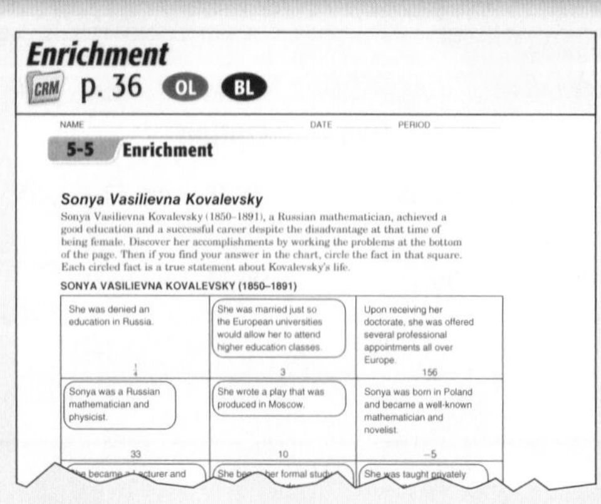
5-5 Enrichment

Sonya Vasilievna Kovalevsky

Sonya Vasilievna Kovalevsky (1850–1891), a Russian mathematician, achieved a good education and a successful career despite the disadvantage at that time of being female. Discover her accomplishments by working the problems at the bottom of the page. Then if you find your answer in the chart, circle the fact in that square. Each circled fact is a true statement about Kovalevsky's life.

SONYA VASILIEVNA KOVALEVSKY (1850–1891)

She was denied an education in Russia.	She was married just so the European universities would allow her to attend higher education classes.	Upon receiving her doctorate, she was offered several professional appointments all over Europe.
4	3	156
Sonya was a Russian mathematician and physicist.	She wrote a play that was produced in Moscow.	Sonya was born in Poland and became a well-known mathematician and novelist.
33	10	−5

Standardized Test Practice

56. Find the value of x so that the polygons have the same perimeter. **C**

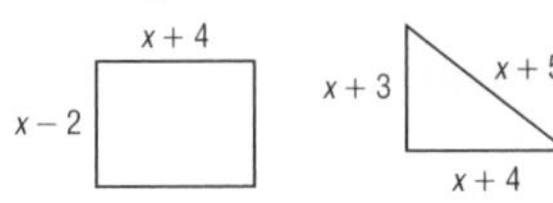

A 3   C 8

B 6   D 12

57. GRIDDED RESPONSE Damon spent \$42, including tax, on shelves he bought at a home improvement store. The price of the shelves, including tax, was \$7 for two shelves. In the equation below, s represents the number of shelves Damon bought.

$$42 = s(7 \div 2)$$

How many shelves s did Damon buy? **12**

58. What is the solution of this inequality? **J**

$$-4x + 16 \geq -4$$

F $x \geq 3$

G $x \leq 3$

H $x \geq 5$

J $x \leq 5$

59. Sandra's scores on the first five science tests are shown. Which inequality represents the score she must receive on the sixth test to have an average score of more than 88? **D**

Test	Score
1	85
2	84
3	90
4	95
5	88

A $s \geq 86$ C $s < 88$

B $s \leq 88$ D $s > 86$

Spiral Review

Solve each inequality. Graph the solution on a number line. (Lesson 5-4) **60–65. See margin for number lines.**

60. $-25t \leq 400$ **$t \geq -16$**

61. $8 > \frac{q}{3}$ **$q < 24$**

62. $14 \geq 7 + a$ **$a \leq 7$**

63. $-13 \geq x - 8$ **$x \leq -5$**

64. $-\frac{3}{4} < w - 1$ **$w > \frac{1}{4}$**

65. $3 \leq \frac{1}{2} + a$ **$a \geq 2\frac{1}{2}$**

Write an inequality for each sentence. (Lesson 5-3)

66. Kyle's earnings were no more than \$60. **$m \leq 60$**

67. The 10 kilometer race time of 86 minutes was greater than the winner's time. **$86 > w$**

Write each fraction or mixed number as a decimal. Use a bar to show a repeating decimal. (Lesson 3-1)

68. $\frac{1}{5}$ **0.2**

69. $-\frac{5}{8}$ **−0.625**

70. $7\frac{3}{10}$ **7.3**

71. $\frac{1}{9}$ **$0.\overline{1}$**

72. $-3\frac{3}{4}$ **−3.75**

73. $-\frac{5}{11}$ **$-0.\overline{45}$**

74. BUSINESS The formula $P = I - E$ is used to find the profit P when income I and expenses E are known. One month a small business has an income of \$19,592 and expenses of \$20,345. (Lesson 2-3)

a. What is the profit for the month? **−\$753**

b. What does a negative profit mean? **expenses > income**

Skills Review

Divide. (Lesson 0-3)

75. $7.2 \div 2$ **3.6**

76. $\$3.75 \div 5$ **\$0.75**

77. $\$25.90 \div 3.5$ **\$7.40**

78. $29.14 \div 4.7$ **6.2**

4 ASSESS

Yesterday's News Have students write about the similarities and differences between solving one-step inequalities in yesterday's lesson and multi-step inequalities in today's lesson.

Formative Assessment

Check for student understanding of concepts in Lesson 5-5.

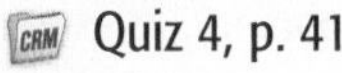

CRM Quiz 4, p. 41

Additional Answers

55. Sample answer: If you get an answer like $5 = 5$ which is always true, all numbers are solutions. If you get an answer like $5 = 9$ which is never true, there are no solutions. If you get an answer like $x = 8$, there is one solution.

60.

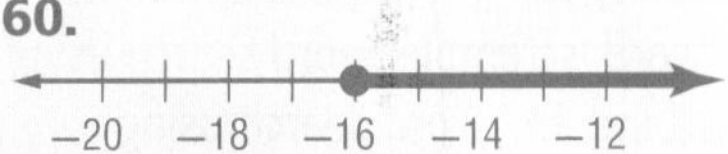

61.

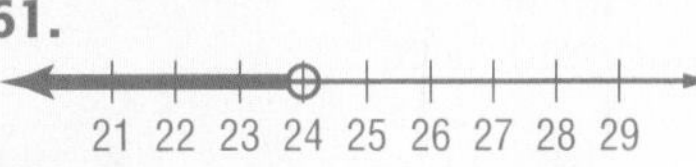

62.

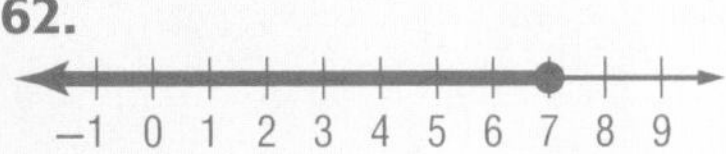

63.

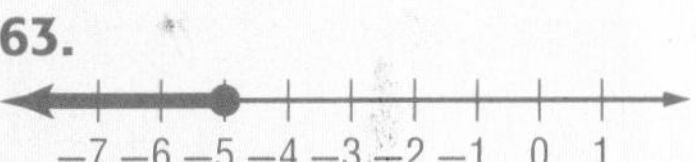

64.

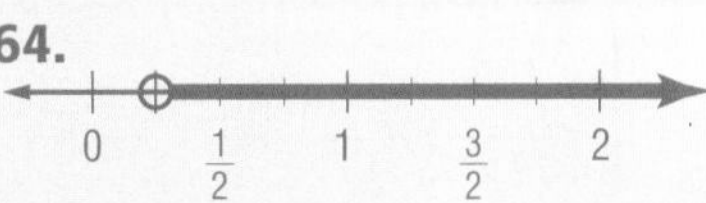

65.

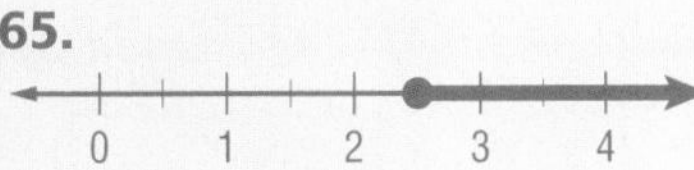

Differentiated Instruction

BL

Extension Ask students to explain how you would graph an inequality, such as $y > 6$ on graph paper. Start by graphing the equation, $y = 6$. How would you represent the solution to the inequality $y > 6$? Answers will vary; show students that by creating a boundary line that is dashed, the set is represented since the solution set does not include 6 but everything greater than 6.

Formative Assessment

Key Vocabulary The page references after each word denote where that term was first introduced. If students have difficulty answering questions 1–10, remind them that they can use these page references to refresh their memories about the vocabulary.

Summative Assessment

 Vocabulary Test, p. 43

Math Online glencoe.com

Vocabulary PuzzleMaker improves students' mathematics vocabulary using four puzzle formats–crossword, scramble, word search using a word list, and word search using clues. Students can work online or from a printed worksheet.

Math Online glencoe.com
- STUDY TO GO
- Vocabulary Review

Chapter Summary

Key Concepts

Perimeter and Area (Lesson 5-1)

- Perimeter is the distance around a geometric figure.
  Rectangle: $P = 2(\ell + w)$
  Triangle: $P = a + b + c$
- Area is the measure of the surface enclosed by a figure.
  Rectangle: $A = \ell w$
  Triangle: $A = \frac{1}{2}bh$

Solving Equations (Lessons 5-2 and 5-5)

- Use the Addition or Subtraction Property of Equality to isolate the variables on one side of an equation.
- Use the Distributive Property to remove the grouping symbols.

Inequalities (Lessons 5-3 to 5-5)

- An inequality is a mathematical sentence that contains $<$, $>$, $\leq$, or $\geq$.
- Solving an inequality means finding values for the variable that make the inequality true.
- When you multiply or divide each side of an inequality by a positive number, the inequality symbol remains the same.
- When you multiply or divide each side of an inequality by a negative number, the inequality symbol must be reversed.
- To solve an inequality that involves more than one operation, work backward to undo the operations.

FOLDABLES® Study Organizer

Be sure the Key Concepts are noted in your Foldable.

Multi-Step Equations/Inequalities
Solving Inequalities
Inequalities
Equations with Variables on Each Side
Perimeter and Area
Chapter 5 Multi-Step Equations and Inequalities

Key Vocabulary

area (p. 222)
formula (p. 221)
identity (p. 250)
inequality (p. 234)
null or empty set (p. 250)
perimeter (p. 221)

Vocabulary Check

Choose the correct term to complete each sentence.

1. An (equation, inequality) is a mathematical sentence that contains a less than or greater than symbol.
2. (Perimeter, Area) is the distance around a geometric figure.
3. The inequality symbol must be reversed when you multiply or divide by a (positive, negative) number.
4. When finding the area of a triangle multiply $\left(2, \frac{1}{2}\right)$ by the product of the base and height.
5. The symbol $\geq$ means (less than, greater than) or equal to.
6. The statement $d + 0 = d$ is an example of the (additive, multiplicative) identity.
7. The area of a rectangle is equal to the (sum, product) of the length and width.
8. The (Addition, Distributive) Property can be used to remove grouping symbols.
9. The measure of the amount of space in a figure is the (perimeter, area).
10. A null or empty set is shown by the symbol ($\varnothing$, λ).

FOLDABLES® Study Organizer

Dinah Zike's Foldables®

Have students look through the chapter to make sure they have included examples in their Foldables.

Suggest that students keep their Foldables handy while completing the Study Guide and Review pages. Point out that their Foldables can serve as a quick review tool when studying for the Chapter Test.

MIXED PROBLEM SOLVING
For mixed problem-solving practice, see page 847.

CHAPTER 5 Study Guide and Review

Lesson-by-Lesson Review

5-1 Perimeter and Area (pp. 221–226)

Find the perimeter and area of each figure.

11. 12.

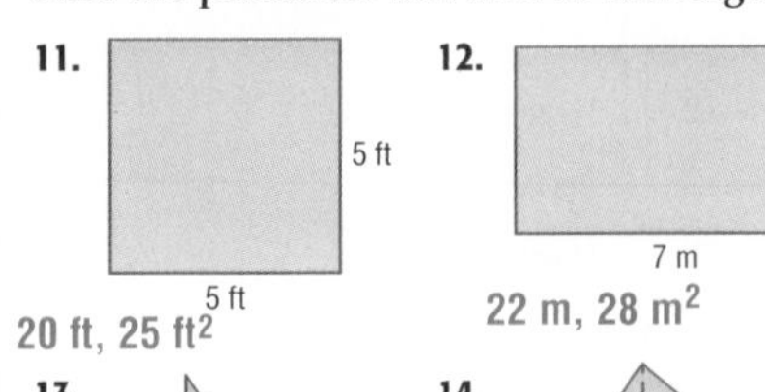

20 ft, 25 ft^2 22 m, 28 m^2

13. 14.

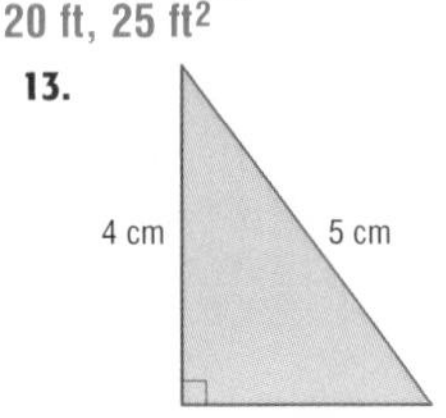

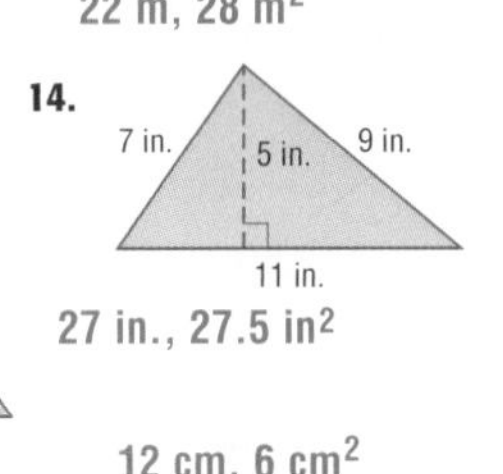

27 in., 27.5 in^2

12 cm, 6 cm^2

15. **GYMNASTICS** The area of a gymnastics mat is 142.5 square feet. If the width of the mat is 9.5 feet, what is the length? 15 ft

EXAMPLE 1

Find the perimeter and area of a 12 inch by 6 inch rectangle.

$P = 2(\ell + w)$	Perimeter of a rectangle
$= 2(12 + 6)$	Replace ℓ with 12 and w with 6.
$= 36$	Simplify.

The perimeter is 36 inches.

$A = \ell w$	Area of a rectangle
$= 12(6)$	Replace ℓ with 12 and w with 6.
$= 72$	Simplify.

The area is 72 square inches.

5-2 Solving Equations with Variables on Each Side (pp. 229–233)

Solve each equation. Check your solution.

16. $3a + 6 = 2a$ -6
17. $10 - x = 9x$ 1
18. $b - 6 = -b + 2$ 4
19. $5 + 2y - 12 = y + 9$ 16
20. $9q + 6 = 6q - 9$ -5
21. $c - 12 = 4c - 12$ 0
22. **MOVIES** An online DVD rental club has two membership plans as shown. Write and solve an equation to find how many months it would take for the total cost of the two plans to be the same.

Plan	Membership Fee	Cost Per Month
A	$20	$5
B	$30	$3

$20 + 5m = 30 + 3m$; 5 months

EXAMPLE 2

Solve $8x + 6 = 4x - 10$. Check your solution.

$8x + 6 = 4x - 10$	Write the equation.
$8x - 4x + 6 = 4x - 4x - 10$	Subtraction Property of Equality
$4x + 6 = -10$	Simplify.
$4x + 6 - 6 = -10 - 6$	Subtraction Property of Equality
$4x = -16$	Simplify.
$x = -4$	Mentally divide each side by 4.

Check $8x + 6 = 4x - 10$

$8(-4) + 6 \stackrel{?}{=} 4(-4) - 10$

$-32 + 6 \stackrel{?}{=} -16 - 10$

$-26 = -26$ ✓

Lesson-by-Lesson Review

Intervention If the given examples are not sufficient to review the topics covered by the questions, remind students that the page references tell them where to review that topic in their textbook.

Two-Day Option Have students complete the Lesson-by-Lesson Review on pp. 255–256. Then you can use ExamView® Assessment Suite to customize another review worksheet that practices all the objectives of this chapter or only the objectives on which your students need more help.

Differentiated Instruction

Super DVD: MindJogger Videoquizzes Use this DVD as an alternative format of review for the test.

CHAPTER 5 Study Guide and Review

Problem Solving Review

For additional practice in problem solving for Chapter 5, see the Mixed Problem Solving Appendix, p. 847, in the Student Handbook section.

Anticipation Guide

Have students complete the Chapter 5 Anticipation Guide and discuss how their responses have changed now that they have completed Chapter 5.

Additional Answers

31.

32.

33.

34.

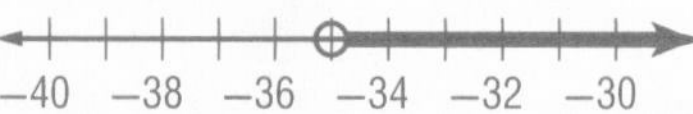

35.

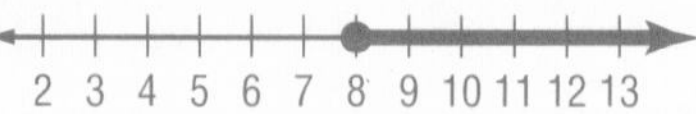

36.

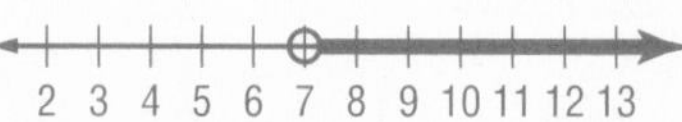

37.

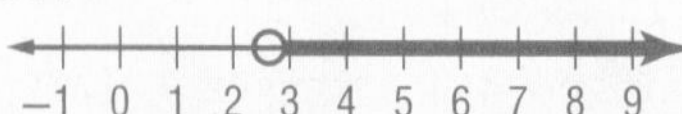

38.

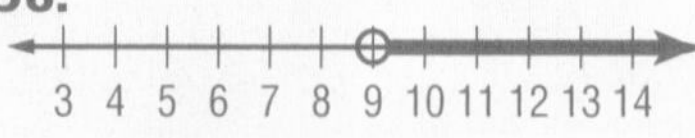

CHAPTER 5 Study Guide and Review

5-3 Inequalities (pp. 234–239)

Write an inequality for each sentence.

23. Jeremiah can spend at most \$15 at the store. $j \leq 15$

24. There are more than 35 students in the band. $b > 35$

For the given value, state whether each inequality is *true* or *false*.

25. $x + 6 > 7, x = 2$ True

26. $13 - a < 9, a = 10$ True

27. $16 \leq 4a, a = 4$ True

28. $3m + 4 \geq 12, m = 2$ False

29. $6x > 18, x = 3$ False

30. $6b + 4 > 12, b = 2$ True

EXAMPLE 3

State whether $x - 6 > 12$ is *true* or *false* for $x = 15$.

$x - 6 > 12$ **Write the inequality.**

$15 - 6 \overset{?}{>} 12$ **Replace *x* with 15.**

$9 \overset{?}{>} 12$ **Simplify.**

The sentence is false. So, $9 \not> 12$.

5-4 Solving Inequalities (pp. 241–247)

Solve each inequality. Graph the solution on a number line. 31–38. See margin for number lines.

31. $x - 4 < 8$ $x < 12$

32. $y + 3 \geq 11$ $y \geq 8$

33. $a - 15 \leq 3$ $a \leq 18$

34. $x + 13 > -22$ $x > -35$

35. $-3z \leq -24$ $z \geq 8$

36. $6h > 42$ $h > 7$

37. $-5x < -13$ $x > \frac{13}{5}$

38. $\frac{2}{3}x > 6$ $x > 9$

39. MUSIC Jose can spend at most \$120 for CDs. If each CD costs \$20, write and solve an inequality to show the maximum number of CDs Jose can buy. $20x \leq 120; x \leq 6$

EXAMPLE 4

Solve $x - 3 < 10$. Then graph the solution on a number line.

$x - 3 < 10$ **Write the inequality.**

$x - 3 + 3 < 10 + 3$ **Addition Property of Inequality**

$x < 13$ **Simplify.**

Graph the solution.

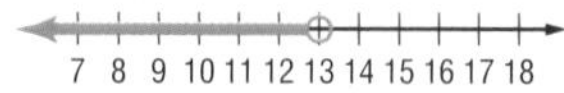

5-5 Solving Multi-Step Equations and Inequalities (pp. 248–253)

Solve. Check your solution.

40. $8b + 5 = 21$ $b = 2$

41. $15 - 4n = -13$ $n = 7$

42. $12 = 6(z - 4)$ $z = 6$

43. $\frac{3}{4}(12 + 4a) = 21$ $a = 4$

44. $-4g - 5 \geq -17$ $g \leq 3$

45. $18 > -12 + 6m$ $m < 5$

46. $24 - 3c \leq 15$ $c \geq 3$

47. $\frac{2}{3}k + 9 < 5$ $k < -6$

48. SALES A car sales associate receives a monthly salary of \$1700 a month plus \$140 for every car he sells. How many cars must he sell monthly to earn at least \$4500? 20 cars

EXAMPLE 5

Solve $-5m + 8 \geq 23$.

$-5m + 8 \geq 23$ **Write the inequality.**

$-5m + 8 - 8 \geq 23 - 8$ **Subtraction Property of Inequality**

$-5m \geq 15$ **Simplify.**

$\frac{-5m}{-5} \leq \frac{15}{-5}$ **Division Property of Inequality**

$m \leq -3$ **Simplify.**

CHAPTER 5 Practice Test

Math Online > glencoe.com
Chapter Test

1. **MULTIPLE CHOICE** The rectangle below has a length of 20 centimeters and a perimeter of P centimeters. Which equation could be used to find the width of the rectangle? **B**

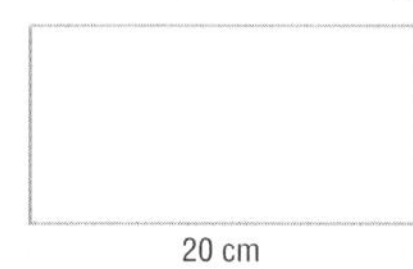

A $P = 40 + \frac{w}{2}$ C $P = 20 + w$

B $P = 40 + 2w$ D $P = 20 + 2w$

2. **MEASUREMENT** If the length of the side of each square is 6 units, what is the perimeter and area of the rectangle? **60 units; 144 units^2**

Solve each equation. Check your solution.

3. $61 = 3b + 7$ **18**
4. $-27 + 15x = 33 - 9x$ **2.5**
5. $16y + 24 = -18 + 9y$ **−6**
6. $7(m + 6) = 105$ **9**
7. $s - 17 = 7(s - 5)$ **3**
8. $9(12 + 4z) = 3(6z - 18)$ **−9**

9. **PROJECTS** The eighth grade class is making digital yearbooks on a DVD. One company charges a rate of $235 plus an additional $0.75 per DVD. Another company charges $125 plus $1.63 per DVD. Write and solve an equation to determine for what number of DVDs the costs will be equal.
$235 + 0.75d = 125 + 1.63d$; 125 DVDs

For the given value, state whether the inequality is *true* or *false*.

10. $3x + 8 > 56$; $x = 15$ **false**
11. $72 < 5x - 3$; $x = 16$ **true**
12. $\frac{124}{x} \geq x + 27$; $x = 4$ **true**

Graph each inequality on a number line.

13. $-5 \leq a$ 14. $w \leq 12$
13–14. See margin.

Write an inequality for each graph.

15. −1 0 1 2 3 4 5 6 7 8 9 **$x \geq 4$**

16. −7 −5 −3 −1 1 3 **$x < -5$**

17. **MULTIPLE CHOICE** A community wants to raise at least $4000 for a new skateboarding park. They have been given a $150 donation, and are selling canvas bags for $55 each to raise the rest of the money. Which inequality describes how many bags they need to sell in order to reach this goal? **J**

F $x \geq 35$ H $x \leq 70$

G $x \leq 35$ J $x \geq 70$

Solve each inequality. Graph the solution on a number line. **18–23. See margin for number lines.**

18. $-9 \geq a + (-3)$ **$a \leq -6$**
19. $54 < 6m$ **$m > 9$**
20. $-5t \geq -60$ **$t \leq 12$**
21. $10 + 4x \geq 3(x - 6)$ **$x \geq -28$**
22. $-7(k - 9) < -21$ **$k > 12$**
23. $14n - 8 \leq (4n - 5)$ **$n \leq \frac{3}{10}$**

24. **TEXT MESSAGES** A cell phone company charges $0.28 for each text message. Paula plans to spend no more than $5.00 on text messages next month. Write and solve an inequality to find how many text messages she will be able to send. **$0.28m \leq 5$; at most 17 messages**

25. **TRANSPORTATION** The minimum amount you can spend for renting a motor scooter is $50. The rental fee is $12 and the cost per hour is $9.50. What is the minimum number of hours you can rent the scooter? **4 h**

CHAPTER 5 Practice Test

ExamView Assessment Suite Customize and create multiple versions of your chapter test and their answer keys. All of the questions from the leveled chapter tests in the *Chapter 5 Resource Masters* are also available on ExamView® Assessment Suite.

Additional Answers

13.

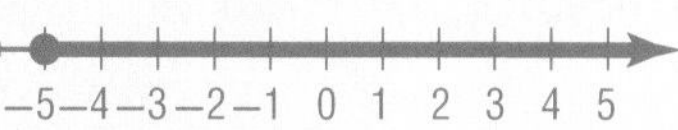

14.
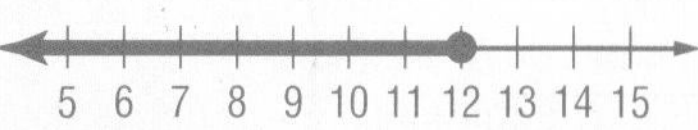

18.
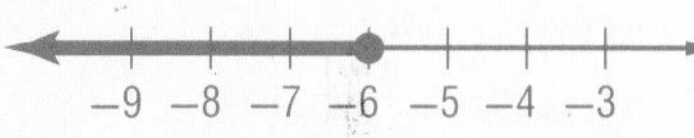

19.
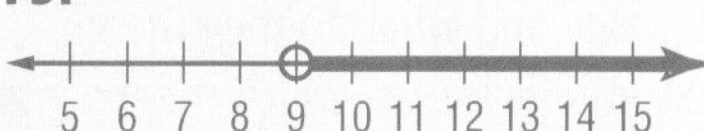

20.
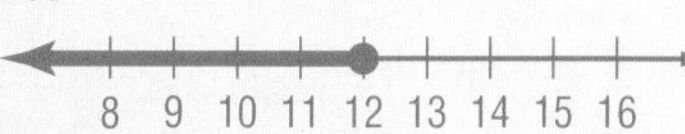

21.
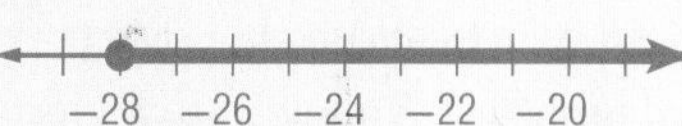

22.
10 12 14 16 18 20

23.
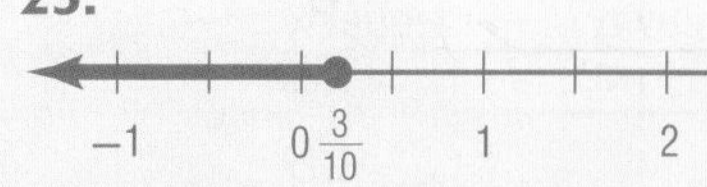

Intervention Planner

Tier 1 On Level	Tier 2 Strategic Intervention approaching grade level	Tier 3 Intensive Intervention 2 or more grades below level
If students miss about 25% of the exercises or less,	 **If** students miss about 50% of the exercises,	**If** students miss about 75% of the exercises,
Then choose a resource:	**Then** choose a resource:	 **Then** use *Math Triumphs, Grade 8,* Ch. 3
SE Lessons 5-1–5-5 **CRM** Skills Practice, pp. 7, 14, 20, 27, and 33 **TE** Chapter Project, p. 218	**CRM** Study Guide and Intervention, Chapter 5, pp. 5, 12, 18, 25, and 31 *Quick Review Math Handbook*	
Math Online > Self-Check Quiz	Math Online > Extra Examples, Personal Tutor, Homework Help	Math Online > Extra Examples, Personal Tutor, Homework Help, Review Vocabulary

CHAPTER 5 Preparing for Standardized Tests

1 FOCUS

Objective Use the strategy of writing and solving an inequality to solve standardized test problems.

2 TEACH

Scaffolding Questions

Ask:

- How is an inequality different from an equation? Sample answer: An equation has an equals sign to show that two statements are equal, while an inequality has an inequality symbol that shows that two statements are not equal.
- What are the symbols used for an inequality and what do they mean? The symbols are $<$, which means less than, $>$, which means greater than, $\leq$, which means less than or equal to, and $\geq$ which means greater than or equal to.
- How can you tell that you can write and solve an inequality to solve a word problem? Sample answer: Just like an equation, there will be an unknown quantity, a known quantity, and words that indicate that the relationship between the known and unknown is an inequality.

Write and Solve an Inequality

Some standardized test questions will require you to be able to write and solve inequalities. The steps below can help you solve these problems.

Strategies for Writing and Solving an Inequality

Step 1

Read the problem statement carefully.

Ask yourself:

- What am I being asked to solve?
- What information is given in the problem?
- What is the unknown quantity that I need to solve for?

A > B

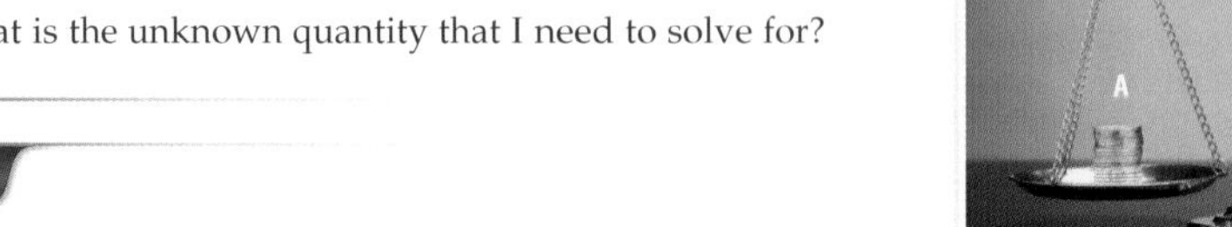

Step 2

Translate the problem statement into an inequality.

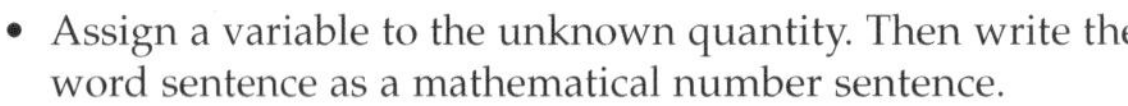

- Assign a variable to the unknown quantity. Then write the word sentence as a mathematical number sentence.

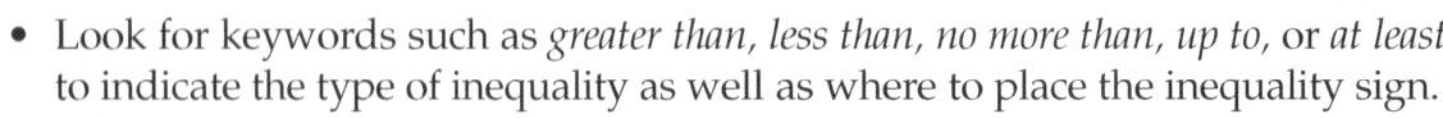

- Look for keywords such as *greater than, less than, no more than, up to,* or *at least* to indicate the type of inequality as well as where to place the inequality sign.

Step 3

Solve the inequality.

- Solve for the unknown in the inequality.
- Multiplying or dividing by a negative reverses the direction of the inequality.
- Check your answer to be sure it makes sense.

EXAMPLE

Read the problem. Identify what you need to know. Then use the information in the problem to solve.

Lorenzo can spend no more than $120 to buy a CD player and some CDs. The CD player costs $65, and each CD costs $11. How many CDs can he buy?

A up to 6 **C** up to 5

B more than 6 **D** more than 5

258 Chapter 5 Multi-Step Equations and Inequalities

Read the problem carefully. You know that Lorenzo can spend no more than $120 for a CD player that costs $65 and CDs that cost $11 each. You want to know how many CDs he can buy.

The unknown quantity that you need to find is the number of CDs Lorenzo can buy.

Words $65 plus $11 per CD is *no more than* $120

Variable Let n represent the number of CDs Lorenzo can buy.

Inequality $\$65 + 11n \leq 120$

Solve the equation for n.

$65 + 11n \leq 120$ **Write the inequality.**

$65 + 11n - 65 \leq 120 - 65$ **Subtract 65 from each side.**

$11n \leq 55$ **Simplify.**

$n \leq 5$ **Divide each side by 11. Simplify.**

The number of CDs that Lorenzo can buy with his gift card is less than or equal to 5, so he can buy up to 5 CDs. The correct answer is C.

Exercises

Read each problem. Identify what you need to know. Then use the information in the problem to solve.

1. Nina solved the problem below, then graphed the solution on a number line.

   Two thirds of a number plus five is greater than eleven.

   Which of the following most appropriately describes the unknown number? A

   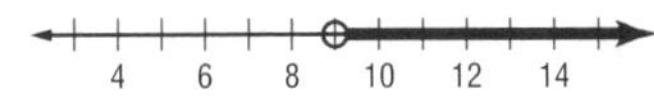

   A more than 9 C at least 9

   B up to 9 D 9 or more

2. Amy added 15 songs to her MP3 player making the total number of songs more than 100. How many songs were originally on the MP3 player? J

   F more than 115 H less than 85

   G less than 115 J more than 85

3. Kara's golden retriever weighs 80 pounds. Her veterinarian told her that a healthy weight for the dog would be less than 62 pounds. If Kara's dog can lose an average of 1.5 pounds per week, how long will it take her dog to reach this goal? B

   A at most 12 weeks C at most 13 weeks

   B more than 12 weeks D more than 13 weeks

Additional Example

Shana wants a photocopying center to make up some flyers for the annual flower sale at the school. She has at least $30 to spend. The photocopying center charges $15 to make the flyers and $0.20 per copy. How many copies can Shana order from the photocopying center? B

A up to 75

B 75 or more

C up to 125

D 125 or more

3 ASSESS

Use Exercises 1–3 to assess students' understanding.

Diagnose Student Errors

Survey student responses for each item. Class trends may indicate common errors and misconceptions.

1. A correct
B guess
C calculation error
D guess

2. F misinterpreted the symbol ≤ to mean at least
G misinterpreted the symbol < to mean at least
H correct
J misinterpreted the symbol > to mean at least

3. A represented negative quantity as positive
B confused relationship between constant and variable and represented negative quantity as positive
C correct
D confused relationship between constant and variable

4. F correct
G misinterpreted *no more* to mean *more than* instead of *is less than or equal to*
H division error
J division error and misinterpreted *no more* to mean *more than* instead of *is less than or equal to*

5. A calculation error such as subtraction error to give $\frac{2}{3}$ instead of $\frac{1}{6}$
B correct
C calculation error such as subtraction error to give 4 instead of 3 for constant
D guess

6. F addition error
G addition error
H correct
J addition error

7. A guess
B correct
C guess
D calculation error

CHAPTER 5 Standardized Test Practice

Standardized Test Practice

Cumulative, Chapters 1 through 5

Multiple Choice

Read each question. Then fill in the correct answer on the answer document provided by your teacher or on a sheet of paper.

1. The table below shows the membership cost for two CD clubs. How many CDs would you need to buy in a year in order for the total cost of both memberships to be the same? **A**

CD Club Membership

	Annual Fee	Cost per CD
Club #1	$50	$7.50
Club #2	$35	$8.00

A 30
B 25
C 20
D 15

2. Georgina wants to practice the piano for at least 45 minutes tonight. Which of the following inequalities represents this situation? **H**

F $t \leq 45$
G $t < 45$
H $t \geq 45$
J $t > 45$

3. On Monday, the price of a share of stock was $79. It fell $3 each day for 11 consecutive days. Which of the following expressions could you use to find the price of the stock on any one of those days? **C**

A $3d + 79$
B $3d - 79$
C $-3d + 79$
D $-3d - 79$

Test-TakingTip

Question 2 Read the problem carefully and look for keywords to help you choose the correct inequality. The words *at least* suggest greater than or equal to.

4. Jonathan has a gift card worth $75. If each DVD costs $12.50, how many DVDs can he buy if he spends no more than $75? **F**

F up to 6 DVDs
G more than 6 DVDs
H up to 7 DVDs
J more than 7 DVDs

5. Solve the following equation. **B**

$$\frac{5}{6}x - 7 = x - 10$$

A $x = 9$
B $x = 18$
C $x = 21$
D $x = 24$

6. What is the perimeter of the triangle below? **H**

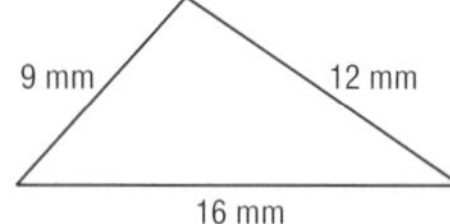

F 32 millimeters
G 35 millimeters
H 37 millimeters
J 41 millimeters

7. The top running speed of a lion is $\frac{5}{7}$ that of a cheetah. If a cheetah can run up to 70 miles per hour, how fast can a lion run? **B**

A 45 mph
B 50 mph
C 55 mph
D 60 mph

260 Chapter 5 Multi-Step Equations and Inequalities

CHAPTER 5 Standardized Test Practice

Short Response/Gridded Response

Record your answers on the answer sheet provided by your teacher or on a sheet of paper.

8. Write an inequality to represent the number line below. $n \leq -9$

9. GRIDDED RESPONSE What is the area, in square meters, of the right triangle shown below? 35

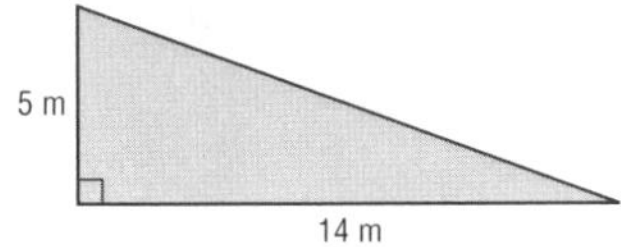

10. GRIDDED RESPONSE Solve the equation. 3

$$7n - 11 = 3(12 - 4n) + 10$$

11. Describe when to flip the direction of an inequality symbol when solving inequalities. Give an example.

12. Forty out of 48 freshmen and 42 out of 50 sophomores had perfect attendance last quarter.

a. What fraction of each class had perfect attendance last quarter? Write your answers in lowest terms. freshmen: $\frac{5}{6}$, sophomores: $\frac{21}{25}$

b. Write each fraction from part **a.** as a decimal. freshmen: 0.83, sophomores: 0.84

c. Which class had a greater portion with perfect attendance last quarter? sophomores

13. The equation $2w + 36 = 88$ represents the relationship between the width w of Daniel's yard and the total amount of fencing he has.

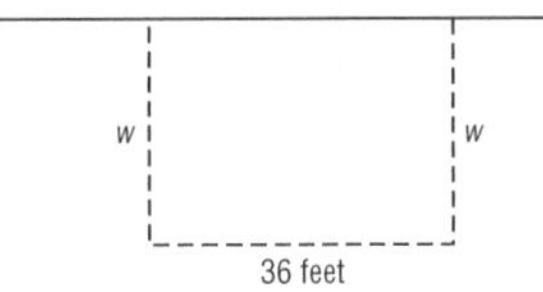

a. Solve the equation for w, the width of the yard. 26 ft

b. If Daniel increased each side by 12 feet, how much total fencing would he need? 124 ft

Extended Response

Record your answers on a sheet of paper. Show your work.

14. The formula $C = \frac{5}{9}(F - 32)$ can be used to convert temperatures in degrees Fahrenheit, F, to degrees Celsius, C.

a. Water boils when it reaches a temperature of 212° Fahrenheit. Write this temperature in degrees Celsius. 100 degrees

b. Water freezes at a temperature of 0° Celsius. Write this temperature in degrees Fahrenheit. 32 degrees

c. Solve the formula for F to find a new formula that converts temperatures from Celsius to Fahrenheit. $F = 1.8C + 32$

11. Sample answer: When multiplying or dividing each side of the inequality by a negative number; $-3n \geq 9$, $n \leq -3$

Need Extra Help?														
If you missed Question...	1	2	3	4	5	6	7	8	9	10	11	12	13	14
Go to Lesson or Page...	5-2	5-3	2-4	5-4	5-5	5-1	4-4	5-3	5-1	5-5	5-4	3-1	4-5	5-2

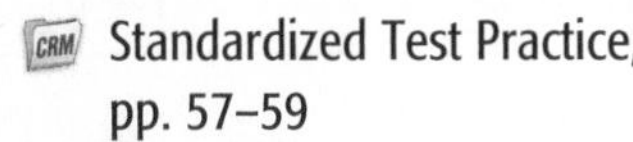

Formative Assessment

You can use these two pages to benchmark student progress.

CRM Standardized Test Practice, pp. 57–59

Answer Sheet Practice

Have students simulate taking a standardized test by recording their answers on practice recording sheets.

CRM Student Recording Sheet, p. 38

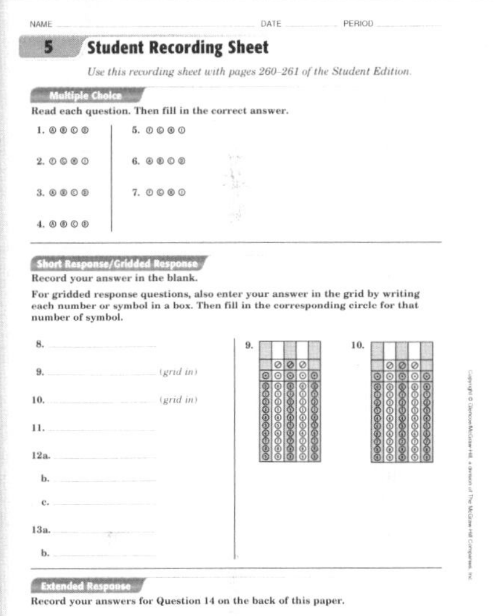

Create practice worksheets or tests that align to your state's standards as well as TIMSS and NAEP tests.

Homework Option

Get Ready for Chapter 6 Assign students the exercises on p. 263 as homework to assess whether they possess the prerequisite skills needed for the next chapter.

Page 228, Explore 5-2

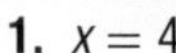

1. $x = 4$

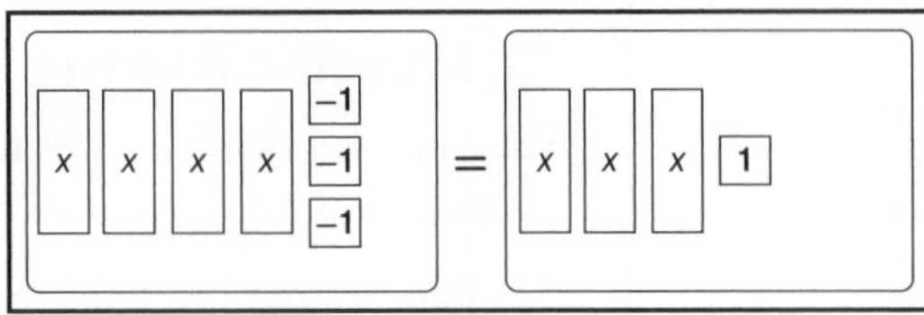

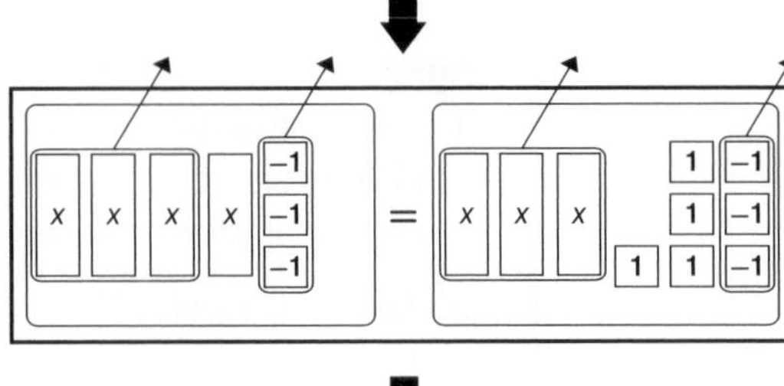

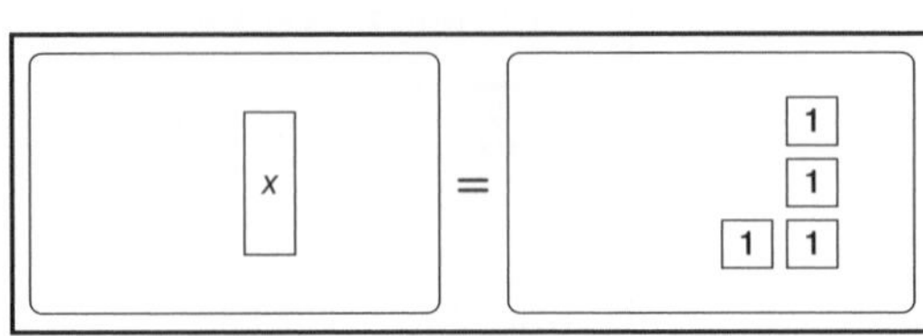

2. $x = 3$

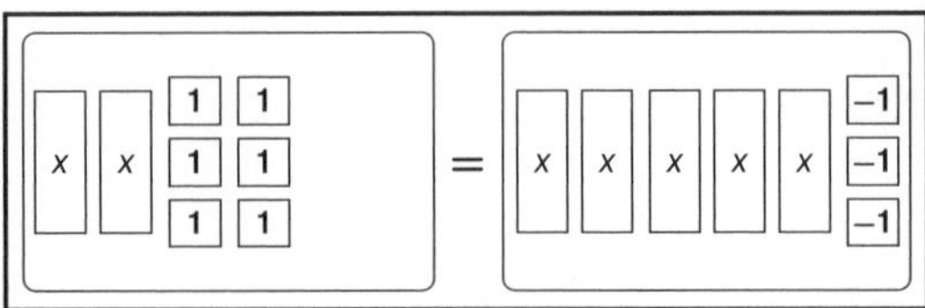

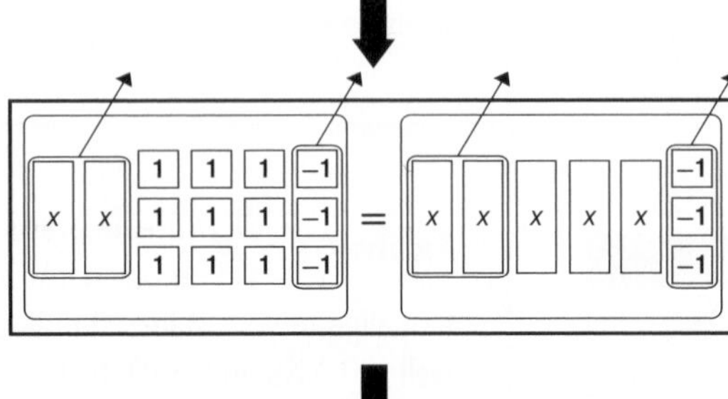

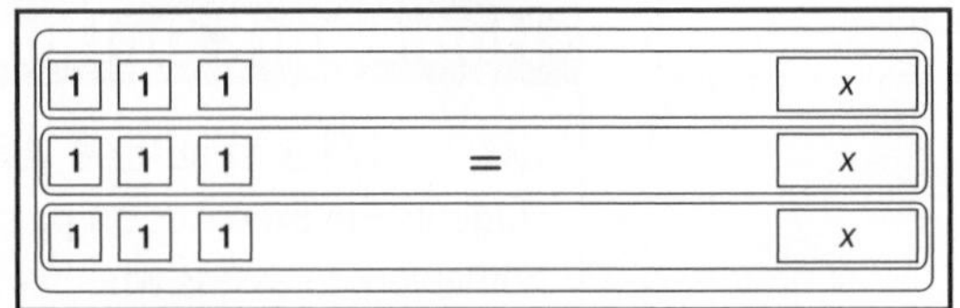

3. $x = 6$

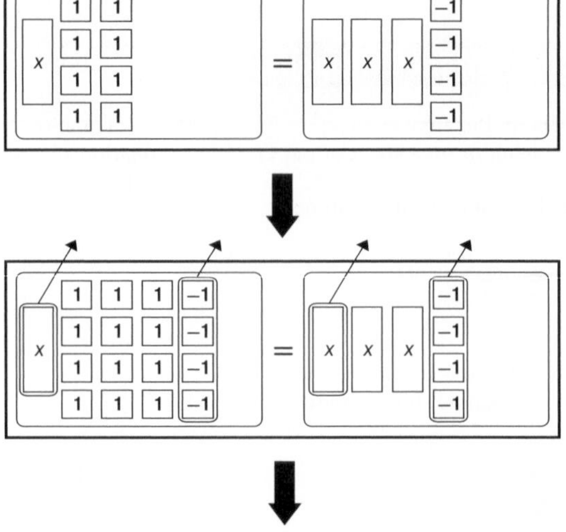

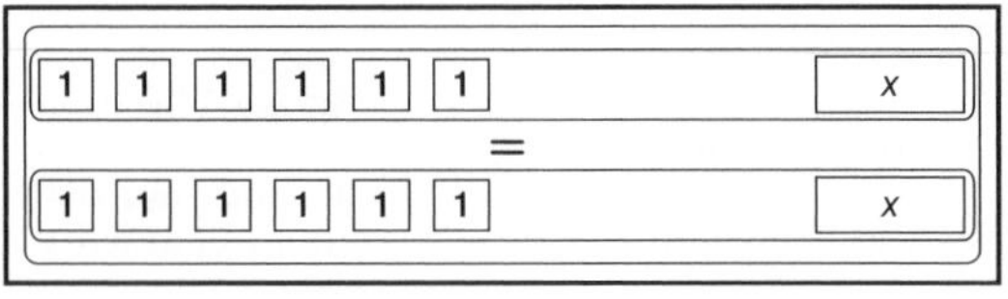

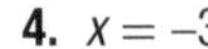

4. $x = -3$

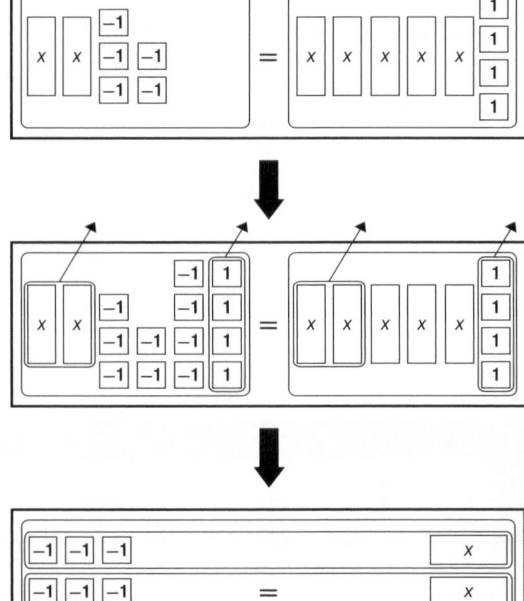

Pages 238–239, Lesson 5-3

39. –13, –14, –15;

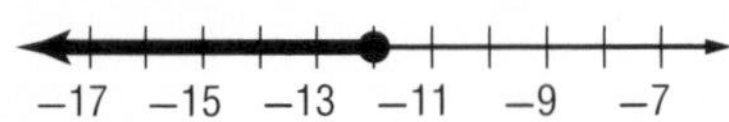

40. Sample answer: You use a closed circle with the symbols $\leq$ or $\geq$ since these both contain the phrase "or equal to." You use the open circle for $<$ and $>$ since they do not equal the value of the point.

Page 251, Lesson 5-5

30. Number line from −4 to 6: open circle at 1, arrow to the left.

31. Number line from −5 to 5: closed circle at −1, arrow to the right.

32. Number line from −5 to 5: closed circle at 2, arrow to the right.

33. Number line from −7 to 3: open circle at −4, arrow to the left.

34. Number line from −2 to 8: open circle at 6, arrow to the left.

35. Number line from −9 to 1: closed circle at −6, arrow to the left.

36. Number line from −14 to −6: closed circle at −9, arrow to the left.

37. Number line from 5 to 15: open circle at 10, arrow to the left.

Page 252, Lesson 5-5

47. −16

$4(y-3) = 2(3y+10)$	Write the equation.
$4y-12 = 6y+20$	Distributive Property
$4y-12+12 = 6y+20+12$	Addition Property of Equality
$4y = 6y+32$	Simplify.
$4y-6y = 6y+32-6y$	Subtraction Property of Equality
$-2y = 32$	Simplify.
$\frac{-2y}{-2} = \frac{32}{-2}$	Division Property of Equality
$y = -16$	Simplify.

48. 2

$5(2f-1) = 3(f+3)$	Write the equation.
$10f-5 = 3f+9$	Distributive Property
$10f-5-3f = 3f+9-3f$	Subtraction Property of Equality
$7f-5 = 9$	Simplify.
$7f-5+5 = 9+5$	Addition Property of Equality
$\frac{7f}{7} = \frac{14}{7}$	Division Property of Equality
$f = 2$	Simplify.

49. $w \geq 6.25$

$-1.2(w+1.1) \leq 6.18$	Write the inequality.
$-1.2w-1.32 \leq 6.18$	Distributive Property
$-1.2w-1.32+1.32 \leq 6.18+1.32$	Addition Property of Inequalities
$-1.2w \leq 7.5$	Simplify.
$\frac{-1.2w}{-1.2} \geq \frac{7.5}{-1.2}$	Division Property of Inequalities
$w \geq -6.25$	Simplify.

50. $p > -1$

$p > \frac{2}{3}(p - \frac{1}{2})$	Write the inequality.
$p > \frac{2}{3}p - \frac{1}{3}$	Distributive Property
$p - \frac{2}{3}p > \frac{2}{3}p - \frac{1}{3} - \frac{2}{3}p$	Subtraction Property of Inequalities
$\frac{1}{3}p > -\frac{1}{3}$	Simplify.
$\frac{1}{3}p \cdot 3 > -\frac{1}{3} \cdot 3$	Multiplication Property of Inequalities
$p > -1$	Simplify.

54a. Identity; All numbers

$5x-6 \geq 3(x-2)+2x$	Write the inequality.
$5x-6 \geq 3x-6+2x$	Distributive Property
$5x-6 \geq 5x-6$	Simplify.
$5x-5x-6 = 5x-5x-6$	Subtraction Property of Inequality
$-6 = -6$	Simplify.

54b. Null set; No solution

$12p+17 \leq 3(4p-8)$	Write the inequality.
$12p+17 \leq 12p-24$	Distributive Property
$12p+17-17 \leq 12p-24-17$	Subtraction Property of Inequality
$12p \leq 12p-41$	Simplify.
$12p-12p \leq 12p-41-12p$	Subtraction Property of Inequality
$0 \leq -41$	Simplify.

CHAPTER 6

Chapter Planner

Diagnostic Assessment
Quick Check, p. 263

	Lesson 6-1 Pacing: 1 day	Lesson 6-2 Pacing: 1 day	Lesson 6-3 Pacing: 1 day
Title	**Ratios**	**Unit Rates**	**Converting Rates and Measurements**
Objectives	• Write ratios as fractions in simplest form. • Simplify ratios involving measurements.	• Find unit rates. • Compare and use unit rates to solve problems.	• Convert rates using dimensional analysis. • Convert between systems of measurement.
Key Vocabulary	ratio	rate unit rate	dimensional analysis
NCTM Focal Points	G7-FP1, G7-FP4C, G8-FP2 For the complete wording of the Focal Points for Grades 7 and 8, please see pages iv, v, FP0, and FP1.		
Multiple Representations		p. 273	
Lesson Resources	**Chapter 6 Resource Masters** • Study Guide and Intervention, pp. 5–6 AL OL ELL • Skills Practice, p. 7 AL OL ELL • Practice, p. 8 AL OL BL ELL • Word Problem Practice, p. 9 AL OL BL • Enrichment, p. 10 OL BL **Transparencies** • 5-Minute Check Transparency 6-1 AL OL BL ELL **Additional Print Resources** • *Study Notebook* AL OL BL ELL	**Chapter 6 Resource Masters** • Study Guide and Intervention, pp. 11–12 AL OL ELL • Skills Practice, p. 13 AL OL ELL • Practice, p. 14 AL OL BL ELL • Word Problem Practice, p. 15 AL OL BL • Enrichment, p. 16 OL BL **Transparencies** • 5-Minute Check Transparency 6-2 AL OL BL ELL **Additional Print Resources** • *Study Notebook* AL OL BL ELL	**Chapter 6 Resource Masters** • Study Guide and Intervention, pp. 17–18 AL OL ELL • Skills Practice, p. 19 AL OL ELL • Practice, p. 20 AL OL BL ELL • Word Problem Practice, p. 21 AL OL BL • Enrichment, p. 22 OL BL • Quiz 1, p. 64 AL OL BL ELL **Transparencies** • 5-Minute Check Transparency 6-3 AL OL BL ELL **Additional Print Resources** • *Study Notebook* AL OL BL ELL
Technology for Every Lesson	Math Online glencoe.com • Extra Examples • Self-Check Quizzes • Personal Tutor	**CD/DVD Resources** IWB INTERACTIVE WHITEBOARD READY IWB StudentWorks Plus IWB Interactive Classroom IWB Diagnostic and Assessment Planner	• TeacherWorks Plus • eSolutions Manual Plus • ExamView Assessment Suite
Math in Motion			
Differentiated Instruction	pp. 266, 269	pp. 271, 274	pp. 276, 280

KEY: 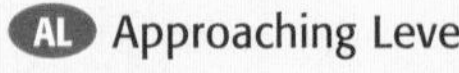 AL Approaching Level  OL On Level 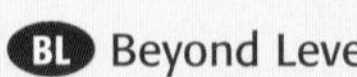 BL Beyond Level ELL English Learners

Suggested Pacing			
Time Periods	Instruction	Review& Asessment	Total
45-minute	11	2	13
90-minute	5.5	1	6.5

Ratio, Proportion, and Similar Figures

Lesson 6-4 Pacing: 1 day	Lesson 6-5 Pacing: 1 day	Extend 6-5 Pacing: 1 day	Lesson 6-6 Pacing: 1 day
Proportional and Nonproportional Relationships	**Solving Proportions**	**Algebra Lab: Inverse Proportions**	**Scale Drawings and Models**
• Identify proportional and nonproportional relationships in tables and graphs. • Describe a proportional relationship using an equation.	• Solve proportions. • Use proportions to solve real-world problems.	• Determine if a given situation is an inverse proportion. • Graph inverse proportions.	• Use scale drawings. • Construct scale drawings.
proportional nonproportional constant of proportionality	proportion cross products	inverse proportion	scale drawing scale model scale scale factor
p. 284	p. 291		
Chapter 6 Resource Masters • Study Guide and Intervention, pp. 23–24 AL OL ELL • Skills Practice, p. 25 AL OL ELL • Practice, p. 26 AL OL BL ELL • Word Problem Practice, p. 27 AL OL BL • Enrichment, p. 28 OL BL **Transparencies** • 5-Minute Check Transparency 6-4 AL OL BL ELL **Additional Print Resources** • *Study Notebook* AL OL BL ELL	**Chapter 6 Resource Masters** • Study Guide and Intervention, pp. 29–30 AL OL ELL • Skills Practice, p. 31 AL OL ELL • Practice, p. 32 AL OL BL ELL • Word Problem Practice, p. 33 AL OL BL • Enrichment, p. 34 OL BL • Quiz 2, p. 64 AL OL BL ELL **Transparencies** • 5-Minute Check Transparency 6-5 AL OL BL ELL **Additional Print Resources** • *Study Notebook* AL OL BL ELL	**Materials:** • grid paper • toothpicks	**Chapter 6 Resource Masters** • Study Guide and Intervention, pp. 35–36 AL OL ELL • Skills Practice, p. 37 AL OL ELL • Practice, p. 38 AL OL BL ELL • Word Problem Practice, p. 39 AL OL BL • Enrichment, p. 40 OL BL • Spreadsheet, p. 41 AL OL BL ELL **Transparencies** • 5-Minute Check Transparency 6-6 AL OL BL ELL **Additional Print Resources** • *Study Notebook* AL OL BL ELL

Math Online glencoe.com
- Extra Examples
- Self-Check Quizzes
- Personal Tutor

CD/DVD Resources IWB INTERACTIVE WHITEBOARD READY
- IWB StudentWorks Plus
- IWB Interactive Classroom
- IWB Diagnostic and Assessment Planner
- TeacherWorks Plus
- eSolutions Manual Plus
- ExamView Assessment Suite

		p. 293	
pp. 282, 285	pp. 288, 292		pp. 295, 299

Formative Assessment
Mid-Chapter Quiz, p. 286

CHAPTER 6

Chapter Planner

	Explore 6-7 Pacing: 1 day	Lesson 6-7 Pacing: 1 day	Lesson 6-8 Pacing: 1 day	Lesson 6-9 Pacing: 1 day
Title	**Geometry Lab: Similar Figures**	**Similar Figures**	**Dilations**	**Indirect Measurement**
Objectives	• Use scale factor to draw enlargements and reductions.	• Find missing measures of similar figures. • Use scale factors to solve problems.	• Graph dilations on a coordinate plane. • Find the scale factor of a dilation.	• Solve problems using shadow reckoning. • Solve problems using surveying methods.
Key Vocabulary		similar figures corresponding parts	dilation	indirect measurement
NCTM Focal Points				
Multiple Representations		p. 305		p. 315
Lesson Resources	**Materials:** • grid paper	**Chapter 6 Resource Masters** • Study Guide and Intervention, pp. 42–43 AL OL ELL • Skills Practice, p. 44 AL OL ELL • Practice, p. 45 AL OL BL ELL • Word Problem Practice, p. 46 AL OL BL • Enrichment, p. 47 OL BL • Quiz 3, p. 65 AL OL BL ELL **Transparencies** • 5-Minute Check Transparency 6-7 AL OL BL ELL **Additional Print Resources** • *Study Notebook* AL OL BL ELL	**Chapter 6 Resource Masters** • Study Guide and Intervention, pp. 48–49 AL OL ELL • Skills Practice, p. 50 AL OL ELL • Practice, p. 51 AL OL BL ELL • Word Problem Practice, p. 52 AL OL BL • Enrichment, p. 53 OL BL • Graphing Calculator, p. 54 AL OL BL ELL **Transparencies** • 5-Minute Check Transparency 6-8 AL OL BL ELL **Additional Print Resources** • *Study Notebook* AL OL BL ELL	**Chapter 6 Resource Masters** • Study Guide and Intervention, pp. 55–56 AL OL ELL • Skills Practice, p. 57 AL OL ELL • Practice, p. 58 AL OL BL ELL • Word Problem Practice, p. 59 AL OL BL • Enrichment, p. 60 OL BL • Quiz 4, p. 65 AL OL BL ELL **Transparencies** • 5-Minute Check Transparency 6-9 AL OL BL ELL **Additional Print Resources** • *Study Notebook* AL OL BL ELL
Technology for Every Lesson	**Math Online** glencoe.com • Extra Examples • Self-Check Quizzes • Personal Tutor	**CD/DVD Resources** IWB INTERACTIVE WHITEBOARD READY IWB StudentWorks Plus IWB Interactive Classroom IWB Diagnostic and Assessment Planner		• TeacherWorks Plus • eSolutions Manual Plus • ExamView Assessment Suite
Math in Motion	p. 300			p. 313
Differentiated Instruction		pp. 302, 306	pp. 308, 312	pp. 314, 317

Summative Assessment
- Study Guide and Review, pp. 318–322
- Practice Test, p. 323

KEY: AL Approaching Level OL On Level BL Beyond Level ELL English Learners

Quick Review Math Handbook*

is Glencoe's mathematical handbook for students and parents.

Hot Words includes a glossary of terms.

Hot Topics consists of two parts:

- explanations of key mathematical concepts
- exercises to check students' understanding

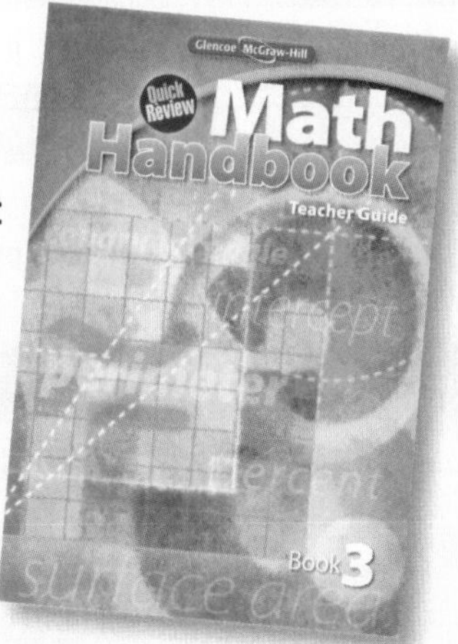

Lesson	Hot Topics Section	Lesson	Hot Topics Section
6-1	6.5	6-6	6.5
6-2	6.5	6-7	8.5
6-3	8.2	6-8	8.5

**Also available in Spanish*

Teacher to Teacher

Barbara Cain
Thomas Jefferson M.S.
Merritt Island, FL

USE WITH LESSON 6-5

“When we multiply a decimal by another number using a multiplication dot in my classroom, we usually put the decimal number in parentheses. This helps to avoid confusion in a handwritten problem with two different uses of the dot.”

NOTES:

CHAPTER 6 Assessment and Intervention

SE = Student Edition, **TE** = Teacher Edition, **CRM** = Chapter Resource Masters

	Diagnosis	Prescription
Diagnostic Assessment	**Beginning Chapter 6**	
	Get Ready for Chapter 6 **SE,** p. 263	Response to Intervention **TE,** p. 263
	Beginning Every Lesson	
	Then, Now, Why? **SE** 5-Minute Check Transparencies	Chapter 0 **SE,** pp. P1–P22 Concepts and Skills Bank **SE,** pp. 856–887 *Quick Review Math Handbook*
Formative Assessment	**During/After Every Lesson**	
	Check Your Progress **SE,** every example Check Your Understanding **SE** H.O.T. Problems **SE** Spiral Review **SE** Additional Examples **TE** Watch Out! **TE** Step 4, Assess **TE** Chapter 6 Quizzes **CRM,** pp. 64–65 Self-Check Quizzes glencoe.com	**Tier 1 Intervention** Concepts and Skills Bank **SE,** 856–887 Skills Practice **CRM,** Ch.1–6 glencoe.com **Tier 2 Intervention** Differentiated Instruction **TE** Study Guide and Intervention Masters **CRM,** Ch. 1–6 *Quick Review Math Handbook* **Tier 3 Intervention** *Math Triumphs, Grade 8,* Ch. 4–5
	Mid-Chapter	
	Mid-Chapter Quiz **SE,** p. 286 Mid-Chapter Test **CRM,** p. 66 ExamView Assessment Suite	**Tier 1 Intervention** Concepts and Skills Bank **SE,** 856–887 Skills Practice **CRM,** Ch. 1–6 glencoe.com **Tier 2 Intervention** Study Guide and Intervention Masters **CRM,** Ch. 1–6 *Quick Review Math Handbook* **Tier 3 Intervention** *Math Triumphs, Grade 8,* Ch. 4–5
	Before Chapter Test	
	Chapter Study Guide and Review **SE,** pp. 318–322 Practice Test **SE,** p. 323 Standardized Test Practice **SE,** pp. 324–327 Chapter Test glencoe.com Standardized Test Practice glencoe.com Vocabulary Review glencoe.com ExamView Assessment Suite	**Tier 1 Intervention** Concepts and Skills Bank **SE,** pp. 856–887 Skills Practice **CRM,** Ch. 1–6 glencoe.com **Tier 2 Intervention** Study Guide and Intervention Masters **CRM,** Ch. 1–6 *Quick Review Math Handbook* **Tier 3 Intervention** *Math Triumphs, Grade 8,* Ch. 4–5
Summative Assessment	**After Chapter 6**	
	Multiple-Choice Tests, Forms 1, 2A, 2B, **CRM,** pp. 68–73 Free-Response Tests, Forms 2C, 2D, 3, **CRM,** pp. 74–79 Vocabulary Test **CRM,** p. 67 Extended Response Test **CRM,** p. 80 Standardized Test Practice **CRM,** pp. 81–83 ExamView Assessment Suite	Study Guide and Intervention Masters **CRM,** Ch. 1–6 *Quick Review Math Handbook* glencoe.com

Differentiated Instruction

Option 1 Reaching All Learners AL OL BL ELL

NATURALIST Have students research the speed in miles per hour of two animals, whether mammals, birds, insects, sea creatures, or other animals. Then have them convert the speeds to feet per second and meters per minute.

Next, ask students to write a problem for each animal involving rate and unit rate. For example:

- A chicken can travel about 286 feet in 22 seconds. How far can it travel in 40 seconds?

Have students trade problems and use unit rates or proportions to solve.

INTERPERSONAL Have students work in small groups. Each group draws a set of three rectangles using metric rulers in centimeters. Two of the rectangles should be similar. The third rectangle should resemble, but not be similar to the other two.

Have groups exchange rectangles and determine which rectangles are similar. Then ask groups to choose one of the rectangles and use a scale factor, known to the group only, to create a similar rectangle to the one chosen. Have students exchange rectangles again and determine the scale factor used to create the new rectangle.

Option 2 Approaching Level AL

Have students bring to class advertisements and coupons from newspapers and magazines. Ask them to explain the different ways in which ratios are used in the ads or coupons. Then have them work together to make a collage of the ads or coupons. Encourage them to highlight the ratios and to include some math problems based on the ratios.

Option 3 English Learners ELL

Many words in this chapter are interrelated. Have students use word webs or other graphic organizers in their math journals to show the relationships. For example, students can begin a word web using *ratio* in the center, with a brief definition and example. They can add to the web as they learn new words, such as unit, unit rate, dimensional analysis, proportional, proportion, and so on. For example,

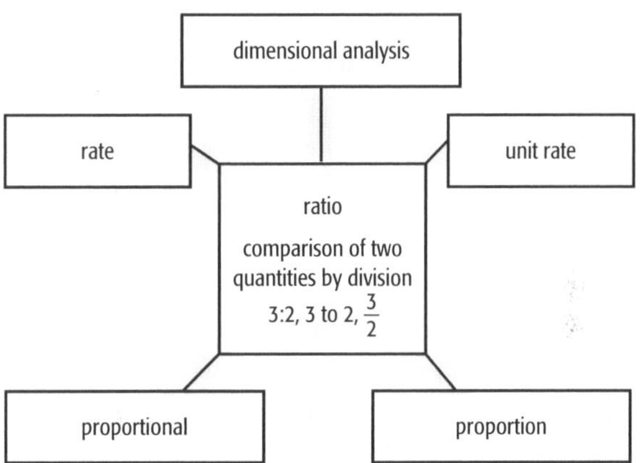

Option 4 Beyond Level BL

Scientists use the "capture-recapture" method to estimate the population of different animals in a wildlife setting. Suppose scientists want to estimate the population of a certain fox in a location. They initially capture a group of fox, humanely mark them, and then release them back into the wildlife population. Later they return and capture another group of fox. How can proportional reasoning help them estimate the total fox population in that location? Sample answer: Set up and solve the following proportion:

$$\frac{\text{number of fox marked in first capture}}{\text{total number of fox}} = \frac{\text{number of fox marked in second capture}}{\text{total number of fox in second capture}}$$

Use this method to estimate the number of black jellybeans in a large jar of jellybeans.

Focus on Mathematical Content

Vertical Alignment

Before Chapter 6

Related Topics before Pre-Algebra

- use division to find unit rates and ratios in proportional relationships

Previous Topics from Pre-Algebra

- select and use appropriate forms of rational numbers to solve real-life problems
- use appropriate operations to solve problems involving rational numbers in problem situations

Chapter 6

Related Topics from Pre-Algebra

- compare and contrast proportional and nonproportional linear relationships
- use proportional relationships in similar two-dimensional figures to find missing measurements

After Chapter 6

Preparation for Algebra 1

- relate direct variation to linear functions and solve problems involving proportional change
- use ratios to solve problems involving similar figures

Lesson-by-Lesson Preview

6-1 Ratios

A ratio is a comparison of two numbers by division. If a basketball player makes 8 out of 10 free throws, the ratio is written as 8 to 10, 8:10, and $\frac{8}{10}$. Ratios can express part to part, part to whole, and whole to part relationships.

6-2 Unit Rates

A *rate* is a ratio of two measurements having different types of units. For example, 18 miles in 2 hours is a rate. A *unit rate* is a rate that has a denominator of 1. The rate 9 miles in 1 hour is a unit rate. To write a rate as a unit rate, divide the numerator and denominator of the rate by the denominator.

Use unit rates to solve problems involving best buys and to find other rates with the same unit rate.

6-3 Converting Rates and Measurements

Dimensional analysis is the process of including units of measurement when computing and is used to write conversion factors when converting rates and measurements. For example, to convert 825 words per hour to words per minute, write a conversion factor that allows you to divide out common units:

$$\frac{825 \text{ words}}{\cancel{1 \text{ hr}}} \cdot \frac{\cancel{1 \text{ hr}}}{60 \text{ min}} = \frac{825 \text{ words}}{60 \text{ min}} = 13.75 \text{ words per min}$$

Dimensional analysis can be used to convert within and between systems of measurement.

6-4 Proportional and Nonproportional Relationships

Two quantities are proportional if they have a constant ratio, and nonproportional if the ratios between them are not equal. For example:

- One aquarium contains 3 clown fish and 1 tetra. A second contains 6 clown fish and 2 tetras. Since both aquariums have a 3:1 ratio of clown fish to tetras, the number of clown fish is proportional to the number of tetras.
- A third aquarium has a ratio of clown fish to tetras of 5 to 2. Since this ratio is not equal to the ratios in the first two aquariums the number of clown fish are not proportional to the number of tetras in all of the aquariums.

Identify proportional and nonproportional relationships by finding and then comparing unit rates.

6-5 Solving Proportions

A proportion is an equation stating that two ratios are equal. For example, $\frac{3}{18} = \frac{13}{78}$ is a proportion because both ratios simplify to $\frac{1}{6}$.

Every proportion has two cross products. In the proportion $\frac{3}{18} = \frac{13}{78}$, the cross products are 3 • 78 and 18 • 13. The cross products of a proportion are equal.

$$\frac{3}{18} = \frac{13}{78}$$

$$3(78) = 13(18)$$

$$234 = 234$$

6-6 Scale Drawings and Models

Scale drawings and models represent objects that are too large or too small to be drawn or built at actual size.

- The lengths and widths of objects in scale drawings and models are proportional to the actual object.
- A scale, such as 1 cm = 3 m, represents the ratio of the length of the scale drawing or model to the length of the actual object. The length of the scale drawing or model is given first.
- If the units of measurement are the same for the scale drawing and the actual object, the scale can be written without units and is called a *scale factor*.

Use proportions or scale factors to find any unknown actual measurement(s) of an object or scale drawing.

6-7 Similar Figures

Figures that have the same shape but not necessarily the same size are similar figures. The following apply to similar figures:

- Corresponding angles have the same measure.
- Corresponding sides are proportional.

In the model, $\triangle ABC \sim \triangle XYZ$. Arcs are used to show congruent angles, and $\frac{AB}{XY} = \frac{BC}{YZ} = \frac{AC}{XZ}$.

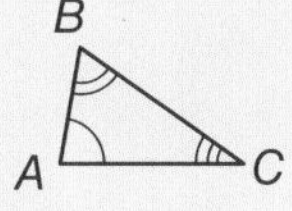

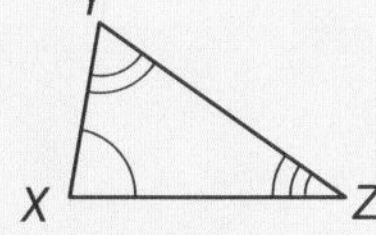

6-8 Dilations

A dilation is a transformation that reduces or enlarges a figure by a scale factor.

- Dilated figures are similar to the original figure.
- Dilations with scale factors greater than 1 are enlargements, between 0 and 1 are reductions, and equal to one are the same size.

6-9 Indirect Measurement

Indirect measurement uses the properties of similar triangles to find measurements that are difficult to measure directly. For example, shadow reckoning uses the similar triangles formed between objects and their shadows. If you know the length and height of one object and its shadow, and the length of the shadow of a second object, you can use a proportion to find the height of the second object.

Targeted professional development has been articulated throughout McGraw-Hill's mathematics program. The **McGraw-Hill Professional Development Video Library** provides short videos that support key topics. For more information, visit glencoe.com.

Model Lessons

Instructional Strategies

CHAPTER 6 Notes

Chapter Project

Designing Spaces

Students use what they have learned about ratios, proportions, and dimensional analysis to make a scale drawing for the floor plan of an 80 ft × 70 ft fun center.

- Divide students into groups. Have each group decide on the number of rooms in the fun center, and what will be located in each room. Remind groups that they should include spaces for an eating or snack area and restrooms.
- Ask groups to decide on and write the dimensions of each room in the fun center. Then have them write the ratio of length to width in simplest form for each room. Which room has the greatest ratio? the least? What do these two ratios mean?
- Have students convert the room dimensions to metric measurements, and then decide whether they will use the customary or metric system for the floor plan.
- Ask each group to decide on a scale for the scale drawing. After they decide on a scale, have groups use grid paper to make and label a scale drawing for the floor plan of the fun center.
- Have students find the scale factor for the scale of the drawing. Ask students how they can use the scale factor to verify that the scale drawing is correct.

CHAPTER 6 Ratio, Proportion, and Similar Figures

Then
In Chapter 4, you solved equations using multiplication and division.

Now
In Chapter 6, you will:
- Write ratios as fractions in simplest form.
- Find and compare unit rates.
- Use and solve proportions.

Why?
ARCHITECTURE The art and science of designing structures is detailed work. Architects produce scale models of their structures for clients. They use proportions and scale factors to draw blueprints for their structures.

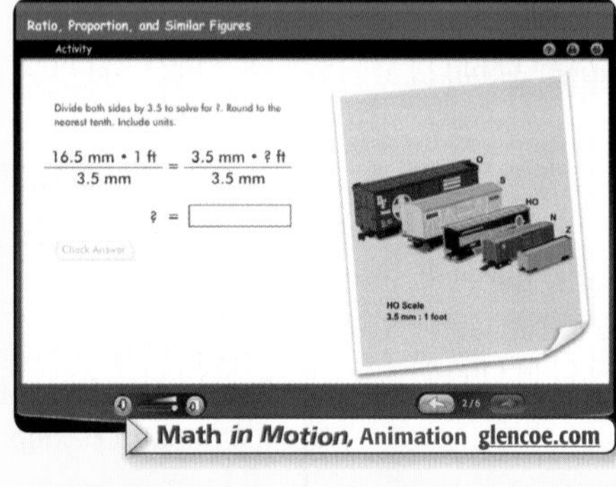

Math *in Motion*, Animation glencoe.com

Key Vocabulary Introduce the key vocabulary in the chapter using the routine below.

Define: A ratio is a comparison of two numbers by division.

Example: The ratio of 2 to 4 can be stated as 2 to 4, 2 : 4, or $\frac{2}{4}$.

Ask: How can you show the ratio of 18 to 7 three different ways? 18 to 7; 18 : 7; $\frac{18}{7}$

Get Ready for Chapter 6

Diagnose Readiness You have two options for checking Prerequisite Skills.

Text Option Take the Quick Check below. Refer to the Quick Review for help.

*Quick*Check

(Used in Lessons 6-1 and 6-2)

Simplify each fraction. If the fraction cannot be simplified, write *simplest form*. (Previous Course)

1. $\frac{12}{15}$ $\frac{4}{5}$
2. $\frac{24}{32}$ $\frac{3}{4}$
3. $\frac{30}{45}$ $\frac{2}{3}$
4. $\frac{5}{11}$ simplest form
5. $\frac{48}{72}$ $\frac{2}{3}$
6. $\frac{16}{43}$ simplest form
7. **PETS** Of the 20 students in Mr. Masuru's class, 15 have pets. Write the fraction of students that own pets in simplest form. $\frac{3}{4}$ students

(Used in Lesson 6-3)

Complete each sentence. (Lesson 0-6)

8. 3 ft = ■ in. 36
9. 2 h = ■ min 120
10. 4 lb = ■ oz 64
11. 2 pt = ■ c 4
12. 3 m = ■ cm 300
13. 4 km = ■ m 4000
14. 1.8 L = ■ mL 1800
15. 13 kg = ■ g 13,000
16. **RUNNING** The high school cross country course is 5-kilometers long. How many meters is this? 5000 m

(Used in Lesson 6-5)

Solve each equation. Check your solution. (Lesson 4-4)

17. $60x = 12$ $\frac{1}{5}$
18. $42 = 7n$ 6
19. $4y = 10$ 2.5
20. $9m = 18$ 2
21. $7 = 3.5a$ 2
22. $11 = 5.5d$ 2
23. **BOOKS** Dyani has 3 times as many books as Mario. If Mario has 27 books, how many books does Dyani have? 81 books

*Quick*Review

EXAMPLE 1

Write $\frac{28}{36}$ as a fraction in simplest form.

Find the GCF of 28 and 36.

factors of 28: 1, 2, 4, 7, 14, 28

factors of 36: 1, 2, 3, 4, 6, 9, 12, 18, 36

The GCF of 28 and 36 is 4.

$\frac{28}{36} = \frac{28 \div 4}{36 \div 4}$ **Divide the numerator and denominator by the GCF, 4.**

$= \frac{7}{9}$ **Simplest form**

EXAMPLE 2

Complete 3 T = ■ oz.

$3\,\cancel{T} \times \frac{2000 \text{ lb}}{1\,\cancel{T}} = 6000 \text{ lb}$ **To convert tons to pounds, multiply by 2000.**

$6000\,\cancel{\text{lb}} \times \frac{16 \text{ oz}}{1\,\cancel{\text{lb}}} = 96{,}000 \text{ oz}$ **To convert pounds to ounces, multiply by 16.**

So, 3 T = 96,000 oz.

EXAMPLE 3

Solve $9.5x = 38$.

$9.5x = 38$ **Write the equation.**

$\frac{9.5x}{9.5} = \frac{38}{9.5}$ **Divide each side by 9.5.**

$x = 4$ **Simplify.**

Online Option Math Online Take a self-check Chapter Readiness Quiz at glencoe.com.

Get Ready for Chapter 6

Response to Intervention (RtI)

Use the *Quick Check* results and the Intervention Planner to help you determine your Response to Intervention. The If-Then statements in the chart help you decide the appropriate tier of RtI and suggest intervention resources for each tier.

Intervention Planner

Tier 1 — On Level

If students miss about 25% of the exercises or less,

Then choose a resource:

SE Lessons 0–6, 4–4

CRM Skills Practice, Chapter 4, p. 25

TE Chapter Project, p. 262

Math Online Self-Check Quiz

Tier 2 — Strategic Intervention approaching grade level

If students miss about 50% of the exercises,

Then choose a resource:

CRM Study Guide and Intervention, Chapter 4, p. 23

Quick Review Math Handbook

Math Online Extra Examples, Personal Tutor, Homework Help

Tier 3 — Intensive Intervention 2 or more grades below level

If students miss about 75% of the exercises,

Then use *Math Triumphs, Grade 8*, Ch. 4–5

Math Online Extra Examples, Personal Tutor, Homework Help, Review Vocabulary

CHAPTER 6 Notes

FOLDABLES® Study Organizer

Dinah Zike's Foldables®

Focus Students write notes about each lesson in this chapter.

Teach Have students make and label the pockets of their Foldables as illustrated. Students should use their Foldables to take notes, define terms, and record concepts about fractions, decimals, and percents throughout the chapter. Have students make flashcards using vocabulary and the Key Concepts in the chapter.

When to Use It Encourage students to add to their Foldable as they work through the chapter, and use them to review ratio, proportion, and percent for the chapter test.

Differentiated Instruction

CRM Student-Built Glossary, pp. 1–2 Students should complete the chart by providing a definition of each term and an example as they progress through Chapter 6. This study tool can also be used to review for the chapter test.

Get Started on Chapter 6

You will learn several new concepts, skills, and vocabulary terms as you study Chapter 6. To get ready, identify important terms and organize your resources. You may wish to refer to **Chapter 0** to review prerequisite skills.

FOLDABLES® Study Organizer

Ratio, Proportion, and Similar Figures Make this Foldable to help you organize your Chapter 6 notes about ratios, proportions, and similar figures. Begin with a piece of 11″ by 17″ paper.

1. **Fold** a two inch tab along the bottom.
2. **Fold** in thirds lengthwise.
3. **Staple** the bottom fold to make a pocket.
4. **Label** each pocket as shown. Place several index cards in each pocket.

Ratio | Proportion | Similar Figures

New Vocabulary

English		Español
ratio	p. 265	razón
rate	p. 270	tasa
unit rate	p. 270	tasa unitaria
dimensional analysis	p. 275	análisis dimensional
proportion	p. 287	proporción
cross products	p. 287	productos cruzados
scale drawing	p. 294	dibujo a escala
scale model	p. 294	modelo a escala
scale	p. 294	escala
scale factor	p. 295	factor de escala
similar figures	p. 301	figures semejantes
congruent	p. 301	congruentes
dilation	p. 301	dilatación
indirect measurement	p. 313	medición indirecta

Review Vocabulary

figure • figura a two-dimensional shape that lies entirely within one plane

simplest form • forma reducida a fraction is in simplest form when the GCF of the numerator and denominator is 1

$\frac{12}{28} = \frac{12 \div 4}{28 \div 4}$ **Divide the numerator and denominator by the GCF, 4.**

$= \frac{3}{7}$ **Simplest form**

Multilingual eGlossary glencoe.com

Math Online glencoe.com

- Study the chapter online
- Explore **Math in Motion**
- Get extra help from your own **Personal Tutor**
- Use **Extra Examples** for additional help
- Take a **Self-Check Quiz**
- **Review Vocabulary** in fun ways

6-1 Ratios

Why?

In mathematics, there are many different ways to compare numbers. Consider the data in the table.

Animal	Life Span (years)
gray whale	70
bottlenose dolphin	30
kangaroo	7
mouse	3

a. On average, how many times as long does a gray whale live as a kangaroo? **10 times**

b. For each year a kangaroo lives, how many years does a gray whale live on average? **10 years**

c. What operation did you use to find parts **a** and **b**? **division**

Then
You have already learned operations with fractions. (Lessons 3-3 and 3-4)

Now
- Write ratios as fractions in simplest form.
- Simplify ratios involving measurements.

New Vocabulary
ratio

Math Online
glencoe.com
- Extra Examples
- Personal Tutor
- Self-Check Quiz
- Homework Help

Write Ratios as Fractions in Simplest Form A **ratio** is a comparison of two quantities by division. If the first number being compared is less than the second, the ratio is usually written as a fraction in simplest form.

Key Concept Ratios
For Your FOLDABLE

Words A **ratio** is a comparison of two quantities by division.

Examples

Numbers			Algebra		
3 to 9	3:9	$\frac{3}{9}$	a to b	$a:b$	$\frac{a}{b}$

Ratios can express part to part, part to whole, or whole to part relationships.

EXAMPLE 1 Write Ratios in Simplest Form

Express the ratio *12 baskets in 18 attempts* as a fraction in simplest form. Explain its meaning.

$$\frac{12}{18} = \frac{2}{3} \quad (\div 6)$$

Divide the numerator and denominator by the GCF, 6.

The ratio of baskets to shots attempted is 2 to 3. This means that for every 3 shots attempted, 2 were made. Also, $\frac{2}{3}$ of the shots attempted were baskets.

Check Your Progress

1. Refer to the table above. Express the ratio of the life span of a bottlenose dolphin to the life span of a mouse as a ratio in simplest form. Explain its meaning. **See Chapter 6 Answer Appendix.**

Personal Tutor glencoe.com

6-1 Lesson Notes

1 FOCUS

Vertical Alignment

Before Lesson 6-1
Learn operations with fractions.

Lesson 6-1
Write ratios as fractions in simplest form. Simplify ratios involving measurements.

After Lesson 6-1
Relate direct variation to linear functions and solve problems involving proportional change.

2 TEACH

Scaffolding Questions

Have students read the *Why?* section of the lesson and answer the questions.

Ask:
- For every three years that a bottlenose dolphin lives, how many years on average does a gray whale live? seven years
- What numbers are factors of both 30 and 70? 1, 2, 5, 10
- How can you simplify $\frac{30}{70}$? $\frac{3}{7}$

Write Ratios as Fractions in Simplest Form

Example 1 shows how to write ratios in simplest form and how to explain the meaning of the ratio.

Lesson 6-1 Resources

Resource	Approaching-Level	On-Level	Beyond-Level	English Learners
Teacher Edition	• Differentiated Instruction, p. 266	• Differentiated Instruction, p. 266	• Differentiated Instruction, p. 269	• Differentiated Instruction, p. 266
Chapter Resource Masters	• Study Guide and Intervention, pp. 5–6 • Skills Practice, p. 7 • Practice, p. 8 • Word Problem Practice, p. 9	• Study Guide and Intervention, pp. 5–6 • Skills Practice, p. 7 • Practice, p. 8 • Word Problem Practice, p. 9 • Enrichment, p. 10	• Practice, p. 8 • Word Problem Practice, p. 9 • Enrichment, p. 10	• Study Guide and Intervention, pp. 5–6 • Skills Practice, p. 7 • Practice, p. 8
Transparencies	• 5-Minute Check Transparency 6-1	• 5-Minute Check Transparency 6-1	• 5-Minute Check Transparency 6-1	• 5-Minute Check Transparency 6-1
Other	• Study Notebook • Teaching Pre-Algebra with Manipulatives	• Study Notebook • Teaching Pre-Algebra with Manipulatives	• Study Notebook	• Study Notebook • Teaching Pre-Algebra with Manipulatives

Formative Assessment

Use the Check Your Progress exercises after each example to determine students' understanding of concepts.

Additional Example

1 Express the ratio *10 roses out of 12 flowers* as a fraction in simplest form. Explain its meaning. $\frac{5}{6}$; This means that for every six flowers, five are roses.

Additional Examples also in Interactive Classroom PowerPoint® Presentations

IWB INTERACTIVE WHITEBOARD READY

Focus on Mathematical Content

Ratios A ratio shows a relationship between two numbers. Ratios compare quantities that are measured in the same unit, but the ratio itself has no units.

Simplify Ratios Involving Measurements

Examples 2 and 3 show how to write ratios as fractions in simplest form.

Additional Examples

2 **SHOPPING** A store found that 25 out of 35 people shopping there were women. Express this ratio as a fraction in simplest form. Explain its meaning. $\frac{5}{7}$; This means that 5 out of every 7 shoppers are women.

3 Express the ratio *21 inches to 2 yards* as a fraction in simplest form. $\frac{7}{24}$

Real-World EXAMPLE 2 Write Ratios as Fractions

MUSIC Ten out of every 30 Americans own a portable MP3 player. Express this ratio as a fraction in simplest form. Explain its meaning.

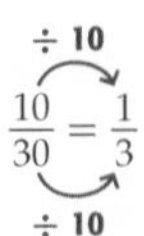

$$\frac{10}{30} = \frac{1}{3}$$ (÷ 10) **Divide the numerator and denominator by the GCF, 10.**

The ratio of Americans who own a portable MP3 player is 1 to 3. This means that for every 3 Americans, 1 owns a portable MP3 player. Also, $\frac{1}{3}$ of Americans own a portable MP3 player.

Check Your Progress

2. **CAMPING** 15 out of 100 campsites at a campground are reserved for campers with pets. Express this ratio as a fraction in simplest form. Explain its meaning.

2. $\frac{3}{20}$; Sample answer: For every 20 campsites, 3 are reserved for campers with pets.

Personal Tutor glencoe.com

Simplify Ratios Involving Measurements When writing a ratio involving measurements, both quantities should have the same unit of measure.

Watch Out!

Units Always double check that the units in a ratio match. If the units do not match, you will not get the correct comparison.

EXAMPLE 3 Write Ratios as Fractions

Express the ratio *8 ounces to 3 pounds* as a fraction in simplest form.

$$\frac{8 \text{ ounces}}{3 \text{ pounds}} = \frac{8 \text{ ounces}}{48 \text{ ounces}}$$ **Convert 3 pounds to ounces.**

$$= \frac{1 \text{ ounce}}{6 \text{ ounces}}$$ **Divide the numerator and denominator by the GCF, 6.**

Written in simplest form, the ratio is 1 to 6.

Check Your Progress

3. Express the ratio *15 inches to 1 foot* as a fraction in simplest form. $\frac{5}{4}$

Personal Tutor glencoe.com

Check Your Understanding

Example 1 p. 265 — **Express each ratio as a fraction in simplest form.**

1. 12 boys to 16 girls $\frac{3}{4}$
2. 24 out of 60 light bulbs $\frac{2}{5}$
3. 36 DVDs out of 84 DVDs $\frac{3}{7}$
4. 50 tiles to 25 tiles $\frac{2}{1}$

Example 2 p. 266

5. **ACTIVITIES** In Mr. Blackwell's class, 15 out of 24 students play sports. Express this ratio as a fraction in simplest form. Explain its meaning. $\frac{5}{8}$; For every 8 students, 5 participate in sports.

Example 3 p. 266 — **Express each ratio as a fraction in simplest form.**

6. 3 pints to 4 quarts $\frac{3}{8}$
7. 2 pounds to 6 ounces $\frac{16}{3}$
8. 9 inches to 1 yard $\frac{1}{4}$
9. 6 gallons to 3 quarts $\frac{8}{1}$

00

Differentiated Instruction

AL OL ELL

Interpersonal

If students are having trouble simplifying ratios or identifying equivalent ratios,

Then on one set of index cards, write ratios that can be simplified, one ratio per card. On a second set of cards, write the simplified ratios. Give one card to each student. Ask students to find the person who has the equivalent ratio. Have them stand in pairs to display the ratios. Encourage students to discuss how they determined which ratio was equivalent to the one they had.

Practice and Problem Solving

● = **Step-by-Step Solutions** begin on page R11. **Extra Practice** begins on page 810.

Example 1 p. 266

Express each ratio as a fraction in simplest form.

10. 9 out of 15 pets $\frac{3}{5}$
11. 20 wins out of 36 games $\frac{5}{9}$
12. 4 players to 52 cards $\frac{1}{13}$
13. 45 out of 60 days $\frac{3}{4}$
14. 16 pens to 10 pencils $\frac{8}{5}$
15. 96 people to 3 buses $\frac{32}{1}$

Example 2 p. 267

16–17. See margin.

16. **PIANOS** On a full size piano, there are 36 black keys and 52 white keys. Express the ratio of black keys to white keys as a fraction in simplest form. Explain its meaning.
17. **RESTAURANTS** In a restaurant, 72 out of 108 tables are booths. Express the ratio of tables that are booths to the total number of tables as a fraction in simplest form. Explain its meaning.

Example 3 p. 267

Express each ratio as a fraction in simplest form.

18. 10 yards to 10 feet $\frac{3}{1}$
19. 4 ounces to 2 pounds $\frac{1}{8}$
20. 18 quarts to 4 gallons $\frac{9}{8}$
21. 6 feet to 14 inches $\frac{36}{7}$

B

22. **STORES** A department store conducted a study to determine what age group shops in their store.

Age Group	Number
0–17	25
18–30	75
31–45	54
46+	26

a. Express the ratio of people ages 0–17 to people ages 18–30 as a fraction in simplest form. $\frac{1}{3}$

b. Express the ratio of people thirty or under to people over the age of 30 as a fraction in simplest form. $\frac{5}{4}$

c. Express the ratio of people age 18–30 to the total number of people as a fraction in simplest form. $\frac{5}{12}$

Real-World Link

Wisconsin Dells, Wisconsin, is recognized as the "Water Park Capital of the World." It is home to both the largest indoor and outdoor water parks in the world.

Source: Wisconsin Dells

23. **WATER PARKS** A water park has 14 body slides, 8 tube slides, 2 types of swimming pools, and 6 water play areas. Use this information to write each ratio as a fraction in simplest form.

a. body slides : tube slides $\frac{7}{4}$

b. play areas : tube slides $\frac{3}{4}$

c. slides : all attractions $\frac{11}{15}$

d. slides : not slides $\frac{11}{4}$

24. **PHONES** A cell phone store displayed the phone at the right on a poster. The length of the phone on the poster is 3 feet 4 inches. Write a ratio comparing the length of the actual cell phone to length of the cell phone on the poster as a fraction in simplest form. $\frac{1}{10}$

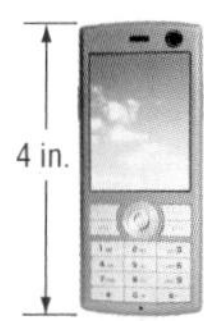

25. **ANIMALS** The table shows the heart rates of different animals.

Animal	Heart Rate (beats/min)	Mass (g)
cat	150	2000
cow	65	800,000
hamster	450	60
horse	44	1,200,000

a. Order the animals from greatest mass to heart rate ratio to least mass to heart rate ratio. horse, cow, cat, hamster

b. Which animal had the greatest ratio? Explain your reasoning.

25b. horse; Sample answer: For every 27,272 grams, a horse's heart will beat 1 time.

TEACH with TECH

BLOG On your secure classroom blog, have students create a running list of ratios they encounter in their daily lives.

3 PRACTICE

Formative Assessment

Use Exercises 1–9 to check for understanding.

Use the chart at the bottom of this page to customize assignments for your students.

Tips for New Teachers

Ratios To compare ratios, it is easier to actually convert each ratio to a decimal and compare.

Additional Answers

16. $\frac{9}{13}$; For every 13 white keys there are 9 black keys or $\frac{9}{13}$ of the keys are black.

17. $\frac{2}{3}$; For every 3 tables, 2 are booths or $\frac{2}{3}$ of the tables are booths.

Differentiated Homework Options

Level	Assignment	Two-Day Option	
AL Basic	10–21, 33, 34–38 even, 39–60	11–21 odd, 39–42	10–20 even, 33, 34–38 even, 43–60
OL Core	11–21 odd, 22–29, 31, 33, 34–38 even, 39–60	10–21, 39–42	22–34, 36, 38, 43–60
BL Advanced	22–56 (optional: 57–60)		

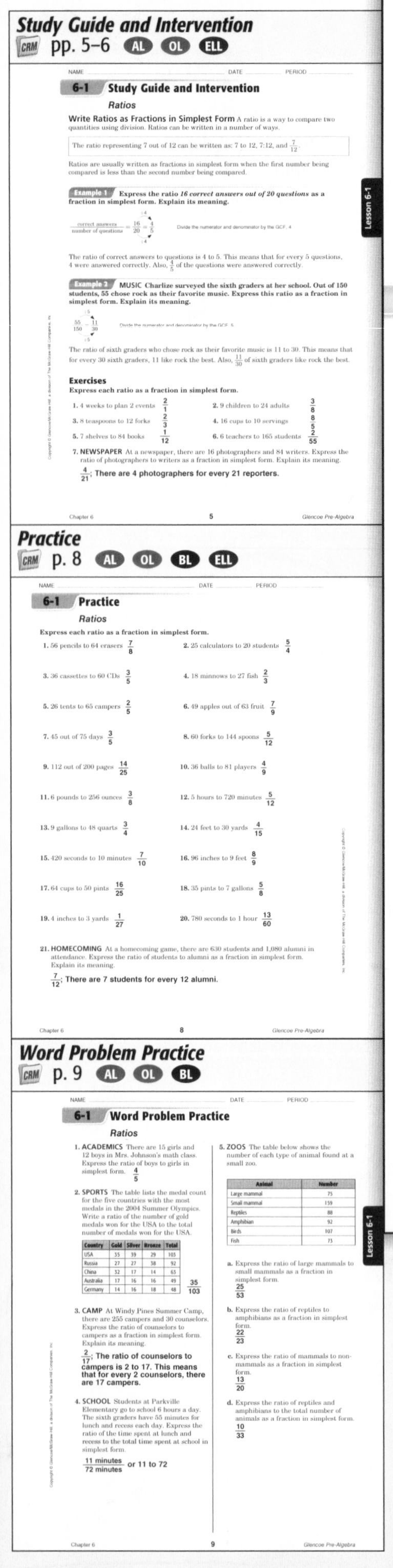
Study Guide and Intervention
CRM pp. 5–6 AL OL ELL

NAME ______ DATE ______ PERIOD ______

6-1 Study Guide and Intervention

Ratios

Write Ratios as Fractions in Simplest Form A ratio is a way to compare two quantities using division. Ratios can be written in a number of ways.

The ratio representing 7 out of 12 can be written as: 7 to 12, 7:12, and $\frac{7}{12}$.

Ratios are usually written as fractions in simplest form when the first number being compared is less than the second number being compared.

Example 1 Express the ratio *16 correct answers out of 20 questions* as a fraction in simplest form. Explain its meaning.

$\frac{\text{correct answers}}{\text{number of questions}} = \frac{16}{20} = \frac{4}{5}$ Divide the numerator and denominator by the GCF, 4.

The ratio of correct answers to questions is 4 to 5. This means that for every 5 questions, 4 were answered correctly. Also, $\frac{4}{5}$ of the questions were answered correctly.

Example 2 MUSIC Charlize surveyed the sixth graders at her school. Out of 150 students, 55 chose rock as their favorite music. Express this ratio as a fraction in simplest form. Explain its meaning.

$\frac{55}{150} = \frac{11}{30}$ Divide the numerator and denominator by the GCF, 5.

The ratio of sixth graders who chose rock as their favorite music is 11 to 30. This means that for every 30 sixth graders, 11 like rock the best. Also, $\frac{11}{30}$ of sixth graders like rock the best.

Exercises

Express each ratio as a fraction in simplest form.

1. 4 weeks to plan 2 events $\frac{2}{1}$
2. 9 children to 24 adults $\frac{3}{8}$
3. 8 teaspoons to 12 forks $\frac{2}{3}$
4. 16 cups to 10 servings $\frac{8}{5}$
5. 7 shelves to 84 books $\frac{1}{12}$
6. 6 teachers to 165 students $\frac{2}{55}$
7. NEWSPAPER At a newspaper, there are 16 photographers and 84 writers. Express the ratio of photographers to writers as a fraction in simplest form. Explain its meaning. $\frac{4}{21}$; There are 4 photographers for every 21 reporters.

Chapter 6 5 Glencoe Pre-Algebra

Practice
CRM p. 8 AL OL BL ELL

NAME ______ DATE ______ PERIOD ______

6-1 Practice

Ratios

Express each ratio as a fraction in simplest form.

1. 56 pencils to 64 erasers $\frac{7}{8}$
2. 25 calculators to 20 students $\frac{5}{4}$
3. 36 cassettes to 60 CDs $\frac{3}{5}$
4. 18 minnows to 27 fish $\frac{2}{3}$
5. 26 tents to 65 campers $\frac{2}{5}$
6. 49 apples out of 63 fruit $\frac{7}{9}$
7. 45 out of 75 days $\frac{3}{5}$
8. 60 forks to 144 spoons $\frac{5}{12}$
9. 112 out of 200 pages $\frac{14}{25}$
10. 36 balls to 81 players $\frac{4}{9}$
11. 6 pounds to 256 ounces $\frac{3}{8}$
12. 5 hours to 720 minutes $\frac{5}{12}$
13. 9 gallons to 48 quarts $\frac{3}{4}$
14. 24 feet to 30 yards $\frac{4}{15}$
15. 420 seconds to 10 minutes $\frac{7}{10}$
16. 96 inches to 9 feet $\frac{8}{9}$
17. 64 cups to 50 pints $\frac{16}{25}$
18. 35 pints to 7 gallons $\frac{5}{8}$
19. 4 inches to 3 yards $\frac{1}{27}$
20. 780 seconds to 1 hour $\frac{13}{60}$
21. HOMECOMING At a homecoming game, there are 630 students and 1,080 alumni in attendance. Express the ratio of students to alumni as a fraction in simplest form. Explain its meaning. $\frac{7}{12}$; There are 7 students for every 12 alumni.

Chapter 6 8 Glencoe Pre-Algebra

Word Problem Practice
CRM p. 9 AL OL BL

NAME ______ DATE ______ PERIOD ______

6-1 Word Problem Practice

Ratios

1. ACADEMICS There are 15 girls and 12 boys in Mrs. Johnson's math class. Express the ratio of boys to girls in simplest form. $\frac{4}{5}$
2. SPORTS The table lists the medal count for the five countries with the most medals in the 2004 Summer Olympics. Write a ratio of the number of gold medals won for the USA to the total number of medals won for the USA.

Country	Gold	Silver	Bronze	Total
USA	35	39	29	103
Russia	27	27	38	92
China	32	17	14	63
Australia	17	16	16	49
Germany	14	16	18	48

$\frac{35}{103}$

3. CAMP At Windy Pines Summer Camp, there are 255 campers and 30 counselors. Express the ratio of counselors to campers as a fraction in simplest form. Explain its meaning. $\frac{2}{17}$; The ratio of counselors to campers is 2 to 17. This means that for every 2 counselors, there are 17 campers.
4. SCHOOL Students at Parkville Elementary go to school 6 hours a day. The sixth graders have 55 minutes for lunch and recess each day. Express the ratio of the time spent at lunch and recess to the total time spent at school in simplest form. $\frac{11 \text{ minutes}}{72 \text{ minutes}}$ or 11 to 72
5. ZOOS The table below shows the number of each type of animal found at a small zoo.

Animal	Number
Large mammal	75
Small mammal	159
Reptiles	88
Amphibian	92
Birds	107
Fish	75

a. Express the ratio of large mammals to small mammals as a fraction in simplest form. $\frac{25}{53}$

b. Express the ratio of reptiles to amphibians as a fraction in simplest form. $\frac{22}{23}$

c. Express the ratio of mammals to non-mammals as a fraction in simplest form. $\frac{13}{20}$

d. Express the ratio of reptiles and amphibians to the total number of animals as a fraction in simplest form. $\frac{10}{33}$

Chapter 6 9 Glencoe Pre-Algebra

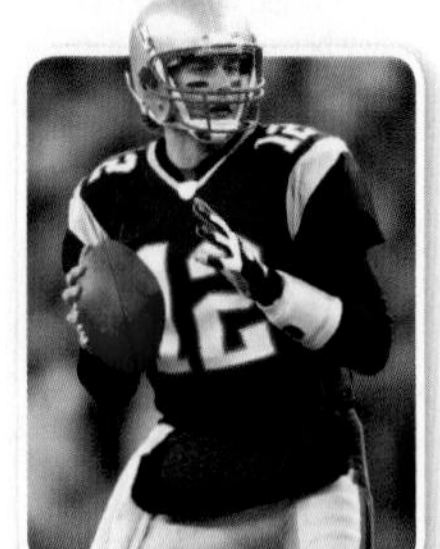

Real-World Link

In the 2007 NFL season, Tom Brady threw for 50 touchdowns, making him the record holder for most touchdown passes in a single season.

Source: NFL

33. Sample answers: number of girls to boys in a class, number of apples to bananas in a fruit basket, a sale price of 3 for $8

34. Estimation; Sample answer: Each of the ratios can be easily rounded to common fraction. $\frac{350}{450}$

36. 2 qt: 3 gal; Sample answer: Since 2 qt: 3 gal involves measurement units, the units need to be the same.

37. Always; Sample answer: No matter what is used to measure the dimensions of the table, the actual dimensions will never change so the ratio will always be the same.

38. Sample answer: He is incorrect. The takeaway/giveaway ratio is 21 to 22 or $\frac{21}{22}$. The sports writer subtracted instead of dividing.

26. SALES Bonnie's Boutique had a T-shirt sale to make room for new inventory. At the end of the sale, 16 T-shirts were left. Of these, 6 of them were blue. Write the ratio of blue shirts to shirts left as a fraction in simplest form. $\frac{3}{8}$

27. BAKING When cooking a turkey, you should bake it for about 1 hour for every four pounds of meat. If an 18 pound turkey is cooked for 4 hours, was it cooked long enough? If not, how long should the turkey have been cooked? **no; Sample answer: An 18 pound turkey should be cooked for $4\frac{1}{2}$ hours.**

28. FOOTBALL The table shows the number of touchdowns and interceptions each NFL quarterback had in a recent season. Which quarterback had the best touchdown to interception ratio? Explain its meaning. **Philip Rivers; for every interception he throws, he throws 2.44 touchdowns.**

Player	Touchdowns	Interceptions
Drew Brees	26	11
Carson Palmer	28	13
Tom Brady	24	12
Philip Rivers	22	9

Compare each pair of ratios using <, >, or =.

29. \$27 for 9 key chains, \$45 for 15 key chains $\frac{27}{9} = \frac{45}{15}$

30. 8 girls out of 18 students, 12 girls out of 22 students $\frac{8}{18} < \frac{12}{22}$

31. 6 cases for \$48, 14 cases for \$88 $\frac{6}{48} < \frac{14}{88}$

32. 24 thriller movies out of 36 DVDs, 10 thriller movies out of 15 DVDs $\frac{24}{36} = \frac{10}{15}$

H.O.T. Problems
Use **H**igher-**O**rder **T**hinking Skills

33. OPEN ENDED Give three different examples of ratios that might occur in a real-world situation.

34. SELECT A TECHNIQUE Which of the technique(s) listed below might you use to determine which of the following ratios is the greatest: 440:1200, 1200: 3750, or 350:450? Justify your selection(s). Then use the technique(s) to solve the problem.

mental math | a calculator | estimation

35. CHALLENGE The ratio of Mieko's age to his brother Sado's age is 2:3. In ten years, the ratio will be 4:5. How old is Mieko? **10**

36. WHICH ONE DOESN'T BELONG? Select the ratio that does not have the same value as the other three. Explain your reasoning.

2 boys: 3 girls | 2 qt: 3 gal | 2 spoons: 3 utensils | 2 ft: 3 ft

37. CHALLENGE Students in Mrs. Miller's class are measuring the length and width of a table using nonstandard materials like pencils and pieces of paper. No matter which tools they use, will the ratio of the length to the width *always*, *sometimes*, or *never* be the same? Explain.

38. WRITING IN MATH In a recent year, the Jacksonville Jaguars took the ball away from their opponents 21 times. They gave the ball up to their opponents 22 times. A sports writer claims the takeaway/giveaway ratio is 21 – 22 or –1. Is this statement correct? Explain.

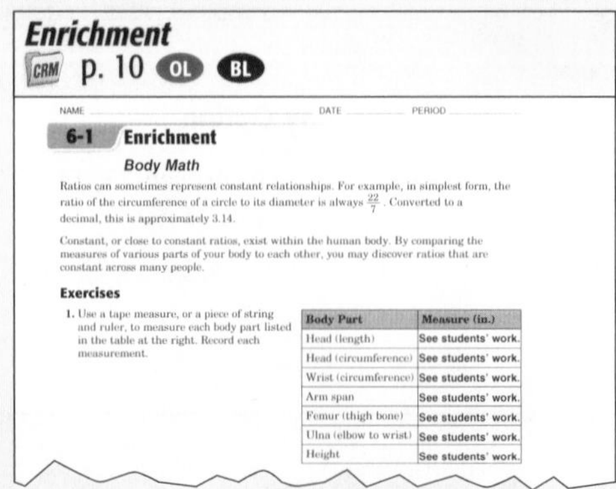
Enrichment
CRM p. 10 OL BL

NAME ______ DATE ______ PERIOD ______

6-1 Enrichment

Body Math

Ratios can sometimes represent constant relationships. For example, in simplest form, the ratio of the circumference of a circle to its diameter is always $\frac{22}{7}$. Converted to a decimal, this is approximately 3.14.

Constant, or close to constant ratios, exist within the human body. By comparing the measures of various parts of your body to each other, you may discover ratios that are constant across many people.

Exercises

1. Use a tape measure, or a piece of string and ruler, to measure each body part listed in the table at the right. Record each measurement.

Body Part	Measure (in.)
Head (length)	See students' work.
Head (circumference)	See students' work.
Wrist (circumference)	See students' work.
Arm span	See students' work.
Femur (thigh bone)	See students' work.
Ulna (elbow to wrist)	See students' work.
Height	See students' work.

268 Chapter 6 Ratio, Proportion, and Similar Figures

Standardized Test Practice

39. Of 48 orchestra members, 30 are girls. What ratio compares the number of boys to girls in the orchestra? **C**

A 3:8 C 3:5
B 8:3 D 5:3

40. Which of the following ratios does *not* describe a relationship between the squares shown? **G**

F 2 black:3 white H 2 black:5 total
G 2 black:5 white J 3 white:5 total

41. Of newly manufactured volleyballs, 12 were defective and 56 passed inspection. What ratio compares the number of defective volleyballs to the total number of volleyballs manufactured? **B**

A 3:14 C 4:14
B 3:17 D 4:17

42. EXTENDED RESPONSE Marisol counted the number of coins she had in her piggy bank. The table shows her results.

pennies	nickels	dimes	quarters
47	14	18	21

a. Write a ratio that compares the number of nickels to the number of quarters. **2:3**

b. Write a ratio that compares the number of dimes to the number of total coins. **9:50**

Spiral Review

Solve. Graph your solution on a number line. (Lesson 5-5) **43–48. See margin for number lines.**

43. $3x + 4 \leq 31$ $x \leq 9$

44. $2n + 5 > 11 - n$ $n > 2$

45. $y + 1 \geq 4y + 4$ $y \leq -1$

46. $16 - 2c < 14$ $c > 1$

47. $18 \leq 12 - 2n$ $n \leq -3$

48. $-3(b - 1) > 18$ $b < -5$

49. APPLES More than 2500 varieties of apples are grown in the United States. Write an inequality to describe the apple varieties. (Lesson 5-3) $a > 2500$

Name the ordered pair for each point graphed at the right. (Lesson 2-6)

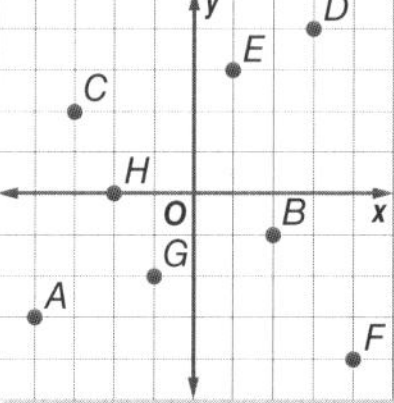

50. A (−4, −3)

51. B (2, −1)

52. C (−3, 2)

53. D (3, 4)

54. E (1, 3)

55. F (4, −4)

56. AEROSPACE To simulate space travel, NASA's Lewis Research Center in Cleveland uses a 430-foot shaft. The free fall of an object in the shaft takes 5 seconds to travel the 430 feet. (Lesson 2-5)

a. Write an integer to represent the change in the height of the object. **−430**

b. On average, how far does the object travel each second? **86 ft**

Skills Review

Divide. Round to the nearest cent. (Previous Course)

57. \$5.75 ÷ 4 **\$1.44**

58. \$8.30 ÷ 6 **\$1.38**

59. \$2.27 ÷ 8 **\$0.28**

60. \$11.50 ÷ 5 **\$2.30**

Differentiated Instruction

Extension Pose the following problem to students: A city has a garden area that is 24 feet wide and 40 feet long. What is the ratio of length to width in simplest form? If both the width and length are decreased by the same amount, will the ratio of length to width remain the same? Explain. $\frac{5}{3}$; Not usually; subtracting the same number from both the numerator and denominator will give the same ratio only if the numerator equals the denominator from the start.

Tips for New Teachers

Order Remind students that the order of the quantities in a problem determines the order of the numbers in the ratio. The first number in the ratio is the first quantity mentioned.

4 ASSESS

Ticket Out the Door Ask students to look around the room for ratios, such as desks per student, windows per door, and so on. Tell students to write at least three ratios, to identify in a sentence what each ratio represents, and to reduce each ratio to simplest form. Have students hand in their papers as they exit.

Additional Answers

43.

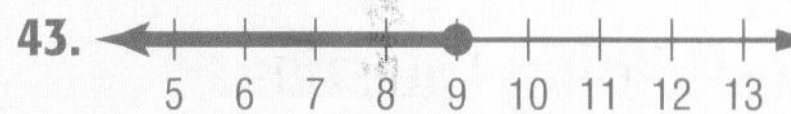

44.

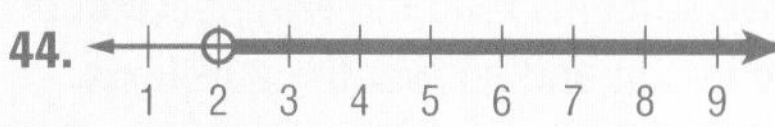

45.

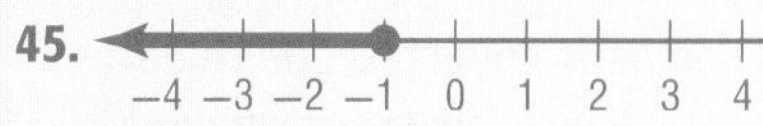

46.

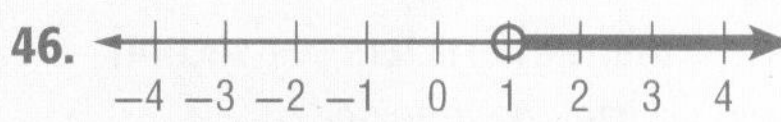

47. −7 −6 −5 −4 −3 −2 −1 0 1

48. −7 −6 −5 −4 −3 −2 −1 0 1

6-2 Lesson Notes

1 FOCUS

Vertical Alignment

Before Lesson 6-2
Learn how to write ratios.

Lesson 6-2
Find unit rates.
Compare and use unit rates to solve problems.

After Lesson 6-2
Relate direct variation to linear functions and solve problems involving proportional change.

2 TEACH

Scaffolding Questions

Have students read the *Why?* section of the lesson and answer the questions.

Ask:

- If someone could text 200 characters at a constant rate for one minute, how many characters per second would they have texted? ≈ 3
- Novice text-messagers type at a rate of about 30 words per minute. Express this ratio as a fraction. $\frac{30 \text{ words}}{\text{minute}}$
- To find how many words a novice could text in 5 minutes, what would you do? multiply 30 by 5

6-2 Unit Rates

Then
You have already learned how to write ratios. (Lesson 6-1)

Now
- Find unit rates.
- Compare and use unit rates to solve problems.

New Vocabulary
rate
unit rate

Math Online
glencoe.com
- Extra Examples
- Personal Tutor
- Self-Check Quiz
- Homework Help

Why?

Eighteen year old Ben Cook set a world record for text messaging by typing 160 characters in a little more than 40 seconds.

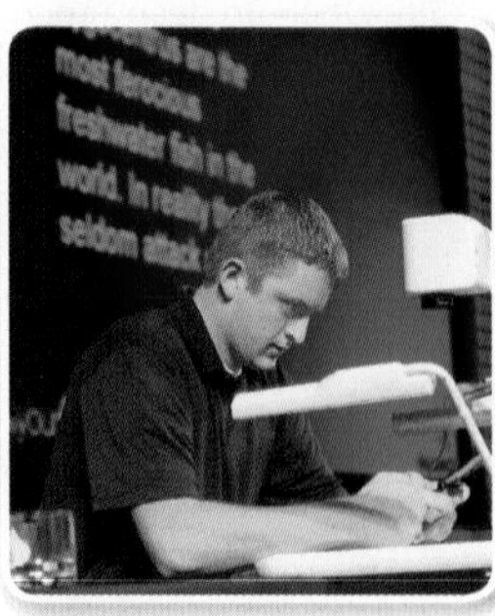

a. If he typed at a constant rate, how many characters did he text each second? **4**

b. It actually took him 42.2 seconds to set the record. Was his rate per second greater or less than the rate in part **a**? Explain. **Less than; as the divisor increases the quotient decreases.**

Find Unit Rates A **rate** is a ratio of two quantities having different kinds of units.

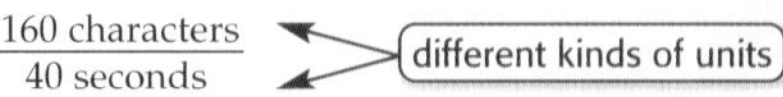

$$\frac{160 \text{ characters}}{40 \text{ seconds}}$$ ← different kinds of units

When a rate is simplified so that it has a denominator of 1, it is called a **unit rate**. To write a rate as a unit rate, divide the numerator and denominator of the rate by the denominator.

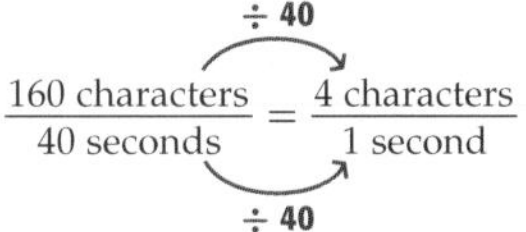

$$\frac{160 \text{ characters}}{40 \text{ seconds}} = \frac{4 \text{ characters}}{1 \text{ second}} \quad (\div 40)$$

EXAMPLE 1 Find Unit Rates

Express each rate as a unit rate. Round to the nearest tenth, if necessary.

a. \$11 for 4 boxes of cereal

Write the rate that compares the cost to the number of boxes.

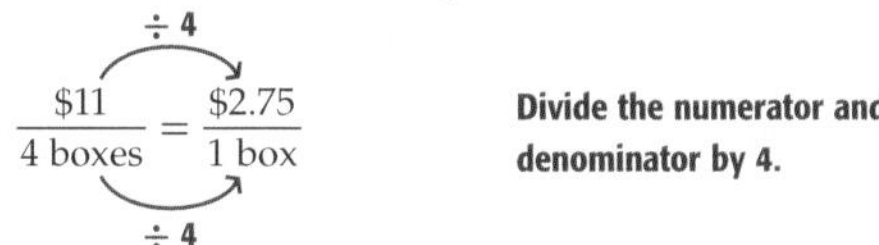

$$\frac{\$11}{4 \text{ boxes}} = \frac{\$2.75}{1 \text{ box}} \quad (\div 4)$$ Divide the numerator and denominator by 4.

So, the cost is \$2.75 per box of cereal.

b. 400 miles on 14 gallons of gasoline

Write the rate that compares the number of miles to the number of gallons.

$$\frac{400 \text{ miles}}{14 \text{ gallons}} = \frac{28.6 \text{ miles}}{1 \text{ gallon}} \quad (\div 14)$$ Divide the numerator and denominator by 14.

So, the car traveled 28.6 miles per gallon of gasoline.

Check Your Progress

1A. \$18.50 for 5 pounds **\$3.70 per pound** **1B.** 100 meters in 14 seconds **7.1 meters per second**

Personal Tutor glencoe.com

Lesson 6-2 Resources

Resource	Approaching-Level	On-Level	Beyond-Level	English Learners
Teacher Edition	• Differentiated Instruction, p. 271	• Differentiated Instruction, p. 271	• Differentiated Instruction, p. 274	
Chapter Resource Masters	• Study Guide and Intervention, pp. 11–12 • Skills Practice, p. 13 • Practice, p. 14 • Word Problem Practice, p. 15	• Study Guide and Intervention, pp. 11–12 • Skills Practice, p. 13 • Practice, p. 14 • Word Problem Practice, p. 15 • Enrichment, p. 16	• Practice, p. 14 • Word Problem Practice, p. 15 • Enrichment, p. 16	• Study Guide and Intervention, pp. 11–12 • Skills Practice, p. 13 • Practice, p. 14
Transparencies	• 5-Minute Check Transparency 6-2	• 5-Minute Check Transparency 6-2	• 5-Minute Check Transparency 6-2	• 5-Minute Check Transparency 6-2
Others	• Study Notebook • Teaching Pre-Algebra with Manipulatives	• Study Notebook • Teaching Pre-Algebra with Manipulatives	• Study Notebook • Teaching Pre-Algebra with Manipulatives	• Study Notebook • Teaching Pre-Algebra with Manipulatives

Compare Unit Rates You can also compare unit rates to solve problems.

Real-World EXAMPLE 2 Compare Unit Rates

FINANCIAL LITERACY An online music store sells 15 songs for $12. Another online music store sells 10 songs for $9. Which online store has the lower cost per song?

Step 1 Find the unit rates of the two stores.

$$\frac{12 \text{ dollars}}{15 \text{ songs}} = \frac{0.8 \text{ dollar}}{1 \text{ song}}$$ (÷ 15 numerator and denominator)

Divide the numerator and denominator by 15.

For the 15 songs, the unit rate is $0.80 per song.

$$\frac{9 \text{ dollars}}{10 \text{ songs}} = \frac{0.9 \text{ dollar}}{1 \text{ song}}$$ (÷ 10 numerator and denominator)

Divide the numerator and denominator by 10.

For the 10 songs, the unit rate is $0.90 per song.

Step 2 Compare the rates. Since $0.80 < $0.90, the first store has a better rate per song.

StudyTip

Alternative Method Use the LCM. In the first case, 30 songs cost $12 × 2 or $24. In the second, 30 songs cost $9 × 3 or $27. The first has the lower cost per song.

Check Your Progress

2. **SUN SCREEN** A store sells two different sizes of the same brand of sun screen, an 8-ounce bottle for $5.76 and a 12-ounce bottle for $8.88. Which size bottle is the better buy per ounce? Explain.

2. 8-ounce bottle; Sample answer: The 8-ounce bottle costs $0.72 per ounce and the 12-ounce bottle costs $0.74 per ounce.

Personal Tutor glencoe.com

Once you know the unit rate, you can use it to solve problems involving any amount.

EXAMPLE 3 Use Unit Rates

DOLPHINS Use the information at the left to find how many breaths a dolphin will take in 7 hours.

Step 1 Find the unit rate.

$$34 \text{ breaths in 4 hours} = \frac{34 \text{ breaths} \div 4}{4 \text{ hours} \div 4} \text{ or } \frac{8.5 \text{ breaths}}{1 \text{ hour}}$$

Step 2 Multiply this unit rate by 7 to find the number of breaths a dolphin will take in 7 hours.

$$\frac{8.5 \text{ breaths}}{1 \text{ hour}} \cdot 7 \text{ hours} = 59.5 \text{ breaths}$$ **Divide out the common units.**

A bottlenose dolphin will take 59.5 breaths in 7 hours.

Real-World Link

Bottlenose dolphins breathe through a nasal opening called a blowhole. A typical dolphin will take about 34 breaths in 4 hours.

Source: Dolphins Plus

Check Your Progress

3. **BAKING** A bakery can make 195 doughnuts in 3 hours. At this rate, how many doughnuts can the bakery make in 8 hours? **520 doughnuts**

Personal Tutor glencoe.com

Find Unit Rates

Example 1 shows how to find unit rates.

Formative Assessment

Use the Check Your Progress exercises after each example to determine students' understanding of concepts.

Additional Example

1. Express each rate as a unit rate. Round to the nearest tenth, if necessary.
   a. $10 for 8 cans of soup. $1.25 per can
   b. 187 miles in 7 days. 26.7 miles per day

Additional Examples also in Interactive Classroom PowerPoint® Presentations

IWB INTERACTIVE WHITEBOARD READY

Focus on Mathematical Content

Rates Rates are a comparison of two numbers. In a rate, the units are different and the units are given as part of the rate. Rates with a denominator of 1 are called unit rates.

Compare Unit Rates

Example 2 shows how to compare unit rates. **Example 3** shows how to use unit rates.

Additional Examples

2. **SHOPPING** A 12-oz bottle of cleaner costs $4.50. A 16-oz bottle of cleaner costs $6.56. Which costs less per ounce? 12-oz bottle: $0.38; 16-oz bottle: $0.41; the 12-oz bottle costs less per ounce.
3. **ANIMALS** A snail moved 5 feet in 2 hours. How many feet will the snail move in 5 hours? 12.5 ft

Differentiated Instruction

AL ELL

If students have difficulty understanding unit rates,

Then bring information to class about cars that have different miles per gallon rates. Compare the cars that are considered fuel efficient. Ask the following questions.

- If Carmen drives a car that gets 20 miles per gallon, how many gallons will she need to drive 230 miles?
- How much will the gas cost?
- If you drive a car that gets 25 miles per gallon, how much gas would you save over Carmen?
- If you rent a car that travels 230 miles with 12 gallons of gasoline, would it be better than Carmen's car?

3 PRACTICE

Formative Assessment

Use Exercises 1–8 to check for understanding.

Use the chart at the bottom of this page to customize assignments for your students.

Additional Answers

22. quart of milk; Multiply the cost of one quart by 4 and then compare the cost to the cost of a gallon. So, $0.76 \times 4 = 3.04$ and $3.04 < 3.18$; $3.18 \div 4 = 0.795$ and $0.76 < 0.795$. Or, divide the cost of a gallon by 4 and then compare the cost to the cost of the quart.

24a.

Time(h)	Distance Traveled (mi)	
	Abigail	Juan
0.5	31	0
1	62	36
2	124	108
3	186	180
4	248	252

24b. **Travel Rates**

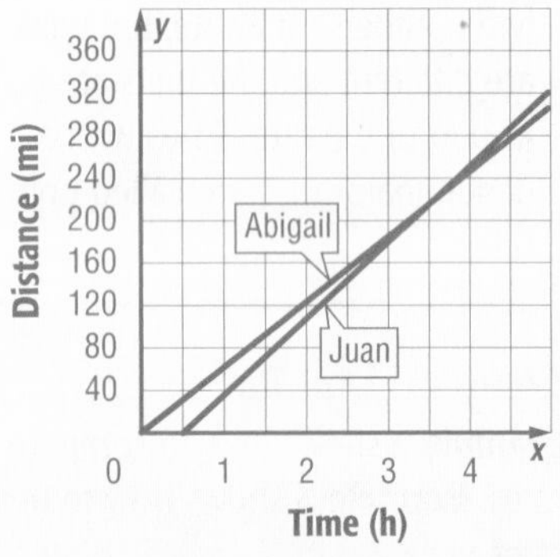

yes; The intersection point represents the time that Juan will catch up to and pass Abigail.

29. \$6.40; Sample answer: The unit rate for the 96 ounce container is \$0.05 per ounce. So, 128 ounces would cost $\$0.05 \times 128$ or \$6.40.

30. Sample answer: The horse runs about 19 yards per second and the sprinter runs about 8 yards per second. Since $19 > 8$, the horse is faster.

Check Your Understanding

Example 1 p. 270

Express each rate as a unit rate. Round to the nearest tenth, if necessary.

1. \$120 for 5 days of work **\$24 per day**
2. 275 miles on 14 gallons **19.6 miles per gallon**
3. 338 points in 16 games **21.1 points per game**
4. 6 pounds for \$19.49 **1 pound for \$3.25**
5. 17 gallons in 4 minutes **4.3 gallons per minute**
6. 180 feet in 19 seconds **9.5 feet per second**

Example 2 p. 271

7. **PEANUTS** Jamal is comparing prices of several different brands of peanuts. Which brand is the best buy? Explain.

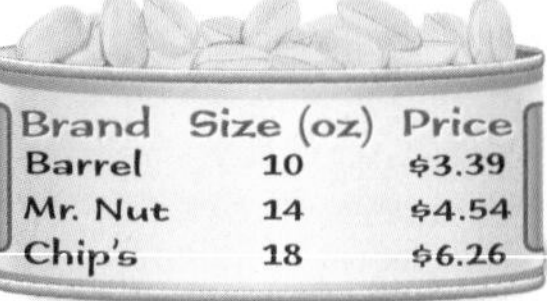

Brand	Size (oz)	Price
Barrel	10	\$3.39
Mr. Nut	14	\$4.54
Chip's	18	\$6.26

7. Mr. Nut; Sample answer: Barrel costs \$0.34 per ounce, Mr. Nut costs \$0.32 per ounce, and Chip's cost \$0.35 per ounce.

Example 3 p. 271

8. **DRIVING** Aisha drove 170 miles in 2.5 hours. At this same rate, how far will she drive in 4 hours? **272 mi**

Practice and Problem Solving

● = **Step-by-Step Solutions** begin on page R11. **Extra Practice** begins on page 810.

Example 1 p. 270

Express each rate as a unit rate. Round to the nearest tenth, if necessary.

9. 156 students in 6 classes **26 students per class**
10. 424 Calories in 3 servings **141.3 Calories per serving**
11. 147.5 miles in 2.5 hours **59 miles per hour**
12. \$29.95 for 4 DVDs **\$7.49 per DVD**
13. \$231 for 3 game tickets **\$77 per ticket**
14. 5 tablespoons in 4 quarts **1.3 tablespoons per quart**
15. \$97.50 for 15 pizzas **1 pizza for \$6.50**
16. 400 meters in 58 seconds **6.9 meters per second**

Example 2 p. 271

17. **PARTIES** The Party Planner sells 10 paper plates for \$2.50. Use the table at the right to determine which company sells paper plates for the same price per plate. **Party Time**

Store	Number of Plates	Price
Party Time	15	\$3.75
Good Times	20	\$6.00
Birthday, Inc.	25	\$7.50

18. **ARCHITECTURE** Building A has 7500 square feet of office space for 320 employees. Building B has 9500 square feet of office space for 370 employees. Which building has more square feet of space per employee?

18. Building B; Sample answer: Building A has 23.44 ft^2 of office space per person and Building B has 25.68 ft^2 of space per person.

Example 3 p. 271

19. **PRODUCE** A farmers market sells ears of sweet corn. At this same rate, how much will it cost to buy 28 ears of sweet corn? **\$12.25**

20. **RECIPES** A recipe that makes 2 dozen cookies calls for $\frac{3}{4}$ cup sugar. How much sugar is needed to make $4\frac{1}{2}$ dozen cookies? $1\frac{11}{16}$ **c**

21. **SWIMMING** Which swimmer shown in the table has the fastest rate? **Jenny**

B

Swimmer	Jenny	Dana	Kaitlin
Event	50 m	100 m	200 m
Time (s)	25.02	119.2	248.07

Differentiated Homework Options

Level	Assignment	Two-Day Option	
AL Basic	9–20, 26–28, 30–47	9–19 odd, 31–34	10–20 even, 26–28, 30, 35–47
OL Core	9–19 odd, 21–28, 30–47	9–20, 31–34	21–28, 30, 35–47
BL Advanced	21–41 (optional: 42–47)		

Real-World Link

The term *salinity* refers to the amount of salt in water. The salinity of Earth's oceans is about 525 grams of dissolved salt for every 15 kilograms of water.

Source: Dolphins Plus

22. **ESTIMATION** A gallon of milk sells for \$3.18, and a quart of milk sells for \$0.76. Which item has the better unit price? Justify your answer using two different methods. **See margin.**

23. **SPORTS** The line graph shows Alicia's and Jermaine's average rates in a race.

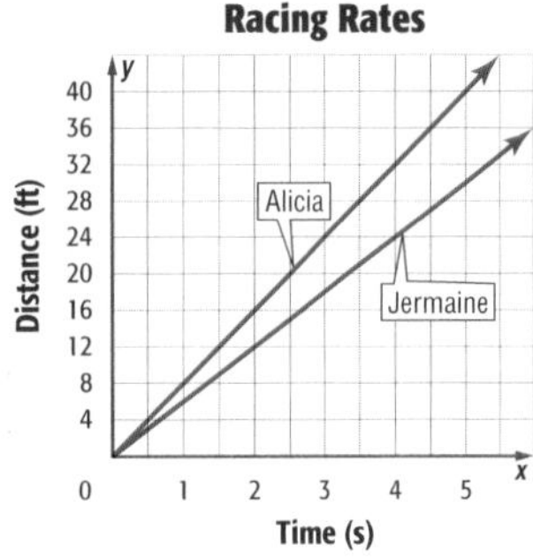

a. Express each person's speed as a unit rate.

b. How long would it take Alicia and Jermaine each to run 1 mile? (*Hint:* One mile = 5280 feet)

c. Suppose Max runs at a rate of 5 feet per second. Predict where the line representing his speed would be graphed. Explain.

24. **MULTIPLE REPRESENTATIONS** In this problem, you will explore rates. Abigail left Charlotte, North Carolina, 30 minutes before Juan to travel to Greenville, South Carolina. Two and a half hours after Abigail left, she had traveled 155 miles and Juan had traveled 144 miles. **a-b. See margin.**

a. **TABULAR** Make a function table to show how far each person has traveled after 1, 2, 3, and 4 hours.

b. **GRAPHICAL** Make a graph of the data. Do the two lines intersect? If so, what does this intersection point represent?

25. **EARTH SCIENCE** Use the information at the left to find the grams of salt for every gram of ocean water. **0.035 gram of salt for every gram of water.**

H.O.T. Problems

Use **H**igher-**O**rder **T**hinking Skills

26. **OPEN ENDED** Give a real-world example of a rate for a unit rate of 40 miles per hour.

27. **REASONING** In which situation will the rate $\frac{x \text{ miles}}{y \text{ hours}}$ decrease? Give an example to explain your reasoning.

a. x increases, y is unchanged

b. x is unchanged, y increases

28. **FIND THE ERROR** Nadia and Josef are writing the rate \$15.75 for 4 pounds as a unit rate. Is either of them correct? Explain your reasoning.

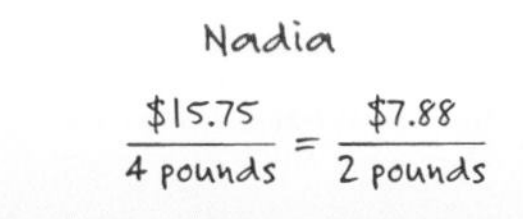

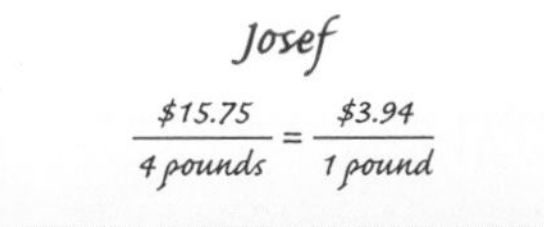

29. **CHALLENGE** A 96-ounce container of orange juice costs \$4.80. At what price should a 128-ounce container be sold in order for the unit rate for both containers to be the same? Explain your reasoning. **29–30. See margin.**

30. **WRITING IN MATH** Explain why a horse that runs $\frac{3}{4}$ mile in 1 minute and 9 seconds is faster than a sprinter who runs a 100-yard dash in 12 seconds.

23a. Alicia: 8 feet per second, Jermaine: 6 feet per second

23b. Alicia: 660 s or 11 min; Jermaine: 880 s or 14 min 40 s

23c. His time would be just below Jermaine's because he ran at a slower speed than him.

26. Sample answer: A freight train traveled 120 miles in 3 hours.

27. situation b; Sample answer: $\frac{120 \text{ mi}}{2\text{h}} = \frac{60 \text{ mi}}{1 \text{ h}}$, $\frac{120 \text{ mi}}{3\text{h}} = \frac{40 \text{ mi}}{1 \text{ h}}$

28. Josef; Sample answer: A unit rate must have a denominator of 1. Nadia incorrectly divided by 2 instead of by 4.

Watch Out!

Find the Error In Exercise 28, students should see that both Nadia and Josef have found rates. However, a unit rate has a denominator of 1.

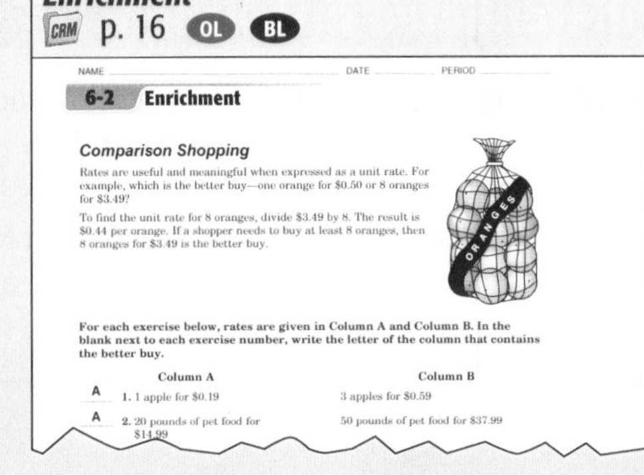

Enrichment
CRM p. 16 OL BL

NAME ______ DATE ______ PERIOD ______

6-2 Enrichment

Comparison Shopping

Rates are useful and meaningful when expressed as a unit rate. For example, which is the better buy—one orange for \$0.50 or 8 oranges for \$3.49?

To find the unit rate for 8 oranges, divide \$3.49 by 8. The result is \$0.44 per orange. If a shopper needs to buy at least 8 oranges, then 8 oranges for \$3.49 is the better buy.

For each exercise below, rates are given in Column A and Column B. In the blank next to each exercise number, write the letter of the column that contains the better buy.

	Column A	Column B
A	1. 1 apple for \$0.19	3 apples for \$0.59
A	2. 20 pounds of pet food for \$14.99	50 pounds of pet food for \$37.99

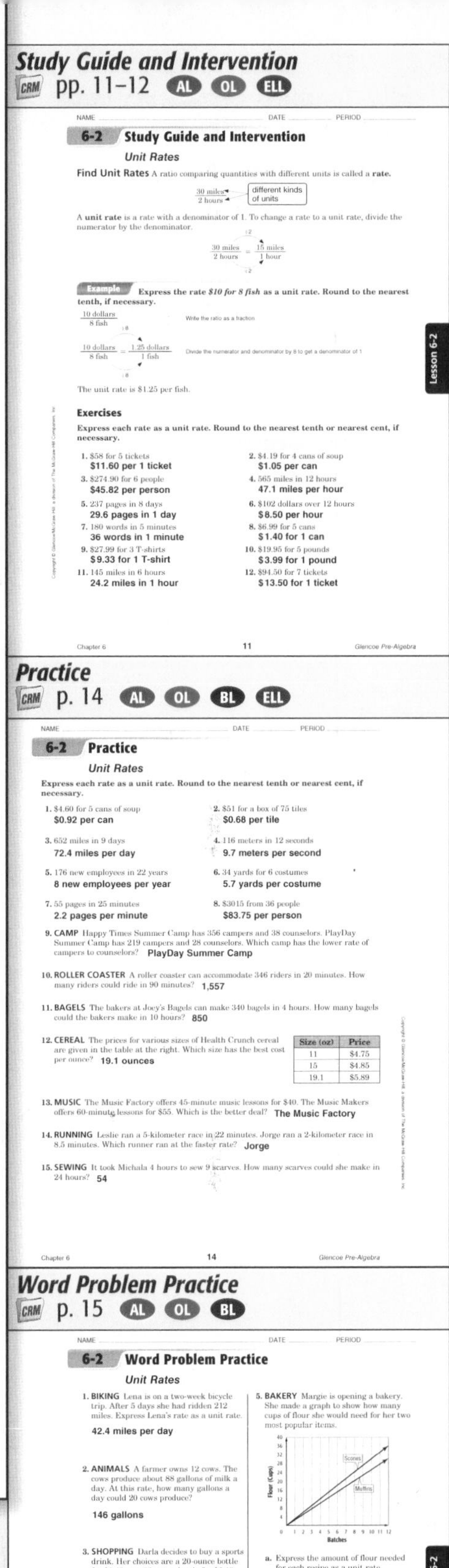

Study Guide and Intervention
CRM pp. 11–12 AL OL ELL

NAME ______ DATE ______ PERIOD ______

6-2 Study Guide and Intervention

Unit Rates

Find Unit Rates A ratio comparing quantities with different units is called a **rate.**

$\frac{30 \text{ miles}}{2 \text{ hours}}$ ← different kinds of units

A **unit rate** is a rate with a denominator of 1. To change a rate to a unit rate, divide the numerator by the denominator.

$\frac{30 \text{ miles}}{2 \text{ hours}} = \frac{15 \text{ miles}}{1 \text{ hour}}$ (÷2)

Example **Express the rate *\$10 for 8 fish* as a unit rate. Round to the nearest tenth, if necessary.**

$\frac{10 \text{ dollars}}{8 \text{ fish}}$ Write the ratio as a fraction

$\frac{10 \text{ dollars}}{8 \text{ fish}} = \frac{1.25 \text{ dollars}}{1 \text{ fish}}$ (÷8) Divide the numerator and denominator by 8 to get a denominator of 1

The unit rate is \$1.25 per fish.

Exercises

Express each rate as a unit rate. Round to the nearest tenth or nearest cent, if necessary.

1. \$58 for 5 tickets **\$11.60 per 1 ticket**
2. \$4.19 for 4 cans of soup **\$1.05 per can**
3. \$274.90 for 6 people **\$45.82 per person**
4. 565 miles in 12 hours **47.1 miles per hour**
5. 237 pages in 8 days **29.6 pages in 1 day**
6. \$102 dollars over 12 hours **\$8.50 per hour**
7. 180 words in 5 minutes **36 words in 1 minute**
8. \$6.99 for 5 cans **\$1.40 for 1 can**
9. \$27.99 for 3 T-shirts **\$9.33 for 1 T-shirt**
10. \$19.95 for 5 pounds **\$3.99 for 1 pound**
11. 145 miles in 6 hours **24.2 miles in 1 hour**
12. \$94.50 for 7 tickets **\$13.50 for 1 ticket**

Lesson 6-2

Chapter 6 11 Glencoe Pre-Algebra

Practice
CRM p. 14 AL OL BL ELL

NAME ______ DATE ______ PERIOD ______

6-2 Practice

Unit Rates

Express each rate as a unit rate. Round to the nearest tenth or nearest cent, if necessary.

1. \$4.60 for 5 cans of soup **\$0.92 per can**
2. \$51 for a box of 75 tiles **\$0.68 per tile**
3. 652 miles in 9 days **72.4 miles per day**
4. 116 meters in 12 seconds **9.7 meters per second**
5. 176 new employees in 22 years **8 new employees per year**
6. 34 yards for 6 costumes **5.7 yards per costume**
7. 55 pages in 25 minutes **2.2 pages per minute**
8. \$3015 from 36 people **\$83.75 per person**

9. **CAMP** Happy Times Summer Camp has 356 campers and 38 counselors. PlayDay Summer Camp has 219 campers and 28 counselors. Which camp has the lower rate of campers to counselors? **PlayDay Summer Camp**

10. **ROLLER COASTER** A roller coaster can accommodate 346 riders in 20 minutes. How many riders could ride in 90 minutes? **1,557**

11. **BAGELS** The bakers at Joey's Bagels can make 340 bagels in 4 hours. How many bagels could the bakers make in 10 hours? **850**

12. **CEREAL** The prices for various sizes of Health Crunch cereal are given in the table at the right. Which size has the best cost per ounce? **19.1 ounces**

Size (oz)	Price
11	\$4.75
15	\$4.85
19.1	\$5.89

13. **MUSIC** The Music Factory offers 45-minute music lessons for \$40. The Music Makers offers 60-minute lessons for \$55. Which is the better deal? **The Music Factory**

14. **RUNNING** Leslie ran a 5-kilometer race in 22 minutes. Jorge ran a 2-kilometer race in 8.5 minutes. Which runner ran at the faster rate? **Jorge**

15. **SEWING** It took Michala 4 hours to sew 9 scarves. How many scarves could she make in 24 hours? **54**

Chapter 6 14 Glencoe Pre-Algebra

Word Problem Practice
CRM p. 15 AL OL BL

NAME ______ DATE ______ PERIOD ______

6-2 Word Problem Practice

Unit Rates

1. **BIKING** Lena is on a two-week bicycle trip. After 5 days she had ridden 212 miles. Express Lena's rate as a unit rate.

42.4 miles per day

2. **ANIMALS** A farmer owns 12 cows. The cows produce about 88 gallons of milk a day. At this rate, how many gallons a day could 20 cows produce?

146 gallons

3. **SHOPPING** Darla decides to buy a sports drink. Her choices are a 20-ounce bottle for \$1.49 or a 32-ounce bottle for \$2.49. Which is the better value? Explain.

Since the 20-ounce bottle costs 7.5 cents per ounce and the 32-ounce bottle costs 7.8 cents per ounce, the 20-ounce bottle is the better value.

4. **MOVIES** FastFilms Video allows you to rent up to 6 movies a month for a flat rate of \$17.75. Videos by Mail allows you to rent up to 8 movies for \$25.00. Which company offers the better value?

FastFilms

5. **BAKERY** Margie is opening a bakery. She made a graph to show how many cups of flour she would need for her two most popular items.

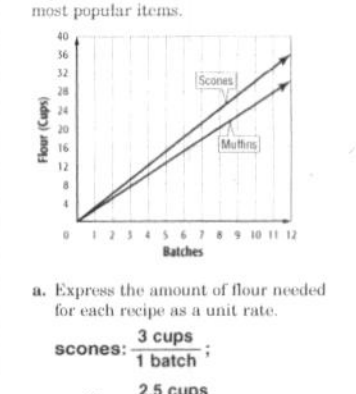

a. Express the amount of flour needed for each recipe as a unit rate.

scones: $\frac{3 \text{ cups}}{1 \text{ batch}}$; muffins: $\frac{2.5 \text{ cups}}{1 \text{ batch}}$

b. How many cups of flour would be needed to make 30 batches of each recipe?

scones: 90 cups; muffins: 75 cups

c. Margie has created a new oatmeal cookie recipe that requires $2\frac{3}{4}$ cups of flour per batch. Predict where the line representing this recipe would be graphed. Explain.

The line representing the new recipe would be graphed exactly halfway between the lines for scones and muffins. The amount of flour needed for one batch of the new recipe is $\frac{1}{4}$ cup more than is needed for the muffins and $\frac{1}{4}$ cup less than is needed for the scones.

Lesson 6-2

Chapter 6 15 Glencoe Pre-Algebra

TEACH with TECH

DIGITAL CAMERA Ask students to take pictures of advertisements or other real-world examples of rates. Then have them find the unit rate for each. Post examples on your class Web site or blog.

ASSESS

Crystal Ball Have students write about how they think what they learned about unit rates will connect to tomorrow's lesson on converting rates and measurements.

Tips for New Teachers

Rates Remind students that a rate is a ratio and that a unit rate is both a ratio and a rate.

Standardized Test Practice

31. On Monday, Ms. Moseley drove 340 miles in 5 hours. On Tuesday, she drove 198 miles in 3 hours. Based on these rates, which statement is true? **B**

A Her rate on Monday was 2 miles per hour slower than her rate on Tuesday.

B Her rate on Tuesday was 2 miles per hour slower than her rate on Monday.

C Her rate on Monday was the same as her rate on Tuesday.

D Her rate on Tuesday was 2 miles per hour faster than her rate on Monday.

32. Kalyin keyboards at a rate of 60 words per minute for 5 minutes and 45 words per minute for 10 minutes. How many words did she type in all? **J**

F 105 H 650

G 510 J 750

33. EXTENDED RESPONSE The table shows the costs of different sized bags of snack mix.

Snack Mix	
Size	**Price**
x-small	$1.96 for 12 oz
small	$2.20 for 16 oz
large	$4.00 for 36 oz
x-large	$5.40 for 48 oz

a. Which size is the most expensive per ounce? **x-small**

b. Pilar wants to buy the one that costs the least per ounce. What size should she buy? Explain. **Large; it has the least cost per ounce.**

34. Sal paid $2.79 for a gallon of milk. Find the cost per quart of milk at this rate. **B**

A $0.55 C $0.93

B $0.70 D $1.40

Spiral Review

Express each ratio as a fraction in simplest form. (Lesson 6-1)

35. 155 apples to 75 oranges $\frac{31}{15}$

36. 7 cups to 9 pints $\frac{7}{18}$

37. 11 gallons to 11 quarts $\frac{4}{1}$

38. 900 pounds to 16 tons $\frac{9}{320}$

39. WEB SITES A company pays Dante to advertise on his web site. The web site earns $10 per month plus $0.05 each time a visitor to the site clicks on the advertisement. What is the least number of clicks he needs to make $45 per month or more from this advertiser? (Lesson 5-5) **700 clicks**

40. SUBMARINES The research submarine *Alvin*, used to locate the wreck of the *Titanic*, descended at a rate of about 100 feet per minute. Write an integer to represent the distance *Alvin* traveled in 5 minutes. (Lesson 2-4) **−500 ft**

41. Evaluate $a - b + c$ if $a = 5$, $b = 7$, and $c = 10$. (Lesson 2-3) **8**

Skills Review

Complete. (Previous Course)

42. 36 in. = ■ ft **3**

43. 4 yd = ■ in. **144**

44. ■ fl oz = 6 c **48**

45. ■ m = 4 cm **0.04**

46. 476 mL = ■ L **0.476**

47. 3.5 km = ■ m **3500**

Differentiated Instruction

BL

Extension Present students with the following problem: A family of four is planning a trip to Florida, which is 658 miles from their home. They plan to take 2.5 days to drive to Florida, spend 7 days there, and take 2.5 days to drive home. They have $5,000 to spend on their vacation. How many miles per day will they have to travel to get to Florida in that length of time? To the nearest dollar, how much money can they spend per day on their vacation including the days of travel? 263.2 miles per day; $417 per day

274 Chapter 6 Ratio, Proportion, and Similar Figures

6-3 Converting Rates and Measurements

Then
You have already learned to find unit rates. (Lesson 6-2)

Now
- Convert rates using dimensional analysis.
- Convert between systems of measurement.

New Vocabulary
dimensional analysis

Math Online
glencoe.com
- Extra Examples
- Personal Tutor
- Self-Check Quiz
- Homework Help

Why?

The record for the fastest land car speed was set at about 760 miles per hour in Black Rock Desert, Nevada, by a thrust powered race car.

a. How many minutes are in 1 hour? **60 min**

b. Write a ratio that compares 1 hour to the number of minutes in 1 hour. $\frac{1\text{ h}}{60\text{ min}}$

Dimensional Analysis **Dimensional analysis** is the process of including units of measurement as factors when you compute. For example, you know that 1 hour = 60 minutes. You can write conversion factors $\frac{1\text{ hour}}{60\text{ minutes}}$ or $\frac{60\text{ minutes}}{1\text{ hour}}$. Each ratio is equivalent to 1 because the numerator and denominator represent the same amount.

Real-World EXAMPLE 1 Use Dimensional Analysis

Convert 760 miles per hour to miles per minute.

Step 1 You need to convert miles per hour to miles per minute. Choose a conversion factor that converts hours to minutes, with minutes in the denominator.

$$\frac{\text{miles}}{\cancel{\text{hour}}} \cdot \frac{\cancel{\text{hour}}}{\text{minute}} = \frac{\text{miles}}{\text{minute}}$$

So, use $\frac{1\text{ h}}{60\text{ min}}$.

Step 2 Multiply.

$\frac{760\text{ mi}}{1\text{ h}} = \frac{760\text{ mi}}{1\text{ h}} \cdot \frac{1\text{ h}}{60\text{ min}}$ **Multiply by $\frac{1\text{ h}}{60\text{ min}}$.**

$= \frac{760\text{ mi}}{\cancel{1\text{ h}}_1} \cdot \frac{\cancel{1\text{ h}}^1}{60\text{ min}}$ **Divide out common units.**

$= \frac{760\text{ mi}}{60\text{ min}}$ **Multiply.**

≈ 12.7 **Divide.**

So, the car traveled about 12.7 miles per minute.

Check Your Progress

1. **MONEY** The average teenager spends $1742 per year on fashion related items. How much is this per week? **$33.50**

Personal Tutor glencoe.com

6-3 Lesson Notes

1 FOCUS

Vertical Alignment

Before Lesson 6-3
Learn how to find unit rates.

Lesson 6-3
Convert rates using dimensional analysis. Convert between systems of measurement.

After Lesson 6-3
Solve problems involving scale drawings and models.

2 TEACH

Scaffolding Questions

Have students read the *Why?* section of the lesson and answer the questions.

Ask:
- How many seconds are in one minute? 60 seconds
- How many seconds are in one hour? 3,600 seconds
- What operation would you use to determine how many miles per minute the race car was moving? division

Lesson 6-3 Resources

Resource	Approaching-Level	On-Level	Beyond-Level	English Learners
Teacher Edition			• Differentiated Instruction, p. 280	• Differentiated Instruction, p. 276
Chapter Resource Masters	• Study Guide and Intervention, pp. 17–18 • Skills Practice, p. 19 • Practice, p. 20 • Word Problem Practice, p. 21	• Study Guide and Intervention, pp. 17–18 • Skills Practice, p. 19 • Practice, p. 20 • Word Problem Practice, p. 21 • Enrichment, p. 22	• Practice, p. 20 • Word Problem Practice, p. 21 • Enrichment, p. 22	• Study Guide and Intervention, pp. 17–18 • Skills Practice, p. 19 • Practice, p. 20
Transparencies	• 5-Minute Check Transparency 6-3	• 5-Minute Check Transparency 6-3	• 5-Minute Check Transparency 6-3	• 5-Minute Check Transparency 6-3
Other	• Study Notebook • Teaching Pre-Algebra with Manipulatives	• Study Notebook • Teaching Pre-Algebra with Manipulatives	• Study Notebook	• Study Notebook • Teaching Pre-Algebra with Manipulatives

Dimensional Analysis

Example 1 shows how to use dimensional analysis. **Example 2** shows how to convert rates.

Formative Assessment

Use the Check Your Progress exercises after each example to determine students' understanding of concepts.

Additional Examples

1. Convert 520 miles per year to miles per month. 43.3 miles per month

2. **SWIMMING POOL** A swimming pool is being filled with water at about 300 gallons per hour. How many quarts per second is this? 0.3 quarts per second

Additional Examples also in Interactive Classroom PowerPoint® Presentations

IWB INTERACTIVE WHITEBOARD READY

Tips for New Teachers

Dimensional Analysis If students are struggling with dimensional analysis, have students write down the rate they want to convert. Leave space to show the conversion factors they need. Then write an equal sign followed by the units of the answer. Color code the units in the problem and the answer. Fill in with color-coded conversion factors. Make sure that colors will divide out, leaving only the colors needed in the answer. Then simplify.

Real-World EXAMPLE 2 Convert Rates

SPORTS **Tyree and three friends attend skydiving class before their first jump. The instructor tells them they will travel at about 176 feet per second. How many miles per hour is this?**

You need to convert feet per second to miles per hour.

Use 1 mi = 5280 ft and 1 h = 3600 s.

$$\frac{176 \text{ ft}}{1 \text{ s}} = \frac{176 \text{ ft}}{1 \text{ s}} \cdot \frac{1 \text{ mi}}{5280 \text{ ft}} \cdot \frac{3600 \text{ s}}{1 \text{ h}}$$ **Multiply by $\frac{1 \text{ mi}}{5280 \text{ ft}}$ and $\frac{3600 \text{ s}}{1 \text{ h}}$.**

$$= \frac{\overset{1}{\cancel{176 \text{ ft}}}}{1 \cancel{\text{s}}} \cdot \frac{1 \text{ mi}}{\underset{\underset{1}{30}}{\cancel{5280 \text{ ft}}}} \cdot \frac{\overset{120}{\cancel{3600 \text{ s}}}}{1 \text{ h}}$$ **Divide the common factors and units.**

$$= \frac{120 \text{ mi}}{1 \text{ h}}$$ **Simplify.**

So, 176 feet per second is equivalent to 120 miles per hour.

Watch Out!

Common Units Make sure that you choose conversion factors that allow you to divide out the common units.

Check Your Progress

2. **TRAINS** The TGV is a high speed rail train in France. At top speed, it runs at an average of 320 kilometers per hour. How many meters per second is this? $88\frac{8}{9}$ meters per second

Personal Tutor glencoe.com

Convert Between Systems The table shows conversion factors between the Customary and Metric systems for units of length, capacity, and mass or weight.

Key Concept Measurement Conversions

For Your FOLDABLE

Customary to Metric	Metric to Customary
Length	
1 in. ≈ 2.540 cm	1 cm ≈ 0.394 in.
1 ft ≈ 0.305 m	1 m ≈ 3.279 ft
1 yd ≈ 0.914 m	1 m ≈ 1.094 yd
1 mi ≈ 1.609 km	1 km ≈ 0.621 mi
Capacity	
Customary to Metric	**Metric to Customary**
1 fl oz ≈ 29.574 mL	1 mL ≈ 0.034 fl oz
1 pt ≈ 0.473 L	1 L ≈ 2.114 pt
1 qt ≈ 0.946 L	1 L ≈ 1.057 qt
1 gal ≈ 3.785 L	1 L ≈ 0.264 gal
Mass or Weight	
Customary to Metric	**Metric to Customary**
1 oz ≈ 28.350 g	1 g ≈ 0.035 oz
1 lb ≈ 0.454 kg	1 kg ≈ 2.203 lb

You can also use dimensional analysis to convert between measurement systems. The two conversion factors $\frac{1 \text{ ft}}{0.305 \text{ m}}$ and $\frac{0.305 \text{ m}}{1 \text{ ft}}$ use the same conversion. Use the factor that will correctly divide out the appropriate common unit.

Differentiated Instruction

ELL

Kinesthetic Many students come from other countries and have limited experience with the customary system of measurement. Allow them time to explore different measurement tools (cm/inch ruler, meter and yard sticks), and learn the units. Then allow them to discuss the difference between 60 miles per hour and 60 kilometers per hour. Which one is faster? Similar activities with bottles and cans can be used to compare capacity measurements.

EXAMPLE 3 Convert Measurements Between Systems

Complete each conversion. Round to the nearest hundredth.

a. 12 centimeters to inches

Use 1 in. ≈ 2.54 centimeters.

$12 \text{ cm} \approx 12 \text{ cm} \cdot \frac{1 \text{ in.}}{2.54 \text{ cm}}$ — Multiply by $\frac{1 \text{ in.}}{2.54 \text{ cm}}$.

$\approx 12 \cancel{\text{cm}} \cdot \frac{1 \text{ in.}}{2.54 \cancel{\text{cm}}}$ — Divide out common units, leaving the desired unit, inch.

$\approx \frac{12 \text{ in.}}{2.54}$ or 4.72 in. — Simplify.

So, 12 centimeters is approximately 4.72 inches.

b. 4 quarts to liters

Use 1 qt ≈ 0.946 L.

$4 \text{ qt} \approx 4 \text{ qt} \cdot \frac{0.946 \text{ L}}{1 \text{ qt}}$ — Multiply by $\frac{0.946 \text{ L}}{1 \text{ qt}}$.

$\approx 4 \cancel{\text{qt}} \cdot \frac{0.946 \text{ L}}{1 \cancel{\text{qt}}}$ — Divide out common units, leaving the desired unit, quart.

$\approx 4 \cdot 0.946$ L or 3.784 L — Simplify.

So, 4 quarts is approximately 3.78 liters.

Check Your Progress

3A. 6 mi ≈ ■ km **9.65** **3B.** 12 oz ≈ ■ g **340.20** **3C.** 11 yd ≈ ■ m **10.05**

Personal Tutor glencoe.com

Real-World Link

At top speed, a giant tortoise can travel about 900 feet per hour.

Source: San Diego Zoo

Real-World EXAMPLE 4 Convert Rates Between Systems

ANIMALS Use the information at the left to determine how many centimeters per second a giant tortoise travels at top speed.

To convert feet to centimeters, use 1 ft = 12 in. and 1 in. ≈ 2.54 cm.

To convert hours to seconds, use 1 h = 60 min and 1 min = 60 s.

$\frac{900 \text{ ft}}{1 \text{ h}} \cdot \frac{12 \text{ in.}}{1 \text{ ft}} \cdot \frac{2.54 \text{ cm}}{1 \text{ in.}} \cdot \frac{1 \text{ h}}{60 \text{ min}} \cdot \frac{1 \text{min}}{60 \text{ s}}$

$= \frac{900 \cancel{\text{ft}}}{1 \cancel{\text{h}}} \cdot \frac{12 \cancel{\text{in.}}}{1 \cancel{\text{ft}}} \cdot \frac{2.54 \text{ cm}}{1 \cancel{\text{in.}}} \cdot \frac{1 \cancel{\text{h}}}{60 \cancel{\text{min}}} \cdot \frac{1 \cancel{\text{min}}}{60 \text{ s}}$ — Divide out common units.

$= \frac{27{,}432 \text{ cm}}{3600 \text{ s}}$ — Multiply.

$= \frac{7.62 \text{ cm}}{1 \text{ s}}$ — Divide.

At top speed, a giant tortoise will travel 7.62 centimeters per second.

Check Your Progress

4. SPORTS At a recent Winter Olympics, USA short track speed skater Apolo Ohno won a gold medal by skating about 12 meters per second. Rounded to the nearest hundredth, how many miles per hour is this? **26.83 mph**

Personal Tutor glencoe.com

Convert Between Systems

Example 3 shows how to convert measurements between systems. **Example 4** shows how to convert rates between systems.

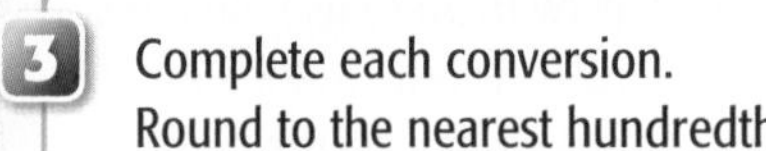

3 Complete each conversion. Round to the nearest hundredth.

a. 4 pounds to kilograms 1.82 kg

b. 15 meters to feet 49.19 ft

4 **CYCLING** A cyclist is cycling about 3 kilometers per hour. Rounded to the nearest hundredth, how many feet per second is this? 2.73 feet per second

Focus on Mathematical Content

Converting Rates and Measurements Rates and measurements can be converted using dimensional analysis, a process of multiplying by factors that include units of measurements. For example, to convert 6 miles per hour into miles per minute, multiply by a conversion factor that eliminates the hour and leaves minutes in the denominator. The hours will cancel, leaving the answer in miles per minute.

$\frac{6 \text{ miles}}{1 \cancel{\text{hour}}} \times \frac{1 \cancel{\text{hour}}}{60 \text{ minutes}} = 0.1$ mile per minute.

Lesson 6-3 Converting Rates and Measurements 277

Tips for New Teachers

Measurement Conversions Suggest to students that they copy the measurement conversions onto an index card. This way they will not have to keep looking up the information as they work through the exercises. You may even allow them to use the index card on quizzes or tests as long as nothing else is written on the card.

3 PRACTICE

Formative Assessment

Use Exercises 1–9 to check for understanding.

Use the chart at the bottom of this page to customize assignments for your students.

Exercise Alert!

Throughout this lesson, answers can vary based on the conversion factor student's use.

Check Your Understanding

Example 1 p. 275

1. **RAINFORESTS** In Brazil, about 20 acres of rainforest are destroyed each minute. At this rate, how much rainforest is destroyed per day? **28,800 acres**

Example 2 p. 276

2. **FENCES** Lexi can paint 5 yards of fencing in one hour. At this rate, how many inches does she paint per minute? **3 inches per minute**

Example 3 p. 277

Complete each conversion. Round to the nearest hundredth.

3. 8 in. ≈ ■ cm **20.32**
4. 5 L ≈ ■ gal **1.32**
5. 15 oz ≈ ■ g **425.25**
6. 24 cm ≈ ■ in. **9.46**
7. 9 pt ≈ ■ L **4.26**
8. 3 m ≈ ■ ft **9.84**

Example 4 p. 277

9. **ELEPHANTS** An elephant can eat up to 440 pounds of vegetation every day. How many grams per minute is this? **138.72 grams per minute**

Practice and Problem Solving

● = **Step-by-Step Solutions** begin on page R11. **Extra Practice** begins on page 810.

Example 1 p. 275

10. **CANDY** A candy company can produce 4800 sour lemon candies per minute. How many candies can they produce each hour? **288,000 candies**
11. **RECYCLING** In a recent year, 51.9 billion aluminum cans were recycled. About how many cans per week is this? **1 billion cans per week**

Example 2 p. 276

12. **TELEVISION** The average American student spends almost 1500 hours per year watching television. How many minutes per day is this? **246.58 minutes per day**
13. **AMUSEMENT PARK** A thrill ride at an amusement park travels 55 miles per hour. How many feet per second is this? **80.67 feet per second**

Example 3 p. 277

Complete each conversion. Round to the nearest hundredth.

14. 4 L ≈ ■ qt **4.23**
15. 16 in. ≈ ■ cm **40.64**
16. 13 m ≈ ■ ft **42.62**
17. 8 yd ≈ ■ m **7.31**
18. 18 lb ≈ ■ kg **8.17**
19. 7 L ≈ ■ gal **1.85**
20. 1500 g ≈ ■ oz **52.91**
21. 15 ft ≈ ■ m **4.58**
22. 28 fl oz ≈ ■ mL **828.07**

Example 4 p. 277

23. **SCIENCE** The velocity of sound through wood at 0° Celsius is 1454 meters per second. How many miles is this per hour? **3250.68 miles per hour**
24. **CARS** A certain car in Canada can travel 15 kilometers per 1 liter of gasoline. How many miles per gallon is this? **35.28 miles per gallon**

Complete each conversion. Round to the nearest hundredth.

25. 8 in. ≈ ■ mm **203.2**
26. 16 L ≈ ■ c **67.65**
27. 2 km ≈ ■ yd **2188**
28. 250 fl oz ≈ ■ L **7.39**
29. 2750 g ≈ ■ lb **6.02**
30. 5 gal ≈ ■ mL **18,925**

B

31. **SPORTS** Crystal's times for each portion of a triathlon are shown in the table.

	Swim	Bike	Run
Distance (km)	1.5	40	10
Time (min)	40	86	64

a. How many meters per second did she run? **2.60 meters per second**

b. What was her speed in miles per hour for the aquabike portion (swimming and biking)? **12.27 miles per hour**

Differentiated Homework Options

Level	Assignment	Two-Day Option	
AL Basic	10–30, 45–47, 49–74	11–29 odd, 51–54	10–30 even, 45–47, 49, 50, 55–74
OL Core	11–35 odd, 36, 37–45 odd, 46, 47, 49–74	10–30, 51–54	31–47, 49, 50, 55–74
BL Advanced	31–70 (optional: 71–74)		

278 Chapter 6 Ratio, Proportion, and Similar Figures

Real-World Link

In the event of a fire, the Willis Tower has a sprinkler system to help extinguish the fire. The pumps that operate the system can pump up to 1500 gallons of water per minute.

Source: Willis Tower

Order each group of rates from least to greatest.

32. 100 oz/min, 2500 g/min, 10 lb/min **2500 g/min, 100 oz/min, 10 lb/min**

33. 500 m/h, 7 yd/min, 6 in./s **7 yd/min, 500 m/h, 6 in./s**

34. 32 mi/gal, 15 m/mL, 6600 yd/qt **6600 yd/qt, 32 mi/gal, 15 m/mL**

35. 500 kg/h, 5 oz/s, 18 lb/min **18 lb/min, 500 kg/h, 5 oz/s**

36. **ARCHITECTURE** Use the information at the left to determine how many liters of water the system in the Willis Tower could pump in $\frac{1}{4}$ minute. Round to the nearest hundredth. **1419.38 L**

37. **FOOD** The average American consumes 20 gallons of ice cream in one year. At this rate, how many liters of ice cream will 50 Americans consume in one week? Round to the nearest hundredth. **72.79 liters per week**

Replace each ● with <, >, or = to make a true sentence.

38. 10 m ● 390 in. **>**

39. 520 oz ● 15 kg **<**

40. 14 pt ● 6622 mL **=**

FINANCIAL LITERACY The table shows the exchange rate between the U.S. dollar and other currencies. Use dimensional analysis to make each conversion.

Exchange Rates Per 1 U.S. Dollar		
Country	**Currency**	**Rate**
European Union	euro	0.729
France	franc	4.784
Japan	yen	122.198
United Kingdom	pound	0.494

41. 150 dollars to euros **109.35 euro**

42. 275 dollars to pounds **135.85 pounds**

43. 90 dollars to yen **10,997.82 yen**

44. 500 francs to dollars **104.52 dollars**

H.O.T. Problems

Use **H**igher-**O**rder **T**hinking Skills

45. **OPEN ENDED** Give two examples of different measurements that are equivalent to 10 centimeters per second.
Sample answers: 600 centimeters per minute, 360 meters per hour

46. **WRITING IN MATH** Macha needs 120 square feet of carpeting for her bedroom. Explain how to use dimensional analysis to convert 120 square feet to square yards if 1 square yard is equal to 9 square feet.

47. **WHICH ONE DOESN'T BELONG?** Select the rate that does not have the same value as the other three. Explain your reasoning.

60 mi/h	88 ft/s	500 ft/min	1440 mi/day

48. **CHALLENGE** A recipe for fruit punch uses the ingredients shown. About how many cups of each ingredient are needed? Round to the nearest tenth.

Fruit Punch	
900 mL	cranberry juice
700 mL	apple juice
300 mL	pineapple juice
150 mL	lemon juice
900 mL	club soda

49. **REASONING** What property of multiplication allows you to multiply a rate by a conversion factor without changing its value? Explain.
Identity Property; the conversion factor is equal to 1.

50. **WRITING IN MATH** Explain how you would convert 10 miles per hour to meters per second.

46. Sample answer: Multiply 120 square feet by $\frac{1 \text{ square yard}}{9 \text{ square feet}}$. Divide out common units and simplify; $13\frac{1}{3}$ yd^2

47. 500 ft/min; Sample answer: All of the other rates are equal to 60 mi/h.

48. cranberry juice: 3.8 cups, apple juice: 3 cups, pineapple juice: 1.3 cups, lemon juice: 0.6 cup, club soda: 3.8 cups

50. Sample answer: Use dimensional analysis. Multiply $\frac{10 \text{ mi}}{1 \text{ h}}$ by $\frac{1 \text{ h}}{3600 \text{ s}}$ and $\frac{1.609 \text{ km}}{1 \text{ mi}}$ and $\frac{1000 \text{ m}}{1 \text{ km}}$ to get 4.47 meters per second.

Study Guide and Intervention

CRM pp. 17–18 AL OL ELL

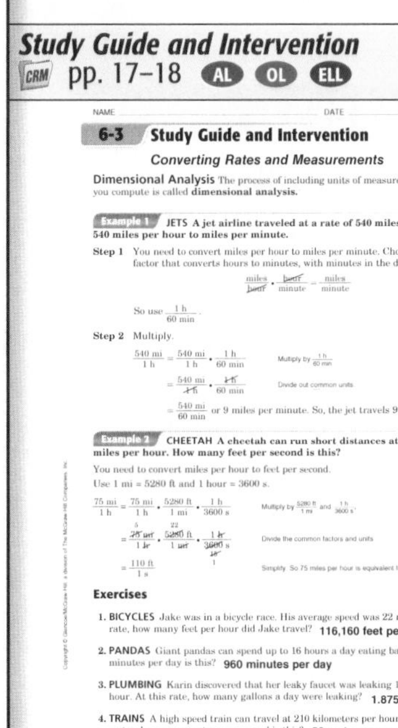

NAME ______ DATE ______ PERIOD ______

6-3 Study Guide and Intervention

Converting Rates and Measurements

Dimensional Analysis The process of including units of measurement as factors when you compute is called **dimensional analysis.**

Example 1 **JETS A jet airline traveled at a rate of 540 miles per hour. Convert 540 miles per hour to miles per minute.**

Step 1 You need to convert miles per hour to miles per minute. Choose a conversion factor that converts hours to minutes, with minutes in the denominator.

$$\frac{\text{miles}}{\text{hour}} \cdot \frac{\text{hour}}{\text{minute}} = \frac{\text{miles}}{\text{minute}}$$

So use $\frac{1 \text{ h}}{60 \text{ min}}$.

Step 2 Multiply.

$\frac{540 \text{ mi}}{1 \text{ h}} = \frac{540 \text{ mi}}{1 \text{ h}} \cdot \frac{1 \text{ h}}{60 \text{ min}}$ Multiply by $\frac{1 \text{ h}}{60 \text{ min}}$

$= \frac{540 \text{ mi}}{1 \text{ h}} \cdot \frac{1 \text{ h}}{60 \text{ min}}$ Divide out common units.

$= \frac{540 \text{ mi}}{60 \text{ min}}$ or 9 miles per minute. So, the jet travels 9 miles per minute.

Example 2 **CHEETAH A cheetah can run short distances at a speed of up to 75 miles per hour. How many feet per second is this?**

You need to convert miles per hour to feet per second.

Use 1 mi = 5280 ft and 1 hour = 3600 s.

$\frac{75 \text{ mi}}{1 \text{ h}} = \frac{75 \text{ mi}}{1 \text{ h}} \cdot \frac{5280 \text{ ft}}{1 \text{ mi}} \cdot \frac{1 \text{ h}}{3600 \text{ s}}$ Multiply by $\frac{5280 \text{ ft}}{1 \text{ mi}}$ and $\frac{1 \text{ h}}{3600 \text{ s}}$.

$= \frac{\overset{5}{75} \text{ mi}}{1 \text{ h}} \cdot \frac{\overset{22}{5280} \text{ ft}}{1 \text{ mi}} \cdot \frac{1 \text{ h}}{\underset{1}{\underset{18}{3600}} \text{ s}}$ Divide the common factors and units.

$= \frac{110 \text{ ft}}{1 \text{ s}}$ Simplify. So 75 miles per hour is equivalent to 110 feet per second.

Exercises

1. **BICYCLES** Jake was in a bicycle race. His average speed was 22 miles per hour. At this rate, how many feet per hour did Jake travel? **116,160 feet per hour**

2. **PANDAS** Giant pandas can spend up to 16 hours a day eating bamboo. How many minutes per day is this? **960 minutes per day**

3. **PLUMBING** Karin discovered that her leaky faucet was leaking 1.25 cups of water an hour. At this rate, how many gallons a day were leaking? **1.875 gallons per day**

4. **TRAINS** A high speed train can travel at 210 kilometers per hour. To the nearest whole meter, how many meters per second is this? **58 meters per second**

Chapter 6 17 Glencoe Pre-Algebra

Lesson 6-3

Practice

CRM p. 20 AL OL BL ELL

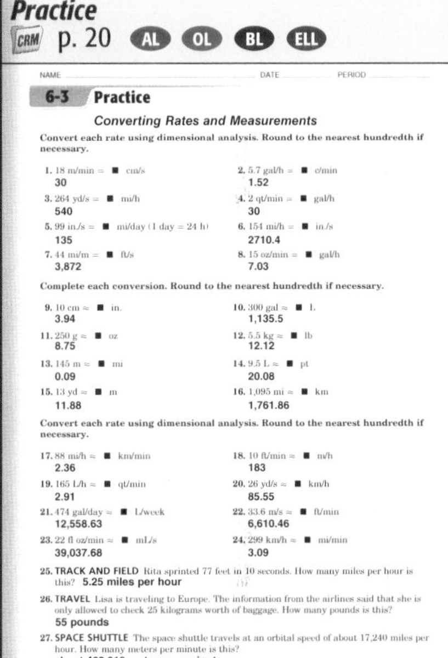

NAME ______ DATE ______ PERIOD ______

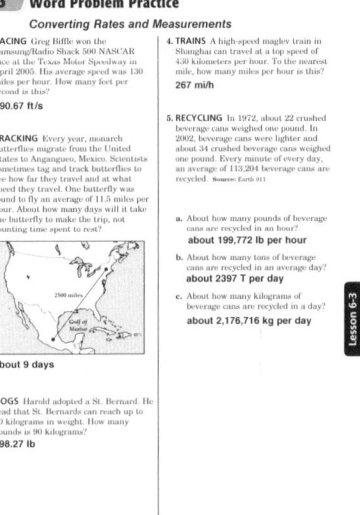

6-3 Practice

Converting Rates and Measurements

Convert each rate using dimensional analysis. Round to the nearest hundredth if necessary.

1. 18 m/min = ■ cm/s **30**
2. 5.7 gal/h = ■ c/min **1.52**
3. 264 yd/s = ■ mi/h **540**
4. 2 qt/min = ■ gal/h **30**
5. 99 in./s = ■ mi/day (1 day = 24 h) **135**
6. 154 mi/h = ■ in./s **2710.4**
7. 44 mi/m = ■ ft/s **3,872**
8. 15 oz/min = ■ gal/h **7.03**

Complete each conversion. Round to the nearest hundredth if necessary.

9. 10 cm ≈ ■ in. **3.94**
10. 300 gal ≈ ■ L **1,135.5**
11. 250 g ≈ ■ oz **8.75**
12. 5.5 kg ≈ ■ lb **12.12**
13. 145 m ≈ ■ mi **0.09**
14. 9.5 L ≈ ■ pt **20.08**
15. 13 yd ≈ ■ m **11.88**
16. 1,095 mi ≈ ■ km **1,761.86**

Convert each rate using dimensional analysis. Round to the nearest hundredth if necessary.

17. 88 mi/h ≈ ■ km/min **2.36**
18. 10 ft/min ≈ ■ m/h **183**
19. 165 L/h ≈ ■ qt/min **2.91**
20. 26 yd/s ≈ ■ km/h **85.55**
21. 474 gal/day ≈ ■ L/week **12,558.63**
22. 33.6 m/s ≈ ■ ft/min **6,610.46**
23. 22 fl oz/min ≈ ■ mL/s **39,037.68**
24. 299 km/h ≈ ■ mi/min **3.09**

25. **TRACK AND FIELD** Rita sprinted 77 feet in 10 seconds. How many miles per hour is this? **5.25 miles per hour**

26. **TRAVEL** Lisa is traveling to Europe. The information from the airlines said that she is only allowed to check 25 kilograms worth of baggage. How many pounds is this? **55 pounds**

27. **SPACE SHUTTLE** The space shuttle travels at an orbital speed of about 17,240 miles per hour. How many meters per minute is this? **about 462,319 meters per minute**

Chapter 6 20 Glencoe Pre-Algebra

Word Problem Practice

CRM p. 21 AL OL BL

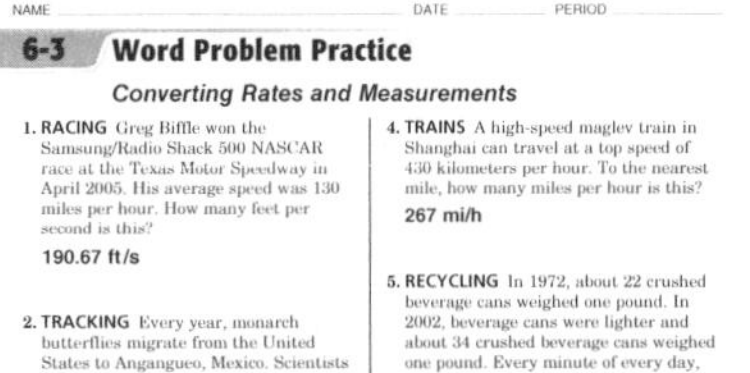

NAME ______ DATE ______ PERIOD ______

6-3 Word Problem Practice

Converting Rates and Measurements

1. **RACING** Greg Biffle won the Samsung/Radio Shack 500 NASCAR race at the Texas Motor Speedway in April 2005. His average speed was 130 miles per hour. How many feet per second is this? **190.67 ft/s**

2. **TRACKING** Every year, monarch butterflies migrate from the United States to Angangueo, Mexico. Scientists sometimes tag and track butterflies to see how far they travel and at what speed they travel. One butterfly was found to fly an average of 11.5 miles per hour. About how many days will it take the butterfly to make the trip, not counting time spent to rest?

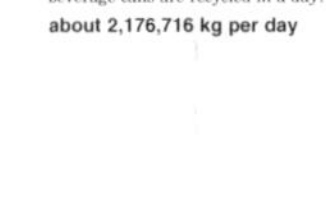

about 9 days

3. **DOGS** Harold adopted a St. Bernard. He read that St. Bernards can reach up to 90 kilograms in weight. How many pounds is 90 kilograms? **198.27 lb**

4. **TRAINS** A high-speed maglev train in Shanghai can travel at a top speed of 430 kilometers per hour. To the nearest mile, how many miles per hour is this? **267 mi/h**

5. **RECYCLING** In 1972, about 22 crushed beverage cans weighed one pound. In 2002, beverage cans were lighter and about 34 crushed beverage cans weighed one pound. Every minute of every day, an average of 113,204 beverage cans are recycled. Source: Earth 911

a. About how many pounds of beverage cans are recycled in an hour? **about 199,772 lb per hour**

b. About how many tons of beverage cans are recycled in an average day? **about 2397 T per day**

c. About how many kilograms of beverage cans are recycled in a day? **about 2,176,716 kg per day**

Chapter 6 21 Glencoe Pre-Algebra

Lesson 6-3

Enrichment

CRM p. 22 OL BL

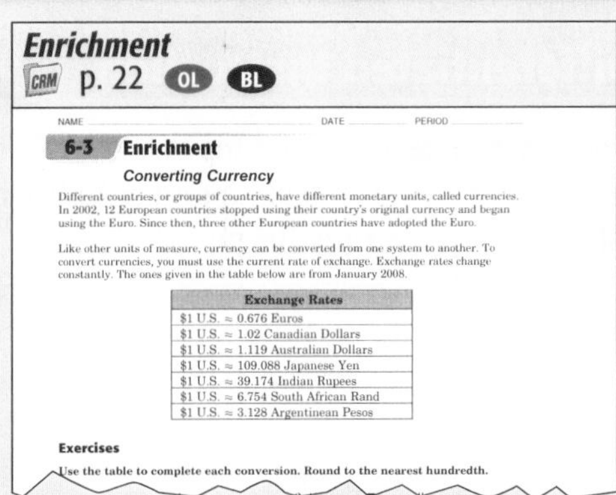

NAME ______ DATE ______ PERIOD ______

6-3 Enrichment

Converting Currency

Different countries, or groups of countries, have different monetary units, called currencies. In 2002, 12 European countries stopped using their country's original currency and began using the Euro. Since then, three other European countries have adopted the Euro.

Like other units of measure, currency can be converted from one system to another. To convert currencies, you must use the current rate of exchange. Exchange rates change constantly. The ones given in the table below are from January 2008.

Exchange Rates
\$1 U.S. ≈ 0.676 Euros
\$1 U.S. ≈ 1.02 Canadian Dollars
\$1 U.S. ≈ 1.119 Australian Dollars
\$1 U.S. ≈ 109.088 Japanese Yen
\$1 U.S. ≈ 39.174 Indian Rupees
\$1 U.S. ≈ 6.754 South African Rand
\$1 U.S. ≈ 3.128 Argentinean Pesos

Exercises

Use the table to complete each conversion. Round to the nearest hundredth.

4 ASSESS

Yesterday's News Have students write how yesterday's lesson on unit rates helped them understand today's lesson on converting rates and measurements.

Formative Assessment

Check for student understanding of the concepts in Lessons 6-1, 6-2, and 6-3.

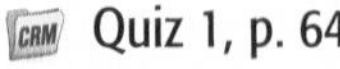 Quiz 1, p. 64

Additional Answer

59. The 6-pack of soda costs about \$0.37 per can. The 12-pack of soda costs about \$0.35 per can. So, the 12-pack is less expensive.

Standardized Test Practice

51. 55 miles per hour is the same rate as which of the following? **C**

A 34 kilometers per hour

B 50 kilometers per hour

C 88 kilometers per hour

D 98 kilometers per hour

52. A piece of notebook paper measures $8\frac{1}{2}$ inches by 11 inches. Which of the following metric approximations is the same? **H**

F 2 m by 2.8 m

G 3 cm by 4 cm

H 22 cm by 28 cm

J 30 m by 40 m

53. A car's mileage is registered at 29,345.5 miles. The driver sees a sign that warns of road work in 1000 feet. What will be the car's mileage when the road work begins? **A**

A 29,345.7

B 29,345.9

C 29,356.2

D 29,356.5

54. SHORT RESPONSE Convert 565 miles per hour to feet per second. Show the procedure you used.
Sample answer: Use dimensional analysis:

$$\frac{\overset{113}{\cancel{565}}\ \cancel{\text{mi}}}{1\ \cancel{\text{hr}}} \cdot \frac{\overset{22}{\cancel{5280}}\ \text{ft}}{1\ \cancel{\text{mi}}} \cdot \frac{1\ \cancel{\text{hr}}}{\underset{\underset{3}{\cancel{15}}}{\cancel{3600}}\ \text{s}} = \frac{2486}{3}$$ **or 828.67 feet per second**

Spiral Review

Express each rate as a unit rate. Round to the nearest tenth, if necessary. (Lesson 6-2)

55. \$183 for 4 concert tickets **\$45.75 per ticket**

56. 100 feet in 14.5 seconds **6.9 feet per second**

57. 254.1 miles on 10.5 gallons **24.2 miles per gallon**

58. 9 inches of snow in 12 hours **0.75 inches per hour**

59. SHOPPING Mrs. Gallagher wants to buy the package of soda that is less expensive per can. Which pack of sodas shown should she buy? Explain your reasoning. (Lesson 6-2) **See margin.**

Express each ratio as a fraction in simplest form. (Lesson 6-1)

60. 12 cars out of 30 vehicles $\frac{2}{5}$

61. 5 cups to 5 quarts $\frac{1}{4}$

62. 15 soccer balls out of 35 balls $\frac{3}{7}$

63. 8 pencils to 20 crayons $\frac{2}{5}$

ALGEBRA Solve each equation. Check your solution. (Lessons 4-3, 4-4)

64. $m - \frac{4}{5} = \frac{7}{10}$ $1\frac{1}{2}$

65. $-7.2 = 9b$ **−0.8**

66. $18 = \frac{2}{3}s$ **27**

67. $6\frac{4}{7} = d - \frac{11}{14}$ $7\frac{5}{14}$

68. $-8.37 = c + (-5.28)$ **−3.09**

69. $\frac{2}{3}t = \frac{1}{6}$ $\frac{1}{4}$

70. HAMBURGERS Clive is making hamburgers for a cookout. How many $\frac{1}{4}$-pound hamburgers can he make from $2\frac{3}{4}$ pounds of ground beef? (Lesson 3-4) **11 hamburgers**

Skills Review

Write each fraction in simplest form. (Previous Course)

71. $\frac{12}{15}$ $\frac{4}{5}$

72. $\frac{18}{24}$ $\frac{3}{4}$

73. $\frac{6}{26}$ $\frac{3}{13}$

74. $\frac{10}{25}$ $\frac{2}{5}$

Differentiated Instruction

Extension Your family takes a trip to Mexico. During your trip, the exchange rate for U.S. dollars to Mexican pesos is 1:11. You pay a cashier 40 U.S. dollars for a souvenir. What is your change in pesos if the souvenir costs 308 pesos? 132 pesos How much is that in U.S. dollars? 12 U.S. dollars

6-4 Proportional and Nonproportional Relationships

Then
You have already used unit rates to convert measurements. (Lesson 6-3)

Now
- Identify proportional and nonproportional relationships in tables and graphs.
- Describe a proportional relationship using an equation.

New Vocabulary
proportional
nonproportional
constant of proportionality

Math Online
glencoe.com
- Extra Examples
- Personal Tutor
- Self-Check Quiz
- Homework Help

Why?

Tom and Jenna are running laps around the gym. The number of laps each runner has completed is shown.

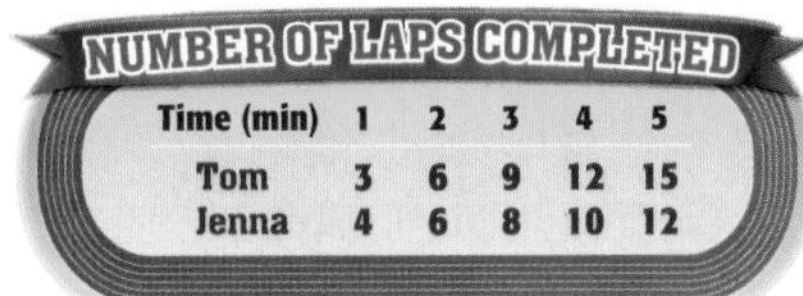

NUMBER OF LAPS COMPLETED

Time (min)	1	2	3	4	5
Tom	3	6	9	12	15
Jenna	4	6	8	10	12

a. For each minute, write a rate in simplest form that compares the number of laps completed by Tom to the time. $\frac{3}{1}, \frac{3}{1}, \frac{3}{1}, \frac{3}{1}, \frac{3}{1}$

b. Repeat for Jenna's times. $\frac{4}{1}, \frac{3}{1}, \frac{8}{3}, \frac{5}{2}, \frac{12}{5}$

c. What pattern(s) do you notice? See Chapter 6 Answer Appendix.

Identify Proportions Two quantities are **proportional** if they have a constant ratio or rate.

Tom's rates: $\frac{3}{1} = \frac{6}{2} = \frac{9}{3} = \frac{12}{4} = \frac{15}{5}$ Jenna's rates: $\frac{4}{1} \neq \frac{6}{2} \neq \frac{8}{3} \neq \frac{10}{4} \neq \frac{12}{5}$

The number of laps completed by Tom is proportional to the time. However, Jenna's rates are not constant. For relationships in which the ratios or rates are *not* constant, the two terms are said to be **nonproportional**.

EXAMPLE 1 Identify Proportional Relationships

Determine whether the cost of coffee is proportional to the number of pounds. Explain your reasoning.

Coffee (pounds)	1	2	3	4
Cost (dollars)	3	6	9	12

Write the rate of coffee to cost for each column in the table. Simplify each fraction.

$\frac{1}{3}$ $\frac{2}{6} = \frac{1}{3}$ $\frac{3}{9} = \frac{1}{3}$ $\frac{4}{12} = \frac{1}{3}$ All the rates are equal.

The number of pounds is proportional to the cost.

Check Your Progress

1. Determine whether the number of legs are proportional to the number of spiders. Explain your reasoning. yes; Each rate is equal to $\frac{1}{8}$.

Number of Spiders	1	2	3	4
Number of Legs	8	16	24	32

Personal Tutor glencoe.com

6-4 Lesson Notes

1 FOCUS

Vertical Alignment

Before Lesson 6-4
Use unit rates to convert measurements.

Lesson 6-4
Identify proportional and nonproportional relationships in tables and graphs. Describe a proportional relationship using an equation.

After Lesson 6-4
Solve problems involving proportional change.

2 TEACH

Scaffolding Questions

Have students read the *Why?* section of the lesson and answer the questions.

Ask:
- How many laps does Tom average per minute in the 5 minutes? 3
- How many laps does Jane average per minute in the 5 minutes? 2.4
- Suppose another runner had averaged 4 laps per minute. What would be his total laps in 5 minutes? 20

Lesson 6-4 Resources

Resource	Approaching-Level	On-Level	Beyond-Level	English Learners
Teacher Edition	• Differentiated Instruction, p. 282		• Differentiated Instruction, p. 285	• Differentiated Instruction, p. 282
Chapter Resource Masters	• Study Guide and Intervention, pp. 23–24 • Skills Practice, p. 25 • Practice, p. 26 • Word Problem Practice, p. 27	• Study Guide and Intervention, pp. 23–24 • Skills Practice, p. 25 • Practice, p. 26 • Word Problem Practice, p. 27 • Enrichment, p. 28	• Practice, p. 26 • Word Problem Practice, p. 27 • Enrichment, p. 28	• Study Guide and Intervention, pp. 23–24 • Skills Practice, p. 25 • Practice, p. 26
Transparencies	• 5-Minute Check Transparency 6-4	• 5-Minute Check Transparency 6-4	• 5-Minute Check Transparency 6-4	• 5-Minute Check Transparency 6-4
Other	• Study Notebook • Teaching Pre-Algebra with Manipulatives	• Study Notebook • Teaching Pre-Algebra with Manipulatives	• Study Notebook	• Study Notebook • Teaching Pre-Algebra with Manipulatives

Identify Proportions

Examples 1 and 2 show how to identify proportional relationships.

Formative Assessment

Use the Check Your Progress exercises after each example to determine students' understanding of concepts.

Additional Examples

1 Determine whether the cost of baseballs is proportional to the number of baseballs. Explain your reasoning. No; the rates are not equal.

Baseballs	1	2	3	4
Cost (dollars)	2	3	4	5

2 Determine whether the number of meters is proportional to the number of seconds. Explain your reasoning. Yes; all the rates are equal.

Time (seconds)	1	2	3	4
Distance (meters)	24	48	72	96

Additional Examples also in Interactive Classroom PowerPoint® Presentations

IWB INTERACTIVE WHITEBOARD READY

Describe Proportional Relationships

Example 3 shows how to describe proportional relationships.

Additional Example

3 WORK Nina charges \$34.50 for 6 days of pet sitting. Write an equation relating the cost of pet sitting to the number of days. What would be the cost of pet sitting for 4 days? $C = 5.75d$; \$23

EXAMPLE 2 Identify Proportional Relationships

Determine whether the number of miles is proportional to the number of hours. Explain your reasoning.

Time (hours)	1	2	3	4
Distance (miles)	50	70	90	110

Write the rate of time to distance for each hour in simplest form.

$\frac{1}{50}$ $\quad \frac{2}{70} = \frac{1}{35}$ $\quad \frac{3}{90} = \frac{1}{30}$ $\quad \frac{4}{100} = \frac{2}{55}$ **The rates are not equal.**

The distance is *not* proportional to the time.

Check Your Progress

2. Determine whether the number of ice cubes is proportional to the number of drinks. Explain your reasoning. no; The rates are not equal.

Number of Drinks	1	2	3	4
Number of Ice Cubes	6	14	22	30

Personal Tutor glencoe.com

ReadingMath

Constant of Proportionality The constant of proportionality is also called the unit rate.

Describe Proportional Relationships Proportional relationships can also be described using equations of the form $y = kx$, where k is the constant ratio. The constant ratio is called the **constant of proportionality**.

Real-World EXAMPLE 3 Describe Proportional Relationships

GEOMETRY A circle's circumference is proportional to its diameter. The circle shown has a circumference of 12.56 meters. Write an equation relating the circumference of the circle to its diameter. What would be the circumference of a circle with a 6-inch diameter?

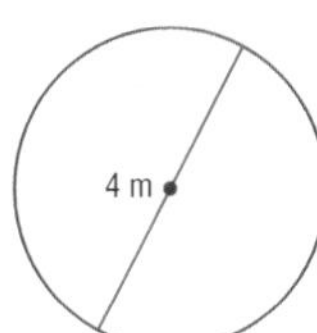

Find the constant of proportionality.

$\frac{\text{circumference}}{\text{diameter}} = \frac{12.56}{4}$ or 3.14

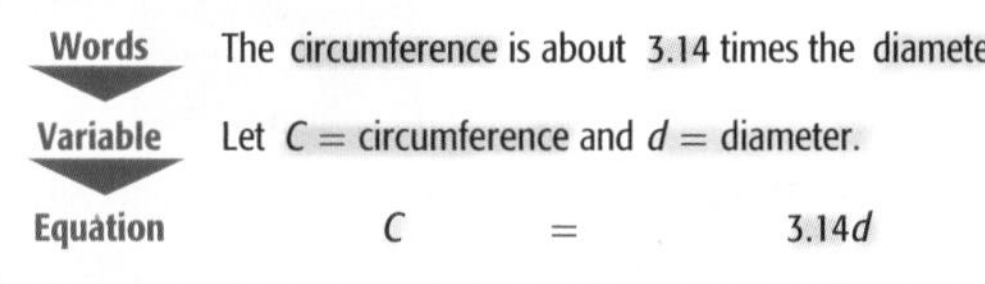

Words The circumference is about 3.14 times the diameter.
Variable Let C = circumference and d = diameter.
Equation $C = 3.14d$

$C = 3.14d$ **Write the equation.**

$C = 3.14(6)$ **Replace d with 6.**

$C = 18.84$ **Multiply.**

The circumference is about 18.84 inches.

Check Your Progress $c = 2.88w$; \$11.52

3. FOOD The cost for $2\frac{1}{2}$ pounds of meat is \$7.20. Write an equation relating cost to the pounds of meat. How much will 4 pounds cost?

Personal Tutor glencoe.com

Differentiated Instruction AL ELL

Verbal/Linguistic Some students will be able to easily describe proportional relationships with an equation. Pair these students with others who are having trouble. Have them practice several examples together.

Check Your Understanding

Examples 1 and 2 pp. 281–282

Determine whether the set of numbers in each table is proportional. Explain.

1.

Blue Paint (quarts)	1	2	3	4
Yellow Paint (quarts)	5	6	7	8

No; the rates are not equal.

2.

Ice Tea Mix (cups)	1	2	3	4
Sugar (cups)	2	4	6	8

2. Yes; each rate is equal to $\frac{1}{2}$.

Example 3 p. 282

3. **GASOLINE** The cost of 13 gallons of gasoline is $41.47. Write an equation relating cost to the number of gallons of gasoline. How much does 18.5 gallons of gasoline cost? $c = 3.19g$; $59.02

Practice and Problem Solving

● = **Step-by-Step Solutions** begin on page R11. **Extra Practice** begins on page 810.

Examples 1 and 2 pp. 281–282

Determine whether the set of numbers in each table is proportional. Explain.

4.

Cans of Concentrate	1	2	3	4
Cans of Water	4	8	12	16

5.

Shaded Squares	1	2	3	4
Total Squares	8	15	30	42

6.

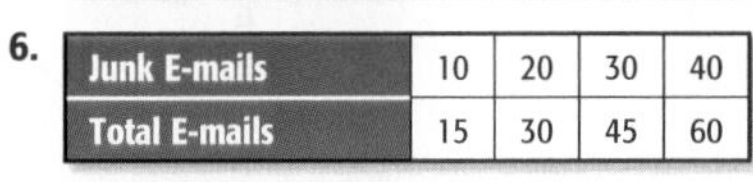

Junk E-mails	10	20	30	40
Total E-mails	15	30	45	60

7.

Weeks	5	6	7	8
Days	35	42	49	56

8.

Heat Index (°F)*	67	73	78	84
Air Temperature (°F)	70	75	80	85

*at 30% Relative Humidity

No; the rates are not equal.

9.

Jars	3	9	12	15
Jelly Beans	18	36	54	72

No; the rates are not equal.

4. Yes; each rate is equal to $\frac{1}{4}$.
5. No; the rates are not equal.
6. Yes; each rate is equal to $\frac{2}{3}$.
7. Yes; each rate is equal to $\frac{1}{7}$.

Example 3 p. 282

For Exercises 10 and 11, write and solve an equation.

10. **FINANCIAL LITERACY** A store is having a sale where all jeans are $\frac{1}{4}$ off the regular price. Write an equation relating the sale price to the regular price. How much would a pair of $29 jeans cost on sale? $s = 0.75r$; $21.75

11. **LAWN SERVICE** Luke earned $54 after mowing 3 lawns. Write an equation comparing earnings to lawns mowed. How much would Luke earn after mowing 7 lawns? $p = 18\ell$; $126

B Copy and complete each table. Determine whether the pattern forms a proportion. 12–14. See Chapter 6 Answer Appendix.

12. **PIZZA** Ms. Rollins had an end-of-year pizza party for the chess team. At the party, every 2 students had 5 slices of pizza.

Number of Students	2	4	6	8	10
Slices of Pizza	■	■	■	■	■

13. **AMUSEMENT PARKS** Admission to an amusement park is $4 plus $1.50 per ride.

Number of Rides	1	2	3	4	5
Cost	■	■	■	■	■

14. **PARTY PLANNING** It will cost $7 per person to hold a birthday party at the recreation center.

Number of Guests	6	7	8	9	10
Cost	■	■	■	■	■

Real-World Link

There are more than 61,000 pizzerias in the United States.

Source: Pizzaware

Tips for New Teachers

Nonproportional Relationships Even though the number of laps Jane completed each minute is a part of a pattern, the ratios of the two quantities are not equal.

Focus on Mathematical Content

Proportional and Nonproportional Relationships Two quantities that have a constant ratio are said to be proportional. They can be represented by an equation of the form $y = kx$, where k is the constant ratio. Nonproportional relationships may have a pattern, but the ratio of the two quantities is not constant.

3 PRACTICE

Formative Assessment

Use Exercises 1–3 to check for understanding.

Use the chart at the bottom of this page to customize assignments for your students.

TEACH with TECH

STUDENT RESPONSE SYSTEM Develop a sequence of proportional and nonproportional relationships with the SRS software. For each relationship, have students respond with 1 for proportional or 2 for nonproportional.

Differentiated Homework Options

Level	Assignment	Two-Day Option	
AL Basic	4–11, 17, 18, 20–40	5–11 odd, 21–24	4–10 even, 17, 18, 20, 25–40
OL Core	5–11 odd, 12–18, 20–40	4–11, 21–24	12–18, 20, 25–40
BL Advanced	12–34 (optional: 35–40)		

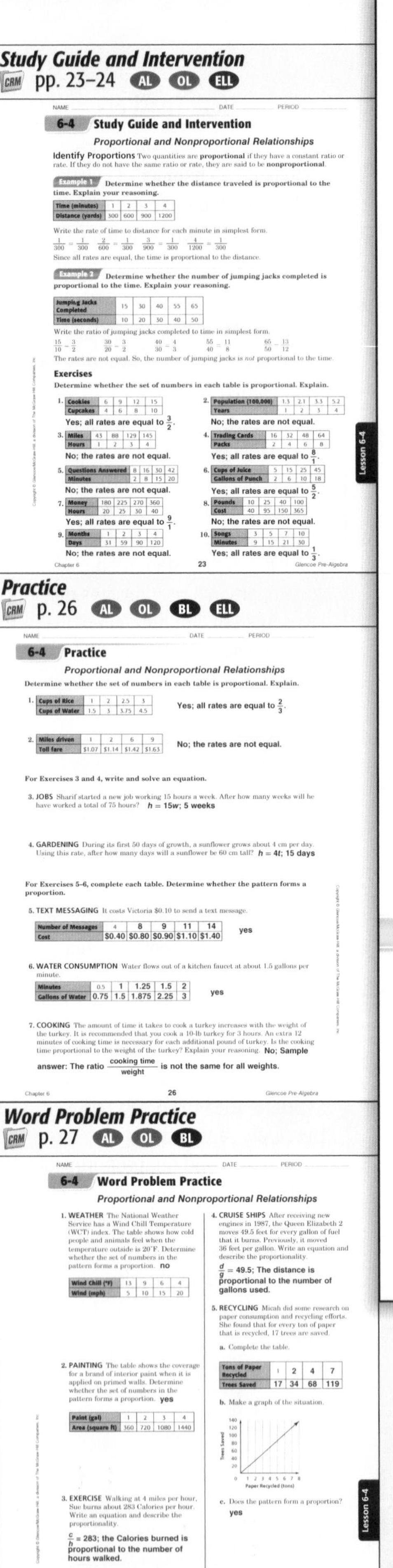

Study Guide and Intervention
CRM pp. 23–24 AL OL ELL

NAME ______ DATE ______ PERIOD ______

6-4 Study Guide and Intervention

Proportional and Nonproportional Relationships

Identify Proportions Two quantities are **proportional** if they have a constant ratio or rate. If they do not have the same ratio or rate, they are said to be **nonproportional**.

Example 1 Determine whether the distance traveled is proportional to the time. Explain your reasoning.

Time (minutes)	1	2	3	4
Distance (yards)	300	600	900	1200

Write the rate of time to distance for each minute in simplest form.

$\frac{1}{300} = \frac{1}{300}$ $\frac{2}{600} = \frac{1}{300}$ $\frac{3}{900} = \frac{1}{300}$ $\frac{4}{1200} = \frac{1}{300}$

Since all rates are equal, the time is proportional to the distance.

Example 2 Determine whether the number of jumping jacks completed is proportional to the time. Explain your reasoning.

Jumping Jacks Completed	15	30	40	55	65
Time (seconds)	10	20	30	40	50

Write the ratio of jumping jacks completed to time in simplest form.

$\frac{15}{10} = \frac{3}{2}$ $\frac{30}{20} = \frac{3}{2}$ $\frac{40}{30} = \frac{4}{3}$ $\frac{55}{40} = \frac{11}{8}$ $\frac{65}{50} = \frac{13}{12}$

The rates are not equal. So, the number of jumping jacks is *not* proportional to the time.

Exercises

Determine whether the set of numbers in each table is proportional. Explain.

1.

Cookies	6	9	12	15
Cupcakes	4	6	8	10

Yes; all rates are equal to $\frac{3}{2}$.

2.

Population (100,000)	1.3	2.1	3.5	5.2
Years	1	2	3	4

No; the rates are not equal.

3.

Miles	43	88	129	145
Hours	1	2	3	4

No; the rates are not equal.

4.

Trading Cards	16	32	48	64
Packs	2	4	6	8

Yes; all rates are equal to $\frac{8}{1}$.

5.

Questions Answered	8	16	30	42
Minutes	2	8	15	20

No; the rates are not equal.

6.

Cups of Juice	5	15	25	45
Gallons of Punch	2	6	10	18

Yes; all rates are equal to $\frac{5}{2}$.

7.

Money	180	225	270	360
Hours	20	25	30	40

Yes; all rates are equal to $\frac{9}{1}$.

8.

Pounds	10	25	40	100
Cost	40	95	150	365

No; the rates are not equal.

9.

Months	1	2	3	4
Days	31	59	90	120

No; the rates are not equal.

10.

Songs	3	5	7	10
Minutes	9	15	21	30

Yes; all rates are equal to $\frac{1}{3}$.

Chapter 6 23 Glencoe Pre-Algebra

Practice
CRM p. 26 AL OL BL ELL

NAME ______ DATE ______ PERIOD ______

6-4 Practice

Proportional and Nonproportional Relationships

Determine whether the set of numbers in each table is proportional. Explain.

1.

Cups of Rice	1	2	2.5	3
Cups of Water	1.5	3	3.75	4.5

Yes; all rates are equal to $\frac{2}{3}$.

2.

Miles driven	1	2	6	9
Toll fare	$1.07	$1.14	$1.42	$1.63

No; the rates are not equal.

For Exercises 3 and 4, write and solve an equation.

3. JOBS Sharif started a new job working 15 hours a week. After how many weeks will he have worked a total of 75 hours? $h = 15w$; 5 weeks

4. GARDENING During its first 50 days of growth, a sunflower grows about 4 cm per day. Using this rate, after how many days will a sunflower be 60 cm tall? $h = 4t$; 15 days

For Exercises 5–6, complete each table. Determine whether the pattern forms a proportion.

5. TEXT MESSAGING It costs Victoria $0.10 to send a text message.

Number of Messages	4	8	9	11	14
Cost	$0.40	$0.80	$0.90	$1.10	$1.40

yes

6. WATER CONSUMPTION Water flows out of a kitchen faucet at about 1.5 gallons per minute.

Minutes	0.5	1	1.25	1.5	2
Gallons of Water	0.75	1.5	1.875	2.25	3

yes

7. COOKING The amount of time it takes to cook a turkey increases with the weight of the turkey. It is recommended that you cook a 10-lb turkey for 3 hours. An extra 12 minutes of cooking time is necessary for each additional pound of turkey. Is the cooking time proportional to the weight of the turkey? Explain your reasoning. No; Sample answer: The ratio $\frac{\text{cooking time}}{\text{weight}}$ is not the same for all weights.

Chapter 6 26 Glencoe Pre-Algebra

Word Problem Practice
CRM p. 27 AL OL BL

NAME ______ DATE ______ PERIOD ______

6-4 Word Problem Practice

Proportional and Nonproportional Relationships

1. WEATHER The National Weather Service has a Wind Chill Temperature (WCT) index. The table shows how cold people and animals feel when the temperature outside is 20°F. Determine whether the set of numbers in the pattern forms a proportion. no

Wind Chill (°F)	13	9	6	4
Wind (mph)	5	10	15	20

2. PAINTING The table shows the coverage for a brand of interior paint when it is applied on primed walls. Determine whether the set of numbers in the pattern forms a proportion. yes

Paint (gal)	1	2	3	4
Area (square ft)	360	720	1080	1440

3. EXERCISE Walking at 4 miles per hour, Sue burns about 283 Calories per hour. Write an equation and describe the proportionality. $\frac{c}{h} = 283$; the Calories burned is proportional to the number of hours walked.

4. CRUISE SHIPS After receiving new engines in 1987, the Queen Elizabeth 2 moves 49.5 feet for every gallon of fuel that it burns. Previously, it moved 36 feet per gallon. Write an equation and describe the proportionality. $\frac{d}{g} = 49.5$; The distance is proportional to the number of gallons used.

5. RECYCLING Micah did some research on paper consumption and recycling efforts. She found that for every ton of paper that is recycled, 17 trees are saved.

a. Complete the table.

Tons of Paper Recycled	1	2	4	7
Trees Saved	17	34	68	119

b. Make a graph of the situation.

c. Does the pattern form a proportion? yes

Chapter 6 27 Glencoe Pre-Algebra

15. **FOOD** Eight hot dogs and ten hot dog buns come in separate packages. **a–b. See margin.**
   a. Is the number of packages of hot dogs proportional to the number of hot dogs? Explain.
   b. Is the number of hot dogs per package proportional to the number of hot dog buns per package? Explain.

16a. Isabel's savings; Sample answer: Isabel starts at $0 and saves $20 per week.

16d. Isabel's savings: $I = 20w$; sister's savings: $S = 20w + 10$

16. **MULTIPLE REPRESENTATIONS** In this problem, you will investigate the relationship between graphs and their corresponding equations. Suppose Isabel decides to save $20 each week for her family vacation. Her sister already has $10 and wants to save an additional $20 each week for the vacation. These situations are modeled in the graphs below.

Graph A

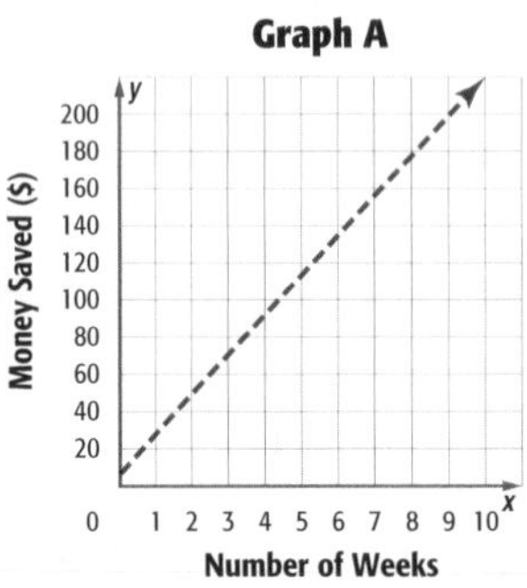

Graph B

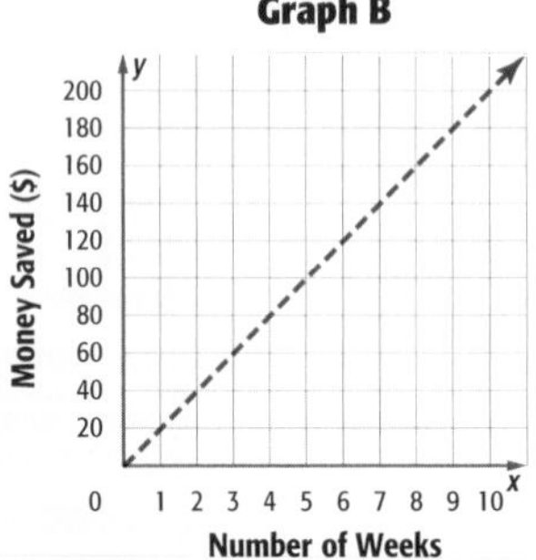

   a. **ANALYTICAL** Which situation is proportional? Explain.
   b. **GRAPHICAL** Compare and contrast the graphs. Which graph represents the proportional situation? Explain. **See margin.**
   c. **TABULAR** Make a table showing the first six weeks of savings for each girl.
   d. **ALGEBRAIC** Write an equation to represent each situation. **c. See Chapter 6 Answer Appendix.**

Math History Link

Golden Rectangle When a square is removed from a golden rectangle, the result is that the remaining rectangle will have the same proportions as the original rectangle. If squares are continually removed from the smaller rectangles, a spiral pattern will result. Greek mathematicians first studied this idea around 500 B.C.

Source: MathWorld

H.O.T. Problems
Use Higher-Order Thinking Skills

17. **OPEN ENDED** Give examples of two similar situations in which one is a proportional relationship and the second one is nonproportional. Then write equations that describe them. **17–18. See Chapter 6 Answer Appendix.**

18. **REASONING** A recipe for paper maché paste includes $\frac{1}{4}$ cup of flour for every cup of water. If there are 6 cups of flour, how many gallons of water are needed? Explain your reasoning.

19. **CHALLENGE** Many objects such as credit cards are shaped like golden rectangles. A *golden rectangle* is a rectangle in which the ratio of the length to the width is approximately 1.618 to 1. This ratio is called the *golden ratio*. **b–c. See Chapter 6 Answer Appendix.**
   a. Find three different objects that are close to a golden rectangle. Make a table to display the dimensions and the ratio found in each object. **Answers will vary.**
   b. Describe how each ratio compares to the golden ratio.
   c. Use the Internet or another source to find three examples of where the golden rectangle is used in architecture.

20. **WRITING IN MATH** This year Monica is 12 years old, and her little sister Patrice is 6 years old. Is Monica's age proportional to Patrice's age? Explain your reasoning using a table of values. **See Chapter 6 Answer Appendix.**

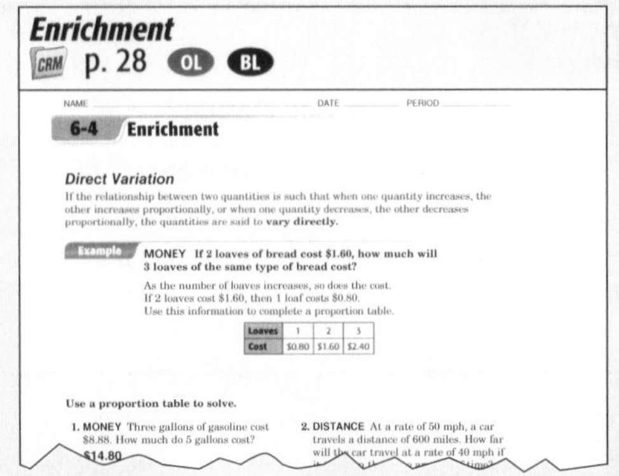

Enrichment
CRM p. 28 OL BL

NAME ______ DATE ______ PERIOD ______

6-4 Enrichment

Direct Variation

If the relationship between two quantities is such that when one quantity increases, the other increases proportionally, or when one quantity decreases, the other decreases proportionally, the quantities are said to **vary directly**.

Example MONEY If 2 loaves of bread cost $1.60, how much will 3 loaves of the same type of bread cost?

As the number of loaves increases, so does the cost.
If 2 loaves cost $1.60, then 1 loaf costs $0.80.
Use this information to complete a proportion table.

Loaves	1	2	3
Cost	$0.80	$1.60	$2.40

Use a proportion table to solve.

1. MONEY Three gallons of gasoline cost $8.88. How much do 5 gallons cost? $14.80

2. DISTANCE At a rate of 50 mph, a car travels a distance of 600 miles. How far will the car travel at a rate of 40 mph if ...

Multiple Representations
In Exercise 16, students use coordinate graphs, tables of values, and equations to compare two savings plans over time.

Exercise Alert

Internet Exercise 19 requires the use of the Internet or some other source to find three places where the golden rectangle is used in architecture.

Standardized Test Practice

21. A bicycle wheel makes 30 revolutions in 45 feet. Which of these represents an equivalent rate of bicycle wheel revolutions? **A**

A 10 revolutions in 15 ft
B 60 revolutions in 100 ft
C 15 revolutions in 10 ft
D 100 revolutions in 60 ft

22. The amount of sales tax paid on a purchase is proportional to the price of the item. Suppose the sales tax rate is 6.25%. If p is the price of the item and t is the sales tax, which equation represents this? **J**

F $p = 0.0625t$
G $p = 6.25t$
H $t = 6.25p$
J $t = 0.0625p$

23. The cost of renting a boat for 4 hours is $51. If the cost of renting a boat is proportional to the number of rental hours, which of the following is *not* an equivalent rate? **D**

A 6 hours for $76.50
B 3 hours for $38.25
C 7 hours for $89.25
D 5 hours for $63.00

24. **EXTENDED RESPONSE** The prices of different sized smoothies at an ice cream shop are shown below. Is the pricing guide based on a constant unit price? Explain. **See margin.**

Size (oz)	16	20	24
Cost ($)	3.25	3.75	4.25

Spiral Review

Complete each conversion. Round to the nearest hundredth, if necessary. (Lesson 6-3)

25. 4 in. ≈ ■ cm **10.16**
26. 5 L ≈ ■ gal **1.32**
27. 1500 lb ≈ ■ kg **681**
28. 14 yd ≈ ■ m **12.8**

Express each rate as a unit rate. Round to the nearest tenth, if necessary. (Lesson 6-2)

29. 140 miles on 6 gallons **23.3 miles per gallon**
30. 19 yards in 2.5 minutes **7.6 yards per minute**
31. 236.7 miles in 4.5 days **52.6 miles per day**
32. 331.5 pages in 8.5 weeks **39 pages per week**

33. **SPORTS** A volleyball uniform costs $15 for the shirt, $10 for the pants, and $8 for the socks. Write two equivalent expressions for the total cost of 12 uniforms. Then find the cost. (Lesson 4-1) **12($15 + $10 + $8), 12($15) + 12($10) + 12($8); $396**

34. **WEATHER** The table shows the record high and low temperatures for selected states. What is the difference between the highest and lowest temperatures for Kentucky? Massachusetts? (Lesson 2-3) **151°F; 142°F**

State	Lowest Temperature (°F)	Highest Temperature (°F)
Kentucky	−37	114
Massachusetts	−35	107

Skills Review

Solve each equation. (Lessons 4-3 and 4-4)

35. $7x = 126$ **18**
36. $150 = 15n$ **10**
37. $42 = 6m$ **7**
38. $12p = 78$ **6.5**
39. $22s = 154$ **7**
40. $245 = 7t$ **35**

Differentiated Instruction

BL

Extension If A = 12, B = 24, C = 15, and D = 30, which of the following are proportional relationships? Explain.

$\frac{A}{B} = \frac{C}{D}$, $\frac{A}{C} = \frac{B}{D}$, $\frac{A}{D} = \frac{C}{B}$, $\frac{A+B}{B} = \frac{C+D}{D}$

$\frac{A}{B} = \frac{C}{D}$, proportional, constant ratio of $\frac{1}{2}$; $\frac{A}{C} = \frac{B}{D}$, proportional, constant ratio of $\frac{4}{5}$;
$\frac{A}{D} = \frac{C}{B}$, nonproportional, ratios not constant; $\frac{A+B}{B} = \frac{C+D}{D}$, proportional, constant ratio of $\frac{3}{2}$.

4 ASSESS

Name the Math Have students explain the mathematical steps they would use to solve the problem:

Nigel paid $126 for 4 tickets to a game. Write an equation relating the cost to the number of tickets. How much would 7 tickets cost? $C = 31.5n$; $220.50

Additional Answers

15a. Yes; sample answer:

Hot Dog Packages	1	2	3	4
Hot Dogs	8	16	24	32

The hot dog packages to hot dogs ratio for hot dog packages of 1, 2, 3, and 4 units is $\frac{1}{8}$, $\frac{2}{16}$ or $\frac{1}{8}$, $\frac{3}{24}$ or $\frac{1}{8}$, and $\frac{4}{32}$ or $\frac{1}{8}$. Since these ratios are all equal to $\frac{1}{8}$, the number of hot dog packages is proportional to the number of hot dogs.

15b. Yes; sample answer:

Hot Dogs	8	16	24	32
Hot Dog Buns	10	20	30	40

The hot dog packages to hot dogs ratio for hot dog packages of 1, 2, 3, and 4 units is $\frac{8}{10}$ or $\frac{4}{5}$, $\frac{16}{20}$ or $\frac{4}{5}$, $\frac{24}{30}$ or $\frac{4}{5}$, and $\frac{32}{40}$ or $\frac{4}{5}$. Since these ratios are all equal to $\frac{4}{5}$, the number of hot dogs is proportional to the number of hot dog buns.

16b. Graph B represents Isabel's saved money and graph A represents her sister's saved money. Sample answer: Isabel's sister already has $10, so the graph representing her saved money starts at 10. The graph representing Isabel's money starts at 0.

24. No; the ratio of ounces to cost is not constant.

Formative Assessment

Use the Mid-Chapter Quiz to assess students' progress in the first half of the chapter.

For problems answered incorrectly, have students review the lessons indicated in parentheses.

Customize and create multiple versions of your Mid-Chapter Quiz and their answer keys.

FOLDABLES Follow-Up

Before students complete the Mid-Chapter Quiz, encourage them to review the information for Lessons 6-1 through 6-4 in their Foldables.

Additional Answer

7. The Swiss cheese costs \$0.17 per ounce. The cheddar cheese costs \$0.14 per ounce. So, the cheddar cheese is less expensive.

CHAPTER 6 Mid-Chapter Quiz

Lessons 6-1 through 6-4

Express each ratio as a fraction in simplest form. (Lesson 6-1)

1. \$16 for 6 gallons $\frac{8}{3}$
2. 200 miles in 4 hours $\frac{50}{1}$
3. 35 people in 7 events $\frac{5}{1}$

Express each rate as a unit rate. Round to the nearest tenth, if necessary. (Lesson 6-2)

4. 875 customers in 7 days **125 customers per day**
5. 12 blocks in 8 minutes **1.5 blocks per min**
6. 7 cars washed in 2 hours **3.5 cars per h**
7. **GROCERIES** Determine which is less expensive per ounce, 16 ounces of Swiss cheese for \$2.75 or 24 ounces of cheddar cheese for \$3.25. Explain. (Lesson 6-2) **See margin.**
8. **CONCERTS** Suppose it costs \$45 to attend a concert where the band plays for 1.5 hours. (Lesson 6-2)
   a. What was the cost to attend the concert per hour? **\$30 per hour**
   b. What was the cost to attend the concert per minute? **\$0.50 per minute**
9. **MULTIPLE CHOICE** Which of the following has the same unit rate as \$5 for 2 pounds? (Lesson 6-2) **A**

   A \$20 for 8 lb C \$24 for 8 lb
   B \$16 for 6 lb D \$12 for 4 lb

Complete each conversion. Round to the nearest hundredth. (Lesson 6-3)

10. 25 lb ≈ ■ kg **11.35**
11. 4 gal ≈ ■ L **15.14**
12. 42 fl oz ≈ ■ mL **1242.11**
13. 36 in. ≈ ■ cm **91.44**
14. **SWIMMING** The Olympic record for the men's 50-meter freestyle is 21.91 seconds. (Lesson 6-3)
    a. Express this speed in meters per second. **2.28 m/s**
    b. At this rate, how many meters could be swum in 1 minute? **136.92 m**
15. **MOUNTAINS** The table shows the heights of tall mountains in the U. S. (Lesson 6-3)

Mountain	Height (ft)
McKinley	20,320
Saint Elias	18,008
Foraker	17,400

    a. What is the height of Mt. McKinley in meters? Round to the nearest hundredth. **6197.6 m**
    b. What is the total height of the three mountains in yards? **18,576 yd**
16. **MULTIPLE CHOICE** An airplane flew 1500 miles in 2.5 hours. How many kilometers is this per hour? (Lesson 6-3) **G**

    F 3750 H 750
    G 966 J 600
17. **ANIMALS** A blue whale's heart beats only 45 times in 5 minutes. Write an equation comparing the number of beats to the number of minutes. At that rate, how many times would the blue whale's heart beat in 20 minutes? (Lesson 6-4) $b = 9m$; **180 times**

Copy and complete each table. Determine whether the pattern forms a proportion. Explain. (Lesson 6-4)

18. **ART MUSEUM** Mr. Dixon takes his fine arts class to the museum. The class has 25 students and museum admission is \$2 per student. **Yes; each rate is equal to $\frac{2}{1}$.**

Number of Students	5	10	15	20	25
Cost (\$)	■	■	■	■	■

10 20 30 40 50

19. **FRUIT** A local apple orchard charges a \$3 entrance fee plus \$2 per barrel of apples. **No; the rates are not equal.**

Number of Barrels	1	2	3	4	5
Cost (\$)	■	■	■	■	■

5 7 9 11 13

20. **DOGS** You earned \$27 for walking 4 dogs. Write an equation comparing earnings to dogs walked. How much would you earn after walking 9 dogs? (Lesson 6-4) $e = 6.75d$; **\$60.75**

Intervention Planner

Tier 1 On Level	Tier 2 Strategic Intervention (approaching grade level)	Tier 3 Intensive Intervention (2 or more grades below level)
If students miss about 25% of the exercises or less,	**If** students miss about 50% of the exercises,	**If** students miss about 75% of the exercises,
Then choose a resource: SE Lessons 6-1 through 6-4 CRM Skills Practice, pp. 7, 13, 19, 25 TE Chapter Project, p. 262 Math Online Self-Check Quiz	**Then** choose a resource: CRM Study Guide and Intervention, Chapter 6, pp. 5, 11, 17, 23 *Quick Review Math Handbook* Math Online Extra Examples, Personal Tutor, Homework Help	**Then** use *Math Triumphs, Grade 8,* Ch. 4–5 Math Online Extra Examples, Personal Tutor, Homework Help, Review Vocabulary

6-5 Solving Proportions

Then
You have already used dimensional analysis to convert measurements. (Lesson 6-3)

Now
- Solve proportions.
- Use proportions to solve real-world problems.

New Vocabulary
proportion
cross products

Math Online
glencoe.com
- Extra Examples
- Personal Tutor
- Self-Check Quiz
- Homework Help

Why?

Bianca wants to make a salt map of the United States for her social studies class. The recipe for the dough is shown.

Salt Map Ingredients

Ingredient	Amount
flour	4 c
salt	2 c
water	1 c

a. Write the ratio of cups of flour to cups of salt as a fraction in simplest form. flour to salt: $\frac{2}{1}$

b. Bianca needs to double the recipe to have enough dough for her map. What is the ratio of cups of flour to cups of salt in simplest form? flour to salt: $\frac{2}{1}$

c. Are the ratios in parts **a** and **b** equal? Explain
Yes; each part was multiplied by the same number.

Proportions In the example above, the ratios of cups of flour to cups of salt for a single batch of dough, $\frac{4}{2}$, or a double batch of dough, $\frac{8}{4}$, are equal. They both simplify to $\frac{2}{1}$.

$$\frac{4}{2} = \frac{2}{1} \qquad \frac{8}{4} = \frac{2}{1}$$

A **proportion** is an equation stating that two ratios or rates are equal. You can use the Multiplication Property of Equality to illustrate an important property of proportions.

	$\frac{4}{2} = \frac{8}{4}$	$\frac{a}{b} = \frac{c}{d}$	
Multiply each side by 2 • 4.	$\frac{4}{2} \cdot (2 \cdot 4) = \frac{8}{4} \cdot (2 \cdot 4)$	$\frac{a}{b} \cdot bd = \frac{c}{d} \cdot bd$	**Multiply each side by *bd*.**
Simplify.	$4 \cdot 4 = 8 \cdot 2$	$ad = cb$	**Simplify.**

The products 4 • 4 and 8 • 2, and *ad* and *cb* are called **cross products** of the proportion. The cross products of any proportion are equal.

$\frac{a}{b} = \frac{c}{d}$, $ad = bc$

Key Concept Property of Proportions — For Your FOLDABLE

Words The cross products of a proportion are equal.

Symbols If $\frac{a}{b} = \frac{c}{d}$, then $ad = cb$.
If $ad = cb$, then $\frac{a}{b} = \frac{c}{d}$ if $b \neq 0$ and $d \neq 0$.

Cross products will help when you use proportional reasoning to solve a problem.

6-5 Lesson Notes

1 FOCUS

Vertical Alignment

Before Lesson 6-5
Use dimensional analysis to convert measurements.

Lesson 6-5
Solve proportions. Use proportions to solve real-world problems.

After Lesson 6-5
Solve problems involving proportional change.

2 TEACH

Scaffolding Questions

Have students read the *Why?* section of the lesson and answer the questions.

Ask:
- Suppose you wanted to make half the recipe for dough. What ratios of the first two ingredients to water would you use? flour to water: $\frac{4}{1}$; salt to water: $\frac{2}{1}$
- Which ingredient has the greater ratio to water? flour
- How many cups of flour would you use in a half batch of dough? 2 cups

Lesson 6-5 Resources

Resource	Approaching-Level	On-Level	Beyond-Level	English Learners
Teacher Edition	• Differentiated Instruction, p. 288		• Differentiated Instruction, p. 292	
Chapter Resource Masters	• Study Guide and Intervention, pp. 29–30 • Skills Practice, p. 31 • Practice, p. 32 • Word Problem Practice, p. 33	• Study Guide and Intervention, pp. 29–30 • Skills Practice, p. 31 • Practice, p. 32 • Word Problem Practice, p. 33 • Enrichment, p. 34	• Practice, p. 32 • Word Problem Practice, p. 33 • Enrichment, p. 34	• Study Guide and Intervention, pp. 29–30 • Skills Practice, p. 31 • Practice, p. 32
Transparencies	• 5-Minute Check Transparency 6-5	• 5-Minute Check Transparency 6-5	• 5-Minute Check Transparency 6-5	• 5-Minute Check Transparency 6-5
Other	• Study Notebook • Teaching Pre-Algebra with Manipulatives	• Study Notebook • Teaching Pre-Algebra with Manipulatives	• Study Notebook	• Study Notebook • Teaching Pre-Algebra with Manipulatives

Tips for New Teachers

Cross Products Carefully go through the steps that lead to the conclusion that cross products of a proportion are equal. You might even suggest that students draw two lines on each problem, forming an x, to show the cross products.

Proportions

Example 1 shows how to solve proportions.

Formative Assessment

Use the Check Your Progress exercises after each example to determine students' understanding of concepts.

Additional Example

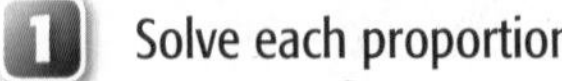

1 Solve each proportion.

a. $\frac{c}{36} = \frac{9}{15}$ $c = 21.6$

b. $\frac{16}{v} = \frac{4.8}{1.5}$ $v = 5$

Additional Examples also in Interactive Classroom PowerPoint® Presentations

IWB INTERACTIVE WHITEBOARD READY

Focus on Mathematical Content

Solving Proportions An equation stating that two ratios are equal is a proportion. To find the unknown value in a proportion, use cross products. For example, the cross products of $\frac{x}{12} = \frac{15}{18}$ are $x \cdot 18$ and $12 \cdot 15$. The solution is $x = 10$.

Use Proportions to Solve Problems

Example 2 shows how to use a proportion to solve a real-world problem. **Example 3** shows how to solve problems using a proportion or an equation.

Just as in solving an equation, solving a proportion means finding the value of the variable that makes a true statement. You can use cross products to solve a proportion in which one of the quantities is not known.

StudyTip

Solve Mentally You can also solve Example 1a mentally. Think: $90 \div 15 = 6$ and $66 \div 6 = 11$.

EXAMPLE 1 Solve Proportions

Solve each proportion.

a. $\frac{b}{15} = \frac{66}{90}$

$\frac{b}{15} = \frac{66}{90}$	
$b \cdot 90 = 15 \cdot 66$	Cross products
$90b = 990$	Multiply.
$\frac{90b}{90} = \frac{990}{90}$	Divide.
$b = 11$	Simplify.

b. $\frac{3.2}{9} = \frac{n}{36}$

$\frac{3.2}{9} = \frac{n}{36}$	
$3.2 \cdot 36 = 9 \cdot n$	Cross products
$115.2 = 9n$	Multiply.
$\frac{115.2}{9} = \frac{9n}{9}$	Divide.
$12.8 = n$	Simplify.

Check Your Progress

1A. $\frac{x}{4} = \frac{7}{20}$ 1.4 **1B.** $\frac{7}{14} = \frac{c}{12}$ 6 **1C.** $\frac{6.8}{t} = \frac{34}{50}$ 10 **1D.** $\frac{m}{8.5} = \frac{42}{51}$ 7

Personal Tutor glencoe.com

Use Proportions to Solve Problems When you solve a real-world problem using a proportion, be sure to compare the quantities in the same order.

Real-World EXAMPLE 2 Use Proportions to Solve Problems

AMUSEMENT PARKS The wait time to ride a roller coaster is 20 minutes when 160 people are in line. At this rate, how long is the wait time when 220 people are in line?

Understand You know how long the wait time is for 160 people. You need to find how long the wait time will be for 220 people.

Plan Write and solve a proportion using ratios that compare people to wait time. Let w represent the wait time for 220 people.

Solve

$\frac{20}{160} = \frac{w}{220}$	← wait time ← number of people
$20 \cdot 220 = 160 \cdot w$	Cross products
$4400 = 160w$	Multiply.
$\frac{4400}{160} = \frac{160w}{160}$	Divide each side by 160.
$27.5 = w$	Simplify.

Check Check the cross products. Since $20 \cdot 220 = 4400$ and $160 \cdot 27.5 = 4400$, the answer is correct. ✓

The wait time is 27.5 minutes.

Check Your Progress

2. COMMUNITY SERVICE Alicia's class is making care packages for a local shelter. They can make 8 care packages with 240 food items. How many care packages can they make with 500 food items? $16\frac{2}{3}$

Personal Tutor glencoe.com

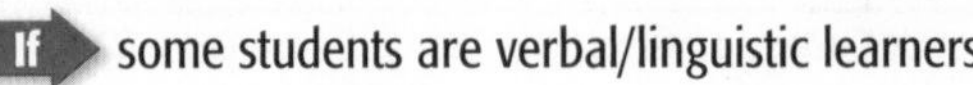

Differentiated Instruction AL

If some students are verbal/linguistic learners,

Then they may find it helpful to talk softly, or even silently, to themselves as they write down the ratios to form a proportion to solve a word problem. They might say, for example, "cost over pencils equals cost over pencils."

StudyTip

Proportions You can set up a proportion in more than one way. In Example 3, the proportion can also be set up as $\frac{4}{20} = \frac{30}{x}$.

EXAMPLE 3 Use Proportions to Solve Problems

MUSEUMS Mrs. Hidalgo paid $30 for 4 students to visit an art museum. Find the cost for 20 students.

Method 1 Write and solve a proportion.

Let x represent the cost for 20 students.

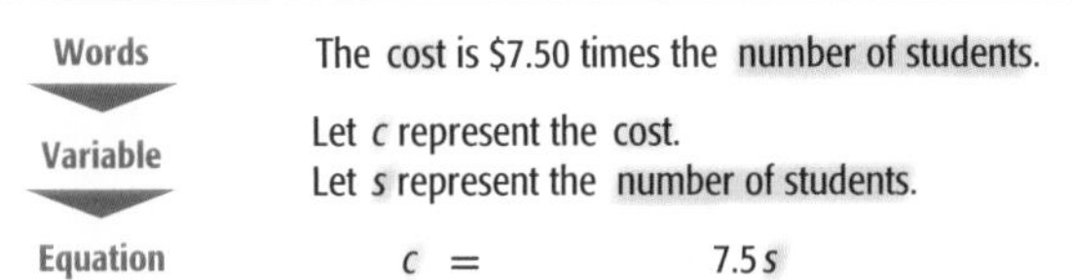

$\frac{30}{4} = \frac{x}{20}$	← cost / ← number of students
$30 \cdot 20 = 4 \cdot x$	**Cross products**
$600 = 4x$	**Multiply.**
$\frac{600}{4} = \frac{4x}{4}$	**Divide each side by 4.**
$150 = x$	**Simplify.**

Method 2 Write and solve an equation.

Find the constant of proportionality, or unit cost, for each student.

$\frac{\text{cost in dollars}}{\text{number of students}} = \frac{30}{4}$ or 7.50 The cost is $7.50 per student.

Words	The cost is $7.50 times the number of students.
Variable	Let c represent the cost. Let s represent the number of students.
Equation	$c = 7.5s$

Use this equation to find the cost for 20 students at the same rate.

$c = 7.5s$	**Write the equation.**
$c = 7.5(20)$	**Replace s with 20.**
$c = 150$	**Multiply.**

So, the cost for 20 students to visit the art museum is $150.

Check Your Progress

3. **DVDS** Matthew paid $49.45 for 5 DVDs at a sale.

A. Write and solve a proportion to find the cost for 8 DVDs at the same rate. $\frac{49.45}{5} = \frac{x}{8}$; **$79.12**

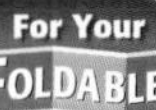

B. Write an equation relating the cost c to the number of DVDs d. How much would it cost for 11 DVDs at the same rate? **$c = 9.89d$; $108.79**

Personal Tutor glencoe.com

Real-World Link

Nearly 150 million DVD players have been sold in the United States since they went on the market in 1997.

Source: Consumer Electronics Association

Concept Summary Solve Proportions

For Your FOLDABLE

Ways to Solve Proportions

- Mental Math
- Cross Products
- Constant of Proportionality

Additional Examples

2 **ARCHITECTURE** An architect builds a model of a building before the actual building is built. The model is 8 inches tall and the actual building will be 22 feet tall. The model is 20 inches wide. Find the width of the actual building. 55 ft

3 **CALORIES** A serving of 4 crackers contains 70 Calories. Write an equation relating the number of Calories, c, to the number of crackers, n. How many Calories are in 7 crackers? $c = 17.5n$; 122.5 Calories

TEACH with TECH

INTERACTIVE WHITEBOARD Write a proportion on the board. Drag the numerators and denominators to show how to form the cross products and rewrite the equation.

3 PRACTICE

Formative Assessment

Use Exercises 1–8 to check for understanding.

Use the chart at the bottom of this page to customize assignments for your students.

Additional Answers

37b.

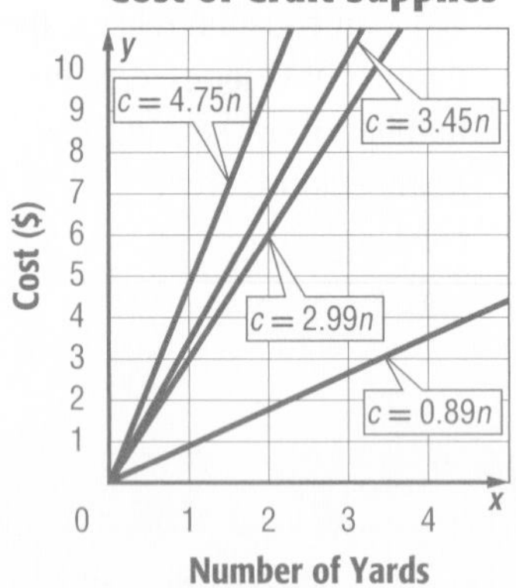

ribbon; fleece; The most expensive fabric is the line that is the steepest. The cheapest fabric is the line that is the least steep.

42. Sample answer: The product of the length and width will remain constant, $lw = k$. The length is not proportional to the width. For example if the area is 36 units^2:

w	3	6	9
l	12	6	4
Ratio	1:4	1:1	9:4

From the table, you can see the proportions are not equal.

Check Your Understanding

Example 1 p. 288

Solve each proportion.

1. $\frac{18}{m} = \frac{27}{36}$ **24**
2. $\frac{t}{21} = \frac{9}{15}$ **12.6**
3. $\frac{8}{17} = \frac{16}{x}$ **34**
4. $\frac{12}{7.2} = \frac{4}{p}$ **2.4**
5. $\frac{n}{13} = \frac{5.8}{2.6}$ **29**
6. $\frac{4.4}{2} = \frac{c}{25}$ **55**

Example 2 p. 288

7. **TELEVISION** *Aspect ratio* is the ratio of width to height of a television screen. A widescreen television screen has an aspect ratio of 16 inches wide to 9 inches high. If a television screen is 48 inches wide, how many inches high is it? **27 in.**

Example 3 p. 289

8. **TIME** Joaquin has a total of 12.5 hours of football practice after school five days a week. Write an equation relating the number of days d to the number of hours h. How many hours of practice will he have for 15 school days? 22 school days? **$2.5d = h$; 37.5 h; 55 h**

Practice and Problem Solving

● = **Step-by-Step Solutions** begin on page R11. **Extra Practice** begins on page 810.

Example 1 p. 288

Solve each proportion.

9. $\frac{6}{8} = \frac{z}{48}$ **36**
10. $\frac{8}{12} = \frac{28}{m}$ **42**
11. $\frac{b}{30} = \frac{4}{5}$ **24**
12. $\frac{18}{15} = \frac{9}{s}$ **7.5**
13. $\frac{7}{c} = \frac{35}{60}$ **12**
14. $\frac{k}{56} = \frac{12}{7}$ **96**
15. $\frac{32}{a} = \frac{12.8}{5.6}$ **14**
16. $\frac{11.5}{6} = \frac{n}{22.8}$ **43.7**
17. $\frac{9.6}{3} = \frac{p}{0.3}$ **0.96**
18. $\frac{14}{w} = \frac{8.4}{4.5}$ **7.5**
19. $\frac{v}{6} = \frac{20.7}{5.4}$ **23**
20. $\frac{10.2}{4} = \frac{h}{12}$ **30.6**

Example 2 p. 288

21. **PAINTING** The classrooms at Lincoln Middle School are painted every summer. If 7 gallons of paint are needed to paint 4 classrooms, how many gallons of paint are needed to paint 16 classrooms? **28 gal**

22. **PIZZA** A principal is ordering pizzas for a school pizza party. He knows that 9 pizzas will feed 25 students. If there are 300 students in the school, how many pizzas will he need to order? **108 pizzas**

Example 3 p. 289

23. **BOATS** A boat traveled 150 feet in 9.7 seconds. Write an equation relating the time t to the distance d. How far would the boat travel in 1 minute? 1 minute 30 seconds? **$d = 15.46t$; 927.6 ft; 1391.4 ft**

24. **RAINFALL** The record for the most amount of rain in the shortest amount of time in the United States was 12 inches in 42 minutes. Write an equation relating the time t to the amount of rain a. How much rain fell in 15 minutes? 28 minutes? **$a = 0.29t$; 4.35 in.; 8.12 in.**

25. **PUNCH** The table shows the amount of each ingredient in 52 ounces of punch.

Ingredient	Amount (ounces)
water	12
lime juice	4
cranberry concentrate	12
sparkling lemon water	24

a. If you have 130 ounces of punch, how much lime juice does the punch contain? **10 oz**

b. If there are 54 ounces of sparkling lemon water in the punch, how many ounces of cranberry concentrate does the punch contain? **27 oz**

c. If the punch contains 44 ounces of water, how many ounces of punch do you have? **190.67 oz**

Differentiated Homework Options

Level	Assignment	Two-Day Option	
AL Basic	9–24, 38, 39, 41, 43–56	9–23 odd, 44–47	10–24 even, 38, 39, 41, 43, 48–56
OL Core	9–29 odd, 30, 31–37 odd, 38, 39, 41, 43–56	9–24, 44–47	25–39, 41, 43, 48–56
BL Advanced	25–52 (optional: 53–56)		

Real-World Link

The Eiffel Tower in Paris, France, was completed in 1889. It has a total weight of 10,100 tons and is 324 meters tall.

Source: SETE

Write a proportion that could be used to solve for each variable. Then solve.

26. 6 goals in 14 games; 9 goals in g games $\frac{6}{14} = \frac{9}{g}$; 21

27. s inches in 0.54 hour; 4.55 inches in 1.89 hours $\frac{s}{0.54} = \frac{4.55}{1.89}$; 1.3

28. 14 gallons for d dollars; 8 gallons for \$24.72 $\frac{14}{d} = \frac{8}{24.72}$; 43.26

29. 20 boxes on 4 shelves; b boxes on 20 shelves $\frac{20}{4} = \frac{b}{20}$; 100

30. ART A 14-inch-wide by 20-inch-long print of the Eiffel Tower is also available as a postcard 6 inches long. What is the width of the postcard? **4.2 in.**

Solve each proportion.

31. $\frac{a}{0.28} = \frac{4}{1.4}$ **0.8**

32. $\frac{3}{14} = \frac{15}{m-3}$ **73**

33. $\frac{16}{x+5} = \frac{4}{5}$ **15**

34. $\frac{x-18}{24} = \frac{15}{8}$ **63**

35. $\frac{9}{7} = \frac{b+11}{14}$ **7**

36. $\frac{15-d}{12} = \frac{37.5}{75}$ **9**

37. **MULTIPLE REPRESENTATIONS** In this problem, you will explore proportions. A craft store is offering the specials shown for different materials.

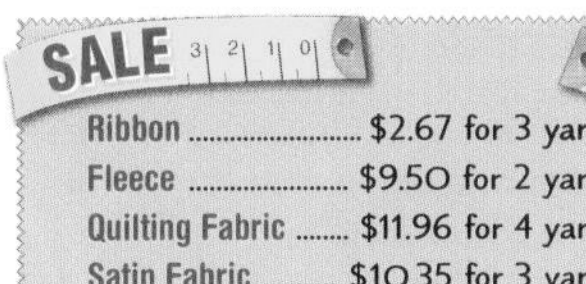

SALE
Ribbon .... $2.67 for 3 yards
Fleece .... $9.50 for 2 yards
Quilting Fabric .... $11.96 for 4 yards
Satin Fabric .... $10.35 for 3 yards

a. **ALGEBRAIC** Write an equation relating the cost c to the number of yards n for each material.

b. **GRAPHICAL** Graph the cost of each material per yard on a coordinate plane. Which item costs the least per yard? the most? How is this shown on the graph? **See margin.**

c. **NUMERICAL** How much would it cost to buy 18 inches of ribbon? How much would it cost to buy 10 meters of fleece? **\$0.45; \$51.97**

37a. ribbon: $c = 0.89n$; fleece: $c = 4.75n$; quilting fabric: $c = 2.99n$; satin fabric: $c = 3.45n$

38. $\frac{12 \text{ hits}}{16 \text{ at bats}}, \frac{3 \text{ hits}}{4 \text{ at bats}}$

43. Sample answer: It is easier to use the constant of proportionality if you are solving the proportion for several unknowns. It is easy to find a unit rate and then multiply the amounts needed to find the equivalent amounts. No, because no matter how you set up and solve a proportion, you will arrive at the same answer.

H.O.T. Problems

Use **H**igher-**O**rder **T**hinking Skills

38. OPEN ENDED Give two examples that are proportional to $\frac{6 \text{ hits}}{8 \text{ at bats}}$.

39. REASONING Suppose $a:b = 2:4$ and $b:c = 4:9$. If $a = 10$, find the value of c. **45**

40. CHALLENGE Solve each proportion.

a. $\frac{4}{x} = \frac{x}{9}$ ± 6 b. $\frac{2}{x} = \frac{x}{8}$ ± 4 c. $\frac{4}{x} = \frac{x}{25}$ ± 10 d. $\frac{9}{x} = \frac{x}{16}$ ± 12

41. FIND THE ERROR Trey and Morgan are solving the proportion $\frac{x}{36} = \frac{4}{9}$. Is either of them correct? Explain your reasoning.
Trey; Sample answer: Morgan cross multiplied incorrectly.

Trey	Morgan
$\frac{x}{36} = \frac{4}{9}$	$\frac{x}{36} = \frac{4}{9}$
$x(9) = 36(4)$	$x(4) = 36(9)$
$x = 16$	$x = 81$

42. CHALLENGE Rectangle $ABCD$ has a fixed area. As the length ℓ and the width w change, what do you know about their product? Is the length proportional to the width? Justify your reasoning. **See margin.**

43. WRITING IN MATH Describe a situation in which it may be easier to solve a proportion using the constant of proportionality. Explain your reasoning. Does it matter which method you use to solve a proportion? Why or why not?

Watch Out!

Find the Error If students are having trouble solving a proportion, as in Exercise 41, remind them they should use cross products to solve the proportion.

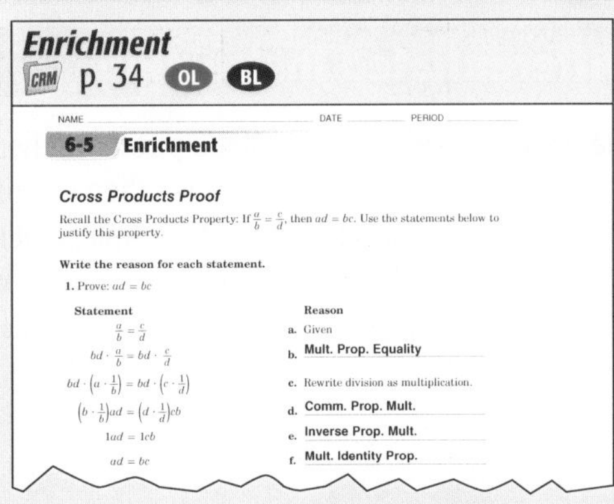

Enrichment CRM p. 34 OL BL

NAME ________ DATE ______ PERIOD ______

6-5 Enrichment

Cross Products Proof

Recall the Cross Products Property: If $\frac{a}{b} = \frac{c}{d}$, then $ad = bc$. Use the statements below to justify this property.

Write the reason for each statement.

1. Prove: $ad = bc$

Statement	Reason
$\frac{a}{b} = \frac{c}{d}$	a. Given
$bd \cdot \frac{a}{b} = bd \cdot \frac{c}{d}$	b. **Mult. Prop. Equality**
$bd \cdot \left(a \cdot \frac{1}{b}\right) = bd \cdot \left(c \cdot \frac{1}{d}\right)$	c. Rewrite division as multiplication.
$\left(b \cdot \frac{1}{b}\right)ad = \left(d \cdot \frac{1}{d}\right)cb$	d. **Comm. Prop. Mult.**
$1ad = 1cb$	e. **Inverse Prop. Mult.**
$ad = bc$	f. **Mult. Identity Prop.**

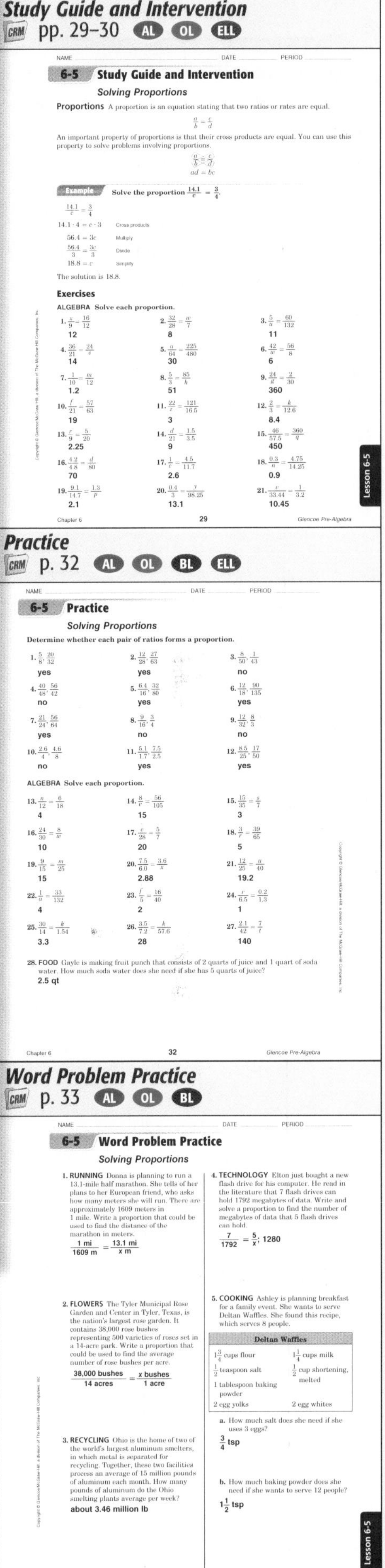

Study Guide and Intervention CRM pp. 29–30 AL OL ELL

NAME ________ DATE ______ PERIOD ______

6-5 Study Guide and Intervention

Solving Proportions

Proportions A proportion is an equation stating that two ratios or rates are equal.

$$\frac{a}{b} = \frac{c}{d}$$

An important property of proportions is that their cross products are equal. You can use this property to solve problems involving proportions.

$$\frac{a}{b} = \frac{c}{d}$$
$$ad = bc$$

Example Solve the proportion $\frac{14.1}{c} = \frac{3}{4}$.

$\frac{14.1}{c} = \frac{3}{4}$

$14.1 \cdot 4 = c \cdot 3$ Cross products

$56.4 = 3c$ Multiply

$\frac{56.4}{3} = \frac{3c}{3}$ Divide

$18.8 = c$ Simplify

The solution is 18.8.

Exercises

ALGEBRA Solve each proportion.

1. $\frac{x}{9} = \frac{16}{12}$ **12**
2. $\frac{32}{28} = \frac{w}{7}$ **8**
3. $\frac{5}{u} = \frac{60}{132}$ **11**
4. $\frac{36}{21} = \frac{24}{s}$ **14**
5. $\frac{a}{64} = \frac{225}{480}$ **30**
6. $\frac{42}{w} = \frac{56}{8}$ **6**
7. $\frac{1}{10} = \frac{m}{12}$ **1.2**
8. $\frac{5}{3} = \frac{85}{h}$ **51**
9. $\frac{24}{g} = \frac{2}{30}$ **360**
10. $\frac{f}{21} = \frac{57}{63}$ **19**
11. $\frac{22}{z} = \frac{121}{16.5}$ **3**
12. $\frac{2}{3} = \frac{k}{12.6}$ **8.4**
13. $\frac{r}{9} = \frac{5}{20}$ **2.25**
14. $\frac{d}{21} = \frac{1.5}{3.5}$ **9**
15. $\frac{46}{57.5} = \frac{360}{q}$ **450**
16. $\frac{4.2}{4.8} = \frac{d}{80}$ **70**
17. $\frac{1}{c} = \frac{4.5}{11.7}$ **2.6**
18. $\frac{0.3}{n} = \frac{4.75}{14.25}$ **0.9**
19. $\frac{9.1}{14.7} = \frac{1.3}{p}$ **2.1**
20. $\frac{0.4}{3} = \frac{y}{98.25}$ **13.1**
21. $\frac{v}{33.44} = \frac{1}{3.2}$ **10.45**

Chapter 6 29 Glencoe Pre-Algebra

Lesson 6-5

Practice CRM p. 32 AL OL BL ELL

NAME ________ DATE ______ PERIOD ______

6-5 Practice

Solving Proportions

Determine whether each pair of ratios forms a proportion.

1. $\frac{5}{8}, \frac{20}{32}$ **yes**
2. $\frac{12}{28}, \frac{27}{63}$ **yes**
3. $\frac{8}{50}, \frac{1}{43}$ **no**
4. $\frac{40}{48}, \frac{56}{42}$ **no**
5. $\frac{6.4}{16}, \frac{32}{80}$ **yes**
6. $\frac{12}{18}, \frac{90}{135}$ **yes**
7. $\frac{21}{24}, \frac{56}{64}$ **yes**
8. $\frac{9}{16}, \frac{3}{4}$ **no**
9. $\frac{12}{32}, \frac{8}{3}$ **no**
10. $\frac{2.6}{4}, \frac{4.6}{8}$ **no**
11. $\frac{5.1}{1.7}, \frac{7.5}{2.5}$ **yes**
12. $\frac{8.5}{25}, \frac{17}{50}$ **yes**

ALGEBRA Solve each proportion.

13. $\frac{n}{12} = \frac{6}{18}$ **4**
14. $\frac{8}{v} = \frac{56}{105}$ **15**
15. $\frac{15}{35} = \frac{s}{7}$ **3**
16. $\frac{24}{30} = \frac{8}{w}$ **10**
17. $\frac{c}{28} = \frac{5}{7}$ **20**
18. $\frac{3}{r} = \frac{39}{65}$ **5**
19. $\frac{9}{15} = \frac{m}{25}$ **15**
20. $\frac{7.5}{6.0} = \frac{3.6}{x}$ **2.88**
21. $\frac{12}{25} = \frac{u}{40}$ **19.2**
22. $\frac{1}{a} = \frac{33}{132}$ **4**
23. $\frac{f}{5} = \frac{16}{40}$ **2**
24. $\frac{r}{6.5} = \frac{0.2}{1.3}$ **1**
25. $\frac{30}{14} = \frac{k}{1.54}$ **3.3**
26. $\frac{3.5}{7.2} = \frac{k}{57.6}$ **28**
27. $\frac{2.1}{42} = \frac{7}{t}$ **140**

28. **FOOD** Gayle is making fruit punch that consists of 2 quarts of juice and 1 quart of soda water. How much soda water does she need if she has 5 quarts of juice? **2.5 qt**

Chapter 6 32 Glencoe Pre-Algebra

Word Problem Practice CRM p. 33 AL OL BL

NAME ________ DATE ______ PERIOD ______

6-5 Word Problem Practice

Solving Proportions

1. **RUNNING** Donna is planning to run a 13.1-mile half marathon. She tells of her plans to her European friend, who asks how many meters she will run. There are approximately 1609 meters in 1 mile. Write a proportion that could be used to find the distance of the marathon in meters.
$\frac{1 \text{ mi}}{1609 \text{ m}} = \frac{13.1 \text{ mi}}{x \text{ m}}$

2. **FLOWERS** The Tyler Municipal Rose Garden and Center in Tyler, Texas, is the nation's largest rose garden. It contains 38,000 rose bushes representing 500 varieties of roses set in a 14-acre park. Write a proportion that could be used to find the average number of rose bushes per acre.
$\frac{38{,}000 \text{ bushes}}{14 \text{ acres}} = \frac{x \text{ bushes}}{1 \text{ acre}}$

3. **RECYCLING** Ohio is the home of two of the world's largest aluminum smelters, in which metal is separated for recycling. Together, these two facilities process an average of 15 million pounds of aluminum each month. How many pounds of aluminum do the Ohio smelting plants average per week?
about 3.46 million lb

4. **TECHNOLOGY** Elton just bought a new flash drive for his computer. He read in the literature that 7 flash drives can hold 1792 megabytes of data. Write and solve a proportion to find the number of megabytes of data that 5 flash drives can hold.
$\frac{7}{1792} = \frac{5}{x}$; 1280

5. **COOKING** Ashley is planning breakfast for a family event. She wants to serve Deltan Waffles. She found this recipe, which serves 8 people.

Deltan Waffles	
$1\frac{3}{4}$ cups flour	$1\frac{1}{4}$ cups milk
$\frac{1}{2}$ teaspoon salt	$\frac{1}{2}$ cup shortening, melted
1 tablespoon baking powder	
2 egg yolks	2 egg whites

a. How much salt does she need if she uses 3 eggs? **$\frac{3}{4}$ tsp**

b. How much baking powder does she need if she wants to serve 12 people? **$1\frac{1}{2}$ tsp**

Chapter 6 33 Glencoe Pre-Algebra

Lesson 6-5

Lesson 6-5 Solving Proportions **291**

4 ASSESS

Crystal Ball Tell students to write how they think today's lesson on solving proportions will connect with tomorrow's lesson on scale drawings and models. Tell them to illustrate with an example how they think they could use a proportion to find the scale of a model.

Formative Assessment

Check for student understanding of concepts in Lessons 6-4 and 6-5.

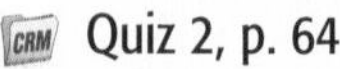 Quiz 2, p. 64

Additional Answers

47a. $\frac{100}{258} = \frac{s}{645}$

47b. 250 students

47c. $\frac{25}{258} = \frac{s}{220}$; about 21 students

Standardized Test Practice

44. Which equation could be used to find the total cost c if Fernando wanted to buy 8 pencils from the school store? **A**

A $c = 0.15 \cdot 8$
B $c = 0.45 \cdot 8$
C $c = 24 \cdot 0.45$
D $c = 0.15 \cdot 24$

45. A line to purchase concert tickets is moving at a rate of 5 feet every 20 minutes. At this rate, how long will a person have been in line if they have moved 30 feet? **J**

F 30 min
G 1 h
H 1 h 30 min
J 2 h

46. During her keyboarding test, Luisa typed 145 words in three minutes. Which of the following could *not* be used to determine the number of minutes it would take her to type 550 words? **D**

A $\frac{145}{3} = \frac{550}{w}$
B $\frac{3}{145} = \frac{w}{550}$
C $\frac{145}{550} = \frac{3}{w}$
D $\frac{145}{550} = \frac{w}{3}$

47. EXTENDED RESPONSE There are 258 eighth graders at Henderson Middle School. The graph shows how many of the eighth graders participate in each sport. **a–c. See margin.**

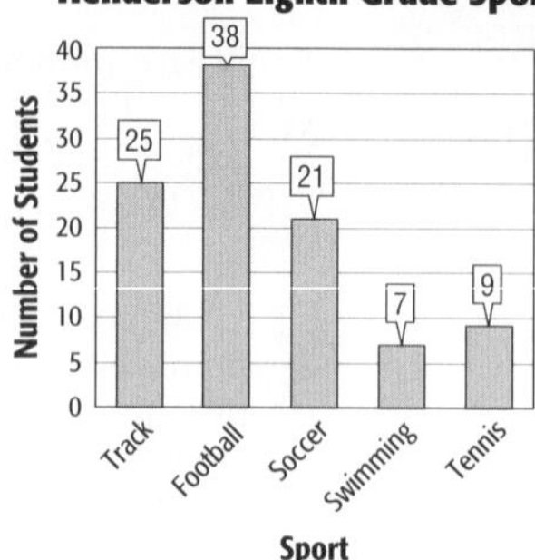

a. If each student participates in only one sport, write a proportion that could be used to predict how many students at Henderson Middle School participate in sports if there are 645 total students.

b. Solve the proportion in part **a.**

c. Write and solve a proportion that could be used to predict the number of eighth graders that participate in track if there are 220 total eighth graders.

Spiral Review

48. Determine whether the rental charge is proportional to the time. Explain your reasoning. (Lesson 6-4) **No; the rates are not equal.**

Time (hours)	1	2	3	4
Rental Charge	$13	$23	$33	$43

Use dimensional analysis to complete each conversion. Round to the nearest hundredth. (Lesson 6-3)

49. 5 in. ≈ ■ cm **12.7** (*Hint:* 1 in. ≈ 2.54 cm)

50. 10 km ≈ ■ mi **6.21** (*Hint:* 1 km ≈ 0.621 mi)

51. 26.3 cm ≈ ■ in. **10.36** (*Hint:* 1 cm ≈ 0.394 in.)

52. PLANES How long will it take an Air Force fighter jet to fly 5200 miles at 650 miles per hour? (Lesson 4-6) **8 h**

Skills Review

Find each product. (Lesson 3-3)

53. $\frac{4}{9} \cdot \frac{2}{3}$ $\frac{8}{27}$

54. $\frac{1}{5} \cdot \frac{1}{8}$ $\frac{1}{40}$

55. $\frac{3}{4} \cdot \frac{3}{5}$ $\frac{9}{20}$

56. $\frac{2}{5} \cdot \frac{5}{6}$ $\frac{1}{3}$

Differentiated Instruction 

Extension Natalie wants to paint a picture on her wall that is 15 feet long and 8 feet wide. First she draws the picture on a piece of paper, then she projects the picture onto the wall. If the drawing is 24 inches long, what is the ratio of the wall painting to the drawing? $\frac{15}{2}$ or 7.5
How wide will the drawing be if it is to fit on her wall? 12.8 in.

Inverse Proportions

Math Online glencoe.com
Math in Motion, Animation

Jon earns money for a class trip by selling T-shirts at a track meet with the Heritage Middle School Service Club. The club earned $220 from the T-shirt sale. The money will be equally divided among all the students who participated in the sale. The equation $d = \frac{220}{s}$ or $sd = 220$ represents this situation, where d is the number of dollars earned per student and s is the number of students.

ACTIVITY

Step 1 Copy and complete the table for the equation $sd = 220$.

Number of Students, s	Dollars Earned per Student, d
2	110
4	55
6	■ 36.67
8	■ 27.50
10	■ 22

Step 2 Copy the blank grid below. Graph the ordered pairs from Step 1. Then connect the points with a smooth curve.

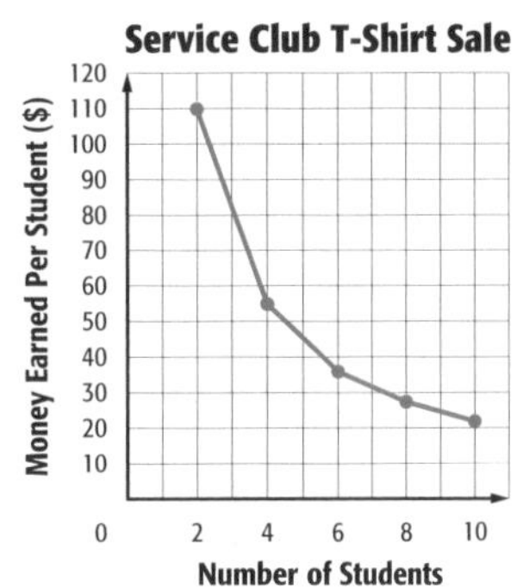

Analyze the Results

1. Is the number of students proportional to the dollars earned per student? Explain. No; Sample answer: The ratio of students to dollars earned is not a constant ratio.
2. What is different about the graph in Step 2 than other functions you have seen? It is not a linear function.
3. An **inverse proportion** is a relationship formed when the product of two variables is a constant. Which situation is an inverse proportion: each student earning $3 per T-shirt sold or the $220 in earnings being equally divided among the total number of students? Explain. 3. The earnings being equally divided among the students; Sample answer: The total amount each student receives multiplied by the number of students will always equal $220.
4. **GARDENS** A rectangular herb garden has an area of 36 square feet.
   a. Make a table of ordered pairs to represent possible dimensions for the garden. Then graph the ordered pairs (length, width). See Chapter 6 Answer Appendix.
   b. Is the relationship in the graph proportional or is it an inverse proportion? Explain. It is an inverse proportion because the product of length and width is a constant.
5. **JOGGING** On Monday, Lola jogs at an average rate of 8 miles per hour around a track. On Wednesday, she jogs 16 miles through a cross-country course at an unknown rate. Make a table of ordered pairs and a graph for each situation. Then decide whether each relationship is a proportion or an inverse proportion. See Chapter 6 Answer Appendix.

1 FOCUS

Objective Determine if a given situation is an inverse proportion. Graph inverse proportions.

Teaching Tip

Discuss with students how to graph points containing a decimal.

2 TEACH

Working in Cooperative Groups

Have students work in pairs of mixed abilities to complete Steps 1 and 2 of the Activity.

Ask:

- What did you notice about the graph? The graph is not a straight line.
- What could have kept the line from being straight? The ratio of students to dollars is not constant.

Practice Have students complete Exercises 1–5.

3 ASSESS

Formative Assessment

Use Exercises 4 and 5 to assess whether students understand inverse proportions.

From Concrete to Abstract

Have students create a problem with a relationship that is a proportion or an inverse proportion. Then trade with another student. Tell them to solve the problem and discuss their solutions.

Extending the Concept

Ask:

- What did you notice about the graphs of inverse proportions? The graphs are curves.

6-6 Lesson Notes

FOCUS

Vertical Alignment

Before Lesson 6-6
Write and solve proportions.

Lesson 6-6
Use and construct scale drawings.

After Lesson 6-6
Use ratios to solve problems involving similar figures.

TEACH

Scaffolding Questions

Have students read the *Why?* section of the lesson and answer the questions.

Ask:

- Suppose a plant in front of the White House has a width of one-half square. What is its actual width? 3.5 feet
- Suppose a sidewalk in front of the White House is 84 feet in length. How many squares long would this be on the drawing? 12 squares

6-6 Scale Drawings and Models

Then
You have already written and solved proportions. (Lesson 6-5)

Now
- Use scale drawings.
- Construct scale drawings.

New Vocabulary
scale drawing
scale model
scale
scale factor

Math Online
glencoe.com
- Extra Examples
- Personal Tutor
- Self-Check Quiz
- Homework Help

Why?

A scale drawing of the White House is drawn on grid paper. The length of one square on the grid paper represents 7 feet.

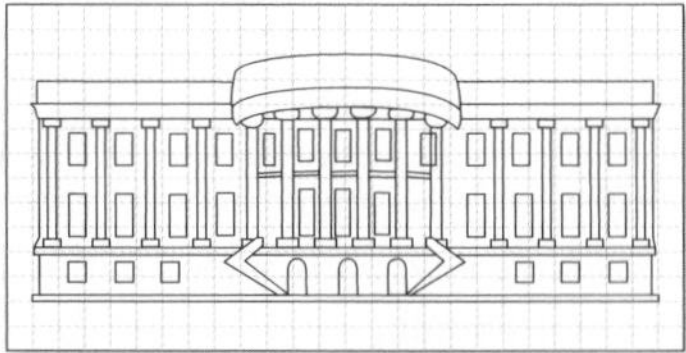

a. What is the actual length of the White House if its length on the drawing is 24 squares? **168 ft**

b. What is the actual height of the White House if its height on the drawing is 10 squares? **70 ft**

Use Scale Drawings and Models A **scale drawing** or a **scale model** is used to represent an object that is too large or too small to be drawn or built at actual size. The lengths and widths of objects on a scale drawing or model are proportional to the lengths and widths of the actual object.

The **scale** is determined by the ratio of a given length on the drawing or model to its corresponding length on the actual object. Consider the following scales.

1 in. = 3 ft — **1 inch represents an actual distance of 3 feet.**

1 cm = 2 mm — **1 centimeter represents an actual distance of 2 millimeters.**

Scales are written so that a unit length on the drawing or model is listed first.

Real-World EXAMPLE 1 Determine the Scale

INSECTS Suppose a model of a dragonfly has a wing length of 4 centimeters. If the length of the insect's actual wing is 6 centimeters, what is the scale of the model?

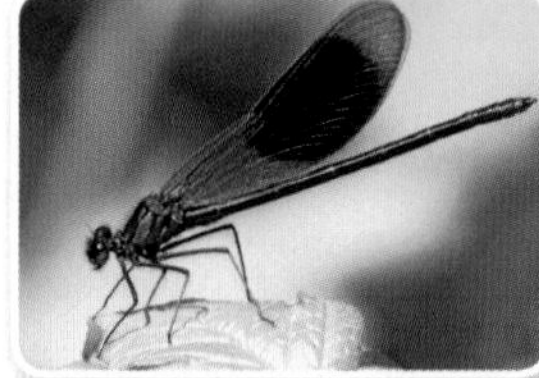

Let x represent the actual length.

Write and solve a proportion.

$$\frac{\text{model length}}{\text{actual length}} \rightarrow \frac{4 \text{ cm}}{6 \text{ cm}} = \frac{1 \text{ cm}}{x \text{ cm}} \leftarrow \frac{\text{model length}}{\text{actual length}}$$

$4 \cdot x = 6 \cdot 1$ — **Find the cross products.**

$4x = 6$ — **Simplify.**

$x = 1.5$ — **Divide each side by 4.**

So, the scale is 1 centimeter = 1.5 centimeters.

Check Your Progress

1. **ARCHITECTURE** The pillars of the World War II memorial in Washington, D.C., are 17 feet tall. A scale model of the memorial has pillars that are 5 inches tall. What is the scale of the model? **1 in. = 3.4 ft**

Personal Tutor glencoe.com

Lesson 6-6 Resources

Resource	Approaching-Level	On-Level	Beyond-Level	English Learners
Teacher Edition	• Differentiated Instruction, p. 295	• Differentiated Instruction, p. 295	• Differentiated Instruction, pp. 295, 299	• Differentiated Instruction, p. 295
Chapter Resource Masters	• Study Guide and Intervention, pp. 35–36 • Skills Practice, p. 37 • Practice, p. 38 • Word Problem Practice, p. 39 • Spreadsheet Activity, p. 41	• Study Guide and Intervention, pp. 35–36 • Skills Practice, p. 37 • Practice, p. 38 • Word Problem Practice, p. 39 • Enrichment, p. 40 • Spreadsheet Activity, p. 41	• Practice, p. 38 • Word Problem Practice, p. 39 • Enrichment, p. 40 • Spreadsheet Activity, p. 41	• Study Guide and Intervention, pp. 35–36 • Skills Practice, p. 37 • Practice, p. 38 • Spreadsheet Activity, p. 41
Transparencies	• 5-Minute Check Transparency 6-6	• 5-Minute Check Transparency 6-6	• 5-Minute Check Transparency 6-6	• 5-Minute Check Transparency 6-6
Other	• Study Notebook • Teaching Pre-Algebra with Manipulatives	• Study Notebook • Teaching Pre-Algebra with Manipulatives	• Study Notebook	• Study Notebook • Teaching Pre-Algebra with Manipulatives

If the scale drawing and model have the same unit of measure, the scale can be written without units. This is called the **scale factor.** Suppose a scale model has a scale of 1 inch = 2 feet.

scale → 1 inch = 2 feet → $\frac{1 \text{ inch}}{2 \text{ feet}}$ → $\frac{1 \text{ inch}}{24 \text{ inches}}$ → 1:24 ← scale factor

One unit on the model represents an actual distance of 24 units. So, the model is $\frac{1}{24}$ the size of the actual object.

Real-World EXAMPLE 2 Find Actual Measurements

ARCHITECTURE The blueprint of a skateboard ramp shows that its length is 11.4 inches. If the scale on the blueprint is 1 inch = 6 feet, what is the length of the actual skateboard ramp?

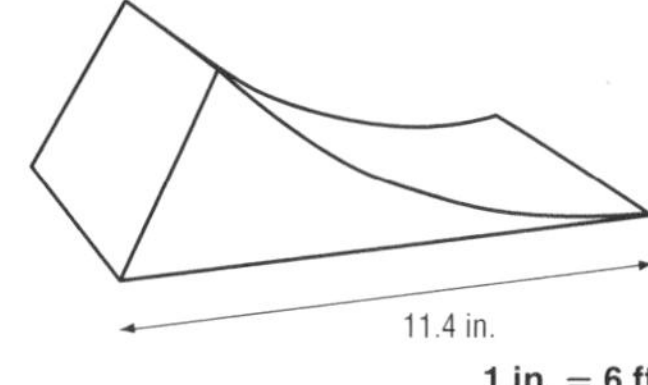

Method 1 Use a proportion.

Let x represent the actual length of the ramp. Write and solve a proportion.

plan length → $\frac{1 \text{ inch}}{6 \text{ feet}} = \frac{11.4 \text{ inches}}{x \text{ feet}}$ ← plan length
actual length → ← actual length

$1 \cdot x = 6 \cdot 11.4$ **Find the cross products.**

$x = 68.4$ **Simplify.**

StudyTip

Alternative Method You can also solve the proportion.

plan actual

$\frac{1 \text{ in.}}{11.4 \text{ in.}} = \frac{6 \text{ ft}}{x \text{ ft}}$

Method 2 Use the scale factor.

The actual length is proportional to the length on the scale drawing with a ratio of $\frac{1 \text{ inch}}{6 \text{ feet}}$.

Find the scale factor.

$\frac{1 \text{ inch}}{6 \text{ feet}} = \frac{1 \text{ inch}}{72 \text{ inches}}$ or $\frac{1}{72}$ **Convert 6 feet to inches and divide out units.**

The scale factor is $\frac{1}{72}$.

So, the actual length is 72 times the blueprint length.

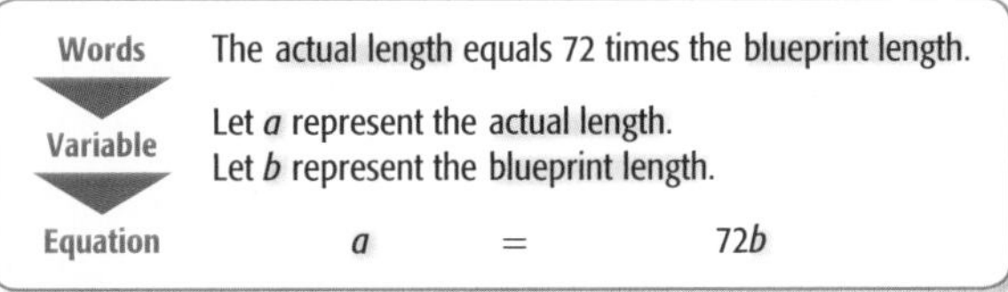

Words	The actual length equals 72 times the blueprint length.
Variable	Let a represent the actual length. Let b represent the blueprint length.
Equation	$a = 72b$

$a = 72b$ **Write the equation.**
$= 72(11.4)$ **Replace b with 11.4.**
$= 820.8$ **Simplify.**

The actual length of the ramp is 820.8 inches or 68.4 feet.

Check Your Progress

2. **EXHIBITS** A map of a natural history museum shows that the dinosaur exhibit room is 7.25 inches wide. If the scale on the map is 1 inch = 8 feet, what is the width of the actual exhibit room? 58 ft

Personal Tutor glencoe.com

Use Scale Drawings and Models

Example 1 shows how to determine the scale of a model. **Example 2** shows how to find actual measurements of an object.

Formative Assessment

Use the Check Your Progress exercises after each example to determine students' understanding of concepts.

Additional Examples

1. **MODEL CAR** A model car is 4 inches long. The actual car is 12 feet long. What is the scale of the model? 1 inch = 3 feet

2. **MAP** A map has a scale of 1 inch = 8 miles. Two towns are 3.25 inches apart on the map. What is the actual distance between the two towns? 26 miles

Additional Examples also in Interactive Classroom PowerPoint® Presentations

Tips for New Teachers

Preventing Errors Have students label terms not only with units of measurement, but also as "actual" and "model." This will help keep the terms in matching order on each side of the equation.

Differentiated Instruction

AL OL BL ELL

Intrapersonal Have each student find a magazine photo and tape a 0.25-inch grid transparency on top of it. Ask students to systematically copy the contents of each grid onto centimeter grid paper to make an enlargement. Encourage them to include both the photo and their drawing in their math journals, and ask them how it helped their understanding of scale and proportions.

Focus on Mathematical Content

Scale The dimensions of a scale model are proportional to the actual object. To find the scale of a model, set up a proportion with measurements in the same units. If the scale is known, use a proportion to find the dimensions of the model or actual object.

Construct Scale Drawings

Example 3 shows how to construct a scale drawing.

Additional Example

3 **PATIO DESIGN** Sheila is designing a patio that is 16 feet long and 14 feet wide. Make a scale drawing of the patio. Use a scale of 0.5 inches = 4 feet. Use $\frac{1}{4}$-inch grid paper. Check students' drawings. The length should be 2 inches and the width should be 1.75 inches.

Tips for New Teachers

Maps You may want to bring in road maps for students to look at as examples of scale drawings. Have them locate the scale and even find the distance between a few cities using the map scale.

Additional Answer

3.

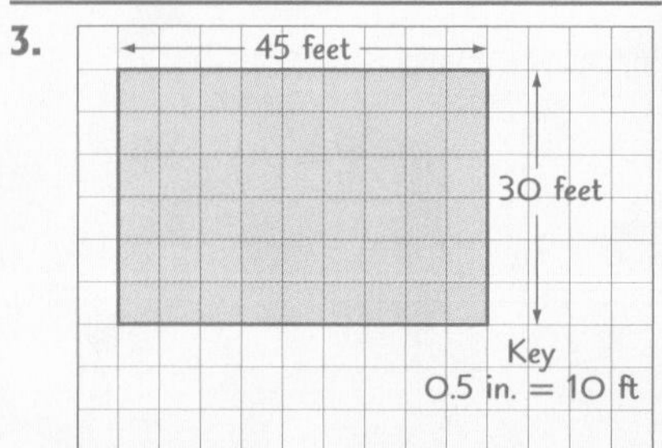

Construct Scale Drawings To construct a scale drawing of an object, use the actual measurements of the object and the scale to which the object is to be drawn.

Real-World EXAMPLE 3 Construct a Scale Drawing

ART Lila is painting a mural on a wall at the community center that measures 18 feet long and 12 feet tall. Make a scale drawing of the mural. Use a scale of $\frac{1}{4}$-inch = 3 feet. Use $\frac{1}{4}$-inch grid paper.

Step 1 Find the measure of the wall's length on the drawing. Let ℓ represent the length.

$$\frac{\text{drawing length} \rightarrow}{\text{actual length} \rightarrow} \quad \frac{\frac{1}{4}\text{ inch}}{3\text{ feet}} = \frac{\ell\text{ inches}}{18\text{ feet}} \quad \frac{\leftarrow \text{drawing length}}{\leftarrow \text{actual length}}$$

$\frac{1}{4} \cdot 18 = 3 \cdot \ell$ — **Find the cross products.**

$4.5 = 3\ell$ — **Simplify.**

$\frac{4.5}{3} = \frac{3\ell}{3}$ — **Divide each side by 3.**

$1.5 = \ell$ — **Simplify.**

On the drawing, the length is 1.5 or $1\frac{1}{2}$ inches.

Step 2 Find the measure of the wall's height on the drawing. Let w represent the width.

$$\frac{\text{drawing width} \rightarrow}{\text{actual width} \rightarrow} \quad \frac{\frac{1}{4}\text{ inch}}{3\text{ feet}} = \frac{w\text{ inches}}{12\text{ feet}} \quad \frac{\leftarrow \text{drawing width}}{\leftarrow \text{actual width}}$$

$\frac{1}{4} \cdot 12 = 3 \cdot w$ — **Find the cross products.**

$3 = 3w$ — **Simplify.**

$\frac{3}{3} = \frac{3w}{3}$ — **Divide each side by 3.**

$1 = w$ — **Simplify.**

On the drawing, the height is 1 inch.

Step 3 Make the scale drawing.

Use $\frac{1}{4}$ inch grid paper. Since $1\frac{1}{2}$ inches = 6 squares and 1 inch = 4 squares, draw a rectangle that is 4 squares by 6 squares.

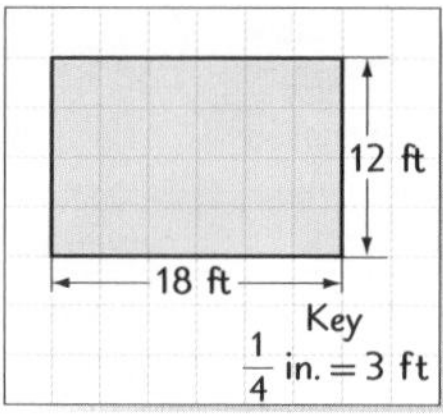

Real-World Career

Landscape Architect Landscape architects use computer sketches and models to design and show outdoor spaces.

A job in this profession requires a degree in landscape architecture which takes 4–5 years to complete.

Source: Bureau of Labor Statistics and ASLA

Check Your Progress

3. **SCHOOL BUILDINGS** An architect is designing a school courtyard that is 45 feet long and 30 feet wide. Make a scale drawing of the courtyard. Use a scale of 0.5 inch = 10 feet. Use $\frac{1}{4}$-inch grid paper. **See margin.**

Personal Tutor glencoe.com

TEACH with TECH

DOCUMENT CAMERA Have students create their own scale drawings and models. Ask several students to present different drawings of the same object, and show how different scales change the appearance of the drawing. Take pictures of the drawings and distribute them to the class.

Check Your Understanding

Example 1 p. 294

1. **CARS** The model of a car is shown at the right. The actual car is $14\frac{1}{2}$ feet long. What is the scale of the model car? **1 in. = 2 ft**

Example 2 p. 295

2. **MAPS** On the map, the scale is 1 inch = 20 miles. What is the actual distance between Kansas City and St. Louis? **260 mi**

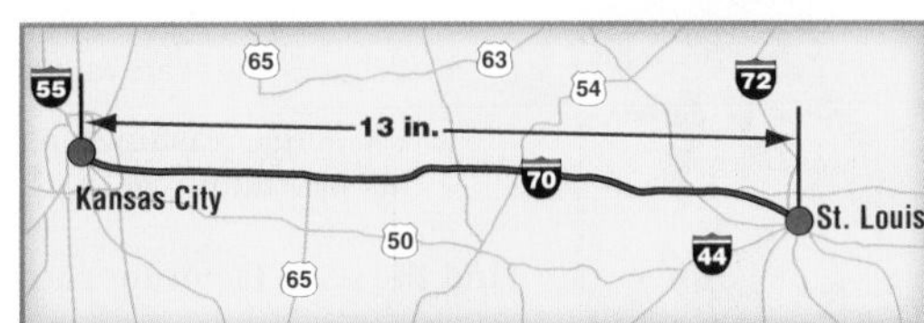

Example 3 p. 296

3. **GARDENS** Marco is designing a flower garden in his backyard that is 12 feet long and 10 feet wide. Make a scale drawing of the room. Use a scale of 0.5 inch = 2 feet. Use $\frac{1}{4}$-inch grid paper. **See margin.**

Practice and Problem Solving

Example 1 p. 294

4. **AIRPLANES** A model airplane is built with a wing span of 23 inches. The actual wing span is 92 feet. Find the scale. **1 in. = 4 ft**

5. **FLAGS** The largest American flag in existence measures 255 feet wide. In an advertisement for renting this flag, the image of the flag is 4 inches wide. What is the scale of the flag? **1 in. = 63.75 ft**

Example 2 p. 295

6. **ARCHITECTURE** A floor plan is shown for the first floor of a new house. If one inch represents 24 feet, what are the actual dimensions of each of the rooms listed?

   a. living room **15 ft by 18 ft** b. deck **30 ft by 9 ft** c. kitchen **9 ft by 18 ft**

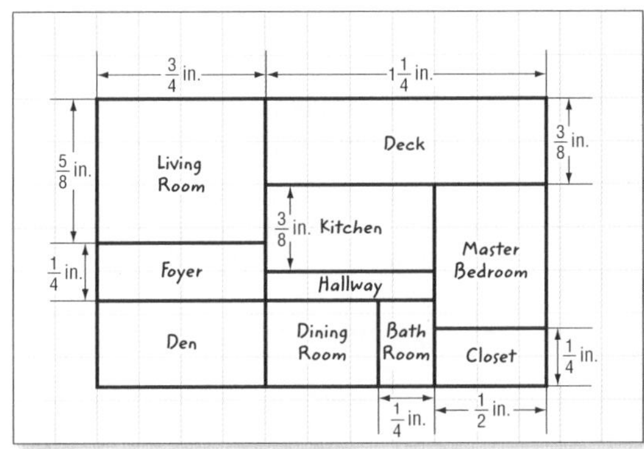

7. **ARCHITECTURE** The actual measurements for rooms are given. Using the floor plan and scale above, find the measurements on the floor plan.

   a. master bedroom 12 feet by 15 feet b. den 18 feet by 9 feet c. dining room 12 feet by 9 feet

7a. $\frac{1}{2}$ in. by $\frac{5}{8}$ in.

7b. $\frac{3}{4}$ in. by $\frac{3}{8}$ in.

7c. $\frac{1}{2}$ in. by $\frac{3}{8}$ in.

3 PRACTICE

Formative Assessment

Use Exercises 1–3 to check for understanding.

Use the chart at the bottom of this page to customize assignments for your students.

Additional Answer

3.

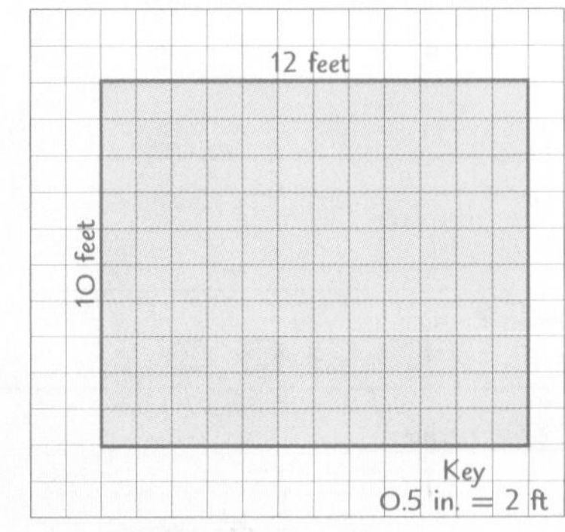

Differentiated Homework Options

Level	Assignment	Two-Day Option	
AL Basic	4–8, 19, 21, 22, 24–42	5, 7, 25–28	4–8 even, 19, 21, 22, 24, 29–42
OL Core	5–9 odd, 10, 11–17 odd, 18, 19, 21, 22, 24–42	4–8, 25–28	9–19, 21, 22, 24, 29–42
BL Advanced	9–36 (optional: 37–42)		

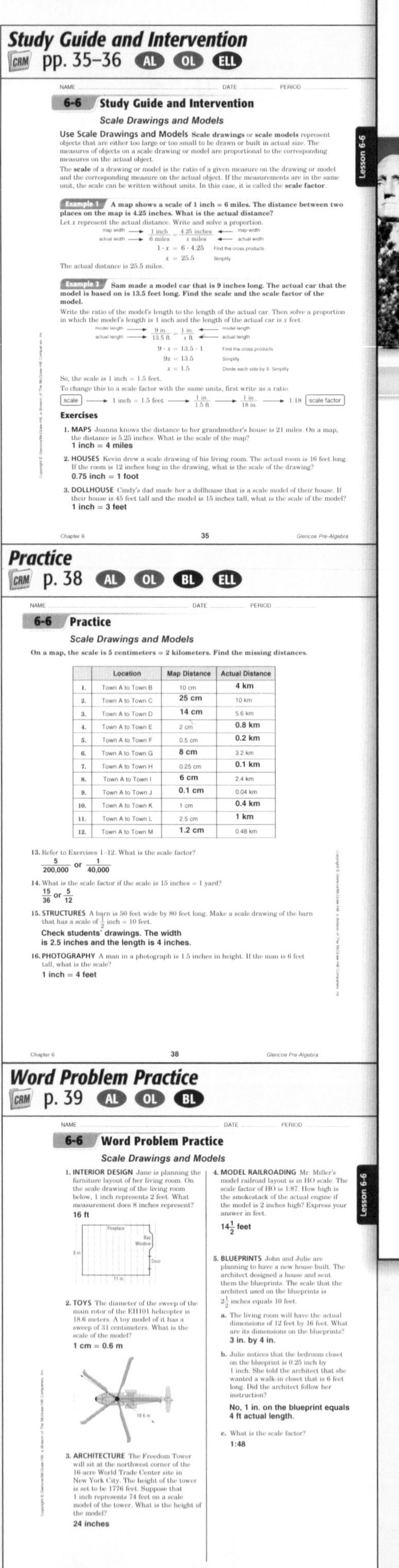
Study Guide and Intervention
CRM pp. 35–36 AL OL ELL

NAME ______ DATE ______ PERIOD ______

6-6 Study Guide and Intervention
Scale Drawings and Models

Use Scale Drawings and Models Scale drawings or scale models represent objects that are either too large or too small to be drawn or built in actual size. The measures of objects on a scale drawing or model are proportional to the corresponding measures on the actual object.
The **scale** of a drawing or model is the ratio of a given measure on the drawing or model and the corresponding measure on the actual object. If the measurements are in the same unit, the scale can be written without units. In this case, it is called the **scale factor**.

Example 1 A map shows a scale of 1 inch = 6 miles. The distance between two places on the map is 4.25 inches. What is the actual distance?
Let x represent the actual distance. Write and solve a proportion.
$\frac{1 \text{ inch}}{6 \text{ miles}} = \frac{4.25 \text{ inches}}{x \text{ miles}}$
$1 \cdot x = 6 \cdot 4.25$ Find the cross products
$x = 25.5$ Simplify
The actual distance is 25.5 miles.

Example 2 Sam made a model car that is 9 inches long. The actual car that the model is based on is 13.5 feet long. Find the scale and the scale factor of the model.
Write the ratio of the model's length to the length of the actual car. Then solve a proportion in which the model's length is 1 inch and the length of the actual car is x feet.
$\frac{9 \text{ in.}}{13.5 \text{ ft}} = \frac{1 \text{ in.}}{x \text{ ft}}$
$9 \cdot x = 13.5 \cdot 1$ Find the cross products
$9x = 13.5$ Simplify
$x = 1.5$ Divide each side by 9. Simplify
So, the scale is 1 inch = 1.5 feet.
To change this to a scale factor with the same units, first write as a ratio.
scale → 1 inch = 1.5 feet → $\frac{1 \text{ in.}}{1.5 \text{ ft}}$ = $\frac{1 \text{ in.}}{18 \text{ in.}}$ → 1:18 scale factor

Exercises
1. MAPS Joanna knows the distance to her grandmother's house is 21 miles. On a map, the distance is 5.25 inches. What is the scale of the map? **1 inch = 4 miles**
2. HOUSES Kevin drew a scale drawing of his living room. The actual room is 16 feet long. If the room is 12 inches long in the drawing, what is the scale of the drawing? **0.75 inch = 1 foot**
3. DOLLHOUSE Cindy's dad made her a dollhouse that is a scale model of their house. If their house is 45 feet tall and the model is 15 inches tall, what is the scale of the model? **1 inch = 3 feet**

Chapter 6 35 Glencoe Pre-Algebra

Practice
CRM p. 38 AL OL BL ELL

NAME ______ DATE ______ PERIOD ______

6-6 Practice
Scale Drawings and Models

On a map, the scale is 5 centimeters = 2 kilometers. Find the missing distances.

	Location	Map Distance	Actual Distance
1.	Town A to Town B	10 cm	4 km
2.	Town A to Town C	25 cm	10 km
3.	Town A to Town D	14 cm	5.6 km
4.	Town A to Town E	2 cm	0.8 km
5.	Town A to Town F	0.5 cm	0.2 km
6.	Town A to Town G	8 cm	3.2 km
7.	Town A to Town H	0.25 cm	0.1 km
8.	Town A to Town I	6 cm	2.4 km
9.	Town A to Town J	0.1 cm	0.04 km
10.	Town A to Town K	1 cm	0.4 km
11.	Town A to Town L	2.5 cm	1 km
12.	Town A to Town M	1.2 cm	0.48 km

13. Refer to Exercises 1–12. What is the scale factor? $\frac{5}{200{,}000}$ or $\frac{1}{40{,}000}$
14. What is the scale factor if the scale is 15 inches = 1 yard? $\frac{15}{36}$ or $\frac{5}{12}$
15. STRUCTURES A barn is 50 feet wide by 80 feet long. Make a scale drawing of the barn that has a scale of $\frac{1}{4}$ inch = 10 feet. **Check students' drawings. The width is 2.5 inches and the length is 4 inches.**
16. PHOTOGRAPHY A man in a photograph is 1.5 inches in height. If the man is 6 feet tall, what is the scale? **1 inch = 4 feet**

Chapter 6 38 Glencoe Pre-Algebra

Word Problem Practice
CRM p. 39 AL OL BL

NAME ______ DATE ______ PERIOD ______

6-6 Word Problem Practice
Scale Drawings and Models

1. INTERIOR DESIGN Jane is planning the furniture layout of her living room. On the scale drawing of the living room below, 1 inch represents 2 feet. What measurement does 8 inches represent? **16 ft**
2. TOYS The diameter of the sweep of the main rotor of the EH101 helicopter is 18.6 meters. A toy model of it has a sweep of 31 centimeters. What is the scale of the model? **1 cm = 0.6 m**
3. ARCHITECTURE The Freedom Tower will sit at the northwest corner of the 16-acre World Trade Center site in New York City. The height of the tower is set to be 1776 feet. Suppose that 1 inch represents 74 feet on a scale model of the tower. What is the height of the model? **24 inches**
4. MODEL RAILROADING Mr. Miller's model railroad layout is in HO scale. The scale factor of HO is 1:87. How high is the smokestack of the actual engine if the model is 2 inches high? Express your answer in feet. **$14\frac{1}{2}$ feet**
5. BLUEPRINTS John and Julie are planning to have a new house built. The architect designed a house and sent them the blueprints. The scale that the architect used on the blueprints is $2\frac{1}{2}$ inches equals 10 feet.
a. The living room will have the actual dimensions of 12 feet by 16 feet. What are its dimensions on the blueprints? **3 in. by 4 in.**
b. Julie notices that the bedroom closet on the blueprint is 0.25 inch by 1 inch. She told the architect that she wanted a walk-in closet that is 6 feet long. Did the architect follow her instruction? **No, 1 in. on the blueprint equals 4 ft actual length.**
c. What is the scale factor? **1:48**

Chapter 6 39 Glencoe Pre-Algebra

Example 3 p. 296

8. **SKATEPARKS** A skatepark is 24 yards wide by 48 yards long. Make a scale drawing of the skatepark that has a scale of $\frac{1}{4}$ in. = 8 yd. **See margin.**

9. **BEDROOMS** Create a scale factor that relates inches to feet and use it to make a scale drawing of your bedroom. **See students' work.**

10. **MONUMENTS Use the information at the left to answer the following.**
    a. Find the length of Roosevelt's moustache on the monument. **20 ft**
    b. What is the scale factor? $\frac{1}{12}$
    c. If George Washington's face is 60 feet tall on the monument, how tall is his face on the model? **60 in. or 5 ft**

Real-World Link

The actual Mount Rushmore carving was made from a scale model with a scale of 1 in. = 1 ft. On the model, Teddy Roosevelt's moustache was 1 foot 8 inches long.

Source: Bureau of Labor Statistics

Find the scale factor for each scale.

11. 6 in. = 10 ft $\frac{1}{20}$
12. 10 cm = 5 m $\frac{1}{50}$
13. 0.5 in. = 3 ft $\frac{1}{72}$
14. 5 ft = 15 yd $\frac{1}{9}$
15. 4 cm = 2.5 mm $\frac{16}{1}$
16. 8 in. = 200 mi $\frac{1}{1584000}$

17. **PLANETS** The 8 planets' distance from the Sun is shown in the table at the right.
    a. What scale would you use to create a scale drawing? **See margin.**
    b. Use centimeter grid paper and your scale from part **a** to create a map of the six planets closest to the Sun. **See Chapter 6 Answer Appendix.**

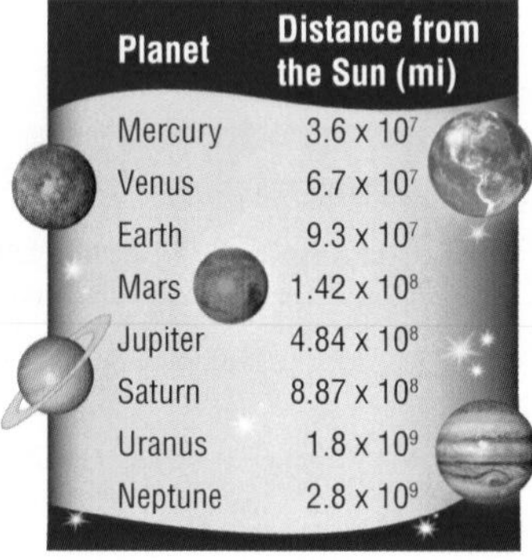

Planet	Distance from the Sun (mi)
Mercury	3.6×10^7
Venus	6.7×10^7
Earth	9.3×10^7
Mars	1.42×10^8
Jupiter	4.84×10^8
Saturn	8.87×10^8
Uranus	1.8×10^9
Neptune	2.8×10^9

18. You build a model with a scale of 1:25. Your friend builds a model of the same object with a scale of 1:50. Which model is bigger? Explain. **your model; Sample answer: $\frac{1}{50} < \frac{1}{25}$**

H.O.T. Problems
Use Higher-Order Thinking Skills

19. **OPEN ENDED** Find a small rectangular item you use on a daily basis. Make a scale drawing of that item. Then write a problem based on your scale drawing. **See students' work.**

20. **CHALLENGE** Rectangle $ABCD$ is reduced by a scale factor $\frac{1}{2}$. What is the area of the new rectangle? **12 in^2**

(Figure: rectangle with vertices A, B, C, D; Area = 48 in^2)

21. **REASONING** Determine whether the following statement is *always*, *sometimes*, or *never* true. Justify your reasoning. *If the scale factor of a scale drawing is greater than one, the scale drawing is larger than the actual object.*

22. **WHICH ONE DOESN'T BELONG?** Identify the scale that does not have the same scale factor. Explain your reasoning.

5 cm = 1 m	10 mm = 20 cm	10 cm = 10 m	25 mm = 0.5 m

23. **CHALLENGE** A model of an insect has a scale of 0.25 cm = 1 mm. Is the model *smaller* or *larger* than the actual insect? Justify your reasoning by using the scale factor.

24. **WRITING IN MATH** Compare and contrast *scale* and *scale factor*. **See margin.**

21. **always; Sample answer: A scale factor of $\frac{3}{1}$ means that 3 units is equal to 1 unit so the scale drawing or model will be larger than the actual object.**

22. **10 cm = 10 m; Sample answer: All of the other scales have a scale factor of $\frac{1}{20}$. 10 cm = 10 m has a scale factor of $\frac{1}{100}$.**

23. **Sample answer: The model is larger than the actual insect. The scale factor is $\frac{2.5}{1}$ which means the model is 2.5 times as large as the insect.**

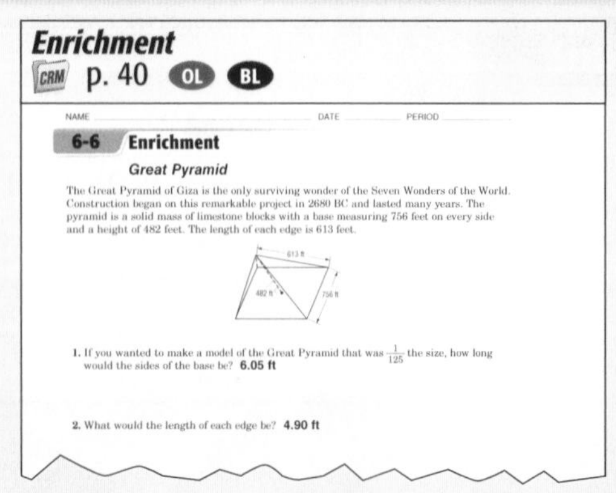
Enrichment
CRM p. 40 OL BL

NAME ______ DATE ______ PERIOD ______

6-6 Enrichment
Great Pyramid

The Great Pyramid of Giza is the only surviving wonder of the Seven Wonders of the World. Construction began on this remarkable project in 2680 BC and lasted many years. The pyramid is a solid mass of limestone blocks with a base measuring 756 feet on every side and a height of 482 feet. The length of each edge is 613 feet.

1. If you wanted to make a model of the Great Pyramid that was $\frac{1}{125}$ the size, how long would the sides of the base be? **6.05 ft**

2. What would the length of each edge be? **4.90 ft**

Tips for New Teachers

Writing in Math You can collaborate with an English teacher to help your students write compare and contrast essays. You and the other teacher can grade for content and form.

Standardized Test Practice

25. Desiree is drawing a model of the Washington Monument which has an actual height of 555.5 feet. **B**

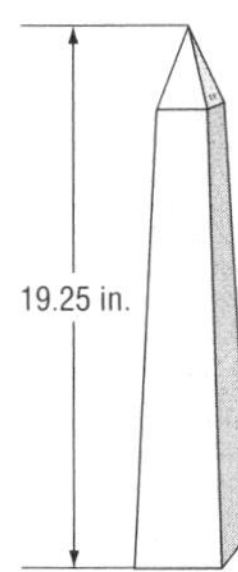

What other information is needed to find the length of the model's sides on the square base?

A the height of the top of the tower
B the length of the actual base side
C the age of the tower
D the height of the tower's first story

26. GRIDDED RESPONSE A blueprint has a scale of 2 inches = 2 feet. What is the scale factor of the blueprint? **1/12**

27. A scale drawing of a swimming pool is shown. **H**

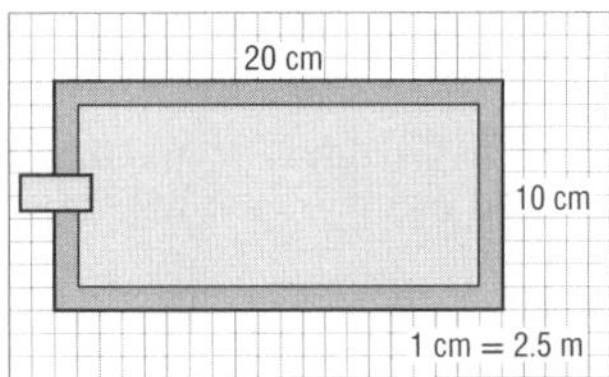

What are the actual dimensions of the swimming pool?

F 8 meters by 4 meters
G 20 meters by 10 meters
H 50 meters by 25 meters
J 80 meters by 40 meters

28. A map has a scale of 1.5 inches = 500 miles. How many inches on the map would represent 850 miles? Round to the nearest tenth. **C**

A 2.2 inches
B 2.4 inches
C 2.6 inches
D 2.8 inches

Spiral Review

ALGEBRA Solve each proportion. (Lesson 6-5)

29. $\frac{p}{6} = \frac{24}{36}$ **4**

30. $\frac{4}{10} = \frac{8}{a}$ **20**

31. $\frac{18}{12} = \frac{24}{q}$ **16**

32. $\frac{5}{h} = \frac{10}{30}$ **15**

33. $\frac{7}{45} = \frac{x}{9}$ **1.4**

34. $\frac{7}{5} = \frac{10.5}{b}$ **7.5**

35. PLANTS Some species of bamboo can grow 245 inches in a week. Write an equation relating the height of the bamboo to the number of days. How much would a bamboo plant have grown after 3 days? (Lesson 6-4) **$h = 35d$; 105 in.**

36. OLYMPICS The conversion factor for changing meters to feet is 1 meter ≈ 3.28 feet. Find the approximate distance in feet of the 110-meter dash. (Lesson 6-3)

$\frac{1 \text{ m}}{3.28 \text{ ft}} = \frac{110 \text{ m}}{x \text{ ft}}$; **about 360.8 ft**

Skills Review

Solve each equation. (Lesson 4-4)

37. $4t = 36$ **9**

38. $52 = 13n$ **4**

39. $6.2m = 114.08$ **18.4**

40. $5x = 3.5$ **0.7**

41. $7.8 = 3b$ **2.6**

42. $9.4 = 4g$ **2.35**

Differentiated Instruction

Extension Ask students to solve the following problem: For a school project, Jorge needs to make a map of the United States. The map will be on paper that is about 24 inches wide. If the actual width of the U.S. is about 3000 miles, what should the scale of the map be? 1 inch = 125 miles

Exercise Alert

Grid Paper Exercise 17 requires the use of centimeter grid paper.

ASSESS

Yesterday's News Have students write how yesterday's lesson on solving proportions helped them in learning today's material. Which ideas are the same? Which are different?

Additional Answers

8.

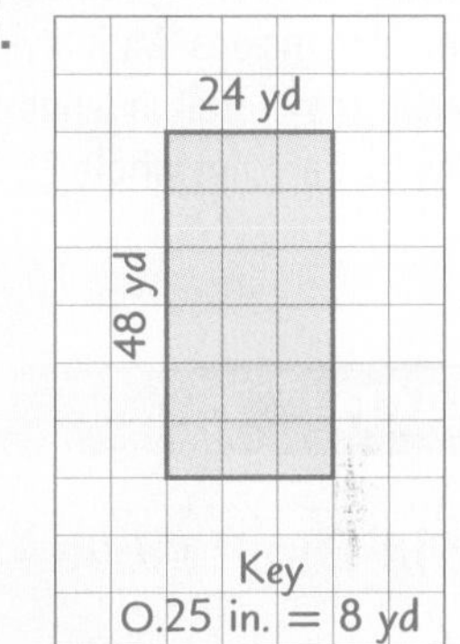

17a. Sample answer: $\frac{1}{4}$ in. = 3.0×10^7mi

24. Sample answer: The scale is the ratio of the length on the model with an actual length. The units of measure can be different. The scale factor is also a ratio, but the units of measure must be the same.

EXPLORE 6-7 Lesson Notes

1 FOCUS

Objective Use scale factor to draw enlargements and reductions.

Materials for Each Student

- grid paper

Teaching Tip

Remind students to be careful as they figure the new dimensions. Multiplying by a scale factor may result in lengths and/or widths that are not whole numbers.

TEACH

Working in Cooperative Groups

Put students in pairs of mixed abilities. Have them do Activities 1 and 2.

Ask:

- What happened to the length of the sides of the figures? In Activity 1, the sides increased, and in Activity 2, the sides decreased.
- What happened to the angles? They remained the same.

Practice Have students complete Exercises 1–5.

ASSESS

Formative Assessment

Use Exercises 4 and 5 to assess whether students understand that multiplying by a scale factor results in similar figures whose angles stay the same and whose sides increase or decrease depending on the size of the scale factor.

EXPLORE 6-7

Geometry Lab Similar Figures

Math Online glencoe.com
Math *in Motion,* Animation

Have you ever used a copy machine to make an enlargement or reduction of a drawing? In these activities, you will draw enlargements and reductions.

ACTIVITY 1

Step 1 On grid paper, draw a rectangle with a length of 5 inches and a width of 2 inches. This is the original figure.

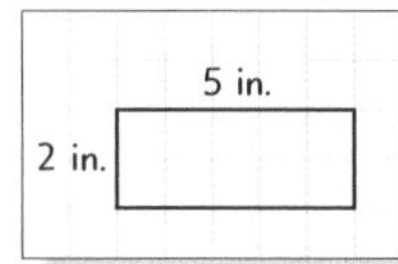

Step 2 Use a scale factor of 1.5. Draw a new rectangle with a length that is 1.5×5 inches and a width that is 1.5×2 inches.

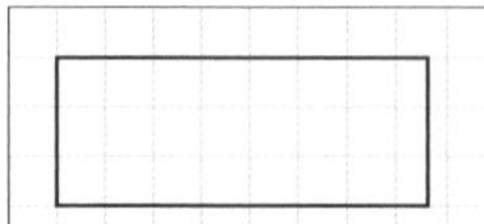

ACTIVITY 2

Step 1 On grid paper, draw a right triangle with legs that measure 3 inches and 4 inches. This is the original figure.

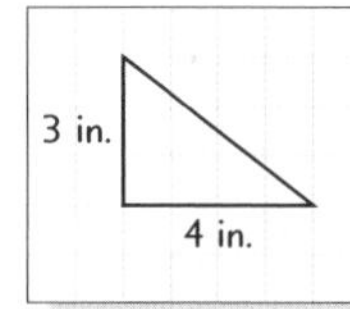

Step 2 Use a scale factor of $\frac{1}{2}$. Draw a new triangle with legs that measure $\frac{1}{2} \times 3$ inches and $\frac{1}{2} \times 4$ inches.

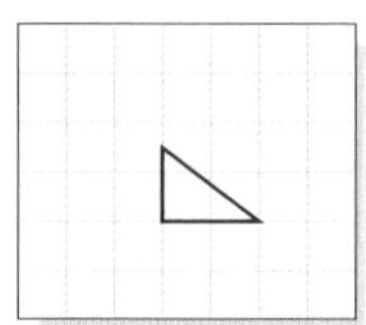

Analyze the Results

1. What are the dimensions of the new rectangle in Activity 1? Is the new rectangle an enlargement or a reduction? **7.5×3 in.; enlargement**
2. What are the dimensions of the new triangle in Activity 2? Is the new triangle an enlargement or a reduction? **$1\frac{1}{2} \times 2$ in.; reduction**
3. How do the sizes of the angles appear to compare in each pair of figures? Do you notice any patterns? **The angles of the scaled figure are equal to the angles of the original figure.**
4. How do the lengths of the sides of the figures compare? **See margin.**
5. **MAKE A CONJECTURE** Repeat Steps 1 and 2 using different figures and different scale factors. What kinds of scale factors result in an enlargement? reduction? **See margin.**

From Concrete to Abstract

A rectangle is 24 centimeters by 30 centimeters. Multiplying the dimensions by a scale factor changes it to 4.8 centimeters by 6 centimeters. What do you know about the size of the scale factor? What is the scale factor? Since the figure is reduced in size, the scale factor is less than 1; $\frac{1}{5}$

Additional Answers

4. The lengths of the sides of the scaled figure are proportional to the sides of the original figure.
5. Scale factors greater than 1 result in enlargements and scale factors less than 1 result in reductions.

Similar Figures

Then

You have already used scales and scale factors to make scale drawings of objects. (Lesson 6-6)

Now

- Find missing measures of similar figures.
- Use scale factors to solve problems.

New Vocabulary

similar figures
corresponding parts
congruent

Math Online

glencoe.com

- Extra Examples
- Personal Tutor
- Self-Check Quiz
- Homework Help

Why?

A fractal is a geometric image that can be divided into parts that are smaller copies of the whole.

a–b. See Chapter 6 Answer Appendix.

a. The image repeats itself infinitely many times. Research the definition of infinity. Does the image represent an infinite pattern?

b. A fractal is considered to be *self-similar*. Using the image, create your own definition of the term *self-similar*.

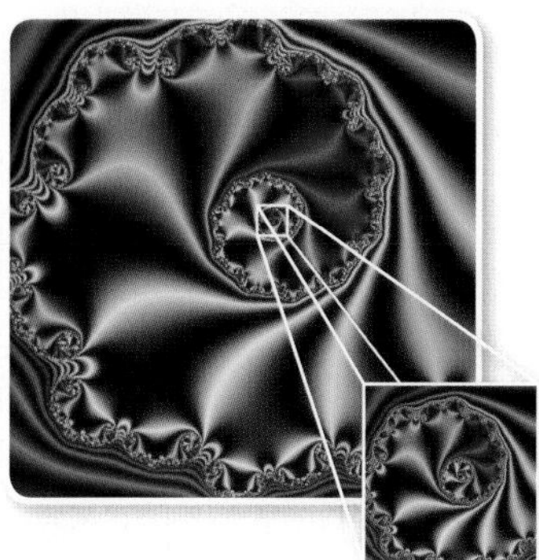

Corresponding Parts of Similar Figures **Similar figures** are figures that have the same shape but not necessarily the same size. Figure *ABCD* is similar to figure *EFGH*. In symbols, $ABCD \sim EFGH$.

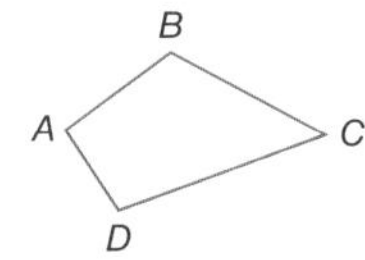

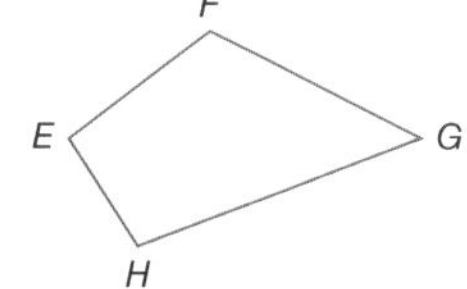

Similar figures have **corresponding parts**. These are angles and sides in the same position.

Corresponding Angles		Corresponding Sides	
$\angle A \leftrightarrow \angle E$	$\angle C \leftrightarrow \angle G$	$\overline{AB} \leftrightarrow \overline{EF}$	$\overline{CD} \leftrightarrow \overline{GH}$
$\angle B \leftrightarrow \angle F$	$\angle D \leftrightarrow \angle H$	$\overline{BC} \leftrightarrow \overline{FG}$	$\overline{DA} \leftrightarrow \overline{HE}$

Key Concept — Similar Triangles

For Your FOLDABLE

Words If two figures are similar, then

- the corresponding angles are **congruent**, or have the same measure, and
- the corresponding sides are proportional and opposite corresponding angles

Model

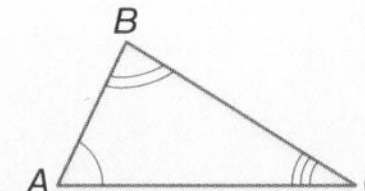

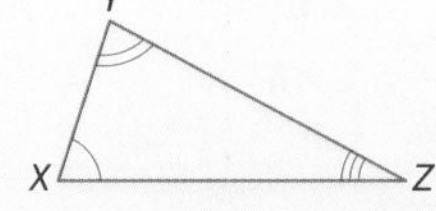

Symbols $\triangle ABC \sim \triangle XYZ$

$\angle A \cong \angle X$, $\angle B \cong \angle Y$, $\angle C \cong \angle Z$ and $\frac{AB}{XY} = \frac{BC}{YZ} = \frac{AC}{XZ}$

The symbol $\cong$ is read *is congruent to*. Arcs are used to show congruent angles.

Vertical Alignment

Before Lesson 6-7
Use scales and scale factors to make scale drawings of objects.

Lesson 6-7
Find missing measures of similar figures. Use scale factors to solve problems.

After Lesson 6-7
Use ratios to solve problems involving similar figures.

Scaffolding Questions

Have students read the *Why?* section of the lesson and answer the questions.

Ask:

- What in nature demonstrates self-similarity? (Think of items that if you looked at a piece, it would resemble the whole.) Sample answer: limbs from trees; one floret from a bunch of broccoli
- Suppose you were going to plant a rectangular garden in your backyard. You draw a scale drawing of the garden to help you plan. How is the drawing like the actual garden? How is it different? The drawing is the same shape as the actual garden, but it is smaller than the actual garden by a proportional amount.

Lesson 6-7 Resources

Resource	Approaching-Level	On-Level	Beyond-Level	English Learners
Teacher Edition	• Differentiated Instruction, p. 302		• Differentiated Instruction, p. 306	
Chapter Resource Masters	• Study Guide and Intervention, pp. 42–43 • Skills Practice, p. 44 • Practice, p. 45 • Word Problem Practice, p. 46	• Study Guide and Intervention, pp. 42–43 • Skills Practice, p. 44 • Practice, p. 45 • Word Problem Practice, p. 46 • Enrichment, p. 47	• Practice, p. 45 • Word Problem Practice, p. 46 • Enrichment, p. 47	• Study Guide and Intervention, pp. 42–43 • Skills Practice, p. 44 • Practice, p. 45
Transparencies	• 5-Minute Check Transparency 6-7	• 5-Minute Check Transparency 6-7	• 5-Minute Check Transparency 6-7	• 5-Minute Check Transparency 6-7
Other	• Study Notebook • Teaching Pre-Algebra with Manipulatives	• Study Notebook • Teaching Pre-Algebra with Manipulatives	• Study Notebook	• Study Notebook • Teaching Pre-Algebra with Manipulatives

Tips for New Teachers

Similarity The symbol ~ is read *is similar to.* When writing $\triangle ABC \sim \triangle XYZ$, make sure that corresponding vertices are listed in the same order.

Corresponding Parts of Similar Figures

Example 1 shows how to find measures of similar figures.

Formative Assessment

Use the Check Your Progress exercises after each example to determine students' understanding of concepts.

Additional Example

1 The figures are similar. Find each missing measure.

a.

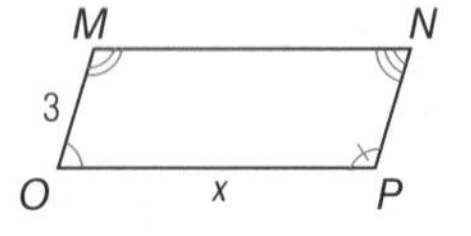

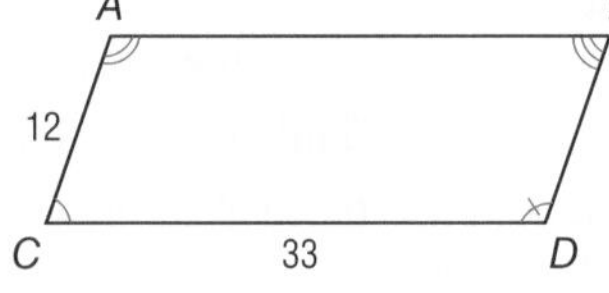

8.25

b.

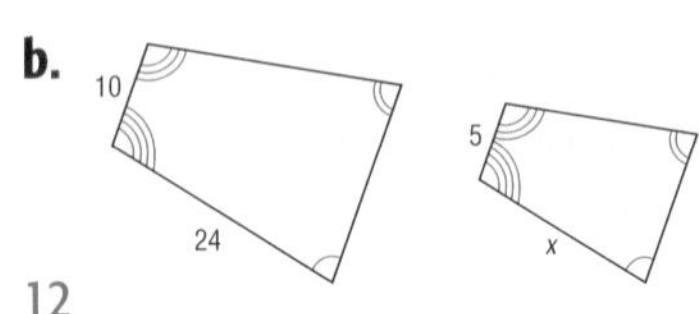

12

Additional Examples also in Interactive Classroom PowerPoint® Presentations

IWB INTERACTIVE WHITEBOARD READY

Since corresponding sides are proportional, you can use a proportion or the scale factor to determine the measures of the sides of similar figures when some measures are known.

EXAMPLE 1 Find Measures of Similar Figures

The figures are similar. Find each missing measure.

a.

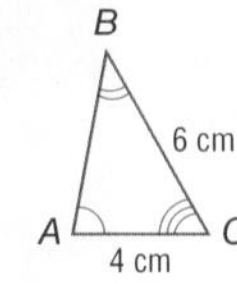

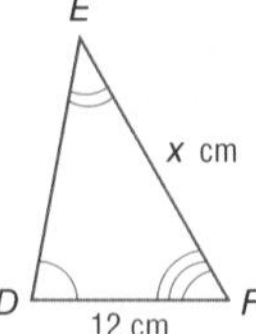

> **StudyTip**
>
> **Alternative Method** You can also use ratios that compare sides within the figures. In Example 1a, you can use $\frac{6}{4} = \frac{x}{12}$.

Since $\triangle ABC \sim \triangle DEF$, the corresponding angles are congruent and the corresponding sides are proportional.

$\frac{BC}{EF} = \frac{AC}{DF}$	**Write a proportion.**
$\frac{6}{x} = \frac{4}{12}$	**Replace *BC* with 6, *EF* with *x*, *AC* with 4, and *DF* with 12.**
$6 \cdot 12 = x \cdot 4$	**Find the cross products.**
$72 = 4x$	**Simplify.**
$18 = x$	**Mentally divide each side by 4.**

The length of $\overline{EF}$ is 18 centimeters.

b.

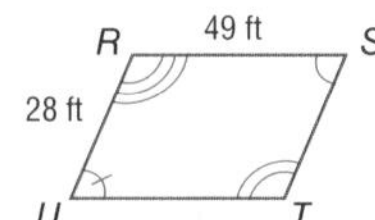

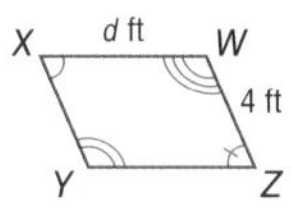

> **StudyTip**
>
> **Segment Notation** $\overline{RS}$ refers to the actual line segment. *RS* refers to the length of $\overline{RS}$.

Figure *RSTU* ~ figure *WXYZ*. The corresponding sides are proportional.

$\frac{RS}{WX} = \frac{RU}{WZ}$	**Write a proportion.**
$\frac{49}{d} = \frac{28}{4}$	**Replace *RS* with 49, *WX* with *d*, *RU* with 28, and *WZ* with 4.**
$49 \cdot 4 = d \cdot 28$	**Find the cross products.**
$196 = 28d$	**Simplify.**
$7 = d$	**Divide each side by 28.**

The length of $\overline{WX}$ is 7 feet.

Check Your Progress

1A. 4

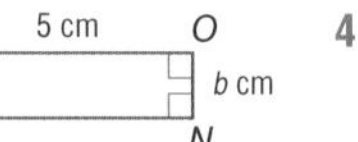

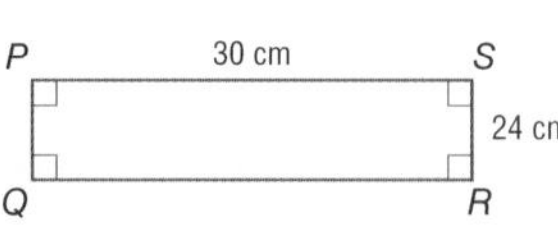

1B. 8

10 cm, 7 cm, 4 cm — G, H, I

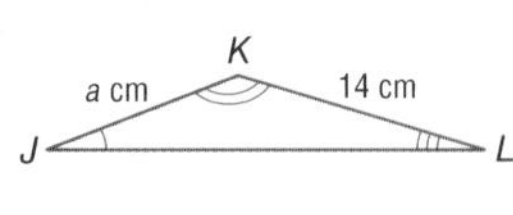

Personal Tutor glencoe.com

Differentiated Instruction

If students have trouble recognizing similar figures because of their orientation,

Then encourage them to copy and cut out the figures. They can then flip or rotate one of them until the corresponding angles align. This should allow students to recognize the corresponding sides and set up a proper proportion.

> **StudyTip**
>
> **Scale Factor** The scale factor is the constant of proportionality. In Lesson 6-4, you learned that proportional relationships can be described using equations of the form $y = kx$, where k is the constant of proportionality.

Scale Factors Recall that the scale factor is the ratio of a length on a scale drawing to the corresponding length on the real object. It is also the ratio of corresponding sides in similar figures.

Real-World EXAMPLE 2 Find Measures of Similar Figures

ARCHITECTURE An architect is designing a decorative window for the entrance of a new office building using similar triangles. If $\triangle ABC \sim \triangle DEF$, find the length of segment DF.

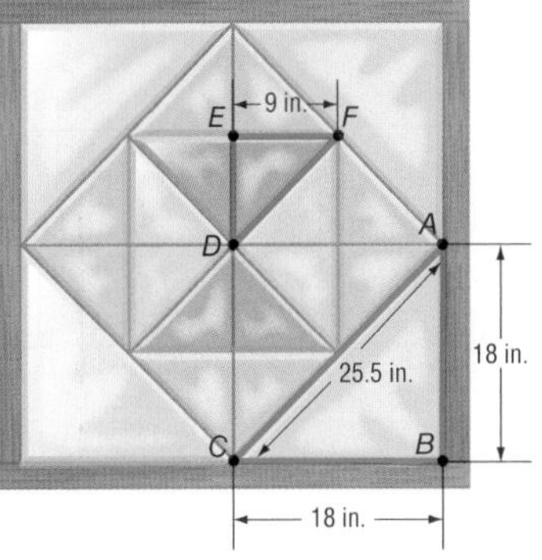

Find the scale factor from $\triangle DEF$ to $\triangle ABC$ by finding the ratio of corresponding sides with known lengths.

scale factor: $\frac{BC}{EF} = \frac{18}{9}$ or 2

Words	2 times a length on triangle *DEF*	is	a corresponding length on triangle *ABC*.
Variable	Let m represent the measure of $\overline{DF}$.		
Expression	$2m$	=	25.5

$2m = 25.5$ **Write the equation.**
$m = 12.75$ **Divide each side by 2.**

So, the length of $\overline{DF}$ is 12.75 inches.

Check Your Progress

2. **TILES** A rectangular blue tile has a length of 4.25 inches and a width of 6.75 inches. A similar red tile has a length of 12.75 inches. What is the width of the red tile? 20.25 in.

Personal Tutor glencoe.com

Check Your Understanding

Example 1 p. 302

The figures are similar. Find each missing measure.

1. $3\frac{1}{3}$

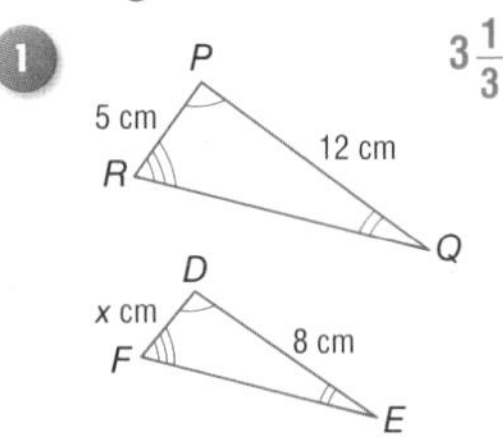

2. 21

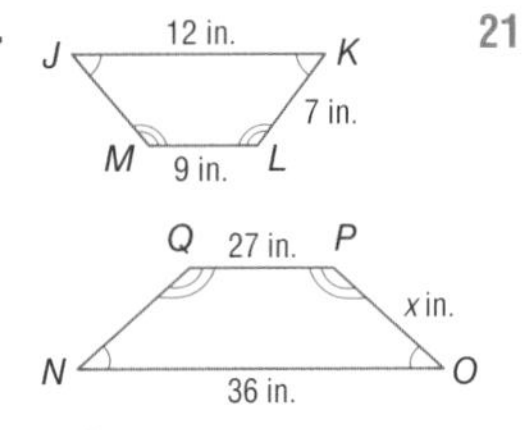

Example 2 p. 303

3. **LOGOS** The logo for an electronics store is made from similar trapezoids as shown. What is the length of the missing measure? 2 units

Tips for New Teachers

Enlargements You may want to display several enlargements and reductions that were made on a copy machine. Ask students to verbalize how the figures are the same and how they are different.

Focus on Mathematical Content

Similar Figures In figures that are similar, their shape is identical but their sizes are not. If the smaller shape were enlarged, it would correspond exactly with the larger one. Since the figures are not the same size, the term used is *similar*.

Scale Factors

Example 2 shows how to find measures of similar figures in a real-world problem.

Additional Example

2. **NESTED BOXES** Nested boxes are a series of boxes that fit inside each other. The faces of the boxes are similar rectangles. A face on a larger box has a length of 24 centimeters and a width of 13.5 centimeters. If the width of a face on a smaller box is 9 centimeters, what is the length of the smaller box? 16 cm

TEACH with TECH

PHOTO EDITING SOFTWARE Give students digital photos of different objects from the classroom. They can use the software to create similar figures by changing the scale of the photograph. Ask students what occurs when only one of the dimensions is changed by the scale factor. The image is skewed.

3 PRACTICE

Formative Assessment

Use Exercises 1–3 to check for understanding.

Use the chart at the bottom of this page to customize assignments for your students.

Additional Answers

11. 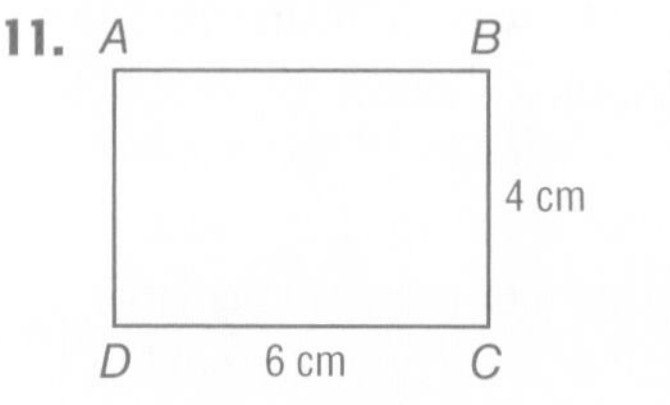

12. 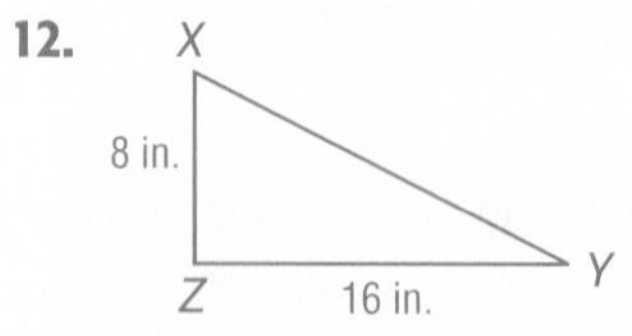

Practice and Problem Solving

= **Step-by-Step Solutions** begin on page R11.
Extra Practice begins on page 810.

Example 1 p. 302

The figures are similar. Find each missing measure.

4. 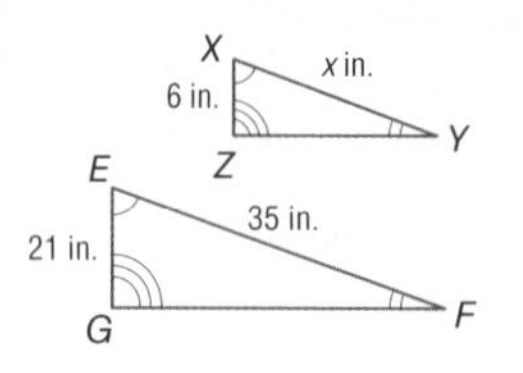

10

5. 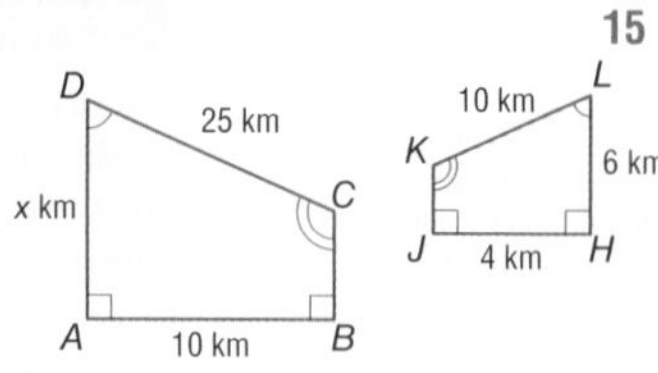

15

6. 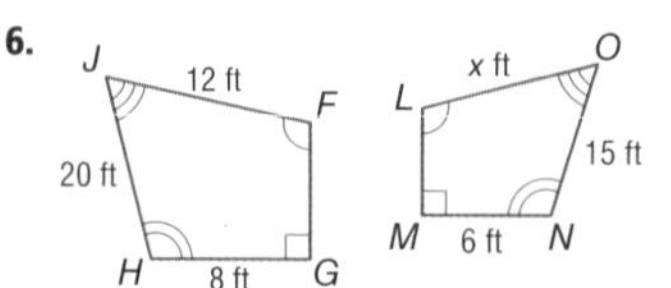

9

7. 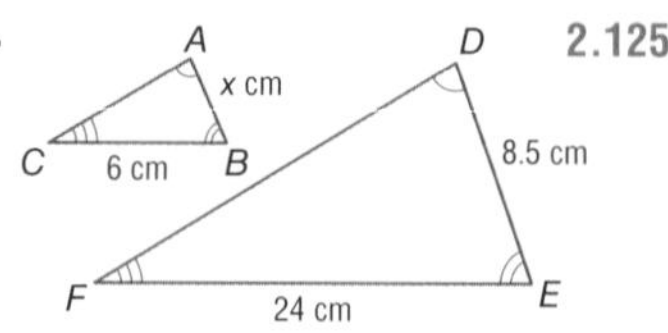

2.125

Example 2 p. 303

8. ART The design shown is made using similar triangles and quadrilaterals. triangle A ~ triangle B and quadrilateral C ~ quadrilateral D.

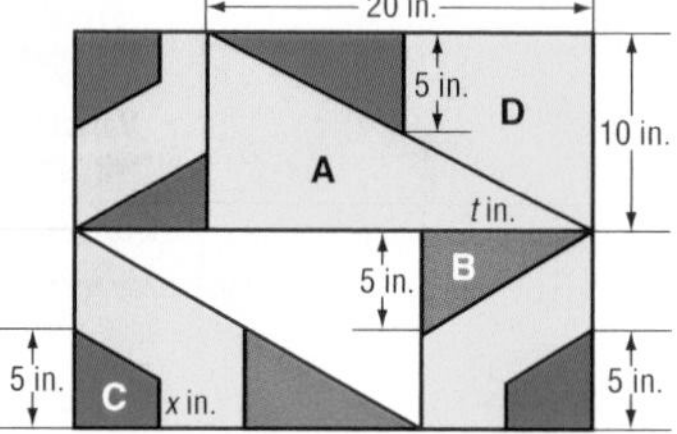

a. Find the missing measure in triangle B. **10 in.**

b. Find the missing measure in quadrilateral C. **2.5 in.**

9. GEOMETRY Triangle LMN is similar to $\triangle RST$. What is the value of LN if RT is 9 inches, MN is 21 inches, and ST is 7 inches? **27 in.**

10. GEOMETRY Quadrilateral $ABCD$ is similar to quadrilateral $WXYZ$. What is the value of WZ if AD is 18 feet, CD is 27 feet, and YZ is 10.8 feet? **7.2 ft**

11. Using a scale factor of $\frac{2}{3}$, draw and label a rectangle similar to rectangle $ABCD$. **See margin.**

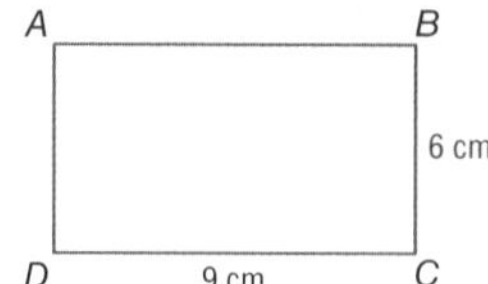

12. Using a scale factor of $\frac{4}{3}$, draw and label a triangle similar to $\triangle XYZ$. **See margin.**

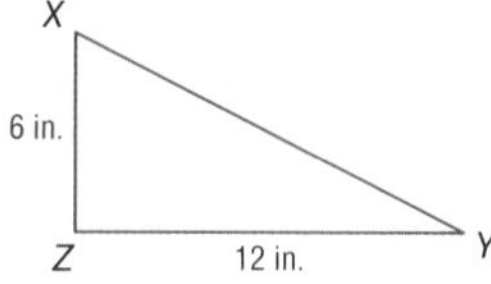

13. PERIMETER Figure $FGHJK$ ~ figure $LMNPQ$. The scale factor from figure $FGHJK$ to figure $LMNPQ$ is $\frac{2}{3}$. What is the perimeter of figure $LMNPQ$? **102 m**

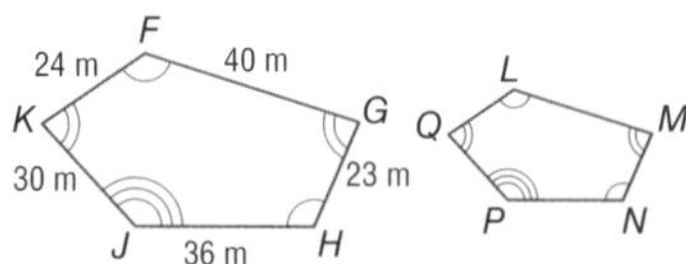

Differentiated Homework Options

Level	Assignment	Two-Day Option	
AL Basic	4–9, 16–19, 21–32	5–9 odd, 22–25	4–8 even, 16–19, 21, 26–32
OL Core	5–9 odd, 10–19, 21–32	4–9, 22–25	10–19, 21, 26–32
BL Advanced	10–28 (optional: 29–32)		

Real-World Link

The film most commonly used in movie productions is called 35 millimeter film because it is 35 millimeters wide. It was first introduced in 1892.

14. **MOVIES** An image that is projected onto a movie screen measures 8.8 meters by 6.4 meters. The projection is similar to the individual frame on the movie reel. If the projection has a scale factor of 400, what are the original dimensions of a frame on a movie reel? **22 mm by 16 mm**

15. **MULTIPLE REPRESENTATIONS** In this problem, you will investigate the relationship between the perimeters of similar figures. In the figures at the right, $\triangle ABC \sim \triangle XYZ$.

    a. **GEOMETRIC** Write an expression for the perimeter of $\triangle ABC$. $a + b + c$

    b. **SYMBOLIC** If the scale factor is represented by d, write algebraic expressions for the measures of the sides of $\triangle XYZ$. ad, bd, cd

    c. **GEOMETRIC** Write an expression for the perimeter of $\triangle XYZ$. $ad + bd + cd$

    d. **SYMBOLIC** Use the Distributive Property to factor the expression from part **c**. Explain the meaning of the expression.

    e. **MAKE A PREDICTION** Suppose $AB = 3$ inches, $BC = 4$ inches, $AC = 5$ inches, and the scale factor from $\triangle ABC$ to $\triangle XYZ$ is 2. Find the perimeter of $\triangle XYZ$ without calculating the lengths of $\overline{XY}$, $\overline{YZ}$, and $\overline{XZ}$. Justify your procedure.

    f. **VERBAL** Explain how the perimeters of similar figures are related to the scale factor. **Sample answer: If the figures are similar, then the perimeters are also similar. So, the perimeters are proportional.**

15d. $d(a + b + c)$; Sample answer: The scale factor times the sum of the measures of the sides of $\triangle ABC$ will give the perimeter of $\triangle XYZ$.

15e. 3 in. + 4 in. + 5 in. = 12 in.; $12 \times 2 = 24$; The perimeter of $\triangle XYZ$ is 24 inches.

17. sometimes; Sample answer: Even though all rectangles have equal corresponding angles, the sides of one rectangle are not always proportional to the sides of another rectangle.

H.O.T. Problems
Use Higher-Order Thinking Skills

16. **OPEN ENDED** Draw two similar triangles whose scale factor is 1:3. Justify your answer. **See Chapter 6 Answer Appendix.**

REASONING Determine whether each statement is *always*, *sometimes*, or *never* true. Explain your reasoning.

17. All rectangles are similar.

18. All squares are similar. **always; Sample answer: All squares are similar because all four sides are of equal length.**

19. **FIND THE ERROR** Carla and Tony are finding the length of $\overline{AB}$ where $\triangle ABC \sim \triangle DEF$, $BC = 16$ feet, $EF = 12$ feet, and $DE = 18$ feet. Is either of them correct? Explain your reasoning. **See Chapter 6 Answer Appendix.**

Carla	Tony
$\frac{16}{18} = \frac{12}{x}$ $x = 13.5$ ft	$\frac{16}{12} = \frac{18}{x}$ $x = 24$ ft

20. **CHALLENGE** *True* or *false*? If $\triangle XYZ \sim \triangle RST$, then $\frac{x}{z} = \frac{r}{t}$, where x is the side opposite $\angle X$, z is the side opposite $\angle Z$, and so on. Justify your answer. If false, provide a counterexample. **20-21. See Chapter 6 Answer Appendix.**

21. **WRITING IN MATH** Suppose you have two triangles. Triangle A is similar to triangle B, and the measures of the sides of triangle A are less than the measures of the sides of triangle B. The scale factor is 0.25. Which is the original triangle? Explain.

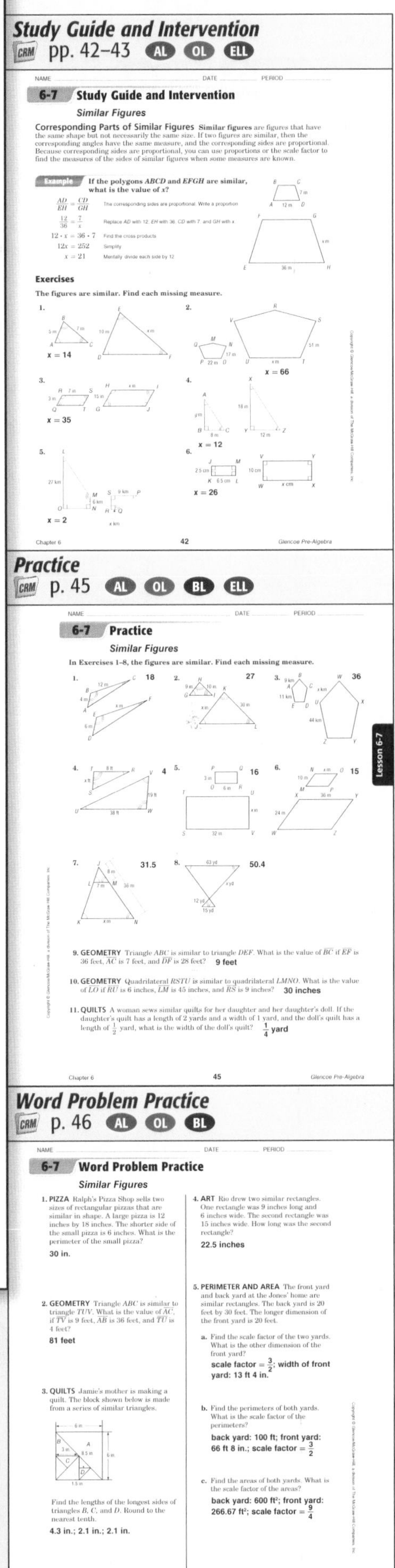

Study Guide and Intervention CRM pp. 42–43 AL OL ELL

6-7 Study Guide and Intervention — Similar Figures

Practice CRM p. 45 AL OL BL ELL

6-7 Practice — Similar Figures

Word Problem Practice CRM p. 46 AL OL BL

6-7 Word Problem Practice — Similar Figures

Watch Out!

Find the Error To choose whether Carla or Tony in Exercise 19 is correct, have students put the symbols for the line segments into the proportion before inserting actual lengths of the line segments. This way, students will be able to see that they have the correct side lengths set up in the proportion before they begin calculating.

Enrichment CRM p. 47 OL BL

6-7 Enrichment

Diagonals of Prisms

To find the length of diagonals in cubes and rectangular solids, a formula can be applied. In the example below, the length of diagonal $\overline{AG}$, or d, can be found using the formula $d^2 = a^2 + b^2 + c^2$ or $d = \sqrt{a^2 + b^2 + c^2}$.

Example 1: The diagonal, d, is equal to the square root of the sum of the squares of the length, a, the width, b, and the height, c.

Example 2: Find the length of the diagonal of a rectangular prism with length of 8 meters, width of 6 meters, and height of 10 meters.

$d = \sqrt{8^2 + 6^2 + 10^2}$

4 ASSESS

Ticket Out the Door Have students answer the following questions and turn them in as they leave. Their responses are to include a drawing with the given information labeled. Quadrilateral *WXYZ* is similar to quadrilateral *PQRS*. What is *QR* if *XY* is 25 meters, *WX* is 52 meters, and *PQ* is 10.4 meters? *QR* = 5 m

Formative Assessment

Check for student understanding of concepts in Lessons 6-6 and 6-7.

CRM Quiz 3, p. 65

Standardized Test Practice

22. Quadrilateral *ABCD* is similar to quadrilateral *EFGH*. What is the length of $\overline{FG}$? **C**

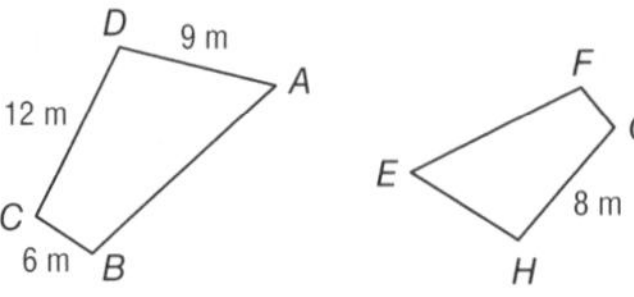

A 1.5 m
B 3.8 m
C 4 m
D 5.3 m

23. If polygon *ABCDE* is similar to polygon *FGHIJ*, which of the following is *not* true? **J**

F $\angle ABC \cong \angle FGH$
G $\angle EDC \cong \angle JIH$
H $\overline{AE}$ corresponds to $\overline{FJ}$
J $\overline{BC}$ corresponds to $\overline{HI}$

24. Triangle *RST* is similar to triangle *XYZ*. **C**

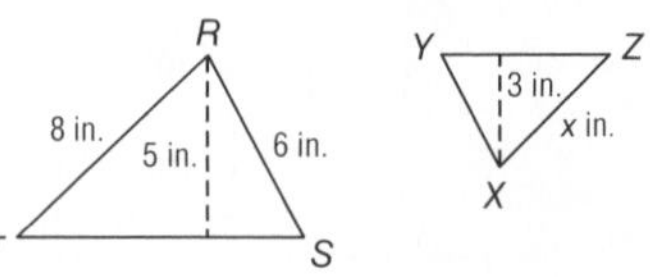

What is the length of $\overline{XZ}$?

A 1.875 in.
B 3.75 in.
C 4.8 in.
D 9.6 in.

25. GRIDDED RESPONSE Triangle *LMN* has a perimeter of 24 centimeters and is similar to triangle *DEF*. If the scale factor relating $\triangle LMN$ to $\triangle DEF$ is $\frac{1}{3}$, what is the perimeter, in centimeters of $\triangle DEF$? **8**

Spiral Review

26. STATUES The Statue of Zeus at Olympia is one of the Seven Wonders of the World. On a scale model of the statue, the height of Zeus is 8 inches. (Lesson 6-6)

a. If the actual height of the statue is 40 feet, what is the scale? **1 in. = 5 ft**

b. What is the scale factor? $\frac{1}{60}$

27. JEWELRY Flor is making bracelets. She knows that 4 bags of beads will make 14 bracelets. If she wants to make 56 bracelets, how many bags of beads will she need? (Lesson 6-5) **16 bags**

28. APPLE CIDER A bushel of apples will make approximately 3 gallons of apple cider. The table shows the relationship between the number of bushels of apples and the number of gallons of apple cider. (Lesson 1-5)

a. Given *b*, the number of bushels needed, write an equation that can be used to find *g*, the number of gallons of apple cider. $g = 3b$

b. How many bushels are needed to make 54 gallons of cider? **18 bushels**

Apple Bushels, *b*	Gallons of Apple Cider, *g*
1	3
2	6
5	15
8	24

Skills Review

Multiply. (Lesson 3-3)

29. $\frac{4}{5} \times 5$ **4**

30. $\frac{7}{4} \times 3$ $\frac{21}{4}$ or $5\frac{1}{4}$

31. $\frac{2}{3} \times 6$ **4**

32. $\frac{8}{5} \times 9$ $\frac{72}{5}$ or $14\frac{2}{5}$

Differentiated Instruction

Extension Two students are discussing the similarities of figures. Kiri says that all squares and isosceles triangles are similar while Tyrique believes the opposite. Who is correct and why? Similar figures must have corresponding angles that are congruent and sides that are proportional. Squares have corresponding angles and proportional sides, so they are similar. Although isosceles triangles have two congruent sides, there is no correspondence from one isosceles triangle to the next, so isosceles triangles are not necessarily similar. An exception is right isosceles triangles which are similar because they meet the criteria for similar polygons. Neither Kiri nor Tyrique are correct, although they are both partially correct.

6-8 Dilations

Why?

As a gift for her grandparents, Sierra is enlarging a favorite 4" inch by 5" inch family photo on her computer.

a. Suppose she enlarges it to 8 by 10 inches. Compare and contrast the original photo and the enlargement.

b. What is the scale factor from the original photo to the enlargement? 1:2

a. The dimensions and the photo double in size.

Then
You have already used transformations such as translations and reflections in the coordinate plane. (Lesson 2-7)

Now
- Graph dilations on a coordinate plane.
- Find the scale factor of a dilation.

New Vocabulary
dilation

Math Online
glencoe.com
- Extra Examples
- Personal Tutor
- Self-Check Quiz
- Homework Help

Dilations Recall that a transformation maps an original figure onto an image. Translations and reflections are two transformations that change the position of the object. A **dilation** is a transformation that enlarges or reduces a figure by a scale factor.

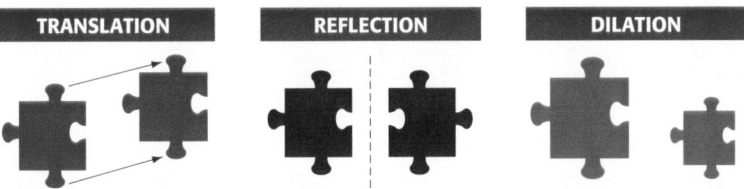

TRANSLATION | REFLECTION | DILATION

When the center of a dilation is the origin, you can find the coordinates of the image by multiplying each coordinate of the figure by the scale factor. Use the notation $(x, y) \rightarrow (kx, ky)$ to describe the dilation.

EXAMPLE 1 Dilation in a Coordinate Plane

A figure has vertices $J(2, 4)$, $K(2, 6)$, $M(8, 6)$, and $N(8, 2)$. Graph the figure and the image of the polygon after a dilation with a scale factor of $\frac{1}{2}$.

The dilation is $(x, y) \rightarrow \left(\frac{1}{2}x, \frac{1}{2}y\right)$. Multiply the coordinates of each vertex by $\frac{1}{2}$. Then graph both figures on the same coordinate plane.

$J(2, 4) \rightarrow J'\left(\frac{1}{2} \cdot 2, \frac{1}{2} \cdot 4\right) \rightarrow J'(1, 2)$

$K(2, 6) \rightarrow K'\left(\frac{1}{2} \cdot 2, \frac{1}{2} \cdot 6\right) \rightarrow K'(1, 3)$

$M(8, 6) \rightarrow M'\left(\frac{1}{2} \cdot 8, \frac{1}{2} \cdot 6\right) \rightarrow M'(4, 3)$

$N(8, 2) \rightarrow N'\left(\frac{1}{2} \cdot 8, \frac{1}{2} \cdot 2\right) \rightarrow N'(4, 1)$

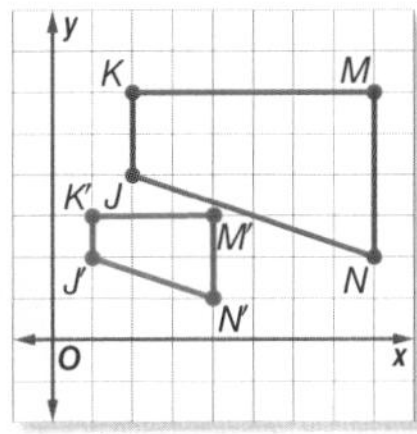

Check Your Progress 1. See Chapter 6 Answer Appendix.

1. A figure has vertices $R(-3, 6)$, $S(3, 12)$, and $T(3, 3)$. Graph the figure and the image of the figure after a dilation with a scale factor of $\frac{1}{3}$.

Personal Tutor glencoe.com

6-8 Lesson Notes

1 FOCUS

Vertical Alignment

Before Lesson 6-8
Use transformations such as translations and reflections.

Lesson 6-8
Graph dilations on a coordinate plane. Find the scale factor of a dilation.

After Lesson 6-8
Solve problems involving dilations.

2 TEACH

Scaffolding Questions

Have students read the *Why?* section of the lesson and answer the questions.

Ask:
- Suppose Sierra had wanted the enlargement to be 12 by 15 inches. What would she have had to do? Multiply the length and width by 3.
- What is the ratio of length to width of the original photo? $\frac{4}{5}$
- If Sierra multiplies by a scale factor of $\frac{1}{3}$, will the resulting photo be larger or smaller than the original? Explain. Smaller; a scale factor between 0 and 1 results in a smaller image.

Lesson 6-8 Resources

Resource	Approaching-Level	On-Level	Beyond-Level	English Learners
Teacher Edition	• Differentiated Instruction, p. 308		• Differentiated Instruction, p. 312	
Chapter Resource Masters	• Study Guide and Intervention, pp. 48–49 • Skills Practice, p. 50 • Practice, p. 51 • Word Problem Practice, p. 52 • Graphing Calculator, p. 54	• Study Guide and Intervention, pp. 48–49 • Skills Practice, p. 50 • Practice, p. 51 • Word Problem Practice, p. 52 • Enrichment, p. 53 • Graphing Calculator, p. 54	• Practice, p. 51 • Word Problem Practice, p. 52 • Enrichment, p. 53 • Graphing Calculator, p. 54	• Study Guide and Intervention, pp. 48–49 • Skills Practice, p. 50 • Practice, p. 51 • Graphing Calculator, p. 54
Transparencies	• 5-Minute Check Transparency 6-8	• 5-Minute Check Transparency 6-8	• 5-Minute Check Transparency 6-8	• 5-Minute Check Transparency 6-8
Other	• Study Notebook • Teaching Pre-Algebra with Manipulatives	• Study Notebook • Teaching Pre-Algebra with Manipulatives	• Study Notebook	• Study Notebook • Teaching Pre-Algebra with Manipulatives

Dilations

Example 1 shows how to graph a figure and an image after a dilation. **Example 2** is a Standardized Test problem that shows how to graph an enlargement in the coordinate plane. **Example 3** shows how to find a scale factor in a real-world problem.

Formative Assessment

Use the Check Your Progress exercises after each example to determine students' understanding of concepts.

Additional Examples

1 A figure has vertices $D(-4, 4)$, $E(4, 8)$, $F(8, 8)$, and $G(4, 0)$. Graph the figure and the image of the polygon after a dilation with a scale factor of $\frac{1}{4}$.

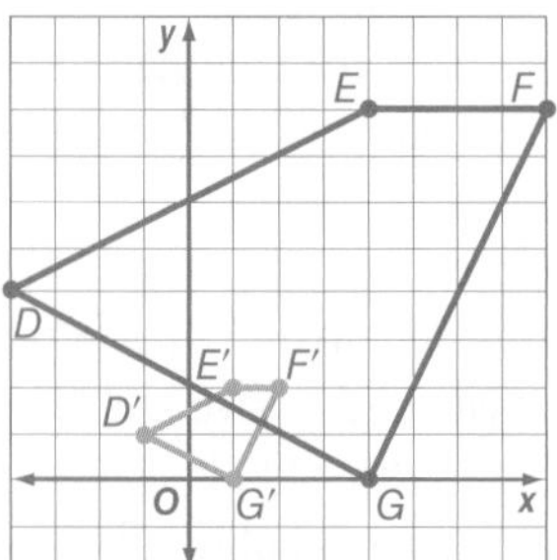

2 **STANDARDIZED TEST PRACTICE** A triangle has vertices $H(-1, -2)$, $I(1, 4)$, and $J(2, 1)$. Find the coordinates of the triangle after a dilation with a scale factor of 4. B

A $H'(4, 8)$, $I'(-4, -16)$, $J'(-8, -4)$

B $H'(-4, -8)$, $I'(4, 16)$, $J'(8, 4)$

C $H'\left(-\frac{1}{4}, -\frac{1}{2}\right)$, $I'\left(\frac{1}{4}, 1\right)$, $J'\left(\frac{1}{2}, \frac{1}{4}\right)$

D $H'(-4, -8)$, $I'(4, 8)$, $J'(8, -4)$

Additional Examples also in Interactive Classroom PowerPoint® Presentations

IWB INTERACTIVE WHITEBOARD READY

Vocabulary Link

Dilate
Everyday Use to expand or widen
Math Use to enlarge or reduce by a scale factor

STANDARDIZED TEST EXAMPLE 2

A triangle has vertices $A(1, -2)$, $B(0, 2)$, and $C(-2, -1)$. Find the coordinates of the triangle after a dilation with a scale factor of 2.

A $A'\left(\frac{1}{2}, -1\right), B'(0, 1), C'\left(-1, -\frac{1}{2}\right)$

B $A'(1, -1), B'(0, 1), C'(-1, -1)$

C $A'(2, -4), B'(0, 4), C'(-4, -2)$

D $A'(2, -4), B'(0, 2), C'(-4, -2)$

Read the Test Item

You are asked to find the coordinates of the image after the dilation. Multiply the coordinates of each vertex by the scale factor.

Solve the Test Item

The dilation is $(x, y) \rightarrow (2x, 2y)$. To dilate the figure, multiply the coordinates of each vertex by 2.

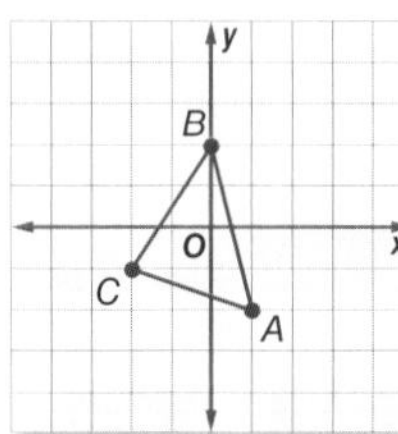

$A(1, -2) \rightarrow (2 \cdot 1, 2 \cdot -2) \rightarrow A'(2, -4)$

$B(0, 2) \rightarrow (2 \cdot 0, 2 \cdot 2) \rightarrow B'(0, 4)$

$C(-2, -1) \rightarrow (2 \cdot -2, 2 \cdot -1) \rightarrow C'(-4, -2)$

The answer is C.

Check Graph the triangle and its image on the coordinate plane.

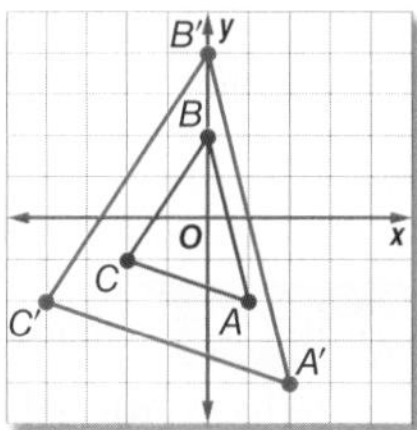

Problem-Solving Tip

Draw a Diagram Draw a diagram when the problem situation involves spatial reasoning or geometric figures. In this example, drawing a diagram helps you check that the coordinates are correct.

Check Your Progress

2. A figure has vertices $X(-3, 6)$, $Y(3, 0)$, and $Z(3, 3)$. Find the coordinates of the figure after a dilation with a scale factor of 3. J

F $X'(0, 9), Y'(6, 3), Z'(6, 6)$

G $X'(-6, -3), Y'(0, -3), Z'(0, 0)$

H $X'(-1, 2), Y'(1, 0), Z'(1, 1)$

J $X'(-9, 18), Y'(9, 0), Z'(9, 9)$

Personal Tutor glencoe.com

Concept Summary — Scale Factor

For Your FOLDABLE

A dilation with a scale factor of k will be:

- an enlargement if $k > 1$,
- a reduction if $0 < k < 1$,
- the same as the original figure if $k = 1$.

Differentiated Instruction

AL

If students have trouble relating the original figure to its image,

Then have students color-code the vertices of a figure before it is dilated. Ask them to write down the coordinates of the point in the same color and show their work for each image point in the same color. Then have them graph the image using the same coding.

StudyTip

Similarity Dilations produce images that are similar (same shape, but not same size).

EXAMPLE 3 Find a Scale Factor

MASCOTS A drawing of a school mascot is to be increased as shown at the right so it can be painted on the gymnasium doors. What is the scale factor of the dilation?

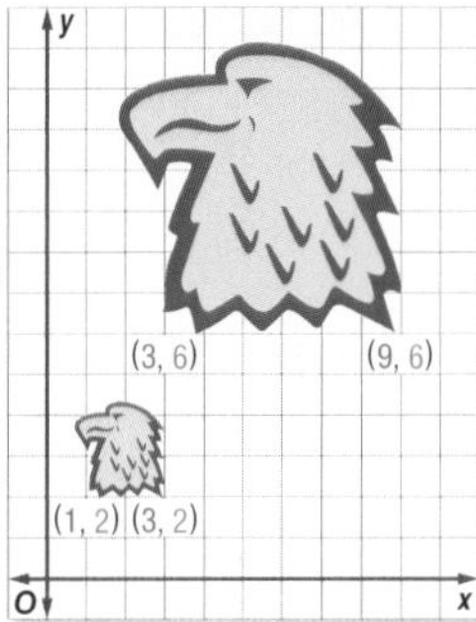

Write a ratio comparing the lengths of the sides of the two images. Subtract the x-coordinates to find the lengths.

$$\frac{\text{length on dilation}}{\text{length on original}} = \frac{9-3}{3-1}$$

$$= \frac{6}{2} \text{ or } 3$$

So, the scale factor of the dilation is 3.

Check Your Progress

3. **PHOTOS** Megan wants to reduce an 8-by-10-inch photo to a 2-by-$2\frac{1}{2}$-inch photo. What is the scale factor of the dilation? $\frac{1}{4}$

Personal Tutor glencoe.com

Focus on Mathematical Content

Dilation A dilation is a transformation that changes the size of a figure by either enlarging or shrinking it. A dilation can occur when a scale factor k is multiplied times the coordinates of a point. For example, the point $P(3, 5)$ after a dilation with a scale factor of 2 becomes $P'(6, 10)$. P' is the notation used to show the image of P.

Additional Example

3 **COPIES** Peri is enlarging a page from a book on the copy machine. The original page measured 14 centimeters by 21 centimeters. If the enlarged image measures 17.5 centimeters by 26.25 centimeters, what is the scale factor of the dilation? $\frac{5}{4}$

Check Your Understanding

Example 1 p. 307

Find the vertices of each figure after a dilation with the given scale factor k. Then graph the image. 1–2. See margin.

1. $k = \frac{1}{2}$

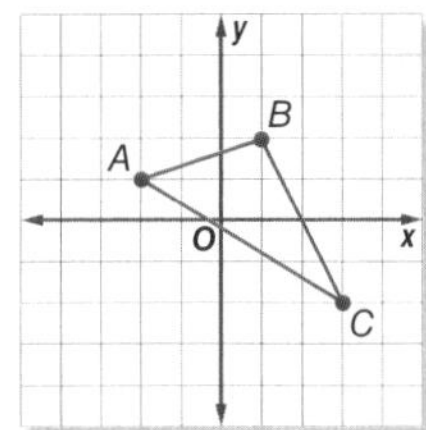

2. $k = \frac{1}{4}$

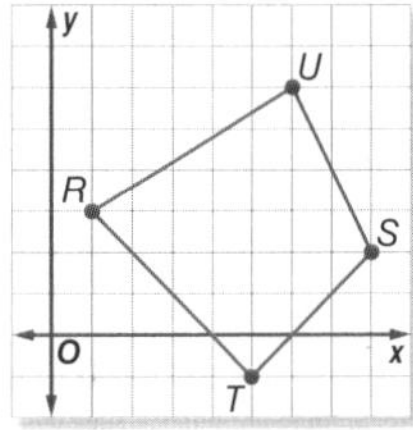

Example 2 p. 308

3. **MULTIPLE CHOICE** A square has vertices $M(0, 0)$, $N(3, -3)$, $O(0, -6)$ and $P(-3, -3)$. Find the coordinates of the square after a dilation with a scale factor of 2.5. A

A $M'(0, 0)$, $N'(7.5, -7.5)$, $O'(0, -15)$, $P'(-7.5, -7.5)$

B $M'(0, 0)$, $N'(2, -2)$, $O'(0, -4)$, $P'(-2, -2)$

C $M'(2.5, 2.5)$, $N'(7.5, -7.5)$, $O'(0, -15)$, $P'(-7.5, -7.5)$

D $M'(2.5, 2.5)$, $N'(2, -2)$, $O'(0, -4)$, $P'(-2, -2)$

Example 3 p. 309

4. **IMAGES** Jorge is using a photocopier to reduce a poster that is 8 inches by 14 inches to 5 inches by $8\frac{3}{4}$ inches. What is the scale factor of the dilation? $\frac{5}{8}$

3 PRACTICE

Formative Assessment

Use Exercises 1–4 to check for understanding.

Use the chart at the bottom of the next page to customize assignments for your students.

Additional Answers

1. $A'(-1, 0.5)$, $B'(0.5, 1)$, $C'(1.5, -1)$

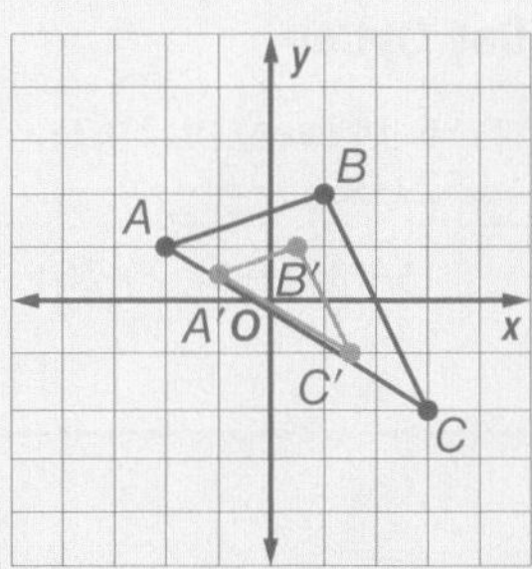

2. $R'(0.25, 0.75)$, $U'(1.5, 1.5)$, $S'(2, 0.5)$, $T'(1.25, -0.25)$

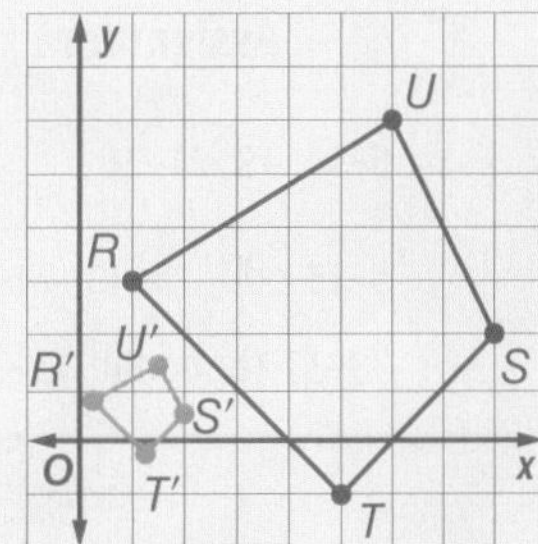

Watch Out!

Preventing Errors Remind students to be sure to multiply both coordinates of a vertex by the scale factor to determine the image of the vertex.

Additional Answers

5. $P'(4, 4)$, $Q'(8, 12)$, $R'(12, 4)$

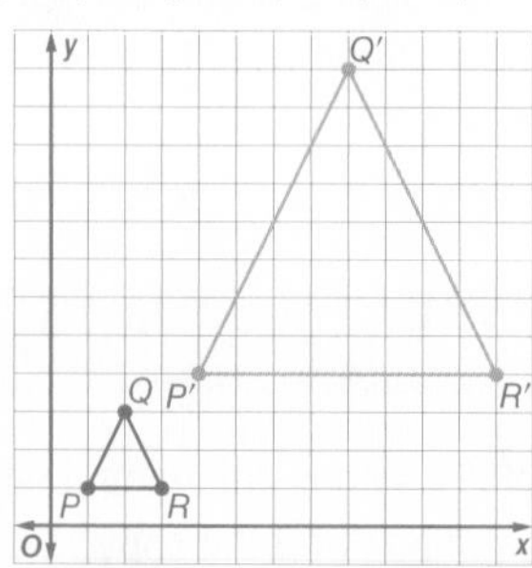

6. $G'(0, 4.5)$, $H'(1.5, 9)$, $I'(6, 1.5)$, $J'(3, 0)$

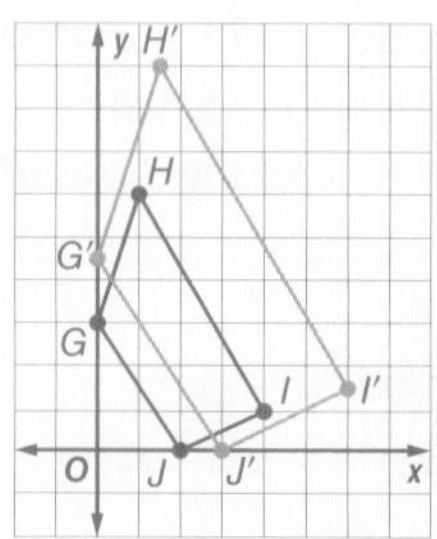

7. $X'(3, 3)$, $Y'(4.5, 6)$, $Z'(6, 0)$

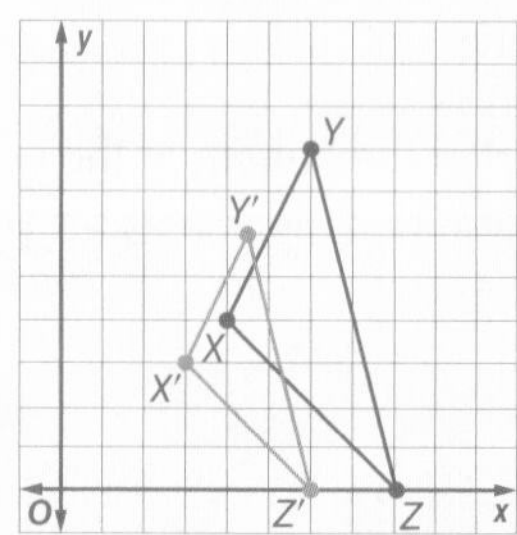

8. $K'(1\frac{2}{3}, 0)$, $L'(2\frac{2}{3}, 1)$, $M'(1, 2\frac{2}{3})$, $N'(0, 1\frac{2}{3})$

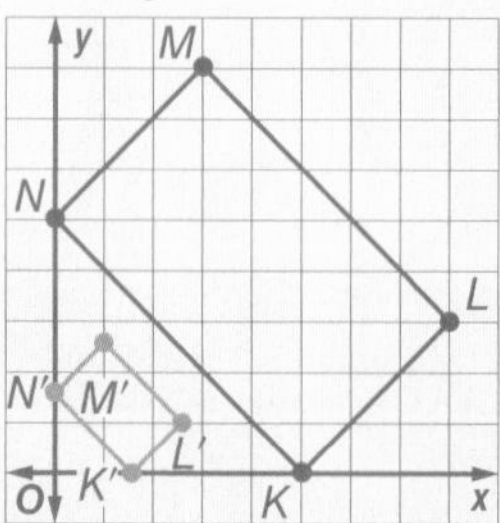

Practice and Problem Solving

= **Step-by-Step Solutions** begin on page R11.
Extra Practice begins on page 810.

Examples 1 and 2 pp. 307–308

Find the vertices of each figure after a dilation with the given scale factor k. Then graph the image. **5–8. See margin.**

5. $k = 4$

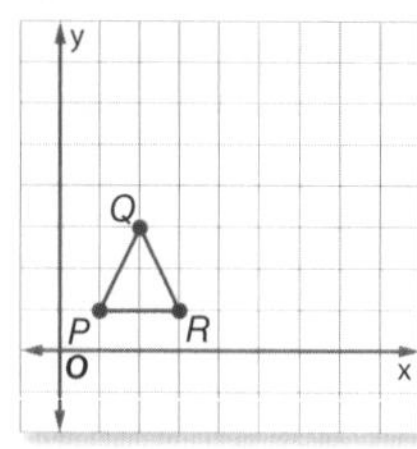

6. $k = 1.5$

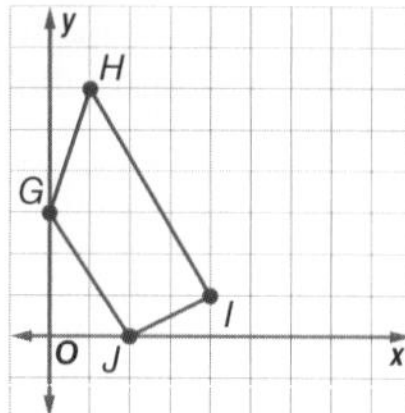

7. $k = \frac{3}{4}$

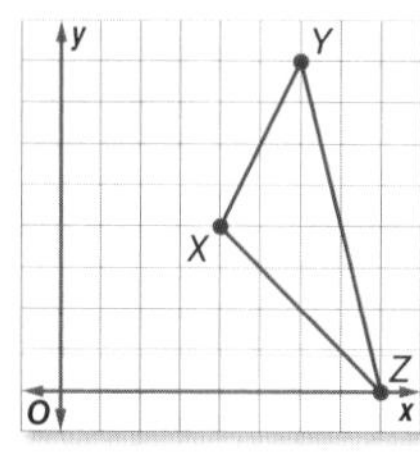

8. $k = \frac{1}{3}$

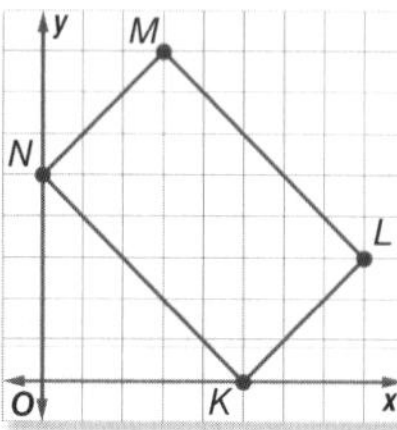

9–12. See Chapter 6 Answer Appendix.

Find the vertices of each figure after a dilation with the given scale factor, k. Then graph the original image and the dilation.

9. $G(-1, 1)$, $H(2, 1)$, $J(3, -2)$, $K(-2, -2)$; $k = 2$

10. $W(0, 0)$, $X(5, -5)$, $Y(5, 10)$; $k = \frac{2}{5}$

11. $R(-1, 2)$, $S(1, 4)$, $T(1, 1)$; $k = 3$

12. $A(-3, -5)$, $B(0, 2)$, $C(3, -1)$, $D(0, -4)$; $k = \frac{1}{2}$

Real-World Link

Optometrists dilate eyes so that they can get a better look at the retina, optic nerve, and blood vessels in the back of your eye.

Source: St. Luke's Cataract and Laser Institute.

Example 3 p. 309

13. **LIFE SCIENCE** In a microscope, the image of a 0.16-millimeter paramecium appears to be 32 millimeters long. What is the scale factor of the dilation? **200**

14. **EYES** During an eye exam, an optometrist dilates her patient's pupils to 7 millimeters. If the diameter of the pupil before dilation was 4 millimeters, what is the scale factor of the dilation? $\frac{7}{4}$

15 **PHOTOGRAPHY** Jung is editing a digital photograph that is 640 pixels wide and 480 pixels high on his computer monitor.

a. If Jung zooms the image on his monitor 150%, what are the dimensions of the image? **960 pixels by 720 pixels**

b. Suppose that Jung is going to use the photograph in a design and wants the image to be 32 pixels wide. What scale factor should he use? $\frac{1}{20}$

c. Jung resizes the photograph so it is 600 pixels high. What scale factor did he use? **1.25**

Differentiated Homework Options

Level	Assignment	Two-Day Option	
AL Basic	5–14, 19, 21–36	5–13 odd, 25–28	6–14 even, 19, 21–24, 29–36
OL Core	5–13 odd, 15–19, 21–36	5–14, 25–28	15–19, 21–24, 29–36
BL Advanced	15–32 (optional: 33–36)		

16. GEOMETRY Triangle $L'M'N'$ is a dilation of triangle LMN. Find the scale factor of the dilation and classify it as an enlargement or a reduction.

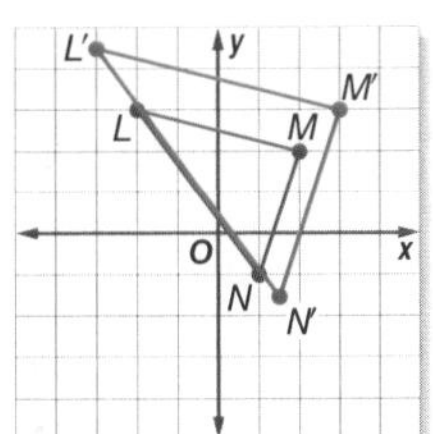

scale factor: 1.5; enlargement

17. GEOMETRY Quadrilateral $A'B'C'D'$ is a dilation of quadrilateral $ABCD$. Find the scale factor of the dilation and classify it as an enlargement or a reduction.

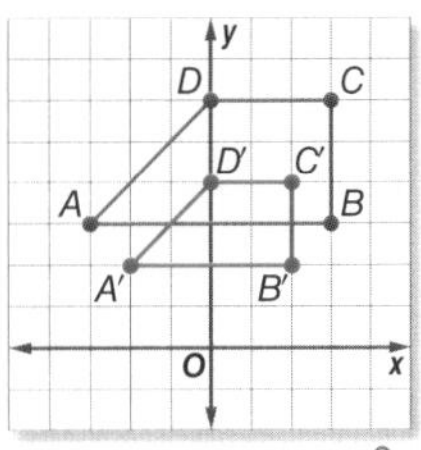

scale factor: $\frac{2}{3}$; reduction

18. PRESENTATIONS Felicia wants to project a 2-inch by 2-inch slide on to a wall to create an image 128 inches by 128 inches. If the slide projector makes the dimensions of the image twice as large for each yard that it is moved away from the wall, how far away should Felicia place the projector? 6 yd

H.O.T. Problems
Use Higher-Order Thinking Skills

19. OPEN ENDED Draw a triangle on grid paper. Then draw the image of the triangle after it is moved 5 units right and then dilated by a scale factor of $\frac{1}{3}$.

19–20. See Chapter 6 Answer Appendix.

20. CHALLENGE Suppose a figure $ABCD$ is dilated by a scale factor of $\frac{1}{2}$ and then reflected over the x-axis and the y-axis. The final image is shown on the graph at the right. Graph the original image and list the coordinates of points A, B, C, and D.

21. REASONING A triangle has coordinates $A(0, 5)$, $B(0, 0)$ and $C(10, 5)$. Find the coordinates of the final image after each set of dilations.

a. $k = 2$ followed by $k = \frac{2}{5}$ $A'(0, 4)$, $B'(0, 0)$, $C'(8, 4)$

b. $k = \frac{2}{5}$ followed by $k = 2$ $A'(0, 4)$, $B'(0, 0)$, $C'(8, 4)$

c. $k = \frac{1}{4}$ followed by $k = 2$ $A'(0, 2.5)$, $B'(0, 0)$, $C'(5, 2.5)$

d. $k = 2$ followed by $k = \frac{1}{4}$ $A'(0, 2.5)$, $B'(0, 0)$, $C'(5, 2.5)$

22. REASONING Refer to Exercise 21. Does the order in which you perform multiple dilations *always*, *sometimes*, or *never* result in the same image? Explain.

23. WHICH ONE DOESN'T BELONG? Which pair of points does not represent a dilation with center at the origin? Explain.

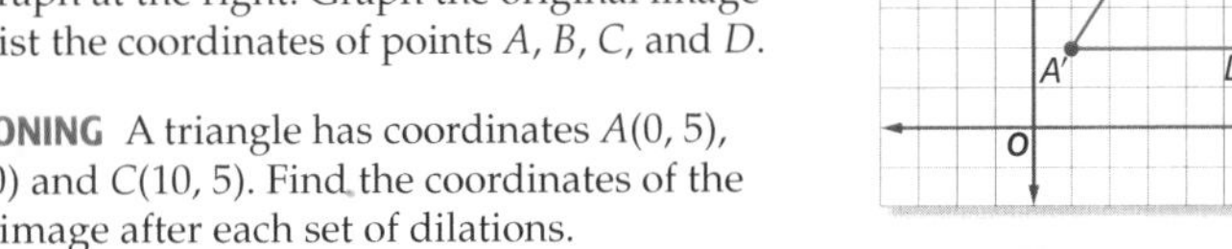

$A(2, 3)$, $A'(4, 6)$	$B(4, 6)$, $B'(2, 3)$	$C(2, 5)$, $C'(4, 7)$	$D(-2, 4)$, $D'(-1, 2)$

24. WRITING IN MATH A triangle has one vertex at point (3, 6). It is dilated with a center at the origin by a scale factor of 3. The resulting image is then dilated with a scale factor of $\frac{1}{3}$. What are the coordinates of that vertex after both dilations? Explain your reasoning.

22. Always. Sample answer: In examples a–d, both sets of two dilations have the same image.

23. $C(2, 5)$, $C'(4, 7)$; Sample answer: Dilations involve multiplying the coordinates by the scale factor. In the points $C(2, 5)$ and $C'(4, 7)$, 2 is added to each coordinate.

24. (3, 6); Sample answer: Multiplying by 3 and then by $\frac{1}{3}$ is the same as multiplying by 1. When multiplied by 1, the point will remain the same.

Problem-Solving Tip

Draw a Picture In Exercise 24, you can draw a picture of the situation to help see each transformation. This can help you write a more concise response.

Enrichment CRM p. 53 OL BL

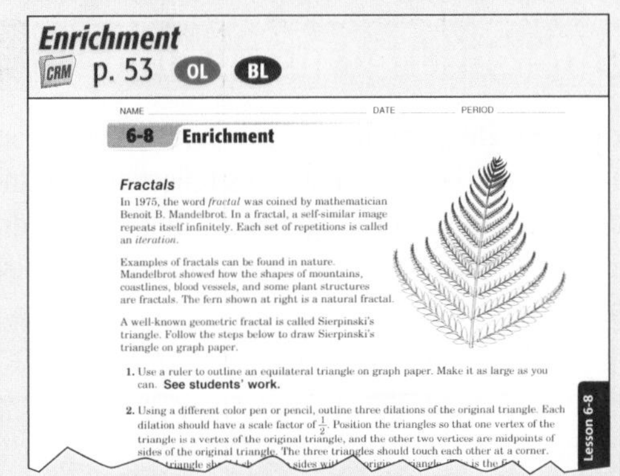

6-8 Enrichment

Fractals

In 1975, the word *fractal* was coined by mathematician Benoit B. Mandelbrot. In a fractal, a self-similar image repeats itself infinitely. Each set of repetitions is called an *iteration*.

Examples of fractals can be found in nature. Mandelbrot showed how the shapes of mountains, coastlines, blood vessels, and some plant structures are fractals. The fern shown at right is a natural fractal.

A well-known geometric fractal is called Sierpinski's triangle. Follow the steps below to draw Sierpinski's triangle on graph paper.

1. Use a ruler to outline an equilateral triangle on graph paper. Make it as large as you can. **See students' work.**

2. Using a different color pen or pencil, outline three dilations of the original triangle. Each dilation should have a scale factor of $\frac{1}{2}$. Position the triangles so that one vertex of the triangle is a vertex of the original triangle, and the other two vertices are midpoints of sides of the original triangle. The three triangles should touch each other at a corner.

Study Guide and Intervention CRM pp. 48–49 AL OL ELL

Practice CRM p. 51 AL OL BL ELL

Word Problem Practice CRM p. 52 AL OL BL

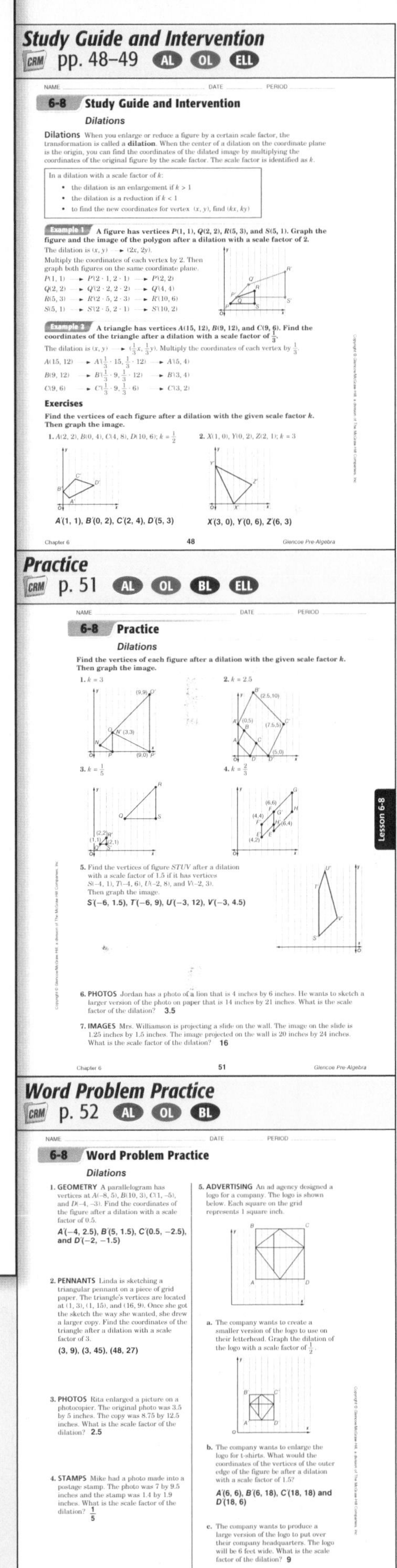

6-8 Study Guide and Intervention

Dilations

Dilations When you enlarge or reduce a figure by a certain scale factor, the transformation is called a **dilation**. When the center of a dilation on the coordinate plane is the origin, you can find the coordinates of the dilated image by multiplying the coordinates of the original figure by the scale factor. The scale factor is identified as k.

In a dilation with a scale factor of k:
- the dilation is an enlargement if $k > 1$
- the dilation is a reduction if $k < 1$
- to find the new coordinates for vertex (x, y), find (kx, ky)

Example 1 A figure has vertices $P(1, 1)$, $Q(2, 2)$, $R(5, 3)$, and $S(5, 1)$. Graph the figure and the image of the polygon after a dilation with a scale factor of 2.

Example 2 A triangle has vertices $A(15, 12)$, $B(9, 12)$, and $C(9, 6)$. Find the coordinates of the triangle after a dilation with a scale factor of $\frac{1}{3}$.

Exercises

1. $A'(1, 1)$, $B'(0, 2)$, $C'(2, 4)$, $D'(5, 3)$
2. $X'(3, 0)$, $Y'(0, 6)$, $Z'(6, 3)$

6-8 Practice

Dilations

5. $S'(-6, 1.5)$, $T'(-6, 9)$, $U'(-3, 12)$, $V'(-3, 4.5)$

6. PHOTOS ... 3.5

7. IMAGES ... 16

6-8 Word Problem Practice

Dilations

1. $A'(-4, 2.5)$, $B'(5, 1.5)$, $C'(0.5, -2.5)$, and $D'(-2, -1.5)$
2. (3, 9), (3, 45), (48, 27)
3. 2.5
4. $\frac{1}{5}$
5. b. $A(6, 6)$, $B(6, 18)$, $C(18, 18)$ and $D(18, 6)$
c. 9

TEACH with TECH

INTERACTIVE WHITEBOARD Display a coordinate plane and draw a figure on the board. Tell students the scale factor for a dilation and have them name the vertices of the dilated figure. Plot these points and draw the image of the figure. Then check the figure to confirm that it is a dilation.

ASSESS

Name the Math Have students draw and label the points $A(-3, 2)$, $B(-2, 4)$, $C(2, 4)$, and $D(3, 2)$. Using a scale factor of 2, have students explain the steps and show the work necessary to dilate the figure. Then have them graph the dilated figure.

Standardized Test Practice

25. Quadrilateral $PQRS$ was dilated to form quadrilateral $P'Q'R'S'$. **C**

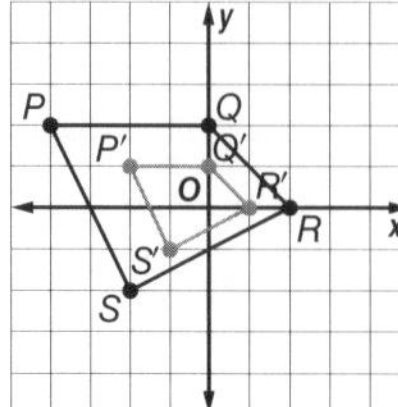

Which number *best* represents the scale factor used to dilate quadrilateral $PQRS$ to quadrilateral $P'Q'R'S'$?

A -2 C $\frac{1}{2}$

B $-\frac{1}{2}$ D 2

26. A triangle has vertices $(1, -1)$, $(-2, 6)$, and $(4, 1)$. If the triangle undergoes a dilation with a scale factor of 3, what will be the vertices of the image? **F**

F $(3, -3)$, $(-6, 18)$, $(12, 3)$

G $(3, 3)$, $(6, 18)$, $(12, 3)$

H $(3, 3)$, $(-6, 18)$, $(12, -3)$

J $(3, -3)$, $(-6, -18)$, $(-12, 3)$

27. Let $G(6, -8)$ be a point on triangle FGH. What are the coordinates of G' if the triangle is dilated by a scale factor of $\frac{1}{2}$? **B**

A $(3, 4)$ C $(-3, 4)$

B $(3, -4)$ D $(-3, -4)$

28. GRIDDED RESPONSE Point $P(-10, 5)$ is on rectangle $PQRS$. If the coordinates of P after a dilation are $(-4, 2)$, what is the scale factor of the dilation? **0.4**

Spiral Review

29. GEOMETRY Triangle RSK is similar to $\triangle RUV$. What is the value of x, rounded to the nearest tenth? (Lesson 6-7) **2.1 km**

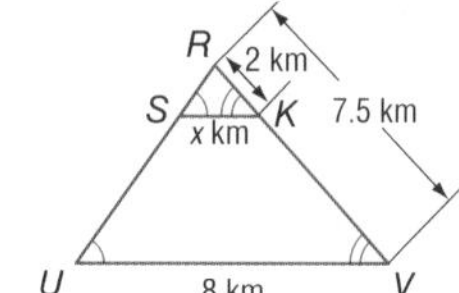

MAPS On a map of South Carolina, the scale is 1 inch = 20 miles. Find the actual distance for each map distance. (Lesson 6-6)

	From	To	Map Distance	
30.	Columbia	Florence	4 inches	80 mi
31.	Myrtle Beach	Greenville	12 inches	240 mi

32. CURRENCY The table at the right shows the exchange rates for certain countries compared to the U.S. dollar on a given day. (Lesson 6-3)

Country	Rate per $1 (U.S.)
Great Britain	0.480 pounds
South Africa	6.568 rands

a. What is the cost of an item in U.S. dollars if it costs 14.99 in British pounds? **$31.23**

b. Find the cost of an item in South African rands if it costs 12.50 in U.S. dollars. **82.1 rands**

Skills Review

Solve each proportion. (Lesson 6-5)

33. $\frac{2}{15} = \frac{c}{72}$ **9.6**

34. $\frac{16}{7} = \frac{4.8}{h}$ **2.1**

35. $\frac{2}{9.4} = \frac{0.2}{v}$ **0.94**

36. $\frac{9}{7.2} = \frac{3.5}{k}$ **2.8**

Differentiated Instruction

Extension On graph paper have students graph a triangle with coordinates of $(-3, 1)$, $(-1, 4)$, and $(-1, 1)$. They are to draw its reflection over the y-axis, draw its translation after being translated 6 units to the right and 1 unit up, and draw the dilated figure after a dilation with a scale factor of 2. What do you notice about the three new figures after the transformations? All three transformations keep the angles the same and the shapes the same. The reflection changes the orientation of the triangle. The dilation changes the size, creating similar figures.

312 Chapter 6 Ratio, Proportion, and Similar Figures

6-9 Indirect Measurement

Then
You have already used similar figures to determine missing measures. (Lesson 6-7)

Now
- Solve problems involving indirect measurement using shadow reckoning.
- Solve problems using surveying methods.

New Vocabulary
indirect measurement

Math Online
glencoe.com
- Extra Examples
- Personal Tutor
- Self-Check Quiz
- Homework Help
- Math in Motion

Why?

On a sunny day, you can see your shadow. The lengths of the shadows around you are proportional to the heights of the objects casting the shadows.

h m | 1.8 m | 1.2 m | 0.8 m

a. What kind of triangles are formed by the objects and their shadows? **similar triangles**

b. **MAKE A CONJECTURE** How could you use your shadow to determine the height of another object? **Set up a proportion comparing shadow length and height. Then solve.**

Indirect Measurement **Indirect measurement** allows you to use the properties of similar triangles to find measurements that are difficult to measure directly.

One type of indirect measurement is called *shadow reckoning*. Two objects and their shadows form two sides of similar triangles.

Math *in Motion*, BrainPOP® glencoe.com

Real-World EXAMPLE 1 Use Shadow Reckoning

MEMORIALS The lead statue of the Korean War Memorial in Washington, D.C., casts a 43.5-inch shadow at the same time a nearby tourist casts a 32-inch shadow. If the tourist is 64 inches tall, how tall is the lead statue?

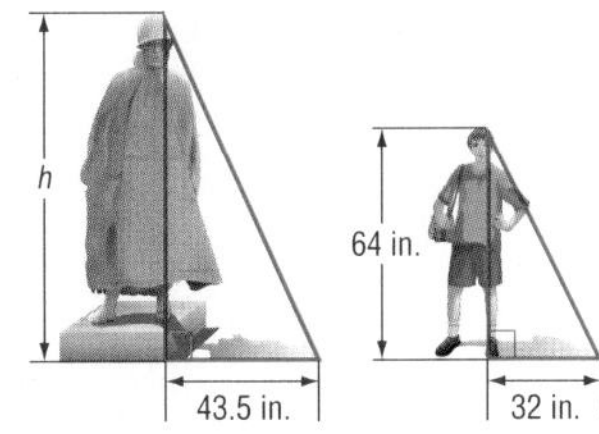

Understand You know the lengths of the shadows and the height of the tourist. You need to find the statue's height.

Plan To find the height of the statue, set up a proportion comparing the tourist's shadow to the statue's shadow. Then solve.

Solve

tourist's height → $\frac{64}{h} = \frac{32}{43.5}$ ← tourist's shadow
statue's height → ← statue's shadow

$64 \cdot 43.5 = 32 \cdot h$ **Find the cross products.**

$2784 = 32h$ **Multiply.**

$87 = h$ **Divide each side by 32.**

Check The tourist's height is 2 times the length of his or her shadow. The statue should be 2 times its shadow, or $2 \cdot 43.5$, which is 87 inches.

Check Your Progress

1. **MONUMENTS** Suppose a bell tower casts a 27.6-foot shadow at the same time a nearby tourist casts a 1.2-foot shadow. If the tourist is 6 feet tall, how tall is the tower? **138 ft**

Personal Tutor glencoe.com

6-9 Lesson Notes

1 FOCUS

Vertical Alignment

Before Lesson 6-9
Use similar figures to determine missing measures.

Lesson 6-9
Solve problems involving indirect measurement using shadow reckoning. Solve problems using surveying methods.

After Lesson 6-9
Use indirect measurement to solve problems involving similar figures.

2 TEACH

Scaffolding Questions

Have students read the *Why?* section of the lesson and answer the questions.

Ask:
- What are the known measures in the diagram? the lengths of the shadows and the height of the tennis player
- What is the unknown measure? the height of the judge sitting in the elevated chair
- What is a proportion you could use to find the unknown measure? Sample answer: $\frac{h \text{ m}}{1.8 \text{ m}} = \frac{1.2 \text{ m}}{0.8 \text{ m}}$

Lesson 6-9 Resources

Resource	Approaching-Level	On-Level	Beyond-Level	English Learners
Teacher Edition		• Differentiated Instruction, p. 314	• Differentiated Instruction, pp. 314, 317	
Chapter Resource Masters	• Study Guide and Intervention, pp. 55–56 • Skills Practice, p. 57 • Practice, p. 58 • Word Problem Practice, p. 59	• Study Guide and Intervention, pp. 55–56 • Skills Practice, p. 57 • Practice, p. 58 • Word Problem Practice, p. 59 • Enrichment, p. 60	• Practice, p. 58 • Word Problem Practice, p. 59 • Enrichment, p. 60	• Study Guide and Intervention, pp. 55–56 • Skills Practice, p. 57 • Practice, p. 58
Transparencies	• 5-Minute Check Transparency 6-9	• 5-Minute Check Transparency 6-9	• 5-Minute Check Transparency 6-9	• 5-Minute Check Transparency 6-9
Other	• Study Notebook • Teaching Pre-Algebra with Manipulatives	• Study Notebook • Teaching Pre-Algebra with Manipulatives	• Study Notebook	• Study Notebook • Teaching Pre-Algebra with Manipulatives

Indirect Measurement

Example 1 shows how to use shadow reckoning.

Formative Assessment

Use the Check Your Progress exercises after each example to determine students' understanding of concepts.

Additional Example

1 **MONUMENTS** Suppose the San Jacinto Monument in La Porte, Texas, casts a shadow of 285 feet. At the same time, a nearby tourist, who is 5 feet tall, casts a 2.5-foot shadow. How tall is the San Jacinto Monument? 570 feet

Additional Examples also in Interactive Classroom PowerPoint® Presentations

IWB INTERACTIVE WHITEBOARD READY

Focus on Mathematical Content

Indirect Measurement Some measurements are difficult to determine such as heights of buildings, trees, flagpoles, etc. By forming a proportional relationship using similar triangles, the heights of these items can be measured indirectly.

Surveying Methods

Example 2 shows how to find measurements using the corresponding parts of similar figures.

Additional Example

2 **MAPS** In the figure, $\triangle PQT \sim \triangle PRS$. Find the distance across the lake. 28.8 m

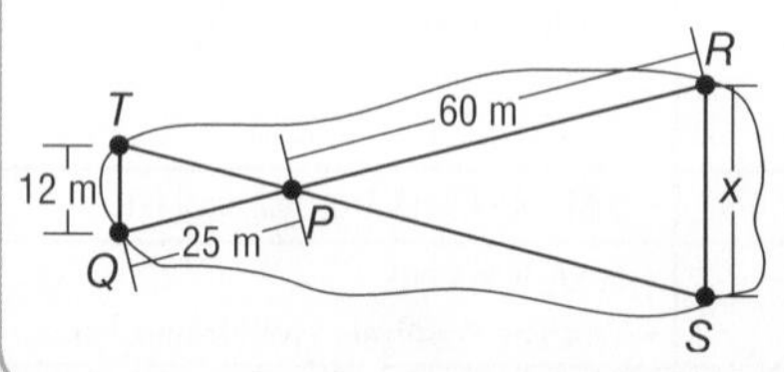

Surveying Methods Surveyors also use similar triangles, but they do not involve shadows. Notice in Example 2 that it is possible to measure three sides of the triangles directly.

EXAMPLE 2 Find Missing Measures

MAPS In the figure, $\triangle STU \sim \triangle VQU$. Find the distance across the pond.

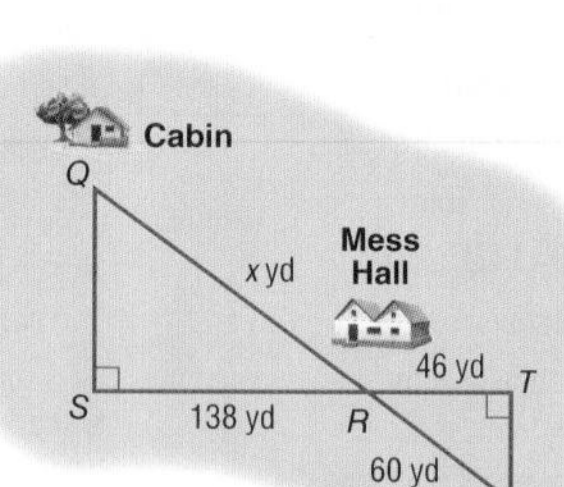

Since the figures are similar, corresponding sides are proportional.

$\frac{UQ}{UT} = \frac{VQ}{ST}$	**Write a proportion.**
$\frac{16}{10} = \frac{x}{20}$	**$UQ = 16$, $UT = 10$, $VQ = x$, and $ST = 20$**
$10 \cdot x = 16 \cdot 20$	**Cross products**
$10x = 320$	**Multiply.**
$\frac{10x}{10} = \frac{320}{10}$	**Divide each side by 10.**
$x = 32$	**Simplify.**

So, the distance across the pond is 32 meters.

Check Your Progress

2. **CAMP** In the figure, $\triangle QRS \sim \triangle URT$. Find the distance from the boys' cabins to the Mess Hall. **180 yd**

Personal Tutor glencoe.com

Check Your Understanding

Examples 1 and 2 pp. 313–314

1. **SPORTS** A basketball hoop in Miguel's backyard casts a shadow that is 8 feet long. At the same time, Miguel casts a shadow that is 4.5 feet long. If Miguel is 5.5 feet tall, how tall is the basketball hoop? Round to the nearest tenth. **9.8 ft**

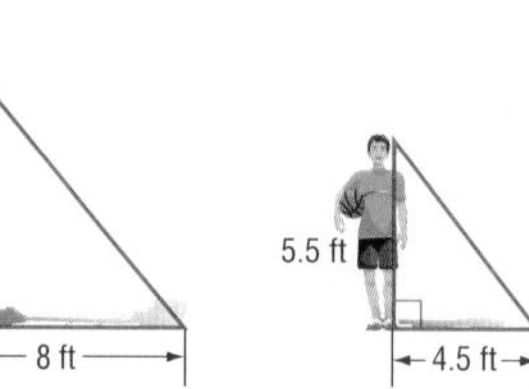

2. **SURVEYING** In the figure, $\triangle ABC \sim \triangle EBD$. Find the distance across Stallion Ravine. **198 m**

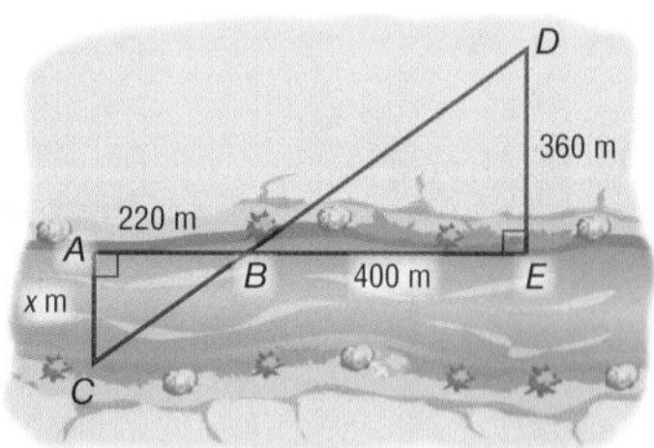

Differentiated Instruction

OL BL

Naturalist Have students work in pairs to use shadow reckoning to measure trees, bushes, or other natural objects in the area. Each pair should use a measuring tape to measure each other's height, shadow's length, and the lengths of the objects' shadows. Have students do their measurements three times a day: in the morning, at noon, and in the afternoon. Discuss whether their calculations for the objects' heights at the three different times remained equal. Discuss why the lengths of the shadows changed during the day.

314 Chapter 6 Ratio, Proportion, and Similar Figures

Practice and Problem Solving

Example 1 p. 313

3. **FLAGS** A flagpole is 30 feet high and a mailbox is 3.5 feet high. The mailbox casts a shadow that is 5.25 feet long. How long is the flagpole's shadow at the same time? **45 ft**

4. **ARCHITECTURE** The height of Medina Middle School is 25 feet tall. A mail service drop box outside the school is 4 feet tall. The drop box casts a shadow that is 6 feet long. At the same time, what is the length of the shadow of the school building? **37.5 ft**

Example 2 p. 314

5. **BRIDGES** The triangles below are similar. Find *x*. **120 yd**

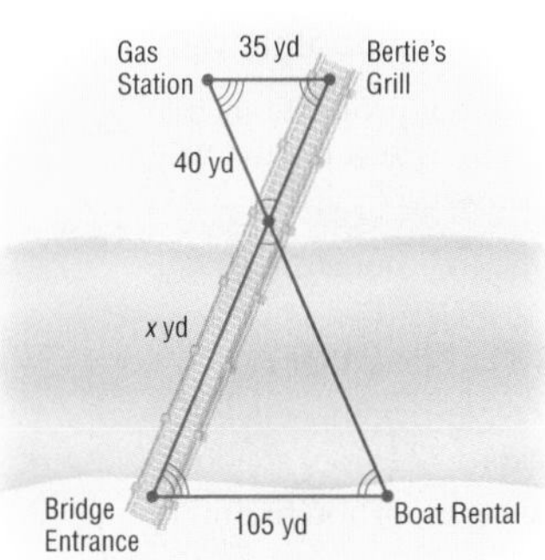

6. **MAPS** The triangles below are similar. How far is it from Athens to Yukon? **40 mi**

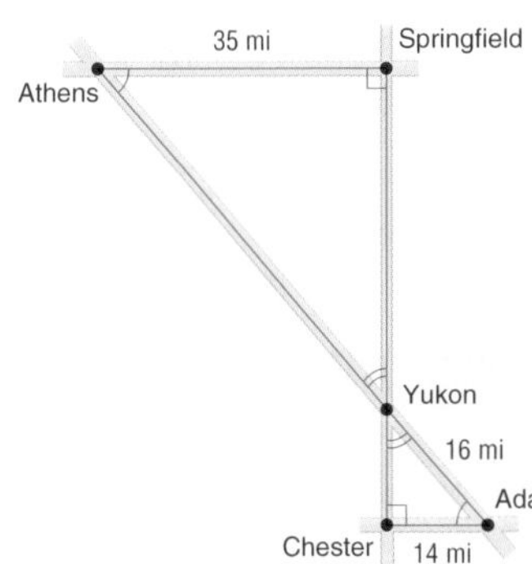

Real-World Link

On July 30, 1909, the U.S. Government bought its first airplane. It was a Wright Brothers biplane. The selling price was $25,000 plus a bonus of $5,000 because it could exceed 40 miles per hour.

Source: Smithsonian

B

7. **ROLLER COASTERS** The height of a roller coaster is 157.5 feet. If the roller coaster's shadow is 60 feet long, how long will a person's shadow be if the person is 5 feet 3 inches tall? **2 ft**

8. **GEOMETRY** All of the triangles in the figure at the right are similar.
   a. Find the measure of segment *GD*. **12 m**
   b. If segment *GF* is congruent to segment *FE*, find the measure of segment *BF*. **6.75 m**
   c. If the length of segment *AD* is 15 meters, what are the lengths of segments *BC* and *CD*? **$CD = 7.5$ m, $BC = 3.75$**

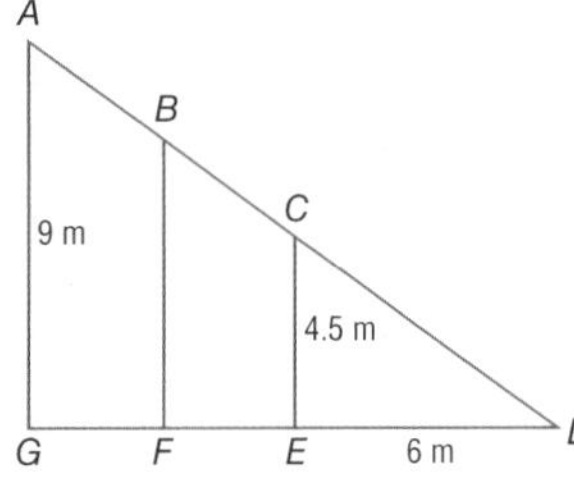

9. **MULTIPLE REPRESENTATIONS** In this problem, you will investigate similar triangles. Consider the following situation. A biplane starts to take-off from the beginning of a runway. When the plane is level with the end of the runway, it is 500 feet above the ground. A bird is flying in the same direction. It is 8 feet above the ground and 15 feet from the beginning of the runway.
   a. **MODEL** Draw a diagram of the situation. **See margin.**
   b. **ALGEBRAIC** Write and solve a proportion to find how far the plane is from the beginning of the runway. $\frac{500}{8} = \frac{x}{15}$; **937.5 ft**

3 PRACTICE

Formative Assessment

Use Exercises 1–2 to check for understanding.

Use the chart at the bottom of this page to customize assignments for your students.

Additional Answer

9a. Sample answer:

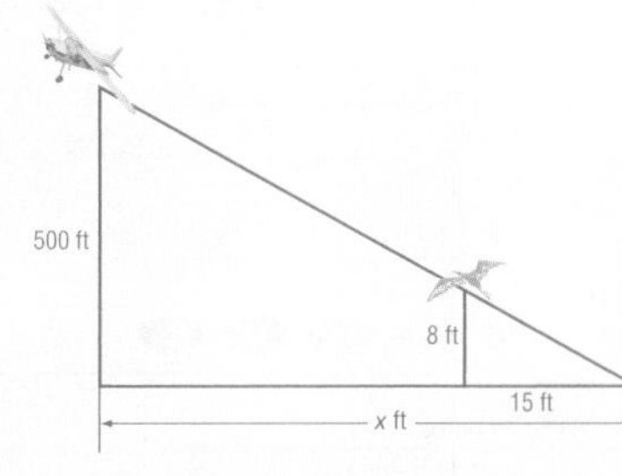

Differentiated Homework Options

Level	Assignment	Two-Day Option	
AL Basic	3–6, 15, 17–29	3, 5, 19–22	4, 6, 15, 17, 18, 23–29
OL Core	3, 5, 7–15, 17–29	3–6, 19–22	7–15, 17, 18, 23–29
BL Advanced	7–25 (optional: 26–29)		

Study Guide and Intervention
CRM pp. 55–56 AL OL ELL

NAME ____________ DATE ________ PERIOD ________

6-9 Study Guide and Intervention
Indirect Measurement

Indirect Measurement The properties of similar triangles can be use to find measurements that are difficult to measure directly. This is called **indirect measurement.**

One type of indirect measurement is *shadow reckoning*. The diagram at the right shows how two objects and their shadows form two sides of similar triangles. You can use a proportion to find measures such as the height of the flag pole.

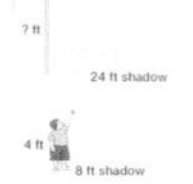

Example SCHOOLS **A school building in casts a 40.5-foot shadow at the same time a 5.8-foot student casts a 4.4-foot shadow. How tall is the school building to the nearest tenth?**

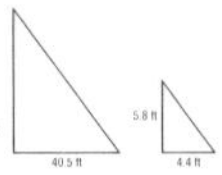

Understand You know the lengths of the shadows and the height of the student. You need to find the building's height.

Plan To find the height of the building, set up a proportion comparing the student's shadow to the building's shadow. Then solve.

Solve

$\frac{5.8}{h} = \frac{4.4}{40.5}$ student's height / building's height; student's shadow / building's shadow

$5.8 \cdot 40.5 = h \cdot 4.4$ Find the cross products

$234.9 = 4.4h$ Multiply

$53.4 = h$ Divide each side by 4.4

The height of the school building is 53.4 feet.

Exercises

1. **HOUSES** Lena's house casts a shadow that is 14 feet long at the same time that Lena casts a shadow that is 3.5 feet long. If Lena is 4.5 feet tall, how tall is her house? **18 feet**
2. **ROCKET** Suppose a rocket outside a science museum cast a shadow that was 176 feet. At the same time, a 5.75-foot-tall person standing next to the rocket casts a shadow that is 9.2 feet long. How tall is the rocket? **110 feet**
3. **TOWERS** A cell phone tower casts a shadow that is 92 feet. A building next to the tower is 28 feet high and casts a shadow that is 11.2 feet long. How tall is the cell phone tower? **230 ft**

Chapter 6 55 Glencoe Pre-Algebra

Lesson 6-9

Practice
CRM p. 58 AL OL BL ELL

NAME ____________ DATE ________ PERIOD ________

6-9 Practice
Indirect Measurement

1. **GEOMETRY** The triangles below are similar. What is the value of x? **50.4**

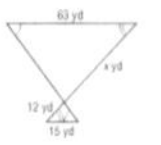

2. **CANYONS** In the figure, $\Delta CDE \sim \Delta GDF$. Find the distance across Rancher Canyon. **21.6 feet**

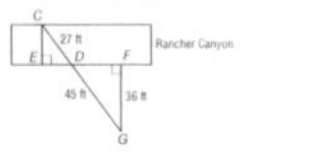

3. **DISTANCES** The triangles below are similar. How far is Dora's house from Micala's house? **7 miles**

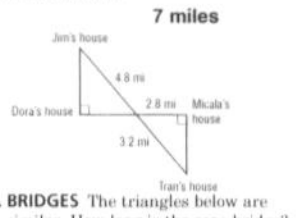

4. **OUTDOOR SPORTS** In the figure, $\Delta ABC \sim \Delta DBE$. How far is the archery range from the soccer field? **60 yards**

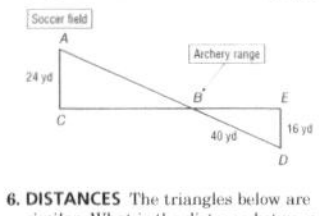

5. **BRIDGES** The triangles below are similar. How long is the rope bridge? **33 feet**

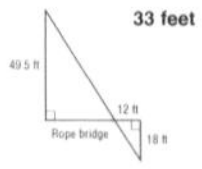

6. **DISTANCES** The triangles below are similar. What is the distance between Tarryhill and Tom's Falls? **105 miles**

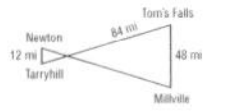

7. **CHIMNEYS** A 6-ft observer casts a 4-ft shadow at the same time a chimney casts a 238-foot shadow. How tall is the chimney? **357 ft**
8. **BUILDINGS** The May Road Apartments in Hong Kong cast a 90-meter shadow at the same time a 1.5-meter tall tenant casts a 0.75-meter shadow. How tall is the apartment building? **180 meters**
9. **WORLD RECORDS** The world's tallest man lived from 1918 to 1940. He cast a 4-foot $5\frac{1}{2}$-inch shadow when a 6-foot pole cast a 3-foot shadow. How tall was he? **8 feet 11 inches**
10. **SHADOWS** A man casts a 14-foot shadow. A 4-foot child casts a 9-foot 4-inch shadow at the same time. How tall is the man? **6 feet**

Chapter 6 58 Glencoe Pre-Algebra

Word Problem Practice
CRM p. 59 AL OL BL

NAME ____________ DATE ________ PERIOD ________

6-9 World Problem Practice
Indirect Measurement

1. **CLIMBING WALLS** Joe's friends are going to climb the climbing wall and have invited Joe to go with them. Joe is afraid of heights and wants to know how high the climbing wall is before he climbs it. Joe is $5\frac{1}{2}$ feet tall and at 3:00 P.M., his shadow is $2\frac{3}{4}$ feet long. At the same time, the shadow of the rock-wall is 35 feet long. How high is the rock-wall? **70 ft**
2. **SHADOWS** Britney is 5 feet tall and casts a $3\frac{1}{2}$-foot shadow at 10:00 A.M. At that time, a nearby tree casts a 17-foot shadow. Two hours later, Britney's shadow is 2 feet long. What is the length of the shadow of the tree at this time? **9.71 ft**
3. **SWIMMING** Tien's camp is having a swim race across the lake. Before the race, Teresa wants to know how many meters it is across the lake. She knows that the flagpole is 22 meters due south from the dock, and that the main cabin is 5 meters due south from the flagpole. She also knows that her cabin is 8 meters due west from the main cabin. Using the diagram below, how far is it across the lake? **35.2 m**

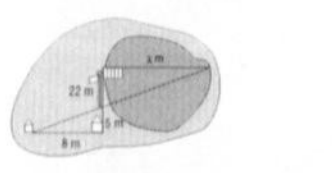

4. **CANALS** In the figure, $\Delta JKL \sim \Delta MKN$. Find the distance across the canal.

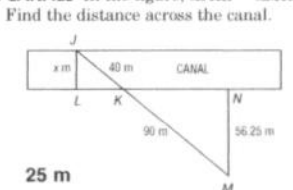

25 m

5. **SHADOWS** Mr. Nolan's math class went out to measure shadows in their school yard. Their data is recorded in the table below.

Item	Shadow Length (ft)
Mr. Nolan	9
flagpole	48
school	63
school bus	16.5

a. If Mr. Nolan is 6 feet tall, how tall is the flagpole? **32 feet**

b. If Mr. Nolan is 5 feet tall, how tall is the school? **35 feet**

c. If Mr. Nolan is 6 feet tall, how tall is the school bus? **11 feet**

d. If a basketball hoop on the playground has a height of 8 feet, how long would its shadow be? **12 feet**

Chapter 6 59 Glencoe Pre-Algebra

Lesson 6-9

10. 1st pole = 50 ft, 2nd pole = 37.5 ft, 3rd pole = 25 ft, 4th pole = 12.5 ft

10. **POLES** Electrical poles that carry electrical wire seem to get smaller the farther away they are. Find the apparent height of each pole if the tallest pole is 50 feet tall and there is 100 feet between each pole.

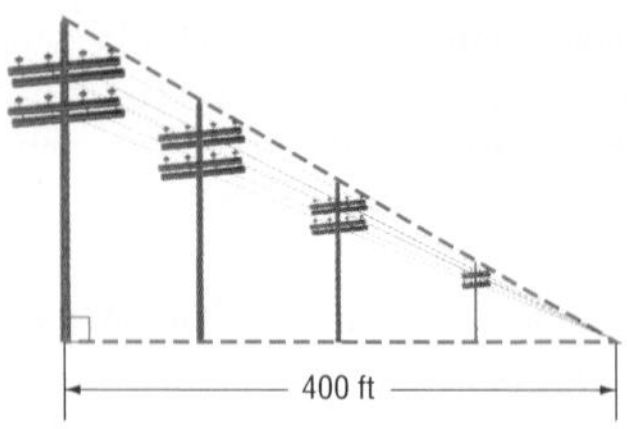

11. **BASKETBALL** During a basketball game, Josh, Devon, and Marco are in the following positions. Josh is 16 feet from Devon, and Devon is $5\frac{1}{3}$ feet from Marco. If Marco is 4 feet from both A and B, how wide is the key? **12 ft**

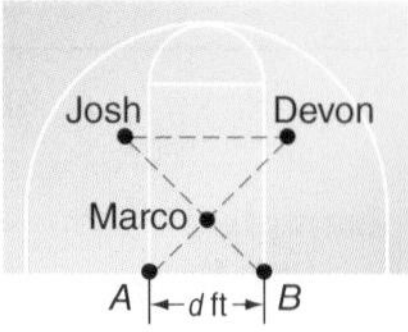

12. **LIGHTHOUSE** Use the figure at the right.
    a. Write two different proportions that could be used to determine the height of the lighthouse. $\frac{x}{120} = \frac{15}{9}, \frac{x}{15} = \frac{120}{9}$
    b. How tall is the lighthouse? **200 ft**

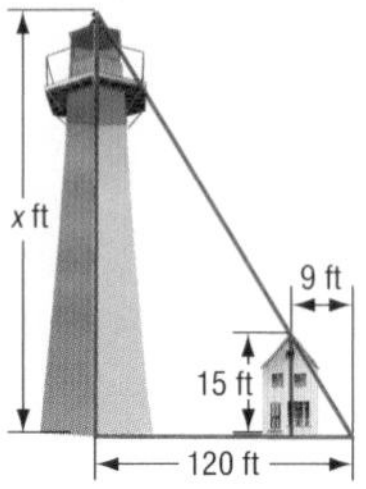

Problem-Solving Tip

To solve Exercise 13, you could draw a diagram.

13. **FERRIS WHEELS** The Navy Pier Ferris Wheel in Chicago is 150 feet tall. If the Ferris wheel casts a $37\frac{1}{2}$-foot shadow, write and solve a proportion to find the height of a nearby woman who casts a $1\frac{1}{2}$-foot shadow. $\frac{37.5}{1.5} = \frac{150}{x}$; **6 ft**
14. **TREE HOUSE** A tree house casts a shadow of 18 feet while Jenet casts a shadow 9 feet. If Jenet is 5 feet tall, how tall is the tree house? **10 ft**

16a. $\frac{h}{ED} = \frac{BC}{DC}$

16b. The distance from the mirror to the person, the distance from the mirror to the base of the flag, the height of the person.

17. false; Sample answer: You also need to know if the angles are congruent as well.

18. Sample answer: If you need to know how tall a tree is to be able to buy enough rope to hang a swing from the tree. I could set up a proportion comparing my height to the height of the tree.

H.O.T. Problems
Use **H**igher-**O**rder **T**hinking Skills

15. **OPEN ENDED** Determine the height of a local landmark or statue in your community using shadow reckoning. **See students' work.**
16. **CHALLENGE** In the diagram shown at the right, $\triangle ABC \sim \triangle EDC$.
    a. Write a proportion that could be used to solve for the height h of the flag pole.
    b. What information would you need to know in order to solve this proportion?

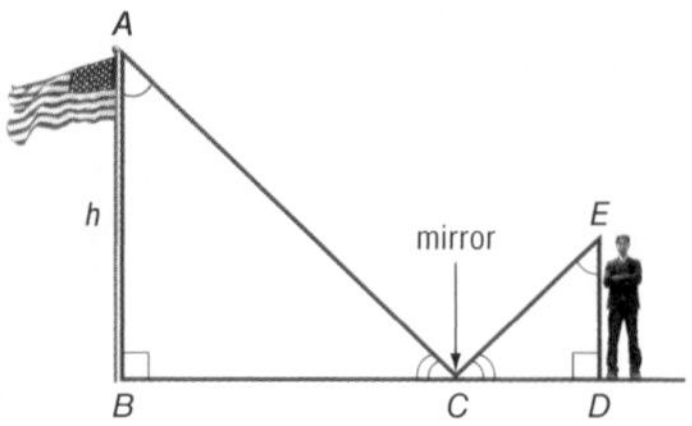

17. **REASONING** *True* or *false?* If two pairs of corresponding sides of two triangles are proportional, then you can use indirect measurement to determine the length of a missing side. Explain your reasoning.
18. **WRITING IN MATH** Give a real-world example of when you might need to use indirect measurement. Explain how you would solve the problem.

Enrichment
CRM p. 60 OL BL

NAME ____________ DATE ________ PERIOD ________

6-9 Enrichment
Sonar

Sonar, which is short for **So**und **Na**vigation and **R**anging, is a form of indirect measurement. Sonar is used to determine the distance of objects when actual measurement is impractical or impossible. Sonar was developed during World War II as a way of tracking enemy submarines and uses sound waves to determine distances. A sound wave is sent from a transmitter. When the wave hits an object, it bounces back to the sonar device, which tracks how long the sound wave took to leave and return. Because sound travels at a constant rate of speed in various environments, the sonar can calculate the distance based on the time it took the sound wave to return.

Example **A sonar transmitter sends out a sound wave. It takes the wave 36 seconds to bounce back. How far is the object that the sound wave bounced off, if sound travels in water at a constant rate of 4800 feet per second?**

Understand You know how long the sound wave took to bounce back and the speed of sound in water. You need to find the distance between the sonar transmitter and the object.

Plan Use a variation of the distance formula, $d = rt$. Because the time given represents the time that the sound wave took to travel *to* and *from* the object, you need to divide the time by 2. So, use the formula $d = \frac{rt}{2}$.

Solve $d = \frac{rt}{2}$ Write the equation

Multiple Representations In Exercise 9, students draw a diagram and use a proportion to find a missing distance dimension.

Standardized Test Practice

19. A bell tower casts a 60-inch shadow. At the same time, a statue that is 4.5 feet tall casts a 15-inch shadow. How tall is the bell tower? **D**

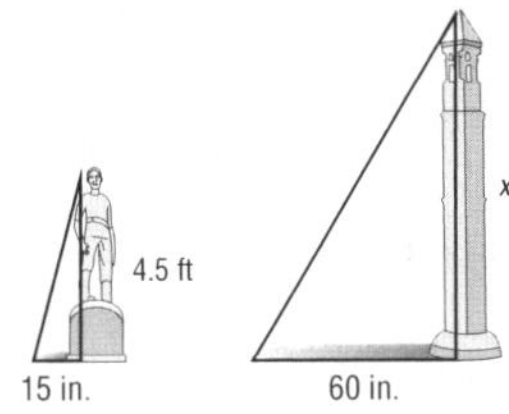

A 200 ft   C 27 ft
B 30 ft   D 18 ft

20. In the figure, $\triangle PRT \sim \triangle SRQ$. Find the distance across the golf green. **J**

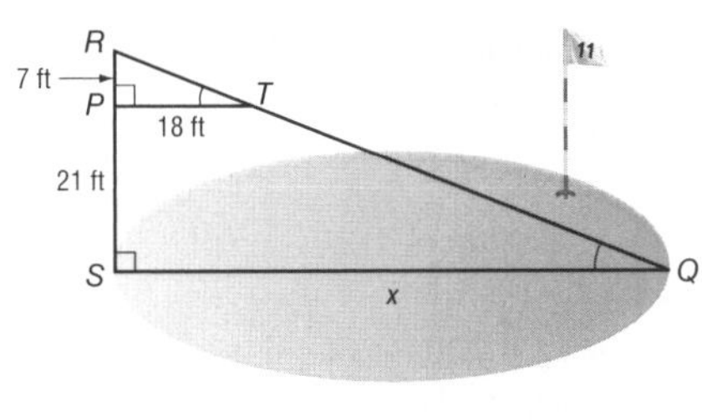

F 4.5 ft   H 48 ft
G 35 ft   J 72 ft

21. SHORT RESPONSE Find the length in kilometers of Beechwold Boulevard. **10 km**

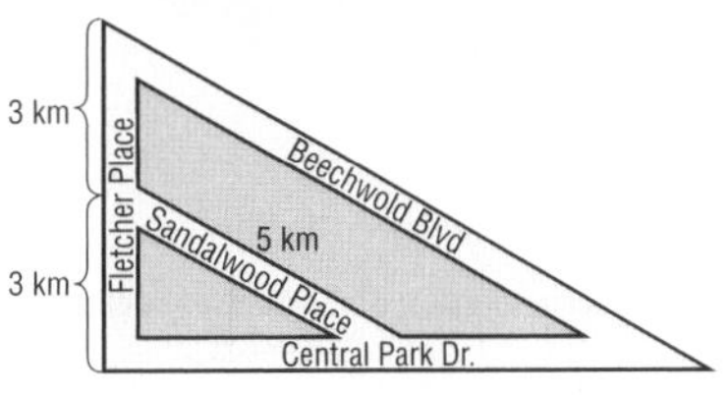

22. How tall is the street sign? **A**

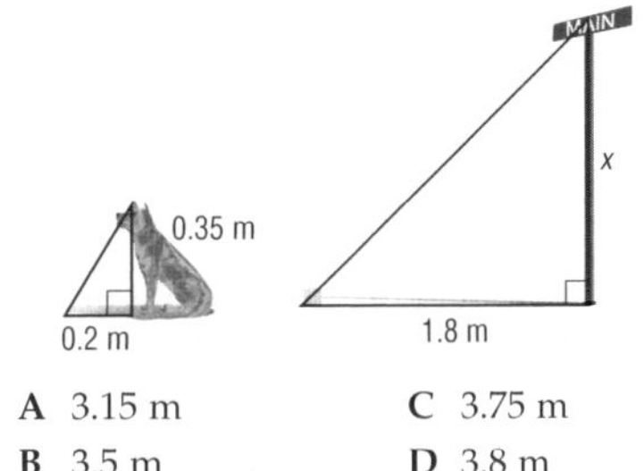

A 3.15 m   C 3.75 m
B 3.5 m   D 3.8 m

Spiral Review

23. A figure has vertices $A(-2, 1)$, $B(1, 2)$, and $C(3, -2)$. Graph the figure and its image after a dilation centered at the origin with a scale factor of 3. (Lesson 6-7) **See margin.**

24. Triangle *JMK* is similar to triangle *PRO*. What is the value of *x*? (Lesson 6-7) **13.5 in.**

25. CRAFTS How many 6-inch long pieces of ribbon can be cut from a piece that is 3 yards long? (Lesson 6-3) **18 pieces**

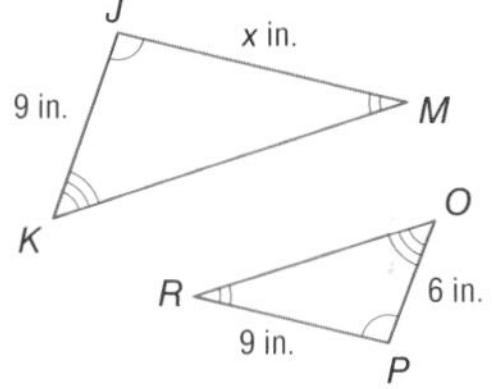

Skills Review

Write each fraction as a decimal. (Lesson 3-1)

26. $\frac{5}{8}$ **0.625**   **27.** $\frac{7}{12}$ **$0.58\overline{3}$**   **28.** $\frac{8}{12}$ **$0.\overline{6}$**   **29.** $\frac{3}{5}$ **0.6**

Differentiated Instruction

Extension A meter stick casts a shadow that is 5 feet long. At the same time, a nearby 90-foot building casts a shadow. How long is the building's shadow in meters? Round your answer to the nearest tenth of a meter. 41.8 meters

Tips for New Teachers

Drawings Encourage students to make drawings to illustrate information in problems. This will help them understand the problem and find the answer.

ASSESS

Ticket Out the Door As students leave, have them turn in to you on a small piece of paper a drawing and the answer to the following question:
A 5-foot parking meter casts a 6-foot shadow. At the same time of day, how long is the shadow of a nearby 80-foot-tall building? 96-foot shadow

Formative Assessment

Check for student understanding of concepts in Lessons 6-8 and 6-9.

CRM Quiz 4, p. 65

Additional Answer

23.

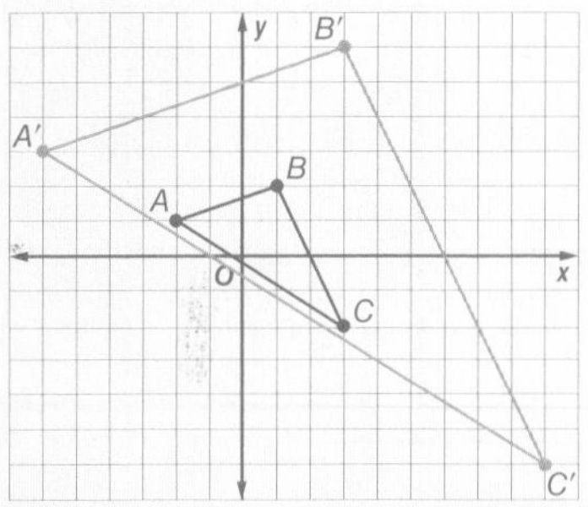

Formative Assessment

Key Vocabulary The page references after each word denote where that term was first introduced. If students have difficulty answering questions 1–8, remind them that they can use these page references to refresh their memories about the vocabulary.

Summative Assessment

CRM Vocabulary Test, p. 67

Math Online glencoe.com

Vocabulary PuzzleMaker improves students' mathematics vocabulary using four puzzle formats–crossword, scramble, word search using a word list, and word search using clues. Students can work online or from a printed worksheet.

CHAPTER 6 Study Guide and Review

Math Online glencoe.com
- STUDY TO GO
- Vocabulary Review

Chapter Summary

Key Concepts

Ratios and Rates (Lessons 6-1 and 6-2)

- A ratio is a comparison of numbers by division.
- A unit rate is a simplified rate whose denominator is 1.

Proportions (Lessons 6-4 and 6-5)

- A proportion is an equation stating two ratios or rates are equal. So, if $\frac{a}{b} = \frac{c}{d}$, then $ad = bc$.
- A proportional relationship exists when the ratios of related terms are equal.

Scale Drawings and Models (Lesson 6-6)

- A scale drawing or model represents an object that is too large or too small to be drawn or built at actual size.
- The ratio of a length on a scale drawing or model to the corresponding length on the real object is the scale.

Similar Figures and Dilations (Lessons 6-7 and 6-8)

- If two figures are similar, then the corresponding angles are congruent and the corresponding sides are proportional.
- A dilation with a scale factor:

  $k > 1$ will result in an enlargement.

  $0 < k < 1$ will result in a reduction.

  $k = 1$ will result in the same figure.

FOLDABLES® Study Organizer

Be sure the Key Concepts are noted in your Foldable.

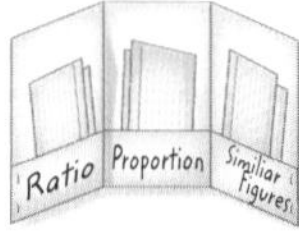

Key Vocabulary

- **congruent** (p. 301)
- **constant of proportionality** (p. 282)
- **corresponding parts** (p. 301)
- **cross products** (p. 287)
- **dilation** (p. 307)
- **dimensional analysis** (p. 275)
- **indirect measurement** (p. 313)
- **inverse proportion** (p. 293)
- **nonproportional** (p. 281)
- **proportion** (p. 287)
- **proportional** (p. 281)
- **rate** (p. 270)
- **ratio** (p. 265)
- **scale** (p. 294)
- **scale drawing** (p. 294)
- **scale factor** (p. 295)
- **scale model** (p. 294)
- **similar figures** (p. 301)
- **unit rate** (p. 270)

Vocabulary Check

Complete each sentence with the correct term. Choose from the list above.

1. A statement of equality of two ratios or rates is called a(n) __proportion__.
2. A(n) __rate__ is a ratio of two measurements having different units.
3. Proportional relationships can be described by using the equation $y = kx$, where k is the ______. **constant of proportionality**
4. The ratio of the length on a scale drawing to the corresponding length on the real object is called the __scale factor__.
5. Figures that have the same shape but not necessarily the same size are called __similar figures__.
6. A (n) __ratio__ is a comparison of two quantities by division.
7. The process of including units of measurement as factors when computing is called ______. **dimensional analysis**
8. Two quantities are __proportional__ if they have a constant ratio or rate.

FOLDABLES® Study Organizer

Dinah Zike's Foldables®

Have students look through the chapter to make sure they have included examples in their Foldables.

Suggest that students keep their Foldables handy while completing the Study Guide and Review pages. Point out that their Foldables can serve as a quick review tool when studying for the Chapter Test.

Lesson-by-Lesson Review

6-1 Ratios (pp. 265–269)

Express each ratio as a fraction in simplest form.

9. 10 girls out of 24 students $\frac{5}{12}$
10. 6 red cars to 4 blue cars $\frac{3}{2}$
11. 10 yards to 8 inches $\frac{45}{1}$
12. 18 ounces to 3 cups $\frac{3}{4}$
13. **BASEBALL** Jean got 12 hits out of 16 times at bat. Express this rate as a fraction in simplest form. Explain its meaning.

13. $\frac{3}{4}$; For every 4 times at bat, Jean got 3 hits or on $\frac{3}{4}$ of his at bats, he got a hit.

EXAMPLE 1

Express the ratio *2 feet to 18 inches* as a fraction in simplest form.

First, convert feet to inches.

$$\frac{2 \text{ ft}}{18 \text{ in.}} = \frac{24 \text{ in.}}{18 \text{ in.}}$$

Next, divide the numerator and denominator by the GCF, 6.

$$\frac{24 \text{ in.} \div 6}{18 \text{ in.} \div 6} = \frac{4 \text{ in.}}{3 \text{ in.}} \text{ or } \frac{4}{3}$$

6-2 Unit Rates (pp. 270–274)

Express each rate as a unit rate. Round to the nearest tenth, if necessary.

14. \$25.97 for 8 boxes **\$3.25 per box**
15. 400 meters in 5 minutes **80 meters per minute**
16. \$175 for 4 concert tickets **\$43.75 per ticket**
17. 125 miles in 200 minutes **0.6 miles per minute**
18. **SHOPPING** An eight pack of juice boxes costs \$4.79, and a twelve pack of juice boxes costs \$6.59. Which is a better buy? Explain. **See margin.**

EXAMPLE 2

Express *274 miles in 14 gallons of gasoline* as a unit rate. Round to the nearest tenth of a mile if necessary.

Write the rate that compares the miles to the number of gallons. Then divide to find the unit rate.

$$\frac{274 \text{ miles}}{14 \text{ gallons}} = \frac{19.6 \text{ miles}}{1 \text{ gallon}} \quad (\div 14)$$

So, the car traveled 19.6 miles on 1 gallon of gasoline.

6-3 Converting Rates and Measurements (pp. 275–280)

Complete each conversion. Round to the nearest hundredth.

19. 7 in. ≈ ■ cm **17.78**
20. 20 m ≈ ■ yd **21.88**
21. 25 fl oz ≈ ■ mL **739.35**
22. 4 L ≈ ■ gal **1.06**
23. 18 pt ≈ ■ L **8.51**
24. 12 oz ≈ ■ g **340.2**
25. **PLANES** A plane is flying at a speed of 425 miles per hour. How far will the plane travel in 0.75 hour? **318.75 mi**
26. **WATER** A swimming pool is being drained at a rate of 50 gallons per hour. How many milliliters per second is this? **52.6 milliliters per second**

EXAMPLE 3

A peregrine falcon can fly at a top speed of 200 miles per hour. How many feet per second is this?

First, convert miles to feet and hours to seconds.

$$\frac{200 \text{ mi}}{1 \text{ h}} = \frac{200 \text{ mi}}{1 \text{ h}} \cdot \frac{5280 \text{ ft}}{1 \text{ mi}} \cdot \frac{1 \text{ h}}{3600 \text{ s}}$$

Next, divide out the common factors.

$$= \frac{\overset{1}{\cancel{200}} \cancel{\text{mi}}}{1 \cancel{\text{h}}} \cdot \frac{\overset{176}{\cancel{5280}} \text{ ft}}{1 \cancel{\text{mi}}} \cdot \frac{1 \cancel{\text{h}}}{\underset{\underset{1}{\cancel{30}}}{\cancel{3600}} \text{ s}}$$

$$= \frac{293.3 \text{ ft}}{1 \text{ s}}$$

The falcon can fly about 293 feet per second.

Lesson-by-Lesson Review

Intervention If the given examples are not sufficient to review the topics covered by the questions, remind students that the page references tell them where to review that topic in their textbook.

Two-Day Option Have students complete the Lesson-by-Lesson Review on pp. 319–322. Then you can use ExamView® Assessment Suite to customize another review worksheet that practices all the objectives of this chapter or only the objectives on which your students need more help.

Differentiated Instruction

Super DVD: MindJogger Videoquizzes Use this DVD as an alternative format of review for the test.

Additional Answer

18. 12 juice boxes for \$6.59; Sample answer: The eight pack of juice boxes costs \$0.60 per juice box and the twelve pack of juice boxes costs \$0.55 per juice box.

CHAPTER 6 Study Guide and Review

6-4 Proportional and Nonproportional Relationships (pp. 281–285)

Determine whether the set of numbers in each table is proportional. Explain.

27.

Boxes	1	2	3	4
Pens	8	16	24	32

Yes; each rate is equal to $\frac{1}{8}$.

28.

Number of People	2	4	6	8
Brownies Eaten	2	5	7	10

No; the rates are not equal.

29. **FESTIVALS** A customer at the ring toss booth gets 8 rings for $2. Write an equation relating the cost to the number of rings. At this same rate, how much would a customer pay for 11 rings? for 20 rings? **$c = 0.25r$, 11 rings cost $2.75; 20 rings cost $5**

EXAMPLE 4

Determine whether the distance is proportional to the time. Explain your reasoning.

Distance (meters)	30	56	69	80
Time (minutes)	1	2	3	4

Write the rate of distance to time for each minute in simplest form.

$\frac{30}{1}$ $\quad \frac{56}{2} = \frac{28}{1}$ $\quad \frac{69}{3} = \frac{23}{1}$ $\quad \frac{80}{4} = \frac{20}{1}$

Since the rates are not equal, the distance is not proportional to the time.

6-5 Solving Proportions (pp. 287–292)

Solve each proportion.

30. $\frac{15}{a} = \frac{5}{4}$ **12**

31. $\frac{m}{6} = \frac{18}{15}$ **7.2**

32. $\frac{28}{24} = \frac{d}{12}$ **14**

33. $\frac{16.5}{21} = \frac{5.5}{t}$ **7**

34. **REAL ESTATE** A homeowner whose house is assessed for $120,000 pays $1800 in taxes. At the same rate, what is the tax on a house assessed at $135,000? **$2025**

EXAMPLE 5

Solve $\frac{4}{9} = \frac{9}{x}$.

$\frac{4}{9} = \frac{9}{x}$	**Write the proportion.**
$4 \cdot x = 9 \cdot 9$	**Cross products**
$4x = 81$	**Multiply.**
$\frac{4x}{4} = \frac{81}{4}$	**Divide each side by 4.**
$x = 20.25$	**Simplify.**

6-6 Scale Drawing and Models (pp. 294–299)

On the scale drawing of a museum, the scale is 0.5 inch = 10 feet. Find the actual length of each gallery.

	Gallery	Drawing Length	
35.	Modern Art	6 in.	**120 ft**
36.	Renaissance	4.25 in.	**85 ft**
37.	Egypt	7.5 in.	**150 ft**

38. **MAPS** The length of a highway is 900 miles. If 0.5 inch on a map represents 50 miles, what is the length of the highway on the map? **9 in.**

EXAMPLE 6

A scale model of a car has a bumper that is 3.5 inches long. The scale on the model is 1 inch = 2 feet. What is the length of the actual car bumper?

model length → / actual length → $\frac{1 \text{ in.}}{2 \text{ ft}} = \frac{3.5 \text{ in.}}{x \text{ ft}}$ ← model length / ← actual length

$1 \cdot x = 2 \cdot 3.5$

$x = 7$

The actual length of the car bumper is 7 feet.

320 Chapter 6 Ratio, Proportion, and Similar Figures

MIXED PROBLEM SOLVING
For mixed problem-solving practice, see page 848.

6-7 Similar Figures (pp. 301–306)

The figures are similar. Determine each missing measure.

39. 7.2 in.

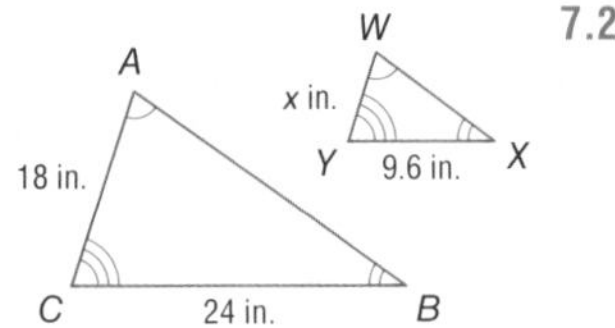

40. 8 cm

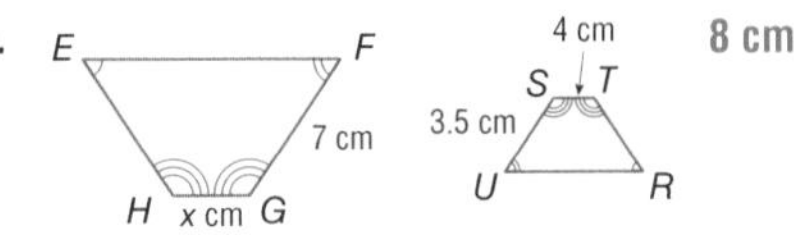

41. **MOSAIC** A mosaic is created using rectangular blocks. Block *A* has a length of 5 centimeters and a width of 2.5 centimeters. Block *B* is similar to block *A* and has a length of 7 centimeters. What is the width of block *B*? 3.5 cm

EXAMPLE 7

If $\triangle LMN \approx \triangle PQR$, what is the value of x?

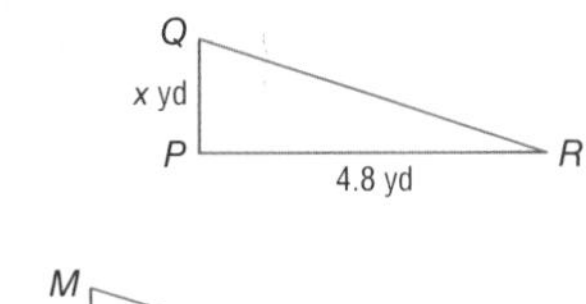

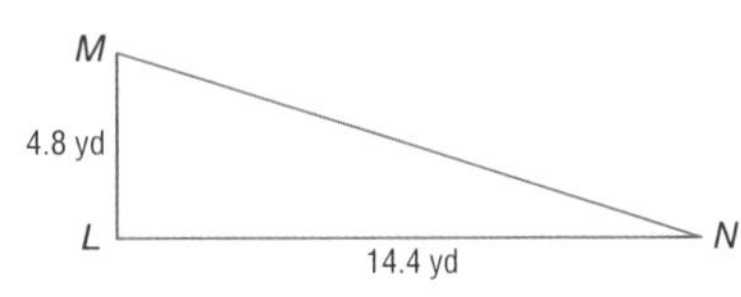

$\frac{LM}{PQ} = \frac{LN}{PR}$ Write a proportion.

$\frac{4.8}{x} = \frac{14.4}{4.8}$ Replace $\overline{LM}$ with 4.8, $\overline{PQ}$ with x, $\overline{LN}$ with 14.4, and $\overline{PR}$ with 4.8.

$x = 1.6$ Find cross products and simplify.

6-8 Dilations (pp. 307–312) 42–45. See margin.

GEOMETRY Find the vertices of each figure after a dilation with the given scale factor, k centered about the origin. Then graph the original image and the dilation.

42. $W(-3, 0), X(2, 6), Y(6, 2), Z(2, -2); k = \frac{2}{3}$
43. $Q(-2, 3), R(1, 2), S(3, -1), T(-2, -2); k = 3$
44. $L(-4, -2), M(-2, 4), N(4, 0); k = \frac{1}{4}$
45. $F(1, 3), G(3, 4), H(2, 1); k = 2.5$

46. **PHOTOGRAPHS** Percy wants to increase the dimensions of his 5-inch by 7-inch photograph by a scale factor of 1.5 on his computer. What is the new size of the photograph? 7.5 in. by 10.5 in.

EXAMPLE 8

A triangle has vertices $A(-2, -1)$, $B(1, 1)$ and $C(3, -3)$. Find the coordinates of the triangle after a dilation centered at the origin with a scale factor of 2.

To dilate the triangle, multiply the coordinates of each vertex by 2.

$A(-2, -1) \rightarrow A'(-2 \cdot 2, -1 \cdot 2) \rightarrow A'(-4, -2)$

$B(1, 1) \rightarrow B'(1 \cdot 2, 1 \cdot 2) \rightarrow B'(2, 2)$

$C(3, -3) \rightarrow C'(3 \cdot 2, -3 \cdot 2) \rightarrow C'(6, -6)$

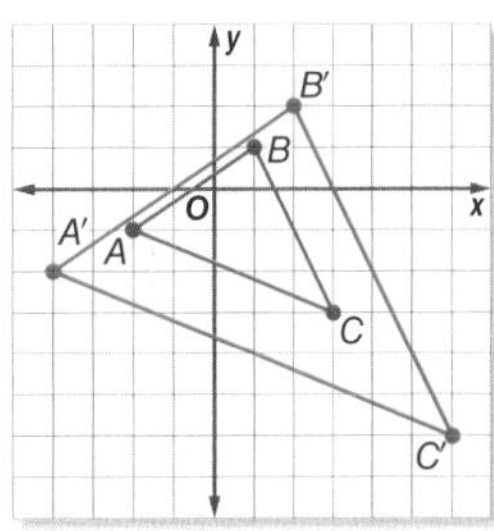

Additional Answers

42.

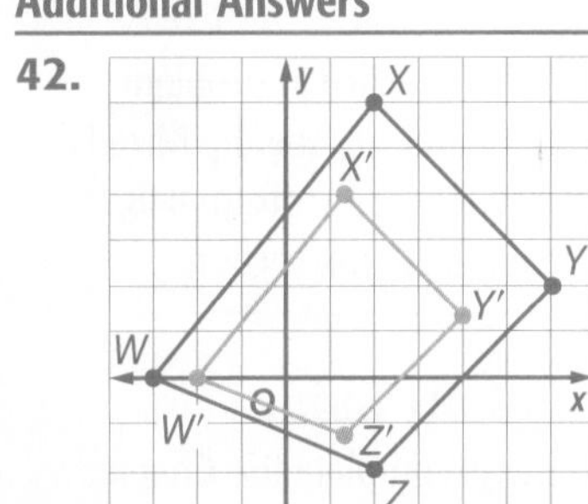

$W'(-2, 0), X'(1\frac{1}{3}, 4), Y'(4, 1\frac{1}{3}), Z'(1\frac{1}{3}, -1\frac{1}{3})$

43.

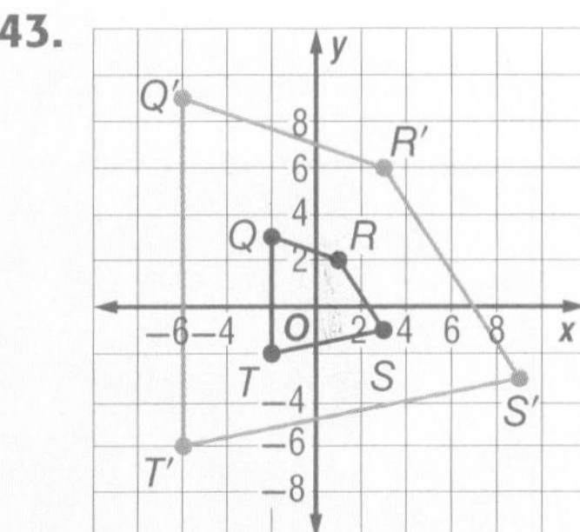

$Q'(-6, 9), R'(3, 6), S'(9, -3), T'(-6, -6)$

44.

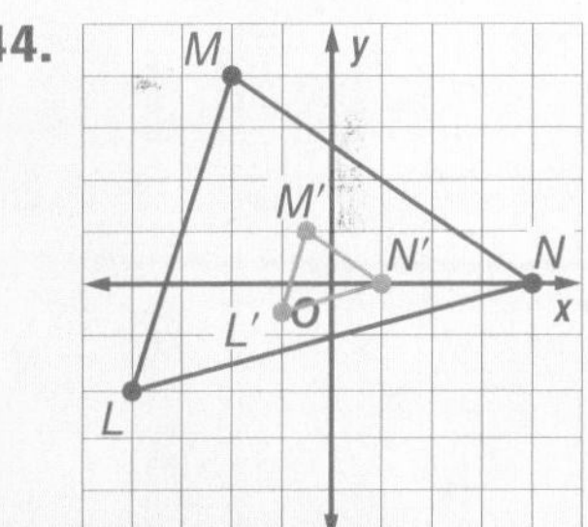

$L'(-1, -0.5), M'(-0.5, 1), N'(1, 0)$

45.

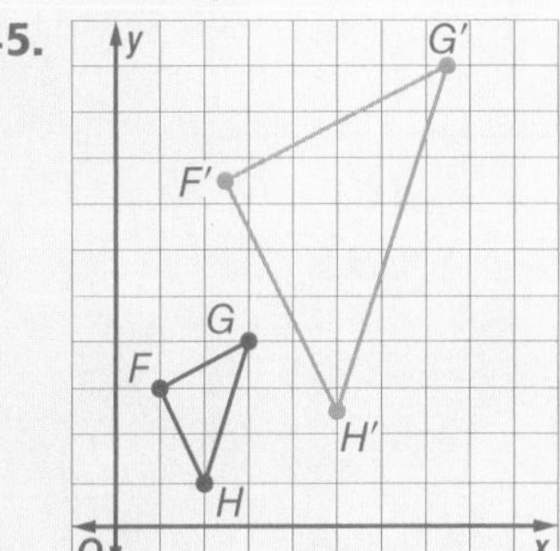

$F'(2.5, 7.5), G'(7.5, 10), H'(5, 2.5)$

Problem Solving Review

For additional practice in problem solving for Chapter 6, see the Mixed Problem Solving Appendix, p. 848, in the Student Handbook section.

Anticipation Guide

Have students complete the Chapter 6 Anticipation Guide and discuss how their responses have changed now that they have completed Chapter 6.

6-9 Indirect Measurement (pp. 313–317)

47. **WORLD RECORDS** At 7 feet 8 inches, the world's tallest woman casts a 46-inch shadow. At the same time, the world's shortest woman casts a 15.5-inch shadow. How tall is the world's shortest woman? **31 in.**

48. **HISTORY** The largest known pyramid is the Pyramid of Khufu. At a certain time of day, a vertical yard stick casts a shadow 1.5 feet long, and the pyramid casts a shadow 241 feet long. How tall is the pyramid? **482 ft**

49. In the figure below, $\triangle ABE \approx \triangle ACD$. What is the distance across the pond? **70 m**

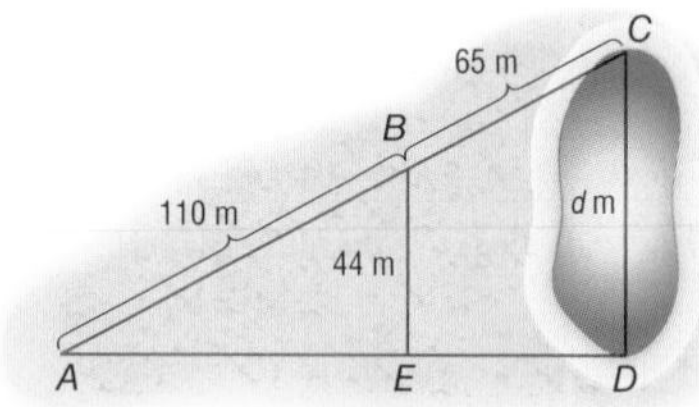

EXAMPLE 9

The Washington Monument casts a 185-foot shadow at the same time a nearby flagpole casts a 3-foot shadow. If the flagpole is 9 feet tall, how tall is the Washington Monument?

Write and solve a proportion.

$$\frac{9 \text{ ft}}{x \text{ ft}} = \frac{3 \text{ ft}}{185 \text{ ft}}$$

(flagpole height → 9 ft; monument height → x ft; 3 ft ← flagpole's shadow; 185 ft ← monument's shadow)

$$9 \cdot 185 = x \cdot 3$$ **Cross products**

$$1665 = 3x$$ **Multiply.**

$$\frac{1665}{3} = \frac{3x}{3}$$ **Divide each side by 3.**

$$555 = x$$

The Washington Monument is 555 feet tall.

Practice Test

Math Online glencoe.com
Chapter Test

1. **ZOOS** The table shows how many of each type of animal are at a zoo. Express each ratio as a fraction in simplest form.

Animal	Types
Mammals	25
Birds	10
Reptiles	8
Arthropods	5

a. birds to mammals $\frac{2}{5}$

b. reptiles to all animals $\frac{1}{6}$

Express each rate as a unit rate.

2. \$75 for 5 DVDs **\$15 per DVD**
3. 300 words in 5 minutes **60 words per minute**
4. **WATER** Which bottle of water costs more per ounce: a 12 ounce bottle for \$1.25 or a 16 ounce bottle for \$1.50? Explain. **See margin.**

Complete each conversion. Round to the nearest hundredth.

5. 15 ft ≈ ■ m **4.58**
6. 11 gal ≈ ■ L **41.64**
7. 50 kg ≈ ■ lb **110.13**
8. 18 oz ≈ ■ g **510.3**
9. **TAXI** The taxi cab company charges a \$2 fee plus \$1.10 for each mile driven. Complete the table and determine whether the pattern forms a proportion. Explain. **No; the rates are not equal.**

Miles Driven	1	2	3	4	5
Cab Fare (\$)	■	■	■	■	■

\$3.10; \$4.20; \$5.30; \$6.40; \$7.50

10. **SALES** Jhan bought an 8-ounce fruit drink for \$1.50. Write and solve a proportion that could be used to find the cost of a gallon of fruit drink. (*Hint*: 1 gal = 128 oz) $\frac{8}{1.50} = \frac{128}{x}$; **\$24**
11. **DRAWING** A scale drawing of a house that is 12 meters tall is being drawn with a scale of 2 centimeters = 3 meters. How many centimeters tall is the scale drawing? **8 cm**
12. **MULTIPLE CHOICE** Brandon is watching a movie clip on his computer in a window that is 6 inches by 3 inches. What is length and width of the window when dilated by a scale factor of $\frac{2}{3}$? **D**

A $\ell = 12$ in., $w = 9$ in.
C $\ell = 3$ in., $w = 6$ in.
B $\ell = 2$ in., $w = 3$ in.
D $\ell = 4$ in., $w = 2$ in.

13. **GEOMETRY** The figures are similar. Find the missing measure. **6 in.**

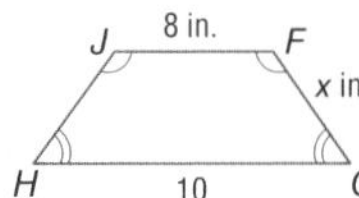

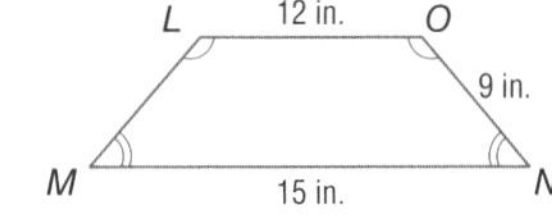

14. **GEOMETRY** Triangle *KLM* is shown. Graph the image of the triangle after a dilation centered at the origin with a scale factor of 2. **See margin.**

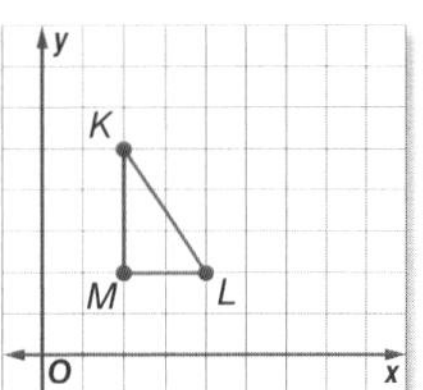

15. **MULTIPLE CHOICE** Triangle *DEF* has vertices *D*(4, 16), *E*(12, −12), and *F*(4, −8). Which of the following gives the vertices of triangle *D′E′F′* after a dilation of $\frac{1}{2}$? **H**

F *D′*(2, 4), *E′*(6, −3), *F′*(2, −2)

G *D′*(16, 32), *E′*(24, −24), *F′*(8, −16)

H *D′*(2, 8), *E′*(6, −6), *F′*(2, −4)

J *D′*(1, 4), *E′*(3, −3), *F′*(1, −2)

16. **GAMES** In the map of Field Games, the triangles are similar. How far is the walk from Gone Fishin′ to the Cake Walk? **3 yd**

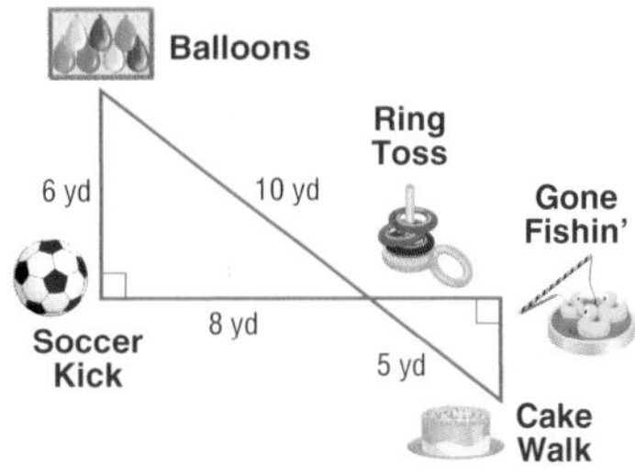

CHAPTER 6 Practice Test

Customize and create multiple versions of your chapter test and their answer keys. All of the questions from the leveled chapter tests in the *Chapter 6 Resource Masters* are also available on ExamView® Assessment Suite.

Additional Answers

4. \$1.25 for 12 ounces; Sample answer: The 12 ounce bottle costs \$0.10 per ounce and the 16 ounce bottle costs \$0.09 per ounce.

14.

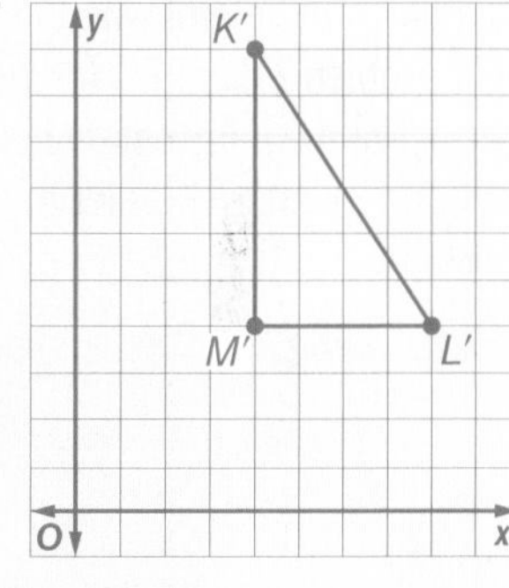

Intervention Planner

Tier 1 On Level	Tier 2 Strategic Intervention approaching grade level	Tier 3 Intensive Intervention 2 or more grades below level
If students miss about 25% of the exercises or less,	**If** students miss about 50% of the exercises,	**If** students miss about 75% of the exercises,
Then choose a resource:	**Then** choose a resource:	**Then** use *Math Triumphs, Grade 8,* Ch. 4–5
SE Lessons 6-1 through 6-9 **CRM** Skills Practice, pp. 7, 13, 19, 25, 31, 37, 44, 50, and 57 **TE** Chapter Project, p. 262	**CRM** Study Guide and Intervention, Chapter 6, pp. 5, 11, 17, 23, 29, 35, 42, 48, and 55 *Quick Review Math Handbook*	
Math Online Self-Check Quiz	**Math Online** Extra Examples, Personal Tutor, Homework Help	**Math Online** Extra Examples, Personal Tutor, Homework Help, Review Vocabulary

 FOCUS

Objective Use the strategy of drawing a diagram to solve standardized test problems.

2 TEACH

Scaffolding Questions

Ask:

- For which types of problems are diagrams useful? Answers will vary.
- Why is a diagram helpful when solving a problem? Sample answer: It helps organize the information in the problem and it makes it easier to see relationships.

CHAPTER 6 Preparing for Standardized Tests

Draw a Diagram

Drawing a diagram can be a helpful way for you to visualize how to solve a problem. You can sketch your diagram on scrap paper or in your test booklet (if allowed). Some questions will require you to include a diagram in your answer. Do *not* make any marks however on your gridded response sheet other than your answers.

Strategies for Drawing a Diagram

Step 1

Read the problem carefully.

Ask yourself:

- What am I being asked to solve?
- What information is given in the problem?

Step 2

Sketch and label your diagram.

- Draw your diagram as clearly and accurately as possible.
- Label the diagram carefully. Be sure to include all of the given information.

Step 3

Solve the problem.

- Use your diagram to help you model the problem situation with an equation. Solve the equation.
- Check to be sure your answer makes sense.

EXAMPLE

Read the problem. Identify what you need to know. Then use the information in the problem to solve. Show your work.

SHORT RESPONSE A flagpole casts a shadow that is 26.25 feet long at the same time Jerome casts a shadow that is 3.5 feet long. If Jerome is 5.6 feet tall, what is the height of the flagpole?

Scoring Rubric	
Criteria	**Score**
Full Credit: The answer is correct and a full explanation is provided that shows each step.	2
Partial Credit: • The answer is correct, but the explanation is incomplete. • The answer is incorrect, but the explanation is correct.	1
No Credit: Either an answer is not provided or the answer does not make sense.	0

Read the problem carefully. You are given information about heights and shadows. Draw a diagram to help you solve the problem.

Example of a 2-point response:

Draw a diagram and use similar triangles to find the height of the flagpole.

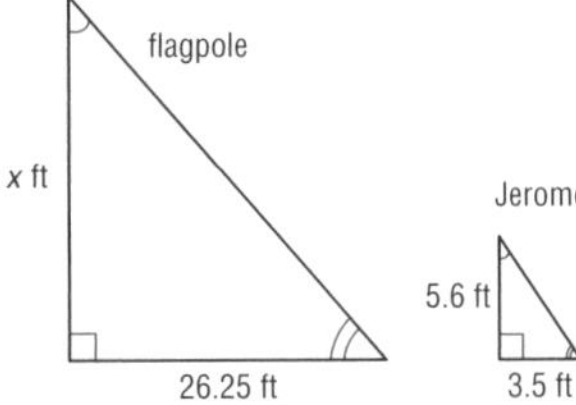

Use the similar triangles to set up and solve a proportion.

$$\text{flagpole}\left\{\frac{x}{26.25}\right. = \left.\frac{5.6}{3.5}\right\}\text{Jerome}$$

$$3.5x = 147$$

$$\frac{3.5x}{3.5} = \frac{147}{3.5}$$

$$x = 42$$

The height of the flagpole is 42 feet.

The steps, calculations, and reasoning are clearly stated. The student also arrives at the correct answer. So, this response is worth the full 2 points.

Exercises

Read each problem. Identify what you need to know. Then use the information in the problem to solve. Show your work.

1. The height of a roller coaster is 155 feet. The roller coaster casts a shadow that is 62 feet long. At the same time, Alexandria casts a shadow that is $2\frac{1}{5}$ feet long. How tall is Alexandria? Round your answer to the nearest inch, if necessary. **5 ft 6 in.**

2. **GRIDDED RESPONSE** A tower casts a 24-foot shadow while a mailbox in the same location casts a 1.2-foot shadow. If the mailbox is 4 feet high, how high is the tower in feet? **80**

3. A surveyor needs to find the distance across the river. Find the distance across the river. **32 m**

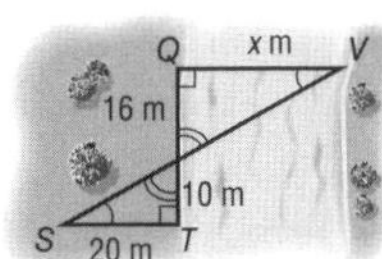

4. In triangle *ABC*, segment *AB* is 5 centimeters long, segment *BC* is 3 centimeters long, and segment *AC* is 6 centimeters long. Triangle *DEF* is similar to triangle *ABC*. If segment *DF* is 7.5 centimeters long, what is the length of segment *DE*? **6.25 cm**

Additional Example

SHORT RESPONSE A townhouse is 35 feet tall. A nearby lamppost is 11.2 feet tall. If the lamppost casts a shadow that is 6.2 feet long, what is the length of the townhouse's shadow?

Sample 2-point response: Draw a diagram and use similar triangles to find the length of the townhouse's shadow.

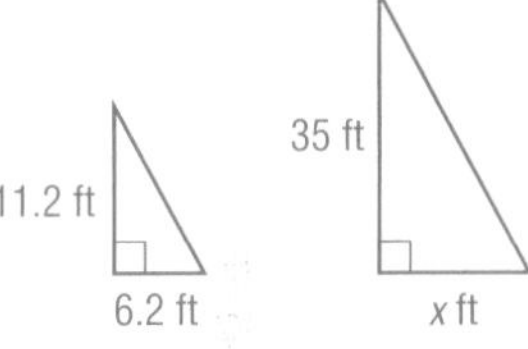

Set up and solve a proportion using the diagrams.

$$\frac{11.2}{6.2} = \frac{35}{x}$$

$$11.2x = 217$$

$$x = 19.375$$

The townhouse's shadow is 19.375 feet long.

3 ASSESS

Use Exercises 1–4 to assess students' understanding.

Diagnose Student Errors

Survey student responses for each item. Class trends may indicate common errors and misconceptions.

1. A divided numerator and denominator by different numbers
   B divided numerator and denominator by different numbers
   C correct
   D division error
2. F used wrong number to multiply unit rate
   G correct
   H used wrong number to multiply unit rate
   J used wrong number to multiply unit rate
3. A guess
   B used wrong number for divisor
   C used wrong number for dividend
   D correct
4. F calculation error
   G guess
   H correct
   J calculation error
5. A confused inches and miles
   B confused inches and miles and set up proportion incorrectly
   C correct
   D set up proportion incorrectly
6. F misunderstood proportional relationship
   G misunderstood proportional relationship
   H misunderstood proportional relationship
   J correct
7. A calculation error
   B correct
   C calculation error
   D guess
8. F guess
   G correct
   H guess
   J calculation error

Multiple Choice

Read each question. Then fill in the correct answer on the answer document provided by your teacher or on a sheet of paper.

1. Of the 60 students in the eighth grade, 24 participate in a school sport. Express this ratio as a fraction in simplest form. **C**

   A $\frac{1}{4}$ C $\frac{2}{5}$

   B $\frac{3}{4}$ D $\frac{3}{5}$

2. A 128-ounce container of orange juice costs \$5.12 at the local supermarket. At what price should the supermarket sell a 96-ounce container of orange juice so that the unit rate of the containers is the same? **G**

Orange Juice Prices	
Size	**Price**
128 oz	\$5.12
96 oz	■

   F \$3.76 H \$3.92

   G \$3.84 J \$4.08

3. Miguel spends \$0.25 for each game ticket at the school carnival. If he has \$4.50, how many game tickets can he buy? **D**

   A 12 C 16

   B 15 D 18

4. Seven more than three times a number is 58. What is the number? **H**

   F 15 H 17

   G 16 J 18

Test-TakingTip

Question 1 Use estimation to eliminate unreasonable answers. Half of 60 is 30 so the fraction should be less than $\frac{1}{2}$.

5. On a map of Terrance's hometown, the distance from the stadium to a park is 3.5 inches. If the actual distance is 7 miles, what is the scale of the map? **C**

   A 1 inch = 0.5 mile

   B 1 inch = 0.25 mile

   C 1 mile = 0.5 inch

   D 1 mile = 0.25 inch

6. Use the table shown below. What number of printer cartridges would result in a proportional relationship? **J**

Boxes	Printer Cartridges
1	16
2	32
3	48
4	■

   F 56 H 60

   G 58 J 64

7. Mrs. Connors is organizing the seventh grade field trip to the museum of natural history. She knows that 3 vans will accommodate 24 passengers. How many vans will be needed for 64 passengers? **B**

   A 7 vans C 9 vans

   B 8 vans D 10 vans

8. Rectangle *ABCD* is similar to rectangle *HIJK*. What is the length of $\overline{IK}$ if BD = 9 centimeters, AB = 12 centimeters, and HI = 8 centimeters? **G**

   F 5.6 cm

   G 6 cm

   H 6.5 cm

   J 7 cm

CHAPTER 6 Standardized Test Practice

Short Response/Gridded Response

Record your answers on the answer sheet provided by your teacher or on a sheet of paper.

9. The right triangles below are similar.

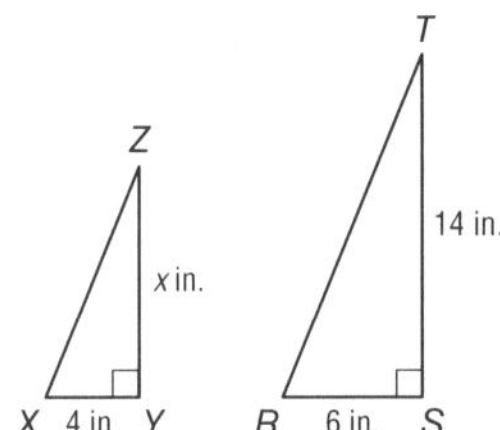

a. Find the scale factor from $\triangle XYZ$ to $\triangle RST$. **1.5**

b. What is the value of x in $\triangle XYZ$? **$9\frac{1}{3}$**

10. GRIDDED RESPONSE In a microscope, the image of a 0.16-millimeter paramecium appears to be 8 millimeters long. What is the scale factor of the dilation? **50**

11. Miley needs to use $\frac{1}{4}$ cup of flour in one recipe and $\frac{2}{3}$ cup in a second recipe. If she doubles both recipes, how much flour does she need in all? **$1\frac{5}{6}$ c**

12. A tree casts a shadow that is 32 feet long at the same time as a stop sign casts a shadow that is 4 feet long. The stop sign is 7 feet tall.

a. Sketch a drawing of the situation. **See Students' work.**

b. How tall is the tree? **56 ft**

13. GRIDDED RESPONSE The length of a rectangle is 5 centimeters longer than twice the width. If the width of the rectangle is 6 centimeters, find the area of the figure in square centimeters. **102**

Extended Response

Record your answers on a sheet of paper. Show your work.

14. The graph shows Jeremy's and Eduardo's average rates in a race.

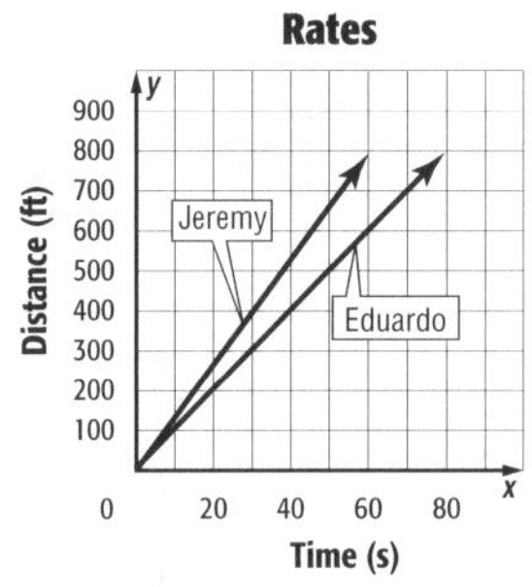

a. Express each person's average speed as a unit rate.

b. At these rates, how long would it take Jeremy and Eduardo each to complete a race of 1800 feet?

c. Suppose Albert races at an average speed of 12.5 feet per second. Predict where the line representing his speed would be graphed. Explain your reasoning.

14a. Jeremy: $13\frac{1}{3}$ feet per second, Eduardo: 10 feet per second

14b. Jeremy: 135 seconds, Eduardo: 180 seconds

14c. Sample answer: Between the two lines on the graph. His speed is greater than Eduardo's but less than Jeremy's.

Need Extra Help?														
If you missed Question...	1	2	3	4	5	6	7	8	9	10	11	12	13	14
Go to Lesson or Page...	6-1	6-2	5-4	4-6	6-6	6-4	6-5	6-7	6-7	6-8	3-6	6-9	5-1	6-2

Formative Assessment

You can use these two pages to benchmark student progress.

CRM Standardized Test Practice, pp. 81–83

Answer Sheet Practice

Have students simulate taking a standardized test by recording their answers on practice recording sheets.

CRM Student Recording Sheet, p. 62

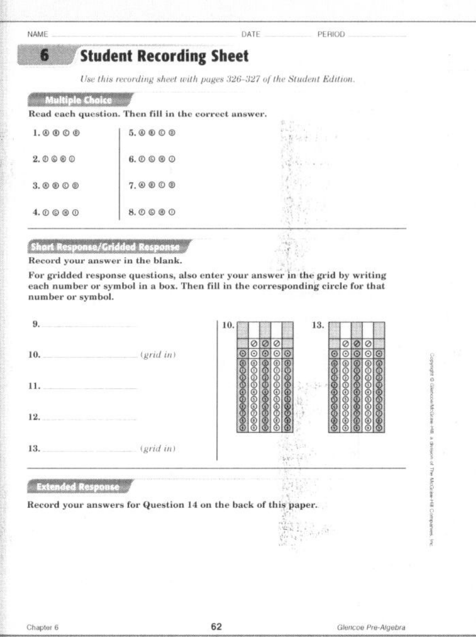

NAME DATE PERIOD

6 Student Recording Sheet

Use this recording sheet with pages 326–327 of the Student Edition.

Multiple Choice

Read each question. Then fill in the correct answer.

1. Ⓐ Ⓑ Ⓒ Ⓓ
2. Ⓐ Ⓑ Ⓒ Ⓓ
3. Ⓐ Ⓑ Ⓒ Ⓓ
4. Ⓐ Ⓑ Ⓒ Ⓓ
5. Ⓐ Ⓑ Ⓒ Ⓓ
6. Ⓐ Ⓑ Ⓒ Ⓓ
7. Ⓐ Ⓑ Ⓒ Ⓓ
8. Ⓐ Ⓑ Ⓒ Ⓓ

Short Response/Gridded Response

Record your answer in the blank.

For gridded response questions, also enter your answer in the grid by writing each number or symbol in a box. Then fill in the corresponding circle for that number or symbol.

9. ______
10. ______ (grid in)
11. ______
12. ______
13. ______ (grid in)

Extended Response

Record your answers for Question 14 on the back of this paper.

Chapter 6 62 Glencoe Pre-Algebra

Create practice worksheets or tests that align to your state's standards as well as TIMSS and NAEP tests.

Homework Option

Get Ready for Chapter 7 Assign students the exercises on p. 329 as homework to assess whether they possess the prerequisite skills needed for the next chapter.

Chapters 1–6 Standardized Test Practice 327

Page 265, Lesson 6-1 (Check Your Progress)

1. $\frac{10}{1}$ or 10; This means that for every 10 years a bottlenose dolphin lives, a mouse lives one year.

Page 281, Lesson 6-4 (Why?)

c. The completed laps per minute for Tom are equivalent. The completed laps for Jenna are not equivalent. Tom ran 3 laps every minute; Jenna ran 4 laps in the first minute, then ran 2 laps every minute thereafter.

Page 283, Lesson 6-4

12. yes

Number of Students	2	4	6	8	10
Slices of Pizza	5	10	15	20	25

13. no

Number of Rides	1	2	3	4	5
Cost	\$5.50	\$7.00	\$8.50	\$10.00	\$11.50

14. yes

Number of Guests	6	7	8	9	10
Cost	\$42	\$49	\$56	\$63	\$70

16c.

Isabel's Savings	
Number of Weeks	Money Saved (\$)
1	20
2	40
3	60
4	80
5	100
6	120

Isabel's Sister's Savings	
Number of Weeks	Money Saved (\$)
1	30
2	50
3	70
4	90
5	110
6	130

17. Sample answer: If the ratio of red to pink flowers is $\frac{2}{8}$, $r = 0.25p$ for r red flowers and p pink flowers. At store A, there are always 2 red flowers for every 8 pink flowers in the bouquet. At store B, their signature bouquet will always have 3 more pink flowers than red flowers. The bouquet for store A is proportional while the bouquet for Store B is nonproportional. Store A: If $\frac{2}{10}$ of the flowers are red, $r = 0.25p$ for r red flowers and p pink flowers. Store B: $r = p - 3$ for r red flowers and p pink flowers.

18. $1\frac{1}{2}$ gal; Sample answer: The ratio of flour to water is $\frac{1}{4}$:1. Since there are 6 cups of flour needed, then there are 24 cups of water needed. There are 16 cups in 1 gallon. $24 \div 16 = 1.5$

19b. The ratios should be close in value.

19c. Sample answer: Pyramid of Khufu in Giza, Egypt; The Taj Mahal in India; The Lincoln Memorial in Washington, D.C.

20. No, their ages are not proportional.

Monica's Age	Patrice's Age
12	6
13	7
14	8
15	9
16	10

Page 293, Extend 6-5

4a.

length (ft)	2	3	4	6
width (ft)	18	12	9	6

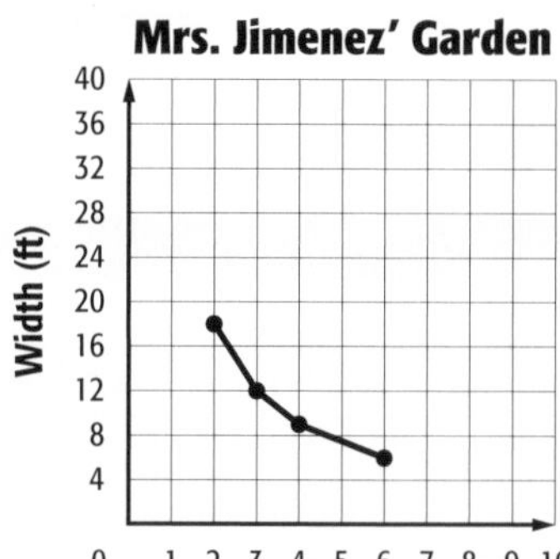

5.

Monday					
time (hours)	0	0.5	1	1.5	2
distance (miles)	0	4	8	12	16

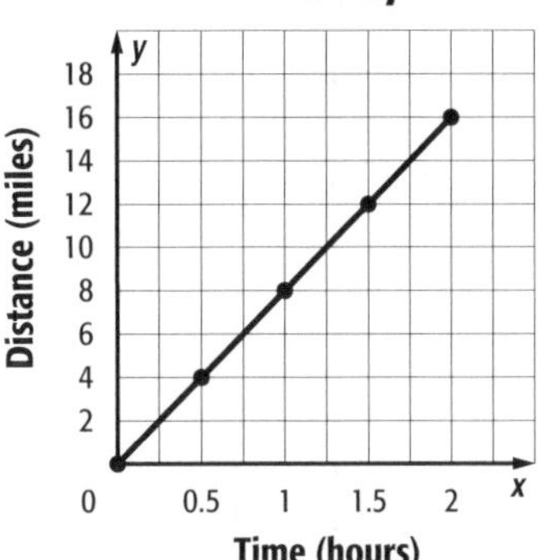

Wednesday				
time (hours)	16	8	4	2
rate (miles per hour)	1	2	4	8

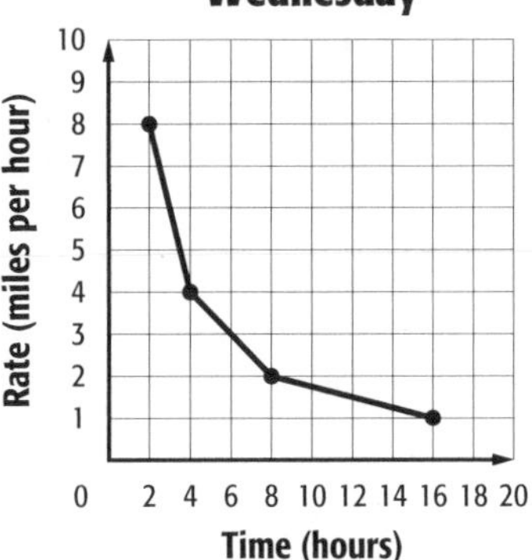

Monday is a proportional relationship and Wednesday is inversely proportional.

Page 298, Lesson 6-6

17b.

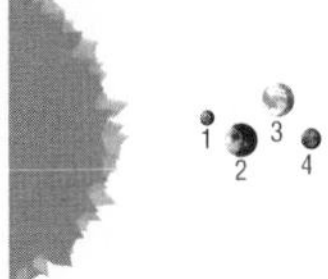

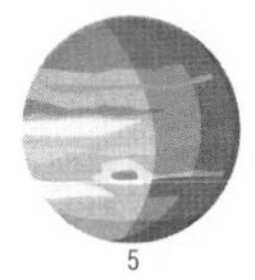

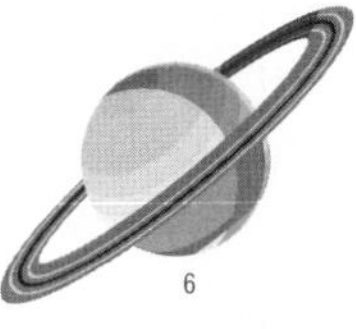

6

Page 301, Lesson 6-7 (Why?)

a. Yes, the pattern continues on forever.

b. A figure that constantly repeats itself with the same image but as a different size is self-similar.

Page 305, Lesson 6-7

16. Sample answer:

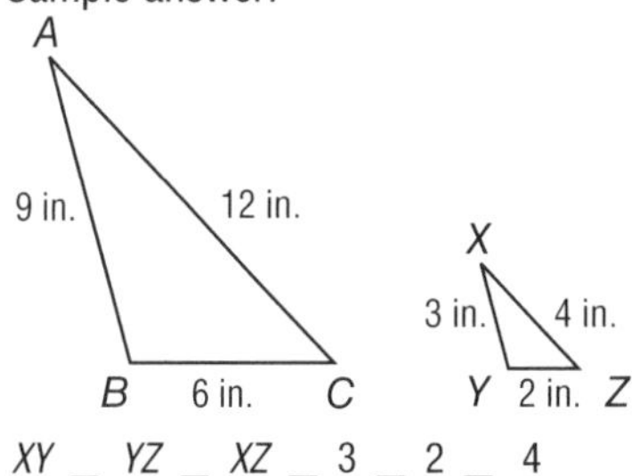

$\frac{XY}{AB} = \frac{YZ}{BC} = \frac{XZ}{AC} = \frac{3}{9} = \frac{2}{6} = \frac{4}{12}$

19. no; Sample answer: Both of them incorrectly set up the proportions. The proportion should be set up as $\frac{BC}{EF} = \frac{AB}{DE}$ or $\frac{16}{12} = \frac{x}{18}$.

20. They are proportional; Sample answer: If $\Delta XYZ \sim \Delta RST$, then corresponding sides are proportional, so $\frac{x}{r} = \frac{z}{t}$.

$\frac{x}{r} = \frac{z}{t}$	Write the proportion.
$xt = rz$	Find the cross products.
$\frac{xt}{zt} = \frac{zr}{zt}$	Divide each side by *zt*.
$\frac{x}{z} = \frac{r}{t}$	Divide out common factors.

21. Triangle *B* is the original triangle. Since the scale factor is less than 1, the original triangle is being reduced, which means that the scaled triangle will be smaller. The measures of the sides of triangle *A* are less than the measures of the sides of triangle *B*, so triangle *B* must be the original triangle.

Page 307, Lesson 6-8 (Check Your Progress)

1.

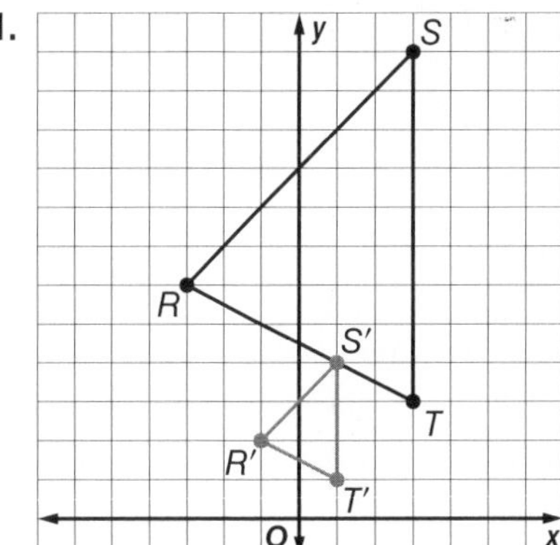

Pages 310–311, Lesson 6-8

9. $G'(-2, 2)$, $H'(4, 2)$, $J'(6, -4)$, $K'(-4, -4)$

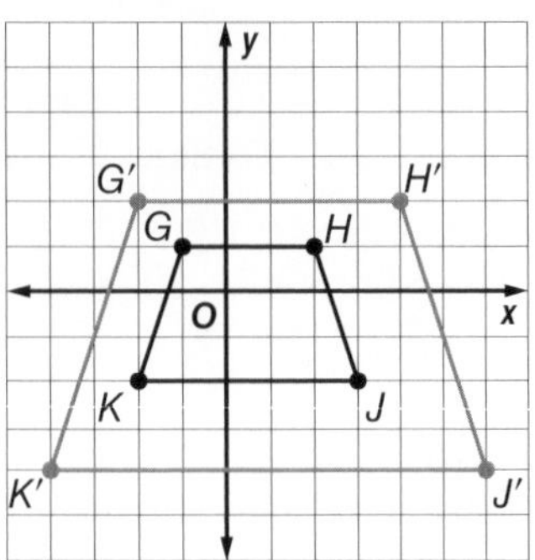

10. $W'(0, 0)$, $X'(2, -2)$, $Y'(2, 4)$

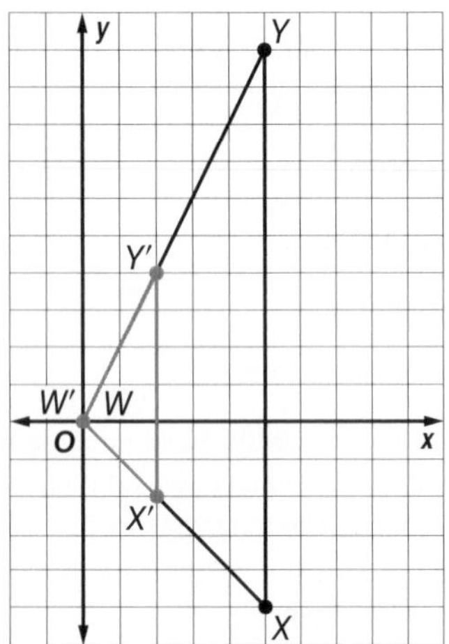

11. $R'(-3, 6)$, $S'(3, 12)$, $T'(3, 3)$

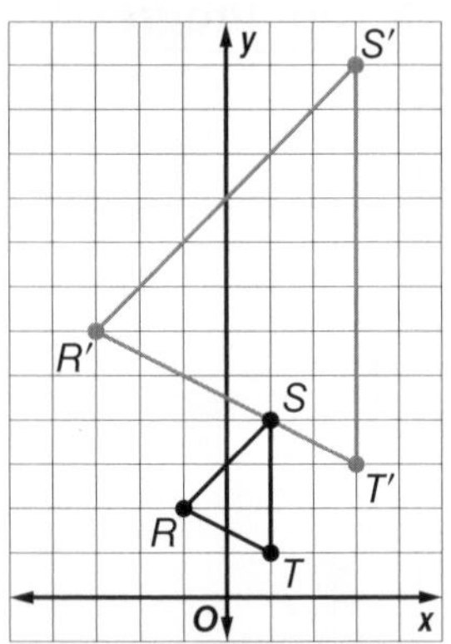

12. $A'(-1.5, -2.5)$, $B'(0, 1)$, $C'(1.5, -0.5)$, $D'(0, -2)$

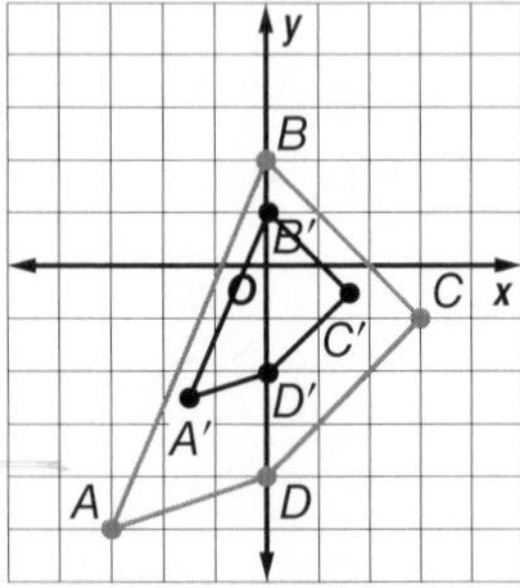

19. Sample answer:

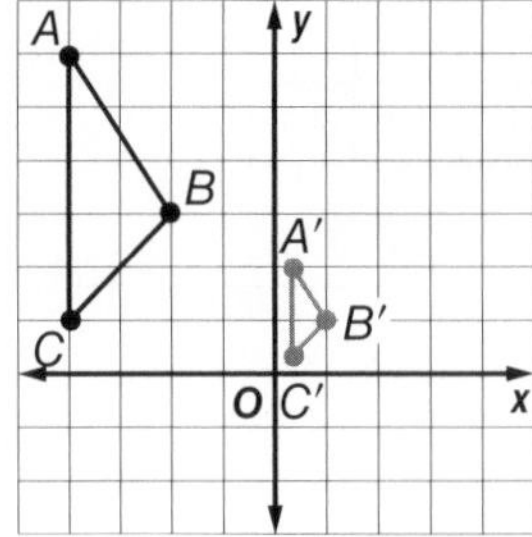

20. Sample answer: $A(-2\ -4)$, $B(-6, -10)$, $C(-10, -8)$, $D(-12, -4)$

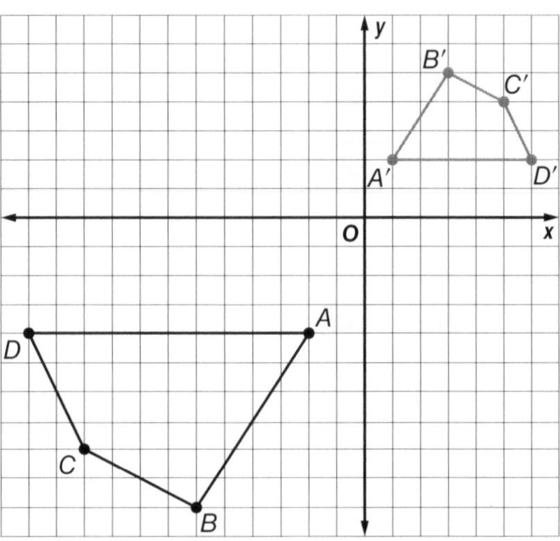

Chapter 6 Answer Appendix

Notes

CHAPTER 7

Chapter Planner

Diagnostic Assessment
Quick Check, p. 329

	Lesson 7-1 Pacing: 1 day	Lesson 7-2 Pacing: 1 day	Explore 7-3 Pacing: 1 day
Title	**Fractions and Percents**	**Fractions, Decimals, and Percents**	**Algebra Lab: Using a Percent Model**
Objectives	• Express percents as fractions. • Express fractions as percents.	• Express percents as decimals and vice versa. • Compare and order fractions, decimals, and percents.	• Use a percent model to find a percent or a part.
Key Vocabulary	percent		
NCTM Focal Points	G7–FP1, G7–FP5C, G7-FP6C For the complete wording of the Focal Points for Grades 7 and 8, please see pages iv, v, FP0, and FP1.		
Multiple Representations		p. 341	
Lesson Resources	**Chapter 7 Resource Masters** • Study Guide and Intervention, pp. 5-6 AL OL ELL • Skills Practice, p. 7 AL OL ELL • Practice, p. 8 AL OL BL ELL • Word Problem Practice, p. 9 AL OL BL • Enrichment, p. 10 OL BL **Transparencies** • 5-Minute Check Transparency 7-1 AL OL BL ELL **Additional Print Resources** • *Study Notebook* AL OL BL ELL	**Chapter 7 Resource Masters** • Study Guide and Intervention, pp. 11–12 AL OL ELL • Skills Practice, p. 13 AL OL ELL • Practice, p. 14 AL OL BL ELL • Word Problem Practice, p. 15 AL OL BL • Enrichment, p. 16 OL BL • Quiz 1, p. 58 AL OL BL ELL **Transparencies** • 5-Minute Check Transparency 7-2 AL OL BL ELL **Additional Print Resources** • *Study Notebook* AL OL BL ELL	**Materials:** • grid paper
Technology for Every Lesson	Math Online glencoe.com • Extra Examples • Self-Check Quizzes • Personal Tutor	**CD/DVD Resources** IWB INTERACTIVE WHITEBOARD READY IWB StudentWorks Plus IWB Interactive Classroom IWB Diagnostic and Assessment Planner	• TeacherWorks Plus • eSolutions Manual Plus • ExamView Assessment Suite
Math in Motion			p. 343
Differentiated Instruction	pp. 332, 333, 336	pp. 339, 342	

KEY: AL Approaching Level OL On Level BL Beyond Level ELL English Learners

Suggested Pacing			
Time Periods	Instruction	Review & Assessment	Total
45-minute	11	2	13
90-minute	5.5	1	6.5

Lesson 7-3 Pacing: 1 day	Lesson 7-4 Pacing: 1 day	Lesson 7-5 Pacing: 1 day	Explore 7-6 Pacing: 1 day
Using the Percent Proportion	**Find Percents of a Number Mentally**	**Using Percent Equations**	**Algebra Lab: Modeling Percents and Change**
• Use the percent proportion to solve problems. • Apply the percent proportion to real-world problems.	• Compute mentally with percents. • Estimate with percents.	• Solve percent problems using percent equations. • Apply the percent equation to real-world problems.	• Use percents to describe a change when a number increases or decreases.
percent proportion		percent equation	
		p. 361	
Chapter 7 Resource Masters • Study Guide and Intervention, pp. 17-18 AL OL ELL • Skills Practice, p. 19 AL OL ELL • Practice, p. 20 AL OL BL ELL • Word Problem Practice, p. 21 AL OL BL • Enrichment, p. 22 OL BL **Transparencies** • 5-Minute Check Transparency 7-3 AL OL BL ELL **Additional Print Resources** • *Study Notebook* AL OL BL ELL	**Chapter 7 Resource Masters** • Study Guide and Intervention, pp. 23–24 AL OL ELL • Skills Practice, p. 25 AL OL ELL • Practice, p. 26 AL OL BL ELL • Word Problem Practice, p. 27 AL OL BL • Enrichment, p. 28 OL BL • Quiz 2, p. 58 AL OL BL ELL **Transparencies** • 5-Minute Check Transparency 7-4 AL OL BL ELL **Additional Print Resources** • *Study Notebook* AL OL BL ELL	**Chapter 7 Resource Masters** • Study Guide and Intervention, pp. 29–30 AL OL ELL • Skills Practice, p. 31 AL OL ELL • Practice, p. 32 AL OL BL ELL • Word Problem Practice, p. 33 AL OL BL • Enrichment, p. 34 OL BL • Quiz 3, p. 59 AL OL BL ELL **Transparencies** • 5-Minute Check Transparency 7-5 AL OL BL ELL **Additional Print Resources** • *Study Notebook* AL OL BL ELL	**Materials:** • grid paper
Math Online glencoe.com • Extra Examples • Self-Check Quizzes • Personal Tutor	**CD/DVD Resources** IWB INTERACTIVE WHITEBOARD READY IWB StudentWorks Plus IWB Interactive Classroom IWB Diagnostic and Assessment Planner	• TeacherWorks Plus • eSolutions Manual Plus • ExamView Assessment Suite	
			p. 363
pp. 346, 350	pp. 352, 355	pp. 358, 362	

Formative Assessment
Mid-Chapter Quiz, p. 356

CHAPTER 7

Chapter Planner

	Lesson 7-6 Pacing: 1 day	Lesson 7-7 Pacing: 1 day	Extend 7-7 Pacing: 1 day	Lesson 7-8 Pacing: 1 day
Title	**Percent of Change**	**Simple and Compound Interest**	**Spreadsheet Lab: Compound Interest**	**Circle Graphs**
Objectives	• Find percent of increase and decrease. • Solve real-world problems involving markup and discount.	• Solve simple interest problems and apply the simple interest equation to real-world problems. • Solve compound interest problems.	• Use a spreadsheet to investigate the impact of compound interest.	• Construct circle graphs. • Analyze circle graphs to solve real-world problems.
Key Vocabulary	percent of change percent of increase percent of decrease	interest principal compound interest		circle graph
NCTM Focal Points				
Multiple Representations	p. 368	p. 373		p. 380
Lesson Resources	**Chapter 7 Resource Masters** • Study Guide and Intervention, pp. 35–36 AL OL ELL • Skills Practice, p. 37 AL OL ELL • Practice, p. 38 AL OL BL ELL • Word Problem Practice, p. 39 AL OL BL • Enrichment, p. 40 OL BL • Graphing Calculator, p. 41 AL OL BL ELL • Quiz 3, p. 59 AL OL BL ELL **Transparencies** • 5-Minute Check Transparency 7-6 AL OL BL ELL **Additional Print Resources** • *Study Notebook* AL OL BL ELL	**Chapter 7 Resource Masters** • Study Guide and Intervention, pp. 42–43 AL OL ELL • Skills Practice, p. 44 AL OL ELL • Practice, p. 45 AL OL BL ELL • Word Problem Practice, p. 46 AL OL BL • Enrichment, p. 47 OL BL • Spreadsheet, p. 48 AL OL BL ELL **Transparencies** • 5-Minute Check Transparency 7-7 AL OL BL ELL **Additional Print Resources** • *Study Notebook* AL OL BL ELL	**Materials:** • computer with spreadsheet software	**Chapter 7 Resource Masters** • Study Guide and Intervention, pp. 49–50 AL OL ELL • Skills Practice, p. 51 AL OL ELL • Practice, p. 52 AL OL BL ELL • Word Problem Practice, p. 53 AL OL BL • Enrichment, p. 54 OL BL • Quiz 4, p. 59 AL OL BL ELL **Transparencies** • 5-Minute Check Transparency 7-8 AL OL BL ELL **Additional Print Resources** • *Study Notebook* AL OL BL ELL
Technology for Every Lesson	Math Online glencoe.com • Extra Examples • Self-Check Quizzes • Personal Tutor **CD/DVD Resources** IWB INTERACTIVE WHITEBOARD READY IWB StudentWorks Plus IWB Interactive Classroom IWB Diagnostic and Assessment Planner • TeacherWorks Plus • eSolutions Manual Plus • ExamView Assessment Suite			
Math in Motion				
Differentiated Instruction	pp. 365, 369	pp. 371, 374		pp. 377, 381

Summative Assessment
• Study Guide and Review, pp. 382–386
• Practice Test, p. 387

KEY: AL Approaching Level OL On Level BL Beyond Level ELL English Learners

Quick Review Math Handbook*

is Glencoe's mathematical handbook for students and parents.

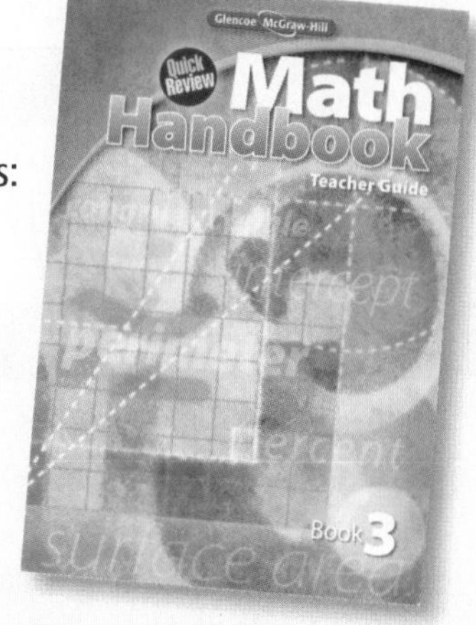

Hot Words includes a glossary of terms.

Hot Topics consists of two parts:

- explanations of key mathematical concepts
- exercises to check students' understanding

Lesson	Hot Topics Section	Lesson	Hot Topics Section
7-2	2.4, 2.6	7-6	2.7
7-3	2.7	7-7	2.7
7-5	2.7	7-8	2.7, 4.2

**Also available in Spanish*

Study Skill

Sequence maps can help students solve problems as they write out the organized steps. As students work through lessons in Chapter 7, encourage them to draw sequence maps describing problem-solving procedures they are learning.

The sequence map describes how to convert percents to decimals. Have students create their own sequence maps for converting decimals to percents, fractions to percents, and ratios to percents.

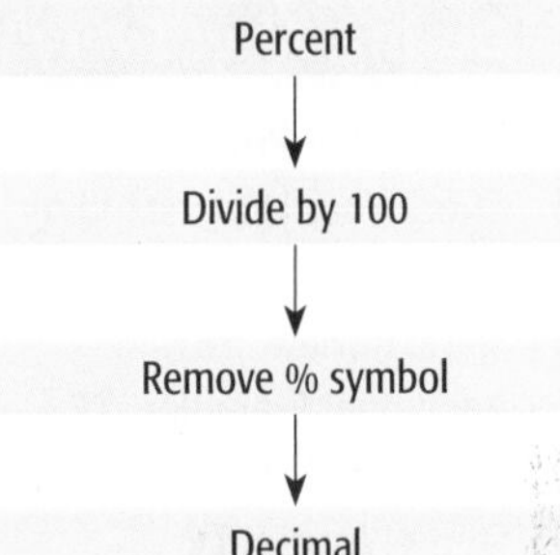

NOTES:

CHAPTER 7

Assessment and Intervention

SE = Student Edition, **TE** = Teacher Edition, **CRM** = Chapter Resource Masters

	Diagnosis	Prescription
Diagnostic Assessment	**Beginning Chapter 7**	
	Get Ready for Chapter 7 **SE,** p. 329	Response to Intervention **TE,** p. 329
	Beginning Every Lesson	
	Then, Now, Why? **SE** 5-Minute Check Transparencies	Chapter 0 **SE,** pp. P1–P22 Concepts and Skills Bank **SE,** pp. 856–887 *Quick Review Math Handbook*
Formative Assessment	**During/After Every Lesson**	
	Check Your Progress **SE,** every example Check Your Understanding **SE** H.O.T. Problems **SE** Spiral Review **SE** Additional Examples **TE** Watch Out! **TE** Step 4, Assess **TE** Chapter 7 Quizzes **CRM,** pp. 58–59 Self-Check Quizzes **glencoe.com**	**Tier 1 Intervention** Concepts and Skills Bank **SE,** pp. 856–887 Skills Practice **CRM,** Ch. 1–7 **glencoe.com** **Tier 2 Intervention** Differentiated Instruction **TE** Study Guide and Intervention Masters **CRM,** Ch. 1–7 *Quick Review Math Handbook* **Tier 3 Intervention** *Math Triumphs, Grade 8,* Ch. 8
	Mid-Chapter	
	Mid-Chapter Quiz **SE,** p. 356 Mid-Chapter Test **CRM,** p. 60 ExamView Assessment Suite	**Tier 1 Intervention** Concepts and Skills Bank **SE,** pp. 856–887 Skills Practice **CRM,** Ch. 1–7 **glencoe.com** **Tier 2 Intervention** Study Guide and Intervention Masters **CRM,** Ch. 1–7 *Quick Review Math Handbook* **Tier 3 Intervention** *Math Triumphs, Grade 8,* Ch. 8
	Before Chapter Test	
	Chapter Study Guide and Review **SE,** pp. 382–386 Practice Test **SE,** p. 387 Standardized Test Practice **SE,** pp. 388–391 Chapter Test **glencoe.com** Standardized Test Practice **glencoe.com** Vocabulary Review **glencoe.com** ExamView Assessment Suite	**Tier 1 Intervention** Concepts and Skills Bank **SE,** pp. 856–887 Skills Practice **CRM,** Ch. 1–7 **glencoe.com** **Tier 2 Intervention** Study Guide and Intervention Masters **CRM,** Ch. 1–7 *Quick Review Math Handbook* **Tier 3 Intervention** *Math Triumphs, Grade 8,* Ch. 8
Summative Assessment	**After Chapter 7**	
	Multiple-Choice Tests, Forms 1, 2A, 2B **CRM,** pp. 62–69 Free-Response Tests, Forms 2C, 2D, 3 **CRM,** pp. 68–73 Vocabulary Test **CRM,** p. 61 Extended Response Test **CRM,** p. 74 Standardized Test Practice **CRM,** pp. 75–77 ExamView Assessment Suite	Study Guide and Intervention Masters **CRM,** Ch. 1–7 *Quick Review Math Handbook* **glencoe.com**

Differentiated Instruction

Option 1 Reaching All Learners AL OL BL ELL

INTRAPERSONAL Have students research the cost of an item they would like to purchase. Ask them to calculate the interest they would earn if they could deposit the cost of the item in a bank that pays simple interest.

Principal	Rate	Time	Interest
	4.5%	3 yr	
	6%	2 yr	

Then have them calculate the interest they would earn if they could deposit the cost of the item in a bank that compounds annually. Remind students that they need to add the interest to the principal at the end of each year.

Principal	Rate	Time	Interest
	4.5%	3 yr	
	4.5%		
	4.5%		
	6%	2 yr	
	6%		

Ask students to compare their calculations for simple and compound interest. In real-world situations, is it better to earn simple interest or compound interest on an investment? Have students use their calculations to support their reasoning.

NATURALIST Have students discuss real-world situations in which it would make sense to estimate with percents. For example, a conservation group might want to know the approximate number of endangered animals in a wildlife habitat. Write the situations on the board as students discuss them. Next, have students choose one of the situations and write a real-world problem about the situation that involves estimating with a percent. Then have them solve the problem.

KINESTHETIC Students can look up statistics on some of their favorite sports players. If a statistic is reported as a decimal, students should convert it to a percentage and vice versa. Follow up by checking the same players at a later date and analyzing any changed that have occurred.

Option 2 Approaching Level AL

Have students work in groups of three to relate fractions, decimals, and percents. One student names a fraction, the second finds an equivalent decimal, and the third finds an equivalent percent. The three students then draw a model to represent the fraction, decimal, and percent. Students switch roles until each has had a turn at finding equivalent decimals and percents.

Option 3 English Learners ELL

Have students make a list of the similarities and differences between the *percent proportion* and the *percent equation*. Then have them write a paragraph that compares and contrasts their use for finding the part; such as 20% of 80, the whole; such as 40 is 10% of what number, and the percent; such as 50 is what percent of 200.

MODELS After introducing the base 10 blocks for the concept of percent and the relation to decimals, use a money model to help illustrate the relationship between decimals and percents. There are 100 pennies in a dollar so a penny is $\frac{1}{100}$ or 1% of a dollar. There are 10 dimes in a dollar so a dime is $\frac{1}{10}$ or 10% of a dollar. You can use the money model in a similar way in which the 10 blocks are used.

Option 4 Beyond Level BL

Give students the following problem to solve:

An electronics store used a 150% markup as the selling price on its newest cell phone. Two months later, the store wants to offer a discount on the cell phone. What is the largest discount the store can offer and not lose money on the phone? 33%

Have students explain their reasoning.

CHAPTER 7

Focus on Mathematical Content

Vertical Alignment

Before Chapter 7

Related Topics before Pre-Algebra

- convert between fractions, decimals, whole numbers, and percents mentally, on paper, or with a calculator

Previous Topics from Pre-Algebra

- select and use appropriate forms of rational numbers to solve real-world problems
- use appropriate operations to solve problems involving rational numbers in problem situations

Chapter 7

Related Topics from Pre-Algebra

- use ratios, proportions, and percent of change to solve problems
- evaluate a solution for reasonableness
- select and use appropriate representations for presenting and displaying relationships among collected data

After Chapter 7

Preparation for Algebra 1

- solve problems involving proportional change
- generate a different representation of data given another representation of data

Lesson-by-Lesson Preview

7-1 Fractions and Percents

A percent is a ratio that compares a number to 100.

- To write a percent as a fraction, express the ratio as a fraction with a denominator of 100. Then simplify, if possible.

$76\% = \frac{76}{100}$ or $\frac{19}{25}$

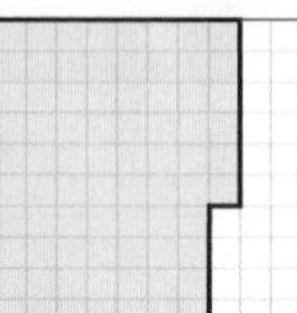

- To write a fraction as a percent, write an equivalent fraction with a denominator of 100. For example,

$$\frac{4}{5} = \frac{80}{100} = 80\%$$

- If the denominator of a fraction is not a factor of 100, use a proportion to write the fraction as a percent.

$$\frac{7}{35} = \frac{n}{100}, 700 = 35n, n = 20, \frac{7}{35} = 20\%$$

7-2 Fractions, Decimals, and Percents

Use the following rules to write decimals as percents and percents as decimals:

- To write a decimal as a percent, multiply by 100 and add the percent symbol. When multiplying by 100, move the decimal point two places to the right.

$$0.155 = 15.5\%$$

- To write a percent as a decimal, divide by 100 and remove the percent symbol. When dividing by 100, move the decimal point two places to the left.

$$2\% = 0.02$$

- To compare fractions, decimals, and percents, first write them in the same form and then compare.

7-3 Using the Percent Proportion

In the percent proportion $\frac{\text{part}}{\text{whole}} = \frac{\text{percent}}{100}$, one of the numbers, called the part, is being compared to the whole quantity, called the whole or base.

- To find the percent, such as *18 is what percent of 54,* write and solve $\frac{18}{54} = \frac{p}{100}$.
- To find the part, such as *what number is 12% of 150,* write and solve $\frac{a}{150} = \frac{12}{100}$.
- To find the whole, such as *28 is 40% of what number,* write and solve $\frac{28}{b} = \frac{40}{100}$.

Find Percent of a Number Mentally

Use fractions or decimals to find the percent of a number mentally.

- When working with percents like 25% and 50%, use the fraction form of the percent. Convert the percent to its fraction equivalent and then calculate. For example, to find 25% of 40, think $25\% = \frac{1}{4}$, and $\frac{1}{4}$ of 40 is 10.
- When computing with 1% or 10%, write the percent as a decimal and then move the decimal point the same number of places to the left of the number. For example, 1% = 0.01, so 1% of 43 is 0.43.

When estimating with percents, use percent or fraction equivalents close to the percent or round percents to decimals close to 1% or 10%.

Using Percent Equations

A percent equation is an equivalent form of the percent proportion in which the percent is written as a decimal. Like in a percent proportion, a percent equation can be used to find the missing part, percent, or whole.

$$\text{Part} = \text{Percent} \cdot \text{Whole}$$

- To find the part, such as *what number is 45% of 80,* write and solve $a = 0.45 \cdot 80$.
- To find the percent, such as *144 is what percent of 320,* write and solve $144 = p \cdot 320$.
- To find the whole, such as *57 is 60% of what number,* write and solve $57 = 0.6 \cdot b$.

Percent of Change

A percent of change gives the percent of increase or decrease in an amount in relation to the original amount. To find the percent of increase or decrease, write a ratio that compares the amount of change to the original amount.

$$\text{percent of change} = \frac{\text{amount of change}}{\text{original amount}}$$

- When the new amount is greater than the original, the percent of change is a percent of increase, such as the percent of markup.
- When the new amount is less than the original, the percent of change is a percent of decrease, such as the percent of discount.

Simple and Compound Interest

Simple interest is paid on the initial principal of a savings account or loan. Compound interest is paid on the initial principal and on interest previously earned.

- To find simple interest, use the formula $I = prt$, where I is interest, p is principal (the amount invested), r is annual interest rate written as a decimal, and t is time in years.
- To find compound interest, use the same formula, but add interest to the principal when compounding occurs to find the new principal.

Circle Graphs

A circle graph compares the parts of a data set to the whole set of data. The percents in a circle graph add up to 100 since the circle represents the whole set. Use the following to construct a circle graph:

- Since there are 360° in a circle, multiply each percent by 360 to find the number of degrees for each section. If necessary, first calculate the percents from the given data.
- Use a compass to draw the circle and radius, and a protractor to draw each angle.
- Label the sections and give the graph a title.

Professional Development

Targeted professional development has been articulated throughout McGraw-Hill's mathematics program. The **McGraw-Hill Professional Development Video Library** provides short videos that support key topics. For more information, visit glencoe.com.

Model Lessons

Instructional Strategies

CHAPTER 7 Notes

Chapter Project

Real World: Stat on Stat

Students use what they have learned about percents and making circle graphs to work with baseball stats. When finding stats, have them round to the nearest tenth, if necessary.

- Divide students into groups. Ask groups to choose a baseball team, and then have each member in the group choose a player on the team and bring to class the following batting statistics: singles (hits), doubles (2B), triples (3B), homeruns (HR), walks (BB), and strikeouts (SO) for the last two seasons.
- Have groups organize the stats into tables for each season. Then ask them to write the ratio of walks to strikeouts for each player as a fraction, percent, and decimal. Which player has the highest percentage of walks to strikeouts?
- Ask groups to choose one stat for each player and determine the percent of change in the stat from one season to the next. Are the percents of change increases or decreases?
- Have each group choose one of the players on the team and find the total number of singles, doubles, triples, and homeruns. Then have them calculate the percents of this total that were singles, doubles, triples, and homeruns. Have them make a circle graph of the data. Then have the groups analyze all of the circle graphs from the different groups. How do the players' stats compare?

CHAPTER 7 Percent

Then

In Chapter 3, you converted fractions and decimals. In Chapter 6, you solved proportions.

Now

In Chapter 7, you will:

- Express percents as fractions and decimals, and fractions as percents.
- Use the percent proportion and percent equations to solve problems.
- Construct and interpret circle graphs.

Why?

SPORTS In baseball, percents are often used to represent statistics of players. In a recent season, Jimmy Rollins, of the Philadelphia Phillies, led the major leagues with the highest on base percent with 0.344. This means he got on base 34.4% of the times he was at bat.

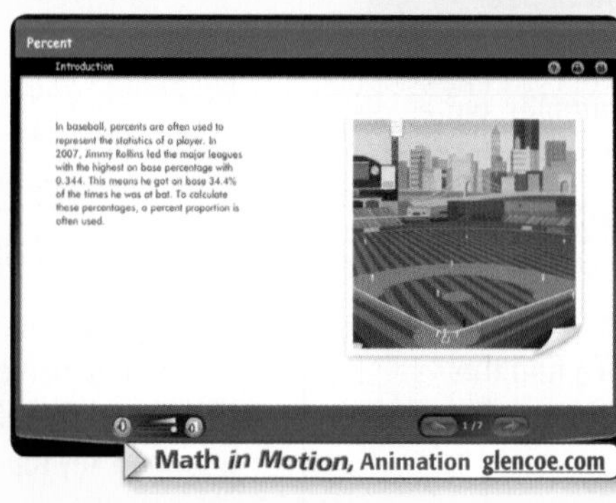

328 Chapter 7 Percent

Key Vocabulary Introduce the key vocabulary in the chapter using the routine below.

Define: A percent equation is an equivalent form of the percent proportion in which the percent is written as a decimal. Part = Percent × Whole

Example: To find 23% of 45, you multiply .23 and 45 to get 10.35. 10.35 is 23% of 45.

Ask: What number is 78% of 67? 52.26

Get Ready for Chapter 7

Diagnose Readiness You have two options for checking Prerequisite Skills.

Text Option Take the Quick Check below. Refer to the Quick Review for help.

*Quick*Check

(Used in Lessons 7-1, 7-2, and 7-4)

Convert each fraction to a decimal. (Lesson 3-1)

1. $\frac{1}{4}$ 0.25
2. $\frac{1}{10}$ 0.1
3. $\frac{3}{8}$ 0.375
4. $\frac{3}{4}$ 0.75
5. **RECIPES** A recipe calls for $\frac{2}{3}$ cup of sugar. Write this amount as a decimal rounded to the nearest hundredth. 0.67

(Used in Lessons 7-3 and 7-5)

Solve each proportion. (Lesson 6-5)

6. $\frac{2}{5} = \frac{n}{15}$ 6
7. $\frac{3}{2} = \frac{n}{10}$ 15
8. $\frac{3}{20} = \frac{n}{100}$ 15
9. $\frac{11}{50} = \frac{n}{200}$ 44
10. **FERRIS WHEEL** The wait time to ride the Ferris wheel at a state fair is 15 minutes when 75 people are in line. At this rate, how long is the wait time when 200 people are in line? 40 min

Solve each equation. Check your solution. (Lesson 4-4) (Used in Lesson 7-6)

11. $25x = 50$ 2
12. $8a = 28$ 3.5
13. $0.1x = 0.5$ 5
14. $6n = 12$ 2
15. **MUSIC** Jan has 4 times as many songs on her computer as Ian has on his computer. If Jan has 516 songs, how many songs does Ian have on his computer? 129 songs

*Quick*Review

EXAMPLE 1

Write $\frac{1}{4}$ as a decimal.

$$\begin{array}{r} 0.25 \\ 4\overline{)1.00} \\ -80 \\ \hline 20 \\ -20 \\ \hline 0 \end{array}$$

So, $\frac{1}{4} = 0.25$.

EXAMPLE 2

Solve $\frac{3}{5} = \frac{n}{20}$.

$\frac{3}{5} = \frac{n}{20}$	
$3 \cdot 20 = 5n$	Cross products
$60 = 5n$	Multiply.
$\frac{60}{5} = \frac{5n}{5}$	Divide each side by 5.
$12 = n$	Simplify.

So, $n = 12$.

EXAMPLE 3

Solve $7.5x = 30$.

$7.5x = 30$	Write the equation.
$\frac{7.5x}{7.5} = \frac{30}{7.5}$	Divide each side by 7.5.
$x = 4$	Simplify.

So, $x = 4$.

Online Option Math Online Take a self-check Chapter Readiness Quiz at glencoe.com.

Response to Intervention (RtI)

Use the *Quick Check* results and the Intervention Planner to help you determine your Response to Intervention. The If-Then statements in the chart below help you decide the appropriate tier of RtI and suggest intervention resources for each tier.

Intervention Planner

Tier 1 On Level

If students miss about 25% of the exercises or less,

Then choose a resource:

- **SE** Lessons 3-1, 4-4, 6-5
- **CRM** Skills Practice, Chapter 3, p. 7; Chapter 4, p. 25; Chapter 6, p. 31
- **TE** Chapter Project, p. 328
- **Math Online** Self-Check Quiz

Tier 2 Strategic Intervention approaching grade level

If students miss about 50% of the exercises,

Then choose a resource:

- **CRM** Study Guide and Intervention, Chapter 3, p. 5; Chapter 4, p. 23; Chapter 6, p. 29
- *Quick Review Math Handbook*
- **Math Online** Extra Examples, Personal Tutor, Homework Help

Tier 3 Intensive Intervention 2 or more grades below level

If students miss about 75% of the exercises,

Then use *Math Triumphs, Grade 8,* Ch. 8

Math Online Extra Examples, Personal Tutor, Homework Help, Review Vocabulary

CHAPTER 7 Notes

FOLDABLES® Study Organizer

Focus Students write notes about functions and graphs as they work through each lesson.

Teach Have students make and label the pages for each lesson of their Foldables as illustrated. Have students use the appropriate pages as they cover each lesson in this chapter. Students should take notes about, draw examples of, and write descriptions of the different types of functions.

When to Use It Encourage students to add to their Foldable as they work through the chapter, and use them to review for the chapter test.

Differentiated Instruction

CRM Student-Built Glossary, pp. 1–2 Students should complete the chart by providing a definition of each term and an example as they progress through Chapter 7. This study tool can also be used to review for the chapter test.

Get Started on Chapter 7

You will learn several new concepts, skills, and vocabulary terms as you study Chapter 7. To get ready, identify important terms and organize your resources. You may wish to refer to **Chapter 0** to review prerequisite skills.

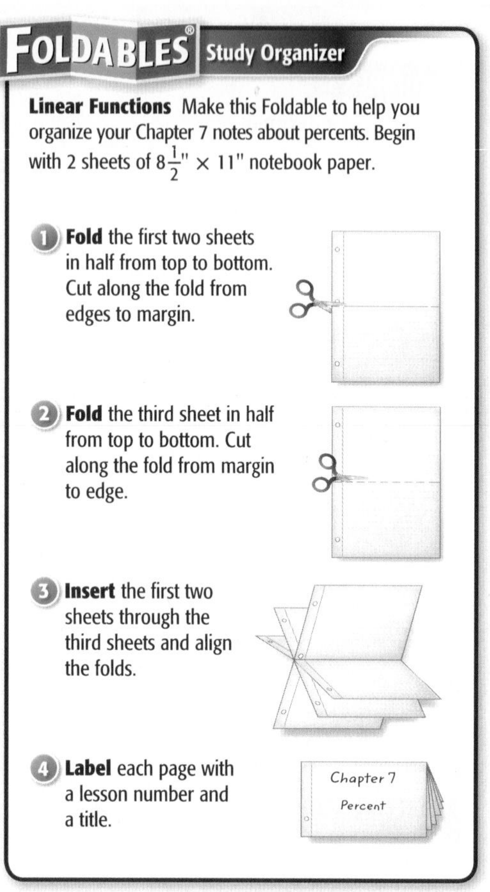

FOLDABLES® Study Organizer

Linear Functions Make this Foldable to help you organize your Chapter 7 notes about percents. Begin with 2 sheets of $8\frac{1}{2}" \times 11"$ notebook paper.

1. **Fold** the first two sheets in half from top to bottom. Cut along the fold from edges to margin.
2. **Fold** the third sheet in half from top to bottom. Cut along the fold from margin to edge.
3. **Insert** the first two sheets through the third sheets and align the folds.
4. **Label** each page with a lesson number and a title.

Math Online glencoe.com

- Study the chapter online
- Explore **Math in Motion**
- Get extra help from your own **Personal Tutor**
- Use **Extra Examples** for additional help
- Take a **Self-Check Quiz**
- **Review Vocabulary** in fun ways

New Vocabulary

English		Español
percent	• p. 331 •	por ciento
percent proportion	• p. 345 •	proporción porcental
percent equation	• p. 357 •	ecuación porcental
percent of change	• p. 364 •	porcentaje de cambio
percent of increase	• p. 364 •	porcentaje de aumento
percent of decrease	• p. 364 •	porcentaje de disminución
markup	• p. 365 •	margen de utilidad
selling price	• p. 365 •	precio de venta
discount	• p. 366 •	descuento
interest	• p. 370 •	interés
simple interest	• p. 370 •	interés simple
principal	• p. 370 •	capital
compound interest	• p. 371 •	interés compuetso
circle graph	• p. 376 •	gráfica circular

Review Vocabulary

cross products • p. 287 • productos cruzados if $\frac{a}{c} = \frac{b}{d}$, then $ad = bc$

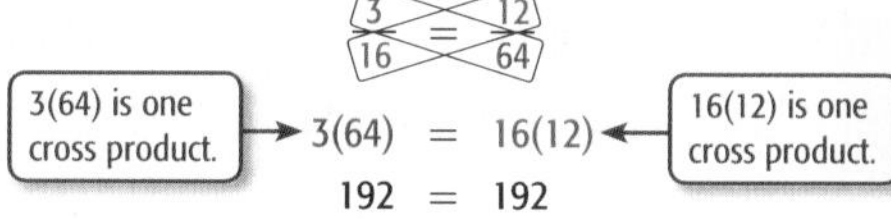

The cross products are equal.

proportion • p. 298 • proporción a statement of equality of two or more ratios

rational number • p. 128 • número racional a number that can be written as a fraction in the form $\frac{a}{b}$, where a and b are integers and $b \neq 0$

Multilingual eGlossary glencoe.com

330 Chapter 7 Percent

7-1 Fractions and Percents

Then

You have already converted fractions and decimals. (Lesson 3-1)

Now

- Express percents as fractions.
- Express fractions as percents.

New Vocabulary

percent

Math Online

glencoe.com

- Extra Examples
- Personal Tutor
- Self-Check Quiz
- Homework Help

Why?

Three players were comparing their basketball free throws.

Basketball Statistics		
Player	Number of Free Throws Made	Number Attempted
Daniel	2	4
Frank	8	10
Dale	15	20

a. For each player, write a ratio that compares the number of free throws made to the number attempted as a fraction in simplest form. a–b. See margin.

b. Rewrite the fractions in part **a** using a denominator of 100.

c. Which player has the greatest ratio of number of free throws made to the number attempted? Frank

d. Was it easier to compare the fractions in parts **a** or **b**? Explain. Part b; the fractions have a common denominator.

Percents as Fractions A **percent** is a ratio that compares a number to 100. To write a percent as a fraction, express the ratio as a fraction with a denominator of 100. Then simplify if possible.

Key Concept Percent — For Your FOLDABLE

Words A percent is a part to whole ratio that compares a number to 100.

Examples 80% 80 out of 100 $\frac{80}{100}$

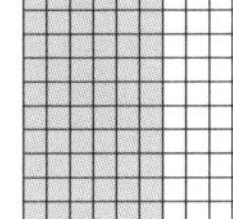

EXAMPLE 1 Percents as Fractions

Write each percent as a fraction in simplest form.

a. 60%

$60\% = \frac{60}{100}$ Definition of percent

$= \frac{3}{5}$ Simplify.

b. $12\frac{1}{2}\%$

$12\frac{1}{2}\% = \frac{12\frac{1}{2}}{100}$ Definition of percent

$= \frac{25}{2} \div 100$ Write $12\frac{1}{2}$ as an improper fraction.

$= \frac{\overset{1}{\cancel{25}}}{2} \cdot \frac{1}{\underset{4}{\cancel{100}}}$ or $\frac{1}{8}$ Simplify.

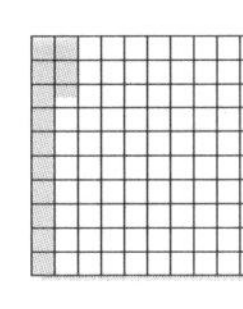

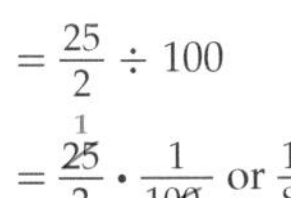

Check Your Progress

1A. 40% $\frac{2}{5}$ **1B.** $20\frac{3}{4}\%$ $\frac{83}{400}$

Personal Tutor glencoe.com

7-1 Lesson Notes

1 FOCUS

Vertical Alignment

Before Lesson 7-1
Convert fractions and decimals.

Lesson 7-1
Express percents as fractions and express fractions as percents.

After Lesson 7-1
Use appropriate operations to convert percents and decimals.

2 TEACH

Scaffolding Questions

Have students read the *Why?* section of the lesson and answer the questions.

Ask:

- What does the numerator represent? the number of free throws made
- What does the denominator represent? the number of free throws attempted
- Why are the fractions rewritten with a common denominator of 100? It makes the fractions easier to compare.

Additional Answers

a. Daniel: $\frac{1}{2}$; Frank: $\frac{4}{5}$; Dale: $\frac{3}{4}$

b. Daniel: $\frac{50}{100}$; Frank: $\frac{80}{100}$; Dale: $\frac{75}{100}$

Lesson 7-1 Resources

Resource	Approaching-Level	On-Level	Beyond-Level	English Learners
Teacher Edition	• Differentiated Instruction, p. 332	• Differentiated Instruction, pp. 332, 333	• Differentiated Instruction, pp. 333, 336	
Chapter Resource Masters	• Study Guide and Intervention, pp. 5–6 • Skills Practice, p. 7 • Practice, p. 8 • Word Problem Practice, p. 9	• Study Guide and Intervention, pp. 5–6 • Skills Practice, p. 7 • Practice, p. 8 • Word Problem Practice, p. 9 • Enrichment, p. 10	• Practice, p. 8 • Word Problem Practice, p. 9 • Enrichment, p. 10	• Study Guide and Intervention, pp. 5–6 • Skills Practice, p. 7 • Practice, p. 8
Transparencies	• 5-Minute Check Transparency 7-1	• 5-Minute Check Transparency 7-1	• 5-Minute Check Transparency 7-1	• 5-Minute Check Transparency 7-1
Other	• Study Notebook • Teaching Pre-Algebra with Manipulatives	• Study Notebook • Teaching Pre-Algebra with Manipulatives	• Study Notebook	• Study Notebook • Teaching Pre-Algebra with Manipulatives

Percents as Fractions

Examples 1 and 2 show how to write percents as fractions in simplest form.

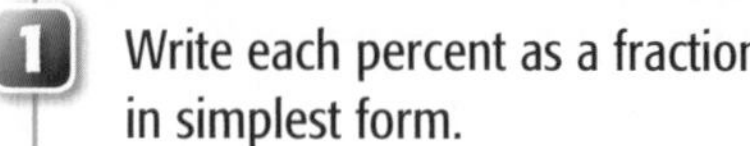

Formative Assessment

Use the Check Your Progress exercises after each example to determine students' understanding of concepts.

Additional Examples

1 Write each percent as a fraction in simplest form.

a. 40% $\frac{2}{5}$

b. $56\frac{1}{4}$% $\frac{9}{16}$

2 Write each percent as a fraction in simplest form.

a. 0.3% $\frac{3}{1000}$

b. 104% $1\frac{1}{25}$

Additional Examples also in Interactive Classroom PowerPoint® Presentations

IWB INTERACTIVE WHITEBOARD READY

Fractions as Percents

Examples 3–5 show how to write a fraction as a percent using equivalent fractions with a denominator of 100.

Additional Example

3 Write each fraction as a percent.

a. $\frac{19}{20}$ 95%

b. $\frac{8}{5}$ 160%

Notice that a percent can be less than 1% or greater than 100%.

Math History Link

Augustus (27 B.C.–14 A.D.) Percents were first used by Roman emperor Augustus. He levied a tax of $\frac{1}{100}$ on all goods sold at auctions.

EXAMPLE 2 Less Than 1% or Greater Than 100%

Write each percent as a fraction in simplest form.

a. 0.8%

$0.8\% = \frac{0.8}{100}$ **Definition of percent**

$= \frac{0.8}{100} \cdot \frac{10}{10}$ **Multiply by $\frac{10}{10}$ to eliminate the decimal in the numerator.**

$= \frac{8}{1000}$ or $\frac{1}{125}$ **Simplify.**

b. 175%

$175\% = \frac{175}{100}$ **Definition of percent**

$= \frac{7}{4}$ or $1\frac{3}{4}$ **Simplify.**

Check Your Progress

2A. 0.2% $\frac{1}{500}$ **2B.** 150% $1\frac{1}{2}$

Personal Tutor glencoe.com

Fractions as Percents To write a fraction as a percent, write an equivalent fraction with a denominator of 100.

EXAMPLE 3 Fractions as Percents

Write each fraction as a percent.

a. $\frac{1}{4}$

First, find the equivalent fraction with a denominator of 100. Then write the fraction as a percent.

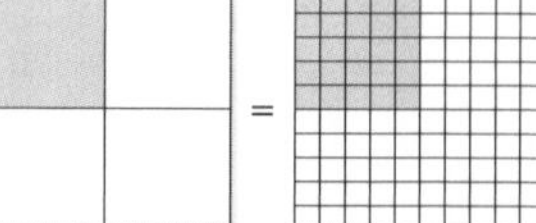

$\frac{1}{4} = \frac{1 \times 25}{4 \times 25} = \frac{25}{100}$ or 25%

So, $\frac{1}{4} = 25\%$.

b. $\frac{6}{5}$

$\frac{6}{5} = \frac{6 \times 20}{5 \times 20}$ or $\frac{120}{100}$ **Write an equivalent fraction with a denominator of 100.**

$= 120\%$ **$\frac{120}{100} = 120\%$**

So, $\frac{6}{5} = 120\%$.

Check Your Progress

3A. $\frac{3}{10}$ 30% **3B.** $\frac{7}{2}$ 350%

Personal Tutor glencoe.com

ReadingMath
Percent

Root Word Cent; comes from the Latin word *centum* which means hundred. There are 100 *cents* in one dollar. *Percent* means *per hundred* or *hundredths*.

Differentiated Instruction

AL OL

Logical Have students make a display or poster showing the following ratios expressed as fractions and percents: 1:8, 1:4, 3:8, 1:3, 1:2, 5:8, 2:3, 3:4, 7:8, and 8:8.

332 Chapter 7 Percent

StudyTip

Choose the Method To write a fraction as a percent,

- use **multiplication** when a fraction has a denominator that is a factor of 100,
- use a **proportion** for any type of fraction.

If the denominator is not a factor of 100, you can write fractions as percents by using a proportion.

Real-World EXAMPLE 4 Fractions as Percents

QUIZZES On her science quiz, Jacinda got 14 questions correct out of 16. Find Jacinda's grade as a percent.

To find her grade, write $\frac{14}{16}$ as a percent.

Estimate $\frac{14}{16}$ is greater than $\frac{12}{16}$ or $\frac{3}{4}$. So, $\frac{14}{16}$ is greater than 75%.

$\frac{14}{16} = \frac{n}{100}$	Write a proportion using $\frac{n}{100}$.
$14 \cdot 100 = 16n$	Cross products
$1400 = 16n$	Multiply.
$\frac{1400}{16} = \frac{16n}{16}$	Divide each side by 16.
$87\frac{1}{2} = n$	Simplify.

So, $\frac{14}{16} = 87\frac{1}{2}\%$ or 87.5%.

Check for Reasonableness 87.5% > 75% ✓

Check Your Progress

4. **MUSIC** Caitlyn has practiced playing the piano 5 out of the last 8 days. What percent is this? 62.5%

Personal Tutor glencoe.com

In real-world situations, the solution of the percent proportion is often a repeating decimal. In these cases, the percent is ususally rounded.

Real-World EXAMPLE 5 Rounding Percents

GAMES After a survey, Ling discovered that 4 out of every 11 eighth graders at his school play games online. Find the percent of eighth graders that play games online. Round to the nearest hundredth.

Estimate $\frac{4}{11}$ is about $\frac{4}{12}$, which equals $\frac{1}{3}$ or about 33%.

$\frac{4}{11} = \frac{n}{100}$	Write a proportion using $\frac{n}{100}$.
$4 \cdot 100 = 11n$	Cross products
$400 = 11n$	Multiply.
400 [÷] 11 [ENTER] 36.36363636	Use a calculator.

So, about 36.36% of the eighth graders play games online.

Check for Reasonableness 36.36% ≈ 33% ✓

Check Your Progress

5. **SPORTS** During baseball season, Theo had 34 hits out of 55 at bats. Find Theo's at-bat percent. Round to the nearest hundredth. 61.82%

Personal Tutor glencoe.com

Real-World Link

A recent survey showed that 35% of Internet users spend their time playing games.

Source: Pew Internet & American Life Project

Additional Examples

4. **GAMES** During the soccer season, the Delta Cougars won 12 of their 16 games. Find the Cougars wins as a percent. 75%

5. **CLUBS** After a survey, Deion discovered that 8 out of 14 eighth graders at his school participate in a club activity. Find the percent of eighth graders that participate in a club. Round to the nearest hundredth. 57.14%

Focus on Mathematical Content

Converting A percent can be written as a fraction by expressing the ratio as a fraction with a denominator of 100. This fraction can then be written in simplest form. Likewise, an equivalent fraction can be written with a denominator of 100, which can easily then be converted to a percent.

TEACH with TECH

PORTABLE MEDIA PLAYER Create a video showing your students how to convert from fractions to percents. Post on your classroom Web site to allow students to download to their own portable media players.

Differentiated Instruction OL BL

Extension Ask students to create a comic strip that shows a student responding to the request "I want you to give me 120% effort today." Have students analyze the statement and compare it to "I want you to give me 120% of the effort you gave yesterday."

3 PRACTICE

Formative Assessment

Use Exercises 1–10 to check for understanding.

Use the chart at the bottom of this page to customize assignments for your students.

Additional Answers

47.

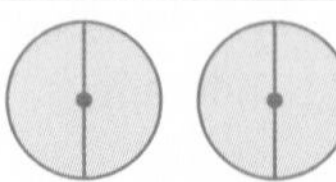

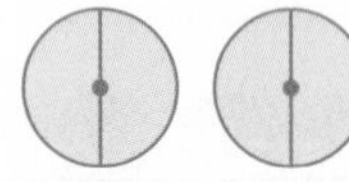

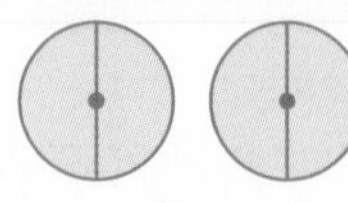

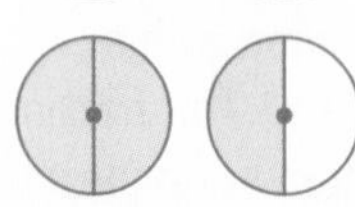

750%

50. Sample answer: You can find the equivalent fraction with a denominator of 100, $\frac{4}{5} = \frac{4 \times 20}{5 \times 20} = \frac{80}{100}$ or 80%. Or you can set up and solve a proportion.

$\frac{4}{5} = \frac{x}{100}$

$5x = 400$

$x = 80$

Check Your Understanding

Examples 1 and 2 (pp. 331–332)

Write each percent as a fraction or mixed number in simplest form.

1. 40% $\frac{2}{5}$ **2.** $14\frac{1}{2}\%$ $\frac{29}{200}$ **3.** 150% $1\frac{1}{2}$ **4.** 0.9% $\frac{9}{1000}$

Example 3 (p. 332)

Write each fraction as a percent. Round to the nearest hundredth.

5. $\frac{19}{20}$ 95% **6.** $\frac{10}{4}$ 250% **7.** $\frac{17}{18}$ 94.44% **8.** $\frac{21}{24}$ 87.5%

Examples 4 and 5 (p. 333)

9. **VACATIONS** Of the students in Ms. Villata's classes, 56 out of 128 are planning to go on a summer vacation. What percent is this? 43.75%

10. **TESTS** On a recent social studies test, Miguel earned 80 out of 90 points. Find Miguel's grade as a percent. Round to the nearest hundredth. 88.89%

Practice and Problem Solving

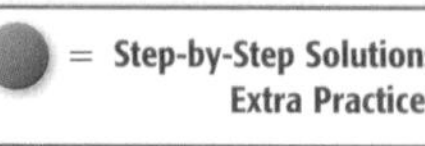

= Step-by-Step Solutions begin on page R11. Extra Practice begins on page 810.

Examples 1 and 2 (pp. 331–332)

Write each percent as a fraction or mixed number in simplest form.

11. 61% $\frac{61}{100}$ **12.** 28% $\frac{7}{25}$ **13.** $20\frac{2}{3}\%$ $\frac{31}{150}$ **14.** $58\frac{1}{2}\%$ $\frac{117}{200}$

15. 116% $\frac{29}{25}$ or $1\frac{4}{25}$ **16.** 425% $\frac{17}{4}$ or $4\frac{1}{4}$ **17.** 0.6% $\frac{3}{500}$ **18.** 0.33% $\frac{33}{10000}$

19. $62\frac{1}{2}\%$ $\frac{5}{8}$ **20.** $33\frac{1}{3}\%$ $\frac{1}{3}$ **21.** 1.2% $\frac{3}{250}$ **22.** 2.3% $\frac{23}{1000}$

23. **GEOGRAPHY** The tallest mountain in the world is Mt. Everest. It is about 140% as tall as the tallest mountain in the United States, Mt. McKinley. Write 140% as a mixed number in simplest form. $1\frac{2}{5}$

24. **POPULATION** According to the U.S. Census Bureau, 0.4% of the population of South Carolina is Native American. Write 0.4% as a fraction in simplest form. $\frac{1}{250}$

Example 3 (p. 332)

Write each fraction as a percent. Round to the nearest hundredth.

25. $\frac{8}{32}$ 25% **26.** $\frac{6}{25}$ 24% **27.** $\frac{18}{4}$ 450% **28.** $\frac{11}{5}$ 220%

29. $\frac{7}{8}$ 87.5% **30.** $\frac{1}{60}$ 1.67% **31.** $\frac{10}{14}$ 71.43% **32.** $\frac{6}{13}$ 46.15%

Examples 4 and 5 (p. 333)

33. **FRIENDS** Of Mark's friends, 5 out of 8 are planning to go to the concert on Friday night. What percent of Mark's friend are planning to go to the concert? 62.5%

34. **SPORTS** There are 18 members on the varsity baseball team. Of these players, 7 are pitchers. What percent of the team are pitchers? Round to the nearest hundredth. 38.89%

35. **ANIMALS** A cheetah can run about $5\frac{1}{2}$ times as fast as a squirrel. What percent is this? 550%

36. **GEOMETRY** The Martin's patio is shown at the right. Part of their patio is covered with a mat. What percent of their patio is covered by the mat? (*Hint:* Area is equal to length times width.) 36%

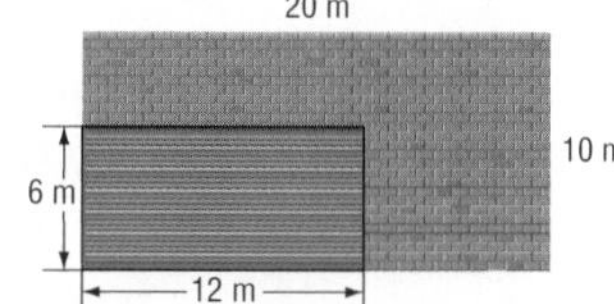

Differentiated Homework Options

Level	Assignment	Two-Day Option	
AL Basic	11–35, 45, 47–48, 50–66	11–35 odd, 51–54	12–34 even, 45, 47–48, 50, 55–66
OL Core	11–35 odd, 36, 37, 39–43 odd, 44–45, 47–48, 50–66	11–35, 51–54	36–45, 47–48, 50, 55–66
BL Advanced	36–62 (optional: 63-66)		

37. GEOMETRY For each model below, write a fraction in simplest form that compares the shaded portion of each figure to its total area. Then write each fraction as a percent. Which figure has the greatest part shaded?

Figure A 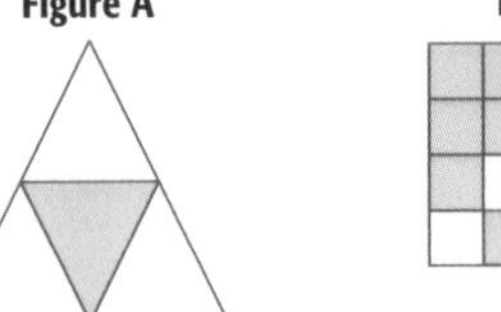

Figure B 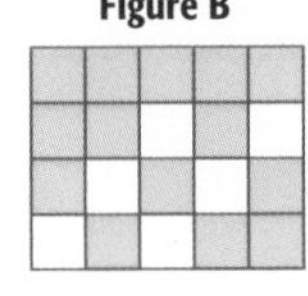

Figure C 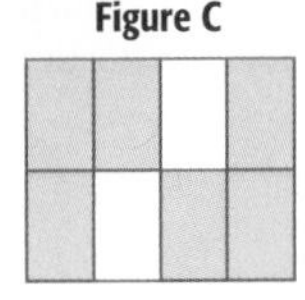

Replace each ● with <, >, or = to make a true sentence.

38. $\frac{8}{20}$ ● 45% <　　**39.** 75% ● $\frac{36}{48}$ =　　**40.** 120% ● $\frac{84}{72}$ >

41. $\frac{7}{10}$ ● $70\frac{1}{4}$% <　　**42.** $\frac{1}{50}$ ● 0.002 % >　　**43.** 300% ● $\frac{3}{10}$ >

Real-World Link

On October 17, 2006, the population of the United States hit the 300 million mark. The population is estimated to be 400 million in 2043.

Source: *USA Today*

44. POPULATION The circle graph shows the percent of the world's population on each continent.

a. Write each percent as a fraction.

b. What fraction of the population lives in the Americas? $\frac{17}{125}$

c. If the world population is about 6.5 billion people, explain how you might determine the number of people who live in Asia.

World Population

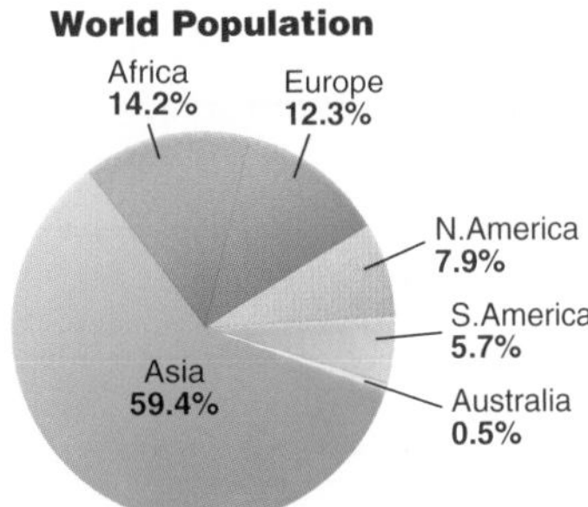

37. figure A: $\frac{1}{4}$, 25%; figure B: $\frac{7}{10}$, 70%; figure C: $\frac{3}{4}$, 75%; figure C

44a. Asia: $\frac{297}{500}$, Africa: $\frac{71}{500}$; Europe: $\frac{123}{1000}$; North America: $\frac{79}{1000}$; South America: $\frac{57}{1000}$; Australia: $\frac{1}{200}$

44c. Sample answer: You can use a proportion to solve. $\frac{59.4}{100} = \frac{x}{6.5}$

45. Sample answer: 76%; $\frac{3}{4} = 0.75$ or 75% and $\frac{7}{9} \approx$ 77.8%. So, 76% is between 75% and 77.8%.

48. Anna; Emma did not multiply by $\frac{10}{10}$ to eliminate the decimal.

H.O.T. Problems　Use Higher-Order Thinking Skills

45. OPEN ENDED Give an example of a percent that is between $\frac{3}{4}$ and $\frac{7}{9}$. Explain your reasoning.

46. CHALLENGE What percent of the larger triangle shown is *not* shaded? Round to the nearest hundredth. **88.89%**

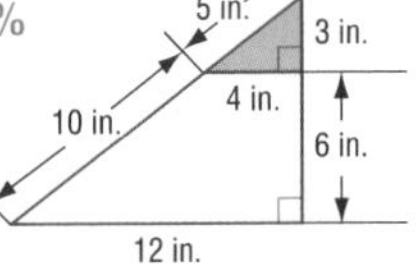

47. NUMBER SENSE Model the fraction $\frac{15}{2}$. Then write the fraction as a percent. **See margin.**

48. FIND THE ERROR Emma and Anna are changing 0.5% to a fraction. Is either of them correct? Explain.

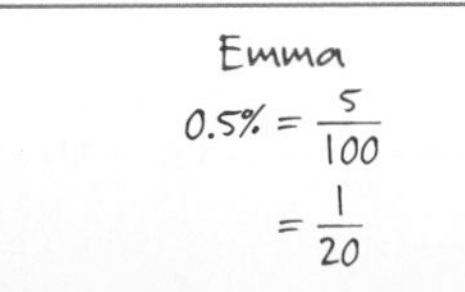

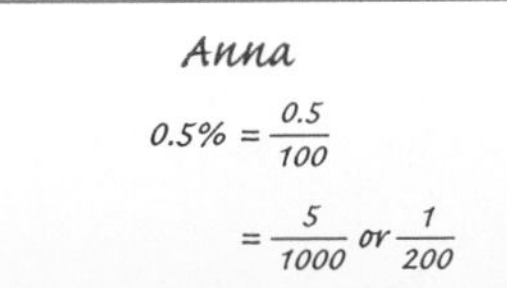

49. CHALLENGE Find the whole number value of x such that $\frac{x}{x+5}$ equals 50%. Explain your reasoning. **5; $\frac{5}{5+5} = 50\%$**

50. WRITING IN MATH Describe two ways to write $\frac{4}{5}$ as a percent. **See margin.**

Watch Out!

Find the Error For Exercise 48, students should see that Emma's and Anna's solutions differ in the first line. Remind students that decimal points cannot be ignored.

Enrichment CRM p. 10 OL BL

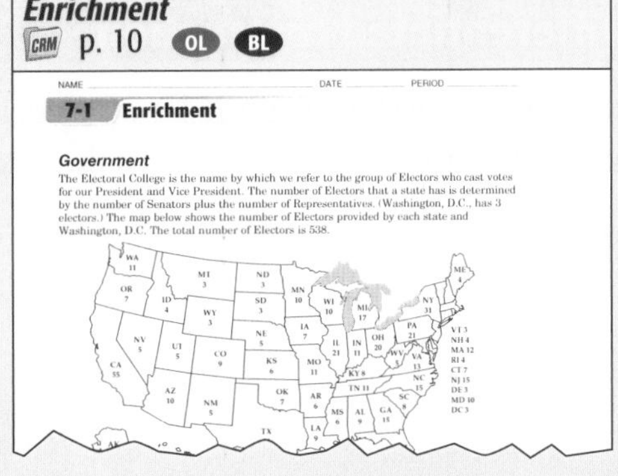

7-1 Enrichment

Government

The Electoral College is the name by which we refer to the group of Electors who cast votes for our President and Vice President. The number of Electors that a state has is determined by the number of Senators plus the number of Representatives. (Washington, D.C., has 3 electors.) The map below shows the number of Electors provided by each state and Washington, D.C. The total number of Electors is 538.

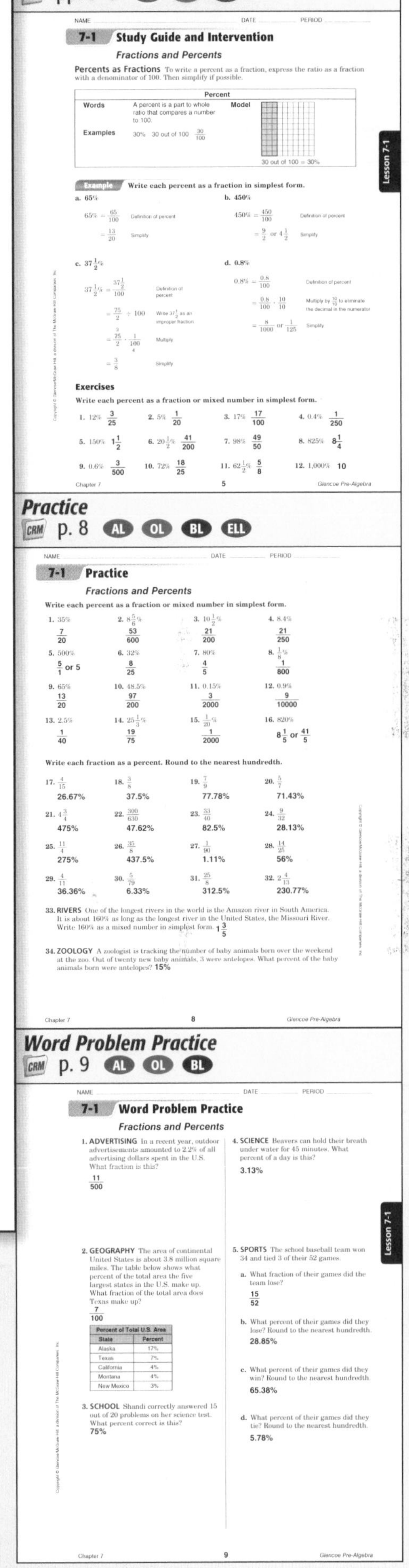

Study Guide and Intervention CRM pp. 5–6 AL OL ELL

7-1 Study Guide and Intervention

Fractions and Percents

Percents as Fractions To write a percent as a fraction, express the ratio as a fraction with a denominator of 100. Then simplify if possible.

Exercises

Write each percent as a fraction or mixed number in simplest form.

1. 12% $\frac{3}{25}$　2. 5% $\frac{1}{20}$　3. 17% $\frac{17}{100}$　4. 0.4% $\frac{1}{250}$

5. 150% $1\frac{1}{2}$　6. $20\frac{1}{2}$% $\frac{41}{200}$　7. 98% $\frac{49}{50}$　8. 825% $8\frac{1}{4}$

9. 0.6% $\frac{3}{500}$　10. 72% $\frac{18}{25}$　11. $62\frac{1}{2}$% $\frac{5}{8}$　12. 1,000% 10

Practice CRM p. 8 AL OL BL ELL

7-1 Practice

Fractions and Percents

Write each percent as a fraction or mixed number in simplest form.

1. 35% $\frac{7}{20}$　2. $8\frac{5}{6}$% $\frac{53}{600}$　3. $10\frac{1}{2}$% $\frac{21}{200}$　4. 8.4% $\frac{21}{250}$

5. 500% $\frac{5}{1}$ or 5　6. 32% $\frac{8}{25}$　7. 80% $\frac{4}{5}$　8. $\frac{1}{8}$% $\frac{1}{800}$

9. 65% $\frac{13}{20}$　10. 48.5% $\frac{97}{200}$　11. 0.15% $\frac{3}{2000}$　12. 0.9% $\frac{9}{10000}$

13. 2.5% $\frac{1}{40}$　14. $25\frac{1}{3}$% $\frac{19}{75}$　15. $\frac{1}{20}$% $\frac{1}{2000}$　16. 820% $8\frac{1}{5}$ or $\frac{41}{5}$

Write each fraction as a percent. Round to the nearest hundredth.

17. $\frac{4}{15}$ 26.67%　18. $\frac{3}{8}$ 37.5%　19. $\frac{7}{9}$ 77.78%　20. $\frac{5}{7}$ 71.43%

21. $4\frac{3}{4}$ 475%　22. $\frac{300}{630}$ 47.62%　23. $\frac{33}{40}$ 82.5%　24. $\frac{9}{32}$ 28.13%

25. $\frac{11}{4}$ 275%　26. $\frac{35}{8}$ 437.5%　27. $\frac{1}{90}$ 1.11%　28. $\frac{14}{25}$ 56%

29. $\frac{4}{11}$ 36.36%　30. $\frac{5}{79}$ 6.33%　31. $\frac{25}{8}$ 312.5%　32. $2\frac{4}{13}$ 230.77%

33. RIVERS One of the longest rivers in the world is the Amazon river in South America. It is about 160% as long as the longest river in the United States, the Missouri River. Write 160% as a mixed number in simplest form. $1\frac{3}{5}$

34. ZOOLOGY A zoologist is tracking the number of baby animals born over the weekend at the zoo. Out of twenty new baby animals, 3 were antelopes. What percent of the baby animals born were antelopes? 15%

Word Problem Practice CRM p. 9 AL OL BL

7-1 Word Problem Practice

Fractions and Percents

1. ADVERTISING In a recent year, outdoor advertisements amounted to 2.2% of all advertising dollars spent in the U.S. What fraction is this? $\frac{11}{500}$

2. GEOGRAPHY The area of continental United States is about 3.8 million square miles. The table below shows what percent of the total area the five largest states in the U.S. make up. What fraction of the total area does Texas make up? $\frac{7}{100}$

State	Percent
Alaska	17%
Texas	7%
California	4%
Montana	4%
New Mexico	3%

3. SCHOOL Shandi correctly answered 15 out of 20 problems on her science test. What percent correct is this? 75%

4. SCIENCE Beavers can hold their breath under water for 45 minutes. What percent of a day is this? 3.13%

5. SPORTS The school baseball team won 34 and tied 3 of their 52 games.

a. What fraction of their games did the team lose? $\frac{15}{52}$

b. What percent of their games did they lose? Round to the nearest hundredth. 28.85%

c. What percent of their games did they win? Round to the nearest hundredth. 65.38%

d. What percent of their games did they tie? Round to the nearest hundredth. 5.78%

4 ASSESS

Ticket Out the Door Have students write the following fractions as percents. As students leave the classroom, have them turn in their solutions.

a. $\frac{41}{50}$ 82%

b. $2\frac{3}{25}$ 212%

Additional Answers

56. $A'(-6, 3), B'(3, 6), C'(9, -6)$

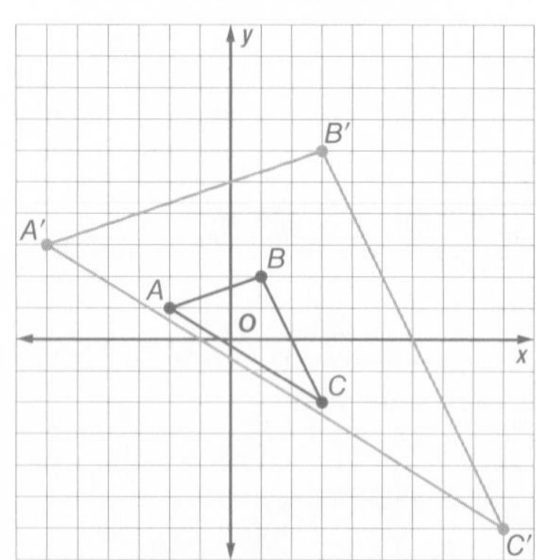

57. $A'(-1, 0.5), B'(0.5, 1), C'(1.5, -1)$

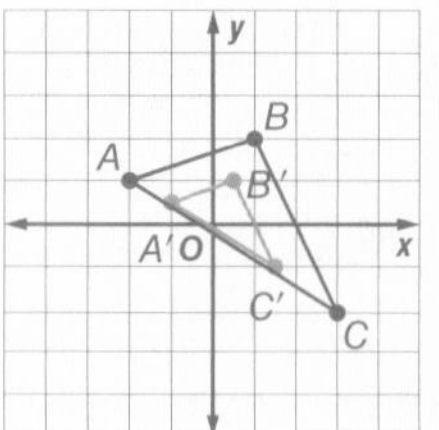

Standardized Test Practice

51. Which of the following represents the shaded portion of the figure below? **B**

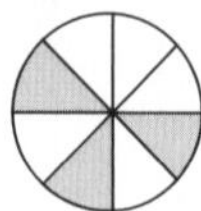

A 25%   C 50%
B 37.5%   D 62.5%

52. During her last basketball game, Carmen made 14 field goals out of 30 attempts. What percent of field goals did she make? **G**

F 45%   H 50%
G 47%   J 51%

53. If 95% of the seventh grade students are going on the trip to the museum, what fraction of the students are *not* going on the field trip? **A**

A $\frac{1}{20}$ C $\frac{9}{10}$
B $\frac{1}{10}$ D $\frac{19}{20}$

54. SHORT RESPONSE Helio is installing some software onto his computer. The screen shows that it is 45% complete. Write 45% as a fraction in simplest form. Show all of your work. $45\% = \frac{45}{100}$ or $\frac{9}{20}$

Spiral Review

55. RIDES Suppose a roller coaster casts a shadow of 31.5 feet. At the same time, a nearby Ferris wheel casts a 19-foot shadow. If the roller coaster is 126 feet tall, how tall is the Ferris wheel? (Lesson 6-9) **76 ft**

For Exercises 56 and 57 use the figure at the right. **56–57. See margin.**

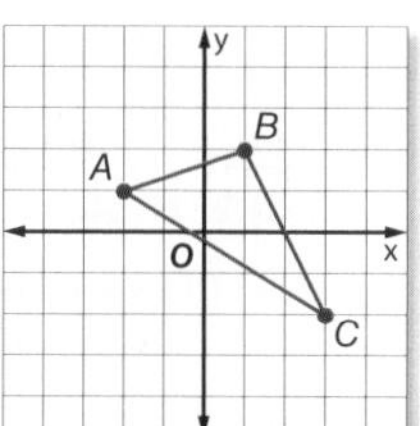

56. Find the vertices of $\triangle ABC$ after a dilation centered at the origin with a scale factor of 3. Then graph the original image and the dilation. (Lesson 6-8)

57. Find the vertices of $\triangle ABC$ after a dilation centered at the origin with a scale factor of $\frac{1}{2}$. Then graph the original image and the dilation. (Lesson 6-8)

Solve each inequality. Check your solution. (Lesson 5-4)

58. $x + 3 < 8$ $\boldsymbol{x < 5}$

59. $14 + y \geq 7$ $\boldsymbol{y \geq -7}$

60. $-13 \geq 9 + b$ $\boldsymbol{b \leq -22}$

61. $a - 5 > 6$ $\boldsymbol{a > 11}$

62. PAINTING A person-day is a unit of measure that represents one person working for one day. A painting contractor estimates that it will take 24 person-days to paint a house. Write and solve an equation to find how many painters the contractor will need to hire to paint the house in 6 days. (Lesson 4-4) **$6p = 24$, 4 painters**

Skills Review

Multiply or divide. (Previous Course)

63. 18.2×100 **1820**

64. 0.04×100 **4**

65. $33.3 \div 100$ **0.333**

66. $0.9 \div 100$ **0.009**

Differentiated Instruction

Extension A student receives a 72.5% on a test. If there are no more than 100 questions on the test, write two ratios comparing correct answers to total questions. $\frac{58}{80}, \frac{29}{40}$

336 Chapter 7 Percent

7-2

Fractions, Decimals, and Percents

Then

You have already expressed fractions as percents and percents as fractions. (Lesson 7-1)

Now

- Express percents as decimals and decimals as percents.
- Compare and order fractions, decimals, and percents.

Math Online

glencoe.com

- Extra Examples
- Personal Tutor
- Self-Check Quiz
- Homework Help

Why?

PETS The table shows the percent of spending on pets in the United States in a recent year. **a–c. See margin.**

a. Write each percent as a fraction. Do not simplify the fractions.

b. Write each fraction in part **a** as a decimal.

c. How could you write a percent as a decimal without writing the percent as a fraction first?

U.S. Spending on Pets

Category	Percent of Sales
Food	40%
Live animal purchases	5%
Grooming & Boarding	7%
Supplies/Medicine	24%
Vet Care	24%

Source: American Pet Products Manufacturers Association

Percents and Decimals You have learned to write percents as fractions and then as decimals.

$24\% = \frac{24}{100} = 0.24$ $\qquad$ $7\% = \frac{7}{100} = 0.07$

You can also write decimals as fractions and then as percents.

$0.40 = \frac{40}{100} = 40\%$ $\qquad$ $0.05 = \frac{5}{100} = 5\%$

These examples suggest the following rules.

Key Concept Percents and Decimals — For Your FOLDABLE

- To write a percent as a decimal, divide by 100 and remove the percent symbol.
- To write a decimal as a percent, multiply by 100 and add the percent symbol.

EXAMPLE 1 Percents as Decimals

Write each percent as a decimal.

a. 16%

$16\% = .16$ — **Remove the % symbol and divide by 100.**

$= 0.16$ — **Add a zero in the ones place.**

b. 9%

$9\% = .09$ — **Remove the % symbol and divide by 100. Add a placeholder zero.**

$= 0.09$ — **Add a zero in the ones place.**

StudyTip

Mental Math To divide a number by 100, move the decimal point two places to the left. To multiply a number by 100, move the decimal point two places to the right.

Check Your Progress

1A. 78% **0.78** $\qquad$ **1B.** 2% **0.02**

Personal Tutor glencoe.com

7-2 Lesson Notes

1 FOCUS

Vertical Alignment

Before Lesson 7-2
Express fractions as percents and percents as fractions.

Lesson 7-2
Express percents as decimals and decimals as percents. Compare and order fractions, decimals, and percents.

After Lesson 7-2
Solve problems using the percent proportion.

2 TEACH

Scaffolding Questions

Have students read the *Why?* section of the lesson and answer the questions.

Ask:

- When converting a percent to a fraction, what should the denominator be? 100
- What does percent mean? per one hundred

Additional Answers

a. $\frac{40}{100}, \frac{5}{100}, \frac{7}{100}, \frac{24}{100}, \frac{24}{100}$

b. 0.4, 0.05, 0.07, 0.24, 0.24

c. Divide each percent by 100 and remove the percent symbol.

Lesson 7-2 Resources

Resource	Approaching-Level	On-Level	Beyond-Level	English Learners
Teacher Edition	• Differentiated Instruction, p. 339		• Differentiated Instruction, p. 342	
Chapter Resource Masters	• Study Guide and Intervention, pp. 11–12 • Skills Practice, p. 13 • Practice, p. 14 • World Problem Practice, p. 15	• Study Guide and Intervention, pp. 11–12 • Skills Practice, p. 13 • Practice, p. 14 • Word Problem Practice, p. 15 • Enrichment, p. 16	• Practice, p. 14 • Word Problem Practice, p. 15 • Enrichment, p. 16	• Study Guide and Intervention, pp. 11–12 • Skills Practice p. 13 • Practice, p. 14
Transparencies	• 5-Minute Check Transparency 7-2	• 5-Minute Check Transparency 7-2	• 5-Minute Check Transparency 7-2	• 5-Minute Check Transparency 7-2
Other	• Study Notebook • Teaching Pre-Algebra with Manipulatives	• Study Notebook • Teaching Pre-Algebra with Manipulatives	• Study Notebook	• Study Notebook • Teaching Pre-Algebra with Manipulatives

Percents and Decimals

Examples 1 and 2 show how to write a percent as a decimal by removing the % symbol and dividing by 100. **Example 3** shows how to write a decimal as a percent. **Example 4** shows how to express a fraction as a percent.

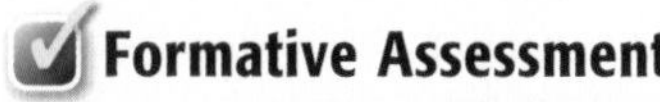

Formative Assessment

Use the Check Your Progress exercises after each example to determine students' understanding of concepts.

Additional Examples

1 Write each percent as a decimal.

a. 23% 0.23

b. 4% 0.04

2 Write each percent as a decimal.

a. 0.7% 0.007

b. 291% 2.91

3 Write each decimal as a percent.

a. 0.6 60%

b. 5.71 571%

c. 0.008 0.8%

Additional Examples also in Interactive Classroom PowerPoint® Presentations

IWB INTERACTIVE WHITEBOARD READY

Watch Out!

Preventing Errors Remind students to be cautious in writing equivalent fractions and percents. Reinforce that $\frac{1}{2} \neq 20\%$ and $\frac{1}{5} \neq 50\%$.

StudyTip

Fractions When the numerator of a fraction is less than the denominator, the fraction is less than 100%. When the numerator is greater than the denominator, the fraction is greater than 100%.

EXAMPLE 2 Percents Less than 1 or Greater than 100

Write each percent as a decimal.

a. 0.7%

0.7 = .007 — **Remove the % symbol and divide by 100. Add placeholder zeros.**

= 0.007 — **Add a zero in the ones place.**

b. 537%

537% = 5.37 — **Remove the % symbol and divide by 100.**

= 5.37

Check Your Progress

2A. 126% **1.26** **2B.** 0.9% **0.009**

Personal Tutor glencoe.com

EXAMPLE 3 Decimals as Percents

Write each decimal as a percent.

a. 0.2

0.2 = 0.20 — **Multiply by 100. Add a placeholder zero.**

= 20% — **Add the % symbol.**

b. 3.84

3.84 = 3.84 — **Multiply by 100.**

= 384% — **Add the % symbol.**

c. 0.005

0.005 = 0.005 — **Multiply by 100.**

= 0.5% — **Add the % symbol.**

Check Your Progress

3A. 0.01 **1%** **3B.** 3.91 **391%** **3C.** 0.002 **0.2%**

Personal Tutor glencoe.com

You have expressed fractions as decimals and decimals as percents. Fractions, decimals, and percents are all different names that represent the same number. The model represents these forms.

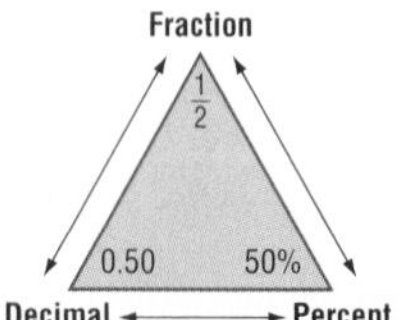

You can express a fraction as a percent by first expressing the fraction as a decimal and then expressing the decimal as a percent.

TEACH with TECH

VIDEO RECORDING Have different groups in the class record themselves converting between fractions, decimals, and percents. Have one group start with a fraction, one group start with a decimal, and one group start with a percent. Show the videos to the entire class.

EXAMPLE 4 Fractions as Percents

Express each fraction as a percent. Round to the nearest tenth, if necessary.

a. $\frac{5}{8}$

$\frac{5}{8} = 0.625$

$= 62.5\%$

b. $\frac{7}{9}$

$\frac{7}{9} = 0.7777777\ldots$

$\approx 77.8\%$

c. $\frac{27}{13}$

$\frac{27}{13} \approx 2.076923077$

$\approx 207.7\%$

d. $\frac{3}{400}$

$\frac{3}{400} = 0.0075$

$= 0.75\%$

Check Your Progress

4A. $\frac{27}{40}$ 67.5% **4B.** $\frac{1}{9}$ 11.1% **4C.** $\frac{1}{250}$ 0.4% **4D.** $\frac{17}{11}$ 154.5%

Personal Tutor glencoe.com

Compare Fractions, Decimals, and Percents You can compare fractions, decimals, and percents by writing them in the same format.

Real-World Link

Of wireless cell phone subscribers, 45% use text messaging, 44% use the camera, 17% play games, and 11% access e-mail.

Source: *ZDNet Research*

Real-World EXAMPLE 5 Compare Numbers

COMMUNICATION In an online survey, one-fifth of teenagers said that their favorite way of communicating with friends is by e-mail, 21% preferred using their cell phones, and 0.15 favored instant messaging. Which of these groups is the largest?

Write one-fifth and 0.15 as percents. Then compare with 21%.

$\frac{1}{5} = 0.20$ or 20% $\quad$ $0.15 = 15\%$

Since 21% > 20% and 21% > 15%, the group that preferred cell phones is the largest.

Check Your Progress

5. **FOOD** At a restaurant, one-eighth of customers prefer fish sandwiches, 14% prefer rib sandwiches, and 0.12 prefer chicken sandwiches. Which of these groups is the largest? rib sandwiches

Personal Tutor glencoe.com

Concept Summary Common Equivalents

For Your FOLDABLE

$\frac{1}{5} = 0.20 = 20\%$	$\frac{1}{3} = 0.\overline{3} = 33.\overline{3}\%$	$\frac{1}{8} = 0.125 = 12.5\%$
$\frac{2}{5} = 0.40 = 40\%$	$\frac{2}{3} = 0.\overline{6} = 66.\overline{6}\%$	$\frac{3}{8} = 0.375 = 37.5\%$
$\frac{3}{5} = 0.60 = 60\%$	$\frac{1}{6} = 0.1\overline{6} = 16.\overline{6}\%$	$\frac{5}{8} = 0.625 = 62.5\%$
$\frac{4}{5} = 0.80 = 80\%$	$\frac{5}{6} = 0.8\overline{3} = 83.\overline{3}\%$	$\frac{7}{8} = 0.875 = 87.5\%$

Additional Example

4 Express each fraction as a percent. Round to the nearest tenth, if necessary.

a. $\frac{3}{8}$ 37.5%

b. $\frac{8}{9}$ 88.9%

c. $\frac{32}{15}$ 213.3%

d. $\frac{1}{125}$ 0.8%

Compare Fractions, Decimals, and Percents

Example 5 shows how to compare fractions, decimals, and percents by writing them in the same format.

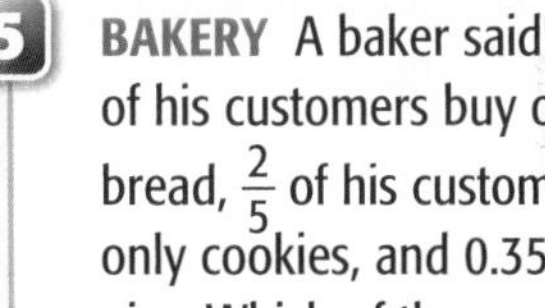

Additional Example

5 **BAKERY** A baker said that 25% of his customers buy only bread, $\frac{2}{5}$ of his customers buy only cookies, and 0.35 buy only pies. Which of these groups is largest? cookies

Focus on Mathematical Content

Reading a Decimal A decimal that is read correctly is read as a fraction. For example, 0.70 is read as "seventy hundredths." This equals seventy parts out of one hundred parts. Because a percent is a ratio that compares a number to one hundred, a decimal can be changed into a percent by moving the decimal two places to the right.

Differentiated Instruction

AL

If students have trouble converting among fractions, decimals, and percents,

Then have students create a number line showing fraction, decimal, and percent equivalents. The number line could be used to help make comparisons. Sample number line:

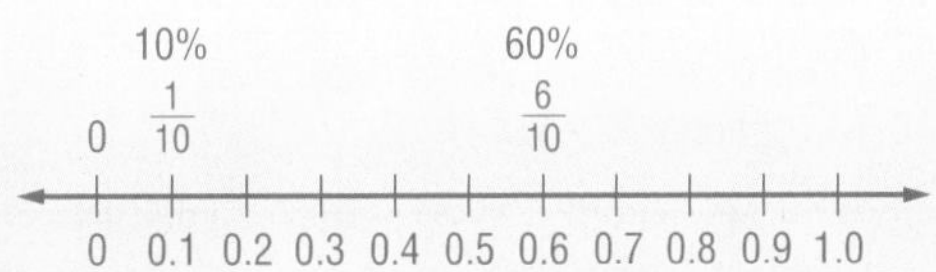

Tips for New Teachers

Decimal Point Multiplying by 100 is the same as moving the decimal point two places to the right. Dividing by 100 is the same as moving the decimal point two places to the left.

3 PRACTICE

Formative Assessment

Use Exercises 1–9 to check for understanding.

Use the chart at the bottom of this page to customize assignments for your students.

Multiple Representations In Exercise 42, students use information from a graph to create a table showing each value as an equivalent fraction, decimal, and percent.

Additional Answers

42a.

Ride	Fraction	Decimal	Percent
Roller Coaster	$\frac{9}{20}$	0.45	45%
Bumper Cars	$\frac{3}{20}$	0.15	15%
Carousel	$\frac{1}{20}$	0.05	5%
Ferris Wheel	$\frac{1}{10}$	0.10	10%
Tilting	$\frac{1}{4}$	0.25	25%

42b. $\frac{9}{20} = \frac{45}{100}, \frac{3}{20} = \frac{15}{100}, \frac{1}{20} = \frac{5}{100}, \frac{1}{10} = \frac{10}{100}, \frac{1}{4} = \frac{25}{100}$

42c. The numerator of the fraction with a denominator of 100 is the same as the percent.

47. Sample answer: Greater than; By dividing by 100 and removing the % symbol, 0.005 > 0.0005. Since 0.005 > 0.0005, 0.5% > 0.0005.

Check Your Understanding

Examples 1 and 2 pp. 337–338

Write each percent as a decimal.

1. 45% **0.45** **2.** 8% **0.08** **3.** 0.6% **0.006** **4.** 455% **4.55**

Examples 3 and 4 pp. 338–339

Express each decimal or fraction as a percent. Round to the nearest tenth, if necessary.

5. $\frac{15}{500}$ **3%** **6.** $\frac{4}{200}$ **2%** **7.** 0.6 **60%** **8.** 1.45 **145%**

Example 5 p. 339

9. PETS Of the students in Miss Han's class 32% own a cat, $\frac{3}{8}$ own a dog, and 0.29 own a bird. Which type of pet do most students own? **dog**

Practice and Problem Solving

= **Step-by-Step Solutions** begin on page R11. **Extra Practice** begins on page 810.

Examples 1 and 2 pp. 337–338

Write each percent as a decimal.

10. 19% **0.19** **11.** 75% **0.75** **12.** 2% **0.02** **13.** 3% **0.03**

14. 0.51% **0.0051** **15.** 0.91% **0.0091** **16.** 166% **1.66** **17.** 284% **2.84**

Examples 3 and 4 pp. 338–339

Write each decimal or fraction as a percent. Round to the nearest tenth, if necessary.

18. 0.57 **57%** **19.** 0.43 **43%** **20.** $\frac{1}{3}$ **33.3%** **21.** $\frac{2}{7}$ **28.6%**

22. $\frac{12}{800}$ **1.5%** **23.** $\frac{7}{200}$ **3.5%** **24.** 0.2 **20%** **25.** 0.8 **80%**

26. 5.43 **543%** **27.** 6.20 **620%** **28.** $\frac{22}{9}$ **244.4%** **29.** $\frac{11}{3}$ **366.7%**

30. $\frac{10}{2000}$ **0.5%** **31.** $\frac{2}{1000}$ **0.2%** **32.** 0.0093 **0.93%** **33.** 0.0002 **0.02%**

Example 5 p. 339

34. FRUIT Thirty percent of high school freshman chose apples as their favorite fruit in a survey. Strawberries were chosen by 0.03 of students, and $\frac{1}{3}$ chose watermelon. Which group is the largest? Explain.

34. Since $\frac{1}{3} \approx 33.3\%$, $0.03 = 3\%$, and 33.3% is greater than 30% and 3%, the group that prefers watermelon is largest.

35. MOVIES Neka was organizing his DVDs. Of his DVDs, $\frac{1}{5}$ were comedies, 18% were drama, and 0.24 were action. Which type of movie makes up most of his collection? **action**

B Write each list of numbers in order from least to greatest.

36. 18%, $\frac{1}{8}$, 0.08 **0.08, $\frac{1}{8}$, 18%**

37. 2.2, 227%, $\frac{5}{22}$ **$\frac{5}{22}$, 2.2, 227%**

38. 0.23, 28%, $\frac{4}{15}$ **0.23, $\frac{4}{15}$, 28%**

39. SPORTS After surveying 200 middle school students about their favorite sports, Antoine and Bartoli made the graph at the right.

Favorite Sports

Auto Racing 14%
Soccer 15%
Baseball 8%
Football 36%
Basketball 27%

a. Estimate the number of students that ranked basketball as their favorite sport. **54 students**

b. About how many students ranked football or soccer as their favorite sport? **100 students**

Differentiated Homework Options

Level	Assignment	Two-Day Option	
AL Basic	10–35, 43–45, 47–67	11–35 odd, 48–51	10–34 even, 43–45, 47, 52–67
OL Core	11–35 odd, 37, 39–45, 47–67	10–35, 48–51	36–45, 47, 52–67
BL Advanced	36–61 (optional: 62–67)		

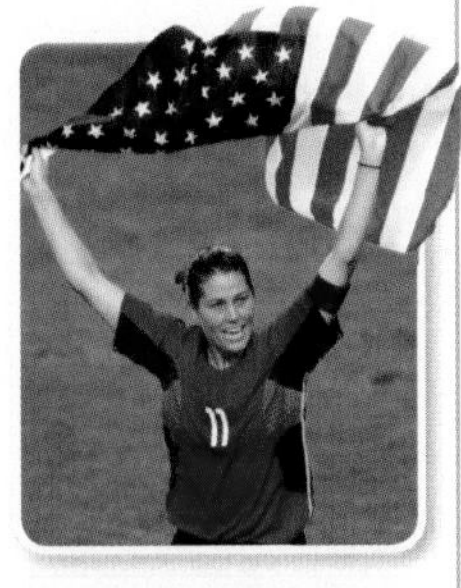

Real-World Link

The U.S. Women's National Soccer team is the only women's team to win the World Cup two times. The team won Olympic gold medals in 1996, 2004, and 2008.

Source: National Soccer Hall of Fame

44. 2.4; 2.4 is the same as 240% which is not equal to the other three ratios

45. Len; Carlita divided by 100 and she should have multiplied by 100

46. No. Sample answer: If the bigger square has side length of 4, the area is 16. The smaller square would have side length of 2 and its area would be 4. The area of the smaller square is $\frac{1}{4}$ or 25% of the larger square.

40. SOCCER Use the table to rank the goalies in order from the greatest percent of saves to the least percent of saves. **Chantel Jones, Amber Campbell, Christina Reuter**

Player	Saves
Christina Reuter	$\frac{64}{71}$
Chantel Jones	0.906
Amber Campbell	90.4%

41. TESTS On his last math test, Luther answered 1 question or 4% of the questions incorrectly. How many questions did Luther answer correctly? **24 questions**

42. MULTIPLE REPRESENTATIONS In this problem, you will investigate bar graphs and percents. The graph shows the results of a recent survey. **a–c. See margin.**

a. **TABULAR** Create a table that shows the fraction of total students that prefer each ride. Write each fraction in simplest form, then as a decimal and percent.

b. **NUMERICAL** Write each fraction as an equivalent fraction with a denominator of 100.

c. **ANALYTICAL** Compare and contrast the results of parts **a** and **b**.

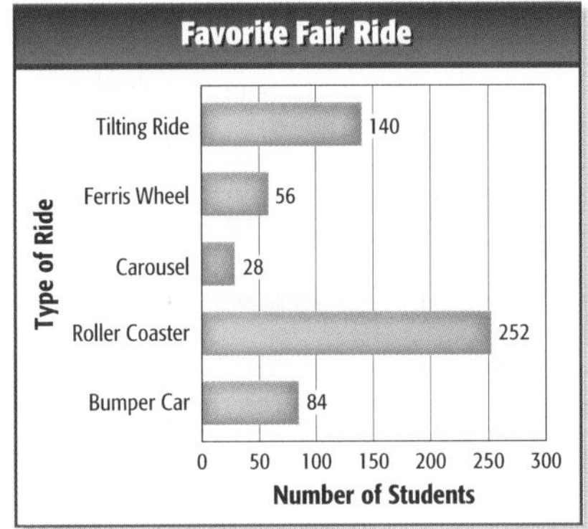

H.O.T. Problems Use Higher-Order Thinking Skills

43. OPEN ENDED Name a percent that is between 0.10 and 0.01. Write it as a decimal and as a fraction. **Sample answer: 9%; 0.09; $\frac{9}{100}$**

44. WHICH ONE DOESN'T BELONG? Identify the ratio that does not have the same value as the other three. Explain your reasoning.

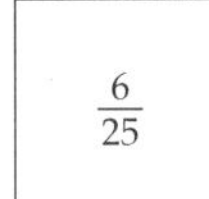

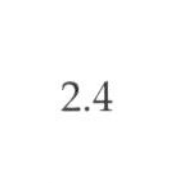

6 out of 25

45. FIND THE ERROR Carlita and Len are writing 1.5 as a percent. Is either of them correct? Explain your reasoning.

Carlita	Len
1.5 = 1.5 ÷ 100 or 0.015%	1.5 = 1.5 × 100 or 150%

46. CHALLENGE Suppose you have two squares. The side length of the smaller square is 50% of the side length of the larger square. Is the area of the smaller square 50% of the area of the larger square? Explain your reasoning.

47. WRITING IN MATH Is 0.5% less than or greater than 0.0005? Explain. **See margin.**

Watch Out!

Find the Error For Exercise 45, ask students if they should multiply or divide when converting a decimal to a percent. multiply

Enrichment CRM p. 16 OL BL

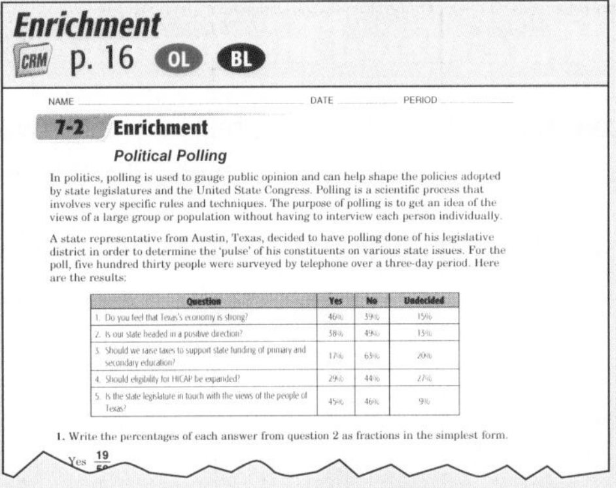

7-2 Enrichment

Political Polling

In politics, polling is used to gauge public opinion and can help shape the policies adopted by state legislatures and the United State Congress. Polling is a scientific process that involves very specific rules and techniques. The purpose of polling is to get an idea of the views of a large group or population without having to interview each person individually.

A state representative from Austin, Texas, decided to have polling done of his legislative district in order to determine the 'pulse' of his constituents on various state issues. For the poll, five hundred thirty people were surveyed by telephone over a three-day period. Here are the results:

Question	Yes	No	Undecided
1. Do you feel that Texas's economy is strong?	46%	39%	15%
2. Is our state headed in a positive direction?	38%	49%	13%
3. Should we raise taxes to support state funding of primary and secondary education?	17%	63%	20%
4. Should eligibility for HICAP be expanded?	29%	44%	27%
5. Is the state legislature in touch with the views of the people of Texas?	45%	46%	9%

1. Write the percentages of each answer from question 2 as fractions in the simplest form.

Yes $\frac{19}{50}$

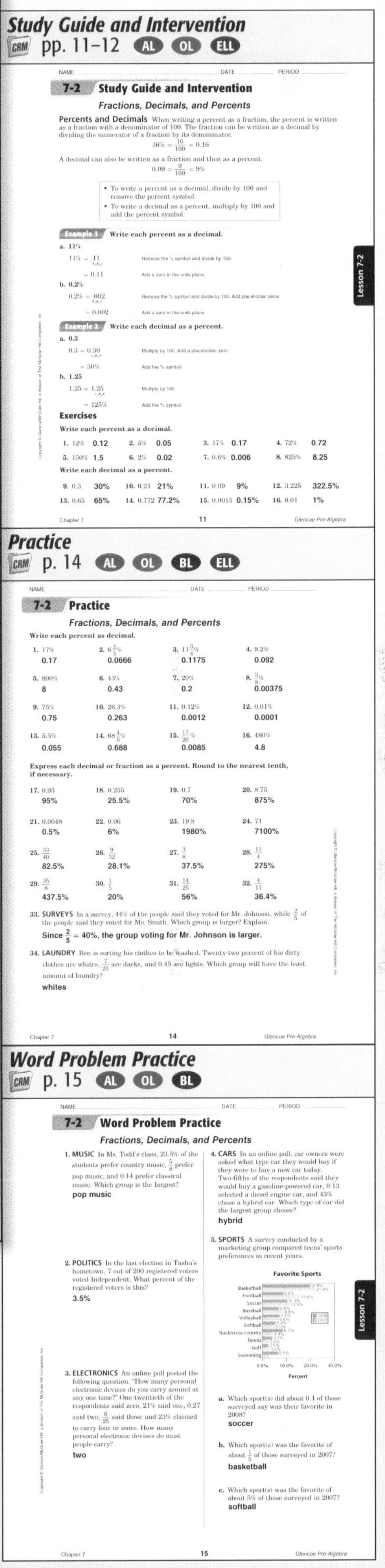

Study Guide and Intervention CRM pp. 11–12 AL OL ELL

7-2 Study Guide and Intervention

Fractions, Decimals, and Percents

Percents and Decimals When writing a percent as a fraction, the percent is written as a fraction with a denominator of 100. The fraction can be written as a decimal by dividing the numerator of a fraction by its denominator.

$16\% = \frac{16}{100} = 0.16$

A decimal can also be written as a fraction and then as a percent.

$0.09 = \frac{9}{100} = 9\%$

- To write a percent as a decimal, divide by 100 and remove the percent symbol.
- To write a decimal as a percent, multiply by 100 and add the percent symbol.

Example 1 Write each percent as a decimal.

a. 11%
11% = .11 Remove the % symbol and divide by 100
= 0.11 Add a zero in the units place.

b. 0.2%
0.2% = .002 Remove the % symbol and divide by 100. Add placeholder zeros.
= 0.002 Add a zero in the units place.

Example 2 Write each decimal as a percent.

a. 0.3
0.3 = 0.30 Multiply by 100. Add a placeholder zero.
= 30% Add the % symbol.

b. 1.25
1.25 = 1.25 Multiply by 100.
= 125% Add the % symbol.

Exercises

Write each percent as a decimal.

1. 12% 0.12 2. 5% 0.05 3. 17% 0.17 4. 72% 0.72
5. 150% 1.5 6. 2% 0.02 7. 0.6% 0.006 8. 825% 8.25

Write each decimal as a percent.

9. 0.3 30% 10. 0.21 21% 11. 0.09 9% 12. 3.225 322.5%
13. 0.65 65% 14. 0.772 77.2% 15. 0.0015 0.15% 16. 0.01 1%

Chapter 7 11 Glencoe Pre-Algebra

Practice CRM p. 14 AL OL BL ELL

7-2 Practice

Fractions, Decimals, and Percents

Write each percent as decimal.

1. 17% 0.17 2. $6\frac{2}{3}\%$ 0.0666 3. $11\frac{3}{4}\%$ 0.1175 4. 9.2% 0.092
5. 800% 8 6. 43% 0.43 7. 20% 0.2 8. $\frac{3}{8}\%$ 0.00375
9. 75% 0.75 10. 26.3% 0.263 11. 0.12% 0.0012 12. 0.01% 0.0001
13. 5.5% 0.055 14. $68\frac{4}{5}\%$ 0.688 15. $\frac{17}{20}\%$ 0.0085 16. 480% 4.8

Express each decimal or fraction as a percent. Round to the nearest tenth, if necessary.

17. 0.95 95% 18. 0.255 25.5% 19. 0.7 70% 20. 8.75 875%
21. 0.0048 0.5% 22. 0.06 6% 23. 19.8 1980% 24. 71 7100%
25. $\frac{33}{40}$ 82.5% 26. $\frac{9}{32}$ 28.1% 27. $\frac{3}{8}$ 37.5% 28. $\frac{11}{4}$ 275%
29. $\frac{35}{8}$ 437.5% 30. $\frac{1}{5}$ 20% 31. $\frac{14}{25}$ 56% 32. $\frac{4}{11}$ 36.4%

33. SURVEYS In a survey, 44% of the people said they voted for Mr. Johnson, while $\frac{2}{5}$ of the people said they voted for Ms. Smith. Which group is larger? Explain.
Since $\frac{2}{5}$ = 40%, the group voting for Mr. Johnson is larger.

34. LAUNDRY Ben is sorting his clothes to be washed. Twenty-two percent of his dirty clothes are whites, $\frac{7}{20}$ are darks, and 0.45 are lights. Which group will have the least amount of laundry?
whites

Chapter 7 14 Glencoe Pre-Algebra

Word Problem Practice CRM p. 15 AL OL BL

7-2 Word Problem Practice

Fractions, Decimals, and Percents

1. MUSIC In Ms. Todd's class, 23.5% of the students prefer country music, $\frac{5}{8}$ prefer pop music, and 0.14 prefer classical music. Which group is the largest?
pop music

2. POLITICS In the last election in Tasha's hometown, 7 out of 200 registered voters voted Independent. What percent of the registered voters is this?
3.5%

3. ELECTRONICS An online poll posted the following question, "How many personal electronic devices do you carry around at any one time?" One-twentieth of the respondents said zero, 21% said one, 0.27 said two, $\frac{6}{25}$ said three and 23% claimed to carry four or more. How many personal electronic devices do most people carry?
two

4. CARS In an online poll, car owners were asked what type car they would buy if they were to buy a new car today. Two-fifths of the respondents said they would buy a gasoline-powered car, 0.13 selected a diesel engine car, and 43% chose a hybrid car. Which type of car did the largest group choose?
hybrid

5. SPORTS A survey conducted by a marketing group compared teens' sports preferences in recent years.

Favorite Sports

a. Which sport(s) did about 0.1 of those surveyed say was their favorite in 2008?
soccer

b. Which sport(s) was the favorite of about $\frac{1}{5}$ of those surveyed in 2007?
basketball

c. Which sport(s) was the favorite of about 5% of those surveyed in 2007?
softball

Chapter 7 15 Glencoe Pre-Algebra

4 ASSESS

Name the Math Have students write about how to compare $\frac{3}{5}$ and 35%. Tell them to be specific in how they decided to compare the two values.

Formative Assessment

Check for student understanding in Lessons 7-1 and 7-2.

CRM Quiz 1, p. 58

Standardized Test Practice

48. Anoki's math teacher drops the lowest quiz score when averaging grades. Which score should his teacher drop? **D**

A 12 correct out of 15

B 79%

C $\frac{56}{70}$

D 0.75

49. A toy company claims that 0.04% of its toys are defective. Which number is *not* equivalent to 0.04%? **J**

F 0.0004

G $\frac{4}{10000}$

H $\frac{1}{2500}$

J 4.0

50. The table shows how Silvia spent her earnings from a paper route. Which represents the part of her money spent at the amusement park? **B**

Item or Activity	Amount
Amusement park	$65
Bicycle	$105
Clothing	$30

A three-eighths

B 32.5%

C 0.65

D $\frac{2}{5}$

51. GRIDDED RESPONSE If 36 out of 80 students voted for Sophia for class president, what percent of the students voted for her? **45**

Spiral Review

Write each percent as a fraction in simplest form. (Lesson 7-1)

52. 30% $\frac{3}{10}$

53. $12\frac{1}{2}\%$ $\frac{1}{8}$

54. 125% $1\frac{1}{4}$

55. ZOO Refer to the graphic shown. If the triangles are similar, how far are the gorillas from the cheetahs? (Lesson 6-8) **80 m**

56. MEDICINE For Jillian's cough, her doctor says that she should take eight tablets the first day and then four tablets each day until her prescription runs out. There are 36 tablets. Solve $8 + 4d = 36$ to find the number of days she will take only four tablets. (Lesson 4-5) **7 days**

Simplify each expression. (Lesson 4-2)

57. $6a + 4 + 2a$ **$8a + 4$**

58. $x + 9x + 3$ **$10x + 3$**

59. $3x + 2y + 4y$ **$3x + 6y$**

60. $6c + 4 + c + 8$ **$7c + 12$**

61. TRAVEL Joshua's family is packing for a trip. The total weight of their luggage cannot exceed 100 pounds. They have 3 suitcases that weigh 24 pounds each and 2 sport bags that weigh 12 pounds each. Is Joshua's family's luggage within the 100-pound limit? Explain. (Lesson 1-1)
$(3 \times 24) + (2 \times 12)$ is 96. So, the luggage is within the limit.

Skills Review

Solve each proportion. (Lesson 6-5)

62. $\frac{20}{4} = \frac{x}{100}$ **500**

63. $\frac{63}{7} = \frac{y}{100}$ **900**

64. $\frac{65}{8} = \frac{n}{100}$ **812.5**

65. $\frac{m}{10} = \frac{4.2}{100}$ **0.42**

66. $\frac{h}{350} = \frac{26}{100}$ **91**

67. $\frac{86.4}{k} = \frac{36}{100}$ **240**

Differentiated Instruction

BL

Extension A percent shows a relationship between a number and 100. If an item was originally priced for $1.00 and it is discounted 22%, then it is $0.22 less than $1.00, or $0.78.

A sweater originally priced at $20.00 is on sale for 30% off. What is the sale price? $14

Algebra Lab: Using a Percent Model

Math Online glencoe.com
Math *in Motion*, Animation

You can use a percent model to represent many real-world situations.

ACTIVITY 1 Finding a Percent

An Internet advertisement claims that 3 out of 5 dentists prefer a certain toothpaste. What percent does this represent?

You can find the *percent* by using a model.

Step 1

Draw a 10-unit by 1-unit rectangle on grid paper. Label the units on the right from 0 to 100, because percent is a ratio that compares a number to 100.

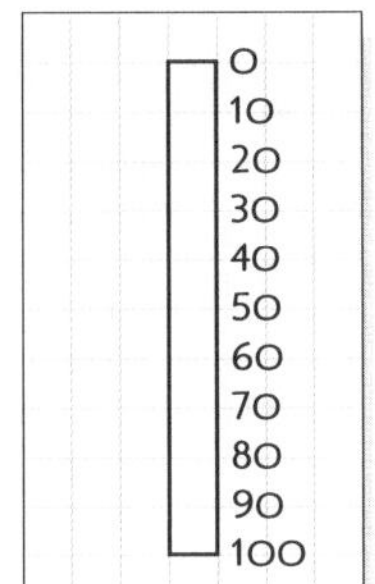

Step 2

On the left side, mark equal units from 0 to 5, because 5 represents the whole quantity. Locate 3 on this scale.

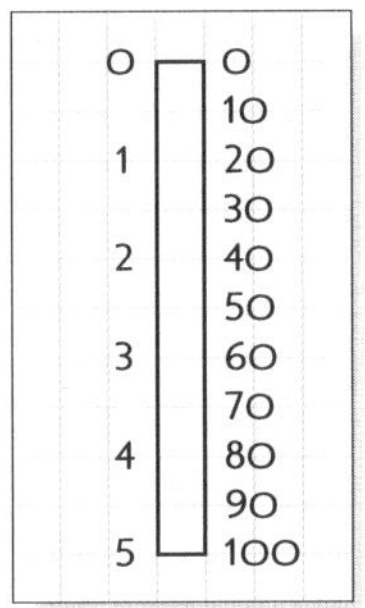

Step 3

Draw a horizontal line from 3 on the left side to the right side of the model. The number on the right side is the percent. Label the model as shown.

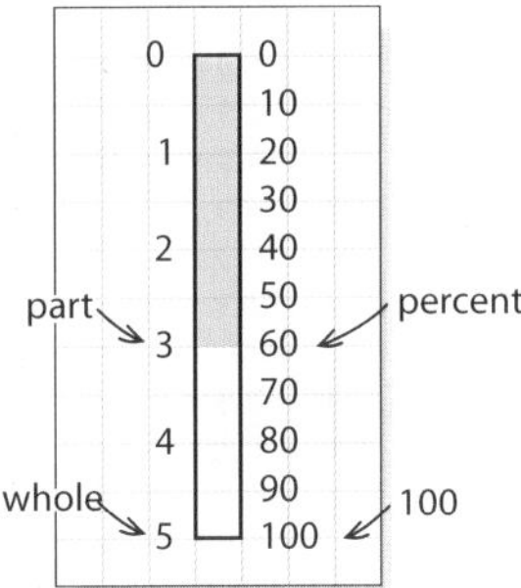

Using the model, you can see that the ratio *3 out of 5* is the same as 60%. So, according to this claim, 60% of dentists prefer this toothpaste.

Exercises

Draw a model and find the percent that is represented by each ratio. If it is not possible to find the exact percent using the model, estimate. 1–10. See Chapter 7 Answer Appendix for models.

1. 4 out of 10 40%
2. 7 out of 10 70%
3. 4 out of 5 80%
4. 2 out of 4 50%
5. 6 out of 20 30%
6. 5 out of 25 20%
7. 8 out of 40 20%
8. 6 out of 24 25%
9. 1 out of 3 33%
10. 4 out of 9 45%

EXPLORE 7-3 Lesson Notes

1 FOCUS

Objective Use a percent model to find a percent or a part.

Materials

- grid paper

Easy to Make Manipulatives

Teaching Pre-Algebra with Manipulatives, template for:

- grid paper, p. 1

Teaching Tip

Have students draw the percent model on the far right-hand side of the page. Then they can reuse the model by folding the grid paper over the left-hand numbers.

2 TEACH

Activity 1

Ask one student to demonstrate Steps 1 and 2 on the board. Encourage students to discuss any questions they may have concerning this model.

Practice Have students complete Exercises 1–10.

Activity 2

Ask one student to demonstrate Steps 1 and 2 on the board. Encourage students to discuss any questions they may have concerning this model.

Have students discuss how to arrive at the percent model on the far right-hand side of the page.

Ask:

- What is 30% of 20? 6
- Which side of the model needs to change when the amount of the whole changes? The scale on the left side of the model.

Practice Have students complete Exercises 11–21.

ASSESS

Formative Assessment

Use Exercises 1–10 to assess whether students comprehend how to write the ratio of two numbers as a percent.

Use Exercises 11–21 to assess whether students comprehend how to find the part that is represented by a percent.

From Concrete to Abstract Have students find the percent represented by the ratio of 4 out of 12. Also have students find the amount that is 35% of 80.

ACTIVITY 2 **Finding a Percent**

Suppose a store advertises a sale in which all merchandise is 30% off its price. If the price of a cell phone case is $20, how much will you save?

In this case, you know the percent. You need to find what part of the original price you'll save.

You can find the *part* by using a similar model.

Step 1

Draw a 10-unit by 1-unit rectangle on grid paper. Label the units on the right from 0 to 100 because percent is a ratio that compares a number to 100.

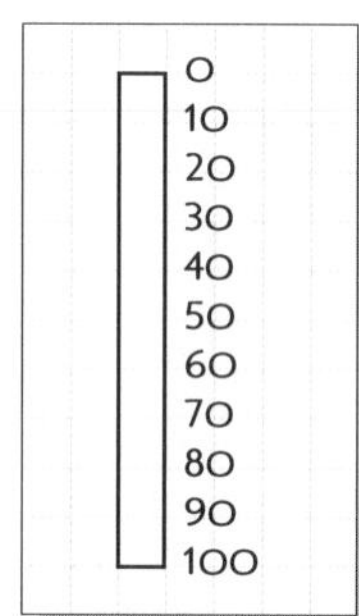

Step 2

On the left side, mark equal units from 0 to 20, because 20 represents the whole quantity.

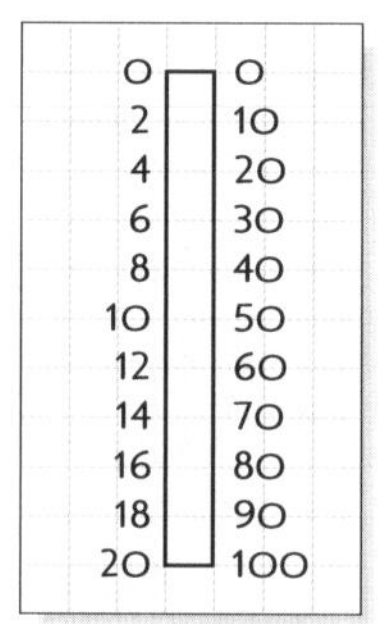

Step 3

Draw a horizontal line from 30% on the right side to the left side of the model. The number on the left side is the part. Label the model as shown.

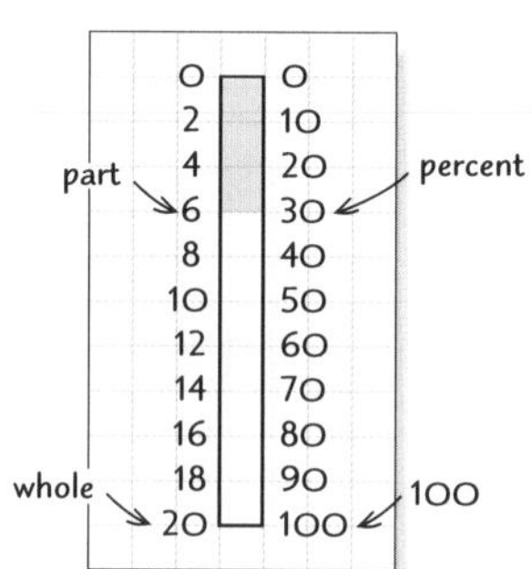

Using the model, you can see that 30% of 20 is 6. So, you will save $6 if you buy the cell phone case.

Exercises

Draw a model and find the part that is represented. If it is not possible to find an exact answer from the model, estimate. 11–20. See Chapter 7 Answer Appendix for models.

11. 20% of 80 16

12. 60% of 15 9

13. 80% of 40 32

14. 30% of 50 15

15. 25% of 50 12.5

16. 75% of 60 45

17. 10% of 150 15

18. 45% of 500 225

19. $33\frac{1}{3}$% of 20 7

20. 90% of 20 18

21. **REASONING** Suppose you know that 60% of some number is 18. Use the model below to find the number x. Explain your reasoning. See Chapter 7 Answer Appendix.

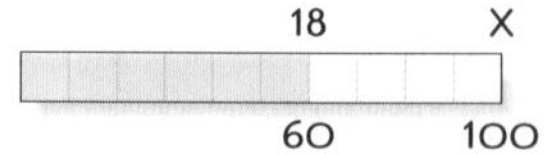

7-3 Using the Percent Proportion

Then
You have already used models to find percents. (Explore 7-3)

Now
- Use the percent proportion to solve problems.
- Apply the percent proportion to real-world problems.

New Vocabulary
percent proportion

Math Online
glencoe.com
- Extra Examples
- Personal Tutor
- Self-Check Quiz
- Homework Help

Why?

A recipe for strawberry lemonade is shown.

a. Write a ratio that compares the number of cups of water to the total number of cups in the recipe. **6 to 12**

b. Write the ratio as a fraction in simplest form and as a percent. $\frac{1}{2}$; **50%**

Strawberry Lemonade
2 cups sugar
1 cup lemon juice
6 cups water
3 cups strawberries

The Percent Proportion From previous lessons, you know that 6 out of 12 is 50%. These numbers form a percent proportion. In a **percent proportion**, one ratio compares *part* of a quantity to the *whole* quantity. The other ratio is the equivalent percent written as a fraction with a denominator of 100.

Key Concept — Percent Proportion (For Your FOLDABLE)

Words $\frac{\text{part}}{\text{whole}} = \frac{\text{percent}}{100}$

Symbols $\frac{a}{b} = \frac{p}{100}$, where a is the part, b is the whole and p is the percent written as a fraction.

EXAMPLE 1 Find the Percent

Twelve is what percent of 32?

Twelve is being compared to 32. So, 12 is the part and 32 is the whole.

Words	Twelve is what percent of 32?
Variable	Let p represent the percent.
Proportion	part → $\frac{12}{32} = \frac{p}{100}$ } percent; whole → 32

$\frac{12}{32} = \frac{p}{100}$ **Write the percent proportion.**

$12 \cdot 100 = 32 \cdot p$ **Find the cross products.**

$1200 = 32p$ **Multiply.**

$\frac{1200}{32} = \frac{32p}{32}$ **Divide each side by 32.**

$37.5 = p$ **Simplify.**

So, 12 is 37.5% of 32.

Check Your Progress

1A. Fifteen is what percent of 20? **75%** **1B.** What percent of 5 is 12? **240%**

Personal Tutor glencoe.com

7-3 Lesson Notes

1 FOCUS

Vertical Alignment

Before Lesson 7-3
Use models to find percents.

Lesson 7-3
Use the percent proportion to solve problems and apply the percent proportion to real-world problems.

After Lesson 7-3
Use appropriate operations to solve problems involving rational numbers in problem situations.

2 TEACH

Scaffolding Questions

Have students read the *Why?* section of the lesson and answer the questions.

Ask:
- What does the first number in the ratio represent? cups of water
- What does the second number in the ratio represent? total number of cups in the recipe
- What ratio represents the strawberries to the total number of cups? $\frac{3}{12}$

Lesson 7-3 Resources

Resource	Approaching-Level	On-Level	Beyond-Level	English Learners
Teacher Edition	• Differentiated Instruction, p. 346	• Differentiated Instruction, p. 346	• Differentiated Instruction, p. 350	
Chapter Resource Masters	• Lesson Reading Guide, pp. 17–18 • Skills Practice, p. 19 • Practice, p. 20 • Word Problem Practice, p. 21	• Study Guide and Intervention, pp. 17–18 • Skills Practice, p. 19 • Practice, p. 20 • Word Problem Practice, p. 21 • Enrichment, p. 22	• Practice, p. 20 • Word Problem Practice, p. 21 • Enrichment, p. 22	• Study Guide and Intervention, pp. 17–18 • Skills Practice, p. 19 • Practice, p. 20
Transparencies	• 5-Minute Check Transparency 7-3	• 5-Minute Check Transparency 7-3	• 5-Minute Check Transparency 7-3	• 5-Minute Check Transparency 7-3
Other	• Study Notebook • Teaching Pre-Algebra with Manipulatives	• Study Notebook • Teaching Pre-Algebra with Manipulatives	• Study Notebook	• Study Notebook • Teaching Pre-Algebra with Manipulatives

Use the Percent Proportion

Example 1 shows how to find the percent of a number. **Example 2** shows how to find the part from a percent using the percent proportion. **Example 3** shows how to find the base or whole from a percent using the percent proportion. **Example 4** shows how to apply the percent proportion to solve a real-world problem.

Formative Assessment

Use the Check Your Progress exercises after each example to determine students' understanding of concepts.

Additional Examples

1. Twenty is what percent of 25? 80%
2. What number is 8.8% of 20? 1.76
3. Seventy is 28% of what number? 250

Additional Examples also in Interactive Classroom PowerPoint® Presentations

IWB INTERACTIVE WHITEBOARD READY

Focus on Mathematical Content

Percent Proportion In a fraction the *whole* is the denominator and the *part* is the numerator. (Note that the whole is sometimes referred to as the *base*.) Percent proportions are the same. The whole or base is on the bottom and the part that is being compared to the base is on top. Therefore the 100, which is the whole, is always in the denominator in a percent proportion.

StudyTip

Check for Reasonableness Ten percent of 450 is 45. So, the answer should be more than 45.

EXAMPLE 2 Find the Part

What number is 15.5% of 450?

The percent is 15.5, and the base is 450. Let a represent the part.

$\frac{a}{450} = \frac{15.5}{100}$ **Write the percent proportion.**

$a \cdot 100 = 450 \cdot 15.5$ **Find the cross products.**

$100a = 6975$ **Multiply.**

$a = 69.75$ **Mentally divide each side by 100.**

So, 69.75 is 15.5% of 450.

Check Your Progress

2A. What number is 11.4% of 330? **37.62**

2B. Find 15.3% of 425. **65.025**

Personal Tutor glencoe.com

StudyTip

Whole In percent problems, the whole usually follows the word *of.*

EXAMPLE 3 Find the Whole

Seventy-eight is 60% of what number?

The percent is 60%, and the part is 78. Let b represent the whole.

$\frac{78}{b} = \frac{60}{100}$ **Write the percent proportion.**

$78 \cdot 100 = b \cdot 60$ **Find the cross products.**

$7800b = 60b$ **Multiply.**

$\frac{7800}{60} = \frac{60b}{60}$ **Divide each side by 60.**

$130 = b$ **Simplify.**

So, 78 is 60% of 130.

Check Your Progress

3A. Thirty percent of what number is 63? **210**

3B. Forty-five is 3% of what number? **1500**

Personal Tutor glencoe.com

Concept Summary: Types of Percent Problems

For Your FOLDABLE

Type	Example	Proportion
Find the Percent	1 is what percent of 5? or What percent of 5 is 1?	$\frac{1}{5} = \frac{p}{100}$
Find the Part	What number is 20% of 5?	$\frac{a}{5} = \frac{20}{100}$
Find the Whole	1 is 20% of what number?	$\frac{1}{b} = \frac{20}{100}$

Differentiated Instruction

AL OL

If some students are visual learners,

Then have them make and fill in a table to aid them in writing a proportion. For example, to find 90% of 15, the table would look like this:

	actual numbers	percent numbers
part	(unknown)	90
whole	15	100

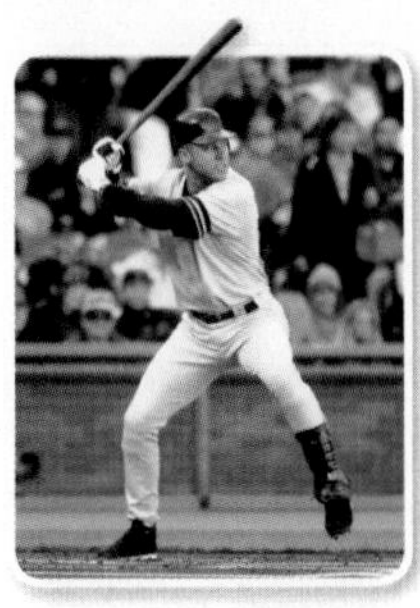

Real-World Link

Derek Jeter's career batting average through the 2007 season was 0.317. This ranks him with the 5th highest lifetime batting average of all active baseball players.

Source: MLB

Real-World EXAMPLE 4 Apply the Percent Proportion

BASEBALL The table shows the batting statistics for one season for Derek Jeter of the New York Yankees. If he had 639 at bats, what percent of his at bats were singles?

Stat	Number
single	151
double	39
triple	4
home run	12
walk	56
strikeout	100

Compare the number of singles, 151, to the total number of at bats, 639. Let p represent the percent.

$\frac{151}{639} = \frac{p}{100}$ **Write the percent proportion.**

$151 \cdot 100 = 639 \cdot p$ **Find the cross products.**

$15{,}100 = 639p$ **Simplify.**

$\frac{15{,}100}{639} = \frac{639p}{639}$ **Divide each side by 639.**

$23.6 \approx p$ **Simplify.**

So, about 23.6% of time Derek's at bats were singles.

Check Your Progress

4. **BASEBALL** What percent of his at bats were strikeouts? 15.6%

Personal Tutor glencoe.com

Check Your Understanding

Examples 1–3 pp. 345–346

Use the percent proportion to solve each problem.

1. 18 is what percent of 72? 25%
2. What percent of 8 is 20? 250%
3. What is 74% of 56? 41.44
4. 9 is 20% of what number? 45
5. What percent of 2 is 8? 400%
6. Find 6% of 300. 18

Example 4 p. 347

7. **TEST SCORES** Of the 120 math tests, 47 were Bs. What percent of the math tests were Bs? 39%

Practice and Problem Solving

 = **Step-by-Step Solutions** begin on page R11. **Extra Practice** begins on page 810.

Examples 1–3 pp. 345–346

Use the percent proportion to solve each problem.

8. 16 is what percent of 64? 25%
9. 21 is what percent of 50? 42%
10. What percent of 145 is 52.2? 36%
11. What percent of 36 is 19.8? 55%
12. What is 60% of 120? 72
13. What is 80% of 125? 100
14. Find 65% of 440. 286
15. Find 83% of 200. 166
16. 12 is 40% of what number? 30
17. 34 is 20% of what number? 170
18. 80% of what number is 12? 15
19. 4% of what number is 15? 375

Example 4 p. 347

20. **DOGS** Sixteen of the 80 dogs at a kennel are golden retrievers. What percent of the dogs at the kennel are golden retrievers? 20%

21. **FLAVORS** The number of lime-flavored gumballs in a gumball machine is 85. If this is 17% of the number of gumballs in the machine, how many gumballs are in the machine? 500 gumballs

Additional Example

4 **TENNIS** From 1999 to 2007, 9 years, Serena Williams won both the U.S. Open and Wimbledon twice. In what percent of both tournaments combined during those years was Serena Williams the women's champion? Round to the nearest tenth. 22.2%

TEACH with TECH

DOCUMENT CAMERA Have a student share his or her work setting up and using the percent proportion. Take pictures of the work and distribute them to the class or post on the classroom Web site.

3 PRACTICE

Formative Assessment

Use Exercises 1–7 to check for understanding.

Use the chart at the bottom of this page to customize assignments for your students.

Differentiated Homework Options

Level	Assignment	Two-Day Option	
AL Basic	8–21, 36, 38, 40–62	9–21 odd, 43–46	8–20 even, 36, 38, 40–42, 47–62
OL Core	9–21 odd, 22–27, 29, 31, 33–36, 38, 40–62	8–21, 43–46	22–36, 38, 40–42, 47–62
BL Advanced	22–58 (optional: 59–62)		

Checking Make sure students write their solutions clearly and verify that their solution is reasonable by rereading the question.

Additional Answers

40. Bethany; Mei set up her proportion incorrectly. She placed the whole over the part.

41. Always; Sample answer: To solve for x % of y, find $\frac{x}{100} = \frac{n}{y}$. So, $n = \frac{xy}{100}$. To solve for y % of x, find $\frac{y}{100} = \frac{n}{x}$. So, $n = \frac{xy}{100}$.

42. Sample answer: His answer is not reasonable because 125% > 100% and 100% of 47 is 47. So, 125% must be greater than 47 and 5.9 < 47.

22. **RESEARCH** Use the Internet or another source to find the percent of states that begin with *A*, *I*, *O*, or *U*. **24%**

23. **SURVEYS** Use the circle graph that shows the results of a survey about New Year's Resolutions.

 a. Determine about how many of the 2947 people surveyed said their most important New Year's resolution was to get organized. **973 people**

 b. About how many said their most important New Year's resolution was to do more reading or to declutter? **766 people**

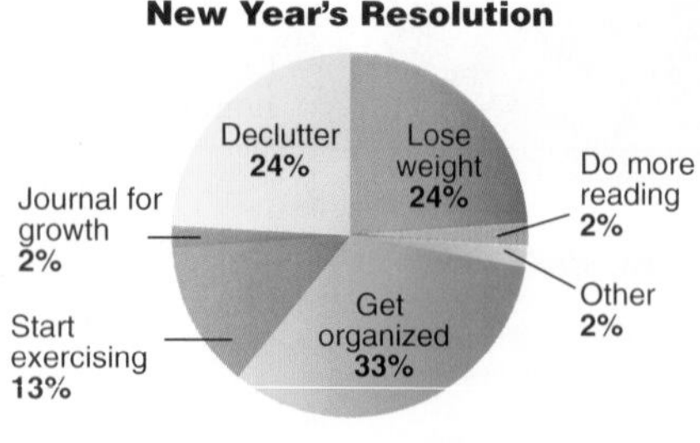

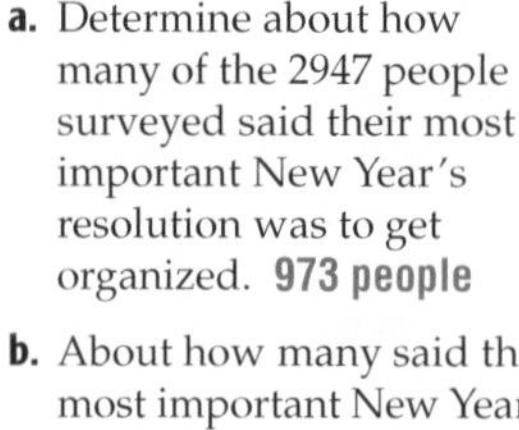

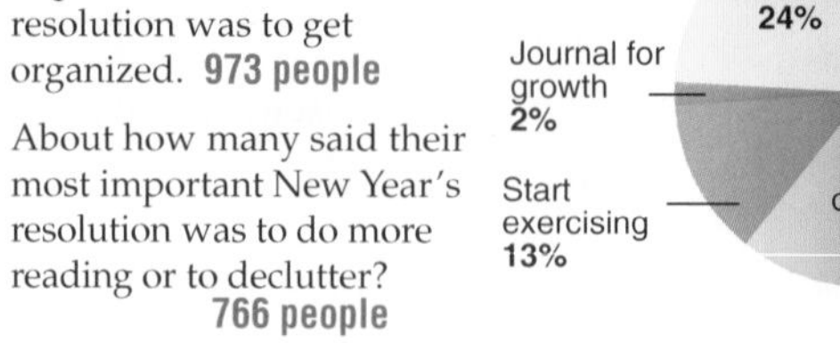

24. **FINANCIAL LITERACY** Accessories Central is having a summer clearance on sunglasses. Maria wants to buy a pair of sunglasses that cost \$48 with a 65% discount. The same pair of sunglasses costs \$38 with a 55% discount at Shades Inc. Which store has the better price for the pair of sunglasses? Explain your reasoning. **Accessories Central; The sunglasses cost \$16.80 at Accessories Central and \$17.10 at Shades Inc. So, \$16.80 < \$17.10.**

25. **PATTERNS** A pattern of equations is shown.

$$2\% \text{ of } 100 = 2$$
$$4\% \text{ of } 50 = 2$$
$$8\% \text{ of } 25 = 2$$
$$16\% \text{ of } 12.5 = 2$$

 a. Describe the pattern. **a. The percent is increased by a factor of 2 and the whole is halved. Each answer is 2.**

 b. Find the next equation in the pattern. **32% of 6.25 = 2**

Real-World Link

An online survey showed that 47% of the 15- to 25-year-olds surveyed voted education as their top concern.

26. **SOCIAL STUDIES** The bar graph shows the results of an online survey of 1242 people aged 15–25 about their political involvement over the last 12 months.

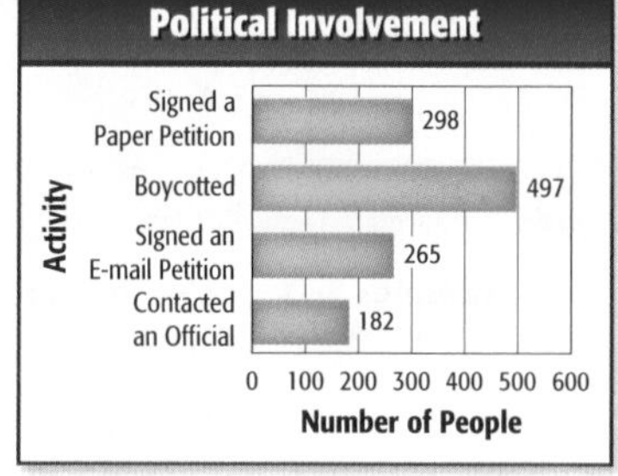

 a. What percent of the people boycotted? Round to the nearest percent. **40%**

 b. Of the people who signed an e-mail petition, 20% were 18 years old. How many 18 year-olds signed an e-mail petition? **53 18 year-olds**

 c. Based on the results of the survey, predict about how many people out of 2000 would contact an official. **293 people**

Watch Out!

Wholes The whole is not always the larger number.

Use the percent proportion to solve each problem. Round to the nearest tenth if necessary.

27. 45 is what percent of 15? **300%**
28. 13 is 25% of what number? **52**
29. What is 58% of 7? **4.1**
30. 8 is what percent of 2000? **0.4%**
31. What is 0.6% of 360? **2.2**
32. 41 is $5\frac{1}{3}$ % of what number? **768.8**

348 Chapter 7 Percent

Real-World Link

The free-throw line in basketball is 2 inches wide, 12 feet long, and 15 feet from the backboard.

Source: NBA

33. BASKETBALL A professional basketball player made 465 out of 520 free throws in one season. The next season the player made 386 out of 437. For both seasons combined, what percent of free throws did the player make? Round to the nearest tenth, if necessary. **88.9%**

34. TALENT SHOWS The table shows the results of a student survey at Crestview Middle School.

Favorite Type of Talent Show Act	
Act	**Number of Students**
stand-up comedy	198
singing	150
dancing	212
playing instruments	80

a. What percent of the students surveyed said their favorite act was playing instruments? **12.5%**

b. If 10 more students vote for stand-up comedy, will the percent be greater than, less than, or equal to the current percent? Explain. **greater than; The new percent would be 32% which is greater than the original percent of 30.9%.**

35. CELL PHONES A cell phone store has 120 cell phones in stock. Of these, 45 have keyboards. The manager of the store wants to add more cell phones with keyboards so that 40% of the stock has keyboards.

a. Write and solve a proportion to find the number of cell phones with keyboards that should be added to the store's inventory.

b. What will be the total number of cell phones in stock? **125 cell phones**

a. $\frac{45 + x}{120 + x} = \frac{40}{100}$; **5 cell phones**

H.O.T. Problems Use Higher-Order Thinking Skills

36. OPEN ENDED Write and solve a real-world problem involving percents.

37. CHALLENGE Without calculating, arrange the following from least to greatest value. Justify your reasoning.

25% of 160, 5% of 80, 25% of 80

38. REASONING Sabrina spelled 82% of her spelling words correctly on her spelling tests this year. If she spells 13 out of 15 words correctly on her next test, will this help or hurt her average? Explain.

39. CHALLENGE Find the value of y so that $y\% = \frac{3y + 9}{600}$. **3**

40. FIND THE ERROR Bethany and Mei are finding what percent of 32 is 18. Is either of them correct? Explain your reasoning. **40–42. See margin.**

Bethany	Mei
$\frac{18}{32} = \frac{x}{100}$	$\frac{32}{18} = \frac{x}{100}$
$x \approx 56$	$x \approx 178$
So, 32 is about 56% of 18.	So, 32 is about 178% of 18.

41. REASONING Is x% of y and y% of x *always*, *sometimes*, or *never* equivalent? Explain your reasoning.

42. WRITING IN MATH Kenji states that 5.9 is 125% of 47. Is his answer reasonable? Explain your reasoning.

36. Sample answer: A girl scout sold 108 boxes of cookies. Of the boxes sold, 27 were peanut butter cookies. What percent of the cookies sold were peanut butter? 25% C

37. 5% of 80, 25% of 80, 25% of 160; If the percent is the same but the whole is bigger, then the part is greater. If the whole is the same but the percent is greater, then the part is greater.

38. Sample answer: This will help her average because $\frac{13}{15} \approx 87\%$ and $87\% > 82\%$.

Watch Out!

Find the Error For Exercise 40, ask students to underline the part and circle the whole. part = 18, whole = 32

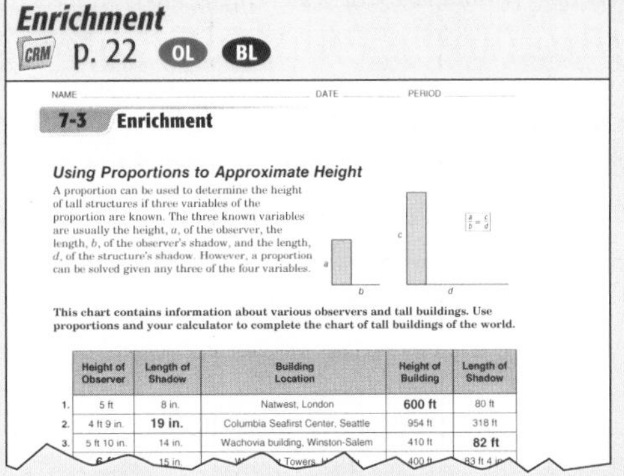

Enrichment CRM p. 22 OL BL

7-3 Enrichment

Using Proportions to Approximate Height

A proportion can be used to determine the height of tall structures if three variables of the proportion are known. The three known variables are usually the height, a, of the observer, the length, b, of the observer's shadow, and the length, d, of the structure's shadow. However, a proportion can be solved given any three of the four variables.

This chart contains information about various observers and tall buildings. Use proportions and your calculator to complete the chart of tall buildings of the world.

	Height of Observer	Length of Shadow	Building Location	Height of Building	Length of Shadow
1.	5 ft	8 in.	Natwest, London	600 ft	80 ft
2.	4 ft 9 in.	19 in.	Columbia Seafirst Center, Seattle	954 ft	318 ft
3.	5 ft 10 in.	14 in.	Wachovia building, Winston-Salem	410 ft	82 ft

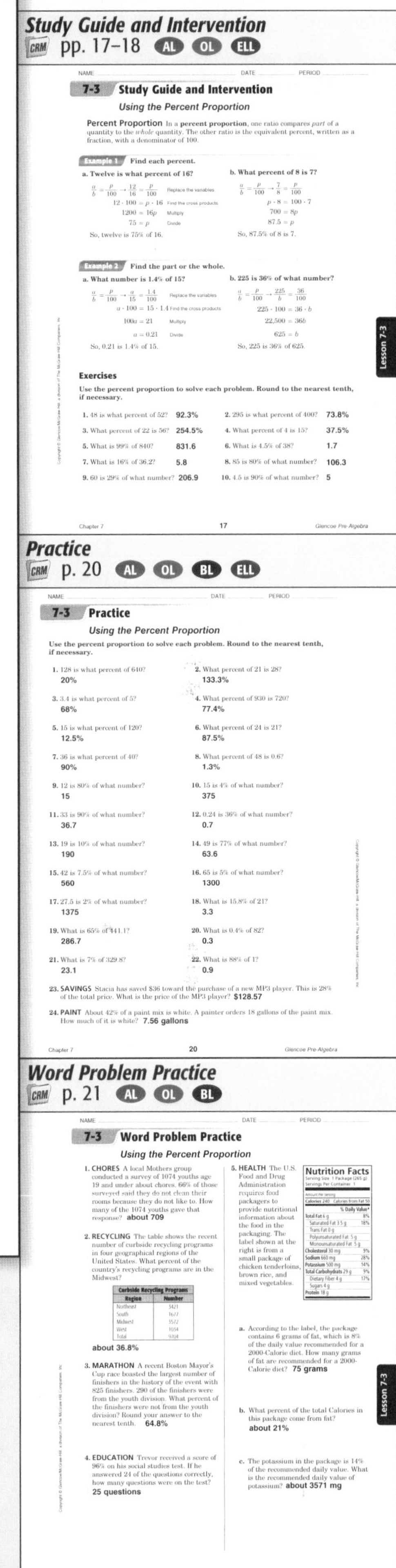

Study Guide and Intervention CRM pp. 17–18 AL OL ELL

7-3 Study Guide and Intervention

Using the Percent Proportion

Percent Proportion In a percent proportion, one ratio compares part of a quantity to the whole quantity. The other ratio is the equivalent percent, written as a fraction, with a denominator of 100.

Example 1 Find each percent.

a. Twelve is what percent of 16? So, twelve is 75% of 16.

b. What percent of 8 is 7? So, 87.5% of 8 is 7.

Example 2 Find the part or the whole.

a. What number is 1.4% of 15? So, 0.21 is 1.4% of 15.

b. 225 is 36% of what number? So, 225 is 36% of 625.

Exercises

Use the percent proportion to solve each problem. Round to the nearest tenth, if necessary.

1. 48 is what percent of 52? 92.3%
2. 295 is what percent of 400? 73.8%
3. What percent of 22 is 56? 254.5%
4. What percent of 4 is 15? 37.5%
5. What is 99% of 840? 831.6
6. What is 4.5% of 38? 1.7
7. What is 16% of 36.2? 5.8
8. 85 is 80% of what number? 106.3
9. 60 is 29% of what number? 206.9
10. 4.5 is 90% of what number? 5

Practice CRM p. 20 AL OL BL ELL

7-3 Practice

Using the Percent Proportion

Use the percent proportion to solve each problem. Round to the nearest tenth, if necessary.

1. 128 is what percent of 640? 20%
2. What percent of 21 is 28? 133.3%
3. 3.4 is what percent of 5? 68%
4. What percent of 930 is 720? 77.4%
5. 15 is what percent of 120? 12.5%
6. What percent of 24 is 21? 87.5%
7. 36 is what percent of 40? 90%
8. What percent of 48 is 0.6? 1.3%
9. 12 is 80% of what number? 15
10. 15 is 4% of what number? 375
11. 33 is 90% of what number? 36.7
12. 0.24 is 36% of what number? 0.7
13. 19 is 10% of what number? 190
14. 49 is 77% of what number? 63.6
15. 42 is 7.5% of what number? 560
16. 65 is 5% of what number? 1300
17. 27.5 is 2% of what number? 1375
18. What is 15.8% of 21? 3.3
19. What is 65% of 441.1? 286.7
20. What is 0.4% of 82? 0.3
21. What is 7% of 329.8? 23.1
22. What is 88% of 1? 0.9
23. SAVINGS Stacia has saved $36 toward the purchase of a new MP3 player. This is 28% of the total price. What is the price of the MP3 player? $128.57
24. PAINT About 42% of a paint mix is white. A painter orders 18 gallons of the paint mix. How much of it is white? 7.56 gallons

Word Problem Practice CRM p. 21 AL OL BL

7-3 Word Problem Practice

Using the Percent Proportion

1. CHORES A local Mothers group conducted a survey of 1074 youths age 19 and under about chores. 66% of those surveyed said they do not clean their rooms because they do not like to. How many of the 1074 youths gave that response? about 709
2. RECYCLING The table shows the recent number of curbside recycling programs in four geographical regions of the United States. What percent of the country's recycling programs are in the Midwest? about 36.8%
3. MARATHON A recent Boston Mayor's Cup race boasted the largest number of finishers in the history of the event with 825 finishers. 290 of the finishers were from the youth division. What percent of the finishers were not from the youth division? Round your answer to the nearest tenth. 64.8%
4. EDUCATION Trevor received a score of 96% on his social studies test. If he answered 24 of the questions correctly, how many questions were on the test? 25 questions
5. HEALTH The U.S. Food and Drug Administration requires food packagers to provide nutritional information about the food in the packaging. The label shown at the right is from a small package of chicken tenderloins, brown rice, and mixed vegetables.

a. According to the label, the package contains 6 grams of fat, which is 8% of the daily value recommended for a 2000-Calorie diet. How many grams of fat are recommended for a 2000-Calorie diet? 75 grams

b. What percent of the total Calories in this package come from fat? about 21%

c. The potassium in the package is 14% of the recommended daily value. What is the recommended daily value of potassium? about 3571 mg

4 ASSESS

Crystal Ball Have students write a sentence on how they think today's lesson on the percent proportion will help them with tomorrow's lesson on finding percent of a number mentally.

Standardized Test Practice

43. The table shows the results of a survey of middle school students about their favorite school mascots. **C**

Mascot	Number of Students
Falcon	60
Stallion	123
Ram	86
Tiger	131

Based on the data, predict how many out of 2000 students would vote for the falcon.

A 600   C 300
B 400   D 200

44. If 40% of a number is 32, what is 35% of the number? **J**

F 8   H 24
G 20   J 28

45. A place kicker expects to make 75% of his field goal attempts this season. If he attempts 36 field goals this season, which of the following statements does *not* represent the place kicker's expectation? **C**

A The place kicker will make 27 field goals.
B The place kicker will miss 9 field goals.
C Less than $\frac{1}{4}$ of the field goal attempts will be missed.
D The place kicker will make more than $\frac{1}{2}$ of his field goal attempts.

46. SHORT RESPONSE If 68 is 25% of a number, what is 600% of the number? **1632**

Spiral Review

47. MEDIA In a survey, 35% of those surveyed said that they get the news from their local television station while three-fifths said that they get the news from a daily newspaper. From which source do more people get their news? (Lesson 7-2) **daily newspaper**

Write each percent as a fraction in simplest form. (Lesson 7-1)

48. 45% $\frac{9}{20}$ **49.** 120% $1\frac{1}{5}$ **50.** 0.5% $\frac{1}{200}$ **51.** $83\frac{1}{3}\%$ $\frac{5}{6}$

52. INSECTS In a drawing of a honeybee, the bee is 4.8 centimeters long. The actual size of the honeybee is 1.2 centimeters. What is the scale of the drawing? (Lesson 5-6) **1 cm = 0.25 cm**

Find each sum or difference. Write in simplest form. (Lesson 3-5)

53. $\frac{17}{18} - \frac{5}{18}$ $\frac{2}{3}$ **54.** $\frac{3}{10} + \frac{7}{10}$ 1   **55.** $\frac{1}{2} - \frac{4}{5}$ $-\frac{3}{10}$

56. $\frac{7}{15} + \frac{1}{6}$ $\frac{19}{30}$ **57.** $\frac{3}{4} - \frac{4}{9}$ $\frac{11}{36}$ **58.** $\frac{1}{2} - \frac{7}{8}$ $-\frac{3}{8}$

Skills Review

Find each product. (Lesson 3-3)

59. $\frac{1}{4} \times 12$ 3   **60.** $\frac{3}{4} \times 24$ 18   **61.** $38 \times \frac{1}{2}$ 19   **62.** $15 \times \frac{1}{3}$ 5

Differentiated Instruction

Extension Have students research their favorite sports team's number of wins and games played. Calculate the percent of wins to predict the outcome of their season. *Hint:* If the team's play performance continues, what is their expected record?

350 Chapter 7 Percent

7-4 Find Percent of a Number Mentally

Then

You have already found percents using the percent proportion. (Lesson 7-3)

Now

- Compute mentally with percents.
- Estimate with percents.

Math Online

glencoe.com

- Extra Examples
- Personal Tutor
- Self-Check Quiz
- Homework Help

Why?

The table shows the final standing of the first, second, and third place finishers in a recent Women's World Cup soccer tournament.

Team	Number of Wins
Germany	5
United States	4
Norway	3

a. If the team from Norway won 50% of their games, use mental math to find the total number of games they played. $3 \div \frac{1}{2} = 6$ games

b. If the team from Germany scored 2 goals in 40% of their winning games, use mental math to find the number of winning games in which they scored 2 goals. $\frac{2}{5} \times 5 = 2$ games

Find Percent of a Number Mentally When you compute with common percents like 40% or 50%, it may be easier to use the fraction form of the percent. The number line shows some common percent-fraction equivalents.

0%	12.5%	25%	40%	50%	$66\frac{2}{3}$%	75%	87.5%	100%
0	$\frac{1}{8}$	$\frac{1}{4}$	$\frac{2}{5}$	$\frac{1}{2}$	$\frac{2}{3}$	$\frac{3}{4}$	$\frac{7}{8}$	1

Concept Summary — Percent-Fraction Equivalents (For Your FOLDABLE)

$25\% = \frac{1}{4}$	$20\% = \frac{1}{5}$	$10\% = \frac{1}{10}$	$12\frac{1}{2}\% = \frac{1}{8}$	$16\frac{2}{3}\% = \frac{1}{6}$
$50\% = \frac{1}{2}$	$40\% = \frac{2}{5}$	$30\% = \frac{3}{10}$	$37\frac{1}{2}\% = \frac{3}{8}$	$33\frac{1}{3}\% = \frac{1}{3}$
$75\% = \frac{3}{4}$	$60\% = \frac{3}{5}$	$70\% = \frac{7}{10}$	$62\frac{1}{2}\% = \frac{5}{8}$	$66\frac{2}{3}\% = \frac{2}{3}$
$100\% = \frac{1}{1}$	$80\% = \frac{4}{5}$	$90\% = \frac{9}{10}$	$87\frac{1}{2}\% = \frac{7}{8}$	$83\frac{1}{3}\% = \frac{5}{6}$

EXAMPLE 1 Use a Fraction to Compute Mentally

Find the percent of each number mentally.

a. 75% of 24

75% of $24 = \frac{3}{4}$ of 24 — THINK $75\% = \frac{3}{4}$

$= 18$ — THINK $\frac{3}{4}$ of 24 is 18.

b. 80% of 60

80% of $60 = \frac{4}{5}$ of 60 — THINK $80\% = \frac{4}{5}$

$= 48$ — THINK $\frac{4}{5}$ of 60 is 48.

Check Your Progress

1A. 40% of 50 20 **1B.** 30% of 70 21

Personal Tutor glencoe.com

7-4 Lesson Notes

1 FOCUS

Vertical Alignment

Before Lesson 7-4
Find percents using the percent proportion.

Lesson 7-4
Compute mentally with percents. Estimate with percents.

After Lesson 7-4
Use mental math with percents to estimate the reasonableness of a solution.

2 TEACH

Scaffolding Questions

Have students read the *Why?* section of the lesson and answer the questions.

Ask:

- How many games did Norway win? 3
- What is 50% as a fraction? $\frac{1}{2}$
- Three is half of what number? 6

Lesson 7-4 Resources

Resource	Approaching-Level	On-Level	Beyond-Level	English Learners
Teacher Edition	• Differentiated Instruction, p. 352	• Differentiated Instruction, p. 352	• Differentiated Instruction, p. 355	• Differentiated Instruction, p. 352
Chapter Resource Masters	• Study Guide and Intervention, pp. 23–24 • Skills Practice, p. 25 • Practice, p. 26 • Word Problem Practice, p. 27	• Study Guide and Intervention, pp. 23–24 • Skills Practice, p. 25 • Practice, p. 26 • Word Problem Practice, p. 27 • Enrichment, p. 28	• Practice, p. 26 • Word Problem Practice, p. 27 • Enrichment, p. 28	• Study Guide and Intervention, pp. 23–24 • Skills Practice, p. 25 • Practice, p. 26
Transparencies	• 5-Minute Check Transparency 7-4	• 5-Minute Check Transparency 7-4	• 5-Minute Check Transparency 7-4	• 5-Minute Check Transparency 7-4
Other	• Study Notebook • Teaching Pre-Algebra with Manipulatives	• Study Notebook • Teaching Pre-Algebra with Manipulatives	• Study Notebook	• Study Notebook • Teaching Pre-Algebra with Manipulatives

Find Percents of a Number Mentally

Examples 1–3 show how to find the percent of a number mentally.

Formative Assessment

Use the Check Your Progress exercises after each example to determine students' understanding of concepts.

Additional Examples

1 Find the percent of each number mentally.

a. 50% of 46 23

b. 70% of 110 77

2 Compute mentally.

a. 10% of 54 5.4

b. 1% of 219 2.19

3 **SHOPPING** Garrett is shopping for a new video game. The original price of the game is $60.00. The game is 10% off. How much will Garrett save? $6.00

Additional Examples also in Interactive Classroom PowerPoint® Presentations

IWB INTERACTIVE WHITEBOARD READY

Estimate with Percents

Example 4 shows how to estimate a percent of a number. **Example 5** shows how to estimate a percent mentally in order to solve a real-world problem.

Additional Example

4 Estimate.

a. 22% of 494 $\approx 100; \frac{1}{5} \cdot 500$ or 100

b. $\frac{1}{4}$% of 1219 3; $\frac{1}{4}\% = \frac{1}{4} \cdot$ 1%. 1% of 1200 is 12. $\frac{12}{4} = 3$

c. 49% of 61 30; $\frac{1}{2} \cdot 60$ or 30

d. 155% of 38 62; 100% of 40 = 40; 55% of 40 is 22, 40 + 22 = 62

EXAMPLE 2 Use Decimals to Compute Mentally

Compute mentally.

a. **10% of 76**

10% of 76 = 0.1 • 76 or 7.6

b. **1% of 122**

1% of 122 = 0.01 • 122 or 1.22

Check Your Progress

2A. 10% of 42 **4.2**

2B. 1% of 264 **2.64**

Personal Tutor glencoe.com

Real-World EXAMPLE 3 Compute Mentally

SALES **Hannah is shopping for school clothes. She has a coupon that will give her 20% off her entire purchase. If the items she buys cost $110 originally, how much will she save with her coupon?**

You need to find 20% of the total cost. First, find 10% of 110.

10% of 110 = 0.1 • 11.0 **Move the decimal point one place to the left.**

= 11

20% is the same as 2 • 10%.

2 • 10% = 2 • 11 or 22 **Replace 10% with 11.**

So, Hannah will save $22 on her purchase.

Real-World Link

Every year nearly 300 billion coupons are distributed nationwide. About 90% of these coupons are distributed in Sunday newspapers.

Source: CMS, Inc.

Check Your Progress

3. **SALES** A television that costs $750 is on sale for 15% off. What is the total discount on the television? **$112.50**

Personal Tutor glencoe.com

Estimate With Percents You can estimate when an exact answer is not needed.

Problem-Solving Tip

Determine Reasonable Answers Deciding whether an answer is reasonable is useful when an exact answer is not necessary.

EXAMPLE 4 Estimate Percent of a Number

Estimate.

a. **26% of 64**

26% is about 25% or $\frac{1}{4}$.

$\frac{1}{4}$ of 64 is 16.

So, 26% of 64 is about 16.

b. $\frac{2}{3}$**% of 891**

$\frac{2}{3}\% = \frac{2}{3} \times 1\%$. 1% of 900 is 9.

891 is almost 900.

So, $\frac{2}{3}$% of 891 is about $\frac{2}{3} \times 9$ or 6.

c. **39% of 81**

39% is about 40% or $\frac{2}{5}$.

81 is about 80.

$\frac{2}{5}$ of 80 is 32.

So, 39% of 81 is about 32.

d. **120% of 51**

100% of 50 is 50.

20% of 50 is 10.

So, 120% of 51 is about 50 + 10 or 60.

Check Your Progress

4A. 92% of 50 **4B.** 63% of 205 **4C.** 75% of 84 **4D.** 130% of 91

Personal Tutor glencoe.com

4A. $\approx 45; \frac{9}{10} \times 50$ or 45

4B. ≈ 126; 1% of 205 is about 2, 63% of 205 is about 63 × 2 or 126

4C. $\approx 63; \frac{3}{4} \times 84$ or 63

4D. ≈ 117; 100% of 90 = 90; 30% of 90 is 27, 90 + 27 = 117

Differentiated Instruction

Verbal/Linguistic Give students one estimation problem at a time. Have them speak their answer as soon as they get it. When students have different estimates, encourage them to compare their strategies and then to explain to the class why the estimates did not match.

Real-World Link

About 3 billion pizzas are sold each year in the United States. The ratio of meat toppings to vegetables toppings preferred by Americans is 31 to 50.

Real-World EXAMPLE 5 Estimate Percent of a Number

PIZZA Mr. Williams ordered 4 pizzas for a birthday party. The cost of the pizzas was $57.96. He wants to tip the delivery person about 15%. What is a reasonable amount for the tip?

Understand You need to find the tip for the delivery person. You know the cost of the pizzas.

Plan Estimate the price of the pizzas. Find 15% of the estimated price.

Solve $57.96 is about $60, and 15% = 10% + 5%.

10% of $60 is $6.00. **Move the decimal point 1 place to the left.**

5% of $60 is $3.00 **5% is one half of 10%.**

So, 15% is about $6.00 + $3.00 or $9.00.

A reasonable amount for the tip is $9.

Check 10% of $58 is $5.80 and 20% of $58 is $11.60.
Since $5.80 < $9 < $11.60, the answer is reasonable. ✓

Check Your Progress

5. **RESTAURANT** Haley went to dinner with her friends. Their bill was $48.61. They want to leave their server a 15% tip. What would be a reasonable amount for the tip? Explain your reasoning.

Personal Tutor glencoe.com

5. $7.50; Sample answer: $48.61 ≈ $50.00, 10% • 50 = 5 and 15% • 50 = 2.50; 5 + 2.50 = 7.50

Check Your Understanding

Examples 1 and 2 pp. 351–352

Find the percent of each number mentally.

1. 75% of 16 12
2. 25% of 32 8
3. 10% of 37 3.7
4. 10% of 115 11.5
5. 1% of 72 0.72
6. 1% of 231 2.31

Example 3 p. 352

7. **HOMEWORK** Jasmine has finished 30% of the exercises on her homework. If there are 40 exercises in all, how many has Jasmine completed? 12 exercises

Example 4 p. 352

Estimate. 8–13. See margin.

8. 11% of 70
9. 53% of 20
10. 40% of 19
11. 87% of 42
12. $\frac{1}{3}$% of 598
13. 110% of 39

Example 5 p. 353

14. **SPORTS** Last basketball season, Carlos made 38% of the baskets he attempted. *At this rate*, about how many baskets will he make if he attempts 30 baskets? 12 baskets

Practice and Problem Solving

= **Step-by-Step Solutions** begin on page R11. **Extra Practice** begins on page 810.

Examples 1 and 2 pp. 351–352

Find the percent of each number mentally.

15. 40% of 80 32
16. 20% of 50 10
17. 25% of 280 70
18. 75% of 96 72
19. $33\frac{1}{3}$% of 27 9
20. $12\frac{1}{2}$% of 48 6
21. $8\frac{1}{3}$% of 72 6
22. $87\frac{1}{2}$% of 32 28
23. 10% of 125 12.5
24. 10% of 259 25.9
25. 1% of 30 0.3
26. 1% of 400 4

Differentiated Homework Options

Level	Assignment	Two-Day Option	
AL Basic	15–41, 45, 47–63	15–41 odd, 48–51	16–40 even, 45, 47, 52–63
OL Core	15–41 odd, 42–45, 47–63	15–41, 48–51	42–45, 47, 52–63
BL Advanced	42–57 (optional: 58–63)		

Focus on Mathematical Content

Finding Percents Mentally Some percents, like 1%, 10%, and 50%, can be figured mentally. More difficult percents can be found using these percents. Ask students to find 10% of 100. 10
Then find 10% of 75. 7.5

Additional Example

5 **MONEY** A restaurant bill totals $21.35. You want to leave a 15% tip. What is a reasonable amount for the tip? $3

3 PRACTICE

Formative Assessment

Use Exercises 1–14 to check for understanding.

Use the chart at the bottom of this page to customize assignments for your students.

Additional Answers

8. 7; 11% is about 10%, $\frac{1}{10} \cdot 70 = 7$
9. 10; 53% is about 50% or $\frac{1}{2}$, $\frac{1}{2} \cdot 20 = 10$
10. 8; 19 is about 20 and 40% is $\frac{2}{5}$, $\frac{2}{5} \cdot 20 = 8$
11. 36; 87% is about 90% or $\frac{9}{10}$, $\frac{9}{10} \cdot 40 = 36$
12. 2; 1% of 598 is about 6, $\frac{1}{3} \cdot 6 = 2$
13. 44; 39 is about 40, 100% of 40 is 40 and 10% of 40 is 4, 40 + 4 = 44

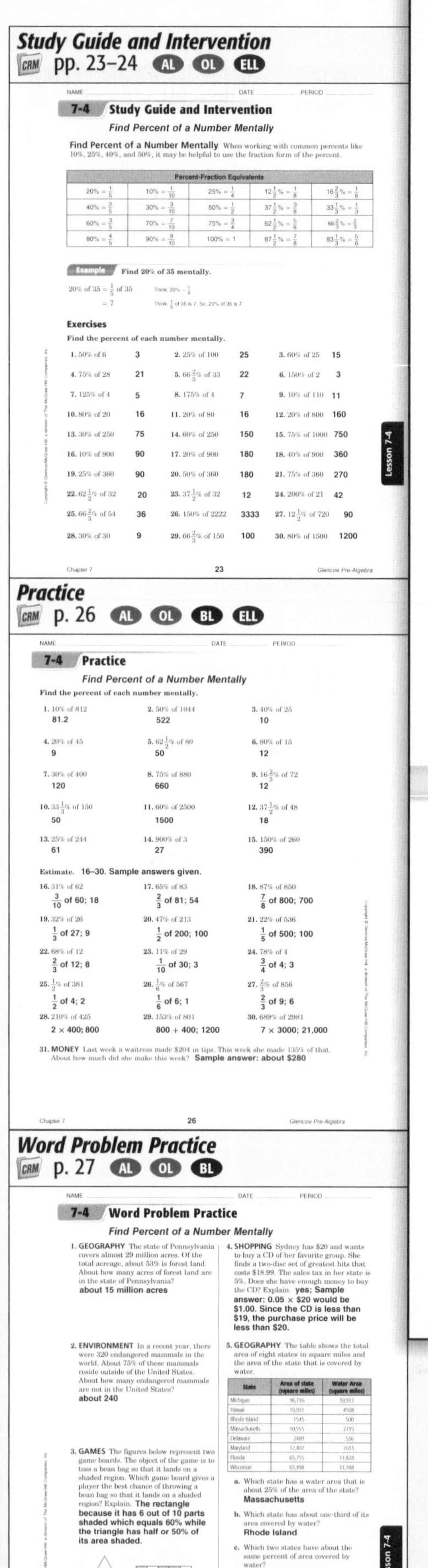
Study Guide and Intervention
CRM pp. 23–24 AL OL ELL

NAME ______ DATE ______ PERIOD ______

7-4 Study Guide and Intervention

Find Percent of a Number Mentally

Find Percent of a Number Mentally When working with common percents like 10%, 25%, 40%, and 50%, it may be helpful to use the fraction form of the percent.

Percent-Fraction Equivalents

$20\% = \frac{1}{5}$	$10\% = \frac{1}{10}$	$25\% = \frac{1}{4}$	$12\frac{1}{2}\% = \frac{1}{8}$	$16\frac{2}{3}\% = \frac{1}{6}$
$40\% = \frac{2}{5}$	$30\% = \frac{3}{10}$	$50\% = \frac{1}{2}$	$37\frac{1}{2}\% = \frac{3}{8}$	$33\frac{1}{3}\% = \frac{1}{3}$
$60\% = \frac{3}{5}$	$70\% = \frac{7}{10}$	$75\% = \frac{3}{4}$	$62\frac{1}{2}\% = \frac{5}{8}$	$66\frac{2}{3}\% = \frac{2}{3}$
$80\% = \frac{4}{5}$	$90\% = \frac{9}{10}$	$100\% = 1$	$87\frac{1}{2}\% = \frac{7}{8}$	$83\frac{1}{3}\% = \frac{5}{6}$

Example Find 20% of 35 mentally.

20% of $35 = \frac{1}{5}$ of 35 Think: $20\% = \frac{1}{5}$

$= 7$ Think: $\frac{1}{5}$ of 35 is 7. So, 20% of 35 is 7.

Exercises

Find the percent of each number mentally.

1. 50% of 6 **3**	2. 25% of 100 **25**	3. 60% of 25 **15**
4. 75% of 28 **21**	5. $66\frac{2}{3}\%$ of 33 **22**	6. 150% of 2 **3**
7. 125% of 4 **5**	8. 175% of 4 **7**	9. 10% of 110 **11**
10. 80% of 20 **16**	11. 20% of 80 **16**	12. 20% of 800 **160**
13. 30% of 250 **75**	14. 60% of 250 **150**	15. 75% of 1000 **750**
16. 10% of 900 **90**	17. 20% of 900 **180**	18. 40% of 900 **360**
19. 25% of 360 **90**	20. 50% of 360 **180**	21. 75% of 360 **270**
22. $62\frac{1}{2}\%$ of 32 **20**	23. $37\frac{1}{2}\%$ of 32 **12**	24. 200% of 21 **42**
25. $66\frac{2}{3}\%$ of 54 **36**	26. 150% of 2222 **3333**	27. $12\frac{1}{2}\%$ of 720 **90**
28. 30% of 30 **9**	29. $66\frac{2}{3}\%$ of 150 **100**	30. 80% of 1500 **1200**

Chapter 7 23 Glencoe Pre-Algebra

Practice
CRM p. 26 AL OL BL ELL

NAME ______ DATE ______ PERIOD ______

7-4 Practice

Find Percent of a Number Mentally

Find the percent of each number mentally.

1. 10% of 812 **81.2**	2. 50% of 1044 **522**	3. 40% of 25 **10**
4. 20% of 45 **9**	5. $62\frac{1}{2}\%$ of 80 **50**	6. 80% of 15 **12**
7. 30% of 400 **120**	8. 75% of 880 **660**	9. $16\frac{2}{3}\%$ of 72 **12**
10. $33\frac{1}{3}\%$ of 150 **50**	11. 60% of 2500 **1500**	12. $37\frac{1}{2}\%$ of 48 **18**
13. 25% of 244 **61**	14. 900% of 3 **27**	15. 150% of 260 **390**

Estimate. **16–30. Sample answers given.**

16. 31% of 62 **$\frac{3}{10}$ of 60; 18**	17. 65% of 83 **$\frac{2}{3}$ of 81; 54**	18. 87% of 850 **$\frac{7}{8}$ of 800; 700**
19. 32% of 26 **$\frac{1}{3}$ of 27; 9**	20. 47% of 213 **$\frac{1}{2}$ of 200; 100**	21. 22% of 536 **$\frac{1}{5}$ of 500; 100**
22. 68% of 12 **$\frac{2}{3}$ of 12; 8**	23. 11% of 29 **$\frac{1}{10}$ of 30; 3**	24. 78% of 4 **$\frac{3}{4}$ of 4; 3**
25. $\frac{1}{2}\%$ of 381 **$\frac{1}{2}$ of 4; 2**	26. $\frac{1}{6}\%$ of 567 **$\frac{1}{6}$ of 6; 1**	27. $\frac{2}{3}\%$ of 856 **$\frac{2}{3}$ of 9; 6**
28. 210% of 425 **2 × 400; 800**	29. 153% of 801 **800 + 400; 1200**	30. 689% of 2981 **7 × 3000; 21,000**

31. MONEY Last week a waitress made $204 in tips. This week she made 135% of that. About how much did she make this week? **Sample answer: about $280**

Chapter 7 26 Glencoe Pre-Algebra

Word Problem Practice
CRM p. 27 AL OL BL

NAME ______ DATE ______ PERIOD ______

7-4 Word Problem Practice

Find Percent of a Number Mentally

1. **GEOGRAPHY** The state of Pennsylvania covers almost 29 million acres. Of the total acreage, about 53% is forest land. About how many acres of forest land are in the state of Pennsylvania? **about 15 million acres**

2. **ENVIRONMENT** In a recent year, there were 320 endangered mammals in the world. About 75% of these mammals reside outside of the United States. About how many endangered mammals are not in the United States? **about 240**

3. **GAMES** The figures below represent two game boards. The object of the game is to toss a bean bag so that it lands on a shaded region. Which game board gives a player the best chance of throwing a bean bag so that it lands on a shaded region? Explain. **The rectangle because it has 6 out of 10 parts shaded which equals 60% while the triangle has half or 50% of its area shaded.**

4. **SHOPPING** Sydney has $20 and wants to buy a CD of her favorite group. She finds a two-disc set of greatest hits that costs $18.99. The sales tax in her state is 5%. Does she have enough money to buy the CD? Explain. **yes; Sample answer: 0.05 × $20 would be $1.00. Since the CD is less than $19, the purchase price will be less than $20.**

5. **GEOGRAPHY** The table shows the total area of eight states in square miles and the area of the state that is covered by water.

State	Area of state (square miles)	Water Area (square miles)
Michigan	96,716	39,912
Hawaii	10,931	4508
Rhode Island	1545	500
Massachusetts	10,555	2715
Delaware	2489	536
Maryland	12,407	2633
Florida	65,755	11,828
Wisconsin	65,498	11,188

a. Which state has a water area that is about 25% of the area of the state? **Massachusetts**

b. Which state has about one-third of its area covered by water? **Rhode Island**

c. Which two states have about the same percent of area covered by water? **About 40% of Michigan and Hawaii are covered by water; about one-sixth or 17% of Florida and Wisconsin are covered by water.**

Chapter 7 27 Glencoe Pre-Algebra

Example 3 p. 352

27. **SALES** A store is having a sale where everything is 15% off. If Jeremy wants to buy items that originally cost $50, how much will he save? **$7.50**

Example 4 p. 352

Estimate. **28–39. See margin.**

28. 16% of 20
29. 73% of 84
30. 46% of 88
31. 25% of 49
32. $\frac{1}{2}\%$ of 507
33. $\frac{1}{6}\%$ of 295
34. 148% of 30
35. 276% of 8
36. $\frac{3}{4}\%$ of 801
37. $\frac{4}{5}\%$ of 30
38. 117% of 50
39. 194% of 15

Example 5 p. 353

40. **FINANCIAL LITERACY** The total cost for Soledad's manicure was $32.99. She wants to give the manicurist a 20% tip. What would be a reasonable amount for the tip? **$6**

41. **INTERNET** In a national survey of 6700 teens, 81% of teens between the ages of 12 and 17 said they use the Internet to e-mail friends or relatives. About how many teens is this? **Sample answer: $\frac{4}{5}$ × 6700 or 5360 teens**

B

42. **MUSIC** The bar graph shows the percent of each age group that owns a portable MP3 player. Suppose there are 825 12–17 year olds in the Louisville School District. About how many of them are likely to own a portable digital music player? **Sample answer: about 330 students**

Portable MP3 Ownership

Percent: 0%, 5%, 10%, 15%, 20%, 25%, 30%, 35%, 40%, 45%

Age Group: 12-17, 18-24, 25-34, 35-44, 45-54, 55-64, 65+

Source: Edison Media Research

43. **TRAVEL** On a family trip, Jenna's family drove 310 miles from Gainesville to Ft. Lauderdale.

a. Her dad drove 52% of the way. About how many miles did he drive? **Sample answer: 155 mi**

b. Jenna's mom drove 58% of the distance her dad drove. About how far did she drive? **Sample answer: 90 mi**

c. Her older brother drove the remaining miles. About how many miles did he drive? **Sample answer: 65 mi**

Real-World Link

Florida is the number one tourist destination in the world. The Florida tourism industry has an annual economic impact of about $57 billion.

Source: Visit Florida

44. **ARTS** About 41% of twelfth graders participated in school performing arts last year. A high school had 1800 students, one-fourth of which were twelfth graders. About how many twelfth graders participated in school performing arts? **about 180 twelfth graders**

H.O.T. Problems
Use Higher-Order Thinking Skills

45. **OPEN ENDED** Suppose you want to find $66\frac{2}{3}\%$ of a. List two values of a for which you could do the computation mentally. Explain your reasoning. **45–47. See Chapter 7 Answer Appendix.**

46. **CHALLENGE** Find two numbers, x and y, such that 10% of x is the same as 40% of y. Explain your reasoning.

47. **WRITING IN MATH** Describe two different ways you could find 20% of 60 mentally.

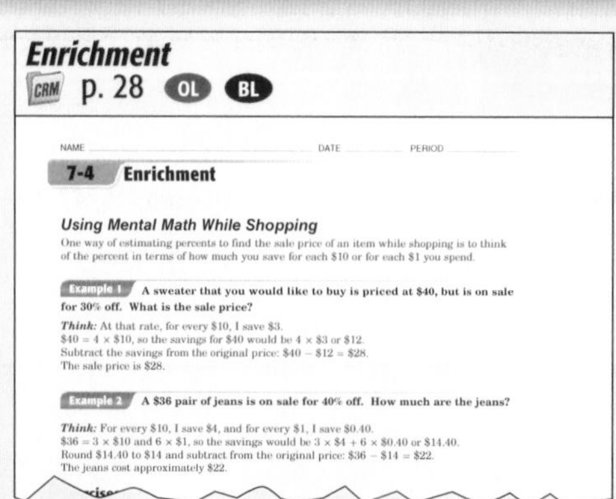
Enrichment
CRM p. 28 OL BL

NAME ______ DATE ______ PERIOD ______

7-4 Enrichment

Using Mental Math While Shopping

One way of estimating percents to find the sale price of an item while shopping is to think of the percent in terms of how much you save for each $10 or for each $1 you spend.

Example 1 A sweater that you would like to buy is priced at $40, but is on sale for 30% off. What is the sale price?

Think: At that rate, for every $10, I save $3.
$40 = 4 × $10, so the savings for $40 would be 4 × $3 or $12.
Subtract the savings from the original price: $40 − $12 = $28.
The sale price is $28.

Example 2 A $36 pair of jeans is on sale for 40% off. How much are the jeans?

Think: For every $10, I save $4, and for every $1, I save $0.40.
$36 = 3 × $10 and 6 × $1, so the savings would be 3 × $4 + 6 × $0.40 or $14.40.
Round $14.40 to $14 and subtract from the original price: $36 − $14 = $22.
The jeans cost approximately $22.

Standardized Test Practice

48. Jerome bought the items listed with the original prices shown on the receipt. If he saved 20% on each item, what is the *best* estimate of how much he saved? **A**

RECEIPT

Qty.	Item	Amount
1	Network Cable	$50.00
1	CD 10-pack	$12.00
1	Mouse	$24.00
1	Memory	$55.00

—Thank you, come again.—

A $28 C $36
B $32 D $40

49. Which fraction is between 85% and 90%? **G**

F $\frac{5}{6}$ H $\frac{9}{10}$
G $\frac{7}{8}$ J $\frac{10}{11}$

50. Lorena, Julian, and Cho completed a group assignment that had 84 questions. Lorena answered $\frac{1}{3}$ of the questions, Julian answered 25% of the questions, and Cho answered the rest. How many questions were answered by the person who answered the greatest number of questions? **D**

A 18 C 28
B 21 D 35

51. EXTENDED RESPONSE The price of Jamila's haircut is $28. There is also a 7% tax added to the bill and Jamila wants to tip the stylist 15% of the total bill. Justify each solution.

a. About how much is the tax on the bill?

b. Find the approximate cost including tax.

c. About how much of a tip will Jamila give the stylist?

d. If she only has $35, does she have enough for tax and tip? Explain.
a–d. See Chapter 7 Answer Appendix.

Spiral Review

52. ACTIVITIES According to a survey about family activities, 35% of people said they enjoy playing games, while three-fifths enjoy watching movies, and $\frac{3}{8}$ enjoy sports. Which group is the largest? Explain. (Lesson 7-3) **movies; Sample answer: $\frac{3}{8}$ = 37.5% and $\frac{3}{5}$ = 60%. Since 60% is greater than 37.5% and 35%, movies are the favorite activity.**

53. GEOGRAPHY The Arctic Ocean contains 3.7% of the world's water. What fraction is this? (Lesson 7-2) $\frac{37}{1000}$

ALGEBRA Solve each proportion. (Lesson 6-5)

54. $\frac{k}{35} = \frac{3}{7}$ **15** **55.** $\frac{3}{t} = \frac{18}{24}$ **4** **56.** $\frac{10}{8.4} = \frac{5}{m}$ **4.2**

57. GEOMETRY The area A of the triangle is 33.75 square inches. Use the formula $A = \frac{1}{2}bh$ to find the height h of the triangle. (Lesson 5-1) **7.5 in.**

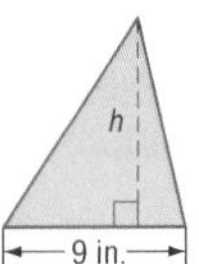

Skills Review

Solve each equation. Check your solution. (Lesson 4-4)

58. $5 = 30b$ $\frac{1}{6}$ **59.** $40n = 10$ **0.25** **60.** $20 = 100k$ **0.20**

61. $34g = 1.7$ **0.05** **62.** $3.6 = 90a$ **0.04** **63.** $200j = 70$ **0.35**

Differentiated Instruction BL

Extension Present the following problem to students: Salespeople often work on a commission, which means they earn a percent of their sales. Suppose a salesperson who earns 10% of her total sales, earned $4300.00 one month. What were her total sales? $43,000

4 ASSESS

Ticket Out the Door Tell students to describe how they mentally calculate 25% of $68.00. Ask them to write the mental process that they use to find the answer. $17.00; methods will vary

Formative Assessment

Check for student understanding of concepts in Lessons 7-3 and 7-4.

CRM Quiz 2, p. 58

Additional Answers

28. 3; 16% is about 15% or $\frac{3}{20}$, $\frac{3}{20} \cdot 20 = 3$

29. 63; 73% is about 75% or $\frac{3}{4}$, $\frac{3}{4} \cdot 84 = 63$

30. 44; 46% is about 50% or $\frac{1}{2}$, $\frac{1}{2} \cdot 88 = 44$

31. 12.5; 49 is about 50, $\frac{1}{4} \cdot 50 = 12.5$

32. 2.5; 1% of 507 is about 5, $\frac{1}{2} \cdot 5 = 2.5$

33. 0.5; 1% of 295 is about 3, $\frac{1}{6} \cdot 3 = 0.5$

34. 45; 148% is about 150%, 100% of 30 is 30 and 50% of 30 is 15, $30 + 15 = 45$

35. 22; 276% is about 275%, 100% of 8 is 8 and 75% of 8 is 6, $8 \cdot 2 + 6 = 22$

36. 6; 1% of 801 is about 8, $\frac{3}{4} \cdot 8 = 6$

37. 0.24; 1% of 30 is 0.3, $\frac{4}{5} \cdot 0.3 = 0.24$

38. 60; 117% is about 120%, 100% of 50 is 50 and 20% of 50 is 10, $50 + 10 = 60$

39. 30; 194% is about 200%, 100% of 15 is 15, $15 \cdot 2 = 30$

CHAPTER 7 Mid-Chapter Quiz

 Formative Assessment

Use the Mid-Chapter Quiz to assess students' progress in the first half of the chapter.

For problems answered incorrectly, have students review the lessons indicated in parentheses.

ExamView Assessment Suite Customize and create multiple versions of your Mid-Chapter Quiz and their answer keys.

FOLDABLES® Follow-Up

Before students complete the Mid-Chapter Quiz, encourage them to review the information for Lessons 7-1 through 7-4 in their Foldables.

CHAPTER 7 Mid-Chapter Quiz

Lessons 7-1 through 7-4

Write each percent as a fraction or mixed number in simplest form. (Lesson 7-1)

1. $33\frac{1}{3}\%$ **$\frac{1}{3}$**
2. 0.25% **$\frac{1}{400}$**
3. 175% **$1\frac{3}{4}$**

Write each fraction as a percent. Round to the nearest hundredth if necessary. (Lesson 7-1)

4. $\frac{1}{6}$ **16.67%**
5. $\frac{50}{40}$ **125%**
6. $\frac{7}{8}$ **87.5%**

7. **ANIMALS** A male lion weighs $\frac{7}{10}$ more than a female lion that weighs 250 pounds. What percent is this? (Lesson 7-1) **70%**

8. **BOXES** What percent of the squares are dark gray? (Lesson 7-1) **30%**

9. **MULTIPLE CHOICE** Monday's average temperature was 70°F. Tuesday's average temperature was 20% hotter than Monday. Write the percent as a fraction. (Lesson 7-1) **C**

A $\frac{2}{7}$ C $\frac{1}{5}$

B $\frac{1}{4}$ D $\frac{1}{7}$

Write each percent as a decimal (Lesson 7-2)

10. 54% **0.54**
11. 87.5% **0.875**
12. 0.163% **0.00163**
13. 225% **2.25**

Express each decimal or fraction as a percent. Round to the nearest tenth, if necessary. (Lesson 7-2)

14. $\frac{8}{64}$ **12.5%**
15. $\frac{56}{32}$ **175%**
16. 0.14 **14%**
17. 1.3 **130%**

18. **STUDENTS** Of the students in Ms. Hillier's class, 27% have blonde hair, 0.33 have black hair, and $\frac{2}{5}$ have brown hair. Which hair color is most common? (Lesson 7-2) **brown hair**

19. **MULTIPLE CHOICE** Jason, Marita, Alice, and Marcus were on a road trip. Jason drove 400 miles, Alice drove $\frac{1}{6}$ of the way, Marita and Marcus each drove 0.25 of the way. If they drove a total of 1200 miles, who drove the longest? (Lesson 7-2) **F**

F Jason H Marita

G Alice J Marcus

Use the percent proportion to solve each problem. (Lesson 7-3)

20. 15 is what percent of 45? **$33\frac{1}{3}\%$**
21. What percent of 7 is 21? **300%**
22. What is 83% of 16? **13.28**
23. 30 is what percent of 75? **40%**
24. Find 8% of 145. **11.6**

25. **POPCORN** Jaime popped a bag of popcorn in the microwave. Thirty percent of the kernels did *not* pop. If there were 120 original kernels, how many did pop? (Lesson 7-3) **84 kernels**

26. **FOOD** The Dragons Soccer Team is having a pizza party and voted on what toppings the players preferred. Of the 25 players, what percent like cheese? (Lesson 7-3) **36%**

Toppings	Number of Players
Cheese	9
Pepperoni	8
Sausage	3
Hawaiian	5

Find the percent of each number mentally. (Lesson 7-4)

27. 1% of 80 **0.8**
28. 25% of 160 **40**
29. $87\frac{1}{2}\%$ of 56 **49**
30. 175% of 200 **350**
31. 20% of 105 **21**
32. $16\frac{2}{3}\%$ of 42 **7**

33. **PLANETS** Mercury's radius is about 40% of Venus' radius. If Venus has a radius of 3800 miles, what is the approximate radius of Mercury? (Lesson 7-4) **about 1600 miles**

Intervention Planner

Tier 1 On Level	Tier 2 Strategic Intervention approaching grade level	Tier 3 Intensive Intervention 2 or more grades below level
If students miss about 25% of the exercises or less,	**If** students miss about 50% of the exercises,	**If** students miss about 75% of the exercises,
Then choose a resource: **SE** Lessons 7-1 through 7-4 **CRM** Skills Practice, pp. 7, 13, 19, and 25 **TE** Chapter Project, p. 328 **Math Online** Self-Check Quiz	**Then** choose a resource: **CRM** Study Guide and Intervention, Chapter 7, pp. 5, 11, 17, and 23 *Quick Review Math Handbook* **Math Online** Extra Examples, Personal Tutor, Homework Help	**Then** use *Math Triumphs, Grade 8*, Ch. 8 **Math Online** Extra Examples, Personal Tutor, Homework Help, Review Vocabulary

7-5 Using Percent Equations

Then
You have already used the percent proportion to solve problems. (Lesson 7-3)

Now
- Solve percent problems using percent equations.
- Apply the percent equation to real-world problems.

New Vocabulary
percent equation

Math Online

glencoe.com
- Extra Examples
- Personal Tutor
- Self-Check Quiz
- Homework Help

Why?

The winner of the New York City Marathon in a recent year was Jelena Prokopcuka. Her total prize money was $130,000.

a. Of her prize money, about 23% was a bonus. Use a proportion to find how much of her prize money was a bonus to the nearest dollar. **about $29,900**

b. Express the percent as a decimal. Multiply the total prize money by the decimal. Round to the nearest dollar. **0.23; about $29,900**

c. Describe how the answers from parts **a** and **b** are related. **They are the same.**

Percent Equations A **percent equation** is an equivalent form of the percent proportion in which the percent is written as a decimal.

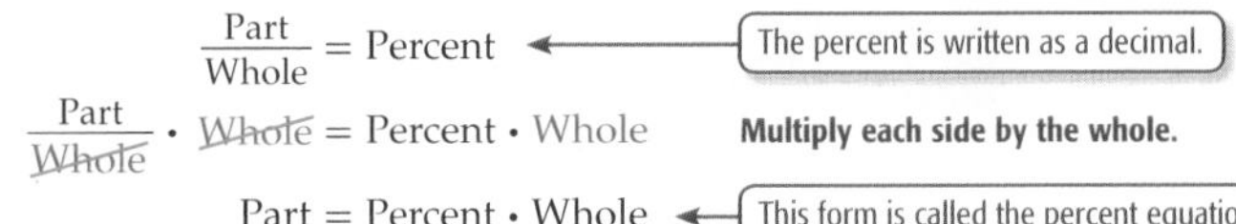

$\frac{\text{Part}}{\text{Whole}} = \text{Percent}$
The percent is written as a decimal.
$\frac{\text{Part}}{\cancel{\text{Whole}}} \cdot \cancel{\text{Whole}} = \text{Percent} \cdot \text{Whole}$
Multiply each side by the whole.
$\text{Part} = \text{Percent} \cdot \text{Whole}$
This form is called the percent equation.

EXAMPLE 1 Find the Part

Find 62% of 75.

Estimate $\frac{3}{5}$ **of 75 is 45.**

The percent is 62 and the whole is 75. You need to find the part.

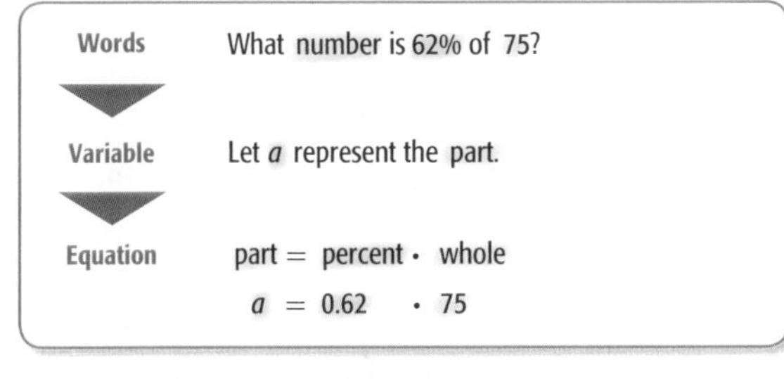

Words
What number is 62% of 75?
Variable
Let a represent the part.
Equation
part = percent · whole
$a = 0.62 \cdot 75$

$a = 0.62 \cdot 75$ **Write the percent equation.**

$= 46.5$ **Multiply.**

Check for Reasonableness $46.5 \approx 45$ ✓

Check Your Progress

1A. Find 60% of 96. **57.6**

1B. Find 45% of 70. **31.5**

Personal Tutor glencoe.com

7-5 Lesson Notes

1 FOCUS

Vertical Alignment

Before Lesson 7-5
Use the percent proportion to solve problems.

Lesson 7-5
Solve percent problems using percent equations. Apply the percent equations to real-world problems.

After Lesson 7-5
Use percent equations to calculate percent of change.

2 TEACH

Scaffolding Questions

Have students read the *Why?* section of the lesson and answer the questions.

Ask:
- About how much of her prize money is a bonus? 20% of $130,000 is $26,000
- What percent of her prize money was not a bonus? 77%
- Use a proportion to find how much of her prize money was not a bonus to the nearest dollar. $100,100

Lesson 7-5 Resources

Resource	Approaching-Level	On-Level	Beyond-Level	English Learners
Teacher Edition	• Differentiated Instruction, p. 358	• Differentiated Instruction, p. 358	• Differentiated Instruction, p. 362	
Chapter Resource Masters	• Study Guide and Intervention, pp. 29–30 • Skills Practice, p. 31 • Practice, p. 32 • Word Problem Practice, p. 33	• Study Guide and Intervention, pp. 29–30 • Skills Practice, p. 31 • Practice, p. 32 • Word Problem Practice, p. 33 • Enrichment, p. 34	• Practice, p. 32 • Word Problem Practice, p. 33 • Enrichment, p. 34	• Study Guide and Intervention, pp. 29–30 • Skills Practice, p. 31 • Practice, p. 32
Transparencies	• 5-Minute Check Transparency 7-5	• 5-Minute Check Transparency 7-5	• 5-Minute Check Transparency 7-5	• 5-Minute Check Transparency 7-5
Other	• Study Notebook • Teaching Pre-Algebra with Manipulatives	• Study Notebook • Teaching Pre-Algebra with Manipulatives	• Study Notebook	• Study Notebook • Teaching Pre-Algebra with Manipulatives

Percent Equations

Examples 1–3 show how to find the part, the percent, and the whole using the percent equation.

Use the Check Your Progress exercises after each example to determine students' understanding of concepts.

Additional Examples

1. Find 38% of 22. 8.36
2. 19 is what percent of 25? 76%
3. 84 is 16% of what number? 525

Additional Examples also in Interactive Classroom PowerPoint® Presentations

IWB INTERACTIVE WHITEBOARD READY

Tips for New Teachers

Rewording Discuss how to write an equation for "find 36% of 120." Explain that it helps to rewrite the sentence as "36% of 120 is what?" Then write the equation: $0.36(120) = n$.

Focus on Mathematical Content

Percent Equation Percents can be written in three equivalent forms: a fraction over 100, a percent symbol, or a decimal. A percent symbol *cannot* be used in a multiplication operation. You must use the fraction or decimal forms. The percent proportion uses the fraction form of the percent. A percent equation often uses the decimal form.

StudyTip

Estimation To determine whether your answer is reasonable, estimate before finding the exact answer.

EXAMPLE 2 Find the Percent

287 is what percent of 410? **Estimate** $\frac{287}{410} \approx \frac{300}{400}$ or $\frac{3}{4}$, which is 75%.

The whole is 410 and the part is 287. Let p represent the percent.

$\underbrace{\text{part}} = \underbrace{\text{percent}} \cdot \underbrace{\text{whole}}$

$287 = p \cdot 410$ **Write the percent equation.**

$\frac{287}{410} = \frac{p \cdot 410}{410}$ **Divide each side by 410.**

$0.7 = p$ **Simplify.**

By definition, the percent is expressed as a decimal. Convert 0.7 to a percent.

Since 0.7 = 70%, 287 is 70% of 410.

Check for Reasonableness $70 \approx 75\%$ ✓

Check Your Progress

2A. 15 is what percent of 125? **12%** **2B.** 20 is what percent of 400? **5%**

Personal Tutor glencoe.com

EXAMPLE 3 Find the Whole

33 is 55% of what number? **Estimate** 33 is 50% of 66.

The part is 33, and the percent is 55%. Let b represent the whole.

$\underbrace{\text{part}} = \underbrace{\text{percent}} \cdot \underbrace{\text{whole}}$

$33 = 0.55 \cdot b$ **Write the percent equation.**

$\frac{33}{0.55} = \frac{0.55b}{0.55}$ **Divide each side by 0.55.**

$60 = b$ **Simplify.**

So, 33 is 55% of 60.

Check for Reasonableness $60 \approx 66$ ✓

StudyTip

Percents Remember that the percent is written as a decimal in the percent equation. So, use 0.55, not 55%.

Check Your Progress

3A. 18 is 30% of what number? **60** **3B.** 79 is 80% of what number? **98.75**

Personal Tutor glencoe.com

The table summarizes the three types of percent problems.

Concept Summary The Percent Equation — For Your FOLDABLE

Type	Example	Equation
Find the Percent	15 is what percent of 60?	$15 = p(60)$
Find the Part	What number is 25% of 60?	$a = 0.25(60)$
Find the Whole	15 is 25% of what number?	$15 = 0.25b$

Differentiated Instruction

AL OL

Kinesthetic Have students play "rock, paper, scissors" by having them randomly make a fist (rock), flatten their hand (paper), or creating cutting scissors with the index and the middle fingers. Count the rocks and determine what percent of students in the class made rocks. Continue playing several rounds, randomly choosing which gesture to count.

Real-World Link

Some states, such as Oregon, Alaska, and New Hampshire, do not have sales tax. California has the highest sales tax average with 7.25%, while the median U.S. sales tax average is 5.5%.

Source: National Tax Administration

Solve Problems The percent equation can be used to solve real-world problems.

Real-World EXAMPLE 4 Use the Percent Equation

SALES TAX Scott wants to buy a digital video recorder that costs $250. If a 6% sales tax is added, what is the total cost?

Method 1 Find the tax first. Then add.

The whole is $250. The percent is 6%. You need to find the amount of the tax, or the part. Let t represent the amount of tax.

$t = 0.06 \cdot 250$ Write the percent equation, writing 6% as a decimal.

$t = 15$ Multiply.

The tax is $15. The total cost is $250 + $15 or $265.

Method 2 Find the total percent first.

Find 100% + 6% or 106% of $250 to find the total cost, including tax.

$t = 1.06 \cdot 250$ Write the percent equation, writing 106% as a decimal.

$t = 1.06 \cdot 250$ or 265 Multiply.

Using either method, the total cost is $265.

Check Your Progress

4. **PROFIT** Last summer, Mr. Potter bought a house for $175,000. Five years later, he sold it for a 24% profit. What was the sale price of the house? $217,000

Personal Tutor glencoe.com

STANDARDIZED TEST EXAMPLE 5

Mr. Li bought a memory card for $137.46 including tax. The card had a sticker price of $129.99. About what percent sales tax did he pay?

A 5% B 6% C 7% D 8%

Read the Test Item

You are asked to find the estimated percent of sales tax.

Solve the Test Item

The tax is $137.46 – $129.99 or $7.47.

$7.47 = p \cdot 129.99$ Write the percent equation.

$\frac{7.47}{129.99} = \frac{p \cdot 129.99}{129.99}$ Divide each side by 129.99.

$0.057 \approx p$ Simplify.

So, 0.057 = 5.7%, and 5.7%, ≈ 6%. The correct choice is B.

Check Your Progress

5. The total cost of a mixer including tax was $47.70. If the original price of the mixer was $45, what was the percent of sales tax? G

F 5.75% G 6% H 6.5% J 7%

Personal Tutor glencoe.com

Use the Percent Equation

Example 4 shows how to find the total cost of an item including sales tax. **Example 5** shows how to find the percent of sales tax given the total cost.

Additional Examples

4 **SALES TAX** Chan wants to buy a cell phone that costs $180. If a 7% sales tax is added, what is the total cost? $192.60

5 **STANDARDIZED TEST PRACTICE** Mr. Wilkins purchased a DVD player for $97.19 including tax. The DVD player had a sticker price of $89.99. About what percent sales tax did he pay? C

A 6%
B 7%
C 8%
D 9%

TEACH with TECH

BLOG Have students write a blog entry about using a percent equation in a real-life situation. Ask them to tell how they calculated the percent, and how it was useful to them.

3 PRACTICE

Formative Assessment

Use Exercises 1–8 to check for understanding.

Use the chart at the bottom of this page to customize assignments for your students.

Additional Answers

25b.

x	y
1.05	126
1.15	138
1.25	150
1.35	162

27b.

x	y
2010	$500
2011	$530
2012	$561.80
2013	$595.51
2014	$631.24
2015	$669.11

Multiple Representations In Exercise 27, students use an equation and a table of values to determine and analyze savings over time.

Check Your Understanding

Examples 1–3 pp. 357–358

Solve each problem using a percent equation.

1. What is 40% of 75? **30**
2. Find 13% of 27. **3.51**
3. 30 is what percent of 90? **$33\frac{1}{3}$%**
4. 15 is what percent of 300? **5%**
5. 55 is 20% of what number? **275**
6. 24 is 80% of what number? **30**

Examples 4 and 5 p. 359

7. **FUNDRAISERS** Last year, Kimberly sold 95 boxes of cookies. This year she wants to sell 20% more boxes than she sold last year. How many boxes will Kimberly have to sell this year to reach her goal? **114 boxes**

8. **MULTIPLE CHOICE** Martin wants to buy a motor scooter. The cost of a motor scooter is $4968. If the total, including tax, is $5290.92, what is the percent of sales tax? **C**

   A 5.5% B 6% C 6.5% D 7%

Practice and Problem Solving

= **Step-by-Step Solutions** begin on page R11. **Extra Practice** begins on page 810.

Examples 1–3 pp. 357–358

Solve each problem using a percent equation.

9. Find 16% of 64. **10.24**
10. What is 36% of 50? **18**
11. 8 is what percent of 40? **20%**
12. 54 is what percent of 60? **90%**
13. 16 is 25% of what number? **64**
14. 64 is 32% of what number? **200**
15. 39 is 50% of what number? **78**
16. 27 is 10% of what number? **270**

Examples 4 and 5 p. 359

17. **SKI JACKETS** Roberto wants to buy a new ski jacket that costs $96. If the total cost, including tax, is $101.28, what is the percent of sales tax? **5.5%**

18. **SHOPPING** A commission is a fee paid to a salesperson based on a percent of sales. Suppose a salesperson at a jewelry store earns a 6% commission. What commission would be earned for selling a ring that costs $1300 dollars? **$78**

Solve each problem using a percent equation.

19. Find 52.5% of 76. **39.9**
20. Find 23.6% of 90. **21.24**
21. 33.8 is what percent of 130? **26%**
22. 79.8 is what percent of 114? **70%**

23. **FINANCIAL LITERACY** The cost, including a 6.75% sales tax, of a digital home theater system with a 40-inch high definition television is $2668.75. What is the original cost of the television and theater system? **$2500**

24. **TENNIS** The results of a Wimbledon Women's Championship match is shown in the table.

	Marion Bartoli	Venus Williams
1st Serves In	40 of 63	35 of 50
Receiving Points Won	16 of 50	30 of 63
Break Point Conversions	1 of 2	4 of 10
Net Approaches	3 of 6	12 of 17

   a. What was Bartoli's percent of receiving points won? **32%**

   b. Which player had a greater percent of their first serves in? **Williams**

   c. Suppose in Williams' next match she has 16 break point opportunities. Based on this match, how many times will she convert on break point opportunities? **6 times**

Differentiated Homework Options

Level	Assignment	Two-Day Option	
AL Basic	9–18, 30, 32–55	9–17 odd, 35–38	10–18 even, 30, 32–34, 39–55
OL Core	9–23 odd, 24–30, 32–55	9–18, 35–38	19–30, 32–34, 39–55
BL Advanced	19–47 (optional: 48–55)		

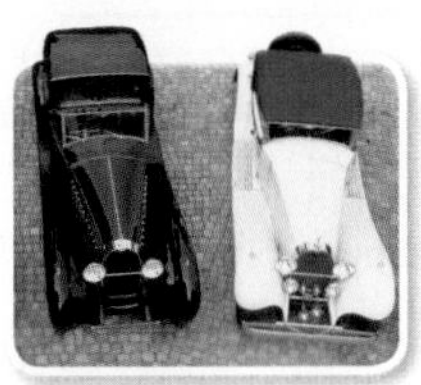

Real-World Link

The National Automobile Museum in Reno, Nevada, features over 200 antique automobiles from 1892 to present.

Source: National Automobile Museum

25. **MUSEUMS** A car museum wants to increase their collection by 20% over the next year. Currently, the museum has 120 cars in its collection.

    a. Write and solve a multiplication equation to find how many cars the museum will have in the next year. How many cars will the museum need to add over the next year to meet its goal? **$c = 1.2 \cdot 120$; 144 cars; 24 cars**

    b. Make a table to find the number of cars in the museum collection if they increase their collection by 5%, 15%, 25%, and 35%. **See margin.**

26. **AREA** The table shows the area of the Great Lakes.

LAKE	AREA (square miles)
Erie	9922
Huron	23,011
Michigan	22,316
Ontario	7320
Superior	31,698

    a. About what percent of the Great Lakes is covered by Lake Erie? **about 11%**

    b. About what percent of the Great Lakes is covered by Lake Huron? **about 24%**

    c. Suppose the area of Lake Michigan was decreased by 8%. Find its new area. **20,530.72 mi²**

27. **MULTIPLE REPRESENTATIONS** In this problem, you will investigate percent relationships. In 2010, Aida saved $500. She plans to save 6% more than her previous' years savings for the next several years.

    a. **ALGEBRAIC** Write and solve a multiplication equation to find how much money she will save next year. **$s = 1.06 \cdot 500$; $530**

    b. **TABULAR** Let x represent the year and y represent the amount of money she has saved. Make a table using the x-values for 2010–2015. **See margin.**

    c. **ANALYTICAL** Does Aida's savings increase by a constant amount each year? Explain. **Sample answer: No; the base amount is different each year so the part changes even though the percent remains constant.**

Use the percent equation to solve each problem if $x = 10$.

28. $(2x)$ is 4% of what number? **500**

29. Find $(4x)$% of 240. **96**

H.O.T. Problems
Use Higher-Order Thinking Skills

30. **OPEN ENDED** Write two percent problems in which the solution is 30%.

31. **CHALLENGE** If you found the percent of a number and the part is greater than the number, what do you know about the percent? Explain.

32. **FIND THE ERROR** Todd and Jon are finding what percent of 80 is 28. Is either of them correct? Explain your reasoning. **Todd; Jon found 28% of 80.**

Todd	Jon
$28 = p \cdot 80$	$p = 80 \cdot 0.28$
$p = 0.35$	$p = 22.4$
So, 28 is 35% of 80.	So, 28 is 22.4% of 80.

33. **REASONING** Does taking a 10% discount on an item then adding a 10% sales tax result in the original price of the item? Support your answer with an example.

34. **WRITING IN MATH** Explain whether you would change the percent to a fraction or a decimal when finding 25% of 128.

30. Sample answer: 27 is what percent of 90?; 54 is what percent of 180?

31. Sample answer: The percent is greater than 100% because otherwise the part would be less than or equal to the whole.

33. No; Suppose an item costs $100. A 10% discount would be a discount of $10, so the discounted price would be $90. Adding a 10% sales tax adds $9. So, $90 + $9 is not $100.

34. Sample answer: a fraction; Change $25\% = \frac{1}{4}$ since 128 is evenly divisible by 4.

Watch Out!

Find the Error For Exercise 32, rephrase the question as "28 is what percent of 80?".

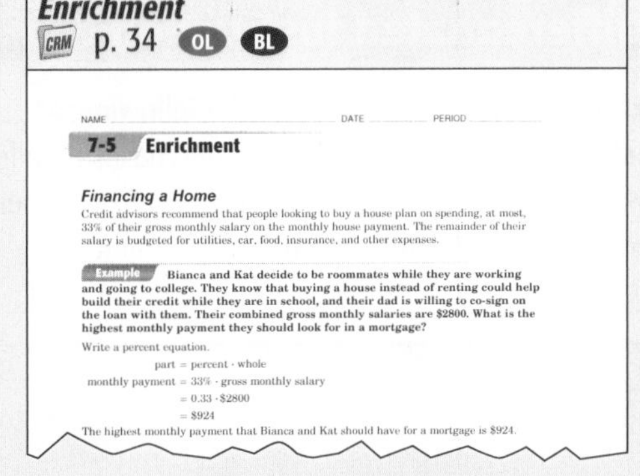

Enrichment
CRM p. 34 OL BL

NAME ______ DATE ______ PERIOD ______

7-5 Enrichment

Financing a Home

Credit advisors recommend that people looking to buy a house plan on spending, at most, 33% of their gross monthly salary on the monthly house payment. The remainder of their salary is budgeted for utilities, car, food, insurance, and other expenses.

Example **Bianca and Kat decide to be roommates while they are working and going to college. They know that buying a house instead of renting could help build their credit while they are in school, and their dad is willing to co-sign on the loan with them. Their combined gross monthly salaries are $2800. What is the highest monthly payment they should look for in a mortgage?**

Write a percent equation.

part = percent · whole
monthly payment = 33% · gross monthly salary
= 0.33 · $2800
= $924

The highest monthly payment that Bianca and Kat should have for a mortgage is $924.

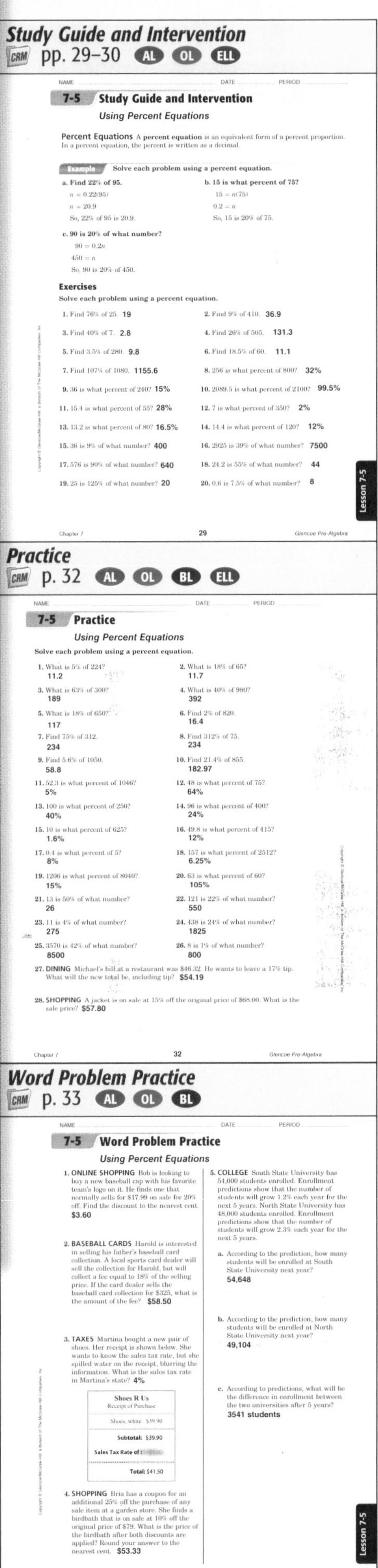

Study Guide and Intervention
CRM pp. 29–30 AL OL ELL

NAME ______ DATE ______ PERIOD ______

7-5 Study Guide and Intervention
Using Percent Equations

Percent Equations A **percent equation** is an equivalent form of a percent proportion. In a percent equation, the percent is written as a decimal.

Example **Solve each problem using a percent equation.**

a. Find 22% of 95.
$n = 0.22(95)$
$n = 20.9$
So, 22% of 95 is 20.9.

b. 15 is what percent of 75?
$15 = n(75)$
$0.2 = n$
So, 15 is 20% of 75.

c. 90 is 20% of what number?
$90 = 0.2n$
$450 = n$
So, 90 is 20% of 450.

Exercises

Solve each problem using a percent equation.

1. Find 76% of 25. **19**
2. Find 9% of 410. **36.9**
3. Find 40% of 7. **2.8**
4. Find 26% of 505. **131.3**
5. Find 3.5% of 280. **9.8**
6. Find 18.5% of 60. **11.1**
7. Find 107% of 1080. **1155.6**
8. 256 is what percent of 800? **32%**
9. 36 is what percent of 240? **15%**
10. 2089.5 is what percent of 2100? **99.5%**
11. 15.4 is what percent of 55? **28%**
12. 7 is what percent of 350? **2%**
13. 13.2 is what percent of 80? **16.5%**
14. 14.4 is what percent of 120? **12%**
15. 36 is 9% of what number? **400**
16. 2925 is 39% of what number? **7500**
17. 576 is 90% of what number? **640**
18. 24.2 is 55% of what number? **44**
19. 25 is 125% of what number? **20**
20. 0.6 is 7.5% of what number? **8**

Lesson 7-5

Chapter 7 29 Glencoe Pre-Algebra

Practice
CRM p. 32 AL OL BL ELL

NAME ______ DATE ______ PERIOD ______

7-5 Practice
Using Percent Equations

Solve each problem using a percent equation.

1. What is 5% of 224? **11.2**
2. What is 18% of 65? **11.7**
3. What is 63% of 300? **189**
4. What is 40% of 980? **392**
5. What is 18% of 650? **117**
6. Find 2% of 820. **16.4**
7. Find 75% of 312. **234**
8. Find 312% of 75. **234**
9. Find 5.6% of 1050. **58.8**
10. Find 21.4% of 855. **182.97**
11. 52.3 is what percent of 1046? **5%**
12. 48 is what percent of 75? **64%**
13. 100 is what percent of 250? **40%**
14. 96 is what percent of 400? **24%**
15. 10 is what percent of 625? **1.6%**
16. 49.8 is what percent of 415? **12%**
17. 0.4 is what percent of 5? **8%**
18. 157 is what percent of 2512? **6.25%**
19. 1206 is what percent of 8040? **15%**
20. 63 is what percent of 60? **105%**
21. 13 is 50% of what number? **26**
22. 121 is 22% of what number? **550**
23. 11 is 4% of what number? **275**
24. 438 is 24% of what number? **1825**
25. 3570 is 42% of what number? **8500**
26. 8 is 1% of what number? **800**
27. **DINING** Michael's bill at a restaurant was $46.32. He wants to leave a 17% tip. What will the new total be, including tip? **$54.19**
28. **SHOPPING** A jacket is on sale at 15% off the original price of $68.00. What is the sale price? **$57.80**

Chapter 7 32 Glencoe Pre-Algebra

Word Problem Practice
CRM p. 33 AL OL BL

NAME ______ DATE ______ PERIOD ______

7-5 Word Problem Practice
Using Percent Equations

1. **ONLINE SHOPPING** Bob is looking to buy a new baseball cap with his favorite team's logo on it. He finds one that normally sells for $17.99 on sale for 20% off. Find the discount to the nearest cent. **$3.60**

2. **BASEBALL CARDS** Harold is interested in selling his father's baseball card collection. A local sports card dealer will sell the collection for Harold, but will collect a fee equal to 18% of the selling price. If the card dealer sells the baseball card collection for $325, what is the amount of the fee? **$58.50**

3. **TAXES** Martina bought a new pair of shoes. Her receipt is shown below. She wants to know the sales tax rate, but she spilled water on the receipt, blurring the information. What is the sales tax rate in Martina's state? **4%**

Shoes R Us
Receipt of Purchase
Shoes, white $39.90
Subtotal: $39.90
Sales Tax Rate of:
Total: $41.50

4. **SHOPPING** Bria has a coupon for an additional 25% off the purchase of any sale item at a garden store. She finds a birdbath that is on sale at 10% off the original price of $79. What is the price of the birdbath after both discounts are applied? Round your answer to the nearest cent. **$53.33**

5. **COLLEGE** South State University has 54,000 students enrolled. Enrollment predictions show that the number of students will grow 1.2% each year for the next 5 years. North State University has 48,000 students enrolled. Enrollment predictions show that the number of students will grow 2.3% each year for the next 5 years.

    a. According to the prediction, how many students will be enrolled at South State University next year? **54,648**

    b. According to the prediction, how many students will be enrolled at North State University next year? **49,104**

    c. According to predictions, what will be the difference in enrollment between the two universities after 5 years? **3541 students**

Lesson 7-5

Chapter 7 33 Glencoe Pre-Algebra

4 ASSESS

Crystal Ball Have students write a sentence explaining how today's lesson on percent equations might help them with tomorrow's lesson on percent of change.

Standardized Test Practice

35. Interest on a savings account is calculated every quarter of a year. During the first quarter, Alejandra earned $54.84 in interest. This was 2% of her savings. How much was Alejandra's savings? **B**

A $274.20 C $5484
B $2742 D $5593.68

36. A lawyer earns an annual salary of $65,490 and receives a raise. The lawyer's new annual salary is $68,109.60. About what percent of a raise did the lawyer receive? **G**

F 3%
G 4%
H 5%
J 6%

37. Nate and some friends went to dinner. The total cost of dinner including a 15% tip was $43.70. What was the cost of dinner alone? **A**

A $38 C $5.70
B $37.50 D $4.30

38. EXTENDED RESPONSE The table shows the capacity of two collegiate football stadiums.

Stadium	Capacity
L.A. Coliseum	91,000
Ben-Hill Griffin	88,548

a. Suppose 75% of Ben-Hill Griffin Stadium is filled, and 73% of L.A. Coliseum is filled. Which stadium has a greater number of people in it? **L.A. Coliseum**

b. How many more people are in that stadium? **19**

Spiral Review

Find the percent of each number mentally. (Lesson 7-4)

39. 75% of 64 **48** **40.** 25% of 52 **13** **41.** $33\frac{1}{3}$% of 27 **9**

42. LIFE SCIENCE Carbon makes up 18.5% of the human body by weight. Determine the amount of carbon in a person who weighs 145 pounds. Round to the nearest tenth. (Lesson 7-3) **26.8 lb**

43. SNACKS The Skyway Snack Company makes a snack mix that contains raisins, peanuts, and chocolate pieces. The ingredients are shown at the right. Suppose the company wants to sell a larger-sized bag that contains 6 cups of raisins. How many cups of chocolate pieces and peanuts should be added? (Lesson 6-5)
chocolate pieces: 2 c; peanuts: 3 c

Convert each rate using dimensional analysis. (Lesson 6-3)

44. 45 mi/h = ■ ft/s **66** **45.** 18 mi/h = ■ ft/s **26.4**

46. 26 cm/s = ■ m/min **15.6** **47.** 32 cm/s = ■ m/min **19.2**

Skills Review

Write each decimal as a percent. (Lesson 7-1)

48. 0.44 **44%** **49.** 0.37 **37%** **50.** 2.06 **206%** **51.** 1.82 **182%**

52. 0.03 **3%** **53.** 0.05 **5%** **54.** 0.004 **0.4%** **55.** 0.007 **0.7%**

Differentiated Instruction

BL

Extension Have students solve the following: Miguel and Isabel both bought identical baseball mitts on sale but they made their purchases at different sporting goods stores. Miguel purchased his mitt for 33% off the original price of $28. Isabel's mitt was originally priced at $33, but it was reduced by 28%. Who paid more? The amount of the discount was the same but the final prices were different. Isabel paid more.

Algebra Lab: Modeling Percents and Change

You can use percents to describe a change when a number increases or decreases.

ACTIVITY 1

Suppose the width of rectangle B is increased from 2 units to 3 units, but the length is unchanged. How is the area affected?

Step 1

Draw a 4 by 2 unit rectangle on grid paper.

Step 2

Increase the width to 3 units. Shade the new units on the rectangle.

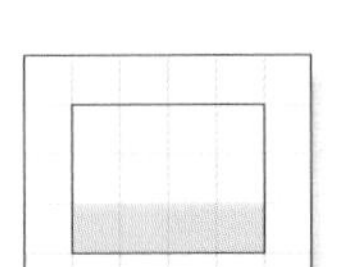

Step 3

Write a ratio comparing the shaded portion to the unshaded portion of the rectangle. Write the ratio as a percent.

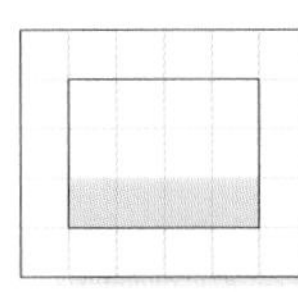

The rectangle has an area of 8 square units.

$\frac{\text{change in area}}{\text{original area}} = \frac{4}{8}$ or 50%

Compared to the original area, the new area increased by 50%.

ACTIVITY 2

Draw a rectangle with dimensions of 5 units by 4 units. Using a percent, describe the change if the width decreases from 4 units to 1 unit.

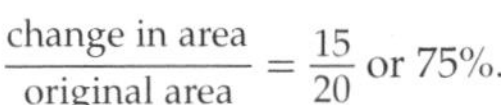

$\frac{\text{change in area}}{\text{original area}} = \frac{15}{20}$ or 75%.

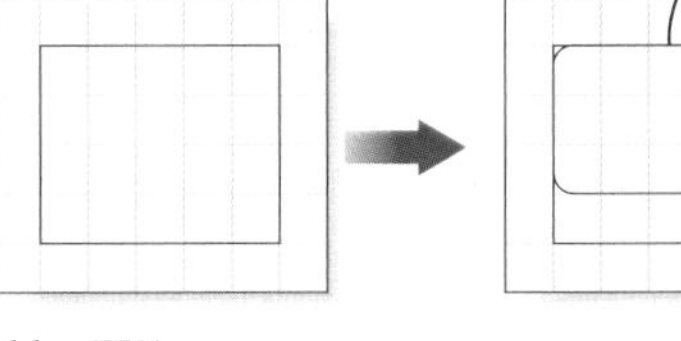

Compared to the original area, the new area decreased by 75%.

Exercises

7. Sample answer: The percents are different because the original amount is different. The denominator changes each time.

Draw each rectangle. Using a percent, describe the change for each set of rectangles.

1. A: 4 units by 1 unit
   B: 4 units by 2 units
   100%
2. C: 4 units by 3 unit $33\frac{1}{3}\%$
   D: 4 units by 4 units
3. W: 4 units by 4 units
   X: 4 units by 5 units
   25%
4. A: 5 units by 4 units 20%
   B: 4 units by 4 units
5. C: 4 units by 4 units 25%
   D: 4 units by 3 units
6. W: 2 units by 3 units $66\frac{2}{3}\%$
   X: 2 units by 1 unit
7. **WRITING IN MATH** For each pair of rectangles in Exercises 1–6, the change in area is 4 square units. Explain why the percent of change is different.

From Concrete to Abstract

Have students find the percent of change for a rectangle that has an area of 8 units increased to an area of 14 units without drawing a model.

Additional Answers

1–6. See Chapter 7 Answer Appendix for rectangles.

EXPLORE 7-6 Lesson Notes

1 FOCUS

Objective Use percents to describe a change when a number increases or decreases.

Materials for Each Student

- grid paper

2 TEACH

Working in Cooperative Groups

Put students in groups of two or three, mixing abilities. Have students work through Activities 1 and 2.

Activity 1

Ask:

- If the original rectangle is smaller than the new rectangle, is the change an increase or decrease? increase
- If a 2 by 4 rectangle is increased to 16 square units, what percent of the original rectangle was added? 100%
- If a 2 by 4 rectangle is increased to 12 square units, what percent of the original rectangle was added? 50%

Activity 2

Ask:

- If the original rectangle is larger than a new rectangle, is the change an increase or a decrease? decrease

Practice Have students complete Exercises 1–7.

3 ASSESS

Formative Assessment

Use Exercise 4 to assess whether students can use percents to describe a change when a number increases or decreases.

7-6 Lesson Notes

1 FOCUS

Vertical Alignment

Before Lesson 7-6
Solve real-world problems using percent equations.

Lesson 7-6
Find percent of increase or decrease. Solve real-world problems involving markup and discount.

After Lesson 7-6
Use percent relationships to calculate simple and compound interest.

2 TEACH

Scaffolding Questions

Have students read the *Why?* section of the lesson and answer the questions.

Ask:

- Has there been an increase or decrease in the number of sea otters? increase
- Does the percent represent an increase or a decrease? increase
- If the percent represented a decrease, how would it be different? It would be a negative number.

7-6 Percent of Change

Then
You have already solved real-world problems using the percent equations. (Lesson 7-5)

Now
- Find percent of increase and decrease.
- Solve real-world problems involving markup and discount.

New Vocabulary
percent of change
percent of increase
percent of decrease
markup
selling price
discount

Math Online
glencoe.com
- Extra Examples
- Personal Tutor
- Self-Check Quiz
- Homework Help

Why?

The table shows the number of California sea otters in recent years.

Year	Number of California Sea Otters
2006	2692
2007	3026

a. How many more sea otters were there in 2007 than in 2006? 334

b. Write the ratio $\frac{\text{amount of increase}}{\text{number of otters in 2006}}$. Then write the ratio as a percent. Round to the nearest tenth. $\frac{334}{2692}$; 12.4%

Find Percent of Change When you subtracted the original amount from the final amount, you found the *amount* of change. When you compared the change to the original amount, you found the *percent* of change.

Key Concept — Percent of Change (For Your FOLDABLE)

Words A **percent of change** is a ratio that compares the change in quantity to the original amount.

Symbols $\text{percent of change} = \frac{\text{amount of change}}{\text{original amount}}$

If the percent is positive, the percent of change is a **percent of increase**. If the percent is negative, the percent of change is called a **percent of decrease**.

EXAMPLE 1 Find the Percent of Change

Find the percent of change from 60°F to 84°F. Then state whether the percent of change is an *increase* or *decrease*.

Step 1 Subtract to find the amount of change.

$84 - 60 = 24$ **final amount – original amount**

Step 2 Write a ratio that compares the amount of change to the original amount. Express the ratio as a percent.

$\text{percent of change} = \frac{\text{amount of change}}{\text{original measurement}}$

$= \frac{24}{60}$ **Substitution**

$= \frac{2}{5}$ or 0.4 **Simplify.**

Step 3 The decimal 0.4 is written as 40%. So, the percent of change is 40%. Since the percent of change is positive, it is a percent of increase.

Check Your Progress

1. **COMICS** Ty had 52 comic books. Now he has 61 books. Find the percent of change. Then state whether the percent of change is an *increase* or *decrease*. Round to the nearest tenth, if necessary. 17.3%; increase

Personal Tutor glencoe.com

Lesson 7-6 Resources

Resource	Approaching-Level	On-Level	Beyond-Level	English Learners
Teacher Edition		• Differentiated Instruction, p. 365	• Differentiated Instruction, pp. 365, 369	
Chapter Resource Masters	• Study Guide and Intervention, pp. 35–36 • Skills Practice, p. 37 • Practice, p. 38 • Word Problem Practice, p. 39 • Graphing Calculator, p. 41	• Study Guide and Intervention, pp. 35–36 • Skills Practice, p. 37 • Practice, p. 38 • Word Problem Practice, p. 39 • Enrichment, p. 40 • Graphing Calculator, p. 41	• Practice, p. 38 • Word Problem Practice, p. 39 • Enrichment, p. 40 • Graphing Calculator, p. 41	• Study Guide and Intervention, pp. 35–36 • Skills Practice, p. 37 • Practice, p. 38 • Graphing Calculator, p. 41
Transparencies	• 5-Minute Check Transparency 7-6	• 5-Minute Check Transparency 7-6	• 5-Minute Check Transparency 7-6	• 5-Minute Check Transparency 7-6
Other	• Study Notebook • Teaching Pre-Algebra with Manipulatives	• Study Notebook • Teaching Pre-Algebra with Manipulatives	• Study Notebook	• Study Notebook • Teaching Pre-Algebra with Manipulatives

Watch Out!

When finding percent of change, don't assume the smaller number is the whole. When the percent of change is a decrease, the original amount will be larger than the new amount.

Real-World EXAMPLE 2 Find the Percent of Change

STAMPS McKenna had 318 stamps. Now she has 273 stamps. Find the percent of change. Round to the nearest tenth, if necessary. Then state whether the percent of change is an *increase* or *decrease*.

$$\text{percent of change} = \frac{\text{amount of change}}{\text{original amount}}$$

$$= \frac{273 - 318}{318} \quad \frac{\text{final amount} - \text{original amount}}{\text{original amount}}$$

$$= \frac{-45}{318} \quad \text{Simplify.}$$

$$\approx -0.141509 \quad \text{Divide. Use a calculator.}$$

To the nearest tenth, the percent of change is −14.2%. Since the percent of change is negative, it is a percent of decrease.

Check Your Progress

2. Find the percent of change from 24 points to 18 points. Then state whether the percent of change is an *increase* or *decrease*. **−25%; decrease**

Personal Tutor glencoe.com

Using Markup and Discount A store sells items for more than it pays for those items. The amount of increase is called the **markup**. The percent of markup is a percent of increase. The **selling price** is the amount the customer pays for an item.

EXAMPLE 3 Find the Selling Price

Find the selling price if a store pays $42 for a pair of roller blades and the markup is 25%.

Method 1 Find the amount of the markup first.

The whole is $42. The percent is 25. You need to find the amount of the markup, or the part. Let m represent the amount of the markup.

$m = 0.25 \cdot 42$ part = percent • whole

$m = 10.5$ Multiply.

Then add the markup to the cost. So, $42 + $10.50 = $52.50.

Method 2 Find the total percent first.

Use the percent equation to find 100% + 25% or 125% of the price. Let p represent the price.

$p = 1.25(42)$ part = percent • whole

$p = 52.50$ Multiply.

Using either method, the selling price is $52.50.

StudyTip

Total Percent In Method 2, the customer will pay 100% of the price plus an extra 25% of the price.

Check Your Progress

3. Find the selling price if a store pays $75 for a bike and the markup is 40%. **$105**

Personal Tutor glencoe.com

Find Percent of Change

Examples 1 and 2 show how to find the percent of change and determine whether the percent of change is an *increase* or *decrease*.

Formative Assessment

Use the Check Your Progress exercises after each example to determine students' understanding of concepts.

Additional Examples

1. Find the percent of change from 20 students to 24 students. State whether the percent of change is an *increase* or *decrease*. 20%; increase

2. Pedro had 325 trading cards. He now has 270 trading cards. Find the percent of change. Round to the nearest tenth, if necessary. Then state whether the percent of change is an *increase* or *decrease*. 16.9%; decrease

Additional Examples also in Interactive Classroom PowerPoint® Presentations

IWB INTERACTIVE WHITEBOARD READY

Using Markup and Discount

Example 3 shows how to find the selling price of an item when given a markup. **Example 4** shows how to find the sale price of an item when given a discount.

Additional Example

3. Find the selling price if a store pays $68 for a portable DVD player, and the markup is 35%. $91.80

Differentiated Instruction

OL BL

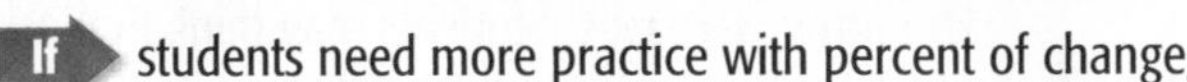

If students need more practice with percent of change,

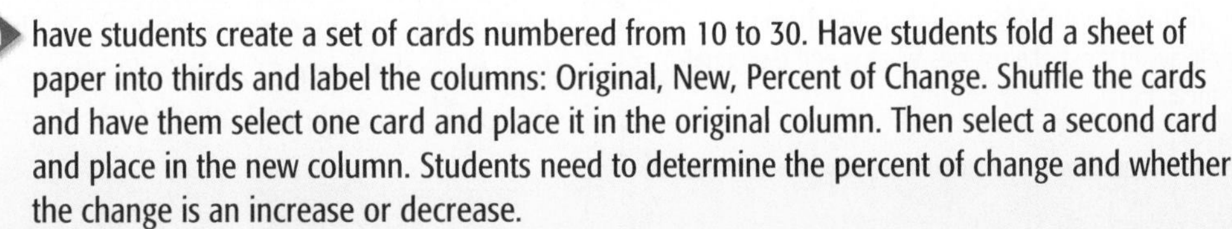

Then have students create a set of cards numbered from 10 to 30. Have students fold a sheet of paper into thirds and label the columns: Original, New, Percent of Change. Shuffle the cards and have them select one card and place it in the original column. Then select a second card and place in the new column. Students need to determine the percent of change and whether the change is an increase or decrease.

Focus on Mathematical Content

Percent of Change A value such as a population can increase, decrease, or remain the same. The original measure is always placed in the denominator of the fraction and is used to determine the percent.

Additional Example

4 **BASEBALL MITT** CR Sporting Goods is having a sale. A baseball mitt has an original price of $89. It is on sale for 25% off the original price. Find the sale price of the baseball mitt. $66.75

TEACH with TECH

WEB SEARCH Ask students to research populations of different cities and states from the U.S. Census Bureau Web site. Have them calculate the percent of change in population over different time periods.

3 PRACTICE

Formative Assessment

Use Exercises 1–6 to check for understanding.

Use the chart at the bottom of the next page to customize assignments for your students.

A **discount** is the amount by which the regular price is reduced. The percent of discount is a percent of decrease.

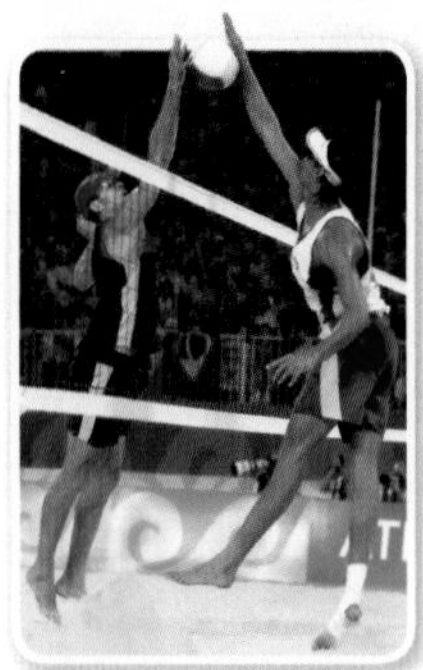

Real-World Link

Beach volleyball became an official Olympic sport in 1996. It is played on a sand court, and each half of the court measures 8 meters by 8 meters.

Source: USA Volleyball

Real-World EXAMPLE 4 Find the Sale Price

VOLLEYBALL Summer Sports is having a sale. A volleyball has an original price of $59. It is on sale for 65% off the original price. Find the sale price of the volleyball.

Method 1 Find the amount of the discount.

The percent is 65 and the whole is 59. You need to find the amount of the discount, or the part.

Let d represent the amount of the discount.

$d = 0.65 \cdot 59$ **part = percent • whole**

$d = 38.35$ **Multiply.**

Subtract the discount from the original cost to find the sale price.
So, $59 − $38.35 = $20.65.

Method 2 Find the total percent first.

If the amount of the discount is 65%, the percent the customer will pay is 100% − 65% or 35%. Find 35% of $59.

Let s represent the sale price.

$s = 0.35(59)$ **part = percent • whole**

$s = 20.65$ **Multiply.**

Using either method, the sale price of the volleyball is $20.65.

Check Your Progress

4. **MAGAZINES** A magazine subscription has a cover price of $35. It is on sale for 67% off the original price. Find the sale price of the magazine subscription. **$11.55**

Personal Tutor glencoe.com

Check Your Understanding

Example 1 p. 364 — **Find the percent of change. Then state whether the percent of change is an *increase* or *decrease*. Round to the nearest tenth, if necessary.**

1. From $40 to $32 **−20%; decrease**
2. From 56 inches to 63 inches **12.5%; increase**

Example 2 p. 365

3. **FINANCIAL LITERACY** On Saturday, Smoothie Central made $1300 in sales. On Sunday, they made $900 in sales. What is the percent of change from Saturday to Sunday? **−30.8%; decrease**

Example 3 p. 365 — **Find the selling price for each item given the cost and the percent of markup.**

4. shoes: $30, 25% markup **$37.50**
5. CD player; $45, 31% markup **$58.95**

Example 4 p. 366

6. **BIKES** Find the sale price of a bike that is regularly $110 and is on sale for 45% off the original price. **$60.50**

Watch Out!

Unlocking Misconceptions Watch for students who systematically want to divide the greater number into the lesser number. Tell them to always first ask themselves what was the original measure.

Tips for New Teachers

Undoing Increases Students may think that a 20% decrease will "undo" a 20% increase. Have them find a 20% increase of $100. $120 Then show them that from $120 to $100 is not a 20% change. The change is about a 16.7% decrease.

Practice and Problem Solving

= Step-by-Step Solutions begin on page R11.
Extra Practice begins on page 810.

Example 1 p. 364

Exercises 3, 15–16, and 28–29 have been rounded to the nearest tenth.

Find the percent of change. Round to the nearest tenth, if necessary. Then state whether the percent of change is an *increase* or *decrease*. 7–14. See margin.

7. From 14 inches to 26 inches
8. From $36 to $48
9. From 82 feet to 74 feet
10. From 16 kilograms to 5 kilograms
11. From $128 to $112
12. From 90 yards to 72 yards
13. From 191 ounces to 270 ounces
14. From 150 minutes to 172 minutes

Example 2 p. 365

15. **GASOLINE** A survey of gas prices in January showed that the cost per gallon one year was $2.649. The following January, the cost per gallon was $2.999. Find the percent change in gas prices from one year to the next. 13.2%; increase

16. **FOOTBALL** Jerome High School's football team scored 38 points in their first game. The next week they only scored 17 points. Find the percent change in the number of points scored by the football team. −55.3%; decrease

Example 3 p. 365

Find the selling price for each item given the cost and the percent of markup.

17. video game: $60; 28% markup $76.80
18. bracelet: $26.50, 35% markup $35.78
19. jacket: $25; 32% markup $33.00
20. stereo: $55, 40% markup $77.00
21. wallet: $14.50, 30% markup $18.85
22. phone: $34, 36% markup $46.24
23. television; $499, 20% markup $598.80
24. mountain bike: $255, 34% mark up $341.70

Example 4 p. 366

25. **SALONS** A salon is having a sale on their hair products. Find the sale price of the shampoo and conditioner set shown at the right that regularly costs $10. $7.50

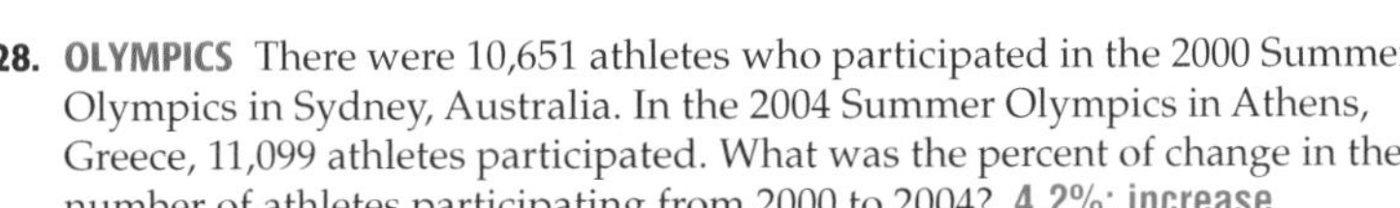

26. **ENTERTAINMENT** The unlimited rental plan at a video store costs $30 a month. It is on sale for 35% off the original price. What is the sale price of the plan? $19.50

Real-World Link

The first modern Olympic games were held in Athens, Greece in 1896. The Olympic rings, designed in 1913, represent the continents Africa, America, Asia, Australia, and Europe and appear on the Olympic flag.

Source: US Olympic Committee

27. **TELEVISION** For the local telethon 3860 viewers called in and donated money on the first night. The next night, there was a 20% decrease in the number of calls from the first night. How many calls did the telethon receive on the second night? 3088 calls

28. **OLYMPICS** There were 10,651 athletes who participated in the 2000 Summer Olympics in Sydney, Australia. In the 2004 Summer Olympics in Athens, Greece, 11,099 athletes participated. What was the percent of change in the number of athletes participating from 2000 to 2004? 4.2%; increase

29. **BICYCLING** According to the National Sporting Goods Association, the number of people who participated in bicycle riding in 2004 was 40.3 million. In 2006, the number was 35.6 million. Find the percent of change from 2004 to 2006. −11.7%

30. **DOGS** Kyla's boxer weighs about 62 pounds. When it was a puppy it only weighed 23 pounds. What is the percent of change in weight? 170%

Additional Answers

7. 85.7%; increase
8. 33.3%; increase
9. −9.8%; decrease
10. −68.8%; decrease
11. −12.5%; decrease
12. −20%; decrease
13. 41.4%; increase
14. 14.7%; increase

Differentiated Homework Options

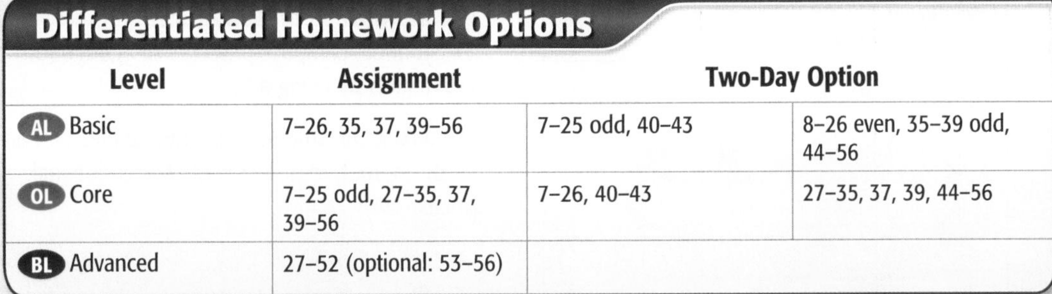

Level	Assignment	Two-Day Option	
AL Basic	7–26, 35, 37, 39–56	7–25 odd, 40–43	8–26 even, 35–39 odd, 44–56
OL Core	7–25 odd, 27–35, 37, 39–56	7–26, 40–43	27–35, 37, 39, 44–56
BL Advanced	27–52 (optional: 53–56)		

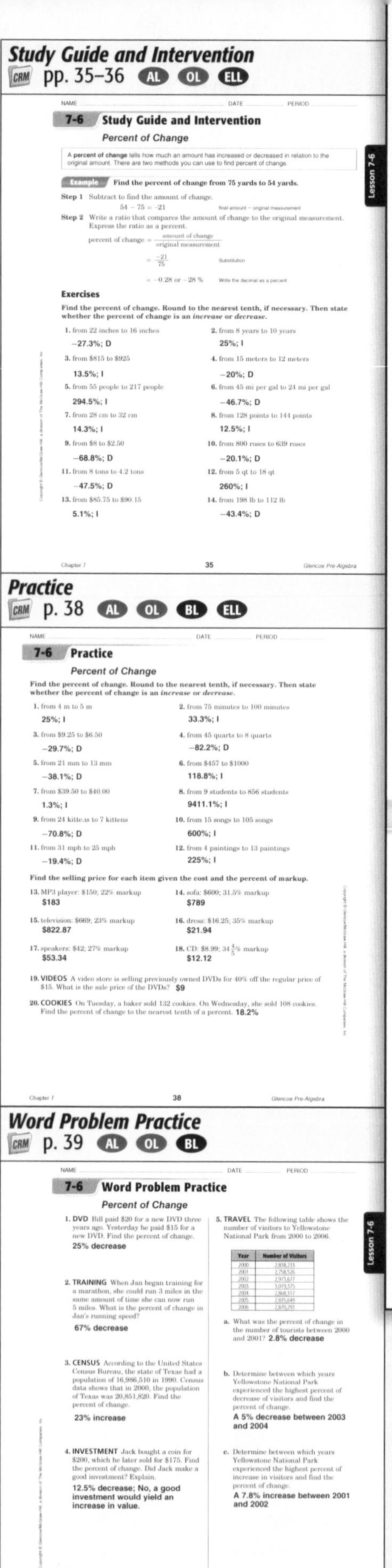

Study Guide and Intervention
CRM pp. 35–36 AL OL ELL

NAME ________ DATE ________ PERIOD ________

7-6 Study Guide and Intervention
Percent of Change

A **percent of change** tells how much an amount has increased or decreased in relation to the original amount. There are two methods you can use to find percent of change.

Example **Find the percent of change from 75 yards to 54 yards.**

Step 1 Subtract to find the amount of change.

$54 - 75 = -21$ final amount − original measurement

Step 2 Write a ratio that compares the amount of change to the original measurement. Express the ratio as a percent.

$\text{percent of change} = \frac{\text{amount of change}}{\text{original measurement}}$

$= \frac{-21}{75}$ Substitution

$= -0.28$ or -28% Write the decimal as a percent

Exercises

Find the percent of change. Round to the nearest tenth, if necessary. Then state whether the percent of change is an *increase* or *decrease*.

1. from 22 inches to 16 inches **−27.3%; D**
2. from 8 years to 10 years **25%; I**
3. from \$815 to \$925 **13.5%; I**
4. from 15 meters to 12 meters **−20%; D**
5. from 55 people to 217 people **294.5%; I**
6. from 45 mi per gal to 24 mi per gal **−46.7%; D**
7. from 28 cm to 32 cm **14.3%; I**
8. from 128 points to 144 points **12.5%; I**
9. from \$8 to \$2.50 **−68.8%; D**
10. from 800 roses to 639 roses **−20.1%; D**
11. from 8 tons to 4.2 tons **−47.5%; D**
12. from 5 qt to 18 qt **260%; I**
13. from \$85.75 to \$90.15 **5.1%; I**
14. from 198 lb to 112 lb **−43.4%; D**

Chapter 7 35 Glencoe Pre-Algebra

Lesson 7-6

Practice
CRM p. 38 AL OL BL ELL

NAME ________ DATE ________ PERIOD ________

7-6 Practice
Percent of Change

Find the percent of change. Round to the nearest tenth, if necessary. Then state whether the percent of change is an *increase* or *decrease*.

1. from 4 m to 5 m **25%; I**
2. from 75 minutes to 100 minutes **33.3%; I**
3. from \$9.25 to \$6.50 **−29.7%; D**
4. from 45 quarts to 8 quarts **−82.2%; D**
5. from 21 mm to 13 mm **−38.1%; D**
6. from \$457 to \$1000 **118.8%; I**
7. from \$39.50 to \$40.00 **1.3%; I**
8. from 9 students to 856 students **9411.1%; I**
9. from 24 kittens to 7 kittens **−70.8%; D**
10. from 15 songs to 105 songs **600%; I**
11. from 31 mph to 25 mph **−19.4%; D**
12. from 4 paintings to 13 paintings **225%; I**

Find the selling price for each item given the cost and the percent of markup.

13. MP3 player: \$150; 22% markup **\$183**
14. sofa: \$600; 31.5% markup **\$789**
15. television: \$669; 23% markup **\$822.87**
16. dress: \$16.25; 35% markup **\$21.94**
17. speakers: \$42; 27% markup **\$53.34**
18. CD: \$8.99; $34\frac{4}{5}$% markup **\$12.12**
19. **VIDEOS** A video store is selling previously owned DVDs for 40% off the regular price of \$15. What is the sale price of the DVDs? **\$9**
20. **COOKIES** On Tuesday, a baker sold 132 cookies. On Wednesday, she sold 108 cookies. Find the percent of change to the nearest tenth of a percent. **18.2%**

Chapter 7 38 Glencoe Pre-Algebra

Word Problem Practice
CRM p. 39 AL OL BL

NAME ________ DATE ________ PERIOD ________

7-6 Word Problem Practice
Percent of Change

1. **DVD** Bill paid \$20 for a new DVD three years ago. Yesterday he paid \$15 for a new DVD. Find the percent of change. **25% decrease**
2. **TRAINING** When Jan began training for a marathon, she could run 3 miles in the same amount of time she can now run 5 miles. What is the percent of change in Jan's running speed? **67% decrease**
3. **CENSUS** According to the United States Census Bureau, the state of Texas had a population of 16,986,510 in 1990. Census data shows that in 2000, the population of Texas was 20,851,820. Find the percent of change. **23% increase**
4. **INVESTMENT** Jack bought a coin for \$200, which he later sold for \$175. Find the percent of change. Did Jack make a good investment? Explain. **12.5% decrease; No, a good investment would yield an increase in value.**
5. **TRAVEL** The following table shows the number of visitors to Yellowstone National Park from 2000 to 2006.

Year	Number of Visitors
2000	2,838,233
2001	2,758,526
2002	2,973,677
2003	3,019,375
2004	2,868,317
2005	2,835,649
2006	2,870,293

a. What was the percent of change in the number of tourists between 2000 and 2001? **2.8% decrease**

b. Determine between which years Yellowstone National Park experienced the highest percent of decrease of visitors and find the percent of change. **A 5% decrease between 2003 and 2004**

c. Determine between which years Yellowstone National Park experienced the highest percent of increase in visitors and find the percent of change. **A 7.8% increase between 2001 and 2002**

Chapter 7 39 Glencoe Pre-Algebra

Lesson 7-6

Problem-Solving Tip

Make a Table In Exercise 32, the data are displayed in a table. This makes finding the percent of change easier.

33b. Sample answer: The percents of change were the same but the amount of change for Columbus was much greater than the amount of change for Columbia. The percents were the same because the original amounts for each city were very different.

Real-World Link

The largest annual population change in the United States in the 20th century was 3,083,287, which occurred from 1949 to 1950. The largest percent of change occurred from 1909 to 1910. It was a 2.1% increase.

Source: U.S. Census Bureau

37a. false; Sample answer: Suppose the cost of an item is \$25 and you want to mark it up 125% of the cost. So, multiply \$25 by 125% or 1.25. The new price is \$25 + \$31.25 or \$56.25.

31. **TRACK** Torie's 400 meter dash time is 74 seconds. Juliette's time is 15% faster than Torie's. What is Juliette's 400 meter dash time? Write an inequality comparing the two times. Use the symbols < or >. **62.9 s; 62.9 < 74**

32. **BUSINESS** The first and second quarter earnings of two restaurants are shown at the right. Which restaurant had the greater percent of change in the second quarter? **B; It increased by 22% and restaurant A increased by about 3%.**

Earnings (\$)		
	A	B
Quarter 1	17,821	8112
Quarter 2	18,331	9920

33. **MULTIPLE REPRESENTATIONS** In this problem, you will compare percents of change. The table shows the population of capital cities for four different states.

City	Population 2000	Population 2006	Amount of Change	% of change
Raleigh, NC	276,093	356,321	80,228	29%
Columbia, SC	116,278	119,961	3683	3%
Frankfort, KY	27,741	27,077	−664	−2%
Columbus, OH	711,470	733,203	21,733	3%

a. **TABULAR** Copy and complete the table. Round to the nearest whole percent.

b. **ANALYTICAL** Compare the amounts of change and the percents of change for Columbia and Columbus. Explain the differences and similarities between the two.

34. **MULTIPLE REPRESENTATIONS** In this problem, you will examine percent of change over time. The table gives the price of milk for various years. **a–b. See margin.**

One Gallon of Milk	
Year	Price (\$)
1970	1.23
1980	1.60
1990	2.15
2000	2.60

a. **ALGEBRAIC** Write two inequalities comparing the percent of increase from 1970 to 1980 to the percent of increase from 1980 to 1990. Round to the nearest percent, if necessary.

b. **GRAPHICAL** Graph the prices of milk over the years. Use the x-axis as the years and y-axis as the prices.

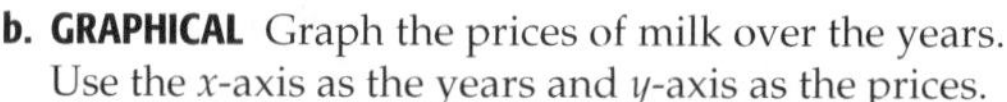

c. **GRAPHICAL** Use the graph to determine which decade had the greatest percent of increase in the price of milk. Explain your reasoning. **1980–1990; The graph is steeper during that time.**

H.O.T. Problems
Use Higher-Order Thinking Skills

35. **OPEN ENDED** Give an example of a percent of increase. **Sample answer: from 80 mi to 160 mi; 100% increase**

36. **CHALLENGE** An item at a consignment shop is marked down 10% each week until it sells. If a bicycle was originally priced at \$150, what is the cost after 3 weeks? 6 weeks? **\$109.35; \$79.72**

37. **REASONING** Determine whether each statement is *true* or *false*. If false, provide a counterexample.

a. It is impossible to increase the cost of an item by more than 100%.

b. It is possible to decrease the cost of an item by less than 1%. **true**

38. **CHALLENGE** Suppose a store has an item on sale for 25% off the original amount. By what percent does the store have to increase the price of the item in order to sell the item for the original amount? Explain. **See margin.**

39. **WRITING IN MATH** Write and solve a real-world problem involving a discount of an item. **See margin.**

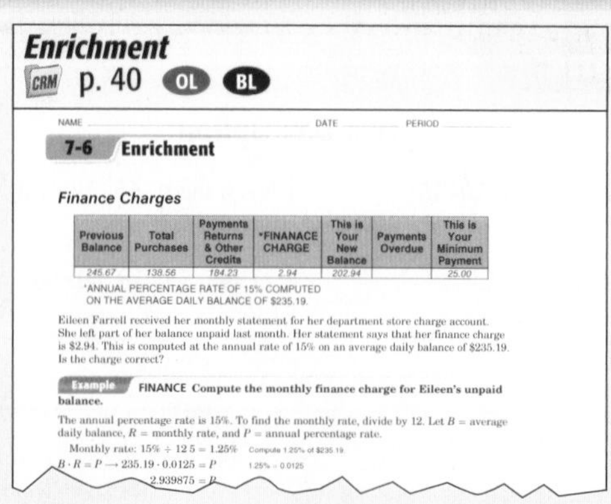

Enrichment
CRM p. 40 OL BL

NAME ________ DATE ________ PERIOD ________

7-6 Enrichment

Finance Charges

Previous Balance	Total Purchases	Payments Returns & Other Credits	*FINANACE CHARGE	This is Your New Balance	Payments Overdue	This is Your Minimum Payment
245.67	138.56	184.23	2.94	202.94		25.00

*ANNUAL PERCENTAGE RATE OF 15% COMPUTED ON THE AVERAGE DAILY BALANCE OF \$235.19.

Eileen Farrell received her monthly statement for her department store charge account. She left part of her balance unpaid last month. Her statement says that her finance charge is \$2.94. This is computed at the annual rate of 15% on an average daily balance of \$235.19. Is the charge correct?

Example **FINANCE Compute the monthly finance charge for Eileen's unpaid balance.**

The annual percentage rate is 15%. To find the monthly rate, divide by 12. Let B = average daily balance, R = monthly rate, and P = annual percentage rate.

Monthly rate: 15% ÷ 12 5 = 1.25% Compute 1.25% of \$235.19

$B \cdot R = P \rightarrow 235.19 \cdot 0.0125 = P$ 1.25% = 0.0125

$2.939875 = P$

Multiple Representations In Exercise 33, students compare percents of change for population by using a table.

In Exercise 34, students use inequalities and a graph to analyze percents of change for milk prices.

Standardized Test Practice

40. If each dimension of the rectangle is tripled, what is the percent of increase in the area? C

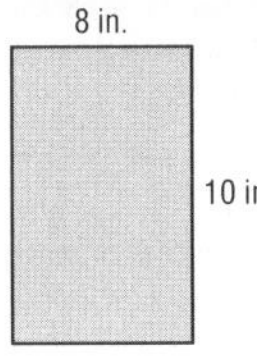

A 300% C 800%

B 600% D 900%

41. Which of the following represents the greatest percent of change? H

F Boots that were originally priced at $90 are on sale for $63.

G A baby that weighed 7 pounds at birth now weighs 10 pounds.

H A bracelet that costs $12 to make is sold for $28.

J A savings account increased from $500 to $600 in 1 year.

42. The table shows the budget of a city. C

Annual Budget	
Year	Budget (millions of $)
2005	45.6
2006	48.3
2007	45.9
2008	55.1

Which statement is supported by the table?

A The budget decreased and then increased.

B The greatest percent of change occurred from 2005 to 2006.

C The budget increased 20% from 2007 to 2008.

D The percent of change from 2005 to 2006 was the same as from 2006 to 2007.

43. GRIDDED RESPONSE The price of a television was $900 on Tuesday. On Wednesday the manager reduced the price 5%. What was the price in dollars of the television after the reduction? 855

Spiral Review

Solve each problem using the percent equation. (Lesson 7-5)

44. Find 12% of 72. 8.64

45. Find 42% of 150. 63

46. What is 37.5% of 89? 33.375

47. What is 24.2% of 60? 14.52

48. FOOD Suppose fifty-six percent of the Calories in corn chips are from fat. If one serving contains 160 Calories, estimate the number of Calories from fat in one serving of corn chips. (Lesson 7-4) about 96 calories

49. FISH Of the fish in an aquarium, 26% are angelfish. If the aquarium contains 50 fish, how many are angelfish? (Lesson 7-3) 13 angelfish

Find each sum. Write in simplest form. (Lesson 3-6)

50. $\frac{1}{10} + \frac{1}{3}$ $\frac{13}{30}$

51. $-\frac{1}{6} + \frac{7}{18}$ $\frac{2}{9}$

52. $6\frac{4}{5} + (-1\frac{3}{4})$ $5\frac{1}{20}$

Skills Review

Write each fraction as a decimal. (Lesson 3-1)

53. $\frac{7}{8}$ 0.875

54. $\frac{1}{5}$ 0.2

55. $\frac{6}{20}$ 0.3

56. $\frac{45}{50}$ 0.9

4 ASSESS

Ticket Out the Door Tell students to solve the following problem. Students will hand in their solutions as they exit.

Suppose 4 desks are removed from a classroom with 30 desks. What is the percent of decrease? 13% decrease

Formative Assessment

Check for student understanding of concepts in Lessons 7-5 and 7-6.

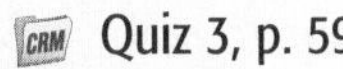

Additional Answers

34a. 30% < 34%; 34% > 30%

34b. **Price of a Gallon of Milk**

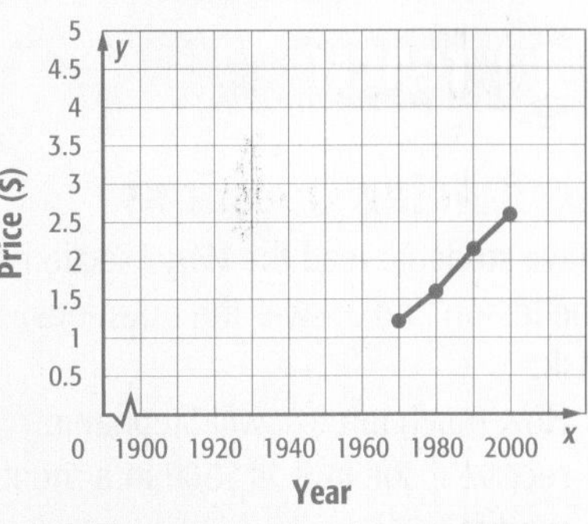

38. $33\frac{1}{3}\%$; Sample answer: Suppose the cost of the item is $100. So, 25% of $100 is $25 and $100 − $25 = $75. Then set a proportion to find what percent of $75 is $25. $75 × p% = $25. Solve for p: $\frac{\$25}{\$75} = \frac{p}{100}$. $p = 33\frac{1}{3}\%$

39. Sample answer: An internet service provider offers a plan for $40 per month. If this month the plan is 45% off, what is the cost of the plan?; $22

Differentiated Instruction

Extension Have students solve the following problem: In December, a video retailer increases the price of DVD's 10%. In January, due to overstock, the same retailer reduces the prices of the DVD's by 10%. How much will a customer pay for a DVD in January if the price in November was $15.00? $14.85

7-7 Lesson Notes

1 FOCUS

Vertical Alignment

Before Lesson 7-7
Solve problems using the percent equation.

Lesson 7-7
Solve simple and compound interest problems and apply the simple interest equation to real-world problems.

After Lesson 7-7
Use circle graphs to display data given as percents.

2 TEACH

Scaffolding Questions

Have students read the *Why?* section of the lesson and answer the questions.

Ask:

- How much interest will Stephanie receive if she invests $500 in a money market? $24.50
- How much interest will Stephanie receive if she invests in a CD? $18.75
- Which investment will give her the greater interest? money market

Additional Answers

b. She will receive $24.50 from a money market and $18.75 from a CD.

7-7 Simple and Compound Interest

Then

You have already solved problems using the percent equation. (Lesson 7-5)

Now

- Solve simple interest problems and apply the simple interest equation to real-world problems.
- Solve compound interest problems.

New Vocabulary

interest
simple interest
principal
compound interest

Math Online

glencoe.com

- Extra Examples
- Personal Tutor
- Self-Check Quiz
- Homework Help

Why?

Stephanie received $500 for graduation. She plans to save it for college. The table shows rates for various investments for one year.

Type of Investment	Rate
Certificate of Deposit (CD)	3.75%
Money Market	4.9%
Savings	2.0%

a. If Stephanie puts her money in a savings account, she will receive 2% of $500 in interest for one year. Find the interest Stephanie will receive if she puts her money in a savings account for one year. **$10**

b. Compare the interest Stephanie will receive in one year from a money market and from a certificate of deposit for one year. **See margin.**

Simple Interest **Interest** is the amount of money paid or earned for the use of money by a bank or other financial institution. **Simple interest** is paid only on the initial principal of a savings account or a loan. To solve problems involving simple interest, use the following formula.

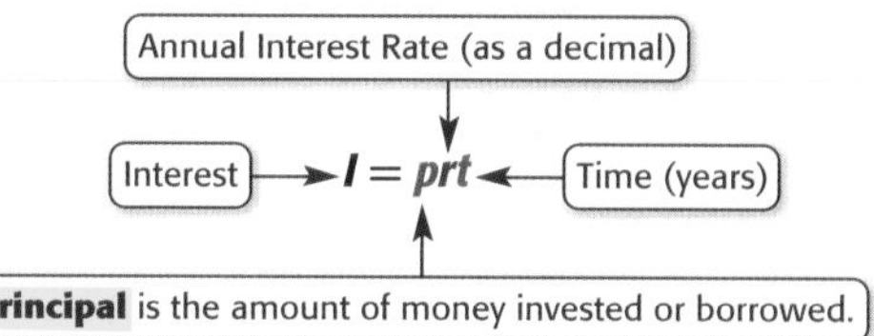

EXAMPLE 1 Find Simple Interest

Find the simple interest to the nearest cent.

a. $1000 at 4.5% for 2 years

$I = prt$ — **Write the simple interest formula.**

$I = 1000 \cdot 0.045 \cdot 2$ — **Replace *p* with 1000, *r* with 0.045, and *t* with 2.**

$I = 90$ — **Simplify.**

The simple interest is $90.

b. $2500 at 6.75% for 3 years

$I = prt$ — **Write the simple interest formula.**

$I = 2500 \cdot 0.0675 \cdot 3$ — **Replace *p* with 2500, *r* with 0.0675, and *t* with 3.**

$I = 506.25$ — **Simplify.**

The simple interest is $506.25.

Check Your Progress

1A. $2250 at 6% for 4 years **$540**

1B. $4000 at 4.25% for 1 year **$170**

Personal Tutor glencoe.com

Lesson 7-7 Resources

Resource	Approaching-Level	On-Level	Beyond-Level	English Learners
Teacher Edition	• Differentiated Instruction, p. 371	• Differentiated Instruction, p. 371	• Differentiated Instruction, pp. 371, 374	• Differentiated Instruction, p. 371
Chapter Resource Masters	• Study Guide and Intervention, pp. 42–43 • Skills Practice, p. 44 • Practice, p. 45 • Word Problem Practice, p. 46 • Spreadsheet Activity, p. 48	• Study Guide and Intervention, pp. 42–43 • Skills Practice, p. 44 • Practice, p. 45 • Word Problem Practice, p. 46 • Enrichment, p. 47 • Spreadsheet Activity, p. 48	• Practice, p. 45 • Word Problem Practice, p. 46 • Enrichment, p. 47 • Spreadsheet Activity, p. 48	• Study Guide and Intervention, pp. 42–43 • Skills Practice, p. 44 • Practice, p. 45 • Spreadsheet Activity, p. 48
Transparencies	• 5-Minute Check Transparency 7-7	• 5-Minute Check Transparency 7-7	• 5-Minute Check Transparency 7-7	• 5-Minute Check Transparency 7-7
Other	• Study Notebook • Teaching Pre-Algebra with Manipulatives	• Study Notebook • Teaching Pre-Algebra with Manipulatives	• Study Notebook	• Study Notebook • Teaching Pre-Algebra with Manipulatives

Watch Out!

Converting Units When using the formula $I = prt$, remember the time is expressed in years. For example, 6 months is 0.5 year.

Real-World EXAMPLE 2 Find the Interest Rate

COMPUTERS Mr. Gabel borrowed $1860 to buy a computer. He will pay $71.30 per month for 30 months. Find the simple interest rate for his loan.

Understand You need to find the simple interest rate.

Plan Use the formula $I = prt$.

Solve First find the amount of interest he will pay.

$\$71.30 \cdot 30 = \$2139$ — **Multiply to find total amount.**

$\$2139 - \$1860 = \$279$ — **Subtract to find the interest.**

So, $I = \$279$.

The principal is $1860. So, $p = 1860$.
The loan will be for 30 months or 2.5 years. So, $t = 2.5$.

$I = prt$ — **Write the simple interest formula.**

$279 = 1860 \cdot r \cdot 2.5$ — **Replace *I* with 279, *p* with 1860, and *t* with 2.5.**

$279 = 4650r$ — **Simplify.**

$\frac{279}{4650} = \frac{4650r}{4650}$ — **Divide each side by 4650.**

$0.06 = r$ — The simple interest rate is 0.06 or 6%.

Check Use the formula $I = prt$. $\$1860 \times 0.06 \times 2.5$ or $279. ✓

Check Your Progress

2. **SAVINGS** Suppose Nantai placed $2400 in the bank for 5 years. He makes $9.20 in interest each month. Find the annual interest rate. **4.6%**

Personal Tutor glencoe.com

Compound Interest **Compound interest** is paid on the initial principal and on interest earned in the past.

StudyTip

Compound Interest Because you are finding the interest after the first year, substitute 1 for *t* instead of 2.

EXAMPLE 3 Find the Total Amount

What is the total amount of money in an account where $600 is invested at an interest rate of 8.75% compounded annually for 2 years?

Step 1 Find the amount of money in the account at the end of the first year.

$I = prt$ — **Write the simple interest formula.**

$I = 600 \cdot 0.0875 \cdot 1$ — **Replace *p* with 600, *r* with 0.0875, and *t* with 1.**

$I = 52.5$ — **Simplify.**

$600 + 52.5 = 652.50$ — **Add the amount invested and the interest.**

At the end of the first year, there is $652.50 in the account.

Step 2 Find the amount of money in the account at the end of the second year.

$I = prt$ — **Write the simple interest formula.**

$I = 652.50 \cdot 0.0875 \cdot 1$ — **Replace *p* with 652.50, *r* with 0.0875, and *t* with 1.**

$I = 57.09$ — **Simplify.**

So, the amount in the account after 2 years is $652.50 + $57.09 or $709.59.

Check Your Progress

3. What is the total amount of money in an account where $5000 is invested at an interest rate of 5% compounded annually after 3 years? **$5788.13**

Personal Tutor glencoe.com

Simple Interest

Example 1 shows how to find the simple interest on a given amount of money. **Example 2** shows how to find the simple interest rate in a real-world application.

Formative Assessment

Use the Check Your Progress exercises after each example to determine students' understanding of concepts.

Additional Examples

1 a. Find the simple interest for $2000 invested at 2.5% for 3 years. $150

b. Find the simple interest for $4500 invested at 4.25% for 2 years. $382.50

2 **SWIMMING POOL** Mr. Webster borrowed $1280 to buy a new swimming pool. He will pay $57.60 each month for the next 24 months. Find the simple interest rate for his loan. 4%

Additional Examples also in Interactive Classroom PowerPoint® Presentations

Compound Interest

Example 3 shows how to calculate the total amount in an account when the investment is compounded annually.

Additional Example

3 What is the total amount of money in an account where $800 is invested at an interest rate of 6.25% compounded annually for 2 years? $903.13

Differentiated Instruction

Intrapersonal To ensure that students understand the difference between simple and compound interest, have them write a paragraph about each of these. Check their explanations to make sure that each student has described the difference correctly.

Focus on Mathematical Content

Compound Interest In contrast to simple interest, compound interest is applied to the original principal and any previously earned interest. There are four ways to increase the amount in a compound-interest account: increase the initial principal, increase the annual interest rate, increase the number of compoundings per year, or increase the time that the money is in the account.

3 PRACTICE

Formative Assessment

Use Exercises 1–9 to check for understanding.

Use the chart at the bottom of this page to customize assignments for your students.

Additional Answers

25. option A; Sample answer: After 3 years, the interest earned with option A is \$281.25. With option B, the interest earned is \$273.91.

32b. **Total Interest Earned**

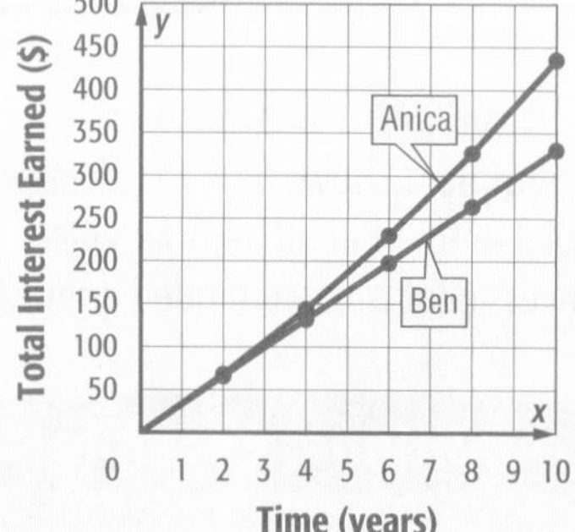

32c. Sample answer: The graph of Ben's interest is in a straight line. The graph of Anica's interest is increasing at a faster rate and is not in a straight line.

Multiple Representations In Exercise 32, students create a table of values and scatter plots to contrast the simple and compound interest.

Check Your Understanding

Example 1 p. 370 — **Find the simple interest to the nearest cent.**

1. \$1350 at 6% for 7 years **\$567**
2. \$240 at 8% for 9 months **\$14.40**
3. \$725 at 3.25% for 5 years **\$117.81**
4. \$3750 at 5.75% for 42 months **\$754.69**

Example 2 p. 371

5. **LOANS** Mateo's sister paid off her student loan of \$5000 in 3 years. If she made a payment of \$152.35 each month, what was her simple interest rate for her loan? Round to the nearest hundredth. **3.23%**

Example 3 p. 371 — **Find the total amount in each account to the nearest cent if the interest is compounded annually.** **6–9. Answers may vary due to rounding.**

6. \$480 at 5% for 3 years **\$555.66**
7. \$515 at 11.8% for 2 years **\$643.71**
8. \$6525 at 6.25% for 4 years **\$8315.65**
9. \$2750 at 8.5% for 3 years **\$3512.55**

Practice and Problem Solving

● = **Step-by-Step Solutions** begin on page R11. **Extra Practice** begins on page 810

Example 1 p. 370 — **Find the simple interest to the nearest cent.**

10. \$275 at 7.5% for 4 years **\$82.50**
11. \$620 at 6.25% for 5 years **\$193.75**
12. \$734 at 12% for 3 months **\$22.02**
13. \$2020 at 8% for 18 months **\$242.40**
14. \$1200 at 6% for 36 months **\$216**
15. \$4380 at 10.5% for 2 years **\$919.80**

Example 2 p. 371

16. **CARS** Thomas borrowed \$4800 to buy a new car. He will be paying \$96 each month for the next 60 months. Find the simple interest rate for his car loan. **4%**

Example 3 p. 371 — **Find the total amount in each account to the nearest cent if the interest is compounded annually.** **17–22. Answers may vary due to rounding.**

17. \$3850 at 5.25% for 2 years **\$4264.86**
18. \$4025 at 6.8% for 6 years **\$5973.01**
19. \$595 at 4.75% for 3 years **\$683.88**
20. \$840 at 7% for 4 years **\$1101.07**
21. \$12,000 at 6.95% for 4 years **\$15,700.17**
22. \$8750 at 12.25% for 2 years **\$11,025.06**

B

23. **CARS** Denise has a car loan of \$8000. Over the course of the loan, she paid a total of \$1680 in interest at a simple interest rate of 6%. How many months was the loan? **42 months**

24. **INVESTMENTS** A certificate of deposit has an annual simple interest rate of 5.25%. If \$567 in interest is earned over a 6 year period, how much was invested? **\$1800**

25. **FINANCIAL LITERACY** A bank offers the options shown for interest rates on their savings accounts. Which option will yield more money after 3 years with an initial deposit of \$1500? Explain. **See margin.**

Kingman Bank		
Option	**Rate**	**Type of Interest**
A	6.25%	simple
B	5.75%	compounded annually

Find the total amount in each account to the nearest cent if the interest is compounded twice a year. **26–29. Answers may vary due to rounding.**

26. \$2500 at 6.75% for 1 year **\$2671.60**
27. \$14,750 at 5% for 1 year **\$15,496.72**
28. \$3750 at 10.25% for 2 years **\$4579.90**
29. \$975 at 7.2% for 2 years **\$1123.16**

Differentiated Homework Options

Level	Assignment	Two-Day Option	
AL Basic	10–22, 33–35, 37–52	11–21 odd, 38–41	10–22 even, 33–35, 37, 42–52
OL Core	11–21 odd, 23–25, 27, 29–35, 37–52	10–22, 38–41	23–35, 37, 42–52
BL Advanced	23–49 (optional: 50–52)		

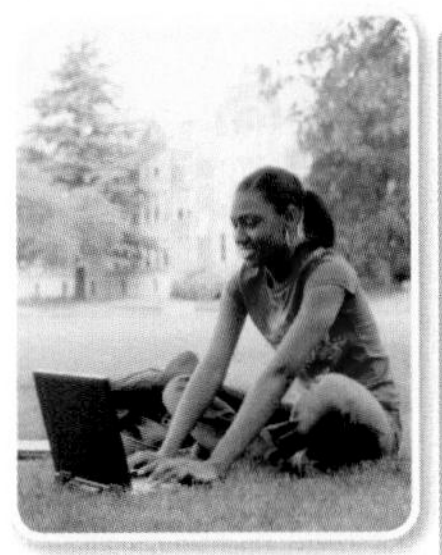

Real-World Link

College tuition continues to rise each year. The average yearly cost of a four-year private college or university is $22,218. The average yearly cost of a four-year pubilc college or university is $5836.

Source: College Board

30. COLLEGE Mrs. Glover placed $15,000 in a certificate of deposit for 18 months for her children's college funds. Each month she makes $56.50 in interest. Find the annual simple interest rate for the certificate of deposit. **4.52%**

31. CREDIT Jameson received his first credit card bill for a total of $325.42. Each month he makes a $50 payment and the remaining balance is charged an interest rate of 1.5%. The register at the right shows his first three monthly bills. If he does not make any more charges, what will be the amount of the fifth bill? the seventh bill? **$137.77; $39.68**

Bill Number	Bill Amount	Payment	New Balance
1	$325.42	$50	$275.42
2	$279.55	$50	$229.55
3	$232.99	$50	$182.99

32. MULTIPLE REPRESENTATIONS In this problem, you will compare simple and compound interest. Consider the following situation. Ben deposits $550 at a 6% simple interest rate and Anica deposits $550 at a 6% interest rate that is compounded annually.

a. TABULAR Copy and complete the table.

Total Interest Earned ($)		
Years	Ben	Anica
2	66	67.98
4	132	144.36
6	198	230.18
8	264	326.61
10	330	434.96

b. GRAPHICAL Graph the data on the coordinate plane. Show the time in years on the x-axis and the total interest earned in dollars on the y-axis. Plot Ben's interest in blue and Anica's interest in red. Then connect the points. **b–c. See margin.**

c. ANALYTICAL Compare the graphs of the two functions.

H.O.T. Problems — Use Higher-Order Thinking Skills

33. OPEN ENDED Give a principal and interest rate where the amount of simple interest earned in four years would be $80. Justify your answer.

34. REASONING Kai-Yo deposits $500 into an account that earns 2% simple interest. Marcos deposits $250 into an account that earns 4% simple interest. How much money does each have after 10 years? Who will have more money over the long run? Explain your reasoning.

35. FIND THE ERROR Sabino and Mya are finding the simple interest on a $2500 investment at a simple interest rate of 5.75% for 18 months. Is either of them correct? Explain your reasoning.

Sabino	Mya
$I = prt$	$I = prt$
$I = 2500 \cdot 0.0575 \cdot 18$	$I = 2500 \cdot 0.575 \cdot 1.5$
$I = \$2587.50$	$I = \$2156.25$

36. CHALLENGE Determine the length of time it will take to double a principal of $100 if deposited into an account that earns 10% simple annual interest. **10 years**

37. WRITING IN MATH Compare simple and compound interest. **See margin.**

33. Sample answer: $2000 at 1%. Using the simple interest formula $I = \$2000 \cdot 0.01 \cdot 4$ or $80

34. Kai-Yo $600, Marcos: $350; Even though Kai-Yo and Marcos earn the same amount of interest after every year, Kai-Yo will always have $250 more than Marcos because that was the difference in the initial deposit.

35. no; Sabino did not convert the time to years and Mya did not change the percent to a decimal correctly.

Additional Answer

37. Sample Answer: With simple interest, the amount of money earned will be the same each year because it is always applied to the initial amount. With compound interest, the amount of interest will increase each year because it is being applied to the new total after the interest is added each year.

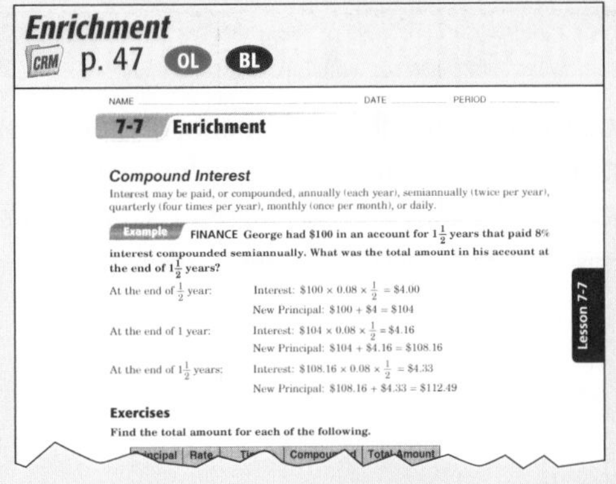

Enrichment CRM p. 47 OL BL

NAME ______ DATE ______ PERIOD ______

7-7 Enrichment

Compound Interest

Interest may be paid, or compounded, annually (each year), semiannually (twice per year), quarterly (four times per year), monthly (once per month), or daily.

Example FINANCE George had $100 in an account for $1\frac{1}{2}$ years that paid 8% interest compounded semiannually. What was the total amount in his account at the end of $1\frac{1}{2}$ years?

At the end of $\frac{1}{2}$ year: Interest: $\$100 \times 0.08 \times \frac{1}{2} = \$4.00$; New Principal: $100 + $4 = $104

At the end of 1 year: Interest: $\$104 \times 0.08 \times \frac{1}{2} = \$4.16$; New Principal: $104 + $4.16 = $108.16

At the end of $1\frac{1}{2}$ years: Interest: $\$108.16 \times 0.08 \times \frac{1}{2} = \$4.33$; New Principal: $108.16 + $4.33 = $112.49

Exercises

Find the total amount for each of the following.

...incipal	Rate	[illegible]	Compou...	Total Amount

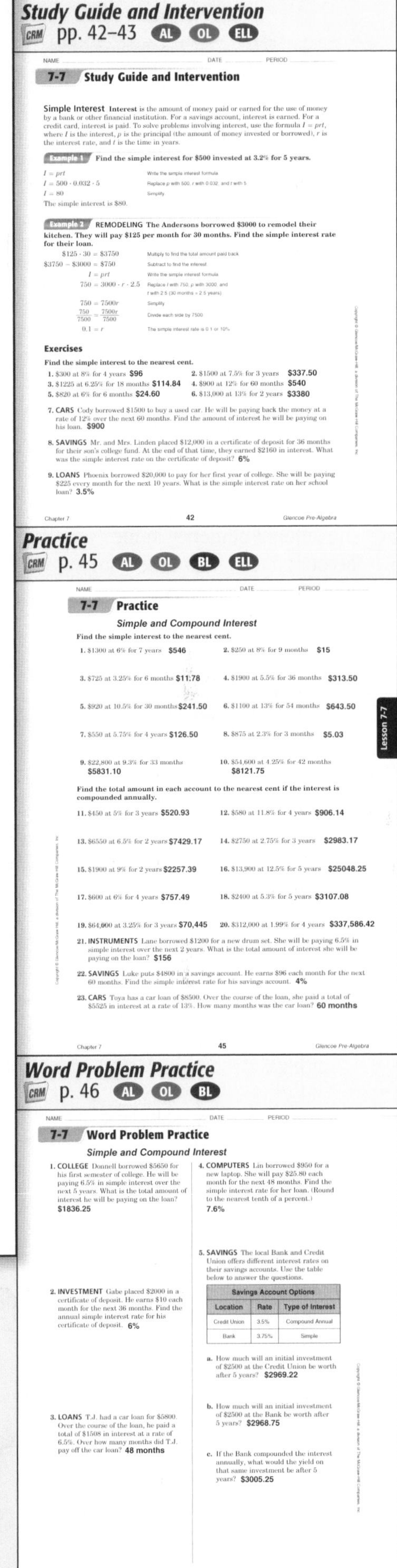

Study Guide and Intervention CRM pp. 42–43 AL OL ELL

NAME ______ DATE ______ PERIOD ______

7-7 Study Guide and Intervention

Simple Interest **Interest** is the amount of money paid or earned for the use of money by a bank or other financial institution. For a savings account, interest is earned. For a credit card, interest is paid. To solve problems involving interest, use the formula $I = prt$, where I is the interest, p is the principal (the amount of money invested or borrowed), r is the interest rate, and t is the time in years.

Example 1 Find the simple interest for $500 invested at 3.2% for 5 years.

$I = prt$ — Write the simple interest formula.
$I = 500 \cdot 0.032 \cdot 5$ — Replace p with 500, r with 0.032, and t with 5.
$I = 80$ — Simplify.
The simple interest is $80.

Example 2 REMODELING The Andersons borrowed $3000 to remodel their kitchen. They will pay $125 per month for 30 months. Find the simple interest rate for their loan.

$\$125 \cdot 30 = \$3750$ — Multiply to find the total amount paid back.
$\$3750 - \$3000 = \$750$ — Subtract to find the interest.
$I = prt$ — Write the simple interest formula.
$750 = 3000 \cdot r \cdot 2.5$ — Replace I with 750, p with 3000, and t with 2.5 (30 months = 2.5 years).
$750 = 7500r$ — Simplify.
$\frac{750}{7500} = \frac{7500r}{7500}$ — Divide each side by 7500.
$0.1 = r$ — The simple interest rate is 0.1 or 10%.

Exercises

Find the simple interest to the nearest cent.

1. $300 at 8% for 4 years **$96**
2. $1500 at 7.5% for 3 years **$337.50**
3. $1225 at 6.25% for 18 months **$114.84**
4. $900 at 12% for 60 months **$540**
5. $820 at 6% for 6 months **$24.60**
6. $13,000 at 13% for 2 years **$3380**

7. CARS Cody borrowed $1500 to buy a used car. He will be paying back the money at a rate of 12% over the next 60 months. Find the amount of interest he will be paying on his loan. **$900**

8. SAVINGS Mr. and Mrs. Linden placed $12,000 in a certificate of deposit for 36 months for their son's college fund. At the end of that time, they earned $2160 in interest. What was the simple interest rate on the certificate of deposit? **6%**

9. LOANS Phoenix borrowed $20,000 to pay for her first year of college. She will be paying $225 every month for the next 10 years. What is the simple interest rate on her school loan? **3.5%**

Practice CRM p. 45 AL OL BL ELL

NAME ______ DATE ______ PERIOD ______

7-7 Practice

Simple and Compound Interest

Find the simple interest to the nearest cent.

1. $1300 at 6% for 7 years **$546**
2. $250 at 8% for 9 months **$15**
3. $725 at 3.25% for 6 months **$11.78**
4. $1900 at 5.5% for 36 months **$313.50**
5. $920 at 10.5% for 30 months **$241.50**
6. $1100 at 13% for 54 months **$643.50**
7. $550 at 5.75% for 4 years **$126.50**
8. $875 at 2.3% for 3 months **$5.03**
9. $22,800 at 9.3% for 33 months **$5831.10**
10. $54,600 at 4.25% for 42 months **$8121.75**

Find the total amount in each account to the nearest cent if the interest is compounded annually.

11. $450 at 5% for 3 years **$520.93**
12. $580 at 11.8% for 4 years **$906.14**
13. $6550 at 6.5% for 2 years **$7429.17**
14. $2750 at 2.75% for 3 years **$2983.17**
15. $1900 at 9% for 2 years **$2257.39**
16. $13,900 at 12.5% for 5 years **$25048.25**
17. $600 at 6% for 4 years **$757.49**
18. $2400 at 5.3% for 5 years **$3107.08**
19. $64,000 at 3.25% for 3 years **$70,445**
20. $312,000 at 1.99% for 4 years **$337,586.42**

21. INSTRUMENTS Lane borrowed $1200 for a new drum set. She will be paying 6.5% in simple interest over the next 2 years. What is the total amount of interest she will be paying on the loan? **$156**

22. SAVINGS Luke puts $4800 in a savings account. He earns $96 each month for the next 60 months. Find the simple interest rate for his savings account. **4%**

23. CARS Toya has a car loan of $8500. Over the course of the loan, she paid a total of $5525 in interest at a rate of 13%. How many months was the car loan? **60 months**

Word Problem Practice CRM p. 46 AL OL BL

NAME ______ DATE ______ PERIOD ______

7-7 Word Problem Practice

Simple and Compound Interest

1. COLLEGE Donnell borrowed $5650 for his first semester of college. He will be paying 6.5% in simple interest over the next 5 years. What is the total amount of interest he will be paying on the loan? **$1836.25**

2. INVESTMENT Gabe placed $2000 in a certificate of deposit. He earns $10 each month for the next 36 months. Find the annual simple interest rate for his certificate of deposit. **6%**

3. LOANS T.J. had a car loan for $5800. Over the course of the loan, he paid a total of $1508 in interest at a rate of 6.5%. Over how many months did T.J. pay off the car loan? **48 months**

4. COMPUTERS Lin borrowed $950 for a new laptop. She will pay $25.80 each month for the next 48 months. Find the simple interest rate for her loan. (Round to the nearest tenth of a percent.) **7.6%**

5. SAVINGS The local Bank and Credit Union offers different interest rates on their savings accounts. Use the table below to answer the questions.

Savings Account Options		
Location	Rate	Type of Interest
Credit Union	3.5%	Compound Annual
Bank	3.75%	Simple

a. How much will an initial investment of $2500 at the Credit Union be worth after 5 years? **$2969.22**

b. How much will an initial investment of $2500 at the Bank be worth after 5 years? **$2968.75**

c. If the Bank compounded the interest annually, what would the yield on that same investment be after 5 years? **$3005.25**

Lesson 7-7 Simple and Compound Interest 373

Watch Out!

Find the Error For Exercise 35, Sabino and Mya are finding the simple interest on an investment. Sabino needs to be aware that the interest must be calculated using years not months. Mya needs to be more careful when she changes percents to decimals.

TEACH with TECH

WEB SEARCH Have students research interest rates for different types of savings accounts. Ask them to calculate the amount of money in the account after 1 year based on an initial deposit of $50.

4 ASSESS

Yesterday's News Have students write how yesterday's lesson on determining discounts and markups helped them with learning today's lesson on interest. What ideas are the same? Which are different?

Additional Answer

41. 6.5% compounded annually; Sample answer: The investment of $500 at a 6.75% simple interest will earn $168.75 and the investment at a 6.5% rate compounded annually will earn $185.04.

Standardized Test Practice

38. A $500 certificate of deposit has a simple interest rate of 7.25%. What is the value of the certificate after 8 years? **C**

A $290 C $790
B $500 D $2900

39. Beatriz borrowed $1500 for student loans. She will make 30 equal monthly payments of $62.50 to pay off the loan. What is the simple interest rate for the loan? **J**

F 4% H 8.5%
G 7% J 10%

40. A savings account with $2250 has an interest rate of 5%. If the interest is compounded annually, how much will be in the account after 2 years? **C**

A $230.63 C $2480.63
B $337.50 D $2587.50

41. EXTENDED RESPONSE Which of the following plans will produce the greater earnings for an investment of $500 over 5 years? Explain. **See margin.**

Plan A	simple interest rate of 6.75%
Plan B	rate of 6.5% compounded annually

Spiral Review

42. ANIMALS In 2000, there were 356 endangered species. Five years later, 389 species were considered endangered. What was the percent of change? (Lesson 7-6) **9.3%**

Solve each problem using the percent equation. (Lesson 7-5)

43. 12 is what percent of 400? **3%**

44. 30 is 60% of what number? **50**

45. MONEY In a recent year, the number of $1 bills in circulation in the United States was about 7 billion. (Lesson 7-4)

a. Suppose the number of $5 bills in circulation was 25% of the number of $1 bills. About how many $5 bills were in circulation? $\frac{1}{4} \times 7$ **or 1.75 billion**

b. If the number of $10 bills was 20% of the number of $1 bills, about how many $10 bills were in circulation? $\frac{1}{5} \times 7$ **or 1.4 billion**

ALGEBRA Find each product. Write in simplest form. (Lesson 3-5)

46. $\frac{2}{x} \cdot \frac{3x}{7}$ $\frac{6}{7}$

47. $\frac{a}{b} \cdot \frac{5b}{c}$ $\frac{5a}{c}$

48. $\frac{4t}{9r} \cdot \frac{18r}{t^2}$ $\frac{8}{t}$

49. EXERCISE The table shows the amount of time Craig spends jogging every day. He increases the time he jogs every week. (Lesson 1-5)

Week	Time Jogging (minutes)
1	7
2	15
3	23
4	31
5	39

a. Write an equation to show the number of minutes spent jogging m for each week w. $m = 8w - 1$

b. How many minutes will Craig jog during week 9? **71 min**

Skills Review

Solve each problem. (Lesson 7-5)

50. Find 66% of 90. **59.4**

51. What is 0.2% of 735? **1.47**

52. Find 250% of 7000. **17,500**

Differentiated Instruction

Extension What is the total amount of money in an account where $500 is invested at an interest rate of 6% compounded quarterly for a year? $530.68 *Hint:* what percent will the balance be multiplied by each time the interest is compounded? 1.5%

EXTEND 7-7

Spreadsheet Lab
Compound Interest

Math Online glencoe.com
• Graphing Technology Personal Tutor

You can use a spreadsheet to investigate the impact of compound interest.

ACTIVITY

George deposits $1600 into an account that earns 8% interest compounded semiannually. What is the value of the account after 5 years?

An 8% interest compounded semiannually means that the interest is paid twice a year, or every 6 months. The interest rate is 8% ÷ 2 or 4%.

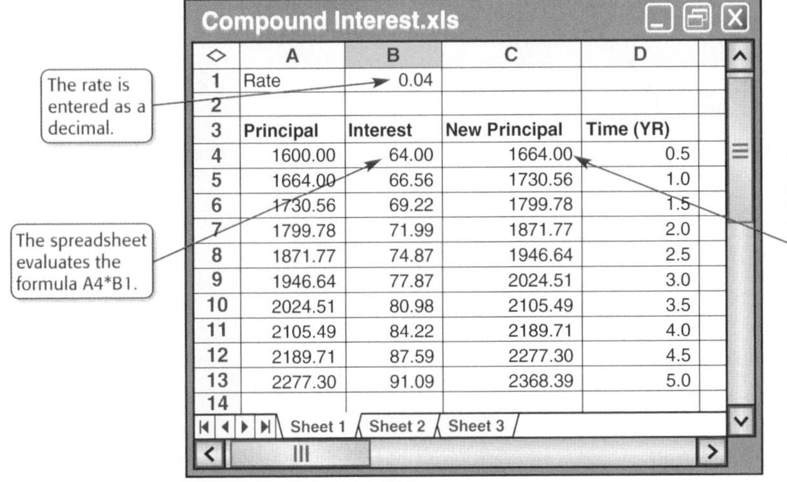

Compound Interest.xls
The rate is entered as a decimal.
The spreadsheet evaluates the formula A4*B1.
The interest is added to the principal every 6 months. The spreadsheet evaluates the formula A4+B4.
Sheet 1
Sheet 2
Sheet 3

◇	A	B	C	D
1	Rate	0.04		
2				
3	Principal	Interest	New Principal	Time (YR)
4	1600.00	64.00	1664.00	0.5
5	1664.00	66.56	1730.56	1.0
6	1730.56	69.22	1799.78	1.5
7	1799.78	71.99	1871.77	2.0
8	1871.77	74.87	1946.64	2.5
9	1946.64	77.87	2024.51	3.0
10	2024.51	80.98	2105.49	3.5
11	2105.49	84.22	2189.71	4.0
12	2189.71	87.59	2277.30	4.5
13	2277.30	91.09	2368.39	5.0
14				

The value of the savings account after five years is $2368.39.

Analyze the Results

1. Suppose you invest $1600 for five years at 8% simple interest. How does the simple interest compare to the compound interest shown above? **The simple interest, $640, is $128.39 less than the compound interest.**
2. Use a spreadsheet to find the amount of money in a savings account if $1600 is invested for five years at 8% interest compounded quarterly. **$2377.52**
3. Suppose you leave $150 in each of three bank accounts paying 6% interest per year. One account pays simple interest, one pays interest compounded semiannually, and one pays interest compounded quarterly. Use a spreadsheet to find the amount of money in each account after three years. **$177.00, $179.11, $179.34**
4. **MAKE A CONJECTURE** If the compounding occurs less frequently, how does the amount of interest change? **The amount of interest earned decreases.**
5. **MAKE A CONJECTURE** If the compounding occurs more frequently, how does the amount of interest change? **The amount of interest earned increases.**

From Concrete to Abstract

Have students discuss the different amounts that would be likely to change when different people deposit an amount of money or money is deposited at different institutions.

Extending the Concept

Ask:

- Suppose you have $5000 to invest for a period of 2 years. You can invest at 4% compounded semi-annually or you can invest at 3.75% compounded quarterly. Which would you choose and why? 4% compounded semiannually; At the end of 2 years, the balance would be $5412.16 versus $5387.54 if invested at 3.75% compounded quarterly.

EXTEND 7-7 Lesson Notes

1 FOCUS

Objective Use a spreadsheet to investigate the impact of compound interest.

Materials for Each Group

- computer with spreadsheet software

Teaching Tip

Remind students that cells in a spreadsheet are named by their row and their column. For example, the cell C5 is located in row 5, column C.

2 TEACH

Working in Cooperative Groups

Arrange students in groups of two or three, mixing abilities. Then have groups complete the Activity and Exercises 1–4.

Ask:

- How are the values in column C used for calculating interest? Each new principal amount is used in the next row as the principal amount in column A. It is then multiplied by the rate to get the interest amount in Column B.
- What information does column D provide? the time that the principal has been earning interest
- If the interest were to change to 3.25%, what cell would you change so that all interest amounts would be recalculated? B1

Practice Have students complete Exercises 1–5.

3 ASSESS

Formative Assessment

Use Exercise 4 to assess whether students comprehend how compounding interest impacts the amount of interest earned.

7-8 Lesson Notes

1 FOCUS

Vertical Alignment

Before Lesson 7-8
Express percents as decimals.

Lesson 7-8
Construct circle graphs.
Analyze circle graphs to solve real-world problems.

After Lesson 7-8
Model data and interpret graphs in everyday situations.

2 TEACH

Scaffolding Questions

Have students read the *Why?* section of the lesson and answer the questions.

Ask:

- How do you determine which instrument was most popular? the instrument with the highest percent
- Which instrument was most popular? your voice
- How does the graph make the survey results easier to interpret? You can tell at a glance which instruments are most and least popular.

7-8 Circle Graphs

Then
You have already expressed percents as decimals. (Lesson 7-2)

Now
- Construct circle graphs.
- Analyze circle graphs to solve real-world problems.

New Vocabulary
circle graph

Math Online
glencoe.com
- Extra Examples
- Personal Tutor
- Self-Check Quiz
- Homework Help

Why?

The graphic shows the results of a recent online survey about what part teens would want to be in a band.

What Part Would You Like To Be In a Band?
guitar 19%
drums 17%
piano 12%
saxophone 7%
vocals 35%
other 10%
Source: PBS Kids

a. Which part was the least favorite? saxophone

b. Are all the parts accounted for in the graphic? How can you tell? Yes; the percents add up to 100.

Circle Graphs A **circle graph** can be used to compare parts of a data set to the whole set of data. The percents in a circle graph add up to 100 since the entire circle represents the whole set.

EXAMPLE 1 Construct a Circle Graph from Percents

Construct a circle graph using the information above.

Step 1 There are 360° in a circle. So, multiply each percent by 360 to find the number of degrees for each section of the graph.

guitar: 19% of $360 = 0.19 \cdot 360 \approx 68$
drums: 17% of $360 = 0.17 \cdot 360 \approx 61$
piano: 12% of $360 = 0.12 \cdot 360 \approx 43$
saxophone: 7% of $360 = 0.07 \cdot 360 \approx 25$
vocals: 35% of $360 = 0.36 \cdot 360 = 126$
other: 10% of $360 = 0.10 \cdot 360 = 36$

Step 2 Use a compass to draw a circle and a radius. Then use a protractor to draw a 43° angle. This section represents the number of people who want to play the piano.

Step 3 From the new radius, draw the next angle. Repeat for each of the remaining angles.

Step 4 Label each section. Then give the graph a title.

What Part Would You Want To Be in a Band?

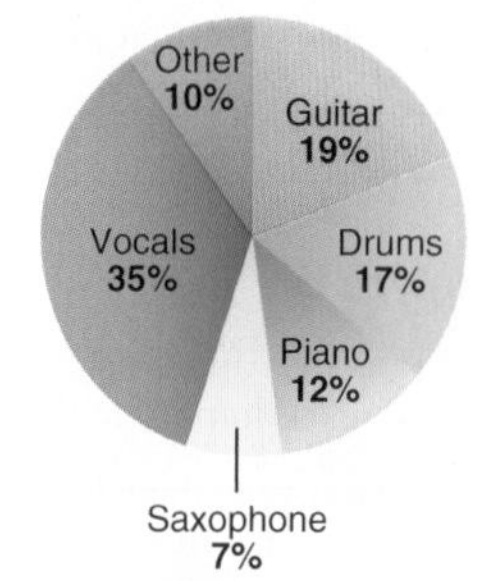

Check Your Progress

1. **PIZZA** The table gives the percent of favorite single pizza toppings. Construct a circle graph using the information in the table. See Chapter 7 Answer Appendix.

Topping	Percent
Cheese	34
Pepperoni	28
Mushroom	21
Other	17

Personal Tutor glencoe.com

Lesson 7-8 Resources

Resource	Approaching-Level	On-Level	Beyond-Level	English Learners
Teacher Edition	• Differentiated Instruction, p. 377	• Differentiated Instruction, p. 377	• Differentiated Instruction, pp. 377, 381	
Chapter Resource Masters	• Study Guide and Intervention, pp. 49–50 • Skills Practice, p. 51 • Practice, p. 52 • Word Problem Practice, p. 53	• Study Guide and Intervention, pp. 49–50 • Skills Practice, p. 51 • Practice, p. 52 • Word Problem Practice, p. 53 • Enrichment, p. 54	• Practice, p. 52 • Word Problem Practice, p. 53 • Enrichment, p. 54	• Study Guide and Intervention, pp. 49–50 • Skills Practice, p. 51 • Practice, p. 52
Transparencies	• 5-Minute Check Transparency 7-8	• 5-Minute Check Transparency 7-8	• 5-Minute Check Transparency 7-8	• 5-Minute Check Transparency 7-8
Other	• Study Notebook • Teaching Pre-Algebra with Manipulatives	• Study Notebook • Teaching Pre-Algebra with Manipulatives	• Study Notebook	• Study Notebook • Teaching Pre-Algebra with Manipulatives

Real-World Link

The United States contributes about 17% of the world's energy supply which makes it the leading producer. However, it is also the leading country in energy usage. The United States uses about 24% of the world's energy supply.

Source: *World Almanac*

When percents are not known, you must first determine what part of the whole each item represents.

EXAMPLE 2 Construct a Circle Graph From Data

Construct a circle graph using the information in the table at the right.

Home Heating	
Type of Fuel	**Number of Homes**
Bottled Gas	12
Electricity	64
Fuel Oil	18
Piped Gas	100
Wood	4
Other	2

Source: U.S. Census Bureau

Step 1 Find the total number of homes.

$12 + 64 + 18 + 100 + 4 + 2 = 200$

Step 2 Find the ratio that compares the number of homes in each group to the total number of homes.

bottled gas: $12 \div 200 = 0.06$
electricity: $64 \div 200 = 0.32$
fuel oil: $18 \div 200 \approx 0.09$
piped gas: $100 \div 200 = 0.50$
wood: $4 \div 200 = 0.02$
other: $2 \div 200 = 0.01$

Step 3 Use these ratios to find the number of degrees of each section.

bottled gas: $0.06 \cdot 360 = 21.6$ or about 22
electricity: $0.32 \cdot 360 = 115.2$ or about 115
fuel oil: $0.09 \cdot 360 = 32.4$ or about 32
piped gas: $0.5 \cdot 360 = 180$
wood: $0.02 \cdot 360 = 7.2$ or about 7
other: $0.01 \cdot 360 = 3.6$ or about 4

Step 4 Use a compass and a protractor to draw a circle and the appropriate sections.

Step 5 Label each section and give the graph a title. Write the ratios as percents.

Type of Fuel Used to Heat Homes

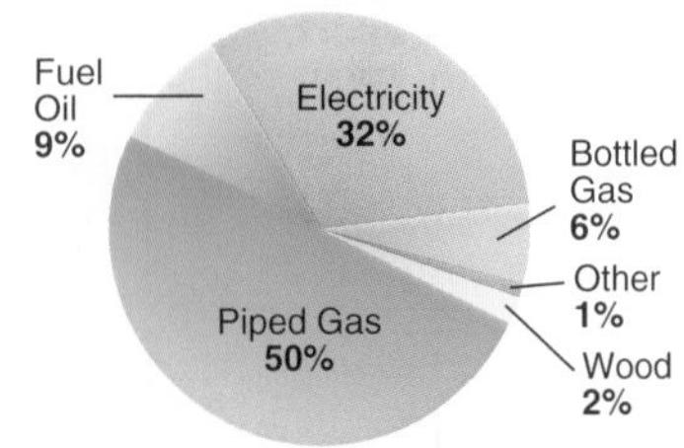

StudyTip

Alternative Method You can also find the angle measure using a proportion.

$\frac{12}{200} = \frac{x}{360}$

$4320 = 200x$

$21.6 = x$

Check Your Progress

2. Make a circle graph using the information in the table at the right that shows the major influences on teens for music choices.
See Chapter 7 Answer Appendix.

Influences on Music Choice	
Influence	**Number of Teens**
Radio	860
Friends	600
Television	320
Parents	140
Other	80

Personal Tutor glencoe.com

Differentiated Instruction

AL OL BL

Tactile The table shows the results of a survey of 25 students: Have students work in groups of two or three, mixing abilities, and make a poster-sized circle graph of the given information. Then tell them to write a paragraph explaining whether they feel the graph fairly represents the results of the survey.

Lunch Options	
Hot Lunch A	11
Lunch B	7
Pack	4
Salad Bar	3

Circle Graphs

Example 1 shows how to construct a circle graph when given percents. **Example 2** shows how to construct a circle graph when given data.

Formative Assessment

Use the Check Your Progress exercises after each example to determine students' understanding of concepts.

Additional Examples

1. Construct a circle graph using the information.

Favorite School Lunch	
Pizza	42%
Tacos	5%
Hamburger	18%
Chicken nuggets	23%
Spaghetti	9%
Other	3%

Favorite Lunch

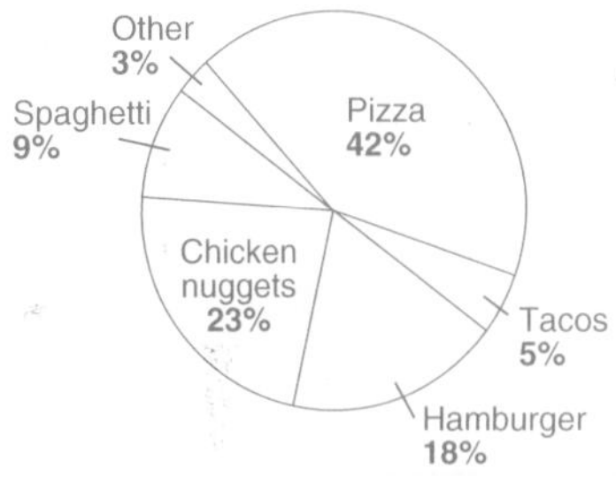

2. Construct a circle graph using the information in the table.

Trisha's Time	
Eating	2
Homework	3
Sleeping	8
Recreation	4
School	7

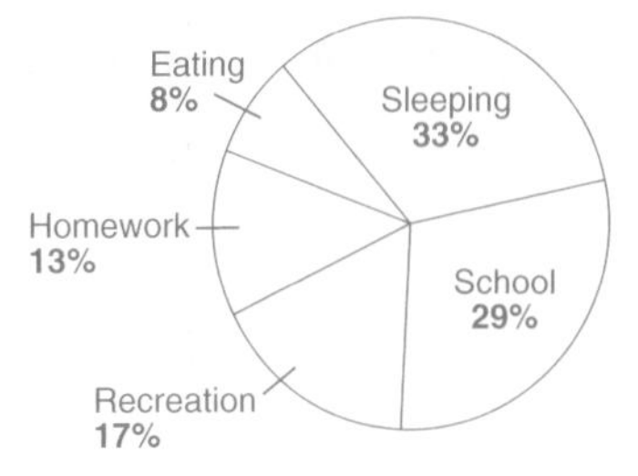

TEACH with TECH

INTERACTIVE WHITEBOARD
Use the IWB to show how to find the percentages for each section of a circle graph. Then use a spreadsheet program to create the circle graph and display it on the IWB.

Analyze Circle Graphs

Example 3 shows how to use percents and central angle measures in a circle graph to solve real-world problems.

Additional Example

3 **PETS** The circle graph shows the results of a survey about favorite pets. If 800 people were surveyed, how many more people prefer dogs to cats? 64 people

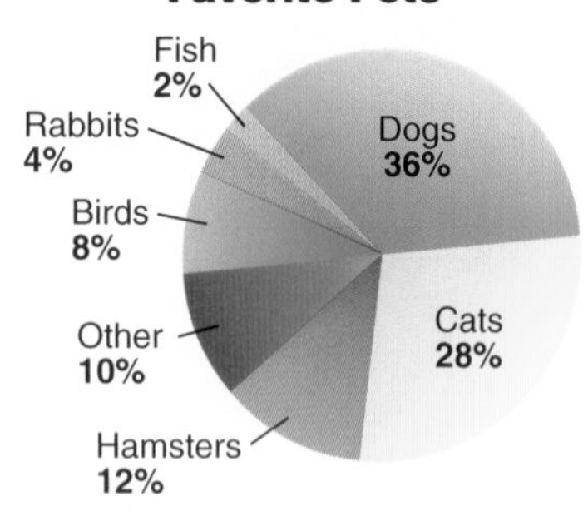

Additional Examples also in Interactive Classroom PowerPoint® Presentations

Analyze Circle Graphs You can use the percents and central angle measures in a circle graph to solve real-world problems.

> **StudyTip**
> **Another Method** To check Example 3, you can solve the problem another way.
> 22% − 20% = 2%
> 2% of $10 billion is $200 million.

Real-World EXAMPLE 3 Analyze Circle Graphs

GOVERNMENT The circle graph at the right shows how the U.S. Government spends its money. Suppose the U.S. Government's budget this year is $10 billion. How much more money is spent on Health than Defense?

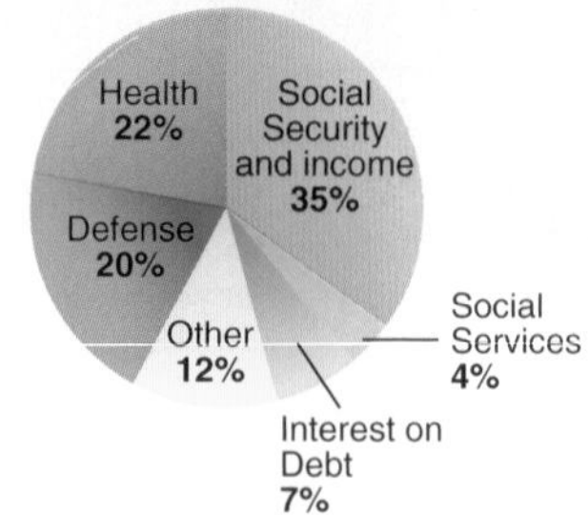

Health
22% of $10.0 billion = 0.22 × $10.0 or $2.2 billion

Defense
20% of $10.0 billion = 0.20 × $10.0 or $2.0 billion

The U.S. Government would spend $2.2 billion − $2.0 billion or $200 million more on Health than Defense.

Check Your Progress

3. Suppose the U.S. Government's budget is $20 billion. How much more money is spent on Interest than on Social Services? **$600 million**

Personal Tutor glencoe.com

Check Your Understanding

Examples 1 and 2 pp. 376–377

Construct a circle graph for each set of data. 1–2. See margin.

1.

Atmospheric Composition	
Element	**Percent**
Nitrogen	78
Oxygen	21
Other	1

Source: NASA

2.

Kingdoms of Life	
Kingdom	**Number of Species**
Bacteria	4,000
Protists	80,000
Animals	1,324,000
Fungi	72,000
Plants	270,000

Source: PBS Kids

Example 3 p. 378

3 **BOOKS** The circle graph at the right shows the results of a survey about favorite kinds of books. If 600 people were surveyed, how many more people prefer mystery books than historical fiction books? **48 people**

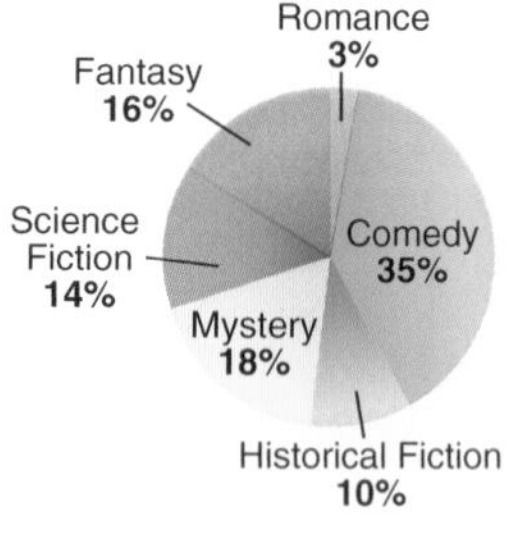

3 PRACTICE

Formative Assessment

Use Exercises 1–3 to check for understanding.

Use the chart at the bottom of the next page to customize assignments for your students.

Additional Answers

1.

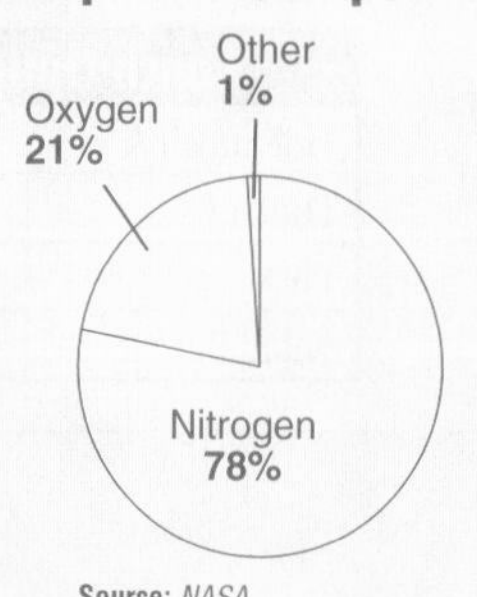

2.

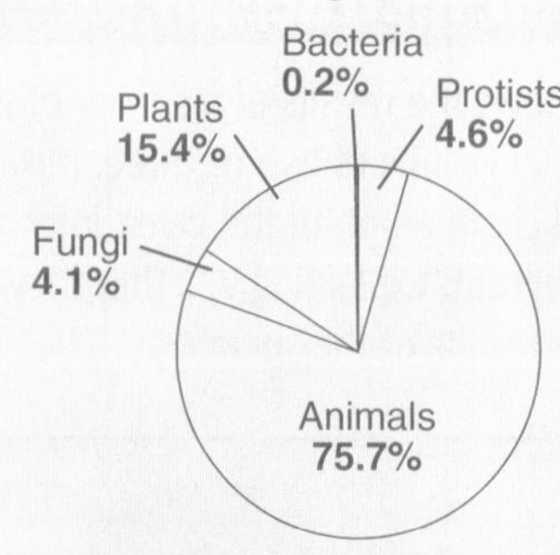

Practice and Problem Solving

= **Step-by-Step Solutions** begin on page R11.
Extra Practice begins on page 810.

Examples 1 and 2 pp. 376–377

Construct a circle graph for each set of data. 4–5. See margin.

4.

Number of U.S. States Visited	
Number of States	**Percent of People**
0	14%
1–5	38%
6–15	26%
16–25	7%
26–50	15%

Source: PBS Kids

5.

Layers of Earth's Atmosphere	
Layer	**Depth (kilometers)**
Troposphere	11.5
Stratosphere	50
Mesosphere	85
Thermosphere	600

Source: *World Almanac*

6–7. See Chapter 7 Answer Appendix.

6.

Athletic Shoe Purchases	
Age	**Number**
Under 14	95
14–17	30
18–24	50
25–34	70
35–44	75
45–64	120
65 & Older	60

7.

U.S. Landfill Composition	
Type	**Percent**
Metal	8%
Plastic	24%
Food and Yard Waste	11%
Rubber and Leather	6%
Other	21%
Paper	30%

Example 3 p. 378

8. **TRAVEL** The circle graph below shows the results of a middle school survey about favorite states to visit on vacation. If 400 students were surveyed, how many more students favor visiting Florida than Colorado? 92 students

9. **TELEVISION** The circle graph below shows the results of a survey about the number of televisions per household. Suppose 250 households were surveyed. How many more households have three televisions than five or more televisions? 45 households

Favorite State to Visit

Number of Televisions in a Household

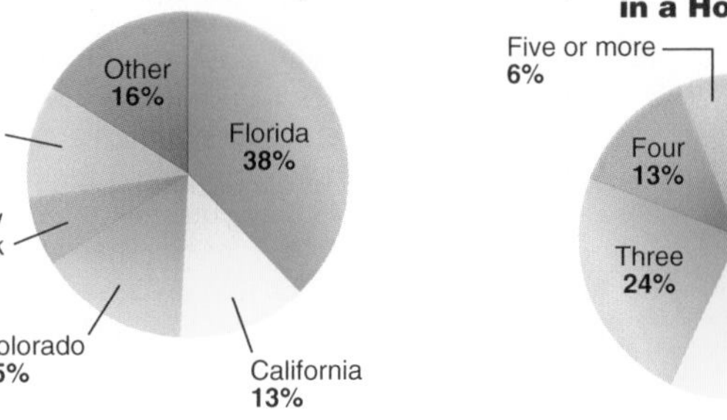

10. **PETS** Samuel surveyed his classmates about their favorite type of pet. He made a circle graph to show the results. The central angle for the section of the graph that represents cats measures 108°. If 45 classmates chose cats as their favorite type of pet, how many classmates did Samuel survey? 150 classmates

Tips for New Teachers

Percent Some students may calculate the percents needed to create a circle graph incorrectly. Remind them to verify that their percents total 100% before constructing a graph.

Focus on Mathematical Content

Circle Graphs A circle graph is a good way to show how 100% of something is divided into parts. To construct a circle graph, percents can be converted into decimals or fractions and then used to determine the number of degrees in each section of the circle. Each section bounded by two radii and an arc of the circle is called a *sector.*

Additional Answers

4. **Number of U.S. States Visited**

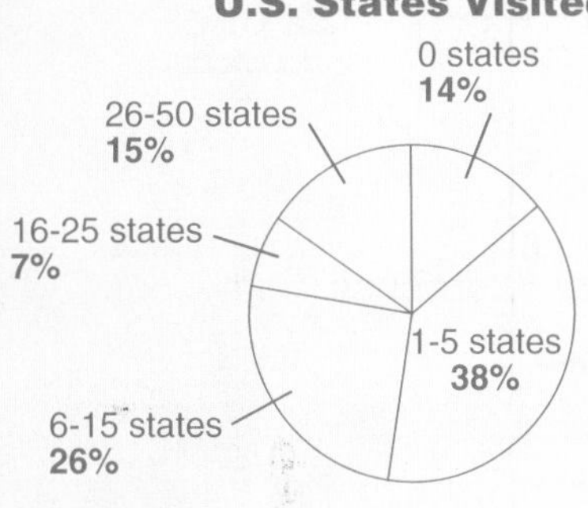

5. **Layers of the Atmosphere**

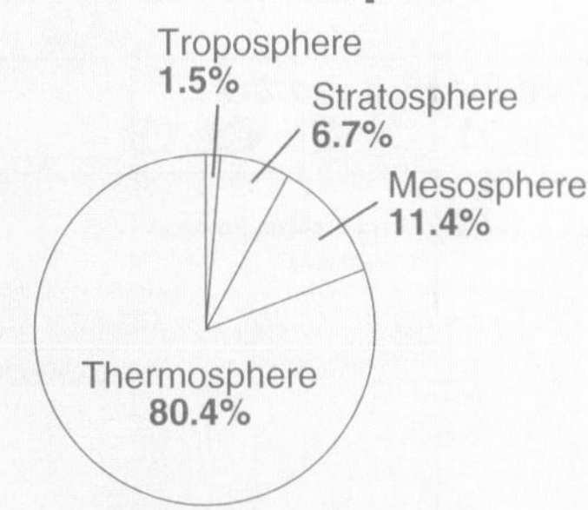

Differentiated Homework Options

Level	Assignment	Two-Day Option	
AL Basic	4–9, 16–29	5–9 odd, 20–23	4–8 even, 16–19, 24–29
OL Core	5–9 odd, 10–14, 16–29	4–9, 20–23	10–14, 16–19, 24–29
BL Advanced	10–26 (optional: 27–29)		

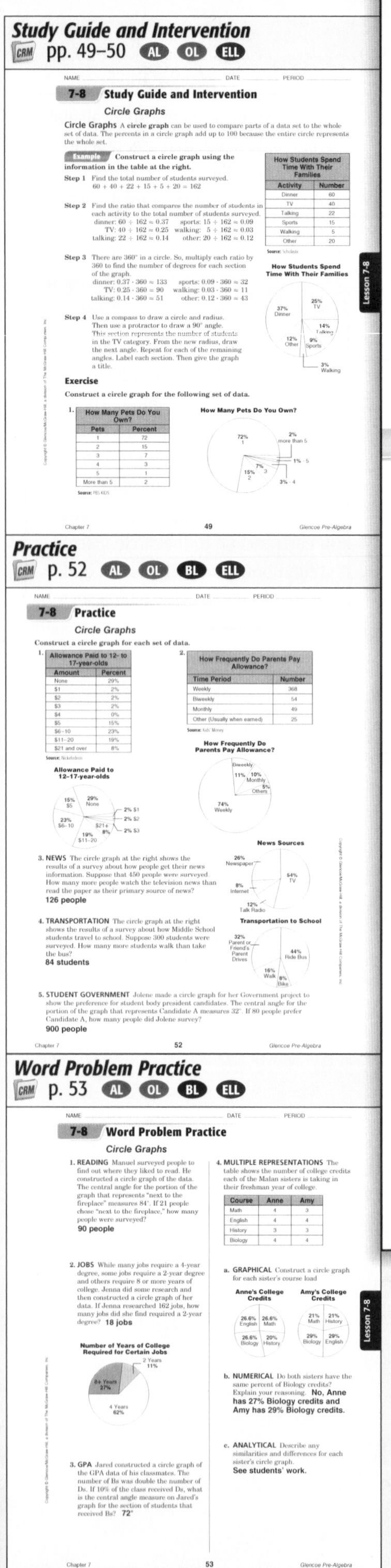

11. **FLOWERS** Yelina surveyed people to find their favorite flower. She made a circle graph of the data. The central angle for the portion of the graph that represents tulips measures 54°. If 75 people chose tulips as their favorite flower, how many people did Yelina survey? **500 people**

12. **SPORTS** Kenard worked at a sporting goods store. To determine trends in footwear, he charted sales for a year. Then he constructed a circle graph of the data. The sales in March were double the sales in May. If the central angle in the graph for March measured 47.5°, what percent of the sales occurred in May? **6.6%**

13. **MULTIPLE REPRESENTATIONS** In this problem, you will investigate circle graphs. The table shows the number of grand slam wins for two different tennis players. **a–b. See margin.**

Grand Slam Tournament	Number of Grand Slam Wins for Steffi Graf	Number of Grand Slam Wins for Pete Sampras
Australian Open	4	2
French Open	6	0
Wimbledon	7	7
U.S. Open	5	5

a. **GRAPHICAL** Construct a circle graph for each player's Grand Slam wins.

b. **NUMERICAL** Do both players have the same percentage of U.S. Grand Slam wins? Explain your reasoning.

c. **ANALYTICAL** Compare the circle graphs. Describe the similarities and differences between the two graphs. **See students' work.**

Real-World Career

Sports Statisticians
Sports statisticians gather and analyze sports data. Statisticians may work for sports teams, associations, or private sports statistics companies. Most jobs require a 4-year degree in computer science or statistics.

Source: Career Prospect

14. **COLLECT DATA** Design a survey to give to your classmates. **a–c. See Chapter 7 Answer Appendix.**

a. Display the data in a table.

b. Create a circle graph of the data.

c. Write two questions based on your data.

H.O.T. Problems

Use **H**igher-**O**rder **T**hinking Skills

15. **CHALLENGE** Explain why a circle graph should *not* be made of the data in the table at the right. **Sample answer: The sum of the percentages is much greater than 100%.**

Favorite Outdoor Activity	
Walking	20%
Gardening	18%
Skiing	31%
Jogging	9%
Rollerblading	12%
Swimming	29%

16. **OPEN ENDED** Construct a circle graph with four categories that shows how you spend your free time. **See Chapter 7 Answer Appendix.**

17. **REASONING** *True* or *false*? You can construct a circle graph without using percents. Support your answer with examples.

18. **NUMBER SENSE** Estimate the percent of the circle graph shown at the right that is represented by Section A and Section B combined. Section C. Section D, Section E and Section F combined. **50%; Sample answer: 22%; 28%**

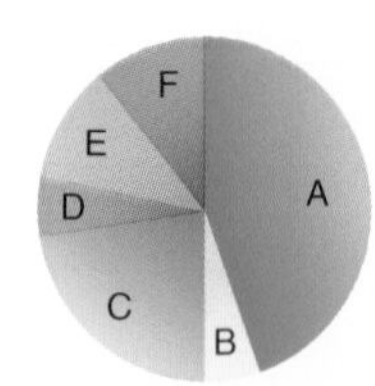

19. **WRITING IN MATH** Explain the steps you would take to create a circle graph if the data are given as percents.

17. **True; Sample answer: You can write a proportion comparing parts to wholes and use 360 as the whole in one of the ratios.**

19. **Sample answer: Change each percent to a decimal. Then multiply each decimal by 360° to find the measure of each angle. Draw a circle and use a protractor to mark each angle. Label each section and add a title.**

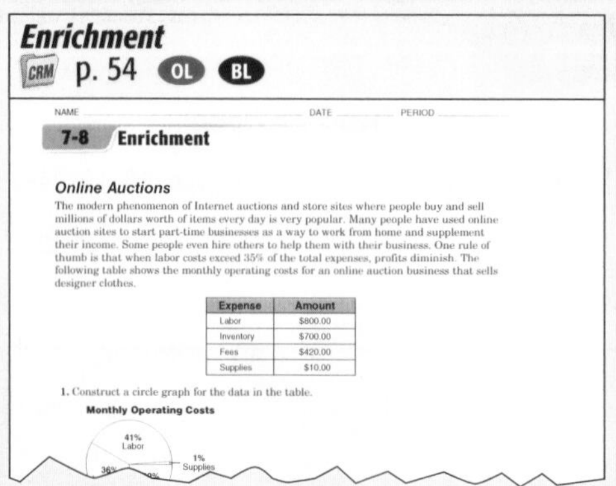

Multiple Representations In Exercise 13, students construct two circle graphs and analyze the careers of two athletes.

Standardized Test Practice

For Exercises 20 and 21 refer to the circle graph below.

Favorite Subject

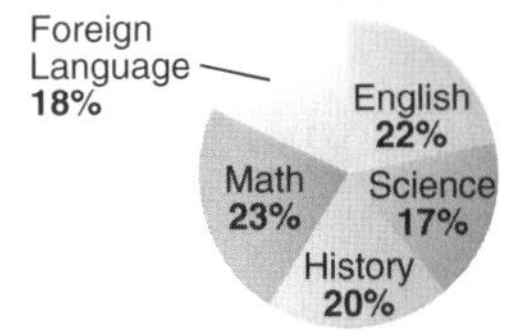

20. Which of the following is supported by the graph? B
    - A Twice as many students prefer math to science.
    - B The favorite subject of most students is math.
    - C More students list history as a favorite than English.
    - D Less than half the students surveyed list Science, Foreign Language and History as their favorite subject.

21. If 800 students were surveyed, what number of students would have math as a favorite subject? H

F 83	H 184
G 180	J 221

22. The table shows the results of a class survey. B

Type of Movie	Number of Students
Comedy	165
Action	160
Drama	92
Science Fiction	83

In a circle graph of the data, how many degrees would make up the central angle of the section titled Action?

A 32°	C 160°
B 115°	D 180°

23. **EXTENDED RESPONSE** The table below shows data about automobile colors. Calculate the degree measures of the central angles of a circle graph for each category.

Car Color	Number of Cars
Red	5
White	10
Green	15
Blue	30
Other	40

See Chapter 7 Answer Appendix.

Spiral Review

Find the simple interest to the nearest cent. (Lesson 7-7)

24. \$4500 at 5.5% for $4\frac{1}{2}$ years **\$1113.75**

25. \$3680 at 6.75% for $2\frac{1}{4}$ years **\$558.90**

26. **SCHOOL** Jiliana is using a copy machine to increase the size of a 2-inch by 3-inch picture of a spider. The enlarged picture needs to measure 3 inches by 4.5 inches. What enlargement setting on the copy machine should she use? (Lesson 7-6) **150%**

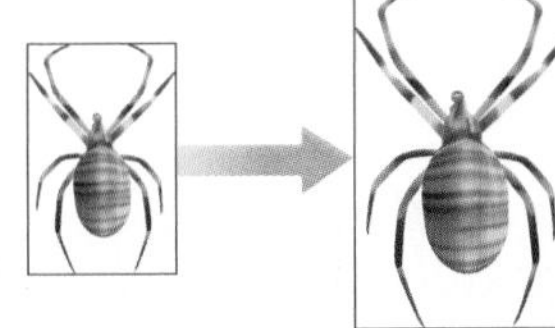

Skills Review

Determine the domain and range of each function (Lesson 1-4)

27. (4, 2), (−7, 9), (0, −1) D: {4, −7, 0}; R: {2, 9, −1}

28. (−2, 12), (−2, 11), (−2, 10) D: {−2}; R: {12, 11, 10}

29. (18, 0), (14, −9), (−6, 6) D: {18, 14, −6}; R: {0, −9, 6}

Differentiated Instruction

BL

Extension Have students conduct a survey of their classmates about their favorite after-school snack. Then have them represent the data in a table and construct a circle graph.

4 ASSESS

Name the Math Have students name two items that must be on a circle graph. Sample answer: title, labels for the sections of the circle graph

Formative Assessment

Check for student understanding of concepts in Lessons 7-7 and 7-8.

CRM Quiz 4, p. 59

Additional Answers

13a.

Sampras's Grand Slam Wins

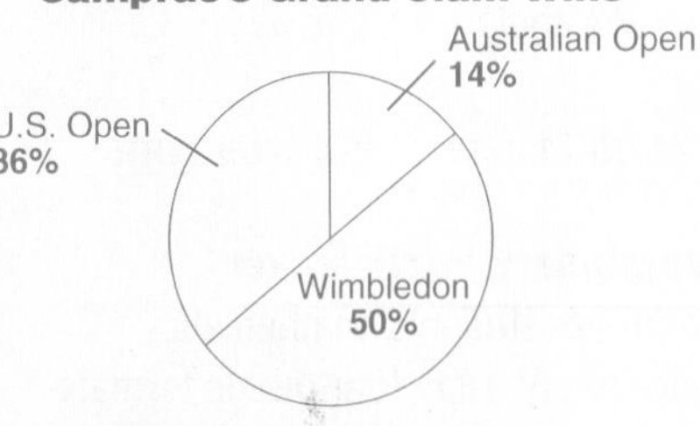

Graf's Grand Slam Wins

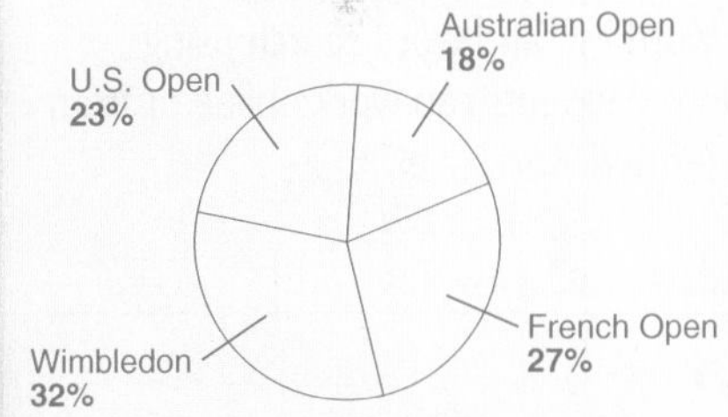

13b. No, even though they each have 5 U.S. Grand Slam wins, the total number of Grand Slam wins for each is different, therefore giving a different percentage for each.

Formative Assessment

Key Vocabulary The page references after each word denote where that term was first introduced. If students have difficulty answering questions 1–8, remind them that they can use these page references to refresh their memories about the vocabulary.

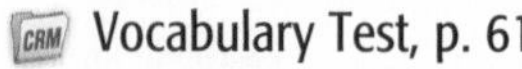

Summative Assessment

CRM Vocabulary Test, p. 61

Math Online glencoe.com

Vocabulary PuzzleMaker improves students' mathematics vocabulary using four puzzle formats–crossword, scramble, word search using a word list, and word search using clues. Students can work online or from a printed worksheet.

Additional Answers

9. $\frac{3}{10}$
10. $\frac{4}{25}$
11. $\frac{23}{25}$
12. $\frac{13}{20}$
13. $\frac{3}{500}$
14. $\frac{9}{2000}$
15. $1\frac{2}{5}$
16. $2\frac{3}{25}$
17. 25%
18. 26.67%
19. 60%
20. 12.5%
21. 33.33%
22. 150%
23. 36%
24. 133.33%

CHAPTER 7 Study Guide and Review

Math Online glencoe.com
- STUDY TO GO
- Vocabulary Review

Chapter Summary

Key Concepts

Fractions, Decimals, and Percents (Lessons 7-1 and 7-2)

- A percent is a ratio that compares a number to 100.
- Fractions, decimals, and percents are all different ways to represent the same number.
- Common fraction, decimal, percent equivalents:

$\frac{1}{5} = 0.2 = 20\%$	$\frac{1}{2} = 0.5 = 50\%$
$\frac{4}{5} = 0.8 = 80\%$	$\frac{1}{4} = 0.25 = 25\%$
$\frac{1}{3} = 0.\overline{3} = 33\frac{1}{3}\%$	$\frac{3}{10} = 0.3 = 30\%$
$\frac{3}{5} = 0.6 = 60\%$	$\frac{9}{10} = 0.9 = 90\%$
$\frac{3}{4} = 0.75 = 75\%$	$\frac{2}{3} = 0.\overline{6} = 66\frac{2}{3}\%$
$\frac{2}{5} = 0.4 = 40\%$	$\frac{7}{10} = 0.7 = 70\%$

Percents (Lessons 7-3 through 7-6)

- A percent proportion is $\frac{\text{part}}{\text{whole}} = \text{percent}$, where the percent is written as a fraction.
- A percent of increase, or decrease, tells how much an amount has increased, or decreased, in relation to the original amount.

Interest (Lesson 7-7)

- Interest is the amount of money paid or earned for the use of money.
- Simple interest can be found using the formula $I = prt$, where I is the interest paid or earned, p is the principal money invested or borrowed, r is the interest rate, and t is the time in years.
- Compound interest is interest paid on the initial principal and on interest earned in the past.

FOLDABLES® Study Organizer

Be sure the Key Concepts are noted in your Foldable.

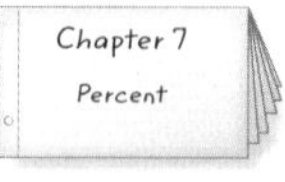

Key Vocabulary

circle graph (p. 376)
compound interest (p. 371)
discount (p. 366)
interest (p. 370)
markup (p. 365)
percent (p. 331)
percent equation (p. 357)
percent of change (p. 364)
percent of decrease (p. 364)
percent of increase (p. 364)
percent proportion (p. 345)
principal (p. 370)
selling price (p. 365)
simple interest (p. 370)

Vocabulary Check

Complete each sentence with the correct term. Choose from the list above.

1. A(n) __markup__ is an increase in price.
2. __Interest__ is the amount of money paid or earned for the use of money.
3. The __percent of change__ is a ratio that compares the change in quantity to the original amount.
4. __Discount__ is the amount by which the regular price of an item is reduced.
5. The money invested or borrowed is called the __principal__.
6. The __selling price__ is the amount of money a customer pays for an item.
7. A(n) __percent__ is a ratio that compares a number to 100.
8. A(n) __circle graph__ is a visual representation that can be used to compare parts of a data set to the whole set of data.

FOLDABLES® Study Organizer

Dinah Zike's Foldables®

Have students look through the chapter to make sure they have included examples in their Foldables. Suggest that students keep their Foldables handy while completing the Study Guide and Review pages. Point out that their Foldables can serve as a quick review tool when studying for the Chapter Test.

Lesson-by-Lesson Review

7-1 Fractions and Percents (pp. 336–336)

Write each percent as a fraction in simplest form. 9–16. See margin.

9. 30% **10.** 16% **11.** 92% **12.** 65%

13. 0.6% **14.** 0.45% **15.** 140% **16.** 212%

Write each fraction as a percent.
17–24. See margin.

17. $\frac{2}{8}$ **18.** $\frac{4}{15}$ **19.** $\frac{3}{5}$ **20.** $\frac{7}{56}$

21. $\frac{11}{33}$ **22.** $\frac{12}{8}$ **23.** $\frac{9}{25}$ **24.** $\frac{36}{27}$

25. **TESTS** In Mr. Henderson's math class, 20 out of 25 students earned a grade of A or B. What percent is this? **80%**

EXAMPLE 1

Write 70% as a fraction in simplest form.

$70\% = \frac{70}{100}$ Definition of percent

$= \frac{7}{10}$ Simplify.

So, $70\% = \frac{7}{10}$.

EXAMPLE 2

Write $\frac{30}{20}$ as a percent.

$\frac{30}{20} = \frac{150}{100}$ Write an equivalent fraction with a denominator of 100.

$= 150\%$ $\frac{150}{100} = 150\%$

7-2 Fractions, Decimals, and Percents (pp. 337–342)

Write each percent as a decimal.
26–34. See margin.

26. 43% **27.** 7.2% **28.** 115% **29.** 0.48%

Write each decimal or fraction as a percent. Round to the nearest tenth if necessary.

30. 0.37 **31.** 2.4 **32.** $\frac{1}{7}$ **33.** $\frac{62}{80}$

34. **PETS** In a survey, 0.2 of American households own a dog, one-fourth own cats, and 7% own a bird. Which group is the largest? Explain.

EXAMPLE 3

Write 8% as a decimal.

$8\% = 0.08$ Remove the % symbol and divide by 100. Add placeholder zero.

$= 0.08$ Add leading zero.

EXAMPLE 4

Write 0.36 as a percent.

$0.36 = 0.36$ Multiply by 100.

$= 36\%$ Add the % symbol.

7-3 Using the Percent Proportion (pp. 345–350)

Use the percent proportion to solve each problem.

35. 12 is what percent of 60? **20%**

36. What is 63% of 130? **81.9**

37. 28 is 80% of what number? **35**

38. **MUSIC** Thirty percent of the CDs that Monique owns are classical. If Monique owns 120 CDs, how many are classical? **36 CDs**

EXAMPLE 5

Thirty six is 24% of what number?

$\frac{36}{b} = \frac{24}{100}$ Write the percent proportion.

$36 \cdot 100 = b \cdot 24$ Find the cross products.

$3600 = 24b$ Simplify.

$150 = b$ Divide each side by 24.

So, 36 is 24% of 150.

Lesson-by-Lesson Review

Intervention If the given examples are not sufficient to review the topics covered by the questions, remind students that the page references tell them where to review that topic in their textbook.

Two-Day Option Have students complete the Lesson-by-Lesson Review on pp. 383–386. Then you can use ExamView® Assessment Suite to customize another review worksheet that practices all the objectives of this chapter or only the objectives on which your students need more help.

Differentiated Instruction

Super DVD: MindJogger Videoquizzes Use this DVD as an alternative format of review for the test.

Additional Answers

26. 0.43

27. 0.072

28. 1.15

29. 0.0048

30. 37%

31. 240%

32. 14.3%

33. 77.5%

34. households with cats; sample answer: 0.2 or 20% of households own dogs, $\frac{1}{4}$ or 25% of households own cats, and 7% of households own birds. $7\% < 20\% < 25\%$

Additional Answers

43. 10; 24% is about 25% or $\frac{1}{4}$, $\frac{1}{4} \cdot 40 = 10$

44. 54; 62% is about 60% or $\frac{3}{5}$, $\frac{3}{5} \cdot 90 = 54$

45. 0.5; 1% of 298 is about 3, $3 \div 6 = 0.5$

46. 325; 100% of 250 is 250 and 30% of 250 is 75, $250 + 75 = 325$

47. 200 free throws; 77% is about 80% or $\frac{4}{5}$ and 244 is about 250, $\frac{4}{5} \cdot 250 = 200$

53. No, the jersey is now 75% off the original price. If the jersey was originally $100, after the first markdown it is $50. Then the manager takes 50% off of $50 making the jersey $25, or 75% off the original price.

CHAPTER 7 Study Guide and Review

7-4 Find Percent of a Number Mentally (pp. 351–355)

Find the percent of each number mentally.

39. 50% of 36 **18**

40. 40% of 55 **22**

41. $33\frac{1}{3}\%$ of 27 **9**

42. 1% of 167 **1.67**

Estimate. **43–47. See margin.**

43. 24% of 40

44. 62% of 90

45. $\frac{1}{6}\%$ of 298

46. 130% of 250

47. SPORTS Tito had 244 free throw attempts in his high school career. If he was successful 77% of the time, about how many free throws did he make?

EXAMPLE 6

Find 40% of 90 mentally.

$40\% \text{ of } 90 = \frac{2}{5} \text{ of } 90$ **Think:** $40\% = \frac{2}{5}$.

$= 36$ **Think:** $\frac{2}{5}$ **of 90 is 36.**

So, 40% of 90 is 36.

EXAMPLE 7

Estimate 78% of 112.

78% is about 75% or $\frac{3}{4}$.

$\frac{3}{4}$ of 112 is 84.

So, 78% of 112 is about 84.

7-5 Using Percent Equations (pp. 357–362)

Solve each problem using a percent equation.

48. 17 is what percent of 68? **25%**

49. What is $16\frac{2}{3}\%$ of 24? **4**

50. 55 is 20% of what number? **275**

51. 48 is what percent of 32? **150%**

52. SOUVENIRS The items in a souvenir shop are on sale for the prices shown. What percent of the original price is the sale price for each item? **hat: 75%, towel: 80%, bag: 70%**

Item	Original Price	Sale Price
hat	$14.00	$10.50
beach towel	$17.50	$14.00
tote bag	$9.00	$6.30

53. SHOPPING A jersey is on sale for 50% off the original price. A week later, the manager takes another 50% off. Is the jersey now free? Explain. **See margin.**

EXAMPLE 8

84 is 60% of what number?

The part is 84 and the percent is 60%. Let w represent the whole.

part = percent · whole

$84 = 0.6 \cdot w$ **Write the percent equation.**

$\frac{84}{0.6} = \frac{0.6w}{0.6}$ **Divide each side by 0.6.**

$140 = w$ **Simplify.**

So, 84 is 60% of 140.

EXAMPLE 9

18 is what percent of 25?

The part is 18 and the whole is 25. Let p represent the percent.

part = percent · whole

$18 = p \cdot 25$ **Write the percent equation.**

$\frac{18}{25} = \frac{25p}{25}$ **Divide each side by 25.**

$0.72 = p$ **Simplify.**

Since 0.72 = 72%, 18 is 72% of 25.

384 Chapter 7 Percent

MIXED PROBLEM SOLVING
For mixed problem-solving practice, see page 849.

7-6 Percent of Change (pp. 364–369)

Find the percent of change. Round to the nearest tenth, if necessary. Then state whether the percent of change is an *increase* or *decrease*.

54. From 55 lb to 24 lb **−56.4%; decrease**

55. From $55.75 to $75.00 **34.5%; increase**

Find the selling price for each item given the cost and the percent of markup or discount.

56. tennis shoes: $85; 24% discount **$64.60**

57. portable MP3 player: $150; 36% markup **$204**

58. CLUBS The number of members in the recycling club increased by 15 people. If the club had 12 members previously, what was the percent of increase of the members in the club? **125%**

59. ICE CREAM The number of pints of mint chocolate chip sold last week was 88. If this week 110 pints were sold, what was the percent of increase? **25%**

EXAMPLE 10

Find the percent of change from 64 minutes to 16 minutes.

$$\text{percent of change} = \frac{\text{amount of change}}{\text{original amount}}$$

$$= \frac{16 - 64}{64}$$

$$= \frac{-48}{64}$$

$$= -\frac{3}{4} \text{ or } -0.75$$

The decimal −0.75 is written as −75%. So, the percent of change is −75%.

Since the percent of change is negative, it is a percent of decrease.

EXAMPLE 11

Find the selling price if a store pays $37 dollars for a video game and the markup is 25%.

$m = 0.25 \cdot 37$ **part = percent • whole**

$m = 9.25$ **Multiply.**

Add the markup and the cost. The selling price is $37 + $9.25 or $46.25.

7-7 Simple and Compound Interest (pp. 370–374)

Find the simple interest to the nearest cent.

60. $575 at 6.25% for 7 years **$251.56**

61. $12,750 at 5% for 10 years **$6375.00**

Find the total amount in each account to the nearest cent if the interest is compounded annually.

62. $2750 at 8% for 3 years **$3464.21**

63. $1500 at 12.5% for 2 years **$1898.44**

64. BOATS Lucas borrowed $10,500 to buy a boat. He will pay $276.50 each month for the next 48 months. Find the simple interest rate for his loan. **6.6%**

EXAMPLE 12

Find the simple interest for $2500 invested at 3.85% for 4 years.

$I = prt$ **Write the simple interest formula.**

$I = 2500 \cdot 0.0385 \cdot 4$ **Substitute**

$I = 385$ **Simplify.**

The simple interest is $385.

Chapter 7 Study Guide and Review 385

Problem Solving Review

For additional practice in problem solving for Chapter 7, see the Mixed Problem Solving Appendix, p. 849, in the Student Handbook section.

Anticipation Guide

Have students complete the Chapter 7 Anticipation Guide and discuss how their responses have changed now that they have completed Chapter 7.

Additional Answers

65.

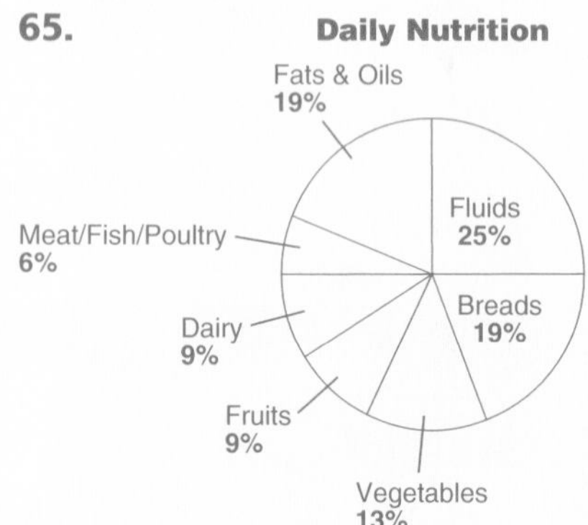

66.

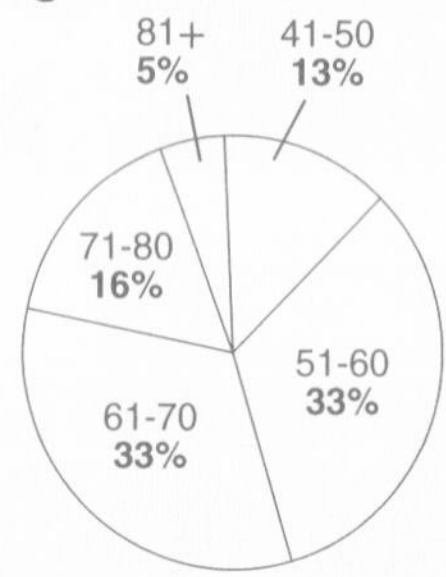

CHAPTER 7 Study Guide and Review

7-8 Circle Graphs (pp. 376–381)

Construct a circle graph for each set of data. **65–66. See margin.**

65.

Daily Nutrition	
Fluids	25%
Breads	19%
Vegetables	13%
Fruits	9%
Dairy	9%
Meat/Fish/ Poultry	6%
Fats & Oils	19%

66.

Age of U.S. Senators	
Age	Number of Senators
41–50	13
51–60	33
61–70	33
71–80	16
81+	5

67. **SPORTS** The circle graph below shows the winners of the NCAA Women's basketball championship by conference. Suppose there have been 25 total championships. How many championships were won by the ACC? **2 championships**

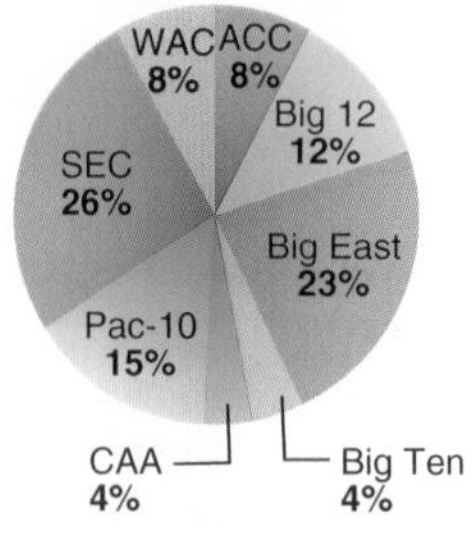

EXAMPLE 13

Construct a circle graph using the information in the table.

Earth's Oceans	
Ocean	Percent of Total
Pacific	47%
Atlantic	23%
Indian	20%
Southern	6%
Arctic	4%

Multiply each percent by 360 to find the number of degrees for each section of graph.

Pacific: 47% of 360 $\approx$ 169
Atlantic: 23% of 360 $\approx$ 83
Indian: 20% of 360 $=$ 72
Southern: 6% of 360 $\approx$ 22
Arctic: 4% of 360 $\approx$ 14

Use a compass to draw a circle and a radius. Then use a protractor to draw a 169° angle to represent the Pacific Ocean.

From the new radius, draw the next angle. Repeat for each of the remaining angles.

Label each section. Then give the graph a title.

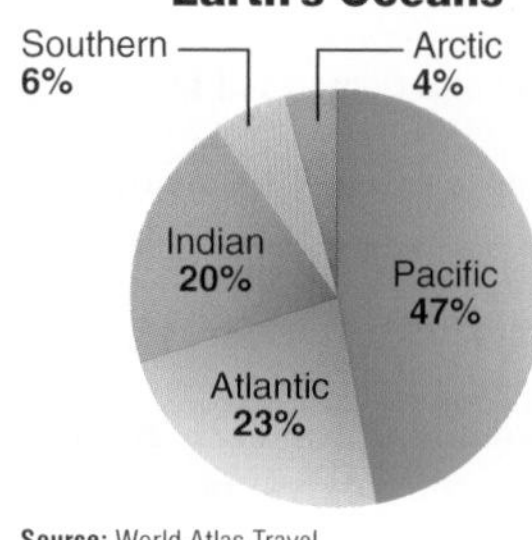

Source: World Atlas Travel

386 Chapter 7 Percent

CHAPTER 7 Practice Test

Math Online glencoe.com Chapter Test

Write each percent as a fraction or mixed number in simplest form.

1. 30% $\frac{3}{10}$
2. 75% $\frac{3}{4}$
3. 62% $\frac{31}{50}$
4. 450% $4\frac{1}{2}$
5. 0.5% $\frac{1}{200}$
6. 120% $1\frac{1}{5}$

Express each decimal or fraction as a percent. Round to the nearest tenth, if necessary.

7. $\frac{21}{25}$ 84%
8. 0.81 81%
9. $\frac{30}{75}$ 40%
10. $\frac{11}{10}$ 110%
11. 12.54 1254%
12. 0.002 0.2%

13. **TRANSPORTATION** Of the players on a football team, 32% ride their bikes to practice, $\frac{6}{20}$ walk to practice, and 0.29 ride the bus to practice. Order the types of transportation used by the football players from least to greatest. bus, walking, bikes

Use the percent proportion to solve each problem.

14. Find 35% of 300. 105
15. What percent of 6 is 9? 150%
16. 34 is 68% of what number? 50
17. What percent of 50 is 32? 64%

18. **CAPACITY** The capacity of a fish tank is 44 gallons. If the aquarium is 23% filled, about how many gallons are in the tank? 10 gal

Solve each problem using the percent equation.

19. What is 30% of 80? 24
20. 60 is what percent of 180? $33\frac{1}{3}\%$
21. 21 is 70% of what number? 30

22. **MULTIPLE CHOICE** Owen wants to buy a snowboard that costs $525. If there is a 5% sales tax added, what is the total cost of the snowboard? D

A $26.25 C $530

B $525 D $551.25

Find the percent of change. Round to the nearest tenth, if necessary. Then state whether the percent of change is an *increase* or *decrease*.

23. From 12 h to 18 h 50%; increase
24. From 87 ft to 21 ft −75.9%; decrease

Find the selling price for each item given the cost and the percent of the markup or discount.

25. shirt: $7, 50% discount $3.50
26. jeans: $32, 40% markup $44.80
27. sweater: $35; 28% discount $25.20
28. DVD: $15; 33% markup $19.95

29. **MULTIPLE CHOICE** Mrs. Olsen wants to buy a DVD player that regularly costs $120 and is on sale for 30% off the original price. What is the sale price of the DVD player? H

F $120 H $84

G $90 J $36

30. What is the simple interest to the nearest cent of $1200 invested at 3% for 5 years? $180.00

31. Find the total amount in an account to the nearest cent if $15,000 is compounded annually at 6% for 2 years. $16,854

32. **SUBJECTS** The student council conducted a survey about students' favorite school subjects. Make a circle graph of the data in the table at the right. See margin.

Favorite Subject	Percent of Students
Math	12
Language Arts	25
Science	30
Physical Education	33

33. **SIBLINGS** The table at the right shows the number of siblings each student in the Science Club has in their family. Make a circle graph of the data. See margin.

Number of Siblings	Number of Students
0	2
1	9
2	7
3	4
4	1
5	1
6	1

CHAPTER 7 Practice Test

ExamView Assessment Suite Customize and create multiple versions of your chapter test and their answer keys. All of the questions from the leveled chapter tests in the *Chapter 7 Resource Masters* are also available on ExamView® Assessment Suite.

Additional Answers

32.

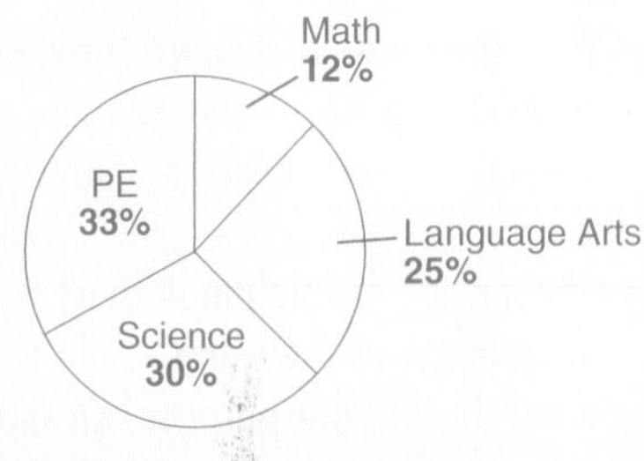

33.

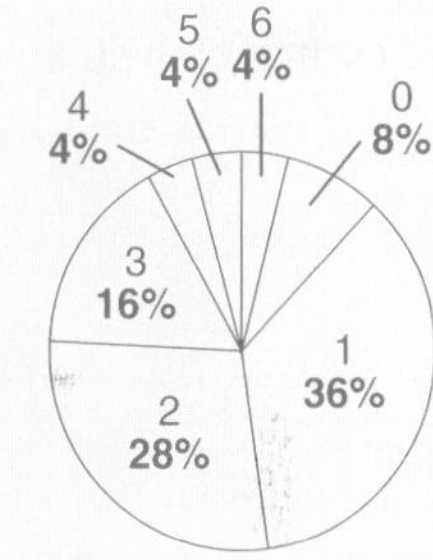

Intervention Planner

Tier 1 On Level	Tier 2 Strategic Intervention approaching grade level	Tier 3 Intensive Intervention 2 or more grades below level
If students miss about 25% of the exercises or less,	**If** students miss about 50% of the exercises,	**If** students miss about 75% of the exercises,
Then choose a resource: **SE** Lessons 7-1 through 7-8 **CRM** Skills Practice, pp. 7, 13, 19, 25, 31, 37, 44, and 51 **TE** Chapter Project, p. 328 Math Online Self-Check Quiz	**Then** choose a resource: **CRM** Study Guide and Intervention, Chapter 7, pp. 5, 11, 17, 23, 29, 35, 42, and 49 *Quick Review Math Handbook* Math Online Extra Examples, Personal Tutor, Homework Help	**Then** use *Math Triumphs, Grade 8,* Ch. 8 Math Online Extra Examples, Personal Tutor, Homework Help, Review Vocabulary

1 FOCUS

Objective Use the strategy of estimation to solve standardized test problems.

2 TEACH

Scaffolding Questions

Ask:

- What are some real-world situations in which you have used estimation? Sample answers: cooking, laundry, shopping
- When using estimation in these situations, was the estimate alone sufficient for your purpose? Or did you use estimation to check that a number was reasonable? Answers will vary.
- How did using estimation help in these situations? Answers will vary.

CHAPTER 7 Preparing for Standardized Tests

Use Estimation

Estimating the solution to a test question before you solve it can be a useful strategy. In some cases, estimation alone might even be enough to identify the correct answer choice.

Strategies for Using Estimation

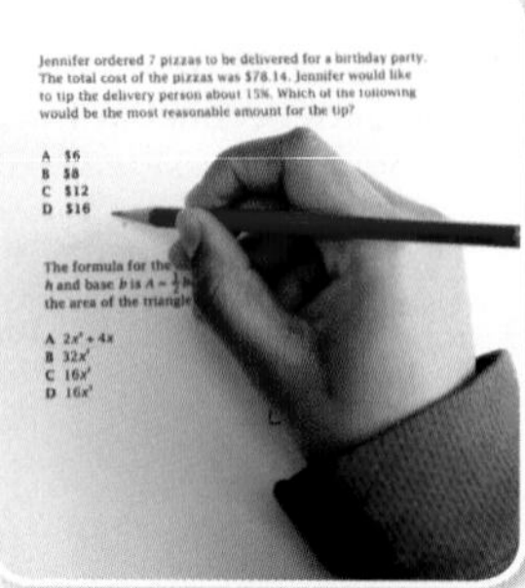

Step 1

Read the question carefully so that you understand what is being asked.

Ask yourself:

- Is an exact answer required to identify the correct answer choice?
- Could I eliminate any of the answer choices as unreasonable by quickly estimating the solution?
- Can I use estimation to check my solution?

Step 2

Use estimation when appropriate. A few examples of when estimation can be used are listed below.

- **Solving the Problem** Use the facts given in the problem to estimate the solution. Then use your estimate to choose the correct answer choice.
- **Eliminating Unreasonable Answers** Estimate the solution to the problem. If any of the answer choices are clearly different than your estimate, eliminate them as unreasonable.
- **Checking Your Answer** If time permits, check to see that your answer is reasonable using estimation.

EXAMPLE

Read the problem. Identify what you need to know. Then use the information in the problem to solve.

Jennifer ordered 7 pizzas to be delivered for a birthday party. The total cost of the pizzas was $78.14. Jennifer would like to tip the delivery person about 15%. Which of the following would be the most reasonable amount for the tip?

A $6	**C** $12
B $8	**D** $16

Read the problem carefully.

Understand You know the total cost of the pizzas. You need to determine the estimated tip for the delivery person.

Plan Estimate the tip by rounding the cost of the pizzas and using mental math.

Solve $\$78.14 \approx \$80$ — **Round the total cost to the nearest $10.**

$15\% = 10\% + 5\%$ — **Break up 15% to make the problem easier to solve.**

10% of $80 is $8. — **Use mental math.**

5% of $80 is $4 — **5% is $\frac{1}{2}$ of 10%. $4 is $\frac{1}{2}$ of $8.**

$\$8 + \$4 = \$12$ — **Add.**

So, 15% of the total cost is about $8 + $4, or $12. A reasonable amount for the tip would be $12.

The correct answer is C.

Check 10% of $78 is $7.80, and 20% of $78 is $15.60. Since $12 is somewhere in the middle between these two values, the answer seems reasonable. ✔

Exercises

Read each question. Identify what you need to know. Then use the information in the question to solve.

1. Orlando has made 69% of his free throws this basketball season. At this rate, about how many free throws would you expect him to make in his next 40 attempts? D

   A about 22
   B about 24
   C about 26
   D about 28

2. Heather spent $48.85 on her haircut. About how much should she leave for a 20% tip? F

   F about $10
   G about $12
   H about $14
   J about $15

3. Gregory is thinking about investing some money in a savings account.

Bank Savings Account		
Option	**Rate**	**Type of Interest**
A	5.00%	simple
B	4.25%	compound

   If Gregory has $1985 to invest, about how much interest would he earn if he invests it for 3 years using option A? B

   A about $150
   B about $300
   C about $400
   D about $450

4. The total area of the state of Michigan is 96,716 square miles. Of that, about 41% of the area is water. Which of the following would be the most reasonable water area for the state? H

   F 4000 square miles
   G 4500 square miles
   H 40,000 square miles
   J 45,000 square miles

Additional Example

Jade wants to buy a surfboard that costs $259. She also wants an airbrushed design on the board that costs $25. The total cost for the board and detailing is $284. Jade has a 35% discount coupon. About how much will the discount be if she uses the coupon? B

A about $70
B about $105
C about $140
D about $175

3 ASSESS

Use Exercises 1–3 to assess students' understanding.

Diagnose Student Errors

Survey student responses for each item. Class trends may indicate common errors and misconceptions.

1. A guess
   B calculation error
   C guess
   D correct
2. F forgot negative sign for *x*-coordinate
   G correct
   H added negative sign for *y*-coordinate
   J used negative sign for wrong coordinate
3. A calculation error
   B correct
   C calculation error
   D calculation error
4. F correct
   G misunderstood concept of estimation
   H misunderstood concept of estimation
   J estimation error
5. A used wrong conversion factors
   B used wrong conversion factors
   C used wrong conversion factors
   D correct
6. F misunderstood concept of finding percentages
   G guess
   H calculation error
   J correct
7. A calculation error
   B calculation error
   C calculation error
   D correct
8. F correct
   G calculation error
   H calculation error
   J calculation error

CHAPTER 7 Standardized Test Practice

Cumulative, Chapters 1 through 7

Multiple Choice

Read each question. Then fill in the correct answer on the answer document provided by your teacher or on a sheet of paper.

1. On a recent social studies exam, Juanita answered 34 out of 40 questions correctly. Find Juanita's grade as a percent. Round to the nearest whole percent if necessary. D

   A 77%
   B 80%
   C 82%
   D 85%

2. Let $X(-12, 6)$ be a point on rectangle *WXYZ*. What are the coordinates of X' if the rectangle is dilated by a scale factor of $\frac{2}{3}$? G

   F (8, 4)
   G (−8, 4)
   H (−8, −4)
   J (8, −4)

3. The table shows the favorite activity of campers at a summer camp. What percent of the campers voted for horseback riding as their favorite activity? Round to the nearest tenth if necessary. C

Activity	Votes
Canoeing	17
Horseback Riding	12
Hiking	5
Swimming	9

   A 24.1%
   B 25.2%
   C 27.9%
   D 33.4%

4. Lunch for the Carlton family was $39.43. They want to leave the server a 15% tip. Which of the following is the most reasonable amount for the tip? F

   F $6.00
   G $6.75
   H $7.50
   J $8.00

5. Heather is riding her bike at a speed of 15 miles per hour. How many feet per second is this? D

   A 17 feet per second
   B 18 feet per second
   C 20 feet per second
   D 22 feet per second

6. The circle graph below shows the results of a survey about students' favorite types of movies. If 400 students were surveyed, how many of them chose comedy as their favorite? J

   F 38
   G 45
   H 146
   J 152

7. Craig played basketball for 56 minutes. This is 10 minutes less than twice the number of minutes that Caleb played. How many minutes did Caleb play basketball? D

   A 27 minutes
   B 29 minutes
   C 31 minutes
   D 33 minutes

8. A washing machine that regularly sells for $329 is on sale for $279. What is the percent discount? Round to the nearest tenth if necessary. F

   F 15.2%
   G 16.5%
   H 17.4%
   J 18.8%

Test-TakingTip

Question 4 Use mental math. Round $39.43 to $40. You know that 10% of $40 is $4, so 5% of $40 must be $2.

Short Response/Gridded Response

9. **GRIDDED RESPONSE** Dr. Bade has 24 patients to see today at his veterinarian's office. Of them, 15 are dogs. What portion of Dr. Bade's patients today are dogs? **0.625 or 5/8**

10. Meredith wants to go on a trip this summer that costs $375. She paid a deposit of $125 and will save an additional $25 per week to pay for the trip. The equation $125 + 25w = 375$ can be used to find the number of weeks Meredith will need to save.

    a. Describe the steps needed to solve the equation. **See margin.**

    b. How many weeks will Meredith need to save to pay for the trip? **10 weeks**

11. The bar graph below shows the number of votes each candidate received for class president.

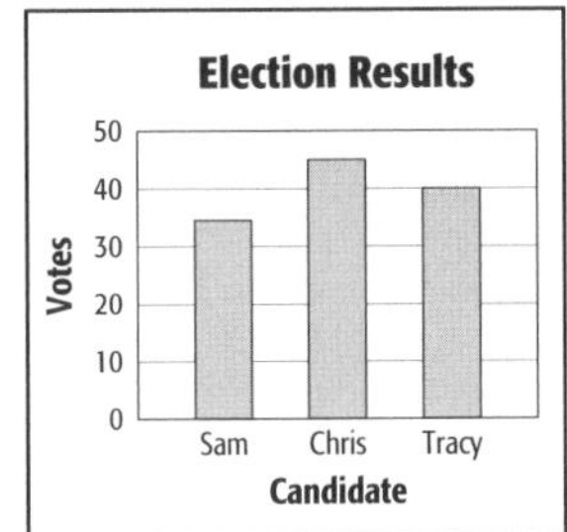

    a. How many students voted in the election? **120 students**

    b. Which candidate received the most votes? What percent of the total votes did he or she receive? **Chris, 37.5%**

12. Find and graph the solution to the following inequality. **See margin.**

$$5x - 3 \geq 9x + 9$$

13. **GRIDDED RESPONSE** Naomi bought the items shown below. She saved 20% on each item by using a store coupon. What was the total amount of money she saved? **24**

The Movie Source Sales Receipt	
Item	**Original Price**
DVD Player	$85
DVD	$10
DVD	$15
Poster	$10

Extended Response

Record your answers on a sheet of paper. Show your work.

14. A retail store currently has annual sales of $160,000. The sales manager's goal is to increase sales by 15% for the following year.

    a. Write and solve an equation to find how much the store manager wants to do in sales volume next year. **$s = 1.15 \times \$160{,}000$; $184,000**

    b. How much will the store's sales volume need to increase next year to meet this goal? **$24,000**

    c. Find the amount of sales volume next year if it is increased by 5%, 10%, 15%, and 20%. **$168,000; $176,000; $184,000; $192,000**

Need Extra Help?														
If you missed Question...	1	2	3	4	5	6	7	8	9	10	11	12	13	14
Go to Lesson or Page...	7-1	6-8	7-3	7-4	6-3	7-8	4-6	7-6	7-2	4-5	7-3	5-5	7-3	7-5

Homework Option

Get Ready for Chapter 8 Assign students the exercises on p. 393 as homework to assess whether they possess the prerequisite skills needed for the next chapter.

Formative Assessment

You can use these two pages to benchmark student progress.

CRM Standardized Test Practice, pp. 75–77

Answer Sheet Practice

Have students simulate taking a standardized test by recording their answers on practice recording sheets.

CRM Student Recording Sheet, p. 55

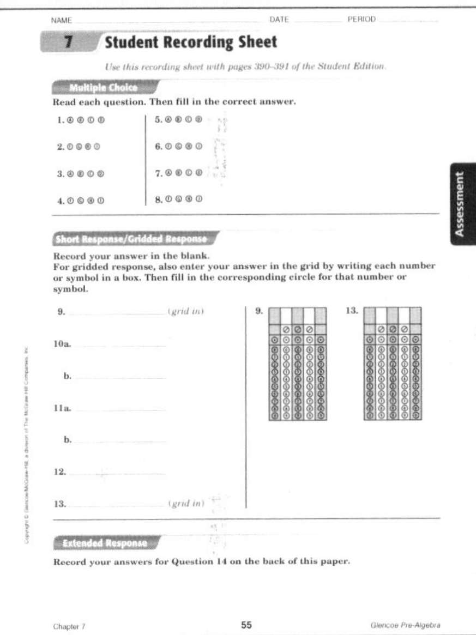
NAME DATE PERIOD

7 Student Recording Sheet

Multiple Choice

Read each question. Then fill in the correct answer.

Short Response/Gridded Response

Record your answer in the blank.

For gridded response, also enter your answer in the grid by writing each number or symbol in a box. Then fill in the corresponding circle for that number or symbol.

Extended Response

Record your answers for Question 14 on the back of this paper.

Chapter 7 55 Glencoe Pre-Algebra

Create practice worksheets or tests that align to your state's standards as well as TIMSS and NAEP tests.

Additional Answers

10a. Write the equation. Use the Subtraction Property of Equality to subtract 125 from both sides of the equation and simplify. Then use the Division Property of Equality to divide both sides by 25 and simplify.

12. $x \leq -3$

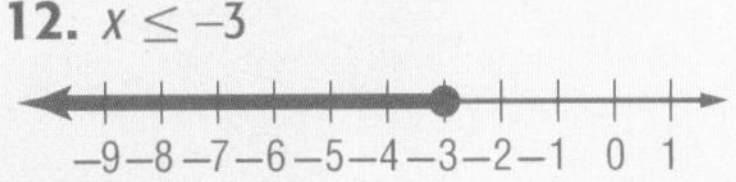

Pages 343–344, Explore 7-3

1.

0	0
1	10
2	20
3	30
4	40
5	50
6	60
7	70
8	80
9	90
10	100

2.

0	0
1	10
2	20
3	30
4	40
5	50
6	60
7	70
8	80
9	90
10	100

3.

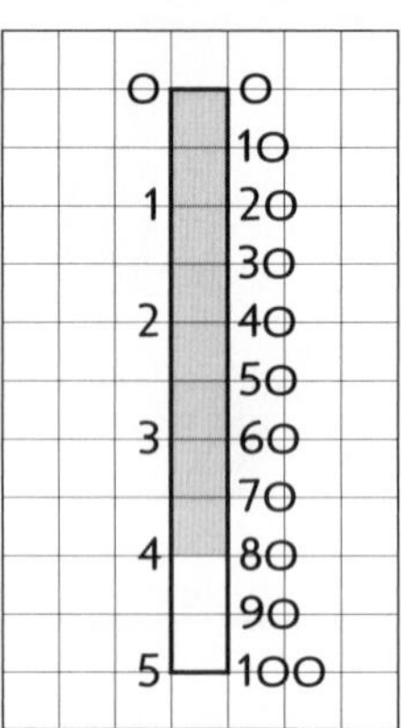

4.

0	0
	10
	20
	30
	40
2	50
	60
	70
	80
	90
4	100

5.

0	0
2	10
4	20
6	30
8	40
10	50
12	60
14	70
16	80
18	90
20	100

6.

0	0
	10
5	20
	30
10	40
	50
15	60
	70
20	80
	90
25	100

7.

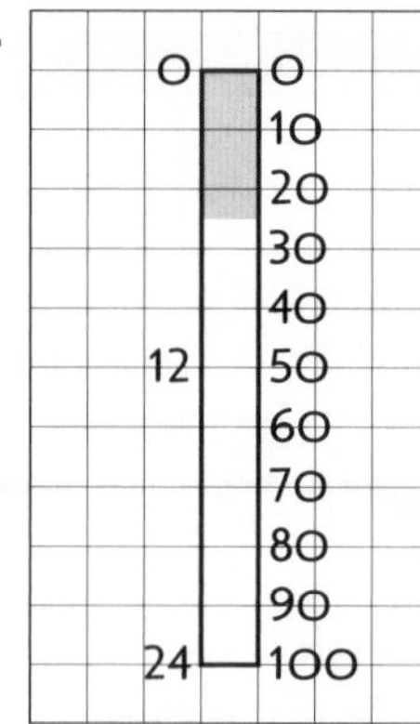

8.

0	0
	10
	20
	30
	40
12	50
	60
	70
	80
	90
24	100

9.

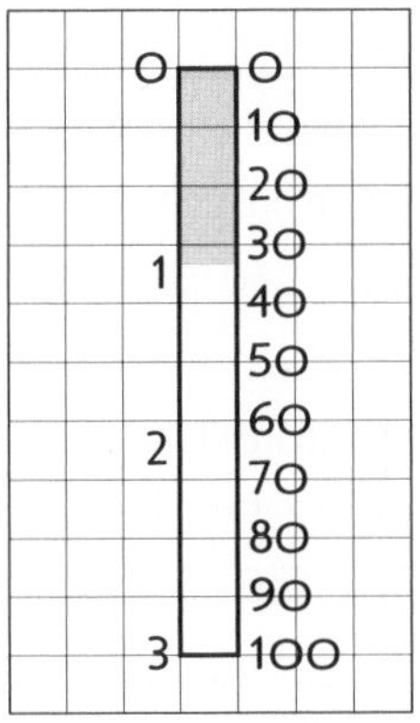

0	0
	10
	20
	30
1	
	40
	50
	60
2	
	70
	80
	90
3	100

10.

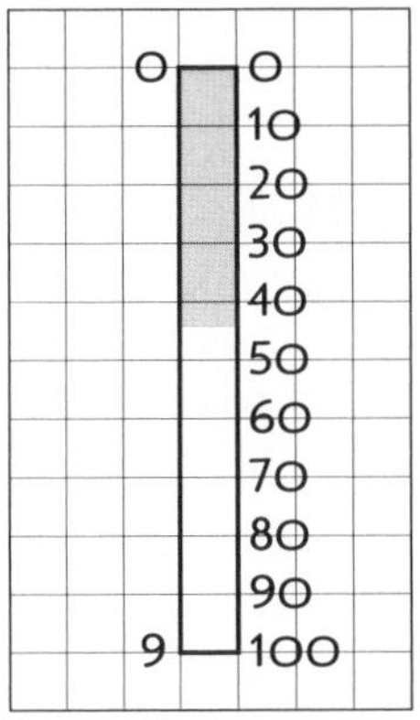

0	0
	10
	20
	30
	40
	50
	60
	70
	80
	90
9	100

11.

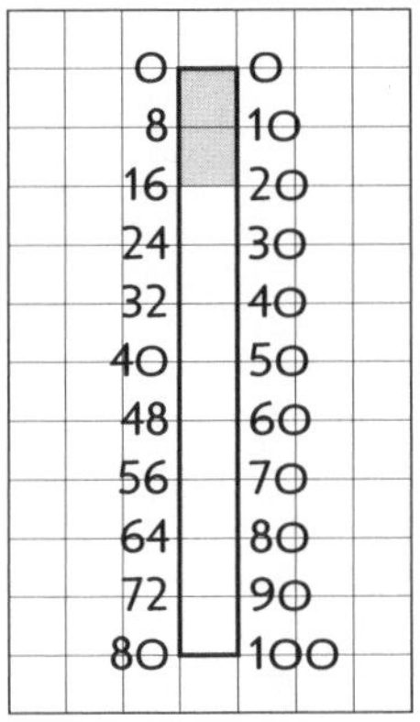

0	0
8	10
16	20
24	30
32	40
40	50
48	60
56	70
64	80
72	90
80	100

12.

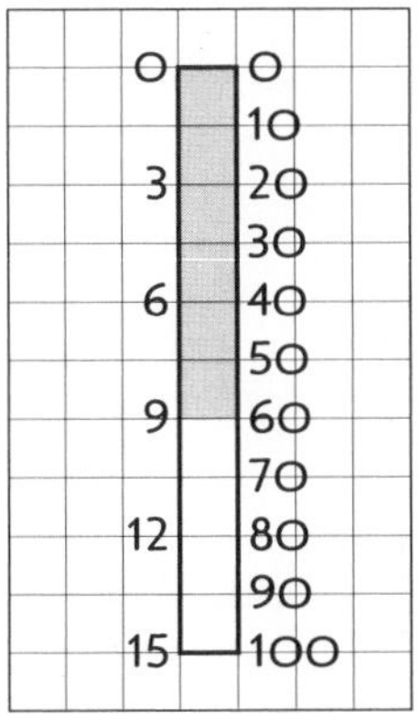

0	0
	10
3	20
	30
6	40
	50
9	60
	70
12	80
	90
15	100

13.

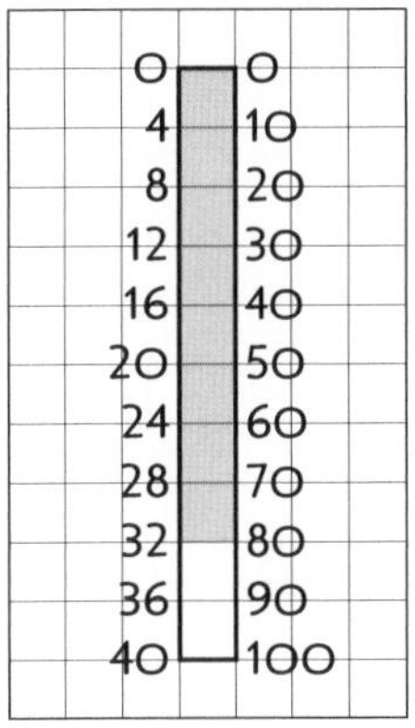

0	0
4	10
8	20
12	30
16	40
20	50
24	60
28	70
32	80
36	90
40	100

14.

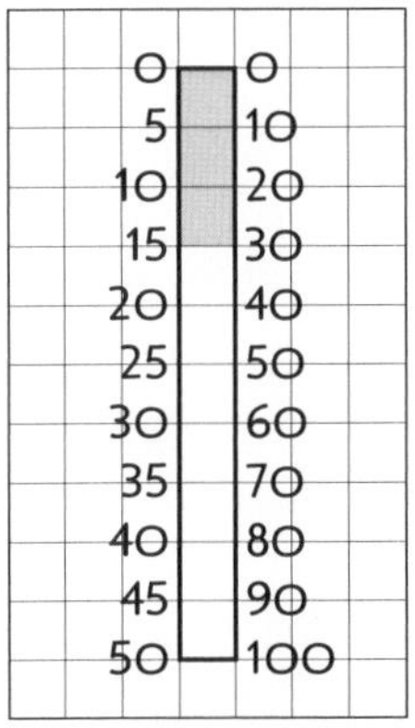

0	0
5	10
10	20
15	30
20	40
25	50
30	60
35	70
40	80
45	90
50	100

15.

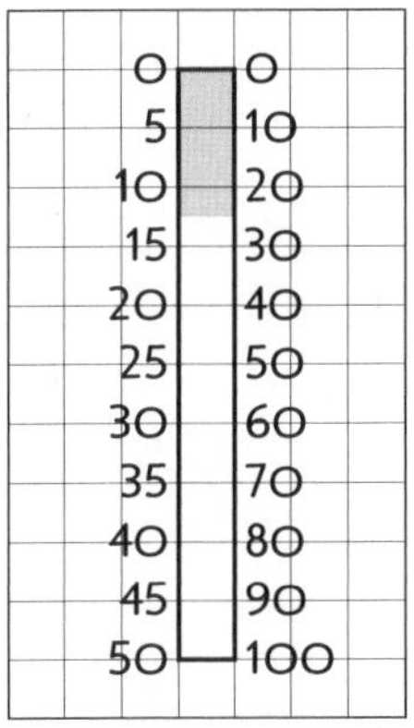

0	0
5	10
10	20
15	30
20	40
25	50
30	60
35	70
40	80
45	90
50	100

16.

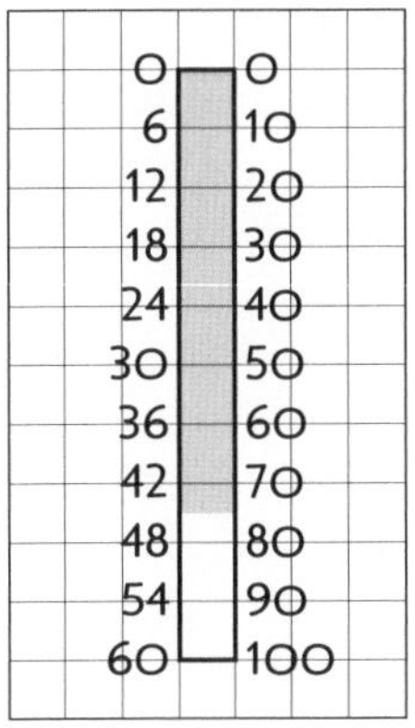

0	0
6	10
12	20
18	30
24	40
30	50
36	60
42	70
48	80
54	90
60	100

17.

0	0
15	10
30	20
45	30
60	40
75	50
90	60
105	70
120	80
135	90
150	100

18.

0	0
50	10
100	20
150	30
200	40
250	50
300	60
350	70
400	80
450	90
500	100

19.

0	0
2	10
4	20
6	30
8	40
10	50
12	60
14	70
16	80
18	90
20	100

20.

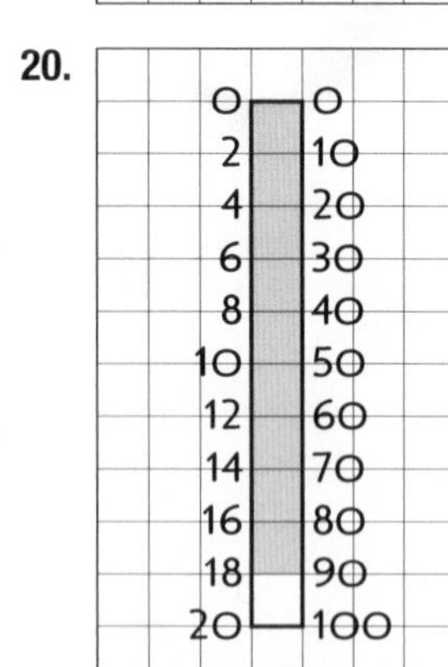

21. Sample answer: Six squares are shaded to make 18 so each square represents 3. There are 10 squares so $x = 30$.

Pages 354–355, Lesson 7-4

45. Sample answer: 60 and 600; These numbers are divisible by 3, making it easy to find $66\frac{2}{3}\%$ or $\frac{2}{3}$ of each number.

46. Sample answer: $x = 400$, $y = 100$; since 40% is 4 times 10%, x must be 4 times y.

47. Sample answer: One way is to use a fractional equivalent. $20\% = \frac{1}{5}$ and $\frac{1}{5} \cdot 60 = 12$. Another way is to find 10% of 60 and multiply the result by 2. $10\% \cdot 60 = 6$, $6 \cdot 2 = 12$

51a. \$2.10; Sample answer: \$28 is about \$30. Since 1% of \$30 is \$0.30, then 7% of \$30 is $7 \cdot 0.30$ or \$2.10

51b. \$30.10; \$28 + \$2.10 = \$30.10

51c. \$4.50; Sample answer: \$30.10 is about \$30. 10% of \$30 is \$3 and 5% of 30 is \$1.50. \$3 + \$1.50 = \$4.50

51d. yes; Sample answer: The total bill with tax will be around \$30.10. The tip is \$4.50. \$30.10 + \$4.50 = \$34.60

Page 363, Explore 7-6

1.

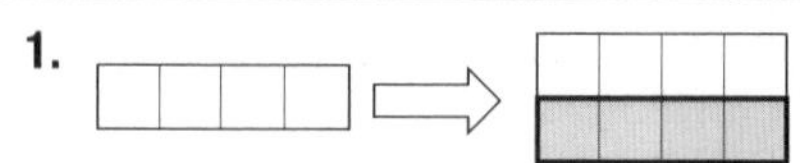

2.

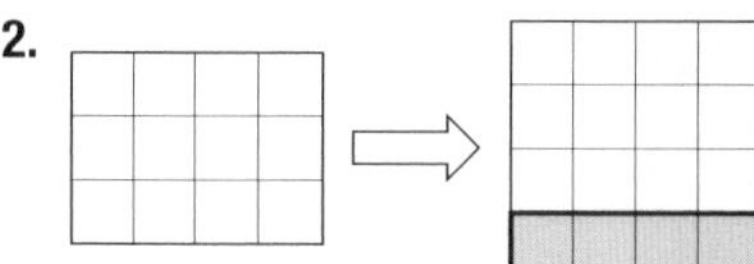

3.

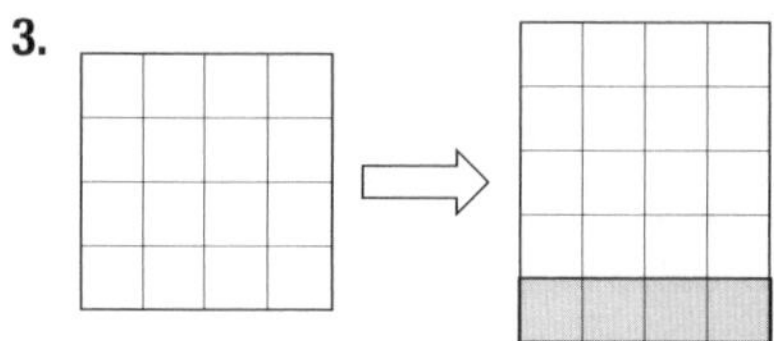

4.

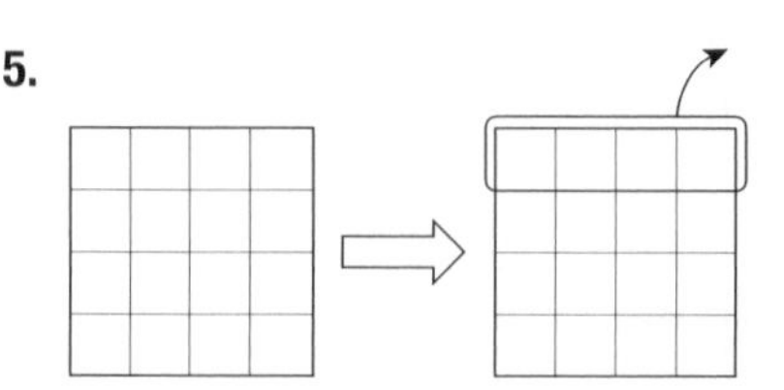

5.

6.

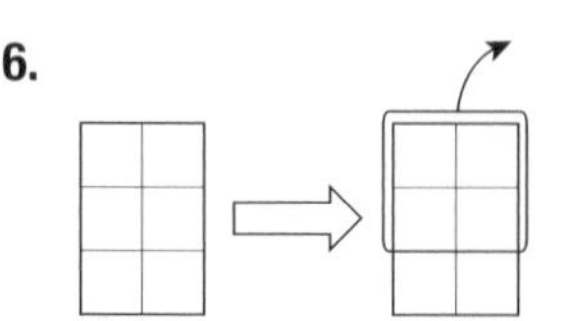

Pages 376-377, Lesson 7-8 (Check Your Progress)

1.

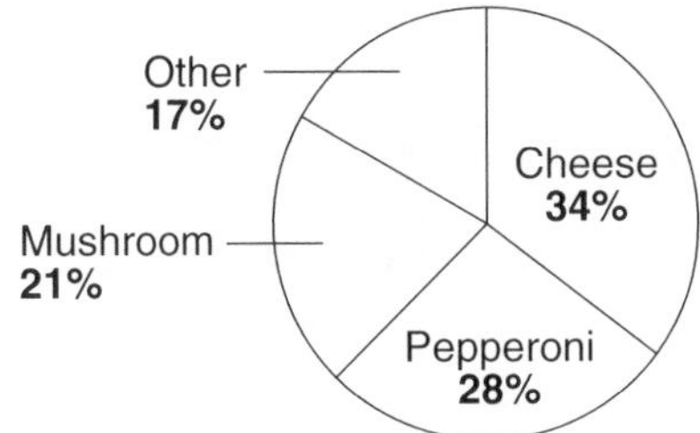

2.

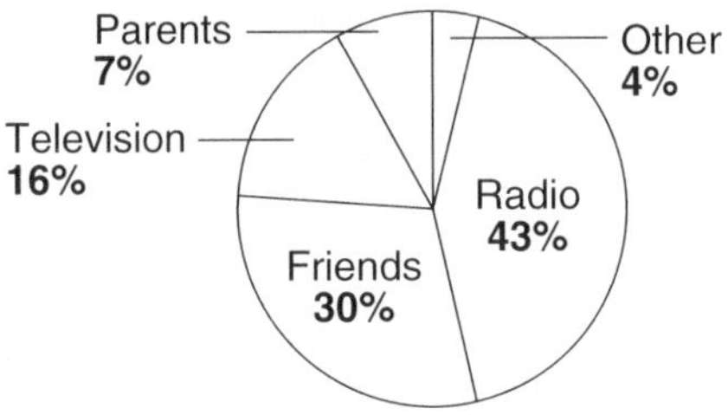

Pages 379–381, Lesson 7-8

6.

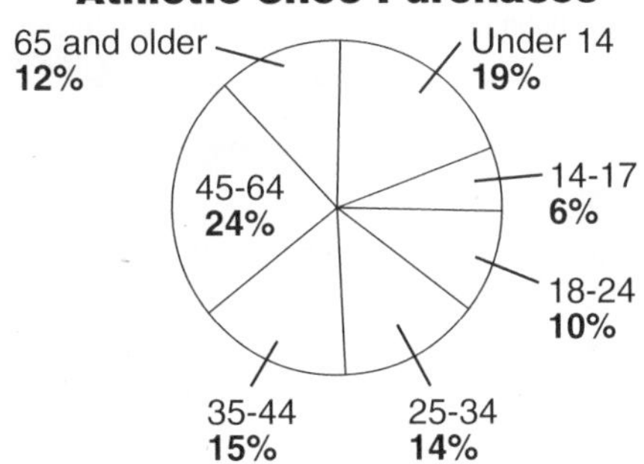

7.

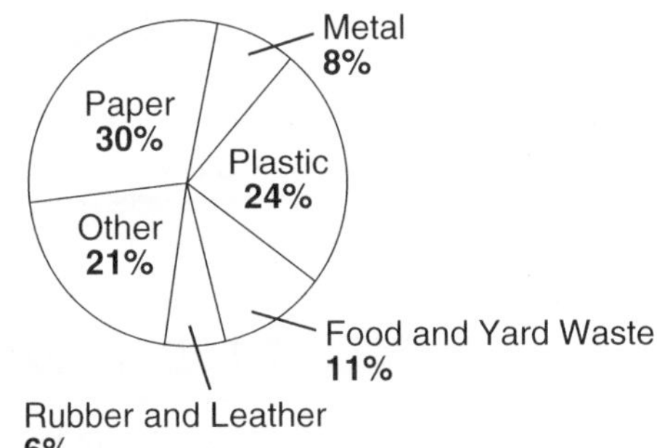

14a. Sample answer:

Favorite Shade of Blue	
Shade	**Number of People**
Aquamarine	30
Navy	35
Light Blue	17
Other	18

14b.

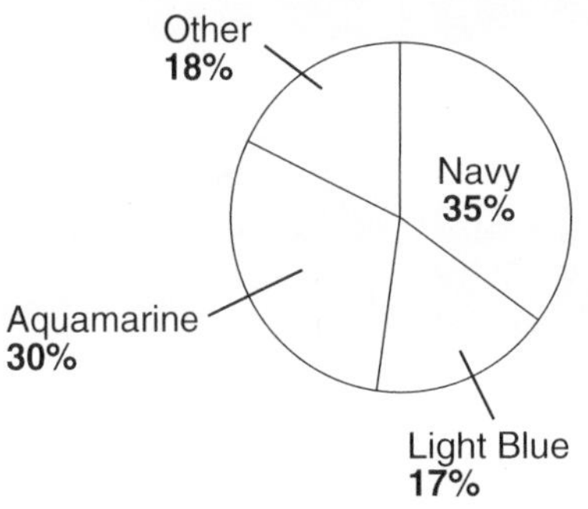

14c. Sample questions: How many more students preferred navy blue than aquamarine? 5 students; How did you determine the angle to use for the light blue color? Multiply 0.17 by $360° \approx 61°$

16.

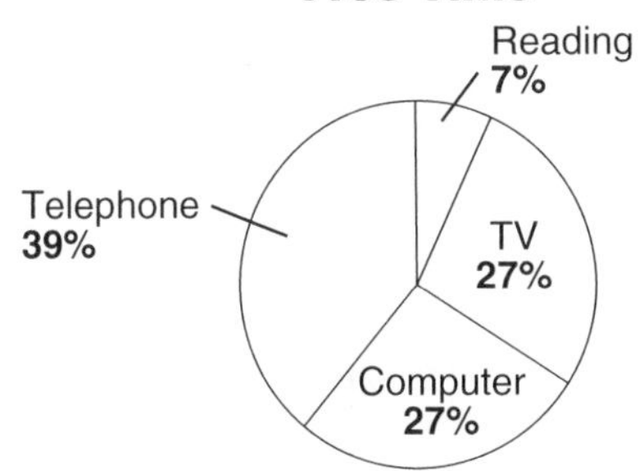

23.

Color	Number of Cars	Angle measure
Red	5	18°
White	10	36°
Green	15	54°
Blue	30	108°
Other	40	144°

Chapter 8 Chapter Planner

Diagnostic Assessment
Quick Check, p. 393

	Lesson 8-1 Pacing: 1 day	Lesson 8-2 Pacing: 1 day	Lesson 8-3 Pacing: 1 day
Title	**Functions**	**Sequences and Equations**	**Representing Linear Functions**
Objectives	• Determine whether a relation is a function. • Write a function using function notation.	• Describe sequences using words and symbols. • Find terms of arithmetic sequences.	• Solve linear equations with two variables. • Graph linear equations using ordered pairs.
Key Vocabulary	independent variable dependent variable vertical line test function notation	sequence term arithmetic sequence common difference	linear equation *x*-intercept *y*-intercept
NCTM Focal Points	G7-FP1, G8-FP1, G8-FP4C, G8-FP5C, G8-FP6C For the complete wording of the Focal Points for Grades 7 and 8, please see page iv, v, FP0, and FP1.		
Multiple Representations		p. 404	p. 410
Lesson Resources	**Chapter 8 Resource Masters** • Study Guide and Intervention, pp. 5–6 AL OL ELL • Skills Practice, p. 7 AL OL ELL • Practice, p. 8 AL OL BL ELL • Word Problem Practice, p. 9 AL OL BL • Enrichment, p. 10 OL BL **Transparencies** • 5-Minute Check Transparency 8-1 AL OL BL ELL **Additional Print Resources** • *Study Notebook* AL OL BL ELL	**Chapter 8 Resource Masters** • Study Guide and Intervention, pp. 11–12 AL OL ELL • Skills Practice, p. 13 AL OL ELL • Practice, p. 14 AL OL BL ELL • Word Problem Practice, p. 15 AL OL BL • Enrichment, p. 16 OL BL **Transparencies** • 5-Minute Check Transparency 8-2 AL OL BL ELL **Additional Print Resources** • *Study Notebook* AL OL BL ELL	**Chapter 8 Resource Masters** • Study Guide and Intervention, pp. 17–18 AL OL ELL • Skills Practice, p. 19 AL OL ELL • Practice, p. 20 AL OL BL ELL • Word Problem Practice, p. 21 AL OL BL • Enrichment, p. 22 OL BL • Quiz 1, p. 68 AL OL BL ELL **Transparencies** • 5-Minute Check Transparency 8-3 AL OL BL ELL **Additional Print Resources** • *Study Notebook* AL OL BL ELL
Technology for Every Lesson	Math Online glencoe.com • Extra Examples • Self-Check Quizzes • Personal Tutor	**CD/DVD Resources** IWB INTERACTIVE WHITEBOARD READY IWB StudentWorks Plus IWB Interactive Classroom IWB Diagnostic and Assessment Planner	• TeacherWorks Plus • eSolutions Manual Plus • ExamView Assessment Suite
Math in Motion			p. 408
Differentiated Instruction	pp. 396, 400	pp. 402, 405	pp. 407, 411

KEY:  AL Approaching Level  OL On Level BL Beyond Level ELL English Learners

Suggested Pacing			
Time Periods	Instruction	Review & Assessment	Total
45-minute	13	2	15
90-minute	6.5	1	7.5

Linear Functions and Graphing

Lesson 8-4 Pacing: 1 day	Lesson 8-5 Pacing: 1 day	Explore 8-6 Pacing: 1 day	Lesson 8-6 Pacing: 1 day
Rate of Change	**Constant Rate of Change and Direct Variation**	**Graphing Technology Lab: Slope and Rate of Change**	**Slope**
• Find rates of change. • Solve problems involving rates of change.	• Identify proportional and nonproportional relationships by finding a constant rate of change. • Solve problems involving direct variation.	• Use technology to describe the slope of a line.	• Find the slope of a line. • Use slope to describe a constant rate of change.
rate of change	linear relationship constant rate of change direct variation constant of variation		slope
			p. 430
Chapter 8 Resource Masters • Study Guide and Intervention, pp. 23–24 AL OL ELL • Skills Practice, p. 25 AL OL ELL • Practice, p. 26 AL OL BL ELL • Word Problem Practice, p. 27 AL OL BL • Enrichment, p. 28 OL BL • Spreadsheet, p. 29 AL OL BL ELL **Transparencies** • 5-Minute Check Transparency 8-4 AL OL BL ELL **Additional Print Resources** • *Study Notebook* AL OL BL ELL	**Chapter 8 Resource Masters** • Study Guide and Intervention, pp. 30–31 AL OL ELL • Skills Practice, p. 32 AL OL ELL • Practice, p. 33 AL OL BL ELL • Word Problem Practice, p. 34 AL OL BL • Enrichment, p. 35 OL BL • Quiz 2, p. 68 AL OL BL ELL **Transparencies** • 5-Minute Check Transparency 8-5 AL OL BL ELL **Additional Print Resources** • *Study Notebook* AL OL BL ELL	**Materials:** • Calculator-Based Lab • grid paper • water • beaker • metric ruler • tablespoon • 1/8-cup measuring cup • paper cups • paper clip	**Chapter 8 Resource Masters** • Study Guide and Intervention, pp. 36–37 AL OL ELL • Skills Practice, p. 38 AL OL ELL • Practice, p. 39 AL OL BL ELL • Word Problem Practice, p. 40 AL OL BL • Enrichment, p. 41 OL BL **Transparencies** • 5-Minute Check Transparency 8-6 AL OL BL ELL **Additional Print Resources** • *Study Notebook* AL OL BL ELL

Math Online glencoe.com
- Extra Examples
- Self-Check Quizzes
- Personal Tutor

CD/DVD Resources IWB INTERACTIVE WHITEBOARD READY
- IWB StudentWorks Plus
- IWB Interactive Classroom
- IWB Diagnostic and Assessment Planner
- TeacherWorks Plus
- eSolutions Manual Plus
- ExamView Assessment Suite

pp. 414, 417	pp. 420, 424		pp. 428, 431

Formative Assessment
Mid-Chapter Quiz p. 425

CHAPTER 8

Chapter Planner

	Explore 8-7 Pacing: 1 day	Lesson 8-7 Pacing: 1 day	Extend 8-7 Pacing: 1 day
Title	**Algebra Lab: Proportional and Nonproportional Linear Relationships**	**Slope-Intercept Form**	**Graphing Technology Lab: Family of Linear Graphs**
Objectives	• Identify direct proportional and nonproportional linear relationships.	• Determine the slopes and y-intercepts of lines. • Graph linear equations using the slope and y-intercept.	• Use the TI-*n*spire to investigate families of linear functions.
Key Vocabulary		slope-intercept form	
NCTM Focal Points			
Multiple Representations		p. 437	
Lesson Resources	**Materials:** • grid paper	**Chapter 8 Resource Masters** • Study Guide and Intervention, pp. 42–43 AL OL ELL • Skills Practice, p. 44 AL OL ELL • Practice, p. 45 AL OL BL ELL • Word Problem Practice, p. 46 AL OL BL • Enrichment, p. 47 OL BL • Quiz 3, p. 69 AL OL BL ELL **Transparencies** • 5-Minute Check Transparency 8-7 AL OL BL ELL **Additional Print Resources** • *Study Notebook* AL OL BL ELL	**Materials:** • TI-*n*spire graphing calculator
Technology for Every Lesson	Math Online glencoe.com • Extra Examples • Self-Check Quizzes • Personal Tutor	**CD/DVD Resources** IWB INTERACTIVE WHITEBOARD READY IWB StudentWorks Plus IWB Interactive Classroom IWB Diagnostic and Assessment Planner	• TeacherWorks Plus • eSolutions Manual Plus • ExamView Assessment Suite
Math in Motion	p. 432	p. 433	
Differentiated Instruction		pp. 434, 438	

KEY: AL Approaching Level OL On Level BL Beyond Level ELL English Learners

Lesson 8-8 Pacing: 1 day	Lesson 8-9 Pacing: 1 day	Lesson 8-10 Pacing: 1 day
Writing Linear Equations	**Prediction Equations**	**Systems of Equations**
• Write equations given the slope and *y*-intercept, a graph, a table, or two points. • Use linear equations to solve problems.	• Draw lines of fit for sets of data. • Use lines of fit to make predictions about data.	• Solve systems of linear equations by graphing. • Solve systems of linear equations by substitution.
point-slope form	line of fit	system of equations substitution
p. 446	p. 451	
Chapter 8 Resource Masters • Study Guide and Intervention, pp. 48–49 AL OL ELL • Skills Practice, p. 50 AL OL ELL • Practice, p. 51 AL OL BL ELL • Word Problem Practice, p. 52 AL OL BL • Enrichment, p. 53 OL BL • Quiz 3, p. 69 AL OL BL ELL **Transparencies** • 5-Minute Check Transparency 8-8 AL OL BL ELL **Additional Print Resources** • *Study Notebook* AL OL BL ELL	**Chapter 8 Resource Masters** • Study Guide and Intervention, pp. 54–55 AL OL ELL • Skills Practice, p. 56 AL OL ELL • Practice, p. 57 AL OL BL ELL • Word Problem Practice, p. 58 AL OL BL • Enrichment, p. 59 OL BL **Transparencies** • 5-Minute Check Transparency 8-9 AL OL BL ELL **Additional Print Resources** • *Study Notebook* AL OL BL ELL	**Chapter 8 Resource Masters** • Study Guide and Intervention, pp. 60–61 AL OL ELL • Skills Practice, p. 62 AL OL ELL • Practice, p. 63 AL OL BL ELL • Word Problem Practice, p. 64 AL OL BL • Enrichment, p. 65 OL BL • Quiz 4, p. 69 OL AL BL ELL **Transparencies** • 5-Minute Check Transparency 8-10 AL OL BL ELL **Additional Print Resources** • *Study Notebook* AL OL BL ELL
Math Online glencoe.com • Extra Examples • Self-Check Quizzes • Personal Tutor	**CD/DVD Resources** IWB INTERACTIVE WHITEBOARD READY IWB StudentWorks Plus IWB Interactive Classroom IWB Diagnostic and Assessment Planner	• TeacherWorks Plus • eSolutions Manual Plus • ExamView Assessment Suite
pp. 442, 447	pp. 449, 452	pp. 454, 457

Summative Assessment
- Study Guide and Review, pp. 458–462
- Practice Test, p. 463

CHAPTER 8 Assessment and Intervention

SE = Student Edition, **TE** = Teacher Edition, **CRM** = Chapter Resource Masters

	Diagnosis	Prescription
Diagnostic Assessment	**Beginning Chapter 8**	
	Get Ready for Chapter 8 **SE,** p. 393	Response to Intervention **TE,** p. 393
	Beginning Every Lesson	
	Then, Now, Why? **SE** 5-Minute Check Transparencies	Chapter 0 **SE,** pp. P1–P22 Concepts and Skills Bank **SE,** pp. 856–887 *Quick Review Math Handbook*
Formative Assessment	**During/After Every Lesson**	
	Check Your Progress **SE,** every example Check Your Understanding **SE** H.O.T. Problems **SE** Spiral Review **SE** Additional Examples **TE** Watch Out! **TE** Step 4, Assess **TE** Chapter 8 Quizzes **CRM,** pp. 68–69 Self-Check Quizzes glencoe.com	Tier 1 Intervention Concepts and Skills Bank **SE,** pp. 856–887 Skills Practice **CRM,** Ch. 1–8 glencoe.com Tier 2 Intervention Differentiated Instruction **TE** Study Guide and Intervention Masters **CRM,** Ch. 1–8 *Quick Review Math Handbook* Tier 3 Intervention *Math Triumphs, Grade 8,* Ch. 2, 6
	Mid-Chapter	
	Mid-Chapter Quiz **SE,** p. 425 Mid-Chapter Test **CRM,** p. 70 ExamView Assessment Suite	Tier 1 Intervention Concepts and Skills Bank **SE,** pp. 856–887 Skills Practice **CRM,** Ch. 1–8 glencoe.com Tier 2 Intervention Study Guide and Intervention Masters **CRM,** Ch. 1–8 *Quick Review Math Handbook* Tier 3 Intervention *Math Triumphs, Grade 8,* Ch. 2, 6
	Before Chapter Test	
	Chapter Study Guide and Review **SE,** pp. 458–462 Practice Test **SE,** p. 463 Standardized Test Practice **SE,** pp. 464–467 Chapter Test glencoe.com Standardized Test Practice glencoe.com Vocabulary Review glencoe.com ExamView Assessment Suite	Tier 1 Intervention Concepts and Skills Bank **SE,** pp. 856–887 Skills Practice **CRM,** Ch. 1–8 glencoe.com Tier 2 Intervention Study Guide and Intervention Masters **CRM,** Ch. 1–8 *Quick Review Math Handbook* Tier 3 Intervention *Math Triumphs, Grade 8,* Ch. 2, 6
Summative Assessment	**After Chapter 8**	
	Multiple-Choice Tests, Forms 1, 2A, 2B **CRM,** pp. 72–77 Free-Response Tests, Forms 2C, 2D, 3 **CRM,** pp. 78–83 Vocabulary Test **CRM,** p. 71 Extended Response Test **CRM,** p. 84 Standardized Test Practice **CRM,** pp. 85–87 ExamView Assessment Suite	Study Guide and Intervention Masters **CRM,** Ch. 1–8 *Quick Review Math Handbook* glencoe.com

CHAPTER 8 Differentiated Instruction

Option 1 Reaching All Learners AL OL BL ELL

VERBAL/LINGUISTIC Have groups of mixed abilities discuss the differences between relations and functions. Then have each student in the group write a paragraph explaining relations and functions in their own words. Ask them to explore which examples, explanations, or demonstrations from class or their text most helped them understand the differences between these concepts.

LOGICAL Pair students of mixed abilities and have them use a graphing calculator to create graphs with slopes of $-\frac{1}{4}$, $-\frac{1}{2}$, -1, -2, -3, -4, $\frac{1}{4}$, $\frac{1}{2}$, 1, 2, 3, and 4. Have them use an equation such as $y = mx$, where m is the slope of the line, and then change the slope for each graph. Next, have them sketch the lines on graph paper and use either labels or a color code to distinguish the lines.

Ask students to compare the lines and consider the following questions:

- How does the slope change as the line approaches a vertical position?
- How does the slope change as the line approaches a horizontal position?

Option 2 Approaching Level AL

Have students work in small groups. Provide each group with several copies of graphs that have positive slopes, negative slopes, zero slopes, and undefined slopes. Ask groups to identify the slopes of the graphs as positive, negative, zero, or undefined and to explain their reasoning. Then have them describe the rates of change represented by the slopes. Encourage groups to compare the graphs to determine which slopes represent greater or smaller rates of change.

Option 3 English Learners ELL

It can be difficult to remember the words associated with linear equations, such as *dependent variable* and *independent variable, domain* and *range, input* and *output, x-values* and *y-values.* Have students discuss strategies that can help them associate independent variable, domain, input, and x-values, on the one hand, and dependent variable, range, output, and y-values on the other.

MULTIPLE REPRESENTATIONS The following chart can be used to support students' understanding of four representations of functions. Students can create the charts or you can give students the chart with one cell completed and have them finish filling it in.

FUNCTION (Use a written description or definition of the function. This can include a real-world problem.)	**TABLE** (Use a table with columns for x and y.)
GRAPH (Show a graph of ordered pairs or a line passing through two or more points.)	**ALGEBRA** (Write an equation or formula. Define the variables.)

Option 4 Beyond Level BL

Have students explore linear equations in the following activity:

- Write an equation of a line that has the same slope as the line $2x - 3y = 3$ and the same y-intercept as the line $3y - 6x = 9$. $y = \frac{2}{3}x + 3$
- Then graph and label the three lines.

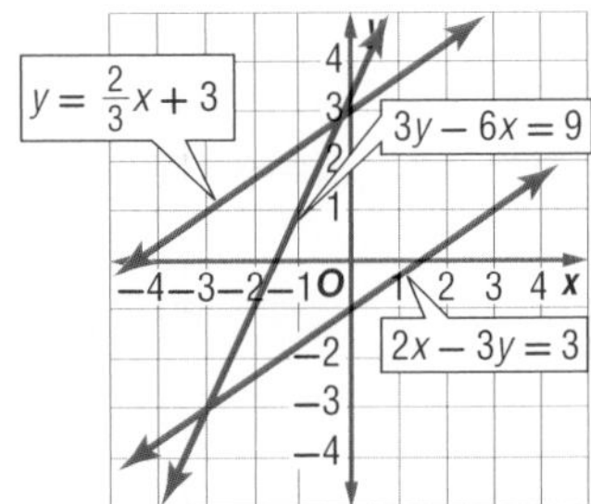

- Ask students to write a few sentences comparing the lines, such as where the lines intersect and which lines are parallel.

CHAPTER 8

Focus on Mathematical Content

Vertical Alignment

Before Chapter 8

Related Topics before Pre-Algebra
- graph data
- use division to find unit rates

Previous Topics from Pre-Algebra
- locate and name points on a coordinate plane
- select appropriate operations

Chapter 8

Related Topics from Pre-Algebra
- generate a different representation of data given another representation of data
- predict, find, and justify solutions to application problems using appropriate tables, graphs, and algebraic equations
- draw conclusions and make predictions by analyzing trends in scatter plots

After Chapter 8

Preparation for Algebra 1
- interpret and predict the effects of changing the slope and *y*-intercept in applied situations
- graph and write equations of lines given characteristics such as two points, a point and a slope, or a slope and *y*-intercept
- develop the concept of slope as rate of change and determine slopes from graphs, tables, and algebraic representations

Lesson-by-Lesson Preview

8-1 Functions

A function is a special relation in which each member of the domain is paired with exactly one member of the range. Functions may be represented using ordered pairs, tables, mappings, graphs, and equations.

Functions can be written using function notation.

equation	function notation
$y = -3x + 4$	$f(x) = -3x + 4$

8-2 Sequences and Equations

A sequence is an ordered list of numbers. An arithmetic sequence is a sequence in which the difference between any two consecutive terms is the same. The arithmetic sequence 6, 10, 14, 18 can be described as follows:

- Words: The terms have a common difference of 4. A term is 2 more than 4 times the term number.
- Equation: $t = 4n + 2$

Equations can be used to extend the pattern and find other terms. For example, in the above sequence, the 52nd term is $t = 4(52) + 2$ or 210.

8-3 Representing Linear Functions

A linear equation is an equation whose graph is a line, such as $y = x + 3$. It is also a function if each *x*-value is paired with exactly one *y*-value. Solutions of linear equations are ordered pairs that make the equation true. You can graph linear equations as follows:

- Find the *x*-intercept of a graph by letting $y = 0$ and solving for *x*. Find the *y*-intercept by letting $x = 0$ and solving for *y*. Plot the two points and draw a line through them.
- Make a table to find ordered pairs solutions by first solving the equation for *y*, and then finding the ordered pairs. Graph the pairs on a coordinate plane and draw a line.

8-4 Rate of Change

A change in one quantity with respect to another quantity is called the rate of change.

Rates of change are:

- positive if *y*-values increase as *x*-values increase,
- negative if *y*-values decrease as *x*-values increase, and
- zero if *y*-values do not change as *x*-values increase.

Constant Rate of Change and Direct Variation

If the rate of change between any two data points in a relationship is the same or constant, then the relationship is a linear relationship that can be described by a linear equation.

A special type of linear equation that describes a constant rate of change is called a direct variation. It can be written in the form $y = kx$, where k is the constant of variation.

- The graph of a direct variation always passes through the origin and represents a proportional situation.
- The ratio of y to x in a direct variation is a constant. As x increases in value, y increases or decreases at a constant rate k and it is said that y varies directly with x or y is directly proportional to x.

Slope

Slope is the ratio of the rise, or vertical change, to the run, or horizontal change of a line: slope $= \frac{\text{rise}}{\text{run}}$.

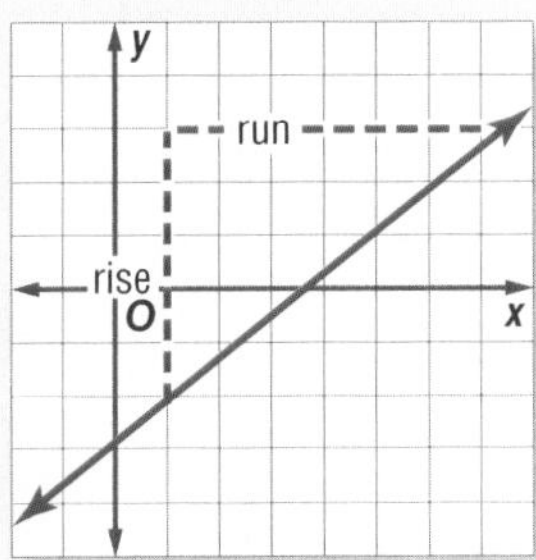

Slope (m) is the same for any two points on a straight line. You can find slope by using the coordinates of any two points on a line: $m = \frac{y_2 - y_1}{x_2 - x_1}$, where $x_2 \neq x_1$.

Slope-Intercept Form

Equations written as $y = mx + b$, where m is the slope and b is the y-intercept, are linear equations in slope-intercept form. For example, the graph of $y = 5x - 6$ is a line that has a slope of 5 and crosses the y-axis at $(0, -6)$.

Sometimes you must first write an equation in slope-intercept form before finding the slope and y-intercept. For example, the equation $2x + 3y = 15$ can be expressed in slope-intercept form by solving the equation for y: $y = -\frac{2}{3}x + 5$, which reveals a slope of $-\frac{2}{3}$ and a y-intercept of 5.

Writing Linear Equations

Linear equations can be written in more than one way:

- If the slope and y-intercept are known or you can find the slope and y-intercept from a graph, substitute the slope m and the y-intercept b in the equation $y = mx + b$.
- If you know the coordinates of two points, use the coordinates to find the slope. Then use the slope and the coordinates of one point to write the equation in the point-slope form: $y - y_1 = m(x - x_1)$.

Prediction Equations

When real-life data are collected, the points graphed usually do not form a straight line, but they may exhibit a linear trend. A line of fit is a line that lies very close to most of the data points. This line can be used to make predictions.

Systems of Equations

A system of equations is a collection of two or more equations with the same variables. A solution to a system of two linear equations is an ordered pair that satisfies both equations in the system. A system can have one, no, or an infinite number of solutions. A system has:

- one solution if the graphs of the equations intersect.
- no solution if the graphs of the equations are parallel.
- an infinite number of solutions if the graphs of the equations are the same line.

Professional Development

Targeted professional development has been articulated throughout McGraw-Hill's mathematics program. The **McGraw-Hill Professional Development Video Library** provides short videos that support key topics. For more information, visit glencoe.com.

Model Lessons

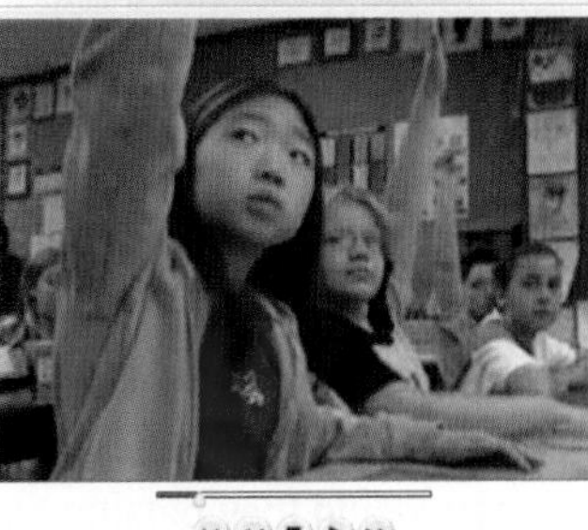

Instructional Strategies

CHAPTER 8 Notes

Chapter Project

Animal Trivia

Students use what they have learned about functions, rates of change and slope, and systems of equations to analyze animal facts on food, heart rate, and speed.

- Ask each student to research the following facts about a favorite wild animal: daily pounds of food eaten, heartbeats per minute, and speed in miles per hour.
- Divide students into groups. Have each group use food facts for each animal to write an equation in function notation that gives pounds of food eaten as a function of the number of days. Why are the relationships functions? How many pounds of food would a zoo of the group's animals need for one month?
- Ask each group to use the heart rates for each animal to write a table of values for x minutes and y heartbeats, and graph the ordered pairs for each animal on the same coordinate plane. How do the heart rates compare? Are the rates of change shown on the graph proportional? How do they know?
- Have each group choose two animals that are close in speed. Have them use the speeds to write two linear equations relating distance and time. For example, if the speed of an animal is 3 miles per hour, the equation would be $d = 3t$, where d is the distance traveled in miles and t is the time in hours. Then have them graph the equations on the same coordinate plane. If the two animals started a race at the same time, how far apart would they be after two hours?

CHAPTER 8 Linear Functions and Graphing

Then

In Chapter 1, you learned how to use multiple representations to represent functions.

Now

In Chapter 8, you will:

- Solve and graph linear equations with two variables.
- Write and graph linear equations using the slope and y-intercept.
- Solve systems of equations by graphing and substitution.

Why?

ANIMALS Did you know that giraffes on average eat about 100 pounds of leaves a day? They spend a majority of their day eating because it takes a lot of leaves to energize these large animals. The amount of food a giraffe eats each day can be represented by a function.

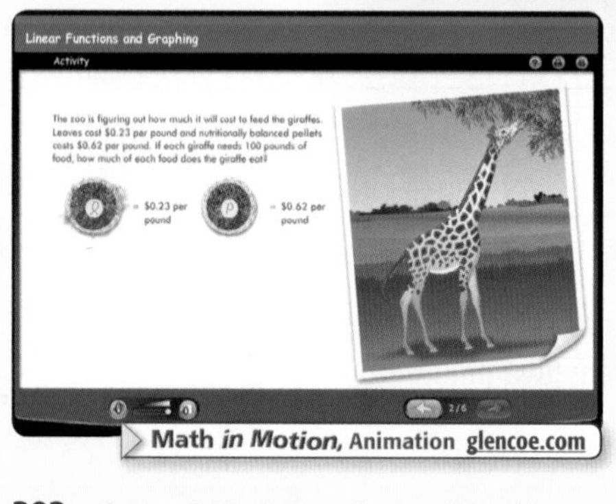

Key Vocabulary Introduce the key vocabulary in the chapter using the routine below.

Define: An equation in slope-intercept form is a linear equation in the form $y = mx + b$, where m is the slope and b is the y-intercept.

Example: The equation $y = 2x + 7$ is in slope-intercept form.

Ask: Is the equation $3x + y = 18$ in slope-intercept form? Explain. No; to be in slope-intercept form it should be written as $-3x + 18 = y$.

Get Ready for Chapter 8

Diagnose Readiness You have two options for checking Prerequisite Skills.

Text Option Take the Quick Check below. Refer to the Quick Review for help.

*Quick*Check

Find the next term in each sequence. (Previous Course) (Used in Lesson 8-2)

1. 1, 5, 9, 13, … 17

2. 5, 10, 20, 40, … 80

3. 32, 29, 26, 23, … 20

4. 50, 48, 46, 44, … 42

5. **EXERCISE** Becky started an exercise program that calls for 12 minutes of jogging each day during the first week. Each week after that, Becky increases the time she jogs by 5 minutes. In which week will she first jog more than 30 minutes? 5th week

(Used in Lesson 8-6)

Use the coordinate plane to name the point for each ordered pair. (Lesson 1-4)

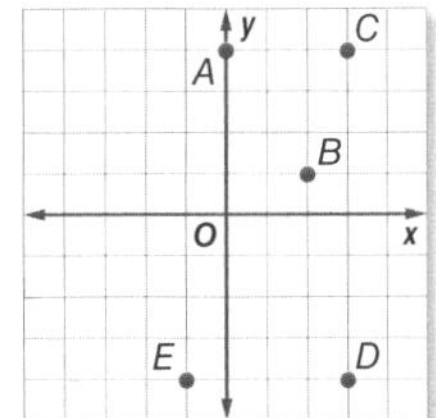

6. (3, −4) D

7. (0, 4) A

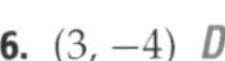

8. (−1, −4) E

9. **DIRECTIONS** On a coordinate plane, the library is located at (4, −3) and the mall is located at (−1, 7). Using north, south, west, and east, write directions on how to walk from the library to the mall.

9. Sample answer: Walk north 10 blocks then west 5 blocks.

(Used in Lessons 8-4 and 8-5)

Write each rate as a unit rate. (Lesson 6-2)

10. 180 gallons in 10 minutes 18 gallons/minute

11. 455 miles in 7 hours 65 mph

12. **SHOPPING** Christa spent $50 for 10 books at the bookstore. What was the unit rate price for each book? $5 per book

*Quick*Review

EXAMPLE 1

Find the next term in the sequence.

4, 7, 10, 13, …

Each term is 3 more than the one before it. So, the next term is 13 + 3 or 16.

EXAMPLE 2

Use the coordinate plane to name the point for (−1, 2).

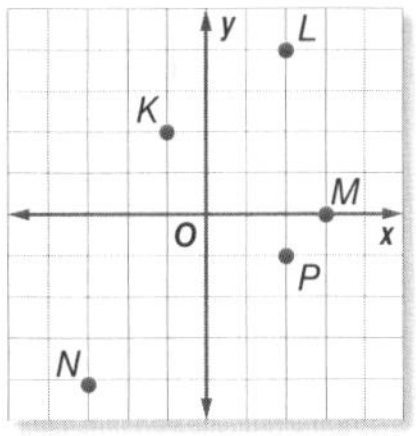

Step 1 Start at the origin, (0, 0).

Step 2 Move 1 unit left.

Step 3 Move 2 units up.

So, point *K* is at (−1, 2).

EXAMPLE 3

Write 150 miles in 2 hours as a unit rate.

To write this as a unit rate, divide 150 by 2.

150 ÷ 2 = 75

So, the unit rate is 75 miles per hour.

Online Option Math Online Take a self-check Chapter Readiness Quiz at glencoe.com.

Get Ready for Chapter 8

Response to Intervention (RtI)

Use the *Quick Check* results and the Intervention Planner to help you determine your Response to Intervention. The If-Then statements in the chart below help you decide the appropriate tier of RtI and suggest intervention resources for each tier.

Intervention Planner

Tier 1 On Level

If students miss about 25% of the exercises or less,

Then choose a resource:

SE Lessons 1–4, 6–2

CRM Skills Practice, Chapter 1, p. 26; Chapter 6, p. 13

TE Chapter Project, p. 392

Math Online Self-Check Quiz

Tier 2 Strategic Intervention approaching grade level

If students miss about 50% of the exercises,

Then choose a resource:

CRM Study Guide and Intervention, Chapter 1, p. 24; Chapter 6, p. 11

Quick Review Math Handbook

Math Online Extra Examples, Personal Tutor, Homework Help

Tier 3 Intensive Intervention 2 or more years below grade level

If students miss about 75% of the exercises,

Then use *Math Triumphs, Grade 8*, Ch. 2, 6

Math Online Extra Examples, Personal Tutor, Homework Help, Review Vocabulary

CHAPTER 8 Notes

FOLDABLES® Study Organizer

Dinah Zike's Foldables®

Focus Students write notes about equations and inequalities.

Teach Have students make and label the tabs for each lesson of their Foldables as illustrated. Have students use the appropriate tabs as they cover each lesson in this chapter. Before beginning each lesson, ask students to look through it and write one question they have about what they see. After each lesson, have them answer the questions they wrote and other questions that may arise.

When to Use It Encourage students to add vocabulary, questions, and answers to questions to their Foldable as they work through the chapter. A completed Foldable is shown on p. 458.

Differentiated Instruction

CRM Student-Built Glossary, p. 1–2
Students should complete the chart by providing a definition of each term and an example as they progress through Chapter 8. This study tool can also be used to review for the chapter test.

Get Started on Chapter 8

You will learn several new concepts, skills, and vocabulary terms as you study Chapter 8. To get ready, identify important terms and organize your resources. You may wish to refer to **Chapter 0** to review prerequisite skills.

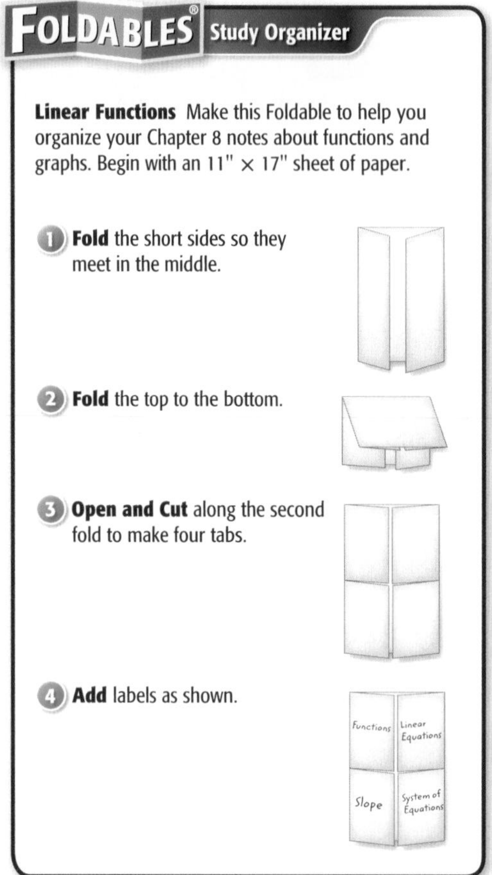

FOLDABLES® Study Organizer

Linear Functions Make this Foldable to help you organize your Chapter 8 notes about functions and graphs. Begin with an 11" × 17" sheet of paper.

1. **Fold** the short sides so they meet in the middle.
2. **Fold** the top to the bottom.
3. **Open and Cut** along the second fold to make four tabs.
4. **Add** labels as shown.

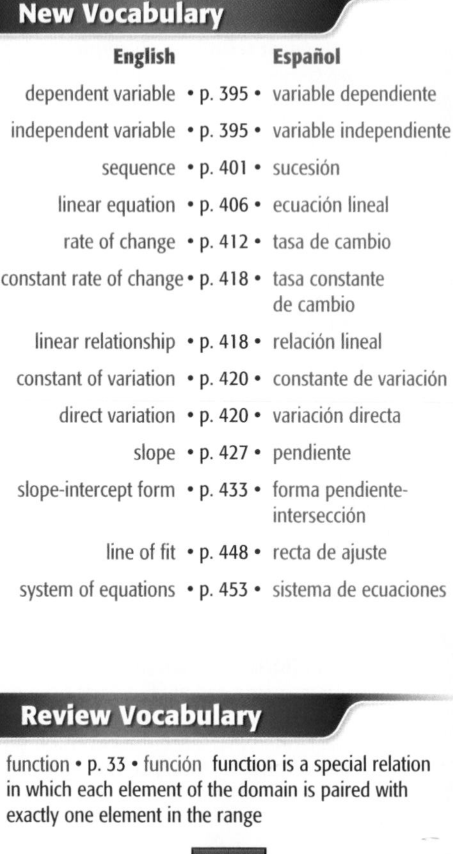

New Vocabulary

English		Español
dependent variable	p. 395	variable dependiente
independent variable	p. 395	variable independiente
sequence	p. 401	sucesión
linear equation	p. 406	ecuación lineal
rate of change	p. 412	tasa de cambio
constant rate of change	p. 418	tasa constante de cambio
linear relationship	p. 418	relación lineal
constant of variation	p. 420	constante de variación
direct variation	p. 420	variación directa
slope	p. 427	pendiente
slope-intercept form	p. 433	forma pendiente-intersección
line of fit	p. 448	recta de ajuste
system of equations	p. 453	sistema de ecuaciones

Review Vocabulary

function • p. 33 • función function is a special relation in which each element of the domain is paired with exactly one element in the range

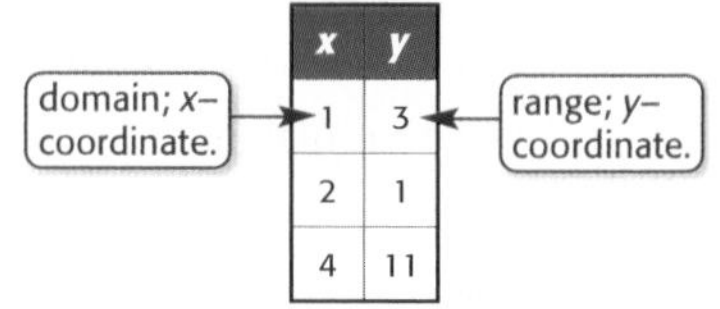

proportional relationship • p. 281 • relación proporcional the ratios of related terms are equal

rate • p. 270 • tasa a ratio of two measurements having different units

Multilingual eGlossary glencoe.com

Math Online glencoe.com

- Study the chapter online
- Explore **Math in Motion**
- Get extra help from your own **Personal Tutor**
- Use **Extra Examples** for additional help
- Take a **Self-Check Quiz**
- **Review Vocabulary** in fun ways

394 Chapter 8 Linear Functions and Graphing

8-1 Functions

Why?

The Thompson Middle School student council is selling school pennants to raise money for a new school welcome sign.

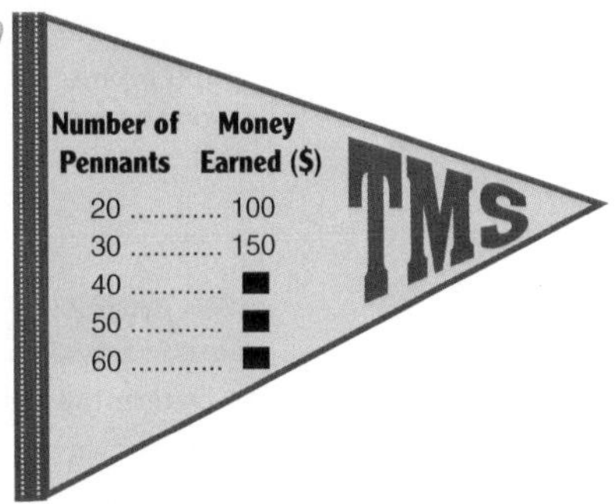

a. Copy and complete the table. **See Chapter 8 Answer Appendix.**

b. If they sell 70 pennants, how much money will they earn? **$350**

c. Explain how to find the total earnings if they sell 100 pennants. **Multiply 100 by 5.**

Then

You have already learned how to find function rules and create function tables. (Lesson 1-5)

Now

- Determine whether a relation is a function.
- Write a function using function notation.

New Vocabulary

independent variable
dependent variable
vertical line test
function notation

Math Online

glencoe.com

- Extra Examples
- Personal Tutor
- Self-Check Quiz
- Homework Help

Relations and Functions The total earnings (output) of the student council depends on, or is a function of, the number of pennants sold (input). The number of pennants sold is called the **independent variable** because the values are chosen and do not depend upon the other variable. The total money earned is called the **dependent variable** because it depends on the input value.

Recall that functions are relations in which each element of the domain is paired with *exactly* one element of the range.

Function

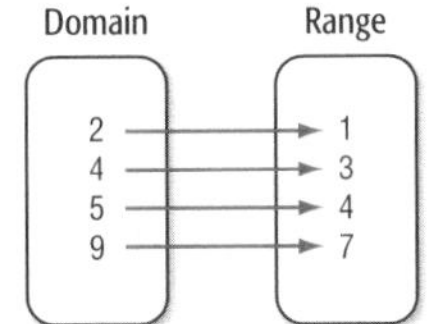

This is a function because each domain value is paired with exactly one range value.

Not a Function

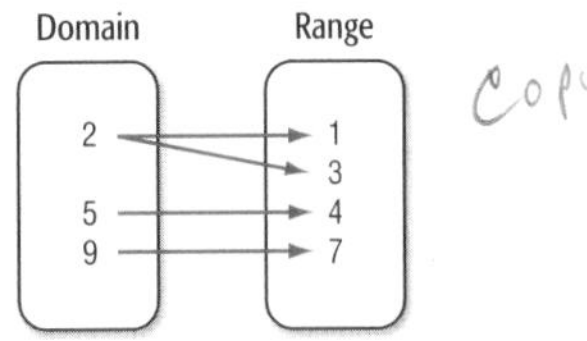

This is *not* a function because 2 in the domain is paired with two range values, 1 and 3.

EXAMPLE 1 Determine Whether a Relation is a Function

Determine whether each relation is a function. Explain.

a. {(54, 112), (56, 130), (55, 145), (54, 123), (56, 128)}

This is not a function because 54 and 56 in the domain are paired with two range values.

b.

x	4	7	6	3	5	2
y	6	10	11	8	4	9

This a function. Each domain value is paired with one range value.

Check Your Progress **1A–1B. See Chapter 8 Answer Appendix.**

1A. {(5, 1), (6, 3), (7, 5), (8, 0)}

1B.

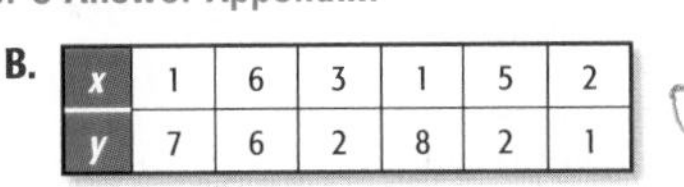

x	1	6	3	1	5	2
y	7	6	2	8	2	1

Personal Tutor glencoe.com

8-1 Lesson Notes

1 FOCUS

Vertical Alignment

Before Lesson 8-1
Learn how to find function rules and create function tables.

Lesson 8-1
Determine whether a relation is a function. Write a function using function notation.

After Lesson 8-1
Find solutions for linear equations.

2 TEACH

Scaffolding Questions

Have students read the *Why?* section of the lesson and answer the questions.

Ask:

- What does the amount of money earned depend upon? The money earned depends upon the number of pennants sold.
- How much does each pennant sell for? $5
- If you know how much each pennant sells for, can you write an equation that allows you to find the amount raised depending on the number of pennants sold? Explain. Yes; assign the variable p to represent the number of pennants sold and m to represent the amount of money raised. The equation $5p = m$ represents the money raised.

Lesson 8-1 Resources

Resource	Approaching-Level	On-Level	Beyond-Level	English Learners
Teacher Edition	• Differentiated Instruction, p. 396		• Differentiated Instruction, p. 400	• Differentiated Instruction, p. 396
Chapter Resource Masters	• Study Guide and Intervention, pp. 5–6 • Skills Practice, p. 7 • Practice, p. 8 • Word Problem Practice, p. 9	• Study Guide and Intervention, pp. 5–6 • Skills Practice, p. 7 • Practice, p. 8 • Word Problem Practice, p. 9 • Enrichment, p. 10	• Practice, p. 8 • Word Problem Practice, p. 9 • Enrichment, p. 10	• Study Guide and Intervention, pp. 5–6 • Skills Practice, p. 7 • Practice, p. 8
Transparencies	• 5-Minute Check Transparency 8-1	• 5-Minute Check Transparency 8-1	• 5-Minute Check Transparency 8-1	• 5-Minute Check Transparency 8-1
Other	• Study Notebook • Teaching Pre-Algebra with Manipulatives	• Study Notebook • Teaching Pre-Algebra with Manipulatives	• Study Notebook	• Study Notebook • Teaching Pre-Algebra with Manipulatives

Relations and Functions

Example 1 shows how to determine whether a relation is a function.
Example 2 shows how to use a graph to identify functions.

Formative Assessment

Use the Check Your Progress exercises after each example to determine students' understanding of concepts.

Additional Examples

1 Determine whether each relation is a function. Explain.

a. {(3, 48), (7, 21), (5, 15), (1, 13), (2, 12)} Yes; each x-value is paired with only one y-value.

b.

x	8	3	10	3	2	5
y	12	5	8	12	9	4

No; 3 is paired with two range values.

2 Determine whether the graph below is a function. Explain your answer.

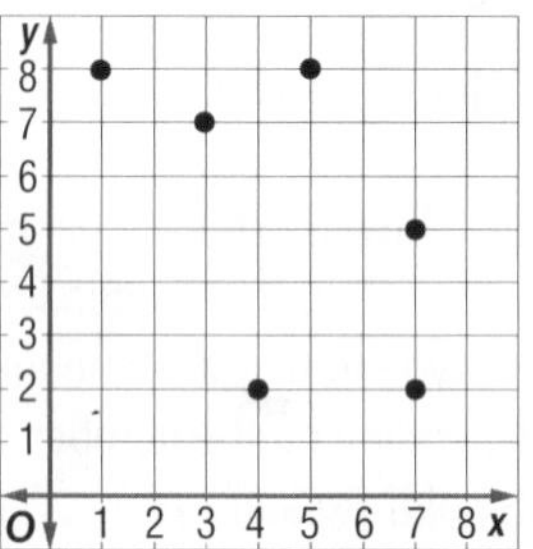

No; the vertical line test shows that it passes through two points on the graph with the same x-value.

Additional Examples also in Interactive Classroom PowerPoint® Presentations

IWB INTERACTIVE WHITEBOARD READY

StudyTip

Vertical Line Test Use a pencil or straightedge to represent a vertical line. Place the pencil at the left of the graph. Move it to the right across the graph.

Another way to determine whether a relation is a function is to apply the **vertical line test** to the graph of the relation. If, for each value of x in the domain, a vertical line passes through no more than one point on the graph, then the graph represents a function. If the line passes through more than one point on the graph, it is *not* a function.

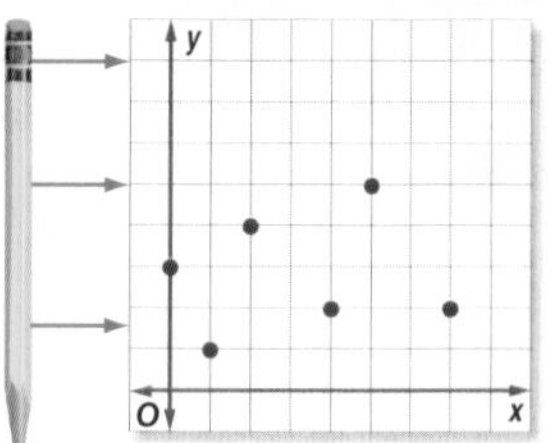

EXAMPLE 2 Use a Graph to Identify Functions

Determine whether the graph above is a function. Explain your answer.

The graph is a function because the vertical line test shows that it passes through no more than one point on the graph for each value of x.

Check Your Progress

2. Determine whether the graph at the right is a function. Explain your answer.
The graph represents a relation that is *not* a function because it does not pass the vertical line test. At least one domain value has more than one range value. By examining the graph, you can see that when $x = 4$, there are two different y values.

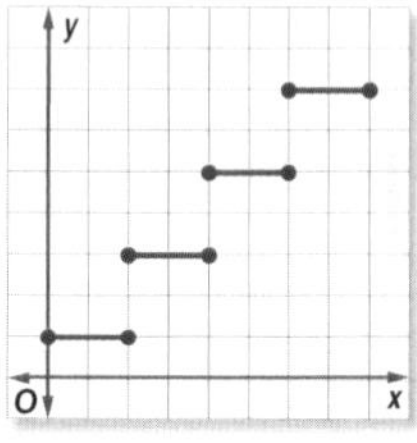

Personal Tutor glencoe.com

Function Notation A function that is written as an equation can also be written in a form called **function notation**. Consider the equation $y = 2x + 3$.

Equation	Function Notation
$y = 2x + 3$	$f(x) = 2x + 3$

The variable y and $f(x)$ both represent the dependent variable. In the example above, when $x = 4$, $f(x) = 11$. In function notation, $f(x)$ is read "f of x" and is equal to the value of the function at x.

Math History Link

Leonhard Euler (1707–1783)
By 1766, Euler lost sight in both of his eyes. Despite being blind, he continued to publish his mathematical results. Euler is credited with being the person who introduced function notation.

EXAMPLE 3 Find a Function Value

If $f(x) = 4x - 7$, find each function value.

a. $f(5)$

$f(x) = 4x - 7$	**Write the function.**
$f(5) = 4(5) - 7$	**Replace x with 5.**
$f(5) = 13$	**Simplify.**

b. $f(-6)$

$f(x) = 4x - 7$	**Write the function.**
$f(-6) = 4(-6) - 7$	**Replace x with -6.**
$f(-6) = -31$	**Simplify.**

Check Your Progress

If $f(x) = 14 + 3x$, find each function value.

3A. $f(4)$ **26**

3B. $f(-7)$ **-7**

Personal Tutor glencoe.com

Differentiated Instruction

AL ELL

If students are visually oriented,

Then have them make a picture called a mapping diagram like those in their book showing the domain, x-values, in one box and the range, y-values, in another. Have students draw arrows pairing each x-value with its corresponding y-value. These drawings can help students in determining whether a relation is a function.

Describe Relationships A function can also describe the relationship between two quantities. For example, the distance you travel in a car depends on how long you are in the car. In other words, *distance is a function of time* or $d(t)$.

StudyTip

Functions A function does not always have to be in the form of $f(x)$. If a function is representing a real-world situation, any variables representing the independent and dependent variables can be used.

Real-World EXAMPLE 4 Use Function Notation

MUSIC Mariah spent $22.50 downloading songs to her digital music player from an online music store for $0.90 each.

a. Use function notation to write an equation that gives the total cost as a function of the number of songs purchased.

Words	total cost =	cost per song times the number of songs
Variables	Let $c(s)$ =	total cost and s = number of songs.
Function	$c(s)$ =	$0.9s$

The function is $c(s) = 0.9s$.

b. Use the equation to determine the number of songs that Mariah downloaded.

$c(s) = 0.9s$ **Write the function.**

$22.5 = 0.9s$ **Substitute 22.5 for $c(s)$.**

$25 = s$ **Divide each side by 0.9.**

So, Mariah downloaded 25 songs.

 **Check Your Progress**

4. **WHALES** A whale watching boat traveled at a speed of 5.5 miles per hour.
   A. Use function notation to write a function that gives the total distance traveled as a function of the time in hours spent whale watching. $d(t) = 5.5t$
   B. Use the function to find how long it took to travel 25 miles. 4.5 h

Personal Tutor glencoe.com

Check Your Understanding

Examples 1 and 2 pp. 395–396

Determine whether each relation is a function. Explain. 1–4. See Chapter 8 Answer Appendix.

1. $\{(8, 2), (4, 3), (6, 5), (1, 5)\}$

2.

x	1	3	8	7	3
y	4	2	9	6	4

3.

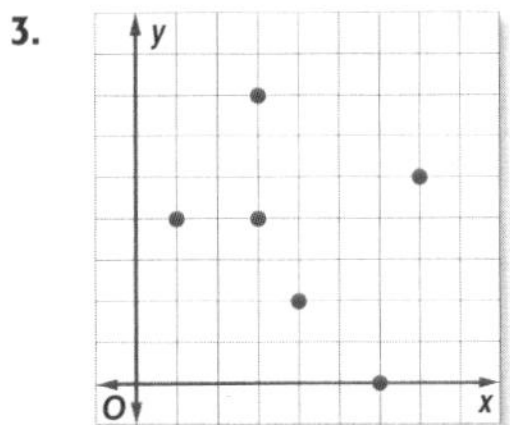

4.

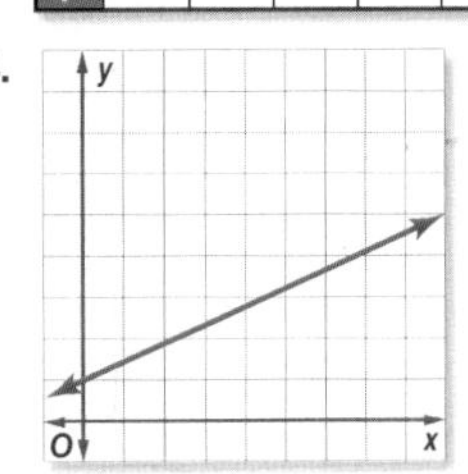

Example 3 p. 396

If $f(x) = 6x - 4$, find each function value.

5. $f(3)$ 14
6. $f(-5)$ −34
7. $f(8)$ 44
8. $f(-9)$ −58

TEACH with TECH

INTERACTIVE WHITEBOARD Display a graph. Draw a vertical line, and drag it from left to right across the graph to demonstrate the vertical line test.

Function Notation

Example 3 shows how to find a function value.

Additional Example

 If $f(x) = 6x + 5$, find each function value.

a. $f(5)$ 35

b. $f(-4)$ −19

Describe Relationships

Example 4 shows how to use function notation to describe relationships in the real world.

Additional Example

 **GREETING CARDS** Ms. Newman spent $8.82 buying cards that sold for $0.49 each.

a. Use function notation to write an equation that gives the total cost as a function of the number of cards purchased. Let $t(c)$ = total cost, c = number of cards; $t(c) = 0.49c$

b. Use the equation to determine the number of cards purchased. 18 cards

Focus on Mathematical Content

Functions A function is a special relation in which exactly one value from the domain x is paired with only one value from the range y. The variable x is usually the independent variable and the variable y the dependent variable.

Watch Out!

Student Misconceptions Students may mistakenly think that both the x- and y-values must be different in a function. Point out that each x-value needs to be different but the y-values do not.

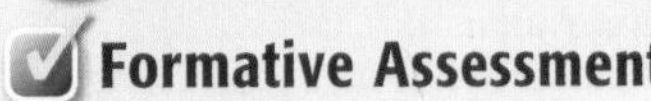

3 PRACTICE

Formative Assessment

Use Exercises 1–9 to check for understanding.

Use the chart at the bottom of the next page to customize assignments for your students.

Tips for New Teachers

Function Notation Remind students that they can choose the letters they use in writing a function, but the independent variable has to be the one in the parentheses and on the right side of the equation.

Exercise Alert

Use Grid/Graph Paper Exercises 38 and 39 require students to graph sets of ordered pairs. You may wish to provide them with grid or graph paper for these exercises.

Tips for New Teachers

Composition of Functions Exercises 40–45 contain a new notation that may be new to students. Explain that $f[g(3)]$ means to find $g(3)$ first, and then use the result in the $f(x)$ function.

Additional Answers

10. This relation is a function because each element of the domain is paired with exactly one element of the range.
11. This is not a function because 24 is paired with two range values, 16 and 17.
12. This relation is a function because each element of the domain is paired with exactly one element of the range.
13. This is not a function because 3 is paired with four range values, 1, 3, 7, and 9.
14. This is not a function because 5 is paired with two range values, 29 and 37.
15. This relation is a function because each element of the domain is paired with exactly one element of the range.

Example 4 p. 397

9. PORTRAITS The Milligan family spent \$215 to have their family portrait taken. The portrait package they would like to purchase costs \$125. In addition, the photographer charges a \$15 sitting fee per person in the portrait.

a. Use function notation to write an equation that gives the total cost as a function of the number of people in the portrait. $c(p) = 125 + 15p$

b. Use the equation to find the number of people in the portrait. **6 people**

Practice and Problem Solving

● = **Step-by-Step Solutions** begin on page R11. **Extra Practice** begins on page 810.

Examples 1 and 2 pp. 395–396

Determine whether each relation is a function. Explain. 10–15. See margin.

10. {(10, 8), (12, 4), (15, 15), (9, 4)}
11. {(24, 16), (25, 16), (24, 17), (26, 17)}

12. {(8, 9), (9, 10), (10, 11), (11, 12)}
13. {(3, 1), (3, 3), (3, 7), (3, 9)}

14.

x	5	8	9	4	5
y	37	42	24	37	29

15.

x	50	75	100	125	150
y	8	12	16	20	24

16–17. See Chapter 8 Answer Appendix.

16.

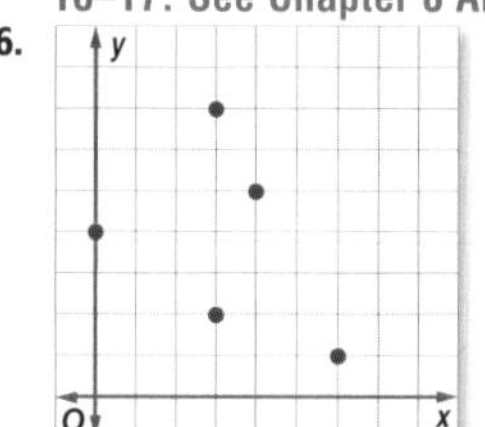

17.

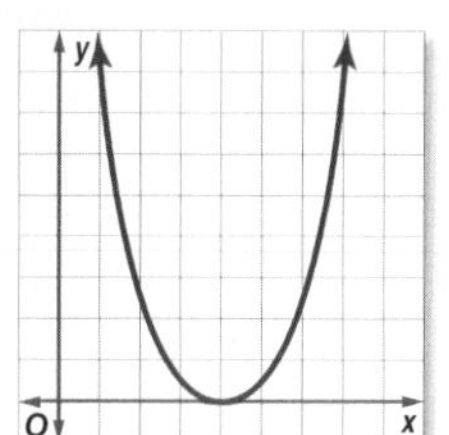

Example 3 p. 396

If $f(x) = 3x - 9$, find each function value.

18. $f(12)$ 27 ● **19** $f(9)$ 18 **20.** $f(-8)$ −33 **21.** $f(-15)$ −54

22. $f(22)$ 57 **23.** $f(3)$ 0 **24.** $f(-4)$ −21 **25.** $f(-11)$ −42

If $g(x) = 5x + 4$, find each function value.

26. $g(7)$ 39 **27.** $g(14)$ 74 **28.** $g(-10)$ −46 **29.** $g(-18)$ −86

30. $g(24)$ 124 **31.** $g(50)$ 254 **32.** $g(-7)$ −31 **33.** $g(-14)$ −66

Example 4 p. 397

34. EXPLORATION A submersible descends to a depth of 1500 feet at a rate of 40 feet per minute to explore an underwater shipwreck.

a. Use function notation to write an equation that gives the total depth of the submersible as a function of the total time (in minutes). $d(t) = 40t$

b. Use the equation to find the total amount of time it took to reach 1500 feet. **37.5 min**

35. TRUCKS Logan spends \$128.10 to rent a moving truck from a rental company. The rental company charges him \$50 for the truck plus an additional fee of \$0.55 per mile that the truck is driven.

a. Use function notation to write an equation that gives the total cost as a function of the number of miles driven. $c(m) = 50 + 0.55m$

b. Use the equation to find the number of miles that he drove the truck. **142 mi**

Differentiated Homework Options

Level	Assignment	Two-Day Option	
AL Basic	10–35, 38, 39, 46–64	11–35 odd, 47–50	10–34 even, 38, 39, 46, 51–64
OL Core	11–35 odd, 36–39, 46–64	10–35, 47–50	36–39, 46, 51–64
BL Advanced	36–60 (optional: 61–64)		

36a. and 36b. yes; Sample answer: Each year (x-value) is paired with only one amount (y-value).

36c. As the years increase, the pounds of whole milk sold decreases and the pounds of reduced and lowfat milk increases.

Real-World Link

Twenty-one percent of the United States' milk supply comes from California. The number two state is Wisconsin with 13%.

Source: USDA

37a. {(1970, 37), (1980, 35), (1990, 34), (2000, 34)} Sample answer: The data represent a function because the x values or years are not repeated.

37b. {(37, 1970), (35, 1980), (34, 1990), (34, 2000)} Sample answer: The inverse does not represent a function because the x-value of 34 has two different y-values.

36. MILK The table shows the sales of milk in the U.S. in different years.

U.S. Milk Sales, 1960–2000 (millions of pounds)		
Year	Whole Milk	Reduced and Lowfat Milk
1960	42,999	389
1970	41,512	6,163
1980	31,253	15,918
1990	21,333	24,509
2000	18,448	23,649

Source: USDA

a. Is the set of ordered pairs (year, whole milk) a function? Explain.

b. Is the set of ordered pairs (year, reduced and lowfat milk) a function? Explain.

c. Describe the relationship between year and million pounds of whole milk purchased. Describe the relationship between year and million pounds of reduced fat and lowfat milk production. Compare the information provided by the two sets of data.

37. PRODUCTION The table shows the average number of hours worked weekly by U.S. production workers for various years.

Year	Hours
1970	37
1980	35
1990	34
2000	34

a. Write the values in the table as a set of ordered pairs. Do the data represent a function? Explain.

b. The *inverse* of a relation is obtained by switching the order of the numbers in each ordered pair. For example, (1970, 37) would be (37, 1970). Write the inverses of the ordered pairs of the data. Do the data represent a function? Explain.

H.O.T. Problems

Use Higher-Order Thinking Skills

38. OPEN ENDED Draw two graphs, one that represents a relation that is a function and one the represents a relation that is not a function. Explain why each graph is or is not a function. **See students' work.**

39. WRITING IN MATH In an arithmetic sequence, a term is found by adding a constant value to the previous term. Consider the terms in this arithmetic sequence: 36, 33, 30, 27, … **39b–c. See Chapter 8 Answer Appendix.**

Term Number	Term
1	36
2	33
3	30
⋮	⋮
7	■

a. What value was added to each term in the sequence? **−3**

b. In a sequence, each number is assigned a term number. Copy and complete the table. Is the set of ordered pairs (term number, term) a function? Explain.

c. Graph the set of ordered pairs. Describe the relationship between term number and term shown in the graph.

CHALLENGE If $f(x) = 4x - 3$ and $g(x) = 8x + 2$, find each function value.

40. $f[g(3)]$ **101**

41. $g[f(5)]$ **138**

42. $f[g(-8)]$ **−251**

43. $g[f(12)]$ **362**

44. $f\{g[f(2)]\}$ **165**

45. $g\{f[g(-4)]\}$ **−982**

46. WRITING IN MATH How can the relationship between water depth and time to ascend to the water's surface be a function? Explain how the two variables are related. Discuss whether water depth can ever correspond to two different times. **See Chapter 8 Answer Appendix.**

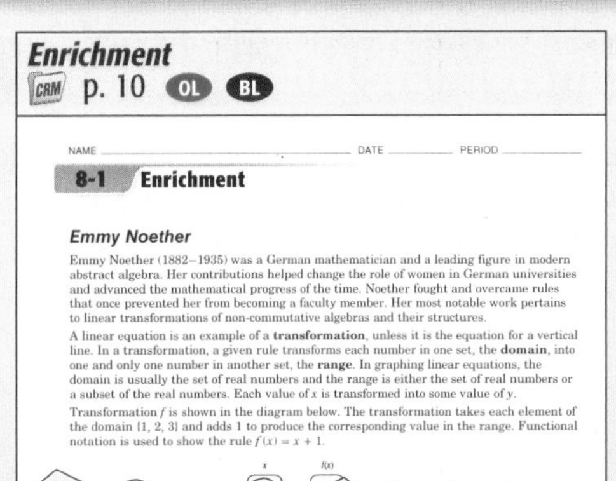

Enrichment
CRM p. 10 OL BL

NAME ______ DATE ______ PERIOD ______

8-1 Enrichment

Emmy Noether

Emmy Noether (1882–1935) was a German mathematician and a leading figure in modern abstract algebra. Her contributions helped change the role of women in German universities and advanced the mathematical progress of the time. Noether fought and overcame rules that once prevented her from becoming a faculty member. Her most notable work pertains to linear transformations of non-commutative algebras and their structures.

A linear equation is an example of a **transformation**, unless it is the equation for a vertical line. In a transformation, a given rule transforms each number in one set, the **domain**, into one and only one number in another set, the **range**. In graphing linear equations, the domain is usually the set of real numbers and the range is either the set of real numbers or a subset of the real numbers. Each value of x is transformed into some value of y.

Transformation f is shown in the diagram below. The transformation takes each element of the domain {1, 2, 3} and adds 1 to produce the corresponding value in the range. Functional notation is used to show the rule $f(x) = x + 1$.

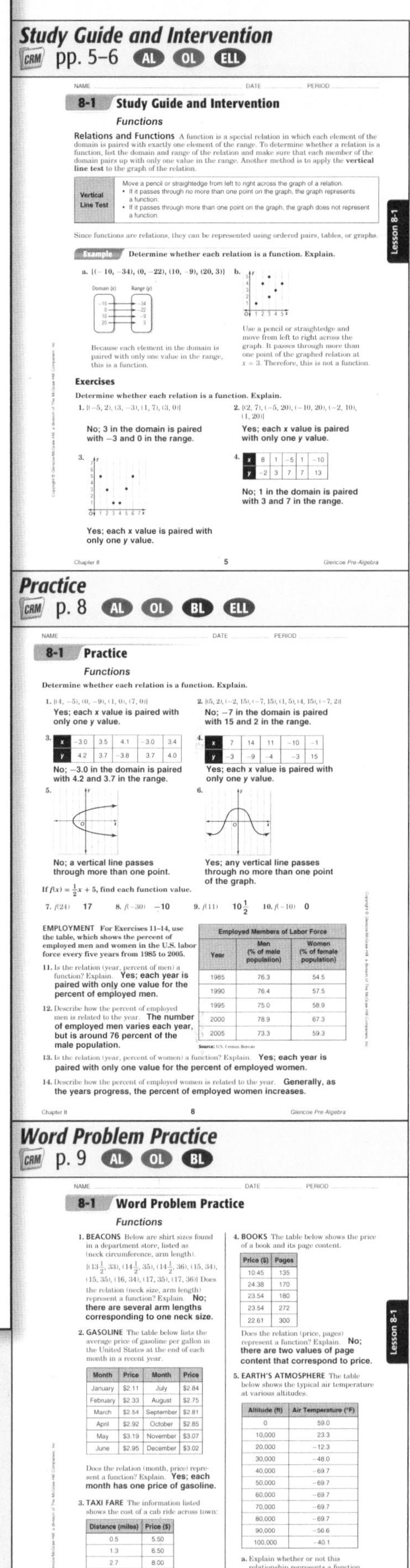

Study Guide and Intervention
CRM pp. 5–6 AL OL ELL

NAME ______ DATE ______ PERIOD ______

8-1 Study Guide and Intervention

Functions

Relations and Functions A function is a special relation in which each element of the domain is paired with exactly one element of the range. To determine whether a relation is a function, list the domain and range of the relation and make sure that each member of the domain pairs up with only one value in the range. Another method is to apply the **vertical line test** to the graph of the relation.

Vertical Line Test	Move a pencil or straightedge from left to right across the graph of a relation. • If it passes through no more than one point on the graph, the graph represents a function. • If it passes through more than one point on the graph, the graph does not represent a function.

Since functions are relations, they can be represented using ordered pairs, tables, or graphs.

Example Determine whether each relation is a function. Explain.

a. {(−10, −34), (0, −22), (10, −9), (20, 3)}

b. [graph]

Because each element in the domain is paired with only one value in the range, this is a function.

Use a pencil or straightedge and move from left to right across the graph. It passes through more than one point of the graphed relation at $x = 3$. Therefore, this is not a function.

Exercises

Determine whether each relation is a function. Explain.

1. {(−5, 2), (3, −3), (1, 7), (3, 0)}
No; 3 in the domain is paired with −3 and 0 in the range.

2. {(2, 7), (−5, 20), (−10, 20), (−2, 10), (1, 20)}
Yes; each x value is paired with only one y value.

3. [graph]
Yes; each x value is paired with only one y value.

4.

x	8	1	−5	1	−10
y	−2	3	7	7	13

No; 1 in the domain is paired with 3 and 7 in the range.

Chapter 8 5 Glencoe Pre-Algebra

Practice
CRM p. 8 AL OL BL ELL

NAME ______ DATE ______ PERIOD ______

8-1 Practice

Functions

Determine whether each relation is a function. Explain.

1. {(4, −5), (0, −9), (1, 0), (7, 0)}
Yes; each x value is paired with only one y value.

2. {(5, 2), (−2, 15), (−7, 15), (1, 5), (4, 15), (−7, 2)}
No; −7 in the domain is paired with 15 and 2 in the range.

3.

x	−3.0	3.5	4.1	−3.0	3.4
y	4.2	3.7	−3.8	3.7	4.0

No; −3.0 in the domain is paired with 4.2 and 3.7 in the range.

4.

x	7	14	11	−10	−1
y	−3	−9	−4	−3	15

Yes; each x value is paired with only one y value.

5. [graph]
No; a vertical line passes through more than one point.

6. [graph]
Yes; any vertical line passes through no more than one point of the graph.

If $f(x) = \frac{1}{2}x + 5$, find each function value.

7. $f(24)$ **17** 8. $f(-30)$ **−10** 9. $f(11)$ **$10\frac{1}{2}$** 10. $f(-10)$ **0**

EMPLOYMENT For Exercises 11–14, use the table, which shows the percent of employed men and women in the U.S. labor force every five years from 1985 to 2005.

Employed Members of Labor Force		
Year	Men (% of male population)	Women (% of female population)
1985	76.3	54.5
1990	76.4	57.5
1995	75.0	58.9
2000	78.9	67.3
2005	73.3	59.3

Source: U.S. Census Bureau

11. Is the relation (year, percent of men) a function? Explain. **Yes; each year is paired with only one value for the percent of employed men.**

12. Describe how the percent of employed men is related to the year. **The number of employed men varies each year, but is around 76 percent of the male population.**

13. Is the relation (year, percent of women) a function? Explain. **Yes; each year is paired with only one value for the percent of employed women.**

14. Describe how the percent of employed women is related to the year. **Generally, as the years progress, the percent of employed women increases.**

Chapter 8 8 Glencoe Pre-Algebra

Word Problem Practice
CRM p. 9 AL OL BL

NAME ______ DATE ______ PERIOD ______

8-1 Word Problem Practice

Functions

1. **BEACONS** Below are shirt sizes found in a department store, listed as (neck circumference, arm length). {$(13\frac{1}{2}, 33)$, $(14\frac{1}{2}, 35)$, $(14\frac{1}{2}, 36)$, (15, 34), (15, 35), (16, 34), (17, 35), (17, 36)} Does the relation (neck size, arm length) represent a function? Explain. **No; there are several arm lengths corresponding to one neck size.**

2. **GASOLINE** The table below lists the average price of gasoline per gallon in the United States at the end of each month in a recent year.

Month	Price	Month	Price
January	$2.11	July	$2.84
February	$2.33	August	$2.75
March	$2.54	September	$2.81
April	$2.92	October	$2.85
May	$3.19	November	$3.07
June	$2.95	December	$3.02

Does the relation (month, price) represent a function? Explain. **Yes; each month has one price of gasoline.**

3. **TAXI FARE** The information listed shows the cost of a cab ride across town:

Distance (miles)	Price ($)
0.5	5.50
1.3	6.50
2.7	8.00
3.1	8.50
3.4	8.50
3.6	9.00

Does the relationship between the distance traveled and the cost represent a function? Explain. **Yes; there is only one price that corresponds to each distance.**

4. **BOOKS** The table below shows the price of a book and its page content.

Price ($)	Pages
10.45	135
24.38	170
23.54	180
23.54	272
22.61	300

Does the relation (price, pages) represent a function? Explain. **No; there are two values of page content that correspond to price.**

5. **EARTH'S ATMOSPHERE** The table below shows the typical air temperature at various altitudes.

Altitude (ft)	Air Temperature (°F)
0	59.0
10,000	23.3
20,000	−12.3
30,000	−48.0
40,000	−69.7
50,000	−69.7
60,000	−69.7
70,000	−69.7
80,000	−69.7
90,000	−56.6
100,000	−40.1

a. Explain whether or not this relationship represents a function. **It does; there is only one temperature value per altitude value.**

b. Describe the relationship between altitude and air temperature. **As the altitude increases, the air temperature decreases, then it remains constant, then it starts increasing.**

Chapter 8 9 Glencoe Pre-Algebra

4 Assess

Ticket Out the Door Have students write on a piece of paper an example of a relation that is a function and explain why it is a function. They should hand the paper to you as they leave.

Additional Answers

49c.

s	$c(s) = 15 + 1.75s$	$c(s)$
15	15 + 1.75(15)	41.25
20	15 + 1.75(20)	50.00
25	15 + 1.75(25)	58.75
30	15 + 1.75(30)	67.50

51.

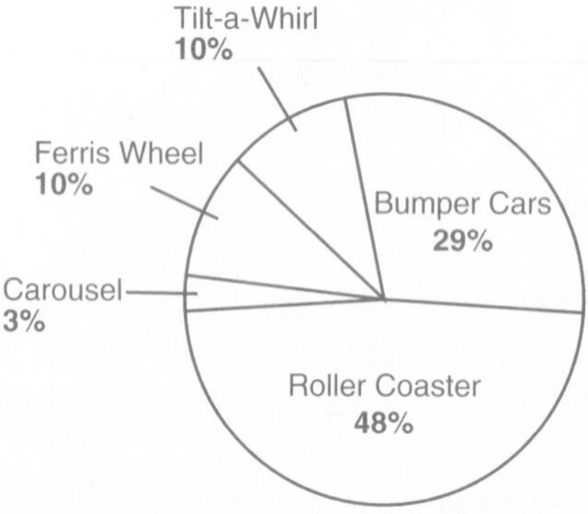

Standardized Test Practice

47. The equation $c(d) = 3.50d$ represents the total cost of renting DVDs as a function of the number of DVDs rented. Which of the following tables contains values that satisfy this function? **A**

A

Cost of Renting DVDs				
d	1	2	3	4
$c(d)$	3.50	7.00	10.50	14.00

B

Cost of Renting DVDs				
d	1	2	3	4
$c(d)$	3.50	6.00	9.00	12.50

C

Cost of Renting DVDs				
d	1	2	3	4
$c(d)$	3.50	7.50	10.50	14.50

D

Cost of Renting DVDs				
d	1	2	3	4
$c(d)$	7.00	10.50	14.00	17.50

48. What is the value of $f(3)$ if $f(x) = -4x + 2$? **G**

F -14 H -6
G -10 J 14

49. EXTENDED RESPONSE For song downloads, Kaylee pays $15 per month plus $1.75 per song.

a. Write an equation using function notation that gives the total cost as a function of the number of songs downloaded. **$c(s) = 15 + 1.75s$**

b. How much would her total bill be if she downloaded 15 songs? **$41.25**

c. Make a function table to show her total bill if she downloads 15, 20, 25, and 30 songs. **See margin.**

50. Which of the following sets of ordered pairs does *not* represent a function? **B**

A {(1, 2), (2, 3), (3, 4), (4, 5)}
B {(2, 3), (2, 4), (2, 5), (2, 6)}
C {(1, 6), (2, 6), (3, 6), (4, 6)}
D {(5, 4), (4, 3), (3, 2), (2, 1)}

Spiral Review

51. RIDES The table shows the results of a survey about the favorite type of ride at an amusement park. Construct a circle graph using the information in the table. (Lesson 7-8) **See margin.**

Type of Ride	Percent
Roller coaster	48
Bumper cars	29
Ferris wheel	10
Carousel	3
Tilt-a-whirl	10

52. BANKING Suppose Marcus invests $750 at an annual rate of 6.25%. How long will it take until Marcus earns $125 in simple interest? (Lesson 7-7) **2.67 years**

Find each product or quotient. (Lessons 3-3 and 3-4)

53. $\frac{8}{9} \cdot \frac{27}{28}$ **$\frac{6}{7}$**

54. $\frac{3}{4}\left(-\frac{1}{3}\right)$ **$-\frac{1}{4}$**

55. $-\frac{7}{8} \cdot \frac{2}{5}$ **$-\frac{7}{20}$**

56. $2 \cdot \frac{7}{12}$ **$\frac{7}{6}$ or $1\frac{1}{6}$**

57. $\frac{2}{9} \div \frac{1}{4}$ **$\frac{8}{9}$**

58. $-\frac{1}{2} \div \frac{5}{6}$ **$-\frac{3}{5}$**

59. $-\frac{3}{5} \div -\frac{5}{9}$ **$\frac{27}{25}$ or $1\frac{2}{25}$**

60. $6\frac{2}{3} \div 5$ **$\frac{4}{3}$ or $1\frac{1}{3}$**

Skills Review

Evaluate each expression if $a = 12$ and $b = 8$. (Lesson 1-2)

61. $4a - b$ **40**

62. $3b - 2a$ **0**

63. $3a + 2b$ **52**

64. $a + 5b$ **52**

Differentiated Instruction BL

Extension Using a graphing calculator, have students graph the relations $y = |x|$, $y = -\sqrt{(16 - x^2)}$ and $y = \sqrt{(16 - x^2)}$, and $y = x^2$. Have students describe what they see. Ask them to determine whether each relation is a function. $y = |x|$, looks like the letter v, function; $y = -\sqrt{(16 - x^2)}$ and $y = \sqrt{(16 - x^2)}$, circle with center at (0, 0) and radius of 4, not a function; $y = x^2$, looks like the letter U, function

8-2 Sequences and Equations

Why?

Giant pandas spend more than 10 hours a day searching for food and eating. The table shows the average amount of bamboo a giant panda eats.

Number of Days	Total Amount of Bamboo (lb)
1	30
2	60
3	90
4	120

Source: Smithsonian National Zoo

a. As the number of days increases by 1, how much does the amount of bamboo increase? **30 lb**

b. How much bamboo would a giant panda eat in 5 days? **150 lb**

Then
You have already used variables to represent patterns. (Lesson 1-2)

Now
- Describe sequences using words and symbols.
- Find terms of arithmetic sequences.

New Vocabulary
sequence
term
arithmetic sequence
common difference

Math Online
glencoe.com
- Extra Examples
- Personal Tutor
- Self-Check Quiz
- Homework Help

Describe Sequences A **sequence** is an ordered list of numbers. Each number is called a **term** of the sequence. When the difference between any two consecutive terms is the same, the sequence is called an **arithmetic sequence**. The difference is called the **common difference**.

EXAMPLE 1 Describe an Arithmetic Sequence

Describe each sequence using words and symbols.

a. 6, 7, 8, 9, …

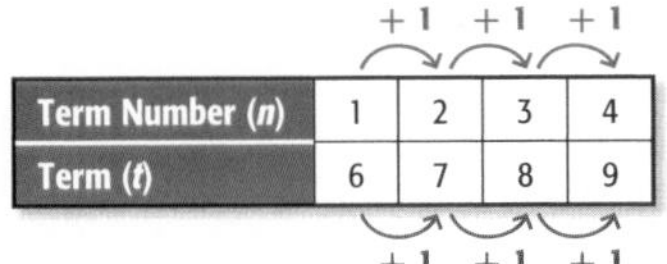

Term Number (n)	1	2	3	4
Term (t)	6	7	8	9

The difference of the term numbers is 1.
The common difference of the terms is 1.

The terms have a common difference of 1. A term is 5 more than the term number. So, the equation that describes the sequence is $t = n + 5$.

b. 4, 8, 12, 16, …

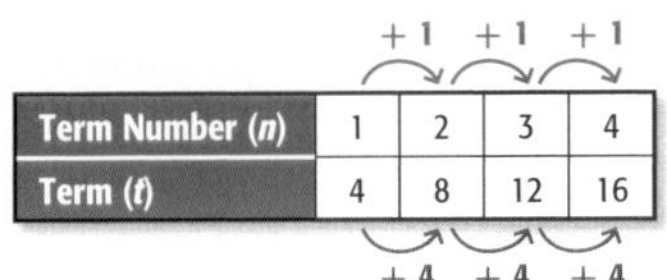

Term Number (n)	1	2	3	4
Term (t)	4	8	12	16

The difference of the term numbers is 1.
The common difference of the terms is 4.

The terms have a common difference of 4. A term is 4 times the term number. So, the equation that describes the sequence is $t = 4n$.

Check Your Progress **1A–1B. See Chapter 8 Answer Appendix.**

1A. 10, 11, 12, 13, … **1B.** 5, 10, 15, 20, …

Personal Tutor glencoe.com

8-2 Lesson Notes

1 FOCUS

Vertical Alignment

Before Lesson 8-2
Use variables to represent patterns.

Lesson 8-2
Describe sequences using words and symbols. Find terms of arithmetic sequences.

After Lesson 8-2
Look for patterns and represent generalizations algebraically.

2 TEACH

Scaffolding Questions

Have students read the *Why?* section of the lesson and answer the questions.

Ask:
- What is the relationship between the days and pounds? The number of pounds is 30 times the number of days.
- What is the relationship between the total amount of bamboo eaten each day? It increases by 30 pounds each day.
- How many pounds would a giant panda eat in a 30-day period? 900 pounds

Lesson 8-2 Resources

Resource	Approaching-Level	On-Level	Beyond-Level	English Learners
Teacher Edition	• Differentiated Instruction, p. 402		• Differentiated Instruction, p. 405	• Differentiated Instruction, p. 402
Chapter Resource Masters	• Study Guide and Intervention, pp. 11–12 • Skills Practice, p. 13 • Practice, p. 14 • Word Problem Practice, p. 15	• Study Guide and Intervention, pp. 11–12 • Skills Practice, p. 13 • Practice, p. 14 • Word Problem Practice, p. 15 • Enrichment, p. 16	• Practice, p. 14 • Word Problem Practice, p. 15 • Enrichment, p. 16	• Study Guide and Intervention, pp. 11–12 • Skills Practice, p. 13 • Practice, p. 14
Transparencies	• 5-Minute Check Transparency 8-2	• 5-Minute Check Transparency 8-2	• 5-Minute Check Transparency 8-2	• 5-Minute Check Transparency 8-2
Other	• Study Notebook • Teaching Pre-Algebra with Manipulatives	• Study Notebook • Teaching Pre-Algebra with Manipulatives	• Study Notebook	• Study Notebook • Teaching Pre-Algebra with Manipulatives

Describe Sequences

Example 1 shows how to describe an arithmetic sequence.

Formative Assessment

Use the Check Your Progress exercises after each example to determine students' understanding of concepts.

Additional Example

1 Describe each sequence using words and symbols.

a. 15, 16, 17, 18... Terms have a common difference of 1 and the term is 14 more than the term number. $t = n + 14$

b. 10, 20, 30, 40... Terms have a common difference of 10 and the term is 10 times the term number. $t = 10n$

Finding Terms

Examples 2 and 3 show how to find the value of a term in an arithmetic sequence.

Additional Examples

2 Write an equation that describes the sequence 6, 9, 12, 15, ... Then find the 11th term of the sequence. $t = 3n + 3$; 36

3 **TELEPHONE CHARGES** For a telephone call to India, a telephone company charges $8 for the first minute and $4 for each additional minute. How much does it cost for a 10-minute call? $44

Additional Examples also in Interactive Classroom PowerPoint® Presentations

IWB INTERACTIVE WHITEBOARD READY

StudyTip

Functions An arithmetic sequence is a function. The equation describing the sequence is the function rule and the term numbers are the inputs.

Finding Terms You can use rules to extend patterns and find other terms.

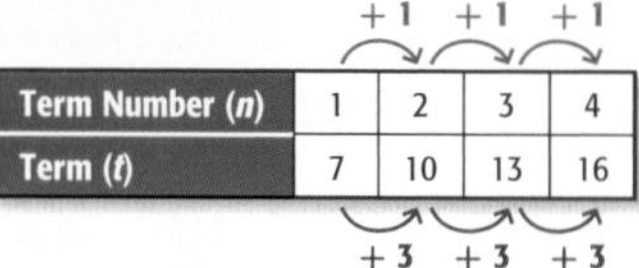

EXAMPLE 2 Find a Term in an Arithmetic Sequence

Write an equation that describes the sequence 7, 10, 13, 16, ... Then find the 15th term of the sequence.

	+1	+1	+1	
Term Number (n)	1	2	3	4
Term (t)	7	10	13	16
	+3	+3	+3	

The difference of the term numbers is 1.

The common difference of the terms is 3.

The terms have a common difference of 3. This difference is 3 times the difference of the term numbers. This suggests that $t = 3n$. However, you need to add 4 to get the value of t. So, $t = 3n + 4$ describes the sequence.

Check If $n = 2$, then $t = 3(2) + 4$ or 10. ✓

Use the equation to find the 15th term. Let $n = 15$.

$t = 3n + 4$ **Write the equation.**

$t = 3(15) + 4$ or 49 **Replace n with 15.**

So, the 15th term is 49.

Check Your Progress

2. Write an equation that describes the sequence 5, 8, 11, 14, ... Then find the 20th term of the sequence. $t = 3n + 2$; 62

Personal Tutor glencoe.com

Real-World Link

About 12.8 million people work in the restaurant industry in the U.S. The only other employer in the country that is larger is the U.S. government.

Source: National Restaurant Association

Real-World EXAMPLE 3 Find a Term in an Arithmetic Sequence

RESTAURANTS The diagram shows the number of square tables needed to seat 4, 6, or 8 people at a restaurant. How many tables are needed to seat 16 people?

Make a table to organize your sequence and find a rule.

Number of Tables (t)	1	2	3
Number of People (p)	4	6	8

The difference of the term numbers is 1.

The common difference of the terms is 2.

The pattern in the table shows the equation $p = 2t + 2$.

$p = 2t + 2$ **Write the equation.**

$16 = 2t + 2$ **Replace p with 16. Solve for t.**

$7 = t$ **Simplify.**

So, 7 tables are needed to seat a party of 16.

Check Your Progress

3. RESTAURANTS How many tables shaped like hexagons are needed for 22 people? **5**

Personal Tutor glencoe.com

Differentiated Instruction

AL ELL

If students have trouble describing sequences using words and symbols,

Then pair them with other students to serve as mentors for practicing these skills.

Check Your Understanding

Example 1 p. 401

Describe each sequence using words and symbols. 1–4. See Chapter 8 Answer Appendix.

1. 2, 3, 4, 5, …
2. 7, 8, 9, 10, …
3. 3, 6, 9, 12, …
4. 7, 14, 21, 28, …

Example 2 p. 402

Write an equation that describes each sequence. Then find the indicated term.

5. 10, 11, 12, 13, …; 10th term $t = 9 + n$; 19
6. 6, 12, 18, 24, …; 11th term $t = 6n$; 66
7. 4, 7, 10, 13, …; 23rd term $t = 3n + 1$; 70
8. 2, 6, 10, 14, …; 14th term $t = 4n - 2$; 54

Example 3 p. 402

9. **GEOMETRY** Suppose each side of a square has a length of 1 foot. Determine which figure will have a perimeter of 60 feet. 15

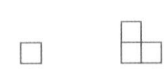

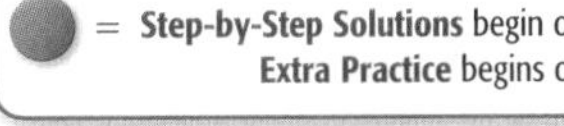

Figure 1 Figure 2 Figure 3

Practice and Problem Solving

● = **Step-by-Step Solutions** begin on page R11. **Extra Practice** begins on page 810.

Example 1 p. 401

Describe each sequence using words and symbols. 10–18. See Chapter 8 Answer Appendix.

10. 3, 4, 5, 6, …
11. 8, 9, 10, 11, …
12. 14, 15, 16, 17,
13. 15, 16, 17, 18, …
14. 2, 4, 6, 8, …
15. 8, 16, 24, 32, …
16. 12, 24, 36, 48, …
17. 20, 40, 60, 80, …
18. 6, 16, 26, 36, ...

Example 2 p. 402

Write an equation that describes each sequence. Then find the indicated term.

19. 16, 17, 18, 19, …; 23rd term
20. 14, 15, 16, 17, …; 16th term
21. 4, 8, 12, 16, …; 13th term
22. 11, 22, 33, 44, …; 25th term
23. 7, 10, 13, 16, …; 20th term
24. 7, 9, 11, 13, …; 33rd term
25. 1, 5, 9, 13, …; 89th term
26. 3, 8, 13, 18, …; 70th term

19. $t = 15 + n$; 38
20. $t = 13 + n$; 29
21. $t = 4n$; 52
22. $t = 11n$; 275
23. $t = 3n + 4$; 64
24. $t = 2n + 5$; 71
25. $t = 4n - 3$; 353
26. $t = 5n - 2$; 348

27. **CONSTRUCTION** A building frame consists of beams in the form of triangles, as shown in the diagram. The frame of a new office building will use 27 beams.

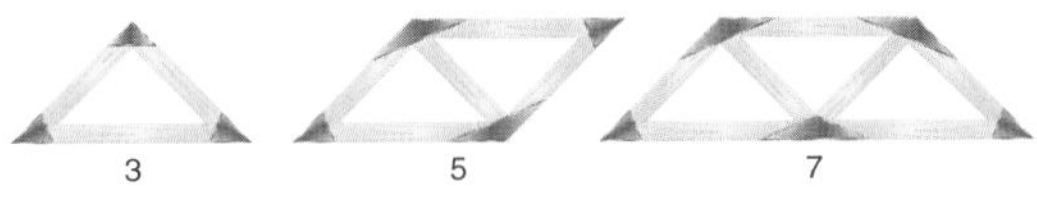

a. Use the pattern to find a rule that describes the sequence. $t = 2n + 1$

b. Find the number of triangles that will be formed for the frame. 13 triangles

Example 3 p. 402

28. **GEOMETRY** Study the pattern at the right. Which figure will have 40 squares? Figure 13

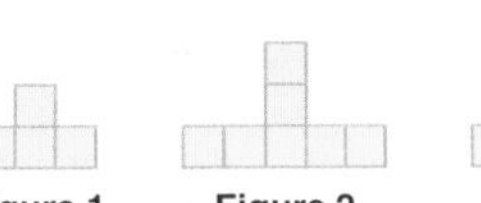

Figure 1 Figure 2 Figure 3

Focus on Mathematical Content

Sequences and Equations An ordered list of numbers such as 18, 13, 8, 3 is a sequence. When the difference between any two consecutive terms is the same number, in this case –5, the sequence is arithmetic. An arithmetic sequence can be described with words and algebraic equations. An equation for this sequence could be $y = -5x + 23$.

Tips for New Teachers

Study Tip Tell students that they can substitute numbers from a table to check whether their equation is true.

Watch Out!

Preventing Errors Have students make a table every time a new sequence problem is introduced. This will allow them to line up the terms and term numbers to help eliminate mistakes.

3 PRACTICE

Formative Assessment

Use Exercises 1–9 to check for understanding.

Use the chart at the bottom of this page to customize assignments for your students.

Differentiated Homework Options

Level	Assignment	Two-Day Option	
AL Basic	10–28, 37, 39–52	11–27 odd, 42–45	10–28 even, 37, 39–41, 46–52
OL Core	11–27 odd, 28, 29–33 odd, 34–37, 39–52	10–28, 42–45	29–37, 39–41, 46–52
BL Advanced	29–48 (optional: 49–52)		

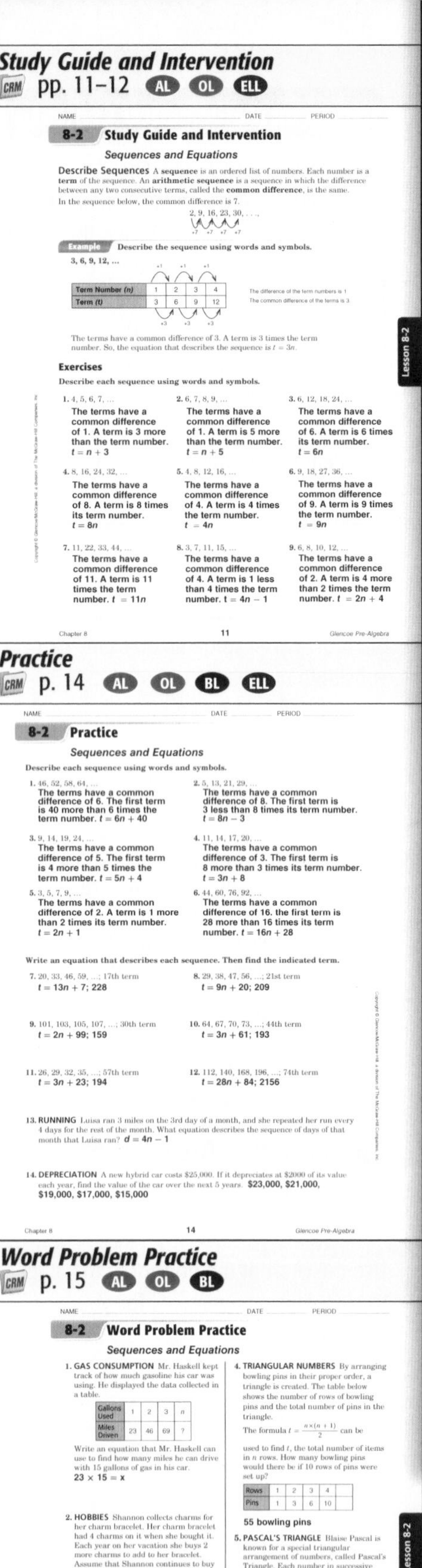

Study Guide and Intervention
CRM pp. 11–12 AL OL ELL

NAME ______ DATE ______ PERIOD ______

8-2 Study Guide and Intervention

Sequences and Equations

Describe Sequences A **sequence** is an ordered list of numbers. Each number is a **term** of the sequence. An **arithmetic sequence** is a sequence in which the difference between any two consecutive terms, called the **common difference**, is the same.

In the sequence below, the common difference is 7.

2, 9, 16, 23, 30, . . .,
+7 +7 +7 +7

Example Describe the sequence using words and symbols.

3, 6, 9, 12, ...

Term Number (*n*)	1	2	3	4
Term (*t*)	3	6	9	12

The difference of the term numbers is 1
The common difference of the terms is 3

The terms have a common difference of 3. A term is 3 times the term number. So, the equation that describes the sequence is $t = 3n$.

Exercises

Describe each sequence using words and symbols.

1. 4, 5, 6, 7, ... **The terms have a common difference of 1. A term is 3 more than the term number. $t = n + 3$**
2. 6, 7, 8, 9, ... **The terms have a common difference of 1. A term is 5 more than the term number. $t = n + 5$**
3. 6, 12, 18, 24, ... **The terms have a common difference of 6. A term is 6 times its term number. $t = 6n$**
4. 8, 16, 24, 32, ... **The terms have a common difference of 8. A term is 8 times its term number. $t = 8n$**
5. 4, 8, 12, 16, ... **The terms have a common difference of 4. A term is 4 times the term number. $t = 4n$**
6. 9, 18, 27, 36, ... **The terms have a common difference of 9. A term is 9 times the term number. $t = 9n$**
7. 11, 22, 33, 44, ... **The terms have a common difference of 11. A term is 11 times the term number. $t = 11n$**
8. 3, 7, 11, 15, ... **The terms have a common difference of 4. A term is 1 less than 4 times the term number. $t = 4n - 1$**
9. 6, 8, 10, 12, ... **The terms have a common difference of 2. A term is 4 more than 2 times the term number. $t = 2n + 4$**

Lesson 8-2

Chapter 8 11 Glencoe Pre-Algebra

Practice
CRM p. 14 AL OL BL ELL

NAME ______ DATE ______ PERIOD ______

8-2 Practice

Sequences and Equations

Describe each sequence using words and symbols.

1. 46, 52, 58, 64, ... **The terms have a common difference of 6. The first term is 40 more than 6 times the term number. $t = 6n + 40$**
2. 5, 13, 21, 29, ... **The terms have a common difference of 8. The first term is 3 less than 8 times its term number. $t = 8n - 3$**
3. 9, 14, 19, 24, ... **The terms have a common difference of 5. The first term is 4 more than 5 times the term number. $t = 5n + 4$**
4. 11, 14, 17, 20, ... **The terms have a common difference of 3. The first term is 8 more than 3 times its term number. $t = 3n + 8$**
5. 3, 5, 7, 9, ... **The terms have a common difference of 2. A term is 1 more than 2 times its term number. $t = 2n + 1$**
6. 44, 60, 76, 92, ... **The terms have a common difference of 16. the first term is 28 more than 16 times its term number. $t = 16n + 28$**

Write an equation that describes each sequence. Then find the indicated term.

7. 20, 33, 46, 59, ...; 17th term **$t = 13n + 7$; 228**
8. 29, 38, 47, 56, ...; 21st term **$t = 9n + 20$; 209**
9. 101, 103, 105, 107, ...; 30th term **$t = 2n + 99$; 159**
10. 64, 67, 70, 73, ...; 44th term **$t = 3n + 61$; 193**
11. 26, 29, 32, 35, ...; 57th term **$t = 3n + 23$; 194**
12. 112, 140, 168, 196, ...; 74th term **$t = 28n + 84$; 2156**
13. **RUNNING** Luisa ran 3 miles on the 3rd day of a month, and she repeated her run every 4 days for the rest of the month. What equation describes the sequence of days of that month that Luisa ran? **$d = 4n - 1$**
14. **DEPRECIATION** A new hybrid car costs $25,000. If it depreciates at $2000 of its value each year, find the value of the car over the next 5 years. **$23,000, $21,000, $19,000, $17,000, $15,000**

Chapter 8 14 Glencoe Pre-Algebra

Word Problem Practice
CRM p. 15 AL OL BL

NAME ______ DATE ______ PERIOD ______

8-2 Word Problem Practice

Sequences and Equations

1. **GAS CONSUMPTION** Mr. Haskell kept track of how much gasoline his car was using. He displayed the data collected in a table.

Gallons Used	1	2	3	*n*
Miles Driven	23	46	69	?

Write an equation that Mr. Haskell can use to find how many miles he can drive with 15 gallons of gas in his car. **23 × 15 = x**

2. **HOBBIES** Shannon collects charms for her charm bracelet. Her charm bracelet had 4 charms on it when she bought it. Each year on her vacation she buys 2 more charms to add to her bracelet. Assume that Shannon continues to buy the same number of charms each year. Write an equation that can be used to find how many charms Shannon will have on her bracelet after 6 years? **(2 × 6) + 4 = x**

3. **PYRAMIDS** When climbing an ancient Mayan pyramid, the Johnson family noticed that the bottom of each side of the pyramid started with 50 large stones. The next level up had 45 large stones, the next level up had 40 stones, and so on. Write an equation to represent the number of stones on each level. How many levels can the pyramid have?

Level	1	2	3	
Stones	45	40	35	?

Number of stones/level = 50 − 5*n* There can be at most 10 levels (0 stones at the top).

4. **TRIANGULAR NUMBERS** By arranging bowling pins in their proper order, a triangle is created. The table below shows the number of rows of bowling pins and the total number of pins in the triangle. The formula $t = \frac{n \times (n+1)}{2}$ can be used to find *t*, the total number of items in *n* rows. How many bowling pins would there be if 10 rows of pins were set up?

Rows	1	2	3	4	
Pins	1	3	6	10	

55 bowling pins

5. **PASCAL'S TRIANGLE** Blaise Pascal is known for a special triangular arrangement of numbers, called Pascal's Triangle. Each number in successive rows of the triangle is created by adding the two numbers in the row above the number.

1
1 1
1 2 1
1 3 3 1
1 4 6 4 1
1 5 10 10 5 1

a. Starting with the second row from the top, what is the sequence of the diagonal (1 2 3 4 5 6 7)? **$n + 1$**

b. The sum of each row represents 2^{n-1}, which means 2 is multiplied by itself $n - 1$ times, where *n* represents the row number. Write an expression for the sum of the values in the sixth row. Simplify the expression. **2 × 2 × 2 × 2 × 2 = 32**

Lesson 8-2

Chapter 8 15 Glencoe Pre-Algebra

Real-World Link

A person on jumping stilts can leap up to 6 feet in the air and travel up to 20 miles per hour.

Source: Xtreme Importz

30. The terms have a common difference of 2. A term is 2 times the term number, plus 1; $t = 2n + 1$.
31. The terms have a common difference of 2. A term is 2 times the term number, plus 2; $t = 2n + 2$.
32. The terms have a common difference of 3. A term is 3 times the term number, minus 2; $t = 3n - 2$.
33. The terms have a common difference of 5. A term is 5 times the term number, minus 1; $t = 5n - 1$.
37. Sample answer: 3, −5, −13, −21, ...
40. Alliyah; you need to add 10 to $4n$ to get the value of t.

B

29. **EXTREME SPORTS** The table shows how far a person on *jumping stilts* can travel. Write an equation that describes the relationship between distance traveled *d* and number of steps taken *s*. Then determine how far a person could travel in 12 steps. **$d = 9s$; 108 ft**

Number of Steps (s)	1	2	3	4	5
Distance Traveled in Feet (d)	9	18	27	36	45

Describe each sequence using words and symbols.

30. 3, 5, 7, 9, ... 31. 4, 6, 8, 10, ... 32. 1, 4, 7, 10, ... 33. 4, 9, 14, 19, ...

34. **MULTIPLE REPRESENTATIONS** In this problem, you will investigate sequences and graphs. Use the graph shown.

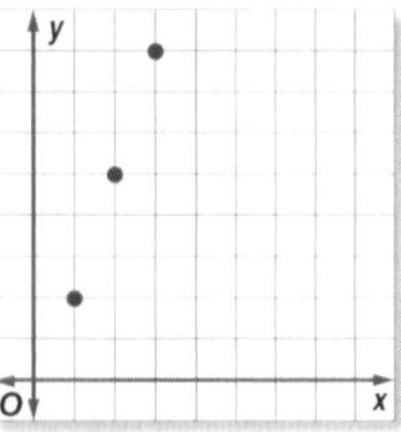

a. **TABULAR** Make a table of ordered pairs (x, y). **See margin.**

b. **VERBAL** Describe how the values of y change as the values of x increase by 1. **The values of y increase by 3.**

c. **ALGEBRAIC** Write an equation relating x and y. Then find x when y is 101. **$y = 3x - 1$; 34**

35. **THEATERS** One section of a movie theater has 26 seats in the first row, 35 seats in the second row, 44 seats in the third row, and so on. If there are 10 rows of seats, how many seats are in the section? **665 seats**

36. **ALGEBRA** The expression $1 + 2n(n + 2)$ describes a pattern of numbers, where n represents a number's position in the sequence. Write the first four terms of the sequence. **7, 17, 31, 49**

H.O.T. Problems

Use **H**igher-**O**rder **T**hinking Skills

C

37. **OPEN ENDED** Write an arithmetic sequence whose common difference is −8.

38. **CHALLENGE** Use an arithmetic sequence to find the number of multiples of 6 between 41 and 523. Justify your reasoning. **See margin.**

39. **WRITING IN MATH** Explain how arithmetic sequences could be used to make real-world predictions. **See margin.**

40. **FIND THE ERROR** Edward and Alliyah are writing a rule for finding the *n*th term of the sequence 14, 18, 22, 26, … . Is either of them correct? Explain.

Edward	Alliyah
The difference is 4, so the rule is $t = 4n$.	The difference is 4 and each term is 10 more than four times the term number, so the rule is $t = 4n + 10$.

41. **WRITING IN MATH** The equation $y = x + 6$ represents the function {(1, 7), (2, 8), (3, 9), (4, 10)}. Write a rule using n and t to describe the arithmetic sequence 7, 8, 9, 10, … . Then compare the input values and the output values of both the function and the sequence. **See margin.**

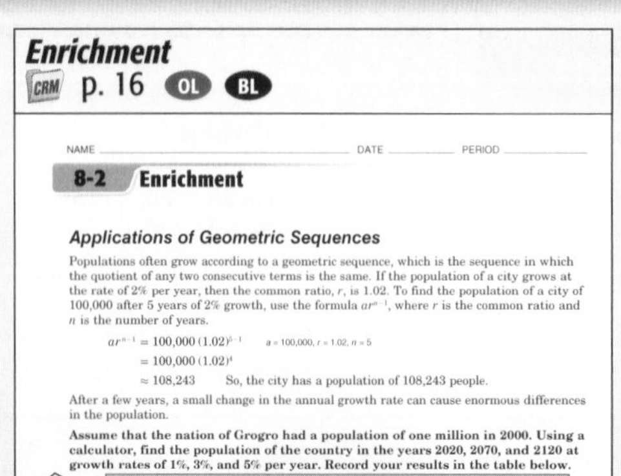

Enrichment
CRM p. 16 OL BL

NAME ______ DATE ______ PERIOD ______

8-2 Enrichment

Applications of Geometric Sequences

Populations often grow according to a geometric sequence, which is the sequence in which the quotient of any two consecutive terms is the same. If the population of a city grows at the rate of 2% per year, then the common ratio, *r*, is 1.02. To find the population of a city of 100,000 after 5 years of 2% growth, use the formula ar^{n-1}, where *r* is the common ratio and *n* is the number of years.

$ar^{n-1} = 100{,}000\,(1.02)^{5-1}$ $a = 100{,}000,\ r = 1.02,\ n = 5$
$= 100{,}000\,(1.02)^4$
$\approx 108{,}243$ So, the city has a population of 108,243 people.

After a few years, a small change in the annual growth rate can cause enormous differences in the population.

Assume that the nation of Grogro had a population of one million in 2000. Using a calculator, find the population of the country in the years 2020, 2070, and 2120 at growth rates of 1%, 3%, and 5% per year. Record your results in the table below.

Population of Grogro

Watch Out!

Find the Error For Exercise 40, students should see that both Edward and Alliyah found the common difference. They need to determine whether the common difference multiplied by the term number will give the term or if a number needs to be added or subtracted, as well.

404 Chapter 8 Linear Functions and Graphing

Standardized Test Practice

42. In a study skills program, students increase the number of minutes they study each week. The first week, they study 40 minutes per day. Each week after that, they increase their study time by 10%, until they are studying 72 minutes per day. In what week of the program should the students begin studying over 60 minutes per day? **D**

A Week 3 C Week 5
B Week 4 D Week 6

43. GRIDDED RESPONSE The table below shows temperatures in degrees Celsius and the equivalent temperature in degrees Fahrenheit.

Celsius	Fahrenheit
40	104
30	86
20	68

If the pattern in the table continues, what will be the temperature in degrees Fahrenheit if the temperature outside is 15 degrees Celsius? **59**

44. Which of the following equations describes the arithmetic sequence 7, 13, 19, 25, 31, ... , where n is the term number? **G**

F $t = 4n + 3$
G $t = 6n + 1$
H $t = 7n$
J $t = 5n + 2$

45. EXTENDED RESPONSE The table below follows a rule.

x	y
1	5
2	7
3	9
4	11
5	13

a. Complete the table by filling in the four missing numbers.

b. Based on the table, write a rule that represents the relationship between x and y. $y = 2x + 3$

Spiral Review

46. ENERGY The circle graph shows the source of the United States' energy. (Lesson 7-8)

a. What is the biggest source of energy for the United States? **petroleum**

b. If the petroleum contributed 40 quadrillion Btu, find the amount of Btu contributed by hydropower. **3 quadrillion**

Where Does U.S. Energy Come From?

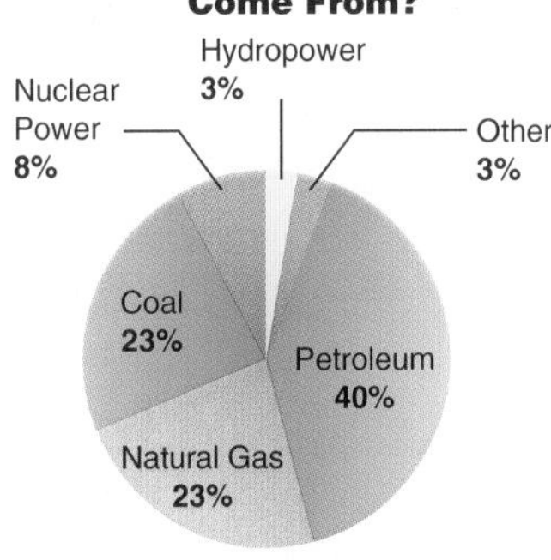

Find the simple interest to the nearest cent. (Lesson 7-7)

47. \$2,400 at 7% for $1\frac{1}{2}$ years **\$252**

48. \$350 at $3\frac{1}{2}$% for 3 years **\$36.75**

Skills Review

Evaluate each expression if $x = -2$ and $y = 3$. (Lesson 1-2)

49. $y + 7$ **10** **50.** $4x$ **−8** **51.** $2y - 1$ **5** **52.** $5x + 3y$ **−1**

4 ASSESS

Name the Math Have students explain the steps they would use to write the equation that describes the sequence 10, 13, 16, 19, ... and to find its 12th term.

Additional Answers

34a.

x	y
1	2
2	5
3	8

38. 81; The multiples of 6 between 41 and 523 can be represented by the sequence 42, 48, 54, . . . 522. The equation that describes this sequence is $t = 6n + 36$. If you let $t = 522$, then $n = 81$. So, the 81st term of the sequence is 522. There are 81 multiples of 6 between 41 and 523.

39. Sample answer: The pattern can be used to create an algebraic expression or equation that is a rule for the sequence. The expression or equation is then used to find values that continue the pattern, and it allows you to make predictions.

41. $t = n + 6$; In both the function and the sequence, the input values are 1, 2, 3, 4 and the output values are 7, 8, 9, 10.

Multiple Representations In Exercise 34, students read ordered pairs from a graph, construct a table, analyze the data verbally, generate an equation relating x- and y-values, and use the equation to predict additional values.

Differentiated Instruction

Extension A special sequence of numbers that appears in nature is the Fibonacci sequence: 1, 1, 2, 3, 5, 8, ... Make a table showing the term number and the Fibonacci number. Extend the table to find the 10th number. Describe in words the pattern you see. 55; the sequence is formed by adding the two previous terms in the sequence to get the next term.

8-3 Lesson Notes

1 FOCUS

Vertical Alignment

Before Lesson 8-3
Use functions to describe relationships between two quantities.

Lesson 8-3
Solve linear equations with two variables. Graph linear equations using ordered pairs.

After Lesson 8-3
Analyze situations involving linear functions.

2 TEACH

Scaffolding Questions

Have students read the *Why?* section of the lesson and answer the questions.

Ask:

- What is the relationship between the time in seconds x and the distance in meters y? As the time in seconds increases, the distance in meters increases.
- How do you find the value of y for $x = 5$? Multiply 60 by 5.
- Describe the graph. How can you use the graph to find other ordered pairs? The graph is a straight line that rises from left to right; extend the line and then locate points on the line.

8-3 Representing Linear Functions

Then
You used functions to describe relationships between two quantities. (Lesson 1-5)

Now
- Solve linear equations with two variables.
- Graph linear equations using ordered pairs.

New Vocabulary
linear equation
x-intercept
y-intercept
discrete data

Math Online
glencoe.com
- Extra Examples
- Personal Tutor
- Self-Check Quiz
- Homework Help
- Math in Motion

Why?

In a tennis match, Venus Williams served a tennis ball at a speed of nearly 60 meters per second.

a–c. See Chapter 8 Answer Appendix.

a. Complete the table to find the number of meters the tennis ball would travel in 1, 2, and 3 seconds at that speed.

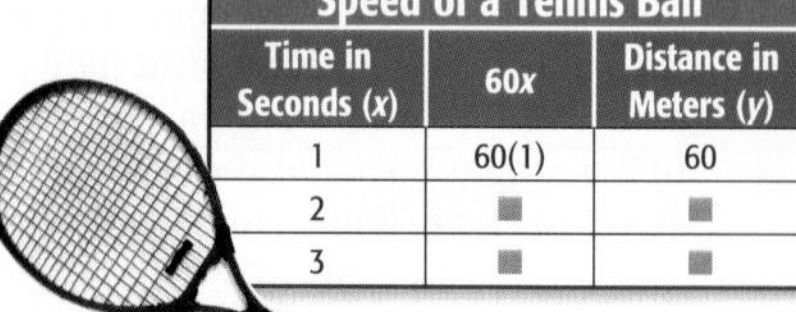

Speed of a Tennis Ball		
Time in Seconds (x)	$60x$	Distance in Meters (y)
1	60(1)	60
2	■	■
3	■	■

b. On grid paper, graph the ordered pairs (time, distance). Then connect the points.

c. Do the data represent a function?

d. Write an equation representing the relationship between time x and number of meters y. **$y = 60x$**

Solve Linear Equations An equation such as $y = 60x$ is called a linear equation. A **linear equation** is an equation whose graph is a line. A linear equation is also a function because each member of the domain (x-value) is paired with exactly one member of the range (y-value).

The solution of an equation with two variables consists of two numbers, one for each variable, that make the equation true. One way to find solutions is to make a table.

EXAMPLE 1 Use a Table of Ordered Pairs

Find four solutions of $y = 7x$. Write the solutions as ordered pairs.

Step 1 Choose four values for x and substitute each value into the equation. We chose -1, 0, 1, and 2.

Step 2 Evaluate the expression to find the value of y.

Step 3 Write the solutions as ordered pairs.

Step 1		Step 2	Step 3
x	$y = 7x$	y	(x, y)
−1	$y = 7(-1)$	−7	(−1, −7)
0	$y = 7(0)$	0	(0, 0)
1	$y = 7(1)$	7	(1, 7)
2	$y = 7(2)$	14	(2, 14)

Four solutions of $y = 7x$ are $(-1, -7)$, $(0, 0)$, $(1, 7)$, and $(2, 14)$.

Check Your Progress **1A–1D. See Chapter 8 Answer Appendix.**

Find four solutions of each equation. Write the solutions as ordered pairs.

1A. $y = x + 2$

1B. $y = 3x - 1$

1C. $y = -2x + 5$

1D. $y = -4x - 6$

Personal Tutor glencoe.com

Lesson 8-3 Resources

Resource	Approaching-Level	On-Level	Beyond-Level	English Learners
Teacher Edition		• Differentiated Instruction, p. 407	• Differentiated Instruction, pp. 407, 411	
Chapter Resource Masters	• Study Guide and Intervention, pp. 17–18 • Skills Practice, p. 19 • Practice, p. 20 • Word Problem Practice, p. 21	• Study Guide and Intervention, pp. 17–18 • Skills Practice, p. 19 • Practice, p. 20 • Word Problem Practice, p. 21 • Enrichment, p. 22	• Practice, p. 20 • Word Problem Practice, p. 21 • Enrichment, p. 22	• Study Guide and Intervention, pp. 17–18 • Skills Practice, p. 19 • Practice, p. 20
Transparencies	• 5-Minute Check Transparency 8-3	• 5-Minute Check Transparency 8-3	• 5-Minute Check Transparency 8-3	• 5-Minute Check Transparency 8-3
Other	• Study Notebook • Teaching Pre-Algebra with Manipulatives	• Study Notebook • Teaching Pre-Algebra with Manipulatives	• Study Notebook	• Study Notebook • Teaching Pre-Algebra with Manipulatives

When solving real-world problems, check that the solution makes sense in the context of the original problem.

Real-World Link

Cell phone companies spend about \$1.4 billion on mobile messaging and display advertisements.

Source: Jupiter Research

Real-World EXAMPLE 2 Use Function Equations

CELL PHONES Games cost \$8 to download onto a cell phone. Ring tones cost \$1. Find four solutions of $8x + y = 20$ in terms of the numbers of games x and ring tones y Darcy can buy with \$20. Explain each solution.

Step 1 Rewrite the equation by solving for y.

$8x + y = 20$ — **Write the equation.**

$8x - 8x + y = 20 - 8x$ — **Subtract 8x from each side.**

$y = 20 - 8x$ — **Simplify.**

Step 2 Choose four x values and substitute them into $y = 20 - 8x$.

x	$y = 20 - 8x$	y	(x, y)
1	$y = 20 - 8(1)$	12	(1, 12)
2	$y = 20 - 8(2)$	4	(2, 4)
$\frac{1}{4}$	$y = 20 - 8\left(\frac{1}{4}\right)$	18	$\left(\frac{1}{4}, 18\right)$
5	$y = 20 - 8(5)$	−20	(5, −20)

Step 3 Explain each solution.

(1, 12) → She can buy 1 game and 12 ring tones.

(2, 4) → She can buy 2 games and 4 ring tones.

$\left(\frac{1}{4}, 18\right)$ → This solution does not make sense in the situation because there cannot be a fractional number of games.

(5, −20) → This solution does not make sense in the situation because you cannot have a negative number of ring tones.

Check Your Progress

2. **FOOD** Michael and his two friends have a total of \$9 to spend on tacos and burritos for lunch. A burrito x costs \$2 and a taco y costs \$1. Find two solutions of the equation $2x + y = 9$ to find how much food they can buy with \$9. Explain each solution.

2. Sample answer: (4, 1) means they can buy 4 burritos and 1 taco; (3, 3) means they can buy 3 burritos and 3 tacos.

Personal Tutor glencoe.com

The solutions in Example 2 represent discrete data because only whole number values are appropriate. **Discrete data** have space between possible data values. Continuous data can take on any value, so there is no space between data values for a given domain. You can determine if data that model real-world situations are discrete or continuous by considering whether all numbers are reasonable as part of the domain.

Discrete Data	Continuous Data
the number of fish a tank can hold	the size of fish in a fish tank the
the number of shirts you can buy	amount of money a shirt costs

StudyTip

Graphs In this book, graphs of discrete functions will be represented by dashed lines. Continuous functions will be represented by solid lines.

Solve Linear Equations

Example 1 shows how to solve a linear equation using a table. **Example 2** shows how to use function equations in real-world applications.

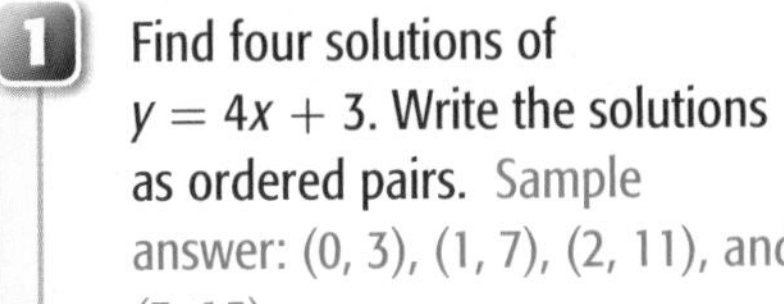

Formative Assessment

Use the Check Your Progress exercises after each example to determine students' understanding of concepts.

Additional Examples

1. Find four solutions of $y = 4x + 3$. Write the solutions as ordered pairs. Sample answer: (0, 3), (1, 7), (2, 11), and (3, 15)

2. **BUSINESS** At a local software company, Level 1 employees x earn \$48,000, and level 2 employees y earn \$24,000. Find four solutions of $48{,}000x + 24{,}000y = 216{,}000$ to determine how many employees at each level the company can hire for \$216,000. Explain each solution. Sample answer: (0, 9) means 0 Level 1, 9 Level 2; (1, 7) means 1 Level 1, 7 Level 2; (2, 5) means 2 Level 1, 5 Level 2; (3, 3) means 3 Level 1, 3 Level 2

Additional Examples also in Interactive Classroom PowerPoint® Presentations

IWB INTERACTIVE WHITEBOARD READY

Tips for New Teachers

Graphing Students should normally use a variety of numbers when finding ordered pair solutions to graph a linear equation. Some equations though, such as in Example 2, require real-world numbers; therefore, only positive integers should be chosen for sample x-values.

Differentiated Instruction

OL BL

If students are familiar with music,

Then bring several passages of sheet music to class. Include scales, melodic strings of notes, and passages with chords. Have students tell which passages are similar to functions and which are dissimilar. Sample answer: scales resemble linear functions; melodic passages have one unique y value for each beat x. Passages with chords do not resemble functions because for each beat x there is more than one note y.

Graph Linear Equations

Example 3 shows how to graph linear equations by plotting points on a coordinate plane.

Additional Example

3 Graph $y = x + 2$.

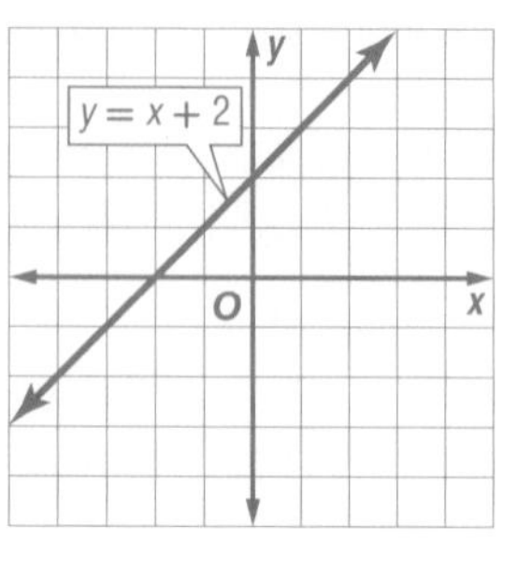

Tips for New Teachers

Choosing x-Values Point out to students that because it is easy to calculate mentally, it is often convenient to choose 0 as an x-value to find a value for y.

Focus on Mathematical Content

Linear Equations The graph of a linear equation is a straight line because the rate of change is constant. If a variable had a degree of more than one, the rate of change would not be constant. Ask students if the equation $y = x^3$ is linear. no

Graph Linear Equations The x-coordinate of the point at which the graph crosses the x-axis is the **x-intercept**. The y-coordinate of the point at which the graph crosses the y-axis is the **y-intercept**.

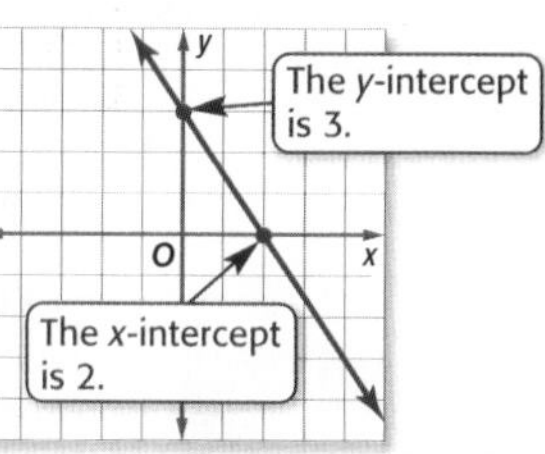

Since two points determine a straight line, a simple method of graphing a linear equation is to find the points where the graph crosses the x-axis and the y-axis and connect them.

StudyTip

An equation written in the form $Ax + By = C$, is written in standard form.

Math *in Motion*, Interactive Lab glencoe.com

EXAMPLE 3 Graph a Linear Function

Graph $-2x + y = 4$.

Step 1 Find the x-intercept.

To find the x-intercept, let $y = 0$.

$-2x + y = 4$	**Write the equation.**
$-2x + (0) = 4$	**Replace y with 0.**
$-2x = 4$	**Divide each side by -2.**
$x = -2$	

Since $x = -2$ when $y = 0$, graph the ordered pair $(-2, 0)$.

Step 2 Find the y-intercept.

To find the y-intercept, let $x = 0$.

$-2x + y = 4$	**Write the equation.**
$-2(0) + y = 4$	**Replace x with 0.**
$y = 4$	

Since $y = 4$ when $x = 0$, graph the ordered pair $(0, 4)$.

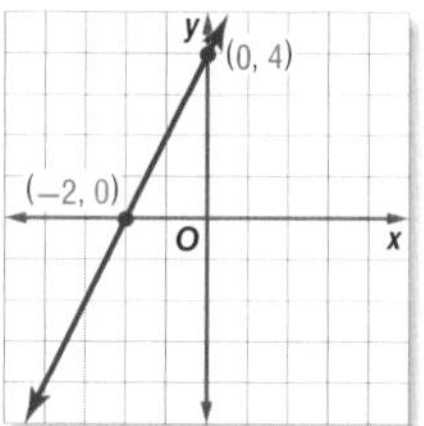

Step 3 Connect the points with a line.

Check Check by solving the equation for y.

$-2x + y = 4$	**Write the equation.**
$-2x + 2x + y = 4 + 2x$	**Add $2x$ to each side.**
$y = 4 + 2x$	**Simplify.**

If $x = -1$, $y = 4 + 2(-1)$ or 2. Notice that the graph of $(-1, 2)$ is on the line. ✔

StudyTip

Although only two points are needed to determine a straight line, always graph at least three to make certain you are correct.

✔ Check Your Progress using intercepts

Graph each equation. 3A–3B. See margin.

3A. $y = x - 4$ **3B.** $x + y = 2$

Personal Tutor glencoe.com

Additional Answers

3A.

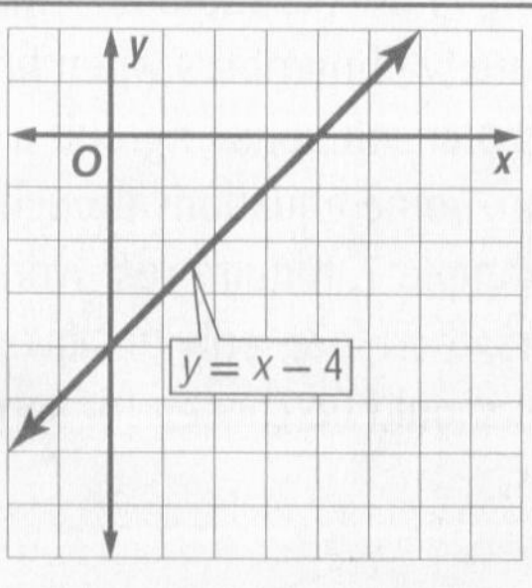

3B.

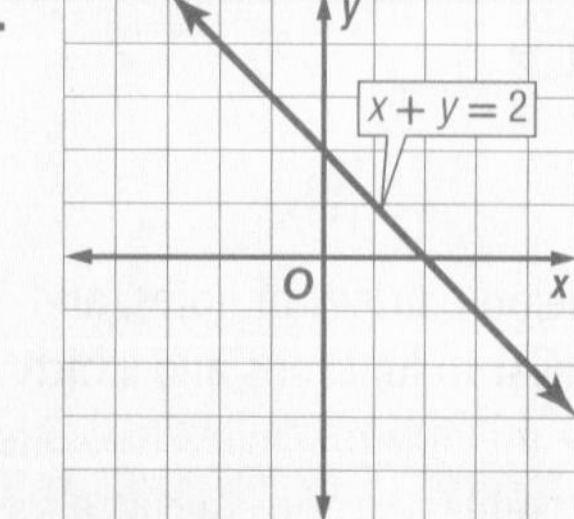

Check Your Understanding

Example 1 p. 406

Copy and complete each table. Use the results to write four ordered pair solutions of the given equation.

1–7. See margin.

1. $y = x + 7$

x	$y = x + 7$	y
−1	■	■
0	■	■
1	■	■
2	■	■

2. $y = 2x - 3$

x	$y = 2x - 3$	y
−2	■	■
0	■	■
2	■	■
4	■	■

Find four solutions of each equation. Write the solutions as ordered pairs.

3. $y = x + 5$ **4.** $y = -4x$ **5.** $y = 3x + 6$ **6.** $-x + y = 7$

Example 2 p. 407

7. WAGES The amount of money Toshiko earns y for working x hours at the library is given by the linear equation $y = 10x$. Find two solutions of this equation. Explain each solution.

Example 3 p. 408

Graph each equation by plotting ordered pairs.

8. $y = x - 1$ **9.** $y = 3x$ **10.** $y = 2x + 4$ **11.** $x + y = 6$

8-11. See Chapter 8 Answer Appendix.

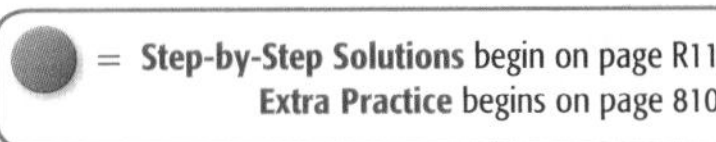
= **Step-by-Step Solutions** begin on page R11.
Extra Practice begins on page 810.

Practice and Problem Solving

Example 1 p. 406

Copy and complete each table. Use the results to write four ordered pair solutions of the given equation. Write the solutions as ordered pairs.

12-25. See Chapter 8 Answer Appendix.

12. $y = x - 2$

x	$y = x - 2$	y
−1	■	■
0	■	■
1	■	■
2	■	■

13. $y = -2x$

x	$y = -2x$	y
−1	■	■
0	■	■
1	■	■
2	■	■

14. $y = 5x + 1$

x	$y = 5x + 1$	y
−2	■	■
−1	■	■
0	■	■
1	■	■

15. $y = -2x + 8$

x	$y = -2x + 8$	y
−1	■	■
0	■	■
2	■	■
4	■	■

Find four solutions of each equation. Write the solutions as ordered pairs.

16. $y = 8x$ **17** $y = -2x$ **18.** $y = x + 7$ **19.** $y = -x + 3$

20. $y = 2x + 5$ **21.** $y = -3x - 4$ **22.** $x + y = -3$ **23.** $2x + y = 9$

Example 2 p. 407

24. GEOMETRY The circumference of a circle C with a radius of r units is approximately given by the linear equation $C \approx 6.3r$. Find two solutions of this equation. Explain each solution.

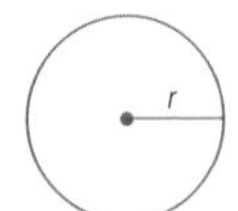
r

25. FAIRS Regular rides cost 3 tickets and children's rides cost 1 ticket. Find three solutions of $3x + y = 12$ to find the number of regular rides x and children's rides y a family can go on with 12 tickets. Explain each solution.

Differentiated Homework Options

Level	Assignment	Two-Day Option	
AL Basic	12–33, 37, 39–54	13–33 odd, 42–45	12–32 even, 37, 39–41, 46–54
OL Core	13–33 odd, 34–37, 39–54	12–33, 42–45	34–37, 39, 46–54
BL Advanced	34–50 (optional: 51–54)		

TEACH with TECH

STUDENT RESPONSE SYSTEM Create slides of several examples of linear functions. For each function, name one of the variables, and ask whether it is the independent or dependent variable. Have students reply with 1 for independent and 2 for dependent.

3 PRACTICE

Formative Assessment

Use Exercises 1–11 to check for understanding.

Use the chart at the bottom of this page to customize assignments for your students.

Additional Answers

1.

x	$y = x + 7$	y
−1	$y = -1 + 7$	6
0	$y = 0 + 7$	7
1	$y = 1 + 7$	8
2	$y = 2 + 7$	9

(−1, 6), (0, 7), (1, 8), (2, 9)

2.

x	$y = 2x - 3$	y
−2	$y = 2(-2) - 3$	−7
0	$y = 2(0) - 3$	−3
2	$y = 2(2) - 3$	1
4	$y = 2(4) - 3$	5

(−2, −7), (0, −3), (2, 1), (4, 5)

3. Sample answer: (−1, 4), (0, 5), (1, 6), (2, 7)

4. Sample answer: (−1, 4), (0, 0), (1, −4), (2, −8)

5. Sample answer: (−1, 3), (0, 6), (1, 9), (2, 12)

6. Sample answer: (−1, 6), (0, 7), (1, 8), (2, 9)

7. Sample answer: (1, 10) means that she earns \$10 for working 1 hour; (2, 20) means that she earns \$20 for working 2 hours.

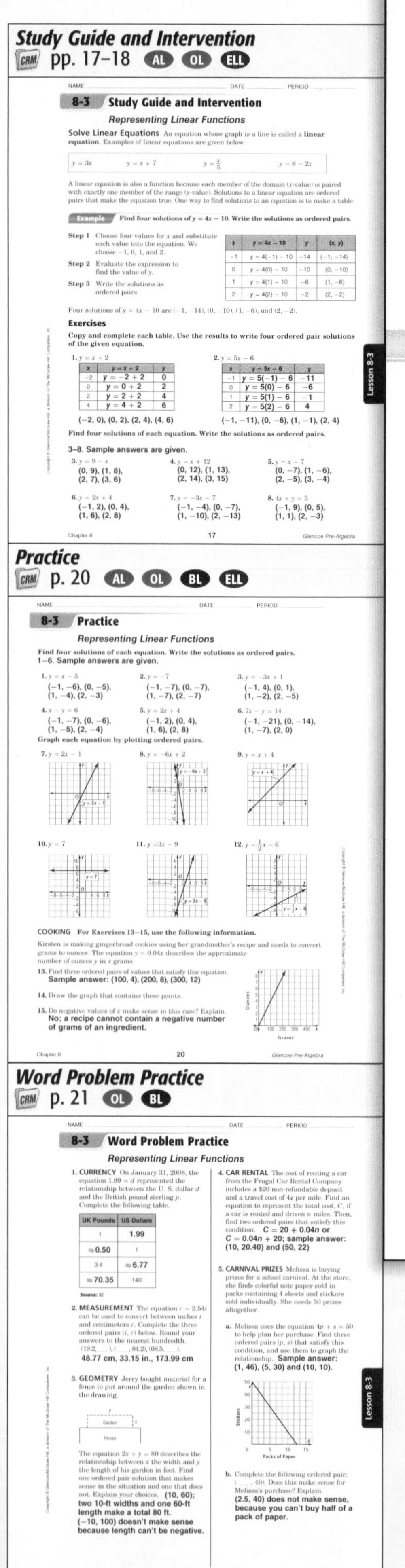

Study Guide and Intervention
CRM pp. 17–18 AL OL ELL

NAME ______ DATE ______ PERIOD ______

8-3 Study Guide and Intervention

Representing Linear Functions

Solve Linear Equations An equation whose graph is a line is called a **linear equation**. Examples of linear equations are given below.

$y = 3x$ $\quad y = x + 7$ $\quad y = \frac{x}{5}$ $\quad y = 8 - 2x$

A linear equation is also a function because each member of the domain (x-value) is paired with exactly one member of the range (y-value). Solutions to a linear equation are ordered pairs that make the equation true. One way to find solutions to an equation is to make a table.

Example **Find four solutions of $y = 4x - 10$. Write the solutions as ordered pairs.**

Step 1 Choose four values for x and substitute each value into the equation. We choose −1, 0, 1, and 2.

Step 2 Evaluate the expression to find the value of y.

Step 3 Write the solutions as ordered pairs.

x	$y = 4x - 10$	y	(x, y)
−1	$y = 4(-1) - 10$	−14	(−1, −14)
0	$y = 4(0) - 10$	−10	(0, −10)
1	$y = 4(1) - 10$	−6	(1, −6)
2	$y = 4(2) - 10$	−2	(2, −2)

Four solutions of $y = 4x - 10$ are (−1, −14), (0, −10), (1, −6), and (2, −2).

Exercises

Copy and complete each table. Use the results to write four ordered pair solutions of the given equation.

1. $y = x + 2$

x	$y = x + 2$	y
−2	$y = -2 + 2$	0
0	$y = 0 + 2$	2
2	$y = 2 + 2$	4
4	$y = 4 + 2$	6

(−2, 0), (0, 2), (2, 4), (4, 6)

2. $y = 5x - 6$

x	$y = 5x - 6$	y
−1	$y = 5(-1) - 6$	−11
0	$y = 5(0) - 6$	−6
1	$y = 5(1) - 6$	−1
2	$y = 5(2) - 6$	4

(−1, −11), (0, −6), (1, −1), (2, 4)

Find four solutions of each equation. Write the solutions as ordered pairs.

3–8. Sample answers are given.

3. $y = 9 - x$ (0, 9), (1, 8), (2, 7), (3, 6)
4. $y = x + 12$ (0, 12), (1, 13), (2, 14), (3, 15)
5. $y = x - 7$ (0, −7), (1, −6), (2, −5), (3, −4)
6. $y = 2x + 4$ (−1, 2), (0, 4), (1, 6), (2, 8)
7. $y = -3x - 7$ (−1, −4), (0, −7), (1, −10), (2, −13)
8. $4x + y = 5$ (−1, 9), (0, 5), (1, 1), (2, −3)

Chapter 8 17 Glencoe Pre-Algebra

Lesson 8-3

Practice
CRM p. 20 AL OL BL ELL

NAME ______ DATE ______ PERIOD ______

8-3 Practice

Representing Linear Functions

Find four solutions of each equation. Write the solutions as ordered pairs.
1–6. Sample answers are given.

1. $y = x - 5$ (−1, −6), (0, −5), (1, −4), (2, −3)
2. $y = -7$ (−1, −7), (0, −7), (1, −7), (2, −7)
3. $y = -3x + 1$ (−1, 4), (0, 1), (1, −2), (2, −5)
4. $x - y = 6$ (−1, −7), (0, −6), (1, −5), (2, −4)
5. $y = 2x + 4$ (−1, 2), (0, 4), (1, 6), (2, 8)
6. $7x - y = 14$ (−1, −21), (0, −14), (1, −7), (2, 0)

Graph each equation by plotting ordered pairs.

7. $y = 2x - 1$
8. $y = -6x + 2$
9. $y = x + 4$
10. $y = 7$
11. $y = 3x - 9$
12. $y = \frac{1}{2}x - 6$

COOKING **For Exercises 13–15, use the following information.**

Kirsten is making gingerbread cookies using her grandmother's recipe and needs to convert grams to ounces. The equation $y = 0.04x$ describes the approximate number of ounces y in x grams.

13. Find three ordered pairs of values that satisfy this equation. **Sample answer: (100, 4), (200, 8), (300, 12)**
14. Draw the graph that contains these points.
15. Do negative values of x make sense in this case? Explain. **No; a recipe cannot contain a negative number of grams of an ingredient.**

Chapter 8 20 Glencoe Pre-Algebra

Word Problem Practice
CRM p. 21 OL BL

NAME ______ DATE ______ PERIOD ______

8-3 Word Problem Practice

Representing Linear Functions

1. **CURRENCY** On January 31, 2008, the equation $1.99 = d$ represented the relationship between the U. S. dollar d and the British pound sterling p. Complete the following table.

UK Pounds	US Dollars
1	1.99
≈0.50	1
3.4	≈6.77
≈70.35	140

Source: XE

2. **MEASUREMENT** The equation $c = 2.54i$ can be used to convert between inches i and centimeters c. Complete the three ordered pairs (i, c) below. Round your answers to the nearest hundredth. (19.2, ___), (___, 84.2), (68.5, ___). **48.77 cm, 33.15 in., 173.99 cm**

3. **GEOMETRY** Jerry bought material for a fence to put around the garden shown in the drawing.

The equation $2x + y = 80$ describes the relationship between x the width and y the length of his garden in feet. Find one ordered pair solution that makes sense in the situation and one that does not. Explain your choices. **(10, 60); two 10-ft widths and one 60-ft length make a total 80 ft. (−10, 100) doesn't make sense because length can't be negative.**

4. **CAR RENTAL** The cost of renting a car from the Frugal Car Rental Company includes a $20 non-refundable deposit and a travel cost of 4¢ per mile. Find an equation to represent the total cost, C, if a car is rented and driven n miles. Then, find two ordered pairs that satisfy this condition. **$C = 20 + 0.04n$ or $C = 0.04n + 20$; sample answer: (10, 20.40) and (50, 22)**

5. **CARNIVAL PRIZES** Melissa is buying prizes for a school carnival. At the store, she finds colorful note paper sold in packs containing 4 sheets and stickers sold individually. She needs 50 prizes altogether.

a. Melissa uses the equation $4p + s = 50$ to help plan her purchase. Find three ordered pairs (p, s) that satisfy this condition, and use them to graph the relationship. **Sample answer: (1, 46), (5, 30) and (10, 10).**

b. Complete the following ordered pair: (___, 40). Does this make sense for Melissa's purchase? Explain. **(2.5, 40) does not make sense, because you can't buy half of a pack of paper.**

Chapter 8 21 Glencoe Pre-Algebra

Lesson 8-3

Example 3 p. 408

Graph each equation. **26-33. See Chapter 8 Answer Appendix.**

26. $y = 5x$
27. $y = -3x$
28. $y = x + 4$
29. $y = -x + 5$
30. $y = 2x + 2$
31. $y = 4x - 1$
32. $x + y = -6$
33. $x - y = 1$

34. **MULTIPLE REPRESENTATIONS** In this problem, you will investigate functions. A whale can swim half a mile per minute.

a. **TABULAR** Make a table to find the number of miles a whale can swim in 5, 10, 15, and 20 minutes. **a-d. See Chapter 8 Answer Appendix.**

b. **VERBAL** As the input values increase by 5, does the difference between the output values increase by the same amount? If not, what is the difference between the output values?

c. **GRAPHICAL** Graph the ordered pairs (time, distance). Then draw a line through the points.

d. **ALGEBRAIC** Write an equation to represent the relationship between time x and number of miles y. Explain your reasoning.

Real-World Career

Marine Mammal Trainer Marine mammal trainers train dolphins, whales, seals, sea lions, walruses, and other marine animals.

A marine mammal trainer needs a Bachelor of Science degree in either zoology, biology, psychology, or marine biology.

35. **GEOMETRY** A rectangle that is x inches long and y inches wide and has a perimeter of 16 inches.

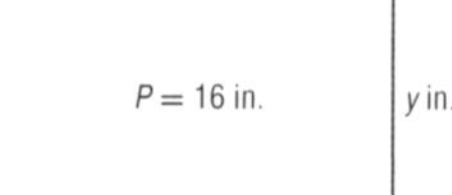

a. Write an equation to represent this situation. **$16 = 2x + 2y$**

b. Find three ordered pairs (width, length) that satisfy the equation. **Sample answer: (1, 7), (2, 6), (3, 5)**

c. Graph the ordered pairs. Then draw a line through the points.

d. Is the ordered pair (−4, 12) a solution of the equation? Does it make sense in the context of the situation? Explain. **c-d. See Chapter 8 Answer Appendix.**

36. **FINANCIAL LITERACY** Mara has $440 to pay a painter to paint her bedroom. The painter charges $55 per hour. The equation $y = 440 - 55x$ represents the amount of money left after x number of hours worked by the painter. What does the solution (7, 55) represent? **Mara has $55 left after 7 hours of painting.**

H.O.T. Problems
Use Higher-Order Thinking Skills

37. **OPEN ENDED** Write a linear equation that has (3, −2) as a solution. Then find another solution of the equation. **Sample answer: $y = x - 5$; (1, −4)**

38. **CHALLENGE** Name a linear equation that is *not* a function. **Sample answer: $x = 1$**

39. **WRITING IN MATH** Explain why a linear function has infinitely many solutions. Then determine which representation shows all the solutions of a linear function: a table, a graph, or an equation. Explain.

39. **Sample answer: Infinitely many values can be substituted for x, or the domain. A table and a graph show some of the solutions. An equation represents all the solutions of a function.**

40. **REASONING** Consider the arithmetic sequence 3, 10, 17, 24, 31, 38, ...

a. Make a scatter plot of the ordered pairs (term number, term). Do the points seem to lie on a line? **a-c. See Chapter 8 Answer Appendix.**

b. In which quadrant(s) would this graph make sense? Explain.

c. If you connect the points, you are including points where the x–value is 1.5, 2.7, or 5.9. Can an arithmetic sequence have these values for x? Explain your reasoning.

41. **WRITING IN MATH** Explain how a linear equation represents a function. Then describe four different real-world representations of a linear function that can be used to express the same relationship. **See Chapter 8 Answer Appendix.**

410 Chapter 8 Linear Functions and Graphing

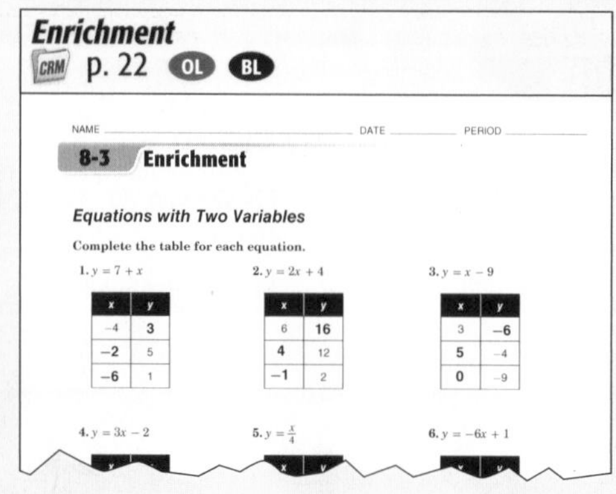

Enrichment
CRM p. 22 OL BL

NAME ______ DATE ______ PERIOD ______

8-3 Enrichment

Equations with Two Variables

Complete the table for each equation.

1. $y = 7 + x$

x	y
−4	3
−2	5
−6	1

2. $y = 2x + 4$

x	y
6	16
4	12
−1	2

3. $y = x - 9$

x	y
3	−6
5	−4
0	−9

4. $y = 3x - 2$

5. $y = \frac{x}{4}$

6. $y = -6x + 1$

Multiple Representations In Exercise 34, students use a table of values, a graph, and an equation to relate time, speed, and distance.

Standardized Test Practice

42. Which equation represents the table of values for the ordered pairs shown? D

x	−1	0	1	2
y	12	9	6	3

A $x - y = -13$ C $x + y = 11$
B $3x - y = 9$ D $3x + y = 9$

43. Which of the following equations represents the line graphed below? F

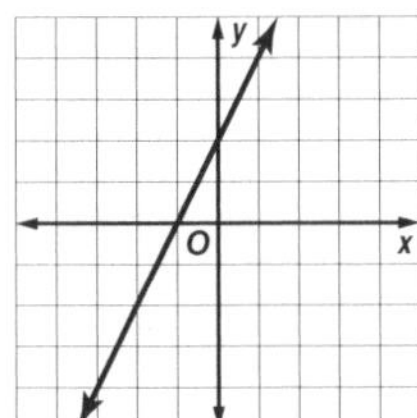

F $2x - y = -2$ H $x - y = 0$
G $x - y = -2$ J $x + 3y = -5$

44. Which of the following sets of ordered pairs represents a linear function? B

A $\{(2, 2), (1, -1), (0, 0), (-1, -1)\}$
B $\{(4, -4), (3, -3), (2, -2), (1, -1)\}$
C $\{(-4, -4), (0, 0), (4, -4), (-8, -8)\}$
D $\{(-3, -5), (-1, 0), (0, 1), (3, -5)\}$

45. **EXTENDED RESPONSE** The equation $y = 64x$ describes the weight y of x cubic feet of water. a–d. See margin.

a. Describe the linear relationship between number of cubic feet and weight of water in words.
b. Make a table of values that describe the relationship.
c. Choose two ordered pairs from your table and describe what they mean.
d. Graph the ordered pairs in your table and draw a line through them.

Spiral Review

Write an equation that describes each sequence. Then find the indicated term. (Lesson 8-2)

46. 7, 8, 9, 10, …; 14th term $t = 6 + n$; 20

47. 6, 10, 14, 18, …; 23rd term $t = 4n + 2$; 94

Determine whether each relation is a function. Explain. (Lesson 8-1)

48. $\{(0, 6), (-3, 9), (4, 9), (-2, 1)\}$ Yes; each x-value is paired with only one y-value.

49. $\{(-0.1, 5), (0, 10), (-0.1, -5)\}$ No; −0.1 in the domain is paired with 5 and −5 in the range.

50. **FOOD** The circle graph shows the results of a survey about favorite pizza toppings. (Lesson 7-8)

a. What is the favorite pizza topping of the people surveyed? just cheese

b. If 250,000 people were surveyed, how many would you expect to rate mushrooms as their favorite topping? 12,500 people

Favorite Pizza Toppings

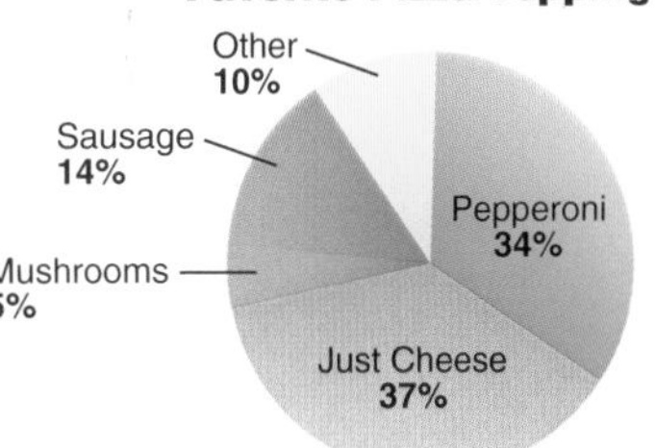

Skills Review

Evaluate each expression. (Lesson 3-4)

51. $\frac{18 - 10}{8 - 4}$ 2

52. $\frac{16 - 7}{1 - 3}$ $-4\frac{1}{2}$ or −4.5

53. $\frac{46 - 22}{2008 - 2004}$ 6

54. $\frac{31 - 25}{46 - 21}$ $\frac{6}{25}$ or 0.24

4 ASSESS

Yesterday's News Ask students to write a sentence on how the lesson about functions helped them with learning today's new concept on linear equations.

Formative Assessment

Check for student understanding of concepts in Lessons 8-1, 8-2, and 8-3.

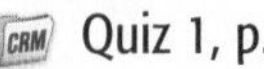 Quiz 1, p. 68

Additional Answers

45a. Water weighs 64 pounds per cubic foot.

45b. Sample answer:

x	y
1	64
2	128
3	192
4	256

45c. Sample answer: (1, 64) means that 1 cubic foot of water weighs 64 pounds; (2, 128) means that 2 cubic feet of water weighs 128 pounds.

45d. Sample answer:

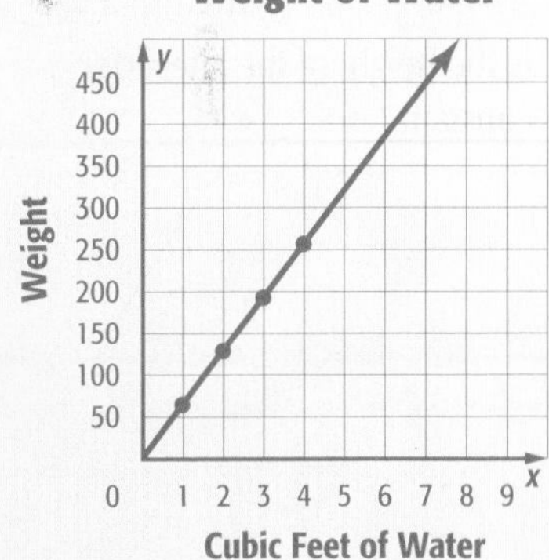

Differentiated Instruction

Extension Pose the following problem to students: Jesse has a hammock tied between 2 trees. He notices that when his friend got into the hammock, it lowered 4 inches. When a second friend got into the hammock along with the first friend, it lowered an additional 6 inches. Write a linear equation to model this situation with x representing the number of people in the hammock and y representing the distance in inches the hammock descends; plot 2–3 points on a graph and determine how many people can get into the hammock before it touches the ground, 28 inches away. $y = -6x + 2$; 5 people

8-4 Lesson Notes

1 FOCUS

Vertical Alignment

Before Lesson 8-4
Use a rate to compare two quantities.

Lesson 8-4
Find rates of change. Solve problems involving rates of change.

After Lesson 8-4
Relate rate of change to the slope of a line.

2 TEACH

Scaffolding Questions

Have students read the *Why?* section of the lesson and answer the questions.

Ask:

- What is happening to the kitesurfer between points *D* and *E*? His height is decreasing.
- What does point *A* represent? the starting point–(0, 0)–of the kitesurfer.
- Is the height of the kitesurfer constant? no

8-4 Rate of Change

Then
You have already used a rate to compare two quantities. (Lesson 5-2)

Now
- Find rates of change.
- Solve problems involving rates of change.

New Vocabulary
rate of change

Math Online
glencoe.com
- Extra Examples
- Personal Tutor
- Self-Check Quiz
- Homework Help

Why?

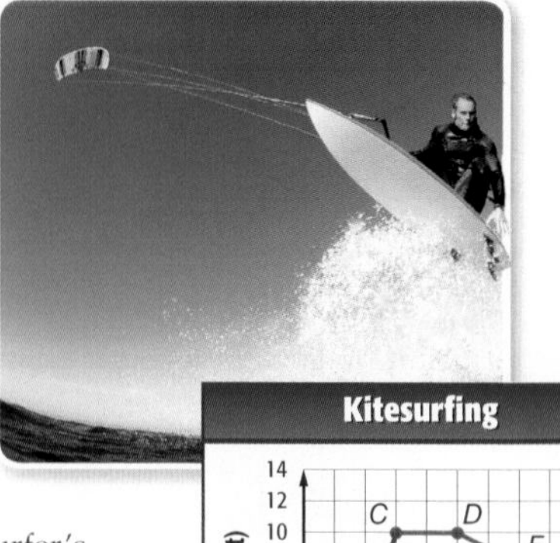

In *kitesurfing*, riders are pulled through the water and up in the air by a kite. The graph shows the change in height of a kitesurfer from 0 to 14 seconds.
a–c. See Chapter 8 Answer Appendix.

a. Between which two consecutive points did the height of the kitesurfer increase the most? How do you know?

b. What is happening to the kitesurfer's height between points C and D?

c. Find the ratio of the change in height to the time for each section of the graph. Which section is the steepest?

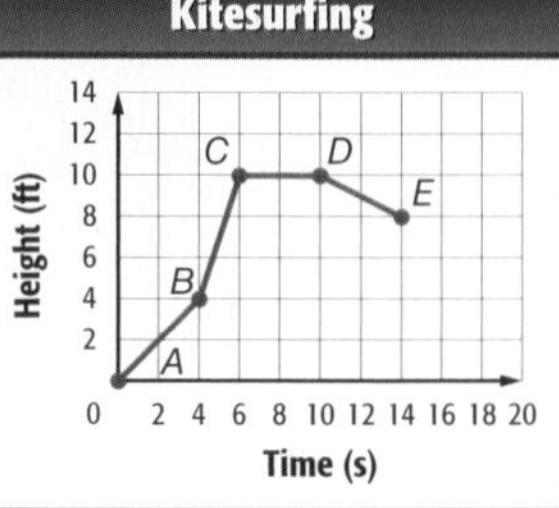

Rate of Change A **rate of change** is a rate that describes how one quantity changes in relation to another quantity. The rate of change of the height of the kitesurfer to the time from point *B* to point *C* is $\frac{10-4}{6-4}$ or 3 feet per second.

Real-World EXAMPLE 1 Find Rate of Change from a Graph

AIRPLANES The graph shows the changes in height and distance of a small airplane. Find the rate of change from point *B* to point *C*.

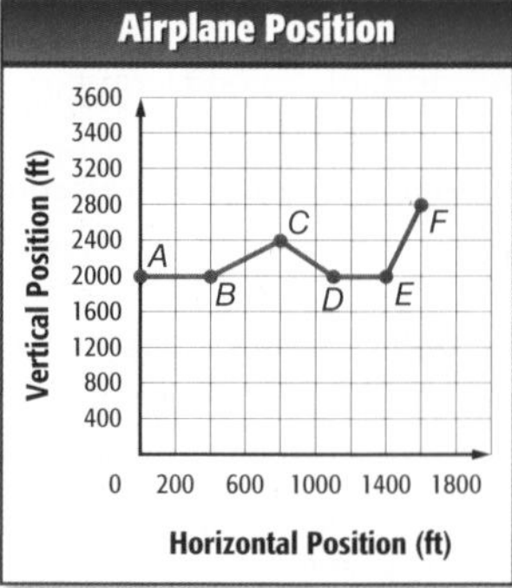

The vertical position changed from 2000 feet to 2400 feet. The horizontal position changed from 400 feet to 800 feet.

$$\frac{\text{change in vertical position}}{\text{change in horizontal position}} = \frac{2400-2000}{800-400}$$

$$= \frac{400}{400}$$

$$= 1$$

The rate of change is an increase of 1 foot in the vertical position for every 1 foot in the horizontal position.

Check Your Progress

1. **AIRPLANES** Find the rate of change from point *E* to point *F* in the airplane position graph above. an increase of 4 feet in the vertical position for every 1 foot in the horizontal position

Personal Tutor glencoe.com

Lesson 8-4 Resources

Resource	Approaching-Level	On-Level	Beyond-Level	English Learners
Teacher Edition	• Differentiated Instruction, p. 414	• Differentiated Instruction, p. 414	• Differentiated Instruction, p. 417	• Differentiated Instruction, p. 414
Chapter Resource Masters	• Study Guide and Intervention, pp. 23–24 • Skills Practice, p. 25 • Practice, p. 26 • Word Problem Practice, p. 27 • Spreadsheet Activity, p. 29	• Study Guide and Intervention, pp. 23–24 • Skills Practice, p. 25 • Practice, p. 26 • Word Problem Practice, p. 27 • Enrichment, p. 28 • Spreadsheet Activity, p. 29	• Practice, p. 26 • Word Problem Practice, p. 27 • Enrichment, p. 28 • Spreadsheet Activity, p. 29	• Study Guide and Intervention, pp. 23–24 • Skills Practice, p. 25 • Practice, p. 26 • Spreadsheet Activity, p. 29
Transparencies	• 5-Minute Check Transparency 8-4	• 5-Minute Check Transparency 8-4	• 5-Minute Check Transparency 8-4	• 5-Minute Check Transparency 8-4
Other	• Study Notebook • Teaching Pre-Algebra with Manipulatives	• Study Notebook • Teaching Pre-Algebra with Manipulatives	• Study Notebook	• Study Notebook • Teaching Pre-Algebra with Manipulatives

Real-World EXAMPLE 2 Find Rate of Change from a Table

MONEY The table shows the amount of money that Joshua earns working at a state park for the summer. Find the rate of change.

Time (h)	Income ($)
x	y
8	76.00
9	85.50

Understand You know the income Joshua receives. You need to find the rate of change.

Plan To find the rate of change, divide the change in income by the change in time.

Solve rate of change $= \dfrac{\text{change in income}}{\text{change in time}}$

$= \dfrac{\$85.50 - \$76.00}{9\text{ h} - 8\text{ h}}$ — Income goes from \$76 to \$85.50. Time goes from 8 to 9 hours.

$= \$9.50/\text{h}$ — Simplify.

The rate of change is \$9.50/h or an increase of \$9.50 per hour.

Check Check by using the rate of change to find Joshua's income if he works 10 hours.

\$9.50/hour × 10 hours = \$95.00. Since 76 + 9.5 = 85.5 and 85.5 + 9.5 = 95, the solution is reasonable. ✓

StudyTip

x and y Values In rates of change, the x values always increase. The y values may increase, decrease, or remain the same.

Check Your Progress

2. **EXERCISE** Alondra uses a pedometer to keep track of the number of steps she takes on a walk. Find the rate of change. **an increase of 96 steps per minute**

Time (min)	Number of Steps
x	y
3	288
5	480

Personal Tutor glencoe.com

Rates of change can be *positive*, *negative*, or *zero*.

Real-World EXAMPLE 3 Negative Rate of Change

ROLLER COASTERS The biggest drop of the *Kingda Ka* roller coaster is described in the table. Find the rate of change. Interpret its meaning.

Time (s)	Height (ft)
x	y
0	456
1	268
2	80

rate of change $= \dfrac{\text{change in height}}{\text{change in time}}$

$= \dfrac{268\text{ ft} - 456\text{ ft}}{1\text{ s} - 0\text{ s}}$ — Height goes from 456 to 268 feet. Time goes from 0 to 1 second.

$= -188\text{ ft/s}$ — Simplify.

The rate of change can be described as a decrease of 188 feet per second.

Real-World Link

The Kingda Ka roller coaster, in Jackson, New Jersey, is 3118 feet long, travels up to 128 miles per hour, and lasts about half a minute.

Source: Coaster Grotto

Check Your Progress

3. **MONEY** The table shows the amount y remaining in Lauren's savings account after x weeks. Find the rate of change. Interpret its meaning. **–\$20/wk; She spends \$20 each week.**

Time (wk)	Amount ($)
x	y
4	160
6	120

Personal Tutor glencoe.com

Rate of Change

Example 1 shows how to find rate of change from a graph. **Example 2** shows how to find rate of change from a table. **Example 3** shows how to find negative rate of change. **Example 4** shows how to compare rates of change.

Formative Assessment

Use the Check Your Progress exercises after each example to determine students' understanding of concepts.

Additional Examples

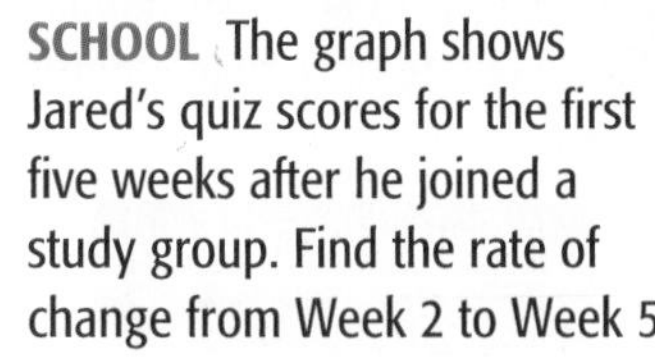

1 **SCHOOL** The graph shows Jared's quiz scores for the first five weeks after he joined a study group. Find the rate of change from Week 2 to Week 5.

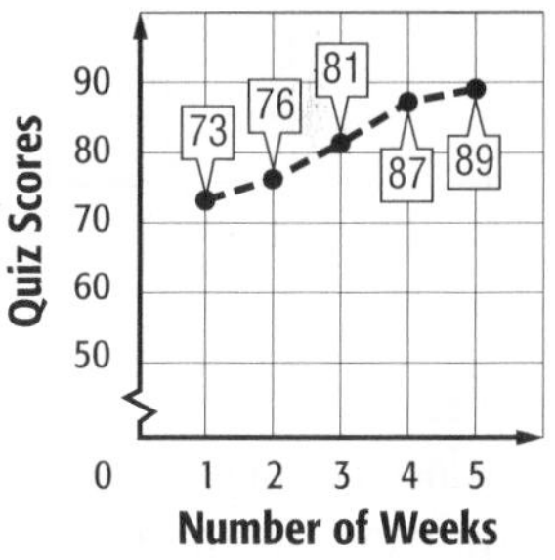

about 4.3 points per week

2 **DISTANCE** The table shows the distance that Amy travels during a week. Find the rate of change. 58 miles per day or an increase of 58 miles per day

Time (d)	Distance (mi)
x	y
3	174
7	406

Additional Examples also in Interactive Classroom PowerPoint® Presentations

IWB INTERACTIVE WHITEBOARD READY

Focus on Mathematical Content

Rate of Change The data needed to find the rate of change in one quantity with respect to another quantity can come from a graph, a table of values, or an equation. The rate of change is found by dividing the change in the vertical position by the change in the horizontal position. The rate of change is positive, negative, or zero.

Tips for New Teachers

Review Vocabulary Remind students that a rate is a ratio of two quantities having different kinds of units. For example, an increase of \$9.50 per hour is a rate.

Tips for New Teachers

Graphs Tell students that when describing the graphs in the Concept Summary, they can say that the first graph "increases from left to right." The second graph "decreases from left to right."

Additional Examples

3 **COOKIES** Natalia is selling cookies. The table below shows the relationship between the hours spent selling and the number of cookies that remain. Find the rate of change. Interpret its meaning.

Hours	Cookies
x	y
0	100
3	40
5	0

−20 cookies/hr; She sells 20 cookies each hour.

4 **INCOME** The table shows the yearly incomes of two families. Compare the rates of change.

Year	Income ($)	
	Miller	King
2004	49,000	50,000
2005	50,000	52,000
2006	51,000	54,000
2007	52,000	56,000

The income of the King family increases at a faster rate than the income of the Miller family.

Real-World Link

The music on a CD is imprinted on a spiral track that is 3.52 miles long.

Real-World EXAMPLE 4 Compare Rates of Change

TECHNOLOGY A CD spins at different speeds when playing songs on the inside tracks (near the center of the CD) than when playing songs on the outside tracks, as shown in the table. Compare the rates of change.

Number of Seconds x	Number of Revolutions y	
	Inside Tracks	Outside Tracks
0	0	0
2	16	6
4	32	12

Source: *Encyclopedia Americana*

Songs on Inside Tracks

$$\text{rate of change} = \frac{\text{change in } y}{\text{change in } x} = \frac{32 - 16}{4 - 2} = 8 \text{ revolutions/s}$$

Songs on Outside Tracks

$$\text{rate of change} = \frac{\text{change in } y}{\text{change in } x} = \frac{12 - 6}{4 - 2} = \frac{6}{2} = 3 \text{ revolutions/s}$$

A CD spins at a faster rate when playing songs on the inside tracks than when playing songs on the outside tracks. A steeper line on the graph indicates a greater rate of change.

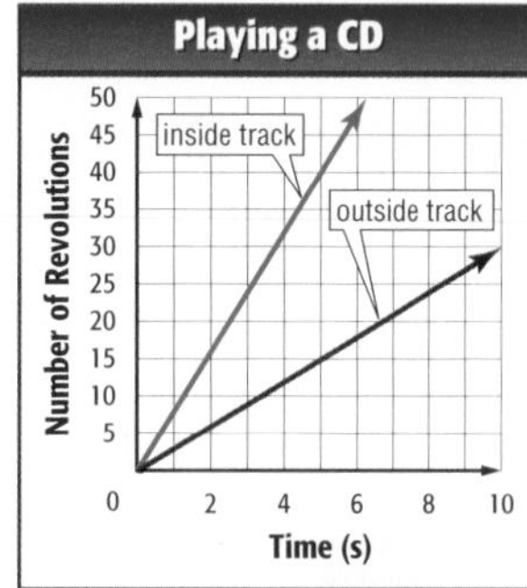

Check Your Progress

4. **GEOMETRY** The perimeter of a regular hexagon changes as its side lengths increase by 1 inch. Compare this rate of change with the rate of change for a square whose side lengths increase by 1 inch.

4. The rate of change in the perimeter of a hexagon is greater than in the perimeter of a square; 6:1 opposed to 4:1

Personal Tutor glencoe.com

ReadingMath

Graphs In the Concept Summary, the rate of change in each graph can be read a different way. In the first graph, as time increases, the temperature increases. In the second graph, as time increases, temperature decreases. In the third graph, as time increases, temperature does not change.

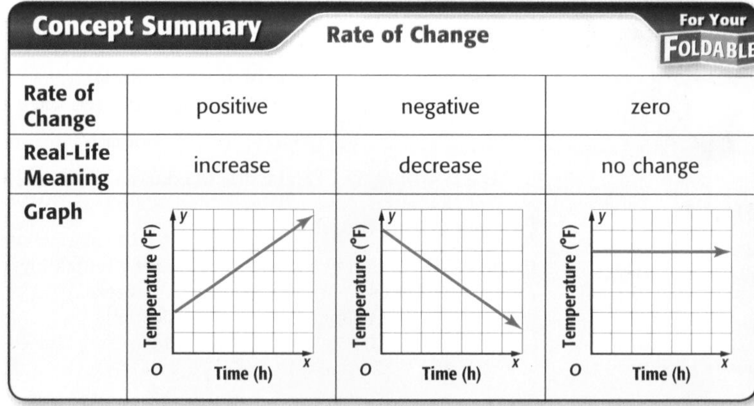

Concept Summary Rate of Change — For Your FOLDABLE

Rate of Change	positive	negative	zero
Real-Life Meaning	increase	decrease	no change
Graph			

Differentiated Instruction

AL OL ELL

 **If** students confuse x- and y-values,

 **Then** provide them with colored pencils to color code the x- and y-values on their tables or graphs. Then when they set up their problems to find the rate of change, they use the same color to keep the values in the correct place in the problem.

Check Your Understanding

Examples 1 and 2 pp. 412–413

Find the rate of change for each linear function.

1. 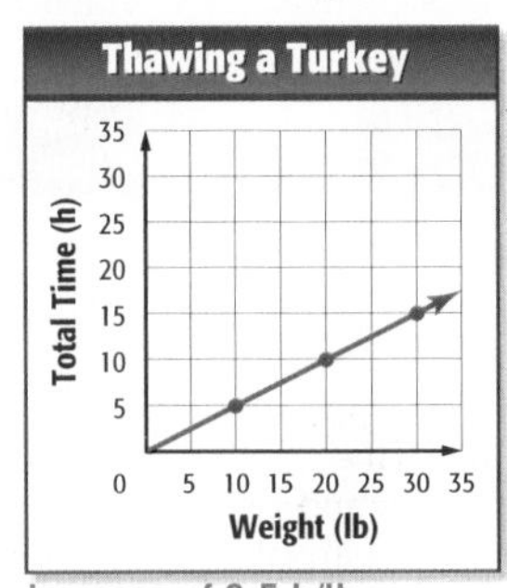

increase of 0.5 h/lb

2.

Filling a Pool	
Time (min)	Depth (in.)
x	y
5	12
10	24
15	36
20	48

increase of 2.4 in./min

Examples 3 and 4 pp. 413–414

3. −0.8 ft/min or decrease of 0.8 ft/min

4. Balloon 1: 8.2 ft/s; balloon 2: 5.6 ft/s; balloon 1 rises at a faster rate than balloon 2.

3. **HIKING** The table shows the altitude of a group of hikers during their hike. Find the rate of change.

Hiking	
Time (min)	Altitude (ft)
x	y
20	170
30	162
40	154

4. **HOT-AIR BALLOONS** The table shows the relationship between time and altitude of two hot-air balloons. Compare the rates of change for the balloons from 3 to 5 seconds.

Time (s)	Altitude (ft)	
	Balloon 1	Balloon 2
3	22.7	30.4
4	30.9	36.0
5	39.1	41.6

Practice and Problem Solving

= **Step-by-Step Solutions** begin on page R11.
Extra Practice begins on page 810.

Examples 1 and 2 pp. 412–413

Find the rate of change for each linear function.

5. increase of 15 miles/h

6. increase of 2.5 oz/serving

7. increase of 10 jumps/min

8. increase of $0.25/message

5. **Riding a Bicycle**

Distance (mi): 0, 5, 10, 15, 20, 25, 30, 35, 40

Time (h): 1, 2, 3, 4

6. 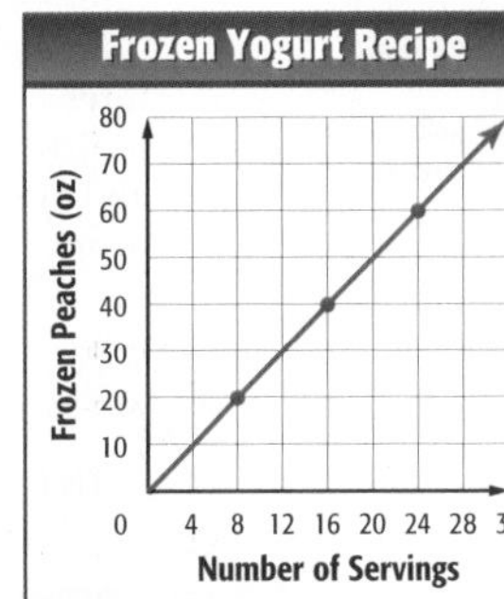

7.

Jumping on a Trampoline	
Time (min)	Number of Jumps
x	y
1	20
2	30
3	40
4	50

8.

Sending Video Messages	
Number of Messages	Cost ($)
x	y
4	1.00
6	1.50
8	2.00
10	2.50

3 PRACTICE

Formative Assessment

Use Exercises 1–4 to check for understanding.

Use the chart at the bottom of this page to customize assignments for your students.

Watch Out!

Preventing Errors Students may confuse horizontal change and vertical change. Remind them that horizontal goes with the x-axis and vertical with the y-axis.

TEACH with TECH

AUDIO RECORDING Have students work in groups. Give each group graphs of several lines without labels. Have students record explanations of real-world situations that could be shown by the graph. Post the recordings on the classroom Web site.

Differentiated Homework Options

Level	Assignment	Two-Day Option	
AL Basic	5–10, 14, 15, 17–35	5–9 odd, 19–22	6–10 even, 14, 15, 17, 18, 23–35
OL Core	5–9 odd, 11–15, 17–35	5–10, 19–22	11–15, 17, 18, 23–35
BL Advanced	11–31, (optional: 32–35)		

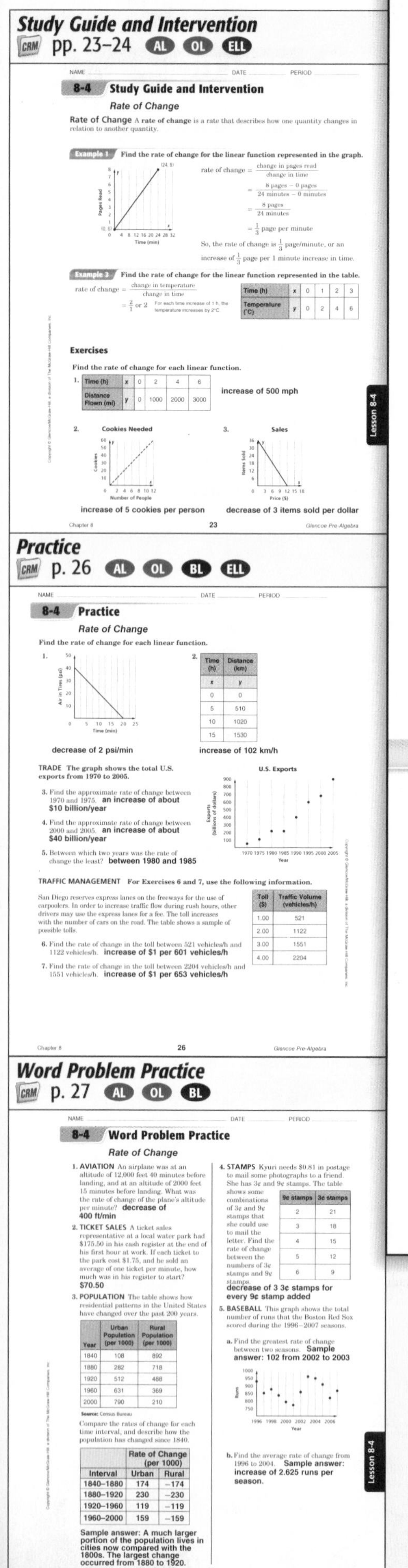

Study Guide and Intervention
CRM pp. 23–24 AL OL ELL

NAME ______ DATE ______ PERIOD ______

8-4 Study Guide and Intervention

Rate of Change

Rate of Change A rate of change is a rate that describes how one quantity changes in relation to another quantity.

Example 1 Find the rate of change for the linear function represented in the graph.

rate of change = $\frac{\text{change in pages read}}{\text{change in time}}$ = $\frac{8 \text{ pages} - 0 \text{ pages}}{24 \text{ minutes} - 0 \text{ minutes}}$ = $\frac{8 \text{ pages}}{24 \text{ minutes}}$ = $\frac{1}{3}$ page per minute

So, the rate of change is $\frac{1}{3}$ page/minute, or an increase of $\frac{1}{3}$ page per 1 minute increase in time.

Example 2 Find the rate of change for the linear function represented in the table.

rate of change = $\frac{\text{change in temperature}}{\text{change in time}}$ = $\frac{2}{1}$ or 2. For each time increase of 1 h, the temperature increases by 2°C.

Time (h)	x	0	1	2	3
Temperature (°C)	y	0	2	4	6

Exercises

Find the rate of change for each linear function.

1.

Time (h)	x	0	2	4	6
Distance Flown (mi)	y	0	1000	2000	3000

increase of 500 mph

2. Cookies Needed — increase of 5 cookies per person

3. Sales — decrease of 3 items sold per dollar

Chapter 8 23 Glencoe Pre-Algebra

Practice
CRM p. 26 AL OL BL ELL

NAME ______ DATE ______ PERIOD ______

8-4 Practice

Rate of Change

Find the rate of change for each linear function.

1. decrease of 2 psi/min

2.

Time (h)	Distance (km)
x	y
0	0
5	510
10	1020
15	1530

increase of 102 km/h

TRADE The graph shows the total U.S. exports from 1970 to 2005.

3. Find the approximate rate of change between 1970 and 1975. an increase of about $10 billion/year

4. Find the approximate rate of change between 2000 and 2005. an increase of about $40 billion/year

5. Between which two years was the rate of change the least? between 1980 and 1985

TRAFFIC MANAGEMENT For Exercises 6 and 7, use the following information.

San Diego reserves express lanes on the freeways for the use of carpoolers. In order to increase traffic flow during rush hours, other drivers may use the express lanes for a fee. The toll increases with the number of cars on the road. The table shows a sample of possible tolls.

Toll ($)	Traffic Volume (vehicles/h)
1.00	521
2.00	1122
3.00	1551
4.00	2204

6. Find the rate of change in the toll between 521 vehicles/h and 1122 vehicles/h. increase of $1 per 601 vehicles/h

7. Find the rate of change in the toll between 2204 vehicles/h and 1551 vehicles/h. increase of $1 per 653 vehicles/h

Chapter 8 26 Glencoe Pre-Algebra

Word Problem Practice
CRM p. 27 AL OL BL

NAME ______ DATE ______ PERIOD ______

8-4 Word Problem Practice

Rate of Change

1. AVIATION An airplane was at an altitude of 12,000 feet 40 minutes before landing, and at an altitude of 2000 feet 15 minutes before landing. What was the rate of change of the plane's altitude per minute? decrease of 400 ft/min

2. TICKET SALES A ticket sales representative at a local water park had $175.50 in his cash register at the end of his first hour at work. If each ticket to the park cost $1.75, and he sold an average of one ticket per minute, how much was in his register to start? $70.50

3. POPULATION The table shows how residential patterns in the United States have changed over the past 200 years.

Year	Urban Population (per 1000)	Rural Population (per 1000)
1840	108	892
1880	282	718
1920	512	488
1960	631	369
2000	790	210

Source: Census Bureau

Compare the rates of change for each time interval, and describe how the population has changed since 1840.

Interval	Rate of Change (per 1000) Urban	Rural
1840–1880	174	−174
1880–1920	230	−230
1920–1960	119	−119
1960–2000	159	−159

Sample answer: A much larger portion of the population lives in cities now compared with the 1800s. The largest change occurred from 1880 to 1920.

4. STAMPS Kyuri needs $0.81 in postage to mail some photographs to a friend. She has 3¢ and 9¢ stamps. The table shows some combinations of 3¢ and 9¢ stamps that she could use to mail the letter. Find the rate of change between the numbers of 3¢ stamps and 9¢ stamps.

9¢ stamps	3¢ stamps
2	21
3	18
4	15
5	12
6	9

decrease of 3 3¢ stamps for every 9¢ stamp added

5. BASEBALL This graph shows the total number of runs that the Boston Red Sox scored during the 1996–2007 seasons.

a. Find the greatest rate of change between two seasons. Sample answer: 102 from 2002 to 2003

b. Find the average rate of change from 1996 to 2004. Sample answer: increase of 2.625 runs per season.

Chapter 8 27 Glencoe Pre-Algebra

Find the rate of change for each linear function.

Examples 3 and 4 pp. 413–414

9. −3°/h or a decrease of 3°/h

12. −10 books/day or a decrease of 10 books/day

9. **TEMPERATURE** The table shows the outside temperature after a number of hours. Find the rate of change.

Time (h)	Temperature (°F)
x	y
1	48
2	45
3	42
4	39

10. **LATE FEES** The table shows late fees for DVDs and video games at a video store. Compare the rates of change. **See margin.**

Days Late	Late Fees ($) DVDs	Video Games
0	0	0
2	3	4
4	6	8
5	7.50	10

11. **INSECTS** The graph shows the speed at which mosquitoes and bees beat their wings. Compare the rates of change. **See margin.**

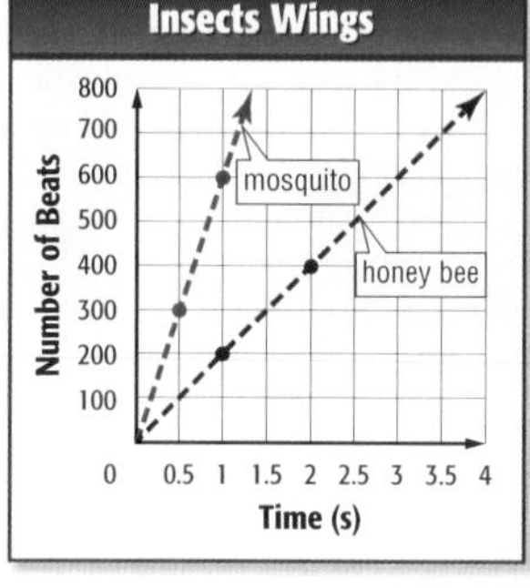

12. **SALES** The graph shows the number of books sold at a book fair. Find the rate of change.

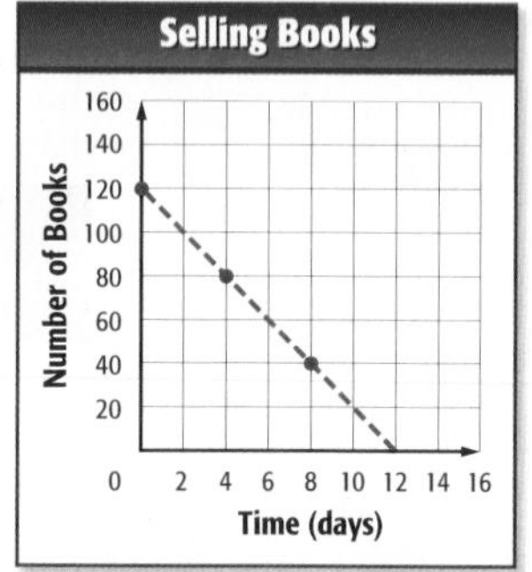

Real-World Link

A puppy should gain about 0.08–0.16 ounce per day per pound of their expected adult weight. For example, a puppy that grows to be 50 pounds should gain 2 to 4 ounces per day.

Source: Foster & Smith, Inc.

13. **PUPPIES** The table shows the number of times puppies should be fed at different ages. Find the three rates of change represented in the table and describe what they mean. **See margin.**

Total Puppy Feedings

Days	Age < 6 Months	6–12 Months	> 12 Months
1	3	2	1
2	6	4	2
3	9	6	3

Source: Foster & Smith, Inc.

H.O.T. Problems

Use Higher-Order Thinking Skills

14–15, 17–18. See margin.

14. **OPEN ENDED** Describe a real-world relationship between two quantities that involve a positive rate of change.

15. **WRITING IN MATH** Refer to the graph in Exercise 11. What is the connection between the steepness of the lines and the rates of change?

16. See Chapter 8 Answer Appendix.

16. **CHALLENGE** A person starts walking, then runs, and then sits down to rest. Sketch a graph of the situation to represent the different rates of change. Label the x-axis "Time" and the y-axis "Distance".

17. **REASONING** Explain why a horizontal line represents a rate of change of zero, but a vertical line cannot be used to represent a rate of change.

18. **WRITING IN MATH** Use the data about airplane position in Example 1 to explain how rate of change affects the graph of the airplane's position.

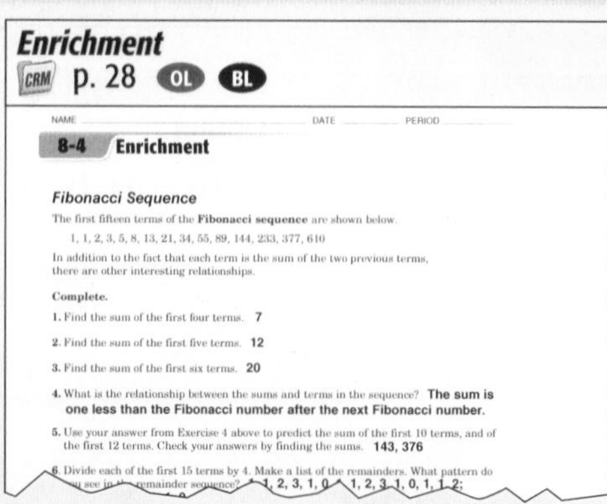

Enrichment
CRM p. 28 OL BL

NAME ______ DATE ______ PERIOD ______

8-4 Enrichment

Fibonacci Sequence

The first fifteen terms of the **Fibonacci sequence** are shown below.

1, 1, 2, 3, 5, 8, 13, 21, 34, 55, 89, 144, 233, 377, 610

In addition to the fact that each term is the sum of the two previous terms, there are other interesting relationships.

Complete.

1. Find the sum of the first four terms. 7

2. Find the sum of the first five terms. 12

3. Find the sum of the first six terms. 20

4. What is the relationship between the sums and terms in the sequence? The sum is one less than the Fibonacci number after the next Fibonacci number.

5. Use your answer from Exercise 4 above to predict the sum of the first 10 terms, and of the first 12 terms. Check your answers by finding the sums. 143, 376

6. Divide each of the first 15 terms by 4. Make a list of the remainders. What pattern do you see in the remainder sequence? 1, 1, 2, 3, 1, 0, 1, 1, 2, 3, 1, 0, 1, 1, 2;

Standardized Test Practice

For Exercises 19 and 20, use the graph.

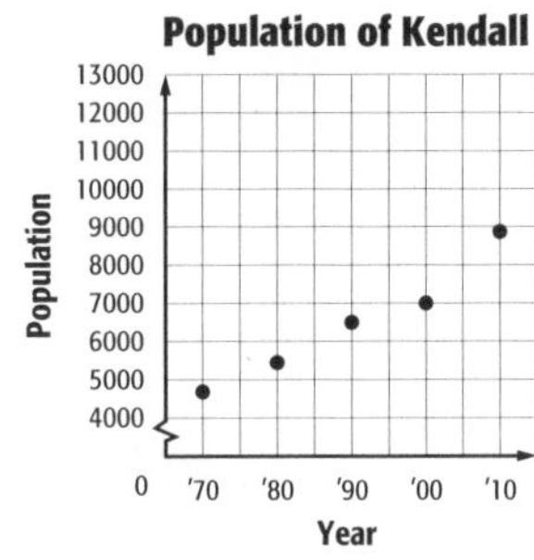

19. In which of the following decades was there the greatest population change? **D**

A 1970–1980 C 1990–2000
B 1980–1990 D 2000–2010

20. In which of the following decades was there the least population change? **H**

F 1970–1980 H 1990–2000
G 1980–1990 J 2000–2010

21. The table shows a relationship between time and altitude of a hot-air balloon. Which is the *best* estimate for the rate of change for the balloon from 1 to 5 seconds? **C**

Time (s)	Altitude (ft)
1	6.3
2	14.5
3	22.7
4	30.9
5	39.1

A 7.6 ft/s C 8.2 ft/s
B 7.8 ft/s D 8.8 ft/s

22. SHORT RESPONSE Find the rate of change for the linear function represented in the table. Round to the nearest hundredth. **increase of 1.08 mi/min**

Time (min)	Distance (mi)
30	32.5
45	48.75
60	65.0
75	81.25
90	97.5

Spiral Review

Find four solutions of each equation. Show each solution in a table of ordered pairs. (Lesson 8-3) **23–28. See Chapter 8 Answer Appendix.**

23. $y = x - 7$ **24.** $y = 2x - 3$ **25.** $3x - y = 10$

Describe each sequence using words and symbols. (Lesson 8-2)

26. 4, 6, 8, 10, ... **27.** 1, 4, 7, 10, ... **28.** 3, 7, 11, 15, ...

29. GEOMETRY Study the pattern at the right. Write an expression that describes the pattern. Which figure will have 45 squares? (Lesson 8-2) **$4n + 1$; figure 11**

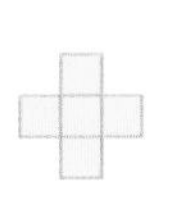
Figure 1

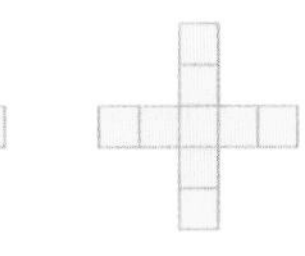
Figure 2

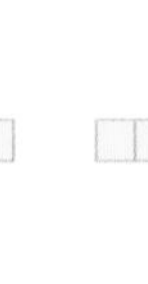
Figure 3

30. Find 95% of 256 using the percent equation. (Lesson 7-5) **243.2**

31. RAIN A raindrop falls from the sky at about 17 miles per hour. How many feet per second is this? Round to the nearest foot per second. (Lesson 6-3) **25 ft/s**

Skills Review

Rewrite $y = kx$ by replacing k with each given value. (Lesson 1-2)

32. $k = 5$ **$y = 5x$** **33.** $k = -2$ **$y = -2x$** **34.** $k = 0.25$ **$y = 0.25x$** **35.** $k = \frac{1}{3}$ **$y = \frac{1}{3}x$**

Differentiated Instruction

BL

Extension Present students with the following problem: Tamika and Rashan are climbing a 150-foot mountain. They begin 48 feet above the ground, at $t = 0$, and climb at a constant rate of 43 feet per hour. Make a graph representing the relationship between the height climbed and the hours climbing.

How long will it take for them to climb the mountain? about $2\frac{1}{2}$ hours

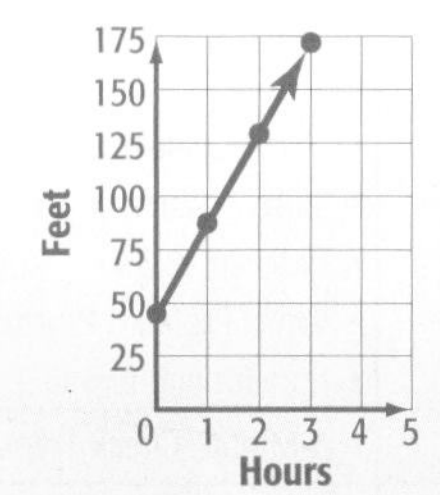

4 ASSESS

Crystal Ball Have students write how they think what they have learned today will connect with tomorrow's theme of constant rate of change and direct variation.

Additional Answers

10. DVDs: $1.50/day; video games: $2/day; The late fee on video games increases at a faster rate than the late fee for DVDs.

11. Mosquito: 600 beats/s; honey bee: 200 beats/s; the number of times a mosquito's wings beats increases at a faster rate than the number of times a honey bee's wings beat.

13. 3 times/day, 2 times/day, 1 time/day; A puppy less than 6 months old should be fed 3 times a day. A puppy between 6 and 12 months old should be fed twice a day. A puppy older than 12 months should be fed once a day.

14. Sample answer: The miles a person jogs changes with the number of minutes they jog. The rate of change is the miles per minute, or their speed.

15. Sample answer: The steeper the line, the greater the rate of change.

16. See Chapter 8 Answer Appendix.

17. Sample answer: For a horizontal line, as x increases, y does not change. So, the rate of change is 0. For a vertical line, x does not change. So, it cannot represent a rate of change.

18. Sample answer: As the absolute value of the rate of change increases, the graph becomes steeper. As the absolute value of the rate of change decreases, the graph becomes less steep. If the rate of change is positive, the graph goes up from left to right. If the rate of change is negative, the graph goes down from left to right.

8-5 Lesson Notes

1 FOCUS

Vertical Alignment

Before Lesson 8-5
Identify proportional and nonproportional relationships in tables and graphs.

Lesson 8-5
Identify proportional and nonproportional relationships by finding a constant rate of change. Solve problems involving direct variation.

After Lesson 8-5
Relate constant rate of change and direct variation to the slope of a line.

2 TEACH

Scaffolding Questions

Have students read the *Why?* section of the lesson and answer the questions.

Ask:

- In four seconds, how many times does a cat's heart beat? 8 In three seconds, how many times does it beat? 6
- Can you predict the number of times the cat's heart will beat in 60 seconds? Explain. Yes, the rate is constant.
- Do the data represent a function? Yes

8-5 Constant Rate of Change and Direct Variation

Then
You have already identified proportional and nonproportional relationships in tables and graphs. (Lesson 6-4)

Now
- Identify proportional and nonproportional relationships by finding a constant rate of change.
- Solve problems involving direct variation.

New Vocabulary
linear relationship
constant rate of change
direct variation
constant of variation

Math Online
glencoe.com
- Extra Examples
- Personal Tutor
- Self-Check Quiz
- Homework Help

Why?

A cat's heart beats about twice as fast as a human heart. The graph shows the average heartbeat of a cat.

a. Choose any two points on the graph and find the rate of change. $\frac{2}{1}$

b. Repeat part **a** with a different pair of points. What is the rate of change? $\frac{2}{1}$

c. **MAKE A CONJECTURE** What is the rate of change between any two points on the line? The rate of change is always $\frac{2}{1}$.

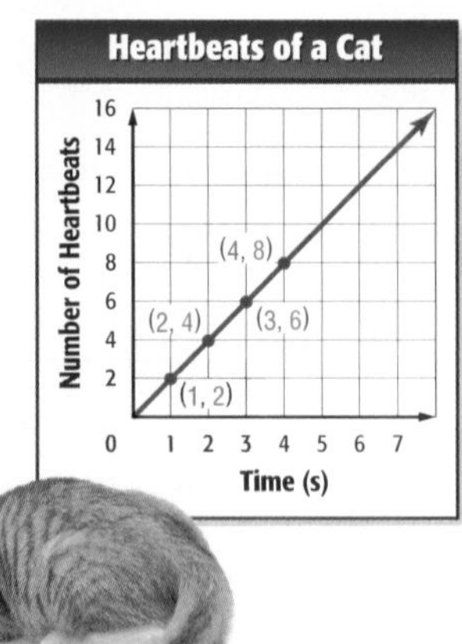

Constant Rates of Change The graph above is a straight line. A relationship that has a straight-line graph is called a **linear relationship**. Notice in the graph above that as time increases by 1, the number of heartbeats increases by 2.

Time (s)	0	1	2	3	4
Number of Heartbeats	0	2	4	6	8

(Time: +1, +1, +1, +1; Heartbeats: +2, +2, +2, +2)

$$\text{rate of change} = \frac{\text{change in heartbeats}}{\text{change in time}} = \frac{2}{1}$$

The rate of change is 2 heartbeats per second.

The rates of change between any two data points in a linear relationship are the same or constant. This is called a **constant rate of change**.

Constant Rate of Change

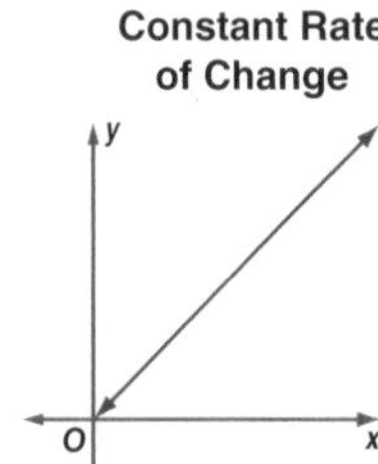

Constant Rate of Change

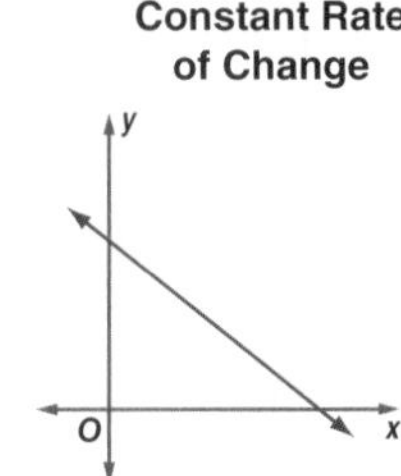

Not a Constant Rate of Change

Lesson 8-5 Resources

Resource	Approaching-Level	On-Level	Beyond-Level	English Learners
Teacher Edition	• Differentiated Instruction, p. 420	• Differentiated Instruction, p. 420	• Differentiated Instruction, pp. 420, 424	
Chapter Resource Masters	• Study Guide and Intervention, pp. 30–31 • Skills Practice, p. 32 • Practice, p. 33 • Word Problem Practice, p. 34	• Study Guide and Intervention, pp. 30–31 • Skills Practice, p. 32 • Practice, p. 33 • Word Problem Practice, p. 34 • Enrichment, p. 35	• Practice, p. 33 • Word Problem Practice, p. 34 • Enrichment, p. 35	• Study Guide and Intervention, pp. 30–31 • Skills Practice, p. 32 • Practice, p. 33
Transparencies	• 5-Minute Check Transparency 8-5	• 5-Minute Check Transparency 8-5	• 5-Minute Check Transparency 8-5	• 5-Minute Check Transparency 8-5
Other	• Study Notebook • Teaching Pre-Algebra with Manipulatives	• Study Notebook • Teaching Pre-Algebra with Manipulatives	• Study Notebook	• Study Notebook • Teaching Pre-Algebra with Manipulatives

Real-World EXAMPLE 1 Find a Constant Rate of Change

DESIGNS **A circular design on an Internet advertisement has two circles, one that is decreasing in size and one that is increasing in size. Find the constant rate of change for the radius of circle 1 in the graph shown. Then interpret its meaning.**

Circle Designs

Radius of Circle (cm) / Number of Seconds — Circle 1, Circle 2

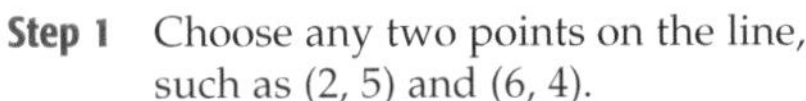

Step 1 Choose any two points on the line, such as (2, 5) and (6, 4).

(2, 5) → 2 seconds, radius 5 cm
(6, 4) → 6 seconds, radius 4 cm

Step 2 Find the rate of change between the points.

$$\text{rate of change} = \frac{\text{change in radius}}{\text{change in time}}$$

$$= \frac{4\text{ cm} - 5\text{ cm}}{6\text{ s} - 2\text{ s}}$$ The radius goes from 5 cm to 4 cm. The time goes from 2 s to 6 s.

$$= -\frac{1\text{ cm}}{4\text{ s}}$$ Simplify.

$$= -0.25\text{ cm/s}$$ Express this as a unit rate.

The rate of change –0.25 cm/s means that the radius of the circle is decreasing at a rate of 0.25 centimeter per second.

Watch Out!

It does not matter which point you use first to find the difference in a rate of change problem. But, it is important that you *always* begin with that point in both the numerator and the denominator.

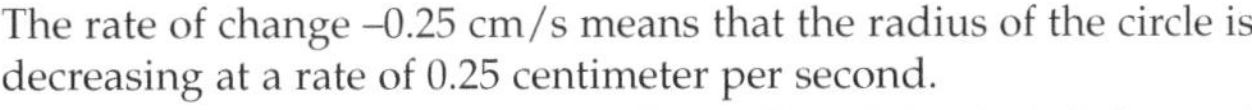

Check Your Progress 1.5 cm/s; The radius of the circle is increasing at a rate of 1.5 cm/s.

1. **DESIGNS** Use the graph above. Find the constant rate of change for circle 2. Then interpret its meaning.

Personal Tutor glencoe.com

Some linear relationships are also *proportional*. That is, the ratio of each non-zero y-value compared to the corresponding x-value is the same.

Time x	1	2	3
Distance y	4	8	12

$$\frac{\text{distance } y}{\text{time } x} \quad \frac{4}{1} = 4 \quad \frac{8}{2} = 4 \quad \frac{12}{3} = 4$$

The ratios are equal, so the linear relationship is proportional.

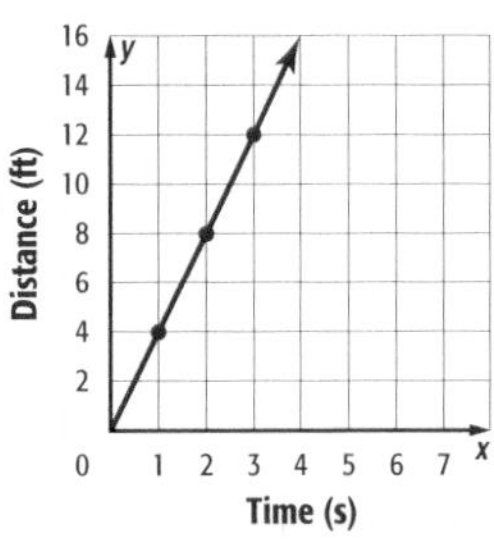

Time x	1	2	3
Distance y	4	6	8

$$\frac{\text{distance } y}{\text{time } x} \quad \frac{4}{1} = 4 \quad \frac{6}{2} = 3 \quad \frac{8}{3} = 2\frac{2}{3}$$

The ratios are *not* equal, so the linear relationship is nonproportional.

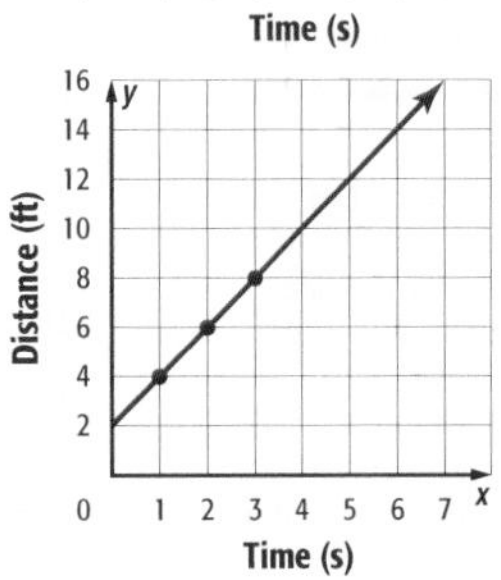

Review Vocabulary

proportional relationship a relationship in which the ratios of related terms are equal *Example:* $\frac{4}{1} = \frac{8}{2} = \frac{12}{3}$ are ratios that represent a proportional relationship. (Lesson 6-4)

Constant Rates of Change

Example 1 shows how to find a constant rate of change using a linear graph. **Example 2** shows how to identify a proportional linear relationship.

Formative Assessment

Use the Check Your Progress exercises after each example to determine students' understanding of concepts.

Additional Example

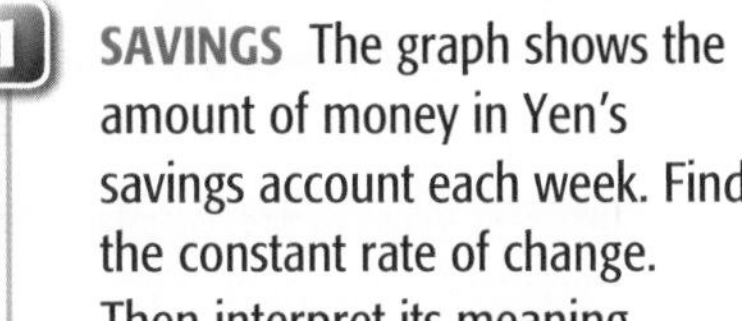

1 **SAVINGS** The graph shows the amount of money in Yen's savings account each week. Find the constant rate of change. Then interpret its meaning.

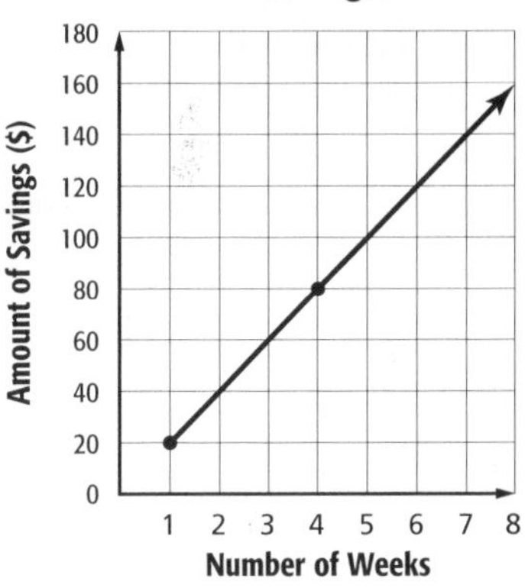

$20/wk; Yen's savings account is increasing at a rate of $20 per week.

Additional Examples also in Interactive Classroom PowerPoint® Presentations

TEACH with TECH

DOCUMENT CAMERA Choose a student to work through an example using the document camera. Give him or her an x-value and a y-value. Have the student find the constant of variation given that y varies directly with x. Take pictures of the work and distribute them to the class or post on the classroom Web site.

Focus on Mathematical Content

Rate of Change A rate of change can be constant, or not constant, and can be negative or positive. Only when the rate of change is constant can predictions be made. Ask students if they did push-ups for 5 minutes, will the number of push-ups per minute likely be constant. Most students should realize that after time, their rate of change (push-ups per minute) would likely decrease as they fatigue.

Additional Example

2 **CYCLING** The graph shows distances that a cyclist rides. Determine if there is a proportional linear relationship between the time and distance.

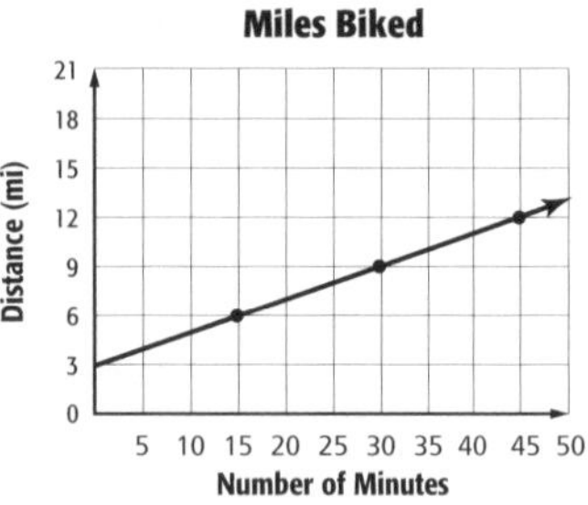

No; the ratio $\frac{\text{distance}}{\text{time}}$ is not the same for every pair of values.

EXAMPLE 2 Use Graphs to Identify Proportional Linear Relationships

TRAIL MIX The graph shows the cost of different amounts of trail mix. Determine if there is a proportional linear relationship between the cost and the weight of the trail mix.

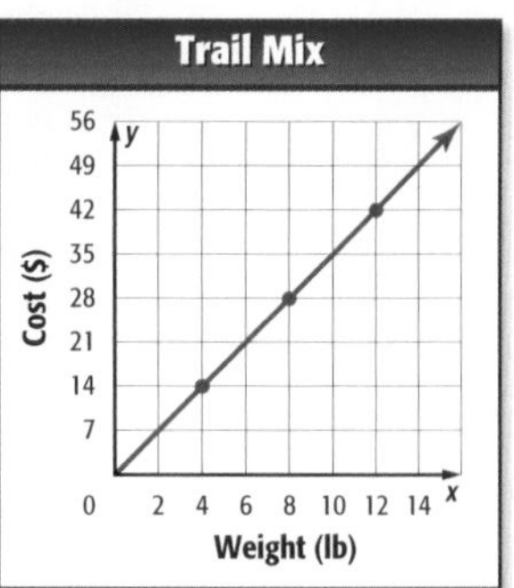

To determine if the quantities are proportional, find $\frac{\text{cost } y}{\text{weight } x}$ for points on the graph.

$\frac{\$14}{4 \text{ lb}} = \$3.50/\text{lb}$

$\frac{\$28}{8 \text{ lb}} = \$3.50/\text{lb}$

$\frac{\$42}{12 \text{ lb}} = \$3.50/\text{lb}$

Since the ratios are the same, the cost of the trail mix is proportional to the weight of the trail mix.

Real-World Link

Trail mix is a popular snack because it is delicious and energy rich. It is usually made from a combination of nuts and dried fruits.

Check Your Progress

2. **DOG WALKING** Tyler charges his customers \$10 per week plus \$5 every time he walks their dogs. Determine whether the relationship between total weekly cost and the number of times the dog is walked is proportional.

2. No; the ratio $\frac{\text{number of walks}}{\text{pay}}$ is different for every pair of values.

Personal Tutor glencoe.com

Direct Variation In the example above, the cost and the weight both vary, but the ratio of the cost to the weight remains constant at \$3.50 per pound.

When the ratio of two variable quantities is constant, their relationship is a **direct variation**. The graph of a direct variation always passes through the origin and represents a proportional linear relationship.

Key Concept Direct Variation

For Your FOLDABLE

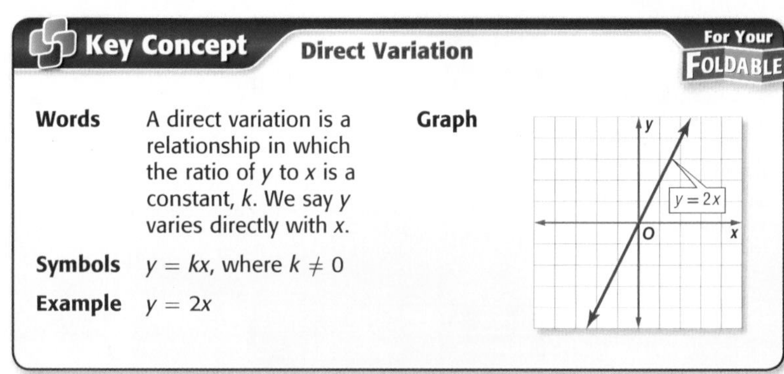

Words A direct variation is a relationship in which the ratio of y to x is a constant, k. We say y varies directly with x.

Symbols $y = kx$, where $k \neq 0$

Example $y = 2x$

Graph

In the equation $y = kx$, k is called the **constant of variation** or *constant of proportionality*. The direct variation $y = kx$ can be written as $k = \frac{y}{x}$. In this form, you can see that the ratio of y to x is the same for any corresponding values of y and x. In other words, x and y vary in such a way that they have a constant ratio, k.

ReadingMath

Directly Proportional Since k is a constant rate of change in a direct variation, we can say the following:

- *y varies directly with x.*
- *y is directly proportional to x.*

Differentiated Instruction

Kinesthetic Have students experience rate of change firsthand. Ask them to choose a physical activity to repeat several times and measure according to performance. For example, how many stomach crunches can they do per minute over 5 minutes? Have students record the number of crunches for each 1-minute period. What is the rate of change from the first minute to the fifth minute? See students' work.

Real-World EXAMPLE 3 Use Direct Variation to Solve Problems

TECHNOLOGY The time it takes to burn amounts of information on a CD varies directly with the amount of information.

Amount of Information (megabytes)	Time (s)
x	y
2.5	10
3.75	15
10	40
25	100

a. Write an equation that relates the amount of information and the time it takes.

Step 1 Find the value of k using the equation $y = kx$. Choose any point in the table. Then solve for k.

$y = kx$ Direct variation equation

$10 = k(2.5)$ Replace y with 10 and x with 2.5.

$4 = k$ Simplify.

Step 2 Use k to write an equation.

$y = kx$ Direct variation equation

$y = 4x$ Replace k with 4.

b. Predict how long it will take to fill a 700-megabyte CD.

$y = 4x$ Write the direct variation equation.

$y = 4(700)$ Replace x with 700.

$y = 2800$ Simplify.

It will take 2800 seconds to fill the CD.

Check Your Progress

3. UNIT COST The graph shows the cost y of x pounds of apples at the local grocery store.

a. Write an equation that relates cost and weight of the apples. $y = 0.8x$

b. Predict how much 5 pounds of apples would cost. $4

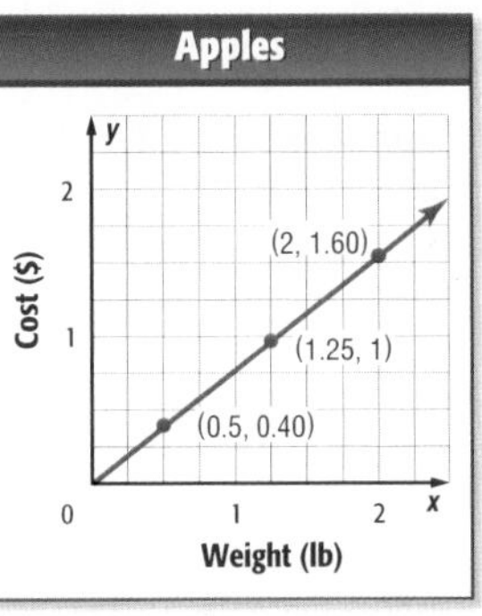

StudyTip

Graphs The graph of a direct variation is always a line that goes through the origin.

Personal Tutor glencoe.com

Concept Summary — Proportional Linear Relationships

For Your FOLDABLE

Words Two quantities a and b have a proportional linear relationship if they have a constant ratio and a constant rate of change.

Symbols $\frac{a}{b}$ and $\frac{\text{change in } b}{\text{change in } a}$ is constant.

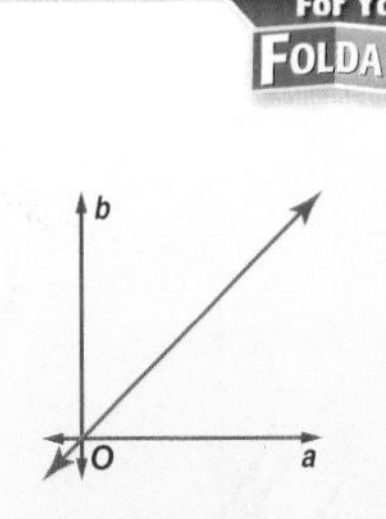

Direct Variation

Example 3 is a real-world example that shows how to use direct variation to solve a problem.

Additional Example

3 **LANDSCAPING** As it is being dug, the depth of a hole for a backyard pond is recorded in a table.

Time (min)	Hole Depth (in.)
x	y
10	8
20	16
30	24
40	32

a. Write an equation that relates time and hole depth. $y = 0.8x$

b. Predict how long it will take to dig a depth of 36 inches. 45 min

Focus on Mathematical Content

Direct Variation The graph of a direct variation goes through the origin and represents a proportional linear relationship. The rate of change is the slope of the line. A linear, or straight line, graph means the slope is constant as is the rate of change.

Watch Out!

Preventing Errors When solving direct variation problems, have students write down the general direct variation equation $y = kx$ for each problem. Then have them replace the x, y, or k with their known values to help them decide whether to multiply or divide.

3 PRACTICE

Formative Assessment

Use Exercises 1–3 to check for understanding.

Use the chart at the bottom of this page to customize assignments for your students.

Watch Out!

Find the Error For Exercise 15, students need to see that Keyshawn and Ramiro have done something different. Both should be finding the constant variation using the ratio of the *y*-value to its corresponding *x*-value.

Additional Answers

6. 5 lb/disk; The additional weight added is 5 pounds per disk. Yes; the ratio $= \frac{\text{total weight}}{\text{number of weights}}$ is the same for every pair of values.

7. -1 ticket available/ticket sold; For each ticket sold, there is one less ticket available to buy. No; the ratio $\frac{\text{tickets available}}{\text{tickets sold}}$ is not the same for every pair of values.

Check Your Understanding

Examples 1 and 2 pp. 419–420

Find the constant rate of change for each linear function and interpret its meaning. Then determine whether a proportional linear relationship exists between the two quantities. Explain your reasoning.

1. $\frac{1}{2}$ in./wk; The plant grows $\frac{1}{2}$ inch per week. No; the ratio $\frac{\text{height}}{\text{time}}$ is not the same for every pair of values.

1. Growth of Plant

Height of Plant (in.)

Number of Weeks

2.

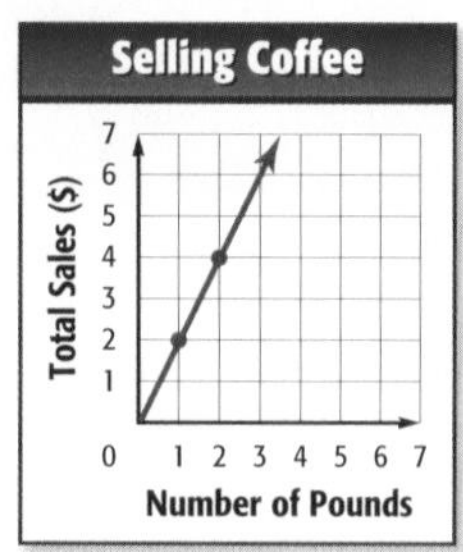

Example 3 pp. 421

2. $\frac{\$2}{\text{lb}}$; The unit cost is \$2 per pound. Yes; the ratio $\frac{\text{total sales}}{\text{number of pounds}}$ is the same for every pair of values.

3. PHYSICAL SCIENCE The length that a spring stretches varies directly with the amount of weight attached to it. When an 8-ounce weight is attached, a spring stretches 2 inches.

a. Write a direct variation equation relating the weight x and the amount of stretch y. $y = 0.25x$

b. Estimate the stretch of the spring when it has a 20-ounce weight attached. **5 in.**

Practice and Problem Solving

= **Step-by-Step Solutions** begin on page R11. **Extra Practice** begins on page 810.

Examples 1 and 2 pp. 419–420

Find the constant rate of change for each linear function and interpret its meaning. Then determine whether a proportional linear relationship exists between the two quantities. Explain your reasoning.

4. $\frac{\$1}{\$2}$ cost/sales; $c = \frac{1}{2}s + 10$. After \$10, every \$1 in cost produces \$2 in sales. No; the ratio $\frac{\text{cost}}{\text{sales}}$ is not the same for every pair of values.

5. $500\ \frac{\text{mi}}{\text{h}}$; The airplane travels 500 miles per hour. Yes; the ratio $\frac{\text{distance}}{\text{time}}$ is the same for every pair of values.

6–7. See margin.

4.

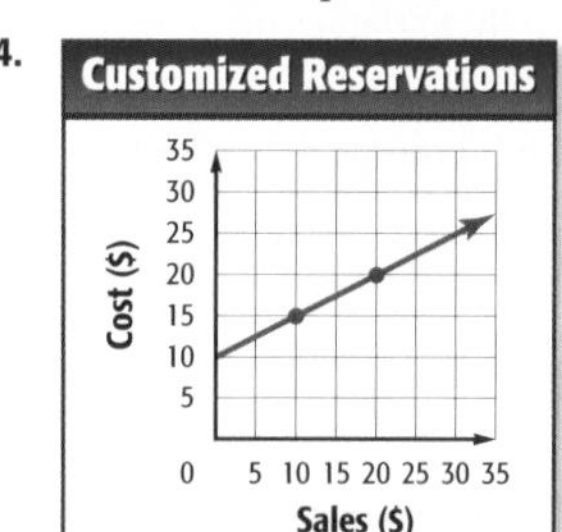

5.

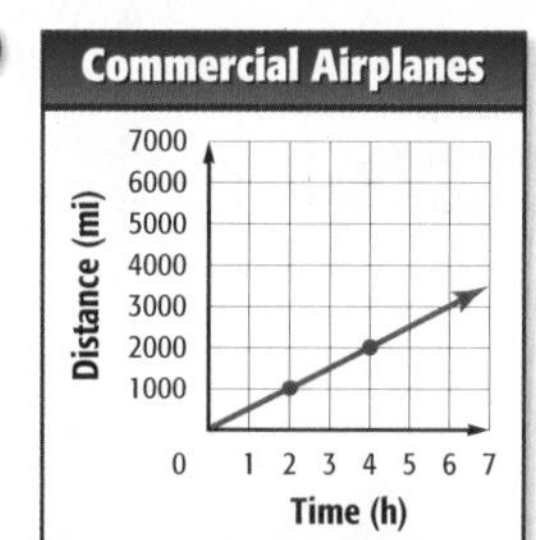

6.

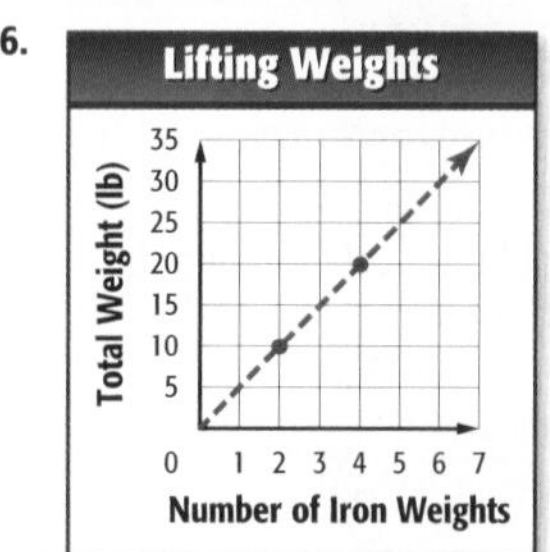

7.

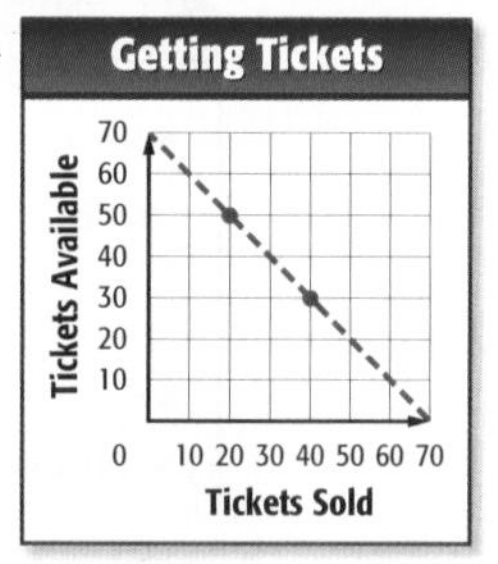

Differentiated Homework Options

Level	Assignment	Two-Day Option	
AL Basic	4–8, 14–16, 18–30	5–7 odd, 19–22	4–8 even, 14–16, 18, 23–30
OL Core	5–7 odd, 8–16, 18–30	4–8, 19–22	8–16, 18, 23–30
BL Advanced	9–26 (optional: 27–30)		

Example 3 p. 421

8. **FOOD COSTS** The cost of cheese varies directly with the number of pounds bought. Suppose 2 pounds cost \$8.40.
   a. Write an equation relating the weight and the cost of the cheese. **$y = 4.2x$**
   b. Find the cost of 3.5 pounds of cheese. **\$14.70**

Real-World Link

Orca whales typically dive to a depth of between 100 and 200 feet. However, the deepest dive ever recorded by an orca whale is 900 feet.

Source: Sea World

9. **PRESSURE** Water pressure is measured in pounds per square inch (psi), which varies directly with the depth of the water. B

Depth (ft)	Pressure (psi)
x	y
33	14.7
66	29.4
99	44.1
132	58.8

   a. Write an equation that relates the depth and the water pressure. Round to the nearest tenth. **$y = 0.4x$**
   b. Use the information at the left to find the water pressure at the depth of the deepest dive by an orca whale. **360 psi**

C

CLEANING Use the graph at the right to determine whether each statement is true or false. Explain your reasoning.

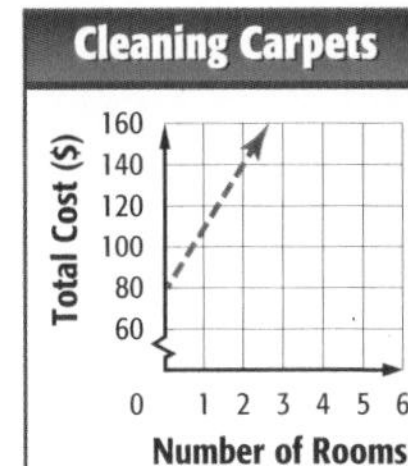

10. There is not a constant rate of change.
11. The two quantities are not proportional.
12. A proportional linear relationship exists.
13. The total cost varies directly with the number of rooms.

10. False; the rate of change $\frac{\text{change in total cost}}{\text{change in number of rooms}}$ is the same for every pair of points, so the rate of change is constant.

11. True; the ratio $\frac{\text{total cost}}{\text{number of rooms}}$ is not the same for every pair of values.

12. False; the ratio $\frac{\text{total cost}}{\text{number of rooms}}$ is not the same for every pair of values.

13. False; the graph of a direct variation always passes through the origin.

H.O.T. Problems

Use Higher-Order Thinking Skills

14–16. See Chapter 8 Answer Appendix.

14. **OPEN ENDED** Graph a line that shows a 3-unit increase in y for every 1-unit increase in x. State the rate of change.

15. **FIND THE ERROR** Keyshawn and Ramiro are determining whether the points with coordinates (2, 12) and (6, 18) represent a proportional linear relationship. Is either of them correct? Explain your reasoning.

Keyshawn

$\frac{y}{x} = \frac{12}{2} = 6 \quad \frac{18}{6} = 3$

Since the ratios are not the same, the relationship is not proportional.

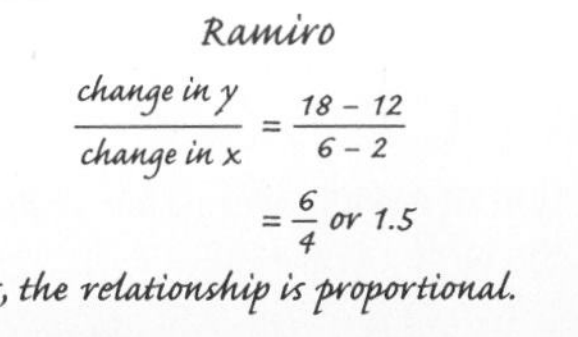

Ramiro

$\frac{\text{change in } y}{\text{change in } x} = \frac{18 - 12}{6 - 2}$

$= \frac{6}{4}$ or 1.5

Yes, the relationship is proportional.

16. **WRITING IN MATH** Determine whether the following statement is *always*, *sometimes*, or *never* true. Justify your reasoning. *A linear relationship that has a constant rate of change is a proportional relationship.*

17. **CHALLENGE** In the equation $d = rt$, d is the distance, r is the rate, and t is the time. Suppose the rate is constant. Explain how the distance changes if the time is increased. **It increases the distance.**

18. **WRITING IN MATH** Write about two real-world quantities that have a proportional linear relationship. Describe how you could change the situation to make the relationship between the quantities nonproportional. **See Chapter 8 Answer Appendix.**

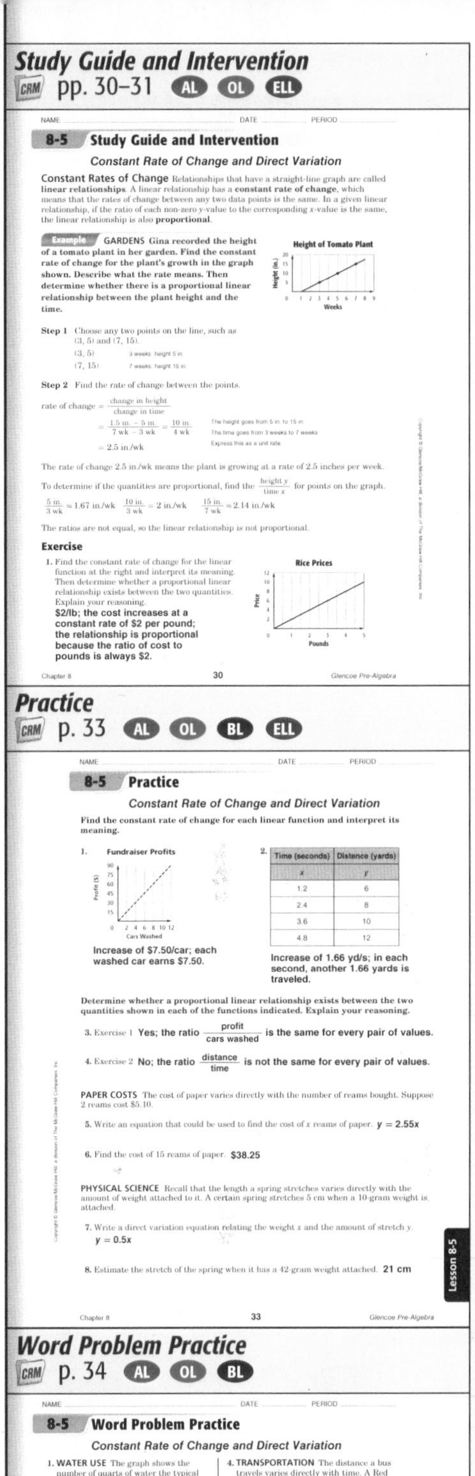

Study Guide and Intervention

CRM pp. 30–31 AL OL ELL

NAME ______ DATE ______ PERIOD ______

8-5 Study Guide and Intervention

Constant Rate of Change and Direct Variation

Constant Rates of Change Relationships that have a straight-line graph are called **linear relationships**. A linear relationship has a **constant rate of change**, which means that the rates of change between any two data points is the same. In a given linear relationship, if the ratio of each non-zero y-value to the corresponding x-value is the same, the linear relationship is also **proportional**.

Example **GARDENS Gina recorded the height of a tomato plant in her garden. Find the constant rate of change for the plant's growth in the graph shown. Describe what the rate means. Then determine whether there is a proportional linear relationship between the plant height and the time.**

Height of Tomato Plant

Step 1 Choose any two points on the line, such as (3, 5) and (7, 15).

(3, 5) 3 weeks, height 5 in.

(7, 15) 7 weeks, height 15 in.

Step 2 Find the rate of change between the points.

rate of change $= \frac{\text{change in height}}{\text{change in time}}$

$= \frac{15 \text{ in.} - 5 \text{ in.}}{7 \text{ wk} - 3 \text{ wk}} = \frac{10 \text{ in.}}{4 \text{ wk}}$ The height goes from 5 in. to 15 in. The time goes from 3 weeks to 7 weeks.

$= 2.5$ in./wk Express this as a unit rate.

The rate of change 2.5 in./wk means the plant is growing at a rate of 2.5 inches per week.

To determine if the quantities are proportional, find the $\frac{\text{height } y}{\text{time } x}$ for points on the graph.

$\frac{5 \text{ in.}}{3 \text{ wk}} \approx 1.67$ in./wk $\quad \frac{10 \text{ in.}}{3 \text{ wk}} = 2$ in./wk $\quad \frac{15 \text{ in.}}{7 \text{ wk}} \approx 2.14$ in./wk

The ratios are not equal, so the linear relationship is not proportional.

Exercise

1. Find the constant rate of change for the linear function at the right and interpret its meaning. Then determine whether a proportional linear relationship exists between the two quantities. Explain your reasoning. **\$2/lb; the cost increases at a constant rate of \$2 per pound; the relationship is proportional because the ratio of cost to pounds is always \$2.**

Rice Prices

Chapter 8 30 Glencoe Pre-Algebra

Practice

CRM p. 33 AL OL BL ELL

NAME ______ DATE ______ PERIOD ______

8-5 Practice

Constant Rate of Change and Direct Variation

Find the constant rate of change for each linear function and interpret its meaning.

1. Fundraiser Profits

Increase of \$7.50/car; each washed car earns \$7.50.

2.

Time (seconds)	Distance (yards)
x	y
1.2	6
2.4	8
3.6	10
4.8	12

Increase of 1.66 yd/s; in each second, another 1.66 yards is traveled.

Determine whether a proportional linear relationship exists between the two quantities shown in each of the functions indicated. Explain your reasoning.

3. Exercise 1 **Yes; the ratio $\frac{\text{profit}}{\text{cars washed}}$ is the same for every pair of values.**

4. Exercise 2 **No; the ratio $\frac{\text{distance}}{\text{time}}$ is not the same for every pair of values.**

PAPER COSTS The cost of paper varies directly with the number of reams bought. Suppose 2 reams cost \$5.10.

5. Write an equation that could be used to find the cost of x reams of paper. **$y = 2.55x$**

6. Find the cost of 15 reams of paper. **\$38.25**

PHYSICAL SCIENCE Recall that the length a spring stretches varies directly with the amount of weight attached to it. A certain spring stretches 5 cm when a 10-gram weight is attached.

7. Write a direct variation equation relating the weight x and the amount of stretch y. **$y = 0.5x$**

8. Estimate the stretch of the spring when it has a 42-gram weight attached. **21 cm**

Chapter 8 33 Glencoe Pre-Algebra

Lesson 8-5

Word Problem Practice

CRM p. 34 AL OL BL

NAME ______ DATE ______ PERIOD ______

8-5 Word Problem Practice

Constant Rate of Change and Direct Variation

1. **WATER USE** The graph shows the number of quarts of water the typical person needs in a certain number of days. Find the constant rate of change for the relationship and interpret its meaning. **2; the typical person needs 2 quarts of water per day.**

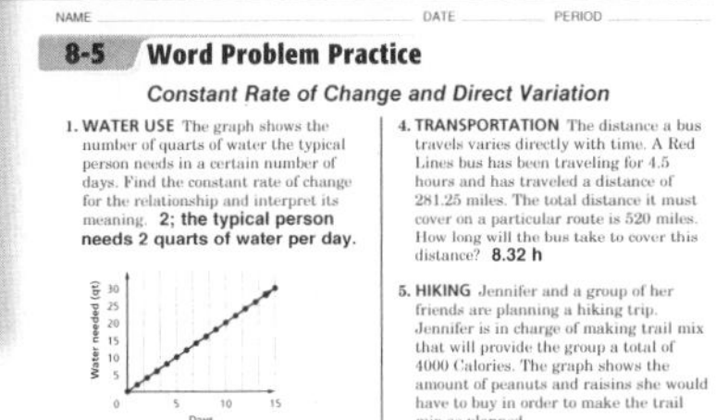

Source: National Park Service

2. **BAKING** The amount of flour needed for a recipe varies directly with the number of servings planned. Three servings require $4\frac{1}{2}$ cups of flour. Write a direct variation equation relating the number of servings s and the required number of cups of flour f. **$f = 1\frac{1}{2}s$**

3. **SCUBA DIVING** Fresh Air Scuba Company leases scuba diving equipment. The following table shows the cost of renting equipment for different lengths of time. Determine if there is a proportional relationship between the cost of the rental and the number of days the equipment is rented. Explain. **No; the ratio $\frac{\text{cost}}{\text{days}}$ is not the same for every pair of values.**

Days	Cost (\$)
3	30
6	50
9	70
12	90

4. **TRANSPORTATION** The distance a bus travels varies directly with time. A Red Lines bus has been traveling for 4.5 hours and has traveled a distance of 281.25 miles. The total distance it must cover on a particular route is 520 miles. How long will the bus take to cover this distance? **8.32 h**

5. **HIKING** Jennifer and a group of her friends are planning a hiking trip. Jennifer is in charge of making trail mix that will provide the group a total of 4000 Calories. The graph shows the amount of peanuts and raisins she would have to buy in order to make the trail mix as planned.

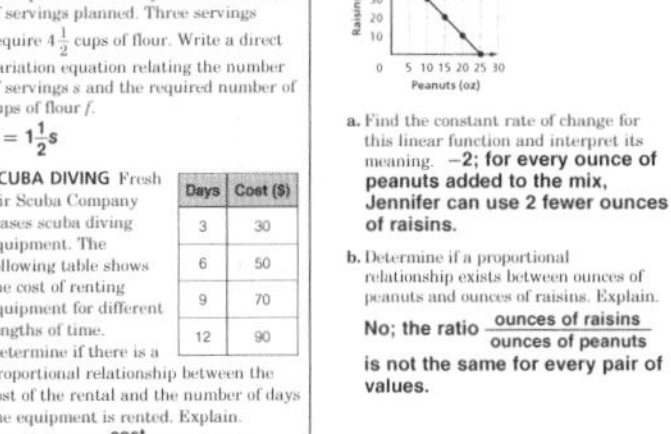

   a. Find the constant rate of change for this linear function and interpret its meaning. **−2; for every ounce of peanuts added to the mix, Jennifer can use 2 fewer ounces of raisins.**
   b. Determine if a proportional relationship exists between ounces of peanuts and ounces of raisins. Explain. **No; the ratio $\frac{\text{ounces of raisins}}{\text{ounces of peanuts}}$ is not the same for every pair of values.**

Chapter 8 34 Glencoe Pre-Algebra

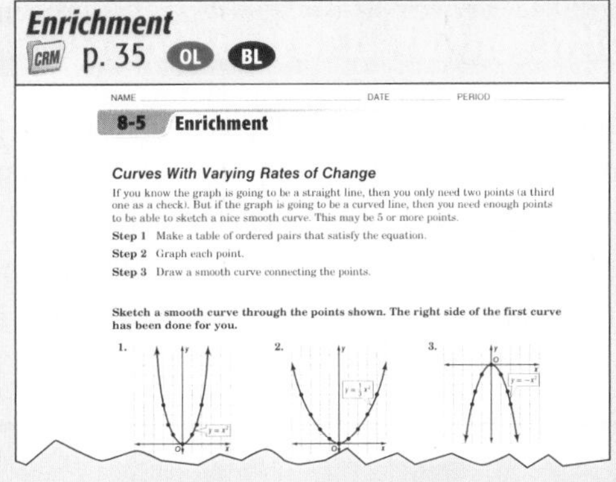

Enrichment

CRM p. 35 OL BL

NAME ______ DATE ______ PERIOD ______

8-5 Enrichment

Curves With Varying Rates of Change

If you know the graph is going to be a straight line, then you only need two points (a third one as a check). But if the graph is going to be a curved line, then you need enough points to be able to sketch a nice smooth curve. This may be 5 or more points.

Step 1 Make a table of ordered pairs that satisfy the equation.

Step 2 Graph each point.

Step 3 Draw a smooth curve connecting the points.

Sketch a smooth curve through the points shown. The right side of the first curve has been done for you.

1. $y = x^2$ 2. $y = \frac{1}{3}x^2$ 3. $y = -x^2$

4 ASSESS

Ticket Out the Door Have students answer this problem: Suppose y varies directly with x and $y = 6$ when $x = 54$. Write an equation that relates x and y, make a graph, and predict y when $x = 135$. Have students hand in their papers as they exit. $y = \frac{1}{9}x$; 15

Formative Assessment

Check for student understanding of concepts in Lessons 8-4 and 8-5.

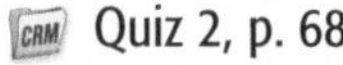 Quiz 2, p. 68

Additional Answers

24. Sample answer: $(-1, -12)$, $(0, 0)$, $(1, 12)$, $(2, 24)$

25. Sample answer: $(-1, -\frac{1}{2})$, $(0, 0)$, $(1, \frac{1}{2})$, $(2, 1)$

26. Sample answer: $(-1, 8)$, $(0, 5)$, $(1, 2)$, $(2, -1)$

Standardized Test Practice

19. Find the constant rate of change for the linear function shown in the graph. **C**

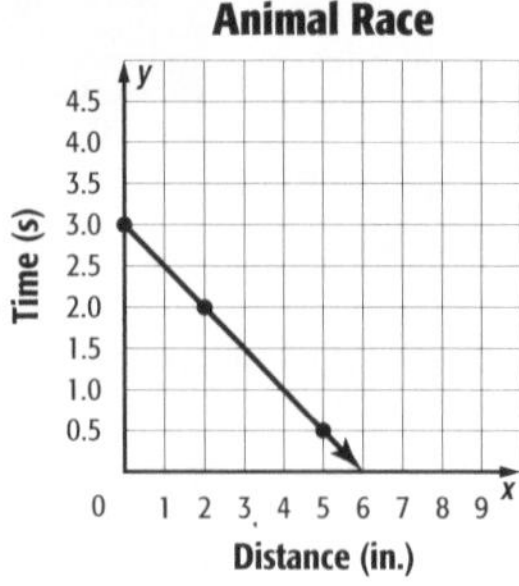

A 2 C $-\frac{1}{2}$

B $\frac{1}{2}$ D -2

20. Which of the following is *not* true about the graph of a function with a constant rate of change? **J**

F The graph can show a positive relationship.

G The graph can show a negative relationship.

H The relationship between x and y values can be proportional.

J The graph will look like a curve.

21. The cost of cookies at a bake sale is shown. **B**

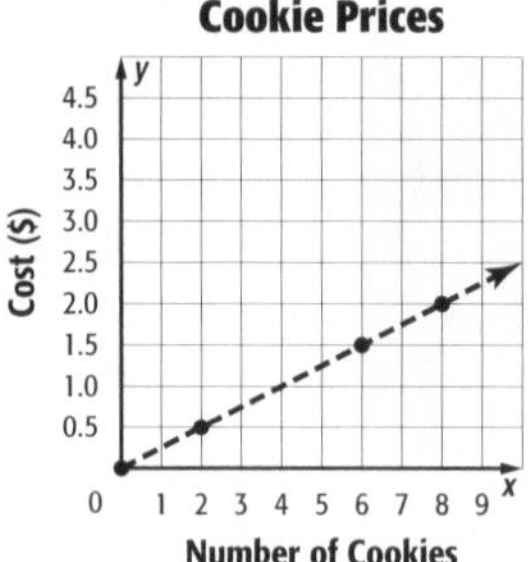

Which of the following is the *best* prediction for the cost of 21 cookies?

A $5.00 C $5.50

B $5.25 D $5.75

22. EXTENDED RESPONSE At an amusement park, the cost of admission varies directly with the number of tickets purchased. Suppose one ticket costs $12.75.

a. Write an equation that could be used to find the cost of any number of admission tickets. $y = 12.75x$

b. Find the cost of 15 tickets. **$191.25**

Spiral Review

23. WATER PARKS Admission costs to a water park are shown in the table. (Lesson 8-4)

a. What is the rate of change? **$12/person**

b. What does the rate mean in this situation? **The cost of admission is $12 per person.**

Water Park Costs	
Number of People	Total Cost ($)
x	y
3	36
4	48
5	60

Find four solutions of each equation. Write the solutions as ordered pairs. (Lesson 8-3) **24–26. See margin.**

24. $y = 12x$ **25.** $y = \frac{1}{2}x$ **26.** $y = -3x + 5$

Skills Review

Subtract. (Lesson 2-3)

27. $-11 - 13$ **−24** **28.** $15 - 31$ **−16** **29.** $-26 - (-26)$ **0** **30.** $9 - (-16)$ **25**

Differentiated Instruction

Extension Have students complete the following problem: Tamika and Rashan are climbing the same 150-foot mountain. They begin on the ground, at $t = 0$, and climb at a constant rate of 43 feet per hour. Write an equation that can be used to determine how long it takes for them to reach the top. $y = 43t$ Another group is climbing the same mountain, although traveling at a different constant rate. They arrive at the top of the cliff in 2.75 hours. How fast are they climbing? about $54\frac{1}{2}$ feet per hour

CHAPTER 8 Mid-Chapter Quiz
Lessons 8-1 through 8-5

Determine whether each relation is a function. Explain. (Lesson 8-1) 1–2. See margin.

1. {(0, 5), (1, 2), (1, −3), (2, 4)}
2. {(−6, 3.5), (−3, 4.0), (0, 4.5), (3, 5.0)}
3. {(3, 2), (−3, 2), (4, 4), (−4, 4)}
Yes, each x-value is paired with only one y-value.

4. **MULTIPLE CHOICE** The relation {(2, 11), (−9, 8), (14, 1), (5, 5)} is *not* a function when which ordered pair is added to the set? (Lesson 8-1) D

A (8, -9) C (0, 0)

B (6, 11) D (2, 18)

Describe each sequence using words and symbols. (Lesson 8-2) 5–8. See Chapter 8 Answer Appendix.

5. 4, 5, 6, 7, … 6. 9, 18, 27, 36, …
7. 3, 5, 7, 9, … 8. 2.5, 5, 7.5, 10, 12.5, …

Write an equation that describes each sequence. Then find the indicated term. (Lesson 8-2)

9. 12, 13, 14, 15, …; 15th term $t = 11 + n$; 26
10. 6, 11, 16, 21, …; 30th term $t = 5n + 1$; 151
11. 7, 12, 17, 22, …; 20th term $t = 5n + 2$; 102

12. **SHORT RESPONSE** Write an expression that could be used to find the value of the term in the nth position in the table below. (Lesson 8-2)

Position	1	2	3	4	n
Value	5	14	23	32	■

$9n - 4$

13–16. See Chapter 8 Answer Appendix.
Find four solutions of each equation. Write the solutions as ordered pairs. (Lesson 8-3)

13. $y = x + 8$ 14. $y = -5x$
15. $y = 2x + 3$ 16. $y = -4x - 7$

17. **CURRENCY** The equation $y = 1.35x$ describes the approximate number of U.S. dollars y that are equal to x euros. (Lesson 8-3)

a. What does the solution (3, 4.05) mean? 3 euros are equal to about \$4.05.

b. About how many U.S. dollars is 15 euros? \$20.25

Graph each equation. (Lesson 8-3) 18–19. See Chapter 8 Answer Appendix.

18. $y = x + 2$ 19. $y = 3x - 4$

Find the rate of change for each linear function. (Lesson 8-4)

20. increase of \$15/wk

Saving Money	
Number of Weeks	Amount Saved (\$)
x	y
3	25
4	40
5	55
6	70

21. −16 oz/s or decrease of 16 oz/s

Water in Bucket	
Time (s)	Amount of Water (oz)
x	y
2	80
4	48
6	16

22. **MONEY** Find the constant rate of change for the linear function shown below and interpret its meaning. (Lesson 8-5)

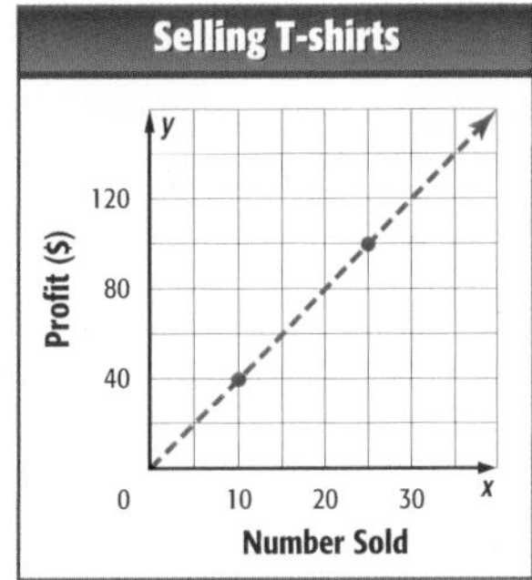

\$4/T-shirt; the profit is \$4 per T-shirt.

Determine whether a proportional linear relationship exists between the two quantities shown in each of the functions indicated. Explain your reasoning. (Lesson 8-5) 23–24. See Chapter 8 Answer Appendix.

23. Exercise 20 24. Exercise 22

25. **CRAFTS** The cost of craft beads varies directly with the number purchased. The cost of 25 beads is \$10. How much do 8 beads cost? (Lesson 8-5) \$3.20

CHAPTER 8 Mid-Chapter Quiz

Formative Assessment

Use the Mid-Chapter Quiz to assess students' progress in the first half of the chapter.

For problems answered incorrectly, have students review the lessons indicated in parentheses.

Customize and create multiple versions of your Mid-Chapter Quiz and their answer keys.

FOLDABLES Follow-Up

Before students complete the Mid-Chapter Quiz, encourage them to review the information for Lessons 8-1 through 8-5 in their Foldables.

Additional Answers

1. No, 1 is paired with 2 and −3.
2. Yes, each x-value is paired with only one y-value.

Intervention Planner

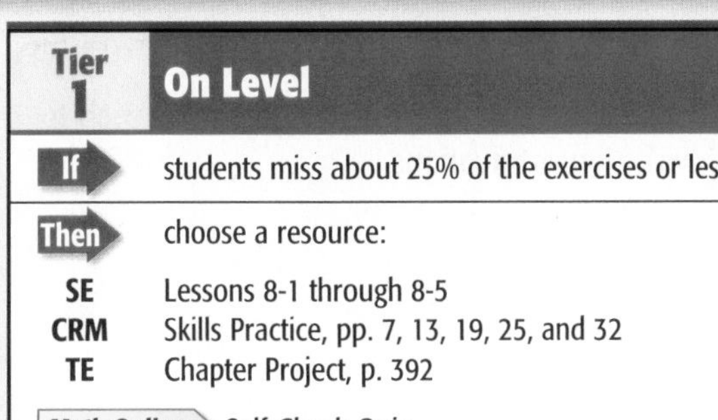

Tier 1 On Level

If students miss about 25% of the exercises or less,

Then choose a resource:

- **SE** Lessons 8-1 through 8-5
- **CRM** Skills Practice, pp. 7, 13, 19, 25, and 32
- **TE** Chapter Project, p. 392

Math Online Self-Check Quiz

Tier 2 Strategic Intervention approaching grade level

If students miss about 50% of the exercises,

Then choose a resource:

- **CRM** Study Guide and Intervention, Chapter 8, pp. 5, 11, 17, 23, and 30

Quick Review Math Handbook

Math Online Extra Examples, Personal Tutor, Homework Help

Tier 3 Intensive Intervention 2 or more grades below level

If students miss about 75% of the exercises,

Then use *Math Triumphs, Grade 8*, Ch. 2, 6

Math Online Extra Examples, Personal Tutor, Homework Help, Review Vocabulary

EXPLORE 8-6 Lesson Notes

1 FOCUS

Objective Use technology to describe the slope of a line.

Materials for Each Group

- Calculator-Based Lab
- grid paper
- water
- beaker
- metric ruler
- tablespoon
- $\frac{1}{8}$-cup measuring cup
- paper cups (2)
- paper clip

Teaching Tip

Run through the Activity ahead of time to become familiar with it. Make sure the calculator and all devices connected to it are working properly ahead of time.

2 TEACH

Working in Cooperative Groups

Arrange students in groups of two or three, mixing abilities. Then have the groups complete Steps 1–3 of the Activity.

Ask:

- Which graph has a steeper slope? graph 2
- Why? The cup with the larger hole empties at a faster rate, so the slope is steeper.
- Suppose your graph exhibited a very gradual slope. What might you conclude? The rate of change was slower; therefore, the amount removed each time was very small.

Practice Have students complete Exercises 1–6.

EXPLORE 8-6 Graphing Technology Lab: Slope and Rate of Change

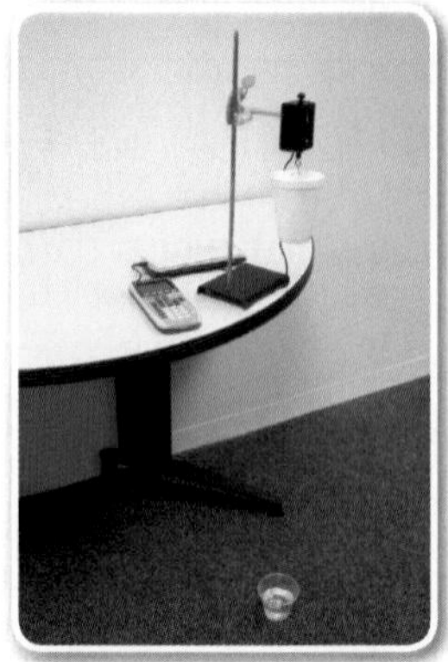

In this activity, you will investigate the relationship between slope and rate of change.

Set Up the Lab

- Connect the force sensor to the Calculator Based Lab (CBL). Then use the unit-to-unit link cable to connect the CBL to the calculator. Place the sensor in a ring stand as shown.
- Make a small hole in the bottom of a paper cup. Straighten a paper clip and use it to create a handle to hang the cup on the force sensor. Place another cup on the floor below.
- Set the device to collect data 100 times at intervals of 0.1 second.

ACTIVITY

Step 1 Hold your finger over the hole in the cup. Fill the cup with water.

Step 2 Begin collecting data as you begin to allow the water to drain.

Step 3 Make the hole in the cup larger. Then repeat Steps 1 and 2 for a second trial.

Analyze the Results 1–7. See Chapter 8 Answer Appendix.

1. Use the calculator to create a graph of the data for Trial 1. The graph will show the weight of the cup y as a function of time x. Describe the graph.
2. Create the graph for Trial 2. Compare the steepness of the two graphs.
3. What happens to the weight of the cup as the time increases?
4. Did the cup empty at a faster rate in Trial 1 or Trial 2? Explain.
5. Describe the relationship between the steepness of the line and the rate at which the cup was emptied.
6. **MAKE A CONJECTURE** Suppose you emptied a cup using a hole half the size of the original hole. Then you emptied a cup using a hole twice the size of the original hole. What would graphs of the data for these trials look like? Explain.
7. Water is emptied at a constant rate from containers that have different shapes. A graph of the water level in each of the containers as a function of time is shown below. Make a sketch of each container.

a. 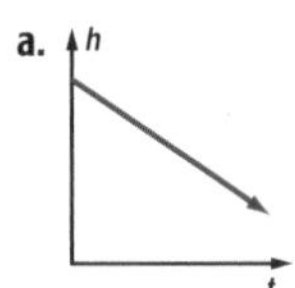

b. 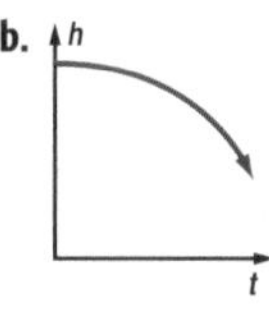

c. 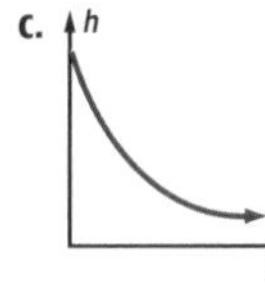

3 ASSESS

Formative Assessment

Allow students to work alone answering Exercise 7. Use this and Exercises 1–6 to assess whether students understand the connection between slope and rate of change.

From Concrete to Abstract

Have students use graphs 1–2 from the trials to write linear equations.

8-6 Slope

Why?

The inflatable water slide shown at the right is 15 feet high and 18 feet long.

a. Write the rate of change comparing the height of the slide to the length as a fraction in simplest form. $\frac{5}{6}$

b. Find the rate of change of a slide that has the same length but is 5 feet higher than the slide at the right. Is this slide steeper or less steep than the original? $\frac{10}{9}$; steeper

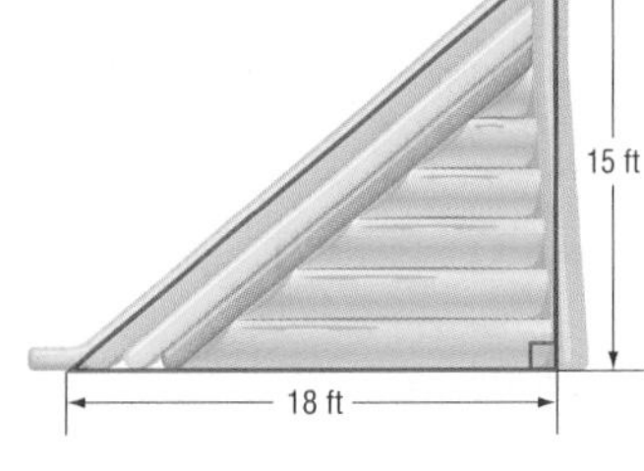

Then

You have already used graphs to find a constant rate of change and interpret its meaning. (Lesson 8-5)

Now

- Find the slope of a line.
- Use slope to describe a constant rate of change.

New Vocabulary

slope

Math Online

glencoe.com

- Extra Examples
- Personal Tutor
- Self-Check Quiz
- Homework Help

Slope **Slope** is the ratio of the *rise*, or the vertical change, to the *run*, or the horizontal change of a line. It describes the steepness of the line. In linear functions, no matter which two points you choose, the slope, or rate of change, of the line is always constant

$$\text{slope} = \frac{\text{rise}}{\text{run}} \quad \begin{matrix} \leftarrow \text{vertical change} \\ \leftarrow \text{horizontal change} \end{matrix}$$

Real-World EXAMPLE 1 Use Rise and Run to Find Slope

SKATEBOARDING Find the slope of a portable skateboard ramp that rises 15 inches for every horizontal change of 54 inches.

$\text{slope} = \frac{\text{rise}}{\text{run}}$ **Write the formula for slope.**

$= \frac{15 \text{ in.}}{54 \text{ in.}}$ **rise = 15 in., run = 54 in.**

$= \frac{5}{18}$ **Simplify.**

The slope of the ramp is $\frac{5}{18}$ or about 0.28.

Check Your Progress

1A. RAMPS What is the slope of a wheelchair ramp that rises 2 inches for every horizontal change of 24 inches? Write as a fraction in simplest form. $\frac{1}{12}$

1B. KITES Arthur is flying a kite in the park. The kite is a horizonal distance of 20 feet from Arthur's position and a vertical distance of 70 feet. Find the slope of the kite string. $\frac{7}{2}$

Personal Tutor glencoe.com

Since slope is a rate of change, it can be positive (slanting upward), negative (slanting downward), or zero.

8-6 Lesson Notes

1 FOCUS

Vertical Alignment

Before Lesson 8-6
Use graphs to find a constant rate of change and interpret its meaning.

Lesson 8-6
Find the slope of a line. Use slope to describe a constant rate of change.

After Lesson 8-6
Determine slopes from graphs, tables, and algebraic representations.

2 TEACH

Scaffolding Questions

Have students read the *Why?* section of the lesson and answer the questions.

Ask:

- How do you know whether the slide is steeper than the original? Sample answer: If the rate of change is greater, the slide is steeper.
- Look at the triangle superimposed on the water slide. Suppose the point where the two legs meet is (18, 0); what is the point at the top of the triangle? (18, 15) the bottom left vertex? (0, 0)

(*continued on next page*)

Lesson 8-6 Resources

Resource	Approaching-Level	On-Level	Beyond-Level	English Learners
Teacher Edition		• Differentiated Instruction, p. 428	• Differentiated Instruction, pp. 428, 431	
Chapter Resource Masters	• Study Guide and Intervention, pp. 36–37 • Skills Practice, p. 38 • Practice, p. 39 • Word Problem Practice, p. 40	• Study Guide and Intervention, pp. 36–37 • Skills Practice, p. 38 • Practice, p. 39 • Word Problem Practice, p. 40 • Enrichment, p. 41	• Practice, p. 39 • Word Problem Practice, p. 40 • Enrichment, p. 41	• Study Guide and Intervention, pp. 36–37 • Skills Practice, p. 38 • Practice, p. 39
Transparencies	• 5-Minute Check Transparency 8-6	• 5-Minute Check Transparency 8-6	• 5-Minute Check Transparency 8-6	• 5-Minute Check Transparency 8-6
Other	• Study Notebook • Teaching Pre-Algebra with Manipulatives	• Study Notebook • Teaching Pre-Algebra with Manipulatives	• Study Notebook	• Study Notebook • Teaching Pre-Algebra with Manipulatives

- If the length of the water slide increases by 7 ft but the height remains the same, would the water slide be steeper or less steep than the original? less steep

Slope

Example 1 shows how to find slope using rise and run. **Example 2** shows how to find a slope from a graph.

Formative Assessment

Use the Check Your Progress exercises after each example to determine students' understanding of concepts.

Additional Examples

1 **HILLS** Find the slope of a hill that rises 30 feet for every horizontal change of 1500 feet. $\frac{1}{50}$

2 Find the slope of each line.

a.

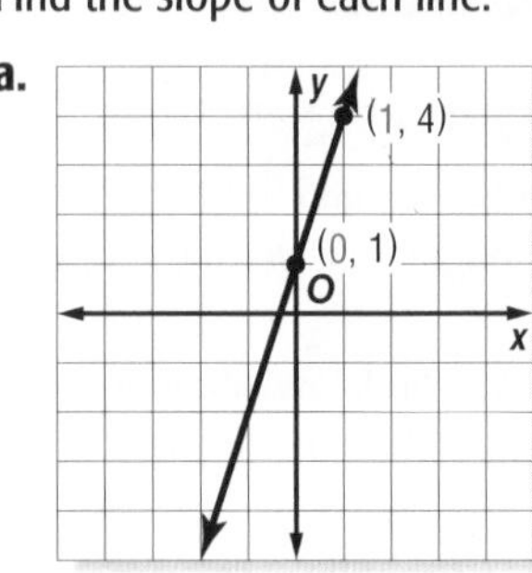

3

b.

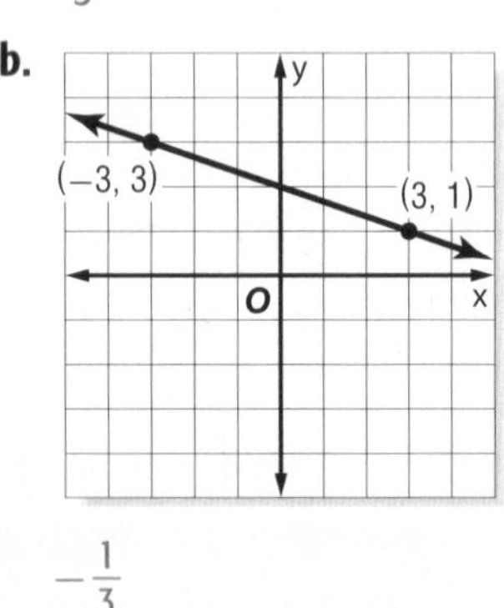

$-\frac{1}{3}$

Additional Examples also in Interactive Classroom PowerPoint® Presentations

IWB INTERACTIVE WHITEBOARD READY

StudyTip

Slopes
- Positive slopes represent a rate of increase.
- Negative slopes represent a rate of decrease.
- Steeper slopes represent greater rates of change.
- Less steep slopes represent lesser rates of change.

EXAMPLE 2 Use a Graph to Find Slope

Find the slope of each line.

a.

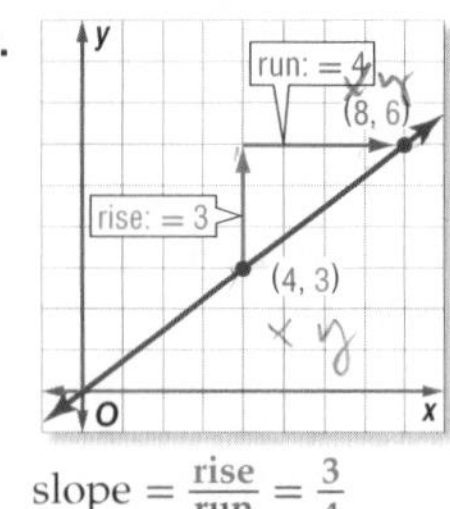

$\text{slope} = \frac{\text{rise}}{\text{run}} = \frac{3}{4}$

b.

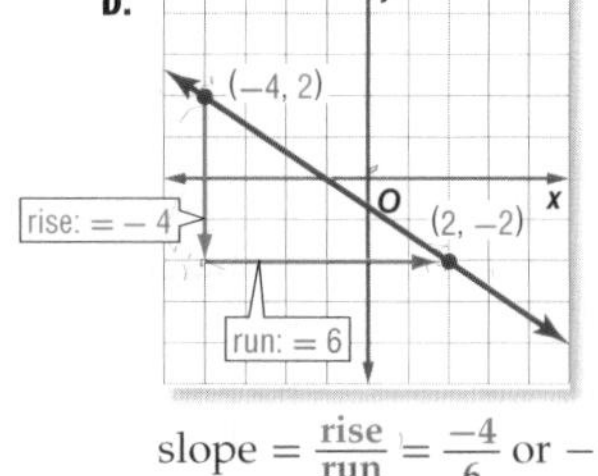

$\text{slope} = \frac{\text{rise}}{\text{run}} = \frac{-4}{6} \text{ or } -\frac{2}{3}$

Check Your Progress

2A.

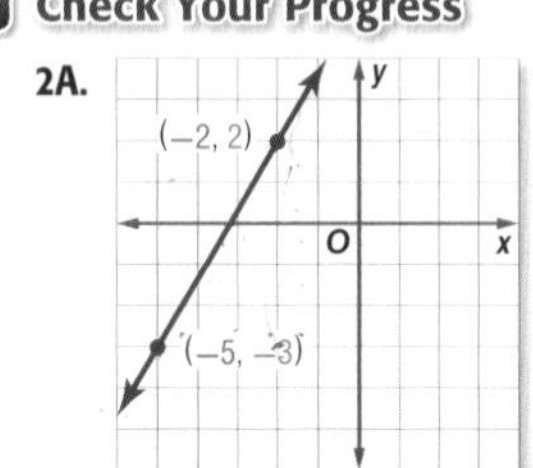

$\frac{5}{3}$

2B.

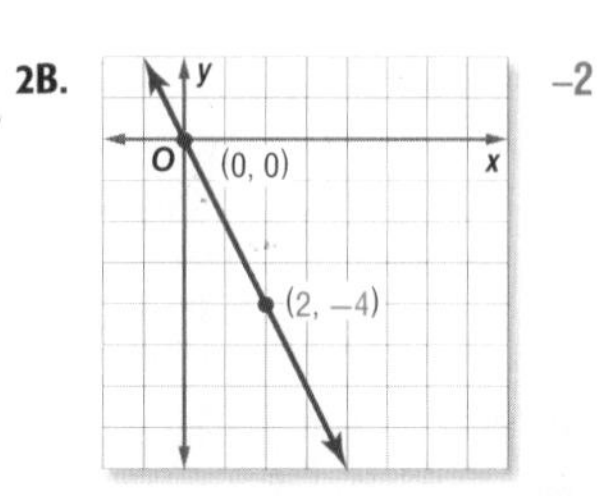

−2

Personal Tutor glencoe.com

Slope and Constant Rate of Change The slope is the same for any two points on a straight line. It represents a constant rate of change.

Key Concept Slope

For Your FOLDABLE

Words The slope m of a line passing through points at (x_1, y_1) and (x_2, y_2) is the ratio of the difference in y-coordinates to the corresponding difference in x-coordinates.

Symbols $m = \frac{y_2 - y_1}{x_2 - x_1}$, where $x_2 \neq x_1$

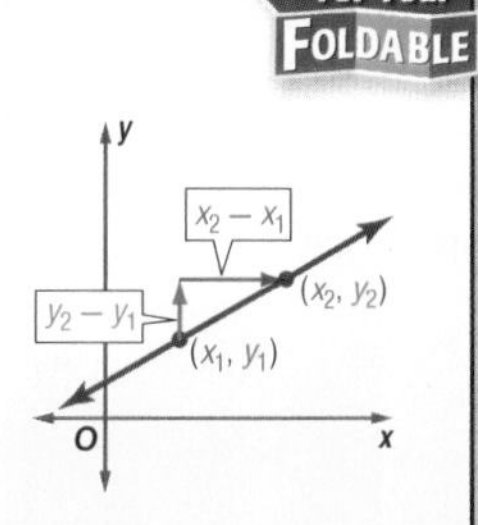

ReadingMath

Multiple Representations There are different methods for finding the slope of a line.

$m = \frac{\text{rise}}{\text{run}}$

$m = \frac{\text{change in } y}{\text{change in } x}$

$m = \frac{y_2 - y_1}{x_2 - x_1}$

EXAMPLE 3 Use Coordinates of Points to Find Slope

Find the slope of the line that passes through $R(-2, 3)$ and $S(4, -1)$.

$m = \frac{y_2 - y_1}{x_2 - x_1}$	**Definition of slope**
$m = \frac{-1 - 3}{4 - (-2)}$	**$(x_1, y_1) = (-2, 3)$, $(x_2, y_2) = (4, -1)$**
$m = \frac{-4}{6}$ or $-\frac{2}{3}$	**Simplify.**

Check Your Progress

3A. $A(-4, 3), B(1, 2)$ $-\frac{1}{5}$

3B. $C(1, -5), D(8, 3)$ $\frac{8}{7}$

Personal Tutor glencoe.com

Differentiated Instruction

OL BL

If students enjoy nature,

Then have them collect data on the slant of several tree branches. They should consider the point where the branch connects to the tree trunk to be the origin. Then they should measure the rise and run. They can number the branches and organize the data in a chart. Then, back in the classroom, they can draw the branches on a graph and label the graph.

StudyTip

Choosing Points
- Any two points on a line can be chosen as (x_1, y_1) and (x_2, y_2).
- The coordinates of both points must be used in the same order.

EXAMPLE 4 Zero and Undefined Slopes

Find the slope of the line that passes through each pair of points.

a. $A(-3, 4), B(2, 4)$

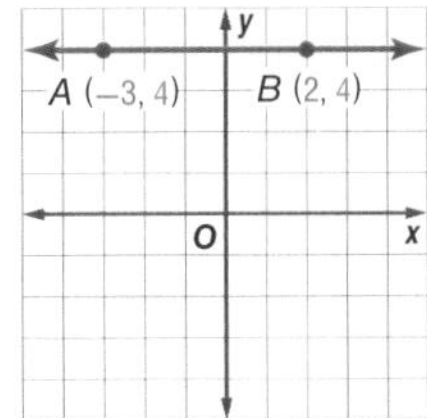

$m = \frac{y_2 - y_1}{x_2 - x_1}$ Definition of slope

$m = \frac{4 - 4}{2 - (-3)}$ $(x_1, y_1) = (-3, 4)$, $(x_2, y_2) = (2, 4)$

$m = \frac{0}{5}$ or 0 Simplify.

b. $T(1, 3), U(1, 0)$

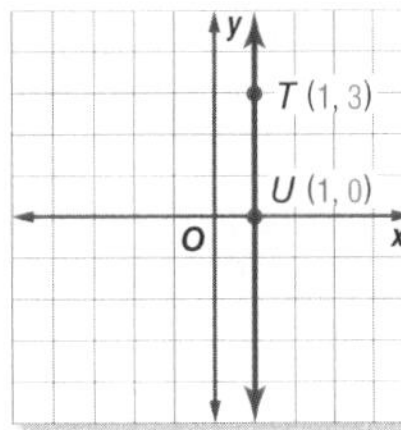

$m = \frac{y_2 - y_1}{x_2 - x_1}$ Definition of slope

$m = \frac{0 - 3}{1 - 1}$ $(x_1, y_1) = (1, 3)$, $(x_2, y_2) = (1, 0)$

$m = \frac{-3}{0}$ Division by 0 is undefined.

The slope is undefined.

Check Your Progress

4A. $E(-1, 7), F(5, 7)$ 0

4B. $G(2, 4), H(2, -1)$ undefined

Personal Tutor glencoe.com

Check Your Understanding

Example 1 p. 427

1. **CLIMBING** Libby and a group of friends are rock climbing. She is climbing up the side of a cliff that rises 18 inches for every horizontal change of 3 inches. Find the slope of the cliff. 6

Example 2 p. 428

Find the slope of each line.

2. −4

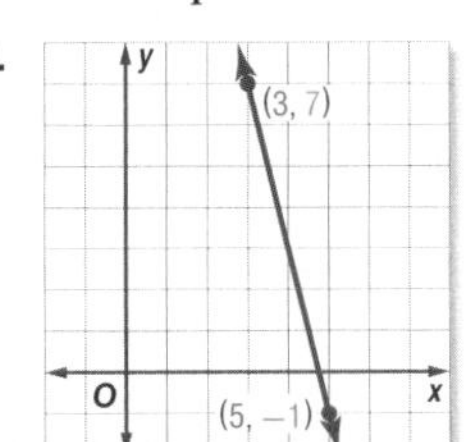

3. $\frac{1}{2}$

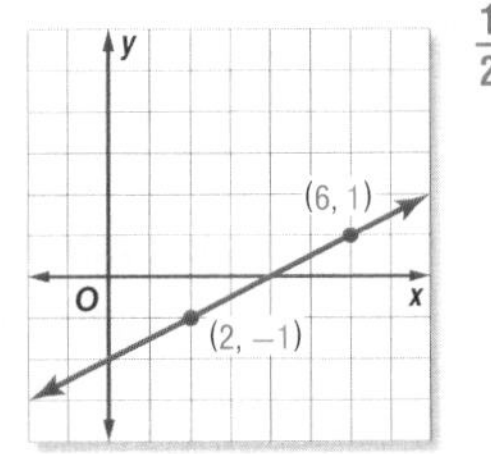

Examples 3 and 4 pp. 428–429

Find the slope of the line that passes through each pair of points.

4. $N(1, 2), P(5, 0)$ $-\frac{1}{2}$

5. $F(-2, -4), G(7, 1)$ $\frac{5}{9}$

6. $A(4, -5), B(9, -5)$ 0

7. $Y(8, 3), Z(-6, 3)$ 0

Differentiated Homework Options

Level	Assignment	Two-Day Option	
AL Basic	8–19, 21, 23–37	9–19 odd, 25–28	8–18 even, 21, 23, 24, 29–37
OL Core	9–19 odd, 20, 21, 23–37	8–19, 25–28	20, 21, 23, 24, 29–37
BL Advanced	20–33, (optional: 34–37)		

Slope and Constant Rate of Change

Example 3 shows how to find the slope of a line using coordinates of points. **Example 4** shows how to find slopes that are either zero or undefined.

Additional Examples

3 Find the slope of the line that passes through $B(2, 7)$ and $C(-3, -2)$. $\frac{9}{5}$

4 Find the slope of the line that passes through each pair of points.

a. $A(-3, 3), B(2, 3)$ 0

b. $P(2, 3), Q(2, -2)$ undefined

Focus on Mathematical Content

Slope The slope (m) between any two points on a straight line is: $m = \frac{y_2 - y_1}{x_2 - x_1}$, where $x_2 \neq x_1$. If $x_2 = x_1$, the line is vertical and has undefined slope. If $y_2 = y_1$, the line is horizontal and has 0 slope.

TEACH with TECH

BLOG Have students write a blog entry explaining how to find the slope of a line. Have them state how the slope describes the appearance of the line.

3 PRACTICE

Formative Assessment

Use Exercises 1–7 to check for understanding.

Use the chart at the bottom of this page to customize assignments for your students.

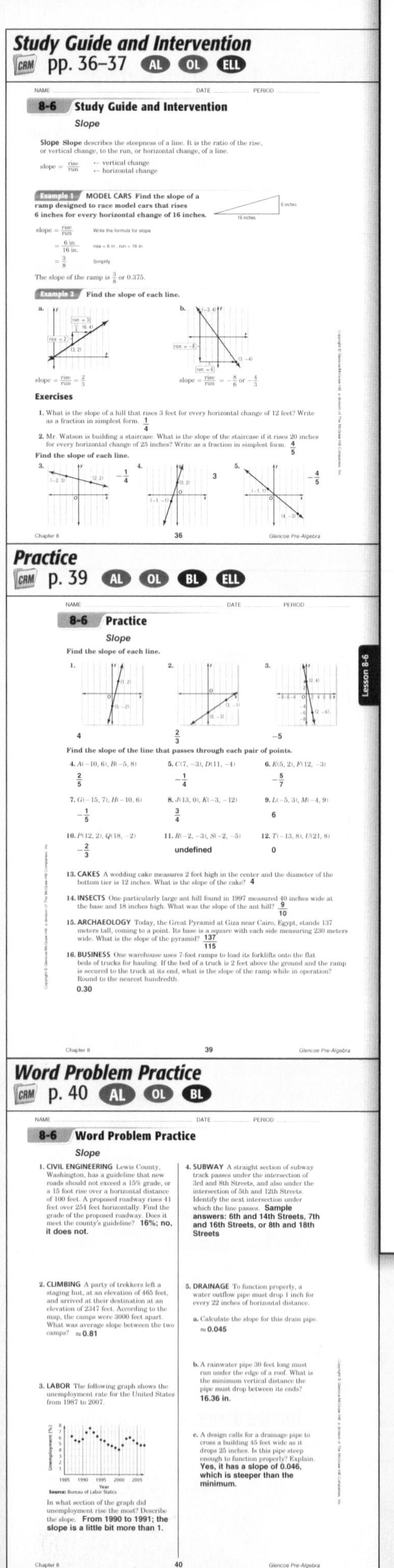
Study Guide and Intervention
CRM pp. 36–37 AL OL ELL

NAME ______ DATE ______ PERIOD ______

8-6 Study Guide and Intervention

Slope

Slope Slope describes the steepness of a line. It is the ratio of the rise, or vertical change, to the run, or horizontal change, of a line.

$\text{slope} = \frac{\text{rise}}{\text{run}}$ ← vertical change ← horizontal change

Example 1 MODEL CARS Find the slope of a ramp designed to race model cars that rises 6 inches for every horizontal change of 16 inches.

$\text{slope} = \frac{\text{rise}}{\text{run}}$ Write the formula for slope.

$= \frac{6 \text{ in.}}{16 \text{ in.}}$ rise = 6 in., run = 16 in.

$= \frac{3}{8}$ Simplify.

The slope of the ramp is $\frac{3}{8}$ or 0.375.

Example 2 Find the slope of each line.

a. slope $= \frac{\text{rise}}{\text{run}} = \frac{2}{3}$

b. slope $= \frac{\text{rise}}{\text{run}} = -\frac{8}{6}$ or $-\frac{4}{3}$

Exercises

1. What is the slope of a hill that rises 3 feet for every horizontal change of 12 feet? Write as a fraction in simplest form. $\frac{1}{4}$

2. Mr. Watson is building a staircase. What is the slope of the staircase if it rises 20 inches for every horizontal change of 25 inches? Write as a fraction in simplest form. $\frac{4}{5}$

Find the slope of each line.

3. $-\frac{1}{4}$ 4. 3 5. $-\frac{4}{5}$

Chapter 8 36 Glencoe Pre-Algebra

Practice
CRM p. 39 AL OL BL ELL

NAME ______ DATE ______ PERIOD ______

8-6 Practice

Slope

Find the slope of each line.

1. 4 2. $\frac{2}{3}$ 3. –5

Find the slope of the line that passes through each pair of points.

4. $A(-10, 6), B(-5, 8)$ $\frac{2}{5}$
5. $C(7, -3), D(11, -4)$ $-\frac{1}{4}$
6. $E(5, 2), F(12, -3)$ $-\frac{5}{7}$
7. $G(-15, 7), H(-10, 6)$ $-\frac{1}{5}$
8. $J(13, 0), K(-3, -12)$ $\frac{3}{4}$
9. $L(-5, 3), M(-4, 9)$ 6
10. $P(12, 2), Q(18, -2)$ $-\frac{2}{3}$
11. $R(-2, -3), S(-2, -5)$ undefined
12. $T(-13, 8), U(21, 8)$ 0

13. CAKES A wedding cake measures 2 feet high in the center and the diameter of the bottom tier is 12 inches. What is the slope of the cake? 4

14. INSECTS One particularly large ant hill found in 1997 measured 40 inches wide at the base and 18 inches high. What was the slope of the ant hill? $\frac{9}{10}$

15. ARCHAEOLOGY Today, the Great Pyramid at Giza near Cairo, Egypt, stands 137 meters tall, coming to a point. Its base is a square with each side measuring 230 meters wide. What is the slope of the pyramid? $\frac{137}{115}$

16. BUSINESS One warehouse uses 7-foot ramps to load its forklifts onto the flat beds of trucks for hauling. If the bed of a truck is 2 feet above the ground and the ramp is secured to the truck at its end, what is the slope of the ramp while in operation? Round to the nearest hundredth. 0.30

Chapter 8 39 Glencoe Pre-Algebra

Word Problem Practice
CRM p. 40 AL OL BL

NAME ______ DATE ______ PERIOD ______

8-6 Word Problem Practice

Slope

1. CIVIL ENGINEERING Lewis County, Washington, has a guideline that new roads should not exceed a 15% grade, or a 15 foot rise over a horizontal distance of 100 feet. A proposed roadway rises 41 feet over 254 feet horizontally. Find the grade of the proposed roadway. Does it meet the county's guideline? 16%; no, it does not.

2. CLIMBING A party of trekkers left a staging hut, at an elevation of 465 feet, and arrived at their destination at an elevation of 2347 feet. According to the map, the camps were 3000 feet apart. What was average slope between the two camps? ≈ 0.81

3. LABOR The following graph shows the unemployment rate for the United States from 1987 to 2007.

In what section of the graph did unemployment rise the most? Describe the slope. From 1990 to 1991; the slope is a little bit more than 1.

4. SUBWAY A straight section of subway track passes under the intersection of 3rd and 8th Streets, and also under the intersection of 5th and 12th Streets. Identify the next intersection under which the line passes. Sample answers: 6th and 14th Streets, 7th and 16th Streets, or 8th and 18th Streets

5. DRAINAGE To function properly, a water outflow pipe must drop 1 inch for every 22 inches of horizontal distance.

a. Calculate the slope for this drain pipe. ≈ 0.045

b. A rainwater pipe 30 feet long must run under the edge of a roof. What is the minimum vertical distance the pipe must drop between its ends? 16.36 in.

c. A design calls for a drainage pipe to cross a building 45 feet wide as it drops 25 inches. Is this pipe steep enough to function properly? Explain. Yes, it has a slope of 0.046, which is steeper than the minimum.

Chapter 8 40 Glencoe Pre-Algebra

Practice and Problem Solving

= **Step-by-Step Solutions** begin on page R11.
Extra Practice begins on page 810.

Example 1 p. 427

8. **SKIING** Find the slope of a snowboarding beginner hill that decreases 24 feet vertically for every 30-foot horizontal increase. $-\frac{4}{5}$

9. **DRIVING** Find the slope of a road that rises 5 feet vertically for every 45-foot horizontal increase. $\frac{1}{9}$

Example 2 p. 428

Find the slope of each line.

10. $\frac{1}{3}$

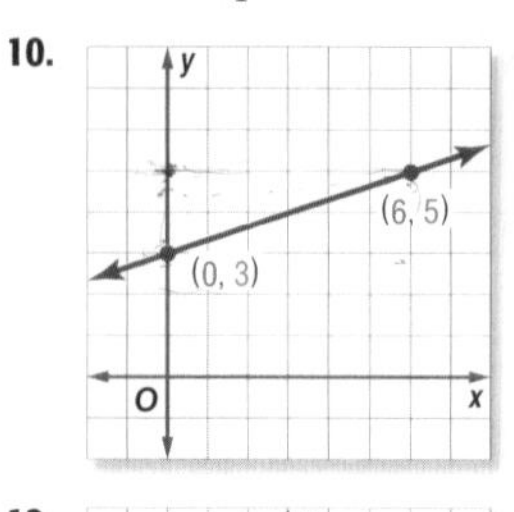

11. –2

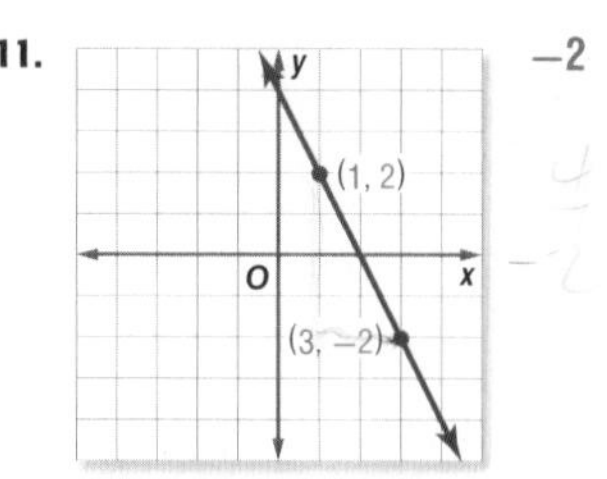

12. 0

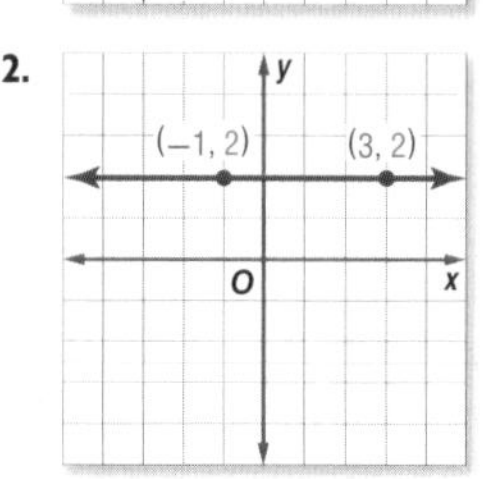

13. $\frac{1}{5}$

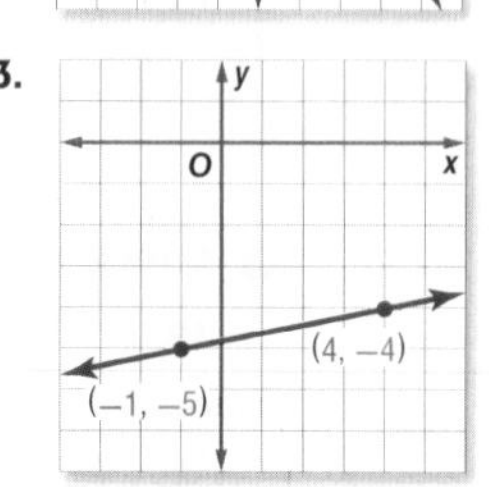

Examples 3 and 4 pp. 428–429

Find the slope of the line that passes through each pair of points.

14. $A(3, 2), B(10, 8)$ $\frac{6}{7}$
15. $R(5, 1), S(0, 4)$ $-\frac{3}{5}$
16. $L(5, -6), M(9, 6)$ 3
17. $J(-1, 3), K(-1, 7)$ undefined
18. $C(-8, 6), D(1, 6)$ 0
19. $V(5, -7), W(-3, 9)$ –2

20. **MULTIPLE REPRESENTATIONS** In this problem, you will investigate ordered pairs. Use the table shown.

x	y
–1	–6
0	–8
1	–10
2	–12

a. **NUMERICAL** What is the slope of the line represented by the data in the table? –2

b. **GRAPHICAL** Graph the points on a coordinate plane. Connect the points with a line. See Chapter 8 Answer Appendix.

c. **VERBAL** What does the point (0, –8) represent? The point is where the line intercepts the y-axis.

H.O.T. Problems
Use **H**igher-**O**rder **T**hinking Skills

21. **OPEN ENDED** Name two points on a line that has a slope of $\frac{5}{8}$.

22. **CHALLENGE** The terms in arithmetic sequence A have a common difference of 3. The terms in arithmetic sequence B have a common difference of 8. In which sequence do the terms form a steeper line when graphed as points on a coordinate plane? Justify your reasoning.

23. **REASONING** *True* or *false*? As the constant of variation increases in a direct variation, the slope of the graph becomes steeper. Explain.

24. **WRITING IN MATH** Explain whether a horizontal line, such as $y = 1$, *always*, *sometimes*, or *never* has 0 slope.

21. Sample answer: (2, 1) and (10, 6)

22. Sample answer: sequence B; since the common difference is greater, its terms increase at a faster rate. So, the points form a steeper line.

23. False; the graph of $y = 100x$ is as steep as the graph of $y = -100x$.

24. Always; the change in y or the vertical change is always 0.

430 Chapter 8 Linear Functions and Graphing

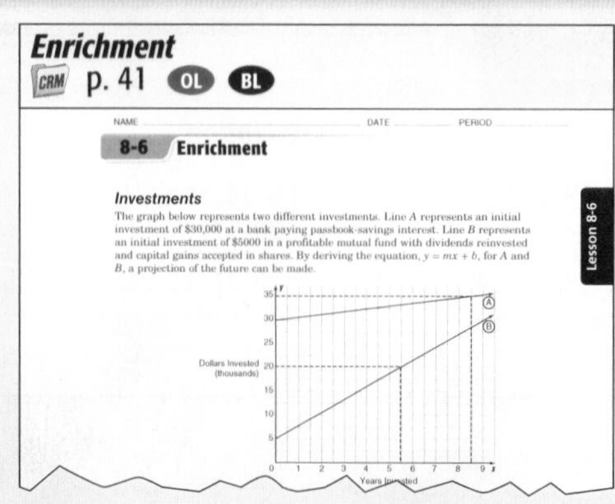
Enrichment
CRM p. 41 OL BL

NAME ______ DATE ______ PERIOD ______

8-6 Enrichment

Investments

The graph below represents two different investments. Line A represents an initial investment of $30,000 at a bank paying passbook-savings interest. Line B represents an initial investment of $5000 in a profitable mutual fund with dividends reinvested and capital gains accepted in shares. By deriving the equation, $y = mx + b$, for A and B, a projection of the future can be made.

Multiple Representations In Exercise 20, students use a table of values and a graph on the coordinate plane to relate x- and y-values to the slope of a line.

Standardized Test Practice

25. The table shows the number of degrees Celsius for certain Fahrenheit temperatures. **C**

Degrees Fahrenheit	Degrees Celsius
5	−15
14	−10
41	5
77	25

What is the slope of the line that fits these data?

A $-\frac{9}{5}$ C $\frac{5}{9}$

B $-\frac{5}{9}$ D $\frac{9}{5}$

26. A wheelchair ramp rises a vertical distance of 2.5 feet over a horizontal distance of 30 feet. Find the slope of the ramp. **F**

F $\frac{1}{12}$ G $\frac{1}{11}$ H $\frac{1}{9}$ J $\frac{1}{8}$

27. Which of the following is true concerning the slope of the line below? **D**

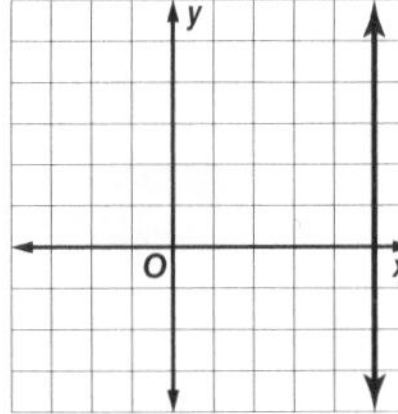

A The slope is −1.

B The slope is zero.

C The slope is 1.

D The slope is undefined.

28. SHORT RESPONSE What is the slope of the line that passes through the points (−3, 5) and (6, −1)? $-\frac{2}{3}$

Spiral Review

29. Determine whether a proportional linear relationship exists between the two quantities shown in the graph. Explain your reasoning. (Lesson 8-5) **Yes; the ratio $\frac{\text{circumference}}{\text{radius}}$ is the same for every pair of values.**

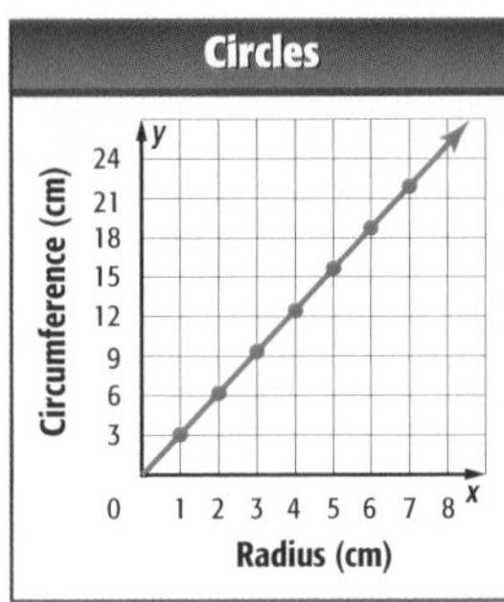

30. FRUIT The table below shows the cost of pears and oranges. Compare the rates of change. (Lesson 8-4) **See margin.**

Weight (lb) x	Cost ($) y	
	Pears	Oranges
0	0	0
2	2.40	2.20
5	6.00	5.50

Solve each equation. (Lesson 4-3)

31. $-123 = x - 183$ **60**   **32.** $-205 + t = -118$ **87**   **33.** $471 = -196 + n$ **667**

Skills Review

Solve each equation for y. (Lesson 5-1)

34. $x + y = 6$ **$y = -x + 6$**   **35.** $3x + y = 1$ **$y = -3x + 1$**   **36.** $-x + 5y = 10$ **$y = \frac{1}{5}x + 2$**   **37.** $\frac{y}{2} - 7x = 5$ **$y = 14x + 10$**

Tips for New Teachers

Working Together This lesson presents itself with good opportunities for cooperative learning. Set up flashcards with the coordinates of a point written on each side. Have students work in two teams to calculate slopes quickly and accurately. Two members of a team each draw a card and find the slope using the coordinates on the cards. Make sure all students get a fair number of turns.

Tips for New Teachers

Slopes of Horizontal Lines Some students may have trouble remembering which line has a slope of 0: a horizontal or a vertical line. Remind them that the word *horizontal* has an *o*, then remind them of 0. A horizontal line has 0 slope.

4 ASSESS

Name the Math Have each student make two line graphs on coordinate graph paper, making sure to label each axis. Instruct the students to trade with a classmate, and find the slope of the lines, naming each step as they work. Encourage them to use mathematical terms to name the parts of the graph, ordered pairs, and so on, as well as the operations they calculate.

Additional Answer

30. Pears: $1.20/lb; oranges: $1.10/lb; the cost of pears increases at a faster rate than the cost of oranges.

Differentiated Instruction 

Extension Ask students to brainstorm the different kinds of ramps they see every day. In one particular case, the ADA (Americans with Disabilities Act) mandates the slope of accessibility ramps. Students can investigate the ramifications of ignoring these mandates. They can present their findings to the class as an oral or visual presentation.

EXPLORE 8-7 Lesson Notes

1 FOCUS

Objective Identify direct proportional and nonproportional linear relationships.

Materials for Each Student

- grid paper

Teaching Tip

Remind students to read directions carefully. Point out that the table and graph require them to extend the pattern.

2 TEACH

Working in Cooperative Groups

Arrange students in groups of two or three, mixing abilities. Then have the groups complete Steps 1 and 2 of the Activity.

Ask:

- Is the rate of change constant in both patterns? yes
- Why? Each pattern increases at a constant rate of 2 blocks.

Practice Have students complete Exercises 1–3.

3 ASSESS

Formative Assessment

Use Exercise 4 to assess whether students can determine which pattern represents a direct proportional relationship or direct variation or nonproportional relationship.

EXPLORE 8-7 Algebra Lab

Proportional and Nonproportional Linear Relationships

Math Online glencoe.com
Math *in Motion*, Animation

Objective
Identify direct proportional and nonproportional linear relationships.

In this lab, you will shade squares on grid paper to develop two different linear functions.

ACTIVITY

Step 1 Using grid paper, draw the two patterns shown.

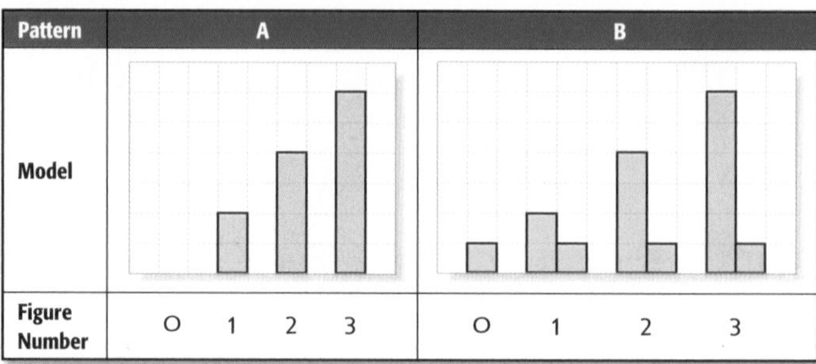

Step 2 Let x represent the figure number and y represent the number of shaded squares in each figure. Copy and complete the table below for each pattern. Then graph and label each set of data on separate coordinate planes. **Step 2. See Chapter 8 Answer Appendix.**

Pattern ______		
x	Process	y
0	■	■
1	■	■
2	■	■
3	■	■
4	■	■
5	■	■
x	■	■

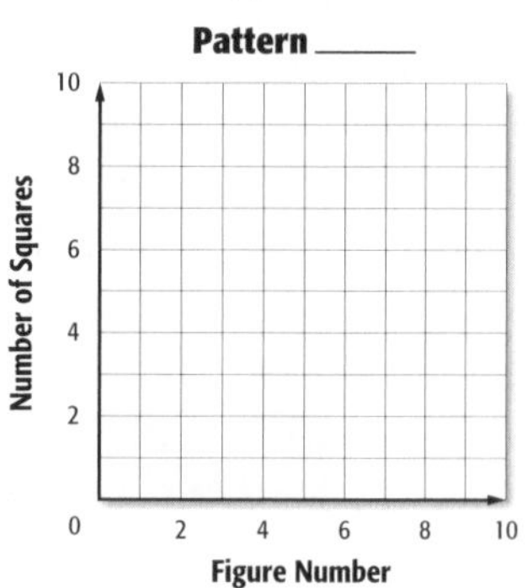

Analyze the Results 1–4. See Chapter 8 Answer Appendix.

1. Describe how the physical models of patterns A and B are alike. Describe how they are different.
2. Compare the processes shown in the tables for patterns A and B.
3. How are the graphs of patterns A and B alike? How are they different?
4. Which pattern represents a direct proportional relationship or direct variation? Which represents a nonproportional relationship? Explain. How can you tell this from the data shown in the table? from the graph?

From Concrete to Abstract

Have students use their graphs and tables to write linear equations for each of the patterns.

Extending the Concept

Ask:

- What is the y-coordinate of the point where each of the lines cross the graph? What is the slope of each line?
- How are the y-coordinate and slope related to the processes you wrote?

8-7 Slope-Intercept Form

Why?

A landscaping company charges a \$20 fee to mow a lawn plus \$8 per hour. The equation $y = 8x + 20$ represents this situation, where x is the number of hours it takes to mow the lawn and y is the total cost of mowing the lawn.

Number Hours, x	Total Cost, y
1	■
2	■
3	■

a. Copy and complete the table to find the total cost of mowing the lawn. **a–c. See Chapter 8 Answer Appendix.**

b. Use the table to graph the equation. In which quadrant does the graph lie? Explain.

c. Find the y-coordinate of the point where the graph crosses the y-axis and the slope of the line. How are they related to the equation?

Then
You have already graphed linear equations using ordered pairs. (Lesson 8-3)

Now
- Determine slopes and y-intercepts of lines.
- Graph linear equations using the slope and y-intercept.

New Vocabulary
slope-intercept form

Math Online
glencoe.com
- Extra Examples
- Personal Tutor
- Self-Check Quiz
- Homework Help
- Math in Motion

Find Slope and *y*-Intercept An equation with a y-intercept that is *not* 0 represents a nonproportional relationship. An equation of the form $y = mx + b$, where m is the slope and b is the y-intercept, is in **slope-intercept form**.

Key Concept Slope-Intercept Form

For Your FOLDABLE

Words The slope-intercept form of an equation is $y = mx + b$, where m is the slope and b is the y-intercept.

Symbols $y = mx + b$

Example $y = 2x + 1$ (2: slope; 1: y-intercept)

Math *in Motion*, BrainPOP® glencoe.com

EXAMPLE 1 Find the Slope and *y*-intercept

State the slope and the y-intercept of the graph of $y = \frac{1}{4}x - 6$.

$y = \frac{1}{4}x - 6$ **Write the equation.**

$y = \frac{1}{4}x + (-6)$ **Write the equation in the form $y = mx + b$.**

The slope is $\frac{1}{4}$ and the y-intercept is -6.

Check Your Progress

State the slope and the y-intercept of the graph of each equation.

1A. $y = 3x + 1$ **3; 1** **1B.** $y = -2x$ **−2; 0**

Personal Tutor glencoe.com

8-7 Lesson Notes

1 FOCUS

Vertical Alignment

Before Lesson 8-7
Graph linear equations using ordered pairs.

Lesson 8-7
Determine slopes and y-intercepts of lines. Graph linear equations using the slope and y-intercept.

After Lesson 8-7
Graph equations of lines given the slope and y-intercept.

2 TEACH

Scaffolding Questions

Have students read the *Why?* section of the lesson and answer the questions.

Ask:
- As x increases, what will happen to y? It will also increase.
- If the company spent five hours mowing, what would the total cost be? \$60
- Is the rate of change constant? yes

Lesson 8-7 Resources

Resource	Approaching-Level	On-Level	Beyond-Level	English Learners
Teacher Edition	• Differentiated Instruction, p. 434	• Differentiated Instruction, p. 434	• Differentiated Instruction, p. 438	• Differentiated Instruction, p. 434
Chapter Resource Masters	• Study Guide and Intervention, pp. 42–43 • Skills Practice, p. 44 • Practice, p. 45 • Word Problem Practice, p. 46	• Study Guide and Intervention, pp. 42–43 • Skills Practice, p. 44 • Practice, p. 45 • Word Problem Practice, p. 46 • Enrichment, p. 47	• Practice, p. 45 • Word Problem Practice, p. 46 • Enrichment, p. 47	• Study Guide and Intervention, pp. 42–43 • Skills Practice, p. 44 • Practice, p. 45
Transparencies	• 5-Minute Check Transparency 8-7	• 5-Minute Check Transparency 8-7	• 5-Minute Check Transparency 8-7	• 5-Minute Check Transparency 8-7
Other	• Study Notebook • Teaching Pre-Algebra with Manipulatives	• Study Notebook • Teaching Pre-Algebra with Manipulatives	• Study Notebook	• Study Notebook • Teaching Pre-Algebra with Manipulatives

Find Slope and y-Intercept

Example 1 shows how to find the slope and y-intercept from a linear equation in slope-intercept form. **Example 2** shows how to write an equation in slope-intercept form and then find the slope and y-intercept.

Additional Examples

1 State the slope and the y-intercept of the graph of $y = \frac{1}{2}x + 3$. $\frac{1}{2}$; 3

2 State the slope and the y-intercept of the graph of $-4x + y = -10$. 4; −10

Tips for New Teachers

Different Forms Write the equations $y = x + (-5)$ and $y = x - 5$ on the board. Lead students to see that both equations are written in slope-intercept form.

Graph Equations

Examples 3 and 4 show how to graph a line from an equation in slope-intercept form.

Additional Example

3 Graph $y = -3x + 9$ using the slope and y-intercept.

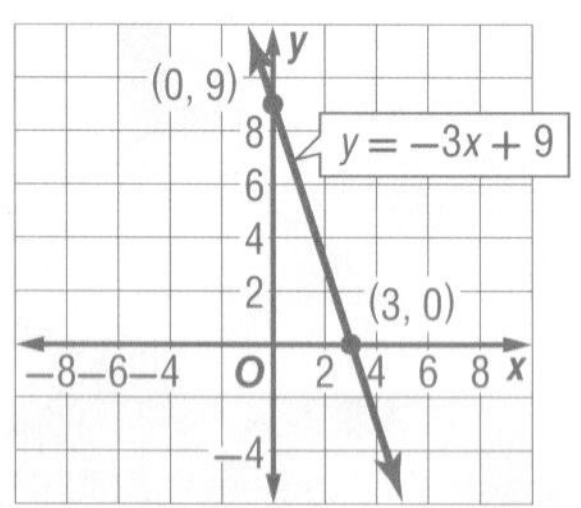

EXAMPLE 2 Find Slope and y-intercept

State the slope and the y-intercept of the graph of $-4x + y = 2$.

First, write the equation in slope-intercept form.

$-4x + y = 2$	**Write the original equation.**
$+4x \quad = \quad +4x$	**Add 4x to each side.**
$y = 2 + 4x$	**Simplify.**
$y = 4x + 2$	**Write in slope-intercept form.**
$y = mx + b$	$m = 4, b = 2$

The slope of the graph is 4 and the y-intercept is 2.

Check Your Progress

State the slope and the y-intercept of the graph of each equation.

2A. $6x + y = -3$ **−6; −3**

2B. $y - 5 = -x$ **−1; 5**

2C. $y - 5x = 10$ **5; 10**

2D. $x = 2 + y$ **1; −2**

Personal Tutor glencoe.com

Graph Equations You can use the slope-intercept form of an equation to graph a line.

StudyTip

Constant of Proportionality The direct variation equation $y = kx$ is a special case of a linear equation of the form $y = mx + b$. The constant of proportionality k is the slope and the y-intercept b is 0.

EXAMPLE 3 Graph an Equation

Graph $y = -\frac{2}{3}x + 3$ using the slope and y-intercept.

Step 1 Find the slope and y-intercept.

slope $= -\frac{2}{3}$

y-intercept = 3

Step 2 Graph the y-intercept point at (0, 3).

Step 3 Write the slope as $\frac{-2}{3}$. Use it to locate a second point on the line.

$m = \frac{-2}{3}$ ← **Change in y: down 2 units** ← **Change in x: right 3 units**

Another point on the line is at (3, 1).

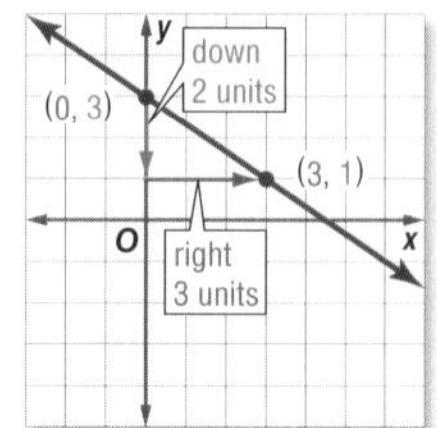

Step 4 Draw a line through the two points and extend the line.

Check Your Progress See Chapter 8 Answer Appendix.

3. Graph $y = -x - 2$ using the slope and y-intercept.

Personal Tutor glencoe.com

Differentiated Instruction

AL OL ELL

If students need help seeing the connection between the equation of a line in slope-intercept form $y = mx + b$ and its graph,

Then have them write m in one color and b in another color. When they graph the equation, use the b color on the graph for the y-intercept and show the slope of the line using the m color.

Real-World EXAMPLE 4 Analyze the Slope and y-Intercept

Real-World Link

Leopard geckos shed their skin every 2 to 4 weeks. The frequency of their shedding is determined by their age and the growth rate.

Source: Golden Gate Geckos

GECKOS A typical leopard gecko is 3 inches long at birth and grows at a rate of about $\frac{1}{3}$ inch per week for the first few months. The total length of a leopard gecko y after x weeks can be represented by $y = \frac{1}{3}x + 3$.

a. Graph the equation.

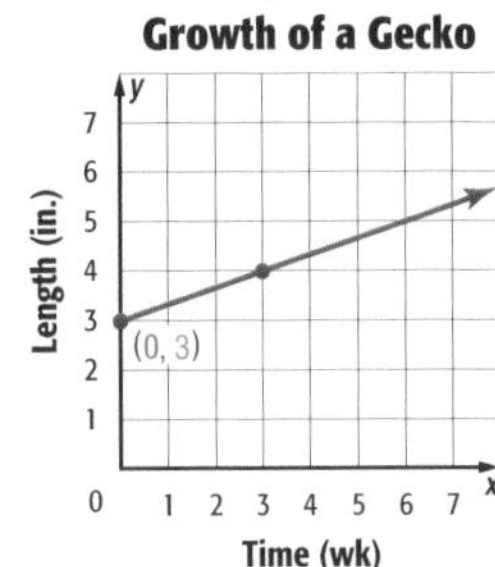

Step 1 First, find the slope and the y-intercept.

slope $= \frac{1}{3}$

y-intercept $= 3$

Step 2 Plot the point at (0, 3). Then go up 1 and right 3 and plot another point.

Step 3 Connect these points and extend the line.

b. Describe what the y-intercept and the slope represent.

The y-intercept 3 represents the length of the gecko at birth. The slope $\frac{1}{3}$ represents the growth rate in inches per week, which is the rate of change.

Check Your Progress

4. **WRITING** Jack has written 30 pages of his novel. He plans to write 12 pages per week until he has completed his novel. The total number of pages written y can be represented by $y = 12x + 30$, where x is the number of weeks. **A–B. See Chapter 8 Answer Appendix.**

   A. Graph the equation.

   B. Describe what the y-intercept and the slope represent.

Personal Tutor glencoe.com

Check Your Understanding

Examples 1 and 2 pp. 433–434

State the slope and the y-intercept of the graph of each equation.

1. $y = 2x + 6$ **2; 6**
2. $y = \frac{3}{4}x - 1$ **$\frac{3}{4}$; −1**
3. $7x + y = 0$ **−7; 0**
4. $4x + y = 3$ **−4; 3**

Example 3 p. 434

Graph each equation using the slope and y-intercept. **5–9. See Chapter 8 Answer Appendix.**

5. $y = \frac{1}{3}x + 1$
6. $y = -x + 2$
7. $y = 2x - 4$
8. $y = -0.75x - 3$

Example 4 p. 435

9. **KITES** A kite flying 60 feet in the air is falling. The altitude of the kite can be represented by $y = -x + 60$, where x is the time in seconds.

   a. Graph the equation.

   b. Describe what the y-intercept and the slope represent.

TEACH with TECH

INTERACTIVE WHITEBOARD Show a coordinate grid on the board. Draw a line on the grid, and have students write the equation of the line in slope-intercept form. Then drag the line to other locations on the board and again have students write the equation of the line. Discuss how the equations are similar and different.

Additional Example

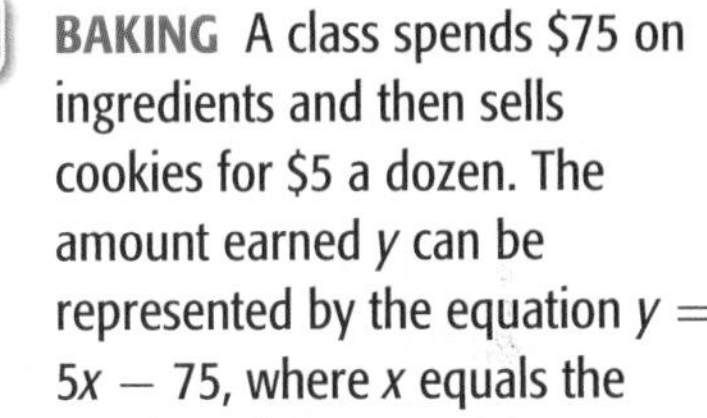

4 **BAKING** A class spends \$75 on ingredients and then sells cookies for \$5 a dozen. The amount earned y can be represented by the equation $y = 5x - 75$, where x equals the number of dozens sold.

a. Graph the equation.

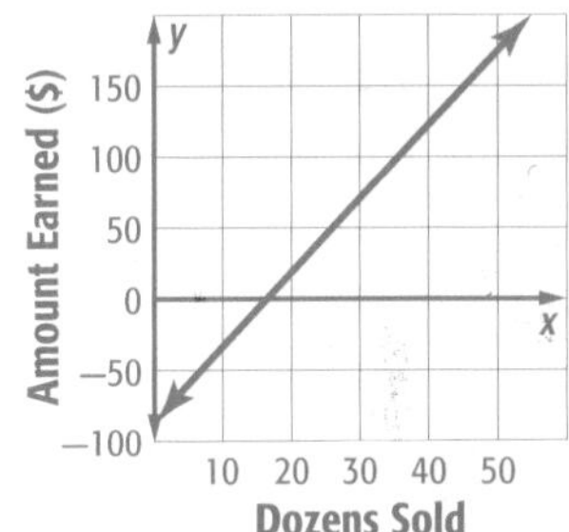

b. Describe what the y-intercept and the slope represent. The y-intercept −75 represents the cost of the ingredients. Slope 5 represents the dollars earned per dozen cookies.

Tips for New Teachers

Slope and Improper Fractions Slope is usually expressed as a fraction or an integer because it gives information about the direction of the line. A mixed number would not reveal that information.

3 PRACTICE

Formative Assessment

Use Exercises 1–9 to check for understanding.

Use the chart at the bottom of the next page to customize assignments for your students.

Watch Out!

Find the Error If students are having difficulty remembering to put an equation into slope-intercept form before they find the slope or y-intercept, like in Exercise 40, remind them of the definition of y-intercept. The variable y must be alone on one side of the equation before proceeding.

Additional Answers

18. 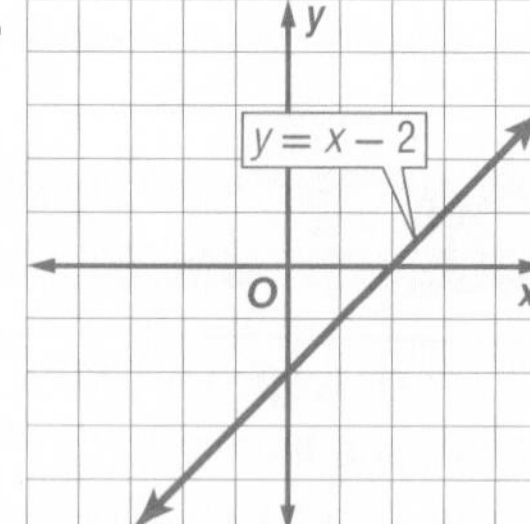

19. 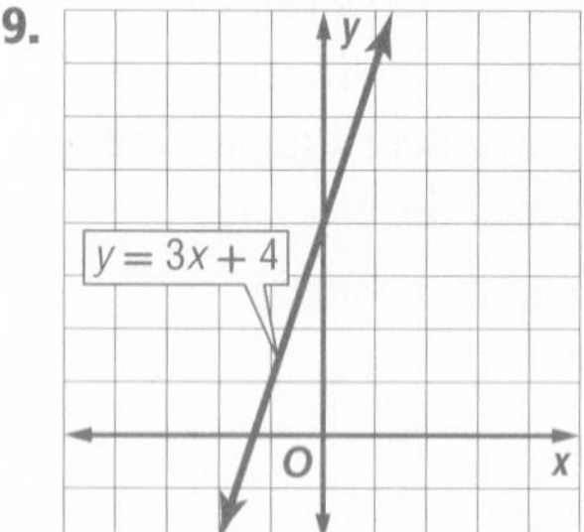

20. 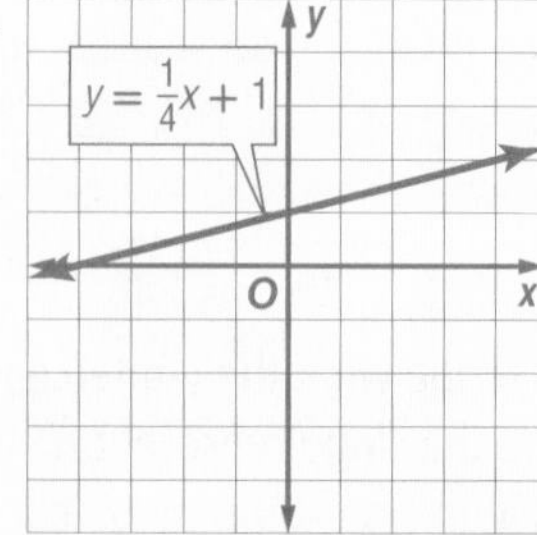

21. 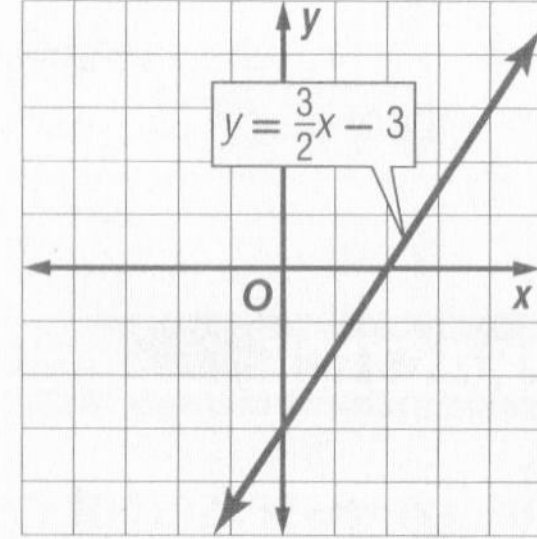

Practice and Problem Solving

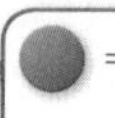 = **Step-by-Step Solutions** begin on page R11. **Extra Practice** begins on page 810.

Examples 1 and 2 pp. 433–434

State the slope and the y-intercept of the graph of each equation.

10. $y = x + 8$ **1; 8**
11. $y = -\frac{5}{2}x - 2$ **$-\frac{5}{2}$; -2**
12. $y = \frac{1}{3}x$ **$\frac{1}{3}$; 0**
13. $y = -9x$ **-9; 0**
14. $-x + y = 5$ **1; 5**
15. $4x + y = 0$ **-4; 0**
16. $-9x + y = -5$ **9; -5**
17. $y - 6 = \frac{1}{2}x$ **$\frac{1}{2}$; 6**

Example 3 p. 434

Graph each equation using the slope and y-intercept. **18–21. See margin.**

18. $y = x - 2$
19. $y = 3x + 4$
20. $y = \frac{1}{4}x + 1$
21. $y = \frac{3}{2}x - 3$
22. $y = -2x - 6$
23. $y = -\frac{4}{3}x + 5$

22–26. See Chapter 8 Answer Appendix.

Example 4 p. 435

24. **FINANCIAL LITERACY** To replace a set of brakes, an auto mechanic charges \$40 for parts plus \$50 per hour. The total cost y can be given by $y = 50x + 40$ for x hours.
    a. Graph the equation using the slope and y-intercept.
    b. State the slope and y-intercept of the graph of the equation and describe what they represent.

StudyTip

Real-World Data Look at the problem to determine how to draw a graph of the data. In Exercise 25, it is not reasonable for the time or the altitude to be negative. So, the graph should be in Quadrant I only.

25. **BIRDS** The altitude in feet y of an albatross who is slowly landing can be given by $y = 300 - 50x$, where x represents the time in minutes.
    a. Graph the equation using the slope and y-intercept.
    b. State the slope and y-intercept of the graph of the equation and describe what they represent.

26. **BAKING** Sam has 15 teaspoons of chopped nuts. She uses $1\frac{1}{2}$ teaspoons for each muffin. The total amount of nuts that she has left y after making x muffins can be given by $y = -\frac{3}{2}x + 15$, as shown in the graph.
    a. State the slope and y-intercept of the graph of the equation and describe what they represent.
    b. Name the x-intercept and describe what it represents.

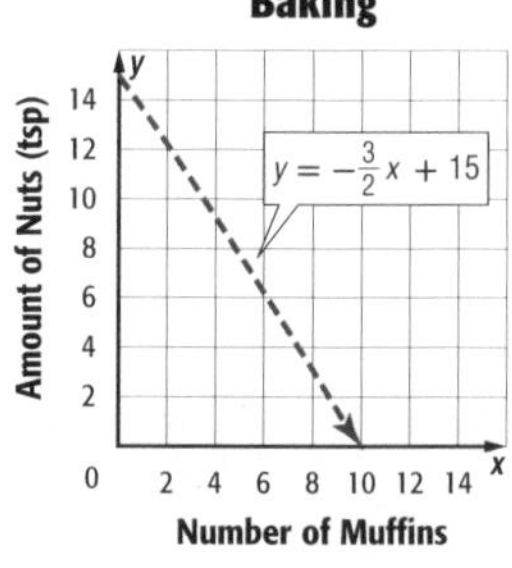

27. **PHOTOS** The table shows the prices of sitting fees and each 5 × 7 portrait for two photography studios.
    a. Write an equation to represent y the total cost of having your photo taken and buying x number of 5 × 7's for each studio.
    b. Graph each equation on the same coordinate plane. **See Chapter 8 Answer Appendix.**
    c. Will the lines ever intersect? Explain.
    d. Compare the slopes of each line.

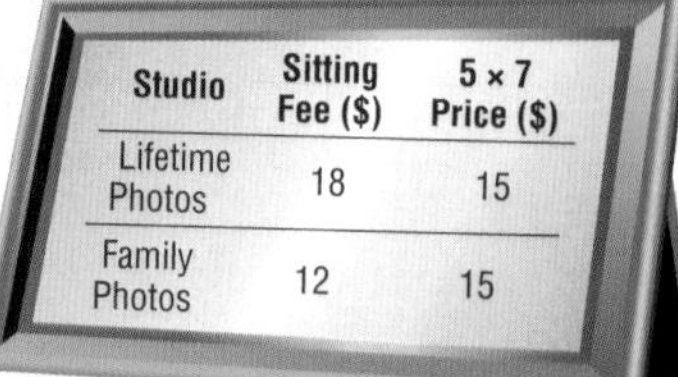

Studio	Sitting Fee (\$)	5 × 7 Price (\$)
Lifetime Photos	18	15
Family Photos	12	15

27a. $y = 15x + 18$; $y = 15x + 12$

27c. No; The lines are parallel and parallel lines do not intersect.

27d. Each line has a slope of 15.

Differentiated Homework Options

Level	Assignment	Two-Day Option	
AL Basic	10–25, 36, 37, 39–56	11–25 odd, 42–45	10–24 even, 36, 37, 39–41, 46–86
OL Core	11–25 odd, 26–27, 29, 31–37, 39–56	10–25, 42–45	26–37, 39–41, 46–56
BL Advanced	26–50 (optional: 51–56)		

436 Chapter 8 Linear Functions and Graphing

Real-World Link

The amusement park with greatest number of rides is Cedar Point located in Sandusky, Ohio. The park has 20 children's rides and 47 major rides.

Source: National Amusement Park Historical Society

Graph each equation using the slope and y-intercept. **28–31. See Chapter 8 Answer Appendix.**

28. $x - 2y = 8$ **29.** $3x + 4y = 12$ **30.** $y = 6$ **31.** $x + 4y = 0$

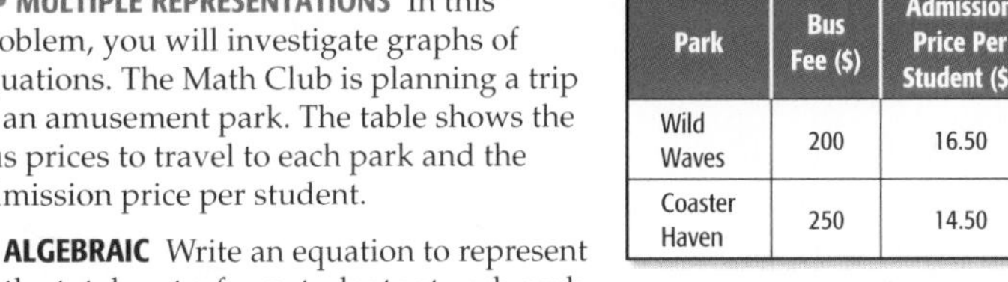

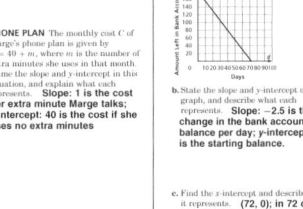

32. **MULTIPLE REPRESENTATIONS** In this problem, you will investigate graphs of equations. The Math Club is planning a trip to an amusement park. The table shows the bus prices to travel to each park and the admission price per student.

Park	Bus Fee ($)	Admission Price Per Student ($)
Wild Waves	200	16.50
Coaster Haven	250	14.50

a. **ALGEBRAIC** Write an equation to represent the total cost y for x students at each park. **$y = 16.5x + 200$; $y = 14.5x + 250$**

b. **GRAPHICAL** Graph the two equations on the same coordinate plane. For how many students is the cost of both trips the same? Explain. **See Chapter 8 Answer Appendix.**

c. **NUMERICAL** If 20 students decide to take the trip, which trip will cost less? If 28 students decide to take the trip, which trip will cost less? **Wild Waves; Coaster Haven**

d. **VERBAL** Is it possible to determine the answers to part **c** by examining the graph you made in part **a**? Explain your reasoning.

32d. Yes; the line for Coaster Heaven is below the line for Wild Waves at 20 and above it at 28.

For Exercises 33–35, use the graph shown at the right.

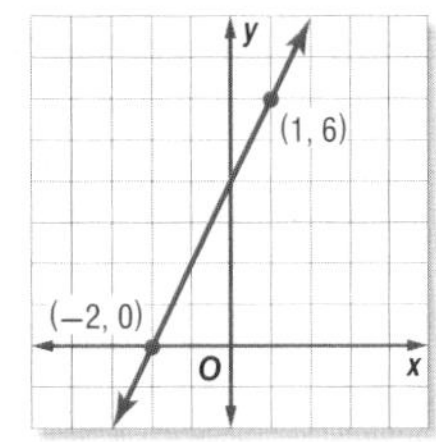

33. What is the slope of the line shown? **2**

34. Identify the x-intercept and y-intercept of the graph. **−2; 4**

35. What is the equation of the line? Write in slope-intercept form. **$y = 2x + 4$**

H.O.T. Problems

Use Higher-Order Thinking Skills

36. **OPEN ENDED** Describe a line that has a y-intercept but no x-intercept. Identify the slope of the line. **horizontal line; slope 0**

37. **WRITING IN MATH** Write a real-world problem that can be represented by an equation in the form $y = mx + b$. Solve by graphing. **37–38. See Chapter 8 Answer Appendix.**

38. **CHALLENGE** Suppose the graph of a line has a negative slope and a positive y-intercept. Through which quadrants does the line pass? Justify your reasoning.

39. **REASONING** Describe what happens to the graph of $y = 3x + 4$ when the slope is changed to $\frac{1}{3}$. **The graph becomes less steep.**

40. **FIND THE ERROR** Maricruz and Francesco are finding the slope and y–intercept of $x - 2y = 3$. Is either of them correct? Explain your reasoning.

Maricruz	Francesco
slope = 1	slope = $\frac{1}{2}$
y-intercept = 3	y-intercept = $\frac{3}{2}$

40. No; Sample answer: Maricruz solved the equation for x instead of y. In Francesco's answer, the y-intercept should be negative.

41. **WRITING IN MATH** Describe the steps you take to graph an equation using the slope and y-intercept.

41. Sample answer: Graph the y-intercept point. Then use the slope to locate a second point on the line. Draw a line through the two points.

Multiple Representations

In Exercise 32, students solve simultaneous equations by graphing the equations as functions on the coordinate plane.

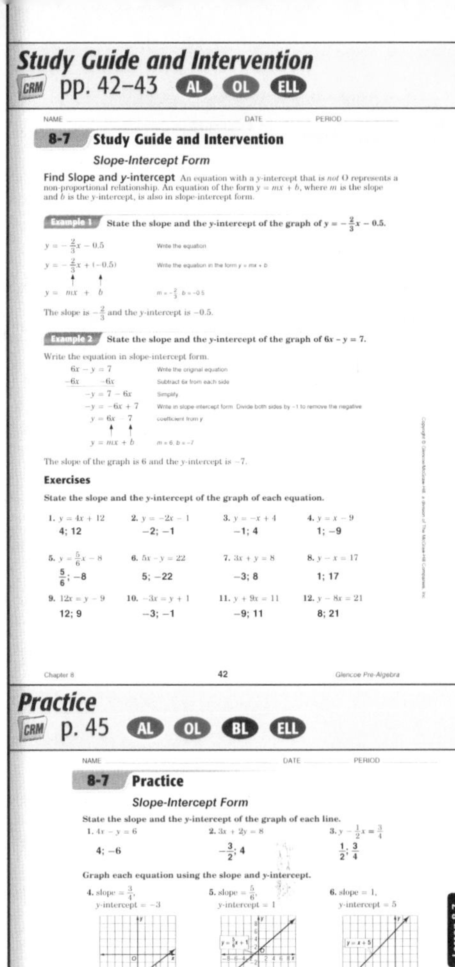

Study Guide and Intervention
CRM pp. 42–43 AL OL ELL

NAME ______ DATE ______ PERIOD ______

8-7 Study Guide and Intervention

Slope-Intercept Form

Find Slope and y-intercept An equation with a y-intercept that is *not* 0 represents a non-proportional relationship. An equation of the form $y = mx + b$, where m is the slope and b is the y-intercept, is also in slope-intercept form.

Example 1 State the slope and the y-intercept of the graph of $y = -\frac{2}{3}x - 0.5$.

$y = -\frac{2}{3}x - 0.5$ Write the equation

$y = -\frac{2}{3}x + (-0.5)$ Write the equation in the form $y = mx + b$

$y = mx + b$ $m = -\frac{2}{3}$, $b = -0.5$

The slope is $-\frac{2}{3}$ and the y-intercept is -0.5.

Example 2 State the slope and the y-intercept of the graph of $6x - y = 7$.

Write the equation in slope-intercept form.

$6x - y = 7$ Write the original equation

$-6x \quad -6x$ Subtract 6x from each side

$-y = 7 - 6x$ Simplify

$-y = -6x + 7$ Write in slope-intercept form. Divide both sides by −1 to remove the negative

$y = 6x - 7$ coefficient from y

$y = mx + b$ $m = 6$, $b = -7$

The slope of the graph is 6 and the y-intercept is -7.

Exercises

State the slope and the y-intercept of the graph of each equation.

1. $y = 4x + 12$ **4; 12**
2. $y = -2x - 1$ **−2; −1**
3. $y = -x + 4$ **−1; 4**
4. $y = x - 9$ **1; −9**
5. $y = \frac{5}{6}x - 8$ **$\frac{5}{6}$; −8**
6. $5x - y = 22$ **5; −22**
7. $3x + y = 8$ **−3; 8**
8. $y - x = 17$ **1; 17**
9. $12x = y - 9$ **12; 9**
10. $-3x = y + 1$ **−3; −1**
11. $y + 9x = 11$ **−9; 11**
12. $y - 8x = 21$ **8; 21**

Chapter 8 42 Glencoe Pre-Algebra

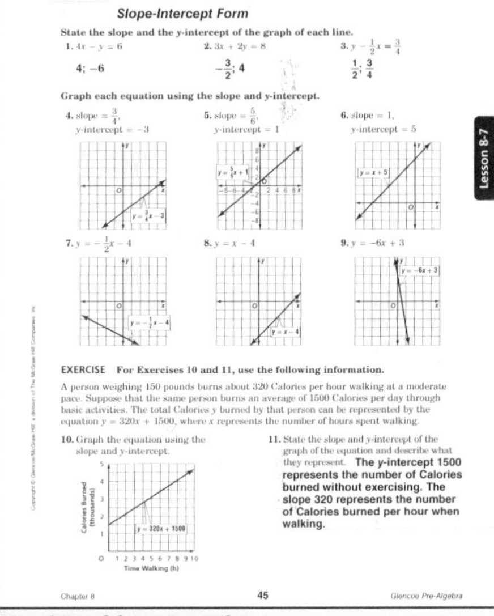

Practice
CRM p. 45 AL OL BL ELL

NAME ______ DATE ______ PERIOD ______

8-7 Practice

Slope-Intercept Form

State the slope and the y-intercept of the graph of each line.

1. $4x - y = 6$ **4; −6**
2. $3x + 2y = 8$ **$-\frac{3}{2}$; 4**
3. $y - \frac{1}{2}x = \frac{3}{4}$ **$\frac{1}{2}$; $\frac{3}{4}$**

Graph each equation using the slope and y-intercept.

4. slope $= \frac{3}{4}$, y-intercept $= -3$
5. slope $= \frac{5}{6}$, y-intercept $= 1$
6. slope $= 1$, y-intercept $= 5$
7. $y = -\frac{1}{2}x - 4$
8. $y = x - 4$
9. $y = -6x + 3$

EXERCISE For Exercises 10 and 11, use the following information.

A person weighing 150 pounds burns about 320 Calories per hour walking at a moderate pace. Suppose that the same person burns an average of 1500 Calories per day through basic activities. The total Calories y burned by that person can be represented by the equation $y = 320x + 1500$, where x represents the number of hours spent walking.

10. Graph the equation using the slope and y-intercept.

11. State the slope and y-intercept of the graph of the equation and describe what they represent. **The y-intercept 1500 represents the number of Calories burned without exercising. The slope 320 represents the number of Calories burned per hour when walking.**

Chapter 8 45 Glencoe Pre-Algebra

Word Problem Practice
CRM p. 46 AL OL BL

NAME ______ DATE ______ PERIOD ______

8-7 Word Problem Practice

Slope-Intercept Form

1. **OVERTIME** Rod is paid an overtime rate of $25 per hour after he earns his basic wage of $600 per week. Write an equation in slope-intercept form for the total pay p if he works h hours of overtime. **$p = 600 + 25h$**

2. **PHONE PLAN** The monthly cost C of Marge's phone plan is given by $C = 40 + m$, where m is the number of extra minutes she uses in that month. Name the slope and y-intercept in this situation, and explain what each represents. **Slope: 1 is the cost per extra minute Marge talks; y-intercept: 40 is the cost if she uses no extra minutes**

3. **ELEVATOR** An elevator travels vertically in a building that has 32 floors, each 11 feet tall. The height h above the first floor after t seconds is given by $h = 297 - 4.4t$. How long will it take for the elevator to reach the second floor? **65 s**

4. **BANK ACCOUNT** Pete's bank account showed a balance at the beginning of the month of $180. He spent $2.50 each day on bus tokens. The amount A left in his bank account after d days can be given by $A = 180 - 2.5d$.

a. Graph the equation using the slope and y-intercept.

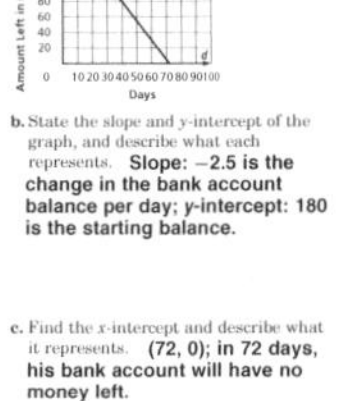

b. State the slope and y-intercept of the graph, and describe what each represents. **Slope: −2.5 is the change in the bank account balance per day; y-intercept: 180 is the starting balance.**

c. Find the x-intercept and describe what it represents. **(72, 0); in 72 days, his bank account will have no money left.**

Chapter 8 46 Glencoe Pre-Algebra

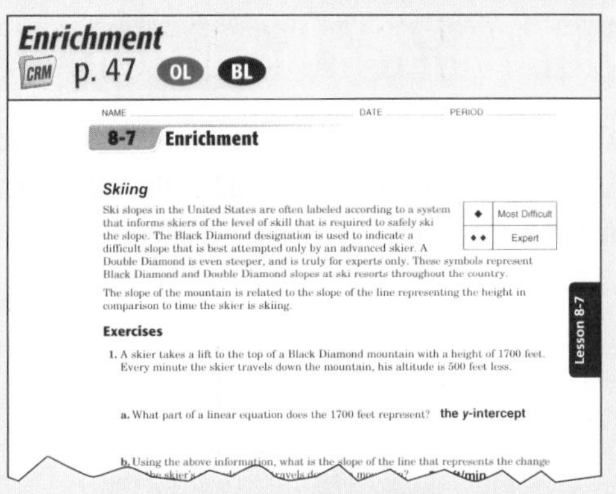

Enrichment
CRM p. 47 OL BL

NAME ______ DATE ______ PERIOD ______

8-7 Enrichment

Skiing

Ski slopes in the United States are often labeled according to a system that informs skiers of the level of skill that is required to safely ski the slope. The Black Diamond designation is used to indicate a difficult slope that is best attempted only by an advanced skier. A Double Diamond is even steeper, and is truly for experts only. These symbols represent Black Diamond and Double Diamond slopes at ski resorts throughout the country.

◆	Most Difficult
◆◆	Expert

The slope of the mountain is related to the slope of the line representing the height in comparison to time the skier is skiing.

Exercises

1. A skier takes a lift to the top of a Black Diamond mountain with a height of 1700 feet. Every minute the skier travels down the mountain, his altitude is 500 feet less.

a. What part of a linear equation does the 1700 feet represent? **the y-intercept**

b. Using the above information, what is the slope of the line that represents the change ...

4 ASSESS

Ticket Out the Door Have students explain how to graph linear equations using slope and y-intercept. Give students the equation $3x + 2y = 12$; instruct them to identify the slope and y-intercept. Students will turn in their papers as they exit.

Additional Answer

45a.

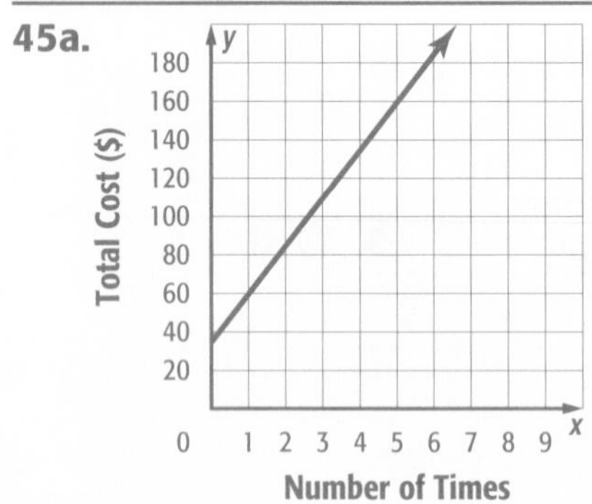

Standardized Test Practice

42. A line has a slope of $\frac{4}{5}$ and a y-intercept of 10. Which of the following represents the equation of the line? **C**

A $4x - 5y = 10$
B $5x - 4y = 10$
C $4x - 5y = -50$
D $5x - 4y = -50$

43. Which *best* represents the graph of $y = 3x - 1$? **J**

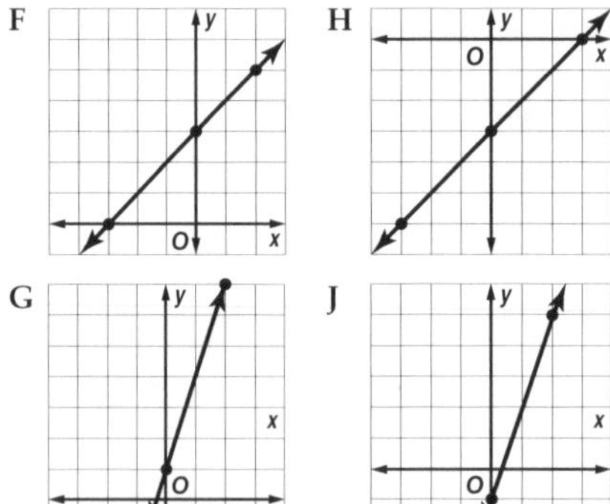

44. The cost of renting a cotton candy machine is \$30 plus \$5 for each hour. The total cost of renting a cotton candy machine is represented by $C(h) = 5h + 30$, where h is number of hours. What does the slope represent? **B**

A number of hours
B cost of each hour
C cost per bag of cotton candy
D cost of renting the machine for no hours

45. EXTENDED RESPONSE Snow Mountain Ski Resort offers a special season pass at the beginning of each ski season. The pass costs \$35, and an additional \$25 is charged each time you ski. The total cost can be represented by $y = 35 + 25x$, where x is number of times you ski.

a. Graph the equation. **See margin.**

b. Explain what the y–intercept and the slope represent. **The y-intercept 35 is the initial cost of the pass and the slope 25 is the cost per time of skiing.**

Spiral Review

46. CARS The cost of gas varies directly with the number of gallons bought. Marty bought 18 gallons of gas for \$49.50. Write an equation that could be used to find the unit cost of a gallon of gas. Then find the unit cost. (Lesson 8-6) **$49.50 = 18x$; \$2.75**

47. BIRDSEED Find the constant rate of change for the linear function in the table and interpret its meaning. (Lesson 8-5)
\$2.80/lb; The birdseed costs \$2.80 per pound.

Amount of Birdseed (lb)	Total Cost (\$)
x	y
4	11.20
8	22.40
12	33.60

Find each sum in simplest form. (Lesson 3-6)

48. $\frac{1}{2} + \frac{7}{10}$ **$1\frac{1}{5}$**

49. $\frac{1}{6} + \frac{3}{12}$ **$\frac{5}{12}$**

50. $\frac{7}{8} + \frac{2}{10}$ **$1\frac{3}{40}$**

Skills Review

Simplify each expression. (Lesson 1-2)

51. $-3(5) - 7$ **-22**

52. $4 + (-5)(6)$ **-26**

53. $(-10 - 8) \div (-9)$ **2**

54. $(32 - 12) \div 4 \times 7$ **35**

55. $(14 - 6) \times 8 \div 2$ **32**

56. $(56 - 28) \div (7 \times 2)$ **2**

Differentiated Instruction

BL

Extension Give students the following equations: $x = -3y + 6$, $x = -3y + 12$, $x = -3y$, and $x = -3y - 6$. Have them put all of the equations in slope-intercept form and graph the equations. What do all of the equations have in common? The lines appear parallel and the equations have the same slope of $-\frac{1}{3}$.

Family of Linear Graphs

Math Online glencoe.com
• Other Calculator Keystrokes

A **family of functions** is a set of functions that is related in some way. The family of linear functions has the parent function $y = x$.

A TI-*n*spire calculator allows you to enter a function and manipulate the graph. This is useful for investigating families of linear functions because you can easily compare characteristics such as slopes and y-intercepts.

ACTIVITY

Graph $y = 2x + 6$ in the default viewing window and move the line to see how the equation relates to the graph.

Step 1 Graph $y = 2x + 6$ in the default viewing window.

- Open a new Graphs & Geometry window by using the following keystrokes. (home) 2
- Enter the function $2x + 6$ in *f1(x)* and press (enter). When a new window is open, the cursor is automatically in the *f(x)* box. The graph and its equation will appear on the coordinate plane.
- Press (tab) twice to move the cursor to the graph screen.

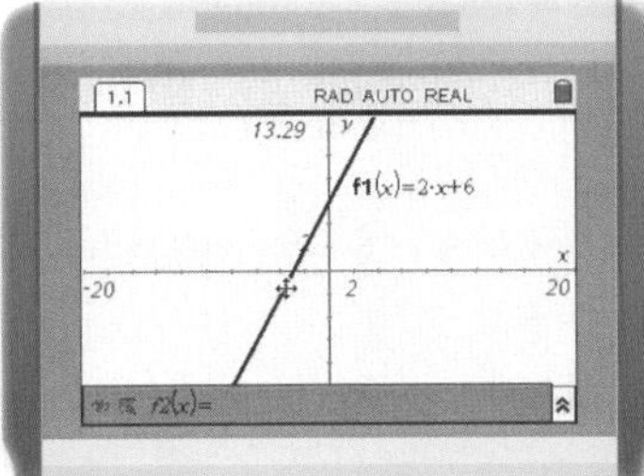

Step 2 Grab the line and translate the line up and down.

- Use the NavPad to move the cursor over the line in the third quadrant near the x-axis until it blinks with a ✣ sign on it. Press (ctrl)(click) to grab the line. Use the NavPad to translate the line up and down.

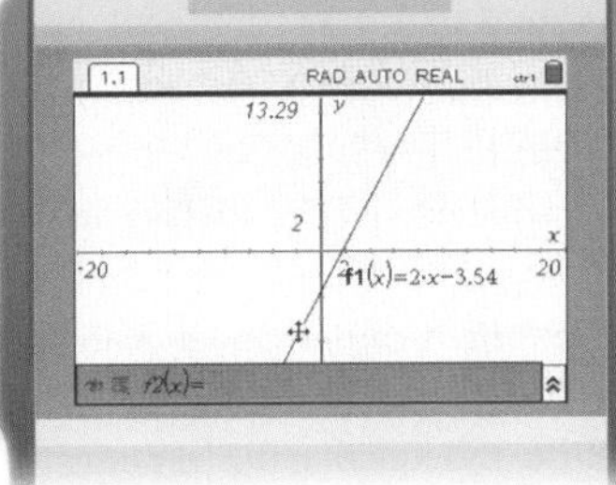

When graphing, be sure to use a viewing window that shows both the x- and y-intercepts of the graph of a function. If you need to set your own minimum and maximum values for the axes and the scale factor, use the WINDOW option from the menu button.

1 FOCUS

Objective Use the TI-*n*spire to investigate families of linear functions.

Materials for Each Group

- TI-*n*spire graphing calculator

Teaching Tip

The graphing calculator opens on the same screen as when it was turned off. Have students press the Home button to begin the lab.

2 TEACH

Working in Cooperative Groups

Have students of mixed abilities work in groups of two or three to complete the Activity and Exercises 1–4.

- In Step 1, point out that the TI-*n*spire uses function notation in the function box. Recall for students that an equation such as $y = 2x + 6$ that is a function can be written in function notation as $f(x) = 2x + 6$.
- In Step 2, students may need to press (tab) twice to make the arrow appear in the graphing window. Make sure students grab the line of the graph near the middle and not at the ends. If they grab the line near the ends, rotating circles will appear and the line will rotate rather than translate.

Ask:

- What happens to the equation of the line as you move the graph up and down? The slope stays the same at 2, but the value of the y-intercept increases as the graph moves up and decreases as it moves down.
- Why do you think the graphs in this activity are a family of linear functions? They all have the same slope, but different y-intercepts.

Practice Have students complete Exercises 5–13.

3 ASSESS

Formative Assessment

Use Exercises 1–4 to assess whether students can move the line of the graph up and down and note the changes in the y-intercept.

Use Exercises 5–8 to assess whether students can rotate the line of the graph and note the changes in the slope of the graph and in the coefficient of x in the equation of the line.

From Concrete to Abstract

Use Exercise 13 to assess whether students understand and can apply changes in slope and y-intercept to real-world situations, and relate the changes to the graph of the function and the equation represented by the graph.

Additional Answers

9. $f(x) = \frac{1}{2}x + 1$ rises from left to right while $f(x) = -2x + 1$ and $f(x) = -2x$ fall from left to right. $f(x) = \frac{1}{2}x + 1$ and $f(x) = -2x + 1$ appear to form a right angle but have the same y-intercept. $f(x) = -2x + 1$ and $f(x) = -2x$ are parallel.

11. Yes; it is perpendicular to the given lines.

Exercises

Graph $y = 3x - 4$. Grab the line and move it up and down as instructed on the previous activity.

1. What changes in the equation? What remains the same? **The y-intercept b changes and the slope m stays constant.**
2. How does adding or subtracting a constant c to a linear function affect its graph? **It shifts the graph vertically c units.**
3. Move the line until it crosses the y-axis as near to 5 as possible. Write the equation of the line. $y = 3x + 5$
4. Write an equation of the line that is parallel to $y = 3x - 4$ and passes through the origin. $y = 3x$

Open a new Graphs & Geometry window. Graph $y = 3x - 4$. Use the NavPad to move over the line until a blinking ↻ appears on it. Grab the line as instructed in the Activity and rotate the line.

5. What changes in the equation? What remains the same? **The slope m changes and the y-intercept b stays constant.**
6. How does changing the coefficient for x affect the graph of a linear function? **As the coefficient of x increases positively, the line becomes steeper.**
7. Without graphing, determine whether the graph of $y = 0.5x$ or the graph of $y = 1.5x$ has a steeper slope. Explain. $y = 1.5x$, **because** $1.5 > 0.5$
8. Rotate the graph until the x coefficient is negative. How does changing the sign of the coefficient of x affect the graph of a linear function? **When the coefficient is negative, the graph falls from left to right. When the coefficient is positive, the graph rises from left to right.**

Open a new Graphs & Geometry window. Graph the following lines.

$f1(x) = -2x$ $\qquad f2(x) = -2x + 1$ $\qquad f3(x) = \frac{1}{2}x + 1$

9. Describe the similarities and differences between the graphs. **See margin.**

Three functions with a slope of 1 are graphed in the standard viewing window, as shown.

10. Write an equation for each, beginning with the left-most graph. $y = x + 5$, $y = x$, $y = x - 5$
11. Does the equation $y = -x - 5$ have any special relationships with any of the above equations? **See margin.**
12. Write another equation that is part of this family of functions. **Sample answer:** $y = x + 3$
13. **GARDENING** A garden center charges $75 per cubic yard for topsoil. The delivery fee is $25.
    a. Write the equation that represents the charges. $y = 75x + 25$
    b. Describe the change in the graph if the delivery fee is changed to $35. **The slope is the same and the y-intercept is 35 instead of 25. The graphs are parallel.**
    c. How does the graph change if the price of a cubic yard of topsoil is increased to $80 when the delivery fee is $35.? **The y-intercept is the same and the slope is 80 instead of 75. The new graph is steeper.**
    d. What are the prices of a cubic yard of topsoil and delivery if the graph has slope 70 and y-intercept 40? **A cubic yard of topsoil is $70 and the delivery fee is $40.**

8-8 Writing Linear Equations

Why? a–b. See margin.

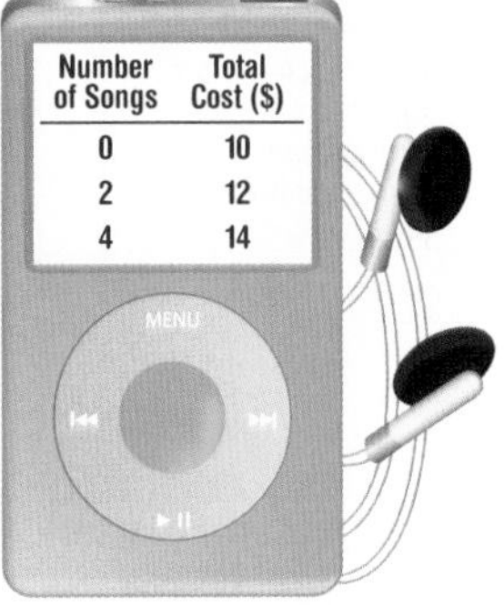

Olivia purchased a music subscription for downloading music from the Internet. The initial fee was $10. She then paid a cost of $1 per song.

a. Graph the ordered pairs (number of songs, total cost). Draw a line through the points.

b. Find the slope and the y-intercept of the line. What do these values represent?

a–b. See Chapter 8 Answer Appendix.

Then
You have already graphed linear equations using the slope and y-intercept. (Lesson 8-6)

Now
- Write equations given the slope and y-intercept, a graph, a table, or two points.
- Use linear equations to solve problems.

New Vocabulary
point-slope form

Math Online
glencoe.com
- Extra Examples
- Personal Tutor
- Self-Check Quiz
- Homework Help

Write Equations in Slope-Intercept Form One way to write a linear equation is to substitute the values for the slope and y-intercept in $y = mx + b$. Sometimes, you may need to find the y-intercept and slope from a graph.

EXAMPLE 1 Write the Equation of a Line in Slope-Intercept Form

Write an equation in slope-intercept form for each line.

a. The slope is $\frac{1}{2}$, and the y-intercept is -5.

$y = mx + b$ — **Slope-intercept form**

$y = \frac{1}{2}x + (-5)$ — **Replace m with $\frac{1}{2}$ and b with -5.**

$y = \frac{1}{2}x - 5$ — **Simplify.**

b.

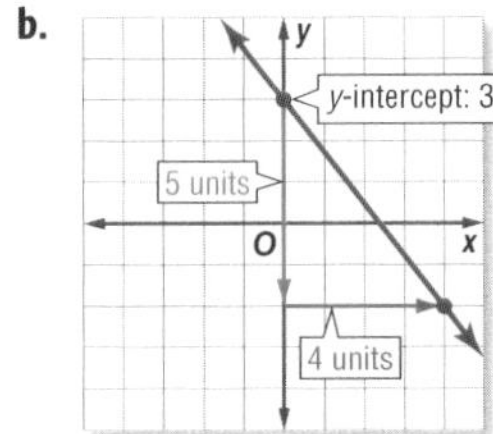

The y-intercept is 3. From (0, 3), you move down 5 units and right 4 units to another point on the line. So, the slope is $-\frac{5}{4}$.

$y = mx + b$ — **Slope-intercept form**

$y = -\frac{5}{4}x + 3$ — **Replace m with $-\frac{5}{4}$ and b with 3.**

Check Your Progress

1A. slope = 2, y-intercept = $\frac{1}{3}$ $y = 2x + \frac{1}{3}$

1B. $y = 2x - 4$

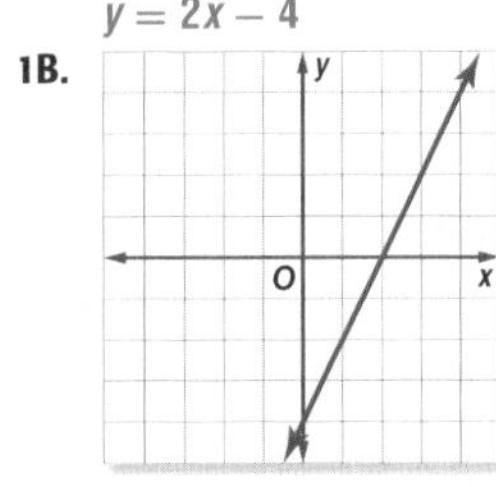

Personal Tutor glencoe.com

8-8 Lesson Notes

1 FOCUS

Vertical Alignment

Before Lesson 8-8
Graph linear equations using the slope and y-intercept.

Lesson 8-8
Write equations given the slope and y-intercept, a graph, a table, or two points. Use linear equations to solve problems.

After Lesson 8-8
Write equations of lines given characteristics such as two points, a table, or a slope and y-intercept.

2 TEACH

Scaffolding Questions

Have students read the *Why?* section of the lesson and answer the questions.

Ask:
- How many songs can be purchased for $10? zero
- How much would eight songs cost? $18
- If the initial fee was $12, how would the graph change? The y-intercept changes to 12 so the graph would move up.

Lesson 8-8 Resources

Resource	Approaching-Level	On-Level	Beyond-Level	English Learners
Teacher Edition	• Differentiated Instruction, p. 442	• Differentiated Instruction, p. 442	• Differentiated Instruction, p. 447	
Chapter Resource Masters	• Study Guide and Intervention, pp. 48–49 • Skills Practice, p. 50 • Practice, p. 51 • Word Problem Practice, p. 52	• Study Guide and Intervention, pp. 48–49 • Skills Practice, p. 50 • Practice, p. 51 • Word Problem Practice, p. 52 • Enrichment, p. 53	• Practice, p. 51 • Word Problem Practice, p. 52 • Enrichment, p. 53	• Study Guide and Intervention, pp. 48–49 • Skills Practice, p. 50 • Practice, p. 51
Transparencies	• 5-Minute Check Transparency 8-8	• 5-Minute Check Transparency 8-8	• 5-Minute Check Transparency 8-8	• 5-Minute Check Transparency 8-8
Other	• Study Notebook • Teaching Pre-Algebra with Manipulatives	• Study Notebook • Teaching Pre-Algebra with Manipulatives	• Study Notebook	• Study Notebook • Teaching Pre-Algebra with Manipulatives

Write Equations in Slope-Intercept Form

Example 1 shows how to write an equation in slope-intercept form. **Examples 2 and 3** show how to write an equation given two points or from a table.

Formative Assessment

Use the Check Your Progress exercises after each example to determine students' understanding of concepts.

Additional Examples

1 Write an equation in slope-intercept form for each line.

a. The slope is $-\frac{1}{4}$ and the y-intercept is 7.

$y = -\frac{1}{4}x + 7$

b.

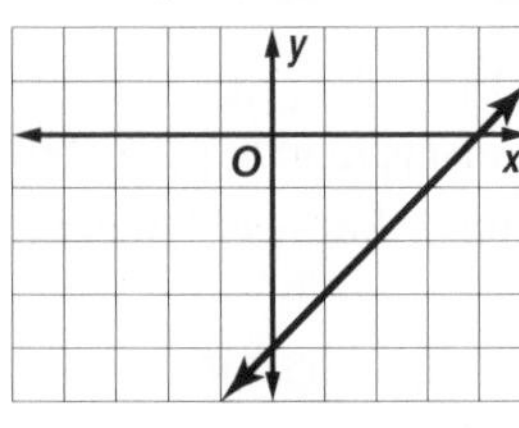

$y = x - 4$

2 Write an equation for the line that passes through the points (7, 0) and (6, 3).

$y - 3 = -3(x - 6)$ or
$y - 0 = -3(x - 7)$ or
$y = -3x + 21$

3 Write an equation of the line in point-slope form that passes through the points shown in the table below.

$y - 16 = -6(x + 2)$

x	y
−2	16
−1	10
0	4
1	−2

Additional Examples also in Interactive Classroom PowerPoint® Presentations

StudyTip

Equations of Lines The point-slope form of an equation can vary depending on the points chosen, but the slope-intercept form is the same regardless of the points chosen.

You can also write an equation for a line if you know the coordinates of two points on the line. An equation in the form $y - y_1 = m(x - x_1)$ where m represents the slope and (x_1, y_1) represents a point on the line, is called **point-slope form** of a line.

EXAMPLE 2 Write an Equation Given Two Points

Write an equation for the line that passes through (4, 8) and (−2, 5).

Step 1 Find the slope m.

$m = \frac{y_2 - y_1}{x_2 - x_1}$ **Definition of slope**

$m = \frac{5 - 8}{-2 - 4}$ **$(x_1, y_1) = (4, 8), (x_2, y_2) = (-2, 5)$**

$m = \frac{-3}{-6}$ or $\frac{1}{2}$ **Simplify.**

Step 2 Use the slope and the coordinates of either point to write the equation in point-slope form.

$y - y_1 = m(x - x_1)$ **Point-slope form**

$y - 8 = \frac{1}{2}(x - 4)$ **Replace (x, y) with (4, 8) and m with $\frac{1}{2}$.**

The equation is $y - 8 = \frac{1}{2}(x - 4)$. In slope-intercept form, $y = \frac{1}{2}x + 6$.

StudyTip

Check Equation To check, substitute the coordinates of the other point in the equation.

$y - 8 = \frac{1}{2}(x - 4)$
$5 - 8 \stackrel{?}{=} \frac{1}{2}(-2 - 4)$
$5 - 8 \stackrel{?}{=} \frac{1}{2}(-6)$
$-3 = -3$ ✓

Check Your Progress

2. Write an equation for the line that passes through (3, 0) and (6, −3).

$y + 3 = -1(x - 6)$ or $y - 0 = -1(x - 3)$ or $y = -x + 3$

Personal Tutor glencoe.com

EXAMPLE 3 Write an Equation from a Table

Write an equation of the line in point-slope form that passes through the points shown in the table at the right.

x	y
4	−2
8	1
12	4
16	7

Step 1 Find the slope m. Use the coordinates of any two points.

$m = \frac{y_2 - y_1}{x_2 - x_1}$ **Definition of slope**

$m = \frac{1 - (-2)}{8 - 4}$ **$(x_1, y_1) = (4, -2), (x_2, y_2) = (8, 1)$**

$m = \frac{3}{4}$ **Simplify.**

Step 2 To write the equation, use the slope and the coordinates of any point.

$y - y_1 = m(x - x_1)$ **Point-slope form**

$y - 1 = \frac{3}{4}(x - 8)$ **Replace (x, y) with (8, 1) and m with $\frac{3}{4}$.**

The equation is $y - 1 = \frac{3}{4}(x - 8)$.

StudyTip

Alternative Strategy If a table includes the y-intercept, simply use this value and the slope to write an equation.

x	y
0	−5
4	−2

y-intercept = −5

Check Your Progress

3. Write an equation of the line in point-slope form that passes through the points shown.

x	−3	0	2	3
y	9	3	−1	−3

Sample answer: $y - 9 = -2(x + 3)$

Personal Tutor glencoe.com

Differentiated Instruction

If students struggle with writing linear equations,

Then have students work in pairs. First, have one partner write down four slopes and the other write down four y-intercepts. Then have them combine the lists to write four linear equations. Afterward, ask them each to state a point on the coordinate grid and then work as a pair to write a linear equation in slope-intercept form that satisfies their two points.

Solve Problems You can write an equation to describe the relationship between two quantities and to make predictions.

Real-World EXAMPLE 4 Write an Equation to Make a Prediction

Real-World Link

Since the boiling point of water is lower at higher altitudes, cooks have to make adjustments in cooking times. A general rule is that for every 1000 feet above 2000 feet elevation, increase the cooking time by 5%.

Source: Kuhn Rikon Switzerland

BOILING POINT The boiling point of water at sea level, or at altitude 0 feet, is 212°F. The boiling point decreases 1°F for every 540-foot increase in altitude. Estimate the boiling point for an altitude of 4000 feet.

Understand You know the rate of change of boiling point temperature to altitude and the temperature at altitude 0 feet. You need to estimate the boiling point for an altitude of 4000 feet.

Plan First, find the slope and y-intercept. Then write an equation to show the relationship between altitude x and temperature y. Use the equation to find the boiling point.

Solve The boiling point decreases 1°F for every 540-foot increase in altitude.

- Find the slope m and the y-intercept b.

$$m = \frac{\text{change in } y}{\text{change in } x} \quad \begin{array}{l}\leftarrow \text{change in boiling point}\\ \leftarrow \text{change in altitude}\end{array}$$

$$= \frac{-1}{540} \quad \begin{array}{l}\leftarrow \text{decrease of 1°F}\\ \leftarrow \text{increase of 540 ft}\end{array}$$

$$\approx -0.002$$

At $x = 0$, $y = 212$. So, the y-intercept b equals 212.

- Write the equation.

$y = mx + b$ **Slope-intercept form**

$y = -0.002x + 212$ **Replace m with -0.002 and b with 212.**

- Find the boiling point.

$y = -0.002x + 212$ **Write the equation.**

$= -0.002(4000) + 212$ **Replace x with 4000.**

$= 204$ **Simplify.**

At an altitude of 4000 feet, the boiling point of water is about 204°F.

Check Since $4000 \div 540$ is about 8, the boiling point would drop 8×1 or 8°F. 212°F − 8°F = 204°F. So, the answer is reasonable. ✓

Problem-SolvingTip

Use a Table Translate the words into a table of values to better understand what the slope represents. For every increase of 540 feet in altitude, the temperature decreases by 1°F.

Altitude (ft) x	Boiling Point (°F) y
0	212
540	211
1,080	210

Check Your Progress

4. **PIANO LESSONS** The cost of 7 half-hour piano lessons is $179. The cost of 11 half-hour lessons is $267.
   - **a.** Write a linear equation that shows the cost y for x half-hour lessons. $y = 22x + 25$
   - **b.** Use the equation from part **a.** to find the cost of 3 half-hour lessons. $91

Personal Tutor glencoe.com

Focus on Mathematical Content

Writing Equations Linear equations can be written using any two points on a straight line even if one of the points is the y-intercept. The intercept is the point $(0, y)$. If a given point is not the y-intercept, use that point and the slope in the slope-intercept form and solve for the y-intercept.

Solve Problems

Example 4 shows how to write an equation to make a prediction.

Additional Example

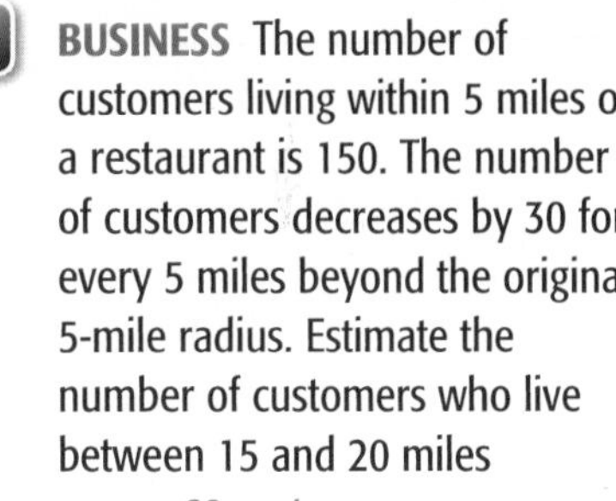

4 **BUSINESS** The number of customers living within 5 miles of a restaurant is 150. The number of customers decreases by 30 for every 5 miles beyond the original 5-mile radius. Estimate the number of customers who live between 15 and 20 miles away. 60 customers

Watch Out!

Preventing Errors Tell students that to check their equations, they can choose another point on the line and substitute its coordinates for x and y in the equation.

Lesson 8-8 Writing Linear Equations 443

3 PRACTICE

Formative Assessment

Use Exercises 1–13 to check for understanding.

Use the chart at the bottom of this page to customize assignments for your students.

Tips for New Teachers

Computing Slope Point out to students that the designation of (x_1, y_1) and (x_2, y_2) is arbitrary. The left-most point doesn't have to be (x_1, y_1) nor the one farthest to the right (x_2, y_2). Tell them to use the order that makes the subtraction the easiest.

Additional Answers

8. $y - 3 = \frac{1}{3}(x - 3)$ or
$y - 4 = \frac{1}{3}(x - 6)$ or
$y = \frac{1}{3}x + 2$

9. $y - 5 = -9(x - 2)$ or
$y + 4 = -9(x - 3)$ or
$y = -9x + 23$

10. $y - 2 = -2(x + 1)$ or
$y + 10 = -2(x - 5)$ or
$y = -2x$

13a. $y = 2.4x$; The speed of the rip current is 2.4 feet per second.

13b. 144 ft

28. $y - 2 = x - 1$ or
$y - 4 = x - 3$ or
$y = x + 1$

29. $y + 2 = \frac{1}{2}(x - 2)$ or
$y + 1 = \frac{1}{2}(x - 4)$ or
$y = \frac{1}{2}x - 3)$

30. $y - 4 = 4(x - 1)$ or
$y - 8 = 4(x - 2)$ or
$y = 4x$

31. $y + 6 = 0(x - 3)$ or
$y + 6 = 0(x - 5)$ or
$y = -6$

32. $y + 4 = -\frac{3}{2}(x - 4)$ or
$y + 10 = -\frac{3}{2}(x - 8)$ or
$y = -\frac{3}{2}x + 2)$

33. $y - 9 = -5(x + 1)$ or
$y + 6 = -5(x - 2)$ or
$y = -5x + 4$

Concept Summary	**Write a Linear Equation** (For Your FOLDABLE)
From Slope and y-Intercept	• Substitute the slope m and y-intercept b in $y = mx + b$.
From a Graph	• Find the y-intercept b and the slope m from the graph. • Substitute the slope and y-intercept in $y = mx + b$.
From Two Points	• Use the coordinates of the two points to find the slope. • Substitute the slope and coordinates of one of the points in $y - y_1 = m(x - x_1)$
From a Table	• Use the coordinates of any two points to find the slope. • Substitute the slope and coordinates of one of the points in $y - y_1 = m(x - x_1)$

Check Your Understanding

Example 1 p. 441

Write an equation in slope-intercept form for each line.

1. slope = 2, y-intercept = 4 **$y = 2x + 4$**
2. slope = 0, y-intercept = 1 **$y = 1$**

3. slope = $-\frac{3}{4}$, y-intercept = 0 **$y = -\frac{3}{4}x$**
4. slope = $\frac{1}{3}$, y-intercept = -6 **$y = \frac{1}{3}x - 6$**

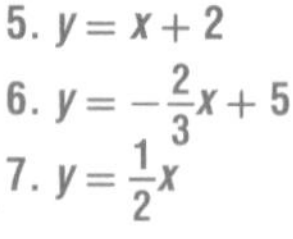
5. $y = x + 2$
6. $y = -\frac{2}{3}x + 5$
7. $y = \frac{1}{2}x$

5.

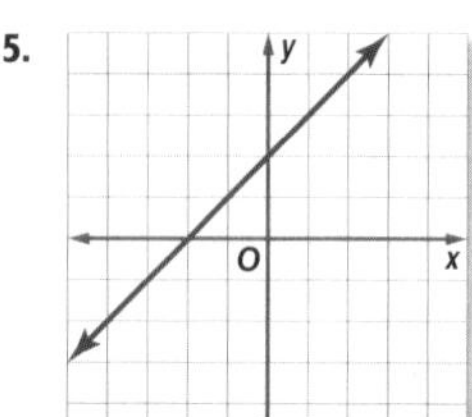

6.

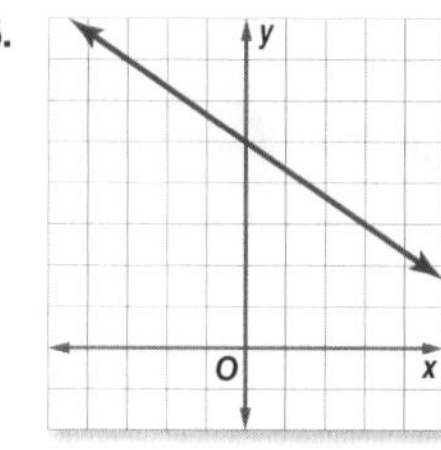

7.

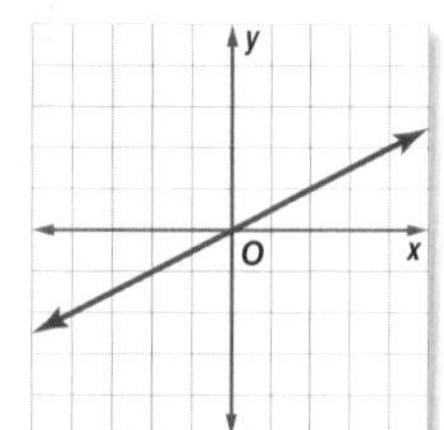

Example 2 p. 442

Write an equation for the line that passes through each pair of points.

8. (3, 3) and (6, 4)
9. (2, 5) and (3, −4)
10. (−1, 2) and (5, −10)
8–10. See margin.

Example 3 p. 442

Write an equation in point-slope form to represent each table of values.

11.

x	−1	0	1	2
y	−6	−2	2	6

Sample answer: $y - 2 = 4(x - 1)$

12.

x	−6	−3	3	6
y	−1	0	2	3

Sample answer: $y - 0 = \frac{1}{3}(x + 3)$

Example 4 p. 443

13. SOUND Use the table that shows the distance that a rip current travels through the ocean.

a. Write an equation in slope-intercept form to represent the data in the table. Describe what the slope means.

b. Estimate how far the rip current travels in 1 minute. **a–b. See margin.**

Time (s)	Distance (ft)
x	y
0	0
1	2.4
2	4.8
3	7.2

444 Chapter 8 Linear Functions and Graphing

Differentiated Homework Options

Level	Assignment	Two-Day Option	
AL Basic	14–39, 43–45, 47–60	15–39 odd, 48–51	14–38 even, 43–45, 47, 52–60
OL Core	15–39 odd, 40–45, 47–60	14–39, 48–51	40–45, 47, 52–60
BL Advanced	41–57 (optional: 58–60)		

Practice and Problem Solving

= **Step-by-Step Solutions** begin on page R11.
Extra Practice begins on page 810.

Example 1 p. 441

Write an equation in slope-intercept form for each line.

14. slope = 3, y-intercept = 2 $y = 3x + 2$
15. slope = 1, y-intercept = −4 $y = x - 4$
16. slope = 0, y-intercept = 1 $y = 1$
17. slope = 2, y-intercept = 0 $y = 2x$
18. slope = $\frac{1}{4}$, y-intercept = −3 $y = \frac{1}{4}x - 3$
19. slope = 0, y-intercept = −7 $y = -7$
20. slope = $-\frac{2}{3}$, y-intercept = 0 $y = -\frac{2}{3}x$
21. slope = $-\frac{5}{3}$, y-intercept = −6 $y = -\frac{5}{3}x - 6$

22. 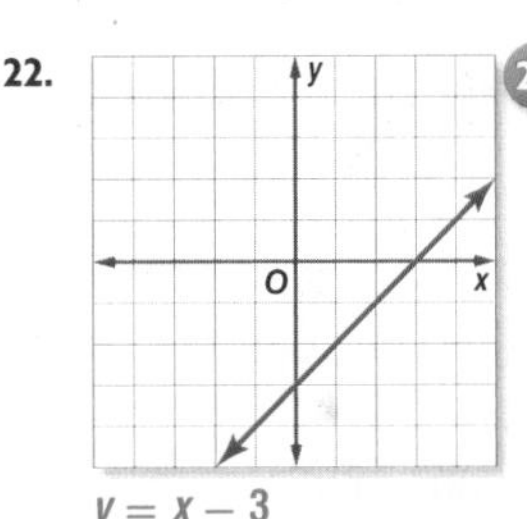
$y = x - 3$

23. 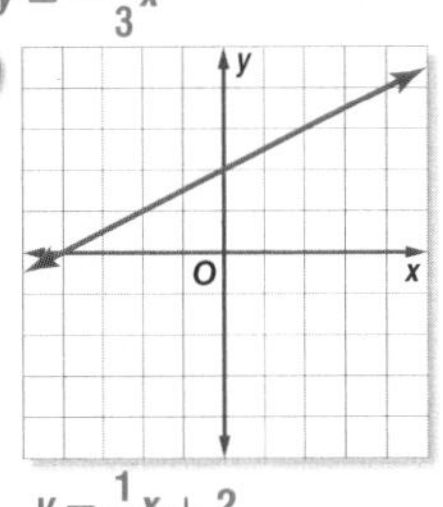
$y = \frac{1}{2}x + 2$

24. 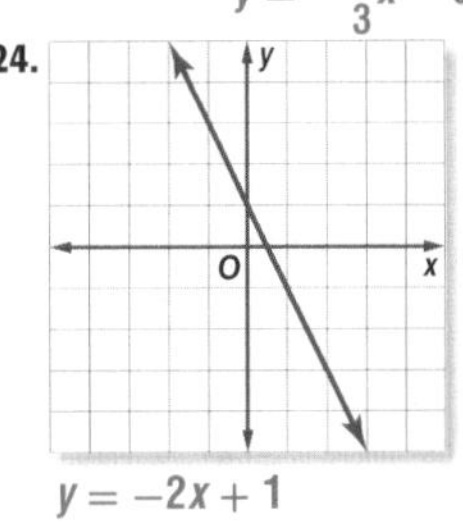
$y = -2x + 1$

25. 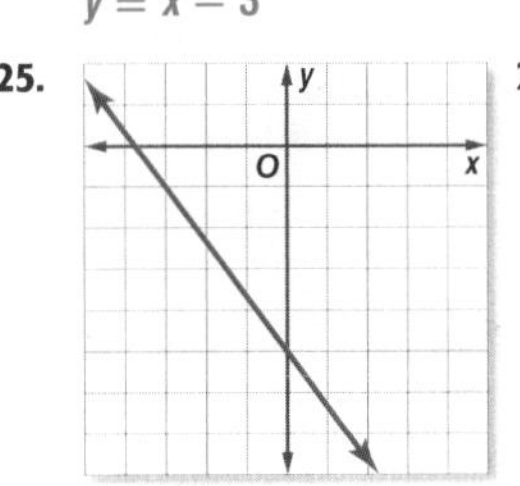
$y = -\frac{4}{3}x - 5$

26. 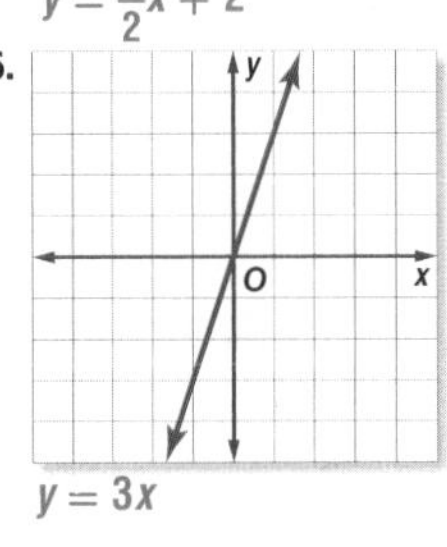
$y = 3x$

27. 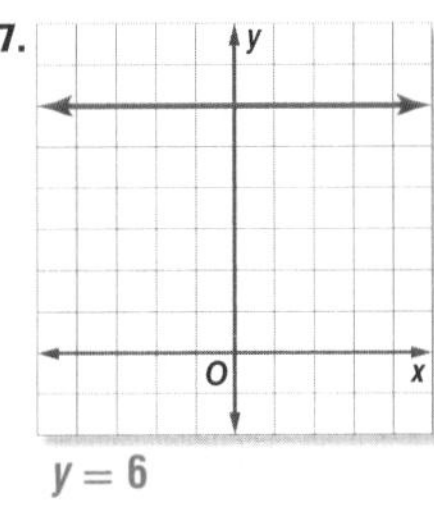
$y = 6$

Example 2 p. 442

Write an equation for the line that passes through each pair of points. 28–33. See margin.

28. (1, 2) and (3, 4)
29. (2, −2) and (4, −1)
30. (1, 4) and (2, 8)
31. (3, −6) and (5, −6)
32. (4, −4) and (8, −10)
33. (−1, 9) and (2, −6)

Example 3 p. 442

Write an equation in point-slope form to represent each table of values.

34.

x	−1	1	2	3
y	4	6	7	8

Sample answer: $y - 4 = 1(x + 1)$

35.

x	−2	−1	1	2
y	−4	−2	2	4

Sample answer: $y + 2 = 2(x + 1)$

36.

x	−4	−3	0	1
y	−3	−4	−7	−8

Sample answer: $y + 8 = -1(x - 1)$

37.

x	−5	5	10	15
y	−1	3	5	7

Sample answer: $y - 5 = \frac{2}{5}(x - 10)$

Example 4 p. 443

38. **COMPUTERS** Compuworks, a computer repair company, charges a fee and an hourly charge. After two hours, the repair bill is \$110, and after three hours, it is \$150.
   a. Write an equation in slope-intercept form to represent the data. $y = 40x + 30$
   b. Describe what the slope and y-intercept mean. The slope 40 is the hourly charge and the y-intercept 30 is the fee.
   c. How much would it cost for 1.5 hours of work? \$90

Study Guide and Intervention
CRM pp. 48–49 AL OL ELL

Practice
CRM p. 51 AL OL BL ELL

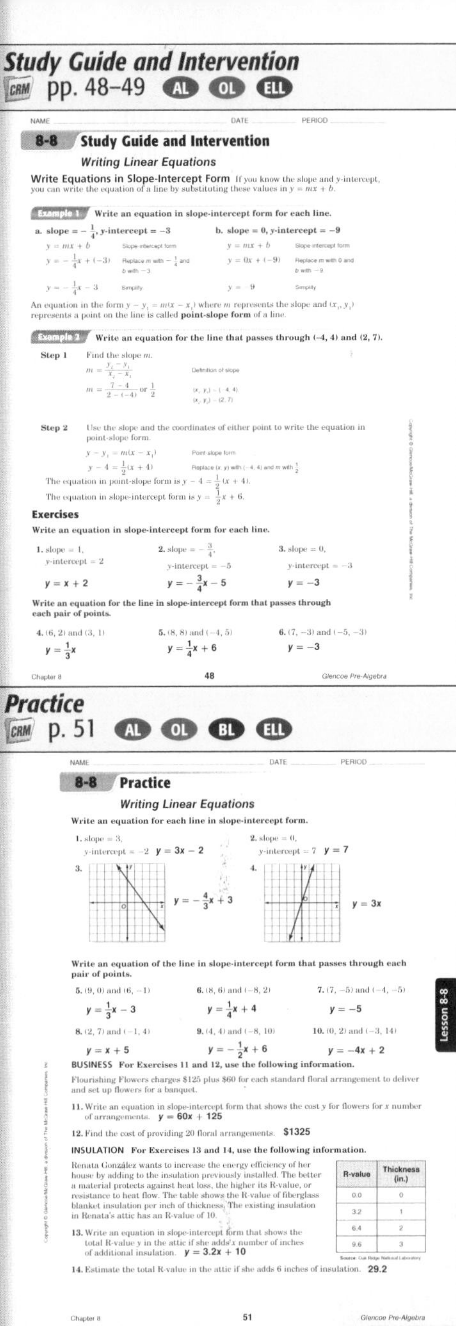

NAME ______ DATE ______ PERIOD ______

8-8 Study Guide and Intervention
Writing Linear Equations

Write Equations in Slope-Intercept Form If you know the slope and y-intercept, you can write the equation of a line by substituting those values in $y = mx + b$.

Example 1 Write an equation in slope-intercept form for each line.

a. slope = $-\frac{1}{4}$, y-intercept = −3
$y = mx + b$ Slope-intercept form
$y = -\frac{1}{4}x + (-3)$ Replace m with $-\frac{1}{4}$ and b with −3
$y = -\frac{1}{4}x - 3$ Simplify

b. slope = 0, y-intercept = −9
$y = mx + b$ Slope-intercept form
$y = 0x + (-9)$ Replace m with 0 and b with −9
$y = -9$ Simplify

An equation in the form $y - y_1 = m(x - x_1)$ where m represents the slope and (x_1, y_1) represents a point on the line is called **point-slope form** of a line.

Example 2 Write an equation for the line that passes through (−4, 4) and (2, 7).

Step 1 Find the slope m.
$m = \frac{y_2 - y_1}{x_2 - x_1}$ Definition of slope
$m = \frac{7 - 4}{2 - (-4)}$ or $\frac{1}{2}$ $(x_1, y_1) = (-4, 4)$, $(x_2, y_2) = (2, 7)$

Step 2 Use the slope and the coordinates of either point to write the equation in point-slope form.
$y - y_1 = m(x - x_1)$ Point-slope form
$y - 4 = \frac{1}{2}(x + 4)$ Replace (x, y) with (−4, 4) and m with $\frac{1}{2}$

The equation in point-slope form is $y - 4 = \frac{1}{2}(x + 4)$.
The equation in slope-intercept form is $y = \frac{1}{2}x + 6$.

Exercises

Write an equation in slope-intercept form for each line.

1. slope = 1, y-intercept = 2 $y = x + 2$
2. slope = $-\frac{3}{4}$, y-intercept = −5 $y = -\frac{3}{4}x - 5$
3. slope = 0, y-intercept = −3 $y = -3$

Write an equation for the line in slope-intercept form that passes through each pair of points.

4. (6, 2) and (3, 1) $y = \frac{1}{3}x$
5. (8, 8) and (−4, 5) $y = \frac{1}{4}x + 6$
6. (7, −3) and (−5, −3) $y = -3$

Chapter 8 48 Glencoe Pre-Algebra

NAME ______ DATE ______ PERIOD ______

8-8 Practice
Writing Linear Equations

Write an equation for each line in slope-intercept form.

1. slope = 3, y-intercept = −2 $y = 3x - 2$
2. slope = 0, y-intercept = 7 $y = 7$
3. $y = -\frac{4}{3}x + 3$
4. $y = 3x$

Write an equation of the line in slope-intercept form that passes through each pair of points.

5. (9, 0) and (6, −1) $y = \frac{1}{3}x - 3$
6. (8, 6) and (−8, 2) $y = \frac{1}{4}x + 4$
7. (7, −5) and (−4, −5) $y = -5$
8. (2, 7) and (−1, 4) $y = x + 5$
9. (4, 4) and (−8, 10) $y = -\frac{1}{2}x + 6$
10. (0, 2) and (−3, 14) $y = -4x + 2$

BUSINESS For Exercises 11 and 12, use the following information.
Flourishing Flowers charges \$125 plus \$60 for each standard floral arrangement to deliver and set up flowers for a banquet.

11. Write an equation in slope-intercept form that shows the cost y for flowers for x number of arrangements. $y = 60x + 125$
12. Find the cost of providing 20 floral arrangements. \$1325

INSULATION For Exercises 13 and 14, use the following information.
Renata González wants to increase the energy efficiency of her house by adding to the insulation previously installed. The better a material protects against heat loss, the higher its R-value, or resistance to heat flow. The table shows the R-value of fiberglass blanket insulation per inch of thickness. The existing insulation in Renata's attic has an R-value of 10.

R-value	Thickness (in.)
0.0	0
3.2	1
6.4	2
9.6	3

Source: Oak Ridge National Laboratory

13. Write an equation in slope-intercept form that shows the total R-value y in the attic if she adds x number of inches of additional insulation. $y = 3.2x + 10$
14. Estimate the total R-value in the attic if she adds 6 inches of insulation. 29.2

Chapter 8 51 Glencoe Pre-Algebra

Word Problem Practice
CRM p. 52 AL OL BL

NAME ______ DATE ______ PERIOD ______

8-8 Word Problem Practice
Writing Linear Equations

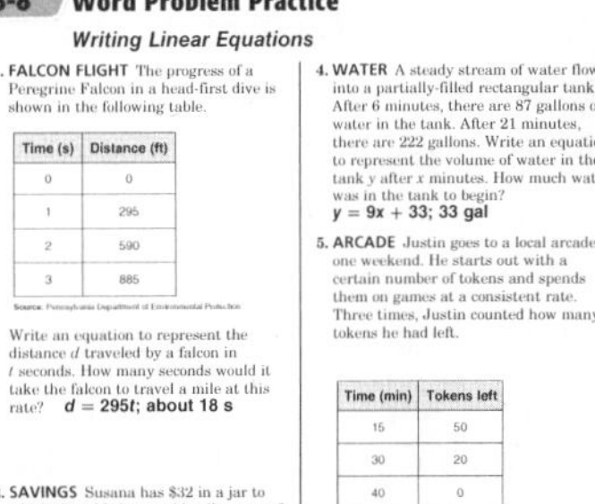

1. **FALCON FLIGHT** The progress of a Peregrine Falcon in a head-first dive is shown in the following table.

Time (s)	Distance (ft)
0	0
1	295
2	590
3	885

Write an equation to represent the distance d traveled by a falcon in t seconds. How many seconds would it take the falcon to travel a mile at this rate? $d = 295t$; about 18 s

2. **SAVINGS** Susana has \$32 in a jar to which she adds her weekly allowance of \$8. Write a linear equation in slope-intercept form to show how much she saves y after x weeks. How much will she have saved after 5 weeks? $y = 32 + 8x$; \$72

3. **ARCHITECTURE** The following diagram shows the design for a symmetrical roof.

Write two equations to represent the two sides of the roof. $y = \frac{2}{3}x + 8$ and $y = -\frac{2}{3}x + 8$

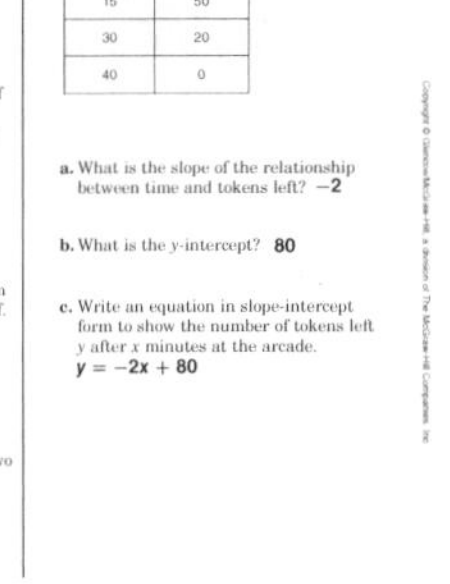

4. **WATER** A steady stream of water flows into a partially-filled rectangular tank. After 6 minutes, there are 87 gallons of water in the tank. After 21 minutes, there are 222 gallons. Write an equation to represent the volume of water in the tank y after x minutes. How much water was in the tank to begin? $y = 9x + 33$; 33 gal

5. **ARCADE** Justin goes to a local arcade one weekend. He starts out with a certain number of tokens and spends them on games at a consistent rate. Three times, Justin counted how many tokens he had left.

Time (min)	Tokens left
15	50
30	20
40	0

a. What is the slope of the relationship between time and tokens left? −2
b. What is the y-intercept? 80
c. Write an equation in slope-intercept form to show the number of tokens left y after x minutes at the arcade. $y = -2x + 80$

Chapter 8 52 Glencoe Pre-Algebra

Enrichment
CRM p. 53 OL BL

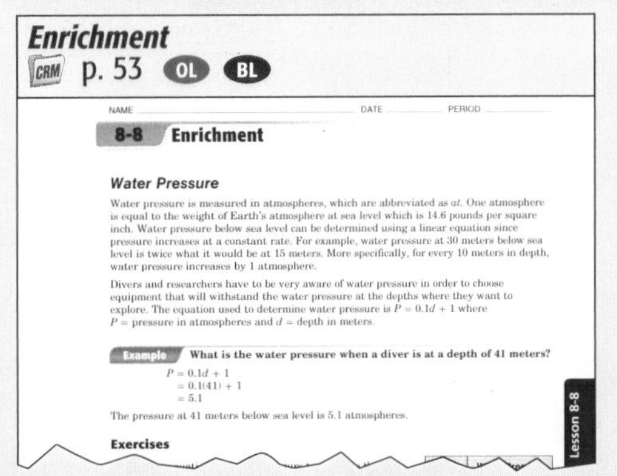

NAME ______ DATE ______ PERIOD ______

8-8 Enrichment

Water Pressure

Water pressure is measured in atmospheres, which are abbreviated as *at*. One atmosphere is equal to the weight of Earth's atmosphere at sea level which is 14.6 pounds per square inch. Water pressure below sea level can be determined using a linear equation since pressure increases at a constant rate. For example, water pressure at 30 meters below sea level is twice what it would be at 15 meters. More specifically, for every 10 meters in depth, water pressure increases by 1 atmosphere.

Divers and researchers have to be very aware of water pressure in order to choose equipment that will withstand the water pressure at the depths where they want to explore. The equation used to determine water pressure is $P = 0.1d + 1$ where P = pressure in atmospheres and d = depth in meters.

Example What is the water pressure when a diver is at a depth of 41 meters?

$P = 0.1d + 1$
$= 0.1(41) + 1$
$= 5.1$

The pressure at 41 meters below sea level is 5.1 atmospheres.

Exercises

Multiple Representations In Exercise 42, students write simultaneous equations modeling time, speed, and distance and solve them by graphing the equations on the coordinate plane.

Watch Out!

Find the Error For Exercise 45, remind students that the slope of a line is found using $m = \frac{y_2 - y_1}{x_2 - x_1}$ and that the y-intercept is of the form $(0, y)$. Have students look at both m and b in Daniel and Kayla's equations.

Additional Answers

39a. $y = 30x + 30$; The height of the fireworks increases 30 meters per 1-inch increase in shell radius.

39b. 300 m

42c.

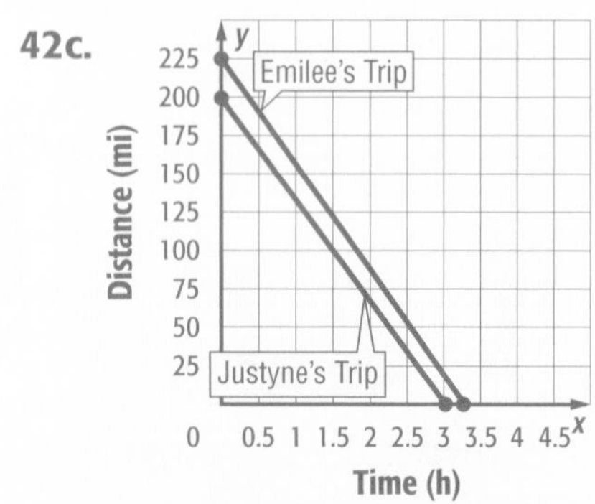

43. Sample answer: $(-1, 2)$ and $(-4, 5)$; $y - 5 = -1(x + 4)$

47. Sample answer: When using an equation in the form $y = mx + b$, the slope is m and the y-intercept is b. When using a table, choose two pairs of x- and y-coordinates to find the slope. The y-intercept is the y value in the table when the corresponding x value is 0. When using a graph, choose two points on the line to find the slope. The y-intercept is the y-coordinate of the point where the graph crosses the y-axis.

Real-World Link

You can see a firework explosion before hearing it because sound travels at about 742 miles per hour, but light travels at about 670 million miles per hour.

Source: Zambelli Fireworks

40. Yes; an equation that represents this situation is $y = 100 + 35x$. If $x = 20$, then the total cost is \$800.

41a. $y = 34.95x$; The slope \$34.95 is the cost per person.

44. False; Sample answer: The equation for a horizontal line is $y = b$, where b represents a constant number. There is no x term in the equation.

45. Daniel; Kayla incorrectly calculated the slope by dividing the change in x by the change in y. Also, the y-intercept is 5, not 0.

39. FIREWORKS The table at the right shows the heights of different firework displays. **a–b. See margin.**

Shell Radius (in.)	Height of Fireworks (m)
3	120
4	150
5	180
6	210

Source: Skylighter

a. Write an equation in slope-intercept form to represent the data. Describe what the slope means.

b. Predict the height of fireworks that have shells with a radius of 9 inches.

40. PAINTING Mr. Awan has budgeted \$860 to have his dining room painted. B The estimated cost for materials is \$100. The painter charges \$35 per hour and estimates that the work will take about 20 hours to complete. Has Mr. Awan budgeted enough money to paint the dining room? Explain.

41. SNORKELING The table at the right shows the cost of a snorkeling trip.

Number of People	Total Cost (\$)
3	104.85
5	174.75

a. Write an equation in slope-intercept form to represent the data. Describe what the slope means.

b. How much would it cost for 9 people to go on the snorkeling trip? **\$314.55**

C **42. MULTIPLE REPRESENTATIONS** Emilee and Justyne are traveling on the same highway to a family reunion at a park. Emilee starts out 225 miles from the park and drives 70 miles per hour. At the same time, Justyne starts out 200 miles from the park and drives 65 miles per hour.

a. ALGEBRAIC Write an equation for Emilee's trip where y is the total distance from the park after x hours. $y = 225 - 70x$

b. ALGEBRAIC Write an equation for Justyne's trip where y is the total distance from the park after x hours. $y = 200 - 65x$

c. GRAPHICAL Graph the two equations on the same coordinate plane. **See margin.**

d. VERBAL Do you think that Emilee will overtake Justyne before they reach the park? Explain your reasoning. **No; Justyne will arrive 0.13 hour or about 8 minutes before Emilee.**

H.O.T. Problems

Use Higher-Order Thinking Skills

43. OPEN ENDED Choose two points in the second quadrant. Write an equation in point-slope form for the line that passes through the points. **See margin.**

44. REASONING *True or false*: The equation for a horizontal line has both an x and y term. Explain your reasoning.

45. FIND THE ERROR Daniel and Kayla are writing an equation for the line that passes through $(-4, 0)$ and $(0, 5)$. Is either of them correct? Explain.

Daniel	Kayla
$m = \frac{5}{4}$ and $b = 5$, so the equation is $y = \frac{5}{4}x + 5$.	$m = \frac{4}{5}$ and the y-intercept is 0, so the equation is $y = \frac{4}{5}x$.

46. CHALLENGE Write an equation in *slope-intercept* form for the line that passes through the points (3, 2) and (9, 4). $y = \frac{1}{3}x + 1$

47. WRITING IN MATH Summarize how to find the slope and y-intercept of a linear function from a(n) equation, table, and graph. **See margin.**

446 Chapter 8 Linear Functions and Graphing

Standardized Test Practice

48. Which of the following equations describes the data in the table below? C

Number of DVDs	2	4	6	8
Cost ($)	16	22	28	34

A $3x + y = 10$
B $x - 3y = -10$
C $3x - y = -10$
D $x + y = 10$

49. Which of the following equations names the line that passes through the points (0, −6) and (2, 3)? F

F $y = \frac{9}{2}x - 6$ H $y = -\frac{2}{9}x - 6$
G $y = \frac{2}{9}x - 6$ J $y = -\frac{9}{2}x - 6$

50. Which of the following equations describes the line graphed below? B

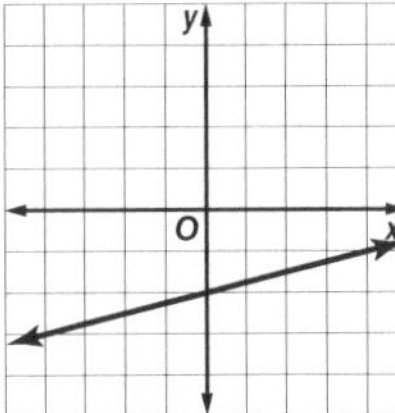

A $y = 4x - 2$ C $y = \frac{1}{3}x - 2$
B $y = \frac{1}{4}x - 2$ D $y = \frac{1}{4}x + 2$

51. SHORT RESPONSE Jan is 320 miles from home and is driving home at a speed of 65 mph. Write an equation to determine her distance from home at any point during her trip. $d = 320 - 65s$

Spiral Review

Graph each equation using the slope and y-intercept. (Lesson 8-7) 52–54. See margin.

52. $y = \frac{3}{4}x + 2$ **53.** $x + y = -3$ **54.** $x + y = 0$

Find the slope of each line. (Lesson 8-6)

55.

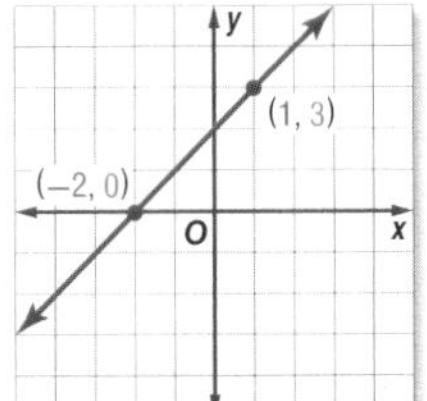

1

56.

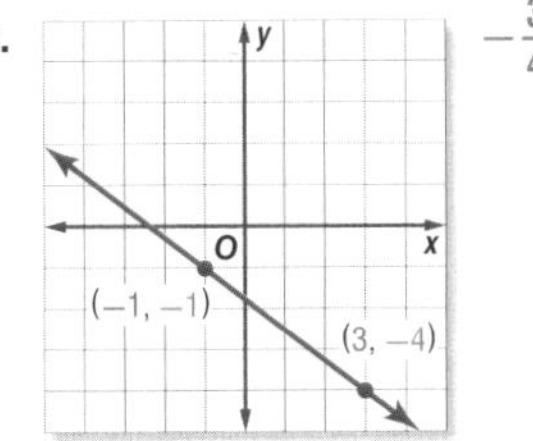

$-\frac{3}{4}$

57. BIRDS If 12 of the 75 animals in a pet store are parakeets, what percent are parakeets? (Lesson 7-3) 16%

Skills Review

Determine whether a scatter plot of the data for the following might show a *positive*, *negative*, or *no* relationship. Explain your answer. (Lesson 1-6)

58. size of household and amount of water bill positive; As a household size increases, the amount of the water bill increases.

59. temperature and heating costs negative; As the temperature decreases, heating costs increase.

60. speed and distance traveled positive; As speed increases, distance traveled increases.

4 ASSESS

Yesterday's News Have students write how yesterday's lesson on the slope-intercept form helped them in today's lesson on writing linear equations.

Formative Assessment

Check for student understanding of concepts in Lessons 8-6 through 8-8.

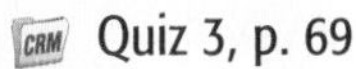

CRM Quiz 3, p. 69

Additional Answers

52.

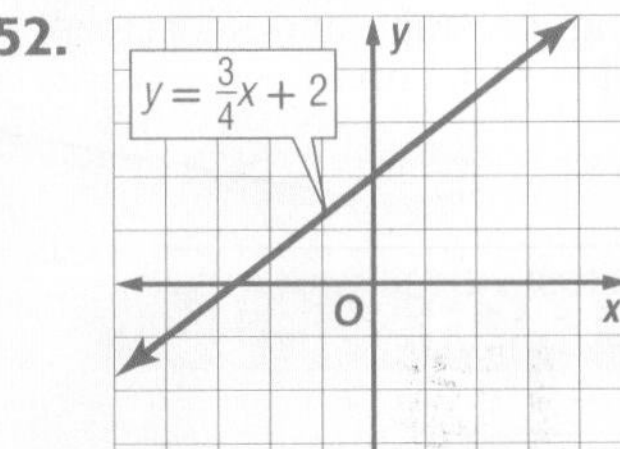

53.

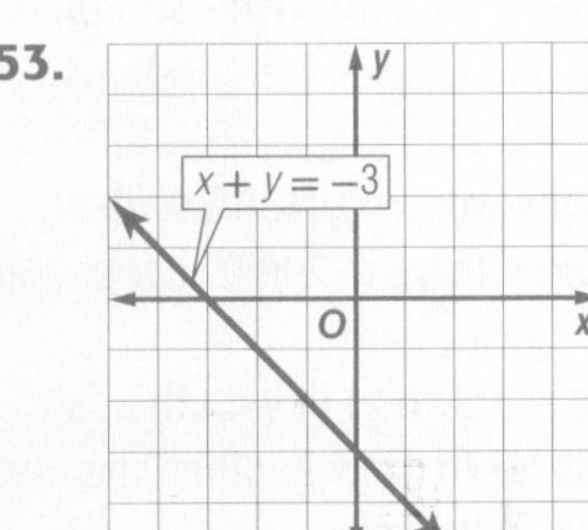

54.

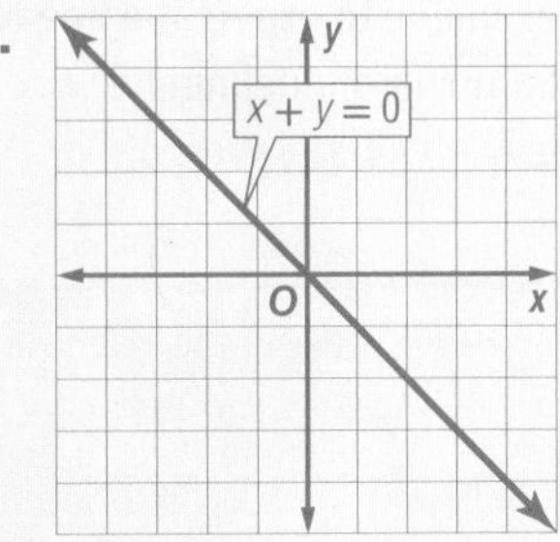

Differentiated Instruction

Extension In 2000, the population of Texas was 20.8 million. The state grew to an estimated 23.5 million six years later. Have students write an equation that represents the population of Texas. They should make a graph and find the slope and y-intercept. Have students predict the population in 2020. See margin for graph; $y = 0.45x + 20.8$; slope $= 0.45$, y-intercept $= 20.8$; prediction: about 30 million

Additional Answer (Differentiated Instruction Extension)

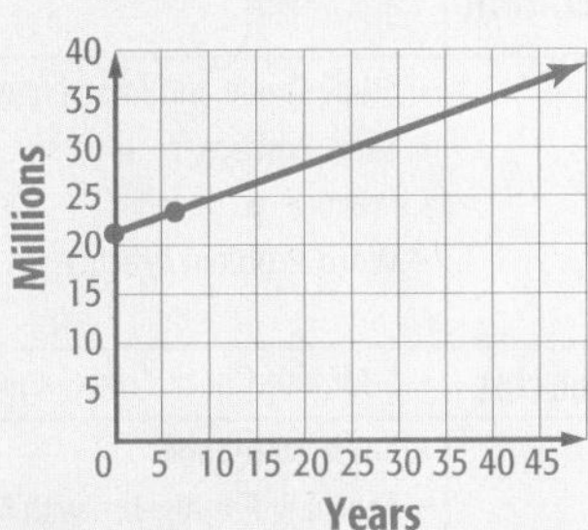

8-9 Lesson Notes

1 FOCUS

Vertical Alignment

Before Lesson 8-9
Analyze trends in data displayed in scatter plots.

Lesson 8-9
Draw lines of fit for sets of data. Use lines of fit to make predictions about data.

After Lesson 8-9
Interpret and predict the effects of changing the slope and y-intercept in applied situations.

2 TEACH

Scaffolding Questions

Have students read the *Why?* section of the lesson and answer the questions.

Ask:

- How many women's NCAA softball teams were there in 2004? about 260 teams
- The line is drawn to fit with the data. Is it possible to draw another line that also fits with the data? yes
- Is it reasonable to expect the line to continue upward indefinitely? No, eventually it would flatten out or plateau.

8-9 Prediction Equations

Then
You have already analyzed trends in data displayed in scatter plots.
(Lesson 1-6)

Now
- Draw lines of fit for sets of data.
- Use lines of fit to make predictions about data.

New Vocabulary
line of fit

Math Online
glencoe.com
- Extra Examples
- Personal Tutor
- Self-Check Quiz
- Homework Help

Why?

The scatter plot shows the number of NCAA Women's softball teams.

NCAA Women's Softball

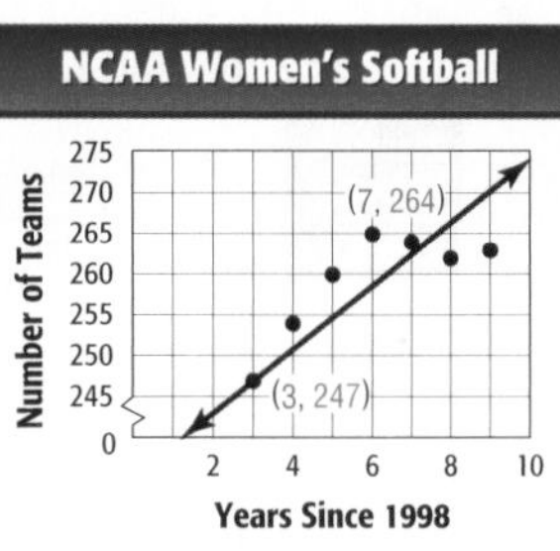

Source: National Collegiate Athletic Association

a. Use the two points that are labeled to find the slope of the line drawn. Describe what the slope means. See Chapter 8 Answer Appendix.

b. Looking at the line, what would you expect the number would be in 2006? Based on the graph, is the actual number greater or less than your prediction? See students' work.

Lines of Fit When real-world data are collected, the points graphed usually do not form a straight line, but may approximate a linear relationship. A **line of fit** is a line that is very close to most of the data points. The line drawn in the graph shown above is a line of fit.

Real-World EXAMPLE 1 Make a Prediction from a Line of Fit

TESTS The table shows the number of college-bound students that took the ACT in different years.

Students Taking ACT

Year	2000	2002	2004	2006
Number (thousands)	1065	1116	1171	1206

Source: ACT, Inc.

a. Make a scatter plot and draw a line of fit for the data.

Graph each of the data points. Draw a line that fits most of the data.

b. Use the line of fit to predict the number of students who will take the ACT in 2015.

Extend the line so that you can estimate the y-value for an x-value of 2015. The y-value for 2015 is about 1480 (thousand). So, we can predict that about 1480 (thousand) students will take the ACT in 2015.

Students Taking ACT

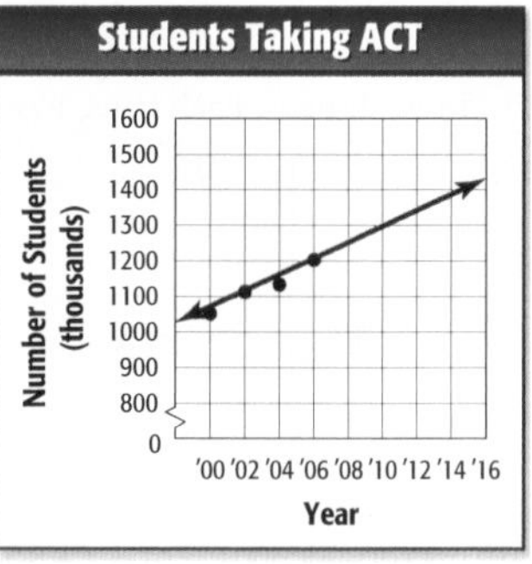

Check Your Progress

1. **ENTERTAINMENT** The table shows the percent of U.S. households that have a digital video camera.

Year	1999	2000	2001	2002	2003	2004	2005	2006
Percent	3	7	10	14	17	19	21	23

A. Make a scatter plot of the data and draw a line of fit. See Chapter 8 Answer Appendix.

B. Predict the percent of households with a digital video camera in 2015. Sample answer: about 53%

Personal Tutor glencoe.com

Lesson 8-9 Resources

Resource	Approaching-Level	On-Level	Beyond-Level	English Learners
Teacher Edition		Differentiated Instruction, p. 449	• Differentiated Instruction, pp. 449, 452	
Chapter Resource Masters	• Study Guide and Intervention, pp. 54–55 • Skills Practice, p. 56 • Practice, p. 57 • Word Problem Practice, p. 58	• Study Guide and Intervention, pp. 54–55 • Skills Practice, p. 56 • Practice, p. 57 • Word Problem Practice, p. 58 • Enrichment, p. 59	• Practice, p. 57 • Word Problem Practice, p. 58 • Enrichment, p. 59	• Study Guide and Intervention, pp. 54–55 • Skills Practice, p. 56 • Practice, p. 57
Transparencies	• 5-Minute Check Transparency 8-9	• 5-Minute Check Transparency 8-9	• 5-Minute Check Transparency 8-9	• 5-Minute Check Transparency 8-9
Other	• Study Notebook • Teaching Pre-Algebra with Manipulatives	• Study Notebook • Teaching Pre-Algebra with Manipulatives	• Study Notebook	• Study Notebook • Teaching Pre-Algebra with Manipulatives

StudyTip

Estimation Drawing a line of fit using the method in this lesson is an estimation. Therefore, it is possible to draw different lines to approximate the same data.

Prediction Equations Predictions can be made from the equation of a line of fit.

Real-World EXAMPLE 2 Make Predictions from an Equation

MOVIES **The scatter plot shows the number of movie theater screens in the U.S. for several years following 1999.**

Movie Theater Screens

(Scatter plot: Number of Screens (thousands), 28–46, vs. Years Since 1999, 0–10; points labeled (2, 37) and (6, 38))

a. Write an equation in slope-intercept form for the line of fit that is drawn.

Step 1 Use two points on the line to find the slope. These may or many not be original data points.

$m = \frac{y_2 - y_1}{x_2 - x_1}$ — **Definition of slope**

$m = \frac{38 - 37}{6 - 2}$ — **Use $(x_1, y_1) = (2, 37)$ and $(x_2, y_2) = (6, 38)$.**

$m = 0.25$ — **Simplify.**

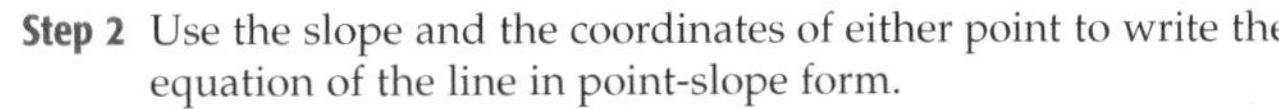

Step 2 Use the slope and the coordinates of either point to write the equation of the line in point-slope form.

$y - y_1 = m(x - x_1)$ — **Point-slope form**

$y - 38 = 0.25(x - 6)$ — **Replace (x_1, y_1) with (6, 38) and m with 0.25.**

Step 3 Solve the point-slope equation for y.

$y - 38 = 0.25(x - 6)$ — **Point-slope equation**

$y - 38 = 0.25x - 1.5$ — **Distributive Property**

$y - 38 + 38 = 0.25x - 1.5 + 38$ — **Add 38 to each side.**

$y = 0.25x + 36.5$ — **Simplify.**

The equation for the line of fit is $y = 0.25x + 36.5$.

b. Predict the number of movie theater screens in 2013.

$y = 0.25x + 36.5$ — **Write the equation of the line of fit.**

$y = 0.25(14) + 36.5$ — **Since 2013 − 1999 = 14, replace x with 14.**

$y = 40$ — **Simplify.**

There should be about 40,000 movie theater screens in 2013.

Real-World Link

In 1987, there were 2084 drive-in, or outdoor, movie screens in the U.S. By 2005, there were only 648.

Source: Motion Picture Association of America

Check Your Progress

2. **SWIMMING** The scatter plot shows the winning Olympic times in the men's 100-meter butterfly for several years following 1964.

   A. Write an equation in slope-intercept form for the line of fit that is drawn.

   B. Predict the winning time in the men's 100-meter butterfly in 2012. **50.8 s**

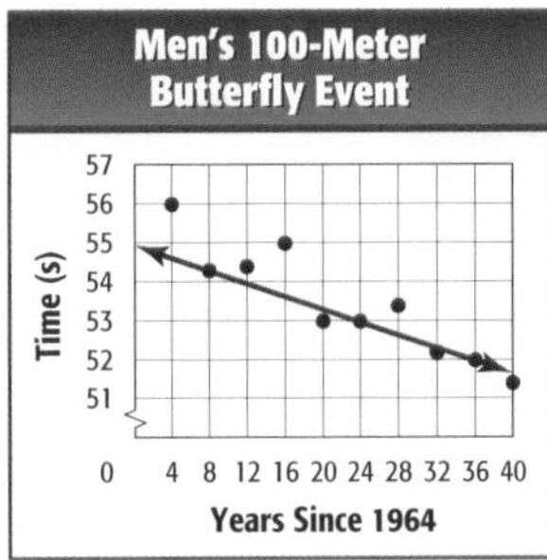

2A. Sample answer: Using (24, 53) and (36, 52), $y = -\frac{1}{12}x + 55$.

Personal Tutor glencoe.com

Lines of Fit

Example 1 shows how to make a prediction from a line of fit.

Formative Assessment

Use the Check Your Progress exercises after each example to determine students' understanding of concepts.

Additional Example

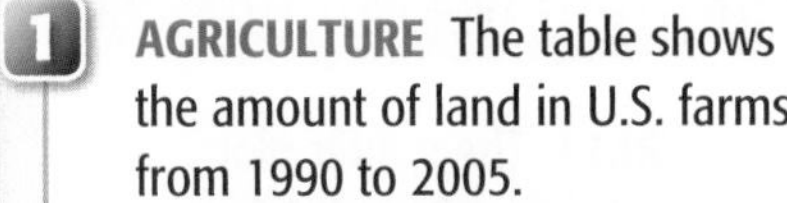

1 **AGRICULTURE** The table shows the amount of land in U.S. farms from 1990 to 2005.

Year	Land (million acres)
1990	987
1995	963
2000	945
2005	933

a. Graph the data. Draw a line that is near most of the data points.

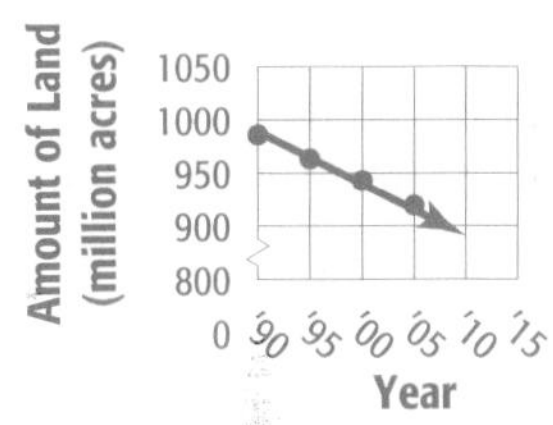

b. Use the line of fit to predict the amount of land in the year 2015. about 875 million acres

Additional Examples also in Interactive Classroom PowerPoint® Presentations

IWB INTERACTIVE WHITEBOARD READY

Differentiated Instruction

OL BL

If students enjoy conducting surveys,

Then have them interview students in the school on an age-related topic, such as how much students earn on average per age. Students should construct a scatter plot of the data, including a line of fit. Then have them interpret the data and make a prediction using the line of fit. They should write a few sentences to explain their predictions. Students can present their results to the class.

Tips for New Teachers

Trends Point out to students that there may be general trends in sets of data. However, not every data point may follow the trend exactly.

Focus on Mathematical Content

Line of Fit A line of fit approximates a relationship but is not exact.

Prediction Equations

Example 2 shows how to make predictions from an equation.

Additional Example

2 **INTERNET** The scatter plot shows the number of U.S. households (millions) with Internet access.

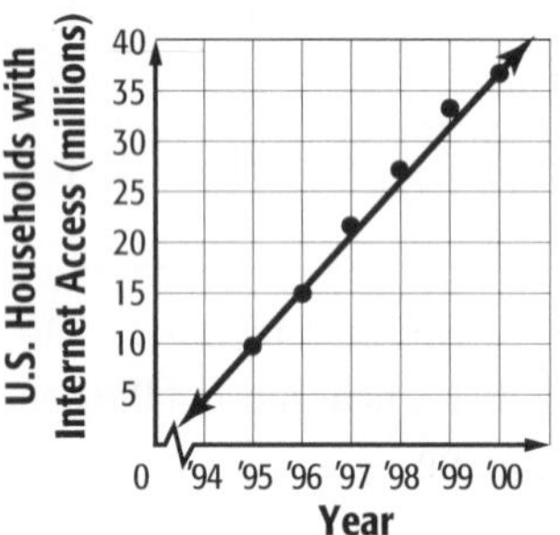

a. Write an equation in slope-intercept form for the line of fit that is drawn. $y = 5.4x - 10{,}763$

b. Predict the number of U.S. households that will have Internet in the year 2010. Sample answer: 91 million households

3 PRACTICE

Formative Assessment

Use Exercises 1–2 to check for understanding.

Use the chart at the bottom of this page to customize assignments for your students.

Check Your Understanding

Example 1 p. 448

1. **NEWSPAPERS** The table shows the number of Sunday newspapers in the U.S.

Year	Number of Sunday Newspapers
2001	913
2002	913
2003	917
2004	915
2005	917
2006	907

   a. Make a scatter plot of the data and draw a line of fit. **See Chapter 8 Answer Appendix.**

   b. Use the line of fit to predict the number of Sunday newspapers in the U.S. in 2014. **Sample answer: 898**

Example 2 p. 449

2. **ONLINE SHOPPING** Use the line of fit drawn that shows the amount of book sales that were purchased online for several years following 1997.

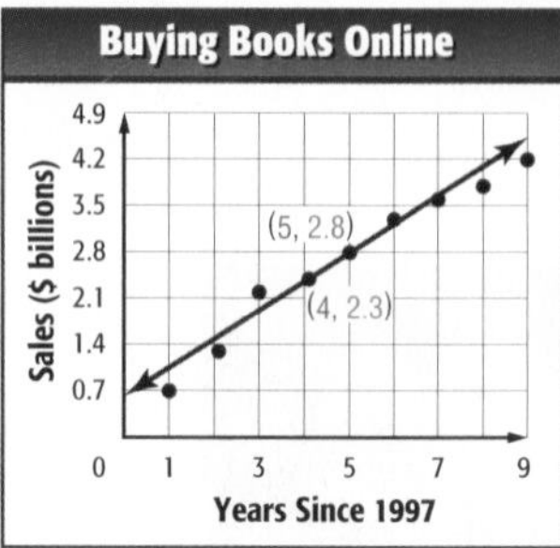

   a. Write an equation in slope-intercept form for the line of fit. **Sample answer: $y = 0.5x + 0.3$**

   b. Use the equation to predict the sales of books online in 2013. **Sample answer: about $8.3 billion**

Practice and Problem Solving

 = **Step-by-Step Solutions** begin on page R11. **Extra Practice** begins on page 810.

Example 1 p. 448

3. **SPORTS** The table shows the sales of athletic equipment.

Year	Equipment Sales ($ millions)	
	Baseball and Softball	Tennis
1999	329	338
2000	319	383
2001	316	371
2002	334	358
2003	340	343
2004	346	362
2005	356	373

   a. Make a scatter plot of the baseball and softball sales and draw a line of fit. **3a, c. See Chapter 8 Answer Appendix.**

   b. Use the line of fit to predict the sales of baseball and softball equipment in 2015. **Sample answer: $492 million**

   c. Make a scatter plot of the tennis sales and draw a line of fit.

   d. Use the line of fit to predict the sales of tennis equipment in 2015. **Sample answer: $490 million**

Example 2 p. 449

4. **FAN CLUBS** Use the line of fit drawn that shows the number of fan clubs in the U.S. for several years following 1999.

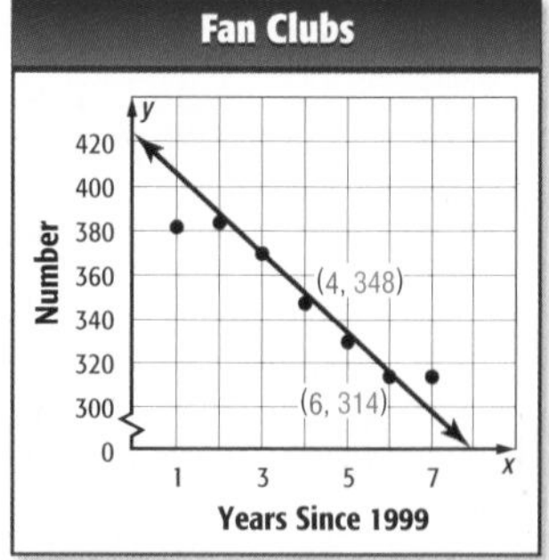

   a. Write an equation in slope-intercept form for the line of fit. **$y = -17x + 416$**

   b. Use the equation to predict the number of fan clubs in the U.S. in 2012. **195**

Differentiated Homework Options

Level	Assignment	Two-Day Option	
AL Basic	3–5, 8, 9, 11–25	3, 5, 13–17	4, 8, 9, 11–12, 18–25
OL Core	3, 5–9, 11–25	3, 4, 5, 13–17	6–9, 11–12, 18–25
BL Advanced	6–22 (optional: 23–25)		

StudyTip

A line of fit can be a good predictor if the relationship between the two variables is a strong positive or strong negative relationship.

5. **SPACE** Use the line of fit drawn that shows the amount of money the government spent on space and other technology for several years following 1998.

Space and Other Technology

a. Write an equation in slope-intercept form for the line of fit. Round to the nearest tenth. Sample answer: $y = 0.4x + 11.9$

b. Use the equation to predict the amount that the government will spend on space and other technology in 2016. Sample answer: $19.1 billion

B

6. **LIFE EXPECTANCY** According to the U.S. Census, the life expectancy of someone born in 2000 is 77.0 years. The life expectancy of someone born in 2010 is 78.5 years.

a. Write an equation in slope-intercept form for the line of fit of the data. $y = 0.15x - 223$

b. Use the equation to predict the life expectancy of a person born in 2015. 79.25

c. What are some limitations in using a line to predict life expectancy?

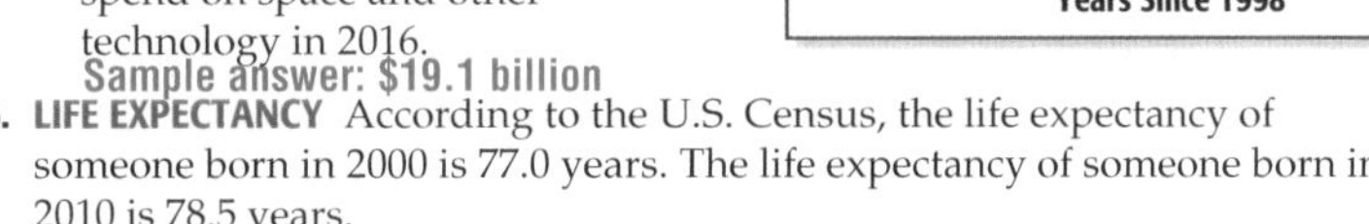

7. **MULTIPLE REPRESENTATIONS** In this problem, you will compare two graphs. Use the table that shows the populations of Illinois and Pennsylvania for several years following 1999. a–d. See Chapter 8 Answer Appendix.

Years Since 1999	Population (millions)	
	Illinois	Pennsylvania
1	12.4	12.3
2	12.5	12.3
3	12.6	12.3
4	12.7	12.4
5	12.7	12.4
6	12.8	12.4

a. **GRAPHICAL** Make a scatter plot and draw a line of fit for each set of data. What does the slope of each line represent?

b. **VERBAL** Which state's population appears to be growing at a faster rate? Explain. If the two lines were to intersect, what does the point of intersection represent?

c. **ALGEBRAIC** Write an equation for each line of fit. Round to the nearest thousandth. Use the equations to verify your answer in part **b**.

d. **NUMERICAL** Estimate the population of both states in 2015.

H.O.T. Problems Use Higher-Order Thinking Skills

C

8. **OPEN ENDED** Find a set of real-world data in which the data change over a span of at least 5 years. Make a scatter plot of the data and draw a line of fit. Write an equation for the line of fit that you drew. See students' work.

9. **WRITING IN MATH** Explain when it is reasonable to make a prediction from a line of fit. Then explain when it is not reasonable.

10. **CHALLENGE** Refer to part **c** of Exercise 7. Suppose you use (Years Since 1998, Population) to write the equations. Is the slope or y-intercept of the graphs of the equations the same? Explain.

11. **REASONING** Describe a scatter plot in which it would not be useful to draw a line of fit. See Chapter 8 Answer Appendix.

12. **WRITING IN MATH** Explain how a line can be used to make predictions. Include a description of a line of fit and an explanation of how a line can represent a set of data that is not exactly linear. See Chapter 8 Answer Appendix.

6c. Sample answer: According to the model, the later a person is born, the longer they will live. However, people's ages will not increase forever.

9. Sample answer: It is reasonable to make a prediction when the data have either a positive or a negative relationship. It is not reasonable if there is no noticeable relationship between the data.

10. Sample answer: The slopes are the same because the rate of change in the population is the same per year whether you use the year or the number of years since 1998. The y-intercepts are different, depending on which scale you use.

Exercise Alert

Data Source Exercise 8 requires Internet access or research materials that can provide real-world data that changes over a span of five years.

Enrichment CRM p. 59 OL BL

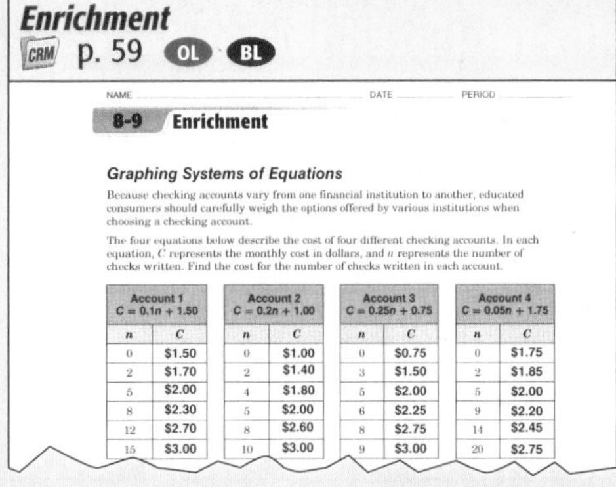

Study Guide and Intervention CRM pp. 54–55 AL OL ELL

Practice CRM p. 57 AL OL BL ELL

Word Problem Practice CRM p. 58 AL OL BL

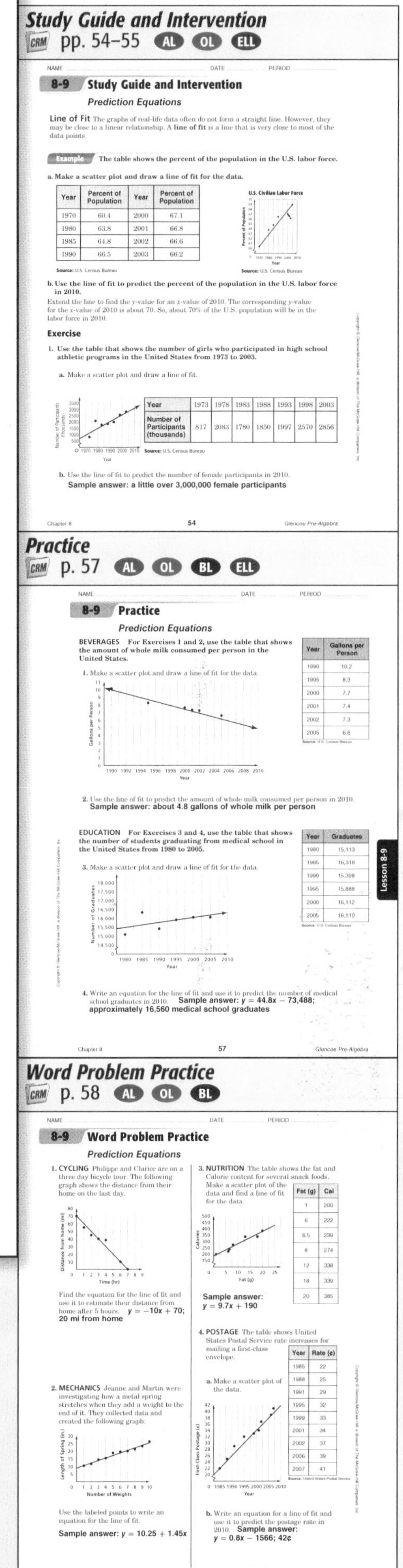

TEACH with TECH

WEB SEARCH Search the Web to find scatter plots for a real-world situation of cost vs. time. Have students use the graphs to find linear equations that appear to fit the data, and use the lines to predict future costs.

ASSESS

Name the Math Have students explain the uses of lines of fit and their equations in making predictions from real-world data. Encourage students to use proper mathematical terminology to name the steps that are taken once data is collected for graphing.

Additional Answers

17a.

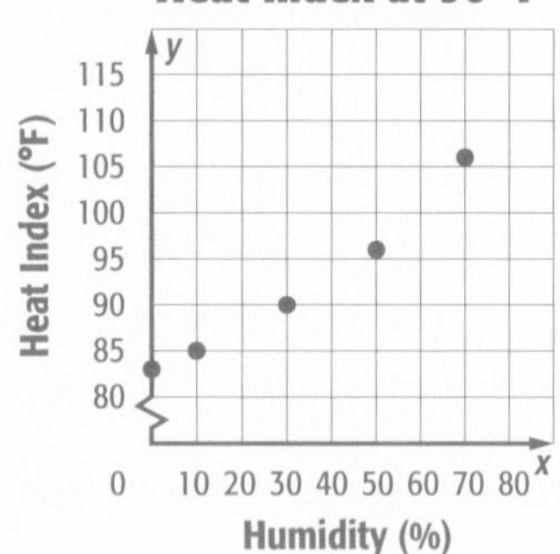

17b. Sample answer: $y = 0.35x + 81.5$

17c. 116.5°F

Standardized Test Practice

For Exercises 13 and 14, use the scatter plot. It shows how much money is in circulation per person in the United States in different years.

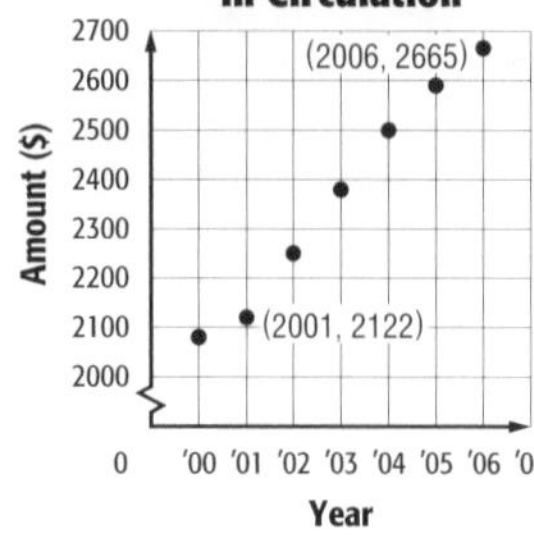

13. Which statement *best* describes the relationship shown on the scatter plot? **B**

A There is no relationship between the data.

B The amount of money in circulation per person increased over time.

C The amount of money in circulation per person decreased over time.

D The amount of money in circulation per person stayed the same over time.

14. Which of the following is the best prediction for the amount of money in circulation per person in 2020? **H**

F \$3605   H \$4185

G \$4050   J \$5240

15. Which of the following shows the equation for a line of fit that contains the data points (4, 534) and (10, 138)? **A**

A $y = -66x + 798$

B $y = -66x - 798$

C $y = 66x + 798$

D $y = 66x - 798$

16. Given the equation $y = 24x + 55$ for a line of fit, which of the following sets of points could be data points? **H**

F $(-3, -127)$ and $(2, 103)$

G $(-3, 127)$ and $(-2, 103)$

H $(3, 127)$ and $(2, 103)$

J $(3, 127)$ and $(-2, 103)$

17. EXTENDED RESPONSE The table shows the heat index at different humidity levels for a temperature of 90°F. **17a–c. See margin.**

Heat Index at 90°F					
Humidity (%)	0	10	30	50	70
Heat Index (°F)	83	85	90	96	106

a. Make a scatter plot of the data.

b. Write an equation in slope-intercept form for a line of fit.

c. Predict the heat index when the humidity is at 100%.

Spiral Review

Write an equation in slope-intercept form for each line. (Lesson 8-8)

18. slope $= -\frac{1}{3}$, y-intercept $= 8$ $y = -\frac{1}{3}x + 8$

19. slope $= \frac{2}{5}$, y-intercept $= 0$ $y = \frac{2}{5}x$

Graph each equation using the slope and y-intercept. (Lesson 8-7) **20–22. See Chapter 8 Answer Appendix.**

20. $y = x + 5$

21. $y = -x + 6$

22. $y = 2x - 3$

Skills Review

Evaluate each expression if $x = 7$, $y = 3$, and $z = 9$. (Lesson 1-2)

23. $\frac{xy}{3} + 2$ **9**

24. $2x + 3z + 5y$ **56**

25. $5z - 3x - 2y$ **18**

Differentiated Instruction

BL

Extension This scatter plot shows the approximate barometric pressure at various altitudes. Ask students to write an equation for the line of fit and use the equation to make a prediction about the barometric pressure at 60,000 feet. Does the prediction make sense? Explain. Sample answer: $y = -0.0006x + 27$; -9; no, the prediction does not make sense because barometric pressure cannot be negative.

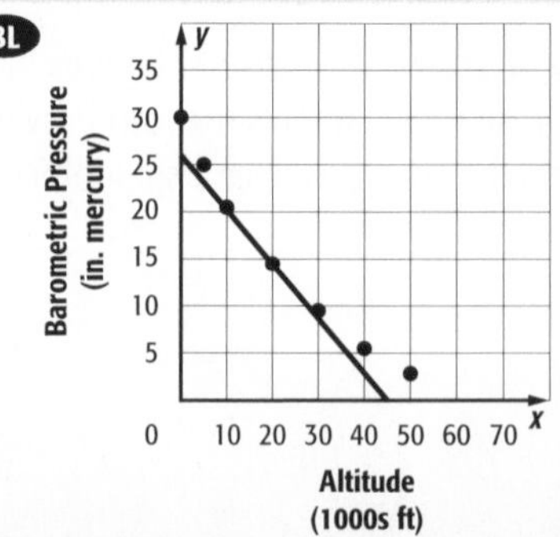

452 Chapter 8 Linear Functions and Graphing

8-10

Systems of Equations

8-10 Lesson Notes

Why?

Then
You have already solved linear equations by graphing. (Lesson 8-2)

Now
- Solve systems of linear equations by graphing.
- Solve systems of linear equations by substitution.

New Vocabulary
system of equations
substitution

Math Online
glencoe.com
- Extra Examples
- Personal Tutor
- Self-Check Quiz
- Homework Help

Hannah and Luis each open a savings account. They make different initial deposits and weekly deposits, as shown in the table.

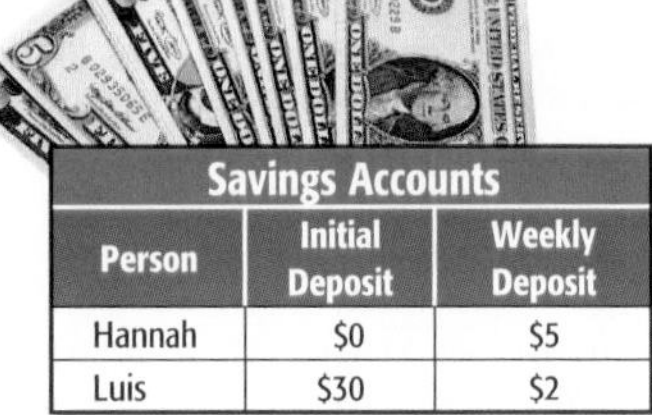

Savings Accounts		
Person	Initial Deposit	Weekly Deposit
Hannah	\$0	\$5
Luis	\$30	\$2

a. Write an equation to represent the amount of money in each person's account. Let y = the amount of money in an account. Let x = the number of weeks. **Hannah: $y = 5x$; Luis: $y = 30 + 2x$**

b. Make a table of values that satisfies each equation. Then graph both equations on the same coordinate plane. **See Chapter 8 Answer Appendix.**

c. What are the coordinates of the point where the two lines meet? What does this point represent? **(10, 50); At 10 weeks, they will have the same amount in their accounts, \$50.**

Solve Systems by Graphing A **system of equations** is a collection of two or more equations with the same set of variables. The equations $y = 5x$ and $y = 30 + 2x$ together are a system of equations. The solution of this system is (10, 50) because the ordered pair is a solution of both equations.

$y = 5x$	**Write the equations.**	$y = 30 + 2x$
$50 \stackrel{?}{=} 5(10)$	**Replace (x, y) with (10, 50).**	$50 \stackrel{?}{=} 30 + 2(10)$
$50 = 50$ ✓	**Simplify.**	$50 \stackrel{?}{=} 30 + 20$
		$50 = 50$ ✓

One way to solve a system of equations is to graph the equations on the same coordinate plane. The coordinates of the point where the graphs intersect is the solution of the system of equations.

EXAMPLE 1 Solve by Graphing

Solve the system of equations by graphing.

$y = x$
$y = -3x + 4$

The graphs appear to intersect at (1, 1). Check this estimate by replacing x with 1 and y with 1.

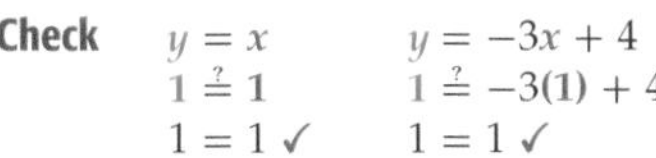

Check $y = x$ $y = -3x + 4$
$1 \stackrel{?}{=} 1$ $1 \stackrel{?}{=} -3(1) + 4$
$1 = 1$ ✓ $1 = 1$ ✓

The solution of the system of equations is (1, 1).

Check Your Progress

1. Solve the system of equations by graphing.
$y = x + 2$ **See Chapter 8 Answer Appendix.**
$y = -2x - 4$

Personal Tutor glencoe.com

1 FOCUS

Vertical Alignment

Before Lesson 8-10
Solve linear equations by graphing.

Lesson 8-10
Solve systems of linear equations by graphing. Solve systems of linear equations by substitution.

After Lesson 8-10
Apply solving systems of equations by graphing or substitution to real-world problems.

2 TEACH

Scaffolding Questions

Have students read the *Why?* section of the lesson and answer the questions.

Ask:
- What do the initial deposit and weekly deposit represent in each equation you wrote? The initial deposit is the y-intercept and the weekly deposit is the slope of the line in each of the equations.
- Which line has the greater slope? the line that represents Hannah's account
- What does this mean? that Hannah's account will likely grow more quickly than Luis's account

Lesson 8–10 Resources

Resource	Approaching-Level	On-Level	Beyond-Level	English Learners
Teacher Edition	• Differentiated Instruction, p. 454	• Differentiated Instruction, p. 454	• Differentiated Instruction, p. 457	• Differentiated Instruction, p. 454
Chapter Resource Masters	• Study Guide and Intervention, pp. 60–61 • Skills Practice, p. 62 • Practice, p. 63 • Word Problem Practice, p. 64	• Study Guide and Intervention, pp. 60–61 • Skills Practice, p. 62 • Practice, p. 63 • Word Problem Practice, p. 64 • Enrichment, p. 65	• Practice, p. 63 • Word Problem Practice, p. 64 • Enrichment, p. 65	• Study Guide and Intervention, pp. 60–61 • Skills Practice, p. 62 • Practice, p. 63
Transparencies	• 5-Minute Check Transparency 8–10	• 5-Minute Check Transparency 8–10	• 5-Minute Check Transparency 8–10	• 5-Minute Check Transparency 8–10
Other	• Study Notebook • Teaching Pre-Algebra with Manipulatives	• Study Notebook • Teaching Pre-Algebra with Manipulatives	• Study Notebook	• Study Notebook • Teaching Pre-Algebra with Manipulatives

Solve Systems by Graphing

Example 1 shows how to solve a system of equations by graphing. **Example 2** shows how to use an extended response question to interpret solutions. **Example 3** shows how to determine if a system of equations has no solution or infinitely many solutions.

Formative Assessment

Use the Check Your Progress exercises after each example to determine students' understanding of concepts.

Additional Examples

1 Solve the system of equations by graphing. (1, 4)

$y = -x + 5$

$y = 2x + 2$

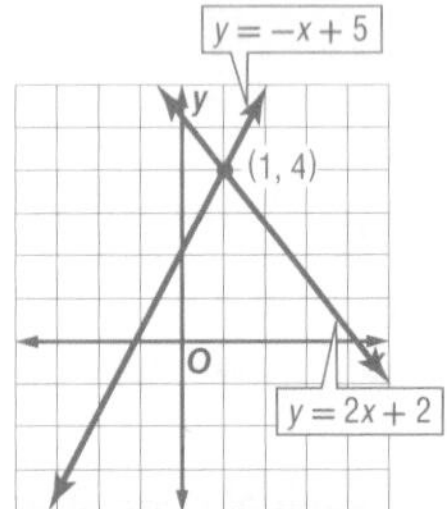

2 **STANDARDIZED TEST PRACTICE** Catori and Mark each download songs. Mark downloaded 4 times as many songs as Catori. Mark also downloaded 6 more songs than Catori.

a. Write a system of equations to represent this situation. $y = 4x$, $y = x + 6$

b. Solve the system by graphing. Explain what the solution means. The solution is $x = 2$ and $y = 8$. Catori downloads 2 songs and Mark downloads 8 songs.

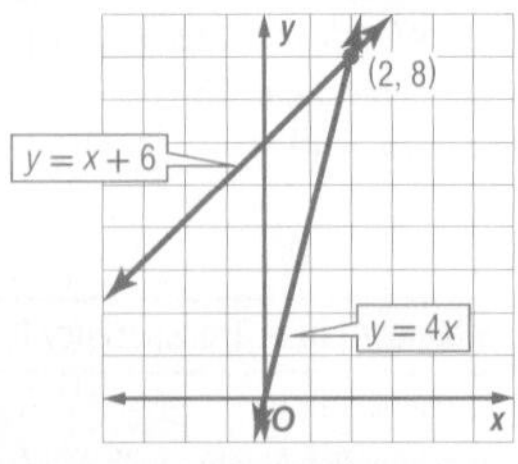

STANDARDIZED TEST EXAMPLE 2

EXTENDED RESPONSE **Marjorie and Bryan are selling magazine subscriptions. Marjorie sells 3 times as many subscriptions as Bryan. Bryan sells 12 fewer subscriptions than Marjorie.**

Test-Taking Tip

When answering extended response questions, make sure your solutions answer all parts of the question. Double check that you covered all parts.

a. Write a system of equations to represent this situation.

Let y represent Marjorie's sales and x represent Bryan's sales.

$y = 3x$ **Marjorie sells 3 times as many subscriptions as Bryan.**

$y = x + 12$ **Bryan sells 12 fewer subscriptions than Marjorie.**

b. Solve the system by graphing. Explain what the solution means.

Graph each equation on the same coordinate grid. The equations intersect at (6, 18).

So, the solution to the system is $x = 6$ and $y = 18$. This means that Marjorie sells 18 subscriptions and Bryan sells 6 subscriptions.

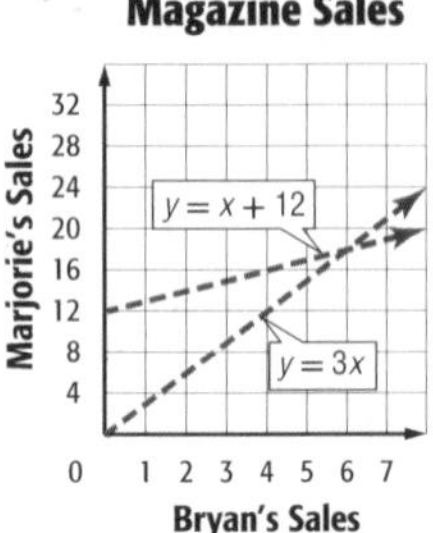

Check Your Progress

2. A doctor's office has twice as many new patients as existing patients. The number of new patients is 22 more than the number of existing patients.

A. Write a system of equations to represent this situation.

B. Solve the system by graphing. Explain what the solution means.

See Chapter 8 Answer Appendix for graph.

2A. $y = 2x$; $y = x + 22$

2B. $x = 22$ and $y = 44$; There are 22 existing patients and 44 new patients.

Personal Tutor glencoe.com

A system of equations can have no solution or infinitely many solutions.

StudyTip

Slopes/Intercepts When the graphs of a system of equations have:

- different slopes → exactly 1 solution
- same slope, different y-intercepts → no solution
- same slope, same y-intercept → infinitely many solutions

EXAMPLE 3 No Solution and Infinitely Many Solutions

Solve each system of equations by graphing.

a. $y = -x + 1$
$y = -x - 3$

The graphs appear to be parallel lines. Since there is no coordinate pair that is a solution to both equations, there is no solution of this system of equations.

b. $y = 2x + 4$
$\frac{1}{2}y - x = 2$

Both equations have the same graph. Any ordered pair on the graph will satisfy both equations. Therefore, there are infinitely many solutions of this system of equations.

3A–B. See Chapter 8 Answer Appendix for graph.

Check Your Progress

3A. $y = x + 4$
$y = x$ no solution

3B. $y = \frac{1}{2}x - 1$
$x - 2y = 2$ infinitely many solutions

Personal Tutor glencoe.com

Differentiated Instruction

AL OL ELL

If students have difficulty solving systems of equations,

Then have them work with a partner. One student graphs one of the equations in the system and the other student graphs the other. They check each other's work and have to agree on the solution to the problem.

Solve Systems by Substitution You can also use algebraic methods to solve a system of equations. One method is called **substitution**.

EXAMPLE 4 Solve by Substitution

StudyTip

Systems The variable y must have the same value in both equations.

Solve the system of equations by substitution.

$y = x + 2$
$y = 5$

Replace y with 5 in the first equation.

$y = x + 2$	**Write the first equation.**
$5 = x + 2$	**Replace y with 5.**
$3 = x$	**Solve for x.**

The solution of this system of equations is (3, 5). You can check the solution by graphing. The graphs appear to intersect at (3, 5).

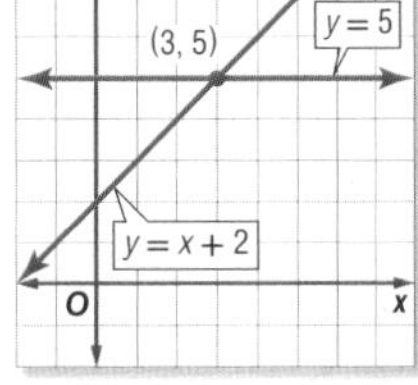

Check Your Progress

4A. $y = 5$
$y = x + 4$ **(1, 5)**

4B. $y = 7 - x$
$x = 3$ **(3, 4)**

Personal Tutor glencoe.com

Concept Summary: Systems of Equations
For Your FOLDABLE

Graph	Intersecting Lines	Parallel Lines	Same Line
Number of Solutions	one solution	no solutions	infinitely many

Check Your Understanding

1–3. See Chapter 8 Answer Appendix for graphs.

Examples 1 and 3 pp. 453–454 — **Solve each system of equations by graphing.**

1. $y = -x$ **(2, −2)**
$y = x - 4$

2. $y = x + 1$ **(3, 4)**
$x + y = 7$

3. $y = \frac{3}{2}x - 1$
$3x - 2y = 2$
infinitely many solutions

Example 2 p. 454

4. EXTENDED RESPONSE Amanda pays an annual fee of \$100 to belong to a gym, plus a monthly fee of \$10. Maria pays only a monthly fee of \$20. **a-b. See Chapter 8 Answer Appendix.**

a. Write a system of equations to represent this situation.

b. Solve the system by graphing. Explain what the solution means.

Example 4 p. 455 — **Solve each system of equations by substitution.**

5. $y = x - 2$
$y = 3$ **(5, 3)**

6. $y = x + 4$
$x = 0$ **(0, 4)**

7. $y = 2x + 3$
$y = 1$ **(−1, 1)**

Additional Example

3 Solve each system of equations by graphing.

a. $y = -x - 3$
$2x + 2y = -6$ infinitely many solutions

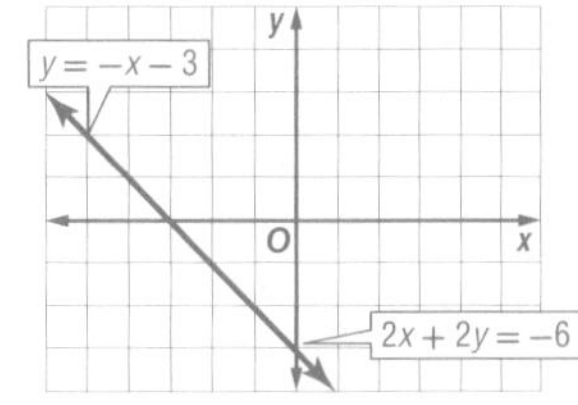

b. $y = 2x$
$y = 2x - 4$ no solution

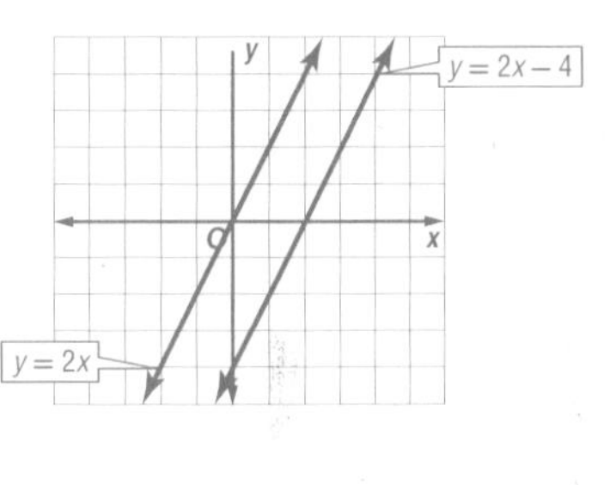

Solve Systems by Substitution
Example 4 shows how to solve systems of equations by substitution.

Additional Example

4 Solve the system of equations by substitution. (6, 7)

$y = 7$
$y = 2x - 5$

Additional Examples also in Interactive Classroom PowerPoint® Presentations

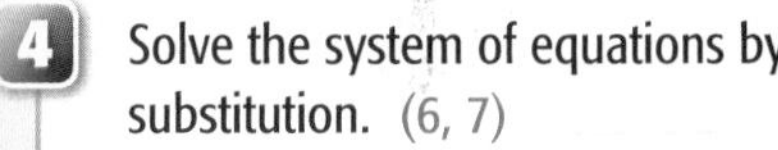

Differentiated Homework Options

Level	Assignment	Two-Day Option	
AL Basic	8–21, 23, 24, 28–40	9–21 odd, 30–33	8–20 even, 23, 24, 28–29, 34–40
OL Core	9–21 odd, 22–24, 28–40	8–21, 30–33	22–24, 28–29, 34–40
BL Advanced	22–36 (optional: 37–40)		

3 PRACTICE

Formative Assessment

Use Exercises 1–7 to check for understanding.

Use the chart at the bottom of this page to customize assignments for your students.

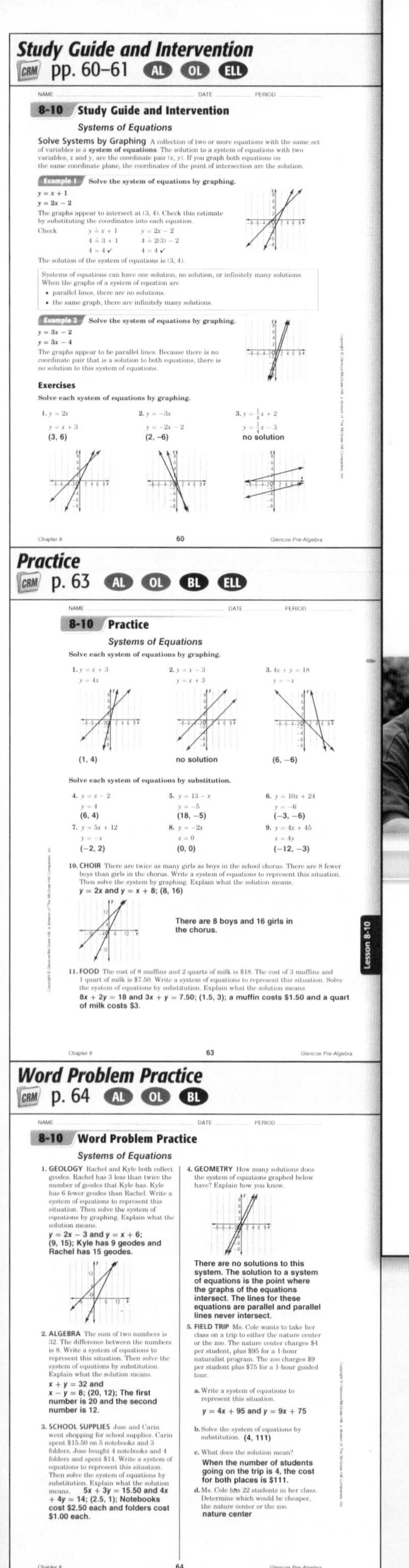

Practice and Problem Solving

= Step-by-Step Solutions begin on page R11.
Extra Practice begins on page 810.

Examples 1 and 3 pp. 453–454

Solve each system of equations by graphing. 8–13. See Chapter 8 Answer Appendix for graphs.

8. $y = 2x$ $(1, 2)$
$y = x + 1$

9. $y = x$ $(2, 2)$
$y = -x + 4$

10. $y = -x + 1$ $(3, -2)$
$y = x - 5$

11. $y = \frac{3}{4}x$
$3x - 4y = 0$ infinitely many solutions

12. $y = \frac{1}{2}x + 1$
$y = \frac{1}{2}x - 2$ no solution

13. $x + y = -3$ $(-3, 0)$
$x - y = -3$

Example 2 p. 454

14. NUMBER SENSE The sum of two numbers is 5, and the difference of the numbers is 3. 14–15. See Chapter 8 Answer Appendix.

a. Write a system of equations to represent this situation.

b. Solve the system of equations by graphing. Explain what the solution means.

15. BASEBALL CARDS Ling starts out with 50 baseball cards and plans to collect 5 per month. Jonathon starts out with 90 baseball cards and plans to sell 5 per month.

a. Write a system of equations to represent this situation.

b. Solve the system of equations by graphing. Explain what the solution means.

Example 4 p. 455

Solve each system of equations by substitution.

16. $y = x + 2$
$x = 1$ $(1, 3)$

17. $y = x + 4$
$y = 0$ $(-4, 0)$

18. $y = 2x - 3$
$y = 5$ $(4, 5)$

19. $y = -x - 4$
$x = 2$ $(2, -6)$

20. $x + y = 2$
$x = -3$ $(-3, 5)$

21. $x - y = 6$
$y = -1$ $(5, -1)$

22. FINANCIAL LITERACY The cost of 2 bagels and 2 cans of orange juice is $4.40. The cost of 3 bagels and 4 cans of orange juice is $7.80.

a. Write a system of equations to represent this situation. $2x + 2y = 4.40$ and $3x + 4y = 7.80$

b. Solve the system of equations by substitution. Explain what the solution means. (1, 1.2); Bagels cost $1.00 each and orange juice costs $1.20 per can.

Real-World Link

Three of the rarest and most valuable baseball cards are from 1951. They are priced between $30,000 and $35,000 each.

Source: USA Today

H.O.T. Problems

Use Higher-Order Thinking Skills

23. OPEN ENDED Write a system of equations that has the solution (1, 7). Write the equations in slope-intercept form. Sample answer: $y = x + 6$ and $y = 8x - 1$

24. WRITING IN MATH Describe the three ways that two lines can be related. Can a system of linear equations have exactly two solutions? Explain. See Chapter 8 Answer Appendix.

CHALLENGE Solve each system of equations by substitution.

25. $y = 2x + 6$
$y = x$ $(-6, -6)$

26. $x + 4y = 33$
$y = -3x$ $(-3, 9)$

27. $5x + y = 8$
$y = x - 4$ $(2, -2)$

28. REASONING Describe when it is better to use substitution to solve a system of equations rather than graphing. 28–29. See Chapter 8 Answer Appendix.

29. WRITING IN MATH Describe the graph of a system of equations if the system has 1 solution, no solution, or infinitely many solutions.

456 Chapter 8 Linear Functions and Graphing

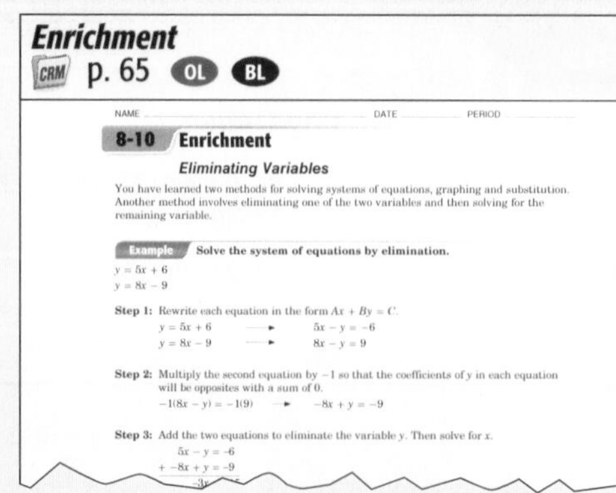

TEACH with TECH

DOCUMENT CAMERA Choose two students to share their work with the class. Select students who solved the same system of equations in different ways (by solving for different variables). Take pictures of the work and distribute them to the class or post on the classroom Web site

Standardized Test Practice

30. Amy took three times as many pictures as Jennifer. Jennifer has 16 fewer pictures than Amy. Which system of equations can be used to find the number of pictures each person took? **A**

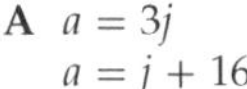

A $a = 3j$, $a = j + 16$

B $a = 3j$, $a = j - 16$

C $j = 3a$, $j = a + 16$

D $j = 3a$, $j = a - 16$

31. Refer to Exercise 30. How many pictures did each person take? **G**

F Amy took 8 pictures and Jennifer took 24 pictures.

G Amy took 24 pictures and Jennifer took 8 pictures.

H Amy took 16 pictures and Jennifer took 6 pictures.

J Amy took 6 pictures and Jennifer took 16 pictures.

32. Which of the following is the solution of the system of equations graphed below? **C**

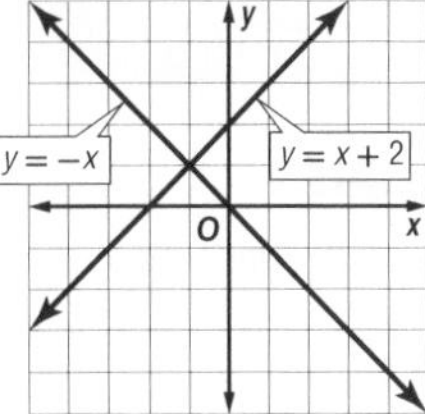

A (1, 1)

B (1, −1)

C (−1, 1)

D (−1, −1)

33. GRIDDED RESPONSE In one season, Tyra made 4 times as many goals as Kailey. Kailey made 9 fewer goals than Tyra. How many goals did Tyra make? **12**

Spiral Review

34. EARTH SCIENCE The table shows the latitude and the average temperature in July for various U.S. cities. (Lesson 8-9)

a. Make a scatter plot of the data and draw a line of fit. **See margin.**

b. Write an equation for the line of fit you drew in part **a**. **See margin.**

c. Use the equation from part **b** to estimate the average July high temperature for a location with latitude 50° north. Round to the nearest degree Fahrenheit. **Sample answer: 59°F**

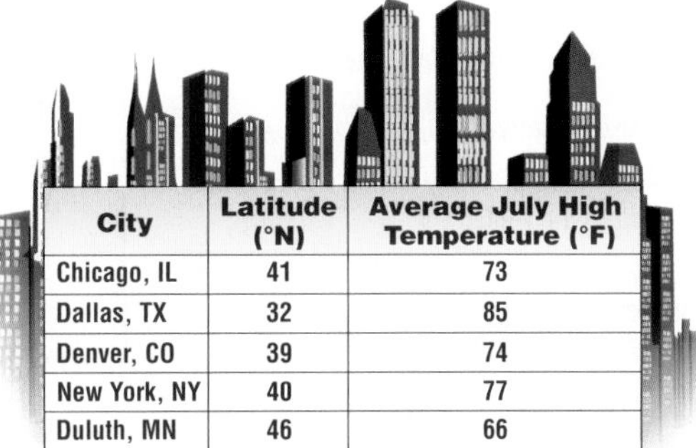

City	Latitude (°N)	Average July High Temperature (°F)
Chicago, IL	41	73
Dallas, TX	32	85
Denver, CO	39	74
New York, NY	40	77
Duluth, MN	46	66

Write an equation in slope-intercept form for each table of values. (Lesson 8-8)

35.

x	−1	0	1	2
y	−7	−3	1	5

$y = 4x - 3$

36.

x	−3	−1	1	3
y	7	5	3	1

$y = -x + 4$

Skills Review

Multiply. (Previous Course)

37. $4 \cdot 4 \cdot 4$ **64**

38. $9 \cdot 9 \cdot 9 \cdot 9$ **6561**

39. $2 \cdot 2 \cdot 2 \cdot 2 \cdot 2$ **32**

40. $5 \cdot 5 \cdot 5$ **125**

4 ASSESS

Ticket Out the Door On a small piece of graph paper, have students solve the system $y = -x - 3$ and $y = 3x + 1$ by graphing. They are to label each line with its equation and write the solution. Students should give you their paper when they leave the room.

Formative Assessment

Check for student understanding of concepts in Lessons 8-9 and 8-10.

CRM Quiz 4, p. 69

Tips for New Teachers

Graphing Tip Remind students that they should graph one equation at a time by either using the slope and y-intercept or a table of values. Encourage them to check the point of intersection in both of the equations of the system.

Additional Answers

34a.

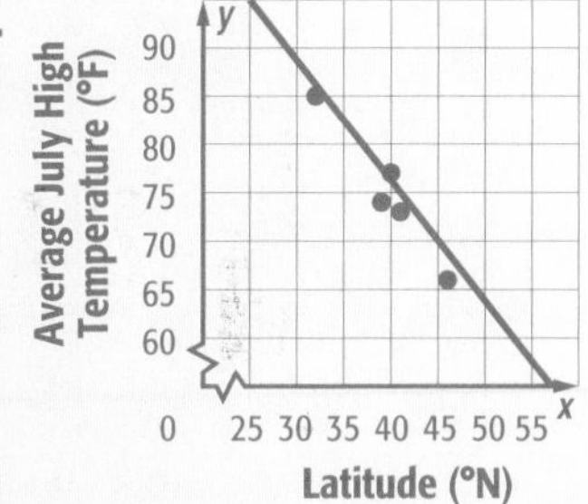

34b. Sample answer: Using (40, 77) and (46, 66), $y = -1.83x + 150.2$

Differentiated Instruction

Extension Give students the following systems of equations to graph: $y = 3x - 1$ and $y = 3x + 2$; $y = x$ and $y = x - 2$; $x + y = 4$ and $x + y = -5$. Have them graph each system on a separate coordinate plane and describe the graphs of each system. Ask: Could you have described the graphs of the systems of equations before you graphed each system? Explain. Each system's graph shows a pair of parallel lines. Yes, parallel lines have the same slopes and different y-intercepts.

CHAPTER 8 Study Guide and Review

Formative Assessment

Key Vocabulary The page references after each word denote where that term was first introduced. If students have difficulty answering questions 1–10, remind them that they can use these page references to refresh their memories about the vocabulary.

Summative Assessment

Vocabulary Test, p. 71

Math Online glencoe.com

Vocabulary PuzzleMaker improves students' mathematics vocabulary using four puzzle formats–crossword, scramble, word search using a word list, and word search using clues. Students can work online or from a printed worksheet.

CHAPTER 8 Study Guide and Review

Math Online glencoe.com
- STUDY TO GO
- Vocabulary Review

Chapter Summary

Key Concepts

Representing Linear Functions (Lesson 8-3)

- A solution of a linear equation is an ordered pair that makes the equation true.
- A linear equation can be represented by a set of ordered pairs, a table of values, or a graph.

Rate of Change and Slope (Lessons 8-4 through 8-6)

- A change in one quantity in relation to another quantity is called the rate of change.
- A quantity that increases over time has a positive rate of change. If it decreases over time, it has a negative rate of change. If it does not change over time, it has a zero rate of change.
- Two quantities a and b have a proportional linear relationship if $\frac{a}{b}$ is constant and $\frac{\text{change in } a}{\text{change in } b}$ is constant.
- Slope can be used to describe rate of change.
- Slope is the ratio of the rise, or the vertical change, to the run, or the horizontal change.

Write and Use Equations (Lessons 8-7 through 8-9)

- In the slope-intercept form $y = mx + b$, m is the slope and b is the y-intercept.
- You can write a linear equation by using the slope and y-intercept, two points on a line, a graph, a table, or a verbal description.

Systems of Equations (Lesson 8-10)

- The solution of a system of equations is the ordered pair that satisfies all equations in the system.

FOLDABLES® Study Organizer

Be sure the Key Concepts are noted in your Foldable.

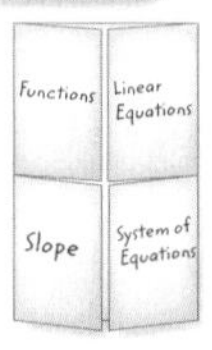

Key Vocabulary

arithmetic sequence (p. 401)
common difference (p. 401)
constant of variation (p. 420)
constant rate of change (p. 418)
dependent variable (p. 395)
direct variation (p. 420)
discrete data (p. 407)
family of functions (p. 439)
function notation (p. 396)
independent variable (p. 395)
line of fit (p. 448)
linear equation (p. 406)
linear relationship (p. 418)
point-slope form (p. 442)
rate of change (p. 412)
sequence (p. 401)
slope (p. 427)
slope-intercept form (p. 433)
substitution (p. 455)
system of equations (p. 453)
term (p. 401)
vertical line test (p. 396)
***x*-intercept** (p. 407)
***y*-intercept** (p. 407)

Vocabulary Check

Choose the term from the list above that best matches each phrase.

1. the ratio of the vertical change to the horizontal change of a line **slope**
2. an equation written in the form $y = mx + b$ **slope-intercept form**
3. an ordered list of numbers **sequence**
4. a description of how one quantity changes in relation to another quantity **rate of change**
5. b in the equation $y = mx + b$ ***y*-intercept**
6. the rate of change between any two data points is the same **constant rate of change**
7. in a linear equation, a variable for the input **independent variable**
8. k in the equation $y = kx$ **constant of variation**
9. a set of equations with the same variables **system of equations**
10. a line that is close to most of the data points in a scatter plot **line of fit**

FOLDABLES® Study Organizer

Dinah Zike's Foldables®

Have students look through the chapter to make sure they have included examples in their Foldables.

Suggest that students keep their Foldables handy while completing the Study Guide and Review pages. Point out that their Foldables can serve as a quick review tool when studying for the Chapter Test.

Lesson-by-Lesson Review

8-1 Functions (pp. 395–400)

11. Determine whether the relation {(5, 3), (−5, 4), (4, 2), (4, 1)} is a function. Explain.

12. **GASOLINE** Use the table that shows the cost of gas in different years. Is the relation a function? Explain.

Year	'02	'04	'06
Cost ($)	1.36	1.82	2.26

11. No; The domain value 4 is paired with 2 range values, 1 and 2.

12. Yes; each domain value is paired with only one range value.

EXAMPLE 1

Determine whether the relation shown in the table is a function. Explain.

x	9	11	13	17	21
y	7	3	−1	−5	−7

Yes, it is a function since each domain value is paired with only one range value.

8-2 Sequences and Equations (pp. 401–405)

13. Describe the sequence 6, 12, 18, 24, … using words and symbols. See margin.

Write an equation that describes each sequence. Then find the indicated term.

14. 6, 10, 14, 18, …; 47th term $t = 4n + 2$; 190

15. 7, 14, 21, 28, …; 50th term $t = 7n$; 350

16. **GEOMETRY** Which figure in the pattern below will have 99 squares? figure 50

Figure 1

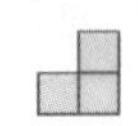
Figure 2

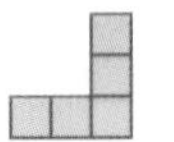
Figure 3

EXAMPLE 2

Write an equation that describes the sequence 9, 18, 27, 36, … . Then find the 16th term of the sequence.

Term Number (n)	1	2	3	4
Term (t)	9	18	27	36

The common difference is 9. Each term is 9 times the term number. So, $t = 9n$.

$t = 9n$ **Write the equation.**
$t = 9(16)$ or 144 **Replace n with 16.**

The 16th term of the sequence is 144.

8-3 Representing Linear Functions (pp. 406–411)

Find four solutions of each equation. Write the solution as ordered pairs. 17–23. See margin.

17. $y = -5x$

18. $y = 4x$

19. $y = x + 9$

20. $x + y = -1$

Graph each equation.

21. $y = -2x$

22. $y = x + 5$

23. **SNACKS** Each small smoothie x costs \$1.50, and each large smoothie y costs \$3. Find two solutions of $1.5x + 3y = 12$ to determine how many of each type Lisa can buy with \$12.

EXAMPLE 3

Find four solutions of $y = -x + 1$. Write the solutions as ordered pairs.

Choose four values for x and substitute each value into the equation. Then solve for y.

x	y = −x + 1	y	(x, y)
−1	y = −(−1) + 1	2	(−1, 2)
0	y = −0 + 1	1	(0, 1)
1	y = −1 + 1	0	(1, 0)
2	y = −2 + 1	−1	(2, −1)

Four solutions: (−1, 2), (0, 1), (1, 0), and (2, −1).

Lesson-by-Lesson Review

Intervention If the given examples are not sufficient to review the topics covered by the questions, remind students that the page references tell them where to review that topic in their textbook.

Two-Day Option Have students complete the Lesson-by-Lesson Review on pp. 459–462. Then you can use ExamView® Assessment Suite to customize another review worksheet that practices all the objectives of this chapter or only the objectives on which your students need more help.

Differentiated Instruction

Super DVD: Mindjogger Videoquizzes
Use this DVD as an alternative format of review for the test.

Additional Answers

13. The terms have a difference of 6. A term is 6 times the term number; $t = 6n$.

17. Sample answer: (−1, 5), (0, 0), (1, −5), (2, −10)

18. Sample answer: (−1, −4), (0, 0), (1, 4), (2, 8)

19. Sample answer: (−1, 8), (0, 9), (1, 10), (2, 11)

20. Sample answer: (−1, 0), (0,−1), (1, −2), (2, −3)

21.

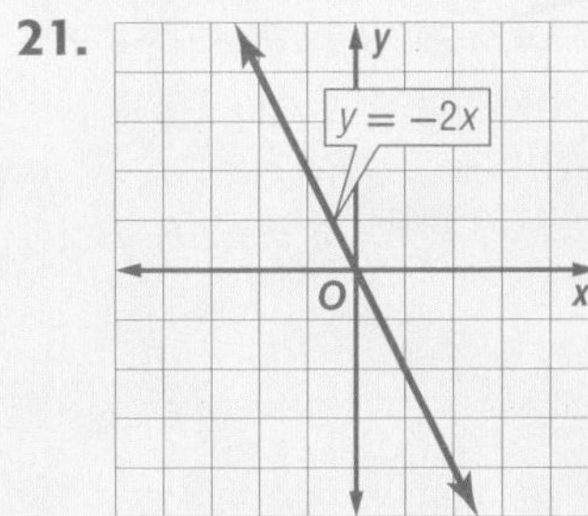

22.

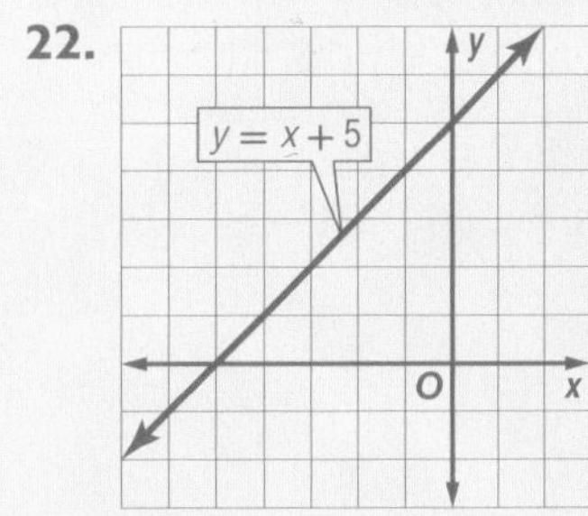

23. Sample answer: (0, 4) means she can buy 0 small smoothies and 4 large smoothies with \$12; (6, 1) means she can buy 6 small smoothies and 1 large smoothie with \$12.

Additional Answers

25. Adults: \$18/person; children: \$12.50/person; the cost for adults increases at a faster rate than the cost for children.

26. 2° per hour; the temperature increases 2° per hour

CHAPTER 8 Study Guide and Review

8-4 Rate of Change (pp. 412–417)

24. Find the rate of change for the linear function shown below. **increase of \$7.75/h**

Time (h) x	0	4	8
Money Earned (\$) y	0	31	62

25. ENTERTAINMENT The table shows the total cost of tickets. Compare the rates of change.

Number of People x	Total Cost (\$) y	
	Adults	Children
2	36	25
4	72	50
6	108	75

See margin.

EXAMPLE 4

The table shows the time and water level of a pool. Find the rate of change.

Time (min) x	0	4	8
Water Level (ft) y	5	4	3

$$\text{rate of change} = \frac{\text{change in water level}}{\text{change in time}} = \frac{5 \text{ ft} - 4 \text{ ft}}{0 \text{ min} - 4 \text{ min}} = \frac{1 \text{ ft}}{-4 \text{ min}} \text{ or } -\frac{1}{4} \text{ ft/min}$$

The rate of change is $-\frac{1}{4}$ ft/min.

8-5 Constant Rate of Change and Direct Variation (pp. 418–424)

26. WEATHER The temperature one day is shown in the graph. Find the constant rate of change and interpret its meaning. See margin.

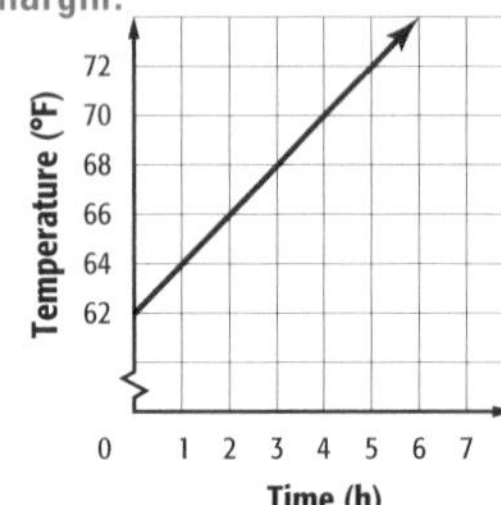

EXAMPLE 5

Find the constant rate of change for the linear function shown at the right and interpret its meaning.

Year x	Population (1000s) y
2001	688
2005	722

$$\text{rate of change} = \frac{\text{change in population}}{\text{change in years}} = \frac{722 - 688}{2005 - 2001} = \frac{34}{4} \text{ or } 8.5$$

The rate of change 8.5 means that the population increased at a rate of 8.5 thousand people per year.

8-6 Slope (pp. 427–431)

Find the slope of the line that passes through each pair of points.

27. $F(0, 1)$, $G(6, 4)$ $\frac{1}{2}$

28. $R(-8, -2)$, $S(4, 9)$ $\frac{11}{12}$

29. $A(-3, 7)$, $G(5, -1)$ -1

30. $P(6, -4)$, $S(-1, 10)$ -2

31. ANIMALS A lizard is crawling up a hill that rises 5 feet for every horizontal change of 30 feet. Find the slope. $\frac{1}{6}$

EXAMPLE 6

Find the slope of the line that passes through $C(6, 1)$ and $D(0, -3)$.

$m = \frac{y_2 - y_1}{x_2 - x_1}$ — **Definition of slope**

$m = \frac{-3 - 1}{0 - 6}$ — $(x_1, y_1) = (6, 1)$, $(x_2, y_2) = (0, -3)$

$m = \frac{-4}{-6}$ or $\frac{2}{3}$ — **Simplify.**

MIXED PROBLEM SOLVING
For mixed problem-solving practice, see page 850.

8-7 Slope-Intercept Form (pp. 433–438)

State the slope and the y-intercept of the graph of each equation.

32. $y = 4x + 7$ 4; 7 **33.** $y = -\frac{4}{3}x$ $-\frac{4}{3}$; 0

34. $5x + y = 0$ −5; 0 **35.** $-x + y = -8$ 1; −8

Graph each equation using the slope and y-intercept. 36–40. See margin.

36. $y = -x + 4$ **37.** $y = 2x - 6$

38. $y = \frac{3}{2}x - 3$ **39.** $y = -\frac{1}{4}x + 5$

40. BALLOONS A balloon is rising above the ground. The height in feet y of the balloon can be given by $y = 7 + 2x$, where x represents the time in seconds. State the slope and y-intercept of the graph of the equation. Describe what they represent.

EXAMPLE 7

State the slope and y-intercept of the graph of $y = 4x - 1$. Then graph the equation.

$y = 4x - 1$ **Write the original equation.**

$y = 4x + (-1)$ **Write the equation in the form $y = mx + b$.**

$y = mx + b$ **$m = 4, b = -1$**

The slope of the graph is 4, and the y-intercept is −1.

Now graph the equation. Write the slope as $\frac{4}{1}$. Plot the point at (0, −1). Then go up 4 and right 1. Connect the points and extend the line.

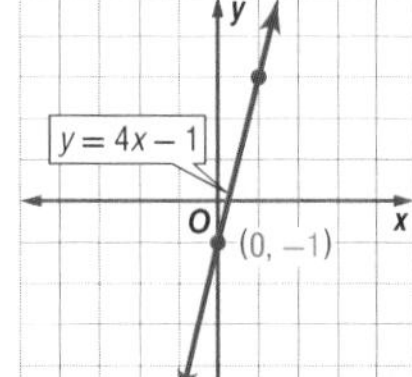

8-8 Writing Linear Equations (pp. 441–447)

Write an equation in slope-intercept form for each line.

41. slope = −2, y-intercept = 5 $y = -2x + 5$

42. slope = $\frac{3}{4}$, y-intercept = −1 $y = \frac{3}{4}x - 1$

43. slope = 4, y-intercept = 0 $y = 4x$

Write an equation in point-slope form for the line passing through each pair of points.

44. (3, 3), (7, −1) $y - 3 = -1(x - 3)$ **45.** (1, 5), (2, 8) $y - 5 = 3(x - 1)$

46. BIRTHDAYS Diem's parents wants to rent the local movie theatre for her birthday party. It costs $100 plus $30 per hour to rent the movie theater.

a. Write an equation in slope-intercept form that shows the cost y for renting the theater for x hours. $y = 30x + 100$

b. Find the cost of renting the theater for 4 hours. $220

EXAMPLE 8

Write an equation in point-slope form for the line that passes through (5, 9) and (2, 0).

Step 1 Find the slope m.

$m = \frac{y_2 - y_1}{x_2 - x_1}$ **Definition of slope**

$m = \frac{9 - 0}{5 - 2}$ **$(x_1, y_1) = (5, 9)$, $(x_2, y_2) = (2, 0)$**

$m = 3$ **Simplify.**

Step 2 Use the slope and the coordinates of either point.

$y - y_1 = m(x - x_1)$ **Point-slope form**

$y - 9 = 3(x - 5)$ **Replace (x, y) with (5, 9) and m with 3.**

An equation of the line through (5, 9) and (2, 0) is $y - 9 = 3(x - 5)$.

Additional Answers

36.

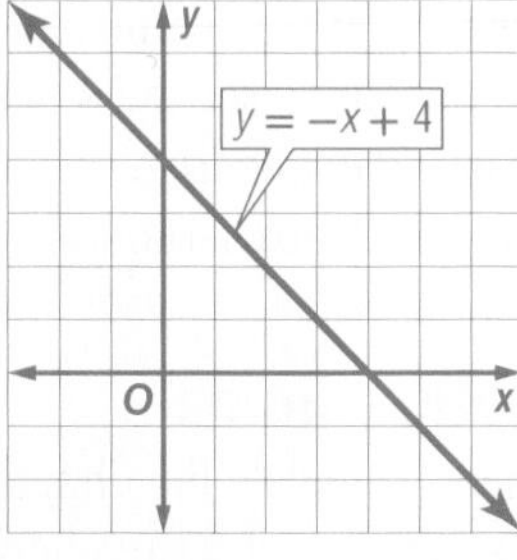

37.

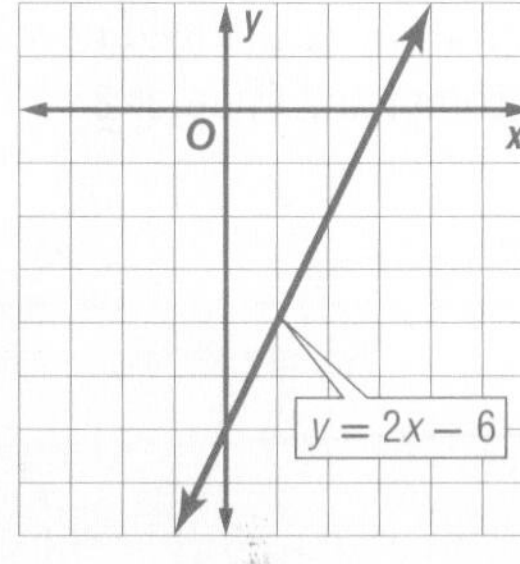

38.

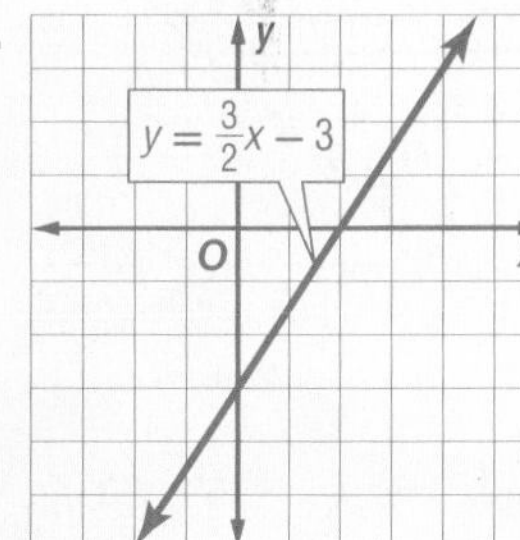

39.

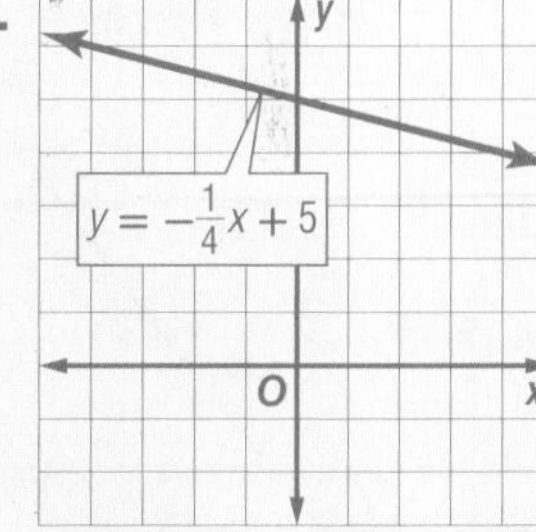

40. The slope 2 represents the ascent in ft per second. The y-intercept 7 represents the initial altitude in ft before the balloon is released.

CHAPTER 8 Study Guide and Review

Problem Solving Review

For additional practice in problem solving for Chapter 8, see the Mixed Problem Solving Appendix, p. 850, in the Student Handbook section.

Anticipation Guide

Have students complete the Chapter 8 Anticipation Guide and discuss how their responses have changed now that they have completed Chapter 8.

Additional Answers

47a.

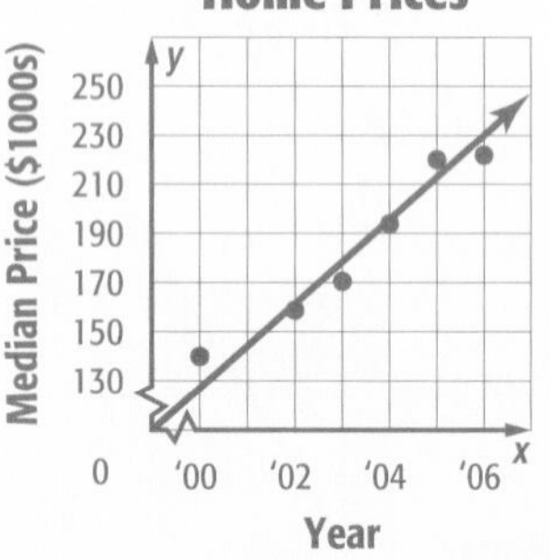

47b. Sample answer: $362,000

48a.

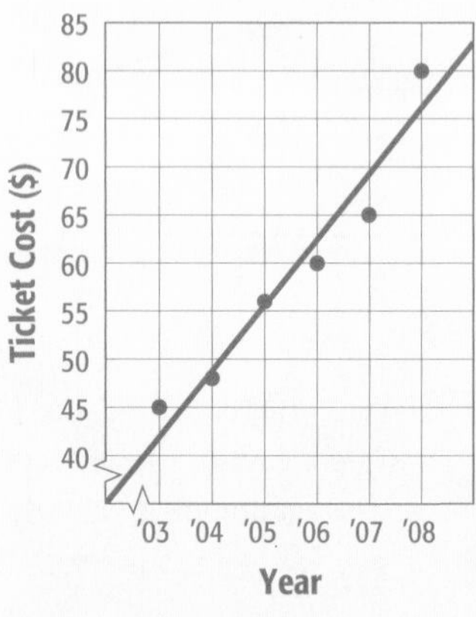

48b. Sample answer: $121

8-9 Prediction Equations (pp. 448–452)

47. HOUSING The table shows the changes in the median price of existing homes. **See margin.**

Year	Median Price ($1000s)
2000	139.0
2002	158.1
2003	170.0
2004	195.2
2005	219.0
2006	221.9

a. Make a scatter plot and draw a line of fit for the data.

b. Use the line of fit to predict the median price for an existing home for the year 2015.

48. MUSIC The table shows the changes in the average concert ticket prices.

Year	'03	'04	'05	'06	'07	'08
Ticket Cost ($)	45	48	56	60	65	80

a. Make a scatter plot and draw a line of fit for the data.

b. Use the line of fit to predict the average price of a concert ticket in 2015.

EXAMPLE 9

Make a scatter plot and draw a line of fit for the table showing the attendance at home games for the first four games of a high school football season. Then use the line of fit to predict the attendance for the seventh home game.

Game	Attendance
1	1100
2	1200
3	1300
4	1500

Plot the points and draw a line as close to the points as possible. For an x value of 7, the y value is about 19. So, a prediction for the attendance is approximately 1900 people.

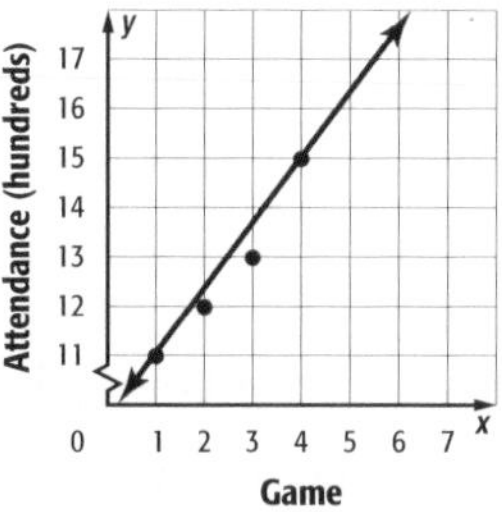

8-10 Systems of Equations (pp. 453–457)

Solve each system of equations by graphing. 49–50. See margin.

49. $y = x$
$y = \frac{1}{2}x - 1$

50. $y = x + 2$
$y = 3x$

Solve each system of equations by substitution.

51. $y = x + 3$
$x = 1$ **(1, 4)**

52. $y = 2x + 6$
$y = 0$ **(−3, 0)**

53. NUMBER SENSE The sum of two numbers is 9, and the difference of the numbers is 1. Write a system of equations to represent this situation. Then solve the system to find the numbers. **Sample answer: $x + y = 9$, $x - y = 1$; 5 and 4; $x = 5$; $y = 4$**

EXAMPLE 10

Solve the system of equations by graphing.

$y = x - 1$

$y = -\frac{2}{3}x + 4$

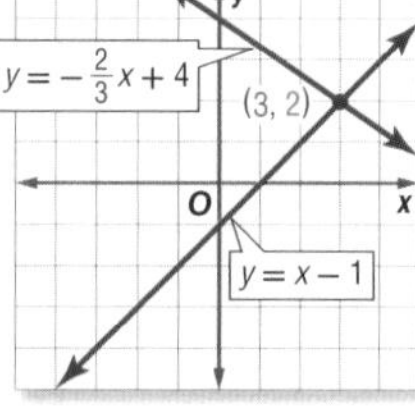

The graphs appear to intersect at (3, 2).

The solution of the system of equations is (3, 2).

49.

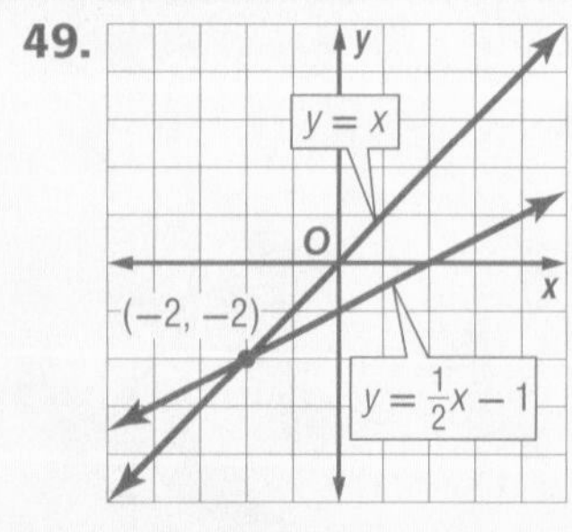

(−2, −2)

50.

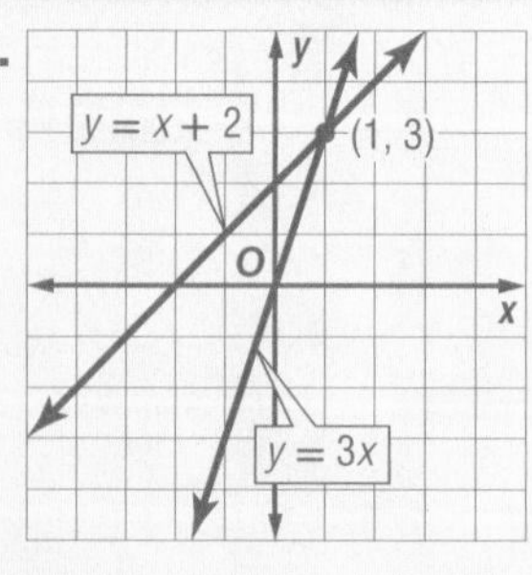

(1, 3)

Math Online glencoe.com Chapter Test

1. Is the relation {(7, 0), (9, 3), (11, 1), (13, 0)} a function? Explain. See margin.

2. Write an equation that describes the sequence 2, 7, 12, 17, … . Then find the 10th term. $t = 5n - 3$; 47

3. **MULTIPLE CHOICE** Which of the following equations shows the relationship between the side length and perimeter of a regular pentagon? B

Side Length (s)	Perimeter (p)
1	5
2	10
3	15
4	20

A $p = 5 + s$ C $s = 5p + 5$

B $p = 5s$ D $s = 5 + p$

Find four solutions of each equation. Write the solutions as ordered pairs. 4–5. See margin.

4. $y = x + 7$ 5. $y = -4x$

Graph each equation by plotting ordered pairs. 6–10. See Chapter 8 Answer Appendix.

6. $y = x - 6$ 7. $y = -2x + 3$

8. **LANDSCAPING** Find the rate of change for the linear function shown below. Then determine whether a proportional linear relationship exists between the two quantities. Explain your reasoning.

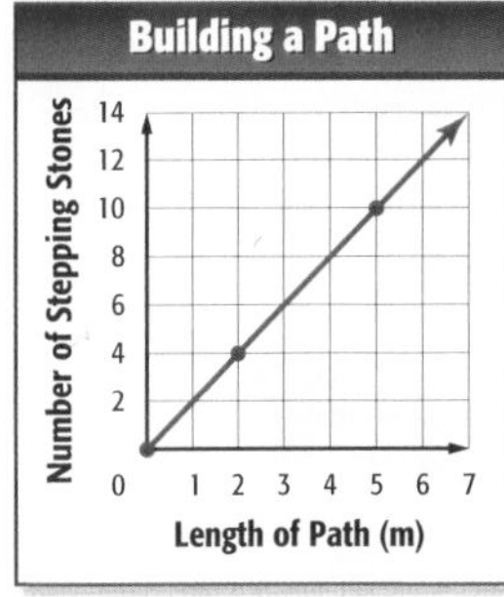

State the slope and y-intercept of the graph of each equation. Then graph each equation using the slope and y-intercept.

9. $y = 3x - 1$ 10. $4x + 3y = 6$

11. **FUNDRAISING** The total profit for a school fundraiser varies directly with the number of potted plants sold. Suppose the school earns $57.60 if 12 plants are sold.

a. Write an equation that could be used to find the profit per plant sold. $y = 4.8x$

b. Find the total profit if 65 plants are sold. $312

12. **MULTIPLE CHOICE** A stylist earns $10 an hour plus $3 per hair cut. Which equation represents the stylist's hourly earnings? F

F $y = 3x + 10$ H $y = 3x - 10$

G $y = 10x + 3$ J $y = 10x - 3$

13. **RECYCLING** Use the graph below to write an equation in slope-intercept form for the line. What does the slope of the line represent?

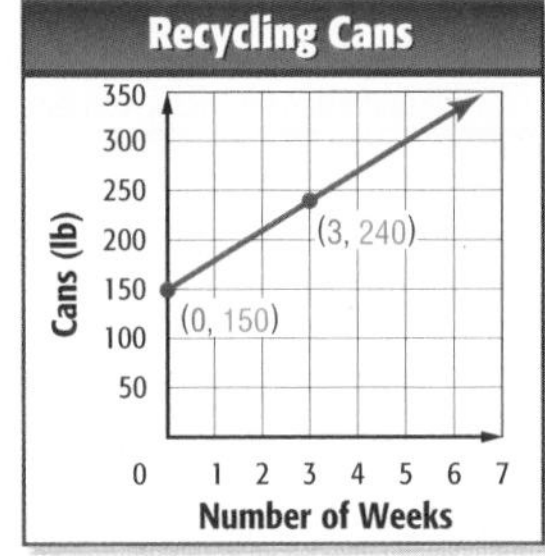

$y = 30x + 150$; 30 pounds of cans are collected per week

Find the slope of the line that passes through each pair of points.

14. $A(8, 5)$, $B(7, 9)$ -4 15. $R(11, 6)$, $S(9, -1)$ $\frac{7}{2}$

16. **FESTIVALS** The table shows the attendance for an annual jazz festival.

Year	People
2008	1400
2009	1520
2010	1650
2011	1740

a. Make a scatter plot and draw a line of fit.

b. Use the line of fit to predict jazz festival attendance in 2014.

a–b. See Chapter 8 Answer Appendix.

Solve each system of equations by graphing. 17–18. See Chapter 8 Answer Appendix.

17. $y = x + 4$
$y = -x + 2$

18. $y = x$
$y = 2x - 1$

Solve each system of equations by substitution.

19. $y = x + 3$
$x = 4$ (4, 7)

20. $y = 2x - 5$
$y = -1$ (2, −1)

CHAPTER 8 Practice Test

ExamView Assessment Suite Customize and create multiple versions of your chapter test and their answer keys. All of the questions from the leveled chapter tests in the *Chapter 8 Resource Masters* are also available on ExamView® Assessment Suite.

Additional Answers

1. This relation is a function because each element of the domain is paired with exactly one element of the range.

4. Sample answer: (−1, 6), (0, 7), (1, 8), (2, 9)

5. Sample answer: (−1, 4), (0, 0), (1, −4), (2, −8).

Intervention Planner

Tier 1 On Level	Tier 2 Strategic Intervention approaching grade level	Tier 3 Intensive Intervention 2 or more grades below level
If students miss about 25% of the exercises or less,	**If** students miss about 50% of the exercises,	**If** students miss about 75% of the exercises,
Then choose a resource:	**Then** choose a resource:	**Then** use *Math Triumphs, Grade 8,* Ch. 2, 6
SE Lessons 8-1 through 8-10 **CRM** Skills Practice, pp. 7, 13, 19, 25, 32, 38, 44, 50, 56, 62 **TE** Chapter Project p. 392	**CRM** Study Guide and Intervention, Chapter 8, pp. 5, 11, 17, 23, 30, 36, 42, 48, 54, 60 *Quick Review Math Handbook*	
Math Online Self-Check Quiz	Math Online Extra Examples, Personal Tutor, Homework Help	Math Online Extra Examples, Personal Tutor, Homework Help, Review Vocabulary

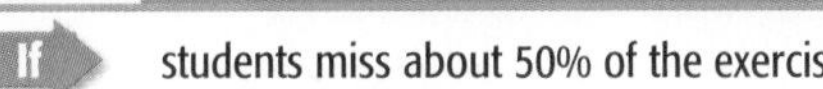

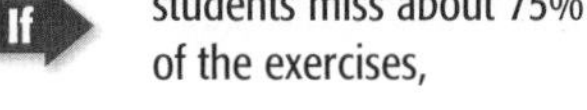

Objective Use a combination of strategies to solve extended-response standardized test problems.

2 TEACH

Scaffolding Questions

Ask:

- How is writing a short two-page report similar to writing a longer five-page report? Sample answer: Both the shorter and longer reports must present a topic, explain what the topic is about, and give details.
- How is writing a short two-page report different from writing a longer five-page report? Sample answer: The longer report will have more sections and more details than the shorter report.
- How do you think an extended response question will differ from a short response question? Sample answer: The extended response question will have more parts and require more explanation and details.

CHAPTER 8 Preparing for Standardized Tests

Extended-Response Questions

Extended-response questions are often called *open-ended* or *constructed-response* questions. These types of questions typically have multiple parts. You must answer all parts to receive full credit.

Strategies for Solving Extended-Response Questions

Step 1

As with short answer, extended-response questions are typically graded using a rubric. The following is an example of an extended-response scoring rubric.

Extended-Response Scoring Rubric		
Credit	Score	Criteria
Full	4	**Full Credit:** A correct solution is given that is supported by well-developed, accurate explanations.
Partial	3, 2, 1	**Partial Credit:** A generally correct solution is given that may contain minor flaws in reasoning or computation or an incomplete solution. The more correct the solution, the greater the score.
None	0	**No Credit:** An incorrect solution is given indicating no mathematical understanding of the concept, or no solution is given.

Step 2

In solving extended-response questions, remember to…

- explain your reasoning or state your approach to solving the problem.
- show all of your work or steps.
- solve each part of the question.
- check your answer if time permits.

EXAMPLE

Read the problem. Identify what you need to know. Then use the information in the problem to solve. Show your work.

The table at the right shows the altitude of a hot air balloon at different times since it began descending to land.

a. Write a linear equation in slope-intercept form to represent the data.

b. Describe what the slope means.

c. Predict how long it will take for the balloon to land.

Time (min)	Altitude (ft)
0	260
2	220
4	180
6	140

Read the problem carefully.

Example of a 4-point response:

a. Let x = time and y = altitude of the balloon.

Use the points (0, 260) and (2, 220) to find the slope.

$m = \frac{260 - 220}{0 - 2}$ or -20

When $x = 0$, $y = 260$, so the y-intercept is 260. The equation of the line is $y = -20x + 260$.

b. The slope gives the change in altitude for the change in time. It is negative because the altitude is decreasing. So, the hot air balloon is descending at a rate of 20 feet per minute.

c. The hot air balloon will have landed when its altitude reaches 0 feet. Let $y = 0$ in the equation and solve for x.

$y = -20x + 260$

$0 = -20x + 260$

$20x = 260$

$x = 13$

So, it will take the balloon 13 minutes to land.

Exercise

Read the question. Identify what you need to know. Then use the information in the question to solve. Show your work.

1. James works as an electrician. He charges a fixed amount per service call plus an hourly fee depending on how long the job takes. His total fee for jobs of different lengths are shown in the graph.

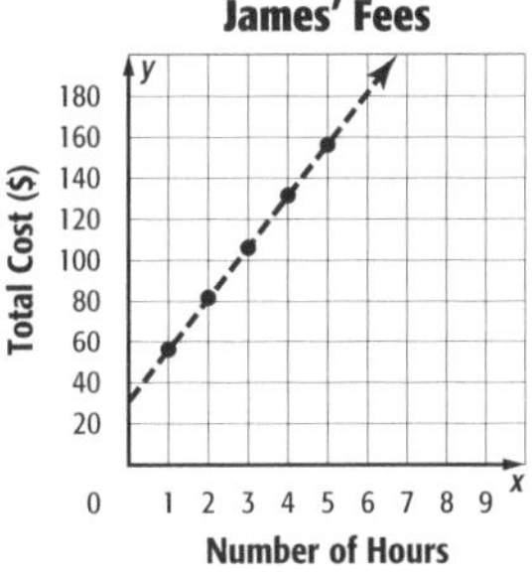

a. Write a linear equation to represent the data. $y = 25x + 30$

b. Describe what the slope means. **James charges $25 per hour.**

c. How much would a job cost if it takes James 7 hours? **$205**

3 ASSESS

Use Exercise 1 to assess students' understanding.

Additional Example

Michaela is using a hose to add water to an inflatable pool. The table shows the number of gallons of water in the pool at different times.

Time (minutes)	Amount of Water (gallons)
0	175
3	211
6	247
9	283

a. Write a linear equation in slope-intercept form to represent the data.

b. Describe what the slope and y-intercept mean.

c. Predict the amount of time it will take to fill the pool to its capacity of 835 gallons.

Example of a 4-point response:

a. Let x = time and let y = gallons of water

Use the points (0, 175) and (3, 211) to find the slope.

$m = \frac{211\text{-}175}{3\text{-}0} = \frac{36}{3}$ or 12

When $x = 0$, $y = 175$, so the y-intercept is 175. The equation of the line is $y = 12x + 175$.

b. The slope gives the rate at which the water flows from the hose. Since the slope is 12, the rate of flow is 12 gallons per minute. The y-intercept represents the gallons of water already in the pool.

c. Substitute 835 for y in the equation $y = 12x + 175$ and solve to find how long it will take to fill the pool.

$835 = 12x + 175$

$835 - 175 = 12x$

$660 = 12x$

$55 = x$

It will take 55 minutes to fill the pool.

Diagnose Student Errors

Survey student responses for each item. Class trends may indicate common errors and misconceptions.

1. A misunderstood concept of area
   B found perimeter instead of area
   C guess
   D correct
2. F correct
   G misunderstood relationship between x and y
   H found relationship for $x = 1$ only
   J guess
3. A chose wrong units
   B chose wrong units and calculation error
   C correct
   D calculation error
4. F calculation error, such as used \$1000 instead of \$2000 to calculate
   G guess
   H correct
   J guess
5. A added 24 and 45 and then divided
   B calculation error or chose wrong sign
   C correct
   D added –24 and –45 and then divided
6. F chose the wrong sign or used wrong signs in calculations
   G switched x- and y-coordinates in calculations and used wrong signs
   H switched x- and y-coordinates in calculations
   J correct
7. A correct
   B misinterpreted real-world meaning of the ordered pair
   C misunderstood concept of real-world meaning of ordered pairs
   D misunderstood concept of real-world meaning of ordered pairs
8. F error in slope
   G error in slope and y-intercept
   H correct
   J error in y-intercept

CHAPTER 8

Standardized Test Practice

Cumulative, Chapters 1 through 8

Multiple Choice

Read each question. Then fill in the correct answer on the answer document provided by your teacher or on a sheet of paper.

1. Find the area of the rectangle below. D

A 32 ft^2 C 58 ft^2
B 34 ft^2 D 66 ft^2

2. The table shows a relationship between x and y. Which equation is true for each ordered pair in the table? G

x	y
0	0
1	42.50
2	85
3	127.5

F $y = 37.5x + 5$ H $y = 27.5x + 15$
G $y = 42.5x$ J $y = 37.5x + 10$

3. Bethany is riding her bike. After 20 seconds she has traveled 360 feet, and after 1 minute she has traveled 1080 feet. What is her rate of change? C

A 18 feet per minute
B 16 feet per minute
C 18 feet per second
D 16 feet per second

Test-TakingTip

Question 7 Be sure your answer choice reflects the correct units.

4. Janelle invested \$2000 in a savings account that pays 7.5% simple interest. How long will it be before she has \$2750 in the account? H

F 10 years H 5 years
G 8 years J 4 years

5. What is the solution of the equation $-24 + 3n = -45$? D

A $n = 23$ C $n = -7$
B $n = 7$ D $n = -23$

6. What is the slope of the line that passes through the points $(-4, 6)$ and $(3, -5)$? J

F $\frac{11}{7}$ H $-\frac{7}{11}$
G $\frac{7}{11}$ J $-\frac{11}{7}$

7. The linear equation $y = 8.50x$ describes Jamie's wages y when she works x hours. Which of the following best describes the real world meaning of the ordered pair (12, 102)? A

A She earns \$102 for working 12 hours.
B She earns \$12 for working 102 hours.
C She earns \$102 for working 102 hours.
D She earns \$12 for working 12 hours.

8. Find the equation of the line in the graph. H

F $y = x + 2$
G $y = x - 2$
H $y = -x + 2$
J $y = -x - 2$

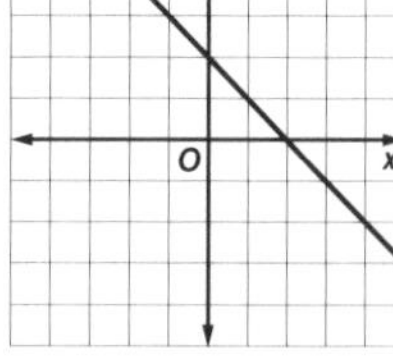

Math Online glencoe.com
Standardized Test Practice

CHAPTER 8 Standardized Test Practice

Short Response/Gridded Response

Record your answers on the answer sheet provided by your teacher or on a sheet of paper.

9. **GRIDDED RESPONSE** The equation $y = 464 - 8x$ describes the altitude y, in feet, of a plane x seconds after it begins its descent. How many seconds will it take the plane to land? **58**

10. Is the relation shown in the graph a function? Explain. **See margin.**

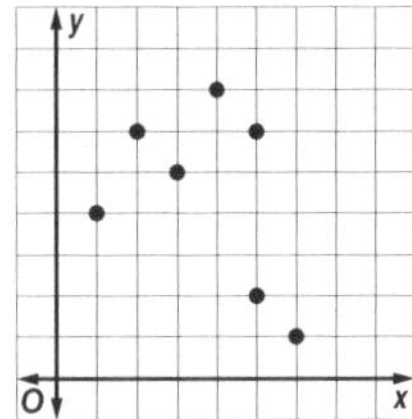

11. Use the sequence 2, 5, 8, 11, 14, ... to answer parts **a** and **b**.
    a. Describe the sequence of numbers using words and symbols. **See margin.**
    b. What is the 24th term of the sequence? **71**

12. At a sport's store, 20 out of 112 sets of golf clubs are junior clubs. Express the ratio of sets of junior golf clubs to the total number of sets of golf clubs as a fraction in simplest form. Explain its meaning. **See margin.**

13. Find the solution of the following system of equations. Show your work. **(1, –5)**

$$4x + 2y = -6$$
$$y = -5x$$

14. H&R Rentals charges $40 to rent a moving van, plus $0.15 per mile.
    a. Write an equation, in slope-intercept form, to show the total cost of renting a van and driving it x miles. $y = 0.15x + 40$
    b. Suppose Marcos rents a moving van and his total cost is $53.20. How many miles did he drive the van? **88 mi**

Extended Response

Record your answers on a sheet of paper. Show your work.

15. The table shows Margo's average keyboarding speed, in words per minute, for five weeks.

Margo's Keyboarding Speed

Week	Speed (wpm)
1	18
2	21
3	26
4	28
5	35

a. Make a scatter plot of Margo's average keyboarding speed versus the number of weeks she has been taking the class. Draw a line of fit. **See Chapter 8 Answer Appendix for graph.**
b. Use the line of fit to predict how fast Margo will be able to type after the sixth week of class. **Sample answer: about 37 wpm**

Need Extra Help?

If you missed Question...	1	2	3	4	5	6	7	8	9	10	11	12	13	14	15
Go to Lesson or Page...	5-1	8-1	8-4	7-7	4-5	8-6	8-3	8-8	8-7	8-10	8-1	8-9	6-1	8-8	8-9

Formative Assessment

You can use these two pages to benchmark student progress.

CRM Standardized Test Practice, pp. 85–87

Answer Sheet Practice

Have students simulate taking a standardized test by recording their answers on practice recording sheets.

CRM Student Recording Sheet, p. 66

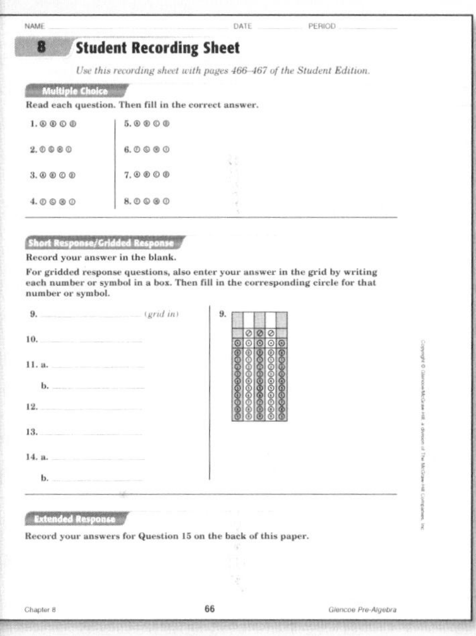
NAME DATE PERIOD
8 Student Recording Sheet
Use this recording sheet with pages 466–467 of the Student Edition.
Multiple Choice
Read each question. Then fill in the correct answer.
1. 2. 3. 4. 5. 6. 7. 8.
Short Response/Gridded Response
Record your answer in the blank.
For gridded response questions, also enter your answer in the grid by writing each number or symbol in a box. Then fill in the corresponding circle for that number or symbol.
9. (grid in) 10. 11. a. b. 12. 13. 14. a. b.
Extended Response
Record your answers for Question 15 on the back of this paper.
Chapter 8 66 Glencoe Pre-Algebra

Create practice worksheets or tests that align to your state's standards as well as TIMSS and NAEP tests.

Additional Answers

10. Sample answer: No, there are two y-values for the same x-value. It fails the vertical line test.

11a. The terms have a common difference of 3. A term is 3 times the term number minus 1. $t = 3n - 1$.

12. $\frac{5}{28}$; for every 28 sets of golf clubs, 5 are junior sets.

Homework Option

Get Ready for Chapter 9 Assign students the exercises on p. 469 as homework to assess whether they possess the prerequisite skills needed for the next chapter.

Page 395, Lesson 8-1 (Why?)

a.

Number of Pennants	Money Earned ($)
20	100
30	150
40	200
50	250
60	300

Page 395, Lesson 8-1 (Check Your Progress)

1A. This relation is a function because each element of the domain is paired with exactly one element of the range.

1B. This is not a function because 1 is paired with two range values, 7 and 8.

Pages 397–399, Lesson 8-1

1. This relation is a function because each element of the domain is paired with exactly one element of the range.

2. This is not a function because 3 is paired with two range values, 2 and 4.

3. The graph represents a relation that is not a function because it does not pass the vertical line test. At least one input value has more than one output value. By examining the graph, you can see that when $x = 3$, there are two different y values.

4. This graph is a function because the vertical line test shows that it passes through no more than one point on the graph for each value of x.

16. The graph represents a relation that is not a function because it does not pass the vertical line test. At least one input value has more than one output value. By examining the graph, you can see that when $x = 3$, there are two different y values.

17. This graph is a function because the vertical line test shows that it passes through no more than one point on the graph for each value of x.

39b.

Term Number	Term
1	36
2	33
3	30
4	27
5	24
6	21
7	18

The set of ordered pairs is a function because each input is paired with only one output.

39c.

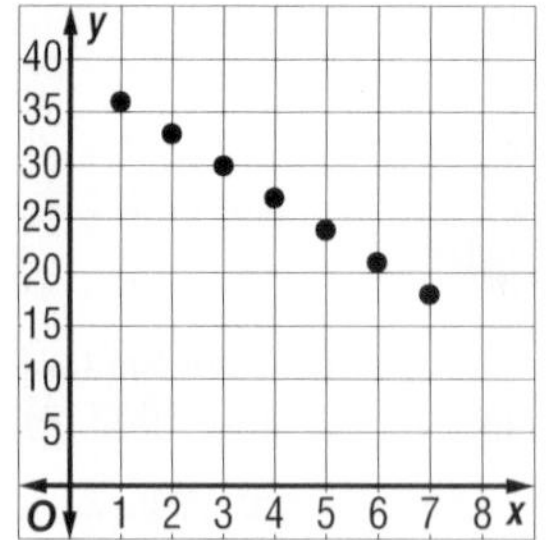

There is a negative relationship.

46. Sample answer: There is only one time to ascend to the water's surface for each water depth. So, the relationship between water depth and time to ascend to the water's surface is a function. As the water depth decreases, the time to ascend to the water's surface decreases. Since the relationship between water depth and time to ascend to the water's surface is a function, there cannot be two different times to ascend to the water's surface for the same water depth.

Page 401, Lesson 8-2 (Check Your Progress)

1A. The terms have a common difference of 1. A term is 9 more than the term number; $t = 9 + n$.

1B. The terms have a common difference of 5. A term is 5 times the term number; $t = 5n$.

Page 403, Lesson 8-2

1. The terms have a common difference of 1. A term is 1 more than the term number; $t = 1 + n$.

2. The terms have a common difference of 1. A term is 6 more than the term number; $t = 6 + n$.

3. The terms have a common difference of 3. A term is 3 times the term number; $t = 3n$.

4. The terms have a common difference of 7. A term is 7 times the term number; $t = 7n$.

10. The terms have a common difference of 1. A term is 2 more than the term number; $t = 2 + n$.

11. The terms have a common difference of 1. A term is 7 more than the term number; $t = 7 + n$.

12. The terms have a common difference of 1. A term is 13 more than the term number; $t = 13 + n$.

13. The terms have a common difference of 1. A term is 14 more than the term number; $t = 14 + n$.

14. The terms have a common difference of 2. A term is 2 times the term number; $t = 2n$.

15. The terms have a common difference of 8. A term is 8 times the term number; $t = 8n$.

16. The terms have a common difference of 12. A term is 12 times the term number; $t = 12n$.

17. The terms have a common difference of 20. A term is 20 times the term number; $t = 20n$.

18. The terms have a common difference of 10. A term is 4 less than 10 times the term number. $t = 10n - 4$.

Page 406, Lesson 8-3 (Why?)

a.

Speed of a Tennis Ball		
Time in Seconds (x)	60x	Distance in Meters (y)
1	60(1)	60
2	60(2)	120
3	60(3)	180

b.

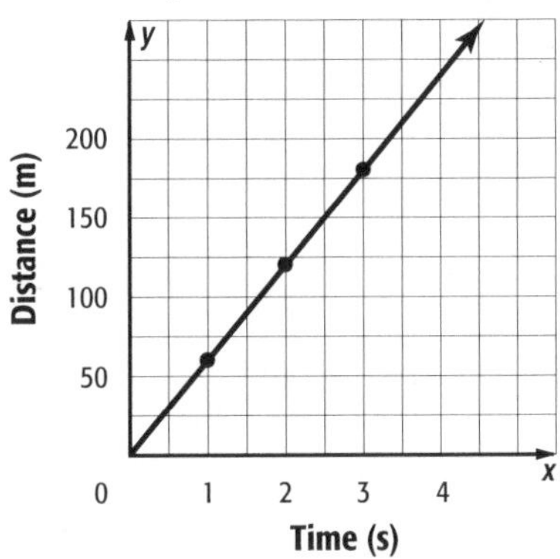

c. Yes; each domain value is paired with exactly one range value.

Page 406, Lesson 8-3 (Check Your Progress)

1A. Sample answer: (–1, 1), (0, 2), (1, 3), (2, 4)

1B. Sample answer: (–1, –4), (0, –1), (1, 2), (2, 5)

1C. Sample answer: (–1, 7), (0, 5), (1, 3), (2, 1)

1D. Sample answer: (–1, –2), (0, –6), (1, –10), (2, –14)

Pages 409–410, Lesson 8-3

8.

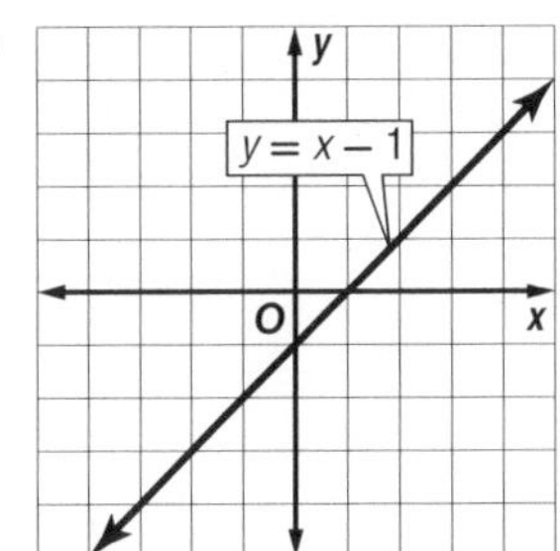

9.

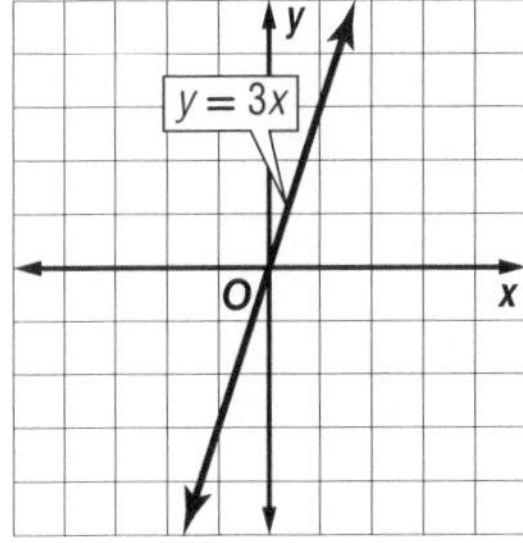

10.

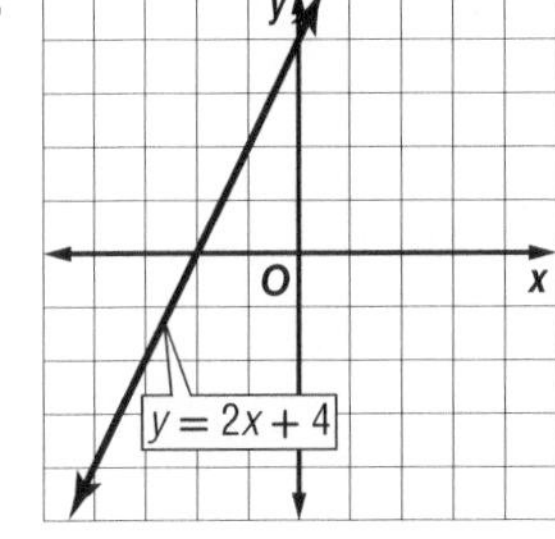

11.

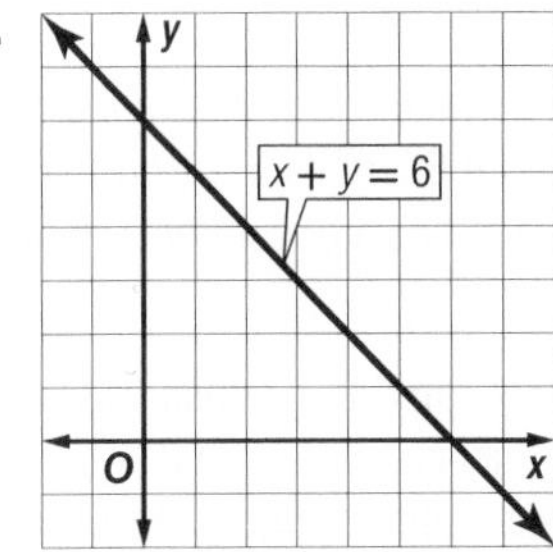

12.

x	$y = x - 2$	y
–1	$y = -1 - 2$	–3
0	$y = 0 - 2$	–2
1	$y = 1 - 2$	–1
2	$y = 2 - 2$	0

(–1, –3), (0, –2), (1, –1), (2, 0)

13.

x	$y = -2x$	y
–1	$y = -2(-1)$	2
0	$y = -2(0)$	0
1	$y = -2(1)$	–2
2	$y = -2(2)$	–4

(–1, 2), (0, 0), (1, –2), (2, –4)

14.

x	$y = 5x + 1$	y
–2	$y = 5(-2) + 1$	–9
–1	$y = 5(-1) + 1$	–4
0	$y = 5(0) + 1$	1
1	$y = 5(1) + 1$	6

(–2, –9), (–1, –4), (0, 1), (1, 6)

15.

x	$y = -2x + 8$	y
–1	$y = -2(-1) + 8$	10
0	$y = -2(0) + 8$	8
2	$y = -2(2) + 8$	4
4	$y = -2(4) + 8$	0

(–1, 10), (0, 8), (2, 4), (4, 0)

16. Sample answer: (–1, –8), (0, 0), (1, 8), (2, 16)

17. Sample answer: (–1, 2), (0, 0), (1, –2), (2, –4)

18. Sample answer: (–1, 6), (0, 7), (1, 8), (2, 9)

19. Sample answer: (–1, 4), (0, 3), (1, 2), (2, 1)

20. Sample answer: (–1, 3), (0, 5), (1, 7), (2, 9)

21. Sample answer: (–1, –1), (0, –4), (1, –7), (2, –10)

22. Sample answer: (–1, –2), (0, –3), (1, –4), (2, –5)

23. Sample answer: (–1, 11), (0, 9), (1, 7), (2, 5)

24. Sample answer: (1, 6.3) means that a circle with a radius of 1 unit has a circumference of about 6.3 units; (2, 12.6) means that a circle with a radius of 2 units has a circumference of about 12.6 units.

25. Sample answer: (1, 9) means they can ride 1 regular ride and 9 children's rides; (2, 6) means they can ride 2 regular rides and 6 children's rides; (3, 3) means they can ride 3 regular rides and 3 children's rides.

26.

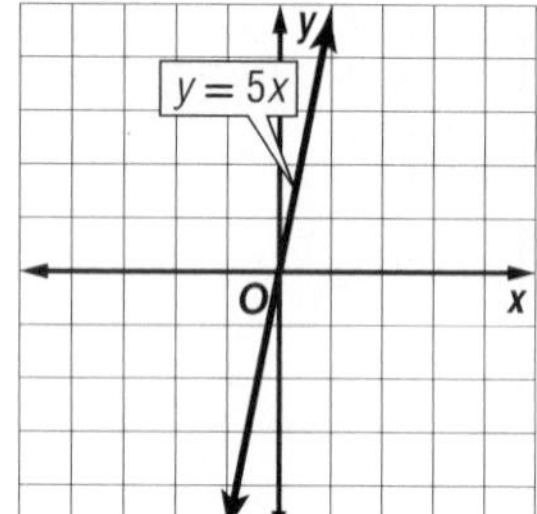

27.

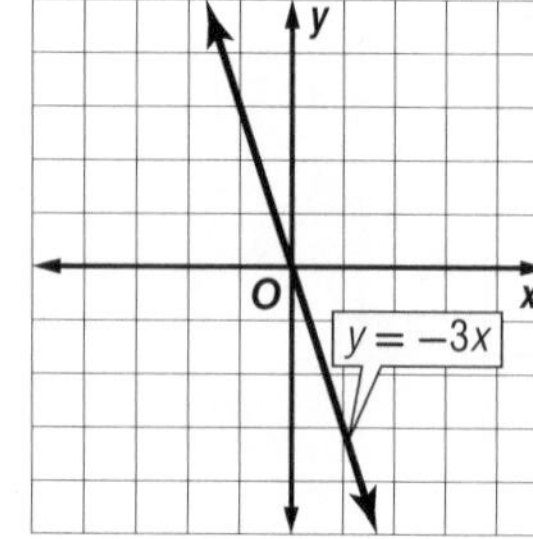

28.

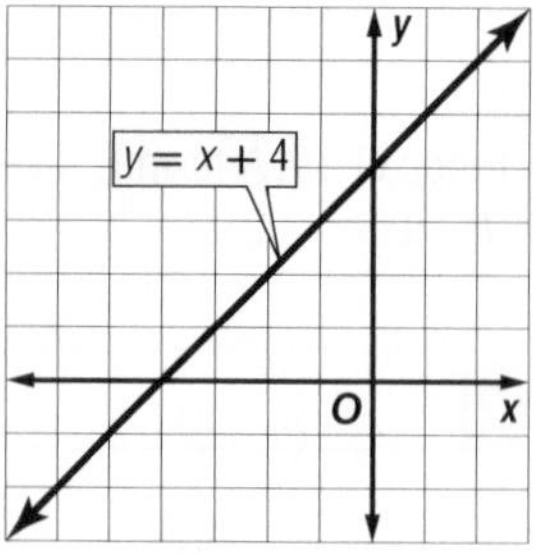

29.

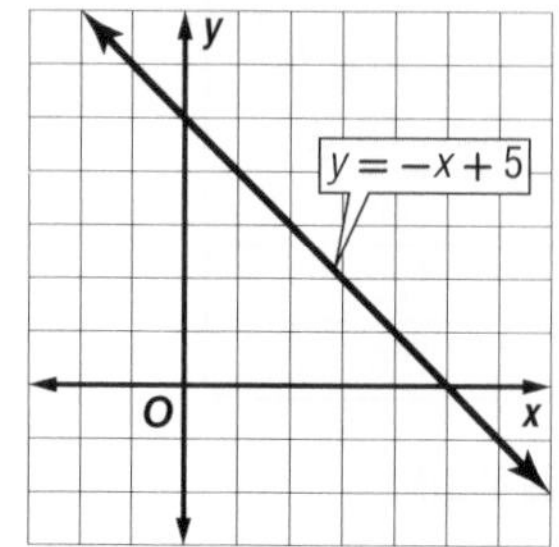

30.

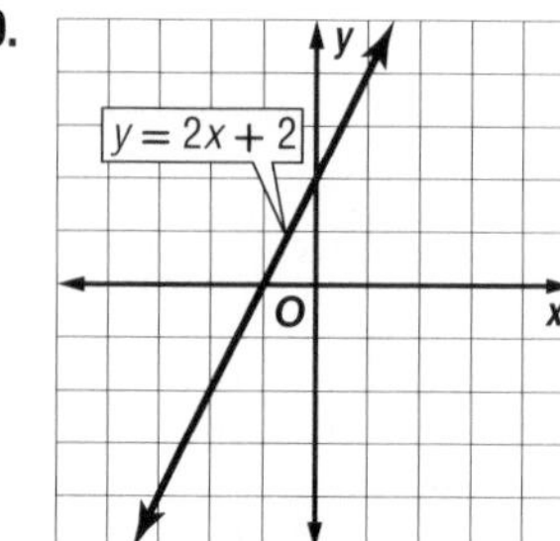

31.

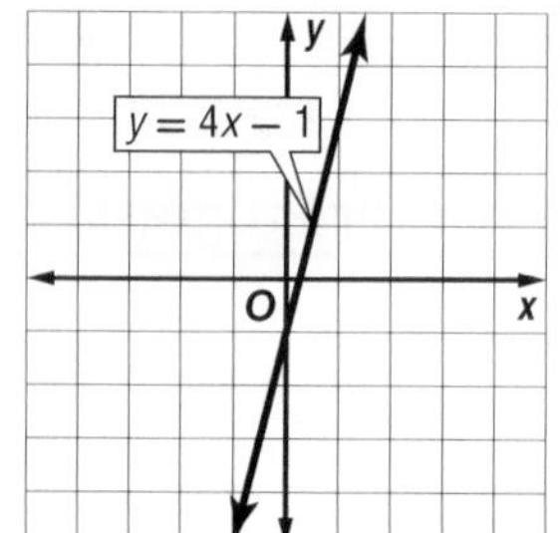

32.

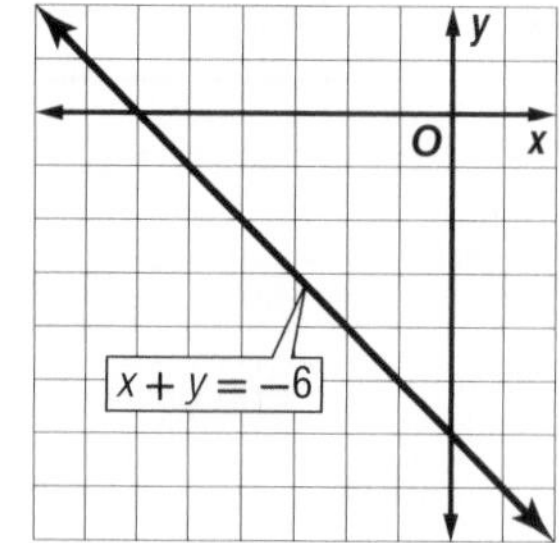

33.

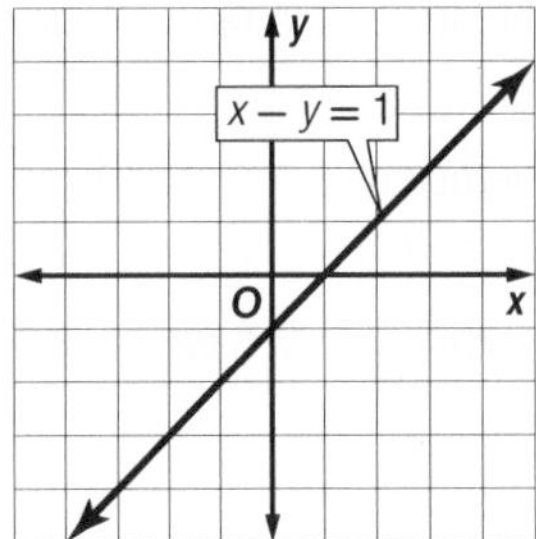

34a.

Time (min) y	$y = 0.5x$	Distance (mi) x
5	$y = 0.5(5)$	2.5
10	$y = 0.5(10)$	5
15	$y = 0.5(15)$	7.5
20	$y = 0.5(20)$	10

34b. No, the output values increase by 2.5.

34c. **Distance a Killer Whale Swims**

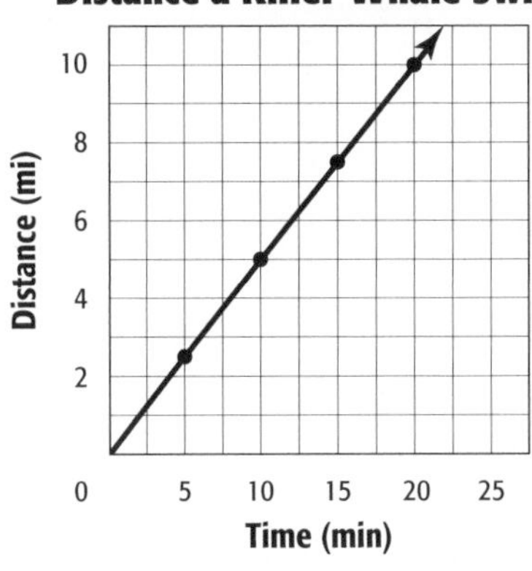

34d. $y = 0.5x$; The miles y that a whale swims is one-half or 0.5 of the time x spent swimming so $y = 0.5x$.

35c. **Perimeter of a Rectangle**

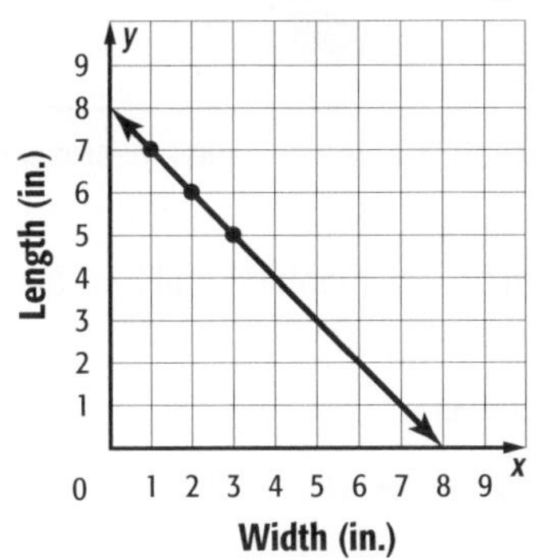

35d. Yes; no, because the width of a rectangle cannot have a negative value.

40a. **Graph of a Sequence**

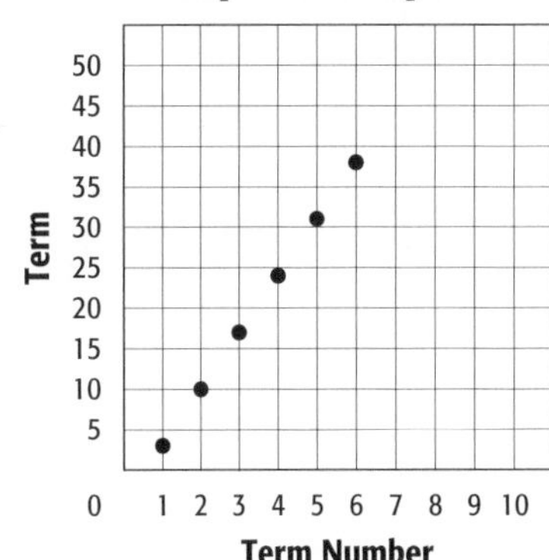

The points lie on one line.

40b. The graph only makes sense in Quadrant I because these term numbers cannot be negative.

40c. Sample answer: An arithmetic sequence can only have natural numbers for the term number x. You should not connect the points with a line as that would imply that there are term numbers between consecutive term numbers.

41. Sample answer: Linear equations use variables to show the relationship between the domain values and the range values of a function. Functions can be represented using a table, a graph, a verbal description, or an equation.

Page 412, Lesson 8-4 (Why?)

a. B and C; the difference in height is 10 – 4 or 6 ft.

b. There is no change in height.

c. A to B: 1; B to C: 3; C to D: 0; D to E: $-\frac{1}{2}$; B to C

Pages 416 – 417, Lesson 8-4

16. Sample answer:

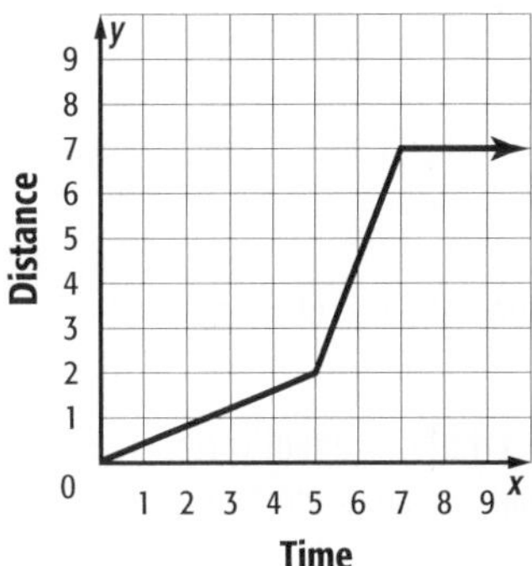

23. Sample answer:

x	y
−1	−8
0	−7
1	−6
2	−5

24. Sample answer:

x	y
−1	−5
0	−3
1	−1
2	1

25. Sample answer:

x	y
−1	−13
0	−10
1	−7
2	−4

26. The difference of the term numbers is 1. The terms have a common difference of 2. A term is 2 times the term number, plus 2. $t = 2n + 2$.

27. The difference of the term numbers is 1. The terms have a common difference of 3. A term is 3 times the term number, minus 2. $t = 3n - 2$.

28. The difference of the term numbers is 1. The terms have a common difference of 4. A term is 4 times the term number, minus 1. $t = 4n - 1$.

Page 423, Lesson 8-5

14. Sample answer:

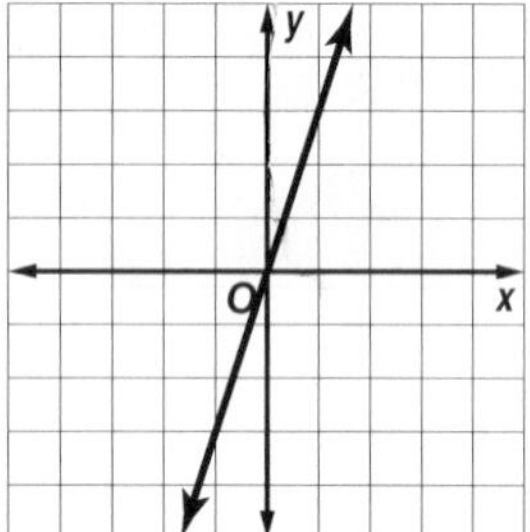

rate of change = 3

15. Keyshawn; Ramiro found the constant rate of change rather than finding the ratios $\frac{y}{x}$ for each point.

16. Sometimes; a linear relationship that is a direct variation is proportional. A linear relationship whose graph does not pass through the origin is not proportional.

18. Sample answer: The total cost y of buying x bags of pretzels involves a proportional linear relationship. If you buy x bags of pretzels and a bottled water for \$2, the relationship between total cost and bags of pretzels becomes nonproportional.

Page 425, Mid-Chapter Quiz

5. The terms have a common difference of 1. A term is 3 more than the term number; $t = 3 + n$.

6. The terms have a common difference of 9. A term is 9 times the term number; $t = 9n$.

7. The terms have a common difference of 2. A term is 1 more than 2 times the term number; $t = 2n + 1$.

8. The terms have a common difference of 2.5. A term is 2.5 times the term number; $t = 2.5n$.

13. Sample answer: (–1, 7), (0, 8), (1, 9), (2, 10)

14. Sample answer: (–1, 5), (0, 0), (1, –5), (2, –10)

15. Sample answer: (–1, 1), (0, 3), (1, 5), (2, 7)

16. Sample answer: (–1, –3), (0, –7), (1, –11), (2, –15)

18.

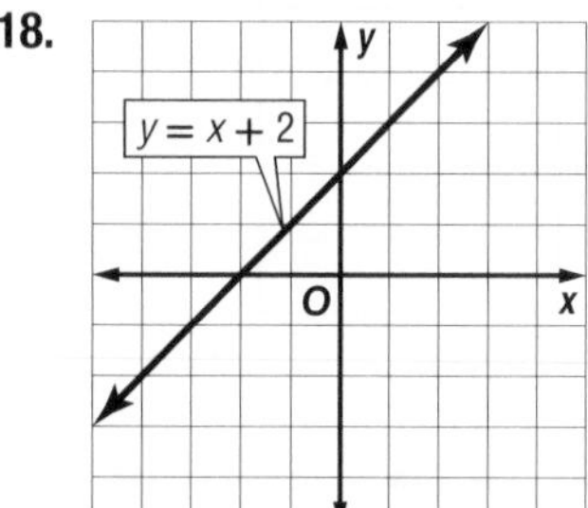

19.

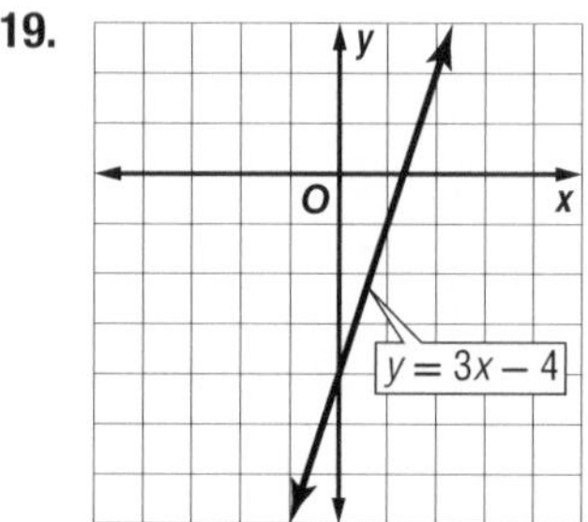

23. No; the ratio $\frac{\text{number of weeks}}{\text{amount saved}}$ is not the same for every pair of values.

24. Yes; the ratio $\frac{\text{profit}}{\text{number sold}}$ is the same for every pair of values.

Page 426, Explore 8-6

1. See students' work for graph. Sample answer: a decreasing linear graph

2. See students' work for graph. The graph for Trial 2 is steeper and has a more negative slope.

3. The weight of the cup decreases.

4. Trial 2; the hole was bigger, so the water drained faster.

5. The greater the slope, the faster the rate.

6. Sample answer: The graph would be less steep than the Trial 1 graph for a hole half the size since the water would drain slower. The graph for a hole twice the size of the second hole would be steeper since the water would drain faster.

7a. Sample answer:

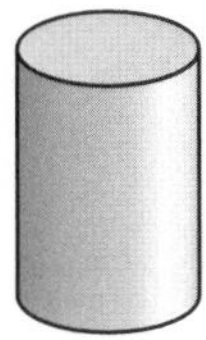

7b. Sample answer:

7c. Sample answer:

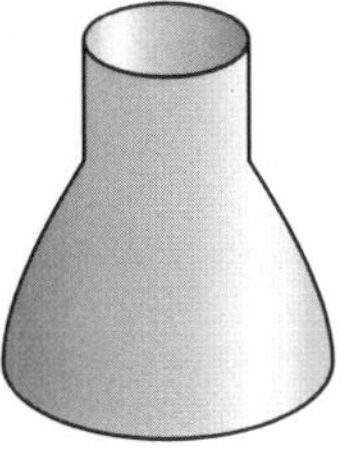

Page 430, Lesson 8-6

20b.

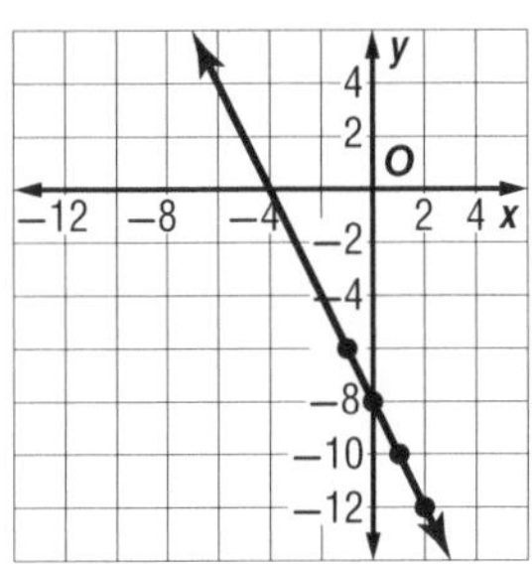

Page 432, Explore 8-7

Step 2 Answers:

Pattern A		
x	Process	y
0	2 • 0	0
1	2 • 1	2
2	2 • 2	4
3	2 • 3	6
4	2 • 4	8
x	2 • x	2x

Pattern B		
x	Process	y
0	2 • 0 + 1	1
1	2 • 1 + 1	3
2	2 • 2 + 1	5
3	2 • 3 + 1	7
4	2 • 4 + 1	9
x	2 • x + 1	2x + 1

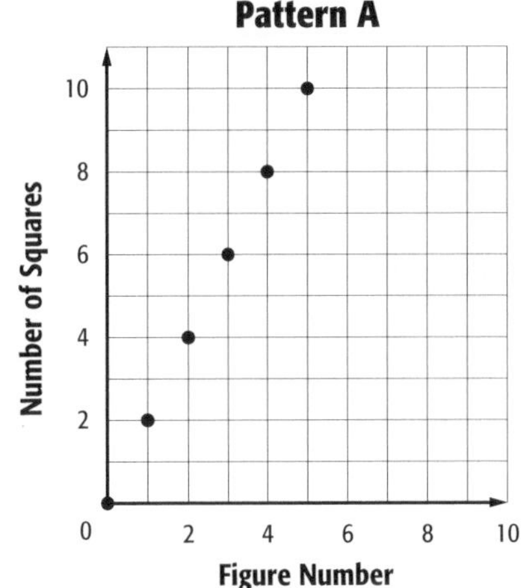

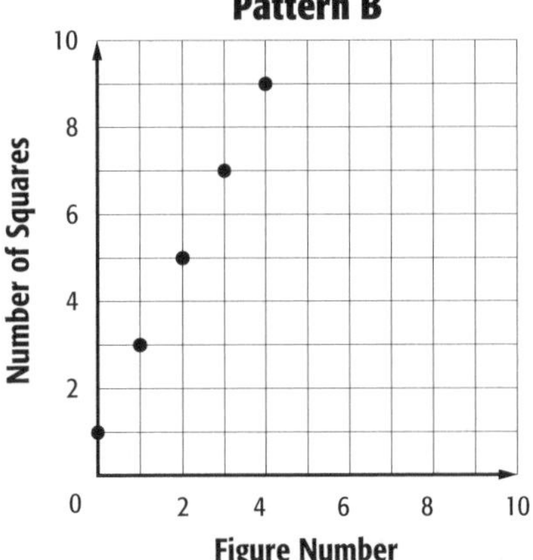

Analyze the Results Answers:

1. Sample answer: Each pattern has a single column of squares that increases by 2 from one figure number to the next. Pattern B has one additional square that remains constant for each figure number.
2. Sample answer: Each pattern has a $2x$ term, but Pattern B has an additional term of 1 added.
3. Sample answer: The points on each graph form a line that rises at the same rate, a two-square increase for every one increase in the figure number. The y-intercepts for the graphs are different, with (0, 0) for Pattern A and (0, 1) for Pattern B.
4. Pattern A is a proportional relationship or direct variation since the ratio $\frac{\text{number of squares}}{\text{figure number}}$ is a constant of 2. Pattern B is a nonproportional relationship since the ratio $\frac{\text{number of squares}}{\text{figure number}}$ is not constant: $\frac{1}{0} \neq \frac{3}{1} \neq \frac{5}{2} \neq \frac{7}{3} \neq \frac{9}{4}$. You can tell that Pattern A is a proportional relationship from the table because the process involves just multiplication. Pattern B is nonproportional because it involves multiplication and addition. You can tell that Pattern A is proportional from the graph because its y-intercept is (0, 0). You can tell that Pattern B is nonproportional from the graph because its y-intercept is not (0, 0).

Page 433, Lesson 8-7 (Why?)

a.

Number of Hours, x	Total Cost, y
1	\$28
2	\$36
3	\$44

b.

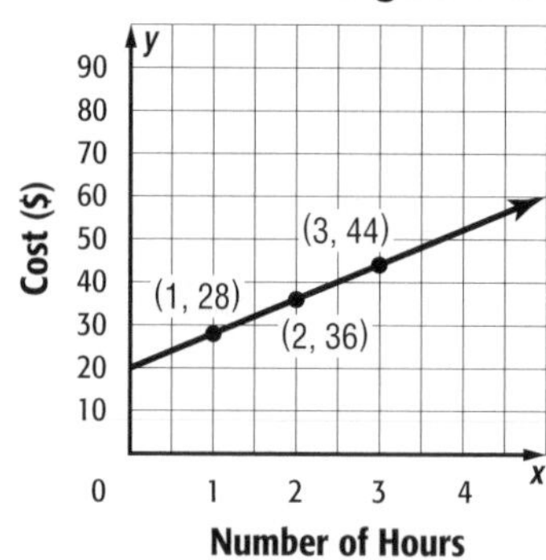

Quadrant 1; the number of hours must be a positive integer, and thus the cost would be positive.

c. 20, 8; The slope is the coefficient of the x-term in the equation and the y-coordinate of the point where the graph crosses the y-axis is the constant.

Pages 434–435, Lesson 8-7 (Check Your Progress)

3.

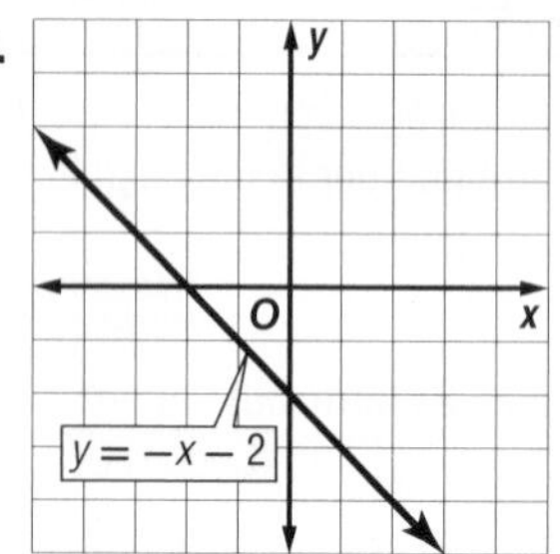

4A.

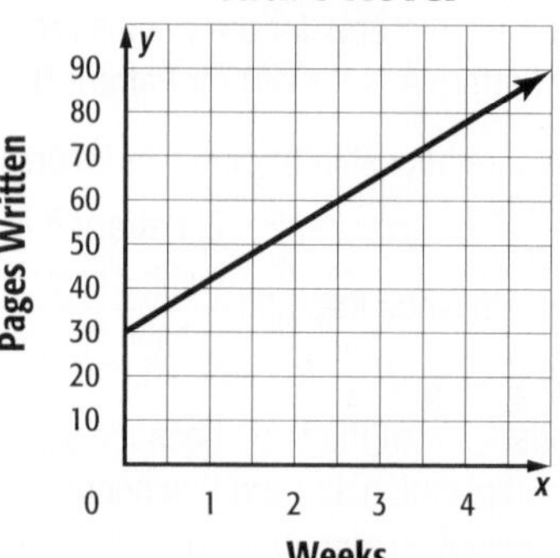

4B. The y-intercept 30 represents the pages that are already written. The slope 12 represents the number of pages he will write per week.

Pages 435–437, Lesson 8-7

5.

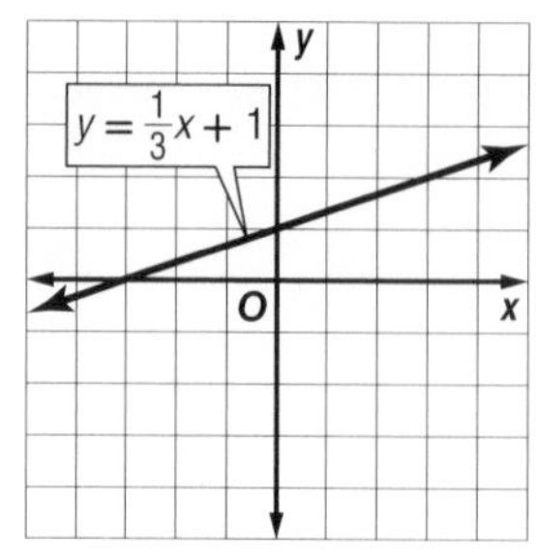

6.

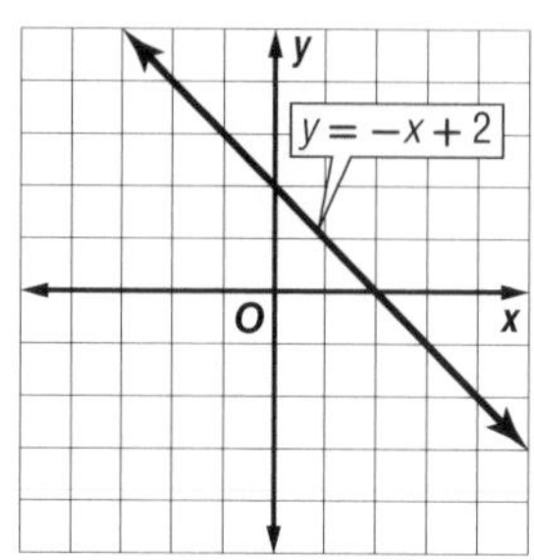

7.

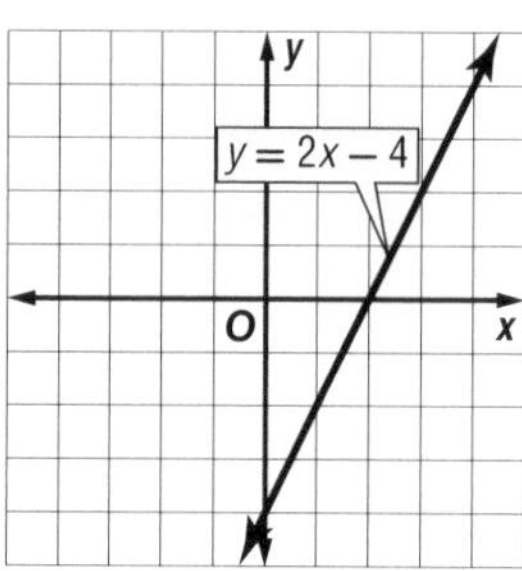

8.

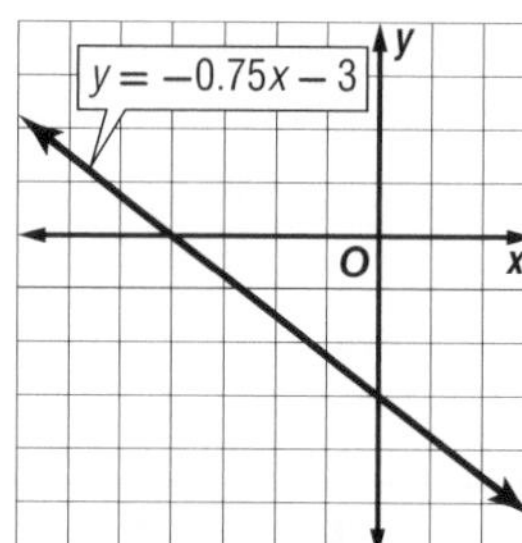

9a.

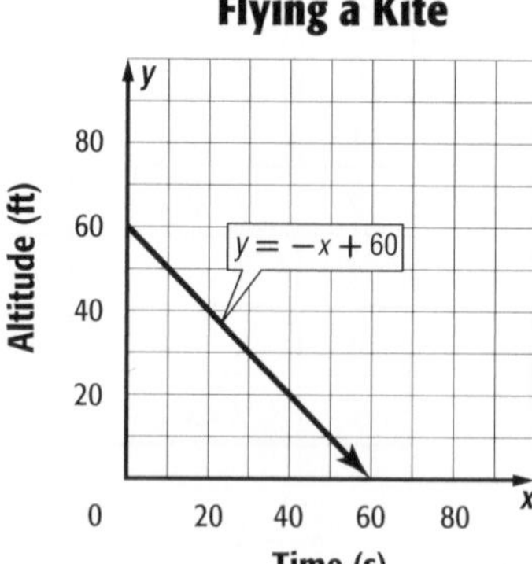

9b. The y-intercept 60 represents the initial height of the kite. The slope –1 represents the descent of 1 foot per second.

22.

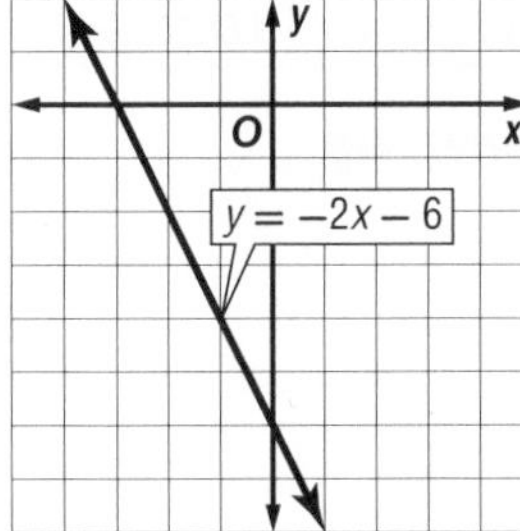

23.

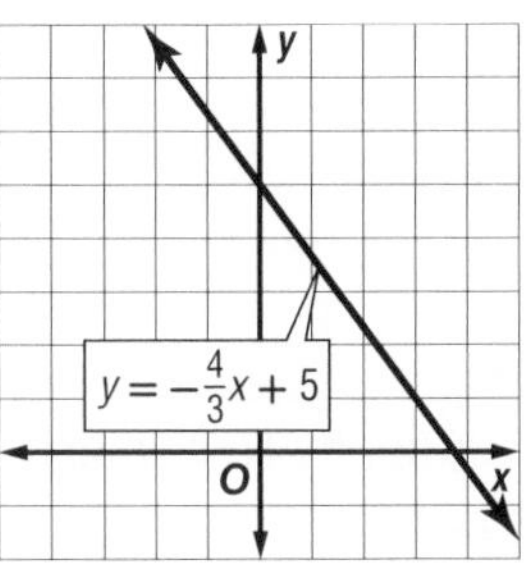

24a.

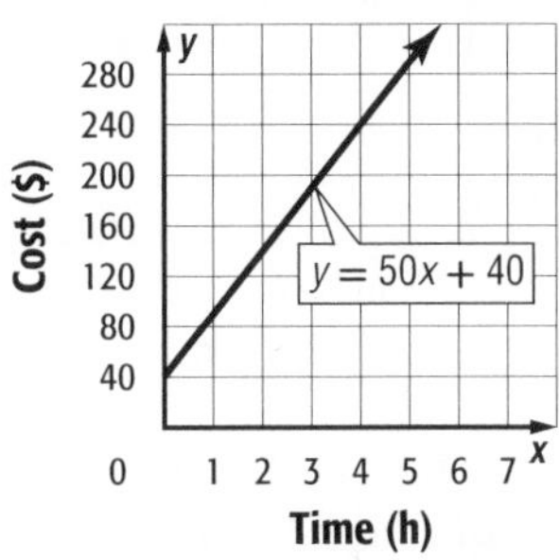

24b. The y-intercept $40 represents the initial fee. The slope $50 represents the price the auto mechanic charges per hour.

25a.

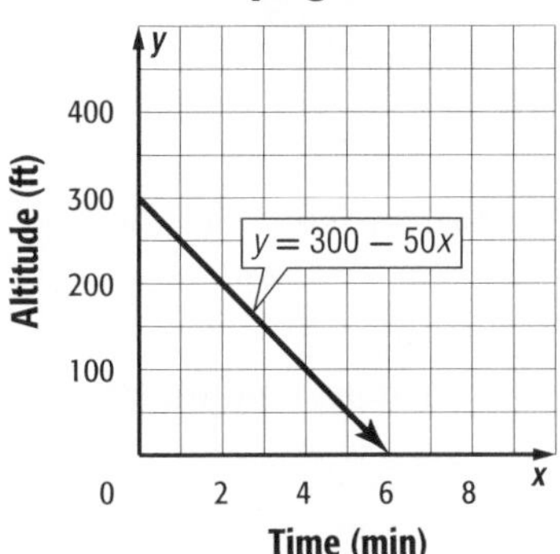

25b. 300 is the y-intercept which represents the original height. The slope is -50 which represents descending at 50 ft/min.

26a. The y-intercept 15 represents the teaspoons of nuts that she starts with. The slope $-\frac{3}{2}$ represents the teaspoons of nuts that she uses for each muffin.

26b. The x-intercept 10 represents the number of muffins that she makes before she runs out of nuts.

27b.

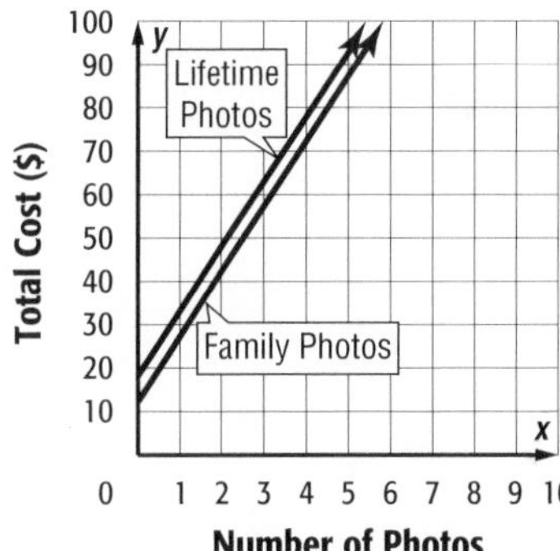

28.

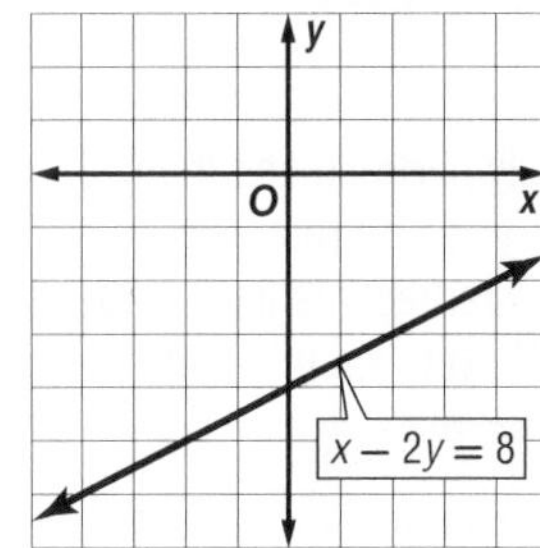

29.

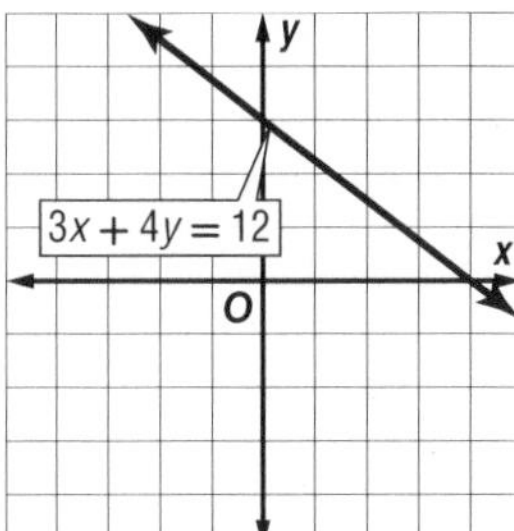

30.

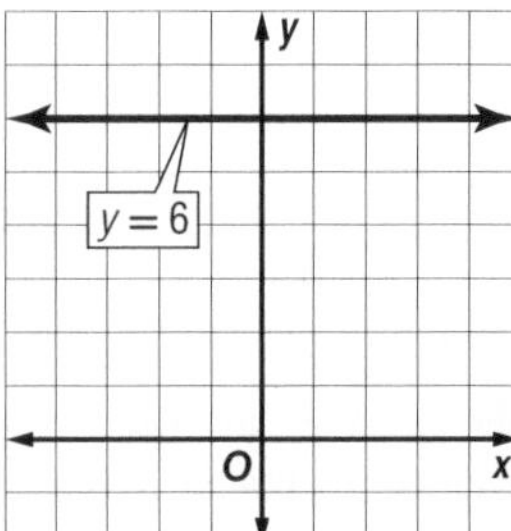

31.

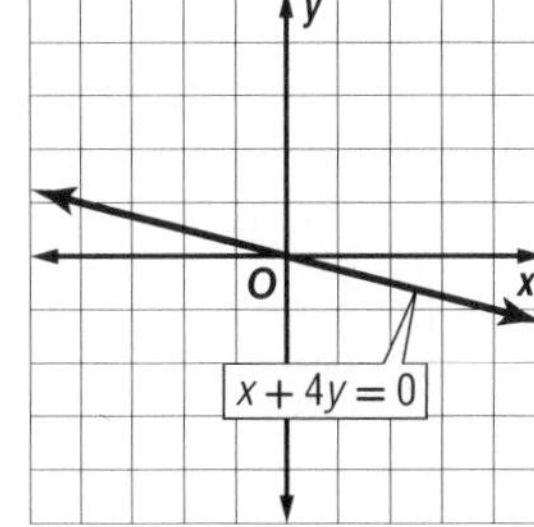

32b.

25 students; If you substitute 25 for the x value in each equation, the resulting y value for each is 612.5.

37. Sample answer: A photographer charges a \$50 sitting fee to come to your house to take family portraits and then \$15 for each 5x7 portrait. The total cost y can be represented by the equation $y = 50 + 15x$, where x represents the number of portraits ordered. A family has \$300 to spend on the portraits. How many portraits can they purchase?; 16

38. Quadrants I, II, and IV; if a y-intercept point is graphed at $(0, b)$, where b is positive, and then a line is drawn through the point so that it has a negative slope, the line will pass through Quadrants I, II, and IV.

Page 441, Lesson 8-8 (Why?)

a.

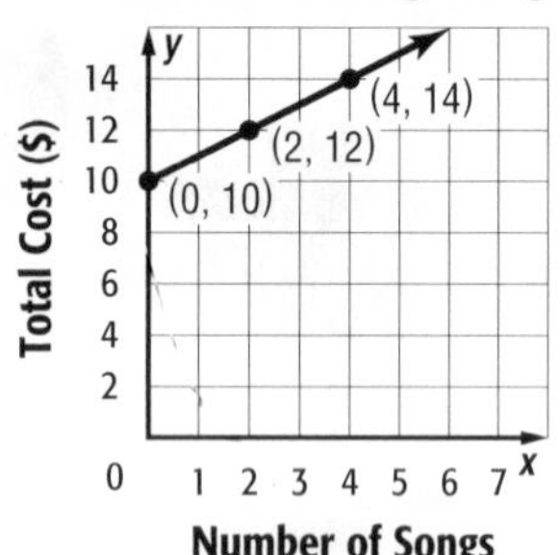

b. Slope = 1 represents the rate of change, \$1 for every song downloaded; y-intercept = 10 represents the initial fee before any songs are downloaded, \$10.

Page 448, Lesson 8-9 (Why?)

a. $\frac{17}{4}$; There is an increase of about 17 teams every 4 years.

Page 448, Lesson 8-9 (Check Your Progress)

1A.

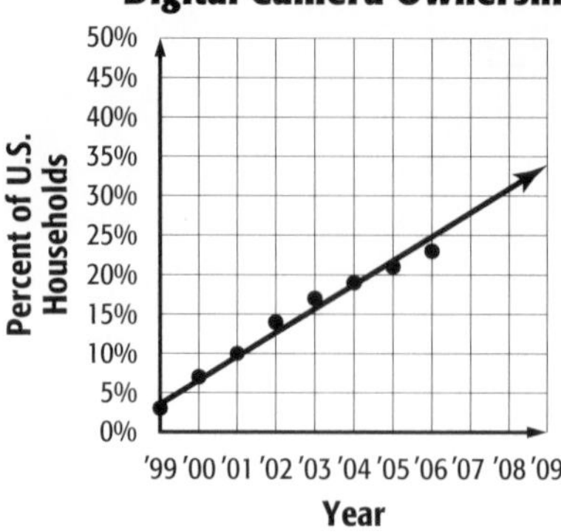

Pages 450–452, Lesson 8-9

1a. Sample answer:

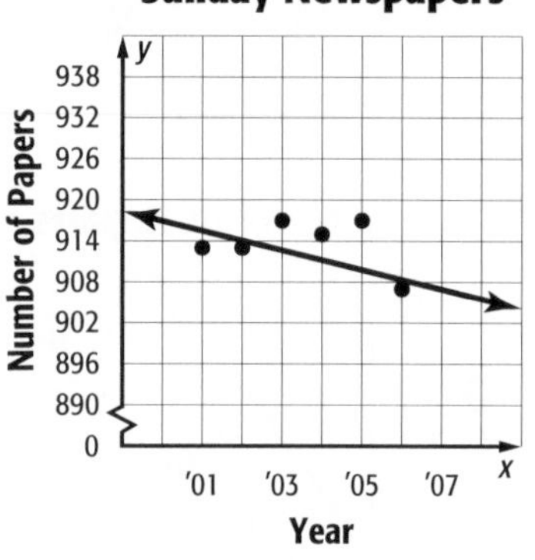

3a. Sample answer:

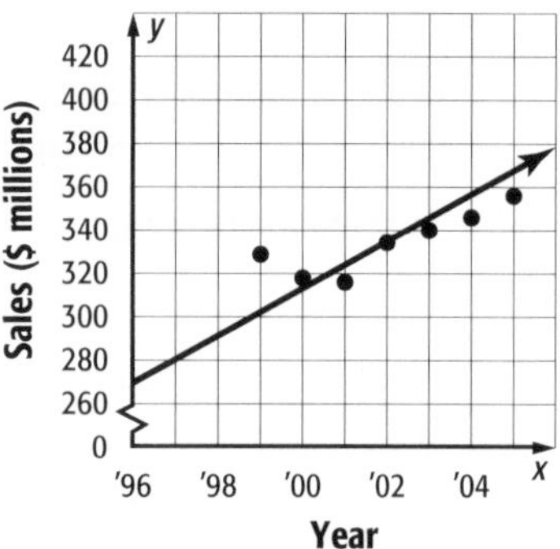

3c. Sample answer:

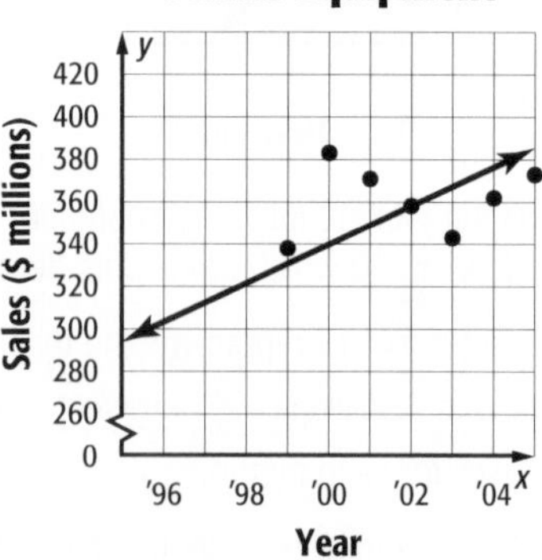

7a.

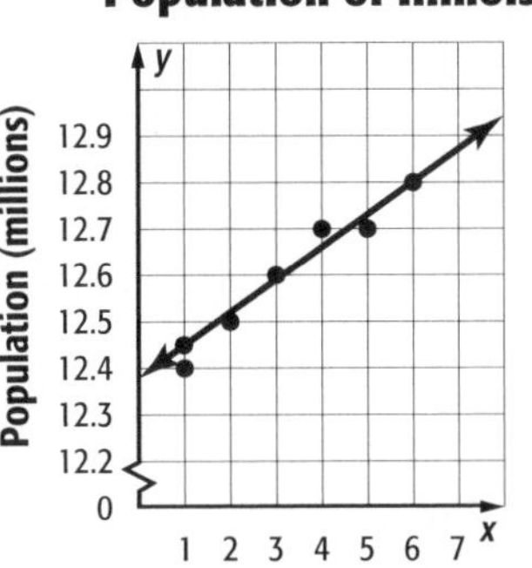

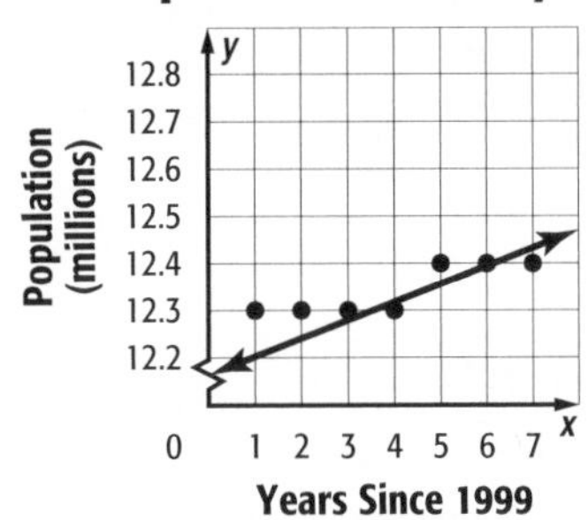

Sample answer: The slope of the line for the population of Illinois means that the population grows by 0.07 million (70,000) people every year. The slope of the line for the population of Pennsylvania means that the population grows by 0.03 million (30,000) people every year.

7b. Ilinois' population; the line of fit is steeper than the line of fit representing the growth of Pennsylvania's population. The intersection would represent the year in which the populations were equal.

7c. Sample answer: Illinois: $y = 0.07x + 12.31$; Pennsylvania: $y = 0.03x + 12.22$; the slope of the Illinois equation is greater than the slope of the Pennsylvania equation. So, it is true that Illinois' population is growing at a faster rate.

7d. Sample answer: Illinois 13.43 million; Pennsylvania 12.7 million

11. Sample answer: a scatter plot in which the data do not appear to be linear

12. Sample answer: Display a set of data using a scatter plot. Then draw a line as close to as many of the points as possible. Then extend the line and use it to make predictions. A line of fit is a line drawn as close to as many of the data points as possible. Although the points may not be exactly linear, a line of fit can be used to approximate the data set.

20.

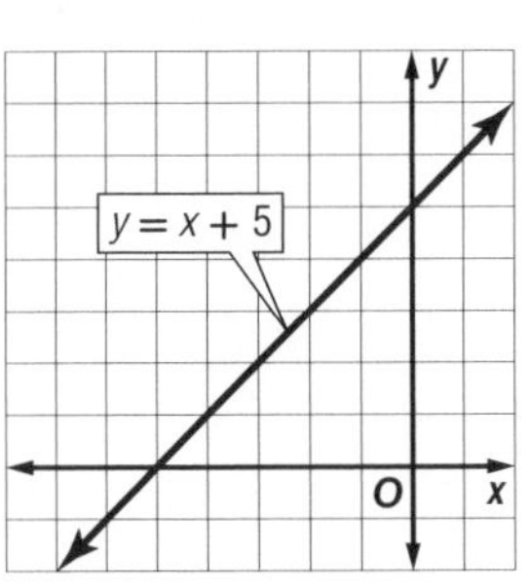

21.

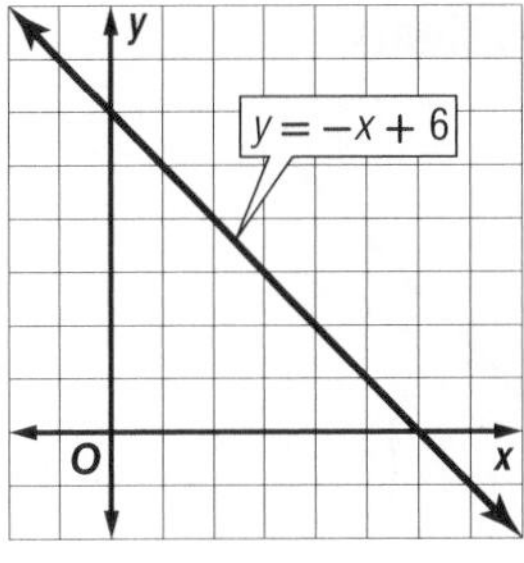

22.

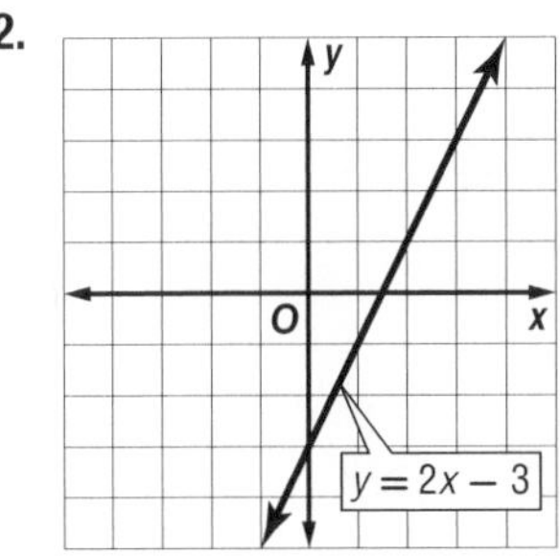

Page 453, Lesson 8-10 (Why?)

b.

x	$y = 30 + 2x$	$y = 5x$
0	30	0
2	34	10
4	38	20
6	42	30
8	46	40

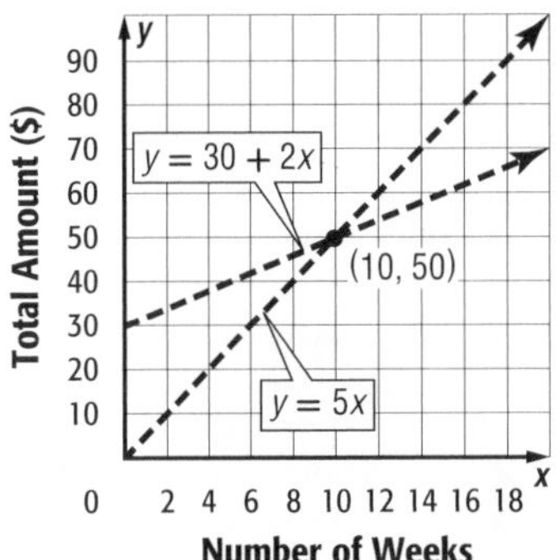

Pages 453–454, Lesson 8-10 (Check Your Progress)

1.

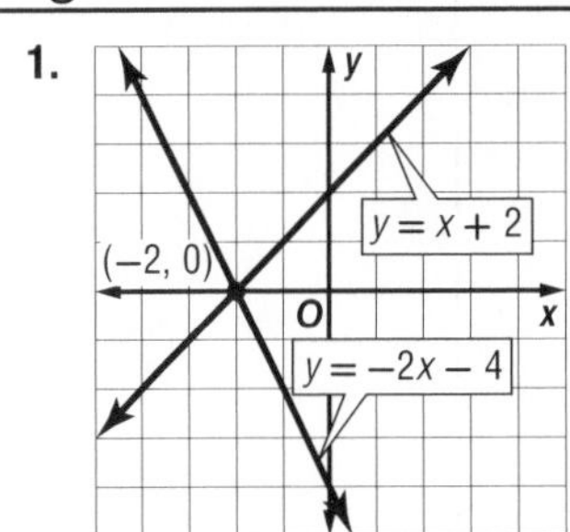

2B.

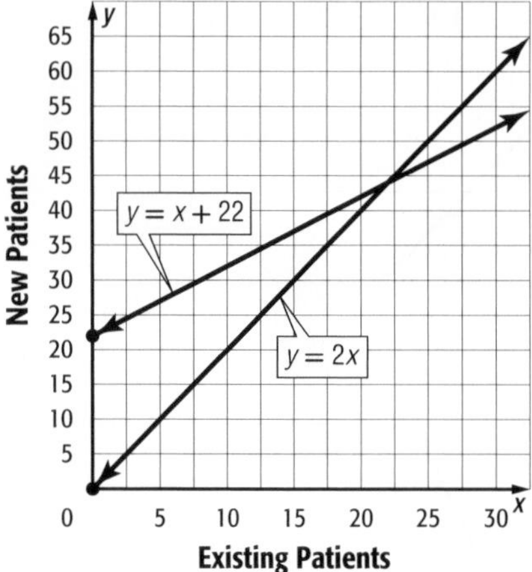

3A.

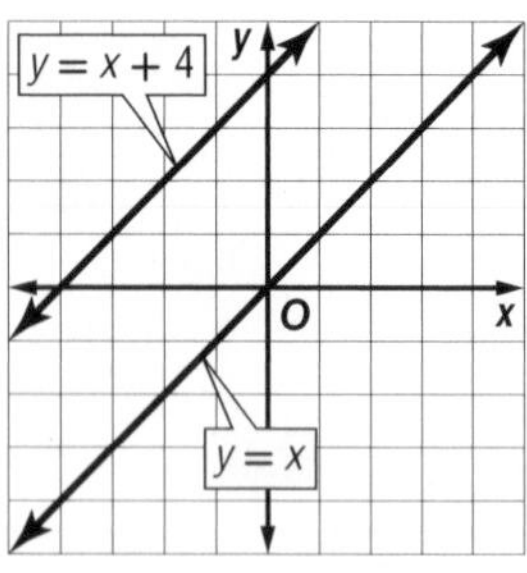

3B.

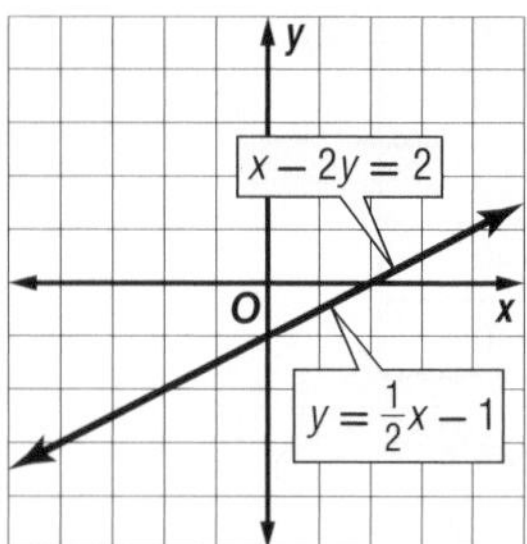

Page 455 – 456, Lesson 8-10

1.

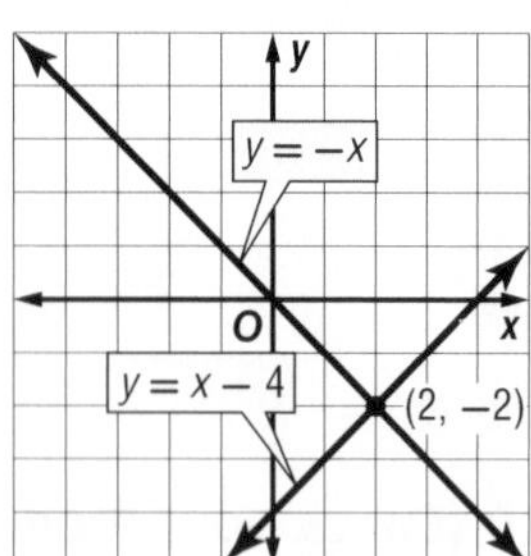

2.

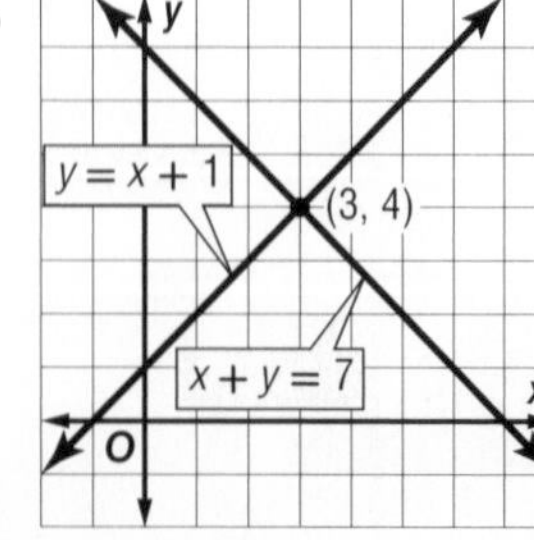

3.

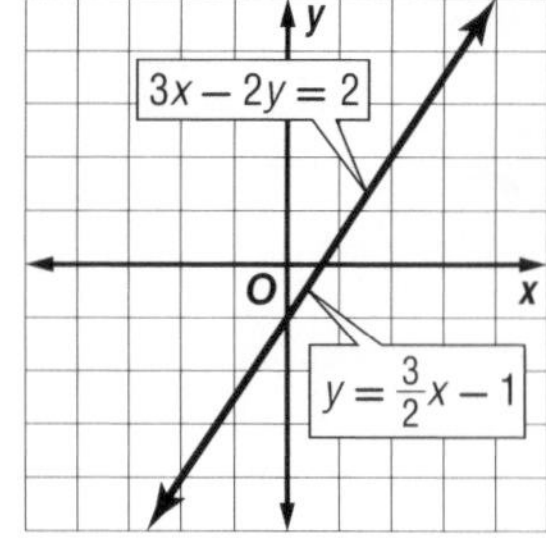

4a. $y = 100 + 10x$ and $y = 20x$

4b.

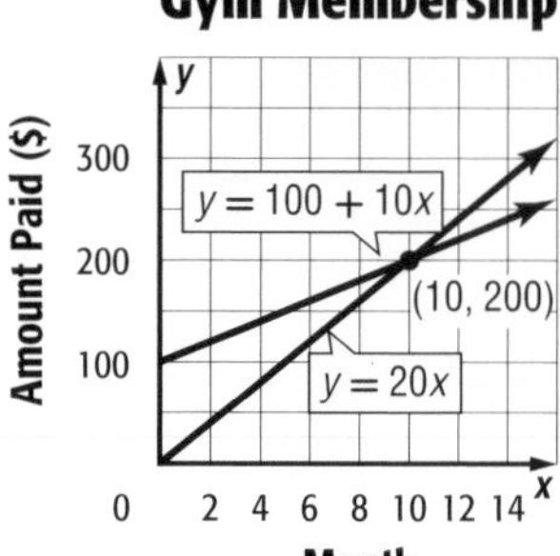

The solution (10, 200) means that the only time Maria and Amanda have paid the same amount is the tenth month in which they have both spent a total of $200.

8.

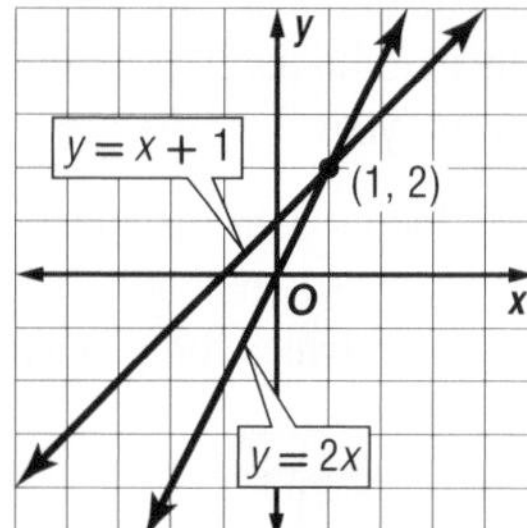

9.

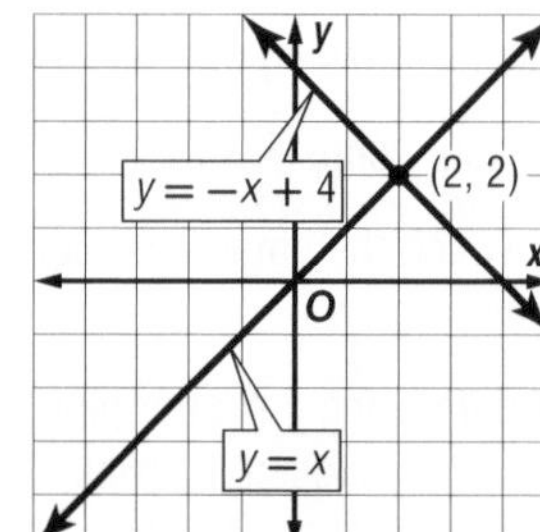

10.

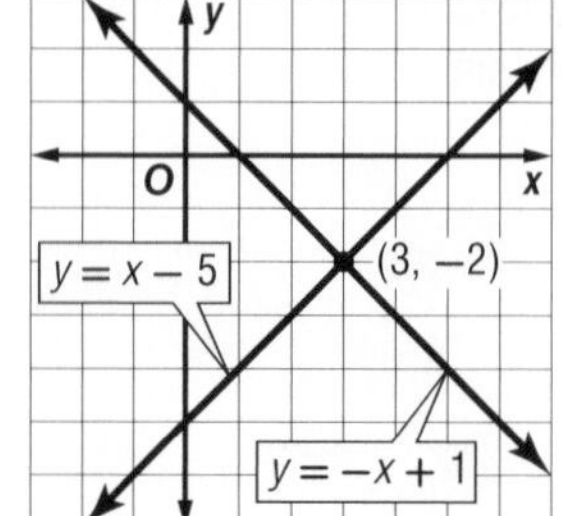

11.

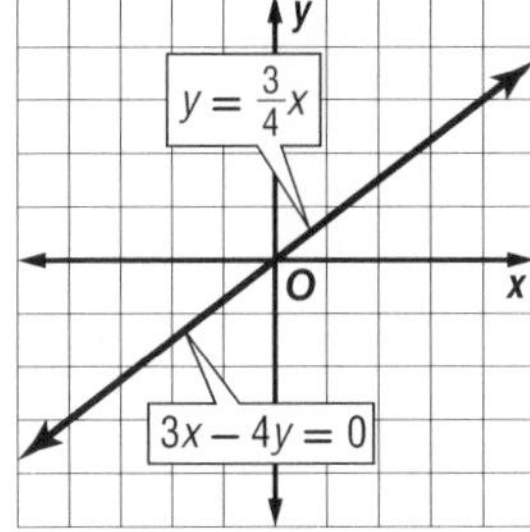

12.

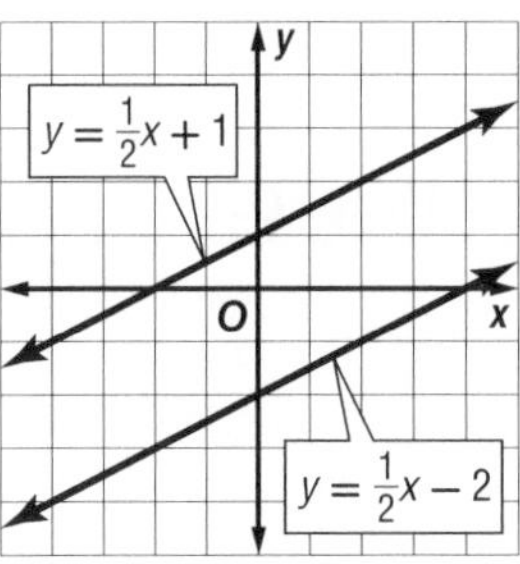

13.

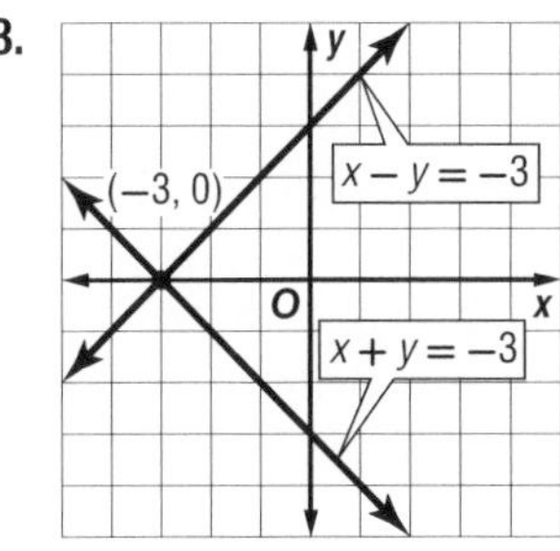

14a. $x + y = 5$ and $x - y = 3$

14b.

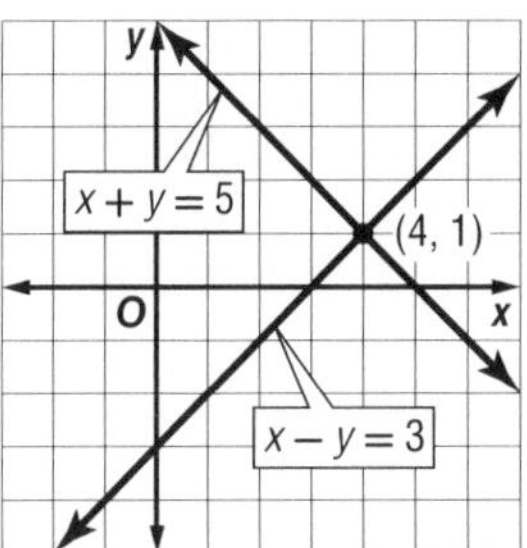

The solution is (4, 1). This means that the numbers 4 and 1 solve both equations.

15a. $y = 5x + 50$ and $y = -5x + 90$

15b.

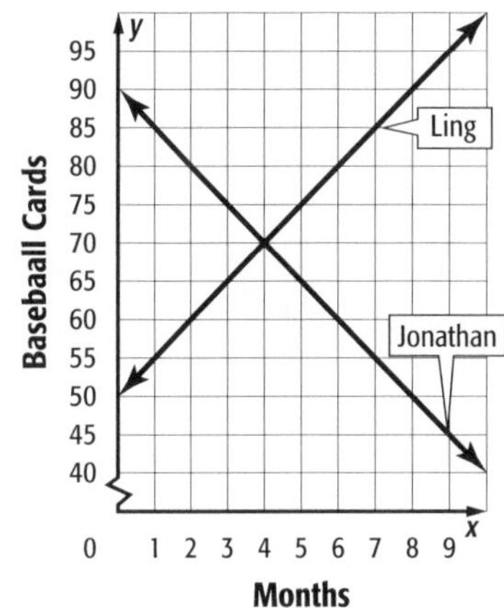

The solution (4, 70) means that after 4 months, they will have the same number of cards (70).

24. Sample answer: Two lines or systems of equations can be parallel and have no solution, intersect and have one solution, or be the same line and have an infinite number of solutions. A system of linear equations cannot have two solutions because two lines cannot intersect twice.

28. Sample answer: When the equations are complex and cannot be easily graphed, or when the solution involves numbers that are not integers, it is better to use substitution to get an accurate solution.

29. Sample answer: If a system of equations has 1 solution, the graphs are intersecting lines. If the system has no solution, the graphs are parallel lines. If the system has infinitely many solutions, then the graphs are the same line.

Page 463, Practice Test

6.

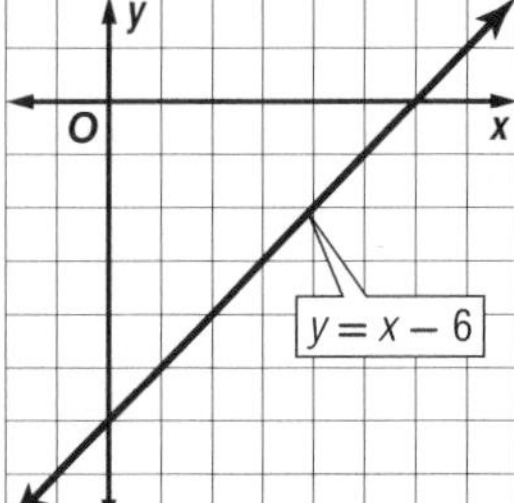

7.

y

O

x

$y = -2x + 3$

8. increase of 2 stones/m; Yes; Sample answer: The ratio $\frac{\text{number of stepping stones}}{\text{length of path}}$ is the same for every pair of values.

9. 3; –1

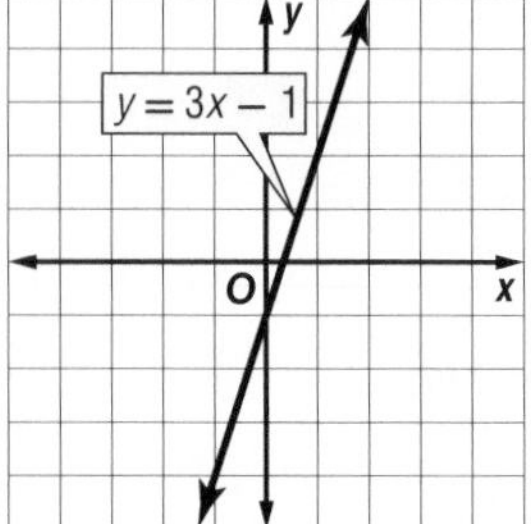

10. $-\frac{4}{3}$; 2

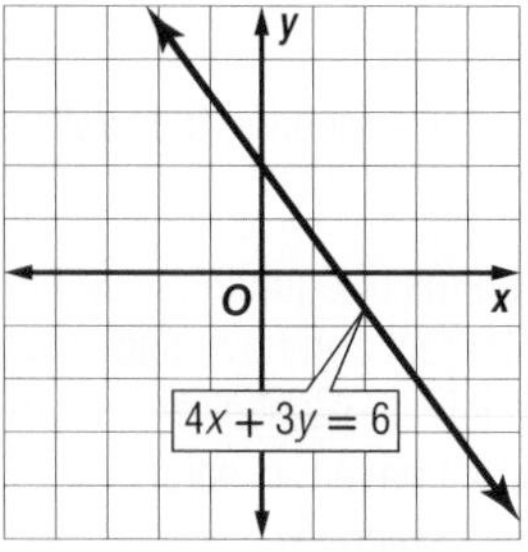

16a. Sample answer:

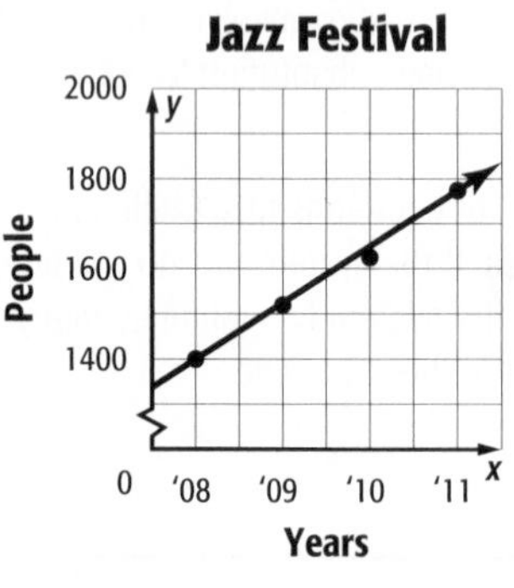

16b. Sample answer: 2,100

17. (–1, 3)

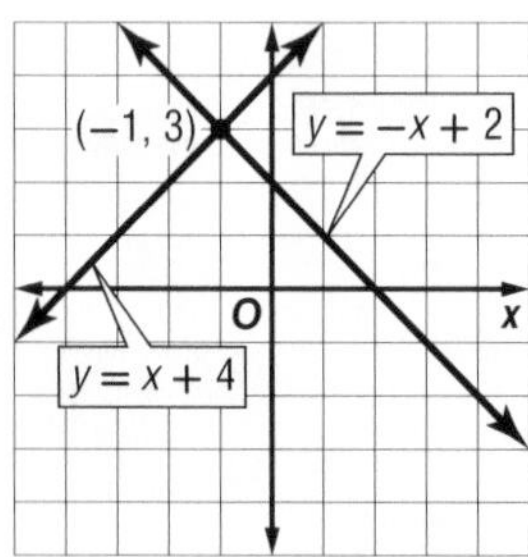

18. (1, 1)

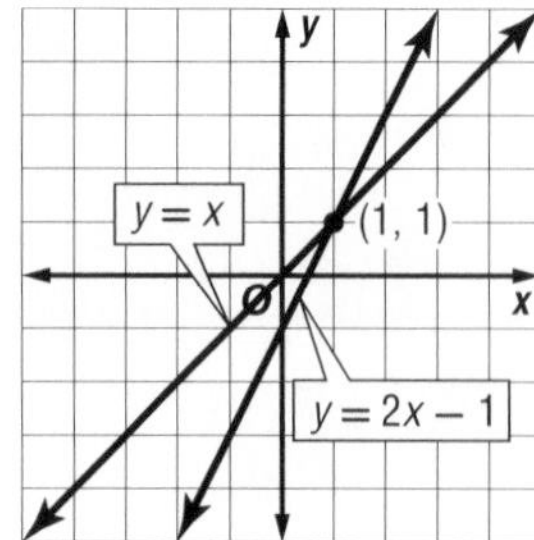

Page 467, Standardized Test Practice

15a.

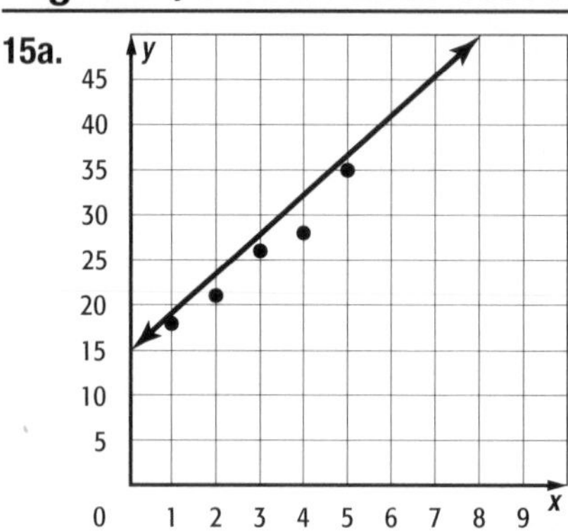

Notes

Chapter Planner

Diagnostic Assessment
Quick Check, p. 469

	Lesson 9-1 Pacing: 1 day	Lesson 9-2 Pacing: 1 day	Lesson 9-3 Pacing: 1 day
Title	**Powers of Exponents**	**Prime Factorization**	**Multiplying and Dividing Monomials**
Objectives	• Write expressions using exponents. • Evaluate expressions containing exponents.	• Write the prime factorizations of composite numbers. • Factor monomials.	• Multiply monomials. • Divide monomials.
Key Vocabulary	exponent power base	prime number composite number prime factorization factor tree monomial factor	
NCTM Focal Points	G8–FP4C, G8–FP7C For the complete wording of the Focal Points for Grades 7 and 8, please see pages iv, v, FP0, and FP1		
Multiple Representations	p. 474		p. 484
Lesson Resources	**Chapter 9 Resource Masters** • Study Guide and Intervention, pp. 5–6 AL OL ELL • Skills Practice, p. 7 AL OL ELL • Practice, p. 8 AL OL BL ELL • Word Problem Practice, p. 9 AL OL BL • Enrichment, p. 10 OL BL • Graphing Calculator, p. 11 AL OL BL ELL **Transparencies** • 5-Minute Check Transparency 9-1 AL OL BL ELL **Additional Print Resources** • *Study Notebook* AL OL BL ELL	**Chapter 9 Resource Masters** • Study Guide and Intervention, pp. 12–13 AL OL BL • Skills Practice, p. 14 AL OL ELL • Practice, p. 15 AL OL BL ELL • Word Problem Practice, p. 16 AL OL BL • Enrichment, p. 17 OL BL **Transparencies** • 5-Minute Check Transparency 9-2 AL OL BL ELL **Additional Print Resources** • *Study Notebook* AL OL BL ELL	**Chapter 9 Resource Masters** • Study Guide and Intervention, pp. 18–19 AL OL ELL • Skills Practice, p. 20 AL OL ELL • Practice, p. 21 AL OL BL ELL • Word Problem Practice, p. 22 AL OL BL • Enrichment, p. 23 OL BL • Quiz 1, p. 64 AL OL BL ELL **Transparencies** • 5-Minute Check Transparency 9-3 AL OL BL ELL **Additional Print Resources** • *Study Notebook* AL OL BL ELL
Technology for Every Lesson	Math Online glencoe.com • Extra Examples • Self-Check Quizzes • Personal Tutor	**CD/DVD Resources** IWB INTERACTIVE WHITEBOARD READY IWB StudentWorks Plus IWB Interactive Classroom IWB Diagnostic and Assessment Planner	• TeacherWorks Plus • eSolutions Manual Plus • ExamView Assessment Suite
Math in Motion	p. 472		p. 482
Differentiated Instruction	pp. 472, 475	pp. 477, 480	pp. 482, 485

KEY:  AL Approaching Level  OL On Level 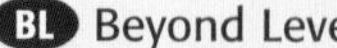 BL Beyond Level ELL English Learners

Suggested Pacing			
Time Periods	Instruction	Review & Assessment	Total
45-minute	11	2	13
90-minute	5.5	1	6.5

Powers and Nonlinear Functions

Lesson 9-4 Pacing: 1 day	Lesson 9-5 Pacing: 1 day	Lesson 9-6 Pacing: 1 day	Lesson 9-7 Pacing: 1 day
Negative Exponents	**Scientific Notation**	**Powers of Monomials**	**Linear and Nonlinear Functions**
• Write expressions using negative exponents. • Evaluate numerical expressions containing negative exponents.	• Express numbers in standard form and in scientific notation. • Compare and order numbers written in scientific notation.	• Find the power of a power. • Find the power of a product.	• Determine whether a function is linear or nonlinear from a graph. • Determine whether a function is linear or nonlinear from an equation or table.
	standard form scientific notation		nonlinear function
p. 490		p. 502	p. 508
Chapter 9 Resource Masters • Study Guide and Intervention, pp. 24–25 AL OL BL • Skills Practice, p. 26 AL OL ELL • Practice, p. 27 AL OL BL ELL • Word Problem Practice, p. 28 AL OL BL • Enrichment, p. 29 OL BL **Transparencies** • 5-Minute Check Transparency 9-4 AL OL BL ELL **Additional Print Resources** • *Study Notebook* AL OL BL ELL	**Chapter 9 Resource Masters** • Study Guide and Intervention, pp. 30–31 AL OL BL • Skills Practice, p. 32 AL OL ELL • Practice, p. 33 AL OL BL ELL • Word Problem Practice, p. 34 AL OL BL • Enrichment, p. 35 OL BL • Quiz 2, p. 64 AL OL BL ELL **Transparencies** • 5-Minute Check Transparency 9-5 AL OL BL ELL **Additional Print Resources** • *Study Notebook* AL OL BL ELL	**Chapter 9 Resource Masters** • Study Guide and Intervention, pp. 36–37 AL OL ELL • Skills Practice, p. 38 AL OL BL • Practice, p. 39 AL OL BL ELL • Word Problem Practice, p. 40 AL OL BL • Enrichment, p. 41 OL BL **Transparencies** • 5-Minute Check Transparency 9-6 AL OL BL ELL **Additional Print Resources** • *Study Notebook* AL OL BL ELL	**Chapter 9 Resource Masters** • Study Guide and Intervention, pp. 42–43 AL OL BL • Skills Practice, p. 44 AL OL BL • Practice, p. 45 AL OL BL ELL • Word Problem Practice, p. 46 AL OL BL • Enrichment, p. 47 OL BL • Quiz 3, p. 66 AL OL BL ELL **Transparencies** • 5-Minute Check Transparency 9-7 AL OL BL ELL **Additional Print Resources** • *Study Notebook* AL OL BL ELL

Math Online > glencoe.com
- Extra Examples
- Self-Check Quizzes
- Personal Tutor

CD/DVD Resources IWB INTERACTIVE WHITEBOARD READY
- IWB StudentWorks Plus
- IWB Interactive Classroom
- IWB Diagnostic and Assessment Planner
- TeacherWorks Plus
- eSolutions Manual Plus
- ExamView Assessment Suite

pp. 487, 491	pp. 494, 498	pp. 500, 503	pp. 505, 509

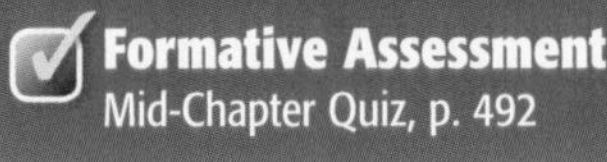
Formative Assessment
Mid-Chapter Quiz, p. 492

Chapter Planner

	Lesson 9-8 Pacing: 1 day	Extend 9-8 Pacing: 1 day	Lesson 9-9 Pacing: 1 day	Extend 9-9 Pacing: 1 day
Title	**Quadratic Functions**	**Graphing Technology Lab: Family of Quadratic Functions**	**Cubic and Exponential Functions**	**Algebra Lab: A Half-Life Simulation**
Objectives	• Graph quadratic functions. • Use quadratic functions to solve problems.	• Investigate families of quadratic functions on a graphing calculator.	• Graph cubic functions. • Graph exponential functions.	• Simulate half-life decay.
Key Vocabulary	quadratic function parabola		cubic function exponential function	
NCTM Focal Points				
Multiple Representations	p. 513			
Lesson Resources	**Chapter 9 Resource Masters** • Study Guide and Intervention, pp. 48–49 AL OL ELL • Skills Practice, p. 50 AL OL ELL • Practice, p. 51 AL OL BL ELL • Word Problem Practice, p. 52 AL OL BL • Enrichment, p. 53 OL BL • Graphing Calculator, p. 54 AL OL BL ELL **Transparencies** • 5-Minute Check Transparency 9-8 AL OL BL ELL **Additional Print Resources** • *Study Notebook* AL OL BL ELL	**Materials:** • graphing calculator	**Chapter 9 Resource Masters** • Study Guide and Intervention, pp. 55–56 AL OL ELL • Skills Practice, p. 57 AL OL ELL • Practice, p. 58 AL OL BL ELL • Word Problem Practice, p. 59 AL OL BL • Enrichment, p. 60 OL BL • Quiz 4, p. 65 AL OL BL ELL **Transparencies** • 5-Minute Check Transparency 9-9 AL OL BL ELL **Additional Print Resources** • *Study Notebook* AL OL BL ELL	**Materials:** • 100 coins • bag • grid paper
Technology for Every Lesson	Math Online glencoe.com • Extra Examples • Self-Check Quizzes • Personal Tutor	**CD/DVD Resources** IWB INTERACTIVE WHITEBOARD READY IWB StudentWorks Plus IWB Interactive Classroom IWB Diagnostic and Assessment Planner		• TeacherWorks Plus • eSolutions Manual Plus • ExamView Assessment Suite
Math in Motion				p. 521
Differentiated Instruction	pp. 511, 514		pp. 517, 520	

Summative Assessment
- Study Guide and Review, pp. 522–526
- Practice Test, p. 527

KEY: AL Approaching Level OL On Level BL Beyond Level ELL English Learners

What the Research Says...

Formative Assessment–ongoing assessments designed to make students' thinking visible to both teachers and students–are essential. They permit the teacher to graph the students' preconceptions, understand where the students are in the "developmental corridor" from informal to formal thinking, and design instruction accordingly. (Bransford et al., 2000)

- Determine students' preconceived ideas about the concepts in the chapter by utilizing the Chapter 4 Anticipation Guide. Make certain to emphasize the areas of misconceptions that are clarified during the lesson.
- Use the assessment activities at the end of each lesson to assess students' understanding of the concepts of the lesson.

Teacher to Teacher

Butch Sloan
Garland ISD
Garland, TX

USE WITH LESSON 9-1

“ Another way to factor is to use what we call the L method. To find the factors of 210, you divide by a prime factor and write the quotient underneath. Then divide the quotient by another prime factor, and so on until the result is 1. This method transfers well to two or more numbers. ”

NOTES:

Chapter 9 Assessment and Intervention

SE = Student Edition, **TE** = Teacher Edition, **CRM** = Chapter Resource Masters

	Diagnosis	Prescription
Diagnostic Assessment	**Beginning Chapter 9**	
	Get Ready for Chapter 9 **SE**, p. 469	Response to Intervention **TE**, p. 469
	Beginning Every Lesson	
	Then, Now, Why? **SE** 5-Minute Check Transparencies	Chapter 0 **SE**, pp. P1–P22 Concepts and Skills Bank **SE**, pp. 856–887 *Quick Review Math Handbook*
Formative Assessment	**During/After Every Lesson**	
	Check Your Progress **SE**, every example Check Your Understanding **SE** H.O.T. Problems **SE** Spiral Review **SE** Additional Examples **TE** Watch Out! **TE** Step 4, Assess **TE** Chapter 9 Quizzes **CRM**, pp. 64–65 Self-Check Quizzes glencoe.com	**Tier 1 Intervention** Concepts and Skills Bank **SE**, pp. 856–887 Skills Practice **CRM**, Ch. 1–9 glencoe.com **Tier 2 Intervention** Differentiated Instruction **TE** Study Guide and Intervention Masters **CRM**, Ch. 1–9 *Quick Review Math Handbook* **Tier 3 Intervention** *Math Triumphs, Grade 8,* Ch. 2, 6
	Mid-Chapter	
	Mid-Chapter Quiz **SE**, p. 492 Mid-Chapter Test **CRM**, p. 66 ExamView Assessment Suite	**Tier 1 Intervention** Concepts and Skills Bank **SE**, pp. 856–887 Skills Practice **CRM**, Ch. 1–9 glencoe.com **Tier 2 Intervention** Study Guide and Intervention Masters **CRM**, Ch. 1–9 *Quick Review Math Handbook* **Tier 3 Intervention** *Math Triumphs, Grade 8,* Ch. 2, 6
	Before Chapter Test	
	Chapter Study Guide and Review **SE**, pp. 522–526 Practice Test **SE**, p. 527 Standardized Test Practice **SE**, pp. 528–531 Chapter Test glencoe.com Standardized Test Practice glencoe.com Vocabulary Review glencoe.com ExamView Assessment Suite	**Tier 1 Intervention** Concepts and Skills Bank **SE**, pp. 856–887 Skills Practice **CRM**, Ch. 1–9 glencoe.com **Tier 2 Intervention** Study Guide and Intervention Masters **CRM**, Ch. 1–9 *Quick Review Math Handbook* **Tier 3 Intervention** *Math Triumphs, Grade 8,* Ch. 2, 6
Summative Assessment	**After Chapter 9**	
	Multiple-Choice Tests, Forms 1, 2A, 2B **CRM**, pp. 68–73 Free-Response Tests, Forms 2C, 2D, 3 **CRM**, pp. 74–80 Vocabulary Test **CRM**, p. 67 Extended Response Test **CRM**, p. 80 Standardized Test Practice **CRM**, pp. 81–83 ExamView Assessment Suite	Study Guide and Intervention Masters **CRM**, Ch. 1–9 *Quick Review Math Handbook* glencoe.com

CHAPTER 9

Differentiated Instruction

Option 1 Reaching All Learners AL OL BL ELL

INTERPERSONAL Have students work in pairs. Ask each student in the pair to create 5 fractions that can be written as numbers with negative exponents and 5 monomials with negative exponents that can be written as fractions. Then have pairs trade papers and complete the tasks. Suggest that students include variables in their problems to increase the challenge.

NATURALIST Have students research examples of natural occurrences that can be modeled by exponential functions, such as the decay of radioactive elements or the growth of bacteria. After students find three or four examples, have them explain why the phenomena exhibit exponential behavior. Ask students to compare the phenomena: Do they think one example will grow or decay faster than the other(s)? If so, how would these differences be shown in the graphs of the functions?

Option 2 Approaching Level AL

Provide each student with a copy of the parent cubic function $y = x^3$ and two other cubic functions graphed on the same coordinate plane. For example, $y = x^3$, $y = x^3 + 1$, and $y = x^3 - 1$ can be graphed on one coordinate plane.

- Have students identify the type of nonlinear function.
- Point out the parent graph and then have students describe the other two graphs in terms of the parent graph.

Option 3 English Learners ELL

To reinforce the meaning of *exponent, power,* and *base,* and the differences between linear and nonlinear functions, have students label the exponent, power, and base for each of the following equations:

- linear: $y = 2x$
- quadratic: $y = 2x^2$
- cubic: $y = 2x^3$
- exponential: $y = 2^x$

Then have students write a sentence describing each of the linear and nonlinear equations in terms of powers and exponents.

Option 4 Beyond Level BL

When an initial amount increases by the same percent over a given period of time, we can say exponential growth occurred. (The equation $y = C(1 + r)^t$ where C represents the initial amount, r represents the rate of change expressed as a decimal, and t represents time, can be used to model exponential growth.) One example of exponential growth is compound interest. In Chapter 7, students solved compound interest problems by repeatedly using the formula $I = prt$. Give students compound interest problems and the exponential growth equation to solve the problems. Then have them compare their answers to answers derived by the repeated use of the $I = prt$ formula.

CHAPTER 9 Focus on Mathematical Content

Vertical Alignment

Before Chapter 9

Related Topics before Pre-Algebra

- simplify numerical expressions
- solve problems involving fractions and decimals

Previous Topics from Pre-Algebra

- communicate mathematical ideas
- select appropriate operations
- use a problem-solving model

Chapter 9

Related Topics from Pre-Algebra

- examine factors and monomials
- evaluate expressions with powers and exponents
- multiply and divide monomials
- express numbers using positive and negative exponents
- use scientific notation
- communicate mathematical ideas using language, efficient tools, appropriate units, and graphical, numerical, physical, or algebraic mathematical models
- predict, find, and justify solutions to application problems using appropriate tables, graphs, and algebraic equations

After Chapter 9

Preparation for Algebra 1

- simplify polynomial expressions and factor in problem situations
- look for patterns and represent generalizations algebraically
- simplify polynomial expressions
- investigate methods for solving linear equations, select a method, and solve the equation

Lesson-by-Lesson Preview

9-1 Powers and Exponents

An expression such as $3 \cdot 3 \cdot 3 \cdot 3$ can be written as a power. A power has a base and an exponent. The base is the number that is multiplied (3). The exponent tells how many times the base is used as a factor (4 times). Thus, $3 \cdot 3 \cdot 3 \cdot 3$ can be written as 3^4.

- Numbers and variables can be written using exponents. For example, $8 \cdot 8 \cdot m \cdot m \cdot m \cdot m$ can be expressed as 8^2m^4.
- Any number, except 0, raised to the zero power is 1: $2^0 = 1$; $x^0 = 1, x \neq 0$.

9-2 Prime Factorization

A prime number is any whole number greater than 1 that has exactly two factors, 1 and itself. A composite number is a whole number greater than 1 that has more than two factors. The whole numbers 0 and 1 are neither prime nor composite.

When a composite number is expressed as the product of prime factors, it is called the prime factorization of the number. One way to find the prime factorization of a number is to use a factor tree:

- Write the number to be factored at the top.
- Choose any pair of whole number factors and continue to factor until there is a row of prime numbers.

Factor trees for 40

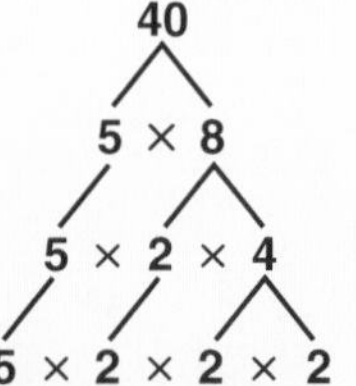

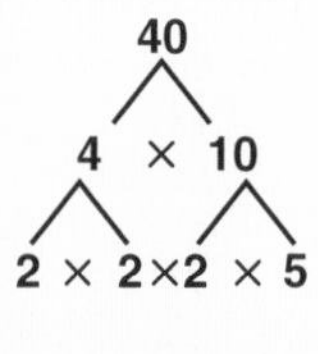

The prime factorization for 40 is $2 \cdot 2 \cdot 2 \cdot 5$ or $2^3 \cdot 5$. A monomial also may be factored. The monomial $8ab^3$ is factored as $3 \cdot 3 \cdot a \cdot b \cdot b \cdot b$.

9-3 Multiplying and Dividing Monomials

Use the Product of Powers Property to multiply monomials and the Quotient of Powers Property to divide monomials.

- To multiply powers with the same base, add their exponents. So, $6^3 \cdot 6^4 = 6^{3+4}$ or 6^7, and $b^2 \cdot b^7 = b^{2+7}$ or b^9.
- To divide powers with the same base, subtract their exponents. So, $\frac{8^9}{8^4} = 8^{9-4}$ or 8^5, and $s^5 \div s = s^{5-1}$ or s^4.

Negative Exponents

For any non-zero real number a and any integer n, $a^{-n} = \frac{1}{a^n}$. For example, 5^{-4} or b^{-7}, can be written as $\frac{1}{5^4}$ or $\frac{1}{b^7}$.

- Prime factorization can be used to write a fraction such as $\frac{1}{216}$ as a power: $\frac{1}{216} = \frac{1}{6} \cdot \frac{1}{6} \cdot \frac{1}{6} = \frac{1}{6^3} = 6^{-3}$
- Negative exponents often are used in science to express small numbers, usually as a power of 10: $\frac{1}{100{,}000} = 10^{-5}$.

Scientific Notation

A number is in *scientific notation* when it is written in the form $a \times 10^n$, where $1 \leq a < 10$ and n is an integer.

- To translate from standard form to scientific notation, move the decimal point to the right of the first non-zero digit, and then write the appropriate power of 10 to the right of the number. The direction in which the decimal point moves indicates the sign of the power.
- To translate from scientific notation to standard form, move the decimal the number of places indicated by the exponent.
- A positive exponent represents a number that is greater than or equal to 10 in standard form. A negative exponent represents a number that is less than 1 in standard form.

Powers of Monomials

To find the power of a power, use the Power of a Power Property and multiply exponents. For example, $(8^2)^3 = 8^{2 \cdot 3}$ or 8^6 and $(m^4)^3 = m^{4 \cdot 3}$ or m^{12}.

To find the power of a product, use the Power of a Product Property and find the power of each factor. Then multiply. For example, $(9y^4)^2 = 9^2 \cdot (y^4)^2$ or $81y^8$.

9-7 Linear and Nonlinear Functions

Linear and nonlinear functions can be identified by looking at graphs, equations, and tables of values.

- Linear functions have graphs that are straight lines. Nonlinear functions have graphs that are curves, *not* straight lines.
- Equations for linear functions can be written in the form $y = mx + b$. Since $-2x + y = 5$ can be written as $y = 2x + 5$, it represents a linear function. The equation $y = \frac{3}{x}$ cannot be written in the form $y = mx + b$, so it represents a nonlinear function.
- Tables with values that increase or decrease at a constant rate represent linear functions, whereas tables with values that do not increase or decrease at a constant rate represent nonlinear functions.

Quadratic Functions

A quadratic function can be described by an equation of the form $y = ax^2 + bx + c$, where $a \neq 0$. The graph of a quadratic function has the shape of a parabola. The parabola opens upward when a is positive and downward when a is negative.

Quadratic functions can be graphed using an equation or a table of values. For example, to graph $y = 3x^2 + 1$, substitute the values –1, –0.5, 0, 0.5, and 1 for x in the equation to yield the coordinates (–1, 4), (–0.5, 1.75), (0, 1), (0.5, 1.75), and (1, 4). Plot the points on a coordinate grid and connect the points to form a parabola.

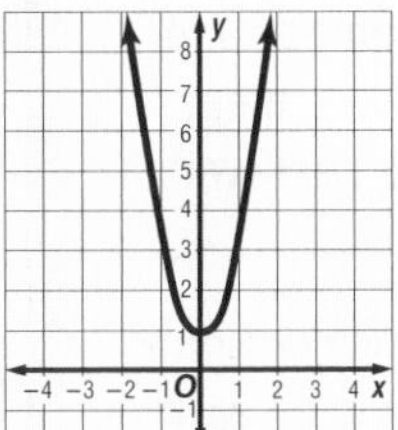

Cubic and Exponential Functions

The graphs of cubic and exponential functions are nonlinear.

- A cubic function can be described by an equation of the form $y = ax^3 + bx^2 + cx + d$, where $a \neq 0$.
- An exponential function can be described by an equation of the form $y = a^x$, where $a > 0$ and $a \neq 1$. In exponential functions, the variable is an exponent.

Professional Development

Targeted professional development has been articulated throughout McGraw-Hill's mathematics program. The **McGraw-Hill Professional Development Video Library** provides short videos that support key topics. For more information, visit glencoe.com.

Model Lessons

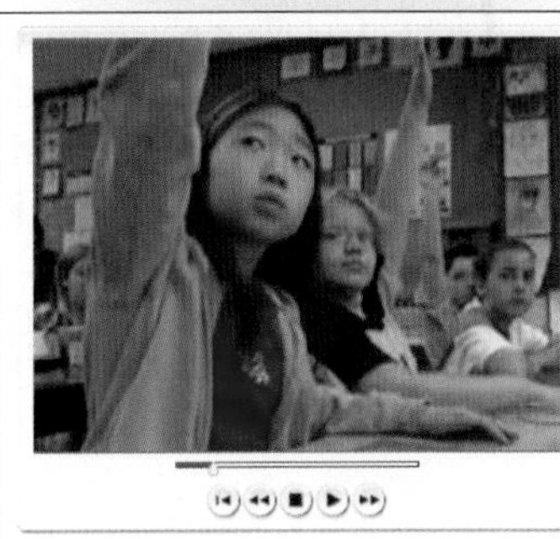

Instructional Strategies

CHAPTER 9 Notes

Chapter Project

A Trip Through the Solar System

Students use what they have learned about exponents, scientific notation, and nonlinear functions to work with space facts. Have students use the metric system for facts.

- Divide students into groups. Have each member choose a planet in our solar system and research information about its diameter and distance from the Sun. Have them bring this information to class written in standard form.
- Have groups examine each person's individual data and then write each diameter in scientific notation. How can you tell which planet is the largest? the smallest?
- Ask groups to imagine an asteroid hitting a planet. If the asteroid is one-millionth the diameter of the planet, what sizes are the asteroids, in scientific notation, that hit each planet?
- Have groups write each planet's distance from the Sun in scientific notation. How long would it take a radio wave travelling at 3×10^5 kilometers per second to reach the Sun from each of the planets?
- Tell groups that the equation $h = -6t^2 + 84$ can be used to find the height of a falling object on Mars after t seconds if it were dropped from a height of 84 feet. Ask students to explain how to find how long it would take the object to hit the ground.

CHAPTER 9 Powers and Nonlinear Functions

Then

In Chapter 8, you learned about linear functions.

Now

In Chapter 9, you will:

- Write and evaluate expressions with exponents.
- Write and compare numbers in scientific notation.
- Use quadratic functions to solve problems.

Why?

SPACE Our solar system has eight main planets. The distance between the Sun and these planets can be millions of miles. When writing numbers that are extremely small or large, you can use scientific notation.

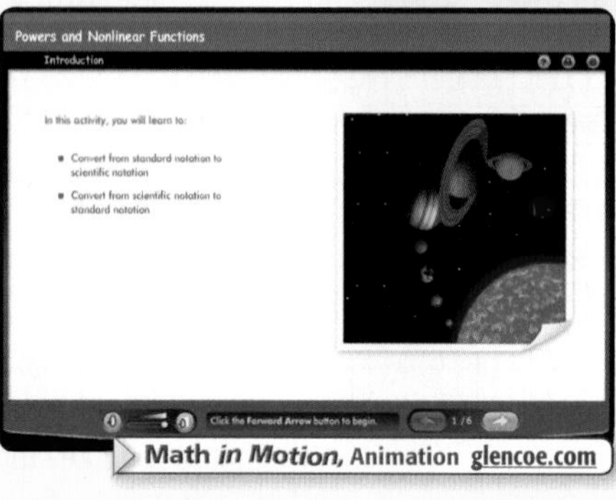

Math *in Motion*, Animation glencoe.com

468 **Chapter 9** Powers and Nonlinear Functions

Key Vocabulary Introduce the key vocabulary in the chapter using the routine below.

Define: To factor a number is to write it as a product of its factors.

Example: $3a^2b^4 = 3 \cdot a \cdot a \cdot b \cdot b \cdot b \cdot b$

Ask: Is $4 \cdot r \cdot r \cdot r \cdot s$ factored correctly?

Explain. No, you need to factor the 4 as well. It should be $2 \cdot 2 \cdot r \cdot r \cdot r \cdot s$.

Get Ready for Chapter 9

Diagnose Readiness You have two options for checking Prerequisite Skills.

Text Option Take the Quick Check below. Refer to the Quick Review for help.

*Quick*Check

Evaluate each expression if $a = 4$, $b = 7$, and $c = 5$. (Lesson 1-2) **(Used in Lesson 9-1)**

1. $3a + 2c$ **22** **2.** $\frac{ac}{2}$ **10**

3. $\frac{ab}{-4} + 2b$ **7** **4.** $4b - 3c$ **13**

5. $-5b + 6a$ **−11** **6.** $\frac{3}{4}(2bc)$ **52.5**

7. SALES Carlita is buying a computer that costs $900. She makes a down payment of $180 and plans to pay the balance in 6 equal installments. How much will each installment be? **$120**

(Used in Lesson 9-4)

Find each sum or difference. (Lessons 2-2 and 2-3)

8. $-27 + (-13)$ **−40** **9.** $11 + (-18)$ **−7**

10. $-9 + 31$ **22** **11.** $22 + (-16)$ **6**

12. $42 - 58$ **−16** **13.** $-15 - 4$ **−19**

14. $6 - (-17)$ **23** **15.** $-24 - (-28)$ **4**

16. CARS The value of Chris' car fell $2365 in the last two years. If the original value was $14,681, what is the value of the car now? **$12,316**

(Used in Lesson 9-5)

Find each product. (Lesson 3-3)

17. $7 \cdot 10$ **70** **18.** $1.25 \cdot 100$ **125**

19. $16.78 \cdot 10$ **167.8** **20.** $0.675 \cdot 1000$ **675**

21. $56 \cdot 0.1$ **5.6** **22.** $162 \cdot 0.001$ **0.162**

23. $97.18 \cdot 0.01$ **0.9718** **24.** $0.316 \cdot 0.01$ **0.00316**

25. HOTELS A hotel costs $159 plus 10% in taxes and fees for each night. The amount of taxes and fees is found by multiplying the cost of the hotel by 10% or 0.1. What is the cost of taxes and fees for one night? **$15.90**

*Quick*Review

EXAMPLE 1

Evaluate $\frac{xy}{z}$ if $x = 3$, $y = 8$, and $z = 6$.

$\frac{xy}{z} = \frac{3(8)}{6}$ **Replace x with 3, y with 8, and z with 6.**

$= \frac{24}{6}$ **Multiply 3 and 8.**

$= 4$ **Divide.**

EXAMPLE 2

Find −25 − (−36).

$-25 - (-36) = -25 + 36$ **To subtract −36, add 36.**

$= 11$ **Simplify.**

EXAMPLE 3

Find 3.76 × 0.01.

3.76 ←**2 decimal places**
× 0.01 ←**2 decimal places**
0.0376 ←**4 decimal places**

The product is 0.0376.

Online Option **Math Online** Take a self-check Chapter Readiness Quiz at glencoe.com.

Response to Intervention (RtI)

Use the *Quick Check* results and the Intervention Planner to help you determine your Response to Intervention. The If-Then statements in the chart help you decide the appropriate tier of RtI and suggest intervention resources for each tier.

Intervention Planner

Tier 1 — On Level

 students miss about 25% of the exercises or less,

 choose a resource:

SE Lessons 1–2, 2–2, 2–3, 3–3

CRM Skills Practice, Chapter 1, p. 14; Chapter 3, p. 21

TE Chapter Project, p. 468

Math Online Self-Check Quiz

Tier 2 — Strategic Intervention approaching grade level

 students miss about 50% of the exercises,

 choose a resource:

CRM Study Guide and Intervention, Chapter 1, pp. 11–12, Chapter 3, pp. 18–19

Quick Review Math Handbook

Math Online Extra Examples, Personal Tutor, Homework Help

Tier 3 — Intensive Intervention 2 or more years below grade level

 students miss about 75% of the exercises,

 use *Math Triumphs, Grade 8,* Ch. 2, 6

 **Math Online** Extra Examples, Personal Tutor, Homework Help, Review Vocabulary

CHAPTER 9 Notes

FOLDABLES® Study Organizer

Dinah Zike's Foldables®

Focus Students write notes about powers and nonlinear functions as they work through this chapter.

Teach Have students make and label the tabs for each lesson of their Foldables as illustrated. Ask them to design a visual for each section such as a graph, diagram, picture, or chart that presents the information in a concise format. Encourage students to label and write captions for their visuals as needed.

When to Use It Have students use their Foldables to take notes, define terms, sketch diagrams, and write formulas as they work through the chapter, and use them to review for the chapter test.

Differentiated Instruction

CRM Student-Built Glossary, pp. 1–2 Students should complete the chart by providing a definition of each term and an example as they progress through Chapter 9. This study tool can also be used to review for the chapter test.

Get Started on Chapter 9

You will learn several new concepts, skills, and vocabulary terms as you study Chapter 9. To get ready, identify important terms and organize your resources. You may wish to refer to **Chapter 0** to review prerequisite skills.

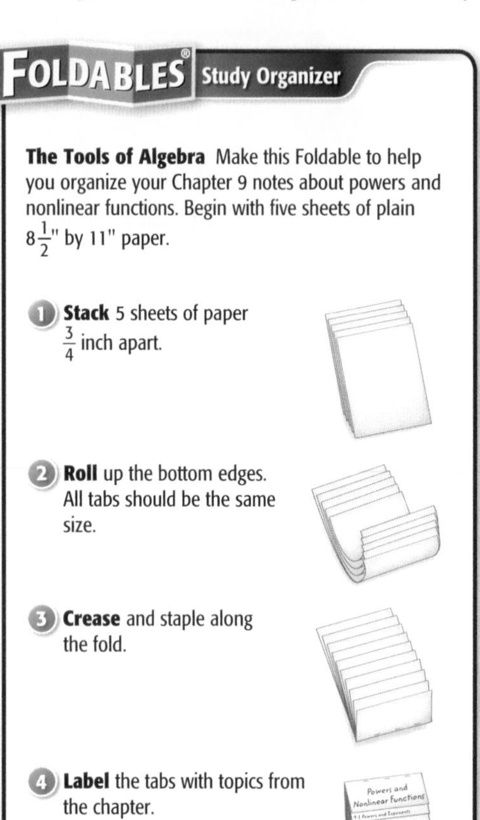

FOLDABLES® Study Organizer

The Tools of Algebra Make this Foldable to help you organize your Chapter 9 notes about powers and nonlinear functions. Begin with five sheets of plain $8\frac{1}{2}$" by 11" paper.

1. **Stack** 5 sheets of paper $\frac{3}{4}$ inch apart.
2. **Roll** up the bottom edges. All tabs should be the same size.
3. **Crease** and staple along the fold.
4. **Label** the tabs with topics from the chapter.

Powers and Nonlinear Functions

Math Online glencoe.com

- Study the chapter online
- Explore **Math in Motion**
- Get extra help from your own **Personal Tutor**
- Use **Extra Examples** for additional help
- Take a **Self-Check Quiz**
- **Review Vocabulary** in fun ways

New Vocabulary

English		Español
exponent	p. 471	exponente
power	p. 471	potencia
base	p. 471	base
prime number	p. 476	número primo
composite number	p. 476	número compuesto
prime factorization	p. 477	factorización prima
factor tree	p. 477	árbol de factores
monomial	p. 477	monomio
factor	p. 478	factorizar
standard form	p. 493	forma estándar
scientific notation	p. 493	notación cientifica
nonlinear function	p. 504	función no lineal
quadratic function	p. 510	función cuadrática
parabola	p. 510	parábola
cubic function	p. 516	función cúbica
exponential function	p. 517	función exponencial

Review Vocabulary

constant rate of change • p. 418 • tasa constante de cambio consistent ratio of vertical change to horizontal change

factors • p. 856 • factores two or more numbers are multiplied to form a product

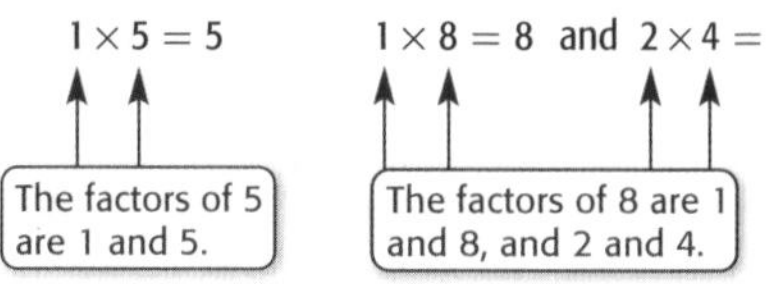

1 × 5 = 5
The factors of 5 are 1 and 5.
1 × 8 = 8 and 2 × 4 = 8
The factors of 8 are 1 and 8, and 2 and 4.

function • p. 33 • función relation in which each member of the domain is paired with exactly one member of the range

Multilingual eGlossary glencoe.com

470 Chapter 9 Powers and Nonlinear Functions

9-1 Powers and Exponents

Why?

Elephants at the National Zoo in Washington, D.C., eat 125 pounds of hay each day. Each elephant weighs more than 10,000 pounds.

a. Using 5 as a factor, write a multiplication expression that equals 125. $5 \cdot 5 \cdot 5$

b. Using 10 as a factor, write a multiplication expression that equals 10,000. $10 \cdot 10 \cdot 10 \cdot 10$

Then
You evaluated expressions without exponents. (Lesson 2-4)

Now
- Write expressions using exponents.
- Evaluate expressions containing exponents.

New Vocabulary
exponent
power
base

Math Online
glencoe.com
- Extra Examples
- Personal Tutor
- Self-Check Quiz
- Homework Help
- Math in Motion

Use Exponents An expression like $5 \cdot 5 \cdot 5$ with equal factors can be written using an exponent. An **exponent** tells how many times a number is used as a factor. A number that is expressed using an exponent is called a **power**. The number that is multiplied is called the **base**. So, $5 \cdot 5 \cdot 5$ equals the power 5^3.

base ⟶ 5^3 ⟵ exponent
↑
power

Read and Write Powers		
Power	Words	Factors
5^1	5 to the first power	5
5^2	5 to the second power or 5 squared	$5 \cdot 5$
5^3	5 to the third power or 5 cubed	$5 \cdot 5 \cdot 5$
5^4	5 to the fourth power or 5 to the fourth	$5 \cdot 5 \cdot 5 \cdot 5$
⋮	⋮	⋮
5^n	5 to the *n*th power or 5 to the *n*th	$\underbrace{5 \cdot 5 \cdot 5 \cdot \ldots \cdot 5}_{n \text{ factors}}$

Any number, except 0, raised to the zero power is defined as 1.

$1^0 = 1$ $2^0 = 1$ $3^0 = 1$ $4^0 = 1$ $5^0 = 1$ $x^0 = 1, x \neq 0$

EXAMPLE 1 Write Expressions using Exponents

Write each expression using exponents.

a. $4 \cdot 4 \cdot 4 \cdot 4 \cdot 4$

The base 4 is a factor 5 times.
So, the exponent is 5.
$4 \cdot 4 \cdot 4 \cdot 4 \cdot 4 = 4^5$

b. $(-8) \cdot (-8) \cdot (-8)$

The base -8 is a factor 3 times.
So, the exponent is 3.
$(-8) \cdot (-8) \cdot (-8) = (-8)^3$

Check Your Progress

1A. $6 \cdot 6 \cdot 6 \cdot 6$ 6^4 **1B.** $(-2)(-2)(-2)$ $(-2)^3$ **1C.** $\left(\frac{1}{2}\right)\left(\frac{1}{2}\right)\left(\frac{1}{2}\right)$ $\left(\frac{1}{2}\right)^3$

Personal Tutor glencoe.com

9-1 Lesson Notes

1 FOCUS

Vertical Alignment

Before Lesson 9-1
Evaluate expressions without exponents.

Lesson 9-1
Write expressions using exponents.
Evaluate expressions containing exponents.

After Lesson 9-1
Express numbers in scientific notation and explore negative exponents.

2 TEACH

Scaffolding Questions

Have students read the *Why?* section of the lesson and answer the questions.

Ask:

- Suppose 5 elephants eat 625 pounds of hay. Using 5 as a factor, what multiplication expression equals 625? $5 \cdot 5 \cdot 5 \cdot 5$
- How many times do you multiply 5 by itself to get a product of 125? 3 625? 4
- Suppose there are 10 elephants at the zoo. Using 10 as a factor, how many times do you multiply 10 by itself to get the total weight of the elephants? Explain. 5; since 10 elephants weigh about 100,000 pounds, you would use the expression $10 \cdot 10 \cdot 10 \cdot 10 \cdot 10$ to equal 100,000 pounds.

Lesson 9-1 Resources

Resource	Approaching-Level	On-Level	Beyond-Level	English Learners
Teacher Edition	• Differentiated Instruction, p. 472	• Differentiated Instruction, p. 472	• Differentiated Instruction, p. 475	• Differentiated Instruction, p. 472
Chapter Resource Masters	• Study Guide and Intervention, pp. 5–6 • Skills Practice, p. 7 • Practice, p. 8 • Word Problem Practice, p. 9 • Graphing Calculator, p. 11	• Study Guide and Intervention, pp. 5–6 • Skills Practice, p. 7 • Practice, p. 8 • Word Problem Practice, p. 9 • Enrichment, p. 10 • Graphing Calculator, p. 11	• Practice, p. 8 • Word Problem Practice, p. 9 • Enrichment, p. 10 • Graphing Calculator, p. 11	• Study Guide and Intervention, pp. 5–6 • Skills Practice, p. 7 • Practice, p. 8 • Graphing Calculator, p. 11
Transparencies	• 5-Minute Check Transparency 9-1	• 5-Minute Check Transparency 9-1	• 5-Minute Check Transparency 9-1	• 5-Minute Check Transparency 9-1
Other	• Study Notebook • Teaching Pre-Algebra with Manipulatives	• Study Notebook • Teaching Pre-Algebra with Manipulatives	• Study Notebook	• Study Notebook • Teaching Pre-Algebra with Manipulatives

Use Exponents

Examples 1 and 2 show how to write expressions using exponents.

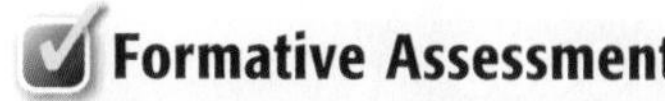

Formative Assessment

Use the Check Your Progress exercises after each example to determine students' understanding of concepts.

Additional Examples

1 Write each expression using exponents.

a. $9 \cdot 9 \cdot 9 \cdot 9$ 9^4

b. $(-1)(-1)$ $(-1)^2$

2 Write each expression using exponents.

a. $w \cdot w \cdot w \cdot w \cdot w$ w^5

b. $(5x + 1)(5x + 1)$ $(5x + 1)^2$

c. $\frac{1}{2} \cdot x \cdot x \cdot x \cdot x \cdot y \cdot y \cdot y$ $\frac{1}{2}x^4y^3$

Additional Examples also in Interactive Classroom PowerPoint® Presentations

IWB INTERACTIVE WHITEBOARD READY

Evaluate Expressions

Example 3 shows how to evaluate numeric expressions. **Example 4** shows how to evaluate algebraic expressions.

Additional Example

3 **HOCKEY** North American hockey rinks are built according to National Hockey League specifications. Evaluate each expression to find these dimensions.

a. The distance from the goal line to the closest blue line is 2^6 feet. 64 ft

b. The length of the rink is $2^3 \cdot 5^2$ feet. 200 ft

Watch Out!

Negative Bases $(-3)^2$ is not the same as -3^2.
- $(-3)^2 = (-3)(-3) = 9$
- $-3^2 = (-1)(3^2) = -9$

EXAMPLE 2 Write Expressions using Exponents

Write each expression using exponents.

a. $y \cdot y \cdot y \cdot y \cdot y \cdot y$

The base y is a factor 6 times.
So, the exponent is 6.
$y \cdot y \cdot y \cdot y \cdot y \cdot y = y^6$

b. $(k + 2)(k + 2)(k + 2)(k + 2)$

The base $(k + 2)$ is a factor 4 times.
So, the exponent is 4.
$(k + 2)(k + 2)(k + 2)(k + 2) = (k + 2)^4$

c. $5 \cdot r \cdot r \cdot s \cdot s \cdot s \cdot s$

$5 \cdot r \cdot r \cdot s \cdot s \cdot s \cdot s = 5 \cdot (r \cdot r) \cdot (s \cdot s \cdot s \cdot s)$ **Group factors with like bases.**

$= 5 \cdot r^2 \cdot s^4$ or $5r^2s^4$ $r \cdot r = r^2, s \cdot s \cdot s \cdot s = s^4$

Check Your Progress

2A. $x \cdot x \cdot x \cdot x \cdot x$ x^5 **2B.** $(c - d)(c - d)$ $(c - d)^2$ **2C.** $9 \cdot f \cdot f \cdot f \cdot f \cdot g$ $9f^4g$

Personal Tutor glencoe.com

Evaluate Expressions Since powers represent repeated multiplication, they need to be included in the rules for order of operations.

Concept Summary Order of Operations

For Your FOLDABLE

Step 1	Simplify the expressions inside grouping symbols first.
Step 2	Evaluate all powers.
Step 3	Do all multiplications or divisions in order from left to right.
Step 4	Do all additions or subtractions in order from left to right.

Real-World EXAMPLE 3 Evaluate Expressions

BEACH VOLLEYBALL The playing area for beach volleyball includes the playing court and the free zone. Evaluate each expression to find the area of the playing court and the free zone.

a. The playing court is a rectangle with an area of 2^7 square meters.

$2^7 = 2 \cdot 2 \cdot 2 \cdot 2 \cdot 2 \cdot 2 \cdot 2$ **2 is a factor 7 times.**

$= 128$ **Simplify.**

The area of the playing court is 128 square meters.

b. The area of the free zone is $2^2 \cdot 3^2 \cdot 5$ square meters.

$2^2 \cdot 3^2 \cdot 5 = 2 \cdot 2 \cdot 3 \cdot 3 \cdot 5$ **Evaluate powers.**

$= 180$ **Multiply.**

The area of the free zone is 180 square meters.

Real-World Link

Beach volleyball began in Santa Monica, California, in the 1920s. It is estimated that about 800 million people play volleyball worldwide.

Source: U.S. Beach-Volleyball

Check Your Progress

3. PHYSICS A tennis ball is dropped from the top of a building. After 8 seconds, the tennis ball hits the ground. The distance in meters the ball traveled is represented by $4.9(8)^2$. How far did the ball drop? 313.6 m

Personal Tutor glencoe.com

Differentiated Instruction

AL OL ELL

If students need extra practice writing expressions as sentences or phrases or translating verbal phrases into algebraic expressions,

Then give students a list of expressions involving exponents. Ask them to practice writing the expressions as sentences or phrases using words. Next, give students verbal phrases describing exponents and have them write the phrase using mathematical symbols. For example, students might describe x^5 as "x raised to the fifth power." If given the phrase "thirty-two squared," they would write 32^2.

StudyTip

Exponents An exponent goes with the number, variable, or quantity in parentheses immediately preceding it.

EXAMPLE 4 Evaluate Algebraic Expressions

Evaluate $x^2 + y^3$ if $x = 6$ and $y = -2$.

$x^2 + y^3 = 6^2 + (-2)^3$ — Replace x with 6 and y with −2.

$= 36 - 8$ — Evaluate powers; $6^2 = (6 \cdot 6)$ or 36; $(-2)^3 = (-2)(-2)(-2)$ or −8.

$= 28$ — Subtract.

Check Your Progress

Evaluate each expression if $a = 5$, $b = -2$, and $c = \frac{3}{4}$.

4A. $10 + b^2$ 14 **4B.** $(a + b)^3$ 27 **4C.** $2 - c^2$ $1\frac{7}{16}$

Personal Tutor glencoe.com

Check Your Understanding

Examples 1 and 2 pp. 471–472

Write each expression using exponents. 4. $4m^3q^3$ 5. $(y - 3)^3$

1. $2 \cdot 2 \cdot 2 \cdot 2 \cdot 2 \cdot 2$ 2^6
2. $d \cdot d \cdot d \cdot d \cdot d \cdot d$ d^6
3. $\left(-\frac{1}{4}\right)\left(-\frac{1}{4}\right)\left(-\frac{1}{4}\right)$ $\left(-\frac{1}{4}\right)^3$
4. $4 \cdot m \cdot m \cdot m \cdot q \cdot q \cdot q$
5. $(y - 3)(y - 3)(y - 3)$
6. $(a + 1)(a + 1)$ $(a + 1)^2$

Example 3 p. 472

7. **INSECTS** The longhorn beetle can have a body length of over 2^4 centimeters. How many centimeters long is this? 16 cm
8. **E-MAIL** Theo sends an e-mail to three friends. Each friend forwards the e-mail to three friends. Each of those friends forwards it to three friends, and so on. Find the number of e-mails sent during the fifth stage as a power. Then find the value of the power. 3^5; 243

Example 4 p. 473

Evaluate each expression if $a = 3$, $b = -4$, and $c = 3.5$.

9. $a^3 + 2$ 29
10. $3(b - 1)^2$ 75
11. $c^2 + b^2$ 28.25

Practice and Problem Solving

= **Step-by-Step Solutions** begin on page R11. **Extra Practice** begins on page 810.

Examples 1 and 2 pp. 471–472

Write each expression using exponents.

12. $11 \cdot 11 \cdot 11 \cdot 11$ 11^4
13. $3 \cdot 3 \cdot 3 \cdot 3 \cdot 3$ 3^5
14. $(-8)(-8)(-8)(-8)(-8)(-8)$ $(-8)^6$
15. $(-14) \cdot (-14) \cdot (-14)$ $(-14)^3$
16. $\left(-\frac{1}{5}\right)\left(-\frac{1}{5}\right)\left(-\frac{1}{5}\right)\left(-\frac{1}{5}\right)$ $\left(-\frac{1}{5}\right)^4$
17. $(-1.5)(-1.5)(-1.5)$ $(-1.5)^3$
18. $ab \cdot ab \cdot ab \cdot ab$ $(ab)^4$
19. $5 \cdot p \cdot p \cdot p \cdot q \cdot q \cdot q$ $5p^3q^3$
20. $3 \cdot 7 \cdot m \cdot m \cdot n \cdot n \cdot n \cdot n$ $21m^2n^4$
21. $8(c + 4)(c + 4)$ $8(c + 4)^2$
22. $(n - 5)(n - 5)(n - 5)$ $(n - 5)^3$
23. $(2x + 3y)(2x + 3y)$ $(2x + 3y)^2$

Example 3 p. 472

24. **VOLCANOES** The longest chain of active volcanoes is in the South Pacific. This chain is more than $3 \cdot 10^4$ miles long and has approximately $3^5 \cdot 5$ volcanoes.
    a. How long is the chain of volcanoes? 30,000 mi
    b. How many volcanoes are there? 1215 volcanoes

TEACH with TECH

INTERACTIVE WHITEBOARD Use the whiteboard while you teach this topic and save each example as a notes page. Send these notes to students so they can have them as a reference in addition to their own notes.

Focus on Mathematical Content

Zero Exponent The exponent indicates how many times the base is multiplied by itself. Observe the pattern: $2^5 = 32$, $2^4 = 16$, $2^3 = 8$, $2^2 = 4$, $2^1 = 2$, $2^0 = 1$. For every decrease of 1 in the exponent, the product is divided by the base. Because $2^1 = 2$, base 2 is divided by 2 for the product of 2^0, which is 1.

Additional Example

Evaluate $x^2 - y^3$ if $x = -5$ and $y = 2$. 17

Tips for New Teachers

Exponents Emphasize to students that 2^4 is not $2 \cdot 4$, but $2 \cdot 2 \cdot 2 \cdot 2$ or 16.

First Power When a number or variable is raised to the first power, the exponent is not usually written. So, 5^1 is written as 5.

Review Vocabulary

Remind students that factors are two or more numbers, variables, or quantities that are multiplied to form a product.

Differentiated Homework Options

Level	Assignment	Two-Day Option	
AL Basic	12–36, 55–59 odd, 60–75	13–35 odd, 60–63	12–36 even, 55, 57, 59, 64–75
OL Core	13–35 odd, 37, 39–53 odd, 54, 55, 57, 59–75	12–36, 60–63	37–55, 57, 59, 64–75
BL Advanced	37–71 (Optional: 72–75)		

3 PRACTICE

Formative Assessment

Use Exercises 1–11 to check for understanding.

Use the chart at the bottom of this page to customize assignments for your students.

Lesson 9-1 Powers and Exponents 473

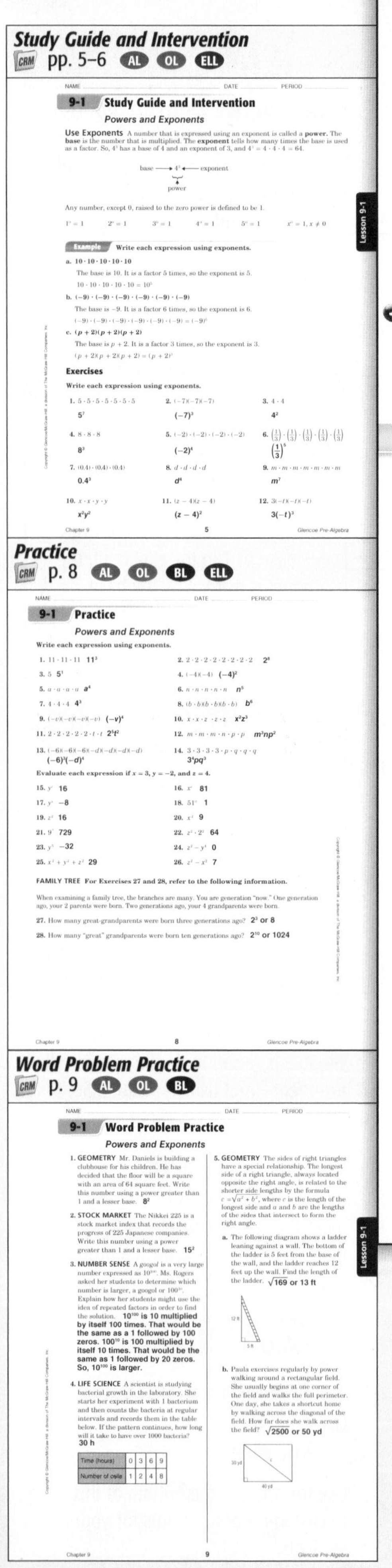

Study Guide and Intervention
CRM pp. 5–6 AL OL ELL

NAME ______ DATE ______ PERIOD ______

9-1 Study Guide and Intervention

Powers and Exponents

Use Exponents A number that is expressed using an exponent is called a **power.** The **base** is the number that is multiplied. The **exponent** tells how many times the base is used as a factor. So, 4^3 has a base of 4 and an exponent of 3, and $4^3 = 4 \cdot 4 \cdot 4 = 64$.

base → 4^3 ← exponent; power

Any number, except 0, raised to the zero power is defined to be 1.

$1^0 = 1$ $2^0 = 1$ $3^0 = 1$ $4^0 = 1$ $5^0 = 1$ $x^0 = 1, x \neq 0$

Example Write each expression using exponents.

a. $10 \cdot 10 \cdot 10 \cdot 10 \cdot 10$
The base is 10. It is a factor 5 times, so the exponent is 5.
$10 \cdot 10 \cdot 10 \cdot 10 \cdot 10 = 10^5$

b. $(-9) \cdot (-9) \cdot (-9) \cdot (-9) \cdot (-9) \cdot (-9)$
The base is -9. It is a factor 6 times, so the exponent is 6.
$(-9) \cdot (-9) \cdot (-9) \cdot (-9) \cdot (-9) \cdot (-9) = (-9)^6$

c. $(p + 2)(p + 2)(p + 2)$
The base is $p + 2$. It is a factor 3 times, so the exponent is 3.
$(p + 2)(p + 2)(p + 2) = (p + 2)^3$

Exercises

Write each expression using exponents.

1. $5 \cdot 5 \cdot 5 \cdot 5 \cdot 5 \cdot 5 \cdot 5$ **5^7**
2. $(-7)(-7)(-7)$ **$(-7)^3$**
3. $4 \cdot 4$ **4^2**
4. $8 \cdot 8 \cdot 8$ **8^3**
5. $(-2) \cdot (-2) \cdot (-2) \cdot (-2)$ **$(-2)^4$**
6. $\left(\frac{1}{3}\right) \cdot \left(\frac{1}{3}\right) \cdot \left(\frac{1}{3}\right) \cdot \left(\frac{1}{3}\right) \cdot \left(\frac{1}{3}\right)$ **$\left(\frac{1}{3}\right)^5$**
7. $(0.4) \cdot (0.4) \cdot (0.4)$ **0.4^3**
8. $d \cdot d \cdot d \cdot d$ **d^4**
9. $m \cdot m \cdot m \cdot m \cdot m \cdot m \cdot m$ **m^7**
10. $x \cdot x \cdot y \cdot y$ **x^2y^2**
11. $(z - 4)(z - 4)$ **$(z - 4)^2$**
12. $3(-t)(-t)(-t)$ **$3(-t)^3$**

Chapter 9 5 Glencoe Pre-Algebra

Lesson 9-1

Practice
CRM p. 8 AL OL BL ELL

NAME ______ DATE ______ PERIOD ______

9-1 Practice

Powers and Exponents

Write each expression using exponents.

1. $11 \cdot 11 \cdot 11$ **11^3**
2. $2 \cdot 2 \cdot 2 \cdot 2 \cdot 2 \cdot 2 \cdot 2 \cdot 2$ **2^8**
3. 5 **5^1**
4. $(-4)(-4)$ **$(-4)^2$**
5. $a \cdot a \cdot a \cdot a$ **a^4**
6. $n \cdot n \cdot n \cdot n \cdot n$ **n^5**
7. $4 \cdot 4 \cdot 4$ **4^3**
8. $(b \cdot b)(b \cdot b)(b \cdot b)$ **b^6**
9. $(-v)(-v)(-v)(-v)$ **$(-v)^4$**
10. $x \cdot x \cdot z \cdot z \cdot z$ **x^2z^3**
11. $2 \cdot 2 \cdot 2 \cdot 2 \cdot 2 \cdot t \cdot t$ **2^5t^2**
12. $m \cdot m \cdot m \cdot n \cdot p \cdot p$ **m^3np^2**
13. $(-6)(-6)(-6)(-d)(-d)(-d)(-d)$ **$(-6)^3(-d)^4$**
14. $3 \cdot 3 \cdot 3 \cdot 3 \cdot p \cdot q \cdot q \cdot q$ **3^4pq^3**

Evaluate each expression if $x = 3$, $y = -2$, and $z = 4$.

15. y^4 **16**
16. x^4 **81**
17. y^3 **−8**
18. 51^0 **1**
19. z^2 **16**
20. x^2 **9**
21. 9^3 **729**
22. $z^2 \cdot 2^2$ **64**
23. y^5 **−32**
24. $z^2 - y^4$ **0**
25. $x^2 + y^2 + z^2$ **29**
26. $z^2 - x^2$ **7**

FAMILY TREE For Exercises 27 and 28, refer to the following information.

When examining a family tree, the branches are many. You are generation "now." One generation ago, your 2 parents were born. Two generations ago, your 4 grandparents were born.

27. How many great-grandparents were born three generations ago? **2^3 or 8**
28. How many "great" grandparents were born ten generations ago? **2^{10} or 1024**

Chapter 9 8 Glencoe Pre-Algebra

Word Problem Practice
CRM p. 9 AL OL BL

NAME ______ DATE ______ PERIOD ______

9-1 Word Problem Practice

Powers and Exponents

1. **GEOMETRY** Mr. Daniels is building a clubhouse for his children. He has decided that the floor will be a square with an area of 64 square feet. Write this number using a power greater than 1 and a lesser base. **8^2**

2. **STOCK MARKET** The Nikkei 225 is a stock market index that records the progress of 225 Japanese companies. Write this number using a power greater than 1 and a lesser base. **15^2**

3. **NUMBER SENSE** A *googol* is a very large number expressed as 10^{100}. Ms. Rogers asked her students to determine which number is larger, a googol or 100^{10}. Explain how her students might use the idea of repeated factors in order to find the solution. **10^{100} is 10 multiplied by itself 100 times. That would be the same as a 1 followed by 100 zeros. 100^{10} is 100 multiplied by itself 10 times. That would be the same as 1 followed by 20 zeros. So, 10^{100} is larger.**

4. **LIFE SCIENCE** A scientist is studying bacterial growth in the laboratory. She starts her experiment with 1 bacterium and then counts the bacteria at regular intervals and records them in the table below. If the pattern continues, how long will it take to have over 1000 bacteria? **30 h**

Time (hours)	0	3	6	9
Number of cells	1	2	4	8

5. **GEOMETRY** The sides of right triangles have a special relationship. The longest side of a right triangle, always located opposite the right angle, is related to the shorter side lengths by the formula $c = \sqrt{a^2 + b^2}$, where c is the length of the longest side and a and b are the lengths of the sides that intersect to form the right angle.

a. The following diagram shows a ladder leaning against a wall. The bottom of the ladder is 5 feet from the base of the wall, and the ladder reaches 12 feet up the wall. Find the length of the ladder. **$\sqrt{169}$ or 13 ft**

b. Paula exercises regularly by power walking around a rectangular field. She usually begins at one corner of the field and walks the full perimeter. One day, she takes a shortcut home by walking across the diagonal of the field. How far does she walk across the field? **$\sqrt{2500}$ or 50 yd**

Chapter 9 9 Glencoe Pre-Algebra

Lesson 9-1

Example 4 p. 473

Evaluate each expression if $x = -2$, $y = 3$, and $z = 2.5$.

25. y^4 **81**
26. z^3 **15.625**
27. $7x^2$ **28**
28. xy^3 **−54**
29. $z^2 + x$ **4.25**
30. $y^0 + 9$ **10**
31. $2y + z^3$ **21.625**
32. $x^2 + 2y - 3$ **7**
33. $y^2 - 3x + 8$ **23**
34. $4(y + 1)^4$ **1024**
35. $3(2z + 4)^2$ **243**
36. $5(x^3 + 6)$ **−10**

Real-World Link

Men's and women's field hockey is played in 132 countries and is the second most popular team sport after soccer.

Source: U.S. Field Hockey

37. **SPORTS** The table shows the minimum areas of different sports fields.

Sport	Minimum Field Area (ft²)
Field Hockey	$2^6 \cdot 10^3$
Men's Lacrosse	$3^2 \cdot 7 \cdot 10^3$
Women's Soccer	$2^4 \cdot 5^2 \cdot 7 \cdot 13$

a. Find the minimum area of each playing field.

b. Order the areas from least to greatest.

c. How much greater is the area of a field hockey field than the area of a men's lacrosse field?

37a. 64,000 ft²; 63,000 ft²; 36,400 ft²

37b. 36,400 ft²; 63,000 ft²; 64,000 ft²

37c. 1000 ft²

Evaluate each expression.

38. 9^2 **81**
39. 11^3 **1331**
40. $\left(-\frac{2}{3}\right)^3$ **$-\frac{8}{27}$**
41. $(-5)^4$ **625**
42. $(-2)^7$ **−128**
43. $2 \cdot 4^4$ **512**
44. $6^3 \cdot 4$ **864**
45. $3^5 \cdot 10$ **2430**
46. $2^0 \cdot 10$ **10**
47. $7^3 \cdot 2^2$ **1372**
48. $5 \cdot 2^4$ **80**
49. $(4.5)^4 \cdot 2$ **820.125**

Replace each ● with <, >, or = to make a true statement.

50. 2^5 ● 5^2 **>**
51. 3^6 ● 6^3 **>**
52. 2^6 ● 8^2 **=**
53. 8^3 ● 4^5 **<**

54. **MULTIPLE REPRESENTATIONS** In this problem, you will explore volume of a cube. The volume of a cube equals the side length cubed. **b–c. See margin.**

a. **SYMBOLIC** Write an equation showing the relationship between side length s and volume V of a cube. **$V = s^3$**

b. **TABULAR** Make a table of values showing the volume of a cube with side lengths of 1, 2, 4, 8, and 16 centimeters.

c. **ANALYTICAL** Use your table to make a conjecture about the change in volume when the side length of a cube is doubled. Justify your response by writing an algebraic expression.

H.O.T. Problems

Use **H**igher-**O**rder **T**hinking Skills **57–59. See margin.**

55. **OPEN ENDED** Use exponents to write two numerical expressions. Then find the product of the expressions. **Sample answer: 6^2, 4^3; 2304**

56. **CHALLENGE** Determine whether x^3 is *always, sometimes,* or *never* a positive number for $x \neq 0$. Explain your reasoning.

56. Sometimes; if x is positive, then x^3 is positive. If x is negative, then x^3 is negative because the product of two negative numbers is always positive and the product of a positive number and a negative number is always negative.

57. **REASONING** Suppose the population of the United States is about 230 million. Is this number closer to 10^7 or 10^8? Explain.

58. **CHALLENGE** Explain why $5^0 = 1$. (*Hint*: Find a pattern in 5^4, 5^3, 5^2, and 5^1 to predict 5^0.)

59. **WRITING IN MATH** Describe the advantages of using exponents to represent numeric values.

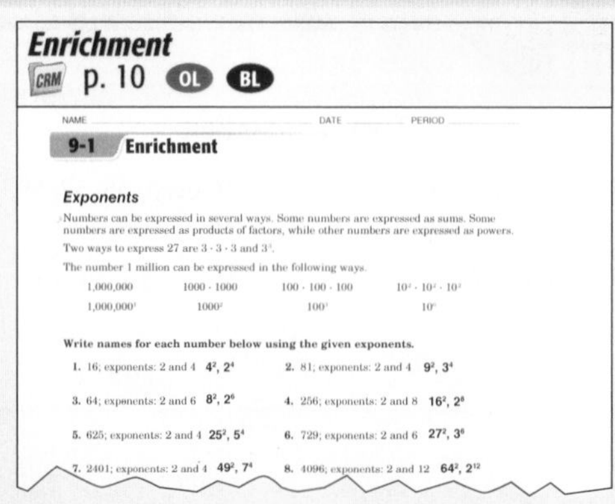

Enrichment
CRM p. 10 OL BL

NAME ______ DATE ______ PERIOD ______

9-1 Enrichment

Exponents

Numbers can be expressed in several ways. Some numbers are expressed as sums. Some numbers are expressed as products of factors, while other numbers are expressed as powers.

Two ways to express 27 are $3 \cdot 3 \cdot 3$ and 3^3.

The number 1 million can be expressed in the following ways.

1,000,000	$1000 \cdot 1000$	$100 \cdot 100 \cdot 100$	$10^2 \cdot 10^2 \cdot 10^2$
$1{,}000{,}000^1$	1000^2	100^3	10^6

Write names for each number below using the given exponents.

1. 16; exponents: 2 and 4 **4^2, 2^4**
2. 81; exponents: 2 and 4 **9^2, 3^4**
3. 64; exponents: 2 and 6 **8^2, 2^6**
4. 256; exponents: 2 and 8 **16^2, 2^8**
5. 625; exponents: 2 and 4 **25^2, 5^4**
6. 729; exponents: 2 and 6 **27^2, 3^6**
7. 2401; exponents: 2 and 4 **49^2, 7^4**
8. 4096; exponents: 2 and 12 **64^2, 2^{12}**

Multiple Representations In Exercise 54, students use an equation and a table of values to show the relation between the length of a side of a cube and its volume.

Standardized Test Practice

60. Marta observed that a bacterium cell doubled every 3 minutes.

Time (min)	Number of Bacteria
0	2^0
3	2^1
6	2^2
9	2^3
12	2^4

Which expression represents the number of cells after one half hour? **A**

A 2^{10} C 2^{20}

B 2^{15} D 2^{30}

61. GRIDDED RESPONSE Suppose a certain forest fire doubles in size every 8 hours. If the initial size of the fire was 1 acre, how many acres will the fire cover in 3 days? **512**

62. Which of the following is equivalent to $4^3 \cdot 5^2$? **H**

F $12 \cdot 25$

G $3 \cdot 3 \cdot 3 \cdot 3 \cdot 2 \cdot 2 \cdot 2 \cdot 2 \cdot 2$

H $4 \cdot 4 \cdot 4 \cdot 5 \cdot 5$

J $4 \cdot 4 \cdot 4 \cdot 5 \cdot 5 \cdot 5$

63. Evaluate $\left(\frac{4}{5}\right)^2$. **B**

A $\frac{8}{25}$ C $\frac{8}{10}$

B $\frac{16}{25}$ D $1\frac{3}{5}$

Spiral Review

Solve each system of equations by substitution. (Lesson 8-10)

64. $y = x + 10$, $y = 2$ **(−8, 2)**

65. $y = x - 5$, $x = 0$ **(0, −5)**

66. $y = 3x - 4$, $y = 1$ $\left(\frac{5}{3}, 1\right)$

67. MULTIPLE REPRESENTATIONS In this problem, you will investigate the approximate barometric pressure at various altitudes. (Lesson 8-9) **a–c. See Chapter 9 Answer Appendix.**

a. **GRAPHICAL** Make a scatter plot of the data and draw a line of fit.

b. **ALGEBRAIC** Write an equation for the line of fit you drew in part **a.** Use it to estimate the barometric pressure at 60,000 feet. Is the estimation reasonable? Explain.

c. **VERBAL** Do you think that a line is the best model for this data? Explain.

Altitude (ft)	Barometric Pressure (in. mercury)
0	30
5000	25
10,000	21
20,000	14
30,000	9
40,000	6
50,000	3

Source: *New York Public Library Science Desk Reference*

Choose the greatest number in each set. (Lesson 7-2)

68. $\left\{\frac{2}{5}, 0.45, 35\%, 3 \text{ out of } 8\right\}$ **0.45**

69. $\left\{\frac{3}{4}, 0.70, 78\%, 4 \text{ out of } 5\right\}$ **4 out of 5**

70. $\left\{19\%, \frac{3}{16}, 0.155, 2 \text{ to } 15\right\}$ **19%**

71. $\left\{89\%, \frac{10}{11}, 0.884, 12 \text{ to } 14\right\}$ $\frac{10}{11}$

Skills Review

List all the whole number factors for each number. (Previous Course)

72. 7 **1 and 7**

73. 15 **1, 3, 5, 15**

74. 18 **1, 2, 3, 6, 9, 18**

75. 40 **1, 2, 4, 5, 8, 10, 20, 40**

Differentiated Instruction

Extension Tell students that a gigabyte contains 1,073,741,824 bytes of memory. This can be written as 2^{30}. Write this number in exponential form, using 10 as a base. (This will be an approximation.) 1,000,000,000 or 10^9

4 ASSESS

Name the Math Give students the expression $6a^2 - a - 2$. Tell them to name a value for a. Have students evaluate the expression, naming the steps or procedures to do so. Sample answer: Let $a = 2$. $6(2)^2 - 2 - 2 = 20$

Multiple Representations In Exercise 67, students create a scatter plot using values from a table, determine a line of best fit, write the equation for the line of best fit, use the equation to predict additional values, and use verbal analysis to determine if a linear equation is the best fit for the data.

Additional Answers

54b.

Side Length (cm)	Volume (cm³)
1	1
2	8
4	64
8	512
16	4096

54c. Sample answer: When the side length is doubled, the volume of the cube is multiplied by 8. $V = (2s)^3$ or $V = 8s^3$.

57. 10^8; Sample answer: $10^7 =$ 10,000,000 and $10^8 =$ 100,000,000. 100,000,000 is much closer to 230,000,000 than 10,000,000.

58. Sample answer: $5^4 = 625$; $5^3 = 125$; $5^2 = 25$; $5^1 = 5$; $5^0 = 1$; Look at the pattern. You will notice that you divide by 5 to get the next product, so $5 \div 5 = 1$. Divide the product by the base, 5 by 5.

59. Using exponents is a more efficient way to describe and compare numbers.

9-2 Lesson Notes

1 FOCUS

Vertical Alignment

Before Lesson 9-2
Simplify expressions by multiplying.

Lesson 9-2
Write the prime factorizations of composite numbers.
Factor monomials.

After Lesson 9-2
Simplify polynomial expressions and factor as necessary.

2 TEACH

Scaffolding Questions

Have students read the *Why?* section of the lesson and answer the questions.

Ask:

- How many different ways can 6 pictures be arranged in rows? 4 ways
- How many different ways can 3 pictures be arranged in rows? 2 ways
- What do you notice about the number of factors each number has and the number of ways the pictures can be arranged in rows? The number of factors is the same as the number of ways the pictures can be arranged in rows.

9-2 Prime Factorization

Then
You simplified expressions by multiplying. (Lesson 2-4)

Now
- Write the prime factorizations of composite numbers.
- Factor monomials.

New Vocabulary
prime number
composite number
prime factorization
factor tree
monomial
factor

Math Online
glencoe.com
- Extra Examples
- Personal Tutor
- Self-Check Quiz
- Homework Help

Why?

Isaiah wants to arrange 6 pictures of his family and friends on the wall.

a. Express 6 as the product of two whole numbers. $1 \cdot 6$, $2 \cdot 3$

b. Suppose he adds two more pictures. Describe the possible rectangular arrangements of 8 pictures. See margin.

c. In how many different ways could he arrange 5 pictures in a rectangle? Explain. 2 ways; 1 row of 5 pictures, 5 rows of 1 picture

Write Prime Factorizations Numbers that have whole number factors can be represented using rectangles.

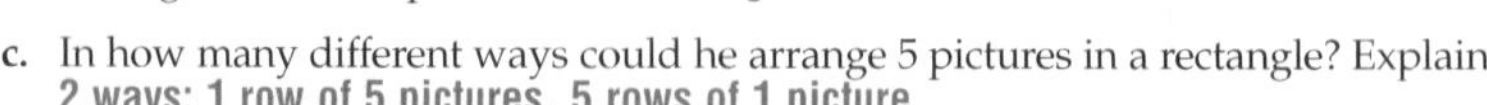

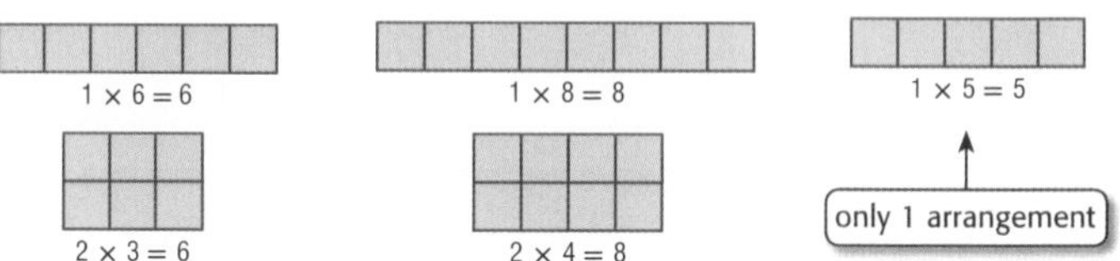

A **prime number** is a whole number that has exactly two unique factors, 1 and itself. So, 5 is a prime number. A **composite number** is a whole number that has more than two factors. The numbers 6 and 8 are composite numbers. The numbers 0 and 1 are neither prime nor composite.

Prime Number	Factors	Composite Number	Factors
2	1, 2	4	1, 2, 4
3	1, 3	6	1, 2, 3, 6
5	1, 5	8	1, 2, 4, 8

EXAMPLE 1 Identify Prime and Composite Numbers

Determine whether each number is *prime* or *composite*.

a. 15

Find factors of 15 by listing whole number pairs whose product is 15.

$15 = 1 \times 15$ $\quad$ $15 = 3 \times 5$

The factors of 15 are 1, 3, 5, and 15. Since the number has more than two factors, it is a composite number.

b. 23

$23 = 1 \times 23$

The number 23 has only two factors, 1 and 23. So, 23 is a prime number.

Check Your Progress

1A. 37 prime $\qquad$ **1B.** 22 composite

Personal Tutor glencoe.com

Lesson 9-2 Resources

Resource	Approaching-Level	On-Level	Beyond-Level	English Learners
Teacher Edition	• Differentiated Instruction, p. 477		• Differentiated Instruction, p. 480	• Differentiated Instruction, p. 477
Chapter Resource Masters	• Study Guide and Intervention, pp. 12–13 • Skills Practice, p. 14 • Practice, p. 15 • Word Problem Practice, p. 16	• Study Guide and Intervention, pp. 12–13 • Skills Practice, p. 14 • Practice, p. 15 • Word Problem Practice, p. 16 • Enrichment, p. 17	• Practice, p. 15 • Word Problem Practice, p. 16 • Enrichment, p. 17	• Study Guide and Intervention, pp. 12–13 • Skills Practice, p. 14 • Practice, p. 15
Transparencies	• 5-Minute Check Transparency 9-2	• 5-Minute Check Transparency 9-2	• 5-Minute Check Transparency 9-2	• 5-Minute Check Transparency 9-2
Other	• Study Notebook • Teaching Pre-Algebra with Manipulatives	• Study Notebook • Teaching Pre-Algebra with Manipulatives	• Study Notebook	• Study Notebook • Teaching Pre-Algebra with Manipulatives

476 Chapter 9 Powers and Nonlinear Functions

StudyTip

Prime Factorization There is exactly one prime factorization for a number. The order in which the prime factors are written does not matter.

When a composite number is expressed as the product of prime factors, it is called the **prime factorization** of the number. One way to find the prime factorization of a number is to use a **factor tree**.

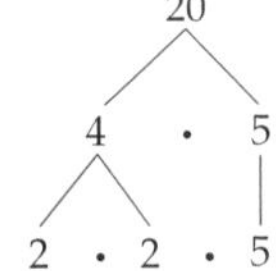

Step 1 Write the number that you are factoring at the top.

Step 2 Choose any pair of whole number factors of the number.

Step 3 Continue to factor any number that is not prime.

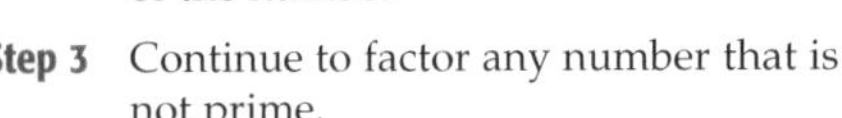

The factor tree is complete when you have a row of prime numbers. The prime factorization of 20 is $2 \cdot 2 \cdot 5$ or $2^2 \cdot 5$.

STANDARDIZED TEST EXAMPLE 2

What is the prime factorization of 90?

A $2 \cdot 5 \cdot 9$	C $3 \cdot 6 \cdot 5$
B $2 \cdot 3^2 \cdot 5$	D $2 \cdot 3 \cdot 15$

Read the Test Item

You are asked to find the factors of 90 that are prime numbers. Construct a factor tree to find all of the prime factors.

Solve the Test Item

Choose any pair of whole number factors of 90.

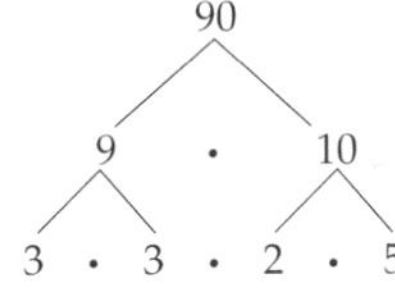

Continue to factor any number that is not prime.

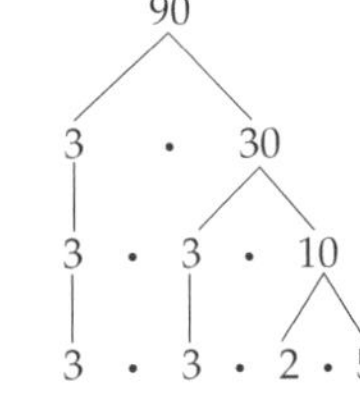

The prime factorization of 90 is $2 \cdot 3 \cdot 3 \cdot 5$ or $2 \cdot 3^2 \cdot 5$. The answer is B.

Check Your Progress

2. What is the prime factorization of 24? G

F $3 \cdot 8$	H $2 \cdot 3 \cdot 4$
G $2^3 \cdot 3$	J $2 \cdot 12$

Personal Tutor glencoe.com

StudyTip

Factors In the equation $8 \times 10 = 80$, 8 and 10 are factors of 80. In the equation $8 \cdot x = 8x$, 8 and x are factors of $8x$.

Factor Monomials A **monomial** is a number, a variable, or a product of numbers and/or variables.

Monomials	Not Monomials
$80, x, 8x$	$x + 5, x^2 - y^2$

To **factor** a number means to write it as a product of its factors. A monomial can also be factored as a product of prime numbers and variables with no exponent greater than 1. Negative coefficients can be factored using -1 as a factor.

Write Prime Factorizations

Examples 1 and 2 show how to identify prime and composite numbers and how to write the prime factorization of a number.

Formative Assessment

Use the Check Your Progress exercises after each example to determine students' understanding of concepts.

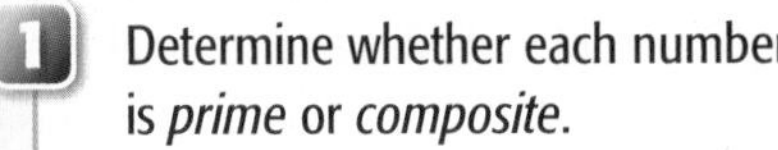

Additional Examples

1 Determine whether each number is *prime* or *composite*.

a. 31 prime

b. 36 composite

2 STANDARDIZED TEST PRACTICE What is the prime factorization of 56? D

A $4 \cdot 14$

B $2^2 \cdot 7^2$

C $2^2 \cdot 7$

D $2^3 \cdot 7$

Additional Examples also in Interactive Classroom PowerPoint® Presentations

IWB INTERACTIVE WHITEBOARD READY

Tips for New Teachers

Mental Math Tell students that to make a factor tree, they can mentally use the divisibility rules to find pairs of factors.

Extension Ask students if other factor trees could have been used to write the prime factorization of 90. Have them discuss if the results are the same.

Additional Answer (Why?)

b. Sample answer: 1 row of 8 pictures, 2 rows of 4 pictures, 4 rows of 2 pictures, 8 rows of 1 picture

Differentiated Instruction

AL ELL

If students struggle with identifying prime and composite numbers,

Then have students find prime numbers using a hundreds chart. Have them cross off number 1. Then have them circle number 2 (the first prime), and cross off all the other numbers divisible by 2. Next, have them go back and circle the next prime, which is 3. Now cross off all numbers divisible by 3. Continue until all numbers not crossed off are circled and are therefore prime. This method is called the Sieve of Eratosthenes, named for Eratosthenes of Cyrene (circa 276–194 B.C.).

Lesson 9-2 Prime Factorization 477

Focus on Mathematical Content

Prime Factorization The prime factorization of a composite number expresses it as the product of its prime number factors. For example, 40 has a prime factorization of $2 \cdot 2 \cdot 2 \cdot 5$ or $2^3 \cdot 5$. The monomial $27ab^3$ can be factored as $3 \cdot 3 \cdot 3 \cdot a \cdot b \cdot b \cdot b$.

Tips for New Teachers

Monomials Clarify that a monomial is the product of variables and rational numbers and may have a number as a denominator, but not a variable. For example, $\frac{x}{2}$ is a monomial, but $\frac{2}{x}$ is not.

Factor Monomials
Example 3 shows how to factor monomials.

Additional Example

3 Factor each monomial.

a. $16p^2q^4$ $2 \cdot 2 \cdot 2 \cdot 2 \cdot p \cdot p \cdot q \cdot q \cdot q \cdot q$

b. $-21x^2y$ $-1 \cdot 3 \cdot 7 \cdot x \cdot x \cdot y$

3 PRACTICE

Formative Assessment

Use Exercises 1–7 to check for understanding.

Use the chart at the bottom of this page to customize assignments for your students.

EXAMPLE 3 Factor Monomials

Factor each monomial.

a. $11r^4s$

$11r^4s = 11 \cdot r \cdot r \cdot r \cdot r \cdot s$ $\quad r^4 = r \cdot r \cdot r \cdot r$

b. $-28a^2b^3$

$-28a^2b^3 = -1 \cdot 2 \cdot 2 \cdot 7 \cdot a^2 \cdot b^3$ $\quad -28 = -1 \cdot 2 \cdot 2 \cdot 7$

$= -1 \cdot 2 \cdot 2 \cdot 7 \cdot a \cdot a \cdot b \cdot b \cdot b$ $\quad a^2 \cdot b^3 = a \cdot a \cdot b \cdot b \cdot b$

Check Your Progress

3A. $10xy$ $2 \cdot 5 \cdot x \cdot y$ **3B.** $12q^2r^3$ **3C.** $-18mn^4$

3B. $2 \cdot 2 \cdot 3 \cdot q \cdot q \cdot r \cdot r \cdot r$

3C. $-1 \cdot 2 \cdot 3 \cdot 3 \cdot m \cdot n \cdot n \cdot n \cdot n$

Personal Tutor glencoe.com

Check Your Understanding

Example 1 p. 476 Determine whether each number is *prime* or *composite*.

1. 26 composite **2.** 19 prime **3.** 35 composite

Example 2 p. 477

4. MULTIPLE CHOICE There are 30 students going on a field trip to an art museum. What is the prime factorization of 30? B

A $2^2 \cdot 3 \cdot 5$ **C** $3^2 \cdot 5$

B $2 \cdot 3 \cdot 5$ **D** $2^2 \cdot 5$

Example 3 p. 478 **ALGEBRA** Factor each monomial. 6. $-1 \cdot 3 \cdot 3 \cdot r \cdot s \cdot s \cdot t$

5. $14a^3$ $2 \cdot 7 \cdot a \cdot a \cdot a$ **6.** $-9rs^2t$ **7.** $20x^2y$ $2 \cdot 2 \cdot 5 \cdot x \cdot x \cdot y$

Practice and Problem Solving

= **Step-by-Step Solutions** begin on page R11. **Extra Practice** begins on page 810.

Example 1 p. 476 Determine whether each number is *prime* or *composite*.

8. 8 composite **9.** 11 prime **10.** 29 prime **11.** 26 composite
12. 13 prime **13.** 41 prime **14.** 57 composite **15.** 63 composite

Example 2 p. 477 Write the prime factorization of each number. Use exponents for repeated factors.

16. 22 $2 \cdot 11$ **17.** 243 3^5 **18.** 105 $3 \cdot 5 \cdot 7$ **19.** 56 $2^3 \cdot 7$
20. 104 $2^3 \cdot 13$ **21.** 196 $2^2 \cdot 7^2$ **22.** 450 $2 \cdot 3^2 \cdot 5^2$ **23.** 198 $2 \cdot 3^2 \cdot 11$

Example 3 p. 478 **ALGEBRA** Factor each monomial. 24–31. See Chapter 9 Answer Appendix.

24. $15y$ **25.** $6n^2$ **26.** $-9p^4$ **27.** $-11n^3$
28. $18ab$ **29.** $20qrs$ **30.** $24f^2g$ **31.** $-35c^3d^2$

32. GEOMETRY The surface area of a cube is given by the expression $6s^2$, where s is the side length. Factor $6s^2$. $2 \cdot 3 \cdot s \cdot s$

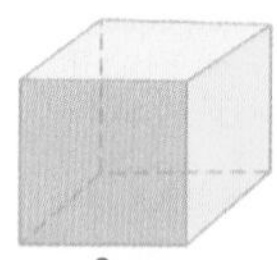

478 Chapter 9 Powers and Nonlinear Functions

Differentiated Homework Options

Level	Assignment	Two-Day Option	
AL Basic	8–33, 39–41, 43–64	9–33 odd, 44–47	8–32 even, 39–41, 43, 48–64
OL Core	9–33 odd, 34–41, 43–64	8–33, 44–47	34–41, 43, 48–64
BL Advanced	34–58 (optional: 59–64)		

33. **REPTILES** The graph shows the maximum age in years of the world's longest-lived reptiles. Write the prime factorization of the age of each reptile.

The World's Longest Lived Reptiles

Maximum age in years

Galapagos Tortoise	Box Turtle	American Alligator	Boa Constrictor
150	120	50	30

a. boa constrictor **2 • 3 • 5**

b. American alligator **$2 \cdot 5^2$**

c. box turtle **$2^3 \cdot 3 \cdot 5$**

d. Galapagos tortoise **$2 \cdot 3 \cdot 5^2$**

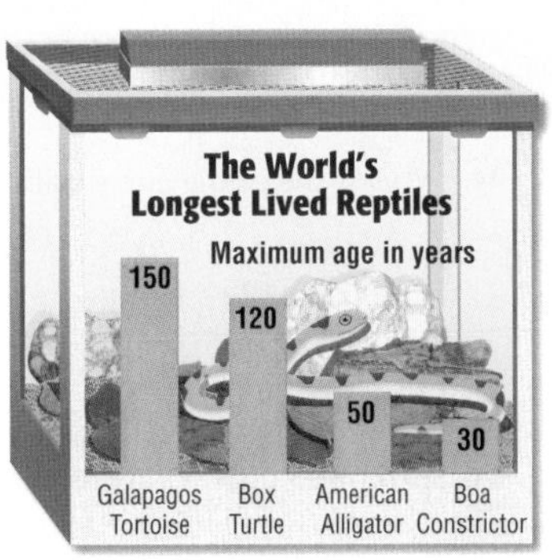

34. **CALENDARS** February 3 is a *prime day* because the month and day (2/3) are represented by prime numbers. How many prime days are there in a nonleap year? **52**

35. **GEOMETRY** Determine how many rectangles with different whole-number dimensions can be drawn for each given area.

a. 30 square inches **4 rectangles** b. 28 square feet **3 rectangles**

Math History Link

Marin Mersenne (1588–1648) Mersenne Primes were first described by the French monk Marin Mersenne. His formula $2^n - 1$ continues to be used by mathematicians today to locate large primes.

Source: The Great Internet Mersenne Prime Search

36. **TECHNOLOGY** *Mersenne primes* are prime numbers in the form $2^n - 1$. In 2006, a group of scientists used special software to discover the greatest prime number so far, $2^{32,582,657} - 1$. Write the prime factorization of each number, or write *prime* if the number is a Mersenne prime.

a. $2^5 - 1$ **prime** b. $2^6 - 1$ **$3^2 \cdot 7$** c. $2^7 - 1$ **prime** d. $2^8 - 1$ **$3 \cdot 5 \cdot 17$**

37. **CODES** Prime numbers are used to help keep messages sent over the Internet private. One step in the process involves multiplying two prime numbers to produce a key N. Determine which number could be N: 27, 29, 31, or 33. **33**

38. **PACKAGING** A beverage company is developing the packaging for a case of soda that contains 36 cans. List the arrangement of the cans that could be used for the package. (*Hint*: The cans can be stacked as well as arranged in a rectangular pattern one-can high.) **1 • 1 • 36; 1 • 2 • 18; 1 • 3 • 12; 1 • 4 • 9; 1 • 6 • 6; 3 • 3 • 4; 2 • 3 • 6; 2 • 2 • 9**

H.O.T. Problems

Use **H**igher-**O**rder **T**hinking Skills

39. **OPEN ENDED** Write three different monomials that have factors of 2, 5, and a^2.

40. **WRITING IN MATH** Explain how you can use the prime factorization of 30 to generate the factors of 30.

41. **FIND THE ERROR** Felipe and Ledell are describing prime numbers. Is either of them correct? Explain your reasoning.

Felipe	Ledell
All odd numbers are prime.	No prime numbers are even.

42. **CHALLENGE** Write five numbers that are divisible by 6 and find the prime factors of the numbers. Then write a rule to describe when a number is divisible by 6. **See Chapter 9 Answer Appendix.**

43. **WRITING IN MATH** Suppose n represents a prime number. Is $2n$ *always*, *sometimes*, or *never* prime? Explain your reasoning. **See Chapter 9 Answer Appendix.**

39. Sample answer: $10a^2$, $10a^2b$, $20a^2$

40. Sample answer: You can multiply all the different combinations of the prime factors to generate all of the factors of 30.

41. Both are incorrect. Felipe did not consider numbers like 9, 15, and 21 and Ledell did not consider 2 as a prime number.

Watch Out!

Find the Error For Exercise 41, encourage students to review the definition of prime numbers and to test some odd numbers to see if they are prime. Ask students to consider whether the number 2 is prime.

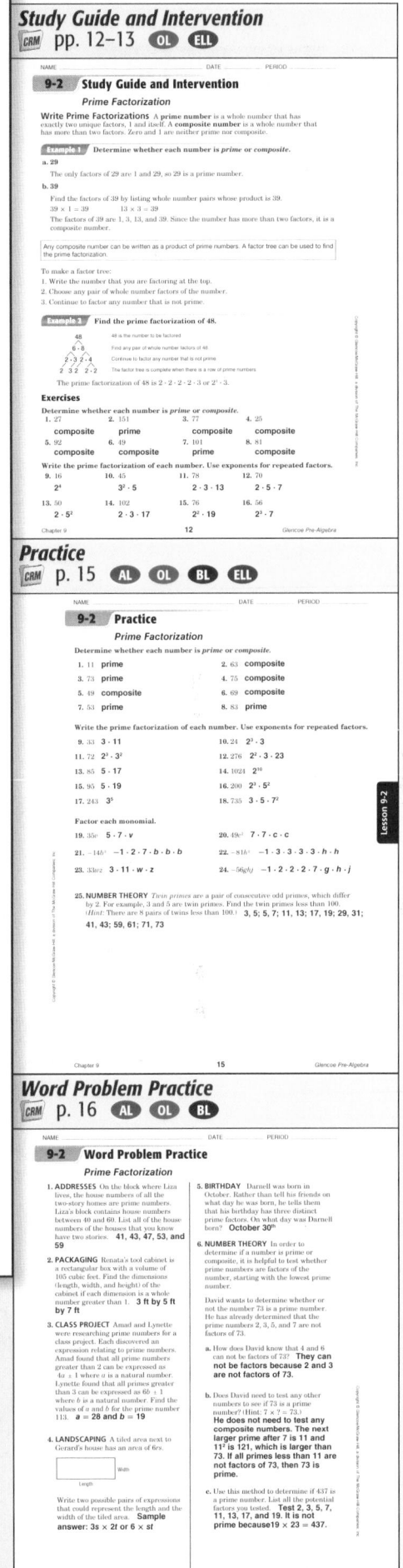

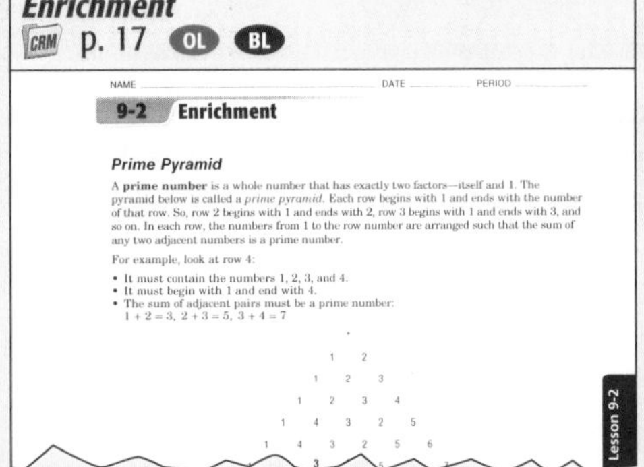
Enrichment

CRM p. 17 OL BL

NAME ______ DATE ______ PERIOD ______

9-2 Enrichment

Prime Pyramid

A **prime number** is a whole number that has exactly two factors—itself and 1. The pyramid below is called a *prime pyramid*. Each row begins with 1 and ends with the number of that row. So, row 2 begins with 1 and ends with 2, row 3 begins with 1 and ends with 3, and so on. In each row, the numbers from 1 to the row number are arranged such that the sum of any two adjacent numbers is a prime number.

For example, look at row 4:

- It must contain the numbers 1, 2, 3, and 4.
- It must begin with 1 and end with 4.
- The sum of adjacent pairs must be a prime number: $1 + 2 = 3$, $2 + 3 = 5$, $3 + 4 = 7$

1 2

1 2 3

1 2 3 4

1 4 3 2 5

1 4 3 2 5 6

Lesson 9-2

Study Guide and Intervention

CRM pp. 12–13 OL ELL

NAME ______ DATE ______ PERIOD ______

9-2 Study Guide and Intervention

Prime Factorization

Write Prime Factorizations A **prime number** is a whole number that has exactly two unique factors, 1 and itself. A **composite number** is a whole number that has more than two factors. Zero and 1 are neither prime nor composite.

Example 1 Determine whether each number is *prime* or *composite*.

a. 29

The only factors of 29 are 1 and 29, so 29 is a prime number.

b. 39

Find the factors of 39 by listing whole number pairs whose product is 39.

$39 \times 1 = 39$ $13 \times 3 = 39$

The factors of 39 are 1, 3, 13, and 39. Since the number has more than two factors, it is a composite number.

Any composite number can be written as a product of prime numbers. A factor tree can be used to find the prime factorization.

To make a factor tree:

1. Write the number that you are factoring at the top.
2. Choose any pair of whole number factors of the number.
3. Continue to factor any number that is not prime.

Example 2 Find the prime factorization of 48.

48 — 48 is the number to be factored

6 · 8 — Find any pair of whole number factors of 48

2 · 3 2 · 4 — Continue to factor any number that is not prime

2 3 2 2 · 2 — The factor tree is complete when there is a row of prime numbers

The prime factorization of 48 is $2 \cdot 2 \cdot 2 \cdot 2 \cdot 3$ or $2^4 \cdot 3$.

Exercises

Determine whether each number is *prime* or *composite*.

1. 27 **composite** 2. 151 **prime** 3. 77 **composite** 4. 25 **composite**

5. 92 **composite** 6. 49 **composite** 7. 101 **prime** 8. 81 **composite**

Write the prime factorization of each number. Use exponents for repeated factors.

9. 16 **2^4** 10. 45 **$3^2 \cdot 5$** 11. 78 **$2 \cdot 3 \cdot 13$** 12. 70 **$2 \cdot 5 \cdot 7$**

13. 50 **$2 \cdot 5^2$** 14. 102 **$2 \cdot 3 \cdot 17$** 15. 76 **$2^2 \cdot 19$** 16. 56 **$2^3 \cdot 7$**

Chapter 9 12 Glencoe Pre-Algebra

Practice

CRM p. 15 AL OL BL ELL

NAME ______ DATE ______ PERIOD ______

9-2 Practice

Prime Factorization

Determine whether each number is *prime* or *composite*.

1. 11 **prime** 2. 63 **composite**

3. 73 **prime** 4. 75 **composite**

5. 49 **composite** 6. 69 **composite**

7. 53 **prime** 8. 83 **prime**

Write the prime factorization of each number. Use exponents for repeated factors.

9. 33 **$3 \cdot 11$** 10. 24 **$2^3 \cdot 3$**

11. 72 **$2^3 \cdot 3^2$** 12. 276 **$2^2 \cdot 3 \cdot 23$**

13. 85 **$5 \cdot 17$** 14. 1024 **2^{10}**

15. 95 **$5 \cdot 19$** 16. 200 **$2^3 \cdot 5^2$**

17. 243 **3^5** 18. 735 **$3 \cdot 5 \cdot 7^2$**

Factor each monomial.

19. $35v$ **$5 \cdot 7 \cdot v$** 20. $49c^2$ **$7 \cdot 7 \cdot c \cdot c$**

21. $-14b^3$ **$-1 \cdot 2 \cdot 7 \cdot b \cdot b \cdot b$** 22. $-81h^2$ **$-1 \cdot 3 \cdot 3 \cdot 3 \cdot 3 \cdot h \cdot h$**

23. $33wz$ **$3 \cdot 11 \cdot w \cdot z$** 24. $-56ghj$ **$-1 \cdot 2 \cdot 2 \cdot 2 \cdot 7 \cdot g \cdot h \cdot j$**

25. **NUMBER THEORY** *Twin primes* are a pair of consecutive odd primes, which differ by 2. For example, 3 and 5 are twin primes. Find the twin primes less than 100. (*Hint*: There are 8 pairs of twins less than 100.) **3, 5; 5, 7; 11, 13; 17, 19; 29, 31; 41, 43; 59, 61; 71, 73**

Chapter 9 15 Glencoe Pre-Algebra

Lesson 9-2

Word Problem Practice

CRM p. 16 AL OL BL

NAME ______ DATE ______ PERIOD ______

9-2 Word Problem Practice

Prime Factorization

1. **ADDRESSES** On the block where Liza lives, the house numbers of all the two-story homes are prime numbers. Liza's block contains house numbers between 40 and 60. List all of the house numbers of the houses that you know have two stories. **41, 43, 47, 53, and 59**

2. **PACKAGING** Renata's tool cabinet is a rectangular box with a volume of 105 cubic feet. Find the dimensions (length, width, and height) of the cabinet if each dimension is a whole number greater than 1. **3 ft by 5 ft by 7 ft**

3. **CLASS PROJECT** Amad and Lynette were researching prime numbers for a class project. Each discovered an expression relating to prime numbers. Amad found that all prime numbers greater than 2 can be expressed as $4a \pm 1$ where a is a natural number. Lynette found that all primes greater than 3 can be expressed as $6b \pm 1$ where b is a natural number. Find the values of a and b for the prime number 113. **$a = 28$ and $b = 19$**

4. **LANDSCAPING** A tiled area next to Gerard's house has an area of $6rs$.

Width

Length

Write two possible pairs of expressions that could represent the length and the width of the tiled area. **Sample answer: $3s \times 2t$ or $6 \times st$**

5. **BIRTHDAY** Darnell was born in October. Rather than tell his friends on what day he was born, he tells them that his birthday has three distinct prime factors. On what day was Darnell born? **October 30th**

6. **NUMBER THEORY** In order to determine if a number is prime or composite, it is helpful to test whether prime numbers are factors of the number, starting with the lowest prime number.

David wants to determine whether or not the number 73 is a prime number. He has already determined that the prime numbers 2, 3, 5, and 7 are not factors of 73.

a. How does David know that 4 and 6 can not be factors of 73? **They can not be factors because 2 and 3 are not factors of 73.**

b. Does David need to test any other numbers to see if 73 is a prime number? (Hint: $7 \times ? = 73$.) **He does not need to test any composite numbers. The next larger prime after 7 is 11 and 11^2 is 121, which is larger than 73. If all primes less than 11 are not factors of 73, then 73 is prime.**

c. Use this method to determine if 437 is a prime number. List all the potential factors you tested. **Test 2, 3, 5, 7, 11, 13, 17, and 19. It is not prime because 19 × 23 = 437.**

Chapter 9 16 Glencoe Pre-Algebra

4 ASSESS

Crystal Ball Tell students to write how they think today's lesson on prime factorization might connect with tomorrow's lesson on multiplying and dividing monomials. Encourage them to flip ahead to the first page of the next lesson if needed.

Additional Answer

45. 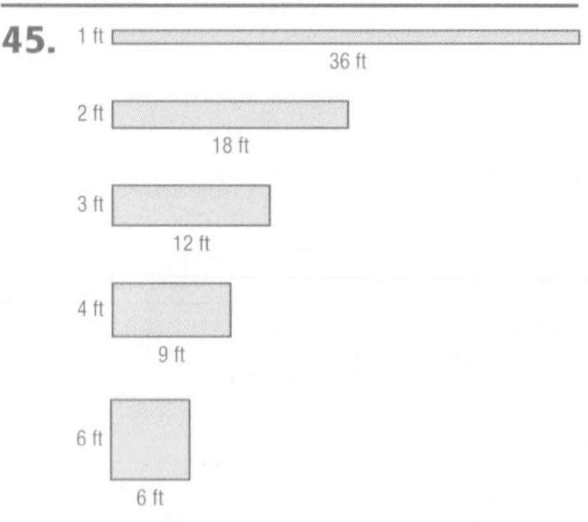

1 ft × 36 ft, 2 ft × 18 ft, 3 ft × 12 ft, 4 ft × 9 ft, 6 ft × 6 ft

Standardized Test Practice

44. What is the prime factorization of $12x^3y^2$? **B**

A $12 \cdot x \cdot x \cdot x \cdot y \cdot y$

B $2 \cdot 2 \cdot 3 \cdot x \cdot x \cdot x \cdot y \cdot y$

C $3 \cdot 4 \cdot x^3 \cdot y^2$

D $12 \cdot x^3 \cdot y^2$

45. SHORT RESPONSE Draw and label all of the rectangles with different whole-number dimensions that have an area of 36 square feet. **See margin.**

46. Which number is *not* a prime factor of 90? **J**

F 2

G 3

H 5

J 9

47. Which is the least whole number that is divisible by 2, 3, 7, and 11? **C**

A 452　　C 462

B 456　　D 468

Spiral Review

Evaluate each expression if $x = 2$, $y = 4$ and $z = -3$. (Lesson 9-1)

48. xz^3 **−54**　**49.** $y^0 - 10$ **−9**　**50.** $x^2 + 3x - 1$ **9**

51. $5(y - 1)^2$ **45**　**52.** $4z^4$ **324**　**53.** $z^2 + x^2$ **13**

54. GAMES Emilio has 17 video games and plans to purchase 2 new games every month. LaShaun has 47 video games and plans to donate 3 games to a charity every month. After how many months will the two have the same number of video games? (Lesson 8-10) **6 months**

55. PIZZA Koto delivers pizzas on weekends. Her average tip is $1.50 for each pizza that she delivers. How many pizzas must she deliver to earn at least $20 in tips? (Lesson 5-4) **14 pizzas**

Write and solve an equation to find each number. (Lesson 4-3)

56. The sum of a number and 9 is −2. $n + 9 = -2; -11$

57. The sum of −5 and a number is −15. $-5 + n = -15; -10$

58. GEOMETRY The area of a trapezoid is the product of one half the height and the sum of both bases. (Lesson 4-6)

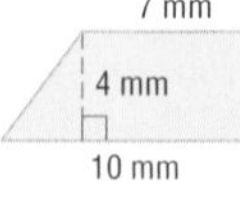

a. If h is the height, b_1 is one base, and b_2 is the second base, write an expression for the area of the trapezoid. $\frac{1}{2}h(b_1 + b_2)$

b. Find the area of the trapezoid shown at the right. **34 mm²**

Skills Review

62. $((-2) \cdot (-7))(t^4 \cdot t^4 \cdot t)$　63. $(-8 \cdot 2)(b^3)(c^2 \cdot c^3)(d^3)$

For each expression, use parentheses to group whole numbers together and powers with like bases together. (Lesson 1-3)

Example: $a \cdot 4 \cdot a^3 \cdot 2 = (4 \cdot 2)(a \cdot a^3)$

59. $3 \cdot a^4 \cdot 5$ $(3 \cdot 5)(a^4)$　**60.** $n \cdot p \cdot p^2 \cdot n^3$ $(n \cdot n^3)(p^2 \cdot p)$　**61.** $b \cdot 5 \cdot 10 \cdot b^4$ $(b \cdot b^4)(5 \cdot 10)$

62. $t \cdot t^4 \cdot (-7) \cdot t^4 \cdot (-2)$　**63.** $2 \cdot c^2 \cdot b^3 \cdot d^3 \cdot c^3 \cdot (-8)$　**64.** $12 \cdot 15 \cdot a \cdot 9 \cdot a^5 \cdot c^3$ $(a \cdot a^5)(c^3)(12 \cdot 15 \cdot 9)$

Differentiated Instruction

BL

Extension Using the form $2^n - 1$ given for Mersenne primes in Exercise 36, ask students to find the first four Mersenne prime numbers. Begin with $n = 2$. 3, 7, 31, 127

9-3 Multiplying and Dividing Monomials

Then
You used the Commutative and Associative Properties of Multiplication to simplify expressions.
(Lesson 1-3)

Now
- Multiply monomials.
- Divide monomials.

Math Online
glencoe.com
- Extra Examples
- Personal Tutor
- Self-Check Quiz
- Homework Help
- Math in Motion

Why?

The table shows the estimated number of songs on an MP3 player with different gigabytes (GB) of capacity.

Capacity (GB)	Estimated Number of Songs
5	$1000 = 10^3$
40	$10{,}000 = 10^4$

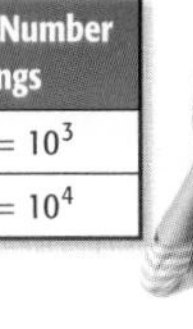

Complete. a. 100; 10^2 b. 1000; 10^3

a. $10 \times \blacksquare = 1000 \quad \rightarrow 10^1 \times \blacksquare = 10^3$

b. $10 \times \blacksquare = 10{,}000 \quad \rightarrow 10^1 \times \blacksquare = 10^4$

c. Examine the exponents of the factors and the exponents of the products above. Then write a rule for determining the exponent of the product when you multiply powers with the same base. Test your rule by multiplying $10^3 \cdot 10^4$ using a calculator. **Sample answer: Add the exponents; 10^7.**

Multiply Monomials Recall that exponents are used to show repeated multiplication. You can use the definition of exponent to help find a rule for multiplying powers with the same base.

$$10^1 \cdot 10^3 = \underbrace{\overbrace{(10)}^{1\text{ factor}} \cdot \overbrace{(10 \cdot 10 \cdot 10)}^{3\text{ factors}}}_{4\text{ factors}} = 10^4$$

Key Concept — Product of Powers Property

For Your FOLDABLE 

Words Multiply powers with the same base by adding their exponents.

Symbols $a^m \cdot a^n = a^{m+n}$ **Example** $2^4 \cdot 2^3 = 2^{4+3}$ or 2^7

EXAMPLE 1 Multiply Powers

Find each product. Express using exponents.

a. $4^3 \cdot 4^5$

$4^3 \cdot 4^5 = 4^{3+5}$ Product of Powers Property; the common base is 4.

$= 4^8$ Add the exponents.

b. $6 \cdot 6^4$

$6 \cdot 6^4 = 6^1 \cdot 6^4$ $6 = 6^1$

$= 6^{1+4}$ Product of Powers Property; the common base is 6.

$= 6^5$ Add the exponents.

Check Your Progress

1A. $5^2 \cdot 5^3$ 5^5

1B. $12^3 \cdot 12$ 12^4

Personal Tutor glencoe.com

Watch Out!
Common Misconception When multiplying powers, do not multiply the bases. $6^1 \cdot 6^4 = 6^5$, not 36^5.

9-3 Lesson Notes

1 FOCUS

Vertical Alignment

Before Lesson 9-3
Use the Commutative and Associative Properties of Multiplication to simplify expressions.

Lesson 9-3
Multiply monomials. Divide monomials.

After Lesson 9-3
Solve problems using scientific notation.

2 TEACH

Scaffolding Questions

Have students read the *Why?* section of the lesson and answer the questions.

Ask:
- How many times is 10 a factor in the monomial 10^7? 7
- Find the product of $10^2 \cdot 10^7$. 10^9
- Given the rule for multiplying powers with the same base, what do you think the rule is for dividing powers with the same base? Use a calculator to test your rule on $10^5 \div 10^2$. Subtract exponents; 10^3

Lesson 9-3 Resources

Resource	Approaching-Level	On-Level	Beyond-Level	English Learners
Teacher Edition	• Differentiated Instruction, p. 482	• Differentiated Instruction, p. 482	• Differentiated Instruction, p. 485	
Chapter Resource Masters	• Study Guide and Intervention, pp. 18–19 • Skills Practice, p. 20 • Practice, p. 21 • Word Problem Practice, p. 22	• Study Guide and Intervention, pp. 18–19 • Skills Practice, p. 20 • Practice, p. 21 • Word Problem Practice, p. 22 • Enrichment, p. 23	• Practice, p. 21 • Word Problem Practice, p. 22 • Enrichment, p. 23	• Study Guide and Intervention, pp. 18–19 • Skills Practice, p. 20 • Practice, p. 21
Transparencies	• 5-Minute Check Transparency 9-3	• 5-Minute Check Transparency 9-3	• 5-Minute Check Transparency 9-3	• 5-Minute Check Transparency 9-3
Other	• Study Notebook • Teaching Pre-Algebra with Manipulatives	• Study Notebook • Teaching Pre-Algebra with Manipulatives	• Study Notebook	• Study Notebook • Teaching Pre-Algebra with Manipulatives

Multiply Monomials

Example 1 shows how to multiply powers. **Example 2** shows how to multiply monomials.

Use the Check Your Progress exercises after each example to determine students' understanding of concepts.

Additional Examples

1 Find each product.

a. $3^4 \cdot 3^6$ 3^{10}

b. $7^8 \cdot 7$ 7^9

2 Find each product.

a. $y^4 \cdot y$ y^5

b. $(3p^4)(-2p^3)$ $-6p^7$

Additional Examples also in Interactive Classroom PowerPoint® Presentations

IWB INTERACTIVE WHITEBOARD READY

Tips for New Teachers

Building Skills Some students will benefit initially from writing out all factors until they understand why exponents are added.

Divide Monomials

Example 3 shows how to divide powers. **Example 4** shows how to use powers to compare values.

Additional Example

3 Find each quotient.

a. $\frac{4^{11}}{4^5}$ 4^6

b. $\frac{x^{12}}{x}$ x^{11}

EXAMPLE 2 Multiply Monomials

Find each product.

a. $b^2 \cdot b^2$

$b^2 \cdot b^2 = b^{2+2}$ — **Product of Powers Property; the common base is *b*.**

$= b^4$ — **Add the exponents.**

b. $2x^3 \cdot 8x^4$

$2x^3 \cdot 8x^4 = 2 \cdot 8 \cdot x^3 \cdot x^4$ — **Commutative Property of Multiplication**

$= 2 \cdot 8 \cdot x^{3+4}$ — **Product of Powers Property; the common base is *x*.**

$= 2 \cdot 8 \cdot x^7$ — **Add the exponents.**

$= 16x^7$ — **Multiply.**

Check Your Progress

2A. $y^6 \cdot y^3$ y^9 **2B.** $(5a^2)(-3a^4)$ $-15a^6$

Personal Tutor glencoe.com

Divide Monomials There is also a property for quotients of powers.

$$\frac{4^5}{4^2} = \frac{\overbrace{4 \cdot 4 \cdot 4 \cdot 4 \cdot 4}^{5 \text{ factors}}}{\underbrace{4 \cdot 4}_{2 \text{ factors}}} = \frac{4 \cdot 4 \cdot 4 \cdot \cancel{4}^1 \cdot \cancel{4}^1}{\cancel{4}_1 \cdot \cancel{4}_1} = \underbrace{4 \cdot 4 \cdot 4}_{3 \text{ factors}} \text{ or } 4^3$$

Key Concept — Quotient of Powers Property

For Your FOLDABLE

Words	Divide powers with the same base by subtracting their exponents.
Symbols	$a^m \div a^n = a^{m-n}$
Example	$3^6 \div 3^2 = 3^{6-2}$ or 3^4

Math *in Motion*, BrainPOP® glencoe.com

Watch Out!

Dividing Monomials When dividing powers, remember that the denominator cannot equal zero. So, in Example 3b, $c \neq 0$.

EXAMPLE 3 Divide Powers

Find each quotient.

a. $\frac{8^5}{8^3}$

$\frac{8^5}{8^3} = 8^{5-3}$ — **Quotient of Powers Property; the common base is 8.**

$= 8^2$ — **Subtract the exponents.**

b. $\frac{c^7}{c^2}$

$\frac{c^7}{c^2} = c^{7-2}$ — **Quotient of Powers Property; the common base is *c*.**

$= c^5$ — **Subtract the exponents.**

Check Your Progress

3A. $\frac{3^9}{3^2}$ 3^7 **3B.** $\frac{b^7}{b^6}$ b^1 or b

Personal Tutor glencoe.com

Differentiated Instruction

If students need help remembering the rules for multiplying and dividing monomials with powers,

Then challenge students to create a catchy phrase, rhyme, or rap that articulates the rules. Provide examples, such as the phrase Please Excuse My Dear Aunt Sally, which indicates the correct order of operations: Parentheses, Exponents, Multiplication, Division, Addition, Subtraction. Have students share ideas with the class.

Real-World Link

Jupiter is the largest planet in the solar system. If Jupiter were hollow, more than 1200 Earths could fit inside.

Source: NASA

Real-World EXAMPLE 4 Use Powers to Compare Values

PLANETS The table shows the approximate diameters of Earth, Mars, and Neptune. About how many times as great is Neptune's diameter than Earth's diameter?

Planet	Approximate Diameter (mi)
Earth	2^{13}
Mars	2^{12}
Neptune	2^{15}

Write a division expression.

$\frac{2^{15}}{2^{13}} = 2^{15-13}$ **Quotient of Powers Property**

$= 2^2$ or 4 **Simplify.**

So, Neptune's diameter is about 4 times as great as Earth's diameter.

Check Your Progress

4. **PLANETS** About how many times as great is the diameter of Earth than the diameter of Mars? 2 times

Personal Tutor glencoe.com

Check Your Understanding

Examples 1 and 2 pp. 481–482

Find each product. Express using exponents.

1. $2^4 \cdot 2^6$ 2^{10}
2. $8^5 \cdot 8$ 8^6
3. $x^{10} \cdot x^6$ x^{16}
4. $-w^2(5w^7)$ $-5w^9$

Example 3 p. 482

Find each quotient. Express using exponents.

5. $\frac{4^5}{4^3}$ 4^2
6. $7^9 \div 7$ 7^8
7. $\frac{r^8}{r^4}$ r^4
8. $b^{11} \div b^2$ b^9

Example 4 p. 483

9. **CANYONS** The Grand Canyon is approximately 2^9 kilometers long. *Mariner Valley* is a canyon on Mars that is approximately 2^{12} kilometers long. About how many times longer is Mariner Valley than the Grand Canyon? 2^3 or 8 times

Practice and Problem Solving

= Step-by-Step Solutions begin on page R11. Extra Practice begins on page 810.

Examples 1 and 2 pp. 481–482

Find each product. Express using exponents. 10–25. See Chapter 9 Answer Appendix.

10. $5^6 \cdot 5^2$
11. $(-2)^3 \cdot (-2)^2$
12. $a^7 \cdot a^2$
13. $(t^3)(t^3)$
14. $(10x)(4x^7)$
15. $6p^7 \cdot 9p^7$
16. $m^5 \cdot (-4m^6)$
17. $(-8s^3)(-3s^4)$

Example 3 p. 482

Find each quotient. Express using exponents

18. $\frac{5^{10}}{5^2}$
19. $\frac{7^6}{7}$
20. $\frac{a^8}{a^7}$
21. $\frac{k^{12}}{k^9}$
22. $(-1.5)^8 \div (-1.5)^3$
23. $8^{15} \div 8^9$
24. $r^{20} \div r^6$
25. $(-n)^6 \div (-n)^4$

Example 4 p. 483

26. **SOUND** Sound intensity is measured in *decibels*. The decibel scale is based on powers of ten as shown.
    a. How many times as intense is a rock concert as normal conversation?
    b. How many times as intense is a vacuum cleaner as a person whispering? 10^6 or 1,000,000 times

26a. 10^5 or 100,000 times

Sound	Decibels	Intensity
rock concert	110	10^{11}
vacuum cleaner	80	10^8
normal conversation	60	10^6
whispering	20	10^2

Additional Example

4 **CLOUDS** The table shows the approximate heights of some clouds. About how many times higher are some high clouds than some low clouds? 2^3 or 8 times

Clouds	Approximate Height (m)
Low	2^{10}
Middle	2^{11}
High	2^{13}

Tips for New Teachers

Reading Math Remind students that *how many times greater* indicates that division is to be used to compare quantities. *How much greater* indicates that subtraction is to be used to compare quantities.

TEACH with TECH

VIDEO RECORDING Have students record themselves multiplying or dividing monomials and explaining their work. Share the videos with the class.

3 PRACTICE

Formative Assessment

Use Exercises 1–9 to check for understanding.

Use the chart at the bottom of this page to customize assignments for your students.

Differentiated Homework Options

Level	Assignment	Two-Day Option	
AL Basic	10–26, 41, 42, 44–66	11–25 odd, 46–49	10–26 even, 41, 42, 44, 45, 50–66
OL Core	11–25 odd, 27–35 odd, 36, 37, 39, 41–42, 44–66	10–26, 46–49	27–42, 44, 45, 50–66
BL Advanced	27–62 (optional: 63–66)		

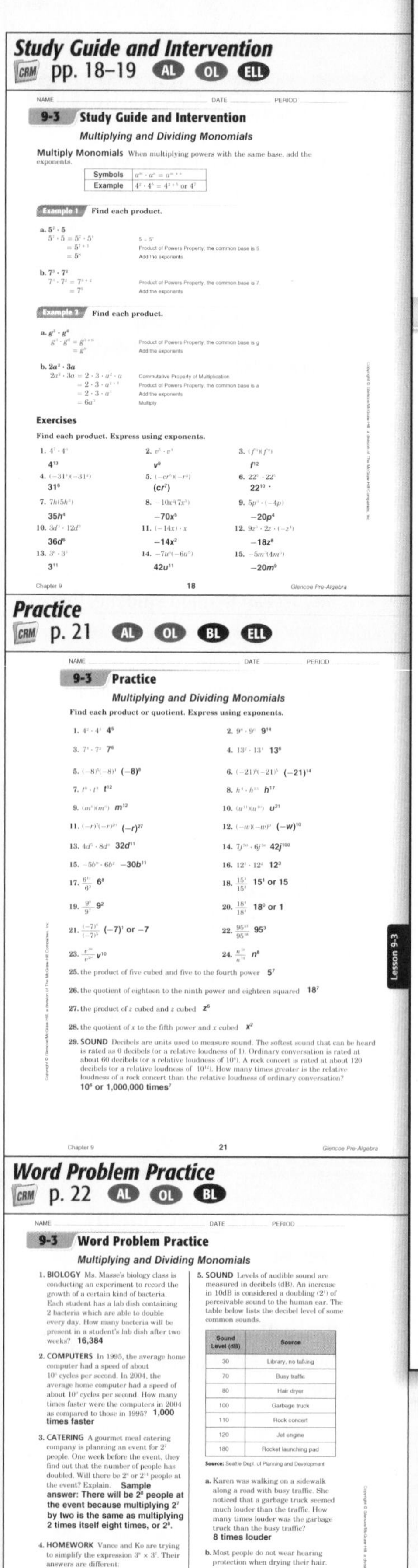
Study Guide and Intervention
CRM pp. 18–19 AL OL ELL

NAME ______ DATE ______ PERIOD ______

9-3 Study Guide and Intervention

Multiplying and Dividing Monomials

Multiply Monomials When multiplying powers with the same base, add the exponents.

Symbols	$a^m \cdot a^n = a^{m+n}$
Example	$4^2 \cdot 4^5 = 4^{2+5}$ or 4^7

Example 1 Find each product.

a. $5^7 \cdot 5$
$5^7 \cdot 5 = 5^7 \cdot 5^1$ — $5 = 5^1$
$= 5^{7+1}$ — Product of Powers Property; the common base is 5
$= 5^8$ — Add the exponents

b. $7^3 \cdot 7^2$
$7^3 \cdot 7^2 = 7^{3+2}$ — Product of Powers Property; the common base is 7
$= 7^5$ — Add the exponents

Example 2 Find each product.

a. $g^3 \cdot g^6$
$g^3 \cdot g^6 = g^{3+6}$ — Product of Powers Property; the common base is g
$= g^9$ — Add the exponents

b. $2a^2 \cdot 3a$
$2a^2 \cdot 3a = 2 \cdot 3 \cdot a^2 \cdot a$ — Commutative Property of Multiplication
$= 2 \cdot 3 \cdot a^{2+1}$ — Product of Powers Property; the common base is a
$= 2 \cdot 3 \cdot a^3$ — Add the exponents
$= 6a^3$ — Multiply

Exercises

Find each product. Express using exponents.

1. $4^7 \cdot 4^6$ **4^{13}**
2. $v^5 \cdot v^4$ **v^9**
3. $(f^3)(f^9)$ **f^{12}**
4. $(-31^3)(-31^3)$ **31^6**
5. $(-cr^5)(-r^2)$ **(cr^7)**
6. $22^5 \cdot 22^5$ **22^{10}**
7. $7h(5h^3)$ **$35h^4$**
8. $-10x^2(7x^3)$ **$-70x^5$**
9. $5p^3 \cdot (-4p)$ **$-20p^4$**
10. $3d^3 \cdot 12d^3$ **$36d^6$**
11. $(-14x) \cdot x$ **$-14x^2$**
12. $9z^3 \cdot 2z \cdot (-z^4)$ **$-18z^8$**
13. $3^8 \cdot 3^3$ **3^{11}**
14. $-7u^6(-6u^5)$ **$42u^{11}$**
15. $-5m^3(4m^6)$ **$-20m^9$**

Chapter 9 18 Glencoe Pre-Algebra

Practice
CRM p. 21 AL OL BL ELL

NAME ______ DATE ______ PERIOD ______

9-3 Practice

Multiplying and Dividing Monomials

Find each product or quotient. Express using exponents.

1. $4^2 \cdot 4^3$ **4^5**
2. $9^8 \cdot 9^6$ **9^{14}**
3. $7^4 \cdot 7^2$ **7^6**
4. $13^2 \cdot 13^4$ **13^6**
5. $(-8)^5(-8)^3$ **$(-8)^8$**
6. $(-21)^9(-21)^5$ **$(-21)^{14}$**
7. $t^9 \cdot t^3$ **t^{12}**
8. $h^4 \cdot h^{13}$ **h^{17}**
9. $(m^6)(m^6)$ **m^{12}**
10. $(u^{11})(u^{10})$ **u^{21}**
11. $(-r)^7(-r)^{20}$ **$(-r)^{27}$**
12. $(-w)(-w)^9$ **$(-w)^{10}$**
13. $4d^5 \cdot 8d^6$ **$32d^{11}$**
14. $7j^{50} \cdot 6j^{50}$ **$42j^{100}$**
15. $-5b^9 \cdot 6b^2$ **$-30b^{11}$**
16. $12^1 \cdot 12^2$ **12^3**
17. $\frac{6^{11}}{6^3}$ **6^8**
18. $\frac{15^3}{15^2}$ **15^1 or 15**
19. $\frac{9^9}{9^7}$ **9^2**
20. $\frac{18^4}{18^4}$ **18^0 or 1**
21. $\frac{(-7)^6}{(-7)^5}$ **$(-7)^1$ or -7**
22. $\frac{95^{21}}{95^{18}}$ **95^3**
23. $\frac{v^{30}}{v^{20}}$ **v^{10}**
24. $\frac{n^{19}}{n^{11}}$ **n^8**
25. the product of five cubed and five to the fourth power **5^7**
26. the quotient of eighteen to the ninth power and eighteen squared **18^7**
27. the product of z cubed and z cubed **z^6**
28. the quotient of x to the fifth power and x cubed **x^2**
29. **SOUND** Decibels are units used to measure sound. The softest sound that can be heard is rated as 0 decibels (or a relative loudness of 1). Ordinary conversation is rated at about 60 decibels (or a relative loudness of 10^6). A rock concert is rated at about 120 decibels (or a relative loudness of 10^{12}). How many times greater is the relative loudness of a rock concert than the relative loudness of ordinary conversation? **10^6 or 1,000,000 times**

Lesson 9-3

Chapter 9 21 Glencoe Pre-Algebra

Word Problem Practice
CRM p. 22 AL OL BL

NAME ______ DATE ______ PERIOD ______

9-3 Word Problem Practice

Multiplying and Dividing Monomials

1. **BIOLOGY** Ms. Masse's biology class is conducting an experiment to record the growth of a certain kind of bacteria. Each student has a lab dish containing 2 bacteria which are able to double every day. How many bacteria will be present in a student's lab dish after two weeks? **16,384**

2. **COMPUTERS** In 1995, the average home computer had a speed of about 10^8 cycles per second. In 2004, the average home computer had a speed of about 10^{11} cycles per second. How many times faster were the computers in 2004 as compared to those in 1995? **1,000 times faster**

3. **CATERING** A gourmet meal catering company is planning an event for 2^7 people. One week before the event, they find out that the number of people has doubled. Will there be 2^8 or 2^{14} people at the event? Explain. **Sample answer: There will be 2^8 people at the event because multiplying 2^7 by two is the same as multiplying 2 times itself eight times, or 2^8.**

4. **HOMEWORK** Vance and Ko are trying to simplify the expression $3^8 \times 3^7$. Their answers are different:

   Ko's work: $3^8 \times 3^7 = (3 \times 3)^{(8+7)} = 9^{15}$

   Vance's work: $3^8 \times 3^7 = 3^{(8+7)} = 3^{15}$

   Which student is correct? Identify the mistake made by the other student. **Sample answer: Vance is correct. Ko should not have multiplied the base by itself.**

5. **SOUND** Levels of audible sound are measured in decibels (dB). An increase in 10dB is considered a doubling (2^1) of perceivable sound to the human ear. The table below lists the decibel level of some common sounds.

Sound Level (dB)	Source
30	Library, no talking
70	Busy traffic
80	Hair dryer
100	Garbage truck
110	Rock concert
120	Jet engine
180	Rocket launching pad

Source: Seattle Dept. of Planning and Development

a. Karen was walking on a sidewalk along a road with busy traffic. She noticed that a garbage truck seemed much louder than the traffic. How many times louder was the garbage truck than the busy traffic? **8 times louder**

b. Most people do not wear hearing protection when drying their hair. However, airport workers often wear ear protection because of the sound produced by jet engines. How many times louder is a jet engine than a hair dryer? **16 times louder**

c. How many times louder is it at a rocket launching pad than in a library? **32,768 times louder**

Chapter 9 22 Glencoe Pre-Algebra

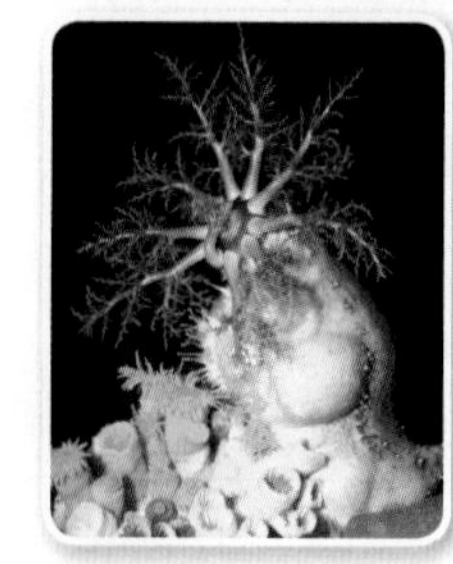

Real-World Link

Sea cucumbers are members of the echinoderm family that live on or near the ocean floor. The smallest species of sea cucumbers are about 10 millimeters long.

Source: OceanLink

27. RUNNING A person weighing 5^3 pounds can experience forces 5 times their body weight while running. Find $5^3 \cdot 5$ to find the number of pounds exerted on a person's foot while running. **5^4 or 625 lb**

28. SEA CUCUMBERS The largest sea cucumbers are more than 10^2 times longer than the smallest sea cucumbers. Use the information at the left to determine the approximate length of the largest sea cucumbers. **10^3 or 1000 mm**

29. HEALTH A nurse draws a sample of blood. A cubic millimeter of the blood contains 22^5 red blood cells and 22^3 white blood cells. Compare the number of red blood cells to the number of white blood cells as a fraction. Explain its meaning. **$\frac{484}{1}$; Sample answer: For every 484 red blood cells, there is one white blood cell.**

Find each missing exponent.

30. $(5^{■})(5^2) = 5^3$ **1**
31. $(9^{10})(9^{■}) = 9^{15}$ **5**
32. $a^{12} \cdot a^{■} = a^{19}$ **7**
33. $\frac{6^{■}}{6^4} = 6^8$ **12**
34. $\frac{x^7}{x^{■}} = 1$ **7**
35. $c^{10} \div c^{■} = c^8$ **2**

36. MULTIPLE REPRESENTATIONS In this problem, you will investigate area and volume. The formulas $A = s^2$ and $V = s^3$ can be used to find the area of a square and the volume of a cube, respectively, with side length s.

a. **TABULAR** Copy and complete the table shown.

Side Length (units)	Area of Square (units²)	Volume of Cube (units³)
s	s^2	s^3
$2s$	■ **$4s^2$**	■ **$8s^3$**
$3s$	■ **$9s^2$**	■ **$27s^3$**
s^2	■ **s^4**	■ **s^6**
s^3	■ **s^6**	■ **s^9**

b. **VERBAL** How are the area and volume each affected if the side length is doubled? tripled? **See margin.**

c. **VERBAL** How are the area and volume each affected if the side length is squared? cubed? **See margin.**

Find each product or quotient. Express using exponents.

37. $ab^5 \cdot 8a^2b^5$ **$8a^3b^{10}$**
38. $10x^3y \cdot (-2xy^2)$ **$-20x^4y^3$**
39. $\frac{n^3(n^5)}{n^2}$ **n^6**
40. $\frac{s^7}{s \cdot s^2}$ **s^4**

H.O.T. Problems
Use Higher-Order Thinking Skills

41. OPEN ENDED Write two algebraic expressions whose quotient is x^5.

42. FIND THE ERROR Addison and Noah are multiplying $(4a^2)(4a^3)$. Is either of them correct? Explain your reasoning.

Addison	Noah
$(4a^2)(4a^3) = 16a^{2+3}$ $= 16a^5$	$(4a^2)(4a^3) = 4a^{2+3}$ $= 4a^5$

43. CHALLENGE Use the Quotient of Powers Property and the equation $\frac{a^n}{a^n} = 1$ to show that a nonzero number raised to the zero power equals 1.

44. REASONING *True* or *false*. For any integer a, $(-a)^2 = -a^2$. If true, explain your reasoning. If false, give a counterexample.

45. WRITING IN MATH Explain how to use division of powers to divide large numbers.

41. Sample answer: x^7, x^2

42. Addison; Noah did not multiply the coefficients together.

43. Sample answer: By the Quotient of Powers, $\frac{a^n}{a^n} = a^{n-n}$ or a^0 for $a \neq 0$. Since $\frac{a^n}{a^n} = 1$, then $a^0 = 1$. So, any nonzero number raised to the zero power must equal 1.

44. False; if $a = 3$, then $(-3)^2 = 9$, but $-3^2 = -9$.

45. Sample answer: Write the numbers as powers with the same base. Then subtract the exponents.

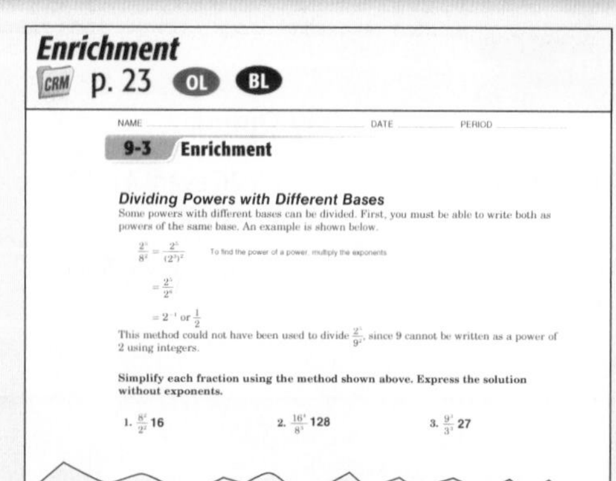
Enrichment
CRM p. 23 OL BL

NAME ______ DATE ______ PERIOD ______

9-3 Enrichment

Dividing Powers with Different Bases

Some powers with different bases can be divided. First, you must be able to write both as powers of the same base. An example is shown below.

$\frac{2^5}{8^2} = \frac{2^5}{(2^3)^2}$ — To find the power of a power, multiply the exponents

$= \frac{2^5}{2^6}$

$= 2^{-1}$ or $\frac{1}{2}$

This method could not have been used to divide $\frac{2^5}{9^2}$, since 9 cannot be written as a power of 2 using integers.

Simplify each fraction using the method shown above. Express the solution without exponents.

1. $\frac{8^2}{2^2}$ **16**
2. $\frac{16^4}{8^3}$ **128**
3. $\frac{9^3}{3^3}$ **27**

Multiple Representations In Exercise 36, students use formulas and a table to relate the length of a side to the area of a square and the volume of a cube, and offer verbal explanations of how the area and volume are affected by a change in the length of a side.

Standardized Test Practice

46. In the metric system, one meter is equal to 10^2 centimeters. One kilometer is 10^3 meters. How many centimeters are in one kilometer? **C**

A 1000 C 100,000
B 10,000 D 1,000,000

47. Which of the following expressions has the same value as $6a^3$? **F**

F $6 \cdot a \cdot a \cdot a$
G $6 + a + a + a$
H $6 + a \cdot a \cdot a$
J $6 \cdot 6 \cdot 6 \cdot a \cdot a \cdot a$

48. Which of the following expressions is equivalent to the product of $5a^3$ and $3a^8$? **C**

A $8a^{11}$ C $15a^{11}$
B $8a^{24}$ D $15a^{24}$

49. **SHORT RESPONSE** The formula $A = \frac{1}{2}bh$ can be used to find the area of a triangle with base b and height h. Write an expression in simplest form to represent the area of the triangle shown below. **See margin.**

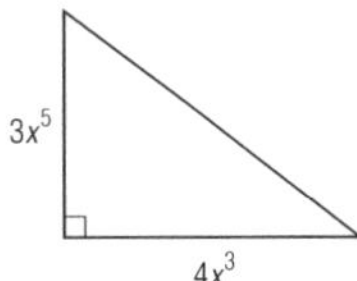

Spiral Review

Write the prime factorization of each number. Use exponents for repeated factors. (Lesson 9-2)

50. 49 7^2 51. 81 3^4 52. 100 $2^2 \cdot 5^2$ 53. 150 $2 \cdot 3 \cdot 5^2$

ALGEBRA Factor each monomial. (Lesson 9-2) **54–57. See margin.**

54. $18x^4$ 55. $54a^6$ 56. $-11m^3$ 57. $-33t^5$

58. **MILEAGE** Which numbers in the table can be expressed as whole numbers raised to a power? Name the cities and express the numbers as powers. (Lesson 9-1) **Chicago: 400 = 20^2; Evansville: 100 = 10^2; Nashville: 125 = 5^3; Paducah: 25 = 5^2; St. Louis: 225 = 15^2**

Miles to Kentucky Dam	
City	**Miles**
Chicago	400
Evansville	100
Lexington	250
Louisville	200
Nashville	125
Paducah	25
St. Louis	225

59. **REAL ESTATE** A commission is a fee paid to a salesperson based on a percent of sales. Suppose a real estate agent earns a 3% commission. What commission would be earned for selling a house for $230,000? (Lesson 7-5) **$6900**

Find each sum or difference. Write in simplest form. (Lesson 3-6)

60. $\frac{3}{5} + \frac{3}{10}$ $\frac{9}{10}$ 61. $-\frac{1}{2} + \frac{3}{8}$ $-\frac{1}{8}$ 62. $-6\frac{2}{3} - \frac{8}{9}$ $-7\frac{5}{9}$

Skills Review

Evaluate each expression if $a = -3$, $b = 7$, and $c = 5$. (Lesson 2-5)

63. $\frac{1}{ab}$ $-\frac{1}{21}$ 64. $\frac{1}{(b)(b)}$ $\frac{1}{49}$ 65. $\frac{c}{75}$ $\frac{1}{15}$ 66. $\frac{ac}{5ab}$ $\frac{1}{7}$

Differentiated Instruction BL

Extension Have students determine the missing exponents in each of the following problems. $\frac{3^8}{3^?} = 3^6$; $x^4 \cdot x^? = x^7$; $\frac{y^6}{y^?} = 1$; $(8x^{10})(2x^?) = 16x^{15}$ 2; 3; 6; 5

Watch Out!

Find the Error Remind students in Exercise 42, to (a) use the Commutative Property of Multiplication to multiply the numbers and (b) use the Product of Powers Property to multiply the powers.

4 ASSESS

Name the Math Have students write an explanation of how to simplify $x^3y \cdot x^2$. Tell them to name the rule and the steps they use in finding the product.

Formative Assessment

Check for student understanding of concepts in Lessons 9-1, 9-2, and 9-3.

CRM Quiz 1, p. 64

Additional Answers

36b. If the side length is doubled, the area is quadrupled and the volume is multiplied by 8. If the side length is tripled, the area is multiplied by 3^2 or 9 and the volume is multiplied by 3^3 or 27.

36c. If the side length is squared, the area is squared and the volume is squared. If the side length is cubed, the area is cubed and the volume is cubed.

49. $A = \frac{1}{2}bh$
$A = \frac{1}{2}(4x^3)(3x^5)$
$A = \frac{1}{2} \cdot 4 \cdot 3 \cdot x^3 \cdot x^5$
$A = \frac{1}{2} \cdot 4 \cdot 3 \cdot x^8$
$A = 6x^8$

54. $2 \cdot 3 \cdot 3 \cdot x \cdot x \cdot x \cdot x$

55. $2 \cdot 3 \cdot 3 \cdot 3 \cdot a \cdot a \cdot a \cdot a \cdot a \cdot a$

56. $-1 \cdot 11 \cdot m \cdot m \cdot m$

57. $-1 \cdot 3 \cdot 11 \cdot t \cdot t \cdot t \cdot t \cdot t$

9-4 Lesson Notes

1 FOCUS

Vertical Alignment

Before Lesson 9-4
Evaluate expressions containing positive exponents.

Lesson 9-4
Write expressions using negative exponents. Evaluate numerical expressions containing negative exponents.

After Lesson 9-4
Express numbers in scientific notation, including negative exponents, in appropriate situations.

2 TEACH

Scaffolding Questions

Have students read the *Why?* section of the lesson and answer the questions.

Ask:

- How many times greater is the maximum thickness of A than the maximum thickness of G, written as a fraction with an exponent in the denominator? $\frac{1}{10^3}$
- What does the fraction $\frac{1}{10^3}$ represent? 1 divided by 10^3
- What is the standard form of the fraction? $\frac{1}{1000}$ the decimal form? 0.001

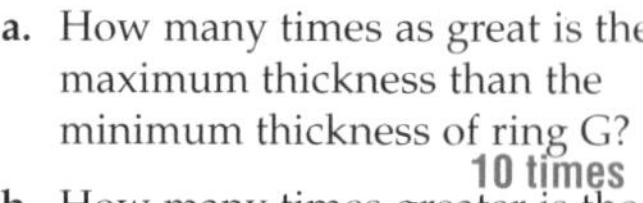

9-4 Negative Exponents

Then
You evaluated expressions containing positive exponents. (Lesson 9-1)

Now
- Write expressions using negative exponents.
- Evaluate numerical expressions containing negative exponents.

Math Online
glencoe.com
- Extra Examples
- Personal Tutor
- Self-Check Quiz
- Homework Help

Why?

Saturn has seven major rings that are made of ice crystals: rings A, B, C, D, E, F, and G.

Thickness of Saturn's Rings		
Ring	Minimum (km)	Maximum (km)
G	100	1000
A	0.1	1

a. How many times as great is the maximum thickness than the minimum thickness of ring G? 10 times

b. How many times greater is the maximum thickness than the minimum thickness of ring A? 10 times

c. How many times greater is the maximum thickness of ring A than the minimum thickness of ring G? Write your answer as a fraction with an exponent in the denominator. $\frac{1}{10^2}$ times

Negative Exponents Negative exponents are the result of repeated division. Extending the pattern below shows that $\frac{1}{100}$ or $\frac{1}{10^2}$ can be defined as 10^{-2}.

Exponential Form	Standard Form	
$10^3 = 10 \cdot 10 \cdot 10$	1000	÷ 10
$10^2 = 10 \cdot 10$	100	÷ 10
10^1	10	÷ 10
10^0	1	÷ 10
10^{-1}	$\frac{1}{10}$	÷ 10
10^{-2}	$\frac{1}{100}$	

You can apply the Quotient of Powers rule and the definition of a power to $\frac{x^3}{x^5}$ and write a general rule about negative exponents.

Method 1 Quotient of Powers

$$\frac{x^3}{x^5} = x^{3-5}$$
$$= x^{-2}$$

Method 2 Definition of Power

$$\frac{x^3}{x^5} = \frac{\overset{1}{\cancel{x}} \cdot \overset{1}{\cancel{x}} \cdot \overset{1}{\cancel{x}}}{\underset{1}{\cancel{x}} \cdot \underset{1}{\cancel{x}} \cdot \underset{1}{\cancel{x}} \cdot x \cdot x}$$
$$= \frac{1}{x \cdot x} \text{ or } \frac{1}{x^2}$$

Since $\frac{x^3}{x^5}$ cannot have two different values, you can conclude that $x^{-2} = \frac{1}{x^2}$.

Key Concept Negative and Zero Exponents — For Your FOLDABLE

Symbols For $a \neq 0$ and any whole number n, $a^{-n} = \frac{1}{a^n}$.
For $a \neq 0$, $a^0 = 1$.

Example $8^{-2} = \frac{1}{8^2}$ $\quad x^0 = 1, x \neq 0$

Lesson 9-4 Resources

Resource	Approaching-Level	On-Level	Beyond-Level	English Learners
Teacher Edition	• Differentiated Instruction, p. 487	• Differentiated Instruction, p. 487	• Differentiated Instruction, p. 491	• Differentiated Instruction, p. 487
Chapter Resource Masters	• Study Guide and Intervention, pp. 24–25 • Skills Practice, p. 26 • Practice, p. 27 • Word Problem Practice, p. 28	• Study Guide and Intervention, pp. 24–25 • Skills Practice, p. 26 • Practice, p. 27 • Word Problem Practice, p. 28 • Enrichment, p. 29	• Practice, p. 27 • Word Problem Practice, p. 28 • Enrichment, p. 29	• Study Guide and Intervention, pp. 24–25 • Skills Practice, p. 26 • Practice, p. 27
Transparencies	• 5-Minute Check Transparency 9-4	• 5-Minute Check Transparency 9-4	• 5-Minute Check Transparency 9-4	• 5-Minute Check Transparency 9-4
Other	• Study Notebook • Teaching Pre-Algebra with Manipulatives	• Study Notebook • Teaching Pre-Algebra with Manipulatives	• Study Notebook	• Study Notebook • Teaching Pre-Algebra with Manipulatives

Watch Out!

Remember 2^{-3} equals $\frac{1}{2^3}$ *not* −6.

EXAMPLE 1 Write Expressions using Positive Exponents

Write each expression using a positive exponent.

a. 2^{-3}

$2^{-3} = \frac{1}{2^3}$ Definition of negative exponent

b. m^{-4}

$m^{-4} = \frac{1}{m^4}$ Definition of negative exponent

Check Your Progress

1A. 3^{-5} $\frac{1}{3^5}$ **1B.** y^{-3} $\frac{1}{y^3}$ **1C.** 2^0 1

Personal Tutor glencoe.com

EXAMPLE 2 Use Negative Exponents

Write each fraction as an expression using a negative exponent other than −1.

a. $\frac{1}{4^2}$

$\frac{1}{4^2} = 4^{-2}$ Definition of negative exponent

b. $\frac{1}{100}$

$\frac{1}{100} = \frac{1}{10^2}$ Definition of exponent

$= 10^{-2}$ Definition of negative exponent

Check Your Progress

2A. $\frac{1}{6^3}$ 6^{-3} **2B.** $\frac{1}{25}$ 5^{-2} **2C.** $\frac{1}{27}$ 3^{-3}

Personal Tutor glencoe.com

Negative exponents are often used in science when dealing with very small numbers. Usually the number is a power of 10.

Real-World Link

Geckos cannot blink because they have a transparent scale that covers each eye rather than eyelids. Most gecko species live for about three years, but some can live for up to 20 years.

Source: Wellington Zoo

Real-World EXAMPLE 3 Use Negative Exponents

REPTILES **Geckos have tiny hairs on the bottom of their feet that are about 0.000001 meter long. Write the decimal as a fraction and as a power of 10.**

$0.000001 = \frac{1}{1{,}000{,}000}$ Write the decimal as a fraction.

$= \frac{1}{10^6}$ $1{,}000{,}000 = 10^6$

$= 10^{-6}$ Definition of negative exponent

Therefore, 0.000001 is $\frac{1}{1{,}000{,}000}$ as a fraction and 10^{-6} as a power of 10.

Check Your Progress

3. FISH The slowest moving fish is a sea horse. It swims at a maximum speed of 0.0001 mile per minute. Write the decimal as a fraction and as a power of ten. $\frac{1}{10{,}000}$ or $\frac{1}{10^4}$ or 10^{-4}

Personal Tutor glencoe.com

Differentiated Instruction

students struggle with the difference between negative numbers and numbers with negative exponents,

have them write a paragraph about each of these. Check their explanations to make sure that each student has correctly described the difference.

Negative Exponents

Examples 1 and 2 show how to write expressions using positive and negative exponents. **Example 3** uses a negative exponent to solve a real-world problem.

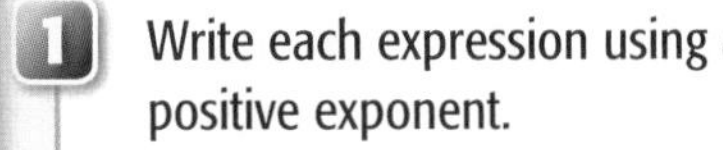

Use the Check Your Progress exercises after each example to determine students' understanding of concepts.

Additional Examples

1 Write each expression using a positive exponent.

a. 3^{-4} $\frac{1}{3^4}$

b. m^{-2} $\frac{1}{m^2}$

2 Write each fraction as an expression using a negative exponent other than −1.

a. $\frac{1}{125}$ 5^{-3}

b. $\frac{1}{8^4}$ 8^{-4}

3 **ATOM** An atom is a small unit of matter. The smallest atom has a diameter of approximately $\frac{1}{10}$ of a nanometer, or 0.0000000001 meter. Write the decimal as a fraction and as a power of 10. $\frac{1}{10{,}000{,}000{,}000}$; 10^{-10}

Additional Examples also in Interactive Classroom PowerPoint® Presentations

IWB INTERACTIVE WHITEBOARD READY

Tips for New Teachers

Say it Out Loud Remind students that saying a decimal properly will automatically name the fraction. So, 0.001 is 1 one thousandth or $\frac{1}{1000}$.

Prime Factorization Tell students that when a number is not a perfect square, use prime factorization to write the number as a power.

$\frac{1}{27} = \frac{1}{3 \cdot 3 \cdot 3} = \frac{1}{3^3} = 3^{-3}$

Evaluate Expressions

Example 4 shows how to evaluate an algebraic expression with a negative exponent.

Additional Example

4 Evaluate $16r^{-3}$ if $r = -4$. $-\frac{1}{4}$

TEACH with TECH

DOCUMENT CAMERA Choose several students to work through examples in front of the class. Have them focus on how to rewrite the expression using positive exponents. Take pictures of the work and distribute them to the class or post on the classroom Web site.

Focus on Mathematical Content

Negative Exponents In science, negative exponents are often used to express small numbers, usually as a power of 10. For example, $\frac{1}{100{,}000}$ can be written as 10^{-5}. The negative exponent indicates that the base is the denominator of a fraction. Think of a negative exponent as the reciprocal of the number expressed. For example, $5^{-4} = \frac{1}{5^4} = \frac{1}{5 \cdot 5 \cdot 5 \cdot 5} = \frac{1}{625}$

3 PRACTICE

Formative Assessment

Use Exercises 1–13 to check for understanding.

Use the chart at the bottom of this page to customize assignments for your students.

StudyTip

Order of Operations Remember to follow the order of operations when evaluating expressions.

Evaluate Expressions Algebraic expressions containing negative exponents can be written using positive exponents and then evaluated.

EXAMPLE 4 Algebraic Expressions with Negative Exponents

Evaluate $4a^{-5}$ if $a = -2$.

$4a^{-5} = 4 \cdot (-2)^{-5}$ **Replace a with -2.**

$= 4 \cdot \frac{1}{(-2)^5}$ **Definition of negative exponent**

$= 4 \cdot \frac{1}{-32}$ **Find $(-2)^5$.**

$= \overset{1}{\cancel{4}} \cdot \frac{1}{\underset{8}{\cancel{-32}}}$ **Simplify.**

$= \frac{1}{-8}$ **Simplify.**

Check Your Progress

Evaluate each expression if $m = 4$ and $n = 3$.

4A. m^{-2} $\frac{1}{16}$ **4B.** $6mn^{-4}$ $\frac{8}{27}$

Personal Tutor glencoe.com

Check Your Understanding

Example 1 p. 487 Write each expression using a positive exponent.

1. 6^{-2} $\frac{1}{6^2}$ **2.** $(-2)^{-3}$ $\frac{1}{(-2)^3}$ **3.** x^{-5} $\frac{1}{x^5}$ **4.** b^{-7} $\frac{1}{b^7}$

Example 2 p. 487 Write each fraction as an expression using a negative exponent other than −1.

5. $\frac{1}{2^6}$ 2^{-6} **6.** $\frac{1}{8^2}$ 8^{-2} **7.** $\frac{1}{9}$ 3^{-2} **8.** $\frac{1}{36}$ 6^{-2}

Example 3 p. 487 **9. BASEBALL** When a baseball is hit, it comes in contact with the bat for less than 0.001 of a second. Write 0.001 using a negative exponent other than −1. 10^{-3}

Example 4 p. 488 Evaluate each expression if $x = -4$ and $y = 2$.

10. y^{-7} $\frac{1}{128}$ **11.** x^{-3} $-\frac{1}{64}$ **12.** 3^x $\frac{1}{81}$ **13.** $8y^{-4}$ $\frac{1}{2}$

Practice and Problem Solving

= **Step-by-Step Solutions** begin on page R11. **Extra Practice** begins on page 810.

Example 1 p. 487 Write each expression using a positive exponent.

14. 11^{-6} $\frac{1}{11^6}$ **15.** 7^{-1} $\frac{1}{7^1}$ or $\frac{1}{7}$ **16.** $(-4)^{-5}$ $\frac{1}{(-4)^5}$ **17.** $(-5)^{-4}$ $\frac{1}{(-5)^4}$

18. a^{-2} $\frac{1}{a^2}$ **19.** k^{-8} $\frac{1}{k^8}$ **20.** b^{-15} $\frac{1}{b^{15}}$ **21.** r^{-20} $\frac{1}{r^{20}}$

Example 2 p. 487 Write each fraction as an expression using a negative exponent other than −1.

22. $\frac{1}{9^4}$ 9^{-4} **23.** $\frac{1}{10^3}$ 10^{-3} **24.** $\frac{1}{7^6}$ 7^{-6} **25.** $\frac{1}{6^5}$ 6^{-5}

26. $\frac{1}{4}$ 2^{-2} **27.** $\frac{1}{49}$ 7^{-2} **28.** $\frac{1}{144}$ 12^{-2} **29.** $\frac{1}{125}$ 5^{-3}

Differentiated Homework Options

Level	Assignment	Two-Day Option	
AL Basic	14–40, 51–53, 55–74	15–39 odd, 57–60	14–40 even, 51–53, 55, 56, 61–74
OL Core	15–39 odd, 41–47, 49, 51–53, 55–74	14–40, 57–60	41–53, 55, 56, 61–74
BL Advanced	41–68 (optional: 69–74)		

Example 3 p. 487

Write each decimal using a negative exponent.

30. SPACE The minimum thickness of Saturn's A ring is one tenth kilometer. **10^{-1}**

31. SCIENCE The diameter of a typical atom is 0.00000001 centimeter. **10^{-8}**

Example 4 p. 488

Evaluate each expression if $n = 3$, $p = -2$, and $q = 6$.

32. n^{-5} $\frac{1}{243}$	**33.** $(pq)^{-2}$ $\frac{1}{144}$	**34.** p^{-3} $-\frac{1}{8}$
35. $-q^{-1}$ $-\frac{1}{6}$	**36.** 9^{p} $\frac{1}{81}$	**37.** 2^{-q} $\frac{1}{64}$
38. $6n^{-3}$ $\frac{2}{9}$	**39.** $4pq^{-2}$ $-\frac{2}{9}$	**40.** $7^{p}q^{2}$ $\frac{36}{49}$

41. SCIENCE The table at the right shows the average lengths of different objects.

Object	Length (m)
pinhead	10^{-3}
cell	10^{-4}
virus	10^{-7}
atom	10^{-10}

Source: NASA

a. How many times as long is a virus than an atom? **10^3 or 1000 times**

b. About how many viruses would fit across a pinhead? **10^4 or 10,000**

c. A football field is about 10^2 meters long. How many times as long is this than a cell? **10^6 or 1,000,000 times**

42. SCIENCE The shortest period of time ever measured directly was a light burst of a laser lasting about 0.000000000000001 second. Write this decimal as a fraction and as a power of ten. **See margin.**

43. PHYSICAL SCIENCE The pH of a substance is a measure of its acidity. The pH scale ranges from 0 to 14, with a pH of 7 being neutral. As the pH decreases, the substance is more acidic. The table shows the pH of several common substances.

	Substance	pH	Hydrogen Ion Concentration
acids	coffee	5	10^{-5}
	milk	6	10^{-6}
neutral	pure water	7	10^{-7}
bases	egg whites	8	10^{-8}
	baking soda	9	10^{-9}

Source: Vision Learning

a. Which substance in the table has the greatest hydrogen ion concentration? How many times as great is that hydrogen ion concentration than that of egg whites? **coffee, 10^3 or 1000 times**

b. Which substance has a hydrogen ion concentration of *one millionth*? **milk**

c. As the pH increases by 1, describe what happens to the concentration of hydrogen ions. **It is divided by 10.**

d. How many times as great is the hydrogen ion concentration of coffee as the hydrogen ion concentration of pure water? **10^2 or 100 times**

Real-World Link

Milk is an excellent source of calcium. People ages 9–13 need about 1300 milligrams of calcium per day to strengthen bones and improve dental health.

Source: Milk Matters

44. SAND A grain of sand has a volume of about $\frac{1}{10{,}000}$ cubic millimeters.

a. Write this number using a negative exponent. **10^{-4}**

b. An empty bottle used to create sand art can hold about 10^{10} grains of sand. What is the approximate volume of the sand art bottle? **10^6mm^3**

c. If one cubic centimeter is equal to 10^3 cubic millimeters, how many cubic centimeters of sand will the bottle hold? **10^3cm^3**

Additional Answer

42. $\frac{1}{10^{15}}$ or $\frac{1}{1{,}000{,}000{,}000{,}000{,}000}$; 10^{-15}

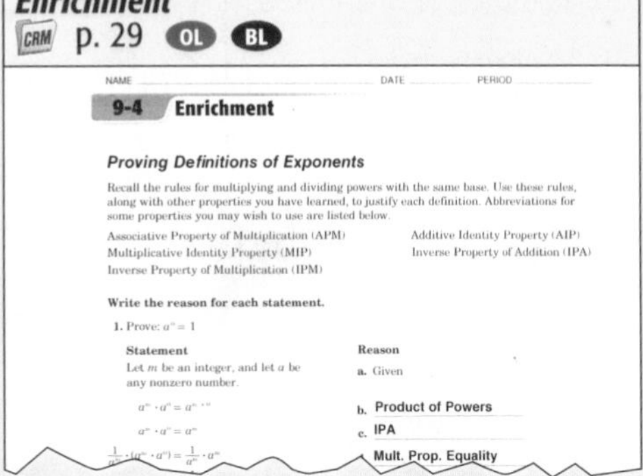

Enrichment
CRM p. 29 OL BL

NAME ______ DATE ______ PERIOD ______

9-4 Enrichment

Proving Definitions of Exponents

Recall the rules for multiplying and dividing powers with the same base. Use these rules, along with other properties you have learned, to justify each definition. Abbreviations for some properties you may wish to use are listed below.

Associative Property of Multiplication (APM)
Multiplicative Identity Property (MIP)
Inverse Property of Multiplication (IPM)
Additive Identity Property (AIP)
Inverse Property of Addition (IPA)

Write the reason for each statement.

1. Prove: $a^0 = 1$

Statement	Reason
Let *m* be an integer, and let *a* be any nonzero number.	a. Given
$a^m \cdot a^0 = a^{m+0}$	b. **Product of Powers**
$a^m \cdot a^0 = a^m$	c. **IPA**
$\frac{1}{a^m} \cdot (a^m \cdot a^0) = \frac{1}{a^m} \cdot a^m$	**Mult. Prop. Equality**

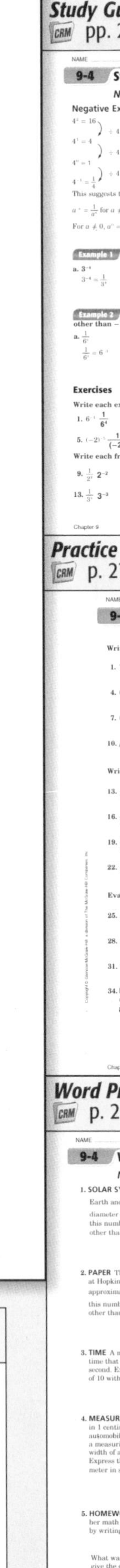

Study Guide and Intervention
CRM pp. 24–25 AL OL ELL

NAME ______ DATE ______ PERIOD ______

9-4 Study Guide and Intervention

Negative Exponents

Negative Exponents Extending the pattern below shows that $4^{-1} = \frac{1}{4}$ or $\frac{1}{4^1}$.

$4^2 = 16$
÷ 4
$4^1 = 4$
÷ 4
$4^0 = 1$
÷ 4
$4^{-1} = \frac{1}{4}$

This suggests the following definition.

$a^{-n} = \frac{1}{a^n}$ for $a \neq 0$ and any whole number *n*. Example: $6^{-4} = \frac{1}{6^4}$

For $a \neq 0$, $a^0 = 1$. Example: $9^0 = 1$

Example 1 Write each expression using a positive exponent.

a. 3^{-4}
$3^{-4} = \frac{1}{3^4}$ Definition of negative exponent

b. y^{-2}
$y^{-2} = \frac{1}{y^2}$ Definition of negative exponent

Example 2 Write each fraction as an expression using a negative exponent other than −1.

a. $\frac{1}{6^1}$
$\frac{1}{6^1} = 6^{-1}$ Definition of negative exponent

b. $\frac{1}{81}$
$\frac{1}{81} = \frac{1}{9^2}$ Definition of exponent
$= 9^{-2}$ Definition of negative exponent

Exercises

Write each expression using a positive exponent.

1. 6^{-4} $\frac{1}{6^4}$ 2. $(-7)^{-8}$ $\frac{1}{(-7)^8}$ 3. b^{-6} $\frac{1}{b^6}$ 4. n^{-1} $\frac{1}{n^1}$ or $\frac{1}{n}$

5. $(-2)^{-5}$ $\frac{1}{(-2)^5}$ 6. 10^{-3} $\frac{1}{10^3}$ 7. j^{-9} $\frac{1}{j^9}$ 8. a^{-2} $\frac{1}{a^2}$

Write each fraction as an expression using a negative exponent other than −1.

9. $\frac{1}{2^2}$ 2^{-2} 10. $\frac{1}{13^4}$ 13^{-4} 11. $\frac{1}{25}$ 5^{-2} 12. $\frac{1}{49}$ 7^{-2}

13. $\frac{1}{3^3}$ 3^{-3} 14. $\frac{1}{9^2}$ 9^{-2} 15. $\frac{1}{121}$ 11^{-2} 16. $\frac{1}{27}$ 3^{-3}

Chapter 9 24 *Glencoe Pre-Algebra*

Practice
CRM p. 27 AL OL BL ELL

NAME ______ DATE ______ PERIOD ______

9-4 Practice

Negative Exponents

Write each expression using a positive exponent.

1. 7^{-8} $\frac{1}{7^8}$ 2. 10^{-6} $\frac{1}{10^6}$ 3. 23^{-1} $\frac{1}{23^1}$

4. $(-5)^{-2}$ $\frac{1}{(-5)^2}$ 5. $(-18)^{-10}$ $\frac{1}{(-18)^{10}}$ 6. m^{-99} $\frac{1}{m^{99}}$

7. $(-1)^{-12}$ $\frac{1}{(-1)^{12}}$ 8. c^{-6} $\frac{1}{c^6}$ 9. p^{-5} $\frac{1}{p^5}$

10. g^{-17} $\frac{1}{g^{17}}$ 11. $5z^{-4}$ $5\left(\frac{1}{z^4}\right)$ 12. $3t^{-1}$ $3\left(\frac{1}{t}\right)$

Write each fraction as an expression using a negative exponent.

13. $\frac{1}{2^{10}}$ 2^{-10} 14. $\frac{1}{29^3}$ 29^{-3} 15. $\frac{1}{4^4}$ 4^{-4}

16. $\frac{1}{39}$ 39^{-1} 17. $\frac{1}{81^7}$ 81^{-7} 18. $\frac{1}{m^4}$ m^{-4}

19. $\frac{1}{x^3}$ x^{-3} 20. $\frac{1}{a^2}$ a^{-2} 21. $\frac{1}{49}$ 7^{-2}

22. $\frac{1}{8}$ 2^{-3} 23. $\frac{1}{144}$ 12^{-2} 24. $\frac{1}{169}$ 13^{-2}

Evaluate each expression if $x = 3$, $y = -2$, and $z = 4$.

25. x^{-4} $\frac{1}{81}$ 26. y^{-2} $\frac{1}{4}$ 27. y^{-5} $-\frac{1}{32}$

28. z^{-4} $\frac{1}{256}$ 29. 5^{y} $\frac{1}{25}$ 30. 10^{y} $\frac{1}{100}$

31. $3z^{-1}$ $\frac{3}{4}$ 32. z^{y} $\frac{1}{16}$ 33. $(xz)^{-2}$ $\frac{1}{144}$

34. **HAIR** Hair grows at a rate of $\frac{1}{64}$ inch per day. Write this number using negative exponents. **8^{-2} or 4^{-3} or 2^{-6}**

Chapter 9 27 *Glencoe Pre-Algebra*

Word Problem Practice
CRM p. 28 AL OL BL

NAME ______ DATE ______ PERIOD ______

9-4 Word Problem Practice

Negative Exponents

1. **SOLAR SYSTEM** The distance between Earth and the Sun is about $\frac{1}{100{,}000}$ the diameter of the solar system. Express this number using a negative exponent other than −1. **10^{-5}**

2. **PAPER** The paper used by the students at Hopkins Middle School is approximately $\frac{1}{216}$ inch thick. Express this number using a negative exponent other than −1. **6^{-3}**

3. **TIME** A microsecond is a measure of time that is equal to one millionth of a second. Express this number as a power of 10 with a negative exponent. **10^{-6}**

4. **MEASUREMENT** There are 10^{-2} meters in 1 centimeter. At the site of an automobile accident, a state trooper uses a measuring tape to determine that the width of a tire track is 20 centimeters. Express this number as a fraction of a meter in simplest form. **$\frac{20}{100} = \frac{1}{5}$ m**

5. **HOMEWORK** As Libby was working on her math homework, she computed 2^{-3} by writing the following equation.

$2^{-3} = -8$

What was Libby's error? Explain. Then give the correct answer. **$2^{-3} = 0.125$; Sample answer: Libby took the opposite of 2^3 instead of taking the reciprocal of 2^3**

6. **INSECTS** Kevin's father is an entomologist. He studies insects. The table below shows the mass of four common insects.

Insect	Mass (g)
Honeybee	8^{-2}
Ant	16^{-2}
Housefly	9^{-2}
Moth	4.5^{-2}

a. Determine which of these insects weighs the most by first expressing each of the masses in decimal form. Round your answers to the nearest thousandth. **honeybee: 0.016 g; ant: 0.004 g; housefly: 0.012 g; moth: 0.049 g; The moth is the heaviest.**

b. How many times heavier is the heaviest insect than the lightest insect? Round your answer to the nearest tenth. **The moth is 12.6 times heavier than the ant.**

c. What percent greater than a housefly's mass is the mass of a honeybee? Round your answer to the nearest tenth. **26.6%**

d. It is estimated that an ant can lift approximately 20 times its own body mass. How many grams can the average ant lift? Write your answer as a fraction in simplest form. **$\frac{20}{16^{-2}} = \frac{5}{64}$ g**

Chapter 9 28 *Glencoe Pre-Algebra*

Lesson 9-4

Watch Out!

Find the Error For Exercise 52, remind students to first rewrite the expression using the definition of a negative exponent. Remember that the exponent only goes with the numbers it is next to.

Additional Answers

45a.

Power	Fraction	Decimal
10^{-1}	$\frac{1}{10}$	0.1
10^{-2}	$\frac{1}{100}$	0.01
10^{-3}	$\frac{1}{1000}$	0.001
10^{-4}	$\frac{1}{10000}$	0.0001
10^{-5}	$\frac{1}{100000}$	0.00001

45b. yes; Sample answer: As the exponents decrease, the number of zeros in the decimal places increase.

45c. Sample answer: The number of zeros in the decimal equivalent is equal to one less than the absolute value of the negative exponent. For example, $10^{-3} = 0.001$.

45d. $10^{-12} = 0.000000000001$

47. a^{-6} or $\frac{1}{a^6}$

48. n^{-6} or $\frac{1}{n^6}$

49. $x^{-1}y^2$ or $\frac{y^2}{x}$

50. $7b^{-4}c^8$ or $\frac{7c^8}{b^4}$

52. Jeannette; Mahala did not follow the order of operations. She multiplied the whole numbers first. She should have first performed the operation with the exponent and then multiplied.

54. They are multiplicative inverses. Sample answer: 2^{-4} and 2^4 are multiplicative inverses because $2^{-4} = \frac{1}{2^4}$, and $\frac{1}{2^4} \cdot \frac{2^4}{1} = 1$.

55. Sample answer: If $n = 3$, $\frac{1}{2^n} = \frac{1}{2^3}$ or $\frac{1}{8}$. If $n = 4$, $\frac{1}{2^n} = \frac{1}{2^4}$ or $\frac{1}{16}$. So, as the value of n increases, the value of $\frac{1}{2^n}$ decreases.

56. Sample answer: $(-3)^4$ is the same as $(-3)(-3)(-3)(-3)$ or 81. 3^{-4} is the same as $\frac{1}{3^4}$ or $\frac{1}{81}$.

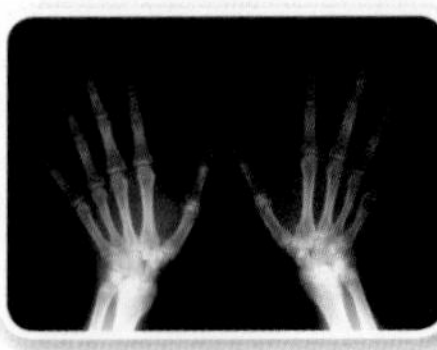

Real-World Link

The wavelengths of X-rays are between 1 and 10 nanometers.

Source: *Biology*, Raven

45. **MULTIPLE REPRESENTATIONS** In this problem, you will explore negative exponents. When using powers of 10, $10^{-1} = \frac{1}{10}$ or 0.1. **a–d. See margin.**

a. TABULAR Copy and complete the table shown.

Power	Fraction	Decimal
10^{-1}	$\frac{1}{10}$	0.1
10^{-2}	■	■
10^{-3}	■	■
10^{-4}	■	■
10^{-5}	■	■

b. VERBAL Do you notice a pattern between the negative powers of 10 and their decimal equivalents? Explain.

c. VERBAL Write a verbal rule that could be used to find the decimal equivalent of any negative power of 10.

d. NUMERICAL Use the rule from part **c** to find the value of 10^{-12}.

46. **SCIENCE** A nanometer is equal to a billionth of a meter. Use the information at the left to express the greatest wavelength of an X-ray in meters. Write the expression using a negative exponent. **10^{-8}m**

C Use the Product of Powers and Quotient of Powers rules to simplify each expression. **47–50. See margin.**

47. $a^3 \div a^9$ **48.** $n^{-4} \cdot n^{-2}$ **49** $\frac{x^{-3}y^4}{x^{-2}y^2}$ **50.** $\frac{28b^4c^3}{4b^8c^{-5}}$

H.O.T. Problems Use Higher-Order Thinking Skills

51. **OPEN ENDED** Write a power that has a negative exponent and show the steps you take to write the power as a fraction.

52. **FIND THE ERROR** Jeannette and Mahala are evaluating the expression $2 \cdot 4^{-2}$. Is either of them correct? Explain your reasoning. **See margin.**

Jeannette	Mahala
$2 \cdot 4^{-2} = 2 \cdot \frac{1}{16}$ $= \frac{2}{16}$ or $\frac{1}{8}$	$2 \cdot 4^{-2} = (2 \cdot 4)^{-2}$ $= 8^{-2}$ or $\frac{1}{64}$

53. **REASONING** Consider the following sets of numbers:

Set 1: $2^{-2}, (-2)^{-2}, (-2)^2, 2^2$

Set 2: $2^{-3}, (-2)^{-3}, (-2)^3, 2^3$

a. Simplify each expression in Set 1. Which expressions, if any, are equal?

b. Simplify each expression in Set 2. Which expressions, if any, are equal?

c. Explain why the number of equal expressions is different for each list.

d. Finish the conjecture: $2^{-x} = (-2)^{-x}$, if and only if ____. **x is an even number**

e. Finish the conjecture: $(-2)^x = 2^x$, if and only if ____. **x is an even number**

54. **CHALLENGE** Compare and contrast x^{-n} and x^n where $x \neq 0$. Then give a numerical example to show the relationship.

55. **REASONING** Investigate the fraction $\frac{1}{2^n}$. Does it increase or decrease as the value of n increases? Explain.

56. **WRITING IN MATH** Explain the difference between the expressions $(-3)^4$ and 3^{-4}.

51. Sample answer: $5^{-2} = \frac{1}{5^2} = \frac{1}{5 \cdot 5} = \frac{1}{25}$

53a. $2^{-2} = \frac{1}{4}$, $(-2)^{-2} = \frac{1}{4}$, $(-2)^2 = 4$, $2^2 = 4$; $2^{-2} = (-2)^{-2}$ and $(-2)^2 = 2^2$

53b. $2^{-3} = \frac{1}{8}$, $(-2)^{-3} = -\frac{1}{8}$, $(-2)^3 = -8$, $2^3 = 8$, none of the expressions are equal

53c. Sample answer: When you square either a positive or a negative value, the answer is positive. When you cube a positive value, you get a positive and when you cube a negative value, you get a negative.

54–56. See margin.

Multiple Representations In Exercise 45, students use a table of values and verbal analysis to relate fractions, decimals, and negative powers of 10.

Standardized Test Practice

57. DNA contains the genetic code of an organism. The length of a DNA strand is about 10^{-7} meter. Which of the following represents the length of the DNA strand as a decimal? **C**

A 0.00001 m
B 0.000001 m
C 0.0000001 m
D 0.00000001 m

58. When simplified, 2^{-5} is equal to which of the following? **H**

F −32
G $-\frac{1}{32}$
H $\frac{1}{32}$
J 32

59. Which of the following shows the expressions $4^0, 4^{-2}, 4^2$, and 4^{-3} in order from least to greatest? **D**

A $4^{-3}, 4^{-2}, 4^2, 4^0$
B $4^0, 4^{-2}, 4^{-3}, 4^2$
C $4^2, 4^0, 4^{-2}, 4^{-3}$
D $4^{-3}, 4^{-2}, 4^0, 4^2$

60. SHORT RESPONSE It takes light 5.3 × 0.000001 seconds to travel one mile. Write 0.000001 as a fraction and as a power of 10. **$\frac{1}{10^6}$ or $\frac{1}{1,000,000}$; 10^{-6}**

Spiral Review

61. ARTS AND CRAFTS When a piece of paper is cut in half, the result is two smaller pieces of paper. When the two smaller pieces are stacked and then cut, the result is four pieces of paper. The number of resulting sheets of paper after c cuts is 2^c. (Lesson 9-3)

a. How many more pieces of paper are there if a piece of paper is cut and stacked 8 times than when a piece of paper is cut and stacked 5 times? **224 pieces**

b. A stack of 500 sheets of notebook paper is about 1 inch thick. How thick would your stack be if you were able to make 10 cuts? **1024 in. or $85\frac{1}{3}$ ft**

ALGEBRA Factor each monomial. (Lesson 9-2)

62. $-105x^2yz^5$ **$-1 \cdot 3 \cdot 5 \cdot 7 \cdot x \cdot x \cdot y \cdot z \cdot z \cdot z \cdot z \cdot z$**

63. $-r^2st$ **$-1 \cdot r \cdot r \cdot s \cdot t$**

64. $53fg$ **$53 \cdot f \cdot g$**

State the slope and y-intercept of each equation. (Lesson 8-7)

65. $2x + y = -3$ **−2; −3**

66. $5x + 4y = 20$ **$-\frac{5}{4}$; 5**

67. $y = 4$ **0; 4**

68. FOOD The results of a survey about favorite hamburger condiments are shown in the table at the right. Which condiment was chosen by the most people? Explain. (Lesson 7-1) **See margin.**

Hamburger Condiment	
Condiment	**Part**
mustard	22%
ketchup	$\frac{2}{5}$
relish	0.2

Skills Review

Find each product. (Lesson 3-3)

69. 25 × 0.001 **0.025**

70. 107 × 0.0001 **0.0107**

71. 3.8 × 0.01 **0.038**

72. 18 × 100 **1800**

73. 76 × 1000 **76,000**

74. 134 × 100,000 **13,400,000**

4 ASSESS

Ticket Out the Door Have students simplify $2x^{-2} \cdot 3x$. Then evaluate the expression if $x = 3$. They are to write both answers on a small piece of paper and hand it to you. $\frac{6}{x}$; 2

Additional Answer

68. Since $\frac{2}{5} = 40\%$, $\frac{2}{10} = \frac{1}{5} = 20\%$, and 40% is greater than 22% and 20%, the group that said they prefer ketchup is largest.

Differentiated Instruction

BL

Extension Have students write the fraction and then the equivalent power of 2 using negative exponents for the shaded part of each figure.
$\frac{1}{2}, \frac{1}{4}, \frac{1}{8}, \frac{1}{16}$; $2^{-1}, 2^{-2}, 2^{-3}, 2^{-4}$

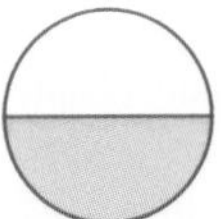
Figure 1

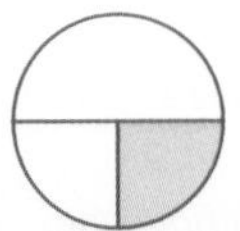
Figure 2

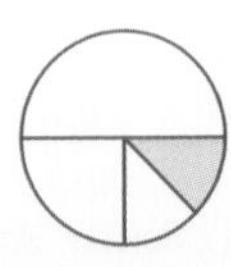
Figure 3

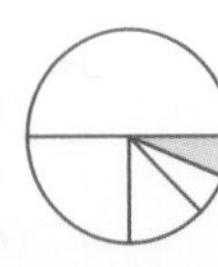
Figure 4

CHAPTER 9 Mid-Chapter Quiz

Formative Assessment

Use the Mid-Chapter Quiz to assess students' progress in the first half of the chapter.

For problems answered incorrectly, have students review the lessons indicated in parentheses.

ExamView Assessment Suite Customize and create multiple versions of your Mid-Chapter Quiz and their answer keys.

FOLDABLES Follow-Up

Before students complete the Mid-Chapter Quiz, encourage them to review the information for Lessons 9-1 through 9-4 in their Foldables.

Additional Answer

29. $\frac{1}{10{,}000{,}000{,}000}$ m; one ten billionth meter

CHAPTER 9 Mid-Chapter Quiz

Lessons 9-1 through 9-4

Write each expression using exponents. (Lesson 9-1)

1. $8 \cdot n \cdot n \cdot n$ **$8n^3$**
2. $(x-1)(x-1)$ **$(x-1)^2$**

Evaluate each expression. (Lesson 9-1)

3. 6^3 **216**
4. $2^5 \cdot 3$ **96**
5. $3^4 \cdot 5$ **405**
6. $4^3 \cdot 2^2 \cdot 3$ **768**

7. **MULTIPLE CHOICE** The number of acres consumed by a forest fire triples every two hours. Which of the following expressions represents the number of acres consumed after 1 day? (Lesson 9-1) **B**

Hours	2	4	6	8	10
Acres Consumed	3^1	3^2	3^3	3^4	3^5

A 3^{10} acres
C 3^{18} acres
B 3^{12} acres
D 3^{24} acres

Evaluate each expression if $x = -3$. (Lesson 9-1)

8. $x^3 - 4$ **−31**
9. $6(x+1)^2$ **24**

Write the prime factorization of each number. Use exponents for repeated factors. (Lesson 9-2)

10. 42 **$2 \cdot 3 \cdot 7$**
11. 99 **$3^2 \cdot 11$**
12. 64 **2^6**

13. **MULTIPLE CHOICE** The kitchen floor shown is to be tiled.

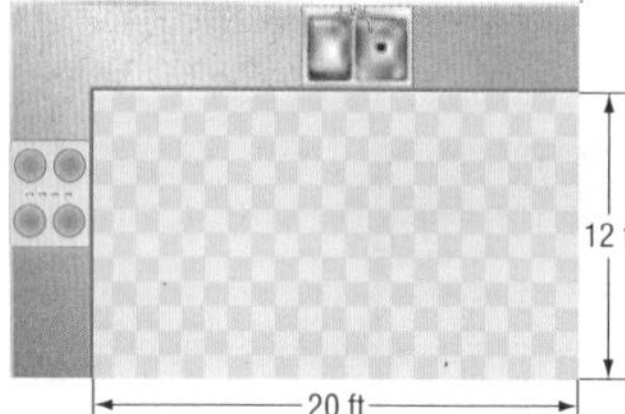

If the tiles are only available in dimensions that are prime numbers, which set of tile dimensions could *not* be used to tile the floor? (Lesson 9-2) **J**

F 2 ft by 2 ft
H 2 ft by 5 ft
G 2 ft by 3 ft
J 3 ft by 3 ft

ALGEBRA Factor each monomial. (Lesson 9-2)

14. $7a^3$ **$7 \cdot a \cdot a \cdot a$**
15. $-12xy^2$ **$-1 \cdot 2 \cdot 2 \cdot 3 \cdot x \cdot y \cdot y$**

Find each product or quotient. Express using exponents. (Lesson 9-3)

16. $8^4 \cdot 8^5$ **8^9**
17. $c^2 \cdot c^6$ **c^8**
18. $\frac{5^9}{5^3}$ **5^6**
19. $\frac{x^7}{x^2}$ **x^5**
20. $(3n)(6n^2)$ **$18n^3$**
21. $2y^3 \cdot 7y^3$ **$14y^6$**

22. **TRAVEL** The table compares the number of people in Wyoming who drive to work to the number of people who walk to work in a recent year. How many times as many people drive than walk to work? (Lesson 9-3) **10^2 or 100 times more**

Mode of Transportation	Number of People
drove	10^5
walked	10^3

Source: U.S. Census Bureau

Write each expression using a positive exponent. (Lesson 9-4)

23. 2^{-5} **$\frac{1}{2^5}$**
24. $(-6)^{-2}$ **$\frac{1}{(-6)^2}$**
25. q^{-11} **$\frac{1}{q^{11}}$**

Write each fraction as an expression using a negative exponent other than −1. (Lesson 9-4)

26. $\frac{1}{5^3}$ **5^{-3}**
27. $\frac{1}{9}$ **3^{-2}**
28. $\frac{1}{16}$ **2^{-4} or 4^{-2}**

For Exercises 29 and 30, use the table that shows wavelengths. (Lesson 9-4)

Wave	Wavelength (m)
radio waves	10^0
microwaves	10^{-2}
X-rays	10^{-10}

Source: NASA

29. Write the wavelength of an X-ray as a fraction without an exponent and in words. **See margin.**
30. How many times as long is the wavelength of a radio wave as that of a microwave? **10^2 or 100 times**

Evaluate each expression if $a = -3$ and $b = 5$. (Lesson 9-4)

31. b^{-2} **$\frac{1}{25}$**
32. a^{-4} **$\frac{1}{81}$**
33. 6^a **$\frac{1}{216}$**

Intervention Planner

Tier 1 On Level	Tier 2 Strategic Intervention approaching grade level	Tier 3 Intensive Intervention 2 or more grades below level
If students miss about 25% of the exercises or less,	**If** students miss about 50% of the exercises,	**If** students miss about 75% of the exercises,
Then choose a resource:	**Then** choose a resource:	**Then** use *Math Triumphs, Grade 8*, Ch. 2, 6
SE Lessons 9-1 through 9-4 **CRM** Skills Practice, pp. 7, 14, 20, 26 **TE** Chapter Project, p. 468	**CRM** Study Guide and Intervention, Chapter 9, pp. 5, 12, 18, 24 *Quick Review Math Handbook*	
Math Online Self-Check Quiz	**Math Online** Extra Examples, Personal Tutor, Homework Help	**Math Online** Extra Examples, Personal Tutor, Homework Help, Review Vocabulary

9-5 Scientific Notation

Why?

The width of Earth is 12.76 million meters. The width of a plant cell is a trillion times smaller with a width of 12.76 millionths of a meter.

a. Write 12.76 million in numbers. **12,760,000**

b. Write 12.76 millionths as a decimal. **0.00001276**

Then
You have already compared and ordered integers. (Lesson 2-1)

Now
- Express numbers in standard form and in scientific notation.
- Compare and order numbers written in scientific notation.

New Vocabulary
standard form
scientific notation

Math Online
glencoe.com
- Extra Examples
- Personal Tutor
- Self-Check Quiz
- Homework Help

Scientific Notation Numbers that do not contain exponents are written in **standard form**. However, when you deal with very large numbers like 12,760,000 or very small numbers like 0.00001276 it is difficult to keep track of the place value. A number that is expressed as a product of a factor and a power of 10 is written in **scientific notation**.

Key Concept — Scientific Notation (For Your FOLDABLE)

Words A number is expressed in scientific notation when it is written as the product of a factor and a power of 10. The factor must be greater than or equal to 1 and less than 10.

Symbols $a \times 10^n$, where $1 \leq a < 10$ and n is an integer.

Examples $3{,}500{,}000 = 3.5 \times 10^6$

$0.00004 = 4 \times 10^{-5}$

left → positive
right → negative

EXAMPLE 1 Express Numbers in Standard Form

Express each number in standard form.

a. 2×10^3

$2 \times 10^3 = 2 \times 1000$ — $10^3 = 1000$

$= 2000$ — Move the decimal point 3 places to the right.

b. 6.8×10^5

$6.8 \times 10^5 = 6.8 \times 100{,}000$ — $10^5 = 100{,}000$

$= 680{,}000$ — Move the decimal point 5 places to the right.

c. 3.25×10^{-4}

$3.25 \times 10^{-4} = 3.25 \times 0.0001$ — $10^{-4} = 0.0001$

$= 0.000325$ — Move the decimal point 4 places to the left.

StudyTip
Powers of Ten The exponent tells you how many places to move the decimal point.

Check Your Progress

1A. 4×10^2 **400** **1B.** 5.94×10^7 **59,400,000** **1C.** 1.3×10^{-3} **0.0013**

Personal Tutor glencoe.com

9-5 Lesson Notes

1 FOCUS

Vertical Alignment

Before Lesson 9-5
Compare and order integers.

Lessson 9-5
Express numbers in standard form and in scientific notation.
Compare and order numbers written in scientific notation.

After Lesson 9-5
Solve problems involving scientific notation.

2 TEACH

Scaffolding Questions

Have students read the *Why?* section of the lesson and answer the questions.

Ask:
- If $1.276 \times 10^3 = 1276$, express 1.276×10^6 as a whole number. 1,276,000
- If $1.276 \times 10^{-3} = 0.001276$, express 1.276×10^{-5} as a decimal. 0.00001276
- What does the exponent tell you? how many places to move the decimal point either right or left

Lesson 9-5 Resources

Resource	Approaching-Level	On-Level	Beyond-Level	English Learners
Teacher Edition	• Differentiated Instruction, p. 494	• Differentiated Instruction, p. 494	• Differentiated Instruction, pp. 494, 498	
Chapter Resource Masters	• Study Guide and Intervention, pp. 30–31 • Skills Practice, p. 32 • Practice, p. 33 • Word Problem Practice, p. 34	• Study Guide and Intervention, pp. 30–31 • Skills Practice, p. 32 • Practice, p. 33 • Word Problem Practice, p. 34 • Enrichment, p. 35	• Practice, p. 33 • Word Problem Practice, p. 34 • Enrichment, p. 35	• Study Guide and Intervention, pp. 30–31 • Skills Practice, p. 32 • Practice, p. 33
Transparencies	• 5-Minute Check Transparency 9-5	• 5-Minute Check Transparency 9-5	• 5-Minute Check Transparency 9-5	• 5-Minute Check Transparency 9-5
Other	• Study Notebook • Teaching Pre-Algebra with Manipulatives	• Study Notebook • Teaching Pre-Algebra with Manipulatives	• Study Notebook	• Study Notebook • Teaching Pre-Algebra with Manipulatives

Scientific Notation

Examples 1 and 2 show how to express numbers in standard and scientific notation. **Example 3** shows how to solve problems using scientific notation.

Formative Assessment

Use the Check Your Progress exercises after each example to determine students' understanding of concepts.

Additional Examples

1 Express each number in standard form.

a. 3×10^5 300,000

b. 4.395×10^4 43,950

c. 6.79×10^{-6} 0.00000679

2 Express each number in scientific notation.

a. 800,000 8×10^5

b. 64,000 6.4×10^4

c. 0.0119 1.19×10^{-2}

3 **DIMES** A dime is 1.35×10^{-3} meters thick. What would the height of a stack of one million dimes be in scientific notation? 1.35×10^3 m

Additional Examples also in Interactive Classroom PowerPoint® Presentations

IWB INTERACTIVE WHITEBOARD READY

TEACH with TECH

INTERACTIVE WHITEBOARD Write a very large or very small number in standard form on the board. Make the decimal point a separate graphic from the digits in the number. Grab the decimal point and drag it to the left or right as you count the number of places you have moved it.

StudyTip

Sign of Exponents
- If a number in standard form is greater than or equal to 1, then the exponent is *positive*.
- If a number is between 0 and 1, the exponent is *negative*.

EXAMPLE 2 Express Numbers in Scientific Notation

Express each number in scientific notation.

a. 4,000,000

$4{,}000{,}000 = 4 \times 1{,}000{,}000$ — **The decimal point moves 6 places.**

$= 4 \times 10^6$ — **The exponent is positive.**

b. 5800

$5800 = 5.8 \times 1000$ — **The decimal point moves 3 places.**

$= 5.8 \times 10^3$ — **The exponent is positive.**

c. 0.072

$0.072 = 7.2 \times 0.01$ — **The decimal point moves 2 places.**

$= 7.2 \times 10^{-2}$ — **The exponent is negative.**

Check Your Progress

2A. 900 9×10^2 **2B.** 18,900 1.89×10^4 **2C.** 0.000064 6.4×10^{-5}

Personal Tutor glencoe.com

Real-World Link

The Amazon Rainforest includes areas in Brazil, Venezuela, Colombia, Ecuador, and Peru. More than 20 percent of the world's oxygen is produced in this rain forest. More than half of the world's estimated 10 million species of plants, animals, and insects live in the tropical rain forests.

Source: Raintree Nutrition

Real-World EXAMPLE 3 Solve Problems using Scientific Notation

RAINFOREST Scientists estimate that there are over 3.5×10^6 ants per acre in the Amazon Rainforest. If the Amazon Rainforest covers approximately 1 billion acres, find the total number of ants. Write in scientific notation.

Understand You know there are about 3.5×10^6 ants per acre and there are about 1 billion acres. You need to know the total number of ants.

Plan Write 1 billion in scientific notation. Multiply the number of ants per acre by the number of acres to find the total number of ants.

Solve 1 billion $= 1 \times 10^9$

total number of ants = number per acre × number of acres

$= (3.5 \times 10^6) \times (1 \times 10^9)$

You can use a calculator to find the product.

3.5 [2nd] [EE] 6 [X] 1 [2nd] [EE] 9 [ENTER] 3.5E15

So, there are about 3.5×10^{15} ants in the Amazon Rainforest.

Check Check using mental math.

$(3.5 \times 10^6)(1 \times 10^9)$

$= (3.5 \times 1)(10^6 \times 10^9)$ — **Commutative Property**

$= 3.5 \times 10^{15}$ ✓ — **Product of Powers Property**

Check Your Progress

3. INSECTS About 1×10^6 fruit flies weigh 1.3×10^2 pounds. How much does one fruit fly weigh? Write in scientific notation. about 1.3×10^{-4} lb

Personal Tutor glencoe.com

Differentiated Instruction

If students need some extra practice writing numbers in scientific notation or are interested in real-world applications of scientific notation,

Then have students research the sizes of very small or very large quantities in science. Have them illustrate these and write the quantities in scientific notation.

Compare and Order Numbers To compare and order numbers in scientific notation, first compare the exponents. With positive numbers, the number with a greater exponent is greater. If the exponents are the same, compare the factors.

Real-World EXAMPLE 4 Order Numbers in Scientific Notation

EARTH SCIENCE The table shows different geologic time periods. Order the time periods from oldest to youngest.

Geologic Time Periods	
Period	Number of Years Ago
Jurassic	2.08×10^8
Silurian	4.38×10^8
Tertiary	6.64×10^7
Triassic	2.45×10^8

Source: U.S. Geological Survey

Step 1 Order the numbers according to their exponents.

The Tertiary period has an exponent of 7. So, it is the youngest period.

Step 2 Order the numbers with the same exponent by comparing the factors.

$$4.38 > 2.45 > 2.08$$

Silurian ↓ Triassic ↓ Jurassic ↓

So, $4.38 \times 10^8 > 2.45 \times 10^8 > 2.08 \times 10^8$.

The time periods ordered from oldest to youngest is Silurian, Triassic, Jurassic, and Tertiary.

Check Your Progress

4. **EARTH SCIENCE** Approximately 1.372×10^7 square kilometers of Antarctica and about 1.834×10^6 square kilometers of Greenland are covered by an ice cap. Which land mass has a greater area covered by ice? **Antarctica**

Personal Tutor glencoe.com

Check Your Understanding

Example 1 p. 493 — **Express each number in standard form.**

1. 4.16×10^3 **4160** **2.** 3.2×10^{-2} **0.032** **3.** 1.075×10^5 **107,500**

Example 2 p. 494 — **Express each number in scientific notation.**

4. 1,600,000 $\mathbf{1.6 \times 10^6}$ **5.** 135,000 $\mathbf{1.35 \times 10^5}$ **6.** 0.008 $\mathbf{8 \times 10^{-3}}$

Example 3 p. 494

7. **ROADS** The U.S. has the most miles of road in the world at about 4×10^6 miles. Japan has about 7.3×10^5 miles. How many more miles of roads does the U.S. have than Japan? Write in scientific notation. $\mathbf{3.27 \times 10^6}$ **mi**

Example 4 p. 495 — **Order each set of numbers from least to greatest.**

8. 3.4×10^2, 3.5×10^2, 3.7×10^{-2}, 400 $\mathbf{3.7 \times 10^{-2}, 3.4 \times 10^2, 3.5 \times 10^2, 400}$

9. 6.5×10^3, 6.12×10^5, 6.01×10^4, 6.1×10^{-2} $\mathbf{6.1 \times 10^{-2}, 6.5 \times 10^3, 6.01 \times 10^4, 6.12 \times 10^5}$

Tips for New Teachers

Reading Scientific Notation Tell students that 3.25×10^{-4} is read as *three point twenty-five times ten to the negative four.*

Focus on Mathematical Content

Scientific Notation In science there are very large numbers, such as the speed of light, and very small numbers, such as the mass of an atom. Scientific notation is a concise way of expressing these numbers. Large numbers are expressed using powers of 10 with positive exponents. Small numbers are expressed using powers of 10 with negative exponents.

Compare and Order Numbers

Example 4 shows how to order numbers in scientific notation.

Additional Example

4 **SPACE** The diameters of Neptune, Saturn, and Uranus, are 4.9×10^4 km, 1.2×10^5 km, and 5.1×10^4 km, respectively. Order the planets from greatest to least diameter. Saturn, Uranus, Neptune

3 PRACTICE

Formative Assessment

Use Exercises 1–9 to check for understanding.

Use the chart at the bottom of the next page to customize assignments for your students.

Watch Out!

Preventing Errors Discuss the following with students prior to the exercises. When multiplying by 10^x and $x > 0$, move the decimal point to the right. When $x < 0$, move the decimal point to the left. Tell students when the inequality sign points to the right to move the decimal right. When the inequality sign points to the left, move the decimal to the left.

Additional Answers

25. 2.4×10^{-2}, 2.45×10^{-2}, 2.4×10^2, 2.45×10^2

26. 3.024×10^2, 2805, 2.81×10^4, 3.2×10^4, 2.08×10^5

27. 5.1×10^{-3}, 5.9×10^4, 5.01×10^5, 5.9×10^6

28. 9.05×10^{-6}, 905,000, 9.5×10^6, 9,562,301

30. New Hampshire, Wisconsin, New York, Maine, Vermont

43. Sample answer: 2×10^2 and 4×10^3; sum: 4.2×10^3; difference: -3.8×10^3; product: 8×10^5; quotient: 5×10^{-2}

45a. 3.8×10^6; 3.8×10^4 is only about 40,000 people, which is not very many for the second largest city in Florida

45b. Sample answer: 3,800,000 or 3.8 million

45c. Sample answer: 3.8 million is easier to read and understand than the standard form (3,800,000) or scientific notation (3.8×10^6) of the number.

Practice and Problem Solving

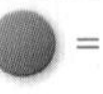 = **Step-by-Step Solutions** begin on page R11. **Extra Practice** begins on page 810.

Example 1 p. 493 — **Express each number in standard form.**

10. 6.89×10^4 **68,900** **11.** 1.5×10^{-4} **0.00015** **12.** 2.3×10^{-5} **0.000023**

13. 9.51×10^{-3} **0.00951** **14.** 3.062×10^6 **3,062,000** **15.** 7.924×10^2 **792.4**

16. MONEY A dollar bill is approximately 1.09×10^{-2} centimeter thick. **0.0109**

17. E-MAILS It is estimated that more than 1.71×10^4 billion e-mails are sent each day around the world. Most of these are spam and viruses. **171,000,000,000**

Example 2 p. 494 — **Express each number in scientific notation.**

18. 700,000 7×10^5 **19.** 32,000,000 3.2×10^7 **20.** 0.045 4.5×10^{-2}

21. 0.000918 9.18×10^{-4} **22.** 1,000,000 1×10^6 **23.** 0.006752 6.752×10^{-3}

Example 3 p. 494

24. WEATHER Each minute, there are approximately 6×10^3 flashes of lightning around the world. The air around a lightning bolt is heated to about 5.4×10^4 degrees Fahrenheit, which is about five times hotter than the Sun.

a. About how many flashes of lightning are there in a day? Write in scientific notation and in standard form. 8.64×10^6; **8,640,000**

b. About how hot is the Sun in degrees Fahrenheit? Write in scientific notation and in standard form. 1.08×10^4; **10,800**

Example 4 p. 495 — **Order each set of numbers from least to greatest.** **25–28. See margin.**

25. 2.4×10^2, 2.45×10^{-2}, 2.45×10^2, 2.4×10^{-2}

26. 2.81×10^4, 2805, 2.08×10^5, 3.2×10^4, 3.024×10^2

27. 5.9×10^6, 5.9×10^4, 5.01×10^5, 5.1×10^{-3}

28. 9,562,301, 9.05×10^{-6}, 9.5×10^6, 905,000

B

29. GOLD A sheet of gold leaf is approximately 1.25×10^{-5} centimeter thick.

a. Write the value of the thickness as a decimal. **0.0000125 cm**

b. Use the formula $V = \ell wh$ to find the volume in cubic meters of a sheet of gold that is 2 meters wide and 5 meters long. 1.25×10^{-6} m^3

Real-World Link

One ounce of gold can be beaten out to 300 square feet. The thinnest sheets of gold are just a few atoms thick.

Source: The Physics Factbook

30. SYRUP List the states in the table from least to greatest production of maple syrup. **See margin.**

State	Amount of Syrup Produced (L)
Maine	1.10×10^6
New Hampshire	3.14×10^5
New York	9.65×10^5
Vermont	1.89×10^6
Wisconsin	3.79×10^5

Source: *Book of World Records*

31. TRAFFIC In a recent year, route U.S. 59 in the Houston area averaged approximately 338,510 vehicles per day. About how many vehicles was this during the entire year? Write the number in scientific notation. Verify your solution by using estimation. 1.24×10^8

32. SPACE The Moon travels around Earth at a speed of about 3.68×10^3 kilometers per hour. If the Moon orbits Earth every 27.3 days, about how far does it travel in one orbit around Earth?

32. about 2.41×10^6 km

Differentiated Homework Options

Level	Assignment	Two-Day Option	
AL Basic	10–28, 43–47 odd, 48–61	11–27 odd, 48–51	10–28 even, 43–47 odd, 52–61
OL Core	11–27 odd, 29–33, 35, 37–39, 41, 43–47 odd, 48–61	10–28, 48–51	29–43, 45, 47, 52–61
BL Advanced	29–58 (optional: 59–61)		

33 **SPEED** The speed of light is about 3×10^5 kilometers per second. The distance between Earth and the Moon is about 3.84×10^5 kilometers. Find how long it would take light to travel from Earth to the Moon. **1.28 s**

Replace each ● with <, >, or = to make a true statement.

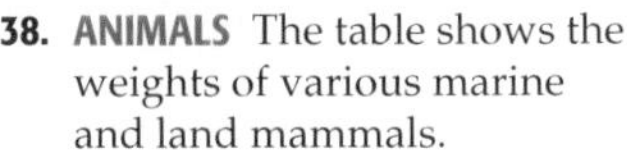

34. 5.72×10^8 ● 5.8×10^8 **<**

35. 35,400 ● 35.4×10^3 **=**

36. 0.042 ● 4.2×10^{-3} **>**

37. 5×10^5 ● 5,000,000 **<**

38. ANIMALS The table shows the weights of various marine and land mammals.

Mammal	Weight (pounds)
African Elephant	1.44×10^4
Blue Whale	2.87×10^5
Fin Whale	9.92×10^4
Right Whale	8.82×10^4
White Rhinoceros	7.94×10^3

a. Order the animals' weights from heaviest to lightest.

b. Which animal is about 10 times lighter than a right whale? **white rhinoceros**

c. About how many times heavier is the blue whale than the African elephant? **20 times**

d. Estimate the combined weight of the fin whale, right whale, and white rhinoceros. Write the combined weight in scientific notation and in standard form. **2.0×10^5; 200,000**

Real-World Link

The hump on the back of the rhino's neck is made up of muscle that is needed to raise its head. This muscle can be $\frac{1}{4}$ of its total body weight.

C **Evaluate each expression. Express in scientific notation and in standard form.**

39. $(6.3 \times 10^5) + (2.7 \times 10^7)$

40. $(8.5 \times 10^{-3}) - (4.8 \times 10^{-5})$

41. $(6.2 \times 10^2)(9.1 \times 10^3)$

42. $\dfrac{16.4 \times 10^{-5}}{3.2 \times 10^{-7}}$

H.O.T. Problems Use Higher-Order Thinking Skills

43. OPEN ENDED Write two numbers in scientific notation with different exponents. Then find the sum, difference, product, and quotient of the two numbers. Write the answers in scientific notation. **See margin.**

44. CHALLENGE A *googol* is a number that is 1 followed by 100 zeros. A *centillion* is a number that is 1 followed by 303 zeros. Write each of these numbers in scientific notation. **googol: 1×10^{100}; centillion: 1×10^{303}**

45. REASONING Miami is the second most populous city in Florida. **See margin.**

a. Which number better describes the population of Miami, 3.8×10^4 or 3.8×10^6? Explain.

b. Express Miami's population in another form.

c. Which notation is best to use when describing population? Explain.

46. CHALLENGE Which number is twice as great as 3×10^2: 6×10^2, 3×10^4, or 6×10^4? Explain. **6×10^2; $3 \times 10^2 = 300$ and $2 \times 300 = 600$ or 6×10^2**

47. WRITING IN MATH Your friend thinks 7.8×10^3 is greater than 6.5×10^2 because 7.8 > 6.5. Explain why your friend's reasoning is incorrect.

38a. blue whale, fin whale, right whale, African elephant, white rhinoceros

39. 2.763×10^7; 27,630,000

40. 8.452×10^{-3}; 0.008452

41. 5.642×10^6; 5,642,000

42. 5.125×10^2; 512.5

47. Sample answer: 7.8×10^3 is greater than 6.5×10^2 because the exponent of 3 is greater than the exponent of 2.

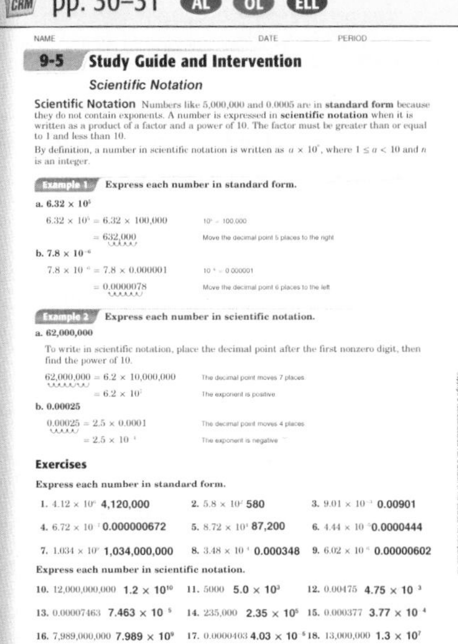

Study Guide and Intervention CRM pp. 30–31 AL OL ELL

NAME ______ DATE ______ PERIOD ______

9-5 Study Guide and Intervention

Scientific Notation

Scientific Notation Numbers like 5,000,000 and 0.0005 are in **standard form** because they do not contain exponents. A number is expressed in **scientific notation** when it is written as a product of a factor and a power of 10. The factor must be greater than or equal to 1 and less than 10.

By definition, a number in scientific notation is written as $a \times 10^n$, where $1 \le a < 10$ and n is an integer.

Example 1 **Express each number in standard form.**

a. 6.32×10^5

$6.32 \times 10^5 = 6.32 \times 100{,}000$ — $10^5 = 100{,}000$

$= 632{,}000$ — Move the decimal point 5 places to the right

b. 7.8×10^{-6}

$7.8 \times 10^{-6} = 7.8 \times 0.000001$ — $10^{-6} = 0.000001$

$= 0.0000078$ — Move the decimal point 6 places to the left

Example 2 **Express each number in scientific notation.**

a. 62,000,000

To write in scientific notation, place the decimal point after the first nonzero digit, then find the power of 10.

$62{,}000{,}000 = 6.2 \times 10{,}000{,}000$ — The decimal point moves 7 places.

$= 6.2 \times 10^7$ — The exponent is positive.

b. 0.00025

$0.00025 = 2.5 \times 0.0001$ — The decimal point moves 4 places.

$= 2.5 \times 10^{-4}$ — The exponent is negative.

Exercises

Express each number in standard form.

1. 4.12×10^6 **4,120,000**
2. 5.8×10^2 **580**
3. 9.01×10^{-3} **0.00901**
4. 6.72×10^{-7} **0.000000672**
5. 8.72×10^4 **87,200**
6. 4.44×10^{-5} **0.0000444**
7. 1.034×10^9 **1,034,000,000**
8. 3.48×10^{-4} **0.000348**
9. 6.02×10^{-6} **0.00000602**

Express each number in scientific notation.

10. 12,000,000,000 **1.2×10^{10}**
11. 5000 **5.0×10^3**
12. 0.00475 **4.75×10^{-3}**
13. 0.00007463 **7.463×10^{-5}**
14. 235,000 **2.35×10^5**
15. 0.000377 **3.77×10^{-4}**
16. 7,989,000,000 **7.989×10^9**
17. 0.0000403 **4.03×10^{-5}**
18. 13,000,000 **1.3×10^7**

Chapter 9 30 *Glencoe Pre-Algebra*

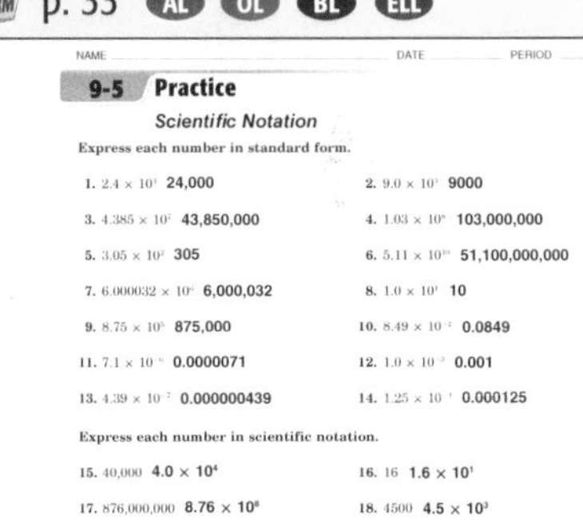

Practice CRM p. 33 AL OL BL ELL

NAME ______ DATE ______ PERIOD ______

9-5 Practice

Scientific Notation

Express each number in standard form.

1. 2.4×10^4 **24,000**
2. 9.0×10^3 **9000**
3. 4.385×10^7 **43,850,000**
4. 1.03×10^8 **103,000,000**
5. 3.05×10^2 **305**
6. 5.11×10^{10} **51,100,000,000**
7. 6.000032×10^6 **6,000,032**
8. 1.0×10^1 **10**
9. 8.75×10^5 **875,000**
10. 8.49×10^{-2} **0.0849**
11. 7.1×10^{-6} **0.0000071**
12. 1.0×10^{-3} **0.001**
13. 4.39×10^{-7} **0.000000439**
14. 1.25×10^{-4} **0.000125**

Express each number in scientific notation.

15. 40,000 **4.0×10^4**
16. 16 **1.6×10^1**
17. 876,000,000 **8.76×10^8**
18. 4500 **4.5×10^3**
19. 151 **1.51×10^2**
20. 0.00037 **3.7×10^{-4}**
21. 83,000,000 **8.3×10^7**
22. 919,100 **9.191×10^5**
23. 5,000,000,000,000 **5.0×10^{12}**
24. 0.13 **1.3×10^{-1}**
25. 0.0000007 **7.0×10^{-7}**
26. 0.0067 **6.7×10^{-3}**

Order each set of numbers from least to greatest.

27. 7.35×10^4, 1.7×10^{-6}, 8.26×10^3, 9.3×10^{-2}
1.7×10^{-6}, 9.3×10^{-2}, 8.26×10^3, 7.35×10^4

28. 0.00048, 4.37×10^{-4}, 4.02×10^{-3}, 0.04
4.37×10^{-4}, 0.00048, 4.02×10^{-3}, 0.04

NIAGARA FALLS **For Exercises 29 and 30, use the following information.**

Every minute, 840,000,000,000 drops of water flow over Niagara Falls.

29. Write this number in scientific notation. **8.4×10^{11}**

30. How many drops flow over the falls in a day? **1.2096×10^{15}**

Chapter 9 33 *Glencoe Pre-Algebra*

Lesson 9-5

Word Problem Practice CRM p. 34 AL OL BL

NAME ______ DATE ______ PERIOD ______

9-5 Word Problem Practice

Scientific Notation

1. **EARTH SCIENCE** Mr. Bell's class is studying the solar system. The circumference of Earth at the equator is about 24,900 miles. Express this number in scientific notation. **2.49×10^4 miles**

2. **LIGHT SPEED** The speed of light is approximately 6.71×10^8 miles per hour. Express this number in standard form. **671,000,000 mi per hr**

3. **EARTH SCIENCE** If it takes light 8.3 minutes to reach the Sun from Earth, use the light speed from Exercise 2 to determine the distance from Earth to the Sun. Write your answer in scientific notation. **9.28×10^7 mi**

4. **EARTH SCIENCE** The students in Mr. Bell's class have learned that the mass of Earth is approximately 5.97×10^{24} kilograms. They have also found that mass of an electron is approximately 9.11×10^{-31} kilograms. How many times greater than the mass of an electron is the mass of Earth? **6.55×10^{54} times**

5. **AIRCRAFT** The SR-71 "Blackbird" is one of the world's fastest airplanes. It is capable of traveling at a cruising speed of Mach 3, or three times the speed of sound. The speed of sound is approximately 7.6×10^2 miles per hour. What is Mach 3 in miles per hour? Write your answer in scientific notation. **2.28×10^3 mi per hr**

6. **POPULATION** Geographers keep track of how many people live in different areas of the world. They are especially interested in how the populations of certain areas change. The table below shows the population of different regions in 1985 and in 2005.

Place	Population 1985	Population 2005
Earth	4.9×10^9	6.4×10^9
China	1.1×10^9	1.3×10^9
India	7.6×10^8	1.1×10^9
United States	2.4×10^8	3.0×10^8

Source: U.S. Census Bureau

a. In 2005, how many times greater than China's population is the population of the world? **4.9 times**

b. How many more people inhabited Earth in 2005 than in 1985? **1.5×10^9**

c. What was the percentage increase in population in India from 1985 to 2005? Round your answer to the nearest percent. **45%**

d. Was India's percent increase in population greater than or less than the percent increase of the whole world for the same time period? Explain. **Larger. The world's population increased by 31%.**

Chapter 9 34 *Glencoe Pre-Algebra*

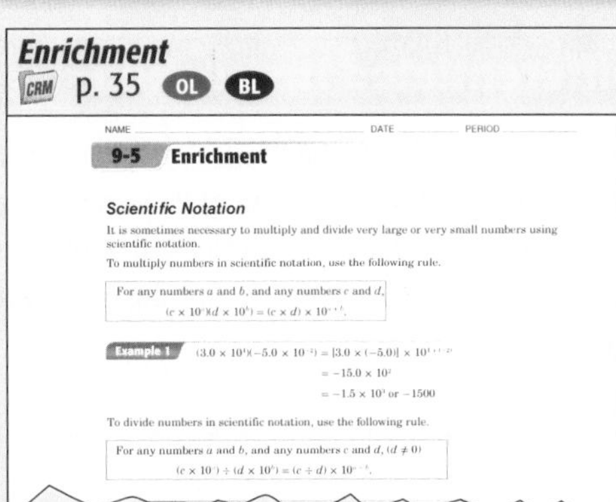

Enrichment CRM p. 35 OL BL

NAME ______ DATE ______ PERIOD ______

9-5 Enrichment

Scientific Notation

It is sometimes necessary to multiply and divide very large or very small numbers using scientific notation.

To multiply numbers in scientific notation, use the following rule.

For any numbers a and b, and any numbers c and d,
$(c \times 10^a)(d \times 10^b) = (c \times d) \times 10^{a+b}$.

Example 1 $(3.0 \times 10^4)(-5.0 \times 10^{-2}) = [3.0 \times (-5.0)] \times 10^{4+(-2)}$
$= -15.0 \times 10^2$
$= -1.5 \times 10^3$ or -1500

To divide numbers in scientific notation, use the following rule.

For any numbers a and b, and any numbers c and d, $(d \neq 0)$
$(c \times 10^a) \div (d \times 10^b) = (c \div d) \times 10^{a-b}$.

4 ASSESS

Yesterday's News Tell students to write how they think what they learned yesterday about negative exponents helped them with today's lesson on scientific notation. Ask them to include reasons negative exponents and scientific notation might be useful. They can illustrate with examples.

Formative Assessment

Check for student understanding of concepts in Lessons 9-4 and 9-5.

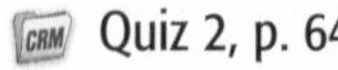

CRM Quiz 2, p. 64

Additional Answers

51a. $(1.832 \times 10^2)(2 \times 10^3) = 3.664 \times 10^5$

51b. $(1.832 \times 10^2)(2 \times 10^3)/(4.5 \times 10^1) = 8.142 \times 10^3$

Standardized Test Practice

48. The slowest land mammal is the three-toed sloth that moves 0.07 mile per hour. Which expression represents this number? **B**

A 7×10^{-3}　　C 7×10^2

B 7×10^{-2}　　D 7×10^3

49. The distance from Earth to the Sun is about 9.6×10^7 miles. Which of the following represents this distance? **G**

F 9,600,000　　H 960,000,000

G 96,000,000　　J 9,600,000,000

50. SHORT RESPONSE The weight of a fruit fly is about 1.3×10^{-4} pound. How much would one million fruit flies weigh? **130 lb**

51. EXTENDED RESPONSE A 45-acre farm in Florida produces 183.2 tons of avocados per year. One ton is 2000 pounds. **a–b. See margin.**

a. Write an expression, in scientific notation, for the number of pounds of avocados produced per year.

b. Write an expression, in scientific notation, for the average number of pounds of avocados produced per acre.

c. Find the average number of pounds produced per acre. Round to the nearest whole number. **8142 lb**

Spiral Review

52. MEDICINE Which type of molecule in the table has a greater mass? How many times greater is it than the other type? (Lesson 9-4) **penicillin; 10^5 times greater**

Molecule	Mass (kg)
penicillin	10^{-18}
insulin	10^{-23}

Find each product or quotient. Express using exponents. (Lesson 9-3)

53. $a \cdot a^5$ a^6

54. $(n^4)(n^4)$ n^8

55. $-3x^2(4x^3)$ $-12x^5$

56. $\frac{3^8}{3^5}$ 3^3

57. MEASUREMENT Use the scale drawing shown. (Lesson 5-1)

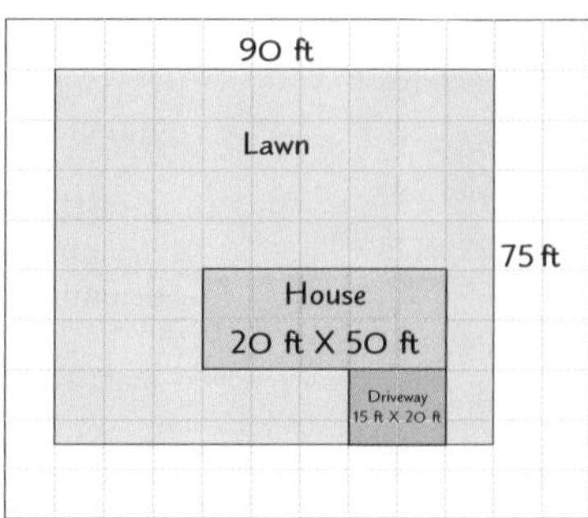

a. What is the area of the lawn? **5450 ft²**

b. Suppose you want to fertilize the lawn. If one bag of fertilizer covers 2500 square feet, how many bags of fertilizer should you buy? **3 bags**

58. RANCHING The largest ranch in the world is in the Australian Outback. It is about 12,000 square miles, which is five times the size of the largest United States ranch. Write and solve a multiplication equation to find the size of the largest United States ranch. (Lesson 4-4) **$12{,}000 = 5x$; 2400 mi²**

Skills Review

Write each expression using exponents. (Lesson 9-1)

59. $4 \cdot 4 \cdot 4 \cdot 4 \cdot 4$ 4^5

60. $(6 \cdot 6 \cdot 6) \cdot 6$ 6^4

61. $3 \cdot 2 \cdot 3 \cdot 2 \cdot 2$ $2^3 \cdot 3^2$

Differentiated Instruction

BL

Extension According to the Product of Powers rule, when multiplying powers with the same base, add the exponents. The Quotient of Powers rule states that when dividing with bases that are the same, subtract the exponents. Evaluate the following expressions. Write answers in scientific notation. Then come up with a rule for multiplying and dividing numbers written in scientific notation.

$\frac{11.2 \times 10^3}{1.4 \times 10^1}$ 8×10^2　　$(2.6 \times 10^3)(1.5 \times 10^{-5})$ 3.9×10^{-2}

9-6 Powers of Monomials

Then
You multiplied and divided monomials. (Lesson 9-3)

Now
- Find the power of a power.
- Find the power of a product.

Math Online
glencoe.com
- Extra Examples
- Personal Tutor
- Self-Check Quiz
- Homework Help

Why?

Refer to Squares A, B, C, and D shown below.

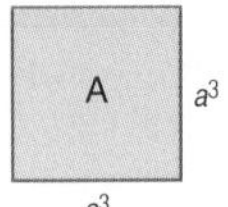

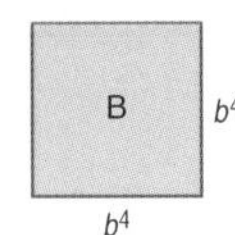

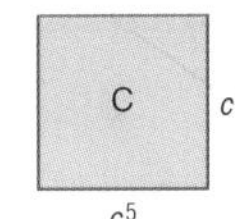

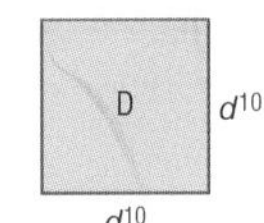

a. Use the squares to complete the table. The first one is done for you. See Chapter 9 Answer Appendix.

Square	Area = Side Length Squared	Area using Product of Powers
A	$(a^3)^2$	$a^3 \cdot a^3 = a^{3+3}$ or a^6
B	■	■
C	■	■
D	■	■

b. What is the relationship between the exponents in column 2 and the final exponent in column 3? Sample answer: The exponent in column 3 is the product of the exponents in column 2.

Power of a Power You can use the property for finding the *product* of powers to find a property for finding the *power* of a power.

$$(4^2)^5 = \underbrace{(4^2)(4^2)(4^2)(4^2)(4^2)}_{\text{5 factors}}$$
$$= 4^{2+2+2+2+2} \leftarrow \text{Product of Powers Property}$$
$$= 4^{10}$$

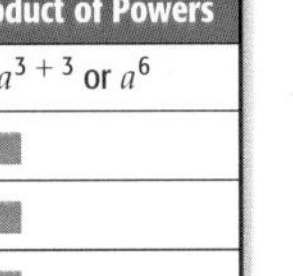

Key Concept Power of a Power Property — For Your FOLDABLE

Words To find the power of a power, multiply exponents.

Symbols $(a^m)^n = a^{m \cdot n}$

Examples $(7^4)^2 = 7^{4 \cdot 2}$ or 7^8 $(n^3)^5 = n^{3 \cdot 5}$ or n^{15}

Watch Out!
Power of a Power When finding the power of a power, do not add the exponent. $(9^6)^2 = 9^{12}$, not 9^8.

EXAMPLE 1 Find the Power of a Power

Simplify.

a. $(9^6)^2$

$(9^6)^2 = 9^{6 \cdot 2}$ Power of a Power

$= 9^{12}$ Simplify.

b. $(q^4)^5$

$(q^4)^5 = q^{4 \cdot 5}$ Power of a Power

$= q^{20}$ Simplify.

Check Your Progress

1A. $(4^3)^7$ 4^{21} **1B.** $(n^4)^4$ n^{16} **1C.** $(2^3)^{-2}$ 2^{-6} or $\frac{1}{2^6}$

Personal Tutor glencoe.com

9-6 Lesson Notes

1 FOCUS

Vertical Alignment

Before Lesson 9-6
Multiply and divide monomials.

Lesson 9-6
Find the power of a power. Find the power of a product.

After Lesson 9-6
Simplify polynomial expressions in problem situations.

2 TEACH

Scaffolding Questions

Have students read the *Why?* section of the lesson and answer the questions.

Ask:
- Using words, what is a rule you can use for finding the power of a power? Sample answer: Multiply the exponents.
- How can you use variables to write a rule for finding the power of a power? Sample answer: $(a^x)^y = a^{x \cdot y}$
- Would your rule for finding the power of a power work to simplify $(2^3x^4)^2$? Explain. Yes; $(2^3x^4)^2 = 2^{3 \cdot 2}x^{4 \cdot 2} = 2^6x^8 = 64x^8$ and $(2^3x^4) \cdot (2^3x^4) = 2^{3+3} \cdot x^{4+4} = 2^6x^8 = 64x^8$.

Lesson 9-6 Resources

Resource	Approaching-Level	On-Level	Beyond-Level	English Learners
Teacher Edition	• Differentiated Instruction, p. 500	• Differentiated Instruction, p. 500	• Differentiated Instruction, p. 503	
Chapter Resource Masters	• Study Guide and Intervention, pp. 36–37 • Skills Practice, p. 38 • Practice, p. 39 • Word Problem Practice, p. 40	• Study Guide and Intervention, pp. 36–37 • Skills Practice, p. 38 • Practice, p. 39 • Word Problem Practice, p. 40 • Enrichment, p. 41	• Practice, p. 39 • Word Problem Practice, p. 40 • Enrichment, p. 41	• Study Guide and Intervention, pp. 36–37 • Skills Practice, p. 38 • Practice, p. 39
Transparencies	• 5-Minute Check Transparency 9-6	• 5-Minute Check Transparency 9-6	• 5-Minute Check Transparency 9-6	• 5-Minute Check Transparency 9-6
Other	• Study Notebook • Teaching Pre-Algebra with Manipulatives	• Study Notebook • Teaching Pre-Algebra with Manipulatives	• Study Notebook	• Study Notebook • Teaching Pre-Algebra with Manipulatives

Power of a Power

Example 1 shows how to find the power of a power.

Formative Assessment

Use the Check Your Progress exercises after each example to determine students' understanding of concepts.

Additional Example

1 Simplify.

a. $(12^2)^3$ 12^6

b. $(f^5)^7$ f^{35}

Additional Examples also in Interactive Classroom PowerPoint® Presentations

IWB INTERACTIVE WHITEBOARD READY

Focus on Mathematical Content

Powers of Monomials The rule for raising a monomial with a power to a power is to keep the base and multiply the exponents. Thus, $(3^5)^2$ equals 3^{10}. This rule can also be used to include a product raised to a power, in which case, each factor is raised to the power. The product $(5x^2y)^3$ becomes $125x^6y^3$.

Power of a Product

Examples 2 and 3 show how to find the power of a product. **Example 4** shows how to use the power of a product to solve a real-world problem.

Additional Examples

2 Simplify.

a. $(2v^6)^4$ $16v^{24}$

b. $(-5a^3b^4)^2$ $25a^6b^8$

3 **GEOMETRY** Find the area of a square with sides of length $9x^3y^5$. $81x^6y^{10}$

Watch Out!

Power of a Product When finding the power of a product, do not multiply the constant by the exponent. $(2x^3)^5 = 32x^{15}$ not $10x^{15}$.

Power of a Product The Power of a Power Property can be extended to find the power of a product.

$$(2x^3)^5 = \underbrace{(2x^3)(2x^3)(2x^3)(2x^3)(2x^3)}_{\text{5 factors}}$$

$= 2^5 \cdot (x^3)^5$	**Associative and Commutative Properties of Multiplication**
$= 2^5 \cdot (x^3) \cdot (x^3) \cdot (x^3) \cdot (x^3) \cdot (x^3)$	**Power of a Power**
$= 2^5 \cdot x^{3+3+3+3+3}$	**Product of Powers Property**
$= 32 \cdot x^{15}$ or $32x^{15}$	**Simplify.**

Notice the power of each factor in the final power above.

Key Concept — Power of a Product Property (For Your FOLDABLE)

Words To find the power of a product, find the power of each factor and multiply.

Symbols $(ab)^m = a^mb^m$, for all numbers a and b and any integer m

Examples $(7x^4)^2 = 7^2 \cdot (x^4)^2$ or $49x^8$

EXAMPLE 2 Find the Power of a Product

Simplify.

a. $(5r^7)^2$

$(5r^7)^2 = 5^2 \cdot (r^7)^2$	**Power of a Product**
$= 5^2 \cdot r^{7 \cdot 2}$	**Power of a Power**
$= 25r^{14}$	**Simplify.**

b. $(2x^6y^3)^4$

$(2x^6y^3)^4 = 2^4 \cdot (x^6)^4 \cdot (y^3)^4$	
$= 2^4 \cdot (x^{6 \cdot 4}) \cdot (y^{3 \cdot 4})$	
$= 16x^{24}y^{12}$	**Simplify.**

Check Your Progress

2A. $(6w^4)^5$ $7776w^{20}$ **2B.** $(-4s^5t^7)^3$ $-64s^{15}t^{21}$ **2C.** $(3x^{-2}y^4)^2$ **2C.** $9x^{-4}y^8$ or $\frac{9y^8}{x^4}$

Personal Tutor glencoe.com

EXAMPLE 3 Find the Power of a Product

GEOMETRY Express the volume of the cube as a monomial.

$V = s^3$	**Formula for volume of a cube**
$= (2xy^5)^3$	**Replace s with $2xy^5$.**
$= 2^3x^3(y^5)^3$	**Power of a Product**
$= 8x^3y^{15}$	**Simplify.**

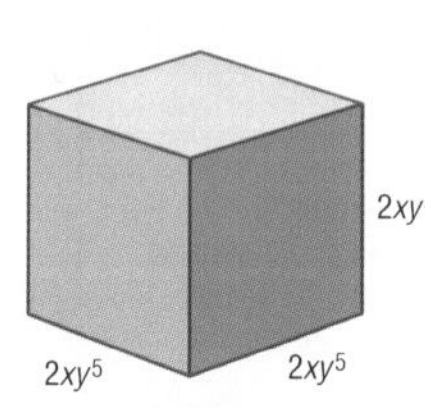

Check Your Progress

3. GEOMETRY Find the area of a square with sides of length $7a^8b^2$. $49a^{16}b^4$

Personal Tutor glencoe.com

500 Chapter 9 Powers and Nonlinear Functions

Differentiated Instruction (AL OL)

If students need a visual reminder of the properties of powers,

Then have students make a display or poster showing each of the following properties: Product of Powers, Quotient of Powers, and Power of Powers. They should include an example of each.

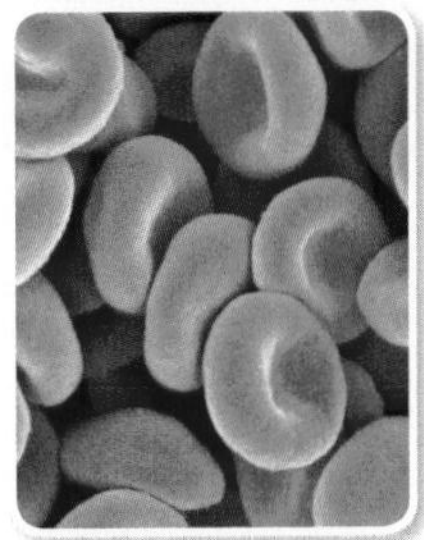

Real-World Link

Red blood cells make up about 40% of total blood volume and carry oxygen to the body. A few drops of whole blood contains approximately one billion red blood cells.

Source: University of Iowa Blood Center

Real-World EXAMPLE 4 Find the Power of a Product

BIOLOGY Ebony wanted to view red blood cells under a microscope with a 1000X magnification. The radius of the circular field she could view is $9 \cdot 10^{-4}$ centimeters. Find the area of the viewing field. Use the formula $A = 3.14r^2$ where A is the area of a circle and r is the radius. Express your answer in scientific notation.

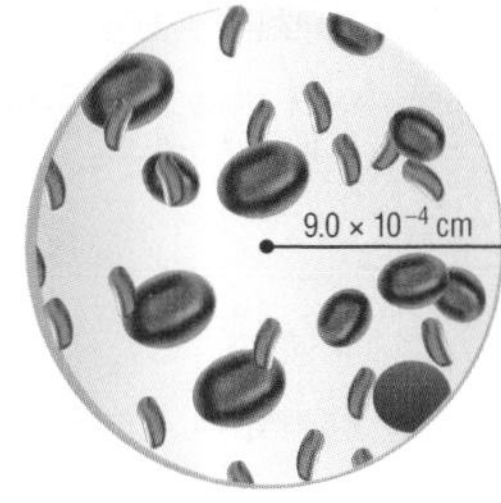

$A = 3.14 \cdot r^2$	Write the equation.
$= 3.14 \cdot (9 \cdot 10^{-4})^2$	Replace r with $9.0 \cdot 10^{-4}$.
$= 3.14 \cdot 9^2 \cdot (10^{-4})^2$	Power of a Product
$= 3.14 \cdot 81 \cdot 10^{-8}$	Simplify.
$= 2.5434 \times 10^{-6}$	Multiply. Write the answer in scientific notation.

The area of the field is 2.5434×10^{-6} square centimeters.

Check Your Progress

4. **BIOLOGY** The radius of a grain of pollen from a certain flower is 2.5×10^{-3} millimeters. Use the formula $V = \frac{4}{3}(3.14)r^3$ to find the volume of the pollen. Express your answer in scientific notation rounded to the nearest hundredth. **6.54×10^{-8}**

Personal Tutor glencoe.com

Concept Summary Powers

For Your FOLDABLE

Product of Powers	Quotient of Powers	Powers of Powers
Add exponents.	Subtract exponents.	Multiply exponents.
$a^m \cdot a^n = a^{m+n}$	$a^m \div a^n = a^{m-n}$	$(ab)^m = a^m b^m$

Check Your Understanding

Examples 1 and 2 pp. 499–500

Simplify.

1. $(6^2)^4$ **6^8**
2. $(a^5)^5$ **a^{25}**
3. $(r^6)^{-2}$ **r^{-12} or $\frac{1}{r^{12}}$**
4. $(3x^4)^3$ **$27x^{12}$**
5. $(4m^2n)^2$ **$16m^4n^2$**
6. $(-2f^3g^4)^7$ **$-128f^{21}g^{28}$**

Example 3 p. 500

7. **GEOMETRY** Express the area of the square at the right as a monomial. **$121n^{12}p^4$**

$11n^6p^2$

$11n^6p^2$

Example 4 p. 501

8. **BUILDINGS** The Lincoln Center for the Performing Arts in New York City takes up most of a square block that measures 2.5×10^2 meters on each side. Find the area of the block that houses the Lincoln Center. Express your answer in scientific notation and in standard notation. **6.25×10^4; 62,500 m^2**

Additional Example

4 **BIOLOGY** A spherical bacterium has a radius of 1.5×10^{-4} millimeters. Use the formula $S = 4 \cdot 3.14 \cdot r^2$ to find the surface area S of a sphere with a radius r. Express your answer in scientific notation. 2.83×10^{-7} mm^2

3 PRACTICE

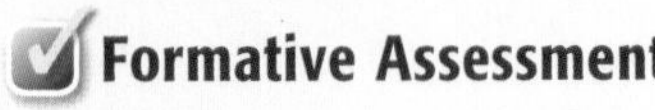

Formative Assessment

Use Exercises 1–8 to check for understanding.

Use the chart at the bottom of this page to customize assignments for your students.

TEACH with TECH

WIKI Create a page for each of the properties of powers on your secure classroom wiki. Students can reply on the wiki with a numerical or algebraic example of each power. All members of the class should contribute to the pages.

Differentiated Homework Options

Level	Assignment	Two-Day Option	
AL Basic	9–24, 32, 34–50	9–23 odd, 36–39	10–24 odd, 32, 34, 35, 40–50
OL Core	9–23 odd, 25, 26, 27–31 odd, 32, 34–50	9–24, 36–39	25–32, 34, 35, 40–50
BL Advanced	25–47 (optional: 48–50)		

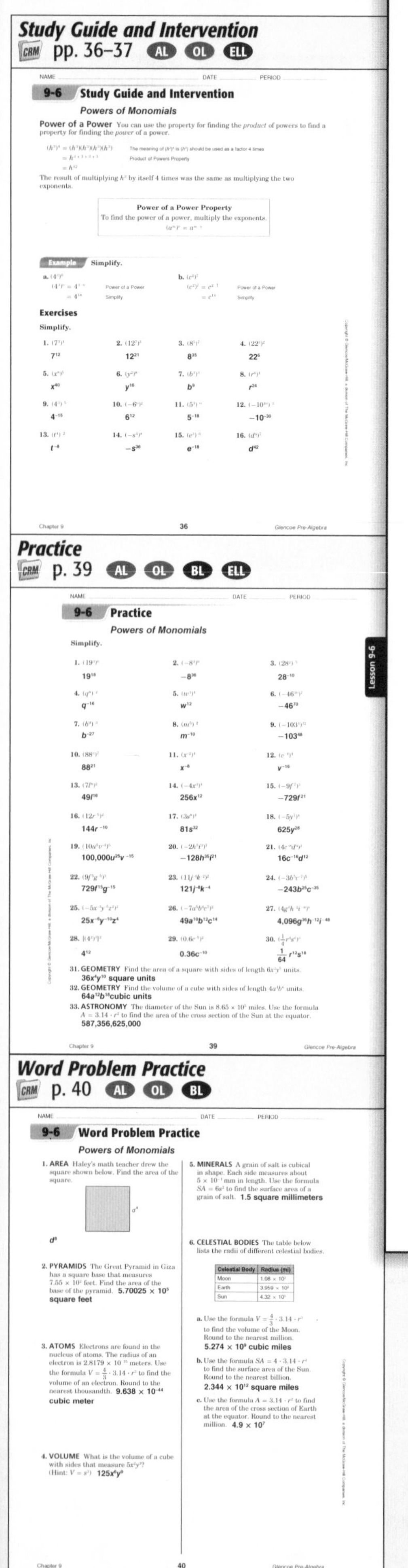
Study Guide and Intervention
CRM pp. 36–37 AL OL ELL

9-6 Study Guide and Intervention
Powers of Monomials

Practice
CRM p. 39 AL OL BL ELL

9-6 Practice
Powers of Monomials

Word Problem Practice
CRM p. 40 AL OL BL

9-6 Word Problem Practice
Powers of Monomials

Practice and Problem Solving

● = **Step-by-Step Solutions** begin on page R11.
Extra Practice begins on page 810.

Examples 1 and 2 pp. 499–500

Simplify.

9. $(2^3)^2$ 2^6 **10.** $(5^4)^6$ 5^{24} **11.** $(3^5)^3$ 3^{15} **12.** $(6^2)^9$ 6^{18}

13. $(b^7)^4$ b^{28} **14.** $(f^6)^{-3}$ **15.** $(2y^2)^8$ $256y^{16}$ **16.** $(7x^{-5})^2$

17. $(3st^3)^4$ $81s^4t^{12}$ **18.** $(10y^5z)^3$ **19.** $(-4n^2p^4)^5$ **20.** $(-5a^8b^3)^4$

14. f^{-18} or $\frac{1}{f^{18}}$

16. $49x^{-10}$ or $\frac{49}{x^{10}}$

Example 3 p. 500

GEOMETRY Express each measure as a monomial.

21. area of square $16a^6b^{14}$

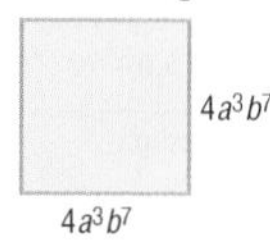

22. volume of cube $27a^9b^{15}$

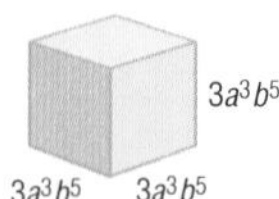

18. $1000y^{15}z^3$

19. $-1024n^{10}p^{20}$

20. $625a^{32}b^{12}$

Example 4 p. 501

23. SPACE The diameter of Saturn at the equator is 6.027×10^4 kilometers. Use the formula $A = 3.14r^2$ to find the area of the cross section of the planet at the equator. Round to the nearest hundred million. 2.9×10^9 km^2

24. COMPUTERS A square microchip for a certain computer measures 1.6×10^{-2} meters on each side. Find the area of the microchip. 2.56×10^{-4} m^2

B Simplify. Express your answer in scientific notation. Round to the nearest hundredth.

25. 6.87×10^{11} stars

25 STARS There are approximately $10(4^9)^2$ stars in the Milky Way Galaxy.

26. EARTH The surface area of Earth is approximately $11.74[(2^3)^4]^2$ square miles. 1.97×10^8 mi^2

Simplify.

27. $[(3^2)^4]^3$ 3^{24} **28.** $(0.4n^3)^2$ $0.16n^6$ **29.** $\left(\frac{1}{2}t^4v^3\right)^4$ $\frac{1}{16}t^{16}v^{12}$ **30.** $(-2w)^{-4}(4w^2)^4$ $16w^4$

C **31. MULTIPLE REPRESENTATIONS** In this problem, you will explore functions.

a. ALGEBRAIC Simplify $(2x^2)^2$ and $[(2x^2)^2]^2$. $4x^4$ and $16x^8$

b. GRAPHICAL Using a graphing calculator, graph the functions $y = 2x^2$, $y = (2x^2)^2$, and $y = [(2x^2)^2]^2$. Sketch the graphs. See margin.

c. VERBAL Compare the graphs. What is similar about the graphs? What is different? Sample answer: All three graphs are shaped like "U." As the coefficient and exponent increase, the graph gets narrower and flatter on the bottom.

H.O.T. Problems

Use **H**igher-**O**rder **T**hinking Skills

32. OPEN ENDED Write three expressions that each are equivalent to x^8: one using the Product of a Power Property; one using the Quotient of a Power Property; and one using the Power of a Power Property.

32. Sample answer: $x^4 \cdot x^4$, $\frac{x^{24}}{x^{16}}$, $(x^2)^4$

33. CHALLENGE Solve $(8^{2x})^3 = 8^{30}$. Explain your reasoning.

33. $x = 5$; $(8^{2x})^3 = 8^{6x}$, so $6x = 30$ or $x = 5$

34. REASONING Compare each pair of monomials. If the pair is not equivalent, explain. a. not equilvalent; $(-6q)^3 = -216q^3 \neq -6q^3$

a. $-6q^3$ and $(-6q)^3$ **b.** $(bc)^4$ and b^4c^4 equivalent

35. WRITING IN MATH Summarize the steps you use to find the power of a power and the power of a product. Sample answer: To find the power of a power, multiply exponents. To find the power of a product, find the power of each factor and multiply.

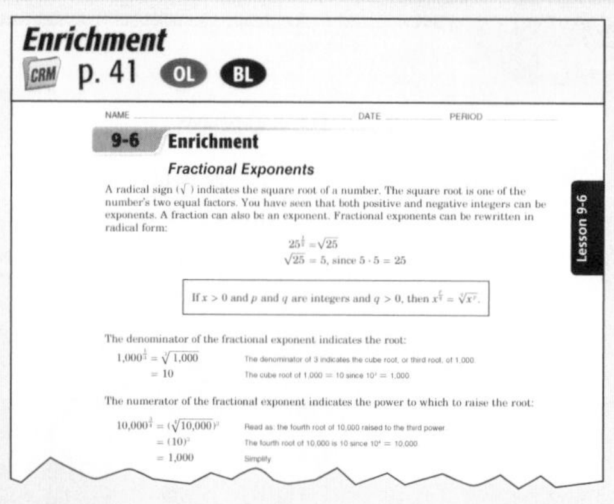
Enrichment
CRM p. 41 OL BL

9-6 Enrichment
Fractional Exponents

Multiple Representations In Exercise 31, students simplify algebraic expressions and use a graphing calculator to compare similar functions and the graphs they produce.

Standardized Test Practice

36. SHORT RESPONSE Find the area of the circle shown below using scientific notation. Use the formula $A = 3.14r^2$. **1.66106×10^{-5} m²**

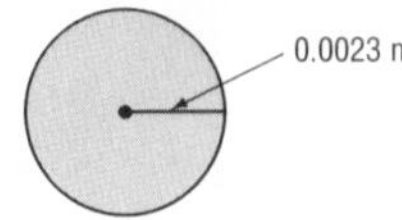

37. The length of the side of a square is $4x^3y^2$ units. Use the formula $A = s^2$ to find the area of the square. **C**

A $4x^5y^4$

B $8x^6y^4$

C $16x^6y^4$

D $64x^6y^4$

38. Simplify the expression $(4x^3y^2)^4$. **J**

F $16x^7y^6$

G $16x^{12}y^8$

H $256x^7y^6$

J $256x^{12}y^8$

39. A star known as Ross 154 is approximately $(3.0 \times 10^8)^2$ miles from Earth. Which of the following represents this distance? **D**

A 6×10^{10}

B 6×10^{16}

C 9×10^{10}

D 9×10^{16}

Spiral Review

Express each number in standard form. (Lesson 9-5)

40. 4.24×10^2 **424**

41. 5.72×10^4 **57,200**

42. 3.347×10^{-1} **0.3347**

Express each number in scientific notation. (Lesson 9-5)

43. 2,000,000 **2×10^6**

44. 499,000 **4.99×10^5**

45. 0.006 **6×10^{-3}**

46. BIRDS A mockingbird uses about 5^{-4} Joules of energy to sing a song. Write the amount of energy the bird uses as an expression using a positive exponent and as a decimal. (Lesson 9-4) **$\frac{1}{5^4}$; 0.0016**

47. BUSINESS To make a profit, stores sell an item for more than it paid for the item. The increase in price is called the *markup*. Suppose a store purchases paint brushes for \$8 each. Find the markup if the brushes are sold for 15% over the price the store paid for them. (Lesson 7-5) **\$1.20**

Skills Review

Copy and complete each table to find the coordinates of three points through which the graph of each function passes. (Lesson 8-3) **48–50. See margin.**

48. $y = 5x + 1$

x	5x + 1	(x, y)
0	■	■
1	■	■
2	■	■

49. $y = 3x^2 - 2$

x	$3x^2 - 2$	(x, y)
0	■	■
1	■	■
2	■	■

50. $y = 2x^3 + 3$

x	$2x^3 + 3$	(x, y)
0	■	■
1	■	■
2	■	■

4 ASSESS

Name the Math Students are to explain and show the work needed to simplify $(-2x^3y^4)^3$.

Additional Answers

31. b.

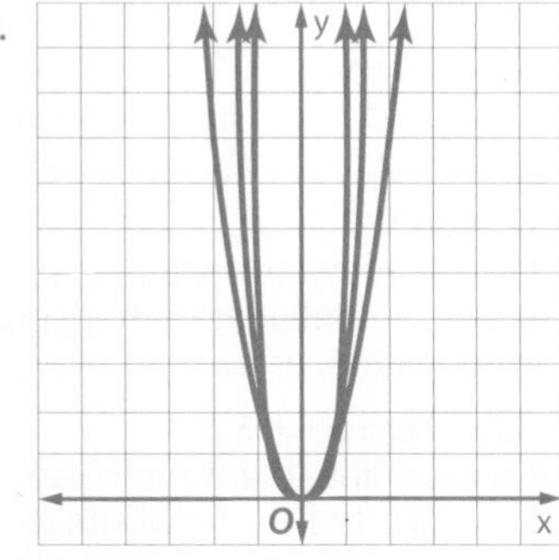

48.

x	5x + 1	(x, y)
0	5(0) + 1	(0, 1)
1	5(1) + 1	(1, 6)
2	5(2) + 1	(2, 11)

49.

x	$3x^2 - 2$	(x, y)
0	$3(0)^2 - 2$	(0, −2)
1	$3(1)^2 - 2$	(1, 1)
2	$3(2)^2 - 2$	(2, 10)

50.

x	$2x^3 + 3$	(x, y)
0	$2(0)^3 + 3$	(0, 3)
1	$2(1)^3 + 3$	(1, 5)
2	$2(2)^3 + 3$	(2, 19)

Differentiated Instruction

BL

Extension Have the students simplify the following problems. $\left(\frac{6x^4}{5y^3}\right)^2$; $\left(\frac{3ef^6}{2g^4h^6}\right)^3$; $\left(\frac{-1}{2x^3y^5}\right)^5$ $\frac{36x^8}{25y^6}$, $\frac{27e^3f^{18}}{8g^{12}h^{18}}$, $\frac{-1}{32x^{15}y^{25}}$

9-7 Lesson Notes

1 FOCUS

Vertical Alignment

Before Lesson 9-7
Represent linear functions using graphs, equations, and tables.

Lesson 9-7
Determine whether a function is linear or nonlinear from a graph, an equation, or a table.

After Lesson 9-7
Connect linear and nonlinear functions to real-world situations.

2 TEACH

Scaffolding Questions

Have students read the *Why?* section of the lesson and answer the questions.

Ask:

- Does the graph show an increase or a decrease in cell phone subscribers? increase
- Does the graph represent a function? Explain. Yes; for each *x*-value there is only one *y*-value.
- How would you describe the graph? Sample answer: The line on the graph is a curve.

9-7 Linear and Nonlinear Functions

Then
You have already represented linear functions using graphs, equations, and tables. (Lesson 8-3)

Now
- Determine whether a function is linear or nonlinear from a graph.
- Determine whether a function is linear or nonlinear from an equation or a table.

New Vocabulary
nonlinear function

Math Online
glencoe.com
- Extra Examples
- Personal Tutor
- Self-Check Quiz
- Homework Help

Why?

The graph shows the number of cell phone subscribers in the United States in recent years.

a. Does the number of cell phone subscribers increase by a constant amount each year? Explain.

b. Does the graph represent a linear relationship? Explain.

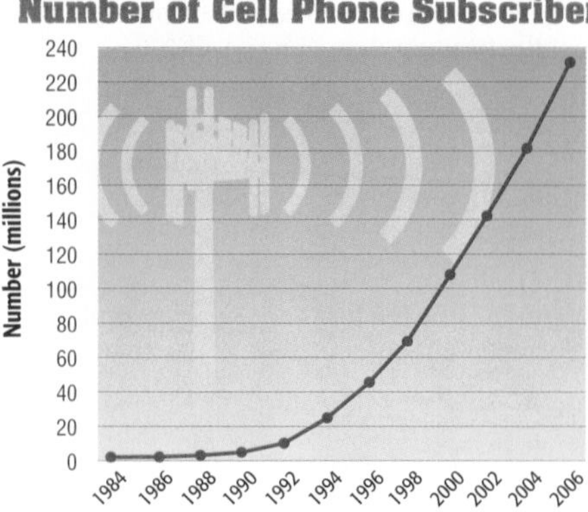

a. No; the number of subscribers increases by a greater amount each year
b. No; it is not a straight line

Graphs of Nonlinear Functions In Lesson 8-3, you learned that linear functions have graphs that are straight lines. These graphs represent constant rates of change. **Nonlinear functions** are functions that do not have constant rates of change. Therefore, their graphs are *not* straight lines.

EXAMPLE 1 Identify Functions Using Graphs

Determine whether each graph represents a *linear* or *nonlinear* function. Explain.

a.

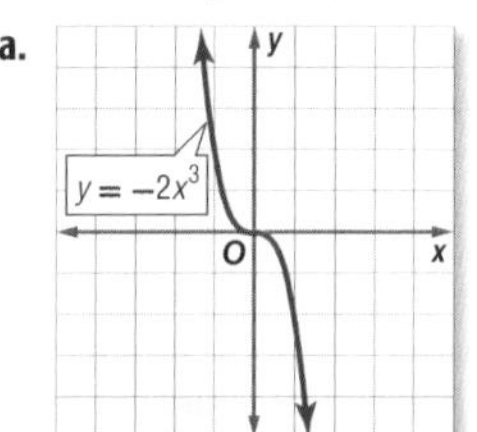

This graph is a curve, not a straight line. So, it represents a nonlinear function.

b.

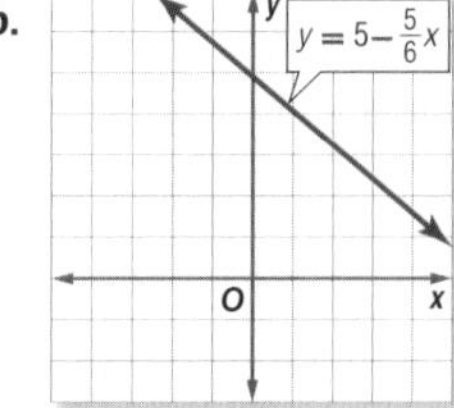

This graph is a line. So, it represents a linear function.

Check Your Progress

1A.

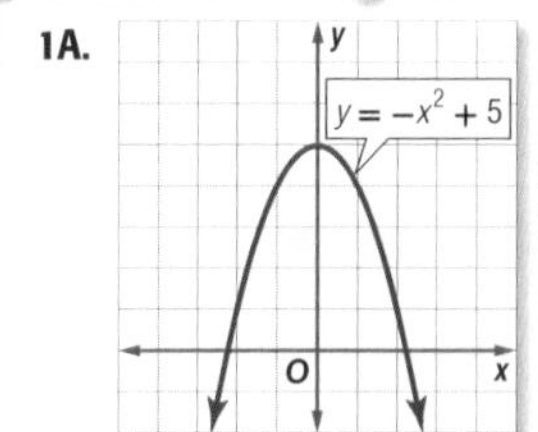

Nonlinear; the graph is a curve.

1B.

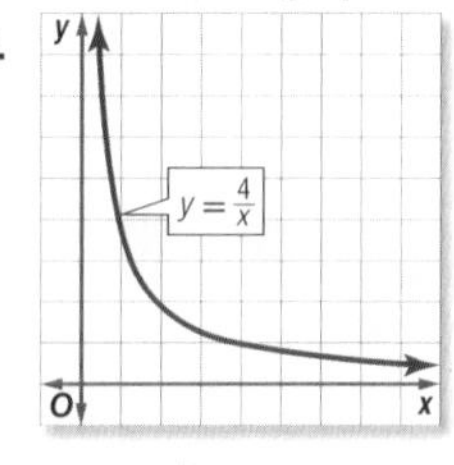

1B. Nonlinear; the graph is a curve.

Personal Tutor glencoe.com

Lesson 9-7 Resources

Resource	Approaching-Level	On-Level	Beyond-Level	English Learners
Teacher Edition		• Differentiated Instruction, p. 505	• Differentiated Instruction, pp. 505, 509	
Chapter Resource Masters	• Study Guide and Intervention, pp. 42–43 • Skills Practice, p. 44 • Practice, p. 45 • Word Problem Practice, p. 46	• Study Guide and Intervention, pp. 42–43 • Skills Practice, p. 44 • Practice, p. 45 • Word Problem Practice, p. 46 • Enrichment, p. 47	• Practice, p. 45 • Word Problem Practice, p. 46 • Enrichment, p. 47	• Study Guide and Intervention, pp. 42–43 • Skills Practice, p. 44 • Practice, p. 45
Transparencies	• 5-Minute Check Transparency 9-7	• 5-Minute Check Transparency 9-7	• 5-Minute Check Transparency 9-7	• 5-Minute Check Transparency 9-7
Other	• Study Notebook • Teaching Pre-Algebra with Manipulatives	• Study Notebook • Teaching Pre-Algebra with Manipulatives	• Study Notebook	• Study Notebook • Teaching Pre-Algebra with Manipulatives

Vocabulary Review

constant rate of change
a consistant ratio of vertical change to horizontal change
Example slope $= \frac{1}{2}$
(Lesson 8-5)

Equations and Tables Recall that the equation for a linear function can be written in the form $y = mx + b$, where m represents the constant rate of change. Therefore, you can determine whether a function is linear from its equation.

EXAMPLE 2 Identify Functions Using Equations

Determine whether each equation represents a *linear* or *nonlinear* function. Explain.

a. $3x + y = 7$

This equation represents a linear function because it can be written as $y = -3x + 7$.

b. $y = 2x^2$

This is nonlinear because x is squared and the equation cannot be written in the form $y = mx + b$.

Check Your Progress

2A. $y = \frac{1}{5}x$

2B. $y = 2^x$

Personal Tutor glencoe.com

2A. Linear; it can be written in the form $y = mx + b$.

2B. Nonlinear; it cannot be written in the form $y = mx + b$.

A nonlinear function does not increase or decrease at the same rate. You can check this by using a table.

The tables represent the functions in Example 2.

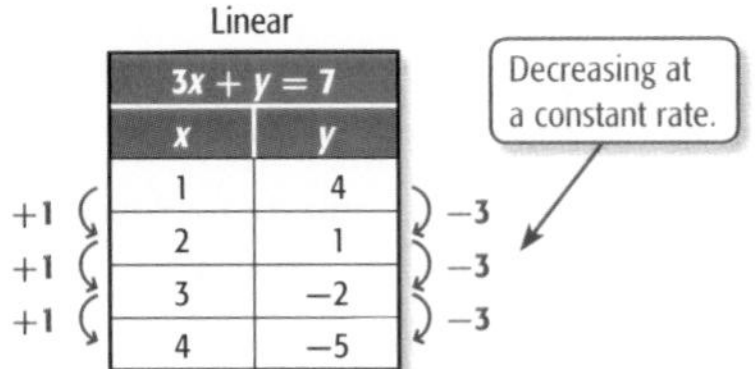
Linear

$3x + y = 7$	
x	y
1	4
2	1
3	−2
4	−5

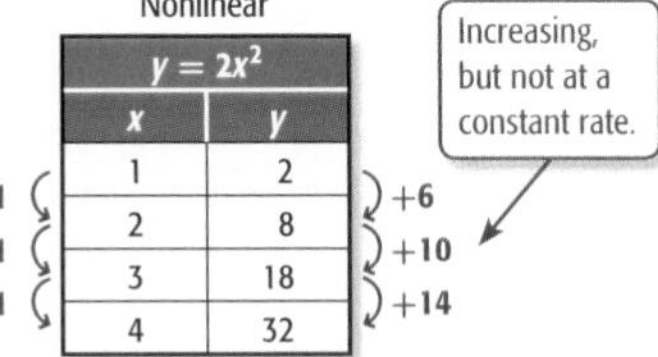
Nonlinear

$y = 2x^2$	
x	y
1	2
2	8
3	18
4	32

Problem-Solving Tip

Make a Graph You can plot a few points on a coordinate plane to determine whether the data in a table represent a linear function.

EXAMPLE 3 Identify Functions Using Tables

Determine whether each table represents a *linear* or *nonlinear* function. Explain.

a.

x	y
2	1
4	2
6	3
8	4

+2, +2, +2; +1, +1, +1

As x increases by 2, y increases by 1. So, this is a linear function.

b.

x	y
1	1
2	4
3	9
4	16

+1, +1, +1; +3, +5, +7

As x increases by 1, y increases by a greater amount each time. So, this is a nonlinear function.

Check Your Progress

3A.

x	y
1	−5
2	−20
3	−45
4	−80

3B.

x	y
3	10
6	14
9	18
12	22

Personal Tutor glencoe.com

3A. Nonlinear; as x increases by 1, y decreases by a greater amount each time.

3B. Linear; as x increases by 3, y increases by 4.

Graphs of Nonlinear Functions

Example 1 shows how to identify linear and nonlinear functions using graphs.

Formative Assessment

Use the Check Your Progress exercises after each Example to determine students' understanding of concepts.

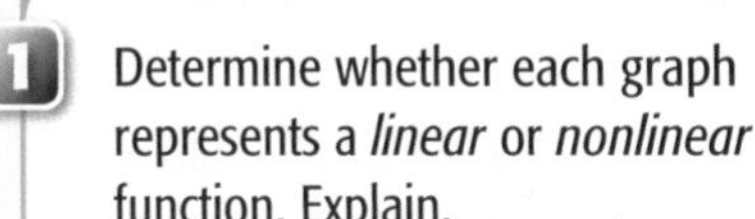

Additional Example

1 Determine whether each graph represents a *linear* or *nonlinear* function. Explain.

a.

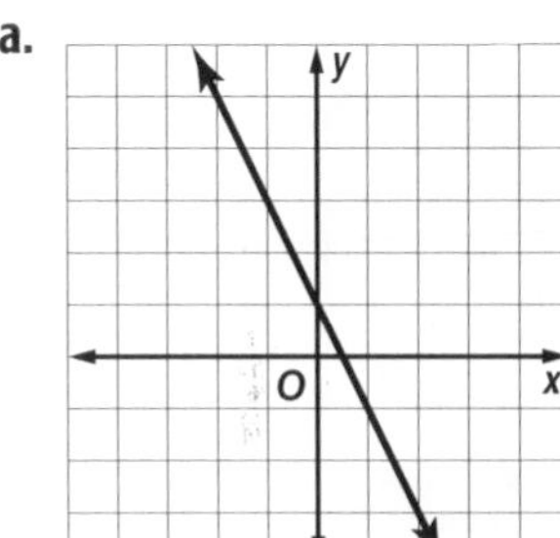

Linear; the graph is a line.

b.

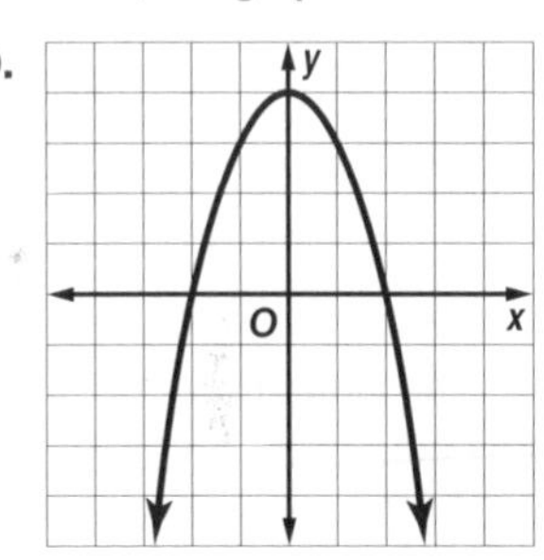

Nonlinear; the graph is a curve.

Additional Examples also in Interactive Classroom PowerPoint® Presentations

Differentiated Instruction

Logical Have students make a function table comparing altitude in feet (x) and temperature in °C (y). The altitudes are 0, 1500, 6000, and 9000 feet. The corresponding temperatures are 15, 5, −26, and −44°C. Have students graph the data and determine the altitude if the temperature is − 32°C. 7000 feet Have them examine their graphs and discuss whether the function is linear or nonlinear. linear

Equations and Tables

Examples 2 and 3 show how to identify functions using equations and tables. **Example 4** uses a table to identify a real-life function.

Additional Examples

2 Determine whether each equation represents a *linear* or *nonlinear* function. Explain.

a. $y = -5x - 4$ Linear; equation is in the form $y = mx + b$.

b. $y = 2x^2 + 3$ Nonlinear; x is squared and equation cannot be written in the form $y = mx + b$.

3 Determine whether each table represents a *linear* or *nonlinear* function. Explain.

a.

x	y
2	25
4	17
6	9
8	1

Linear; as x increases by 2, y decreases by 8.

b.

x	y
5	2
8	4
11	8
14	16

Nonlinear; as x increases by 3, y increases by a greater amount each time.

4 **OIL** The table shows the price of oil futures per barrel for six months. Describe whether the data represent a *linear* or *nonlinear* function. Nonlinear; as the months increase by 1, the price changes by a different amount each time.

Oil Futures	
Month	Price
1	94.44
2	94.57
3	94.44
4	94.26
5	94.00
6	93.50

Real-World Career

Aerospace Technician Aerospace technicians construct, test, and maintain aircraft and space vehicles. They use software to produce drawings and models used to construct aircraft. A minimum of a two-year degree in engineering or aerospace technology is usually required.

Source: Virginia Department of Education

Real-World EXAMPLE 4 Real-Life Functions

SPACE The table shows the flight data for a model rocket launch. Describe whether the data for the ascent more closely represent a *linear* or *nonlinear* function.

Ascent		Descent	
Time (s)	Height (m)	Time (s)	Height (m)
0	0	7	140
1	38	8	130
2	74	9	120
3	106	10	110
4	128	11	100
5	138	12	90
6	142	13	80

Understand You need to determine whether the data represent a linear or nonlinear function.

Plan Find the change in height for each second. Make a table.

Solve Subtract to find the changes in height.

s	0	1	2	3	4	5	6
m	0	38	74	106	128	138	142

+38 +36 +31 +22 +10 +4

As the seconds increase by 1, the height of the rocket changes by a different amount each time. So, this is a nonlinear function.

Check If you were to graph the function, you would see that the points do not lie on a straight line.

Check Your Progress 4. Linear; as the seconds increase by 1, the height of the rocket decreases by 10.

4. **SPACE** Use the data for the model rocket launch shown above. Describe whether the data for the descent more closely represent a *linear* or *nonlinear* function. Explain.

Personal Tutor glencoe.com

Check Your Understanding

Example 1 p. 504

Determine whether each graph, equation, or table represents a *linear* or *nonlinear* function. Explain. 2. Nonlinear; graph is a curve.

1. 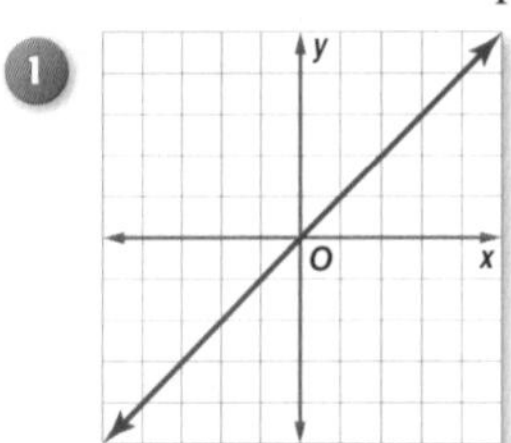

Linear; graph is a straight line.

2. 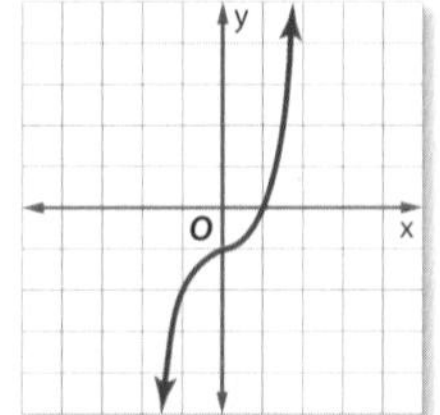

Examples 2 and 3 p. 505

3. $y = -x - 12$ 4. $5xy = 25$

3–6. See margin.

5.

x	y
1	6
2	9
3	12
4	15

6.

x	y
1	1
2	8
3	27
4	64

7. Nonlinear; the rate of change is not constant.

Example 4 p. 506

7. **FINANCIAL LITERACY** The amount of money in Juana's savings account for each of the last six months is \$100, \$100.50, \$101.00, \$101.51, \$102.02, and \$102.53. Do these data represent a *linear* or *nonlinear* function? Explain.

Tips for New Teachers

Linear Functions Point out that the degree of the independent variable in a function determines the shape of its graph. In the equation for a linear function $y = mx + b$, x has a degree of 1. So, its graph is a straight line.

Additional Answers

3. Linear; the equation is written in the form $y = mx + b$.
4. Nonlinear; the equation cannot be written in the form $y = mx + b$.
5. Linear; as x increases by 1, y increases by 3.
6. Nonlinear; as x increases by 1, y increases by a greater amount each time.

Practice and Problem Solving

= **Step-by-Step Solutions** begin on page R11. **Extra Practice** begins on page 810.

Example 1 p. 504

Determine whether each graph, equation, or table represents a *linear* or *nonlinear* function. Explain.

8. Nonlinear; graph is a curve.
9. Linear; graph is a straight line.
10. Nonlinear; graph is a curve.
11. Nonlinear; graph is a curve.
12. Linear; the equation is written in the form $y = mx + b$.
13. Linear; the equation is written in the form $y = mx + b$.

8.

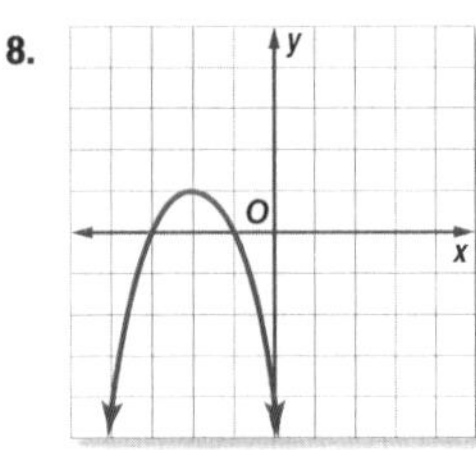

9.

10.

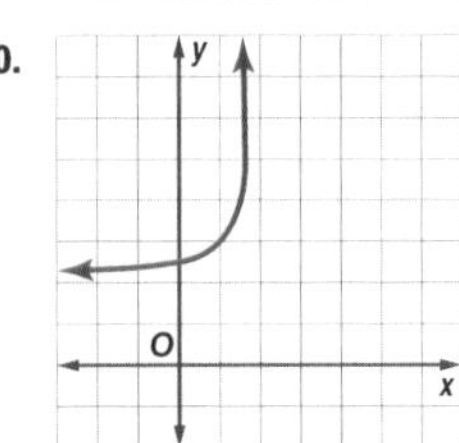

11

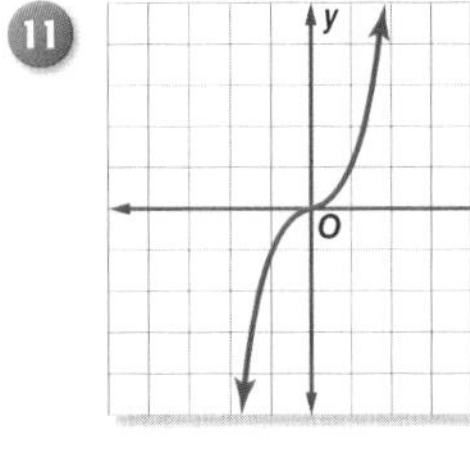

Example 2 p. 505

12. $3x = y$ **13.** $y = 7$ **14.** $xy = -4$ **15.** $y = \frac{10}{x}$

Example 3 p. 505

14. Nonlinear; the equation cannot be written in the form $y = mx + b$.

16.

x	y
1	21
2	16
3	11
4	6

17.

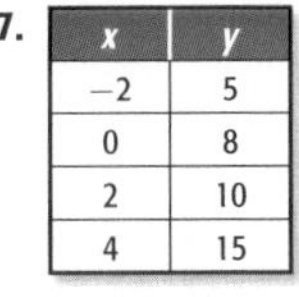

x	y
−2	5
0	8
2	10
4	15

18.

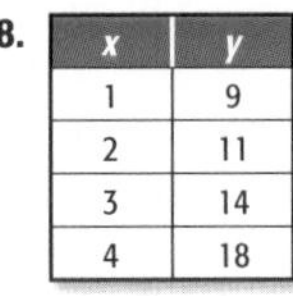

x	y
1	9
2	11
3	14
4	18

19.

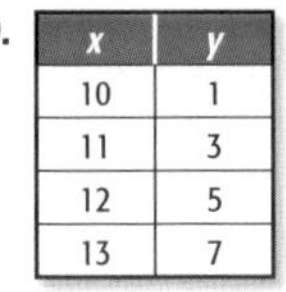

x	y
10	1
11	3
12	5
13	7

Example 4 p. 506

15. Nonlinear; the equation cannot be written in the form $y = mx + b$.
16. Linear; as x increases by 1, y decreases by 5.
17. Nonlinear; as x increases by 2, y increases by a different amount each time.
18. Nonlinear; as x increases by 1, y increases by a greater amount each time.
19. Linear; as x increases by 1, y increases by 2.

20. HEALTH The chart below shows the average height in centimeters of a teenage boy. Do these data represent a linear or nonlinear function? Explain.

Age	13	14	15	16	17	18
Height (cm)	156	163	170	173	175	176

20–22. See margin.

21. BASEBALL The graph shows the average price of a baseball ticket in recent years. Would you describe the change in price as a linear function? Explain.

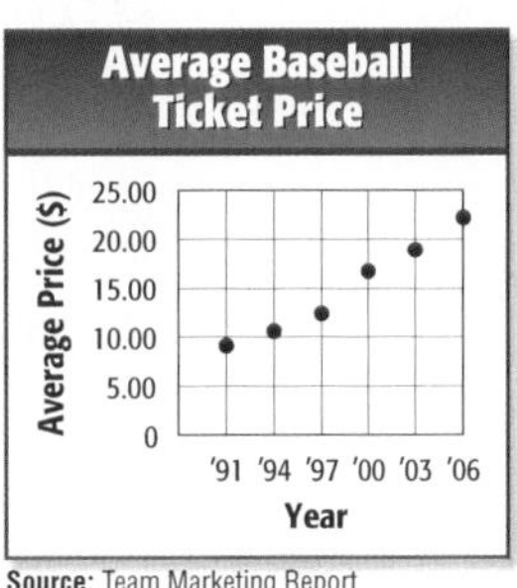

Source: Team Marketing Report

22. FINANCIAL LITERACY Adam puts $15 into his savings account every month. Suzanne tries to double the amount of money in her bank account every month. Not including interest, which person's monthly balance represents a linear function? Explain why the other person's balance is best represented by a nonlinear function.

Focus on Mathematical Content

Linear and Nonlinear Functions Linear functions have graphs that are straight lines, representing a constant rate of change between any two points on the graph. Nonlinear functions do not have a constant rate of change. They are represented by graphs that are curves. Any equation that cannot be written in the form $y = mx + b$ is not linear. For example, $y = \frac{3}{x}$ is nonlinear. It cannot be written in the form $y = mx + b$ because x is in the denominator.

TEACH with TECH

STUDENT RESPONSE SYSTEM Create a presentation with several functions and ask students if each is linear or nonlinear. Have students respond with 1 for linear or 2 for nonlinear.

3 PRACTICE

Formative Assessment

Use Exercises 1–7 to check for understanding.

Use the chart at the bottom of this page to customize assignments for your students.

Additional Answers

20. Nonlinear; the amount of change in height for each age is not constant.

21. Nonlinear; the amount of change in price each year is not constant.

22. Adam's bank account; his account increases by a fixed amount each month. Suzanne's bank account increases by a different amount each month.

Differentiated Homework Options

Level	Assignment	Two-Day Option	
AL Basic	8–21, 29–31, 33–52	9–21 odd, 34–37	8–20 even, 29–31, 33, 38–52
OL Core	9–21 odd, 22–31, 33–52	8–21, 34–37	22–31, 33, 38–52
BL Advanced	22–46 (optional: 47–52)		

Study Guide and Intervention
CRM pp. 42–43 AL OL ELL

Practice
CRM p. 45 AL OL BL ELL

Word Problem Practice
CRM p. 46 AL OL BL

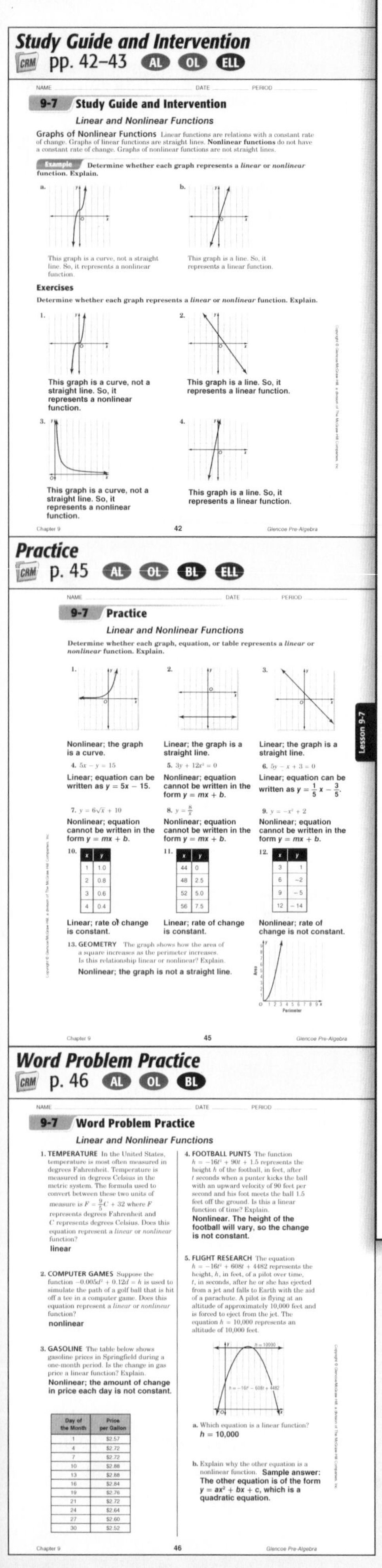

> **StudyTip**
> The area of a circle is the amount of surface *inside* the circle. The circumference of a circle is the distance *around* the circle.

23. **MULTIPLE REPRESENTATIONS** In this problem, you will investigate area and circumference of circle *S*. The formula for finding the area *A* of a circle given the radius *r* is $A = 3.14r^2$. The formula for finding the circumference of a circle is $C = 6.28r$.

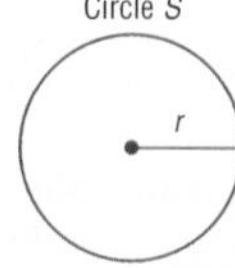

a. **TABULAR** Copy and complete the table at the right. **a–d. See Chapter 9 Answer Appendix.**

b. **GRAPHICAL** Graph the points whose ordered pairs are (r, C).

c. **GRAPHICAL** Graph the points whose ordered pairs are (r, A).

d. **ANALYTICAL** Does either graph represent a linear relationship? If so, name the slope of the line.

Radius r	Circumference C	Area A
1	■	■
2	■	■
3	■	■
4	■	■
5	■	■

Determine whether each situation represents a *linear* or *nonlinear* function. Explain your reasoning.

24. Amanda earns $7.80 per hour.

25. As the number of inches increases by 1, the number of centimeters increases by about 2.54. **Linear; the rate of change is constant.**

26. The population of a city increases by 3% each year.

27. **MONEY** Ben does yard work to earn extra money. Mrs. Rodriquez pays him $10 per hour. Mrs. Benson pays him $100 per weekend. For which situation is Ben's pay a linear function of the number of hours he works? Explain.

28. **GEOMETRY** The table below shows the corresponding width for the possible different lengths of a rectangle with a fixed area of 20 square feet. Graph these data on a coordinate plane. Do the data represent a linear function? Justify your solution. **No; the graph is a curve. See Chapter 9 Answer Appendix.**

Length (ft)	1	2	3	4	5	6	8	10
Width (ft)	20	10	$6\frac{2}{3}$	5	4	$3\frac{1}{3}$	$2\frac{1}{2}$	2

H.O.T. Problems
Use Higher-Order Thinking Skills

29. **WRITING IN MATH** Describe your preferred method for determining whether a function is linear or nonlinear given its equation. **See students' work.**

30. **OPEN ENDED** Describe a real-world situation that represents a linear function.

31. **WHICH ONE DOESN'T BELONG?** Identify the equation that does not belong with the other three. Explain your reasoning.

$y = \frac{1}{3}x - x$	$xy = 3$	$5x + y = 6$	$x = 5y$

32. **CHALLENGE** Are all straight lines linear functions? Explain.

33. **WRITING IN MATH** Describe the different representations that are possible for a function. Explain how you can use each representation to determine whether a function is linear. **See Chapter 9 Answer Appendix.**

Answers:

24. Linear; $7.80 per hour is the constant rate of change

26. No; the graph is a curve.

27. Sample answer: Ben's pay from Mrs. Rodriquez is a linear relationship. As his hours increase, his pay increases by $10. His pay does not increase when he works for Mrs. Benson.

30. Sample answer: The cost of movie tickets for students. As the number of movie tickets increases by 1, the total cost increases by the amount of a movie ticket.

31. $xy = 3$ because it is not a linear equation.

32. No; a vertical line based on a rule such as $x = 3$ is not a function because there is more than one y value for the x value

Enrichment
CRM p. 47 OL BL

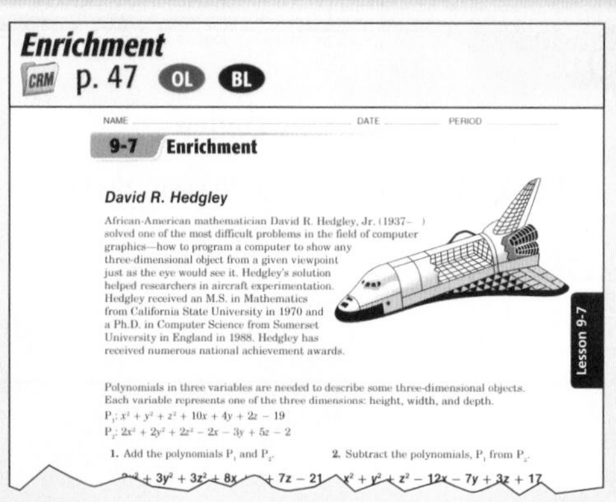

Multiple Representations In Exercise 23, students use formulas, a table, and function graphs to relate radius, circumference, and area of a circle.

Standardized Test Practice

34. Which graph represents a linear function? C

A

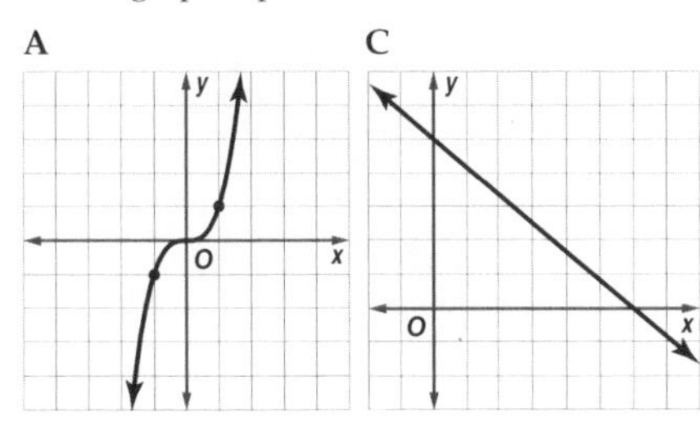

C

B

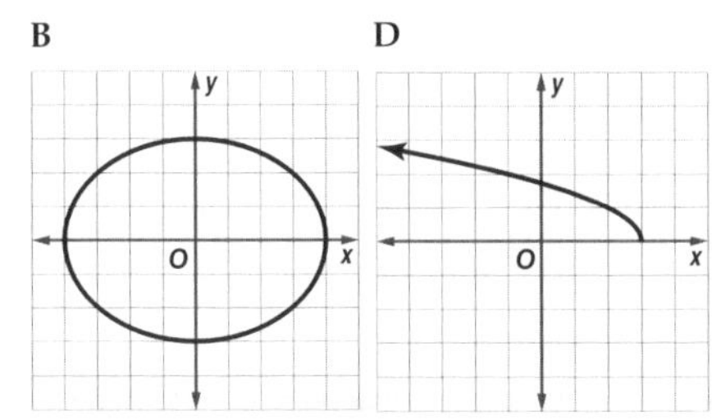

D

35. **EXTENDED RESPONSE** Does the equation for the area of a square represent a linear or nonlinear function? Use a table to explain your reasoning. See margin.

36. Which of the following equations represents a nonlinear function? J

F $y = 3x + 9$ H $x = -2$
G $y = 9$ J $xy = -3$

37. Which of the following equations describes the data in the table? B

x	−6	−4	−2	0	2
y	32	12	0	−4	0

A $y = 2x - 4$ C $y = 4x + 8$
B $y = x^2 - 4$ D $x^2 + y = 8$

Spiral Review

Simplify. (Lesson 9-6)

38. $4(x^3)^4$ $4x^{12}$
39. $(-6p^2)^3$ $-216p^6$
40. $(2yw^5)^6$ $64y^6w^{30}$

Express each number in scientific notation. (Lesson 9-5)

41. 80,000,000 8×10^7
42. 697,000 6.97×10^5
43. 0.059 5.9×10^{-2}

44. **OCEANS** Rank the oceans in the table by area from least to greatest. (Lesson 9-5) Arctic, Indian, Atlantic, Pacific

Ocean	Area (sq mi)
Arctic	5.44×10^6
Atlantic	3.18×10^7
Indian	2.89×10^7
Pacific	6.40×10^7

45. **MONEY** If Simone wants to leave a tip of about 15% on a dinner check of \$23.85, how much should she leave? (Lesson 7-4) About \$3.60

46. **COOKING** Gabriel used $3\frac{3}{4}$ cups of sugar to make $2\frac{1}{2}$ batches of cookies. How much sugar is needed for one batch of cookies? (Lesson 4-4) $1\frac{1}{2}$c

Skills Review

Use a table to graph each function. (Lesson 8-3) 47–52. See Chapter 9 Answer Appendix.

47. $y = x + 5$
48. $y = -2x - 6$
49. $x + y = -8$
50. $x - 3y = -12$
51. $y = -\frac{2}{3}x + 9$
52. $y = \frac{1}{2}x - 4$

Tips for New Teachers

Functions Remind students that not every straight line represents a function. An equation whose graph is a vertical line is not a function. You might also wish to point out to students that the degree of the independent variable determines the shape of the graph of a function.

4 ASSESS

Ticket Out the Door Have students write the answer to the following problem on a small piece of paper and hand it to you. Have them determine whether the equation $x = 8y$ is linear or nonlinear and explain why.

Formative Assessment

Check for student understanding of concepts in Lessons 9-6 and 9-7.

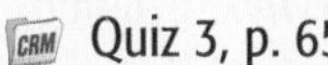

CRM Quiz 3, p. 65

Additional Answer

35. The equation for the area of a square $A = s^2$ represents a nonlinear function. You can construct a table of values and graph the points (s, A) to see that the graph is a curve.

Side	Area
1	1
2	4
3	9
4	16

Differentiated Instruction

BL

Extension In Exercise 15, the graph of the equation $y = \frac{10}{x}$ contains asymptotes. An asymptote is a line that the graph approaches but never crosses. Ask students to graph $y = \frac{10}{x}$ and determine its asymptotes. Discussion questions could include: What makes this graph approach a line and never cross it? What kind of equation could have an asymptote? What would cause a graph like this to shift left or right, up or down?

9-8 Lesson Notes

1 FOCUS

Vertical Alignment

Before Lesson 9-8
Use linear functions to solve problems.

Lesson 9-8
Graph quadratic functions. Use quadratic functions to solve problems.

After Lesson 9-8
Connect nonlinear functions to real-world situations.

2 TEACH

Scaffolding Questions

Have students read the *Why?* section of the lesson and answer the questions.

Ask:

- What is the maximum height that the flight reaches? 32,000 ft
- Is the rate of change constant? no
- What kind of values are used for the domain and range of the function shown by the flight? Explain. Only positive values are used because time and altitude for the flight cannot be negative.

Additional Answer

a. The graph looks like a curve that goes up and back down at the same angle.

9-8 Quadratic Functions

Then
You used linear functions to solve problems. (Lesson 8-7)

Now
- Graph quadratic functions.
- Use quadratic functions to solve problems.

New Vocabulary
quadratic function
parabola

Math Online
glencoe.com
- Extra Examples
- Personal Tutor
- Self-Check Quiz
- Homework Help

Why?

People on *zero-gravity flights* experience weightlessness, similar to what astronauts experience in space flight. Weightlessness occurs because the plane is flown in a *parabolic* path, climbing and diving at slopes of about 45 degrees.

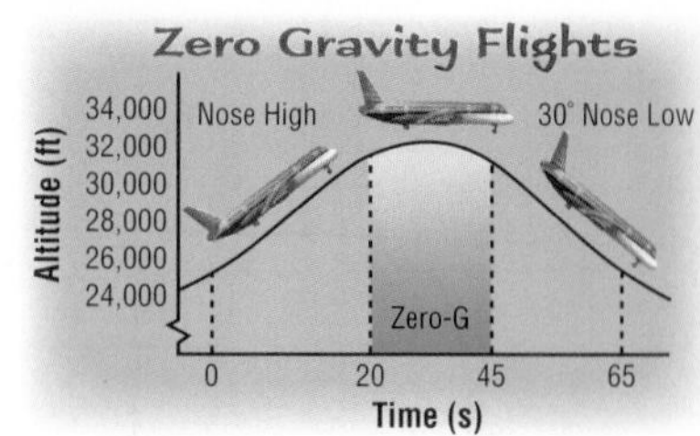

a. Describe the graph. **See margin.**

b. How is this graph different from linear graphs? **It does not have a constant rate of change. It is a curve, not a line.**

Graph Quadratic Functions The function that describes the flight path above is an example of a quadratic function. A **quadratic function** can be written in the form $y = ax^2 + bx + c$, where $a \neq 0$. The graph of a quadratic function is called a **parabola**.

Key Concept — Quadratic Function

For Your FOLDABLE

Words A quadratic function can be described by an equation of the form $y = ax^2 + bx + c$, where $a \neq 0$.

Example $y = x^2 - 4$

Graph

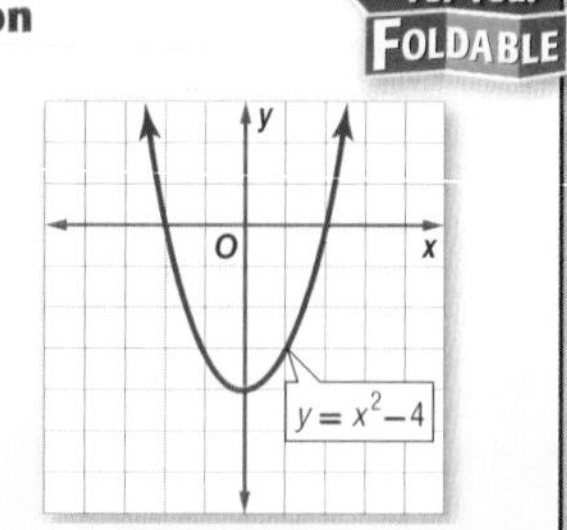

EXAMPLE 1 Graph Quadratic Functions

Graph $y = x^2 - 2$.

Make a table of values, plot the ordered pairs, and connect the points with a curve.

x	$y = x^2 - 2$	(x, y)
−2	$y = (-2)^2 - 2 = 2$	(−2, 2)
−1	$y = (-1)^2 - 2 = -1$	(−1, −1)
0	$y = (0)^2 - 2 = -2$	(0, −2)
1	$y = (1)^2 - 2 = -1$	(1, −1)
2	$y = (2)^2 - 2 = 2$	(2, 2)

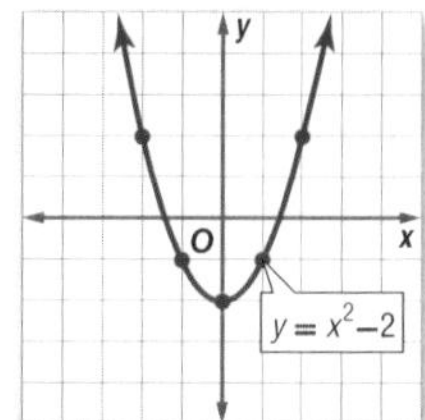

Check Your Progress

1. Graph $y = \frac{1}{4}x^2$. **See Chapter 9 Answer Appendix.**

Personal Tutor glencoe.com

Lesson 9-8 Resources

Resource	Approaching-Level	On-Level	Beyond-Level	English Learners
Teacher Edition	• Differentiated Instruction, p. 511	• Differentiated Instruction, p. 511	• Differentiated Instruction, p. 514	
Chapter Resource Masters	• Study Guide and Intervention, pp. 48–49 • Skills Practice, p. 50 • Practice, p. 51 • Word Problem Practice, p. 52 • Graphing Calculator, p. 54	• Study Guide and Intervention, pp. 48–49 • Skills Practice, p. 50 • Practice, p. 51 • Word Problem Practice, p. 52 • Enrichment, p. 53 • Graphing Calculator, p. 54	• Practice, p. 51 • Word Problem Practice, p. 52 • Enrichment, p. 53 • Graphing Calculator, p. 54	• Study Guide and Intervention, pp. 48–49 • Skills Practice, p. 50 • Practice, p. 51 • Graphing Calculator, p. 54
Transparencies	• 5-Minute Check Transparency	• 5-Minute Check Transparency	• 5-Minute Check Transparency	• 5-Minute Check Transparency
Other	• Study Notebook • Teaching Pre-Algebra with Manipulatives	• Study Notebook • Teaching Pre-Algebra with Manipulatives	• Study Notebook	• Study Notebook • Teaching Pre-Algebra with Manipulatives

Watch Out!

Squares Square x before finding the opposite.

EXAMPLE 2 Graph Quadratic Functions

Graph $y = -x^2$.

Make a table of values, then plot the ordered pairs.

x	$y = -x^2$	(x, y)
−2	$y = -(-2)^2 = -4$	(−2, −4)
−1	$y = -(-1)^2 = -1$	(−1, −1)
0	$y = -(0)^2 = 0$	(0, 0)
1	$y = -(1)^2 = -1$	(1, −1)
2	$y = -(2)^2 = -4$	(2, −4)

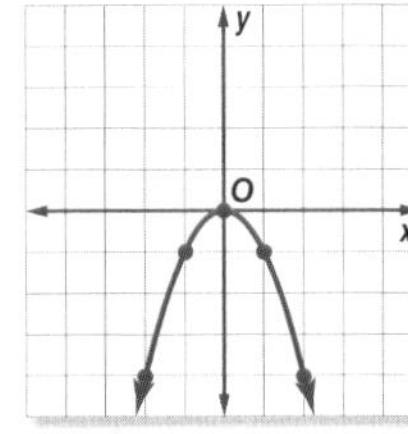

Check Your Progress

2. Graph $y = 2x^2 + 1$. **See Chapter 9 Answer Appendix.**

Personal Tutor glencoe.com

Use Quadratic Functions You can use quadratic functions to model and analyze real-world situations.

EXAMPLE 2 Use Quadratic Functions

BASEBALL Georgia threw a baseball into the air. The equation that gives the ball's height in meters h as a function of time t is $h = -4.9t^2 + 16t + 1.4$.

a. Graph this equation and interpret your graph. What was the height of the ball after 3 seconds?

Make a table of values, then plot the ordered pairs.

t	$h = -4.9t^2 + 16t + 1.4$	(t, h)
0	$1.4 = -4.9(0)^2 + 16(0) + 1.4$	(0, 1.4)
1	$12.5 = -4.9(1)^2 + 16(1) + 1.4$	(1, 12.5)
2	$13.8 = -4.9(2)^2 + 16(2) + 1.4$	(2, 13.8)
3	$5.3 = -4.9(3)^2 + 16(3) + 1.4$	(3, 5.3)

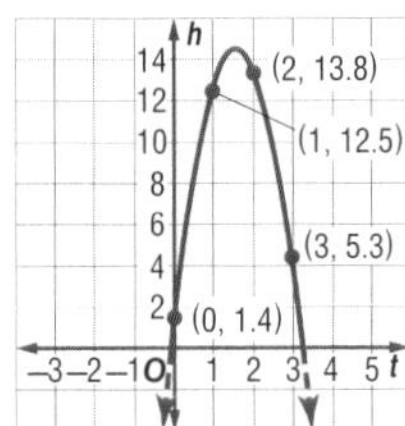

- The maximum height of the ball occurred between 1 and 2 seconds.
- The ball was released at 1.4 meters (0 seconds).
- The ball hit the ground between 3 and 4 seconds (0 meters).
- At 3 seconds, the ball was 5.3 meters above the ground (3, 5.3).

b. What values of the domain and range are unreasonable? Explain.

Unreasonable values for the domain and range would be any negative numbers because neither time nor height can be negative.

Review Vocabulary

Domain the set of x-values, or input, of a function (Lesson 1-4)
Range the set of y-values, or output, of a function (Lesson 1-4)

Check Your Progress

3. **FRAMES** Mei is building a picture frame, and she wants the width to be $\frac{2}{3}$ the length. Graph the equation that models the area of the framed picture. What is the area of the picture if the width is 6 inches? **54 in^2; See Chapter 9 Answer Appendix for graph.**

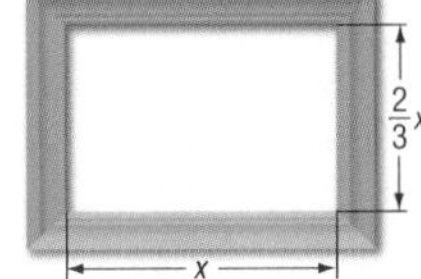

Personal Tutor glencoe.com

Differentiated Instruction

students have difficulty graphing quadratic functions that do not model real-world situations,

suggest that they first make a table using only zero and positive values for x. Graph the ordered pairs for these values and sketch the curve. Then put the opposite values for x on the table, graph these points, and sketch that of the curve. Have students fold their papers along the y-axis to see that the two parts of the parabola match.

Graph Quadratic Functions

Examples 1 and 2 show how to graph quadratic functions.

Formative Assessment

Use the Check Your Progress exercises after each example to determine students' understanding of concepts.

Additional Examples

Graph $y = -x^2 - 3$.

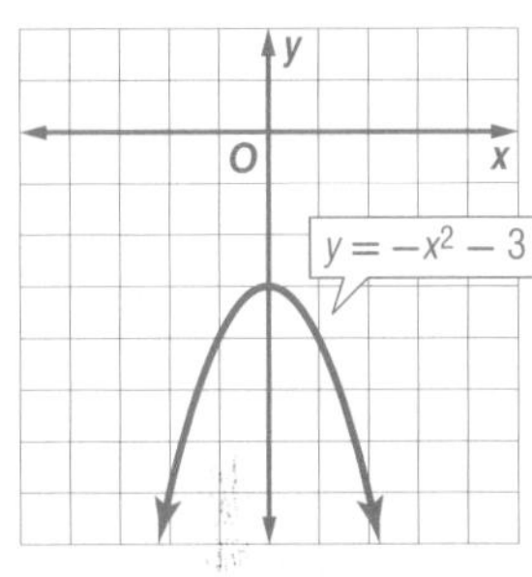

Graph $y = -2x^2$.

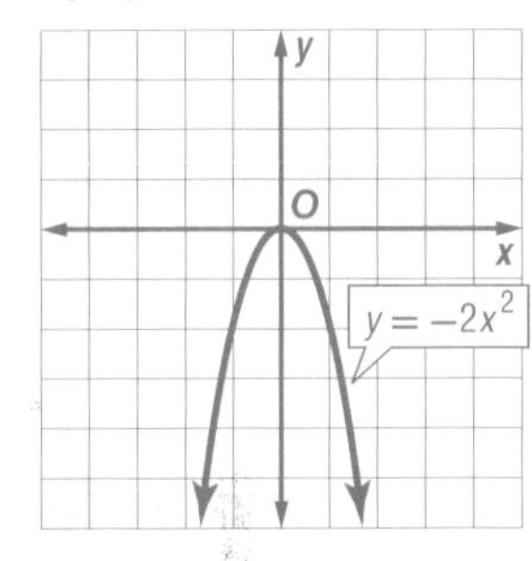

Additional Examples also in Interactive Classroom PowerPoint® Presentations

IWB INTERACTIVE WHITEBOARD READY

Use Quadratic Functions

Example 3 shows how to use quadratic functions to solve a real-world problem.

Tips for New Teachers

Analyze Graphs Students can solve problems by analyzing graphs. Important points on the graph include where the graph crosses the x- and y-axes at the top or bottom of the graph, also called the *maximum* and *minimum.*

Additional Example

3 **SKYDIVING** The distance, d, in feet that a skydiver falls can be found using the equation $d = 16t^2$.

a. Graph this equation and interpret your graph. How far will the skydiver fall in 4.5 seconds? 324 ft

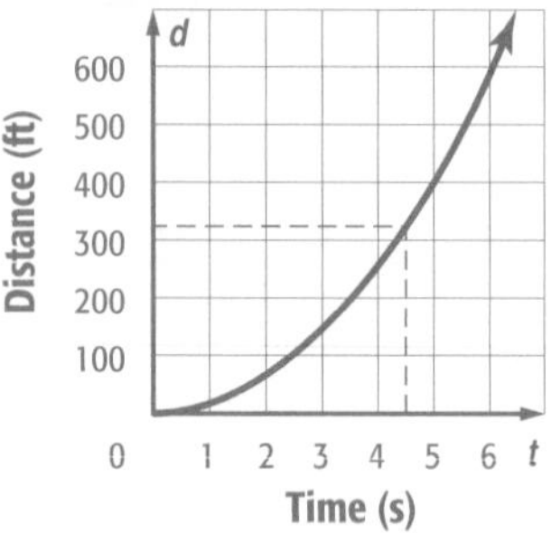

b. What values of the domain and range are unreasonable? Explain. Any negative numbers would be unreasonable for both domain and range because neither the time nor the distance can be negative.

Focus on Mathematical Content

Quadratic Functions The graph of a quadratic equation in the form $y = ax^2 + bx + c$, where $a \neq 0$, is a parabola that can open up or down. The vertex is the highest or lowest point. An axis of symmetry divides a parabola into halves that are mirror images of each other.

3 PRACTICE

Formative Assessment

Use Exercises 1–7 to check for understanding.

Use the chart at the bottom of this page to customize assignments for your students.

Check Your Understanding

Examples 1 and 2 pp. 510 and 511

Graph each function. **1–6. See Chapter 9 Answer Appendix.**

1. $y = 2x^2$ **2.** $y = -4x^2$ **3.** $y = \frac{1}{2}x^2$

4. $y = 2x^2 - 2$ **5.** $y = \frac{1}{4}x^2 + 1$ **6.** $y = -3x^2 - 3$

Example 3 p. 511

7. SPORTS A soccer ball is kicked straight up into the air. The height of the ball h after t seconds can be modeled by the equation. $h = -16t^2 + 40t + 2$.

a. Graph this equation and interpret the graph. What is the height of the ball after 2 seconds? **See Chapter 9 Answer Appendix.**

b. What values of the domain and range are unreasonable? Explain. **Sample answer: Any negative values because height and time cannot be negative.**

Practice and Problem Solving

 = **Step-by-Step Solutions** begin on page R11. **Extra Practice** begins on page 810.

Examples 1 and 2 pp. 510 and 511

Graph each function. **8–19. See Chapter 9 Answer Appendix.**

8. $y = x^2$ **9.** $y = x^2 + 1$ **10.** $y = -3x^2$

11. $y = 4x^2$ **12.** $y = x^2 + 2$ **13.** $y = x^2 + 4$

14. $y = -x^2 + 3$ **15.** $y = 2x^2 + 4$ **16.** $y = 2x^2 - 3$

17. $y = -\frac{1}{2}x^2 + 1$ **18.** $y = \frac{1}{2}x^2 + 1$ **19.** $y = -2x^2 + 5$

Example 3 p. 511

20. SPACE Refer to the graph at the beginning of the lesson.

a. Estimate the maximum height of the aircraft during the parabolic maneuver. Round to the nearest thousand **Sample answer: 32,000 ft**

b. Describe the altitude of the aircraft between 20 and 45 seconds, the time in which zero gravity is achieved. **See Chapter 9 Answer Appendix.**

B

21. CARS The function $d = \frac{1}{2}at^2$ represents the distance d that a race car will travel over an amount of time t given the rate of acceleration a.

a. Suppose a car is accelerating at a rate of 7 feet per second each second. Graph this function on the coordinate plane. **See Chapter 9 Answer Appendix.**

b. Use your graph to find the time it would take the car to travel 125 feet. **about 6 seconds**

22a. See Chapter 9 Answer Appendix.

22. CRAFTS Meghan has 30 inches of ribbon to make a rectangular border for a scrapbook page.

a. Write and graph a function to represent the area A of the section inside the border.

b. What should the dimensions of the section be to enclose the maximum area inside the border? (*Hint*: Find the coordinates of the maximum point of the graph.) **8 in. × 8 in.**

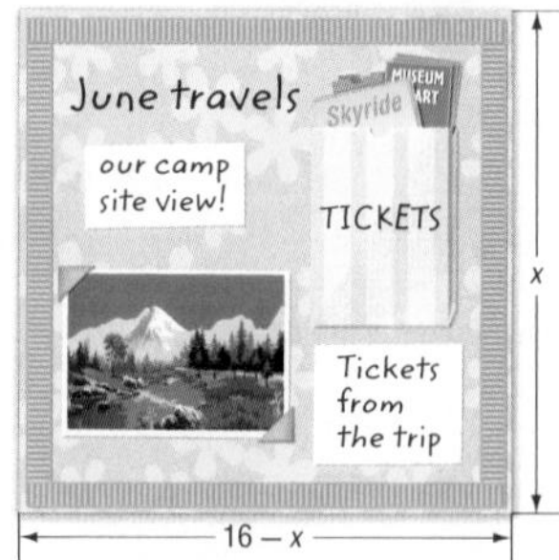

StudyTip

Vertex Form A quadratic equation can also be written in *vertex form* or $y = a(x - h)^2 + k$. In this form, the maximum or minimum point of the graph called the vertex is located at the point (h, k).

Differentiated Homework Options

Level	Assignment	Two-Day Option	
AL Basic	8–20, 25, 26, 29–45	9–19 odd, 30–33	8–20 even, 25, 26, 29, 34–45
OL Core	9–19 odd, 20–26, 29–45	8–20, 30–33	21–26, 29, 34–45
BL Advanced	21–41 (optional: 42–45)		

23. **MULTIPLE REPRESENTATIONS** In this problem, you will examine a system of equations. A square has side length s. **See Chapter 9 Answer Appendix.**

a. **SYMBOLIC** Write equations to represent the perimeter P and the area A of the square in terms of side length s.

b. **TABULAR** Make a table showing the perimeter and area of the square for side lengths 0, 1, 2, 3, and 4 units.

c. **GRAPHICAL** Graph the points whose ordered pairs are (side length, perimeter) and (side length, area). Describe the graphs.

d. **ANALYTICAL** Are there any values for s that have the same numerical value for A and P? How can you tell from the table or graph?

Real-World Link

The tallest waterfall in the world is Angel Falls in Venezuela. It is 979 meters (3212 feet) tall and 107 meters (350 feet) wide.

Source: World Waterfall Database

24. **WATERFALLS** The function $d = -16t^2 + h$ models the distance d in feet a drop of water falls t seconds after it begins its descent from the top of a waterfall of height h. **See students' work.**

a. Choose two waterfalls from the table and graph the function for each waterfall.

b. Use your graph to estimate the time it will take a drop of water to reach the river at the base of each waterfall.

Tallest U.S. Waterfalls

Waterfall	State	Height (meters)
Olo'upena Falls	Hawaii	900
Pu'uka'oku Falls	Hawaii	840
Waihilau	Hawaii	792
Colonial Creek Falls	Washington	788
Johannesburg Falls	Washington	751

Source: World Waterfall Database

H.O.T. Problems Use Higher-Order Thinking Skills

C

25. **OPEN ENDED** Sketch the graph of a quadratic function that has x-intercepts at 2 and 6. **25–29. See Chapter 9 Answer Appendix.**

26. **REASONING** Consider the two equations $y = x^2 + 1$ and $y = -x^2 + 1$.

a. Make a table of values for each equation including 7 ordered pairs. Be sure to include $x = 0$ in each table.

b. Graph the two functions on the same coordinate plane.

c. Compare and contrast both graphs.

d. Make a conjecture about the value of a in the equation $y = ax^2 + bx + c$ and the direction that the curve opens.

e. Make a conjecture about the value of c and the placement of the graph on the y-axis.

CHALLENGE The graph of quadratic functions may have one maximum or one minimum point. The *maximum point* of a graph is the point with the greatest y-value coordinate. The *minimum point* is the point with the least y-value coordinate. Graph each equation. Find the coordinates of each point.

27. the maximum point of the graph of $y = -x^2 + 7$

28. the minimum point of the graph of $y = x^2 - 6$

29. **WRITING IN MATH** Describe the relationships between the different representations of quadratic functions and explain how to translate among these representations.

Multiple Representations In Exercise 23, students use formulas, a table, and function graphs to relate side length to the perimeter and area of a square.

Enrichment
CRM p. 53 OL BL

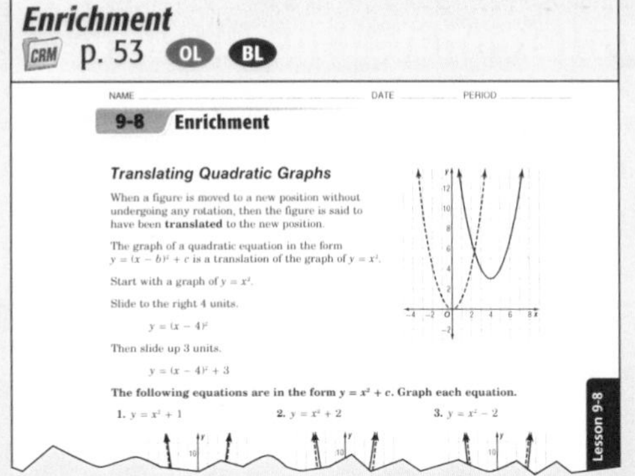

Study Guide and Intervention
CRM pp. 48–49 AL OL ELL

Practice
CRM p. 51 AL OL BL ELL

Word Problem Practice
CRM p. 52 AL OL BL

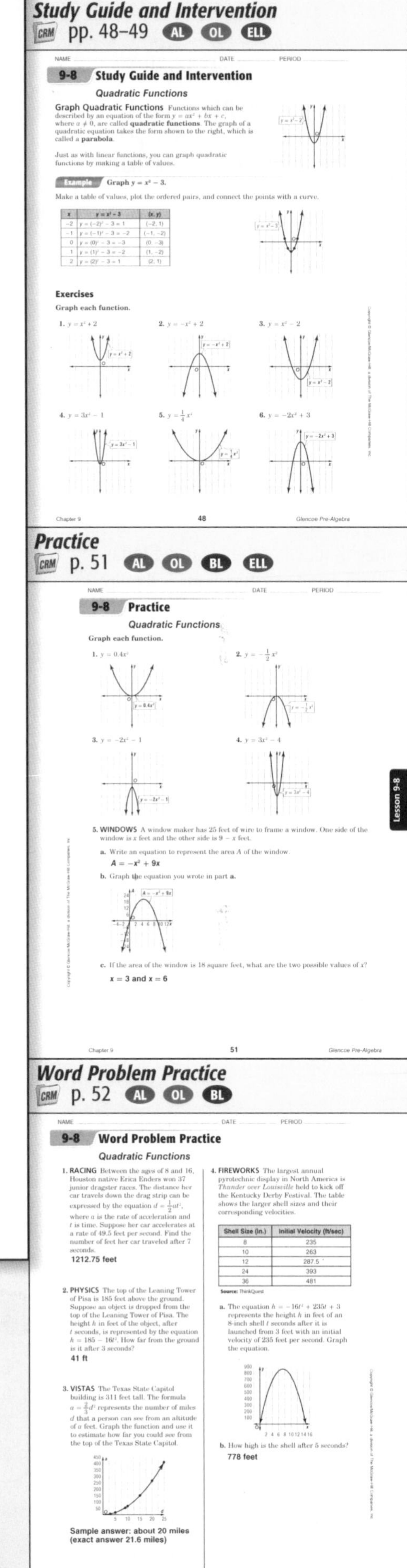

TEACH with TECH

AUDIO RECORDING Give students combinations of graphs, formulas, and tables, and have them record themselves describing the function. Make sure they describe whether the function opens up or down, identify the vertex, and describe how wide or narrow the parabola is.

4 ASSESS

Crystal Ball Have students write how they think what they learned today about quadratic functions will help them on tomorrow's lesson about cubic and exponential functions.

Additional Answer

33a.

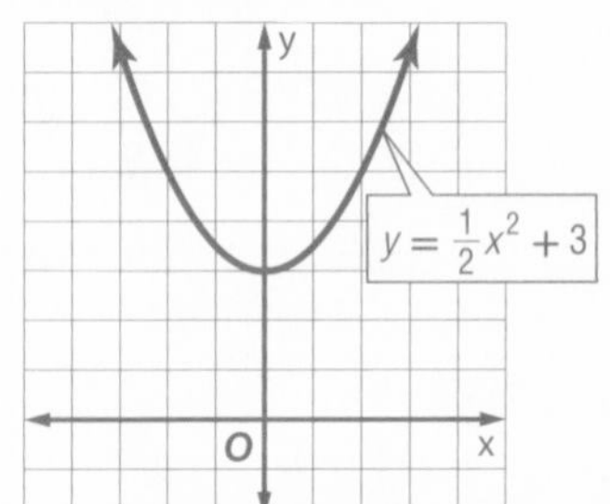

Standardized Test Practice

30. Which graph represents the function $y = -2x^2 - 3$? **C**

A

C

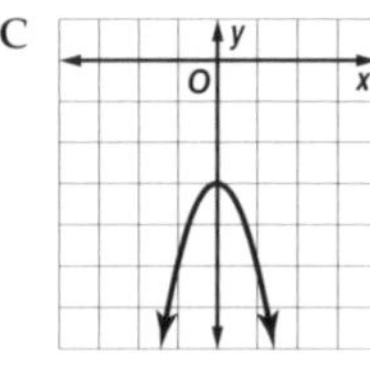

B

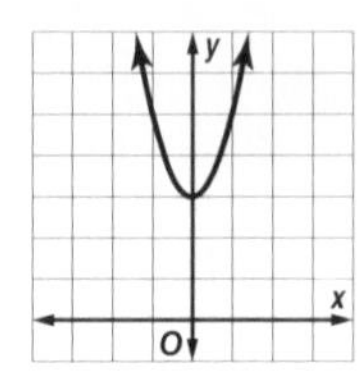

D

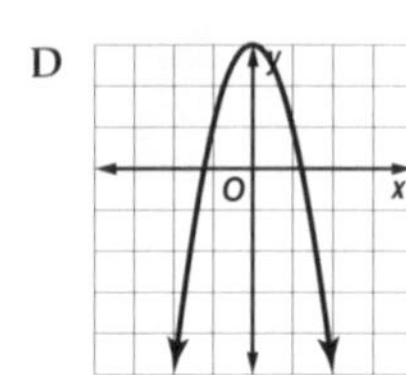

31. What are the x-intercepts of the graph of $y = x^2 - 4$? **G**

F −3, 3

G −2, 2

H 0

J −1, 3

32. The equation $d = \frac{s^2}{20}$, modeled below, can be used to determine the stopping distance d in feet of a car moving at a speed s feet per second. Which of the following is the *best* estimate for the stopping distance of a car traveling at a speed of 15 feet per second? **B**

A 10 ft

B 11 ft

C 12 ft

D 13 ft

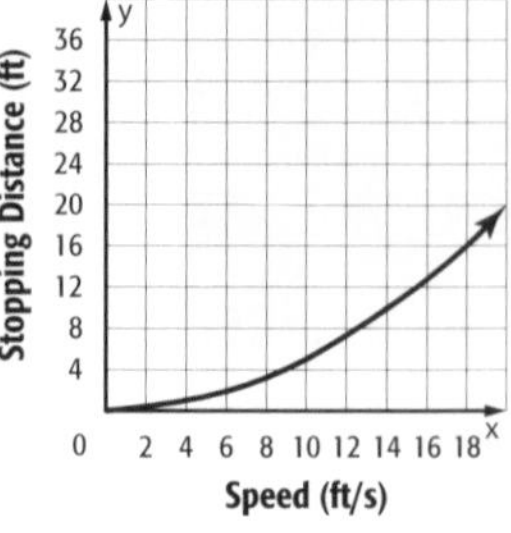

33. EXTENDED RESPONSE The equation $y = \frac{1}{2}x^2 + 3$ is a quadratic function.

a. Graph the function. **See margin.**

b. What is the minimum value of the function? **(0, 3)**

Spiral Review

Determine whether each table represents a *linear* or *nonlinear* function. Explain. (Lesson 9-7)

34.

x	y
−4	13
−2	0
0	4
2	0

Nonlinear; rate of change is not constant.

35.

x	y
8	19
9	22
10	25
11	28

Linear; rate of change is constant.

36.

x	y
9	−2
11	−8
13	−14
15	−20

Linear; rate of change is constant.

Simplify. (Lesson 9-6)

37. $(7^4)^2$ **7^8 or 5,764,801**

38. $(3^4)^0$ **3^0 or 1**

39. $(2c^5d)^3$ **$8c^{15}d^3$**

40. $(10x^3y^4)^2$ **$100x^6y^8$**

41. SCHOOL A biology class had 28 students. Four students transferred out of the class to take chemistry. Find the percent of change in the number of students in the biology class. Round to the nearest tenth. (Lesson 7-6) **−14.3%**

Skills Review

Evaluate each expression. (Lesson 9-1)

42. 2^4 **16**

43. 6^3 **216**

44. $3 \cdot 4^2$ **48**

45. $2 \cdot 4^3$ **128**

Differentiated Instruction BL

Extension Have students graph the equation $x = y^2$. Determine whether it represents a quadratic function. Explain. Not a quadratic function; the graph is a parabola with a vertex at (0, 0) that opens to the right. Two points will have the same x-value with different y-values, such as (4, −2) and (4, 2).

EXTEND **9-8**
Graphing Technology Lab: Family of Quadratic Functions

Math Online glencoe.com
- Other Calculator Keystrokes
- Graphing Technology Personal Tutor

You can use a graphing calculator to investigate families of quadratic functions. The family of quadratic functions has the parent function $y = x^2$.

ACTIVITY

Graph $y = x^2$ and $y = x^2 - 5$ in the standard viewing window and describe how the graphs are related.

Step 1 Clear any existing equations from the [Y=] list by pressing [Y=] [CLEAR].

Step 2 Enter $y = x^2$ in [Y1] and $y = x^2 - 5$ in [Y2] and graph:

[Y=] [X,T,θ,n] [x^2] [ENTER]

[Y=] [X,T,θ,n] [x^2] [–] 5 [Zoom] 6

Press [Trace] and move along each function using the right and left arrow keys. Move from one function to another using the up and down arrow keys.

The graphs are similar in that they are both parabolas. However, the graph of $y = x^2$ has its vertex at (0, 0), and the graph of $y = x^2 - 5$ has its vertex at (0, –5).

Analyze the Results

For Exercises 1–3, graph $y = x^2$, $y = x^2 + 4$, and $y = x^2 - 6$ on the same screen.

1. Compare and contrast the graphs. **See margin.**

2. How does adding or subtracting a constant c from a quadratic function affect its graph? **It shifts the graph vertically c units.**
3. The three parabolas at the right are graphed in the standard viewing window and have the same shape as the graph of $y = x^2$. Write an equation for each, beginning with the lowest parabola. **$y = x^2 - 3$, $y = x^2 + 2$, $y = x^2 + 5$**

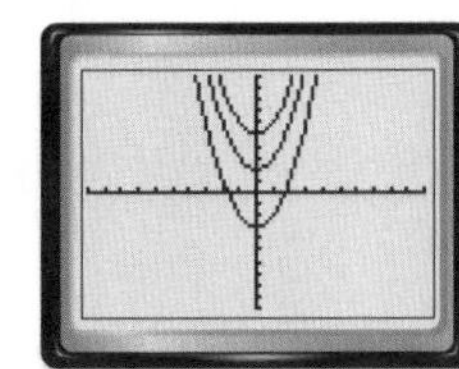

For Exercises 4–6, graph $y = x^2$, $y = 0.5x^2$, and $y = 4x^2$ on the same screen.

4. Compare and contrast the graphs. **They all have the different shapes, the same y-intercept.**
5. How does changing the coefficient of x^2 affect the graph of a parabolic function? **As the absolute value of the coefficient increases, the parabola is narrower.**
6. Without graphing, determine whether the graph of $y = 0.2x^2$ or the graph of $y = 1.2x^2$ is more narrow. Explain. **$y = 1.2x^2$, because $1.2 > 0.2$**
7. **MAKE A CONJECTURE** Compare and contrast the graph of $y = x^2 + 1$ and the graph of each function listed below. **a–c. See margin.**

   a. $y = x^2 - 1$ **b.** $y = 2x^2 + 1$ **c.** $y = -x^2 + 1$

EXTEND **9-8** Lesson Notes

1 FOCUS

Objective Investigate families of quadratic functions on a graphing calculator.

Materials for Each Student
- graphing calculator

Teaching Tip
Students may need to adjust their calculator settings. Have students use the arrow keys to place the cursor on any plot currently highlighted, then press [ENTER], then turn the plot off.

The mode settings determine what type of graph will result. Check that students' mode settings are as follows, in order from top to bottom: Normal, Float, Radian, Func, Connected, Sequential, Real, and Full.

2 TEACH

Working in Cooperative Groups
Have students work in pairs of mixed abilities to complete the Activity.

Ask:
- How does changing the constant affect the graph and the shape of the parabola? The graph shifts vertically, but the shape of the parabola does not change.

Practice Have students complete Exercises 1–7.

3 ASSESS

Formative Assessment
Use Exercise 2 to assess whether students can determine the effect of adding or subtracting a constant c on the graph of a quadratic function. Use Exercise 5 to assess whether students can determine the effect of the coefficient on the graph of a quadratic function.

Additional Answers

1. All the parabolas have the same shape. The graph of $y = x^2 + 4$ is shifted up 4 units from the graph of $y = x^2$. The graph of $y = x^2 - 6$ is shifted down 6 units from the graph of $y = x^2$.

7a. same shape; different y-intercepts

7b. same y-intercept; graph of $y = 2x^2 + 1$ is more narrow

7c. same y-intercept and shape; graph of $y = x^2 + 1$ faces upward and graph of $y = -x^2 + 1$ faces downward

From Concrete to Abstract
Ask students to graph $y = x^2$ and $y = 2x^2 + 6$ on the same screen. Have them compare the graphs.

9-9 Lesson Notes

1 FOCUS

Vertical Alignment

Before Lesson 9-9
Graph linear functions.

Lesson 9-9
Graph cubic functions. Graph exponential functions.

After Lesson 9-9
Connect nonlinear functions to real-world situations.

2 TEACH

Scaffolding Questions

Have students read the *Why?* section of the lesson and answer the questions.

Ask:

- Is the rate of change constant? no
- Describe the graph and what it means. The graph curves upward, which means that the values increase.
- Why do you think no negative values of *x* were used? The length of the dog carrier cannot be negative, nor can its volume. Neither domain nor range can be negative in this situation.

9-9 Cubic and Exponential Functions

Then
You have already graphed linear functions. (Lesson 8-3)

Now
- Graph cubic functions.
- Graph exponential functions.

New Vocabulary
cubic function
exponential function

Math Online
glencoe.com
- Extra Examples
- Personal Tutor
- Self-Check Quiz
- Homework Help

Why?

Dog cages like the one shown come in different sizes that are $4x$ units long, $3x$ units wide, and $3x$ units high. The volume V of the dog cage can be found by multiplying the length, width, and height.

a. Write an equation to represent the volume of the cage. $V = 4x \cdot 3x \cdot 3x$ or $V = 36x^3$

b. In the first quadrant of the coordinate plane, graph the volume as a function of side length. Use 0, 0.5, 1, 1.5, and 2 for the values of x. See Chapter 9 Answer Appendix.

c. Is the function linear, quadratic, or neither? Explain.

c. Neither; the equation cannot be written in the form $y = mx + b$ or $y = ax^2 + bx + c$

Cubic Functions A **cubic function** is a function that can be described by an equation of the form $y = ax^3 + bx^2 + cx + d$, where $a \neq 0$. You can make a table of values to graph a cubic function.

EXAMPLE 1 Graph Cubic Functions

Graph each cubic function.

a. $y = 2x^3$

Make a table of values, plot the ordered pairs, and connect the points with a curve.

x	$y = 2x^3$	(x, y)
−1.2	$y = 2(-1.2)^3 \approx -3.5$	(−1.2, −3.5)
−1	$y = 2(-1)^3 = -2$	(−1, −2)
0	$y = 2(0)^3 = 0$	(0, 0)
1	$y = 2(1)^3 = 2$	(1, 2)
1.2	$y = 2(1.2)^3 \approx 3.5$	(1.2, 3.5)

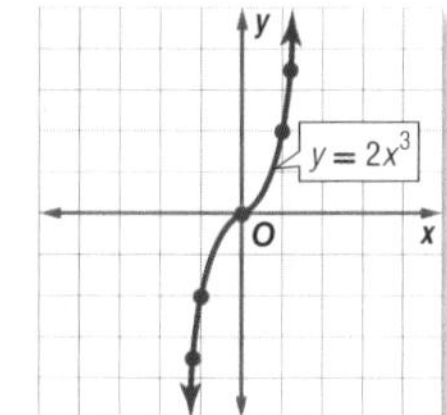

b. $y = x^3 + 3$

x	$y = x^3 + 3$	(x, y)
−1.5	$y = (-1.5)^3 + 3 \approx -0.4$	(−1.5, −0.4)
−1	$y = (-1)^3 + 3 = 2$	(−1, 2)
0	$y = (0)^3 + 3 = 3$	(0, 3)
1	$y = (1)^3 + 3 = 4$	(1, 4)
1.5	$y = (1.5)^3 + 3 \approx 6.4$	(1.5, 6.4)

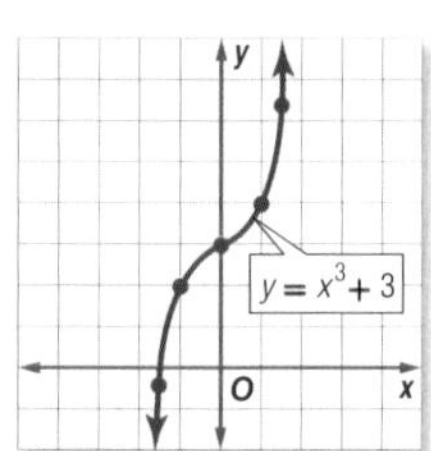

Check Your Progress 1A–1B. See Chapter 9 Answer Appendix.

1A. $y = -4x^3$ **1B.** $y = x^3 + 4$

Personal Tutor glencoe.com

Lesson 9-9 Resources

Resource	Approaching-Level	On-Level	Beyond-Level	English Learners
Teacher Edition			• Differentiated Instruction, pp. 517, 520	
Chapter Resource Masters	• Study Guide and Intervention, pp. 55–56 • Skills Practice, p. 57 • Practice, p. 58 • Word Problem Practice, p. 59	• Study Guide and Intervention, pp. 55–56 • Skills Practice, p. 57 • Practice, p. 58 • Word Problem Practice, p. 59 • Enrichment, p. 60	• Practice, p. 58 • Word Problem Practice, p. 59 • Enrichment, p. 60	• Study Guide and Intervention, pp. 55–56 • Skills Practice, p. 57 • Practice, p. 58
Transparencies	• 5-Minute Check Transparency 9-9	• 5-Minute Check Transparency 9-9	• 5-Minute Check Transparency 9-9	• 5-Minute Check Transparency 9-9
Other	• Study Notebook • Teaching Pre-Algebra with Manipulatives	• Study Notebook • Teaching Pre-Algebra with Manipulatives	• Study Notebook	• Study Notebook • Teaching Pre-Algebra with Manipulatives

EXAMPLE 2 Investigate Cubic Functions

GEOMETRY **The equation $y = \frac{1}{3}(3.14)x^3$ represents the volume of the cone. Graph the equation in the first quadrant.**

x	$y = \frac{1}{3}(3.14)x^3$	(x, y)
0	$y = \frac{1}{3}(3.14)(0)^3 = 0$	(0, 0)
1	$y = \frac{1}{3}(3.14)(1)^3 \approx 1.0$	(1, 1)
2	$y = \frac{1}{3}(3.14)(2)^3 \approx 8.4$	(2, 8.4)
3	$y = \frac{1}{3}(3.14)(3)^3 \approx 28.3$	(3, 28.3)

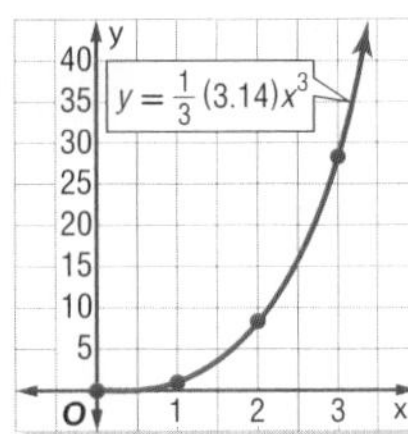

Check Your Progress

2. The volume V of a cube with side length s equals the cube of the side length. Write an equation for the volume and graph the equation in the first quadrant. **$V = s^3$; See Chapter 9 Answer Appendix for graph.**

Personal Tutor glencoe.com

Exponential Functions In equations of linear, quadratic, and cubic functions, the variable was a base. In exponential functions, the variable is an exponent. An **exponential function** is a function that can be described by an equation of the form $y = a^x + c$, where $a \neq 0$ and $a \neq 1$.

Real-World EXAMPLE 3 Graph Exponential Functions

TEXT MESSAGES **Hannah sends a text message to two of her friends. Each of her two friends forwards the text to two friends. Each of those friends forwards it to two friends, and so on. The function $N = 2^x$ represents the total number of text messages sent, where x is the stage of text messages.**

a. Make a table of values.

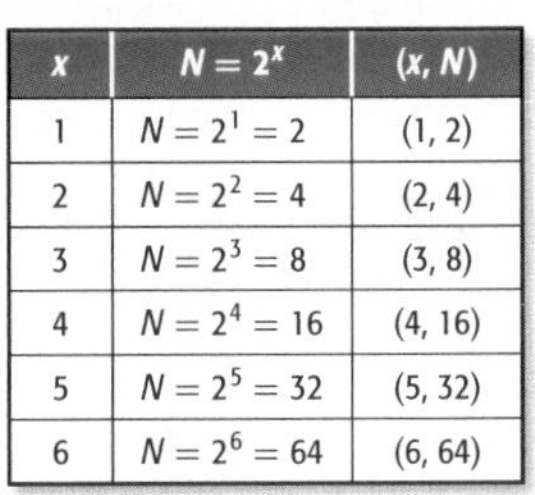

x	$N = 2^x$	(x, N)
1	$N = 2^1 = 2$	(1, 2)
2	$N = 2^2 = 4$	(2, 4)
3	$N = 2^3 = 8$	(3, 8)
4	$N = 2^4 = 16$	(4, 16)
5	$N = 2^5 = 32$	(5, 32)
6	$N = 2^6 = 64$	(6, 64)

b. Graph the values.

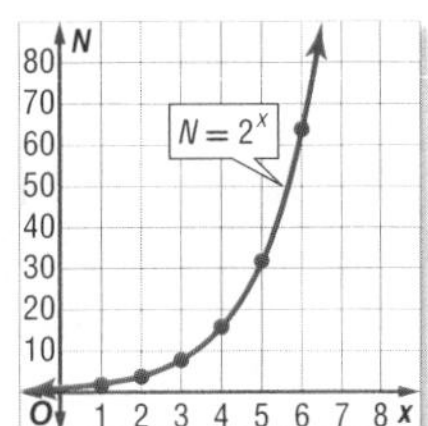

c. In what stage will the number of text messages sent be 64?

Use the graph. The x value that corresponds to the N value of 64 is 6. So, 64 messages will be sent at the 6th stage.

Check Your Progress **6 rounds; See Chapter 9 Answer Appendix for graph.**

3. **TABLE TENNIS** A table tennis tournament has 64 players. Half of the players are eliminated after each round. The function $y = 64\left(\frac{1}{2}\right)^x$ represents the total number of players remaining after each round, where x is number of rounds played. Graph the function. After how many rounds will there be a champion?

Personal Tutor glencoe.com

Real-World Link

The world record for hitting the most balls back and forth in 60 seconds was set in 1993 with 173.

Source: USA Table Tennis

Differentiated Instruction BL

If students would like to explore exponential functions in more depth,

Then have students use a graphing calculator to graph the exponential equation $y = 4^x$. Now have them graph the exponential equation $y = \frac{1}{4^x}$. Ask students to describe the differences between the two graphs.

Cubic Functions

Example 1 shows how to graph cubic functions. **Example 2** shows how to investigate cubic functions.

Formative Assessment

Use the Check Your Progress exercises after each example to determine students' understanding of concepts.

Additional Examples

1 Graph each cubic function.

a. $y = -\frac{1}{2}x^3$

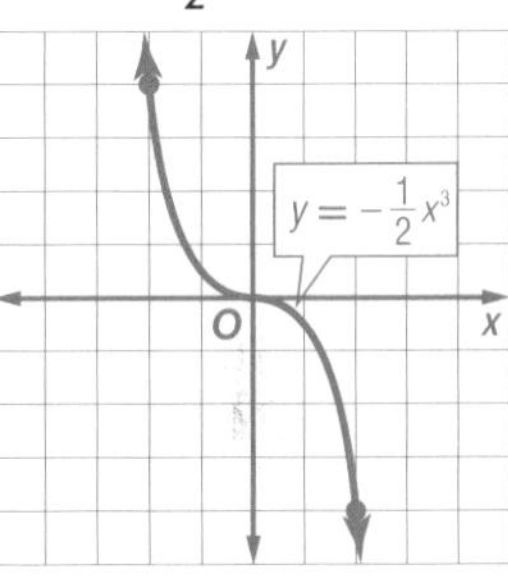

b. $y = 2x^3 + 2$

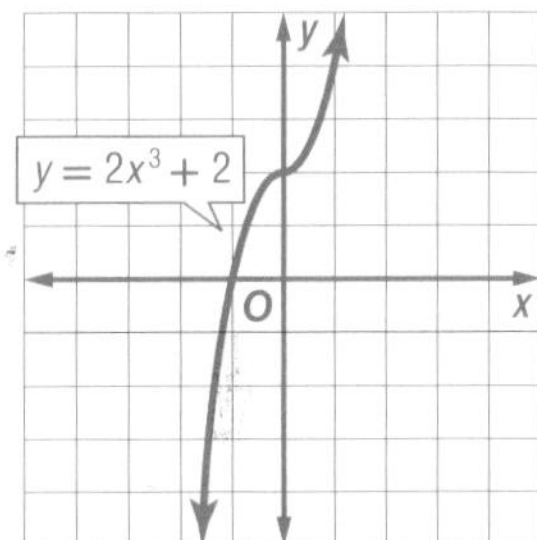

2 **GEOMETRY** The equation $y = \frac{1}{8}x^3$ represents the volume of a cube. Graph the equation in the first quadrant.

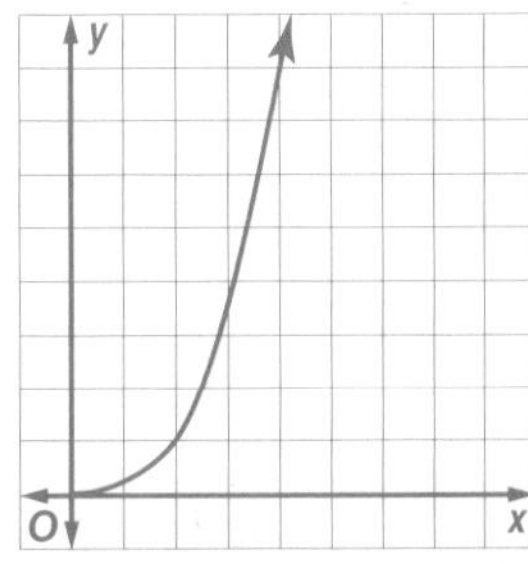

Additional Examples also in Interactive Classroom PowerPoint® Presentations

IWB INTERACTIVE WHITEBOARD READY

Exponential Functions

Examples 3 and **4** show how to graph exponential functions.

Additional Examples

3 Alex has $400. For each week that goes by, he spends half of the money he has remaining. The function $N = 400\left(\frac{1}{2}\right)^x$ represents the amount of money remaining at the end of each week x.

a. Make a table of values.

x	y
0	400
1	200
2	100
3	50
4	25

b. Graph the values.

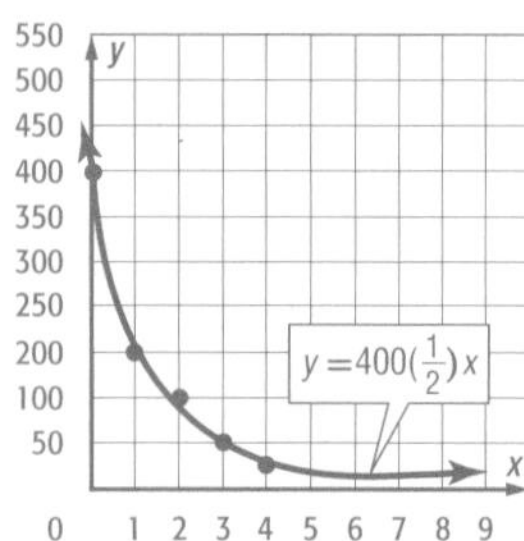

c. After how many weeks will he have $6.25 remaining? 6 weeks

4 Graph $y = 2^x - 2$.

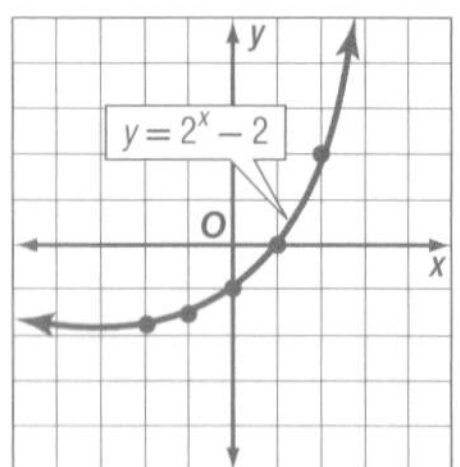

3 PRACTICE

Formative Assessment

Use Exercises 1–8 to check for understanding.

Use the chart at the bottom of this page to customize assignments for your students.

EXAMPLE 4 Graph Exponential Functions

Graph $y = 2^x + 1$.

First, make a table of ordered pairs. Then graph the ordered pairs.

x	$y = 2^x + 1$	(x, y)
−2	$y = 2^{-2} + 1 = 1.25$	(−2, 1.25)
−1	$y = 2^{-1} + 1 = 1.5$	(−1, 1.5)
0	$y = 2^0 + 1 = 2$	(0, 2)
1	$y = 2^1 + 1 = 3$	(1, 3)
2	$y = 2^2 + 1 = 5$	(2, 5)

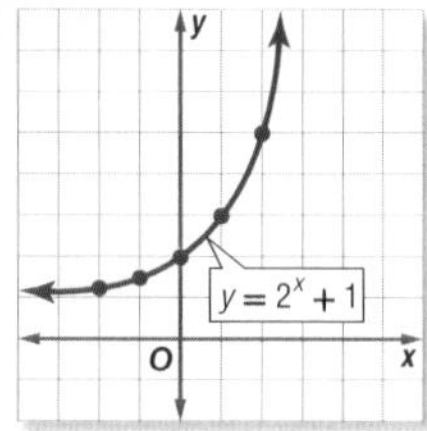

Check Your Progress

4. Graph $y = 3^x - 4$. See Chapter 9 Answer Appendix.

Personal Tutor glencoe.com

Concept Summary Functions — For Your FOLDABLE

Linear	Nonlinear: Quadratic	Nonlinear: Cubic	Nonlinear: Exponential
$y = mx + b$	$y = ax^2 + bx + c$	$y = ax^3 + bx^2 + cx + d$	$y = a^x + c$

Check Your Understanding

Examples 1 and 2 pp. 516–517

Graph each function. 1–4. See Chapter 9 Answer Appendix.

1. $y = x^3$ **2.** $y = x^3 + 1$ **3.** $y = \frac{1}{3}x^3$ **4.** $y = -2x^3$

Example 3 p. 517

5. FINANCIAL LITERACY The amount of money spent at an amusement park continues to increase. The total $T(x)$ in millions of dollars can be estimated by the function $T(x) = 12(1.12)^x$, where x is the number of years after it opened in 2005.

a. Make a table of values showing the amount of money spent after the park has been open 1, 2, 3, and 4 years. a–b. See Chapter 9 Answer Appendix.

b. Graph the function.

c. What does the y-intercept represent in this problem? $12 million sales in 2005

Example 4 p. 518

Graph each function. 6–8. See Chapter 9 Answer Appendix.

6. $y = 3^x$ **7** $y = 2^x - 3$ **8.** $y = 3^x + 3$

Differentiated Homework Options

Level	Assignment	Two-Day Option	
AL Basic	9–24, 31, 33–50	9–23 odd, 36–39	10–24 even, 31, 33–35, 40–50
OL Core	9–23 odd, 25–31 odd, 33–50	9–24, 36–39	25–31, 33–35, 40–50
BL Advanced	25–46 (optional: 47–50)		

Practice and Problem Solving

= **Step-by-Step Solutions** begin on page R11. **Extra Practice** begins on page 810.

Examples 1 and 2 pp. 516–517

Graph each function. 9–24. See Chapter 9 Answer Appendix.

9. $y = -x^3$ **10.** $y = 3x^3$ **11.** $y = 4x^3$ **12.** $y = x^3 - 2$

13. $y = x^3 - 1$ **14.** $y = -x^3 + 1$ **15.** $y = -x^3 + 3$ **16.** $y = 2x^3 - 1$

Example 3 p. 517

17 **MONEY** Jax opened a savings account with an interest rate of 5%. The balance of his account is represented by the function $y = 1000(1.05)^x$, where x represents the number of years the money has been in the account.

a. Graph the function. Identify the y-intercept. Explain its meaning.

b. In how many years will the balance be greater than $2000?

18. **BACTERIA** The population of bacteria in a culture increases according to the function $y = 500(2.1)^{0.01t}$, where t represents the number of hours.

a. Estimate the number of bacteria after 10 hours. Graph the function.

b. Identify the y-intercept and explain what it represents.

25. quadratic
26. linear
27. exponential
28. cubic
29. linear
30. quadratic

Example 4 p. 518

Graph each function.

19. $y = 2^x + 2$ **20.** $y = 4^x$ **21.** $y = 3^x + 1$

22. $y = 2^x - 1$ **23.** $y = 3^x - 2$ **24.** $y = 2^x + 4$

Identify each function as *linear, quadratic, cubic,* or *exponential.*

25. $y = 3x^2 + 4x$ **26.** $5x + 2y = 10$ **27.** $y = 2.4^x$

28.

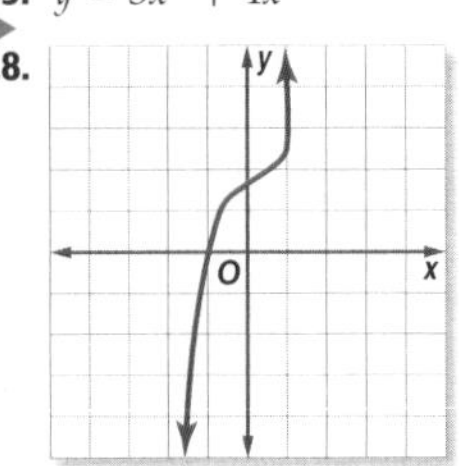

29.

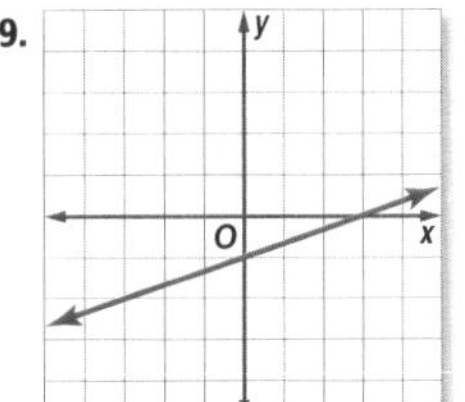

30.

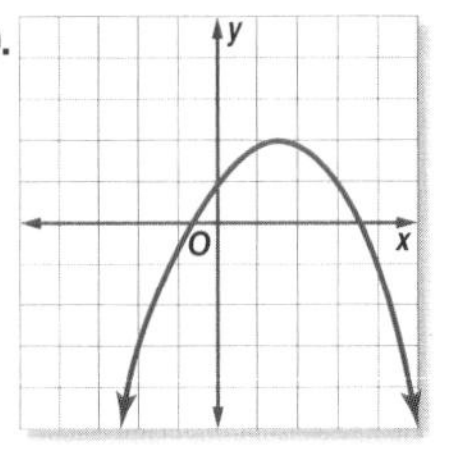

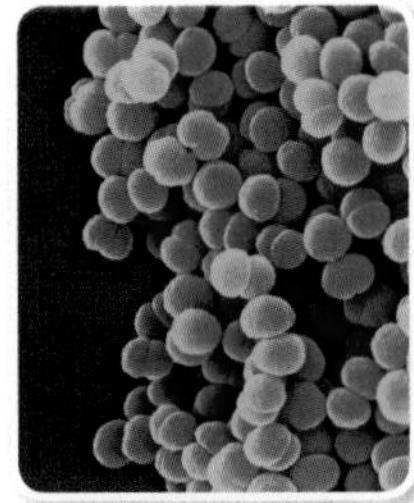

Real-World Link

Bacteria cells grow exponentially, but at different rates. In the time that it takes a single *Nitrosomonas* cell to double in population, a single *E. coli* bacterium can produce a population of more than 35 trillion cells.

Source: Fritz Industries

H.O.T. Problems

Use Higher-Order Thinking Skills

31–35. See Chapter 9 Answer Appendix.

31. **OPEN ENDED** Write a linear function and an exponential function. Then compare and contrast the rates of change represented by the functions.

32. **CHALLENGE** Analyze the graph of an exponential function by describing how each change in $y = a^x + c$ affects the graph of the function.

a. c increases **b.** for $a > 1$, a decreases

33. **WHICH ONE DOESN'T BELONG?** Identify the equation that is not the same as the other three. Explain your reasoning.

$y = 5 + 3^x$	$y + 3^x = 5$	$y + 3x = 5$	$3^x + y = 5$

34. **REASONING** Graph $y = x^2$ and $y = x^3$ in the first quadrant on the same coordinate plane. Explain which graph shows faster growth.

35. **WRITING IN MATH** Describe the general shape of the exponential function $y = a^x$.

TEACH with TECH

WEB PAGE Have groups of students work together to create a Web page for your classroom Web site describing how to graph cubic and exponential functions. Have them start from an equation and describe how to determine which points to use and plot to sketch the graph.

Enrichment CRM p. 60 OL BL

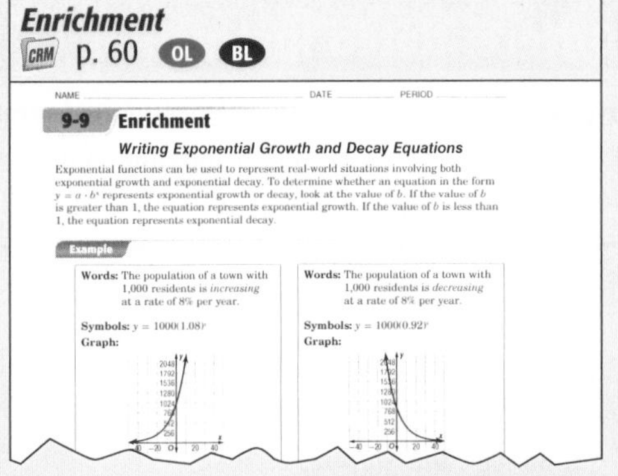

Study Guide and Intervention CRM pp. 55–56 AL OL ELL

Practice CRM p. 58 AL OL BL ELL

Word Problem Practice CRM p. 59 AL OL BL

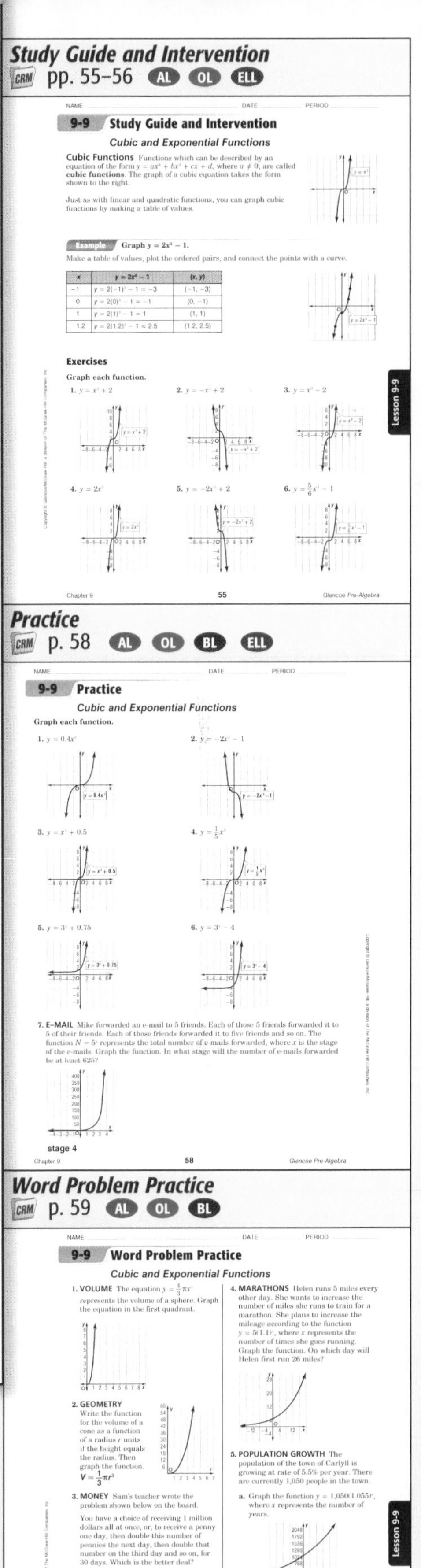

Tips for New Teachers

Graphs Sometimes it is not possible to identify the type of function from the graph. For example, when only one quadrant is shown, graphs of cubic or exponential functions may appear to be quadratic. Tell students they can check for a pattern among the range values.

4 ASSESS

Ticket Out the Door Have students graph either $y = x^3$ or $y = 3^x$ and identify whether it is an exponential or cubic function. Ask students to hand in their graphs as they go out the door.

Formative Assessment

Check for student understanding of concepts in Lessons 9-8 and 9-9.

CRM Quiz 4, p. 65

Additional Answers

39a.

x	y
−2	$-\frac{8}{9}$
−1	$-\frac{2}{3}$
0	0
1	2
2	8

39b.

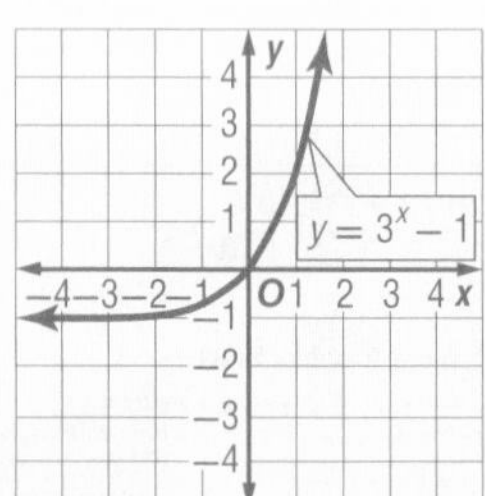

39c. Exponential; the variable is an exponent.

40a. $A = 50x - x^2$

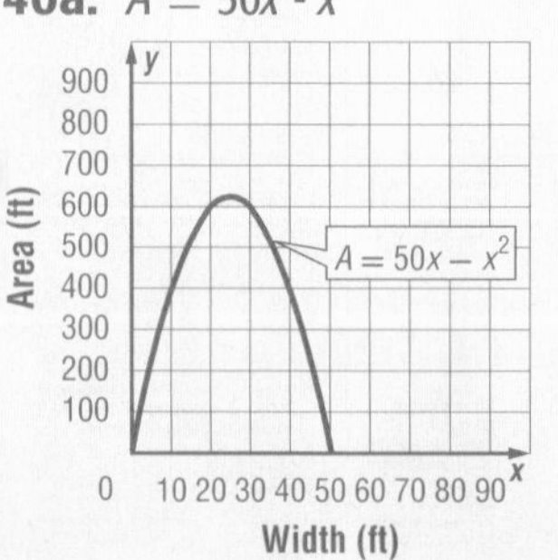

Standardized Test Practice

36. Which of the following equations represents the graph? **A**

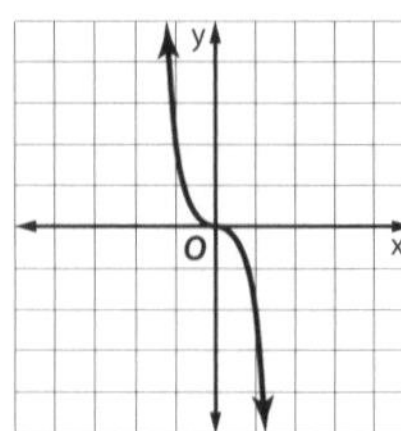

A $y = -2x^3$ C $y = -2x^2$
B $y = 2x^3$ D $y = 2x^2$

37. Which of the following equations represents a cubic function? **J**

F $y = 5^x$ H $y = 5x^2$
G $y = 5x$ J $y = 5x^3$

38. Of the following, which describes the equation $y = 5^x - 4$? **C**

A quadratic function
B linear function
C exponential function
D cubic function

39. EXTENDED RESPONSE Use the function $y = 3^x - 1$. **See margin.**

a. Make a table of values.
b. Graph the ordered pairs.
c. Does the equation represent a linear, quadratic, cubic, or exponential function? Explain your reasoning.

Spiral Review

40. CONSTRUCTION Use the figure at the right. A dog pen is being built with a 100-foot roll of chain link fence. (Lesson 9-8)

a. Write and graph an equation to represent the area A of the pen.
b. What dimensions of the dog pen would enclose the maximum area inside the fence? (*Hint*: Find the maximum point of the graph.) **a–b. See margin.**

Determine whether each graph represents a *linear* or *nonlinear* function. Explain. (Lesson 9-7) **41–43. See margin.**

41.
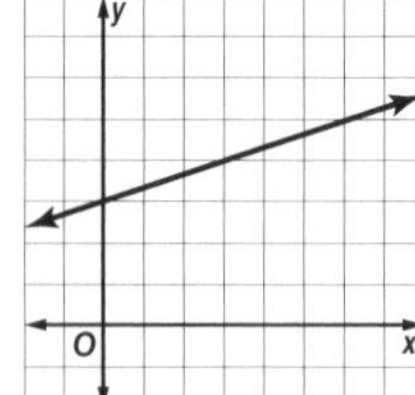

42.
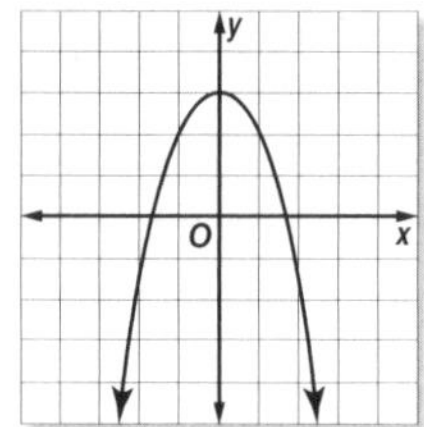

43.
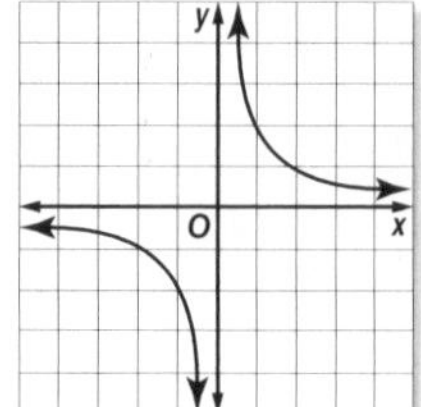

Express each number in standard form. (Lesson 9-1)

44. 3.08×10^{-4} **0.000308** **45.** 1.4×10^2 **140** **46.** 8.495×10^5 **849,500**

Skills Review

Multiply. (Previous Course)

47. $4 \times 4 \times 4 \times 4$ **256** **48.** $2 \times 2 \times 2 \times 2 \times 2$ **32** **49.** 9×9 **81** **50.** $3 \times 3 \times 3$ **27**

Differentiated Instruction

BL

Extension Some savings accounts compound semiannually or twice a year. The function $y = 5000 (1.025)^{2x}$ can be used to find the amount of money in an account after x years if \$5000 is deposited at 5% and the money is compounded semiannually. How much money is there after 4 years? ≈\$6092

40b. 25 ft by 25 ft
41. Linear; graph is a straight line.
42. Nonlinear; graph is a curve.
43. Nonlinear; the graph is a curve.

Algebra Lab: A Half-Life Simulation

Math Online glencoe.com
Math *in Motion*, Animation

Objective
Students will make predictions about half-lives.

The *half-life* of a radioactive element such as uranium is the time that it takes for one-half a quantity of the element to decay.

ACTIVITY

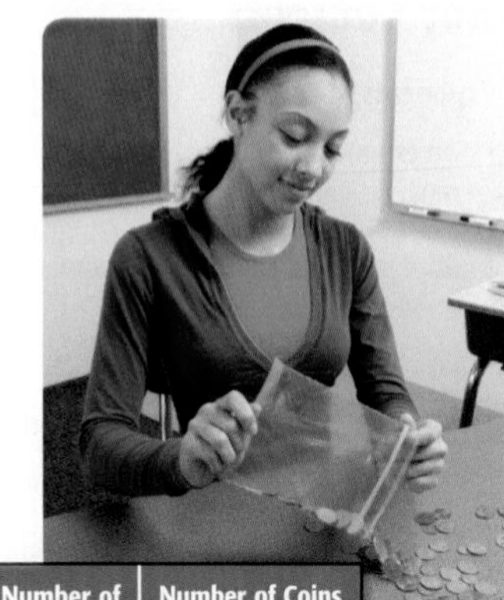

Step 1 Place 100 coins in a bag. Shake the bag and empty the coins on a table. This simulates one half-life.

Step 2 Remove all the coins that are tails up. In a table like the one shown, record the number of coins that remain.

Step 3 Place the remaining coins in the bag and shake it again. Then empty the coins on a table. This represents another half life.

Step 4 Remove all the coins that are tails up. Count the number of coins that remain and record it in the table.

Step 5 Repeat the activity until fewer than 5 coins remain.

Number of Half-Lives	Number of Coins That Remain
1	■ 54
2	■ 28
3	■ 10
4	■ 5
5	■ 2

Analyze the Results

1. On a coordinate plane, let the x-axis represent the number of half-lives and the y-axis represent the number of coins that remain. Plot the points (number of half-lives, number of remaining coins) from your table. See Chapter 9 Answer Appendix.
2. Describe the graph of the data. Points descend from left to right in a curve.

The expressions below represent the average number of coins that remain after three simulations of the half-life activity.

1 Half-Life	2 Half-Lives	3 Half-Lives
$100\left(\frac{1}{2}\right) = 100\left(\frac{1}{2}\right)^1$	$100\left(\frac{1}{2}\right)\left(\frac{1}{2}\right) = 100\left(\frac{1}{2}\right)^2$	$100\left(\frac{1}{2}\right)\left(\frac{1}{2}\right)\left(\frac{1}{2}\right) = 100\left(\frac{1}{2}\right)^3$

3. Use the expressions to predict how many coins remain after three half-lives. Compare this number to the number in the table. Explain any differences. 12.5 or about 13 coins; see students' work.
4. Suppose you started with 50 coins. Predict how many coins would remain after 4 half-lives. about 3 coins

EXTEND 9-9 Lesson Notes

1 FOCUS

Objective Simulate half-life decay.

Materials for Each Group

- 100 coins
- bag
- grid paper

Teaching Tip

Ask students to predict how many coins will remain after each half-life. Discuss discrepancies between their predictions and the actual number of coins.

2 TEACH

Working in Cooperative Groups

Arrange students in pairs, mixing abilities, to complete the Activity and Exercises 1–2.

Ask:

- Why would you expect an average of half of the coins removed after each half-life? Because there are 2 sides to the coin, there is a 50/50 chance that a coin will turn tails up.

Practice Have students complete Exercises 3–4.

3 ASSESS

Formative Assessment

Use Exercises 1–4 to assess if students comprehend how the expressions relate to the data.

From Concrete to Abstract

Describe a regular tetrahedron that has the faces numbered 1–4. Tell students there are 50 of these tetrahedrons in a shoebox. The box is shaken, and the tetrahedrons with 1s not showing are removed. Have students calculate how many tetrahedrons they would expect to remain after each shake, for five shakes.

Formative Assessment

Key Vocabulary The page references after each word denote where that term was first introduced. If students have difficulty answering questions 1–10, remind them that they can use these page references to refresh their memories about the vocabulary.

Summative Assessment

Vocabulary Test, p. 67

Math Online glencoe.com

Vocabulary PuzzleMaker improves students' mathematics vocabulary using four puzzle formats–crossword, scramble, word search using a word list, and word search using clues. Students can work online or from a printed worksheet.

CHAPTER 9 Study Guide and Review

Math Online glencoe.com
- STUDY TO GO
- Vocabulary Review

Chapter Summary

Key Concepts

Exponents (Lesson 9-1)

- An exponent is a way of writing repeated multiplication.

Multiplying and Dividing Monomials (Lesson 9-3)

- Powers with the same base can be:
  - multiplied by adding their exponents.
  - divided by subtracting their exponents.

Negative Exponents and Scientific Notation (Lessons 9-4 and 9-5)

- For $a \neq 0$ and any whole number n, $a^{-n} = \frac{1}{a^n}$.
- A number in scientific notation is the product of a number between 1 and 10 and a power of 10.

Powers of Monomials (Lesson 9-6)

- To find the power of a power, multiply exponents.
- To find the power of a product, find the power of each factor and multiply.

Linear and Nonlinear Functions (Lesson 9-7)

- Nonlinear functions do not have constant rates of change.

Graphing Quadratic and Cubic Functions (Lessons 9-8 and 9-9)

- Quadratic and cubic functions can be graphed by plotting points.

FOLDABLES® Study Organizer

Be sure the Key Concepts are noted in your Foldable.

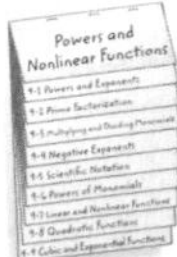

Key Vocabulary

base (p. 471)
composite number (p. 476)
cubic function (p. 516)
exponent (p. 471)
exponential function (p. 517)
factor (p. 478)
factor tree (p. 477)
monomial (p. 477)
nonlinear function (p. 504)
parabola (p. 510)
power (p. 471)
prime factorization (p. 477)
prime number (p. 476)
quadratic function (p. 510)
scientific notation (p. 493)
standard form (p. 493)

Vocabulary Check

Determine whether each statement is *true* or *false*. If *false*, replace the underlined word or number to make a true statement.

1. The exponent of a number raised to the first power can be omitted. **true**
2. A number is in scientific notation when it does not contain exponents. **false; standard form**
3. In 5^7, the number 7 is the base. **false; exponent**
4. The number 49 is an example of a(n) prime number. **false; composite number**
5. The equation $y = 5^x + 2$ is an example of a(n) exponential function. **true**
6. The graph of a(n) cubic function is called a parabola. **false; quadratic function**
7. To multiply powers with the same base, add the exponents. **true**
8. A(n) nonlinear function has a constant rate of change. **false; linear function**
9. To simplify $(n^6)^5$, the first step is to add 6 and 5. **false; multiply**
10. The graph of a(n) quadratic function is symmetric. **true**

FOLDABLES® Study Organizer

Dinah Zike's Foldables®

Have students look through the chapter to make sure they have included examples in their Foldables.

Suggest that students keep their Foldables handy while completing the Study Guide and Review pages. Point out that their Foldables can serve as a quick review tool when studying for the Chapter Test.

Lesson-by-Lesson Review

9-1 Powers and Exponents (pp. 471–475)

Write each expression using exponents.

11. $6 \cdot 6 \cdot 6 \cdot 6 \cdot 6$ 6^5 **12.** 4 4^1

13. $x \cdot x \cdot x$ x^3 **14.** $f \cdot f \cdot g \cdot g \cdot g \cdot g$ f^2g^4

Evaluate each expression.

15. 3^5 243 **16.** $2 \cdot 4^3$ 128

Evaluate each expression if $w = -\frac{3}{4}$, $x = 4$, $y = 1$, and $z = -5$.

17. $x^2 - 6$ 10 **18.** $w^3 + y^2$ $\frac{37}{64}$

19. $2(y + z^3)$ −248 **20.** w^4x^2yz $-\frac{405}{16}$ or $-25\frac{5}{16}$

21. TEETH Adult humans have 2^5 teeth. How many teeth do adults have? 32 teeth

EXAMPLE 1

Write $a \cdot a \cdot b \cdot b \cdot b \cdot b \cdot b$ using exponents.

Group the factors with like bases. Then write using exponents.

$$a \cdot a \cdot b \cdot b \cdot b \cdot b \cdot b = (a \cdot a) \cdot (b \cdot b \cdot b \cdot b \cdot b)$$
$$= a^2b^5$$

EXAMPLE 2

Evaluate $(a + 2b)^2$ if $a = 3$ and $b = -2$.

$(a + 2b)^2 = [3 + 2(-2)]^2$ **$a = 3$ and $b = -2$**

$= (-1)^2$ **Simplify inside the brackets.**

$= 1$ **Simplify.**

9-2 Prime Factorization (pp. 476–480)

Write the prime factorization of each number. Use exponents for repeated factors.

22. 34 $2 \cdot 17$ **23.** 40 $2^3 \cdot 5$

24. 63 $3^2 \cdot 7$ **25.** 225 $3^2 \cdot 5^2$

Factor each monomial.

26. $18x$ $2 \cdot 3 \cdot 3 \cdot x$ **27.** $10r^2$ $2 \cdot 5 \cdot r \cdot r$

28. $32pq$ $2 \cdot 2 \cdot 2 \cdot 2 \cdot 2 \cdot p \cdot q$ **29.** $-25ab^2$ $-1 \cdot 5 \cdot 5 \cdot a \cdot b \cdot b$

30. PHOTOGRAPHS Jacy has 24 photographs to put in a rectangular arrangement. How many different numbers of rows and columns can she display them if each row has the same number of photographs? Name each arrangement. 8; $1 \cdot 24$, $24 \cdot 1$, $2 \cdot 12$, $12 \cdot 2$, $3 \cdot 8$, $8 \cdot 3$, $4 \cdot 6$, $6 \cdot 4$

EXAMPLE 3

Write the prime factorization of 52. Use exponents for repeated factors.

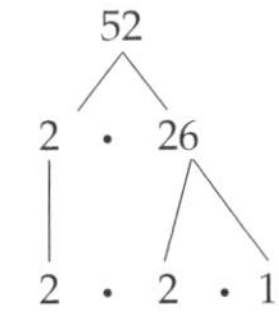

The prime factorization of 52 is $2 \cdot 2 \cdot 13$ or $2^2 \cdot 13$.

EXAMPLE 4

Factor $-21gh^3$.

$-21gh^3 = -1 \cdot 3 \cdot 7 \cdot g \cdot h^3$ **$-21 = -1 \cdot 3 \cdot 7$**

$= -1 \cdot 3 \cdot 7 \cdot g \cdot h \cdot h \cdot h$ **$g \cdot h^3 = g \cdot h \cdot h \cdot h$**

CHAPTER 9 Study Guide and Review

Lesson-by-Lesson Review

Intervention If the given examples are not sufficient to review the topics covered by the questions, remind students that the page references tell them where to review that topic in their textbook.

Two-Day Option Have students complete the Lesson-by-Lesson Review on pp. 523–526. Then you can use ExamView® Assessment Suite to customize another review worksheet that practices all the objectives of this chapter or only the objectives on which your students need more help.

Differentiated Instruction

Super DVD: MindJogger Videoquizzes Use this DVD as an alternative format of review for the test.

CHAPTER 9 Study Guide and Review

9-3 Multiplying and Dividing Monomials (pp. 481–485)

Find each product or quotient. Express using exponents.

31. $3^5 \cdot 3^2$ **3^7**
32. $(-7) \cdot (-7)^4$ **$(-7)^5$**
33. $m^3 \cdot m^6$ **m^9**
34. $x^8 \cdot x$ **x^9**
35. $(2h^7)(6h)$ **$12h^8$**
36. $(5a^3)(-6a^4)$ **$-30a^7$**
37. $\frac{9^6}{9^5}$ **9^1 or 9**
38. $\frac{k^{10}}{k^4}$ **k^6**

39. PLANETS Venus is about 10^8 kilometers from the Sun. Saturn is about 10^9 kilometers from the Sun. About how many times farther from the Sun is Saturn than Venus? **39. about 10 times**

EXAMPLE 5

Find each product or quotient.

a. $4t^5 \cdot 2t^8$

$4t^5 \cdot 2t^8 = (4 \cdot 2)(t^5 \cdot t^8)$ — **Commutative Property of Multiplication**
$= (8)(t^{5+8})$ — **The common base is *t*.**
$= 8t^{13}$ — **Add exponents.**

b. $\frac{n^{15}}{n^9}$

$\frac{n^{15}}{n^9} = n^{15-9}$ — **The common base is *n*.**
$= n^6$ — **Subtract exponents.**

9-4 Negative Exponents (pp. 486–491)

Write each expression using a positive exponent.

40. 9^{-4} **$\frac{1}{9^4}$**
41. $(-10)^{-2}$ **41. $\frac{1}{(-10)^2}$**
42. m^{-5} **$\frac{1}{m^5}$**

Write each fraction as an expression using a negative exponent other than −1.

43. $\frac{1}{6^3}$ **6^{-3}**
44. $\frac{1}{64}$ **2^{-6}, 4^{-3}, or 8^{-2}**
45. $\frac{1}{125}$ **5^{-3}**

46. MEASUREMENT If 1 millimeter is equal to 10^{-3} meter and 1 nanometer is equal to 10^{-9} meter, how many nanometers are in 1 millimeter? Write using a positive exponent. **10^6**

EXAMPLE 6

Write $\frac{1}{32}$ as an expression using a negative exponent other than −1.

$\frac{1}{32} = \frac{1}{2 \cdot 2 \cdot 2 \cdot 2 \cdot 2}$ — **Find the prime factorization of 32.**
$= \frac{1}{2^5}$ — **Definition of exponent**
$= 2^{-5}$ — **Definition of negative exponent**

9-5 Scientific Notation (pp. 493–498)

Express each number in standard form.

47. 5.82×10^3 **5820**
48. 9×10^{-2} **0.09**
49. 3.4×10^{-4} **0.00034**
50. 1.705×10^5 **170,500**

Express each number in scientific notation.

51. 379 **3.79×10^2**
52. 26,880 **2.688×10^4**
53. 0.0014 **1.4×10^{-3}**
54. 0.000561 **5.61×10^{-4}**

55. SPACE The mass of the Sun is 1.98892×10^{15} exagrams. Express in standard form. **1,988,920,000,000,000 exagrams**

EXAMPLE 7

Express 0.0049 in scientific notation.

$0.0049 = 4.9 \times 0.001$ — **The decimal point moves 3 places.**
$= 4.9 \times 10^{-3}$ — **The exponent is negative.**

524 Chapter 9 Powers and Nonlinear Functions

MIXED PROBLEM SOLVING
For mixed problem-solving practice, see page 851.

9-6 Powers of Monomials (pp. 499–503)

Simplify.

56. $(2^6)^3$ 2^{18}

57. $(r^2)^8$ r^{16}

58. $(3x^7)^2$ $9x^{14}$

59. $(-2n^4)^6$ $64n^{24}$

60. $(4a^9b)^4$ $256a^{36}b^4$

61. $(5w^5x^8)^3$ $125w^{15}x^{24}$

62. GEOMETRY Find the area of the square shown below. $64h^{10}$

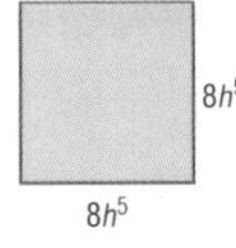

EXAMPLE 8

Simplify.

a. $(8^5)^3$

$(8^5)^3 = 8^{5 \cdot 3}$ Power of a Power

$= 8^{15}$ Simplify.

b. $(3rs^4)^5$

$(3rs^4)^5 = 3^5 \cdot r^5 \cdot (s^4)^5$ Power of a product

$= 3^5 \cdot r^5 \cdot s^{4 \cdot 5}$ Power of a power

$= 243r^5s^{20}$ Simplify.

9-7 Linear and Nonlinear Functions (pp. 504–509)

Determine whether each graph, equation, or table represents a *linear* or *nonlinear* function. Explain. 63–69. See margin.

63.

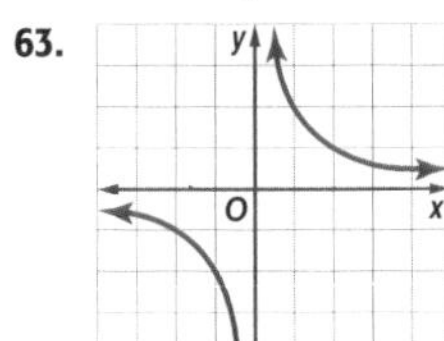

64.

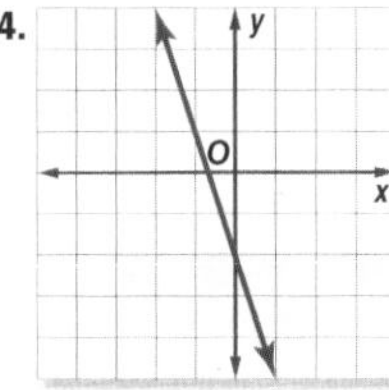

65. $y = \frac{3}{4}x$

66. $y = \frac{5}{x} + 1$

67.

x	y
1	8
2	6
3	4
4	2

68.

x	y
6	10
7	20
8	30
9	40

69. SCHOOLS A school district's spending on students over the last five years is represented by the equation $y = 325x^2 + 0.2x + 1427$. Is this equation linear? Explain.

EXAMPLE 9

Determine whether each graph, equation, or table represents a *linear* or *nonlinear* function. Explain.

a.

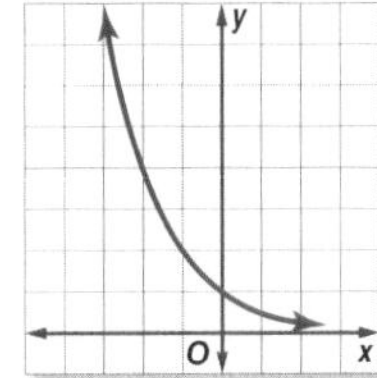

The graph is a curve, not a straight line. So, it represents a nonlinear function.

b. $2y = 8x + 1$

This equation represents a linear function because it can be written as $y = 4x + \frac{1}{2}$.

c.

	x	y	
	−6	5	
+2	−4	10	+5
+2	−2	20	+10
+2	0	40	+20

The table represents a nonlinear function because the rate of change is not constant.

Additional Answers

63. Nonlinear; the graph is a curve.

64. Linear; the graph is a straight line.

65. Linear; the equation is written in the form $y = mx + b$.

66. Nonlinear; the equation cannot be written in the form $y = mx + b$.

67. Linear; as x increases by 1, y decreases by 2.

68. Linear; as x increases by 1, y increases by 10.

69. No; the equation cannot be written in $y = mx + b$ form.

Chapter 9 Study Guide and Review 525

Problem Solving Review

For additional practice in problem solving for Chapter 9, see the Mixed Problem Solving Appendix, p. 851, in the Student Handbook section.

Anticipation Guide

Have students complete the Chapter 9 Anticipation Guide and discuss how their responses have changed now that they have completed Chapter 9.

Additional Answers

70.

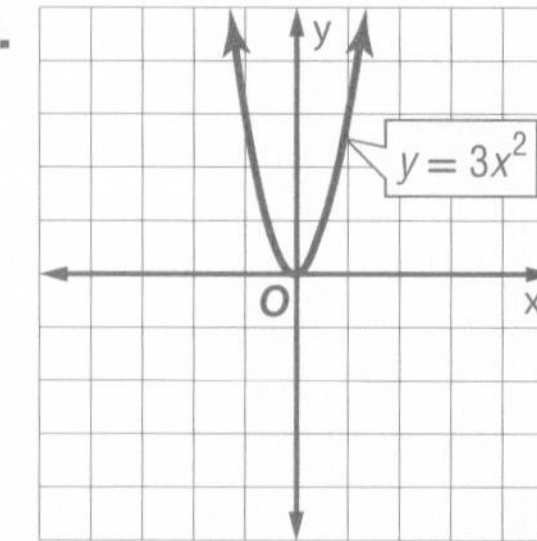

71.

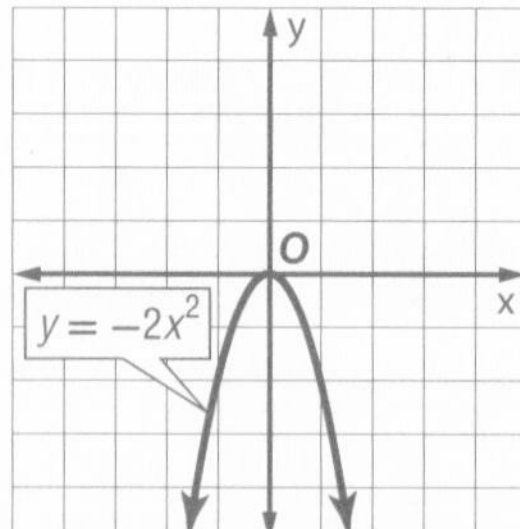

72.

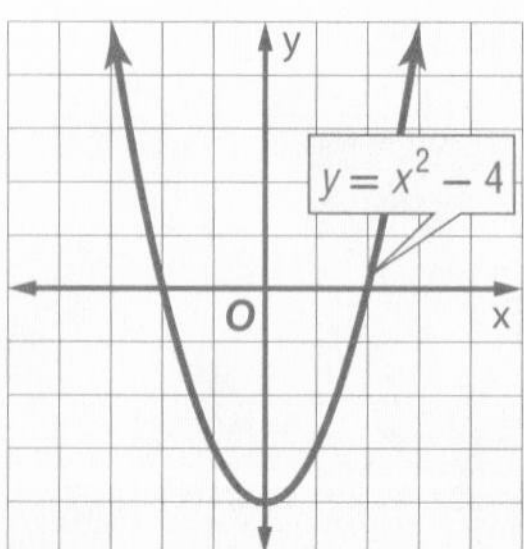

73.

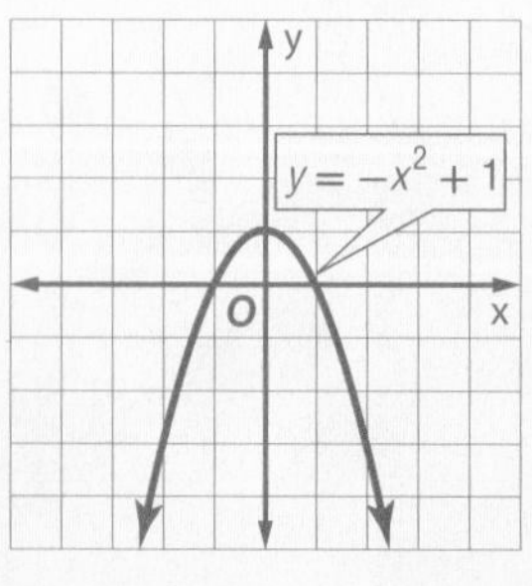

CHAPTER 9 Study Guide and Review

9-8 Quadratic Functions (pp. 510–514)

Graph each function. **70–76. See margin.**

70. $y = 3x^2$ **71.** $y = -2x^2$

72. $y = x^2 - 4$ **73.** $y = -x^2 + 1$

74. $y = 2x^2 + 2$ **75.** $y = \frac{1}{2}x^2 - 3$

76. GEOMETRY The volume of a cylinder with a height of 8 inches can be found using the equation $V = 8(3.14)r^2$ where r is the radius of the cylinder. Graph the equation

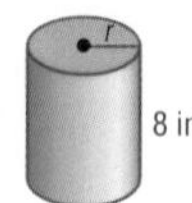

EXAMPLE 10

Graph $y = x^2 + 3$.

x	$x^2 + 3$	(x, y)
−2	$(-2)^2 + 3 = 7$	(−2, 7)
−1	$(-1)^2 + 3 = 4$	(−1, 4)
0	$(0)^2 + 3 = 3$	(0, 3)
1	$(1)^2 + 3 = 4$	(1, 4)
2	$(2)^2 + 3 = 7$	(2, 7)

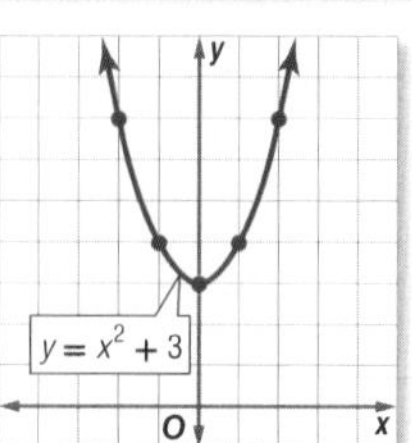

9-9 Cubic and Exponential Functions (pp. 516–520)

Graph each function. **77–82. See Chapter 9 Answer Appendix.**

77. $y = x^3 + 1$ **78.** $y = -3x^3$

79. $y = x^3 - 4$ **80.** $y = 2^x + 2$

81. $y = 3^x$ **82.** $y = 2^x - 1$

83. LIFE SCIENCE Starting from a single bacterium in a dish, the number of bacteria after t cycles of reproduction is 2^t. A bacterium reproduces every 30 minutes. If there are 1000 bacteria in a dish now, how many will there be in 1 hour? **4000**

EXAMPLE 11

Graph $y = -2^x$. The equation $y = -2^x$ is the same as $y = (-1)(2^x)$.

x	$y = -2^x$	(x, y)
−2	$y = -2^{-2}$	(−2, −0.25)
−1	$y = -2^{-1}$	(−1, −0.5)
0	$y = -2^0$	(0, −1)
1	$y = -2^1$	(1, −2)
2	$y = -2^2$	(2, −4)

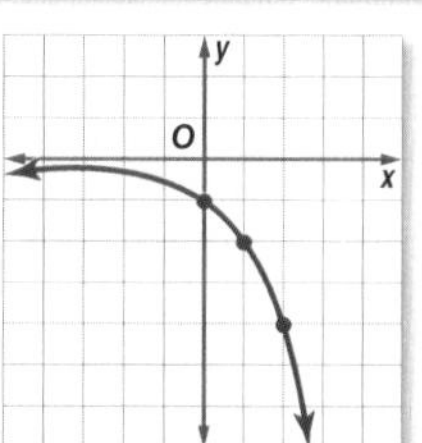

74.

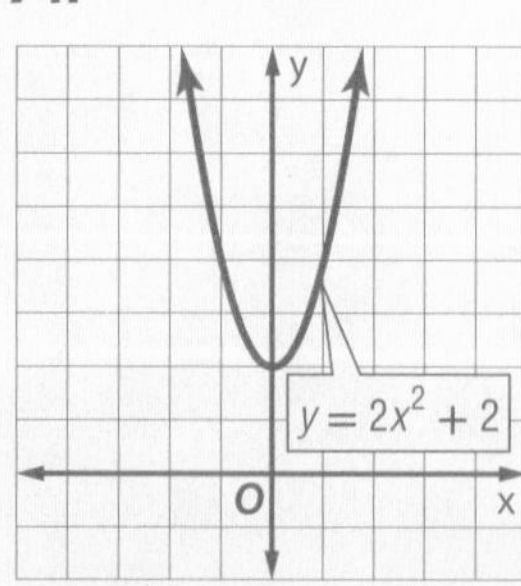

75.

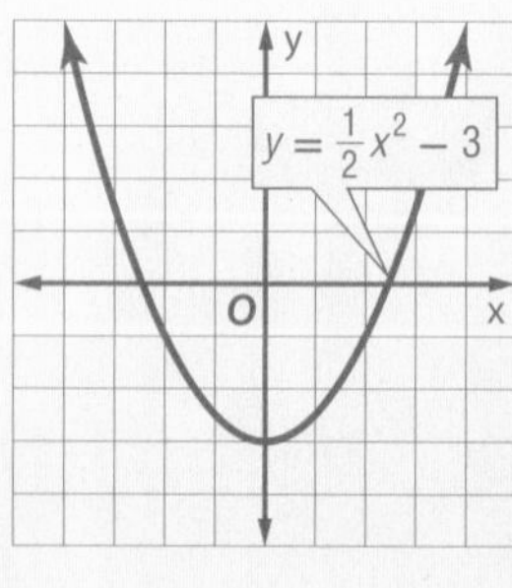

76.

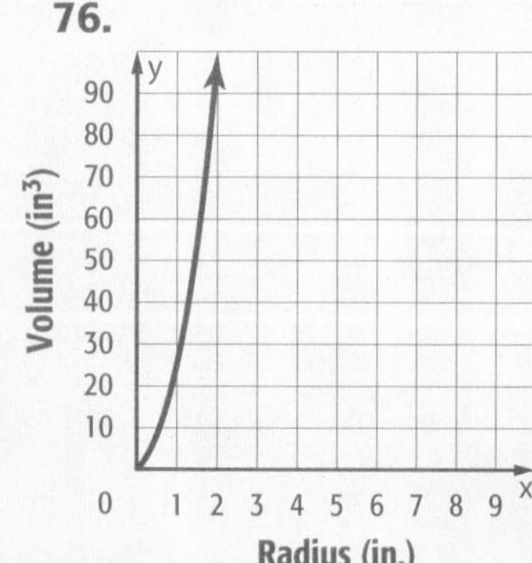

Math Online  glencoe.com
Chapter Test

Write each expression using exponents.

1. $(-2)(-2)(-2)$ $(-2)^3$
2. $3 \cdot b \cdot b \cdot b \cdot b \cdot b$ $3b^5$

Evaluate each expression if $c = 2$ and $d = -3$.

3. $c^3 + 5$ 13
4. $c - 4d^2$ −34

5. **MULTIPLE CHOICE** When the United States had 48 states, the stars on the flag were in a 6×8 rectangular arrangement. Which of the following rectangular arrangements of the 48 stars would be impossible? D

A 2×24 C 4×12
B 3×16 D 5×10

Factor each monomial.

6. $-15rs$ $-1 \cdot 3 \cdot 5 \cdot r \cdot s$
7. $26b^3c^2d$ $2 \cdot 13 \cdot b \cdot b \cdot b \cdot c \cdot c \cdot d$

8. **MULTIPLE CHOICE** Which of the following expressions represents the area of the square? J

F $3ab^2$ H $9ab^2$
G $3a^2b^2$ J $9a^2b^2$

Find each product or quotient. Express using exponents.

9. $9^2 \cdot 9^6$ 9^8
10. $k \cdot k^5$ k^6
11. $(-2)^5 \div (-2)^2$ $(-2)^3$
12. $(11y^3)(-3y^7)$ $-33y^{10}$

13. **MEASUREMENT** How many square centimeters is equivalent to one square millimeter? Write as an expression with a positive exponent. $\frac{1}{10^2}$

Write each expression using a positive exponent.

14. 10^{-10} $\frac{1}{10^{10}}$
15. m^{-5} $\frac{1}{m^5}$

16. Write $\frac{1}{121}$ as an expression using a negative exponent other than −1. 11^{-2}

Write each number in standard form.

17. 3.4×10^{-5} 0.000034
18. 7.29×10^3 7290

Write each number in scientific notation.

19. 50,300 5.03×10^4
20. 0.008 8×10^{-3}

VOLCANOES The table shows the greatest amounts of lava in cubic meters per second that erupted from six volcanoes in the last century.

Volcano	Date	Eruption Rate
Mount St. Helens	1980	2×10^4
Ngauruhoe	1975	2×10^3
Hekla	1970	4×10^3
Agung	1963	3×10^4
Bezymianny	1956	2×10^5
Hekla	1947	2×10^4
Santa Maria	1902	4×10^4

21. Order the volcano eruption rates from greatest to least eruption rate. See margin.

22. How many times as great was the Santa Maria eruption rate than the Mount St. Helens eruption rate? 2 times

Simplify.

23. $(4^2)^6$ 4^{12}
24. $(p^7)^3$ p^{21}
25. $(3c^4d^6)^4$ $81c^{16}d^{24}$

Determine whether each equation or table represents a *linear* or *nonlinear* function. Explain. 26–29. See margin.

26. $y = x^2 + 1$
27. $3x + 2y = 9$

28.

x	y
1	5
2	16
3	27
4	38

29.

x	y
7	−1
8	0
9	1
10	2

Graph each function. 30–33. See Chapter 9 Answer Appendix.

30. $y = -\frac{1}{3}x^2$
31. $y = 2x^2 - 1$
32. $y = 2x^3 + 1$
33. $y = 2^x - 2$

CHAPTER 9 Practice Test

ExamView Assessment Suite Customize and create multiple versions of your chapter test and their answer keys. All of the questions from the leveled chapter tests in the *Chapter 9 Resource Masters* are also available on ExamView® Assessment Suite.

Additional Answers

21. Bezymianny; Santa Maria; Agung; Mount St. Helens tied with Hekla, 1947; Hekla, 1970; Ngauruhoe

26. Nonlinear; the equation cannot be written in the form $y = mx + b$.

27. Linear; the equation can be written in the form $y = mx + b$.

28. Linear; as x increases by 1, y increases by 11.

29. Linear; as x increases by 1, y increases by 1.

Intervention Planner

Tier 1 On Level	Tier 2 Strategic Intervention approaching grade level	Tier 3 Intensive Intervention 2 or more grades below level
If students miss about 25% of the exercises or less,	**If** students miss about 50% of the exercises,	**If** students miss about 75% of the exercises,
Then choose a resource: SE Lessons 9-1 through 9-9; CRM Skills Practice, pp. 7, 14, 20, 26, 32, 38, 44, 50 and 57; TE Chapter Project p. 468	**Then** choose a resource: CRM Study Guide and Intervention, Chapter 9, pp. 5, 12, 18, 24, 30, 36, 42, 48, and 55; *Quick Review Math Handbook*	**Then** use *Math Triumphs, Grade 8,* Ch. 2, 6
Math Online Self-Check Quiz	Math Online 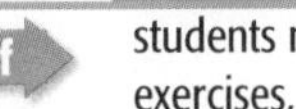 Extra Examples, Personal Tutor, Homework Help	Math Online Extra Examples, Personal Tutor, Homework Help, Review Vocabulary

1 FOCUS

Objective Use the strategy of eliminating unreasonable answers to solve standardized test problems.

2 TEACH

Scaffolding Questions

Ask:

- Have you ever thought that someone gave an unreasonable explanation for something that occurred? In general terms, what made you think the explanation was unreasonable? Sample answer: The explanation did not fit the circumstances or was unusual.
- In general terms, how would a reasonable explanation differ from an unreasonable explanation? Sample answer: A reasonable explanation would fit the facts or details of the situation whereas the unreasonable explanation would not.

CHAPTER 9 Preparing for Standardized Tests

Eliminate Unreasonable Answers

You can eliminate unreasonable answers to help you find the correct choice when solving multiple choice test items. Doing so may save you time by narrowing down the list of possible correct answers.

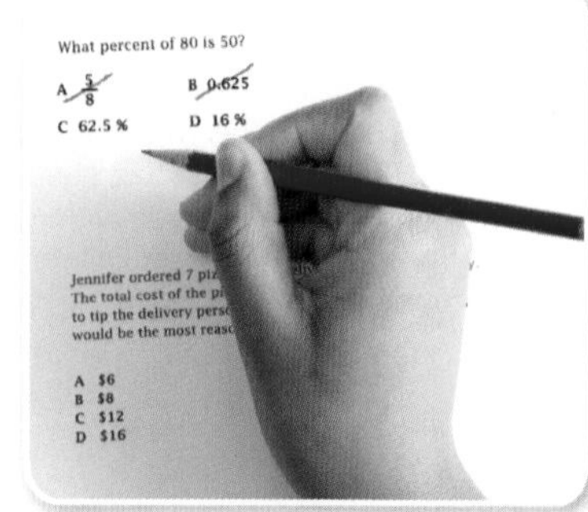

Strategies for Eliminating Unreasonable Answers

Step 1

Read the problem carefully to determine exactly what you are being asked to find.

Ask yourself:

- What am I being asked to solve?
- In what format (fraction, integer, decimal, percent, or graph) will the correct answer be?
- What units (if any) will the correct answer have?

Step 2

Carefully look over each possible answer choice and evaluate for reasonableness.

- Identify any answer choices that are clearly incorrect and eliminate them.
- Eliminate any answer choices that are not in the proper format.
- Eliminate any answer choices that do not have the correct units.

Step 3

Solve the problem and choose the correct answer from those remaining. Check your answer.

EXAMPLE

Read the problem. Identify what you need to know. Then use the information in the problem to solve.

The formula for the area A of a triangle with height h and base b is $A = \frac{1}{2}bh$. Write an expression to represent the area of the triangle below.

A $2x^2 + 4x$
B $32x^3$
C $16x^2$
D $16x^3$

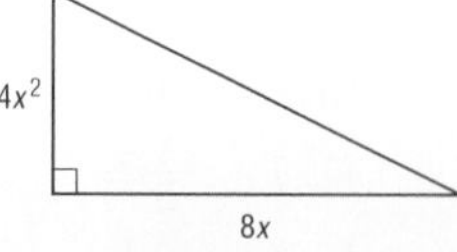

528 Chapter 9 Powers and Nonlinear Functions

Finding the area of the triangle will result in multiplying a monomial by a monomial. You know by the product of powers property that the answer will have an x^3 term. Answer choices A and C are not in the proper form for the correct answer, so they can be eliminated.

So, the correct answer choice will be either B or D. Use the formula to multiply the monomials and find the correct answer.

$A = \frac{1}{2}bh$	**Write the formula.**
$A = \frac{1}{2}(8x)(4x^2)$	**Replace b with $8x$ and h with $4x^2$.**
$A = (4x)(4x^2)$	**Multiply.**
$A = 16x^3$	**Multiply then simplify.**

The area of the triangle is $16x^3$. The correct answer is D.

Exercises

Read each question. Eliminate any unreasonable answers. Then use the information in the question to solve.

1. The table shows the surface areas, in square kilometers, of the oceans.

Ocean	Area (km^2)
Pacific	156,000,000
Atlantic	77,000,000
Indian	69,000,000
Southern	20,000,000
Arctic	14,000,000

Which of the following represents the area of the Arctic Ocean in scientific notation? B

A 0.14×10^8

B 1.4×10^7

C 1.4×10^8

D 14×10^6

2. The graph below represents a function.

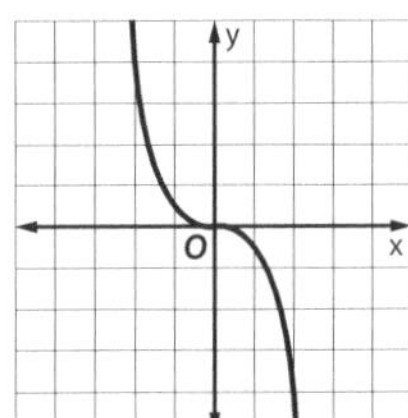

Which of the following equations represents the function? H

F $y = 2^x - 1$

G $y = -2^x$

H $y = -\frac{1}{2}x^3$

J $y = \frac{1}{2}x^3$

Additional Example

The formula for the area of a rectangle is $A = \ell w$, where ℓ is the length of the rectangle and w is the width. Which expression represents the area of the rectangle below? C

A $7x^5$

B $7x^6$

C $10x^5$

D $10x^6$

3 ASSESS

Use Exercises 1–2 to assess students' understanding.

CHAPTER 9 Standardized Test Practice

Diagnose Student Errors

Survey student responses for each item. Class trends may indicate common errors and misconceptions.

1. A moved decimal point 6 places instead of 8
B moved decimal point 7 places instead of 8
C correct
D moved decimal point 9 places instead of 8

2. F interest added to initial deposit
G calculation error on interest and interest added to initial deposit
H correct
J calculation error

3. A correct
B added instead of multiplied coefficients and multiplied instead of added exponents
C forgot to halve product of base and height
D multiplied instead of added exponents

4. F correct
G calculation error
H calculation error and error in choosing or using signs in calculations
J error in choosing or using signs in calculations

5. A correct
B misunderstood concept of nonlinear function
C misunderstood meaning of parabola
D misunderstood concept of quadratic function

6. F misunderstood definition of negative exponent
G misunderstood definition of negative exponent
H misunderstood definition of negative exponent
J correct

CHAPTER 9 Standardized Test Practice

Cumulative, Chapters 1 through 9

Multiple Choice

Read each question. Then fill in the correct answer on the answer document provided by your teacher or on a sheet of paper.

1. In 2007, the population of the United States was about 3.0×10^8. Which of the following represents this number in standard form? **C**

A 3,000,000
B 30,000,000
C 300,000,000
D 3,000,000,000

2. Michelle deposits $1200 in a savings account with a 6% interest rate. How much simple interest will she have earned after three years? **H**

F $1,416
G $1,396
H $216
J $196

3. The area of a triangle is one half the product of its base and its height. Which of the following expressions represents the area of the right triangle shown? **A**

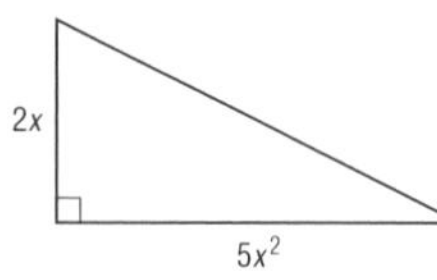

A $5x^3$
B $7x^2$
C $10x^3$
D $5x^2$

4. Find the slope of the line that passes through points $R(4, 1)$ and $S(-2, 6)$? **F**

F $-\frac{5}{6}$
G $-\frac{2}{3}$
H $\frac{2}{3}$
J $\frac{5}{6}$

5. Which term does *not* describe the function graphed below? **A**

A linear
B nonlinear
C parabola
D quadratic

6. Write b^{-2} using a positive exponent. **J**

F $\frac{1}{2b}$
G $\frac{1}{2^b}$
H $\frac{1}{b+2}$
J $\frac{1}{b^2}$

7. The radius of the Moon is about 1.7×10^6 meters. Use the formula $V = \frac{4}{3}\pi r^3$ to find the volume of the moon. **D**

A 2.1×10^9 m^3
B 3.7×10^9 m^3
C 3.7×10^{18} m^3
D 2.1×10^{19} m^3

8. Which of the following expressions is equivalent to $3p - 4r + 4p - 5r$? **J**

F $-p - r$
G $-p - 9r$
H $7p - r$
J $7p - 9r$

Test-TakingTip

Question 6 If time permits, you can check your answer using substitution. For example, let $b = 5$. Using a calculator, $5^{-2} = 0.04$, which is the same as $\frac{1}{25}$.

7. A added instead of multiplied to find power of a power
B calculation error and added instead of multiplied to find power of a power
C calculation error and forgot to add exponents for $10^1 \cdot 10^{18}$
D correct

8. F misunderstood concept of adding and subtracting integers
G used wrong numbers in calculating *p*
H used wrong numbers in calculating *r*
J correct

Short Response/Gridded Response

Record your answers on the answer sheet provided by your teacher or on a sheet of paper.

9. Describe the transformation shown on the coordinate plane below.

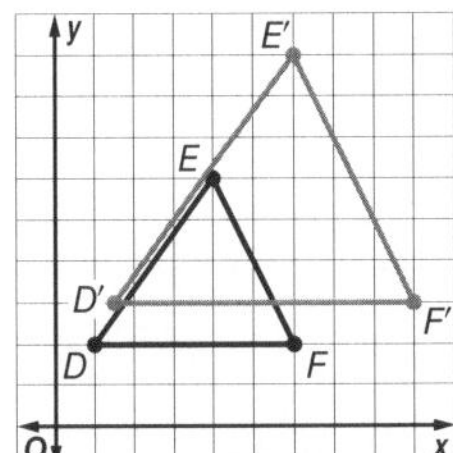

Sample answer: The transformation is a dilation with a scale factor of $1\frac{1}{2}$.

10. **GRIDDED RESPONSE** In a single elimination tournament, the function $y = 32\left(\frac{1}{2}\right)^x$ can be used to find the number of teams y left in the tournament after x rounds. If there are 32 teams in the tournament, how many rounds will be needed to determine the champion? 5

11. The width of a cotton fiber is about 0.001 centimeter.
    a. Write the width of a cotton fiber as a fraction. $\frac{1}{1000}$
    b. Write the width of a cotton fiber using a negative exponent. 10^{-3}
    c. How many cotton fibers would need to be stacked on top of each other to reach a height of 5 centimeters? 5000

12. **GRIDDED RESPONSE** Write $\frac{8}{25}$ as a decimal. 0.32

13. Suppose a wild fire is doubling in size every 6 hours. If the initial size of the fire was 1 acre, how many acres will the fire cover in 2 days? 256 acres

Extended Response

Record your answers on a sheet of paper. Show your work.

14. The quadratic function $y = -16x^2 + 128x$ models the height y of a toy rocket x seconds after it is launched.

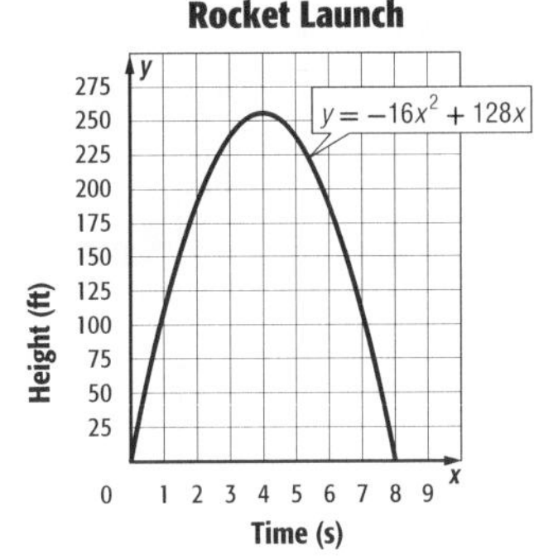

a. How long does it take the rocket to reach its peak height? 4 s
b. What is the peak height reached by the toy rocket? 256 ft
c. How long does it take the rocket to land? 8 s

Need Extra Help?														
If you missed Question...	1	2	3	4	5	6	7	8	9	10	11	12	13	14
Go to Lesson or Page...	9-5	7-7	9-3	8-6	9-8	9-4	9-6	4-2	6-8	9-9	9-4	7-2	9-1	9-8

Formative Assessment

You can use these two pages to benchmark student progress.

CRM Standardized Test Practice, pp. 81–83

Answer Sheet Practice

Have students simulate taking a standardized test by record their answers on practice recording sheets.

CRM Student Recording Sheet, p. 62

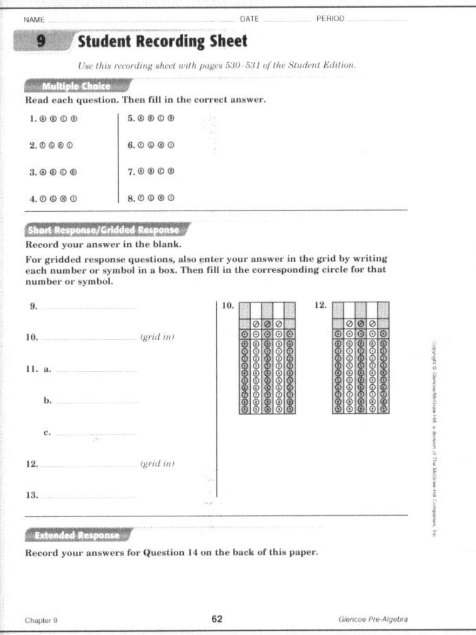
NAME DATE PERIOD

9 Student Recording Sheet

Use this recording sheet with pages 530–531 of the Student Edition.

Multiple Choice

Read each question. Then fill in the correct answer.

1. Ⓐ Ⓑ Ⓒ Ⓓ　5. Ⓐ Ⓑ Ⓒ Ⓓ
2. Ⓐ Ⓑ Ⓒ Ⓓ　6. Ⓐ Ⓑ Ⓒ Ⓓ
3. Ⓐ Ⓑ Ⓒ Ⓓ　7. Ⓐ Ⓑ Ⓒ Ⓓ
4. Ⓐ Ⓑ Ⓒ Ⓓ　8. Ⓐ Ⓑ Ⓒ Ⓓ

Short Response/Gridded Response

Record your answer in the blank.

For gridded response questions, also enter your answer in the grid by writing each number or symbol in a box. Then fill in the corresponding circle for that number or symbol.

9. ______
10. ______ (grid in)
11. a. ______
b. ______
c. ______
12. ______ (grid in)
13. ______

Extended Response

Record your answers for Question 14 on the back of this paper.

Chapter 9　62　Glencoe Pre-Algebra

Create practice worksheets or tests that align to your state's standards as well as TIMSS and NAEP tests.

Homework Option

Get Ready for Chapter 10 Assign students the exercises on p. 533 as homework to assess whether they possess the prerequisite skills needed for the next chapter.

Page 475, Lesson 9-1

67a.

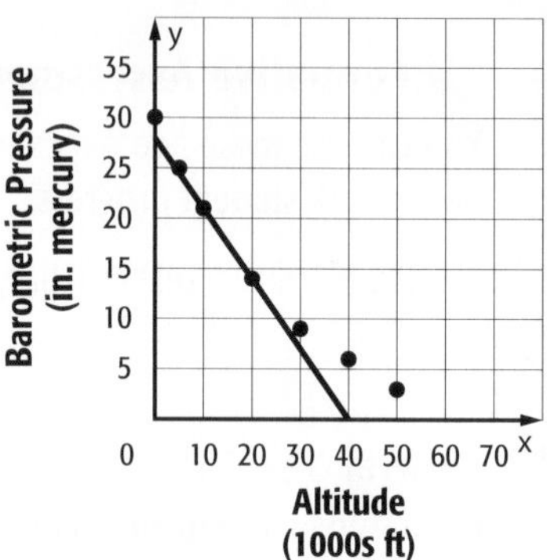

67b. Sample answer: Using (10,000, 21) and (30,000, 9), $y = -0.0006x + 27$; -9; this is not reasonable because barometric pressure cannot be negative.

67c. No, the equation gives a negative value for barometric pressure, which is not possible. Also, the data in the scatter plot do not appear to be linear.

Pages 478–479, Lesson 9-2

24. $3 \cdot 5 \cdot y$

25. $2 \cdot 3 \cdot n \cdot n$

26. $-1 \cdot 3 \cdot 3 \cdot p \cdot p \cdot p \cdot p$

27. $-1 \cdot 11 \cdot n \cdot n \cdot n$

28. $2 \cdot 3 \cdot 3 \cdot a \cdot b$

29. $2 \cdot 2 \cdot 5 \cdot q \cdot r \cdot s$

30. $2 \cdot 2 \cdot 2 \cdot 3 \cdot f \cdot f \cdot g$

31. $-1 \cdot 5 \cdot 7 \cdot c \cdot c \cdot c \cdot d \cdot d$

42. Sample answer: 6, 12, 18, 24, 30; $6 = 2 \cdot 3$; $12 = 2^2 \cdot 3$; $18 = 2 \cdot 3^2$; $24 = 2^3 \cdot 3$; $30 = 2 \cdot 3 \cdot 5$; Sample answer: A number is divisible by 6 if the number is divisible by 2 and 3.

43. Sample answer: The number $2n$ is never prime. Since you are multiplying a number by 2, you have an additional set of factor pairs, 2 and n.

Pages 483–484, Lesson 9-3

10. 5^8

11. $(-2)^5$

12. a^9

13. t^6

14. $40x^8$

15. $54p^{14}$

16. $-4m^{11}$

17. $24s^7$

18. 5^8

19. 7^5

20. a^1 or a

21. k^3

22. $(-1.5)^5$

23. 8^6

24. r^{14}

25. $(-n)^2$

Page 490, Lesson 9-4

55. Sample answer: If $n = 3$, $\frac{1}{2^n} = \frac{1}{2^3}$ or $\frac{1}{8}$. If $n = 4$, $\frac{1}{2^n} = \frac{1}{2^4}$ or $\frac{1}{16}$. So, as the value of n increases, the value of $\frac{1}{2^n}$ decreases.

Page 499, Lesson 9-6 (Why?)

a.

Square	Area = Side Length Squared	Area using Product of Powers
A	$(a^3)^2$	$a^3 \cdot a^3 = a^{3+3}$ or a^6
B	$(b^4)^2$	$b^4 \cdot b^4 = b^{4+4}$ or b^8
C	$(c^5)^2$	$c^5 \cdot c^5 = c^{5+5}$ or c^{10}
D	$(d^{10})^2$	$d^{10} \cdot d^{10} = d^{10+10}$ or d^{20}

Pages 508–509, Lesson 9-7

23a.

Radius r	Circumference C	Area A
1	6.28	3.14
2	12.56	12.56
3	18.84	28.26
4	25.12	50.24
5	31.4	78.5

23b.

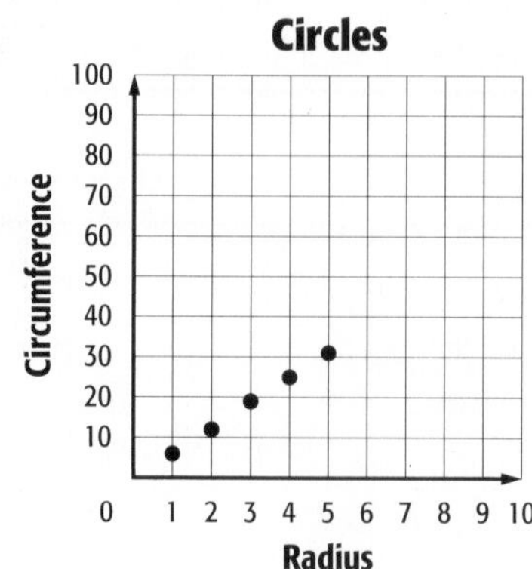

23c. **Circles**

Area: 100, 90, 80, 70, 60, 50, 40, 30, 20, 10

0 1 2 3 4 5 6 7 8 9 10

Radius

23d. Yes, the circumference is a linear relationship. The slope is 6.28.

28. **Area**

Width (ft): 20, 18, 16, 14, 12, 10, 8, 6, 4, 2

0 1 2 3 4 5 6 7 8 9 10

Length (ft)

33. Sample answer: Functions can be represented using graphs, equations, or tables. A non-vertical graph that is a straight line represents a linear function. An equation that can be written in the form $y = mx + b$, is a linear function. If a table of values shows a constant defined rate of change, the function is linear.

47.

x	y
−1	4
0	5
1	6

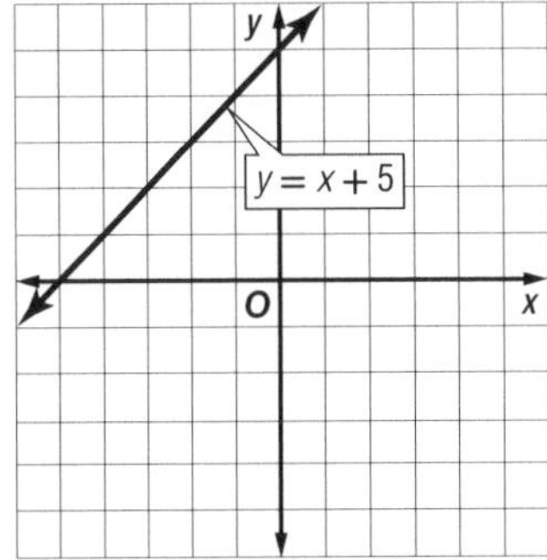

48.

x	y
−1	−4
0	−6
1	−8

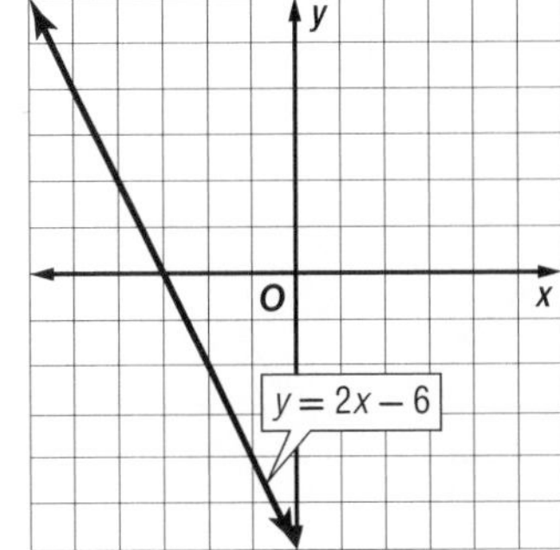

49.

x	y
−1	−7
0	−8
1	−9

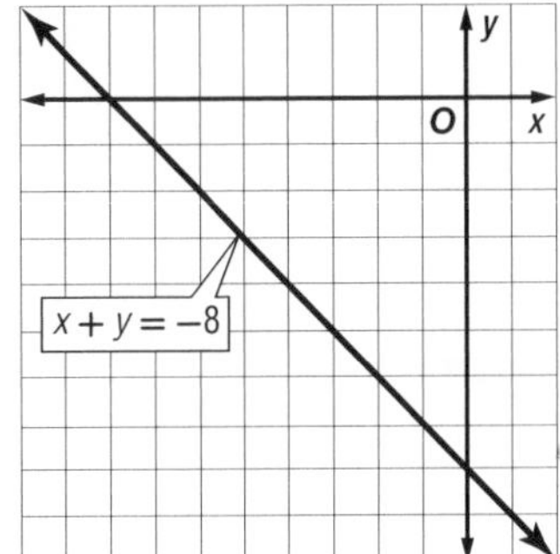

50.

x	y
−3	3
0	4
3	5

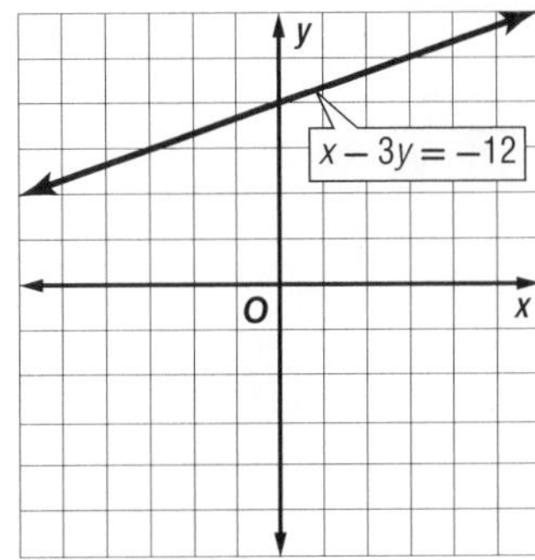

51.

x	y
−3	11
0	9
3	7

$y = -\frac{2}{3}x + 9$

52.

x	y
−2	−5
0	−4
2	−3

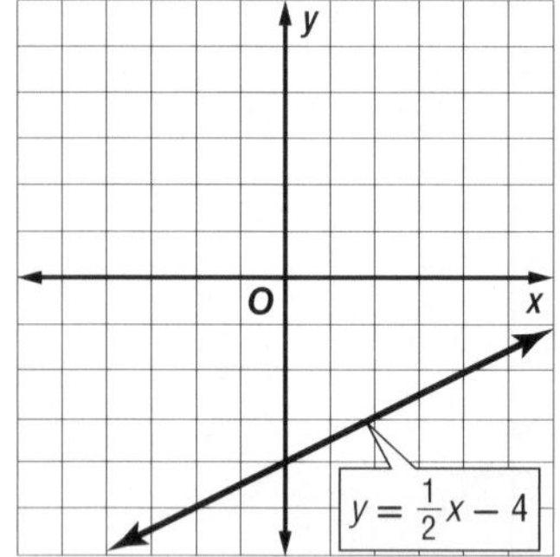

Pages 510–511, Lesson 9-8 (Check Your Progress)

1.

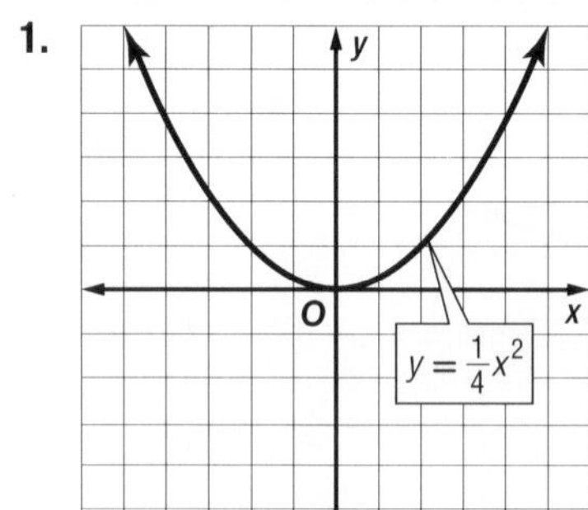

2.

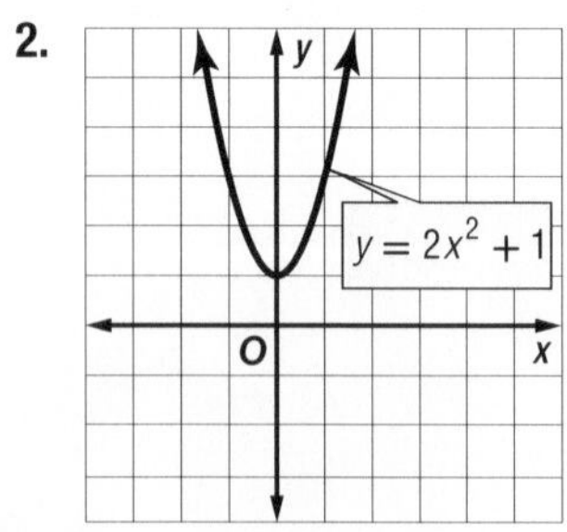

3.

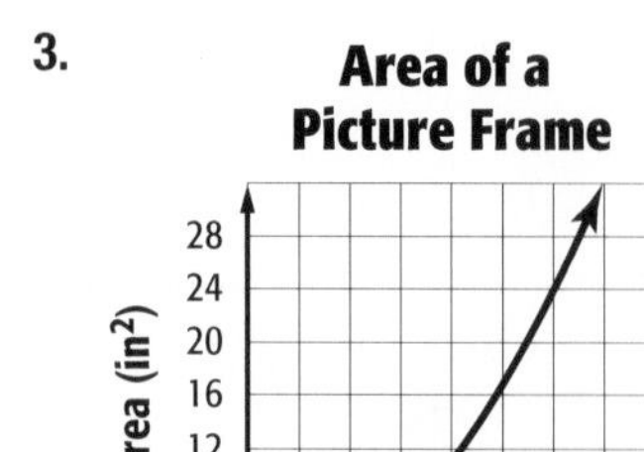

Pages 512–513, Lesson 9-8

1.

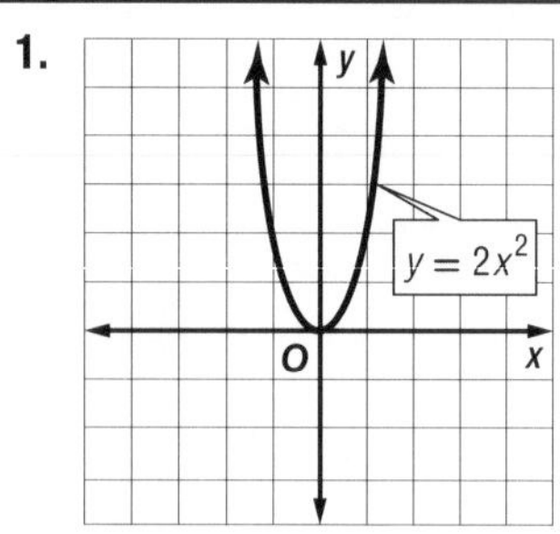

2.

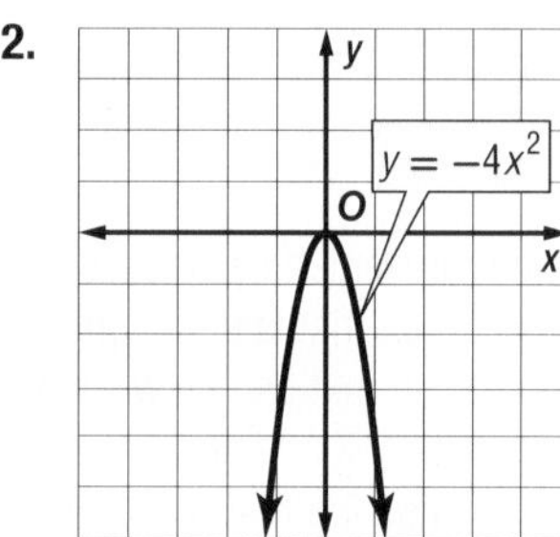

3.

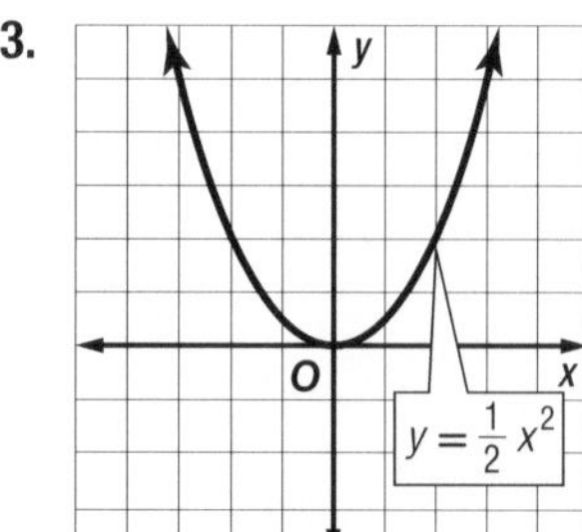

4.

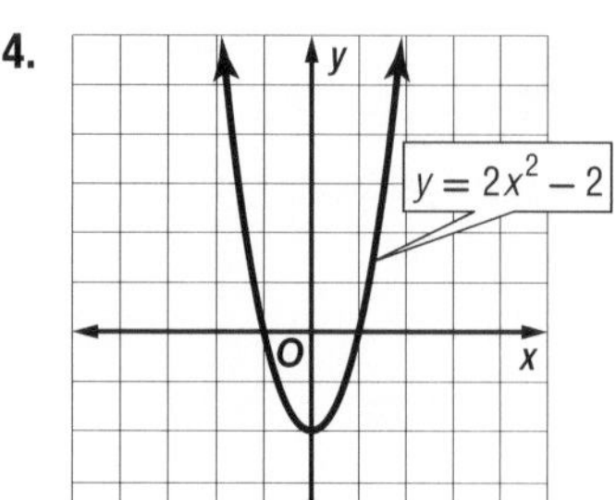

5. 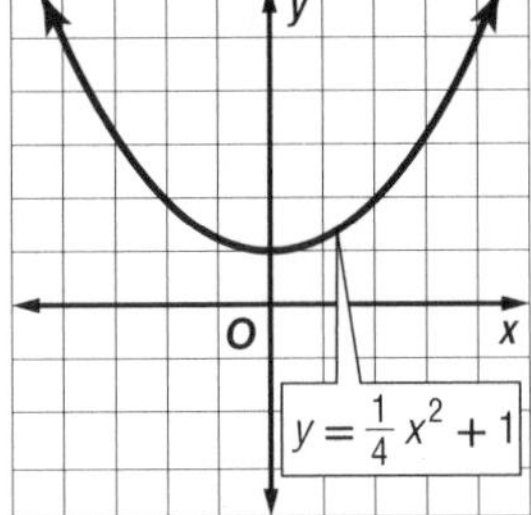

6. 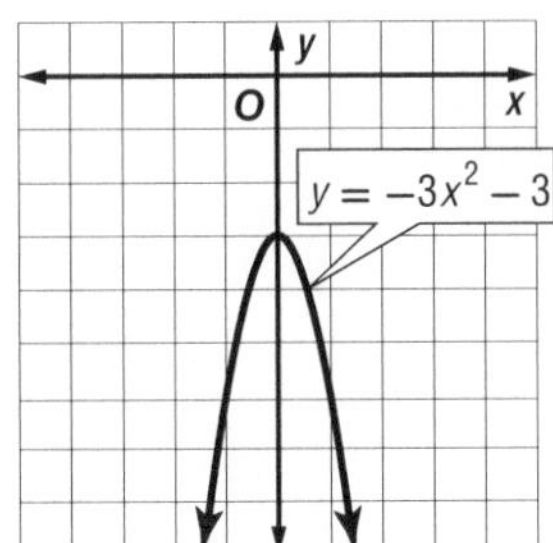

7a. 

18 ft

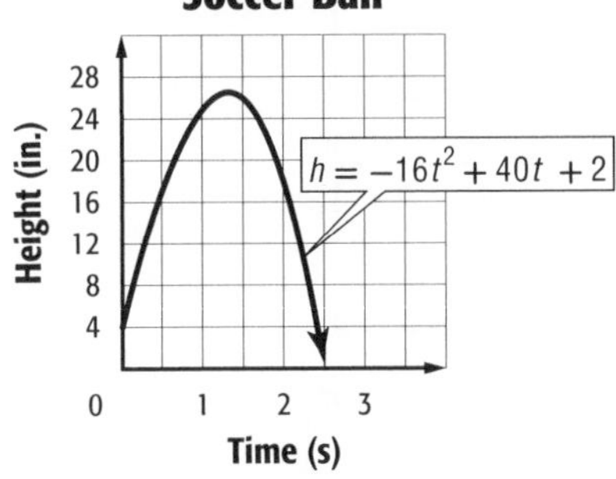

As the time increases up to about 1.5 seconds, the height of the ball increases. Then, the height of the ball decreases until it reaches 0 feet at about 2.5 seconds; 18 ft.

8. 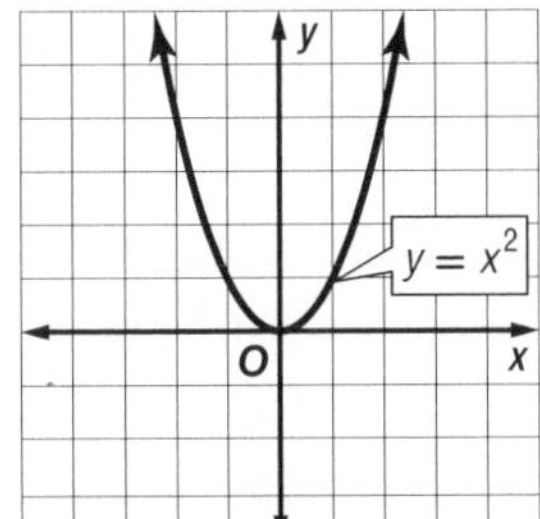

9. 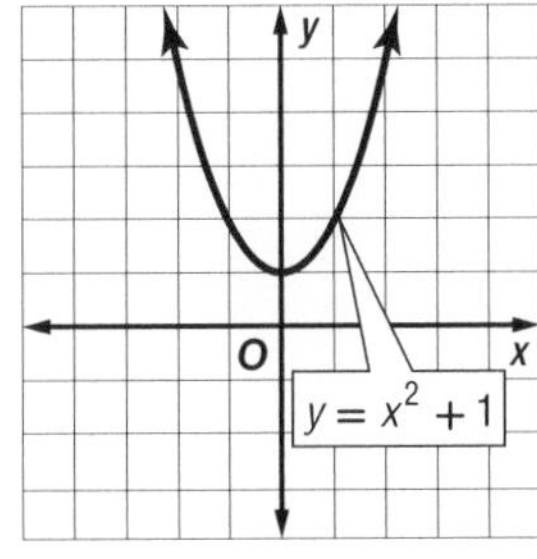

10. 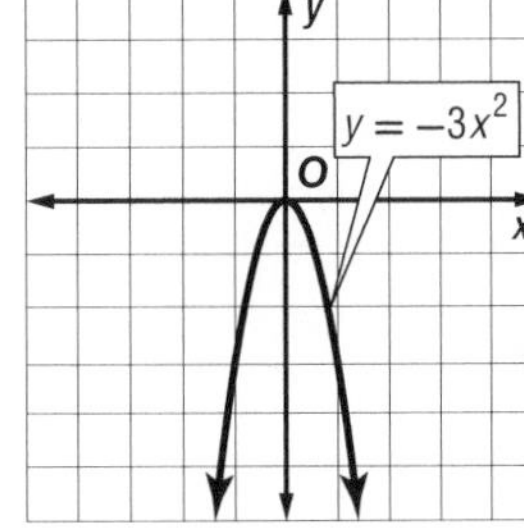

11. 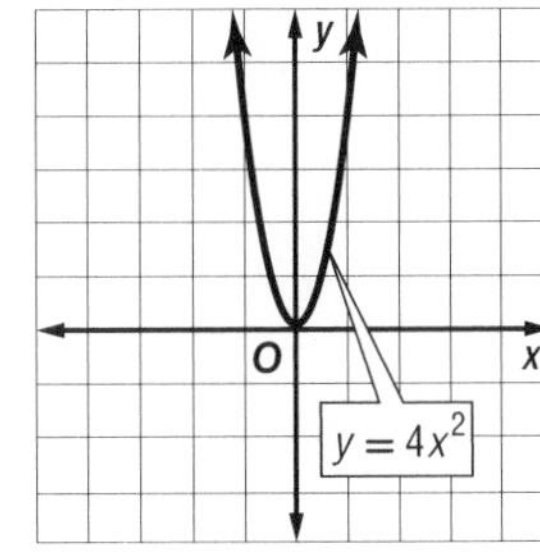

12. 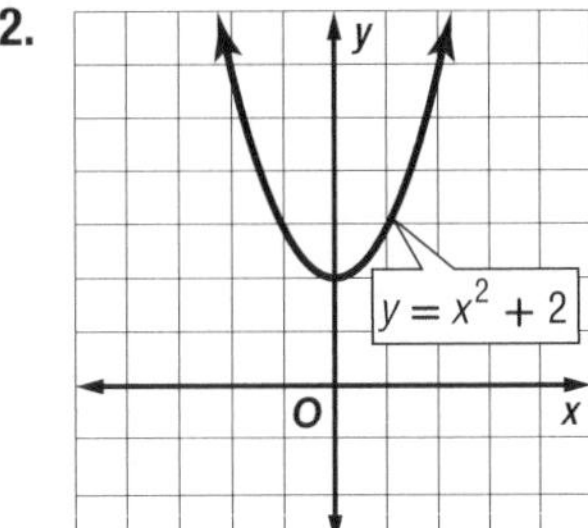

13. 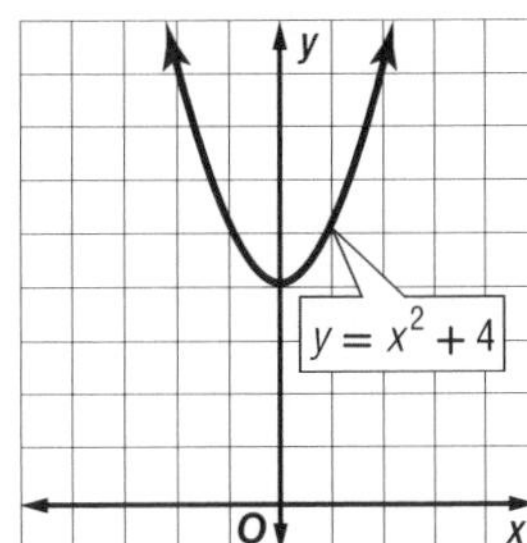

14. 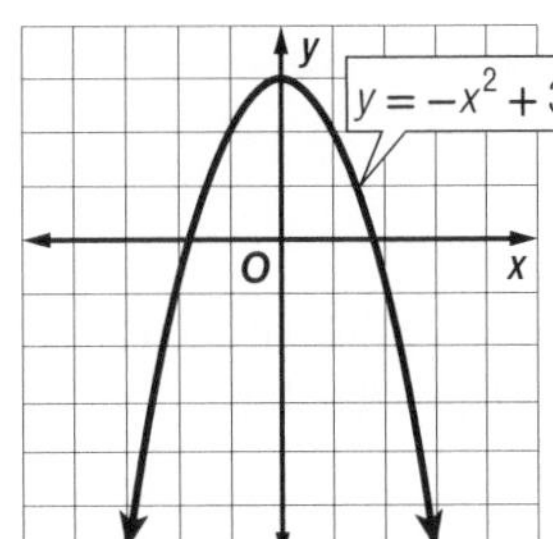

15. 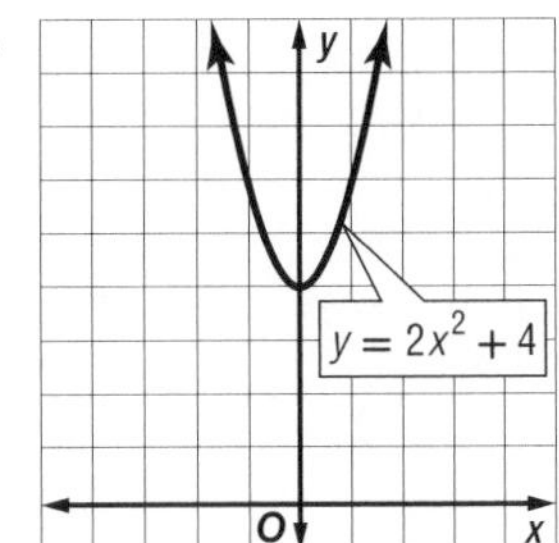

16. 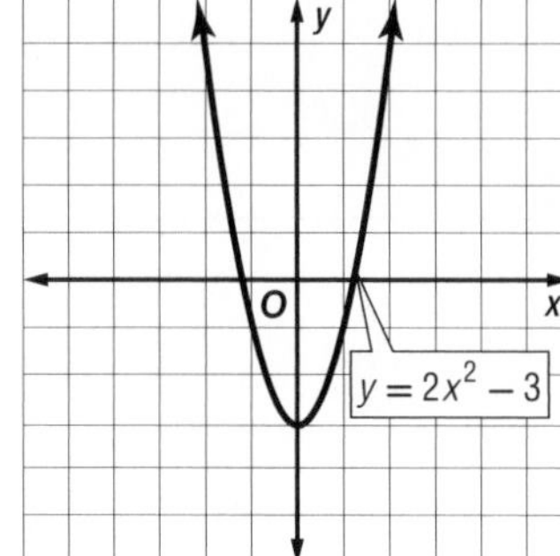

17. 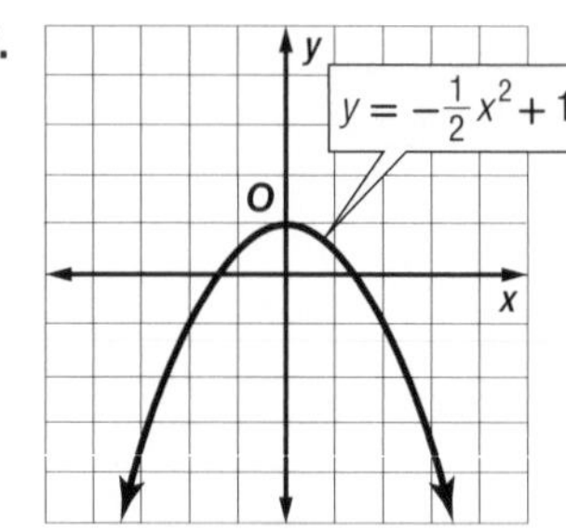

18. 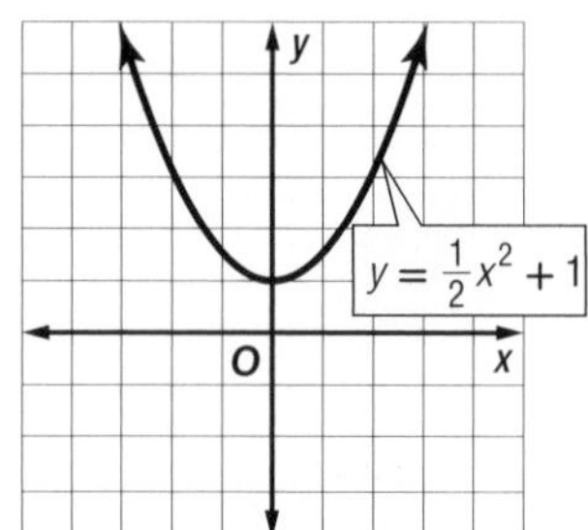

19. 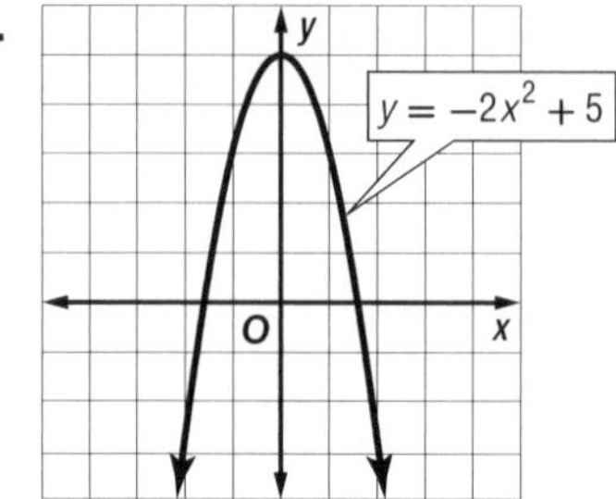

20b. Sample answer: The plane begins at 31,000 ft, increases to about 32,000 ft, then decreases to 31,000 ft.

21a.

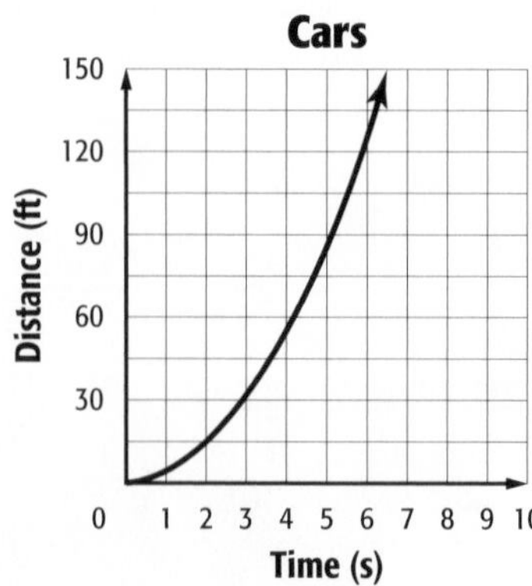

22a. $A = -x^2 + 16x$

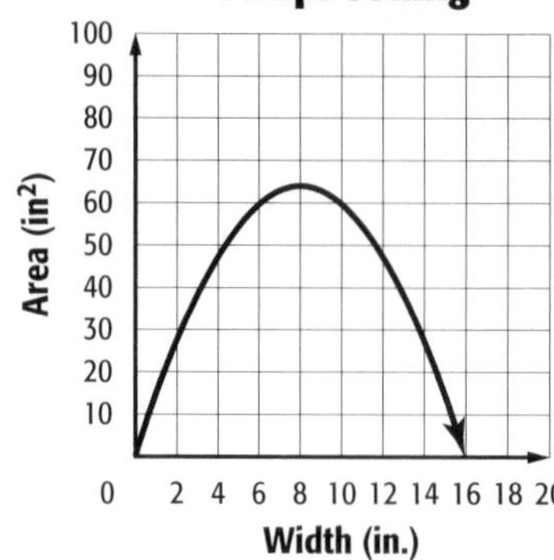

23a. $P = 4s$; $A = s^2$

23b.

s	$P = 4s$	$A = s^2$
0	$4 \cdot 0 = 0$	$0^2 = 0$
1	$4 \cdot 1 = 4$	$1^2 = 1$
2	$4 \cdot 2 = 8$	$2^2 = 4$
3	$4 \cdot 3 = 12$	$3^2 = 9$
4	$4 \cdot 4 = 16$	$4^2 = 16$

23c.

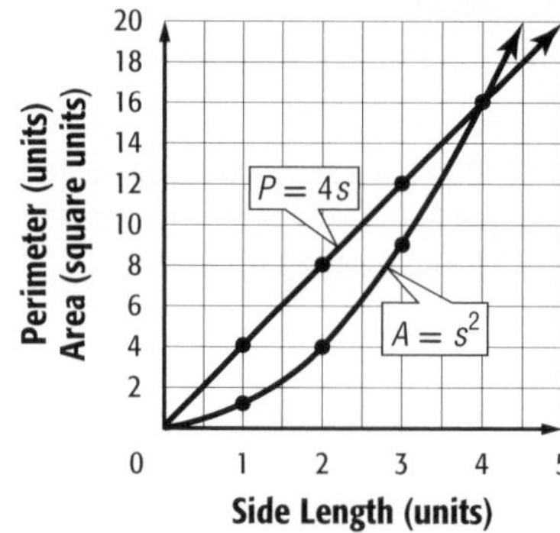

The graph for the perimeter is a linear function, the graph for the area is a quadratic function.

23d. Yes, when the side length is 4 units both the perimeter and area are 16. In the table, the values are the same. On the graph, it is where the two functions intersect.

25. Sample answer:

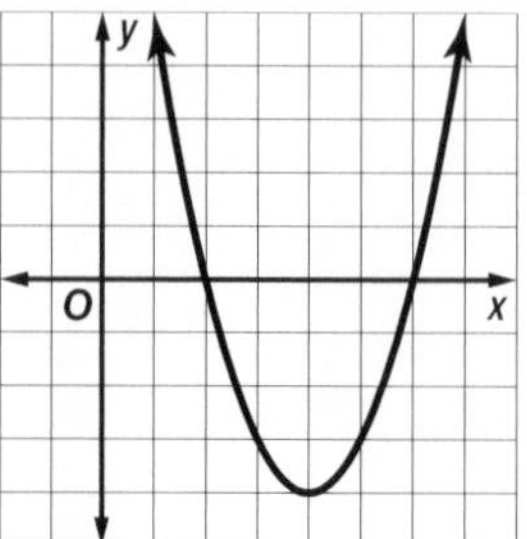

26a.

x	$y = x^2 + 1$	(x, y)
-3	$10 = (-3)^2 + 1$	$(-3, 10)$
-2	$5 = (-2)^2 + 1$	$(-2, 5)$
-1	$2 = (-1)^2 + 1$	$(-1, 2)$
0	$1 = (0)^2 + 1$	$(0, 1)$
1	$2 = (1)^2 + 1$	$(1, 2)$
2	$5 = (2)^2 + 1$	$(2, 5)$
3	$10 = (3)^2 + 1$	$(3, 10)$

x	$y = -x^2 + 1$	(x, y)
-3	$-8 = -(-3)^2 + 1$	$(-3, -8)$
-2	$-3 = -(-2)^2 + 1$	$(-2, -3)$
-1	$0 = -(-1)^2 + 1$	$(-1, 0)$
0	$1 = -(0)^2 + 1$	$(0, 1)$
1	$0 = -(1)^2 + 1$	$(1, 0)$
2	$-3 = -(2)^2 + 1$	$(2, -3)$
3	$-8 = -(3)^2 + 1$	$(3, -8)$

26b.

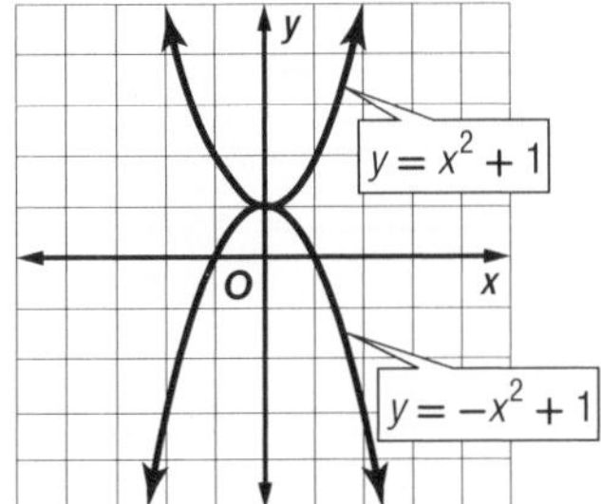

26c. Sample answer: One graph opens upward and the other opens downward. They also have the same shape and the same y-intercept at (0, 1).

26d. Sample answer: If a is positive, the graph opens upward. If a is negative, the graph opens downward.

26e. Sample answer: The y-intercept of the graph of a quadratic is c for $ax^2 + c$.

27. (0, 7)

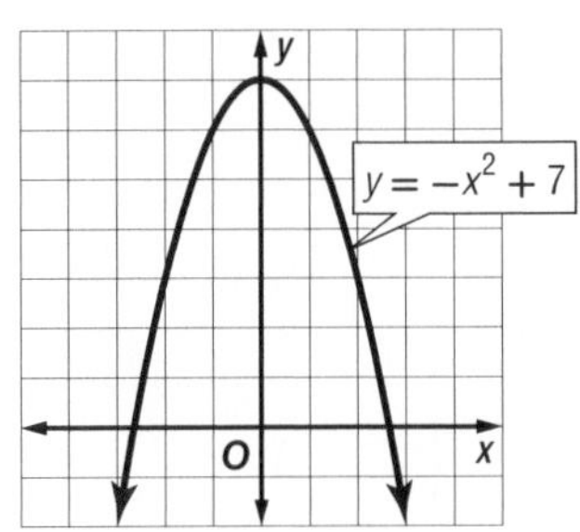

28. (0, –6)

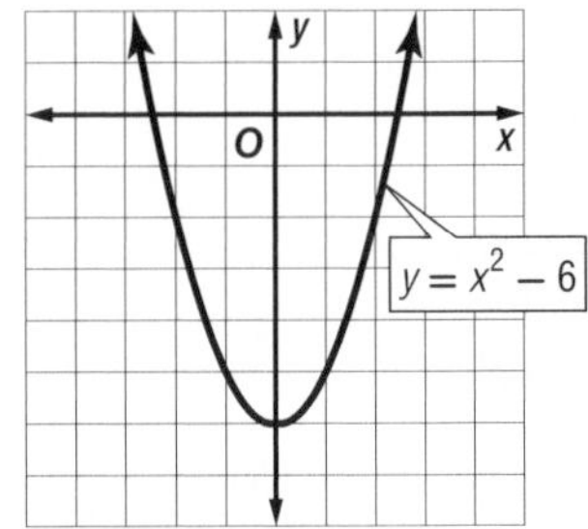

29. Sample answer: Formulas and tables can be used to make graphs. Tables and graphs can be used to write rules. To make a graph, use a rule to make a table of values. Then plot the points. To write a rule, find points that lie on the graph and make a table using the coordinates. Look for a pattern and write a rule that describes the pattern.

Page 516, Lesson 9-9 (Why?)

b.

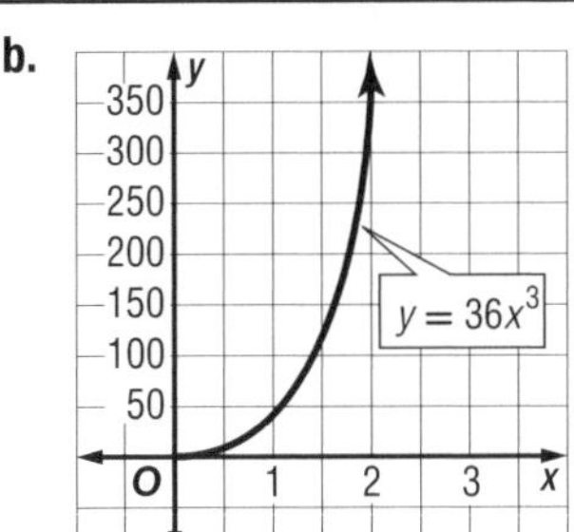

Pages 516–518, Lesson 9-9 (Check Your Progress)

1A.

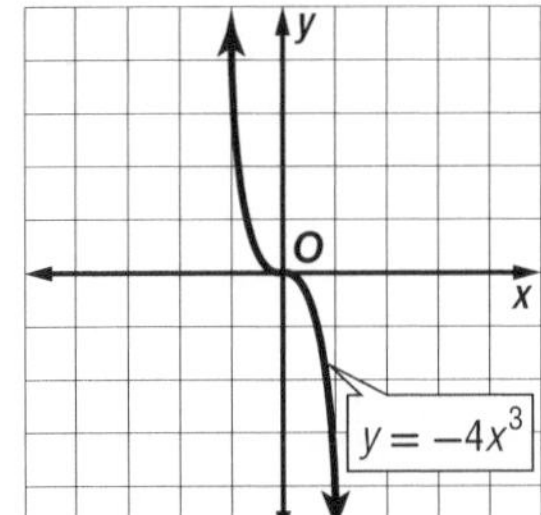

1B.

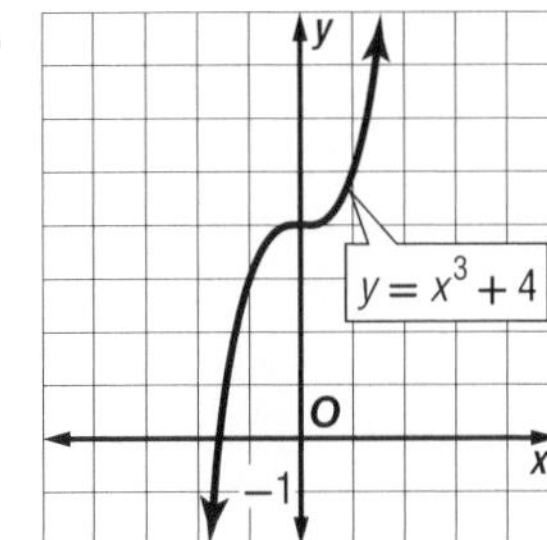

2. 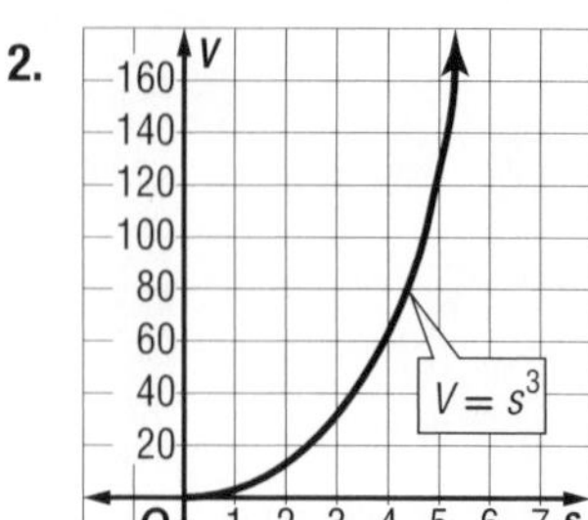

3. 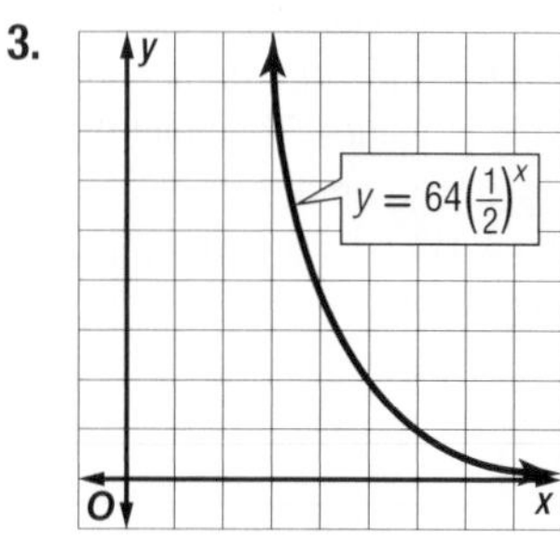

4. 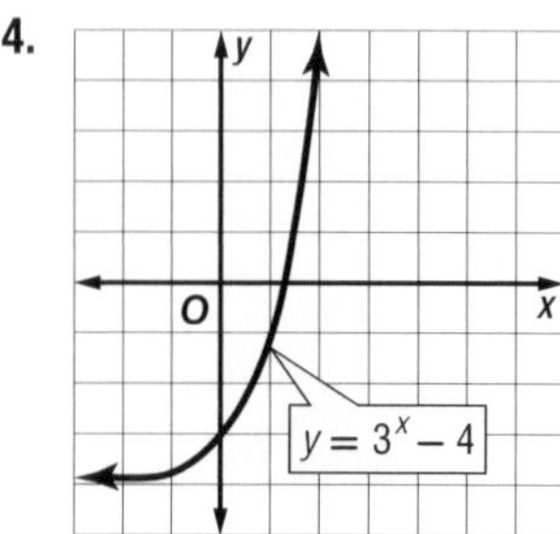

Pages 518–519, Lesson 9-9

1. 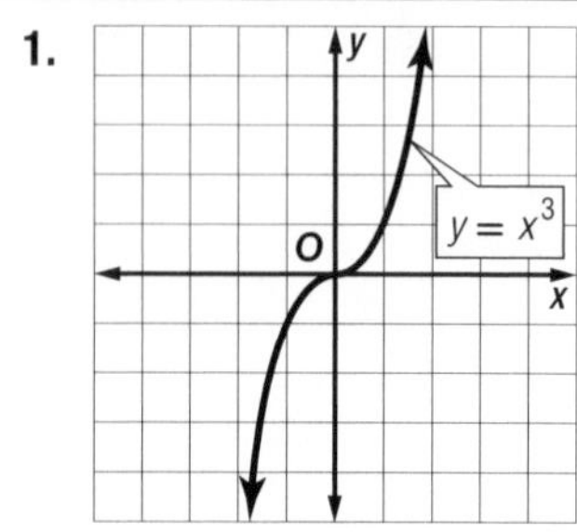

2. 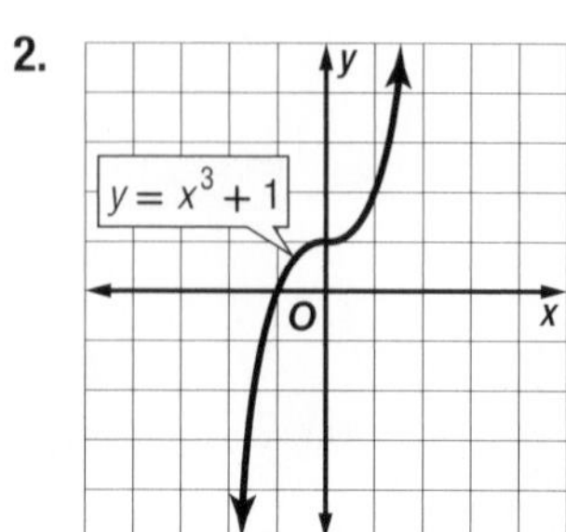

3. 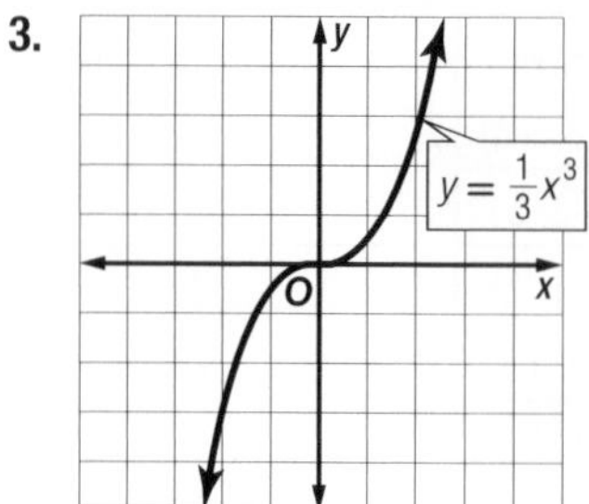

4. 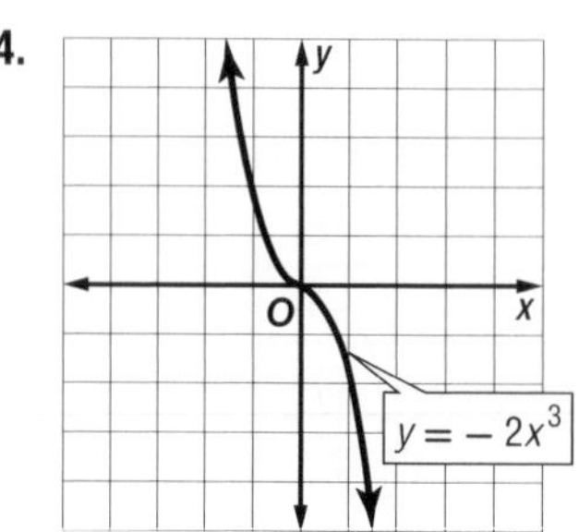

5a.

Years	Money Spent (in millions)
1	13.4
2	15.1
3	16.9
4	18.9

5b. 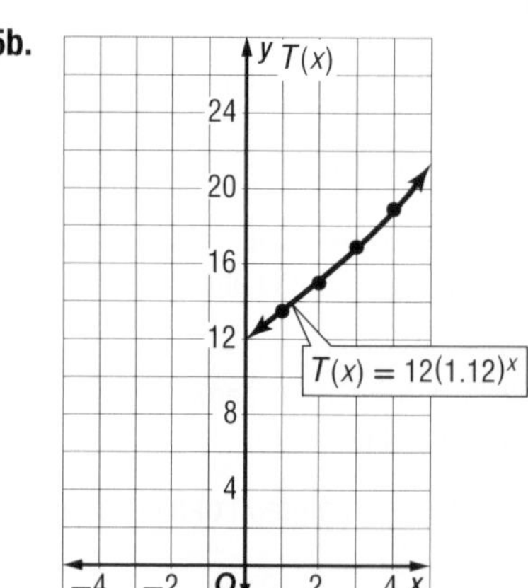

6. 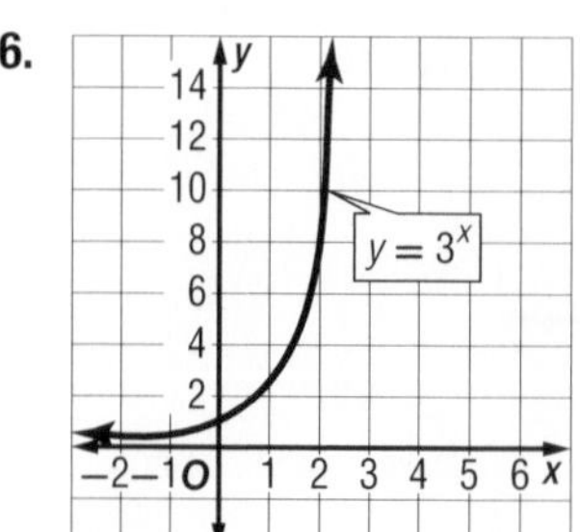

Chapter 9 Answer Appendix

7.

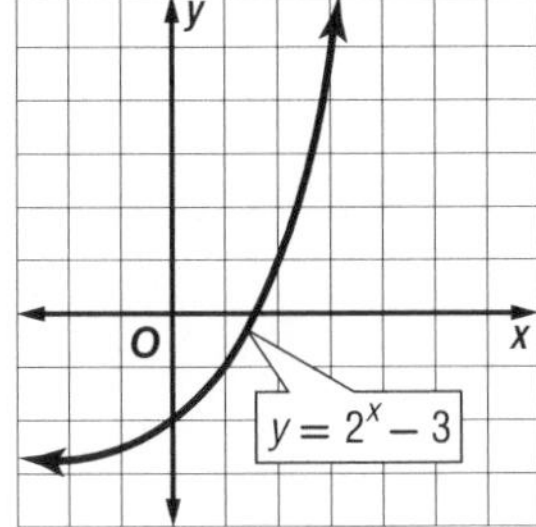

8.

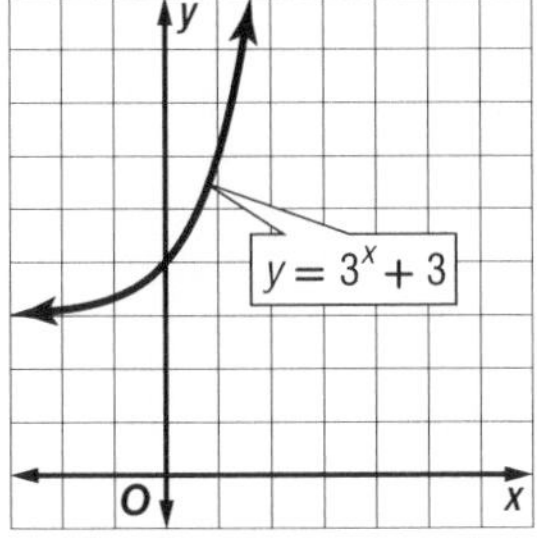

9.

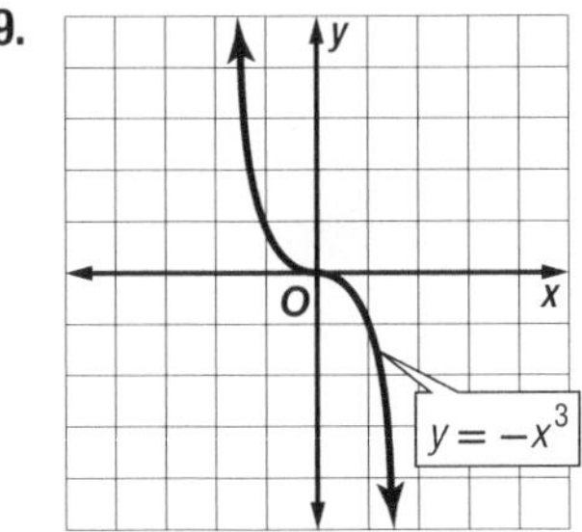

10.

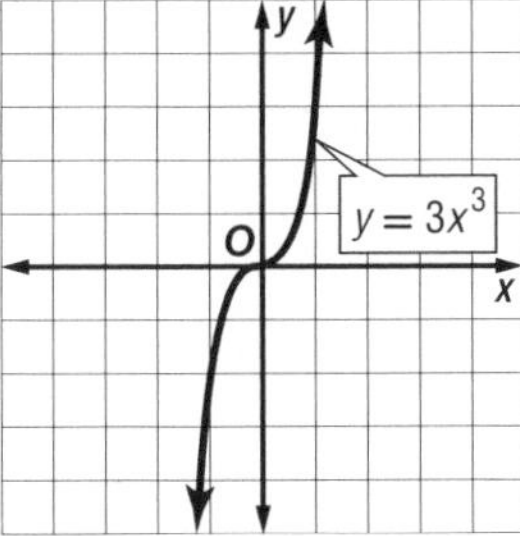

11.

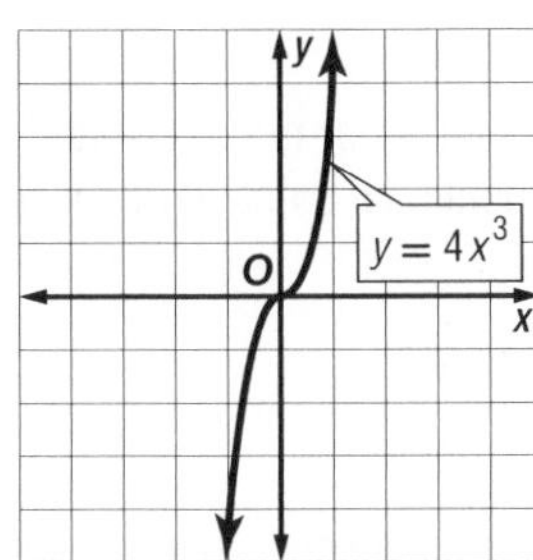

12.

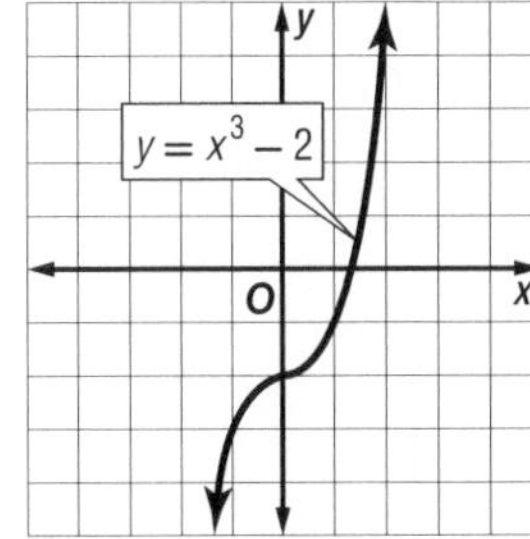

13.

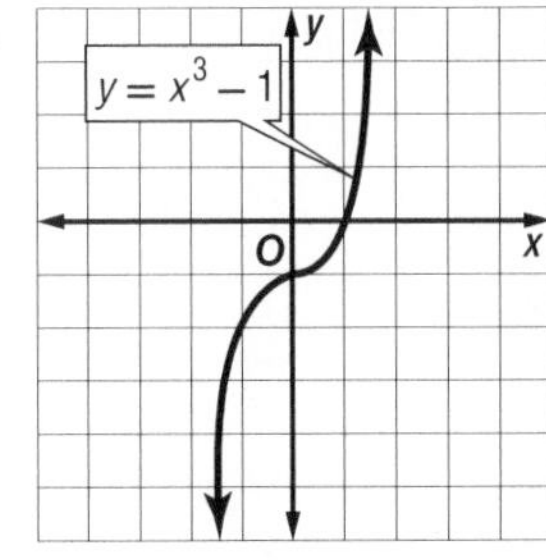

14.

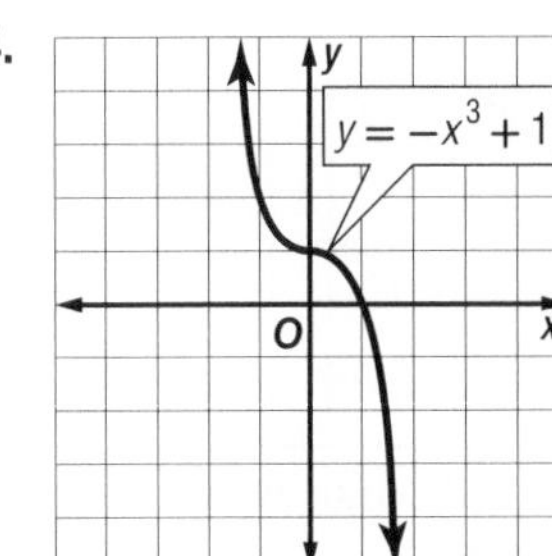

15.

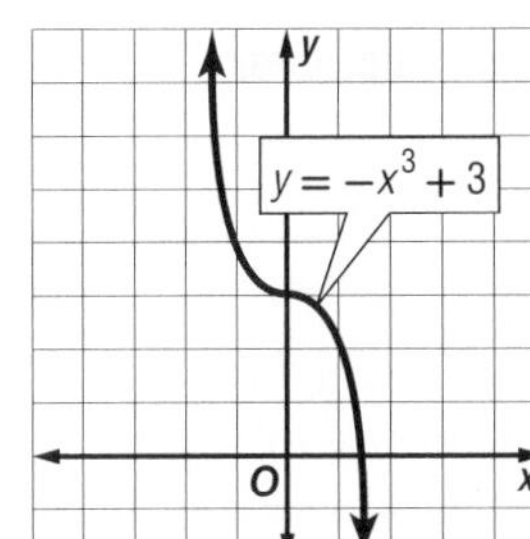

16.

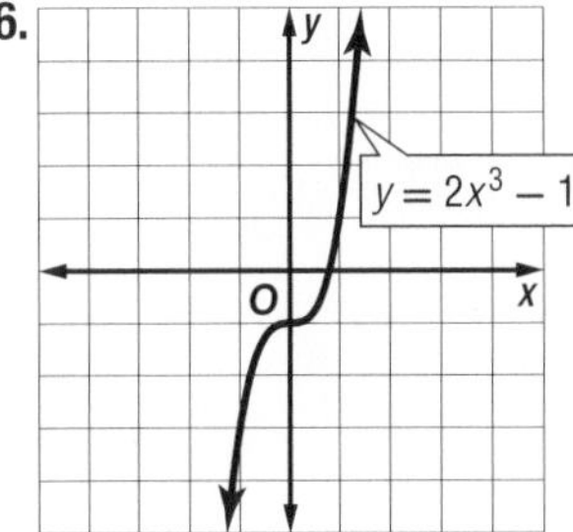

17a.

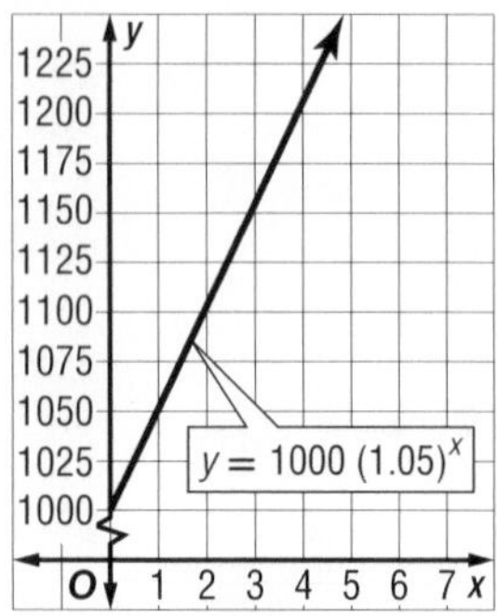

1000; The initial amount of money put into the account.

17b. after 15 years

18a. 538.5

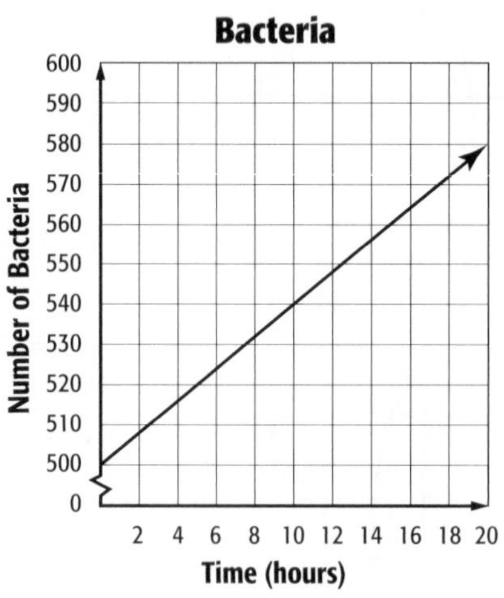

18b. 500; The initial amount of bacteria in a culture.

19.

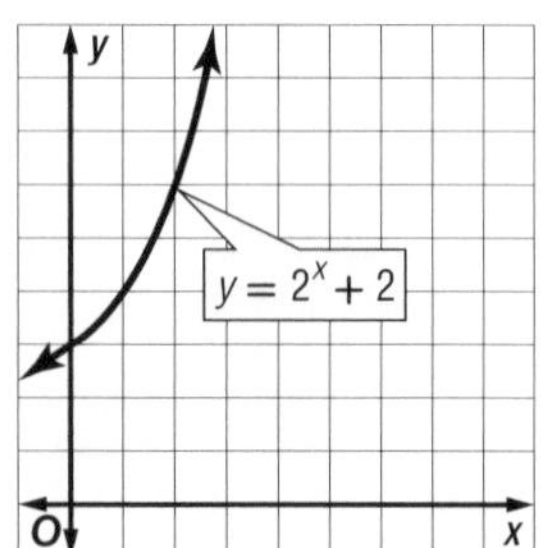

20.

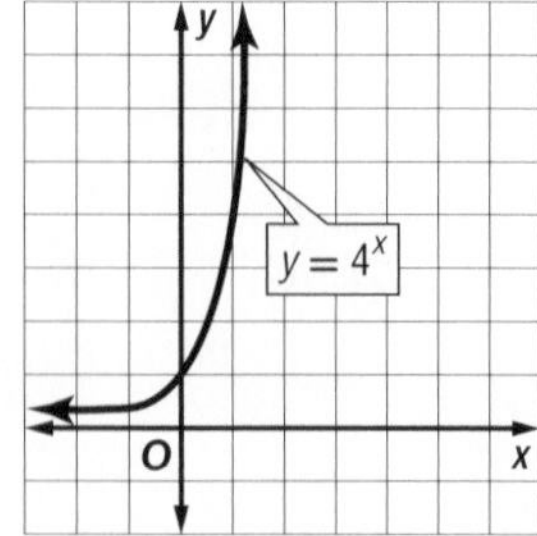

21.

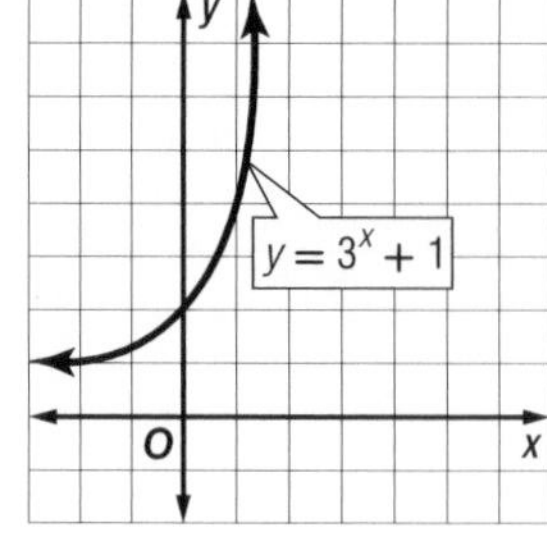

22.

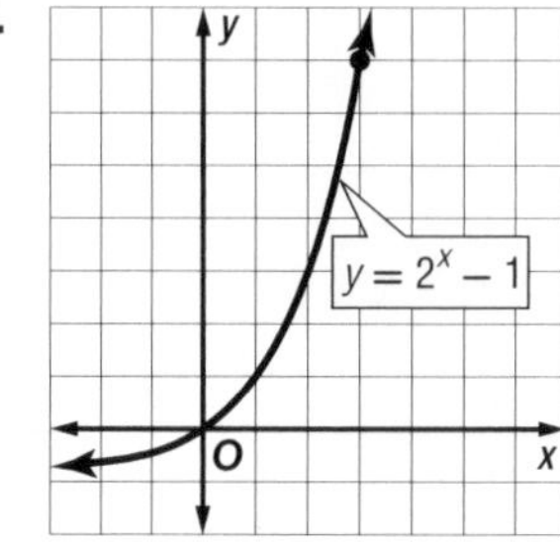

23.

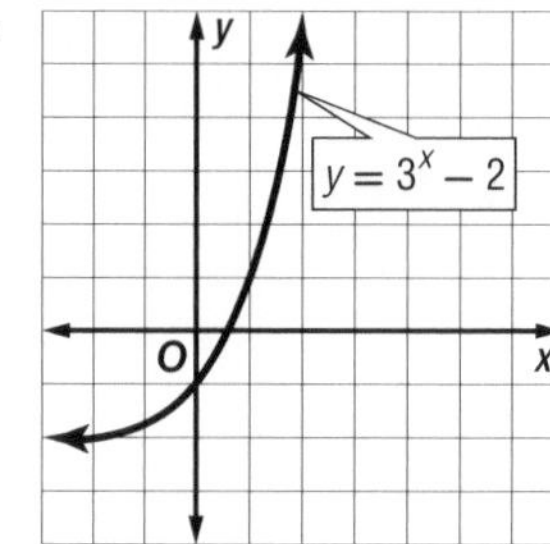

24.

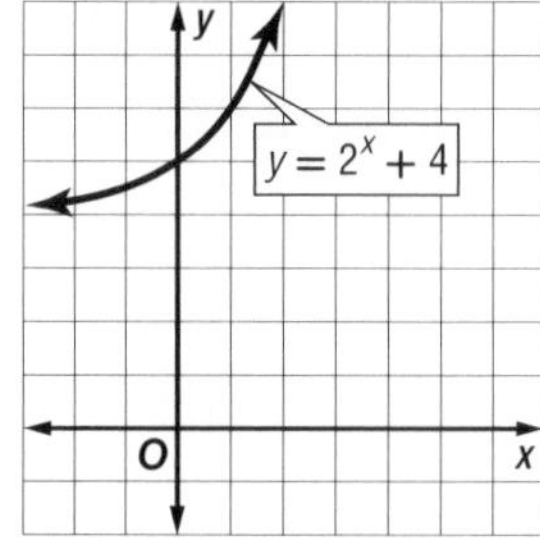

31. Sample answer: $y = 3x$, $y = 3^x$; the linear function has a constant rate of change. The exponential function has a greater rate of change.

32a. The *y*-intercept of the graph increases.

32b. The graph becomes less steep.

33. $y + 3x = 5$; This equation represents a linear function and the others represent exponential functions.

34.

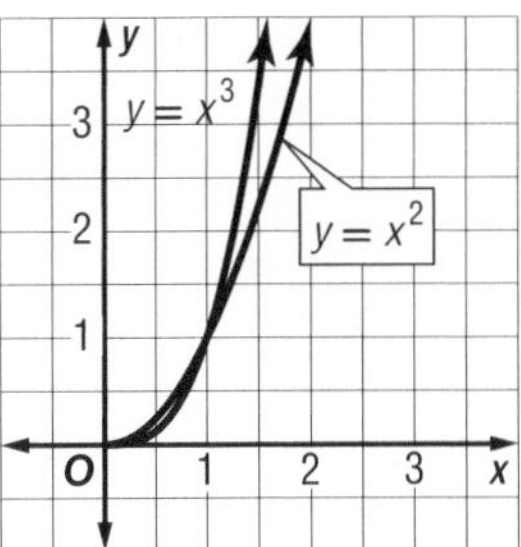

For $x > 1$, $y = x^3$ shows faster growth because the graph has a steeper slope.

35. Sample answer: The graph begins almost flat, but then for increasing x values, it becomes more steep.

Page 521, Extend 9-9

1. Sample answer:

Number of Half-Lives	Number of Coins That Remain
1	54
2	28
3	10
4	5
5	2

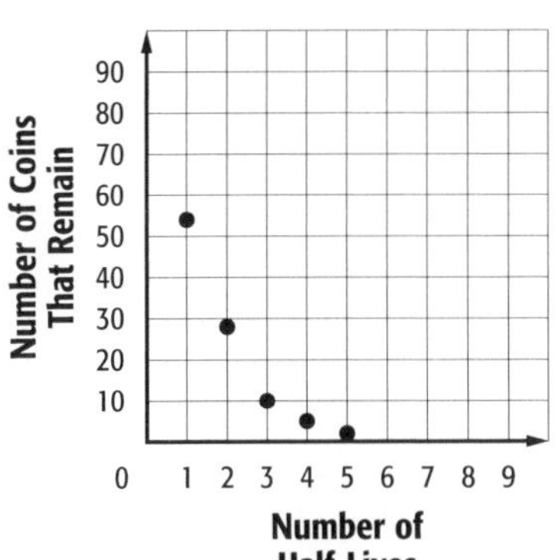

Page 526, Study Guide and Review

77.

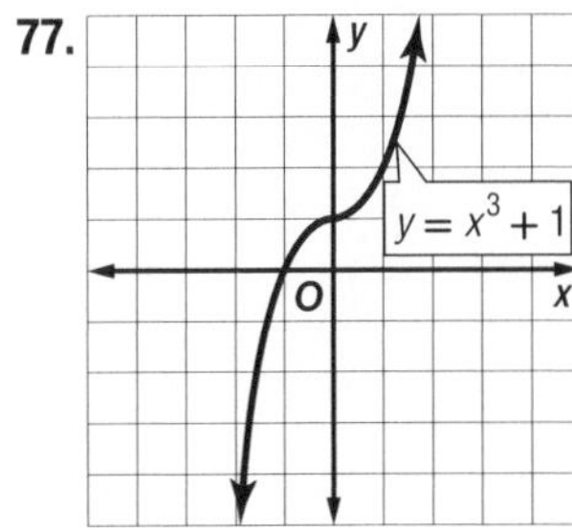

78.

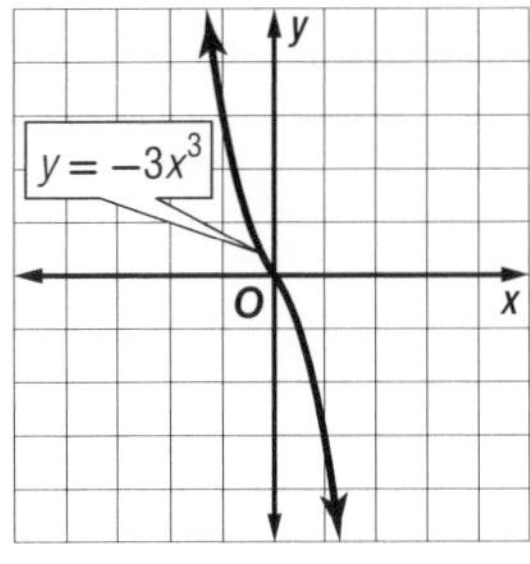

79.

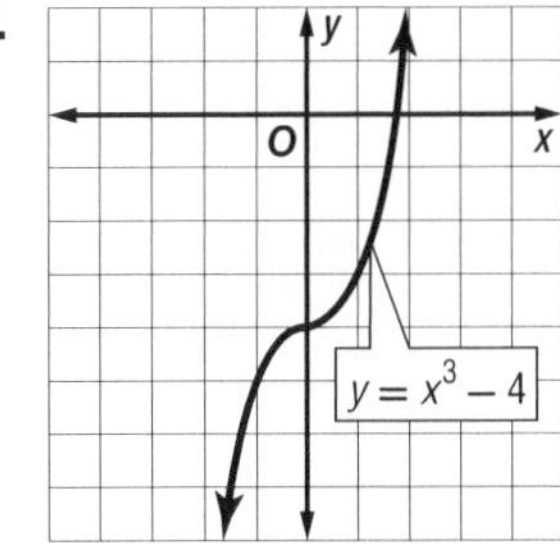

80.

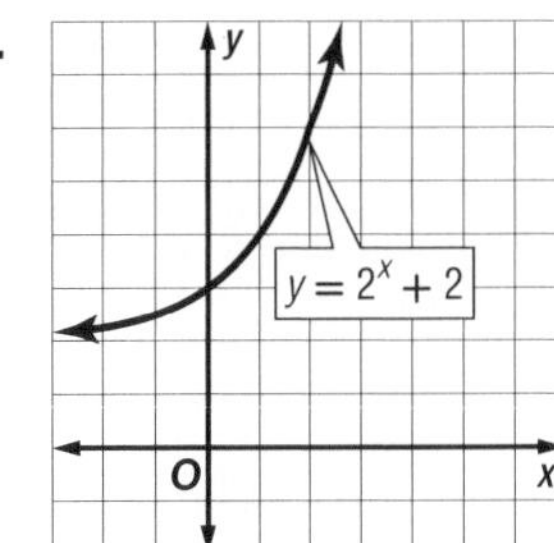

81.

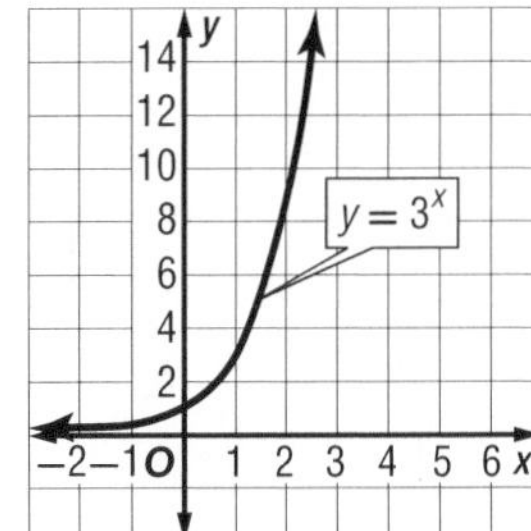

82.

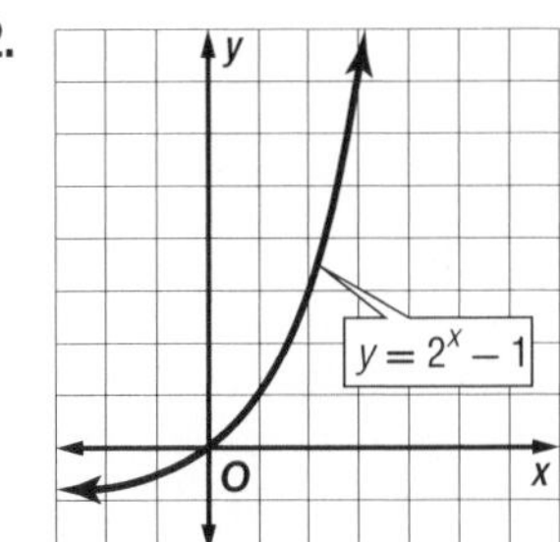

Page 527, Practice Test

30.

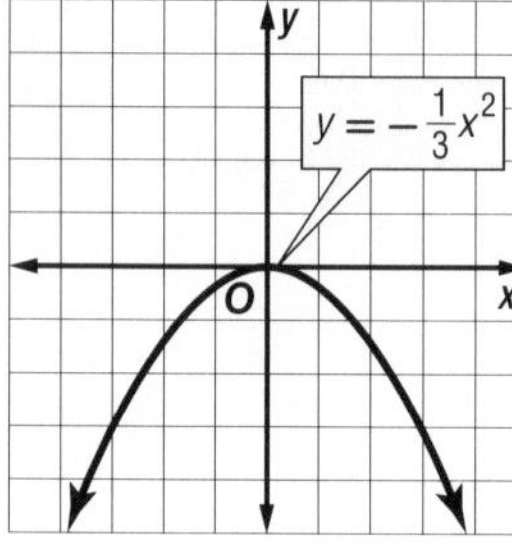

31.

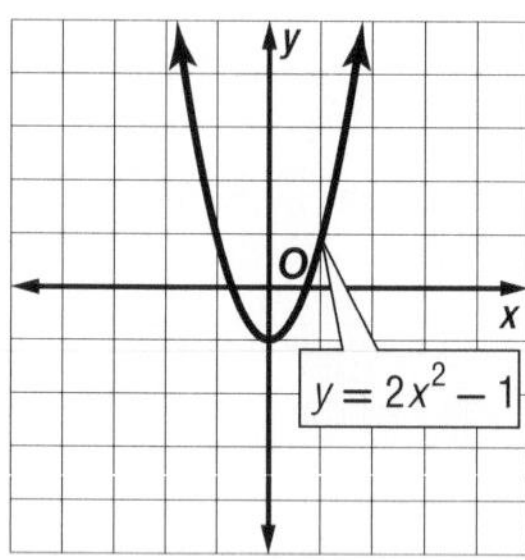

32.

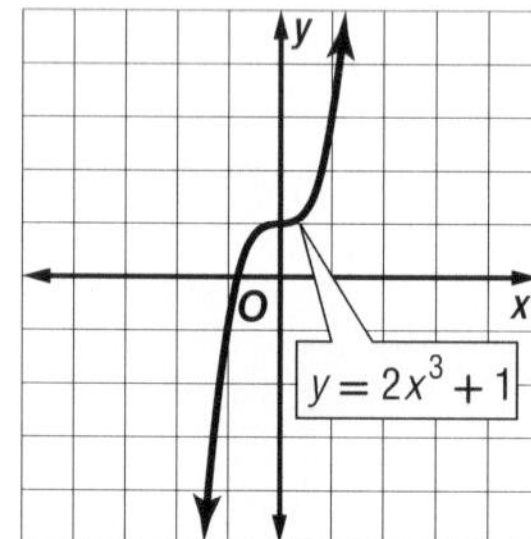

33.

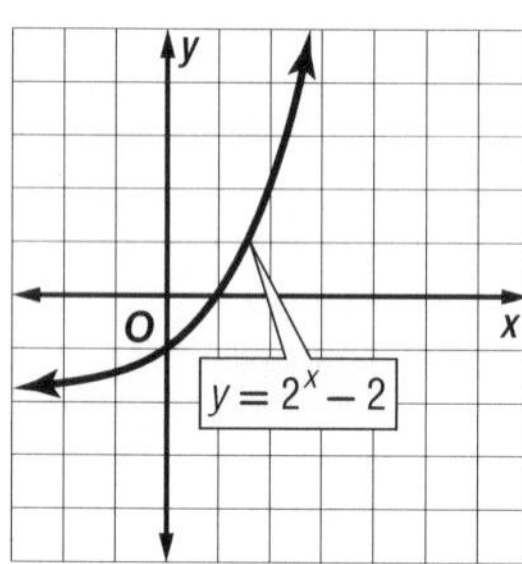

Notes

CHAPTER 10 Chapter Planner

Diagnostic Assessment
Quick Check, p. 533

	Explore 10-1 Pacing: 1 day	Lesson 10-1 Pacing: 1 day	Lesson 10-2 Pacing: 1 day
Title	**Algebra Lab: Squares and Square Roots**	**Squares and Square Roots**	**The Real Number System**
Objectives	• Model and evaluate squares and square roots.	• Find square roots. • Estimate square roots.	• Identify and compare numbers in the real number system. • Solve equations by finding square roots.
Key Vocabulary		perfect square square root radical sign	irrational numbers real numbers
NCTM Focal Points	G8–FP2, G8, FP7C For the complete wording of the Focal Points for Grades 7 and 8, please see pages iv, v, FP0 and FP1		
Multiple Representations		p. 541	
Lesson Resources	**Materials:** • algebra tiles	**Chapter 10 Resource Masters** • Study Guide and Intervention, pp. 5–6 AL OL ELL • Skills Practice, p. 7 AL OL ELL • Practice, p. 8 AL OL BL ELL • Word Problem Practice, p. 9 AL OL ELL • Enrichment, p. 10 OL BL **Transparencies** • 5-Minute Check Transparency 10–1 AL OL BL ELL **Additional Print Resources** • *Study Notebook* AL OL BL ELL	**Chapter 10 Resource Masters** • Study Guide and Intervention, pp. 11–12 AL OL ELL • Skills Practice, p. 13 AL OL ELL • Practice, p. 14 AL OL BL ELL • Word Problem Practice, p. 15 AL OL ELL • Enrichment, p. 16 OL BL • Graphing Calculator, p. 17 AL OL BL ELL • Quiz 1, p. 44 AL OL BL ELL **Transparencies** • 5-Minute Check Transparency 10–2 AL OL BL ELL **Additional Print Resources** • *Study Notebook* AL OL BL ELL
Technology for Every Lesson	Math Online glencoe.com • Extra Examples • Self-Check Quizzes • Personal Tutor	**CD/DVD Resources** IWB INTERACTIVE WHITEBOARD READY IWB StudentWorks Plus IWB Interactive Classroom IWB Diagnostic and Assessment Planner	• TeacherWorks Plus • eSolutions Manual Plus • ExamView Assessment Suite
Math in Motion	p. 535		
Differentiated Instruction		pp. 538, 542	pp. 544, 548

KEY: AL Approaching Level OL On Level BL Beyond Level ELL English Learners

Suggested Pacing			
Time Periods	Instruction	Review & Assessment	Total
45-minute	10	2	12
90-minute	5	1	6

Real Numbers and Right Triangles

Explore 10-3 Pacing: 1 day	Lesson 10-3 Pacing: 1 day	Explore 10-4 Pacing: 1 day	Lesson 10-4 Pacing: 1 day
Geometry Lab: Angles in a Triangle	**Triangles**	**Algebra Lab: The Pythagorean Theorem**	**The Pythagorean Theorem**
• Investigate the relationship among measures of the angles of a triangle.	• Find the missing angle measure of a triangle. • Classify triangles by properties and attributes.	• Investigate the relationship among the sides of a right triangle.	• Use the Pythagorean Theorem to find the length of a side of a right triangle. • Use the converse of the Pythagorean Theorem to determine whether a triangle is a right triangle.
	vertex; acute angle right angle; obtuse angle straight angle; congruent acute triangle obtuse triangle right triangle scalene triangle isosceles triangle equilateral triangle		legs hypotenuse Pythagorean Theorem solving a right triangle converse
			p. 562
Materials: • straightedge • sheet of paper • protractor	**Chapter 10 Resource Masters** • Study Guide and Intervention, pp. 18–19 AL OL ELL • Skills Practice, p. 20 AL OL ELL • Practice, p. 21 AL OL BL ELL • Word Problem Practice, p. 22 AL OL ELL • Enrichment, p. 23 OL BL • Quiz 2, p. 44 AL OL BL ELL **Transparencies** • 5-Minute Check Transparency 10–3 AL OL BL ELL **Additional Print Resources** • *Study Notebook* AL OL BL ELL	**Materials:** • rectangular dot paper	**Chapter 10 Resource Masters** • Study Guide and Intervention, pp. 24–25 AL OL ELL • Skills Practice, p. 26 AL OL ELL • Practice, p. 27 AL OL BL ELL • Word Problem Practice, p. 28 AL OL ELL • Enrichment, p. 29 OL BL **Transparencies** • 5-Minute Check Transparency 10–4 AL OL BL ELL **Additional Print Resources** • *Study Notebook* AL OL BL ELL
Math Online glencoe.com • Extra Examples • Self-Check Quizzes • Personal Tutor	**CD/DVD Resources** IWB INTERACTIVE WHITEBOARD READY IWB StudentWorks Plus IWB Interactive Classroom IWB Diagnostic and Assessment Planner	• TeacherWorks Plus • eSolutions Manual Plus • ExamView Assessment Suite	
p. 549		p. 557	
	pp. 552, 556		pp. 559, 560, 563

Formative Assessment
Mid-Chapter Quiz, p. 556

Chapter Planner

	Extend 10-4 Pacing: 1 day	Lesson 10-5 Pacing: 1 day	Lesson 10-6 Pacing: 1 day
Title	**Algebra Lab: Graphing Irrational Numbers**	**The Distance Formula**	**Special Right Triangles**
Objectives	• Graph irrational numbers on a number line.	• Use the Distance Formula to find the distance between two points on a coordinate plane. • Apply the Distance Formula to solve problems about figures on the coordinate plane.	• Find missing measures in 45°-45°-90° triangles. • Find missing measures in 30°-60°-90° triangles.
Key Vocabulary		Distance Formula	
NCTM Focal Points			
Multiple Representations			p. 575
Lesson Resources	**Materials:** • grid paper • compass	**Chapter 10 Resource Masters** • Study Guide and Intervention, pp. 30–31 AL OL ELL • Skills Practice, p. 32 AL OL ELL • Practice, p. 33 AL OL BL ELL • Word Problem Practice, p. 34 AL OL ELL • Enrichment, p. 35 OL BL • Quiz 3, p. 45 AL OL BL ELL **Transparencies** • 5-Minute Check Transparency 10–5 AL OL BL ELL **Additional Print Resources** • *Study Notebook* AL OL BL ELL	**Chapter 10 Resource Masters** • Study Guide and Intervention, pp. 36–37 AL OL ELL • Skills Practice, p. 38 AL OL ELL • Practice, p. 39 AL OL BL ELL • Word Problem Practice, p. 40 AL OL ELL • Enrichment, p. 41 OL BL • Graphing Calculator, p. 42 AL OL BL ELL • Quiz 4, p. 45 AL OL BL ELL **Transparencies** • 5-Minute Check Transparency 10–6 AL OL BL ELL **Additional Print Resources** • *Study Notebook* AL OL BL ELL
Technology for Every Lesson	Math Online glencoe.com • Extra Examples • Self-Check Quizzes • Personal Tutor	**CD/DVD Resources** IWB INTERACTIVE WHITEBOARD READY IWB StudentWorks Plus IWB Interactive Classroom IWB Diagnostic and Assessment Planner	• TeacherWorks Plus • eSolutions Manual Plus • ExamView Assessment Suite
Math in Motion	p. 564		
Differentiated Instruction		pp. 566, 570	pp. 573, 576

Summative Assessment
- Study Guide and Review, pp. 577–580
- Practice Test, p. 581

KEY: AL Approaching Level OL On Level BL Beyond Level ELL English Learners

Quick Review Math Handbook

is Glencoe's mathematical handbook for students and parents.

Hot Words includes a glossary of terms.

Hot Topics consists of two parts:

- explanations of key mathematical concepts
- exercises to check students' understanding.

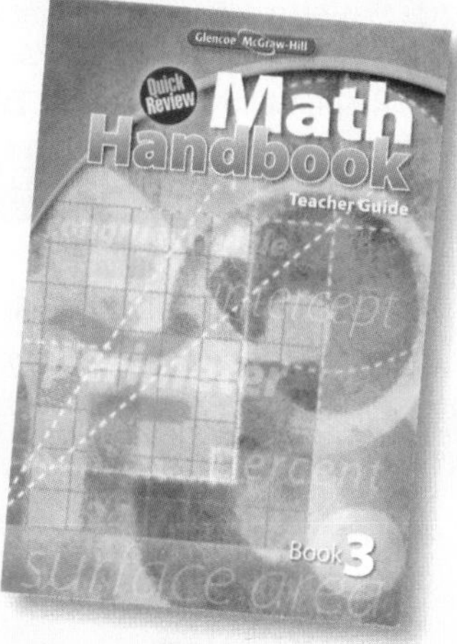

Lesson	Hot Topics Section	Lesson	Hot Topics Section
10-1	3.1, 3.2	10-4	7.9
10-3	7.1	10-5	7.9

What the Research Says...

Wood and Turner-Vorbeck (2001) state that it is critical that students be involved in the lessons, listen to each other, and engage in a variety of interaction with the material being studied.

- In Lesson 10-3, have students form different types of triangles between three towns on state maps. Have them discuss and present their results.
- Have students work cooperatively in the Explore and Extend activities throughout the chapter. This will provide a chance for dialogue, debate, and problem solving.

NOTES:

CHAPTER 10

Assessment and Intervention

SE = Student Edition, **TE** = Teacher Edition, **CRM** = Chapter Resource Masters

	Diagnosis	Prescription
Diagnostic Assessment	**Beginning Chapter 10**	
	Get Ready for Chapter 10 **SE,** p. 533	Response to Intervention **TE,** p. 533
	Beginning Every Lesson	
	Then, Now, Why? **SE** 5-Minute Check Transparencies	Chapter 0 **SE,** pp. P1–P22 Concepts and Skills Bank **SE,** pp. 856–887 *Quick Review Math Handbook*
Formative Assessment	**During/After Every Lesson**	
	Check Your Progress **SE,** every example Check Your Understanding **SE** H.O.T. Problems **SE** Spiral Review **SE** Additional Examples **TE** Watch Out! **TE** Step 4, Assess **TE** Chapter 10 Quizzes **CRM,** pp. 44–45 Self-Check Quizzes **glencoe.com**	Tier 1 Intervention Concepts and Skills Bank **SE,** pp. 856–887 Skills Practice **CRM,** Ch. 1–10 **glencoe.com** Tier 2 Intervention Differentiated Instruction **TE** Study Guide and Intervention Masters **CRM,** Ch. 1–10 *Quick Review Math Handbook* Tier 3 Intervention *Math Triumphs, Grade 8,* Ch. 4, 6
	Mid-Chapter	
	Mid-Chapter Quiz **SE,** p. 556 Mid-Chapter Test **CRM,** p. 46 ExamView Assessment Suite	Tier 1 Intervention Concepts and Skills Bank **SE,** pp. 856–887 Skills Practice **CRM,** Ch. 1–10 **glencoe.com** Tier 2 Intervention Study Guide and Intervention Masters **CRM,** Ch. 1–10 *Quick Review Math Handbook* Tier 3 Intervention *Math Triumphs, Grade 8,* Ch. 4, 6
	Before Chapter Test	
	Chapter Study Guide and Review **SE,** pp. 577–580 Practice Test **SE,** p. 581 Standardized Test Practice **SE,** pp. 582–585 Chapter Test **glencoe.com** Standardized Test Practice **glencoe.com** Vocabulary Review **glencoe.com** ExamView Assessment Suite	Tier 1 Intervention Concepts and Skills Bank **SE,** pp. 856–887 Skills Practice **CRM,** Ch. 1–10 **glencoe.com** Tier 2 Intervention Study Guide and Intervention Masters **CRM,** Ch. 1–10 *Quick Review Math Handbook* Tier 3 Intervention *Math Triumphs, Grade 8,* Ch. 4, 6
Summative Assessment	**After Chapter 10**	
	Multiple-Choice Tests, Forms 1, 2A, 2B, **CRM,** pp. 48–53 Free-Response Tests, Forms 2C, 2D, 3, **CRM,** pp. 54–60 Vocabulary Test **CRM,** p. 47 Extended Response Test **CRM,** p. 60 Standardized Test Practice **CRM,** pp. 61–63 ExamView Assessment Suite	Study Guide and Intervention Masters **CRM,** Ch. 1–10 *Quick Review Math Handbook* **glencoe.com**

Chapter 10 Differentiated Instruction

Option 1 Reaching All Learners AL OL BL ELL

VISUAL/SPATIAL Have students explore square roots and special triangles using geodot paper.

- Provide students with a sheet of geodot paper that has at least 12 rows and 12 columns of dots.
- Have students connect the dots to form as many squares as possible.
- Ask students to write equations for each square, first as a square and then as a square root. For example, for a 9-by-9 square, students would write $9^2 = 81$ and $\sqrt{81} = 9$.
- Then have students draw a diagonal through the squares and identify the type of special triangles formed by the diagonal. Have them find the hypotenuse of each right triangle to the nearest tenth. For example, the hypotenuse of a right triangle formed by the diagonal of a 9-by-9 square is $9\sqrt{2}$ or about 12.73 units.

INTERPERSONAL Have students work in groups of three to write statements about triangles that are true or false. For example:

- A true statement could be *you can represent the sum of the measures of the angles of an equilateral triangle by the equation $3x = 180$.*
- A false statement could be *scalene triangles can have a right angle and an obtuse angle.*

Ask groups to prepare five true and five false statements and then trade their statements with another group. Have the groups determine whether the statements are true or false, and if false, explain why.

Option 2 Approaching Level AL

Have students work in small groups to create their own representation of the real number system. Have a variety of materials available such as poster board, cardboard, foil, construction paper, glue, markers, string, and scissors. Ask students to include examples of rational, irrational, integers, natural, and whole numbers. Have them give an oral presentation of their work when finished.

Option 3 English Learners ELL

To help students master the vocabulary associated with triangles, have them create a table with these headings:

Acute	Obtuse	Right

Ask them to include the following in each column, with sketches:

- a short description of the triangle
- whether the triangle can be equilateral, isosceles, or scalene, with tick marks on sketches to indicate congruent sides

Have students check each others' tables for accuracy and completeness.

Many of the words used in this chapter have multiple meanings in the English language. Discuss these multiple meanings with students. For example, the word **root** can also be used as part of a plant or tree (the tree's roots ran underground), origin or cause of something (the root of a problem), or nationality (I have Puerto Rican roots).

Option 4 Beyond Level BL

Have students compare and contrast the following equations with and without absolute value symbols.

$$\sqrt{x^2} = |x| \qquad \sqrt{x^4} = x^2$$

$$\sqrt{x^6} = |x^3| \qquad \sqrt{x^8} = x^4$$

Then have students explain the following:

- Why are absolute value symbols required for some square roots and not others?
- What are two more examples of square roots which require and do not require absolute value symbols?

CHAPTER 10 Focus on Mathematical Content

Vertical Alignment

Before Chapter 10

Related Topics before Pre-Algebra
- use properties to classify triangles
- estimate and find solutions involving proportional relationships, such as similarity

Previous Topics from Pre-Algebra
- estimate and find solutions involving percents and proportional relationships
- compare and contrast proportional and nonproportional linear relationships

Chapter 10

Related Topics from Pre-Algebra
- communicate mathematical ideas using algebraic mathematical models
- use geometric concepts and properties to solve problems in fields such as art and architecture
- use the Pythagorean Theorem to solve real-world problems

After Chapter 10

Preparation for Geometry
- make generalizations about geometric properties of angle relationships in polygons
- derive, extend, and use the Pythagorean Theorem and its converse
- derive and use formulas involving length, slope, and midpoint

Lesson-by-Lesson Preview

10-1 Squares and Square Roots

The square root of a number is one of two equal factors of the number.

- A number such as 64 is a perfect square because it is the square of an integer: $8^2 = 64$ and $(-8)^2 = 64$.
- Every positive number has a positive and negative square root: The radical sign $\sqrt{}$ indicates the positive square root, $-\sqrt{}$ indicates the negative square root, and $\pm\sqrt{}$ indicates both square roots. Examples include $\sqrt{81} = 9$, $-\sqrt{49} = -7$, and $\pm\sqrt{4} = \pm 2$ or 2 and -2.
- A negative number does not have a square root that is a real number because the square of a number is never negative.
- If an integer is not a perfect square, estimate the square root by using perfect squares. For example, to find $\sqrt{19}$, 19 lies between the perfect squares 16 and 25, and since $\sqrt{16} = 4$ and $\sqrt{25} = 5$, $\sqrt{19}$ is between 4 and 5. Since 19 is closer to 16 than 25, the square root is closer to 4 than 5.

10-2 The Real Number System

The real number system is made up of the sets of rational and irrational numbers.

- Rational numbers are numbers that can be written in the form $\frac{a}{b}$ where a and b are integers and $b \neq 0$. Examples are 0.45, $\frac{1}{4}$, and $\sqrt{0.36}$.
- Irrational numbers are non-repeating, non-terminating decimals. Examples include $\sqrt{71}$, π, and 0.020020002....
- All real numbers can be represented on the same number line.

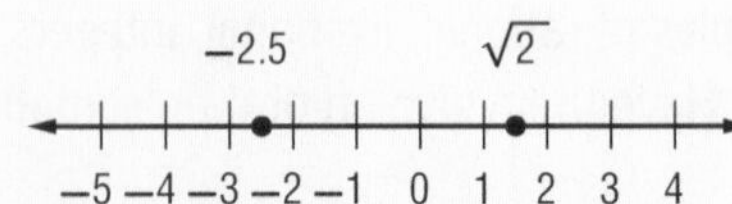

Real Numbers and Right Triangles

Triangles

A triangle is a figure formed by three line segments that intersect only at their endpoints. The points where the segments intersect are called vertices. The sum of the measures of the angles of a triangle is 180°.

Triangles can be classified by their angles:

- An acute triangle contains all acute angles. An acute angle is an angle whose measure is less than 90°.
- An obtuse triangle has one obtuse angle. An obtuse angle is an angle whose measure is greater than 90°. An obtuse triangle has one obtuse angle and two acute angles.
- A right triangle has one right angle. A right triangle has one right angle and two acute angles.

Triangles can also be classified by their sides:

- A scalene triangle has no congruent sides.
- An isosceles triangle has at least two congruent sides.
- An equilateral triangle has all sides congruent.

The Pythagorean Theorem

In a right triangle, the sides that are adjacent to the right angle are called the legs. The side opposite the right angle is the hypotenuse.

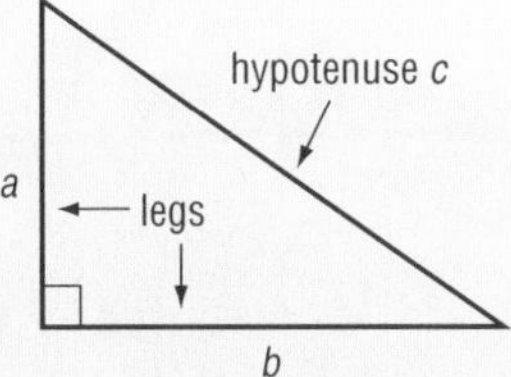

The Pythagorean Theorem describes the relationship between the lengths of the legs, a and b, and the hypotenuse c. It states that if a triangle is a right triangle, then the square of the length of the hypotenuse is equal to the sum of the squares of the lengths of the legs: $c^2 = a^2 + b^2$.

- When you *solve a right triangle*, you use the Pythagorean Theorem to find the length of an unknown side given the lengths of the other two sides.
- The converse of the Pythagorean Theorem states that if $c^2 = a^2 + b^2$, then the triangle is a right triangle. For example, given side lengths of 3 mm, 4 mm, and 5 mm, you can use the converse of the Pythagorean Theorem to determine whether the triangle is a right triangle: Since $5^2 = 3^2 + 4^2$ or $25 = 9 + 16$, a triangle with side lengths 3 mm, 4 mm, and 5 mm is a right triangle.

The Distance Formula

The Distance Formula, based on the Pythagorean Theorem, can be used to find the distance between two points on a coordinate plane. It states that the distance d between two points with coordinates (x_1, y_1) and (x_2, y_2) is given by $d = \sqrt{(x_2 - x_1)^2 + (y_2 - y_1)^2}$. You can use the Distance Formula to draw conclusions about a figure drawn on the coordinate plane. For example, you can find the length of each side of a triangle using the Distance Formula, and then add the lengths of the sides to find the perimeter.

Special Right Triangles

You can use the relationships between the hypotenuse and the legs of 45°-45°-90° triangles and 30°-60°-90° triangles to find the measures of missing side lengths.

In a 45°-45°-90° triangle,

- hypotenuse = leg · $\sqrt{2}$. So, if each leg is 4 cm, the hypotenuse is $4\sqrt{2}$ mm or about 5.66 cm.

In a 30°-60°-90° triangle,

- hypotenuse = 2 · shorter leg, and
- longer leg = $\sqrt{3}$ · shorter leg. So, if the shorter leg is 5 ft, the hypotenuse is 10 ft and the longer leg is $5\sqrt{3}$ ft or about 8.66 ft.

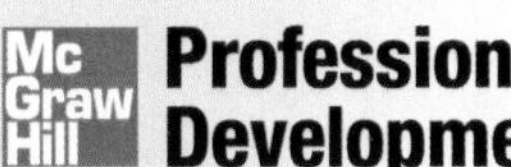

Targeted professional development has been articulated throughout McGraw-Hill's mathematics program. The **McGraw-Hill Professional Development Video Library** provides short videos that support key topics. For more information, visit glencoe.com.

Instructional Strategies

CHAPTER 10 Notes

Chapter Project

Recreational Tips

Students use what they have learned about square roots, the Pythagorean Theorem, special right triangles, and the Distance Formula to write a how-to guide on recreation.

- Divide students into groups. Ask each group member to choose a recreational activity, such as sailing. Find a formula involving square roots related to that activity, like $s = 1.34\sqrt{l}$ to find the hull speed s of a sailboat where l is the length of the hull at the waterline. *Hint: Look for formulas on the Internet and in the lesson examples and exercises.*
- Have each group write a how-to section on using formulas in each of their activities. For example, hikers might want to know how far they can see from the top of a peak. Have them explain how to use the formulas and give examples.
- Ask each group to write a section in their guide on how to use the Pythagorean theorem or special right triangles in each of their activities. For example, someone might want to estimate the distance from their sailboat to a dock or the height of a cliff.
- Have each group include a section on how to use a coordinate system and the Distance Formula to find distances. Ask them to draw a map of three places in a recreational area, with a key that gives the value per unit on the grid. Then have them show how to find the distances between the places.

CHAPTER 10 Real Numbers and Right Triangles

Then

In Chapter 3 you learned how all fractions and some decimals are classified as rational numbers.

Now

In Chapter 10, you will:

- Identify irrational numbers and classify real numbers.
- Classify triangles.
- Solve problems using the Pythagorean Theorem and the Distance Formula.

Why?

RECREATION Looking for a sport that requires great skill, balance, and flexibility? Then give windsailing a try. Windsailing is a cross between sailing and surfing. Windsail designers use mathematics such as square roots when trying to create the best sail.

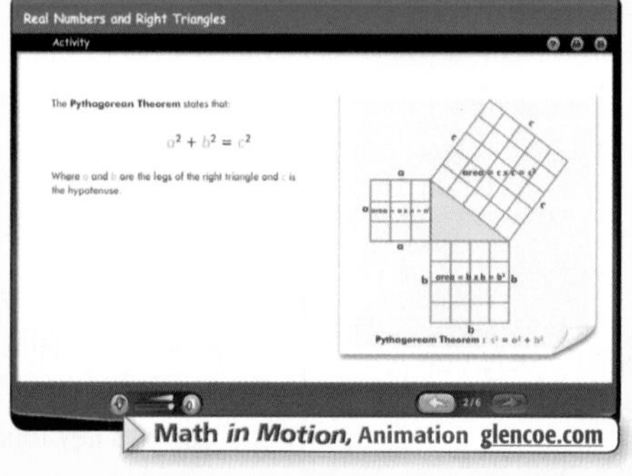

Math *in Motion*, Animation glencoe.com

Key Vocabulary Introduce the key vocabulary in the chapter using the routine below.

<u>Define:</u> The square root of a number is one of two equal factors of a number.

<u>Example:</u> The square root of 25 is 5 since $5^2 = 25$.

<u>Ask:</u> What is the square root of 144? 12

Get Ready for Chapter 10

Diagnose Readiness You have two options for checking Prerequisite Skills.

Text Option Take the Quick Check below. Refer to the Quick Review for help.

*Quick*Check

(Used in Lesson 10–2)

Replace each ● with <, >, or = to make a true statement. (Concepts and Skills Bank)

1. 5.19 ● 5.187 > **2.** 19.45 ● 19.5 <

3. 24.56 ● 24.56 = **4.** 9.734 ● 9.73 >

5. 16.892 ● 16.9 < **6.** 42.641 ● 42.64 >

7. **FIELD HOCKEY** Order the following winning averages of five field hockey teams from greatest to least.

0.523, 0.546, 0.601, 0.594, 0.509
0.601, 0.594, 0.546, 0.523, 0.509

(Used in Lesson 10–3)

Solve each equation. (Lesson 4-4)

8. $9a = 72$ 8 **9.** $36 = 3m$ 12

10. $16x = 64$ 4 **11.** $144 = 16b$ 9

12. $90 = 18c$ 5 **13.** $120 = 40f$ 3

14. **COOKIES** A batch of cookies contains 2 cups of sugar. How many batches of cookies contain 16 cups of sugar? **8 batches**

(Used in Lesson 10–5)

Evaluate each expression. (Lesson 9-1)

15. $(8 - 3)^2 + (12 - 9)^2$ 34

16. $(5 - 2)^2 + (8 - 4)^2$ 25

17. $(-4 - 6)^2 + [(-2 - (-3)]^2$ 101

18. $(-3 - 1)^2 + (5 - 3)^2$ 20

19. $[(7 - (-4)]^2 + [(6 - (-2)]^2$ 185

20. **BIOLOGY** Suppose a virus splits into two viruses every 45 minutes. How many viruses are there after 5 hours 15 minutes? **128 viruses**

*Quick*Review

EXAMPLE 1

Replace ● with <, >, or = to make 34.29 ● 34.3 a true statement.

34.29 Line up the decimal points.

34.3 The digits in the tenths place are not the same.

2 tenths < 3 tenths

So, 34.29 < 34.3.

EXAMPLE 2

Solve $14w = 56$.

$14w = 56$ Write the equation.

$\frac{14w}{14} = \frac{56}{14}$ Divide each side by 14.

$w = 4$ Simplify.

EXAMPLE 3

Evaluate $(6 - 2)^2 + (9 - 7)^2$.

$(6 - 2)^2 + (9 - 7)^2$

$= 4^2 + 2^2$ Simplify the expressions inside parentheses first.

$= 16 + 4$ Evaluate 4^2 and 2^2.

$= 20$ Simplify.

Online Option Math Online Take a self-check Chapter Readiness Quiz at glencoe.com.

Get Ready for Chapter 10

Response to Intervention (RtI)

Use the *Quick Check* results and the Intervention Planner to help you determine your Response to Intervention. The If-Then statements in the chart help you decide the appropriate tier of RtI and suggest intervention resources for each tier.

Intervention Planner

Tier 1 On Level

 students miss about 25% of the exercises or less,

 choose a resource:

SE Lessons 0-3, 4-4, and 9-1

CRM Skills Practice, Chapter 4, p. 25, Chapter 9, p. 7

TE Chapter Project, p. 532

Math Online Self-Check Quiz

Tier 2 Strategic Intervention approaching grade level

 students miss about 50% of the exercises,

Then choose a resource:

CRM Study Guide and Intervention, Chapter 4, pp. 23–24, Chapter 9, pp. 5–6

Quick Review Math Handbook

Math Online Extra Examples, Personal Tutor, Homework Help

Tier 3 Intensive Intervention 2 or more grades below level

 students miss about 75% of the exercises,

 use *Math Triumphs, Grade 8,* Ch. 4, 6

Math Online Extra Examples, Personal Tutor, Homework Help, Review Vocabulary

CHAPTER 10 Notes

FOLDABLES® Study Organizer

Dinah Zike's Foldables®

Focus Students write notes about two-dimensional figures in this chapter.

Teach Have students make and label the sections for each topic of their Foldables as illustrated. Have students use the appropriate sections as they cover each lesson in this chapter. Encourage students to use each pocket for a specific figure in the chapter. Students can include lesson numbers with the diagrams and definitions they record.

When to Use It Students should record names, formulas, and attributes of two-dimensional figures and their measurements, and use them to review for the chapter test.

Differentiated Instruction

CRM Student-Built Glossary, pp. 1–2
Students should complete the chart by providing a definition of each term and an example as they progress through Chapter 10. This study tool can also be used to review for the chapter test.

Get Started on Chapter 10

You will learn several new concepts, skills, and vocabulary terms as you study Chapter 10. To get ready, identify important terms and organize your resources. You may wish to refer to **Chapter 0** to review prerequisite skills.

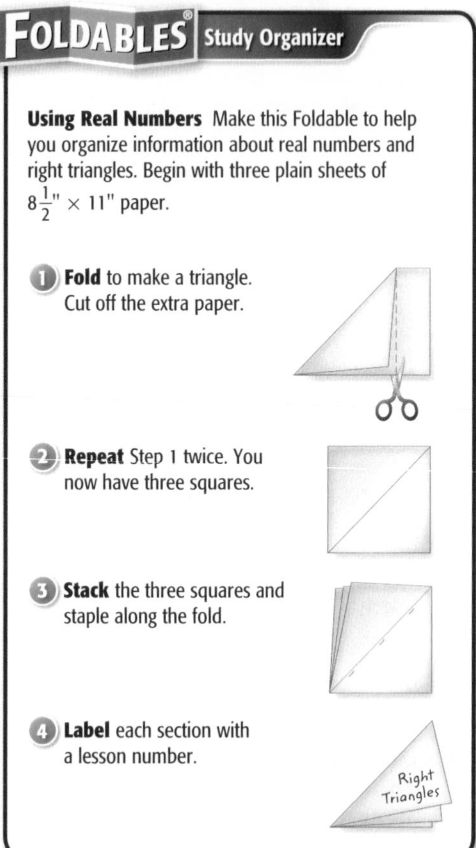

FOLDABLES® Study Organizer
Using Real Numbers Make this Foldable to help you organize information about real numbers and right triangles. Begin with three plain sheets of $8\frac{1}{2}$" × 11" paper.
1 Fold to make a triangle. Cut off the extra paper.
2 Repeat Step 1 twice. You now have three squares.
3 Stack the three squares and staple along the fold.
4 Label each section with a lesson number.
Right Triangles

New Vocabulary

English		Español
square root	p. 537	raíz cuadrada
irrational numbers	p. 543	número irracional
real numbers	p. 543	número reales
acute angle	p. 551	ángulo agudo
right angle	p. 551	ángulo recto
obtuse angle	p. 551	ángulo obtuso
straight angle	p. 551	ángulo llano
acute triangle	p. 552	triángulo acutángulo
obtuse triangle	p. 552	triángulo obtusángulo
right triangle	p. 552	triángulo rectángulo
congruent	p. 552	congruentes
scalene triangle	p. 552	triángulo escaleno
isosceles triangle	p. 552	triángulo isósceles
equilateral triangle	p. 552	triángulo equilátero
hypotenuse	p. 558	hipotenusa
Pythagorean Theorem	p. 558	Teorema de Pitágoras
converse	p. 560	recíproca
Distance Formula	p. 565	Fórmula de la distancia

Review Vocabulary

integer • p. 61 • enteros whole numbers and their opposites

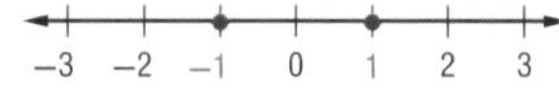

rational number • p. 128 • número racional a number that can be written in the form $\frac{a}{b}$, where a and b are integers and $b \neq 0$

Multilingual eGlossary glencoe.com

Math Online glencoe.com

- Study the chapter online
- Explore **Math in Motion**
- Get extra help from your own **Personal Tutor**
- Use **Extra Examples** for additional help
- Take a **Self-Check Quiz**
- **Review Vocabulary** in fun ways

EXPLORE **10-1**

Algebra Lab: Squares and Square Roots

Math Online > glencoe.com
Math *in Motion*, Animation

Numbers raised to the second power are called *squares*. You can use a geometric model to discover the reason they are called squares.

ACTIVITY 1

Use algebra tiles to evaluate 6^2.

- The power 6^2 is the product 6×6. The product can be represented by a square with one factor as the length and the other as the width.
- Arrange tiles in a 6-by-6 square.
- Since $6 \times 6 = 36$, $6^2 = 36$.

The opposite of squaring a number is finding a *square root*. These are inverse operations. To find the square root of a number, find two equal factors whose product is that number. The positive square root of a number is the *principal square root*. The symbol for the principal square root is $\sqrt{\ }$.

ACTIVITY 2

Use algebra tiles to find $\sqrt{25}$.

- You know that a square number can be represented by the area of a square. To find the square root of 25, arrange 25 tiles into a square.
- Twenty-five tiles can be arranged in a 5-by-5 square. So, $25 = 5 \times 5$, or 5^2.
- The length of each side of the square is 5 units. So, the principal square root of 25 is 5.

Analyze the Results

Model each power. Apply what you learned to evaluate it. 1–6. See Chapter 10 Answer Appendix for models.

1. 3^2 9 **2.** 5^2 25 **3.** 7^2 49

4. 8^2 64 **5.** 10^2 100 **6.** 12^2 144

7. Explain why n^2 is called *n squared*. The product can be represented by the area of a square with a side of length n.

Model each square root. Apply what you learned to evaluate it. 8–13. See Chapter 10 Answer Appendix for models.

8. $\sqrt{4}$ 2 **9.** $\sqrt{16}$ 4 **10.** $\sqrt{81}$ 9

11. $\sqrt{49}$ 7 **12.** $\sqrt{100}$ 10 **13.** $\sqrt{121}$ 11

14. What part of the model represents the square root of the area of the square? the length of the edge of the square

EXPLORE **10-1** Lesson Notes

1 FOCUS

Objective Model and evaluate squares and square roots.

Materials for Each Group

- algebra tiles

Easy to Make Manipulatives
Teaching Mathematics with Manipulatives template for algebra tiles, p. 7.

2 TEACH

Working in Cooperative Groups

Have students work in groups of two or three to complete Activities 1–3.

Activity 1

Ask:

- Can you use algebra tiles to represent a number with an exponent and have the sides not be the same length? No, since the factors are equal the lengths will always be the same.
- Suppose there was a square with lengths of 20 on each side. How would you write this value as an exponential expression? 20^2

Practice Have students complete Exercises 1–7.

Activity 2

Explain to students that the square root of a number is the opposite of squaring the number.

Ask:

- What is the principal square root of 36? 6 How could you represent that using algebra tiles? A square with side lengths of 6.

Practice Have students complete Exercises 8–14.

Activity 3

Show students how algebra tiles can be used to represent a base with an exponent or a square root of a number, and how they can be used to estimate square roots.

Ask:

- If the side length of a square is 6, the principal square root is 6. Can you use algebra tiles to represent a number such as 35? Explain. No. The lengths of the rectangle would have to be equal and multiply together to be 35. The lengths would be less then 6, but more than 5 so tiles could not be used.

Practice Have students complete Exercises 15–21.

Formative Assessment

Use Exercises 1–21 to assess whether students understand the relation between the length of a side of a square and the square root of a number.

From Concrete to Abstract

Use Exercise 21 to assess whether students can find or estimate the square root of a number without using models.

Additional Answer

21. Sample answer: The square root is greater than 20 because $20^2 = 400$. Try 21^2, 22^2, and so on until you find a perfect square close to the number.

A **perfect square** is a number with a whole number square root but most whole numbers are not perfect squares. You can estimate the square roots of numbers that are not perfect squares.

ACTIVITY 3

Use algebra tiles to estimate the principal square root of 50.

Step 1 Arrange 50 tiles into the largest square possible. The largest square possible has 49 tiles, with 1 left over.

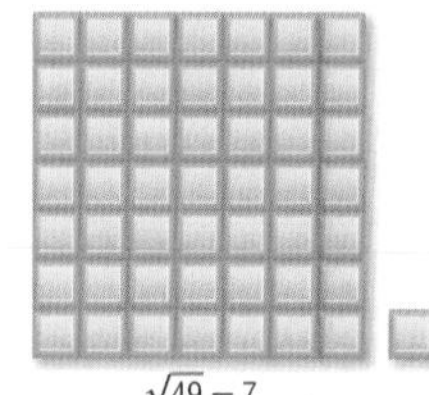

Step 2 Add tiles until you have the next larger square. So, 14 new tiles are needed for the next square.

Step 3 The square root of 49 is 7 and the square root of 64 is 8. Therefore, the square root of 50 is between the whole numbers 7 and 8.

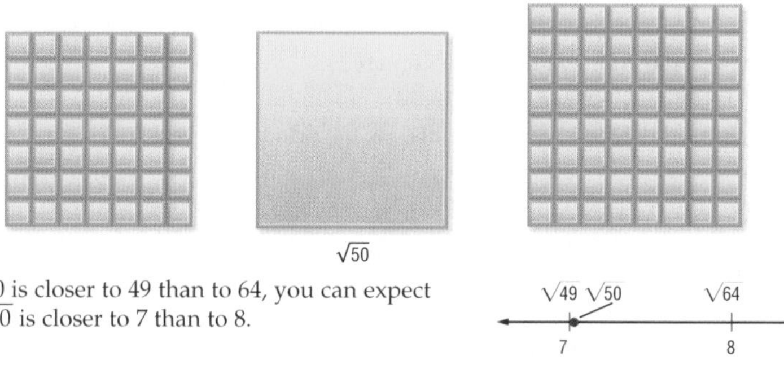

Since 50 is closer to 49 than to 64, you can expect that $\sqrt{50}$ is closer to 7 than to 8.

$\sqrt{49}$ $\sqrt{50}$ $\sqrt{64}$
7 8

Check the estimate with a calculator. 2nd [√] 50 ENTER 7.071067812 ✓

Analyze the Results

Use a number line to model each square root. Apply what you learned to estimate the principal square root. 15–20. See Chapter 10 Answer Appendix for number lines.

15. $\sqrt{20}$ 4 **16.** $\sqrt{44}$ 7 **17.** $\sqrt{58}$ 8 **18.** $\sqrt{69}$ 8 **19.** $\sqrt{91}$ 10 **20.** $\sqrt{111}$ 11

21. MAKE A CONJECTURE Describe how to use the guess and check strategy to find the square root of a number between 400 and 500. See margin.

10-1 Squares and Square Roots

Then
You have already evaluated expressions containing squares of numbers. (Lesson 8-1)

Now
- Find square roots.
- Estimate square roots.

New Vocabulary
perfect square
square root
radical sign

Math Online
glencoe.com
- Extra Examples
- Personal Tutor
- Self-Check Quiz
- Homework Help

Why?

The Space Needle in Seattle, Washington, was built on a square lot with an area of 14,400 square feet.

a. What number when multiplied by itself equals 144? 14,400? **12; 120**

b. What are the dimensions of the square lot? **120 ft by 120 ft**

Find Square Roots A number like 144 is a **perfect square** because it is the square of an integer. The opposite of squaring a number is finding the square root.

Key Concept Square Root

For Your FOLDABLE

Words A **square root** of a number is one of its two equal factors.

Symbols If $x^2 = y$, then x is a square root of y.

A **radical sign**, $\sqrt{\ }$, is used to indicate a positive square root. Every positive number has both a positive and a negative square root.

$$\sqrt{36} = 6 \qquad -\sqrt{36} = -6 \qquad \pm\sqrt{36} = \pm 6 \text{ or } 6, -6$$

A negative number like -36 has no real-number square root because the square of a number cannot be negative.

EXAMPLE 1 Find Square Roots

Find each square root.

a. $\sqrt{9}$

$\sqrt{9} = 3$ Find the positive square root of 9; $3^2 = 9$.

b. $-\sqrt{64}$

$-\sqrt{64} = -8$ Find the negative square root of 64; $8^2 = 64$.

c. $\pm\sqrt{4}$

$\pm\sqrt{4} = \pm 2$ Find both square roots of 4; $2^2 = 4$.

d. $\sqrt{-81}$

There is no real square root because no number times itself is equal to -81.

Check Your Progress

1A. $\sqrt{49}$ **7** **1B.** $-\sqrt{16}$ **−4** **1C.** $\pm\sqrt{100}$ **±10** **1D.** $\sqrt{-49}$ **no real solution**

Personal Tutor glencoe.com

10-1 Lesson Notes

1 FOCUS

Vertical Alignment

Before Lesson 10-1
Evaluate expressions containing squares of numbers.

Lesson 10-1
Find square roots. Estimate square roots.

After Lesson 10-1
Distinguish between rational and irrational numbers.

2 TEACH

Scaffolding Questions

Have students read the *Why?* section of the lesson and answer the questions.

Ask:

- How are the area of the lot and the dimensions of the lot related? Since the lot is a square, the square root of the area of the lot is equal to the dimensions of the lot.
- Suppose a garden in the shape of a square has a total area of 36 square feet. What are the dimensions of the garden? 6×6
- How did you find your answer? The garden is square, so the lengths must be 6 or –6 since both equal 36 when squared. Length cannot be negative, so the length and width are 6.

Lesson 10-1 Resources

Resource	Approaching-Level	On-Level	Beyond-Level	English Learners
Teacher Edition		• Differentiated Instruction, p. 538	• Differentiated Instruction, p. 542	
Chapter Resource Masters	• Study Guide and Intervention, pp. 5–6 • Skills Practice p. 7 • Practice p. 8 • Word Problem Practice, p. 9	• Study Guide and Intervention, pp. 5–6 • Skills Practice p. 7 • Practice p. 8 • Word Problem Practice, p. 9 • Enrichment, p. 10	• Practice p. 8 • Word Problem Practice, p. 9 • Enrichment, p. 10	• Study Guide and Intervention, pp. 5–6 • Skills Practice p. 7 • Practice p. 8
Transparencies	• 5-Minute Check Transparency 10-1	• 5-Minute Check Transparency 10-1	• 5-Minute Check Transparency 10-1	• 5-Minute Check Transparency 10-1
Other	• Study Notebook • Teaching Pre-Algebra with Manipulatives	• Study Notebook • Teaching Pre-Algebra with Manipulatives	• Study Notebook	• Study Notebook • Teaching Pre-Algebra with Manipulatives

Find Square Roots

Example 1 shows how to find square roots of perfect squares.

Formative Assessment

Use the Check Your Progress exercises after each example to determine students' understanding of concepts.

Additional Examples

1 Find each square root.

a. $\sqrt{64}$ 8

b. $-\sqrt{121}$ −11

c. $\pm\sqrt{256}$ ± 16

d. $\sqrt{-9}$ no real solution

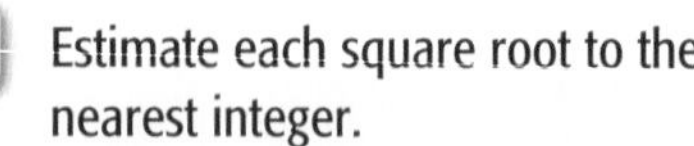

2 Estimate each square root to the nearest integer.

a. $\sqrt{22}$ 5

b. $-\sqrt{319}$ −18

3 Use a calculator to find $\sqrt{57}$ to the nearest tenth. 7.5

Additional Examples also in Interactive Classroom PowerPoint® Presentations

IWB INTERACTIVE WHITEBOARD READY

Focus on Mathematical Content

Negative Square Root The real square root of a negative number is *not possible;* two equal factors cannot be multiplied to produce a negative product. The negative square root of a number *is possible* because two negatives multiplied equal a positive. There exists both a positive (principal) and negative square root for every positive number; zero has only one, zero. Ask students, what is the square root of –16? There is no real-number square root of –16.

Math History Link

Aryabhata (476–550) Aryabhata, an Indian mathematician, published a very good approximation of the square roots of 2 and 3. He also wrote a summary of astronomy and Hindu mathematics.

Estimate Square Roots When integers are not perfect squares, you can estimate square roots mentally by using perfect squares.

EXAMPLE 2 Estimate Square Roots

Estimate each square root to the nearest integer.

a. $\sqrt{33}$

The first perfect square less than 33 is 25. $\sqrt{25} = 5$

The first perfect square greater than 33 is 36. $\sqrt{36} = 6$

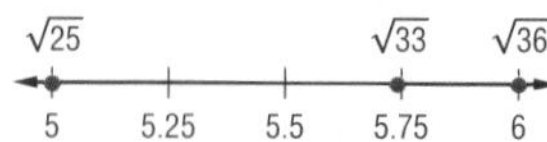

The square root of 33 is between the integers 5 and 6. Since 33 is closer to 36 than to 25, you can expect $\sqrt{33}$ to be closer to 6 than to 5.

b. $-\sqrt{129}$

The first perfect square less than 129 is 121. $\sqrt{121} = 11$

The first perfect square greater than 129 is 144. $\sqrt{144} = 12$

$-\sqrt{144}$ $-\sqrt{129}$ $-\sqrt{121}$

−12 −11.75 −11.50 −11.25 −11

The negative square root of 129 is between the integers −11 and −12. Since 129 is closer to 121 than to 144, you can expect $-\sqrt{129}$ to be closer to −11 than −12.

Check Your Progress

2A. $\sqrt{60}$ 8

2B. $-\sqrt{23}$ −5

Personal Tutor glencoe.com

StudyTip

Choose a Form Express a number as a square root if an exact answer is needed. Express a number as a decimal if an approximation is sufficient.

EXAMPLE 3 Use a Calculator to Find a Square Root

Use a calculator to find $\pm\sqrt{40}$ to the nearest tenth.

2nd [√] 40 ENTER 6.32455532 **Use a calculator.**

$\sqrt{40} \approx 6.3$ **Round to the nearest tenth.**

So, $\pm\sqrt{40}$ is $\approx \pm 6.3$ because you must find both square roots.

Check for Reasonableness Since $6^2 = 36$, the answer is reasonable. ✓

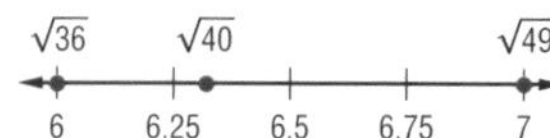

Check Your Progress

Use a calculator to find each square root to the nearest tenth.

3A. $\sqrt{14}$ 3.7

3B. $\sqrt{79}$ 8.9

Personal Tutor glencoe.com

Differentiated Instruction

OL

Intrapersonal Have students write in their journals about when and why squares and square roots are used. Have them ask their science teachers how squares are used in science and include the answer in their entry.

EXAMPLE 4 Use a Calculator to Find a Negative Square Root

Use a calculator to find $-\sqrt{18}$ to the nearest tenth.

[(-)] [2nd] [$\sqrt{\ }$] 18 [ENTER] 4.24264069 Use a calculator.

$-\sqrt{18} \approx -4.2$ Round to the nearest tenth.

Check for Reasonableness Since $4^2 = 16$, the answer is reasonable. ✓

Number line: $-\sqrt{25}$ at -5; $-\sqrt{18}$ at about -4.25; $-\sqrt{16}$ at -4. Tick marks: -5, -4.75, -4.5, -4.25, -4

Check Your Progress

Use a calculator to find each square root to the nearest tenth.

4A. $-\sqrt{27}$ **−5.2**

4B. $-\sqrt{92}$ **−9.6**

4C. $\pm\sqrt{67}$ **±8.2**

4D. $-\sqrt{135}$ **−11.6**

Personal Tutor glencoe.com

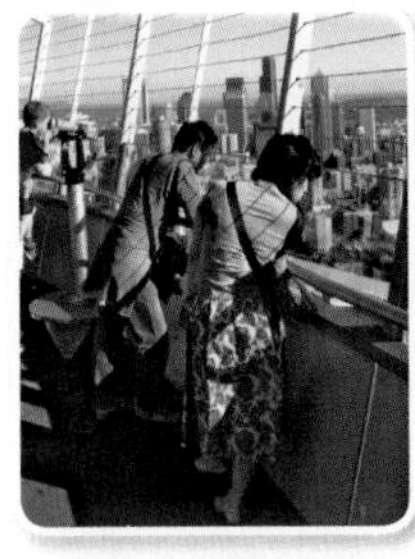

Real-World Link

The Space Needle has 848 steps from the bottom of the basement to the top of the Observation Deck.

Source: Space Needle Fun Facts

When finding square roots in real-world situations, use the positive, or *principal*, square root when a negative answer does not make sense.

Real-World EXAMPLE 5 Use Square Roots to Solve Problems

RECREATION On a clear day, the number of miles a person can see to the horizon can be found using the formula $d = 1.22 \cdot \sqrt{h}$, where d is the distance to the horizon in miles and h is the person's distance from the ground in feet. The observation deck of Seattle's Space Needle is 520 feet high. How far to the horizon can a person standing on the observation deck see? Round to the nearest tenth.

ESTIMATE The distance is between $1 \cdot \sqrt{400}$ and $1 \cdot \sqrt{900}$. So, it's between 20 and 30.

$d = 1.22 \cdot \sqrt{h}$ Write the equation.

$= 1.22 \cdot \sqrt{520}$ Replace h with 520.

$\approx 1.22 \cdot 22.8$ Use a calculator.

≈ 27.8 Simplify.

The approximate distance to the horizon is 27.8 miles to the nearest tenth.

Check for Reasonableness $20 < 27.8 < 30$ ✓

Check Your Progress

5. **RECREATION** Spring Port Ledge Lighthouse in Maine is approximately 55 feet high. Estimate and then calculate about how far a person who is standing on the observation deck can see on a clear day. Round to the nearest tenth of a mile. **Sample answer: 7 mi; 9.0 mi**

Personal Tutor glencoe.com

Estimate Square Roots

Example 2 shows how to estimate square roots to the nearest integer. **Examples 3 and 4** show how to use a calculator to estimate square roots. **Example 5** demonstrates how a square root is used in a real-world problem.

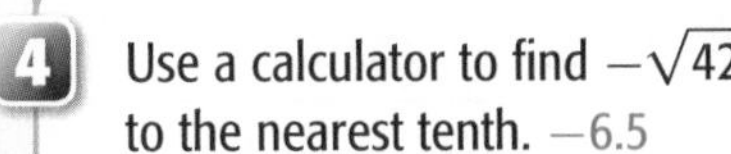

4 Use a calculator to find $-\sqrt{42}$ to the nearest tenth. −6.5

5 **SKYSCRAPER** The tallest building in Houston, Texas is the JP Morgan Chase Tower, standing at 1002 feet. About how far to the horizon can a person standing on the top floor see? Round your answer to the nearest tenth. 38.6 mi

Focus on Mathematical Content

Mathematical Language The square root is one of two equal factors of the radicand. The radicand, the value under the radical sign, is any positive number. A radicand is a perfect square if its square root is a whole number.

Tips for New Teachers

For Example 5. When estimating, students should use a number that results in a number that can be converted into a square easily.

3 PRACTICE

Formative Assessment

Use Exercises 1–10 to check for understanding.

Use the chart at the bottom of this page to customize assignments for your students.

Tips for New Teachers

Estimating Students should first practice estimating square roots before using a calculator. This allows the student opportunity to become more familiar with square roots and will help to avoid errors.

Additional Answers

38. $-10, -\sqrt{83}, -\sqrt{76}, -8, \sqrt{65}, \sqrt{77}, 9$

39c. Sample answer: For $0 < x < 1$, the graph of $y = x^2$ has a gradual climb then gets steeper as it approaches 1. The graph of $y = \sqrt{x}$ starts out steeper, then begins to flatten out. At $x = 1$, the graphs intersect. When $x > 1$, the first graph continues to get steeper while the second graph levels out.

39d. Sample answer: The graph for $y = x^2$; it is steeper for most of the graph.

42. Sample answer: A number that has a rational square root will have an ending digit of 0, 1, 4, 5, 6, or 9. The last digit is the ending digit in one of the squares from 1–100. There are just six ending digits. 1513, 1997, 1158

Check Your Understanding

Example 1 p. 537

Find each square root.

1. $\sqrt{16}$ 4 **2.** $-\sqrt{100}$ −10 **3.** $\pm\sqrt{81}$ ±9

Example 2 p. 538

Estimate each square root to the nearest integer. Do not use a calculator.

4. $\sqrt{27}$ 5 **5.** $-\sqrt{48}$ −7 **6.** $\pm\sqrt{39}$ ±6

Examples 3 and 4 pp. 538–539

Use a calculator to find each square root to the nearest tenth.

7. $\sqrt{21}$ 4.6 **8.** $-\sqrt{56}$ −7.5 **9.** $\pm\sqrt{37}$ ±6.1

Example 5 p. 539

10. **RECREATION** A baseball diamond is actually a square with an area of 8100 square feet. Most baseball teams cover their diamond with a tarp to protect it from the rain. The sides are all the same length. How long is the tarp on each side? **90 ft**

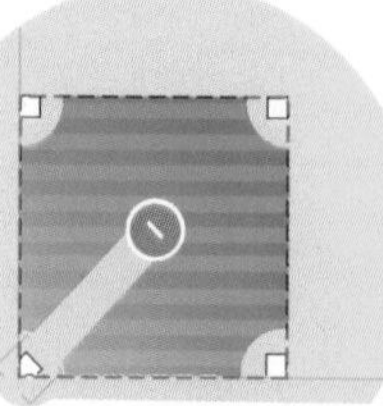

Practice and Problem Solving

● = **Step-by-Step Solutions** begin on page R11.
Extra Practice begins on page 810.

Example 1 p. 537

Find each square root.

11. $\sqrt{36}$ 6 **12.** $\sqrt{9}$ 3 **13.** $-\sqrt{169}$ −13

14. $-\sqrt{144}$ −12 **15.** $\pm\sqrt{-25}$ no real solution **16.** $\pm\sqrt{1}$ ±1

Example 2 p. 538

Estimate each square root to the nearest integer. Do not use a calculator.

17. $\sqrt{83}$ 9 **18.** $\sqrt{34}$ 6 **19.** $-\sqrt{102}$ −10

20. $-\sqrt{14}$ −4 **21.** $\pm\sqrt{78}$ ±9 **22.** $\pm\sqrt{146}$ ±12

Examples 3 and 4 pp. 538–539

Use a calculator to find each square root to the nearest tenth.

23. $\sqrt{7}$ 2.6 **24.** $\sqrt{32}$ 5.7 **25.** $\pm\sqrt{71}$ ±8.4 **26.** $-\sqrt{48}$ −6.9

27. $-\sqrt{155}$ −12.4 **28.** $\sqrt{162}$ 12.7 **29.** $\sqrt{310}$ 17.6 **30.** $\pm\sqrt{215}$ ±14.7

Example 5 p. 539

31. **RECREATION** Cedar Point in Ohio is known as the "Roller Coaster Capital of the World." The table shows the heights of their tallest coasters. Use the formula from Example 5 to determine how far a rider can see from the highest point of each ride. Round to the nearest tenth.

Cedar Point Attractions

Roller Coaster	Height (ft)
Magnum XL-200	205
Mean Streak	161
Millennium Force	310
Top Thrill Dragster	420
Wicked Twister	215

a. Millennium Force **21.5 mi**

b. Mean Streak **15.5 mi**

c. How much farther can a rider see on the Top Thrill Dragster than on the Magnum XL-200? **7.5 mi**

Differentiated Homework Options

Level	Assignment	Two-Day Option	
AL Basic	11–32, 40, 42–62	11–31 odd, 44–47	12–32 even, 40, 42–43, 48–62
OL Core	11–31 odd, 33–40, 42–62	11–32, 44–47	33–40, 42–43, 48–62
BL Advanced	33–54 (Optional: 55–62)		

Real-World Link

Chess is thought to be the oldest skill game in the world. Viswanathan Anand was named the 2007 World Chess Champion in Mexico City, Mexico. The top prize for the tournament was $390,000.

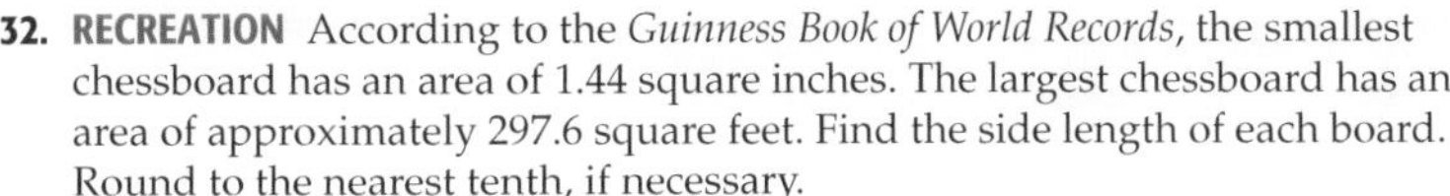

32. **RECREATION** According to the *Guinness Book of World Records*, the smallest chessboard has an area of 1.44 square inches. The largest chessboard has an area of approximately 297.6 square feet. Find the side length of each board. Round to the nearest tenth, if necessary.

    a. smallest board **1.2 in.** b. largest board **17.3 ft**

33. **GEOMETRY** The area of the square at the right is given. Find the length of a side to the nearest tenth. Then find its approximate perimeter. **14.7 cm; 58.8 cm**

215 cm^2

34. **GARDENS** The recommended space needed for a certain plant is 2 square feet. You want to plant 32 of these plants in a square garden. What is the length of each side of the garden if you follow the recommendations? **8 ft**

Complete each of the following mentally.

35. Which is greater, $\sqrt{79}$ or 8? Explain your reasoning.
36. Which is less, -2 or $-\sqrt{6}$? Explain your reasoning.
37. Between which two consecutive whole numbers on a number line does $\sqrt{85}$ lie? **9 and 10**
38. Order $\sqrt{77}$, -8, $-\sqrt{83}$, 9, -10, $-\sqrt{76}$, $\sqrt{65}$ from least to greatest. **See margin.**

39. **MULTIPLE REPRESENTATIONS** In this problem, you will investigate the graphs of $y = x^2$ and $y = \sqrt{x}$.

    a. **TABULAR** Copy and complete each of the tables shown. Choose an appropriate domain **a–b. See Chapter 10 Answer Appendix.**

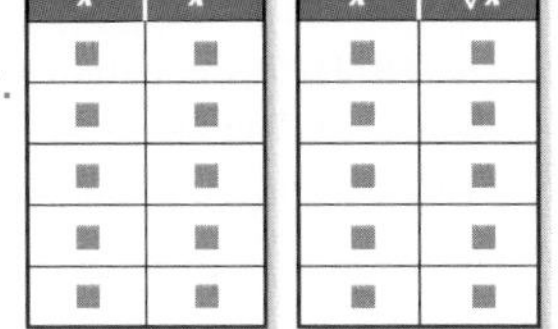

x	x^2
■	■
■	■
■	■
■	■
■	■

x	$\sqrt{x}$
■	■
■	■
■	■
■	■
■	■

    b. **GRAPHICAL** Using the ordered pairs from each table, graph $y = x^2$ and $y = \sqrt{x}$.

    c. **VERBAL** Describe each graph for $0 < x < 1$, for $x = 1$, and for $x > 1$. **c–d. See margin.**

    d. **ANALYTICAL** Which has the greater average rate of change? Explain.

35. $\sqrt{79}$; Sample answer: $\sqrt{79}$ is between $\sqrt{64}$ and $\sqrt{81}$, which is greater than 8.

36. $-\sqrt{6}$; Sample answer: $-\sqrt{6}$ is between $-\sqrt{9}$ and $-\sqrt{4}$, which is less than -2.

40. Sample answer: $\sqrt{300}$.

41d. finding the square root of a number

43. Sample answer: The exact value of a square root is given using the square root symbol, such as $\sqrt{13}$. An approximation is a decimal value, such as $\sqrt{13} \approx 3.6$.

H.O.T. Problems Use Higher-Order Thinking Skills

40. **OPEN ENDED** Find a square root that lies between 17 and 18.
41. **CHALLENGE** Addition and subtraction are *inverse operations* because one operation undoes the other operation. Use inverse operations to evaluate the following.

    a. $(\sqrt{246})^2$ **246** b. $(\sqrt{811})^2$ **811** c. $(\sqrt{732})^2$ **732**

    d. Describe the inverse operation of squaring a number.

42. **NUMBER SENSE** What are the possibilities for the ending digit of a number that has a whole number square root? Explain your reasoning. Then write three numbers between 1000 and 2000 that are *not* perfect squares. **See margin.**
43. **WRITING IN MATH** Describe the difference between an exact value and an approximation when finding square roots of numbers that are not perfect squares. Give an example of each.

Multiple Representations In Exercise 39, students create two tables of function values and use them to graph quadratic and radical equations; then the students use words to describe and analyze the graphs created.

Enrichment CRM p. 10 OL BL

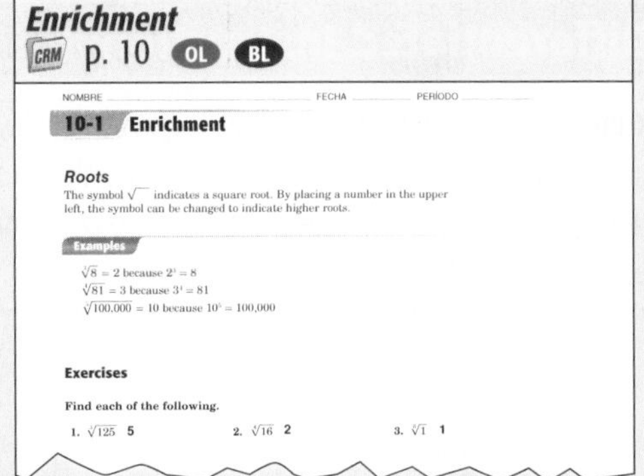

NOMBRE ____ FECHA ____ PERIODO ____

10-1 Enrichment

Roots

The symbol $\sqrt{\ }$ indicates a square root. By placing a number in the upper left, the symbol can be changed to indicate higher roots.

Examples

$\sqrt[3]{8} = 2$ because $2^3 = 8$

$\sqrt[4]{81} = 3$ because $3^4 = 81$

$\sqrt[5]{100{,}000} = 10$ because $10^5 = 100{,}000$

Exercises

Find each of the following.

1. $\sqrt[3]{125}$ **5** 2. $\sqrt[4]{16}$ **2** 3. $\sqrt[5]{1}$ **1**

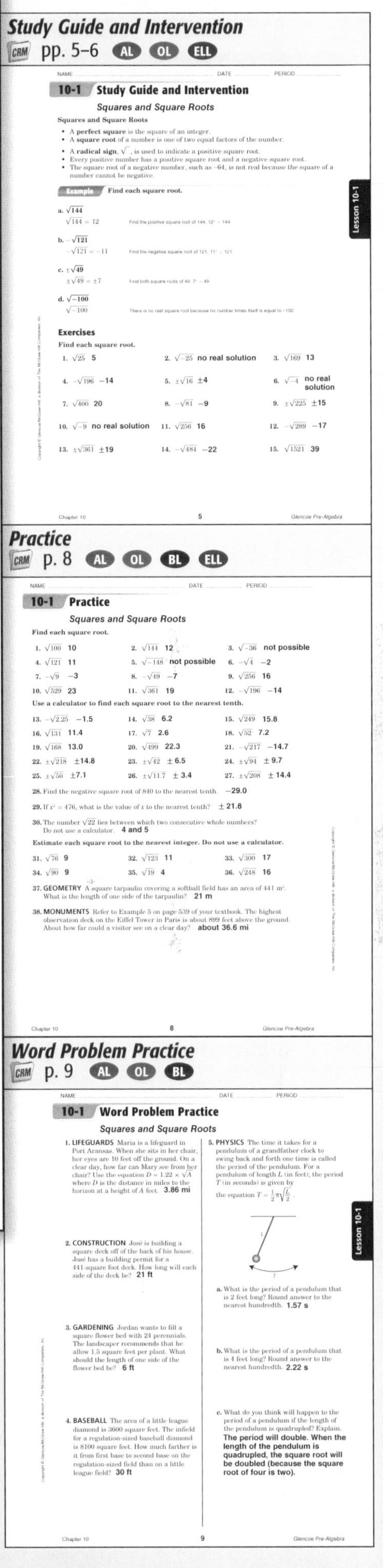

Study Guide and Intervention CRM pp. 5–6 AL OL ELL

NAME ____ DATE ____ PERIOD ____

10-1 Study Guide and Intervention

Squares and Square Roots

Squares and Square Roots

- A **perfect square** is the square of an integer.
- A **square root** of a number is one of two equal factors of the number.
- A **radical sign**, $\sqrt{\ }$, is used to indicate a positive square root.
- Every positive number has a positive square root and a negative square root.
- The square root of a negative number, such as −64, is not real because the square of a number cannot be negative.

Example Find each square root.

a. $\sqrt{144}$ — $\sqrt{144} = 12$ Find the positive square root of 144. $12^2 = 144$

b. $-\sqrt{121}$ — $-\sqrt{121} = -11$ Find the negative square root of 121. $11^2 = 121$

c. $\pm\sqrt{49}$ — $\pm\sqrt{49} = \pm 7$ Find both square roots of 49. $7^2 = 49$

d. $\sqrt{-100}$ — $\sqrt{-100}$ There is no real square root because no number times itself is equal to −100.

Exercises

Find each square root.

1. $\sqrt{25}$ **5** 2. $\sqrt{-25}$ **no real solution** 3. $\sqrt{169}$ **13**
4. $-\sqrt{196}$ **−14** 5. $\pm\sqrt{16}$ **±4** 6. $\sqrt{-4}$ **no real solution**
7. $\sqrt{400}$ **20** 8. $-\sqrt{81}$ **−9** 9. $\pm\sqrt{225}$ **±15**
10. $\sqrt{-9}$ **no real solution** 11. $\sqrt{256}$ **16** 12. $-\sqrt{289}$ **−17**
13. $\pm\sqrt{361}$ **±19** 14. $-\sqrt{484}$ **−22** 15. $\sqrt{1521}$ **39**

Chapter 10 5 Glencoe Pre-Algebra

Practice CRM p. 8 AL OL BL ELL

NAME ____ DATE ____ PERIOD ____

10-1 Practice

Squares and Square Roots

Find each square root.

1. $\sqrt{100}$ **10** 2. $\sqrt{144}$ **12** 3. $\sqrt{-36}$ **not possible**
4. $\sqrt{121}$ **11** 5. $\sqrt{-148}$ **not possible** 6. $-\sqrt{4}$ **−2**
7. $-\sqrt{9}$ **−3** 8. $-\sqrt{49}$ **−7** 9. $\sqrt{256}$ **16**
10. $\sqrt{529}$ **23** 11. $\sqrt{361}$ **19** 12. $-\sqrt{196}$ **−14**

Use a calculator to find each square root to the nearest tenth.

13. $-\sqrt{2.25}$ **−1.5** 14. $\sqrt{38}$ **6.2** 15. $\sqrt{249}$ **15.8**
16. $\sqrt{131}$ **11.4** 17. $\sqrt{7}$ **2.6** 18. $\sqrt{52}$ **7.2**
19. $\sqrt{168}$ **13.0** 20. $\sqrt{499}$ **22.3** 21. $-\sqrt{217}$ **−14.7**
22. $\pm\sqrt{218}$ **±14.8** 23. $\pm\sqrt{42}$ **±6.5** 24. $\pm\sqrt{94}$ **±9.7**
25. $\pm\sqrt{50}$ **±7.1** 26. $\pm\sqrt{11.7}$ **±3.4** 27. $\pm\sqrt{208}$ **±14.4**

28. Find the negative square root of 840 to the nearest tenth. **−29.0**

29. If $x^2 = 476$, what is the value of x to the nearest tenth? **±21.8**

30. The number $\sqrt{22}$ lies between which two consecutive whole numbers? Do not use a calculator. **4 and 5**

Estimate each square root to the nearest integer. Do not use a calculator.

31. $\sqrt{76}$ **9** 32. $\sqrt{123}$ **11** 33. $\sqrt{300}$ **17**
34. $\sqrt{90}$ **9** 35. $\sqrt{19}$ **4** 36. $\sqrt{248}$ **16**

37. **GEOMETRY** A square tarpaulin covering a softball field has an area of 441 m^2. What is the length of one side of the tarpaulin? **21 m**

38. **MONUMENTS** Refer to Example 5 on page 539 of your textbook. The highest observation deck on the Eiffel Tower in Paris is about 899 feet above the ground. About how far could a visitor see on a clear day? **about 36.6 mi**

Chapter 10 8 Glencoe Pre-Algebra

Word Problem Practice CRM p. 9 AL OL BL

NAME ____ DATE ____ PERIOD ____

10-1 Word Problem Practice

Squares and Square Roots

1. **LIFEGUARDS** Maria is a lifeguard in Port Aransas. When she sits in her chair, her eyes are 10 feet off the ground. On a clear day, how far can Mary see from her chair? Use the equation $D = 1.22 \times \sqrt{A}$ where D is the distance in miles to the horizon at a height of A feet. **3.86 mi**

2. **CONSTRUCTION** José is building a square deck off of the back of his house. José has a building permit for a 441-square foot deck. How long will each side of the deck be? **21 ft**

3. **GARDENING** Jordan wants to fill a square flower bed with 24 perennials. The landscaper recommends that he allow 1.5 square feet per plant. What should the length of one side of the flower bed be? **6 ft**

4. **BASEBALL** The area of a little league diamond is 3600 square feet. The infield for a regulation-sized baseball diamond is 8100 square feet. How much farther is it from first base to second base on the regulation-sized field than on a little league field? **30 ft**

5. **PHYSICS** The time it takes for a pendulum of a grandfather clock to swing back and forth one time is called the period of the pendulum. For a pendulum of length L (in feet), the period T (in seconds) is given by the equation $T = \frac{1}{2}\pi\sqrt{\frac{L}{2}}$.

a. What is the period of a pendulum that is 2 feet long? Round answer to the nearest hundredth. **1.57 s**

b. What is the period of a pendulum that is 4 feet long? Round answer to the nearest hundredth. **2.22 s**

c. What do you think will happen to the period of a pendulum if the length of the pendulum is quadrupled? Explain. **The period will double. When the length of the pendulum is quadrupled, the square root will be doubled (because the square root of four is two).**

Chapter 10 9 Glencoe Pre-Algebra

4 ASSESS

Yesterday's News Ask students to explain how previous lessons on squaring numbers helped them with today's lesson on finding and estimating square roots.

Additional Answers

48.

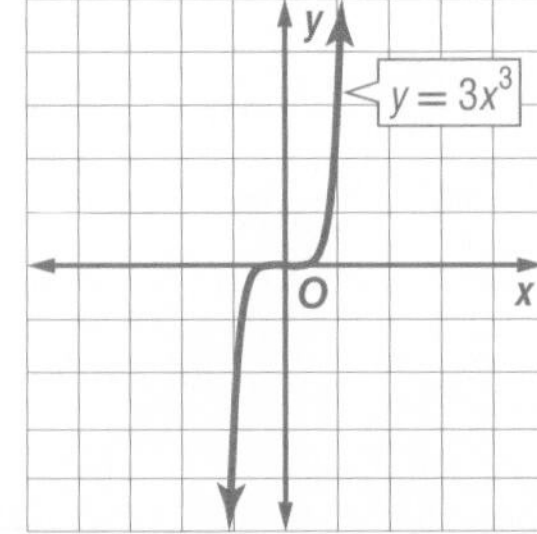

49.

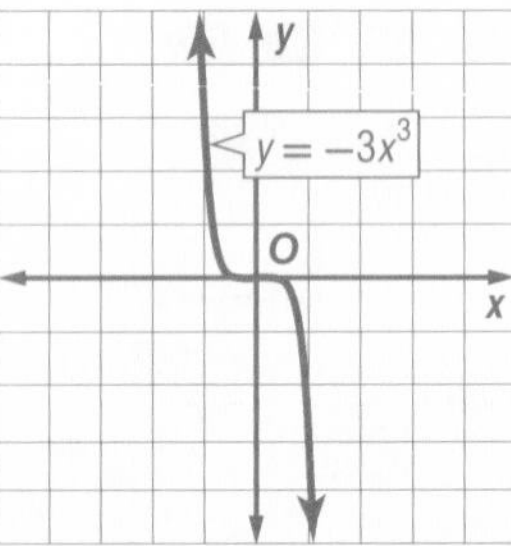

50.

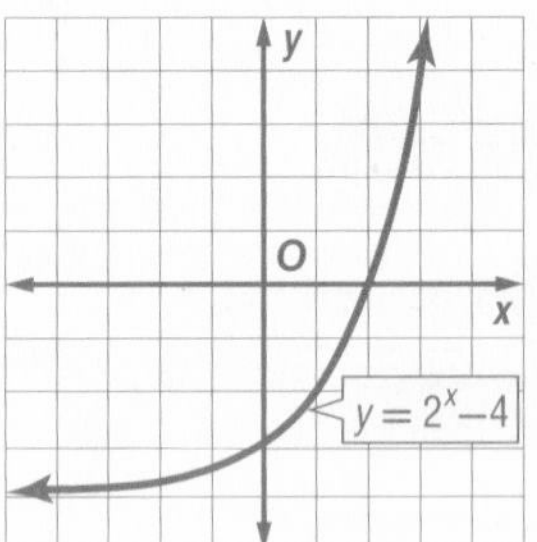

51a.

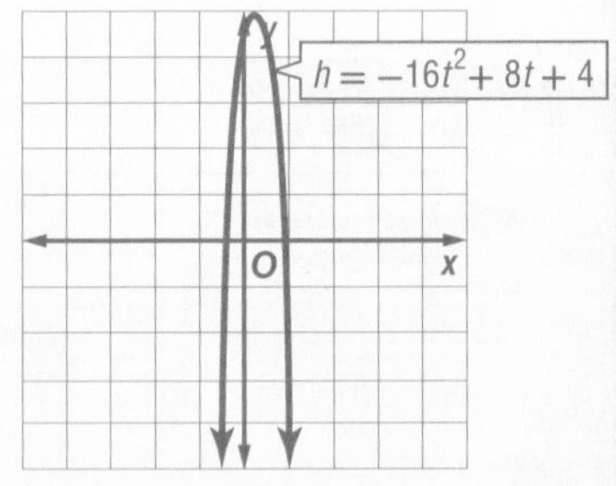

54b. Sample answer: You can use the fraction form of two-fifths since the area of the rectangle is a multiple of 5.

Standardized Test Practice

44. Which point on the number line best represents $\sqrt{210}$? **C**

A B C D
13.5 13.75 14 14.25 14.5 14.75 15

A A C C
B B D D

45. SHORT RESPONSE The area of each square is 25 square units. Find the perimeter of the figure shown below. **60 units**

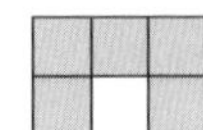

46. The new gymnasium at Oakdale Middle School has a hardwood floor in the shape of a square. If the area of the floor is 62,500 square feet, what is the length of one side of the square floor? **H**

F 200 ft   H 250 ft
G 225 ft   J 275 ft

47. A surveyor determined the distance across a field was $\sqrt{1568}$ feet. What is the approximate distance? **C**

A 25.6 ft   C 39.6 ft
B 30.6 ft   D 42.6 ft

Spiral Review

Graph each equation. (Lesson 9-9) **48–50. See margin.**

48. $y = 3x^3$ **49.** $y = -3x^3$ **50.** $y = 2^x - 4$

51. BASEBALL The equation $h = -16t^2 + 8t + 4$ can be used to model the height h of a baseball t seconds after it is hit. (Lesson 9-8)

a. Graph the equation on a coordinate plane. **See margin.**

b. After how many seconds will the ball hit the ground? **about 0.85 s**

Solve each problem using the percent equation. (Lesson 7-5)

52. 9 is what percent of 25? **36%**

53. 48 is 64% of what number? **75**

54. GEOMETRY Suppose that two-fifths of the rectangle at the right is shaded. (Lesson 5-1)

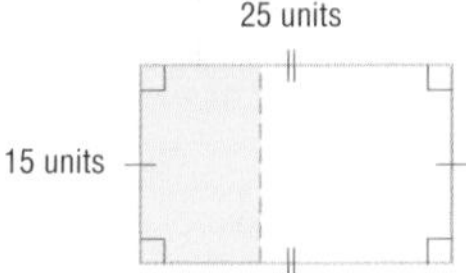

a. What is the area of the shaded region? **150 square units**

b. Is it better to use the decimal or fractional form of two-fifths in this situation? Explain. **See margin.**

Skills Review

55. natural, whole, integer, rational   **58. natural, whole, integer, rational**

Identify all sets to which each number belongs. (Lesson 3-2)

55. 4   **56.** -7 **integer, rational**   **57.** $-2\frac{5}{8}$ **rational**   **58.** $\frac{6}{3}$

59. 15.8 **rational**   **60.** 9.0202020… **rational**   **61.** 1.2345… **not rational**   **62.** 30.151151115… **not rational**

Differentiated Instruction

BL

Extension In algebra, students will learn to evaluate a radical expression, which is an expression under a radical sign. The expression under the radical sign must be evaluated first, before finding the square root. Have students evaluate $\sqrt{b^2 - 4ac}$ for $a = 3$, $b = 10$, $c = 2$, rounding to the nearest hundredth. 8.72

542 Chapter 10 Real Numbers and Right Triangles

10-2 The Real Number System

10-2 Lesson Notes

Then
You have already compared fractions and decimals. (Lesson 3-1)

Now
- Identify and compare numbers in the real number system.
- Solve equations by finding square roots.

New Vocabulary
irrational numbers
real numbers

Math Online
glencoe.com
- Extra Examples
- Personal Tutor
- Self-Check Quiz
- Homework Help

Why?

A roller coaster drops 100 feet at a 95-degree angle. The ride is 0.84 mile long and covers 5.5 acres.

a. Express the length of the ride as a fraction in simplest form. $\frac{21}{25}$

b. Express the number of acres that the ride covers as an improper fraction. $\frac{11}{2}$

Identify and Compare Real Numbers Recall that *rational numbers* are numbers that can be written as fractions. Examples of rational numbers are given below.

$$1\frac{2}{5} = \frac{7}{5} \quad -4 = -\frac{4}{1} \quad 0.15 = \frac{15}{100}$$

$$0.\overline{3} = \frac{1}{3} \quad \sqrt{25} = \frac{5}{1}$$

An **irrational number** is a number that cannot be written as a fraction. When written as decimals, irrational numbers neither terminate nor repeat.

Key Concept Irrational Number — For Your FOLDABLE

Words An irrational number is a number that cannot be expressed as $\frac{a}{b}$, where a and b are integers and $b \neq 0$.

Examples $\pi \approx 3.14159...$ $\quad -\sqrt{5} \approx -2.2360679...$

The sets of rational numbers and irrational numbers together make up the set of **real numbers**. The diagram shows the relationship among the real numbers.

Real Numbers

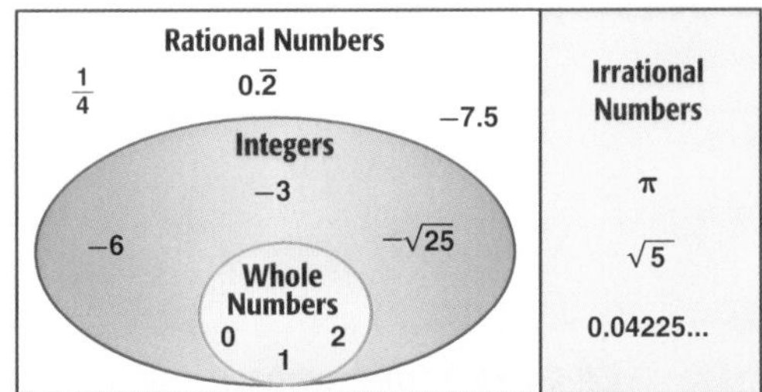

Computations with an irrational number and a rational number (other than zero) produce an irrational number.

1 FOCUS

Vertical Alignment

Before Lesson 10-2
Compare fractions and decimals.

Lesson 10-2
Identify and compare numbers in the real number system. Solve equations by finding square roots.

After Lesson 10-2
Use different representations of real numbers to solve problems involving triangles.

2 TEACH

Scaffolding Questions

Have students read the *Why?* section of the lesson and answer the questions.

Ask:

- What is similar about the way in which the length of the roller coaster and the number of acres it covers is expressed? Both are decimals that can be expressed as fractions.
- Can all decimals be expressed as fractions? Explain. No; decimals such as 1.7320508... that neither terminate nor repeat cannot be expressed as fractions.

(continued on next page)

Lesson 10-2 Resources

Resource	Approaching-Level	On-Level	Beyond-Level	English Learners
Teacher Edition	• Differentiated Instruction, p. 544	• Differentiated Instruction, p. 544	• Differentiated Instruction, pp. 544, 548	• Differentiated Instruction, p. 544
Chapter Resource Masters	• Study Guide and Intervention, pp. 11–12 • Skills Practice, p. 13 • Practice, p. 14 • Word Problem Practice, p. 15 • Graphing Calculator, p. 17	• Study Guide and Intervention, pp. 11–12 • Skills Practice, p. 13 • Practice, p. 14 • Word Problem Practice, p. 15 • Enrichment, p. 16 • Graphing Calculator, p. 17	• Practice, p. 14 • Word Problem Practice, p. 15 • Enrichment, p. 16 • Graphing Calculator, p. 17	• Study Guide and Intervention, pp. 11–12 • Skills Practice, p. 13 • Practice, p. 14 • Graphing Calculator, p. 17
Transparencies	• 5-Minute Check Transparency 10-2	• 5-Minute Check Transparency 10-2	• 5-Minute Check Transparency 10-2	• 5-Minute Check Transparency 10-2
Other	• Study Notebook • Teaching Pre-Algebra with Manipulatives	• Study Notebook • Teaching Pre-Algebra with Manipulatives	• Study Notebook	• Study Notebook • Teaching Pre-Algebra with Manipulatives

- Can whole numbers and integers be expressed as fractions? Explain. Yes; sample answer: 12 can be expressed as $\frac{12}{1}$ and -6 can be expressed $\frac{-12}{2}$.

Identify and Compare Real Numbers

Example 1 shows how to classify real numbers. **Example 2** shows how to compare real numbers. **Example 3** shows how to order real numbers.

Formative Assessment

Use the Check Your Progress exercises after each example to determine students' understanding of concepts.

Additional Examples

1 Name all of the sets of numbers to which each real number belongs. Write *whole*, *integer*, *rational*, or *irrational*.

a. $0.\overline{246}$ rational

b. $\sqrt{225}$ whole, integer, rational

c. -7.25 rational

d. $\sqrt{17}$ irrational

2 Replace ● with <, >, or = to make $\sqrt{125}$ ● $11\frac{7}{8}$ a true statement. <

3 Order $6\frac{1}{4}$, $\sqrt{38}$, $6.\overline{5}$, and $\sqrt{36}$ from least to greatest. $\sqrt{36}$, $\sqrt{38}$, $6\frac{1}{4}$, $6.\overline{5}$

Additional Examples also in Interactive Classroom PowerPoint® Presentations

IWB INTERACTIVE WHITEBOARD READY

StudyTip

Square Roots If an integer is not a perfect square, then its square root is an irrational number.

EXAMPLE 1 Classify Real Numbers

Name all of the sets of numbers to which each real number belongs. Write *whole*, *integer*, *rational*, or *irrational*.

a. $\frac{21}{7}$ Since $\frac{21}{7} = 3$, this number is a whole number, an integer, and a rational number.

b. -2.5 Since $-2.5 = -\frac{10}{4}$, this number is a rational number.

c. $0.\overline{2}$ Since $0.\overline{2} = 0.22222...$ or $\frac{2}{9}$, this number is a rational number.

d. $\sqrt{38}$ Since $\sqrt{38} = 6.16441400...$ It is not the square root of a perfect square so it is irrational.

Check Your Progress

1A. 0.7 rational

1B. $\sqrt{100}$ whole, integer, rational

1C. $\frac{9}{5}$ rational

1D. -6 integer, rational

Personal Tutor glencoe.com

Review Vocabulary

Integers Integers are the whole numbers and their opposites. ..., −3, −2, −1, 0, 1, 2, 3, ... (Lesson 2-1)

EXAMPLE 2 Compare Real Numbers

Replace ● with <, >, or = to make $3\frac{1}{3}$ ● $\sqrt{15}$ a true statement.

Express each number as a decimal. Then compare the decimals.

$3\frac{1}{3} = 3.33333333...$

$\sqrt{15} = 3.87298334...$

Since 3.333... is less than 3.872..., $3\frac{1}{3} < \sqrt{15}$.

Check Your Progress

2. Replace ● with <, >, or = to make $7\frac{2}{5}$ ● $\sqrt{57}$ a true statement. <

Personal Tutor glencoe.com

EXAMPLE 3 Order Real Numbers

Order $8\frac{4}{5}$, $\sqrt{64}$, $8.\overline{3}$, $\sqrt{76}$ from least to greatest.

Express each number as a decimal. Then order the decimals.

$8\frac{4}{5} = 8.8$

$\sqrt{64} = 8$

$8.\overline{3} = 8.33333333...$

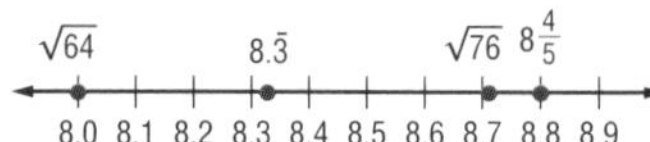

$\sqrt{76} = 8.71779788...$

From least to greatest, the order is $\sqrt{64}$, $8.\overline{3}$, $\sqrt{76}$, and $8\frac{4}{5}$.

Check Your Progress

3. Order $\sqrt{30}$, 5.6, $\frac{15}{3}$, and $5\frac{2}{3}$ from greatest to least. $5\frac{2}{3}$, 5.6, $\sqrt{30}$, $\frac{15}{3}$

Personal Tutor glencoe.com

Differentiated Instruction

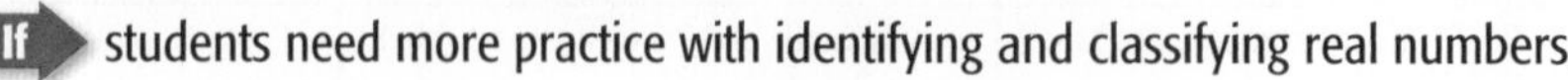

If students need more practice with identifying and classifying real numbers,

Then have teams of students find real-world examples for each type of number in the real number system. Have students present their findings to the class. Encourage students to look for unique examples. For example, the bus has four tires. Four is a whole number, an integer, and a rational number.

Solve Equations By the definition of a square root, if $x^2 = y$, then $x = \pm\sqrt{y}$. You can use this relationship to solve equations involving squares.

EXAMPLE 4 Solve Equations

Solve each equation. Round to the nearest tenth, if necessary.

a. $a^2 = 36$

$a^2 = 36$	Write the equation.
$a = \pm\sqrt{36}$	Definition of square root
$a = 6$ and -6	Check $6 \cdot 6 = 36$ and $(-6) \cdot (-6) = 36$

The solutions are 6 and −6.

b. $2n^2 = 170$

$2n^2 = 170$	Write the equation.
$n^2 = 85$	Divide each side by 2.
$n = \pm\sqrt{85}$	Definition of square root
$n \approx 9.2$ and -9.2	Use a calculator.

The solutions are approximately 9.2 and −9.2.

StudyTip

Check Reasonableness Check the results by calculating 9^2 and $(-9)^2$. $9^2 = 81$ $(-9)^2 = 81$ Since 81 is close to 85, the solutions are reasonable.

Check Your Progress

4A. $363 = 3d^2$ 11, −11

4B. $y^2 = 30$ ≈ 5.5, −5.5

Personal Tutor glencoe.com

In most real-world situations, a negative square root does not make sense. Consider only the positive, or *principal*, square root.

Real-World EXAMPLE 5 Use Real Numbers to Solve Problems

HANG GLIDING The *aspect ratio* of a hang glider allows it to glide through the air. The formula for the aspect ratio R is $R = \frac{s^2}{A}$, where s is the wingspan and A is the area of the wing. What is the wingspan of a hang glider if its aspect ratio is 4.5 and the area of the wing is 50 square feet?

$R = \frac{s^2}{A}$	Write the formula.
$4.5 = \frac{s^2}{50}$	Replace R with 4.5 and A with 50.
$225 = s^2$	Multiply each side by 50.
$\sqrt{225} = s$	Consider the positive square root.
$15 = s$	Simplify.

The wingspan of the hang glider is 15 feet.

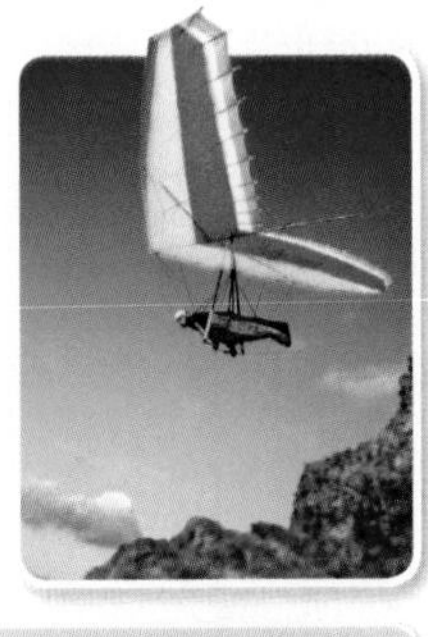

Real-World Link

The longest hang gliding trip lasted 36 hours. The highest altitude reached by a hang glider was 18,000 feet.

Source: HowStuffWorks

Check Your Progress 5. 77.9 m/s

5. SEISMIC WAVES A *tsunami* is caused by an earthquake on the ocean floor. The speed of a tsunami can be measured by the formula $\frac{s^2}{d} = 9.61$, where s is the speed of the wave in meters per second and d is the depth of the ocean in meters where the earthquake occurs. What is the speed of a tsunami if an earthquake occurs at a depth of 632 meters? Round to the nearest tenth.

Personal Tutor glencoe.com

Focus on Mathematical Content

Irrational Numbers Real numbers include irrational and rational numbers. A number can be rational or irrational but not both. The difference is whether a number can be expressed as a fraction or not. If it can, it is rational. If a number is irrational it will belong to no other subgroups.

Solve Equations

Examples 4 and 5 show how to solve equations that involve finding square roots.

Additional Examples

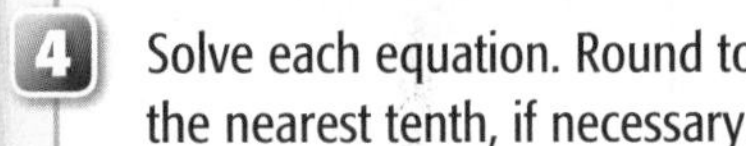

4 Solve each equation. Round to the nearest tenth, if necessary.

a. $w^2 = 169$ 13, −13

b. $r^2 = 50$ ≈ 7.1, −7.1

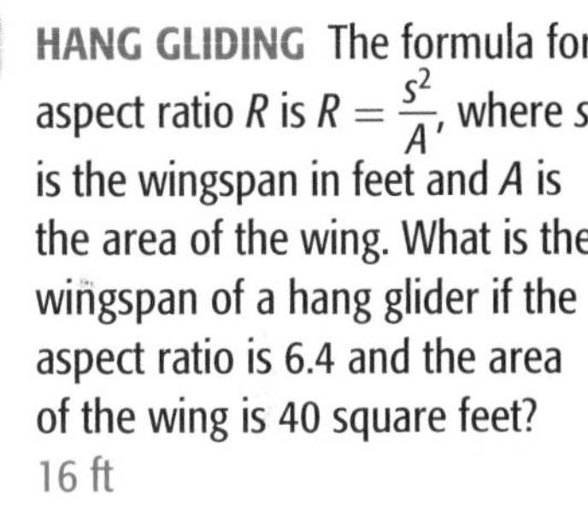

5 **HANG GLIDING** The formula for aspect ratio R is $R = \frac{s^2}{A}$, where s is the wingspan in feet and A is the area of the wing. What is the wingspan of a hang glider if the aspect ratio is 6.4 and the area of the wing is 40 square feet? 16 ft

TEACH with TECH

INTERACTIVE WHITEBOARD Draw a set diagram on the board showing how the set of real numbers is separated into rational and irrational numbers, integers, whole numbers, etc. Create a list of 12 real numbers, and choose students to come to the board to drag them into the correct set in the diagram.

3 PRACTICE

Formative Assessment

Use Exercises 1–13 to check for understanding.

Use the chart at the bottom of this page to customize assignments for your students.

Additional Answers

45. Sometimes; Sample answer: $\frac{4}{9}$ can be written as $0.\overline{4}$, but $\frac{1}{2}$ is written as 0.5.

59. If a square has an area that is not a perfect square, the lengths of the sides will be irrational. Sample answer: A square with an area of 25 square units has sides that are rational. A square with an area of 26 square units has sides that are irrational.

Check Your Understanding

Example 1 p. 544

Name all of the sets of numbers to which each real number belongs. Write *whole, integer, rational,* or *irrational.*

1. 10 whole, integer, rational **2.** $\frac{1}{5}$ rational **3.** $\sqrt{35}$ irrational **4.** $-\frac{14}{2}$ integer, rational

Example 2 p. 544

Replace each ● with <, >, or = to make a true statement.

5. $\sqrt{6}$ ● $2\frac{3}{8}$ > **6.** $-5.\overline{2}$ ● $-\sqrt{29}$ > **7.** $-\sqrt{42}$ ● $-6\frac{2}{3}$ >

Example 3 p. 544

Order each set of numbers from least to greatest. 8. $-\sqrt{4}, -1\frac{3}{4}, -1.5, -\frac{5}{4}$

8. $-\frac{5}{4}, -\sqrt{4}, -1.5, -1\frac{3}{4}$ **9.** $\sqrt{110}, 10\frac{1}{5}, 10.\overline{5}, 10.15$ $10.15, 10\frac{1}{5}, \sqrt{110}, 10.\overline{5}$

Example 4 p. 545

ALGEBRA Solve each equation. Round to the nearest tenth, if necessary.

10. $x^2 = 16$ 4, −4 **11.** $3m^2 = 222$ 8.6, −8.6 **12.** $42 = 1.4r^2$ 5.5, −5.5

Example 5 p. 545

13. PIZZA The formula $A \approx 3.14r^2$ can be used to determine the area of a circle where A is the area and r is the distance from the center of the circle to the outside edge. If the area of the largest pizza ever made was approximately 11,818 square feet, about how far is the distance from the center of the pizza to the outside edge? Round to the nearest tenth. 61.3 ft

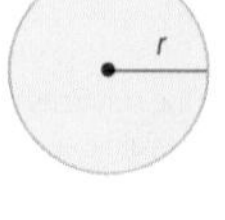

Practice and Problem Solving

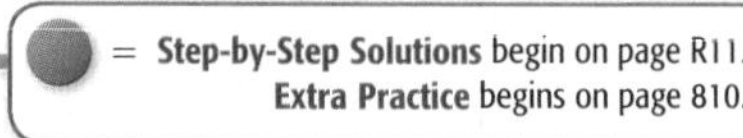
= **Step-by-Step Solutions** begin on page R11.
Extra Practice begins on page 810.

Example 1 p. 544

Name all of the sets of numbers to which each real number belongs. Write *whole, integer, rational,* or *irrational.* 14. whole, integer, rational

14. 4 **15.** $\frac{3}{5}$ rational **16.** $-\frac{7}{2}$ rational **17.** $\sqrt{26}$ irrational

18. $-\frac{36}{4}$ integer, rational **19.** 8.2 rational **20.** 0.55555… rational **21.** $-\sqrt{81}$ integer, rational

22. 6.01 rational **23.** $\frac{42}{7}$ whole, integer, rational **24.** $\sqrt{144}$ whole, integer, rational **25.** $0.\overline{18}$ rational

Example 2 p. 544

Replace ● with <, >, or = to make a true statement.

26. $\sqrt{17}$ ● 4.2 < **27.** $5.\overline{15}$ ● $\sqrt{26}$ > **28.** $3\frac{5}{6}$ ● $\sqrt{10}$ >

29. $\sqrt{2.56}$ ● $1\frac{3}{5}$ = **30.** $-\sqrt{0.25}$ ● $-\frac{1}{2}$ = **31.** $-7\frac{5}{8}$ ● $-\sqrt{55}$ <

Example 3 p. 544

Order each set of numbers from least to greatest.

32. $2.\overline{71}, 2\frac{3}{4}, \sqrt{5}, \frac{5}{2}$ $\sqrt{5}, \frac{5}{2}, 2.\overline{71}, 2\frac{3}{4}$ **33.** $\sqrt{64}, 8\frac{1}{7}, 8.\overline{14}, \frac{15}{2}$ $\frac{15}{2}, \sqrt{64}, 8.\overline{14}, 8\frac{1}{7}$

34. $-\sqrt{11}, -3.\overline{3}, -3.4, -\frac{16}{5}$ $-3.4, -3.\overline{3}, -\sqrt{11}, -\frac{16}{5}$ **35.** $-\frac{5}{6}, -5, -\sqrt{26}, -\frac{31}{6}$ $-\frac{31}{6}, -\sqrt{26}, -5, -\frac{5}{6}$

Example 4 p. 545

ALGEBRA Solve each equation. Round to the nearest tenth, if necessary.

36. $y^2 = 64$ 8, −8 **37.** $130 = n^2$ 11.4, −11.4 **38.** $5p^2 = 315$ 7.9, −7.9

39. $2d^2 = 162$ 9, −9 **40.** $190.5 = 1.5b^2$ 11.3, −11.3 **41.** $0.1x^2 = 0.169$ 1.3, −1.3

Differentiated Homework Options

Level	Assignment	Two-Day Option	
AL Basic	14–42, 53–56, 58–80	15–41 odd, 60–63	14–42 even, 53–56, 58–59, 64–80
OL Core	15–41 odd, 42–47, 49, 51–56, 58–80	14–42, 60–63	43–56, 58–59, 64–80
BL Advanced	43–74 (Optional: 75–80)		

Example 5
p. 545

42. **TRACK AND FIELD** The height h in feet that a pole vaulter can reach can be estimated using the formula $h = \frac{v^2}{64}$, where v is the velocity of the athlete in feet per second. Use the information at the left to determine about how fast the record holder was running. **about 32 ft/s**

Real-World Link

The women's pole vault world record was set at the World Championships in 2005. A height of 5.01 meters, which is about 16 feet, was cleared.

Source: International Association of Athletics Federations

43. **PHYSICS** The formula $h = 16t^2$ describes the time t in seconds that it takes for an object to fall from a height of h feet. A thrill ride has a 60-foot tall freefall drop. How long does it take for the ride to complete its freefall? Round to the nearest tenth. **1.9 s**

Determine whether each statement is *always, sometimes,* or *never* true. Explain your reasoning.

44. An integer is a rational number. **Always; Sample answer: All integers are rational numbers.**
45. A real number can be written as a repeating decimal. **See margin.**
46. An irrational number can be written as a terminating decimal. **Never; Sample answer: Irrational numbers when written as decimals do not terminate or repeat.**
47. A whole number is an integer. **Always; Sample answer: All whole numbers are integers.**

Tell whether each expression is *rational or irrational.* Explain.

48. $4 \times \sqrt{2}$
49. $\sqrt{49} - 15$
50. $\sqrt{10} \div 2$
51. $9 \cdot \pi$

52. **CARS** In the formula $s = \sqrt{30fd}$, s is the speed of a car in miles per hour, d is the distance the car skidded in feet, and f is friction. The table shows different values of f. At an accident scene, a car made 100-foot skid marks before hitting another car. If the speed limit was 55 miles per hour, was the car speeding before applying the brakes on a dry, concrete road? Explain.

Road Conditions	Type of Surface	
	Concrete	Asphalt
Wet	0.4	0.5
Dry	0.8	1.0

48. **Irrational; $\sqrt{2}$ is irrational.**
49. **Rational; $\sqrt{49}$ is rational.**
50. **Irrational; $\sqrt{10}$ is irrational.**
51. **Irrational; π is irrational.**
52. **Sample answer: The length of the skid marks show that the car was traveling about 49 mph before the driver applied the brake. The car could have skid farther if it weren't for the collision. Therefore, the skid marks would have been longer and thus, the car would have been traveling at a higher rate than 55 mph.**

H.O.T. Problems

Use Higher-Order Thinking Skills

53. **OPEN ENDED** Find a rational number and an irrational number that are between 6.2 and 6.5. Include the decimal approximation of the irrational number to the nearest hundredth. **Sample answer: 6.4; $\sqrt{40} \approx 6.32$**

REASONING Tell whether each expression is *true* or *false*. If false, give a counterexample.

54. All whole numbers are integers. **true**
55. All square roots are irrational numbers. **False; $\sqrt{16}$ is rational.**
56. All rational numbers are integers. **False; 4.5 is rational.**
57. **CHALLENGE** What is the value of x to the nearest tenth if $x^2 - 4^2 = \sqrt{15^2}$? **5.6 or −5.6**
58. **WHICH ONE DOESN'T BELONG?** Identify the number that does not belong with the other three. Explain your reasoning.

$50.\overline{1}$	$-\frac{50}{2}$	-50.1	$\sqrt{50}$

$\sqrt{50}$ because it is irrational; the other numbers are rational.

59. **WRITING IN MATH** Explain the relationship between the area of a square and the length of its sides. Give an example of a square whose side length is rational and an example of a square whose side length is irrational. **See margin.**

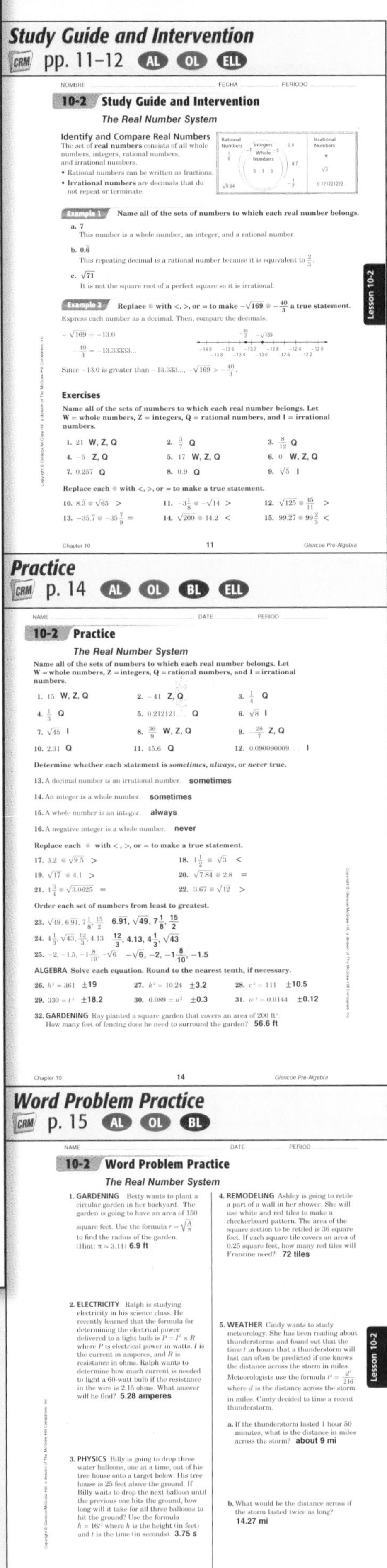

Study Guide and Intervention
CRM pp. 11–12 AL OL ELL

10-2 Study Guide and Intervention
The Real Number System

Identify and Compare Real Numbers The set of **real numbers** consists of all whole numbers, integers, rational numbers, and irrational numbers.
- Rational numbers can be written as fractions.
- **Irrational numbers** are decimals that do not repeat or terminate.

Example 1 Name all of the sets of numbers to which each real number belongs.

a. 7 — This number is a whole number, an integer, and a rational number.

b. $0.\overline{6}$ — This repeating decimal is a rational number because it is equivalent to $\frac{2}{3}$.

c. $\sqrt{71}$ — It is not the square root of a perfect square so it is irrational.

Example 2 Replace ● with <, >, or = to make $-\sqrt{169}$ ● $-\frac{40}{3}$ a true statement.

Express each number as a decimal. Then, compare the decimals.

$-\sqrt{169} = -13.0$

$-\frac{40}{3} = -13.33333...$

Since −13.0 is greater than −13.333..., $-\sqrt{169} > -\frac{40}{3}$.

Exercises

Name all of the sets of numbers to which each real number belongs. Let W = whole numbers, Z = integers, Q = rational numbers, and I = irrational numbers.

1. 21 **W, Z, Q**
2. $\frac{3}{7}$ **Q**
3. $\frac{8}{12}$ **Q**
4. −5 **Z, Q**
5. 17 **W, Z, Q**
6. 0 **W, Z, Q**
7. 0.257 **Q**
8. 0.9 **Q**
9. $\sqrt{5}$ **I**

Replace each ● with <, >, or = to make a true statement.

10. 8.3 ● $\sqrt{65}$ **>**
11. $-3\frac{1}{8}$ ● $-\sqrt{14}$ **>**
12. $\sqrt{125}$ ● $\frac{45}{4}$ **>**
13. -35.7 ● $-35\frac{7}{9}$ **=**
14. $\sqrt{200}$ ● 14.2 **<**
15. 99.27 ● $99\frac{2}{3}$ **<**

Chapter 10 — 11 — Glencoe Pre-Algebra

Practice
CRM p. 14 AL OL BL ELL

10-2 Practice
The Real Number System

Name all of the sets of numbers to which each real number belongs. Let W = whole numbers, Z = integers, Q = rational numbers, and I = irrational numbers.

1. 15 **W, Z, Q**
2. −41 **Z, Q**
3. $\frac{1}{4}$ **Q**
4. $\frac{1}{3}$ **Q**
5. 0.212121... **Q**
6. $\sqrt{8}$ **I**
7. $\sqrt{45}$ **I**
8. $\frac{36}{9}$ **W, Z, Q**
9. $-\frac{28}{7}$ **Z, Q**
10. 2.31 **Q**
11. 45.6 **Q**
12. 0.090090009... **I**

Determine whether each statement is *sometimes, always,* or *never* true.

13. A decimal number is an irrational number. **sometimes**
14. An integer is a whole number. **sometimes**
15. A whole number is an integer. **always**
16. A negative integer is a whole number. **never**

Replace each ● with <, >, or = to make a true statement.

17. 3.2 ● $\sqrt{9.5}$ **>**
18. $1\frac{1}{2}$ ● $\sqrt{3}$ **<**
19. $\sqrt{17}$ ● 4.1 **>**
20. $\sqrt{7.84}$ ● 2.8 **=**
21. $1\frac{3}{4}$ ● $\sqrt{3.0625}$ **=**
22. 3.67 ● $\sqrt{12}$ **>**

Order each set of numbers from least to greatest.

23. $\sqrt{49}$, 6.91, $7\frac{1}{8}$, $\frac{15}{2}$ **$6.\overline{91}$, $\sqrt{49}$, $7\frac{1}{8}$, $\frac{15}{2}$**
24. $4\frac{1}{3}$, $\sqrt{43}$, $\frac{12}{3}$, 4.13 **$\frac{12}{3}$, 4.13, $4\frac{1}{3}$, $\sqrt{43}$**
25. −2, −1.5, $-1\frac{8}{10}$, $-\sqrt{6}$ **$-\sqrt{6}$, −2, $-1\frac{8}{10}$, −1.5**

ALGEBRA Solve each equation. Round to the nearest tenth, if necessary.

26. $h^2 = 361$ **±19**
27. $k^2 = 10.24$ **±3.2**
28. $c^2 = 111$ **±10.5**
29. $330 = t^2$ **±18.2**
30. $0.089 = a^2$ **±0.3**
31. $w^2 = 0.0144$ **±0.12**

32. GARDENING Ray planted a square garden that covers an area of 200 ft². How many feet of fencing does he need to surround the garden? **56.6 ft**

Chapter 10 — 14 — Glencoe Pre-Algebra

Word Problem Practice
CRM p. 15 AL OL BL

10-2 Word Problem Practice
The Real Number System

1. GARDENING Betty wants to plant a circular garden in her backyard. The garden is going to have an area of 150 square feet. Use the formula $r = \sqrt{\frac{A}{\pi}}$ to find the radius of the garden. (Hint: π ≈ 3.14) **6.9 ft**

2. ELECTRICITY Ralph is studying electricity in his science class. He recently learned that the formula for determining the electrical power delivered to a light bulb is $P = I^2 \times R$ where P is electrical power in watts, I is the current in amperes, and R is resistance in ohms. Ralph wants to determine how much current is needed to light a 60-watt bulb if the resistance in the wire is 2.15 ohms. What answer will he find? **5.28 amperes**

3. PHYSICS Billy is going to drop three water balloons, one at a time, out of his tree house onto a target below. His tree house is 25 feet above the ground. If Billy waits to drop the next balloon until the previous one hits the ground, how long will it take for all three balloons to hit the ground? Use the formula $h = 16t^2$ where h is the height (in feet) and t is the time (in seconds). **3.75 s**

4. REMODELING Ashley is going to retile a part of a wall in her shower. She will use white and red tiles to make a checkerboard pattern. The area of the square section to be retiled is 36 square feet. If each square tile covers an area of 0.25 square feet, how many red tiles will Francine need? **72 tiles**

5. WEATHER Cindy wants to study meteorology. She has been reading about thunderstorms and found out that the time t in hours that a thunderstorm will last can often be predicted if one knows the distance across the storm in miles. Meteorologists use the formula $t^2 = \frac{d^3}{216}$ where d is the distance across the storm in miles. Cindy decided to time a recent thunderstorm.

a. If the thunderstorm lasted 1 hour 50 minutes, what is the distance in miles across the storm? **about 9 mi**

b. What would be the distance across if the storm lasted twice as long? **14.27 mi**

Chapter 10 — 15 — Glencoe Pre-Algebra

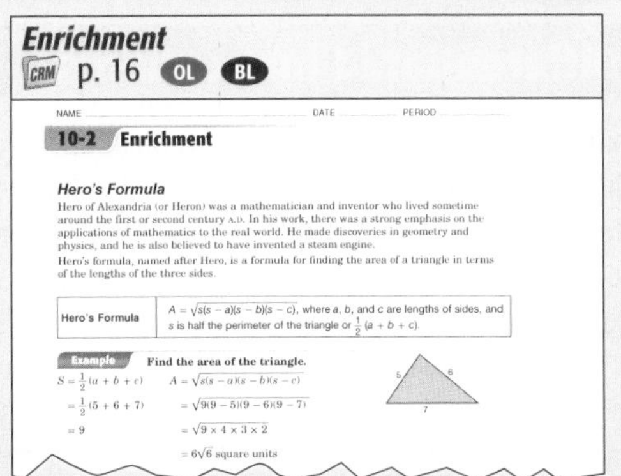

Enrichment
CRM p. 16 OL BL

10-2 Enrichment

Hero's Formula

Hero of Alexandria (or Heron) was a mathematician and inventor who lived sometime around the first or second century A.D. In his work, there was a strong emphasis on the applications of mathematics to the real world. He made discoveries in geometry and physics, and he is also believed to have invented a steam engine.

Hero's formula, named after Hero, is a formula for finding the area of a triangle in terms of the lengths of the three sides.

Hero's Formula	$A = \sqrt{s(s-a)(s-b)(s-c)}$, where a, b, and c are lengths of sides, and s is half the perimeter of the triangle or $\frac{1}{2}(a+b+c)$.

Example Find the area of the triangle.

$S = \frac{1}{2}(a+b+c)$ — $A = \sqrt{s(s-a)(s-b)(s-c)}$

$= \frac{1}{2}(5+6+7)$ — $= \sqrt{9(9-5)(9-6)(9-7)}$

$= 9$ — $= \sqrt{9 \times 4 \times 3 \times 2}$

$= 6\sqrt{6}$ square units

4 ASSESS

Name the Math Tell students to write about the relationship between the real number system and rational numbers, irrational numbers, integers, and whole numbers. Encourage them to use mathematical terms to name the relationships and to include examples or a Venn diagram to illustrate.

Formative Assessment

Check for student understanding of concepts in Lessons 10-1 and 10-2.

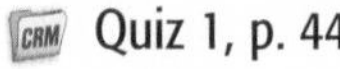

Quiz 1, p. 44

Additional Answers

70.

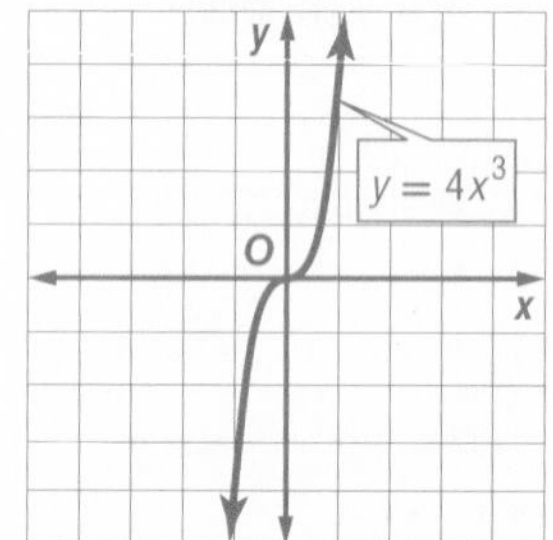

71.

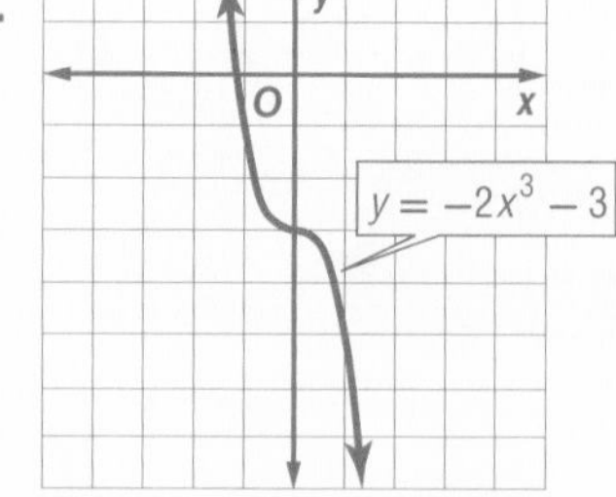

72.

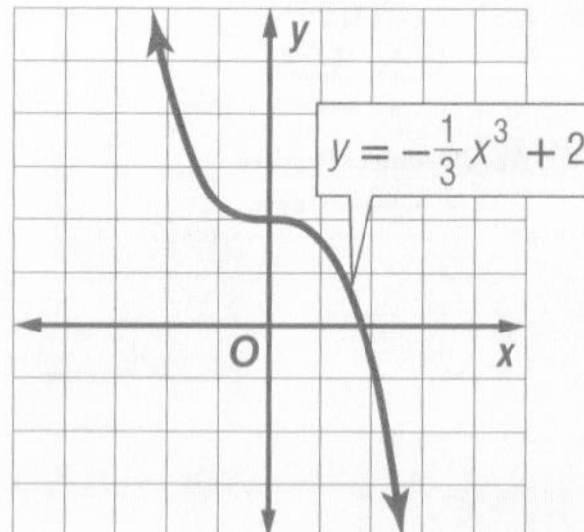

73.

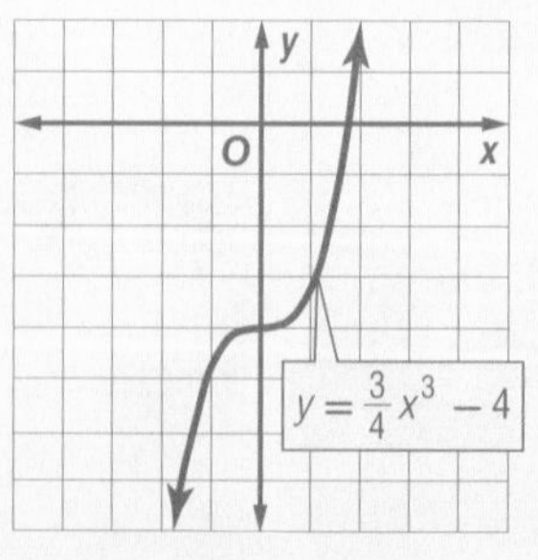

Standardized Test Practice

60. For what value of x is $\frac{1}{\sqrt{x}} < \sqrt{x} < x$? **D**

A -2 C $\frac{1}{2}$

B $\frac{1}{4}$ D 2

61. The formula $h = 16t^2$ describes the time t in seconds that it takes for an object to fall from a height of h feet. How long would it take a basketball to hit the ground from a height of 50 feet? **F**

F 1.77 s
G 10.36 s
H 28.28 s
J 200 s

62. Which of the following is an example of an irrational number? **C**

A -8 C $\sqrt{10}$

B $\frac{3}{4}$ D $\sqrt{16}$

63. GRIDDED RESPONSE The area of a triangle that has three equal sides can be found using the expression $\frac{s^2\sqrt{3}}{4}$, where s is the length of one side. What is the area in square inches of the triangle below to the nearest tenth? **43.3**

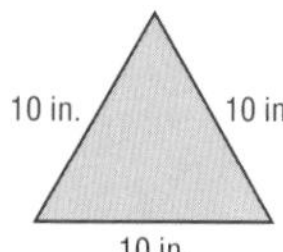

Spiral Review

Estimate each square root to the nearest integer. Do not use a calculator. (Lesson 10-1)

64. $\sqrt{79}$ **9** **65.** $\sqrt{95}$ **10** **66.** $-\sqrt{54}$ **−7**

67. $-\sqrt{125}$ **−11** **68.** $\pm\sqrt{200}$ **±14** **69.** $\pm\sqrt{396}$ **±20**

Graph each function. (Lesson 9-9) **70–73. See margin.**

70. $y = 4x^3$ **71.** $y = -2x^3 - 3$ **72.** $y = -\frac{1}{3}x^3 + 2$ **73.** $y = \frac{3}{4}x^3 - 4$

74. FORESTRY The table shows the percent of forest land in different states. (Lesson 7-3)

a. For each state in the table, how many square miles of land are covered by forests? Round to the nearest square mile.

b. Which state has the greatest amount of forest land?

STATE	PERCENT OF LAND COVERED BY FOREST	AREA OF STATE (SQUARE MILES)
Illinois	11.0%	55,584
Kentucky	49.1%	39,728
Michigan	44.7%	56,804
New York	56.1%	47,214
Ohio	27.3%	40,948

Source: U.S. Census Bureau

74a. Illinois: 6114 mi^2; Kentucky: 19,506 mi^2; Michigan: 25,391 mi^2; New York: 26,487 mi^2; Ohio: 11,179 mi^2

74b. New York

Skills Review

Solve each equation. (Lesson 5-5)

75. $18 + 57 + x = 180$ **105** **76.** $x + 27 + 54 = 180$ **99** **77.** $85 + x + 24 = 180$ **71**

78. $x + x + x = 180$ **60** **79.** $2x + 3x + 4x = 180$ **20** **80.** $2x + 3x + 5x = 180$ **18**

Differentiated Instruction

BL

Extension Present the following problem to students: Bettina and Stephan are purchasing hang gliders. Bettina prefers a hang glider with a low aspect ratio around 5.1 for easy maneuvering. Stephan prefers a high aspect ratio around 7.4 for performance. If the area of both wings is about 160 square feet, will Bettina's hang glider have a shorter or longer wingspan than Stephan's? Explain. Shorter; sample answer: Since the area is the same, multiplying the wingspan by a lower aspect ratio will result in a smaller number. Finding the square root of the smaller number also results in a smaller number, which means the wingspan is shorter for the lower aspect ratio.

Angles in a Triangle

Math Online glencoe.com
Math in Motion

There is a relationship among the measures of the angles of a triangle.

ACTIVITY

Step 1 Use a straightedge or ruler to draw a triangle on a piece of paper. Then cut out the triangle and label the vertices *X*, *Y*, and *Z*.

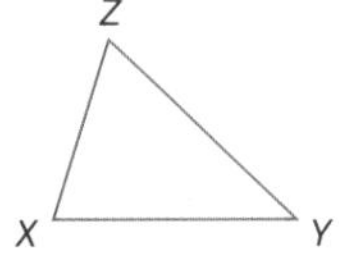

Step 2 Fold the triangle as shown so that point *Z* lies on side XY as shown. Label the back of $\angle Z$ as $\angle 2$.

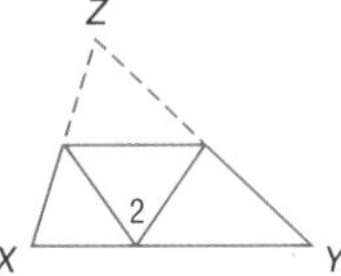

Step 3 Fold again so point *X* meets point *Z*. Label the back of $\angle X$ as $\angle 1$.

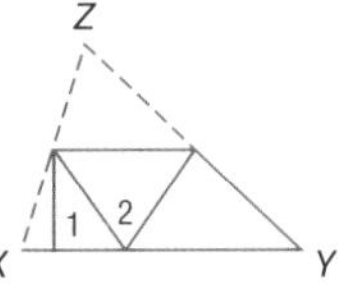

Step 4 Fold so point *Y* meets point *Z*. Label the back of $\angle Y$ as $\angle 3$.

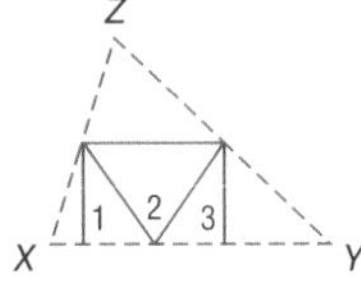

Analyze the Results

1. What kind of figure is formed by angles 1, 2, and 3? **straight line**
2. Repeat the activity using a different triangle. Label the vertices *R*, *S*, and *T*. What kind of figure is formed by angles *R*, *S*, and *T*? **straight line**
3. Make a table like the one shown at the right. Use a protractor to measure the angles of triangles *XYZ* and *RST*. Find the sum of the angle measures. **The sum of the angle measures in both triangles is 180°.**

Triangle	Angle Measures	Sum of Angle Measures
XYZ		
RST		

4. **MAKE A CONJECTURE** Without measuring, make a conjecture about the sum of the measures of the angles of any triangle. **The sum of the measure is 180°.**

EXPLORE 10-3 Lesson Notes

1 FOCUS

Objective Investigate the relationship among the measures of the angles of a triangle.

Materials for Each Student

- straightedge
- protractor

2 TEACH

Working in Cooperative Groups

Have students work in groups of two or three, mixing abilities, to complete the Activity and Exercises 1 and 2.

Teaching Tip

Some students may be distracted by the rectangular shape of the folds when analyzing the results of the Activity. Suggest that students redraw the angles on a sheet of paper to clearly see that $\angle 1$, $\angle 2$, and $\angle 3$ form a straight line.

Ask:

- The triangle in the model does not have a right angle. What would be the sum of the angles of a triangle if one of the angle measures were 90º? 180º

Practice Have students complete Exercises 3 and 4.

3 ASSESS

Formative Assessment

Use Exercise 3 to assess whether students understand that the sum of the measures of the angles of a triangle is 180º.

From Concrete to Abstract

Use Exercise 4 to assess whether students understand that the sum of the measures of the angles of all triangles is 180º and is known without measuring the angles.

10-3 Lesson Notes

1 FOCUS

Vertical Alignment

Before Lesson 10-3
Solve equations by adding or subtracting.

Lesson 10-3
Find the missing angle measure of a triangle.
Classify triangles by properties and attributes.

After Lesson 10-3
Use relationships between triangles and sides of triangles to solve problems.

2 TEACH

Scaffolding Questions

Have students read the *Why?* section of the lesson and answer the questions.

Ask:

- Given the side lengths of the figures, what conjecture can you make about the angle measures of the figures? Sample answer: The angles have the same measure.
- What do you know about the sum of the measures of the angles in a triangle? The sum of the angles is 180°.
- What is the measure of the angles in the triangles on the geodesic dome? Explain. 60° ; since the angle measures are equal, divide 180° by 3 to give 60°.

10-3 Triangles

Then
You solved equations by adding or subtracting. (Lesson 4-3)

Now
- Find the missing angle measure of a triangle.
- Classify triangles by properties and attributes.

New Vocabulary
line segment
triangle
vertex
congruent

Math Online
glencoe.com
- Extra Examples
- Personal Tutor
- Self-Check Quiz
- Homework Help

Why?

Geodesic domes are structures that are almost spherical. They are stronger and are able to cover more space than any other type of structure without internal supports.

a. Name the geometric figures that form the surface of the geodesic dome shown. triangles

b. Describe the side lengths of the geometric figures. They are the same length.

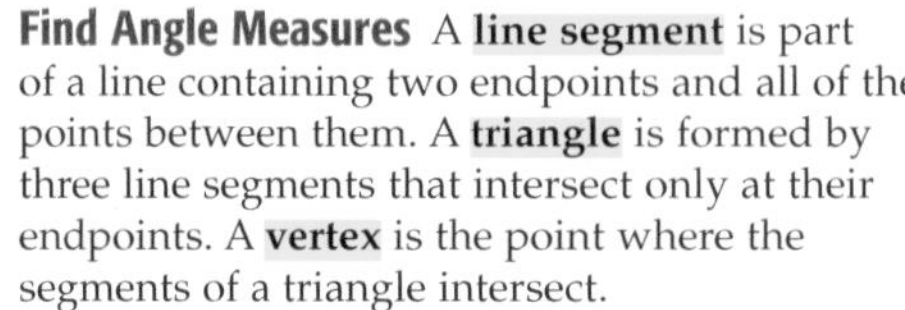

Find Angle Measures A **line segment** is part of a line containing two endpoints and all of the points between them. A **triangle** is formed by three line segments that intersect only at their endpoints. A **vertex** is the point where the segments of a triangle intersect.

Triangle XYZ, written $\triangle XYZ$, is shown at the right. When finding the measures of angles in a triangle, the notation $m\angle X$ means the measure of angle X.

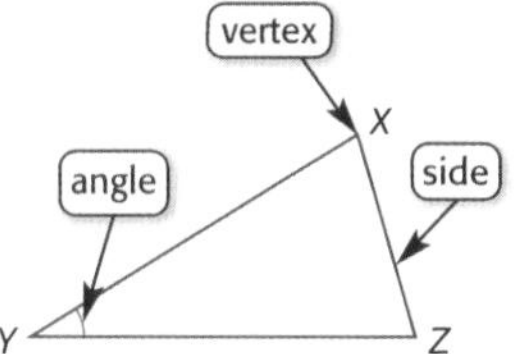

sides: $\overline{XY}$, $\overline{YZ}$, $\overline{XZ}$
vertices: X, Y, Z
angles: $\angle X$, $\angle Y$, $\angle Z$

Key Concept Angles of a Triangle — For Your FOLDABLE

Words The sum of the measures of the angles of a triangle is 180°.

Symbols $x + y + z = 180$

Model

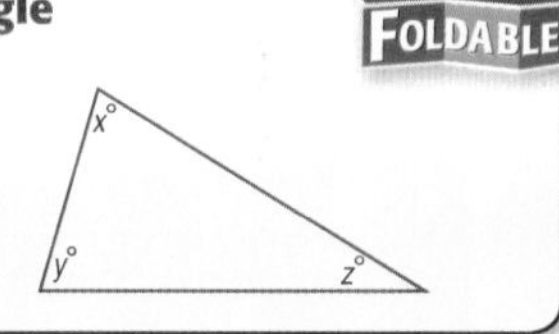

EXAMPLE 1 Find Angle Measures

Find the value of x in $\triangle PQR$.

$m\angle P + m\angle Q + m\angle R = 180$	Write an equation.
$x + 54 + 89 = 180$	Substitution
$x + 143 = 180$	Simplify.
$x + 143 - 143 = 180 - 143$	Subtract 143 from each side.
$x = 37$	Simplify.

So, $m\angle P = 37°$.

Check Your Progress

1. Find the $m\angle E$ in $\triangle DEF$ if $m\angle D = 62°$ and $m\angle F = 39°$. 79°

Personal Tutor glencoe.com

Lesson 10-3 Resources

Resource	Approaching-Level	On-Level	Beyond-Level	English Learners
Teacher Edition	• Differentiated Instruction, p. 552	• Differentiated Instruction, p. 552	• Differentiated Instruction, p. 555	• Differentiated Instruction, p. 552
Chapter Resource Masters	• Study Guide and Intervention, pp. 18–19 • Skills Practice, p. 20 • Practice, p. 21 • Word Problem Practice, p. 22	• Study Guide and Intervention, pp. 18–19 • Skills Practice, p. 20 • Practice, p. 21 • Word Problem Practice, p. 22 • Enrichment, p. 23	• Practice, p. 21 • Word Problem Practice, p. 22 • Enrichment, p. 23	• Study Guide and Intervention, pp. 18–19 • Skills Practice, p. 20 • Practice, p. 21
Transparencies	• 5-Minute Check Transparency 10-3	• 5-Minute Check Transparency 10-3	• 5-Minute Check Transparency 10-3	• 5-Minute Check Transparency 10-3
Other	• Study Notebook • Teaching Pre-Algebra with Manipulatives	• Study Notebook • Teaching Pre-Algebra with Manipulatives	• Study Notebook	• Study Notebook • Teaching Pre-Algebra with Manipulatives

EXAMPLE 2 Use Ratios to Find Angle Measures

The measures of the angles of $\triangle ABC$ are in the ratio 1:3:8. What are the measures of the angles?

Words	The sum of the measures of the angles is 180°.
Variables	Let x represent the measure of the first angle, $3x$ the measure of a second angle, and $8x$ the measure of the third angle.
Equation	$x + 3x + 8x = 180$

$x + 3x + 8x = 180$ **Write the equation.**

$12x = 180$ **Combine like terms.**

$\frac{12x}{12} = \frac{180}{12}$ **Divide each side by 12.**

$x = 15$ **Simplify.**

Since $x = 15$, $3x = 3(15)$ or 45, and $8x = 8(15)$ or 120.

The measures of the angles are 15°, 45°, and 120°.

> **StudyTip**
> **Check Solutions** $15 + 45 + 120 = 180$. So, the answer is correct.

Check Your Progress

2. The measures of the angles of a triangle are in the ratio 1:3:6. What are the measures of the angles? 18°, 54°, 108°

Personal Tutor glencoe.com

Classify Triangles Angles can be classified by their degree measure.

Key Concept Types of Angles — For Your FOLDABLE

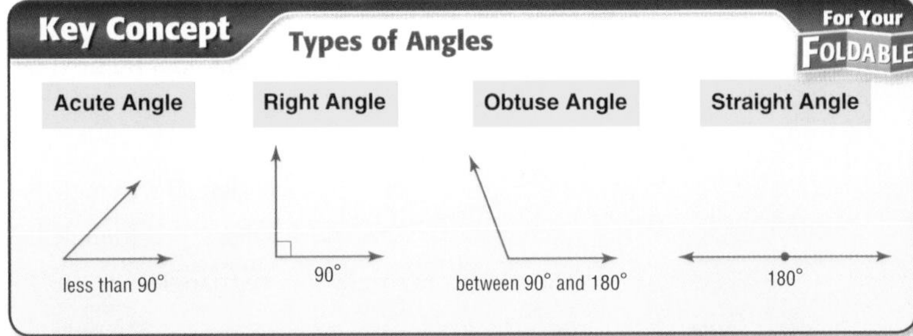

Real-World Link

Smilodons were about 4–5 feet long, 3 feet tall, and weighed about 440 pounds. Their saber-like teeth were up to 7 inches long.

Source: Enchanted Learning

Real-World EXAMPLE 3 Classify Angles

ANIMALS ***Smilodons*** **were saber-toothed cats that lived 11,000 years ago. Smilodons had jaws that opened to an angle of about 120°. What type of angle is formed by the jaws of a smilodon?**

S 120°

The measure of $\angle S$ is greater than 90°, so $\angle S$ is obtuse. The jaws of a smilodon form an obtuse angle.

Check Your Progress

3. ANIMALS Modern lions can open their jaws to an angle of about 65°. What type of angle is formed by the jaws of a lion? acute

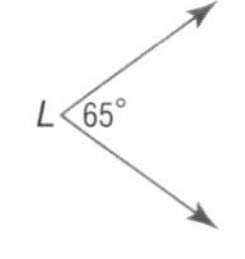

Personal Tutor glencoe.com

Tips for New Teachers

Estimation Point out to students that they can use estimation to mentally check their solutions. For example, in Example 1, $89 + 54 + 37 \approx 90 + 50 + 40 = 180$. The solution is reasonable.

Find Angle Measures

Examples 1 and 2 show how to find an unknown angle measure in a triangle and how to find the measures of the angles in a triangle using ratios.

Formative Assessment

Use the Check Your Progress exercises after each example to determine students' understanding of concepts.

Additional Examples

1 Find the value of x in $\triangle DEF$. 47

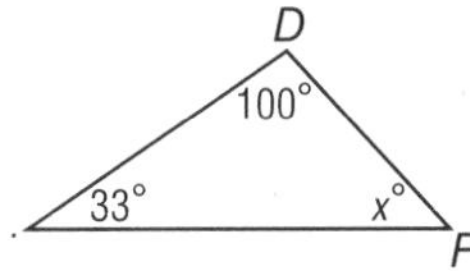

2 ALGEBRA The measures of the angles of a triangle are in the ratio 2:3:5. What are the measures of the angles? 36°, 54°, 90°

3 HUMAN JAWS Humans have jaws that can open to about 45°. What type of angle is formed by the jaws of a human? acute

Additional Examples also in Interactive Classroom PowerPoint® Presentations

IWB INTERACTIVE WHITEBOARD READY

TEACH with TECH

STUDENT RESPONSE SYSTEM Create a presentation consisting of a series of triangles and ask students to classify what type of triangle is shown. First classify the triangles by angles. Then classify the triangles by sides. Provide students with a numerical key for how to respond.

Classify Triangles

Example 3 shows how to classify an angle in a real-world problem. **Example 4** shows how to classify triangles by their angles and their sides.

Focus on Mathematical Content

Classifying Triangles Triangles can be classified by their angles (which must add up to 180°) or by their sides. For example, a triangle with an angle greater than 90° and no congruent sides is an obtuse scalene triangle. Ask students if they can draw a right obtuse triangle. No, if one angle is 90°, it is not possible to have an angle over 90° because the sum of three angles must be 180°.

Additional Example

4 Classify each triangle by its angles and by its sides.

a.

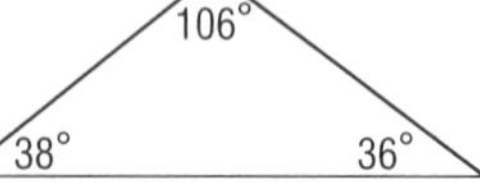

obtuse scalene

b.

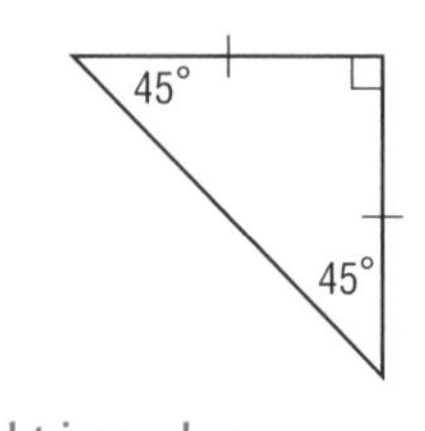

right isosceles

Triangles can be classified by their angles.

Key Concept — Classify Triangles by Angles

For Your FOLDABLE

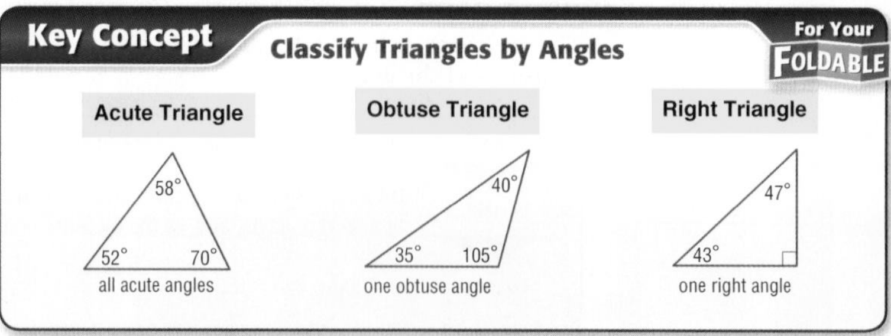

Triangles can also be classified by their sides. **Congruent** sides are sides that have the same length.

ReadingMath

Congruent Segments Tick marks on the sides of a triangle indicate that those sides are congruent. Sides without tick marks are not congruent.

Key Concept — Classify Triangles by Sides

For Your FOLDABLE

Scalene Triangle	Isosceles Triangle	Equilateral Triangle
no congruent sides	at least two sides congruent	all sides congruent

EXAMPLE 4 Classify Triangles

Classify each triangle by its angles and by its sides.

a.

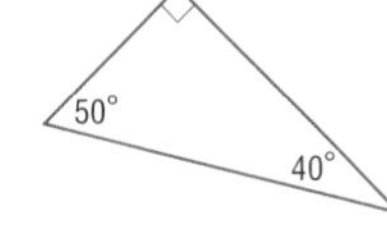

Angles: The triangle has a right angle.

Sides: The triangle has no congruent sides.

The triangle is a right scalene triangle.

b.

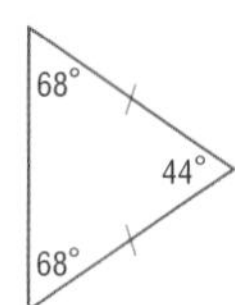

Angles: The triangle has all acute angles.

Sides: The triangle has two congruent sides.

The triangle is an acute isosceles triangle.

Check Your Progress

4A. acute scalene

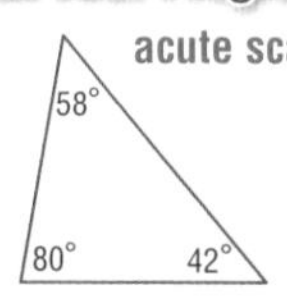

4B. acute equilateral

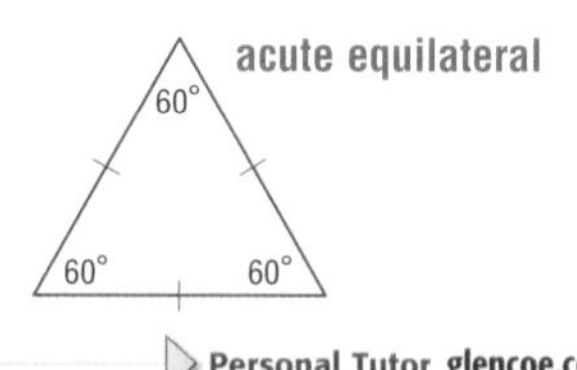

Personal Tutor glencoe.com

Differentiated Instruction

AL OL ELL

If students are confused by the fact that all triangles, including right and obtuse triangles, contain acute angles,

Then tell students to look carefully for right and obtuse angles before they classify a triangle.

552 Chapter 10 Real Numbers and Right Triangles

Check Your Understanding

Examples 1 and 4 pp. 550, 552

Find the value of x in each triangle. Then classify each triangle by its angles and by its sides.

1. 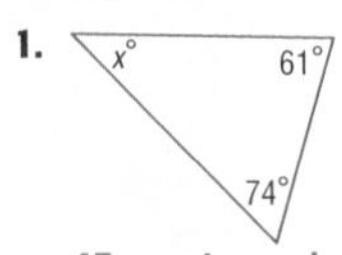

45; acute scalene

2. 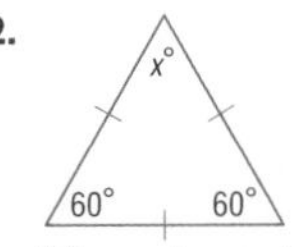

60; acute equilateral

3. 45° x° 8 cm 8 cm
45; right isosceles

Example 2 p. 551

4. The measures of the angles of a triangle are in the ratio 2:3:5. What are the measures of the angles? 36°, 54°, 90°

Example 3 p. 551

5. **ANIMALS** A hippopotamus can open its jaws to an angle of about 180°. What type of angle is formed by the jaws of a hippo? straight

Practice and Problem Solving

 = **Step-by-Step Solutions** begin on page R11.
Extra Practice begins on page 810.

Examples 1 and 4 pp. 550, 552

Find the value of x in each triangle. Then classify each triangle by its angles and by its sides.

6. 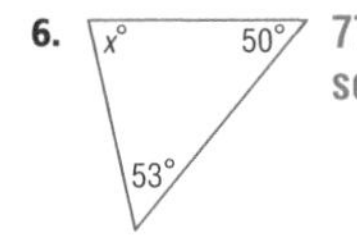

77; acute scalene

7. 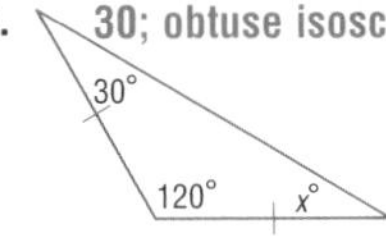

30; obtuse isosceles

8. 12 in. x° 60° 12 in. 12 in. 60°
60; acute equilateral

9. 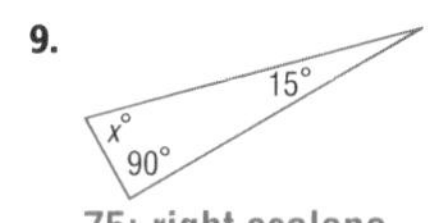

75; right scalene

10. 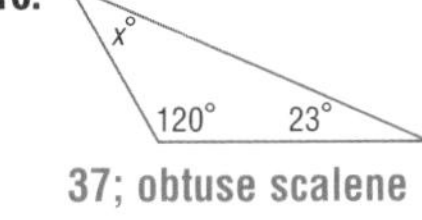

37; obtuse scalene

11. 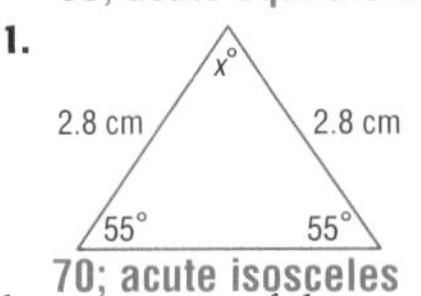

70; acute isosceles

Example 2 p. 551

12. Determine the measures of the angles of $\triangle ABC$ if the measures of the angles are in the ratio 1:1:16. 10°, 10°, 160°

13. Determine the measures of the angles of $\triangle TUV$ if the measures of the angles are in the ratio 1:6:8. 12°, 72°, 96°

Example 3 p. 551

TIME What type of angle is formed by the hands on a clock at each time?

14. 3:00 right
15. 6:00 straight
16. 10:30 obtuse
17. 4:30 acute

Classify each angle as *acute, obtuse, right,* or *straight.*

18. 30° acute
19. 86° acute
20. 90° right
21. 145° obtuse
22. 116° obtuse
23. 55° acute
24. 42° acute
25. 125° obtuse
26. 92° obtuse

3 PRACTICE

Formative Assessment

Use Exercises 1–5 to check for understanding.

Use the chart at the bottom of this page to customize assignments for your students.

Differentiated Homework Options

Level	Assignment	Two-Day Option	
AL Basic	6–26, 35, 36, 38–56	7–25 odd, 40–43	6–26 even, 35, 36, 38, 39, 44–56
OL Core	7–25 odd, 27–28, 29–35 odd, 36, 38–56	6–26, 40–43	27–36, 38, 39, 44–56
BL Advanced	27–52 (Optional: 53–56)		

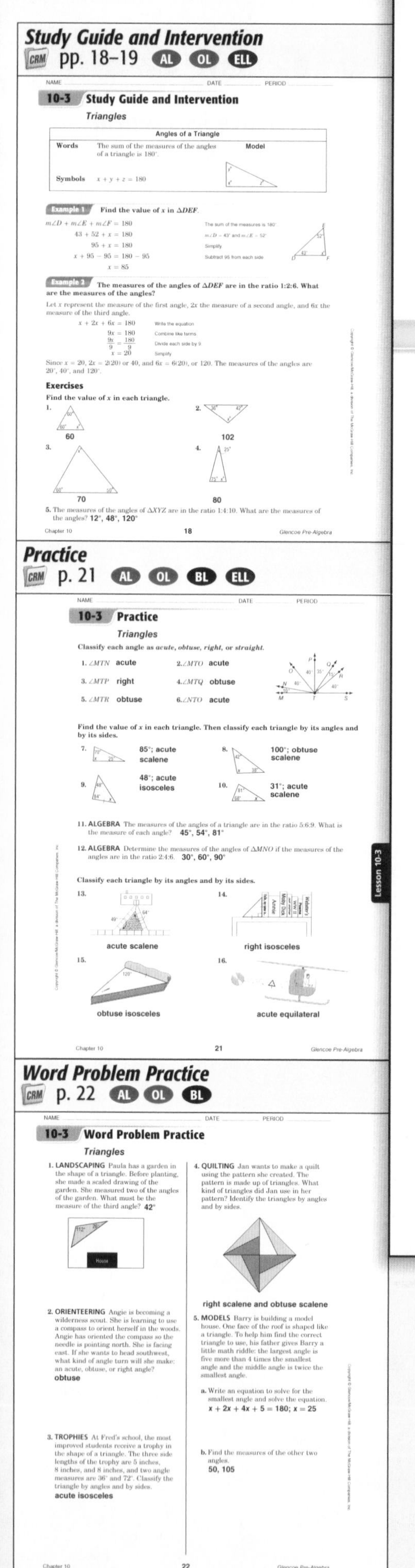

Study Guide and Intervention

CRM pp. 18–19 AL OL ELL

NAME ______ DATE ______ PERIOD ______

10-3 Study Guide and Intervention

Triangles

Angles of a Triangle		
Words	The sum of the measures of the angles of a triangle is 180°.	**Model**
Symbols	$x + y + z = 180$	

Example 1 Find the value of x in $\triangle DEF$.

$m\angle D + m\angle E + m\angle F = 180$ The sum of the measures is 180°.
$43 + 52 + x = 180$ $m\angle D = 43°$ and $m\angle E = 52°$
$95 + x = 180$ Simplify.
$x + 95 - 95 = 180 - 95$ Subtract 95 from each side.
$x = 85$

Example 2 The measures of the angles of $\triangle DEF$ are in the ratio 1:2:6. What are the measures of the angles?

Let x represent the measure of the first angle, $2x$ the measure of a second angle, and $6x$ the measure of the third angle.

$x + 2x + 6x = 180$ Write the equation.
$9x = 180$ Combine like terms.
$\frac{9x}{9} = \frac{180}{9}$ Divide each side by 9.
$x = 20$ Simplify.

Since $x = 20$, $2x = 2(20)$ or 40, and $6x = 6(20)$, or 120. The measures of the angles are 20°, 40°, and 120°.

Exercises

Find the value of x in each triangle.

1. **60**
2. **102**
3. **70**
4. **80**
5. The measures of the angles of $\triangle XYZ$ are in the ratio 1:4:10. What are the measures of the angles? **12°, 48°, 120°**

Chapter 10 18 Glencoe Pre-Algebra

Practice

CRM p. 21 AL OL BL ELL

NAME ______ DATE ______ PERIOD ______

10-3 Practice

Triangles

Classify each angle as *acute, obtuse, right,* or *straight*.

1. $\angle MTN$ **acute**
2. $\angle MTO$ **acute**
3. $\angle MTP$ **right**
4. $\angle MTQ$ **obtuse**
5. $\angle MTR$ **obtuse**
6. $\angle NTO$ **acute**

Find the value of x in each triangle. Then classify each triangle by its angles and by its sides.

7. **85°; acute scalene**
8. **100°; obtuse scalene**
9. **48°; acute isosceles**
10. **31°; acute scalene**
11. **ALGEBRA** The measures of the angles of a triangle are in the ratio 5:6:9. What is the measure of each angle? **45°, 54°, 81°**
12. **ALGEBRA** Determine the measures of the angles of $\triangle MNO$ if the measures of the angles are in the ratio 2:4:6. **30°, 60°, 90°**

Classify each triangle by its angles and by its sides.

13. **acute scalene**
14. **right isosceles**
15. **obtuse isosceles**
16. **acute equilateral**

Chapter 10 21 Glencoe Pre-Algebra

Lesson 10-3

Word Problem Practice

CRM p. 22 AL OL BL

NAME ______ DATE ______ PERIOD ______

10-3 Word Problem Practice

Triangles

1. **LANDSCAPING** Paula has a garden in the shape of a triangle. Before planting, she made a scaled drawing of the garden. She measured two of the angles of the garden. What must be the measure of the third angle? **42°**
2. **ORIENTEERING** Angie is becoming a wilderness scout. She is learning to use a compass to orient herself in the woods. Angie has oriented the compass so the needle is pointing north. She is facing east. If she wants to head southwest, what kind of angle turn will she make: an acute, obtuse, or right angle? **obtuse**
3. **TROPHIES** At Fred's school, the most improved students receive a trophy in the shape of a triangle. The three side lengths of the trophy are 5 inches, 8 inches, and 8 inches, and two angle measures are 36° and 72°. Classify the triangle by angles and by sides. **acute isosceles**
4. **QUILTING** Jan wants to make a quilt using the pattern she created. The pattern is made up of triangles. What kind of triangles did Jan use in her pattern? Identify the triangles by angles and by sides. **right scalene and obtuse scalene**
5. **MODELS** Barry is building a model house. One face of the roof is shaped like a triangle. To help him find the correct triangle to use, his father gives Barry a little math riddle: the largest angle is five more than 4 times the smallest angle and the middle angle is twice the smallest angle.
   a. Write an equation to solve for the smallest angle and solve the equation. **$x + 2x + 4x + 5 = 180$; $x = 25$**
   b. Find the measures of the other two angles. **50, 105**

Chapter 10 22 Glencoe Pre-Algebra

Real-World Link

According to a recent survey, the average age of a skateboarder is 14.

Source: The Skate Park Association of the United States

B

27. **ASTRONOMY** The Big Dipper may be the best known group of stars in the sky. The figures below show how the Big Dipper probably looked 100,000 years ago, how it looks today, and how it will look 100,000 years from now.

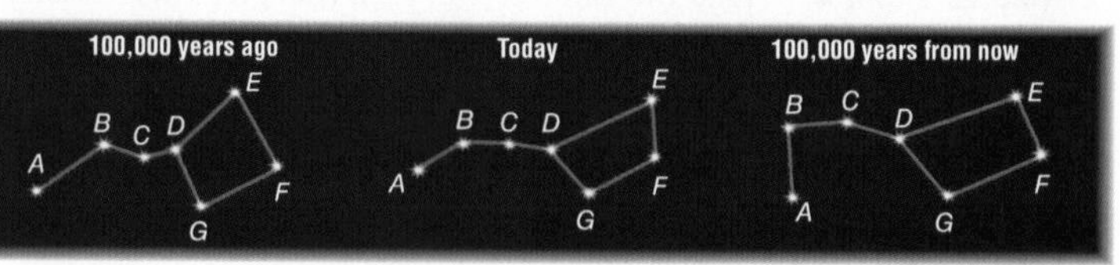

a. Which angle was acute 100,000 years ago and will be obtuse 100,000 years from now? **$\angle E$**

b. Identify an angle that appears to be a right angle. **$\angle G$ from 100,000 years ago**

28. **SKATEBOARDING** Tony Hawk was the first skateboarder to perform the 900 during the X-Games. He rode off a ramp and spun 900° in mid-air while on a skateboard. How many revolutions did Tony make performing the 900? **2.5 revolutions**

ALGEBRA Find the measures of the angles in each triangle.

29. 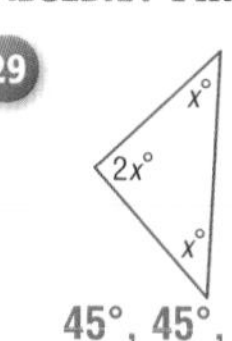

45°, 45°, 90°

30. (x–2)°, 72°, x° **53°, 55°, 72°**

31. 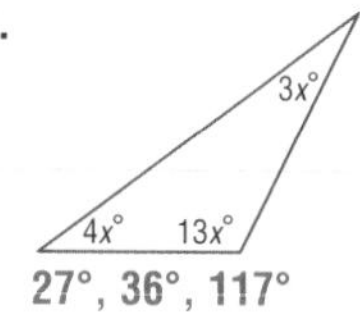

27°, 36°, 117°

C

ALGEBRA The measures of the sides of a triangle are given. Classify each triangle by its sides.

32. $2x, 3x, 4x$ **scalene**
33. y, y, y **equilateral**
34. $3x, 3x, 2x$ **isosceles**

H.O.T. Problems Use **H**igher-**O**rder **T**hinking Skills

35. **OPEN ENDED** Sketch each triangle. If it is not possible to sketch the triangle, write *not possible.* **a–b. See margin.**
    a. acute scalene
    b. obtuse and *not* scalene
    c. right equilateral **not possible**
    d. obtuse equilateral **not possible**

36. **FIND THE ERROR** Miguel says that an equilateral triangle is sometimes an obtuse triangle. Jane says that an equilateral triangle is always an acute triangle. Is either of them correct? Explain your reasoning.

37. **CHALLENGE** Find the value of x and y in the figure. **50; 80**

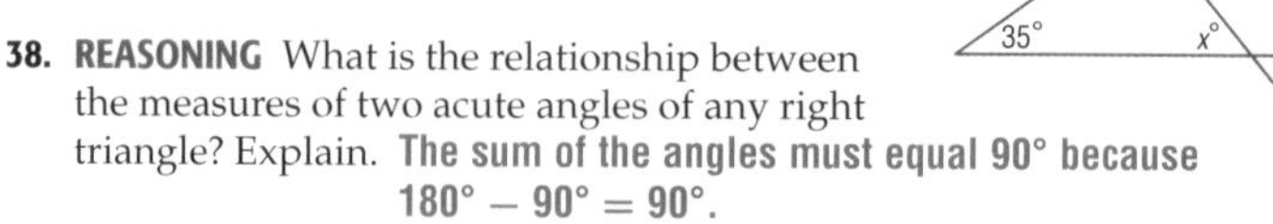

38. **REASONING** What is the relationship between the measures of two acute angles of any right triangle? Explain. **The sum of the angles must equal 90° because $180° - 90° = 90°$.**

39. **WRITING IN MATH** *True* or *false*? Every triangle has at least 2 acute angles. Justify your reasoning.

36. **Jane; an equilateral triangle has all sides congruent and all angles congruent. So, each angle measures 60°. Therefore, an equilateral triangle is always acute.**

39. **True; Sample answer: There can be at most one right or one obtuse angle. So, the sum of the two remaining angles must be ≤ 90°.**

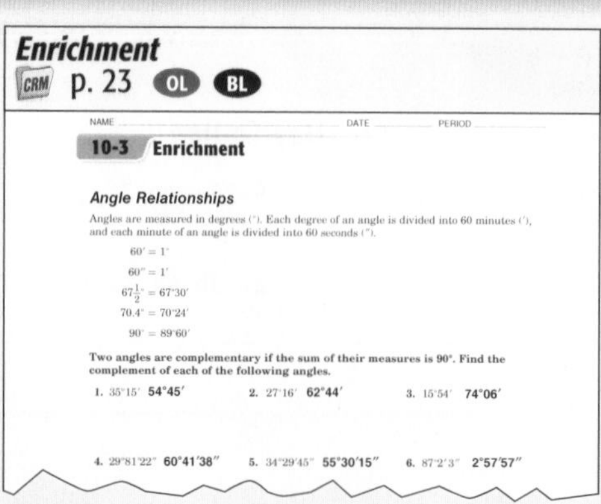

Enrichment

CRM p. 23 OL BL

NAME ______ DATE ______ PERIOD ______

10-3 Enrichment

Angle Relationships

Angles are measured in degrees (°). Each degree of an angle is divided into 60 minutes (′), and each minute of an angle is divided into 60 seconds (″).

$60' = 1°$
$60'' = 1'$
$67\frac{1}{2}° = 67°30'$
$70.4° = 70°24'$
$90° = 89°60'$

Two angles are complementary if the sum of their measures is 90°. Find the complement of each of the following angles.

1. 35°15′ **54°45′**
2. 27°16′ **62°44′**
3. 15°54′ **74°06′**
4. 29°81′22″ **60°41′38″**
5. 34°29′45″ **55°30′15″**
6. 87°2′3″ **2°57′57″**

Standardized Test Practice

40. How would you find the value of x? **D**

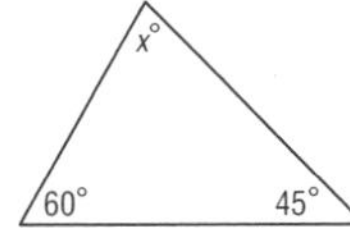

A Subtract 60 from 105.
B Add 180 to 105.
C Add 45 to 105.
D Subtract 105 from 180.

41. Which of the following best describes the triangle with the given measures? **F**

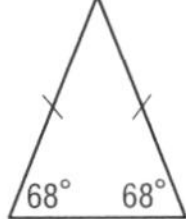

F acute isosceles triangle
G acute scalene triangle
H obtuse isosceles triangle
J acute equilateral triangle

42. Which of the following is an obtuse triangle? **C**

A 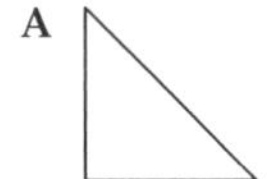

C 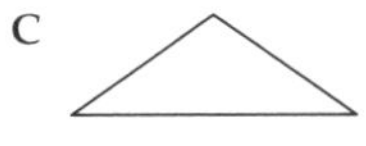

B 

D 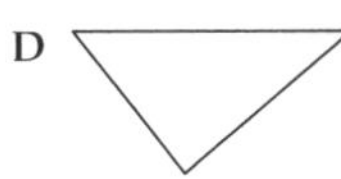

43. **EXTENDED RESPONSE** Use the triangle shown below.

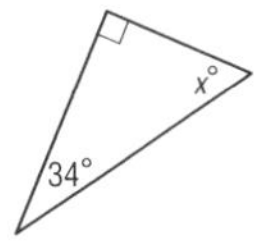

a. Find the value of x. **56°**
b. Explain how you found the value of x in part **a**.
c. Classify the triangle by its angles and by its sides. **right scalene**

b. $90 + 34 = 124$, $180 - 124° = 56$

Spiral Review

ALGEBRA **Solve each equation. Round to the nearest tenth, if necessary.** (Lesson 10-2)

44. $m^2 = 81$ **9, −9**
45. $196 = y^2$ **14, −14**
46. $168 = 2p^2$ **9.2, −9.2**
47. $\frac{f^2}{2} = 51$ **10.1, −10.1**

Estimate each square root to the nearest integer. Do not use a calculator. (Lesson 10-1)

48. $-\sqrt{52}$ **−7**
49. $-\sqrt{17}$ **−4**
50. $\sqrt{38}$ **6**
51. $\sqrt{140}$ **12**

52. **WEATHER** The time a storm will hit an area can be predicted using $d \div s = t$ where d is the distance in miles an area is from the storm, s is the speed in miles per hour of the storm, and t is the travel time in hours of the storm. Suppose it is 11:00 A.M. and a storm is heading toward a town at a speed of 30 miles per hour. The storm is about 150 miles from the town. What time will the storm hit? (Lesson 3-4) **4:00 P.M.**

Skills Review

Find the value of each expression. (Lesson 9-1)

53. 11^2 **121**
54. 3^2 **9**
55. 16^2 **256**
56. 17^2 **289**

Watch Out!

Find the Error Suggest that students attempt to sketch Jane and Miguel's triangles in Exercise 36, and then explain whether either of them is correct. Encourage students to make sketches when reasoning about the angles of triangles and other polygons.

4 ASSESS

Crystal Ball Have students predict how this lesson helps prepare them for the next lesson on the Pythagorean Theorem.

Formative Assessment

Check for student understanding of Lesson 10-3.

CRM Quiz 2, p. 44

Additional Answers

35a.

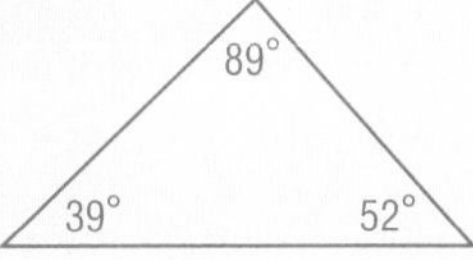

35b.

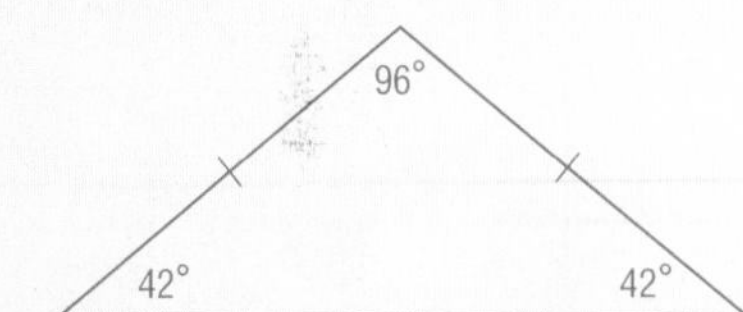

Differentiated Instruction

Extension Present the following problem to students: The measure of $\angle S$ in $\triangle RST$ is one-half the measure of $\angle R$, and the measure of $\angle T$ is twice the measure of $\angle S$ plus 5°. What are the measures of the angles in $\triangle RST$? $m\angle R = 70°, m\angle S = 35°, m\angle T = 75°$

CHAPTER 10 Mid-Chapter Quiz

Formative Assessment

Use the Mid-Chapter Quiz to assess students' progress in the first half of the chapter.

For problems answered incorrectly, have students review the lessons indicated in parentheses.

ExamView Assessment Suite Customize and create multiple versions of your Mid-Chapter Quiz and their answer keys.

FOLDABLES Follow-Up

Before students complete the Mid-Chapter Quiz, encourage them to review the information for Lessons 10-1 through 10-3 in their Foldables.

CHAPTER 10 Mid-Chapter Quiz

Lessons 10-1 through 10-3

Find each square root. (Lesson 10-1)

1. $\pm\sqrt{49}$ **±7**
2. $\sqrt{144}$ **12**
3. $\sqrt{64}$ **8**
4. $-\sqrt{121}$ **−11**

5. **GARDENING** A square vegetable garden has an area of 169 square feet. If $\sqrt{A} = s$, where s is the length of one side and A is the area, how many feet of fencing is needed to enclose the garden? (Lesson 10-1) **52 ft**

Estimate each square root to the nearest whole number. Do not use a calculator. (Lesson 10-1)

6. $\sqrt{51}$ **7**
7. $-\sqrt{88}$ **−9**
8. $\sqrt{17}$ **4**
9. $\pm\sqrt{111}$ **±11**
10. $\pm\sqrt{41}$ **±6**
11. $-\sqrt{1000}$ **−30**

12. **MULTIPLE CHOICE** Which statement is *not* true? (Lesson 10-1) **D**

A $6 < \sqrt{39} < 7$

B $9 < \sqrt{89} < 10$

C $-8 < -\sqrt{56} < -7$

D $-4 < -\sqrt{17} < -5$

Name all of the sets of numbers to which each real number belongs. Write *whole, integer, rational,* or *irrational*. (Lesson 10-2)

13. 0.3 **rational**
14. $-\sqrt{49}$ **integer, rational**
15. $15.\overline{1}$ **rational**
16. $\frac{56}{8}$ **whole, integer, rational**

17. **GEOMETRY** Use $A = \pi r^2$ to find the radius of a circle with an area of 28.26 square inches. In the formula, A represents the area of a circle, r represents the radius, and $\pi \approx 3.14$. (Lesson 10-2) **3 in.**

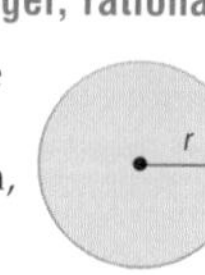

ALGEBRA Solve each equation. Round to the nearest tenth, if necessary. (Lesson 10-2)

18. $k^2 = 74$ **−8.6, 8.6**
19. $131 = n^2$ **−11.4, 11.4**
20. $2b^2 = 98$ **−7, 7**
21. $3.6r^2 = 518.4$ **−12, 12**

Replace each ● with <, >, or = to make a true statement. (Lesson 10-2)

22. $\sqrt{7}$ ● 2.5 **>**
23. $1\frac{4}{5}$ ● $\sqrt{3.24}$ **=**

24. **HORIZON** On a clear day, the number of miles a person can see to the horizon can be found using the formula $d = 1.22 \cdot \sqrt{h}$, where d is the distance in miles to the horizon and h is the person's distance from the ground. If a person is standing on the roof of a skyscraper at a height of 1200 feet, about how many miles could he see? (Lesson 10-2) **about 42 mi**

Classify each angle measure as *acute, obtuse, right,* or *straight*. (Lesson 10-3)

25. 77° **acute**
26. 180° **straight**
27. 90° **right**
28. 165° **obtuse**

Classify each triangle by its angles and by its sides. (Lesson 10-3)

29. 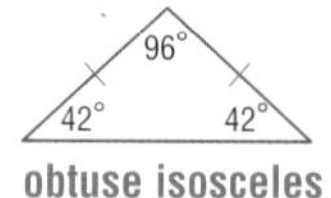

obtuse isosceles

30. 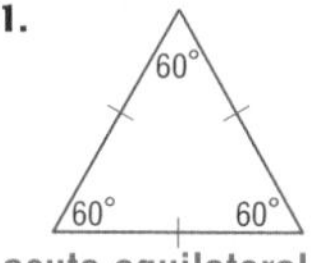

right scalene

31. 60°, 60°, 60° **acute equilateral**

32. 30°, 60° **right scalene**

33. **MULTIPLE CHOICE** Refer to the figure shown. Lloyd lives in Salsburg, does his grocery shopping in Richmond, and sees a doctor in Thornville. What is the measure of the angle formed when Lloyd travels from Salsburg to Richmond and then to Thornville? (Lesson 10-3) **G**

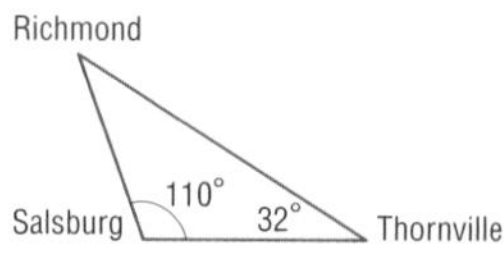

F 28°

G 38°

H 48°

J 180°

Intervention Planner

Tier 1 On Level	Tier 2 Strategic Intervention approaching grade level	Tier 3 Intensive Intervention 2 or more grades below level
 **If** students miss about 25% of the exercises or less,	 **If** students miss about 50% of the exercises,	 **If** students miss about 75% of the exercises,
Then choose a resource: **SE** Lessons 10-1, 10-2, and 10-3; **CRM** Skills Practice, pp. 7, 13, and 20; **TE** Chapter Project, p. 532	**Then** choose a resource: **CRM** Study Guide and Intervention, Chapter 10, pp. 5, 11, and 18; *Quick Review Math Handbook*	 **Then** use *Math Triumphs, Grade 8,* Ch. 4, 6
 **Math Online** Self-Check Quiz	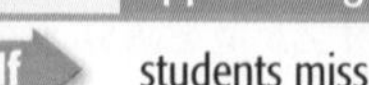 **Math Online** Extra Examples, Personal Tutor, Homework Help	**Math Online** Extra Examples, Personal Tutor, Homework Help, Review Vocabulary

The Pythagorean Theorem

Math Online glencoe.com
Math *in Motion*, Animation

You can use grid paper to investigate the relationship that exists among the sides of a right triangle. Each square □ represents 1 square unit.

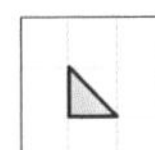

$A = \frac{1}{2}(1)$ or $\frac{1}{2}$ unit^2

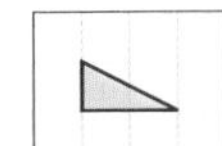

$A = \frac{1}{2}(2)$ or 1 unit^2

ACTIVITY

In each diagram shown below, a square is attached to each side of a right triangle.

Triangle 1

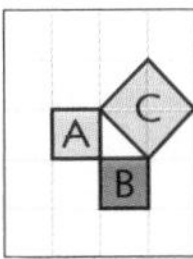

Triangle 2

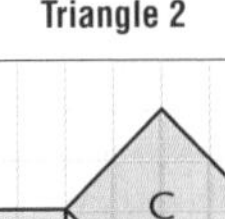

Triangle 3

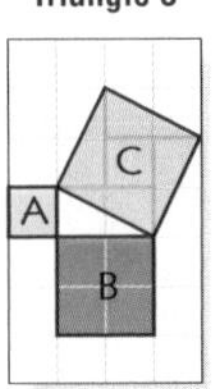

Triangle 4

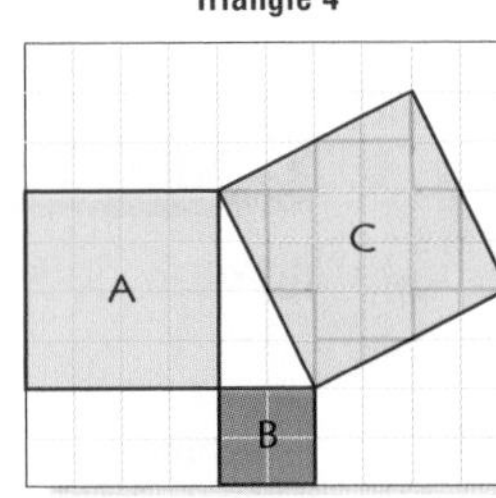

Copy and complete the table. Then find the area of each square that is attached to the triangle. Record the results in your table.

Triangle	Area of Square A (units^2)	Area of Square B (units^2)	Area of Square C (units^2)
1	1	1	2
2	4	4	8
3	1	4	5
4	16	4	20

Analyze the Results

1. How does the sum of the areas of square A and square B compare to the area of square C? **The sum of the areas of squares A and B is equal to the area of square C.**
2. Draw a right triangle on centimeter grid paper. Count to find the measures of the shorter sides and use the relationship you discovered to calculate the measure of the longest side. Measure to verify your answer. **See students' work.**
3. Refer to the diagram at the right. If the lengths of the sides of a right triangle are whole numbers such that $a^2 + b^2 = c^2$, the numbers a, b, and c are called a **Pythagorean Triple**. Tell whether each set of numbers is a Pythagorean Triple. Explain.

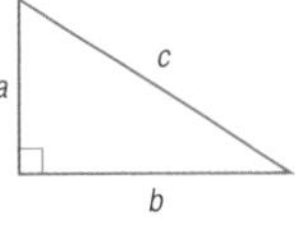

a. 3, 4, 5 **yes; $3^2 + 4^2 = 5^2$**
b. 5, 7, 9 **no; $5^2 + 7^2 \neq 9^2$**
c. 6, 9, 12 **no; $6^2 + 9^2 \neq 12^2$**

Tips for New Teachers

This activity could also be completed using a geoboard.

From Concrete to Abstract

Exercise 3 uses Pythagorean Triples to test whether a triangle is a right triangle. Use this exercise to assess whether students understand that the Pythagorean Theorem applies to all right triangles.

EXPLORE 10-4 Lesson Notes

1 FOCUS

Objective Investigate the relationship between the sides of a right triangle.

Materials for Each Student

- centimeter grid paper

Easy to Make Manipulatives

Teaching Mathematics with Manipulatives, template for:

- centimeter grid paper, p. 12

2 TEACH

Working in Cooperative Groups

Have students work in groups of two or three, mixing abilities, to complete the Activity and Exercise 1.

- Though counting and recording activities can be divided among the students, all students in the group should discuss Exercise 2.
- For Triangle 4, suggest that students count the whole squares first and then the partial squares along the edge of the square.

Ask:

- What do you notice about the placement of the right angle in Triangles 1–4? It is adjacent to the shorter sides of the triangle and opposite the largest side.

Practice Have students complete Exercises 2–3.

3 ASSESS

Formative Assessment

Use Exercise 2 to assess whether students comprehend the relationship between the lengths of the shorter sides and the longest side of a right triangle.

10-4 Lesson Notes

1 FOCUS

Vertical Alignment

Before Lesson 10-4
Find the missing measures of similar triangles.

Lesson 10-4
Use the Pythagorean Theorem to find the length of a side of a right triangle.
Use the converse of the Pythagorean Theorem to determine whether a triangle is a right triangle.

After Lesson 10-4
Derive, extend, and use the Pythagorean Theorem.

2 TEACH

Scaffolding Questions

Have students read the *Why?* section of the lesson and answer the questions.

Ask:

- What do you know about the relationship between the shorter sides of a right triangle and the longer side? The sum of the squares of the lengths of the shorter sides is equal to the square of the length of the longest side.
- Suppose the horizontal support measures 60 m and the vertical support measures 80 m. How long is the straight part of the slide? 100 m

(continued on next page)

10-4 The Pythagorean Theorem

Then
You have already found missing measures of similar triangles. (Lesson 6-7)

Now
- Use the Pythagorean Theorem to find the length of a side of a right triangle.
- Use the converse of the Pythagorean Theorem to determine whether a triangle is a right triangle.

New Vocabulary
legs
hypotenuse
Pythagorean Theorem
solving a right triangle
converse

Math Online
glencoe.com
- Extra Examples
- Personal Tutor
- Self-Check Quiz
- Homework Help

Why?

You are probably not thinking about right triangles as you speed down a water slide. But the figure at the right shows how they are related.

a. What parts of the water slide make up the right triangle? the horizontal and vertical supports and the straight part of the slide
b. Which side of the triangle is the longest side? The side opposite the right angle.

Use the Pythagorean Theorem In a right triangle, the sides adjacent to the right angle are called the **legs**. The side opposite the right angle is the **hypotenuse**. It is the longest side of a right triangle.

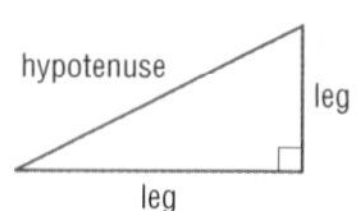

The **Pythagorean Theorem** describes the relationship between the lengths of the legs and the hypotenuse for any right triangle.

Key Concept: Pythagorean Theorem

For Your FOLDABLE

Words In a right triangle, the sum of the squares of the lengths of the legs is equal to the square of the length of the hypotenuse.

Symbols $a^2 + b^2 = c^2$

Model (right triangle with legs a, b and hypotenuse c)

EXAMPLE 1 Find the Hypotenuse Length

Find the length of the hypotenuse of the right triangle.

(right triangle with legs 8 mm and 15 mm, hypotenuse c)

$a^2 + b^2 = c^2$	Pythagorean Theorem
$8^2 + 15^2 = c^2$	Replace a with 8 and b with 15.
$64 + 225 = c^2$	Evaluate 8^2 and 15^2.
$289 = c^2$	Add 64 and 225.
$\pm\sqrt{289} = c$	Definition of square root
$17 = c$	Use the principal square root.

The length of the hypotenuse is 17 millimeters.

Check Your Progress

1. Find the length of the hypotenuse of a right triangle if the legs are 24 inches and 45 inches long. 51 in.

Personal Tutor glencoe.com

Lesson 10-4 Resources

Resource	Approaching-Level	On-Level	Beyond-Level	English Learners
Teacher Edition	• Differentiated Instruction, p. 559	• Differentiated Instruction, p. 559	• Differentiated Instruction, pp. 560, 563	• Differentiated Instruction, p. 559
Chapter Resource Masters	• Study Guide and Intervention, pp. 24–25 • Skills Practice, p. 26 • Practice, p. 27 • Word Problem Practice, p. 28	• Study Guide and Intervention, pp. 24–25 • Skills Practice, p. 26 • Practice, p. 27 • Word Problem Practice, p. 28 • Enrichment, p. 29	• Practice, p. 27 • Word Problem Practice, p. 28 • Enrichment, p. 29	• Study Guide and Intervention, pp. 24–25 • Skills Practice, p. 26 • Practice, p. 27
Transparencies	• 5-Minute Check Transparency 10-4	• 5-Minute Check Transparency 10-4	• 5-Minute Check Transparency 10-4	• 5-Minute Check Transparency 10-4
Other	• Study Notebook • Teaching Pre-Algebra with Manipulatives	• Study Notebook • Teaching Pre-Algebra with Manipulatives	• Study Notebook	• Study Notebook • Teaching Pre-Algebra with Manipulatives

STANDARDIZED TEST EXAMPLE 2

GRIDDED RESPONSE A volleyball court is 30 feet wide and 60 feet long. A player serves the ball from one corner of the court to the opposite corner. How far is this? Round to the nearest tenth.

Problem-Solving Tip

Make a Model You can draw and label a model of the volleyball court to help you determine which values to substitute for the variables in $a^2 + b^2 = c^2$.

Read the Test Item

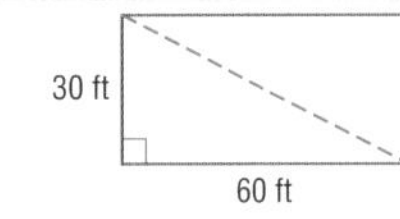

The sides of the court and the diagonal form a right triangle. Find the measure of the hypotenuse.

Solve the Test Item

$a^2 + b^2 = c^2$	Pythagorean Theorem
$30^2 + 60^2 = c^2$	Replace *a* with 30 and *b* with 60.
$900 + 3600 = c^2$	Evaluate 30^2 and 60^2.
$4500 = c^2$	Add.
$\pm\sqrt{4500} = c$	Definition of square root
$67.1 \approx c$	Use the principal square root.

Fill in the Answer Grid

The distance from corner to corner is about 67.1 feet.

6	7	.	1

Check Your Progress

2. GRIDDED RESPONSE A doorway is 2.7 feet wide and 8.4 feet high. What is the longest piece of drywall that can be taken through the doorway? Round to the nearest tenth. **8.8 ft**

Personal Tutor glencoe.com

If you know the lengths of two sides of a right triangle, you can use the Pythagorean Theorem to find the length of the third side. This is called **solving a right triangle**.

Real-World EXAMPLE 3 Solve a Right Triangle

ADVERTISEMENTS A balloon advertising the opening of a store is tethered to the ground as shown. About how many feet above the ground is the balloon?

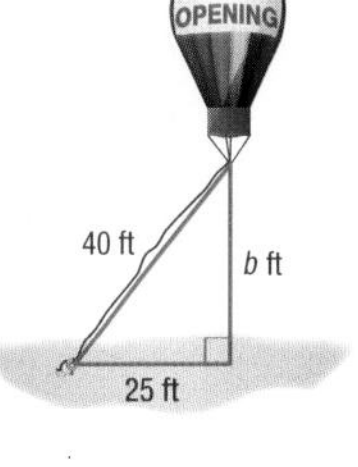

$a^2 + b^2 = c^2$	Pythagorean Theorem
$25^2 + b^2 = 40^2$	Replace *a* with 25 and *c* with 40.
$625 + b^2 = 1600$	Evaluate 25^2 and 40^2.
$625 - 625 + b^2 = 1600 - 625$	Subtract 625 from each side.
$b^2 = 975$	Simplify.
$b = \pm\sqrt{975}$	Definition of square root

 [$\sqrt{\ }$] 975  31.22498999 Use a calculator.

The balloon is about 31.2 feet above the ground.

StudyTip

Square Roots In Lesson 10-1, you learned that a number has both a positive and negative square root. Since you are finding the lengths of sides of triangles, calculate the positive square root only.

Check Your Progress

3. **LADDERS** A 15-foot ladder is leaning against a house. The base of the ladder is 3.5 feet from the house. About how many feet does the ladder reach on the side of the house? **14.6 ft**

Personal Tutor glencoe.com

- How can you check your answer? Check that $60^2 + 80^2 = 100^2$: $3600 + 6400 = 10{,}000$ or $10{,}000 = 10{,}000$, so 100 m is correct

Use the Pythagorean Theorem

Examples 1–3 show how to use the Pythagorean Theorem to find the length of a leg or the length of the hypotenuse of a right triangle.

Formative Assessment

Use the Check Your Progress exercises after each Example to determine students' understanding of concepts.

Differentiated Instruction

AL OL ELL

 students have difficulty remembering the Pythagorean Theorem and Pythagorean Triples,

Then have students split into groups to create jingles to help commit Pythagorean Triples and the Pythagorean Theorem to memory. Sample jingles: *a* times *a*, plus *b* times *b*, will always come to *c* times *c*. Sides 3, 4 and long side 5, make the Theorem come alive.

Additional Examples

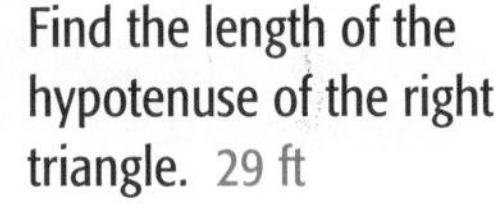

1. Find the length of the hypotenuse of the right triangle. 29 ft

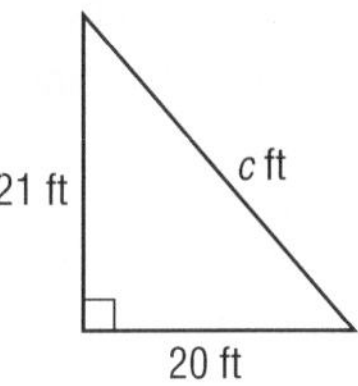

2. **STANDARDIZED TEST PRACTICE** A ladder positioned against a 10-foot building reaches its top. Its base is 3 feet from the building. About how long is the ladder in feet? Round to the nearest tenth. 10.4

3. **LANDSCAPING** A diagonal path through a rectangular garden is 32 feet long. The length of the garden is 24 feet. About how many feet wide is the garden? about 21.2 ft

Additional Examples also in Interactive Classroom PowerPoint® Presentations

Use the Converse of the Pythagorean Theorem

Example 4 shows how to use the converse of the Pythagorean Theorem to identify right triangles.

Focus on Mathematical Content

Identifying Right Triangles Right triangles can be identified by their right angle, though that information is not always provided. When the lengths of the legs and hypotenuse are put into the Pythagorean Theorem, the left side of the equation equals the right. If the sides of the equation are not equal, then it is not a right triangle. Ask students: Are the lengths 5, 11, and 12 a right triangle? no

Additional Example

4 The measures of three sides of a triangle are given. Determine whether each triangle is a right triangle.

a. 48 ft, 60 ft, 78 ft no

b. 24 cm, 70 cm, 74 cm yes

3 PRACTICE

Formative Assessment

Use Exercises 1–8 to check for understanding.

Use the chart at the bottom of the next page to customize assignments for your students.

Use the Converse of the Pythagorean Theorem The Pythagorean Theorem is written in if-then form. If you reverse the statements after *if* and *then*, you have formed the **converse of the Pythagorean Theorem**.

Pythagorean Theorem	If a triangle is a right triangle, then $c^2 = a^2 + b^2$.
Converse	If $c^2 = a^2 + b^2$, then a triangle is a right triangle.

Not all converses are true. However, the converse of the Pythagorean Theorem *is* true. Use the converse to determine whether a triangle is a right triangle.

EXAMPLE 4 Identify a Right Triangle

The measures of three sides of a triangle are given. Determine whether each triangle is a right triangle.

a. 6 cm, 8 cm, 10 cm

$a^2 + b^2 = c^2$	Pythagorean Theorem
$6^2 + 8^2 \stackrel{?}{=} 10^2$	$a = 6, b = 8, c = 10$
$36 + 64 \stackrel{?}{=} 100$	Evaluate.
$100 = 100$	Simplify.

The triangle is a right triangle.

b. 4 in., 5 in., 6 in.

$a^2 + b^2 = c^2$	Pythagorean Theorem
$4^2 + 5^2 \stackrel{?}{=} 6^2$	$a = 4, b = 5, c = 6$
$16 + 25 \stackrel{?}{=} 36$	Evaluate.
$41 \neq 36$	Simplify.

The triangle is *not* a right triangle.

Check Your Progress

4A. 8 in., 9 in., 12 in. no

4B. 15 mm, 20 mm, 25 mm yes

Personal Tutor glencoe.com

Check Your Understanding

Example 1 p. 558 — **Find the length of the hypotenuse of each right triangle. Round to the nearest tenth, if necessary.**

1. 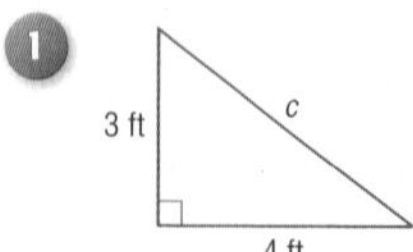

5 ft

2. 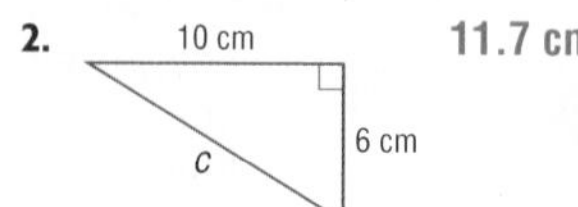

11.7 cm

Example 2 p. 559

3. GRIDDED RESPONSE A gymnastics tumbling mat is a square that measures 40 feet on each side. During the floor routine, a gymnast makes a tumbling pass along the length of the diagonal of the mat. How many feet long is their tumbling pass? Round to the nearest tenth. 56.6 ft

Example 3 p. 559

4. SHADOWS Marian's shadow is 94 inches long. The distance from the top of Marian's head to the end of her shadow is 115 inches. How many inches tall is Marian? Round to the nearest tenth. 66.2 in.

Example 4 p. 560 — **The lengths of three sides of a triangle are given. Determine whether each triangle is a right triangle.**

5. $a = 9, b = 12, c = 15$ yes

6. $a = 6, b = 10, c = 12$ no

7. $a = 12, b = 14, c = 20$ no

8. $a = 15, b = 20, c = 25$ yes

Differentiated Instruction BL

Extension After students have mastered the Pythagorean Theorem, have them graph the points (1,2) and (4,6) and connect them with a segment. Ask them to use the Pythagorean Theorem to find the length of the segment. 5 units

Practice and Problem Solving

Step-by-Step Solutions begin on page R11.
Extra Practice begins on page 810.

Example 1 p. 558

Find the length of the hypotenuse of each right triangle. Round to the nearest tenth, if necessary.

9. 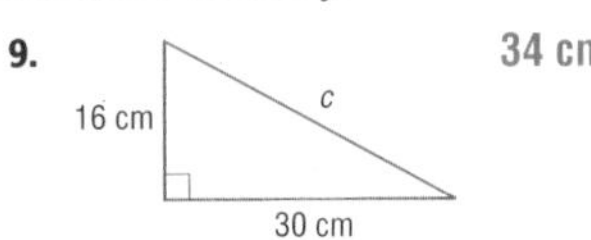

34 cm

10. 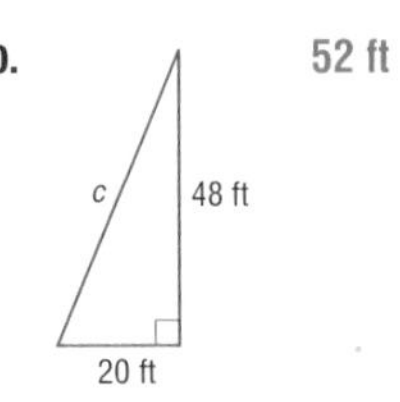

52 ft

11. 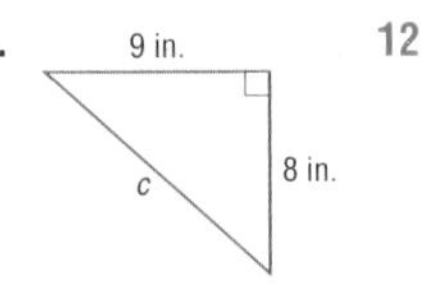

12.0 in.

12. 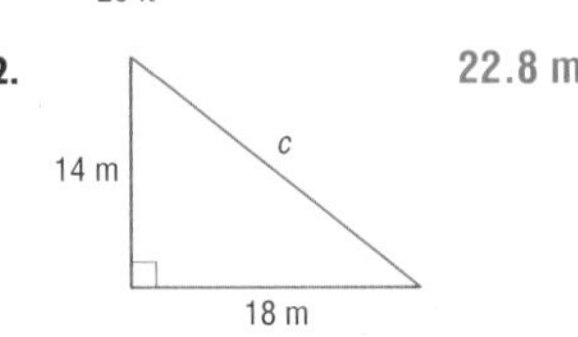

22.8 m

Example 2 p. 559

13. **MAPS** It is 68 miles from Columbia to Augusta and 130 miles from Augusta to Charleston. How many miles is it from Charleston to Columbia to the nearest tenth? 110.8 mi

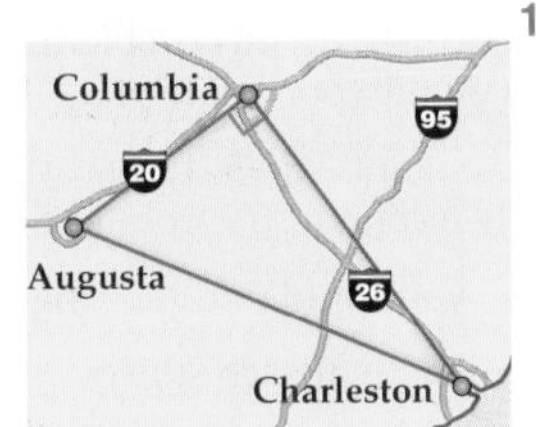

14. **MODELS** Inez is building a model sailboat. How long must she cut a piece of wood to make a brace for the mainsail? 9 in.

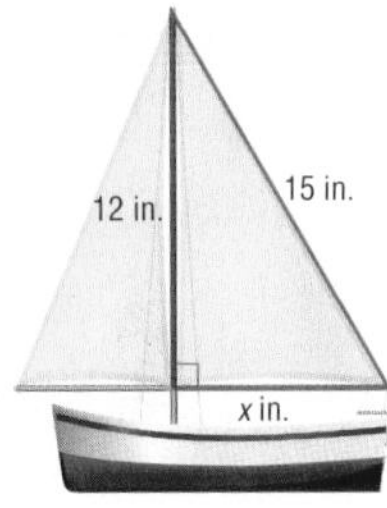

Example 3 p. 559

15 **DESIGN** A square courtyard in the center of an office building measures 35 feet on each side. The designer of the building is constructing a walkway diagonally through the center of the courtyard. What is the length of the walkway to the nearest tenth? 49.5 ft

Example 4 p. 560

The lengths of three sides of a triangle are given. Determine whether each triangle is a right triangle.

16. $a = 4, b = 9, c = 12$ no

17. $a = 7, b = 24, c = 25$ yes

18. $a = 12, b = 16, c = 20$ yes

19. $a = 16, b = 30, c = 32$ no

HOME THEATERS Projection screens for home movie theaters are described according to the measure of the diagonal. Find each missing dimension. Round to the nearest inch.

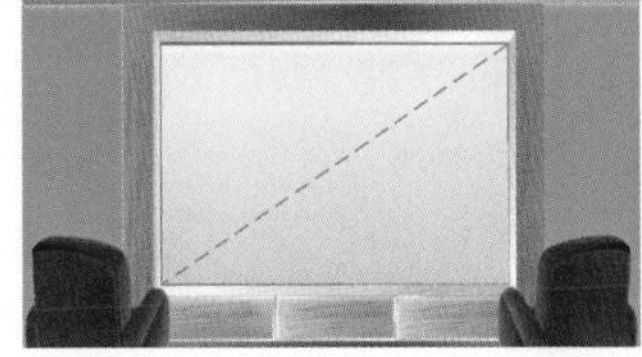

20. A screen is 80 inches long and 45 inches high. What is the diagonal of the screen? 92 in.

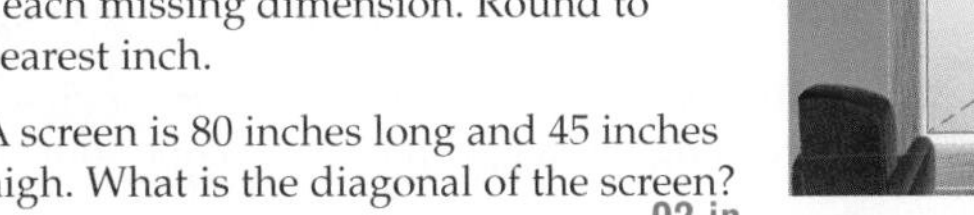

21. An 84-inch screen is 73 inches long. What is the height? 42 in.

22. A 120-inch screen is 59 inches high. What is the length? 104 in.

Tips for New Teachers

PROBLEM SOLVING Suggest that students draw diagrams to help solve problems such as Exercises 3, 4, and 15.

TEACH with TECH

WIKI Assign one student the role of note taker for this lesson. His or her job will be to post the notes on the secure classroom wiki. All other students should read and respond with corrections, additions, and comments.

Differentiated Homework Options

Level	Assignment	Two-Day Option	
AL Basic	9–19, 34, 36–53	9–19 odd, 39–42	10–18 even, 34, 36–38, 43–53
OL Core	9–19 odd, 20–22, 23–31 odd, 32–34, 36–53	9–19, 39–42	20–34, 36–38, 43–53
BL Advanced	20–50 (Optional: 51–53)		

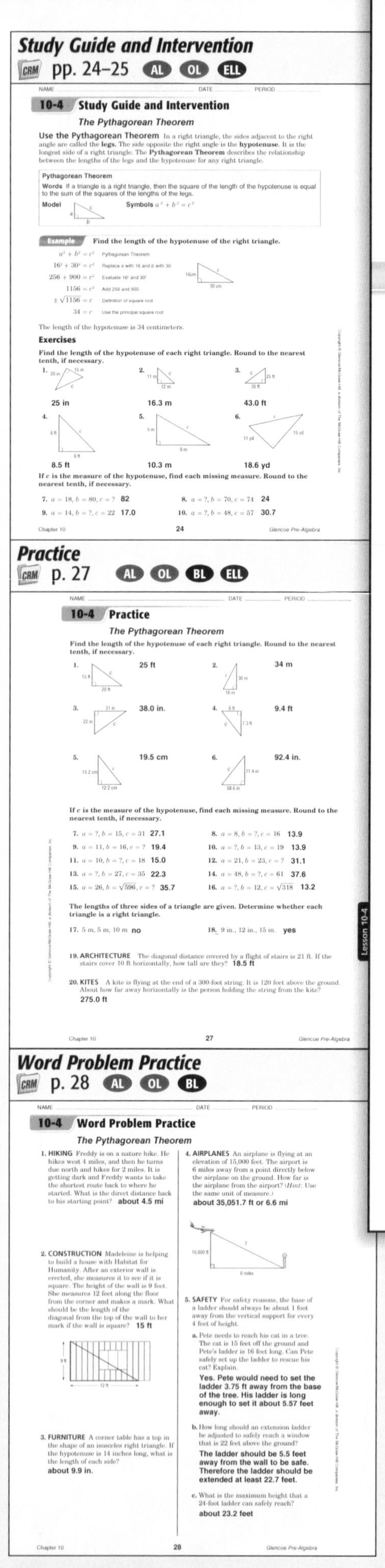

Study Guide and Intervention
CRM pp. 24–25 AL OL ELL

NAME ______ DATE ______ PERIOD ______

10-4 Study Guide and Intervention

The Pythagorean Theorem

Use the Pythagorean Theorem In a right triangle, the sides adjacent to the right angle are called the **legs.** The side opposite the right angle is the **hypotenuse**. It is the longest side of a right triangle. The **Pythagorean Theorem** describes the relationship between the lengths of the legs and the hypotenuse for any right triangle.

Pythagorean Theorem
Words If a triangle is a right triangle, then the square of the length of the hypotenuse is equal to the sum of the squares of the lengths of the legs.
Model **Symbols** $a^2 + b^2 = c^2$

Example **Find the length of the hypotenuse of the right triangle.**

$a^2 + b^2 = c^2$ Pythagorean Theorem
$16^2 + 30^2 = c^2$ Replace a with 16 and b with 30
$256 + 900 = c^2$ Evaluate 16^2 and 30^2
$1156 = c^2$ Add 256 and 900
$\pm\sqrt{1156} = c$ Definition of square root
$34 = c$ Use the principal square root

The length of the hypotenuse is 34 centimeters.

Exercises

Find the length of the hypotenuse of each right triangle. Round to the nearest tenth, if necessary.

1. **25 in** 2. **16.3 m** 3. **43.0 ft**
4. **8.5 ft** 5. **10.3 m** 6. **18.6 yd**

If c is the measure of the hypotenuse, find each missing measure. Round to the nearest tenth, if necessary.

7. $a = 18, b = 80, c = ?$ **82**
8. $a = ?, b = 70, c = 74$ **24**
9. $a = 14, b = ?, c = 22$ **17.0**
10. $a = ?, b = 48, c = 57$ **30.7**

Chapter 10 24 Glencoe Pre-Algebra

Practice
CRM p. 27 AL OL BL ELL

NAME ______ DATE ______ PERIOD ______

10-4 Practice

The Pythagorean Theorem

Find the length of the hypotenuse of each right triangle. Round to the nearest tenth, if necessary.

1. **25 ft** 2. **34 m**
3. **38.0 in.** 4. **9.4 ft**
5. **19.5 cm** 6. **92.4 in.**

If c is the measure of the hypotenuse, find each missing measure. Round to the nearest tenth, if necessary.

7. $a = ?, b = 15, c = 31$ **27.1**
8. $a = 8, b = ?, c = 16$ **13.9**
9. $a = 11, b = 16, c = ?$ **19.4**
10. $a = ?, b = 13, c = 19$ **13.9**
11. $a = 10, b = ?, c = 18$ **15.0**
12. $a = 21, b = 23, c = ?$ **31.1**
13. $a = ?, b = 27, c = 35$ **22.3**
14. $a = 48, b = ?, c = 61$ **37.6**
15. $a = 26, b = \sqrt{596}, c = ?$ **35.7**
16. $a = ?, b = 12, c = \sqrt{318}$ **13.2**

The lengths of three sides of a triangle are given. Determine whether each triangle is a right triangle.

17. 5 m, 5 m, 10 m **no**
18. 9 in., 12 in., 15 in. **yes**

19. **ARCHITECTURE** The diagonal distance covered by a flight of stairs is 21 ft. If the stairs cover 10 ft horizontally, how tall are they? **18.5 ft**

20. **KITES** A kite is flying at the end of a 300-foot string. It is 120 feet above the ground. About how far away horizontally is the person holding the string from the kite? **275.0 ft**

Chapter 10 27 Glencoe Pre-Algebra

Lesson 10-4

Word Problem Practice
CRM p. 28 AL OL BL

NAME ______ DATE ______ PERIOD ______

10-4 Word Problem Practice

The Pythagorean Theorem

1. **HIKING** Freddy is on a nature hike. He hikes west 4 miles, and then he turns due north and hikes for 2 miles. It is getting dark and Freddy wants to take the shortest route back to where he started. What is the direct distance back to his starting point? **about 4.5 mi**

2. **CONSTRUCTION** Madeleine is helping to build a house with Habitat for Humanity. After an exterior wall is erected, she measures it to see if it is square. The height of the wall is 9 feet. She measures 12 feet along the floor from the corner and makes a mark. What should be the length of the diagonal from the top of the wall to her mark if the wall is square? **15 ft**

3. **FURNITURE** A corner table has a top in the shape of an isosceles right triangle. If the hypotenuse is 14 inches long, what is the length of each side? **about 9.9 in.**

4. **AIRPLANES** An airplane is flying at an elevation of 15,000 feet. The airport is 6 miles away from a point directly below the airplane on the ground. How far is the airplane from the airport? (*Hint*: Use the same unit of measure.) **about 35,051.7 ft or 6.6 mi**

5. **SAFETY** For safety reasons, the base of a ladder should always be about 1 foot away from the vertical support for every 4 feet of height.
   a. Pete needs to reach his cat in a tree. The cat is 15 feet off the ground and Pete's ladder is 16 feet long. Can Pete safely set up the ladder to rescue his cat? Explain. **Yes. Pete would need to set the ladder 3.75 ft away from the base of the tree. His ladder is long enough to set it about 5.57 feet away.**
   b. How long should an extension ladder be adjusted to safely reach a window that is 22 feet above the ground? **The ladder should be 5.5 feet away from the wall to be safe. Therefore the ladder should be extended at least 22.7 feet.**
   c. What is the maximum height that a 24-foot ladder can safely reach? **about 23.2 feet**

Chapter 10 28 Glencoe Pre-Algebra

If c is the measure of the hypotenuse, find each missing measure. Round to the nearest tenth, if necessary.

23. $a = 9$ m, $b = ?, c = 12$ m **7.9 m**
24. $a = ?, b = 21$ cm, $c = 35$ cm **28 cm**
25. $a = ?, b = 16$ ft, $c = 29$ ft **24.2 ft**
26. $a = 30$ in., $b = ?, c = 40$ in. **26.5 in.**
27. $a = 8.1$ mi, $b = 3.5$ mi, $c = ?$ **8.8 mi**
28. $a = 10.4$ yd, $b = 16.9$ yd, $c = ?$ **19.8 yd**
29. $a = ?, b = \sqrt{123}$ ft, $c = 22$ ft **19 ft**
30. $a = \sqrt{127}$ m, $b = ?, c = 31$ m **28.9 m**

31. **RECREATION** Parasailing is a popular water activity where a person with a parachute is attached to a boat by a long rope.

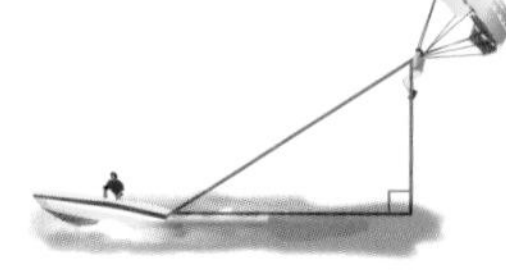

   a. In Myrtle Beach, the maximum height off the water a parasailor can be is 500 feet. If the rope is 800 feet long, about how many feet from the boat is the parasailor to the nearest tenth? **624.5 ft**
   b. In Daytona Beach, parasailors can soar to 2000 feet above the ground. If the parasailor is 1500 feet from the boat, about how long is the rope? **2500 ft**

Real-World Link

There are three main parasailing methods. The most popular method is called Winchboat parasailing. This is where the launch and recovery of the parasailor take place directly on the boat.

Source: Parasailing USA

32. **TRAVEL** Europe's largest town square is the Rynek Glowny located in Krakow, Poland. It covers approximately 48,400 square yards.
   a. How many feet long is a side of the square? **660 ft**
   b. To the nearest foot, what is the diagonal distance across Rynek Glowny? **b. 933 ft**

33. **MULTIPLE REPRESENTATIONS** In this problem, you will investigate the Pythagorean Theorem on the coordinate plane.
   a. **GRAPHICAL** Graph the points $A(-5, 1)$, $B(1, 1)$, and $C(1, -3)$ on a coordinate plane. Then connect the points. **See margin.**
   b. **VERBAL** Explain how you could find the length of segment $\overline{AC}$.
   c. **NUMERICAL** Find the length of each side of $\triangle ABC$ to the nearest tenth.
   d. **NUMERICAL** What are the perimeter and area of $\triangle ABC$? $P = 17.2$ **units,** $A = 12$ **units**^{2}

H.O.T. Problems
Use Higher-Order Thinking Skills

34. **OPEN ENDED** The hypotenuse of a right triangle is 23 centimeters long. Find possible measures for the legs of the triangle. Round to the nearest hundredth. Justify your answer.

35. **CHALLENGE** In the figure, $\overline{BD}$ is the diagonal of the base and $\overline{FD}$ is the diagonal of the figure. Find $\overline{FD}$ to the nearest tenth.

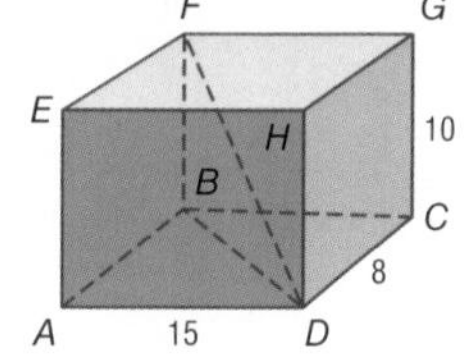

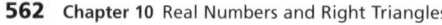

36. **FIND THE ERROR** The legs of a right triangle are 13 and 22 inches. Needa says that the hypotenuse is 17.7 inches long and Monifa says that it is 25.6 inches. Is either of them correct? Explain.

37. **REASONING** Find the length of the legs x of the isosceles right triangle shown. Describe your steps. **See Chapter 10 Answer Appendix.**

38. **WRITING IN MATH** Explain how you can use the measures of a triangle to determine whether a triangle is a right triangle. Give an example. **See Chapter 10 Answer Appendix.**

33b. Sample answer: Find the length of the legs using the units on the coordinate plane. Then use the Pythagorean Theorem to find the length of the hypotenuse.

33c. $\overline{AB} = 6$ units, $\overline{BC} = 4$ units, $AC \approx 7.2$ units

34. Sample answer: 15 cm and 17.44 cm; $23^2 = 529$ and $15^2 + 17.44^2 = 529.1536$. So, $23^2 \approx 15^2 + 17.44^2$.

35. 19.7 units

36. Monifa; Needa incorrectly calculated $22^2 - 13^2$ instead of $22^2 + 13^2$.

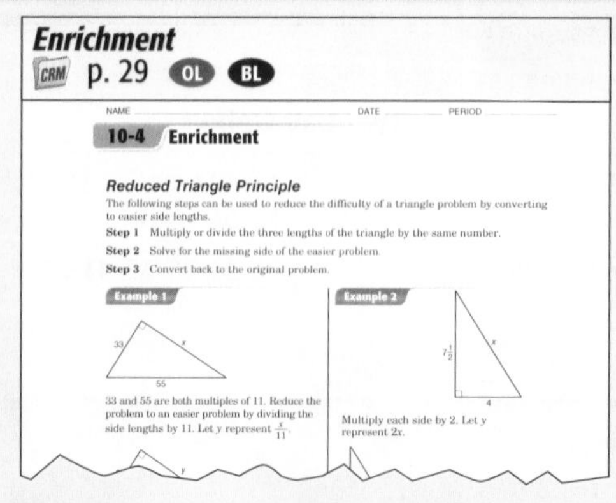

Enrichment
CRM p. 29 OL BL

NAME ______ DATE ______ PERIOD ______

10-4 Enrichment

Reduced Triangle Principle

The following steps can be used to reduce the difficulty of a triangle problem by converting to easier side lengths.

Step 1 Multiply or divide the three lengths of the triangle by the same number.
Step 2 Solve for the missing side of the easier problem.
Step 3 Convert back to the original problem.

Example 1

33 and 55 are both multiples of 11. Reduce the problem to an easier problem by dividing the side lengths by 11. Let y represent $\frac{x}{11}$.

Example 2

Multiply each side by 2. Let y represent $2x$.

Multiple Representations In Exercise 33, students use a graph on the coordinate plane and the Pythagorean Theorem to compute the length of a line segment and the perimeter and area of a triangle.

Standardized Test Practice

39. Find the amount of edging needed to enclose the triangular flower bed. D

A 8 yd
B 12 yd
C 18 yd
D 24 yd

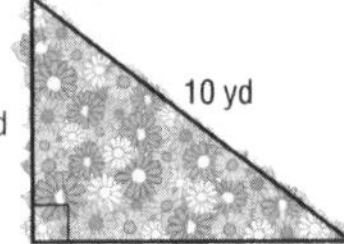

40. SHORT RESPONSE Is the triangle formed by the buildings below a right triangle? Explain your reasoning. See margin.

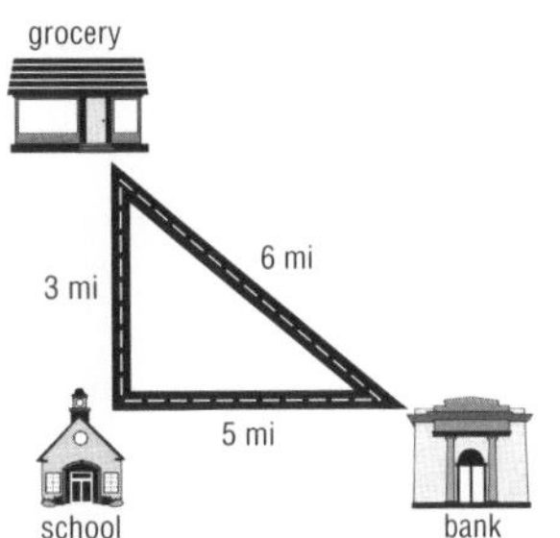

41. Which of the following *cannot* be the measures of sides of a right triangle? G

F 6 cm, 8 cm, 10 cm
G 14 cm, 18 cm, 20 cm
H 10 cm, 24 cm, 26 cm
J 20 cm, 21 cm, 29 cm

42. EXTENDED RESPONSE Use the figure below.

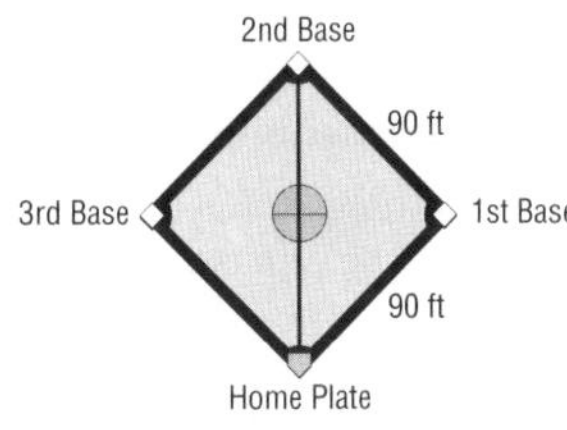

a. Explain how to determine the distance from home plate to second base. See margin.

b. About how many feet is it from home plate to second base? Show and justify all your steps. See Chapter 10 Answer Appendix.

Spiral Review

Find the value of x in each triangle. Then classify each triangle by its angles and by its sides. (Lesson 10-3)

43. 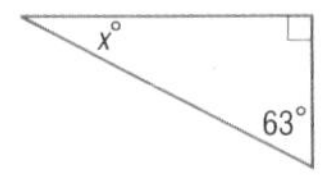

27; right scalene

44. 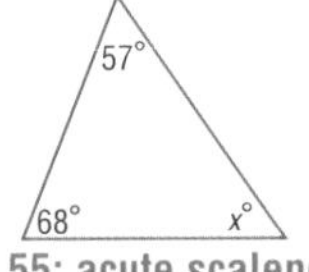

55; acute scalene

45. 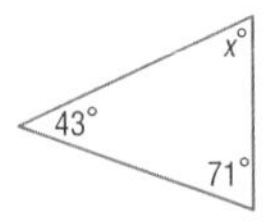

66; acute scalene

Name all of the sets of numbers to which each real number belongs. Write *whole, integer, rational,* or *irrational*. (Lesson 10-2)

46. -5 integer, rational **47.** $0.\overline{4}$ rational **48.** $\sqrt{63}$ irrational **49.** 7.4 rational

50. GRADES Tobias' average for five quizzes is 86. He wants to have an average of at least 88 for six quizzes. What is the lowest score he can receive on his sixth quiz to obtain this average? (Lesson 4-6) 98

Skills Review

Simplify each expression. (Lesson 9-1)

51. $(10 - 3)^2 + (4 - 8)^2$ 65 **52.** $[7 - (-2)]^2 + (5 - 3)^2$ 85 **53.** $(-4 - 6)^2 + (-1 - 5)^2$ 136

Watch Out!

Find the Error For Exercise 36, suggest that students draw a right triangle, label the sides whose lengths are known, and put a question mark for the length of the missing side. They should refer to this diagram to help them determine whether Needa and Monifa used the Pythagorean Theorem correctly.

4 ASSESS

Name the Math Have students describe the Pythagorean Theorem, including examples of when to use it or its converse.

Additional Answers

33a.

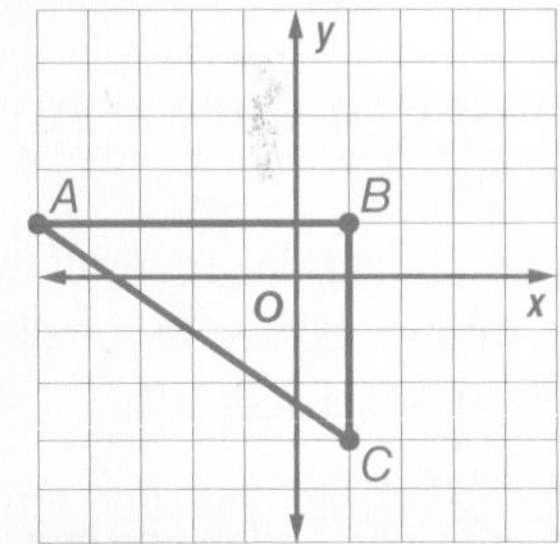

40. No; Sample answer: To be a right triangle, the converse of the Pythagorean Theorem must be true. So, $3^2 + 5^2$ must equal 6^2. Since $3^2 + 5^2 \neq 6^2$, it is not a right triangle.

42a. Sample answer: Use the Pythagorean Theorem to find the distance.

Differentiated Instruction

Extension In a right triangle, the Pythagorean Theorem describes the relationship between the sides as shown in the equation $c^2 = a^2 + b^2$, where c is the hypotenuse. Suppose three girls are tossing a football, each standing at a corner, or vertex, of the triangle shown. Tasha, at point T, is standing 6 feet from Alicia, who is at point A. Carissa is throwing the ball from point C. She is 10 feet away from Alicia. What is the distance between Tasha and Carissa? $\sqrt{136}$ or ≈ 11.7 ft

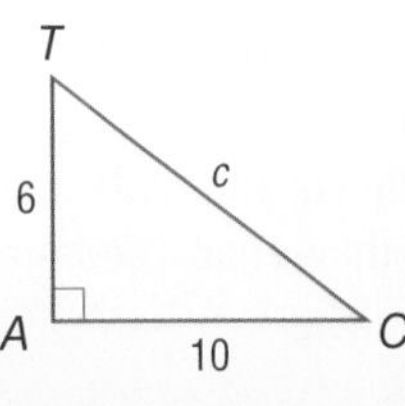

FOCUS

Objective Graph irrational numbers on a number line.

Materials for Each Student

- grid paper
- compass

Easy to Make Manipulatives

Teaching Mathematics with Manipulatives, template for:

- grid paper, p. 1

TEACH

Working in Cooperative Groups

Arrange students in groups of two or three, mixing abilities, to complete the Activity and Exercises 1–4.

Ask:

- How can you find the square root of 17? Find the two numbers whose squares have a sum of 17; $1^2 + 4^2 = 17$. Graph using 4 and 1 as the legs of the triangle. $\sqrt{17} \approx 4.1$
- Why does this work? It works because of the Pythagorean Theorem; the hypotenuse squared is equal to the sum of the legs squared.

Practice Have students complete Exercises 5–6.

ASSESS

Formative Assessment

Use Exercise 5 to assess whether students comprehend how to graph irrational numbers.

EXTEND 10-4 Algebra Lab: Graphing Irrational Numbers

Math Online glencoe.com
Math *in Motion,* Animation

You have already graphed integers and rational numbers on a number line. You can use right triangles to graph irrational numbers like $\sqrt{5}$ or $\sqrt{34}$ on a number line.

ACTIVITY

Graph $\sqrt{34}$ on a number line.

Step 1 Find two square numbers with a sum of 34. Since $34 = 9 + 25$ or $3^2 + 5^2$, you can use the numbers 3 and 5.

Step 2 Use the numbers to draw a right triangle.

- First, draw a number line on grid paper.
- Next, draw a right triangle with legs that measure 3 units and 5 units. Notice that this triangle can be drawn in two ways.

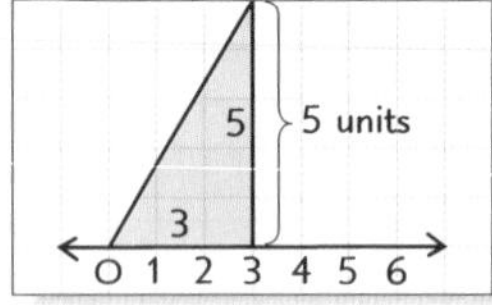

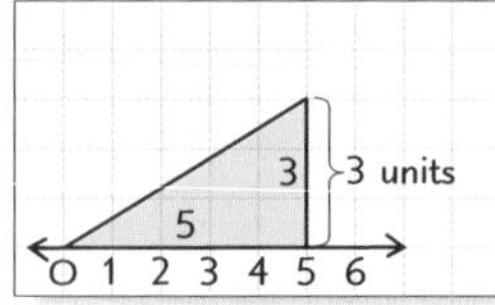

Step 3 Graph $\sqrt{34}$.

- Open your compass to the length of the hypotenuse.
- With the tip of the compass at 0, draw an arc that intersects the number line. Label the intersection point *A*.
- The distance from 0 to *A* is $\sqrt{34}$ units. From the graphs, $\sqrt{34} \approx 5.8$.

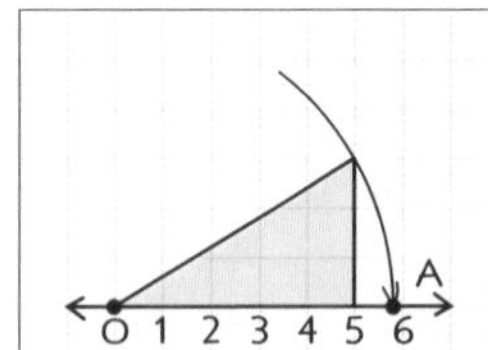

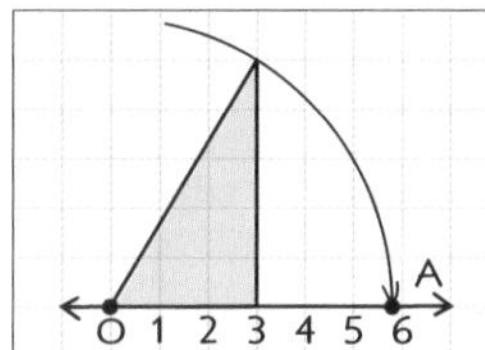

Analyze the Results 1–6. See Chapter 10 Answer Appendix.

Use a compass and grid paper to graph each irrational number on a number line.

1. $\sqrt{5}$
2. $\sqrt{20}$
3. $\sqrt{97}$
4. $\sqrt{45}$
5. Describe two different ways to graph $\sqrt{61}$.
6. Explain how the graph of $\sqrt{2}$ can be used to locate the graph of $\sqrt{3}$.

From Concrete to Abstract

Have students draw the lengths of the legs of the right triangle and pass their incomplete triangle to another student. That student will finish the triangle and write an equation, using the Pythagorean Theorem, that represents the triangle.

Extending the Concept

Ask:

- What is the hypotenuse length, to the nearest tenth, of an isosceles right triangle whose legs measure 4 units? $\sqrt{32} \approx 5.7$ units

10-5 The Distance Formula

10-5 Lesson Notes

Why?

Dakota is biking on the trail shown on the map at the right. His brother timed his ride from point B to point A.

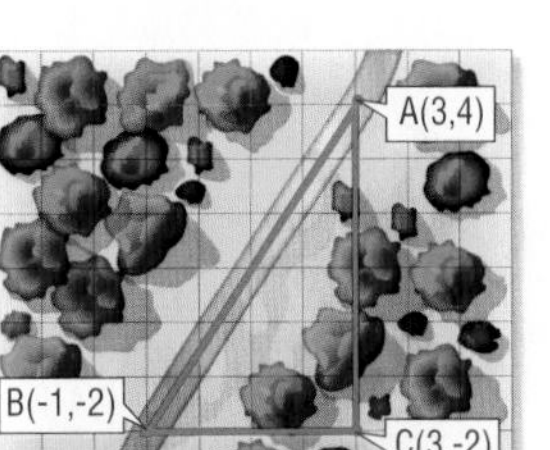

a. What type of triangle is formed by points A, B, and C? **right scalene**

b. How can you find the length of $\overline{BC}$ without counting the number of grids? $\overline{AC}$?

c. How can you find the distance between points A and B? **Use the Pythagorean Theorem; $4^2 + 6^2 = (AB)^2$; $AB = \sqrt{52}$ or about 7.2**

b. **Subtract the x-coordinates; subtract the y-coordinates**

Find the Distance between Points The figure above shows that you can find the distance between points A and B by drawing a right triangle. You can also use the **Distance Formula**, which is based on the Pythagorean Theorem.

Then
You found the slope of a line passing through two points on a coordinate plane. (Lesson 8-6)

Now
- Use the Distance Formula to find the distance between two points on a coordinate plane.
- Apply the Distance Formula to solve problems about figures on the coordinate plane.

New Vocabulary
Distance Formula

Math Online
glencoe.com
- Extra Examples
- Personal Tutor
- Self-Check Quiz
- Homework Help

Key Concept — Distance Formula

For Your FOLDABLE

Symbols The distance d between two points with coordinates (x_1, y_1) and (x_2, y_2) is given by $d = \sqrt{(x_2 - x_1)^2 + (y_2 - y_1)^2}$.

Model
(x_2, y_2), (x_1, y_1), O, x, y

EXAMPLE 1 Find the Distance Between Two Points

Find the distance between $A(-2, 1)$ and $B(4, 3)$.

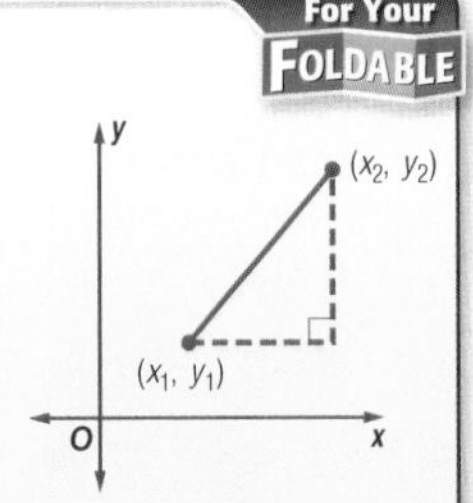

$d = \sqrt{(x_2 - x_1)^2 + (y_2 - y_1)^2}$	**Distance Formula**
$AB = \sqrt{[4 - (-2)]^2 + (3 - 1)^2}$	$(x_1, y_1) = (-2, 1)$, $(x_2, y_2) = (4, 3)$
$AB = \sqrt{6^2 + 2^2}$	**Simplify.**
$AB = \sqrt{36 + 4}$	**Evaluate 6^2 and 2^2.**
$AB = \sqrt{40}$	**Add 36 and 4.**
$AB \approx 6.3$	**Simplify.**

So, the distance between points A and B is about 6.3 units.

Check Your Progress

1. Find the distance between $F(5, -6)$ and $G(1, 2)$. Round to the nearest tenth, if necessary. **8.9 units**

Personal Tutor glencoe.com

StudyTip

Midpoint To find the coordinates of the midpoint of a line segment, use the formula $M = \left(\frac{x_1 + x_2}{2}, \frac{y_1 + y_2}{2}\right)$. The midpoint of $\overline{AB}$ in Example 1 is at the point $\left(\frac{-2 + 4}{2}, \frac{1 + 3}{2}\right)$ or (1, 2).

1 FOCUS

Vertical Alignment

Before Lesson 10-5
Find the slope of a line passing through two points on a coordinate plane.

Lesson 10-5
Use the Distance Formula to find the distance between two points on a coordinate plane. Apply the Distance Formula to solve problems about figures on the coordinate plane.

After Lesson 10-5
Derive and use formulas involving length, slope, and midpoint.

2 TEACH

Scaffolding Questions

Have students read the *Why?* section of the lesson and answer the questions.

Ask:
- How do you know which coordinates to subtract to find $\overline{BC}$? $\overline{BC}$ lies along the x-axis, so subtract the x-coordinates.
- How do you know which coordinates to subtract to find $\overline{AC}$? $\overline{AC}$ lies along the y-axis, so subtract the y-coordinates.
- Why can you use the Pythagorean Theorem to find the distance between A and B? $\triangle ABC$ is a right triangle.

Lesson 10-5 Resources

Resource	Approaching-Level	On-Level	Beyond-Level	English Learners
Teacher Edition	• Differentiated Instruction, p. 566	• Differentiated Instruction, p. 566	• Differentiated Instruction, p. 570	
Chapter Resource Masters	• Study Guide and Intervention, pp. 30–31 • Skills Practice, p. 32 • Practice, p. 33 • Word Problem Practice, p. 34	• Study Guide and Intervention, pp. 30–31 • Skills Practice, p. 32 • Practice, p. 33 • Word Problem Practice, p. 34 • Enrichment, p. 35	• Practice, p. 33 • Word Problem Practice, p. 34 • Enrichment, p. 35	• Study Guide and Intervention, pp. 30–31 • Skills Practice, p. 32 • Practice, p. 33
Transparencies	• 5-Minute Check Transparency 10-5	• 5-Minute Check Transparency 10-5	• 5-Minute Check Transparency 10-5	• 5-Minute Check Transparency 10-5
Other	• Study Notebook • Teaching Pre-Algebra with Manipulatives	• Study Notebook • Teaching Pre-Algebra with Manipulatives	• Study Notebook	• Study Notebook • Teaching Pre-Algebra with Manipulatives

Find the Distance Between Points

Examples 1 and 2 show how to find the distance between two points using the Distance Formula.

Use the Check Your Progress exercises after each example to determine students' understanding of concepts.

Additional Examples

1 Find the distance between $M(8, 4)$ and $N(-6, -2)$. Round to the nearest tenth, if necessary. 15.2 units

2 **SOCCER** Javy kicks a ball from a position that is 2 yards behind the goal line and 4 yards from the sideline $(-2, 4)$. The ball lands 8 yards past the goal line and 2 yards from the same sideline $(8, 2)$. What distance, to the nearest tenth, was the ball kicked? 10.2 yd

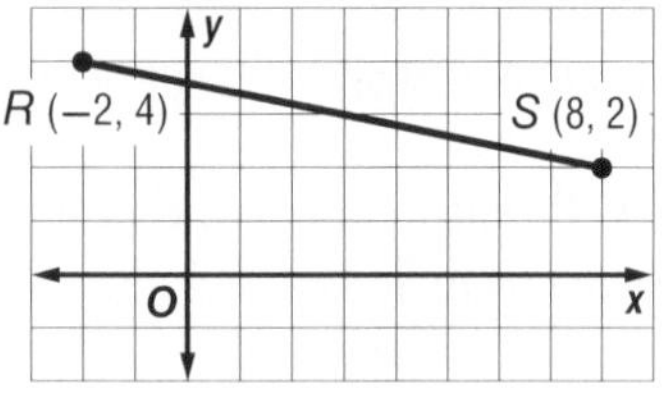

Additional Examples also in Interactive Classroom PowerPoint® Presentations

IWB INTERACTIVE WHITEBOARD READY

Real-World Link

The District of Columbia is 67 square miles and is divided into four quadrants. The U.S. Capitol building is at the point where the quadrants meet. Numbered streets run north and south. Lettered streets run east and west.

Source: Washington, D.C., Convention and Tourism Corp.

Real-World EXAMPLE 2 Use the Distance Formula

RECREATION The Yeager family is visiting Washington, D.C. One unit on the coordinate system of their map is 0.05 mile. Find the distance between the Department of Defense at (−2, 9) and the Madison Building at (3, −3).

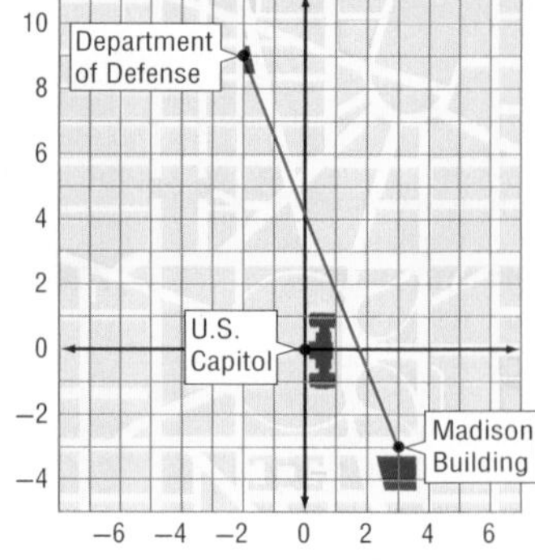

Understand You know the coordinates of the two locations and that each unit represents 0.05 mile You need to find the distance between the two points.

Plan Use the Distance Formula to find the distance between the two points. Then multiply to find the distance in miles.

Solve

$d = \sqrt{(x_2 - x_1)^2 + (y_2 - y_1)^2}$	Distance Formula
$d = \sqrt{[3 - (-2)]^2 + (-3 - 9)^2}$	$(x_1, y_1) = (-2, 9), (x_2, y_2) = (3, -3)$
$d = \sqrt{5^2 + (-12)^2}$	Simplify.
$d = \sqrt{25 + 144}$	Evaluate 5^2 and $(-12)^2$.
$d = \sqrt{169}$	Add 25 and 144.
$d = 13$	Simplify.

The distance between the two buildings is 13 units on the map. Since each unit is equal to 0.05 mile, the distance between the two buildings is 0.05 · 13 or 0.65 mile.

Check The distance is slightly greater than 12 units or 0.6 mile. So, the answer is reasonable. ✓

Check Your Progress

2. **RECREATION** Find the distance between the Madison Building at (3, −3) and the U.S. Capitol at (0, 0) to the nearest hundredth. **0.21 mi**

Personal Tutor glencoe.com

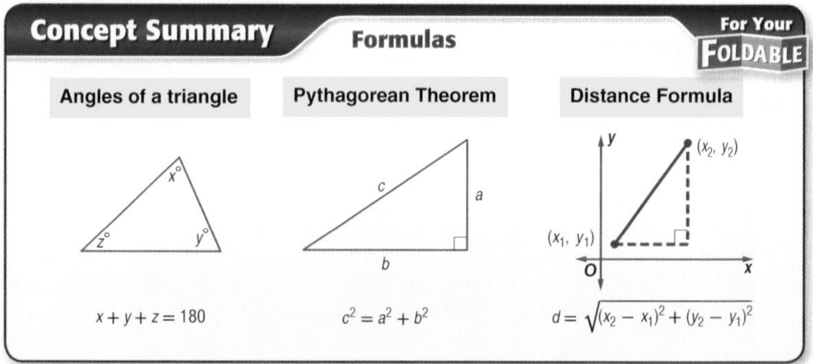

Concept Summary
Formulas
For Your FOLDABLE
Angles of a triangle
Pythagorean Theorem
Distance Formula
x + y + z = 180
c² = a² + b²
d = √((x₂ − x₁)² + (y₂ − y₁)²)

Differentiated Instruction AL OL

 students struggle with using the Distance Formula,

 using masking tape, lay out a grid on the floor in the gymnasium or classroom. Mark the origin and axes with different colored tape. Have each student choose a spot on the grid and determine its coordinates. Then have students find the distance between themselves and three other classmates. Use ropes marked off in grid units to check the answers.

Apply the Distance Formula If you know the coordinates of points of a figure, you can draw conclusions and solve real-world problems on the coordinate plane.

EXAMPLE 3 Find the Perimeter

GEOMETRY Classify $\triangle JKL$ by its sides. Then find its perimeter to the nearest tenth.

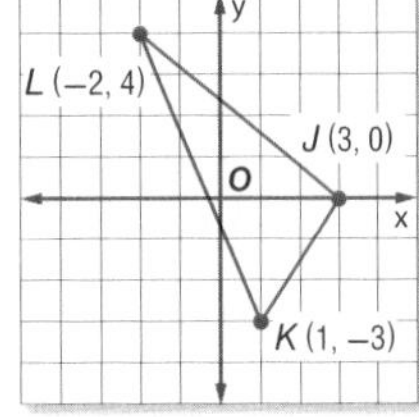

Step 1 Use the Distance Formula to find the length of each side of the triangle.

Side $\overline{JK}$

$\overline{JK}$ has endpoints $J(3, 0)$ and $K(1, -3)$.

$d = \sqrt{(x_2 - x_1)^2 + (y_2 - y_1)^2}$

$JK = \sqrt{(1 - 3)^2 + (-3 - 0)^2}$

$JK = \sqrt{(-2)^2 + (-3)^2}$

$JK = \sqrt{4 + 9}$ or $\sqrt{13}$

Side $\overline{KL}$

$\overline{KL}$ has endpoints $K(1, -3)$ and $L(-2, 4)$.

$d = \sqrt{(x_2 - x_1)^2 + (y_2 - y_1)^2}$

$KL = \sqrt{(-2 - 1)^2 + [4 - (-3)]^2}$

$KL = \sqrt{(-3)^2 + 7^2}$

$KL = \sqrt{9 + 49}$ or $\sqrt{58}$

Side $\overline{LJ}$

$\overline{LJ}$ has endpoints $L(-2, 4)$ and $J(3, 0)$.

$d = \sqrt{(x_2 - x_1)^2 + (y_2 - y_1)^2}$

$LJ = \sqrt{[3 - (-2)]^2 + (0 - 4)^2}$

$LJ = \sqrt{5^2 + (-4)^2}$

$LJ = \sqrt{25 + 16}$ or $\sqrt{41}$

None of the sides are congruent. So, $\triangle JKL$ is scalene.

Step 2 Round each side length to the nearest tenth. Then add the lengths of the sides to find the perimeter.

$$JK + KL + LJ = \sqrt{13} + \sqrt{58} + \sqrt{41}$$
$$\approx 3.6 + 7.6 + 6.4$$
$$\approx 17.6$$

The perimeter is about 17.6 units.

Check Your Progress

3. **GEOMETRY** Classify $\triangle XYZ$ with vertices $X(-2, 8)$, $Y(-3, 1)$, and $Z(3, 3)$ by its sides. Then find its perimeter to the nearest tenth. **isosceles; 20.5 units**

Personal Tutor glencoe.com

StudyTip

Substitution You can use either point as (x_1, y_1). The distance will be the same.

Watch Out!

To simplify the sum of square roots, do not add the numbers inside the square root symbol. Simplify first, then add the rounded numbers.

Apply the Distance Formula

Example 3 uses the Distance Formula to find the perimeter of a triangle.

Additional Example

3 **GEOMETRY** Classify $\triangle XYZ$ by its sides. Then find its perimeter to the nearest tenth. scalene; 15.8 units

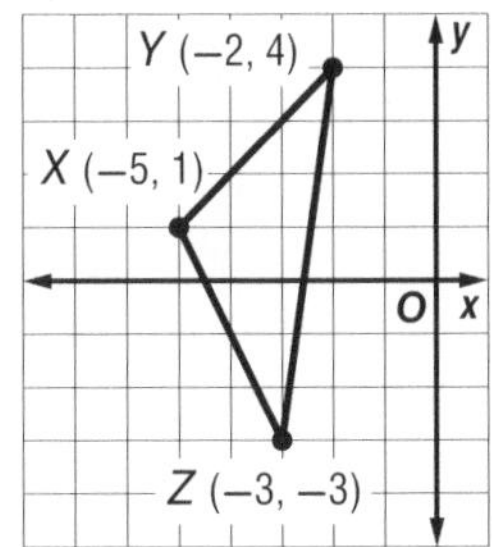

Tips for New Teachers

Endpoints Point out to students that given two points, it is always possible to make them the endpoints of the hypotenuse of a right triangle.

Focus on Mathematical Content

Distance and the Pythagorean Theorem The Pythagorean Theorem describes the relationship between sides of a right triangle: $c^2 = a^2 + b^2$. In the Distance Formula, the lengths of the legs, a and b, are represented on a coordinate plane as the difference between two coordinates. The hypotenuse, c, is represented by the distance, d, in the formula.

3 PRACTICE

Formative Assessment

Use Exercises 1–5 to check for understanding.

Use the chart at the bottom of this page to customize assignments for your students.

Additional Answers

29. Mental math; Sample answer: the cup is located at (0, 0) on a coordinate system with points at (-2, -3) and (1, 4). You can use mental math to find the distance between the cup and the two balls; $\sqrt{(-2)^2 + (-3)^2} = \sqrt{13}$; $\sqrt{(1)^2 + (4)^2} = \sqrt{17}$. Since $\sqrt{13} < \sqrt{17}$, Joan's ball is closer to the cup.

30a–b.

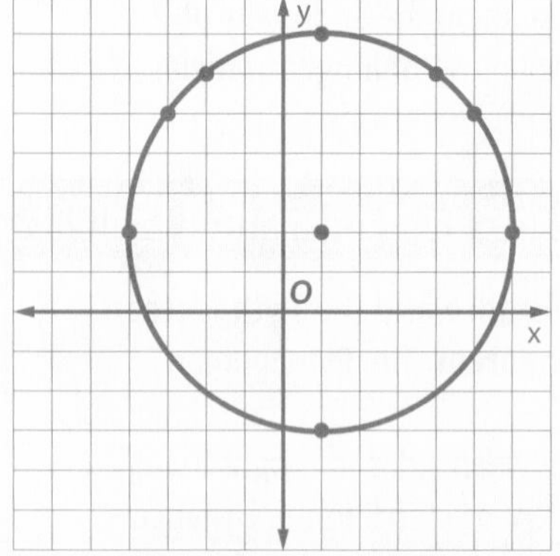

30c. A circle; Sample answer: All of the points are 5 units away from (1, 2). Since all the points are the same distance from a given point, a circle is formed.

Check Your Understanding

Example 1 p. 565

Find the distance between each pair of points. Round to the nearest tenth, if necessary.

1. $G(1, 5)$, $H(9, 5)$ **8**
2. $R(0, -4)$, $S(-2, 6)$ **10.2**

Example 2 p. 566

3. **ARCHAEOLOGY** An archaeologist creates a coordinate plane to record where artifacts were discovered. A unit on the grid represents 5 feet. Find the distance between two artifacts if one artifact was found at (−3, 1) and the other was found at (−6, −5) on the grid. Round to the nearest tenth. **33.5 ft**

Example 3 p. 567

4. **GEOMETRY** Classify $\triangle MNP$ shown at the right by its sides. Then find its perimeter. Round to the nearest tenth. **scalene; 17.7**

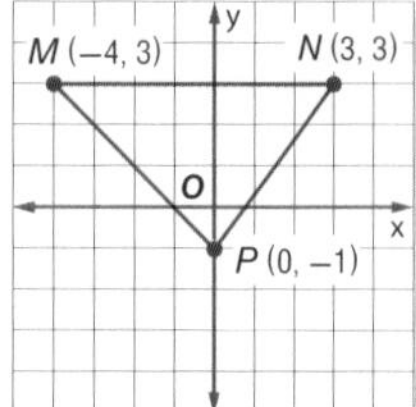

5. **GEOMETRY** Classify $\triangle ABC$ with vertices $A(4, 0)$, $B(-1, 6)$, and $C(7, -2)$ by its sides. Then find its perimeter to the nearest tenth. **scalene; 22.7**

Practice and Problem Solving

= **Step-by-Step Solutions** begin on page R11. **Extra Practice** begins on page 810.

Example 1 p. 565

Find the distance between each pair of points. Round to the nearest tenth, if necessary.

6. $F(1, 3)$, $G(6, 3)$ **5**
7. $C(5, 1)$, $D(8, 4)$ **4.2**
8. $H(-3, -1)$, $J(8, 0)$ **11**
9. $L(-2, 2)$, $M(4, 7)$ **7.8**
10. $A(-2, 7)$, $B(0, 5)$ **2.8**
11. $P(9, -3)$, $Q(4, 4)$ **8.6**

Example 2 p. 566

12. **MAPS** Ashland, Kentucky, has a longitude of 82° W and a latitude of 38° N. Bowling Green, Kentucky, is located at 86° W and 35° N. Each degree is about 46.6 miles at this longitude/latitude. Find the distance between Ashland and Bowling Green. **233 mi**

13. **AIRPORTS** A distance of 3 units on a coordinate plane equals an actual distance of 1 mile. The locations of two airports on a map are at (121, 145) and (218, 401). Find the actual distance between these airports to the nearest mile. **91 mi**

Example 3 p. 567

GEOMETRY Classify each triangle by its sides. Then find the perimeter of each triangle. Round to the nearest tenth.

14. 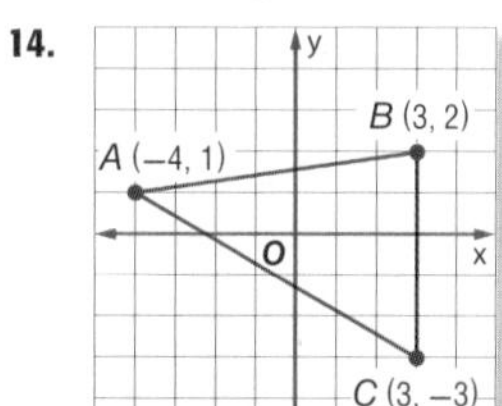

scalene; 20.2

15. 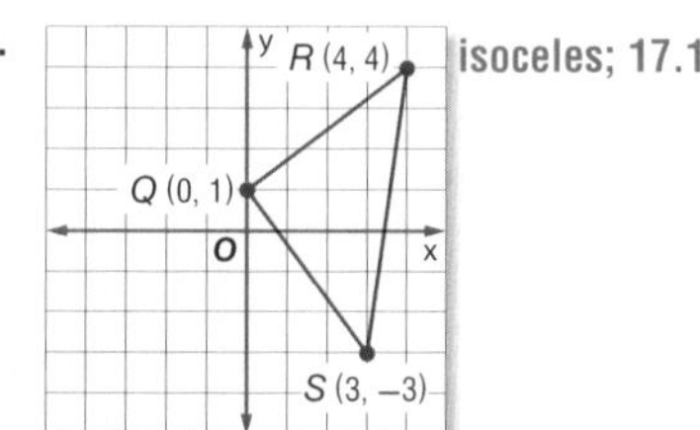

isoceles; 17.1

B

16. $H(-4, 8)$, $J(1, 5)$, $K(-4, 1)$ **scalene; 19.2**
17. $L(0, 7)$, $M(3, -4)$, $N(-6, -7)$ **scalene; 36.1**

Differentiated Homework Options

Level	Assignment	Two-Day Option	
AL Basic	6–17, 27, 29, 31–42	7–17 odd, 32–35	6–16 even, 27, 29, 31, 36–42
OL Core	7–17 odd, 18, 19, 21–23, 25, 27, 29, 31–42	6–17, 32–35	18–27, 29, 31, 36–42
BL Advanced	18–39 (optional: 40–42)		

Park Ranger
Responsibilities for a ranger in a nature park may include using maps to maintain trails. The coordinate plane is involved in the process of using maps.

This career may require a 4-year degree in parks management, or natural sciences.

18. **PARKS** Rosa is looking at a map of the park that is laid out on a coordinate system. Rosa is at (1, −1). The shelter house is at (−2, −4) and the fossil exhibit is at (3, 2). Is Rosa closer to the shelter house or the fossil exhibit? **fossil exhibit**

19. **RECREATION** Darnell's first dart lands 2 inches to the right and 7 inches below the bull's-eye. What is the distance between the bull's-eye and where his first shot hit the target? Round to the nearest tenth of an inch. **7.3 in.**

Find the area of each rectangle.

20. 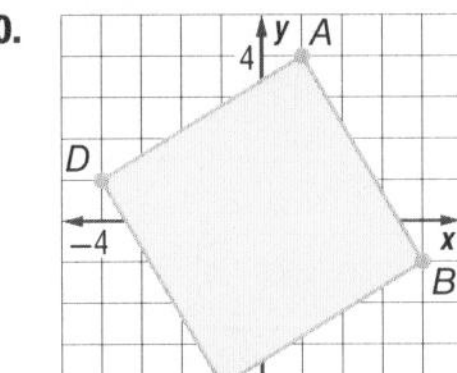

34 square units

21. 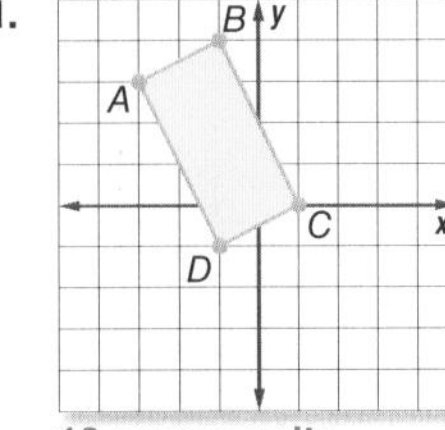

10 square units

22. **RECREATION** Tomas is hiking the Appalachian Trail in Pennsylvania between Hamburg and Harrisburg at an average rate of 4 miles per hour. Hamburg is located at 40.56°N and 76.01°W, while Harrisburg is located at 40.30°N and 76.84°W. At this longitude/latitude, each degree is about 57.8 miles. Find about how long it will take him to hike the trail. **12.6 h**

C

Find the distance between each pair of points. Round to the nearest tenth, if necessary.

23. $Q\left(5\frac{1}{4}, 3\right), R\left(2, 6\frac{1}{2}\right)$ **4.8**

24. $A\left(-2\frac{1}{2}, 0\right), B\left(-8\frac{3}{4}, -6\frac{1}{4}\right)$ **8.8**

25. $S(6.5, 3.2), T(-5.1, 9.3)$ **13.1**

26. $N(-0.4, -4.8), P(1.8, -8.8)$ **4.6**

H.O.T. Problems

Use **H**igher-**O**rder **T**hinking Skills

27. **OPEN ENDED** Name the coordinates of the endpoints of a line segment that is neither horizontal nor vertical and has a length of 5 units.

28. **CHALLENGE** Find x if the distance between (1, 2) and (x, 7) is 13 units. **−11 or 13**

29. **REASONING** In a golf tournament, Joan's ball landed 2 feet to the left and 3 feet short of the cup. Carolina's ball landed 1 foot to the right and 4 feet beyond the cup. Which of the following techniques would you use to determine who is closer to the cup? Justify your selection(s). Then use the technique(s) to solve the problem. **See margin.**

mental math	number sense	estimation

30. **CHALLENGE** Plot the point (1, 2) on the coordinate plane. **a–c. See margin.**
    a. Graph eight points that are 5 units away from (1, 2) on the plane.
    b. Connect the points with a smooth curve.
    c. What figure is formed? Explain.

31. **WRITING IN MATH** Compare the steps for using the Pythagorean Theorem and for using the Distance Formula to find the distance between two points on the coordinate plane.

27. Sample answer: (1, 3) and (5, 6)

31. Sample answer: To use the Pythagorean Theorem, connect the points. Then draw vertical and horizontal lines so that a right triangle is formed. Determine the lengths of the legs. Then use the Pythagorean Theorem formula to find the length of the hypotenuse. To use the Distance Formula, replace (x_1, y_1) and (x_2, y_2) in the formula with the coordinates of the two points. Then simplify.

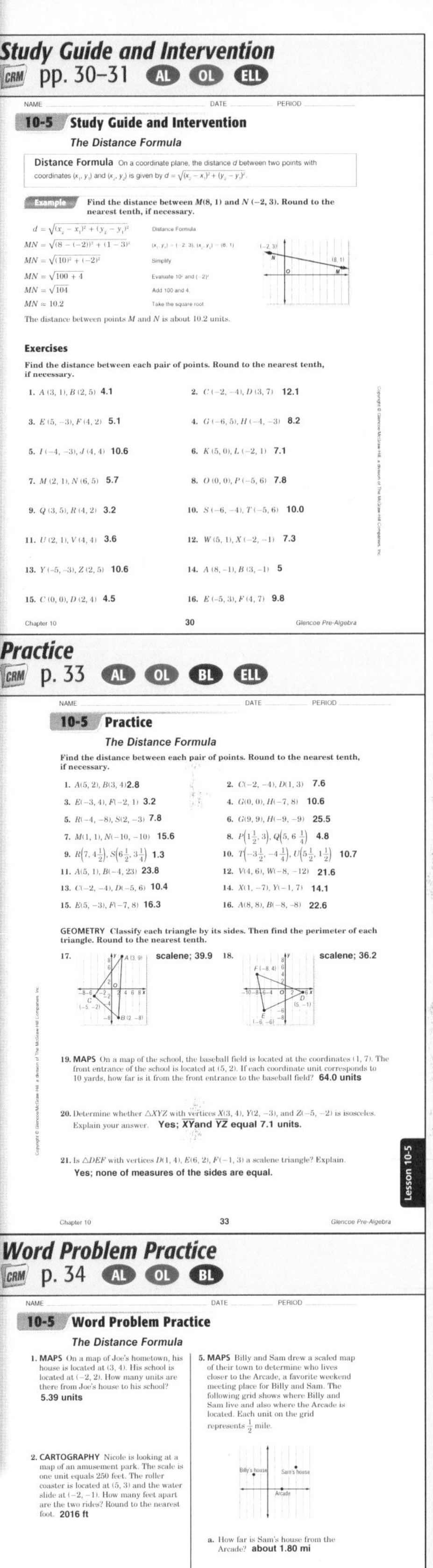

Study Guide and Intervention
CRM pp. 30–31 AL OL ELL

NAME ______ DATE ______ PERIOD ______

10-5 Study Guide and Intervention

The Distance Formula

Distance Formula On a coordinate plane, the distance d between two points with coordinates (x_1, y_1) and (x_2, y_2) is given by $d = \sqrt{(x_2 - x_1)^2 + (y_2 - y_1)^2}$.

Example Find the distance between $M(8, 1)$ and $N(-2, 3)$. Round to the nearest tenth, if necessary.

$d = \sqrt{(x_2 - x_1)^2 + (y_2 - y_1)^2}$ Distance Formula

$MN = \sqrt{(8 - (-2))^2 + (1 - 3)^2}$ $(x_1, y_1) = (-2, 3), (x_2, y_2) = (8, 1)$

$MN = \sqrt{(10)^2 + (-2)^2}$ Simplify

$MN = \sqrt{100 + 4}$ Evaluate 10^2 and $(-2)^2$

$MN = \sqrt{104}$ Add 100 and 4

$MN \approx 10.2$ Take the square root

The distance between points M and N is about 10.2 units.

Exercises

Find the distance between each pair of points. Round to the nearest tenth, if necessary.

1. $A(3, 1), B(2, 5)$ **4.1**
2. $C(-2, -4), D(3, 7)$ **12.1**
3. $E(5, -3), F(4, 2)$ **5.1**
4. $G(-6, 5), H(-4, -3)$ **8.2**
5. $I(-4, -3), J(4, 4)$ **10.6**
6. $K(5, 0), L(-2, 1)$ **7.1**
7. $M(2, 1), N(6, 5)$ **5.7**
8. $O(0, 0), P(-5, 6)$ **7.8**
9. $Q(3, 5), R(4, 2)$ **3.2**
10. $S(-6, -4), T(-5, 6)$ **10.0**
11. $U(2, 1), V(4, 4)$ **3.6**
12. $W(5, 1), X(-2, -1)$ **7.3**
13. $Y(-5, -3), Z(2, 5)$ **10.6**
14. $A(8, -1), B(3, -1)$ **5**
15. $C(0, 0), D(2, 4)$ **4.5**
16. $E(-5, 3), F(4, 7)$ **9.8**

Chapter 10 30 Glencoe Pre-Algebra

Practice
CRM p. 33 AL OL BL ELL

NAME ______ DATE ______ PERIOD ______

10-5 Practice

The Distance Formula

Find the distance between each pair of points. Round to the nearest tenth, if necessary.

1. $A(5, 2), B(3, 4)$ **2.8**
2. $C(-2, -4), D(1, 3)$ **7.6**
3. $E(-3, 4), F(-2, 1)$ **3.2**
4. $G(0, 0), H(-7, 8)$ **10.6**
5. $R(-4, -8), S(2, -3)$ **7.8**
6. $G(9, 9), H(-9, -9)$ **25.5**
7. $M(1, 1), N(-10, -10)$ **15.6**
8. $P\left(1\frac{1}{2}, 3\right), Q\left(5, 6\frac{1}{4}\right)$ **4.8**
9. $R\left(7, 4\frac{1}{2}\right), S\left(6\frac{1}{2}, 3\frac{1}{4}\right)$ **1.3**
10. $T\left(-3\frac{1}{2}, -4\frac{1}{4}\right), U\left(5\frac{1}{2}, 1\frac{1}{2}\right)$ **10.7**
11. $A(5, 1), B(-4, 23)$ **23.8**
12. $V(4, 6), W(-8, -12)$ **21.6**
13. $C(-2, -4), D(-5, 6)$ **10.4**
14. $X(1, -7), Y(-1, 7)$ **14.1**
15. $E(5, -3), F(-7, 8)$ **16.3**
16. $A(8, 8), B(-8, -8)$ **22.6**

GEOMETRY Classify each triangle by its sides. Then find the perimeter of each triangle. Round to the nearest tenth.

17. $A(3, 9)$, $B(2, -8)$, $C(-5, -2)$ **scalene; 39.9**

18. $F(-8, 4)$, $D(5, -1)$, $E(-6, -6)$ **scalene; 36.2**

19. **MAPS** On a map of the school, the baseball field is located at the coordinates (1, 7). The front entrance of the school is located at (5, 2). If each coordinate unit corresponds to 10 yards, how far is it from the front entrance to the baseball field? **64.0 units**

20. Determine whether $\triangle XYZ$ with vertices $X(3, 4)$, $Y(2, -3)$, and $Z(-5, -2)$ is isosceles. Explain your answer. **Yes; $\overline{XY}$ and $\overline{YZ}$ equal 7.1 units.**

21. Is $\triangle DEF$ with vertices $D(1, 4)$, $E(6, 2)$, $F(-1, 3)$ a scalene triangle? Explain. **Yes; none of measures of the sides are equal.**

Chapter 10 33 Glencoe Pre-Algebra

Lesson 10-5

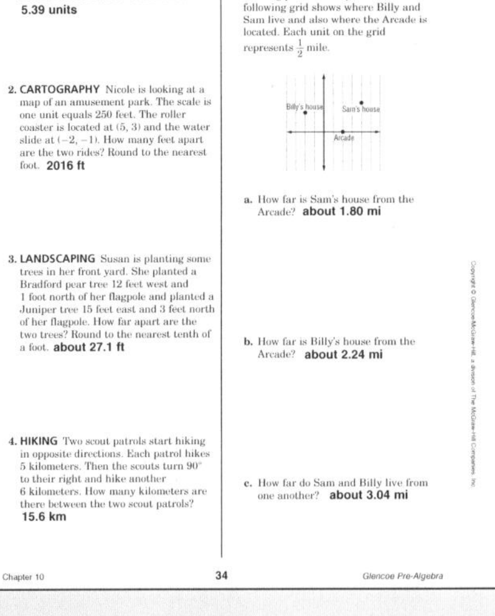

Word Problem Practice
CRM p. 34 AL OL BL

NAME ______ DATE ______ PERIOD ______

10-5 Word Problem Practice

The Distance Formula

1. **MAPS** On a map of Joe's hometown, his house is located at (3, 4). His school is located at (−2, 2). How many units are there from Joe's house to his school? **5.39 units**

2. **CARTOGRAPHY** Nicole is looking at a map of an amusement park. The scale is one unit equals 250 feet. The roller coaster is located at (5, 3) and the water slide at (−2, −1). How many feet apart are the two rides? Round to the nearest foot. **2016 ft**

3. **LANDSCAPING** Susan is planting some trees in her front yard. She planted a Bradford pear tree 12 feet west and 1 foot north of her flagpole and planted a Juniper tree 15 feet east and 3 feet north of her flagpole. How far apart are the two trees? Round to the nearest tenth of a foot. **about 27.1 ft**

4. **HIKING** Two scout patrols start hiking in opposite directions. Each patrol hikes 5 kilometers. Then the scouts turn 90° to their right and hike another 6 kilometers. How many kilometers are there between the two scout patrols? **15.6 km**

5. **MAPS** Billy and Sam drew a scaled map of their town to determine who lives closer to the Arcade, a favorite weekend meeting place for Billy and Sam. The following grid shows where Billy and Sam live and also where the Arcade is located. Each unit on the grid represents $\frac{1}{2}$ mile.

Billy's house — Sam's house — Arcade

a. How far is Sam's house from the Arcade? **about 1.80 mi**

b. How far is Billy's house from the Arcade? **about 2.24 mi**

c. How far do Sam and Billy live from one another? **about 3.04 mi**

Chapter 10 34 Glencoe Pre-Algebra

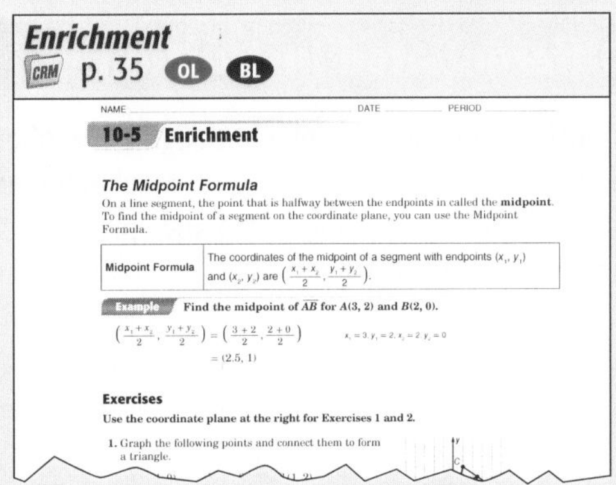

Enrichment
CRM p. 35 OL BL

NAME ______ DATE ______ PERIOD ______

10-5 Enrichment

The Midpoint Formula

On a line segment, the point that is halfway between the endpoints in called the **midpoint**. To find the midpoint of a segment on the coordinate plane, you can use the Midpoint Formula.

Midpoint Formula	The coordinates of the midpoint of a segment with endpoints (x_1, y_1) and (x_2, y_2) are $\left(\frac{x_1 + x_2}{2}, \frac{y_1 + y_2}{2}\right)$.

Example Find the midpoint of $\overline{AB}$ for $A(3, 2)$ and $B(2, 0)$.

$\left(\frac{x_1 + x_2}{2}, \frac{y_1 + y_2}{2}\right) = \left(\frac{3 + 2}{2}, \frac{2 + 0}{2}\right)$ $x_1 = 3, y_1 = 2, x_2 = 2, y_2 = 0$

$= (2.5, 1)$

Exercises

Use the coordinate plane at the right for Exercises 1 and 2.

1. Graph the following points and connect them to form a triangle.

Lesson 10-5 The Distance Formula 569

TEACH with TECH

BLOG Have students write a blog entry on your secure classroom blog explaining how the distance formula and Pythagorean Theorem are similar to each other, and how they are different.

4 ASSESS

Ticket Out the Door Have students draw a right triangle on a piece of graph paper and label the points. Have them trade triangles with another student. Have each student use the Distance Formula to find the length of the hypotenuse of the triangle. As students leave the classroom, have them turn in their work.

Formative Assessment

Check for student understanding of concepts in Lessons 10-4 and 10-5.

CRM Quiz 3, p. 45

Standardized Test Practice

32. Which expression could be used to find the distance between points A and B? **A**

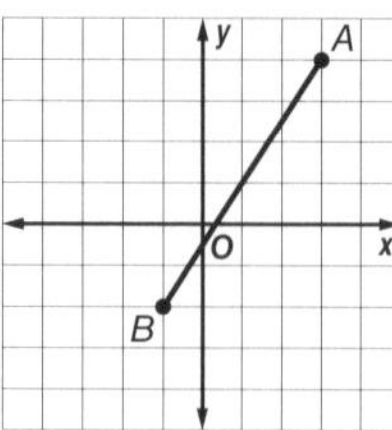

A $\sqrt{(3+1)^2+(4+2)^2}$
B $\sqrt{(3-1)^2+(4-2)^2}$
C $\sqrt{(-2+1)^2+(4+3)^2}$
D $\sqrt{(3-1)^2-(4-2)^2}$

33. What is the distance between S and T in quadrilateral $RSTU$? Round to the nearest tenth. **H**

F 4.5
G 5.4
H 5.7
J 10.8

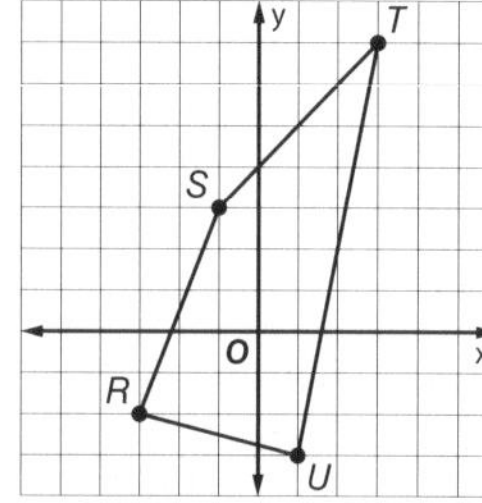

34. EXTENDED RESPONSE Ayana is hiking the trail shown on the graph below.

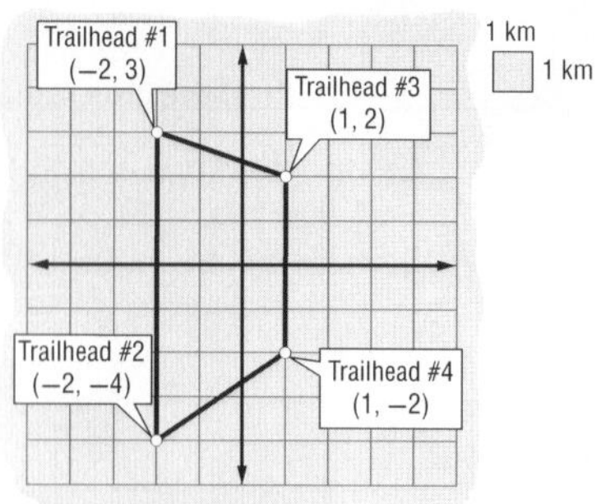

a. To the nearest tenth kilometer, find the total distance Ayana hikes if she completes the entire trail. **17.8 kilometers**

b. If there are paths between Trailheads 2 and 3 and between Trailheads 1 and 4, which path is shorter?
The path between Trailheads 1 and 4

35. To the nearest tenth unit, what is the distance between (1, −5) and (5, −1)? **B**

A 5.6
B 5.7
C 6.4
D 6.7

Spiral Review

Find the length of the hypotenuse in each right triangle. Round to the nearest tenth, if necessary. (Lesson 10-4)

36. **10**

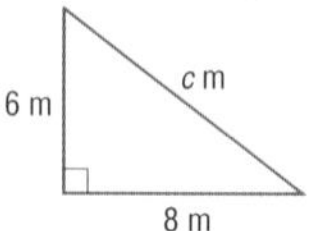

37. **51**

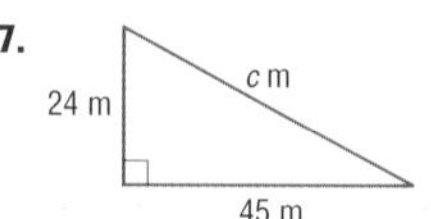

38. **7.7**

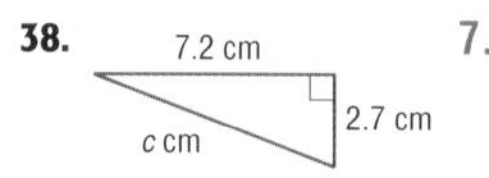

39. ALGEBRA The measures of the angles of a triangle are in the ratio 1:3:5. What is the measure of each angle? (Lesson 10-3) **20°, 60°, 100°**

Skills Review

Estimate each square root to the nearest integer. Do not use a calculator. (Lesson 10-1)

40. $\sqrt{45}$ **7** **41.** $-\sqrt{139}$ **−12** **42.** $\pm\sqrt{170}$ **±13**

Differentiated Instruction

BL

Extension The midpoint of a line segment is often useful to locate. Draw a horizontal line segment on graph paper and find its midpoint. Label the endpoints and midpoint. How could you find the midpoint without counting units? Now, plot $M(4, 5)$ and $N(-8, -3)$ on a coordinate graph. Find the midpoint without counting. The midpoint can be calculated by adding the two x-coordinates and dividing by 2 to get the x-coordinate of the midpoint, and by adding the two y-coordinates and dividing by 2 to get the y-coordinate of the midpoint; (−2, 1).

10-6 Special Right Triangles

Why?

The diagram at the right shows the first step in making a paper airplane.

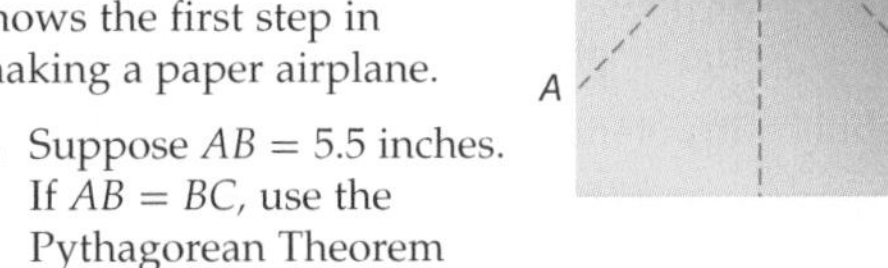

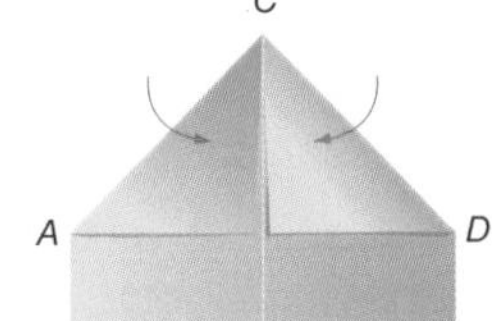

a. Suppose $AB = 5.5$ inches. If $AB = BC$, use the Pythagorean Theorem to find AC to the nearest tenth. **7.8 in.**

b. Use a calculator to find $AB \cdot \sqrt{2}$ and $BC \cdot \sqrt{2}$ to the nearest tenth. Compare the results to the answer in part **a.** **7.8 in.; They are the same.**

Then
You used the Pythagorean Theorem to find missing measures in right triangles. (Lesson 10-4)

Now
- Find missing measures in 45°-45°-90° triangles.
- Find missing measures in 30°-60°-90° triangles.

Math Online
glencoe.com
- Extra Examples
- Personal Tutor
- Self-Check Quiz
- Homework Help

Find Measures in 45°–45°–90° Triangles Study the triangles shown. The corresponding angles have the same measure and the corresponding sides are proportional with a scale factor of 2. This and other examples suggest that all 45°-45°-90° triangles are similar. In addition to the Pythagorean Theorem, you can use similar triangles to find missing measures in a 45°-45°-90° triangle.

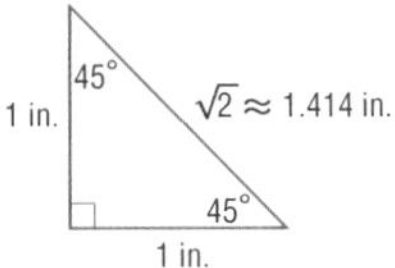

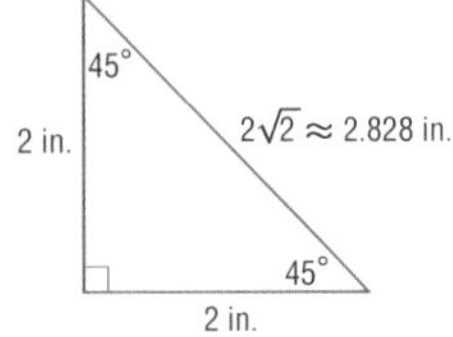

EXAMPLE 1 Find the Hypotenuse in a 45°–45°–90° Triangle

Triangle ABC and triangle DEF are 45°-45°-90° triangles. Find the length of the hypotenuse in $\triangle DEF$.

The scale factor from $\triangle ABC$ to $\triangle DEF$ is $\frac{3}{1}$ or 3. Use the scale factor to find the hypotenuse.

$x = 3 \cdot \sqrt{2}$ **Multiply the length of $\overline{AC}$ by the scale factor, 3.**

$= 3\sqrt{2}$

A: 1 in., 45°, √2 in., 45°, B 1 in. C — D: 45°, 3 in., x, 45°, E 3 in. F

So, the hypotenuse of $\triangle DEF$ measures $3\sqrt{2}$ inches.

Check Your Progress

Find the length of each hypotenuse.

1A. $11\sqrt{2}$ m

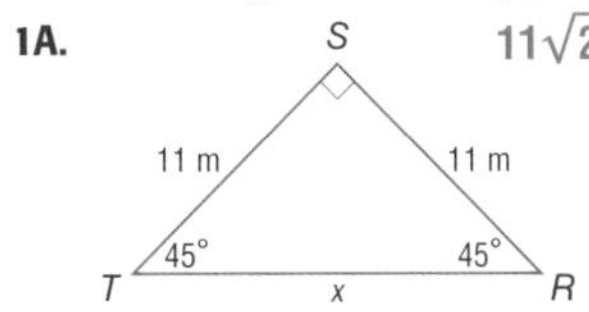

1B. $8\sqrt{2}$ cm

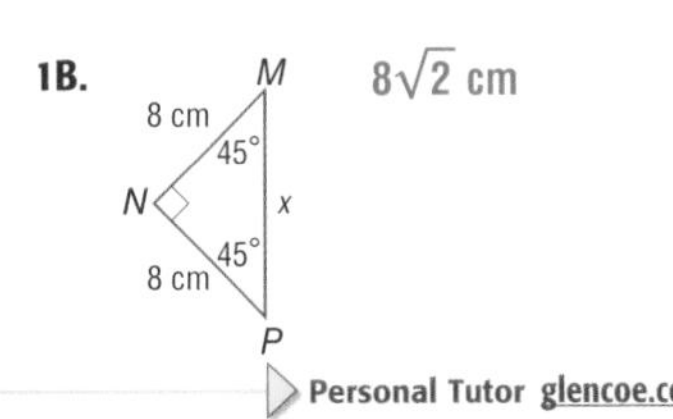

Personal Tutor glencoe.com

10-6 Lesson Notes

1 FOCUS

Vertical Alignment

Before Lesson 10-6
Use the Pythagorean Theorem to find missing measures in right triangles.

Lesson 10-6
Find missing measures in 45°-45°-90° triangles. Find missing measures in 30°-60°-90° triangles.

After Lesson 10-6
Use the sine, cosine, and tangent ratios to solve problems involving right triangles.

2 TEACH

Scaffolding Questions

Have students read the *Why?* section of the lesson and answer the questions.

Ask:
- What are the types of triangles in the diagram? Isosceles right triangles
- What are the measures of their angles? two 45° angles, one 90° angle
- What can you conclude about the length of the hypotenuse in this type of special right triangle? It is the length of a leg × $\sqrt{2}$.

Lesson 10-6 Resources

Resource	Approaching-Level	On-Level	Beyond-Level	English Learners
Teacher Edition	• Differentiated Instruction, p. 573	• Differentiated Instruction, p. 573	• Differentiated Instruction, p. 576	
Chapter Resource Masters	• Study Guide and Intervention, pp. 36–37 • Skills Practice, p. 38 • Practice, p. 39 • Word Problem Practice, p. 40	• Study Guide and Intervention, pp. 36–37 • Skills Practice, p. 38 • Practice, p. 39 • Word Problem Practice, p. 40 • Enrichment, p. 41	• Practice, p. 39 • Word Problem Practice, p. 40 • Enrichment, p. 41	• Study Guide and Intervention, pp. 36–37 • Skills Practice, p. 38 • Practice, p. 39
Transparencies	• 5-Minute Check Transparency 10-6	• 5-Minute Check Transparency 10-6	• 5-Minute Check Transparency 10-6	• 5-Minute Check Transparency 10-6
Others	• Study Notebook • Teaching Pre-Algebra with Manipulatives	• Study Notebook • Teaching Pre-Algebra with Manipulatives	• Study Notebook	• Study Notebook • Teaching Pre-Algebra with Manipulatives

Find Measures in 45°-45°-90° Triangles

Example 1 shows how to find the hypotenuse of a 45°-45°-90° triangle.

Formative Assessment

Use the Check Your Progress exercises after each example to determine students' understanding of concepts.

Additional Example

1 $\triangle RST$ is a 45°-45°-90° triangle. Find the length of the hypotenuse. $9\sqrt{2}$ mm

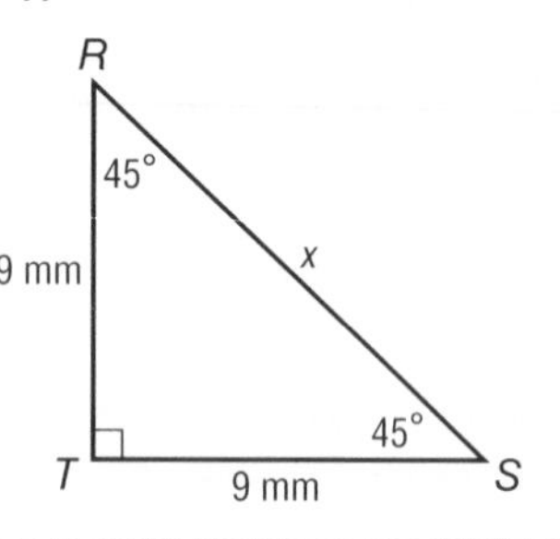

Find Measures in 30°-60°-90° Triangles

Example 2 shows how to find the exact lengths of missing measures in 30°-60°-90° triangles. **Example 3** shows how to use a 30°-60°-90° triangle to solve a real-world problem.

Additional Example

2 $\triangle PQR$ is a 30°-60°-90° triangle. Find the exact length of the missing measures. $x = 16$ ft; $y = 8\sqrt{3}$ ft

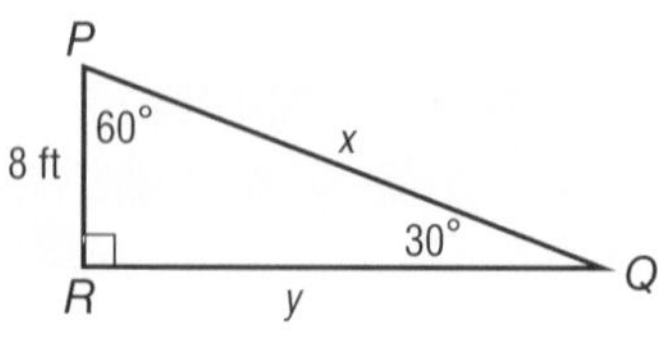

Additional Examples also in Interactive Classroom PowerPoint® Presentations

IWB INTERACTIVE WHITEBOARD READY

Example 1 suggests the following relationship for 45°-45°-90° triangles.

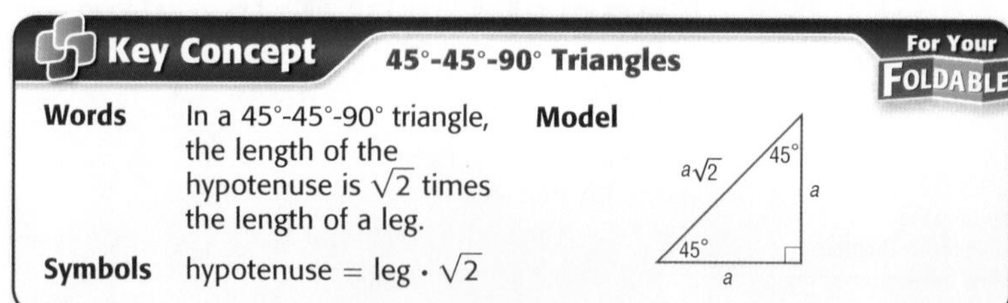

Key Concept 45°-45°-90° Triangles — For Your FOLDABLE

Words In a 45°-45°-90° triangle, the length of the hypotenuse is $\sqrt{2}$ times the length of a leg.

Symbols hypotenuse = leg $\cdot \sqrt{2}$

Model

Find Measures in 30°-60°-90° Triangles Study the triangles shown. Just as 45° -45°-90° triangles are similar, 30°-60°-90° triangles are similar.

EXAMPLE 2 Find Missing Measures in a 30°-60°-90° Triangle

$\triangle ABC$ and $\triangle DEF$ are 30°-60°-90° triangles. Find the exact length of the missing measures.

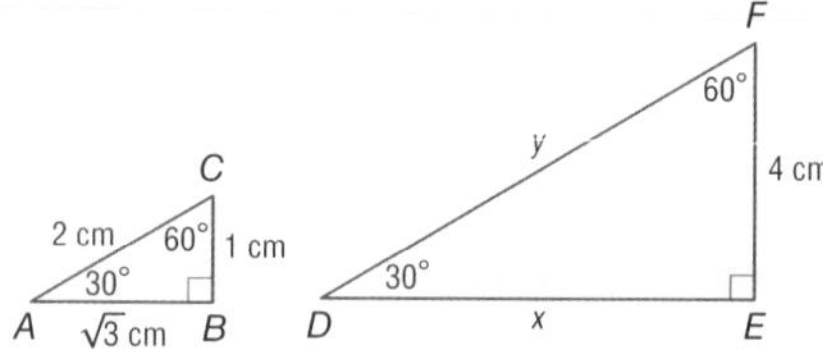

The scale factor from $\triangle ABC$ to $\triangle DEF$ is $\frac{4}{1}$ or 4.

Use the scale factor to find the missing measures.

$x = 4 \cdot 2$ **Multiply the length of $\overline{AC}$ by the scale factor.**

$= 8$

So, x is 8 centimeters.

$y = 4 \cdot \sqrt{3}$ **Multiply $\overline{AB}$ by the scale factor.**

$= 4\sqrt{3}$

So, y is $4\sqrt{3}$ centimeters.

StudyTip

Alternative Method You can also use a proportion to find the missing measures of corresponding sides. In Example 2, you can use $\frac{2}{1} = \frac{x}{4}$.

Check Your Progress

2. Triangle RST is a 30°-60°-90° triangle. Find the exact length of the missing measures.
$x = 3$ cm; $y = 3\sqrt{3}$ cm

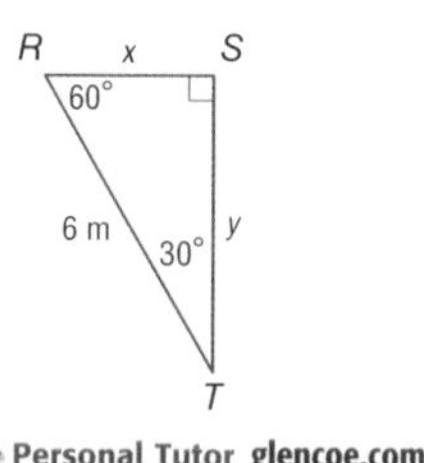

Personal Tutor glencoe.com

TEACH with TECH

INTERACTIVE WHITEBOARD Use the whiteboard to work through finding the side lengths of a 45°-45°-90° and 30°-60°-90° triangle. Save your work and distribute it to students at the end of class or post on the class Web site.

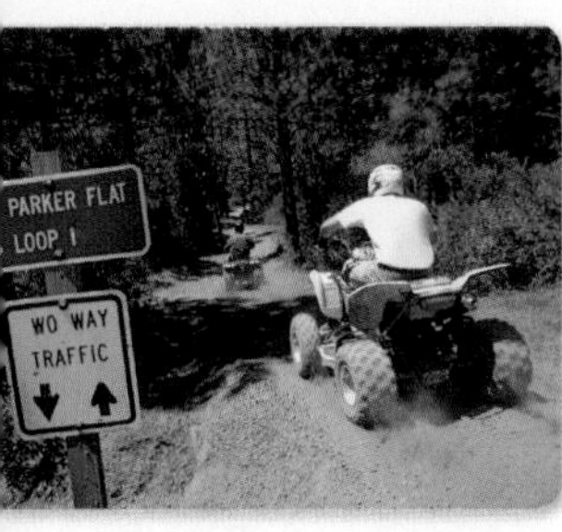

Real-World Link

(ATV) The all-terrain vehicle was initially developed in Japan as a means of transportation through mountainous areas. When ATVs were first sold in the U.S. in the early 1970s, they had 3 wheels.

Source: American Honda Motor Company

Example 2 suggests the following relationship for 30°-60°-90° triangles.

Key Concept 30°-60°-90° Triangles

For Your FOLDABLE

Words In a 30°-60°-90° triangle,
- the length of the hypotenuse is 2 times the length of the shorter leg, and
- the length of the longer leg is $\sqrt{3}$ times the length of the shorter leg.

Model

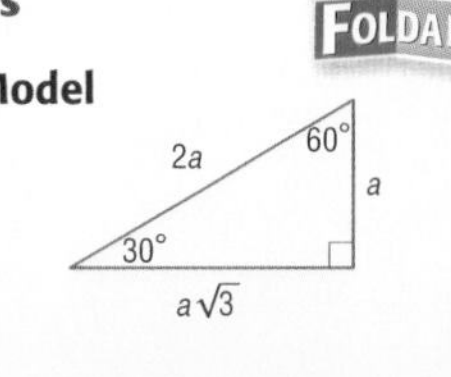

Symbols hypotenuse = 2 · shorter leg
longer leg = $\sqrt{3}$ · shorter leg

In real-world situations, use the decimal value for the square root.

Real-World EXAMPLE 3 Use Special Right Triangles

RAMPS A ten foot ramp for loading an all-terrain vehicle onto a truck makes a 30°-angle with the ground. Find y, the distance from the truck to the end of the ramp. Round to the nearest tenth.

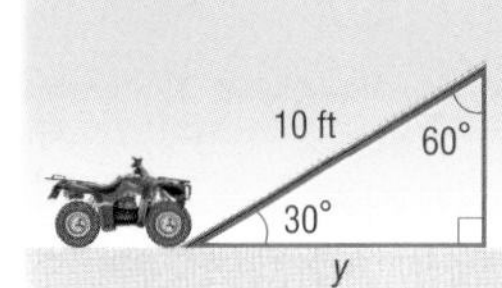

Understand You know the hypotenuse of the 30°-60°-90° triangle. You need to find the distance from the truck to the end of the ramp.

Plan To find y, use the relationship between the shorter leg and the longer leg in a 30°-60°-90° triangle. The shorter leg is half the length of the hypotenuse or 5 feet.

Solve longer leg = $\sqrt{3}$ · shorter leg **Relationship between sides**

$y = \sqrt{3} \cdot 5$ **Substitution**

To find the decimal value of y use a calculator.

[2nd] [√‾] 3 [ENTER] [×] 5 [ENTER] 8.660254038

$\sqrt{3} \cdot 5 \approx 8.7$ **Round to the nearest tenth.**

The distance from the truck to the end of the ramp is about 8.7 feet.

Check Use the Pythagorean Theorem to check the solution. Since $5^2 + 8.7^2 = 100.69$ and $100.69 \approx 100$, the answer is correct. ✓

ReadingMath

Exact Values Since 8.6 is rounded, it is an approximate value, while $5\sqrt{3}$ is an exact value.

Check Your Progress

3. **KICKBALL** A kickball field is in the shape of a square. The distance from first base to second base is 60 feet. Find x the distance from home base to second base. Round to the nearest tenth. **84.9 ft**

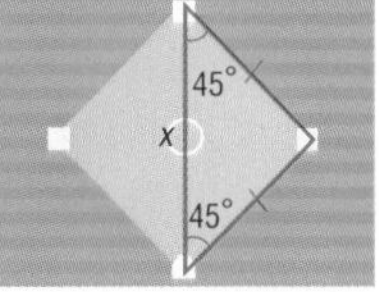

Personal Tutor glencoe.com

Tips for New Teachers

Have students investigate equilateral triangles. Then have students fold triangles in half to create two 30°-60°-90° triangles.

Additional Example

3 **GATES** A gate has a metal diagonal bar that forms a 30° angle with the bottom edge of the frame. The height of the gate is 2 feet. Find y, the length of the gate. Round to the nearest tenth. 3.5 ft

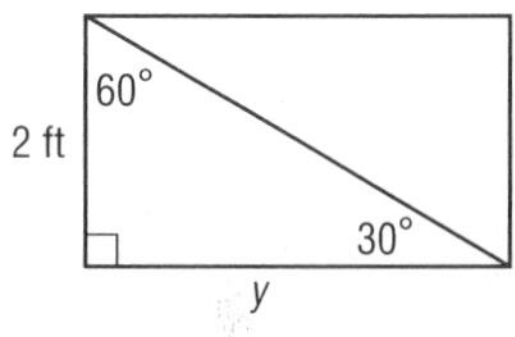

Focus on Mathematical Content

Special Right Triangles You can create congruent 45°-45°-90° triangles by drawing the diagonal of a square. The legs of each triangle are congruent, and the hypotenuse is $\sqrt{2}$ times the length of a leg. You can create congruent 30°-60°-90° triangles by drawing one of the altitudes of an equilateral triangle. In each triangle, the hypotenuse is twice the length of the shorter leg and the longer leg is $\sqrt{3}$ times the length of the shorter leg.

Differentiated Instruction AL OL

If students find it difficult to remember the relationships for the special right triangles,

Then suggest that they use index cards to draw diagrams of the relationships, which they can refer to while working on the exercises. It may be helpful to use units for the diagrams rather than variables, such as: 1, 1, $1\sqrt{2}$ and 1, 2, $1\sqrt{3}$.

3 PRACTICE

Formative Assessment

Use Exercises 1–8 to check for understanding.

Use the chart at the bottom of this page to customize assignments for your students.

Watch Out!

Preventing Errors Make sure students understand that the relationships described for 45°-45°-90° triangles and 30°-60°-90° triangles apply to those triangles only and cannot be used interchangeably or with other triangles.

Watch Out!

Find the Error For Exercise 24, suggest that students draw a 30°-60°-90° triangle in the same orientation as $\triangle JKL$ and label the sides as a, $2a$, and $a\sqrt{3}$. Students can use this triangle to keep track of the proportions between the sides.

Additional Answers

19a.

Leg Length	Hypotenuse
1	1.4
2	2.8
3	4.2
4	5.7
5	7.1

19b.

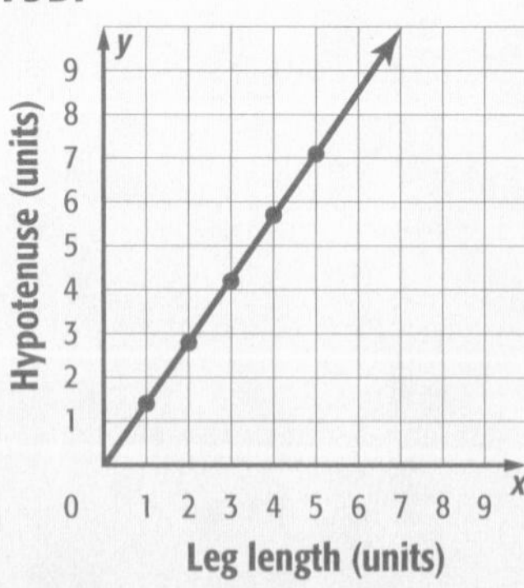

The points lie in a straight line.

Check Your Understanding

Examples 1 and 2 pp. 571–572

Find each missing measure.

1. 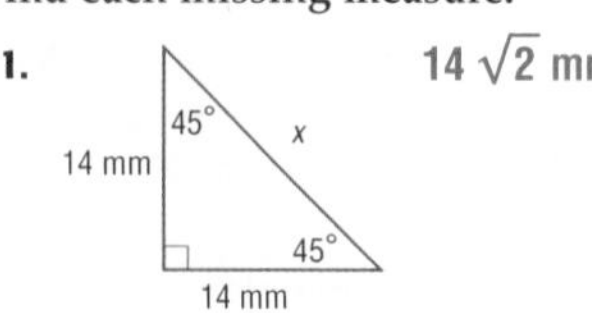

$14\sqrt{2}$ mm

2. 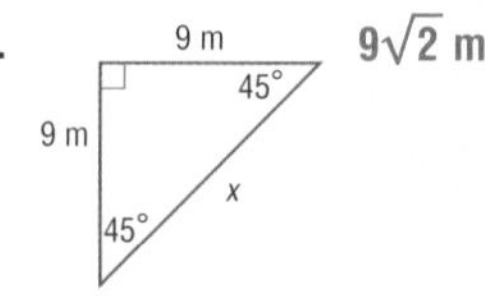

$9\sqrt{2}$ m

3. 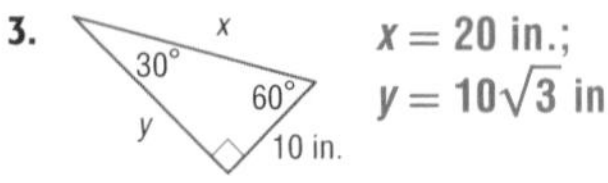

$x = 20$ in.; $y = 10\sqrt{3}$ in.

4. $x = 13$ ft; $y = 13\sqrt{3}$ ft

5. In a 45°-45°-90° triangle, a leg is 2 centimeters long. Find the exact length of the hypotenuse. $2\sqrt{2}$ cm

6. In a 30°-60°-90° triangle, the shorter leg is 9 feet long. Find the exact length of the hypotenuse and the length of the longer leg. 18 ft; $9\sqrt{3}$ ft

Example 3 p. 573

AIR HOCKEY An air hockey table is 40 inches wide, as shown at the right. Find each measure. Round to the nearest tenth, if necessary.

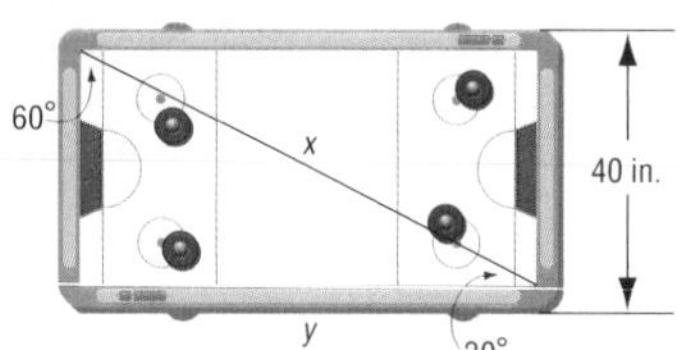

7. length of table 69.3 in.

8. distance the puck can go from one corner of the table to another 80 in.

Practice and Problem Solving

= **Step-by-Step Solutions** begin on page R11. **Extra Practice** begin on page 810.

Examples 1 and 2 pp. 571–572

Find each missing measure.

9. 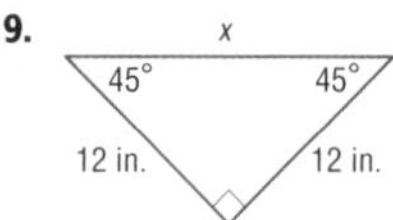

10. 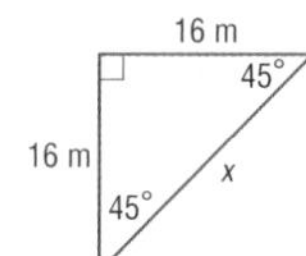

11. 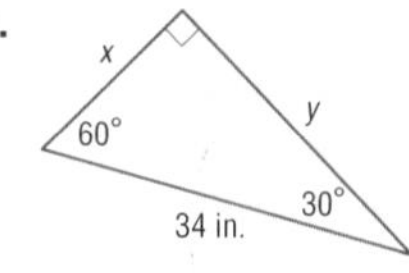

12.

13. 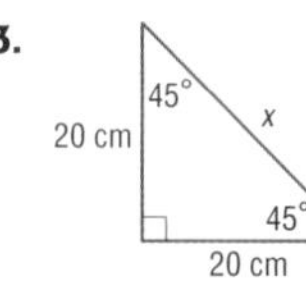

14. 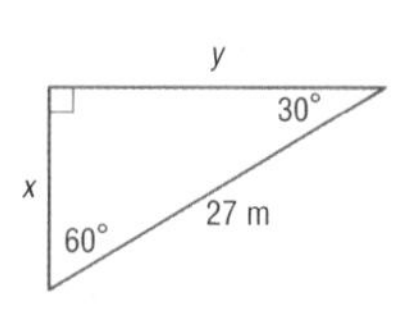

9. $12\sqrt{2}$ in.
10. $16\sqrt{2}$ m
11. $x = 17$ in., $y = 17\sqrt{3}$ in.
12. $x = 14$ km, $y = 7\sqrt{3}$ km
13. $20\sqrt{2}$ cm
14. $x = 13.5$ m, $y = 13.5\sqrt{3}$ m

15. In a 45°-45°-90° triangle, a leg is 15 inches long. Find the exact length of the hypotenuse. $15\sqrt{2}$ in.

16. In a 30°-60°-90° triangle, the hypotenuse is 26 inches long. Find the exact length of the shorter leg and the length of the longer leg. 13 in.; $13\sqrt{3}$ in.

Differentiated Homework Options

Level	Assignment	Two-Day Option	
AL Basic	9–18, 23–25, 27–48	9–17 odd, 28–31	10–18 even, 23–25, 27, 32–48
OL Core	9–19 odd, 20, 21, 23–25, 27–40	9–18, 28–31	19–25, 27, 32–48
BL Advanced	19–40 (Optional: 41-48)		

574 Chapter 10 Real Numbers and Right Triangles

Example 3 p. 573

Real-World Link

Visitors to the Tate Modern museum in the United Kingdom will be able to sit in canvas sacks and slide from the fifth floor to the ground, accelerating up to 30 miles per hour.

Source: Tate Modern

17. SLIDES A slide forms a 60° angle with its ladder. If the slide is 12 feet tall, how long is it? **24 ft**

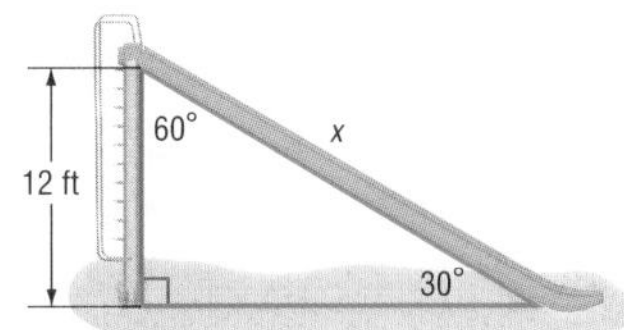

18. MAZES The corn maze below is a square. If the diagonal is $420\sqrt{2}$ feet long, what is the perimeter of the maze? **1680 ft**

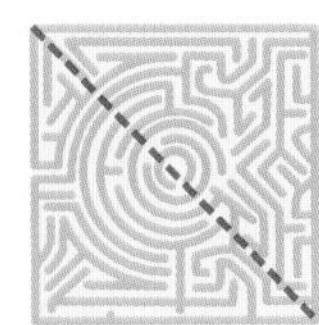

19. MULTIPLE REPRESENTATIONS In this problem, you will explore 45°-45°-90° triangles. **a–b. See margin.**

a. **TABULAR** Find the hypotenuse of isosceles right triangles with the following leg lengths: 1, 2, 3, 4, and 5. Round to the nearest tenth. Record the results in a table.

b. **GRAPHICAL** Graph the points (leg length, hypotenuse) on a coordinate plane. Describe the pattern of the points.

c. **SYMBOLIC** Write an equation that you could use to approximate the hypotenuse y if you know the side length x of a 45°-45°-90° triangle. $y = x\sqrt{2}$

20. SIGNS What is the perimeter of the school crossing sign shown at the right? Round to the nearest tenth. **123.1 in.**

Find each missing measure.

21.

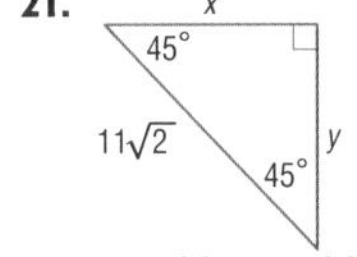

$x = 11$, $y = 11$

22.

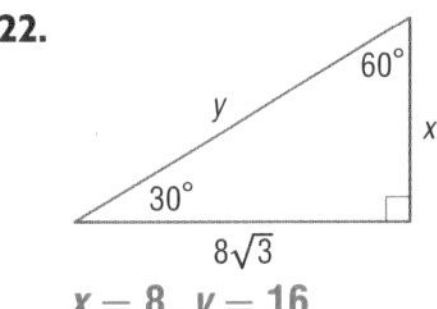

$x = 8$, $y = 16$

H.O.T. Problems

Use **H**igher-**O**rder **T**hinking Skills

23. OPEN ENDED Draw a 30°-60°-90° triangle. Measure the length of the shorter leg. Then use the measure to find the length of the longer leg and the hypotenuse. Check your answers by measuring the other two sides. **See students' work.**

24. FIND THE ERROR Ava says that the length of $\overline{JK}$ in the figure is 16 inches. Deondre says the length is about 22.6 inches. Is either of them correct? Explain.

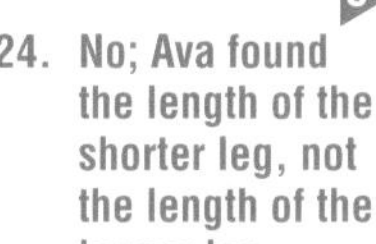

24. No; Ava found the length of the shorter leg, not the length of the longer leg. Deondre multiplied 16 by $\sqrt{2}$ instead of $\sqrt{3}$.

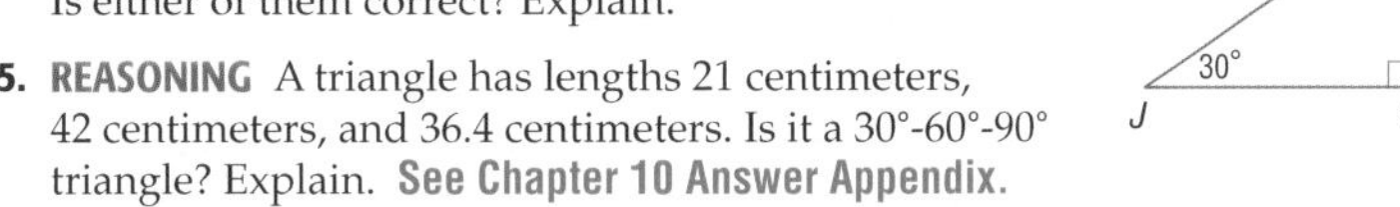

25. REASONING A triangle has lengths 21 centimeters, 42 centimeters, and 36.4 centimeters. Is it a 30°-60°-90° triangle? Explain. **See Chapter 10 Answer Appendix.**

26. CHALLENGE In a 45°-45°-90° triangle, the ratio of the smaller angles to the larger angle is 1:2. Is the ratio of the leg lengths to the hypotenuse also 1:2? Explain your reasoning. **No; the ratio is $1:\sqrt{2}$.**

27. WRITING IN MATH Describe the relationships among the side lengths of a 30°-60°-90° triangle.

27. The hypotenuse is twice the length of the shorter leg. The longer leg is $\sqrt{3}$ times the length of the shorter leg.

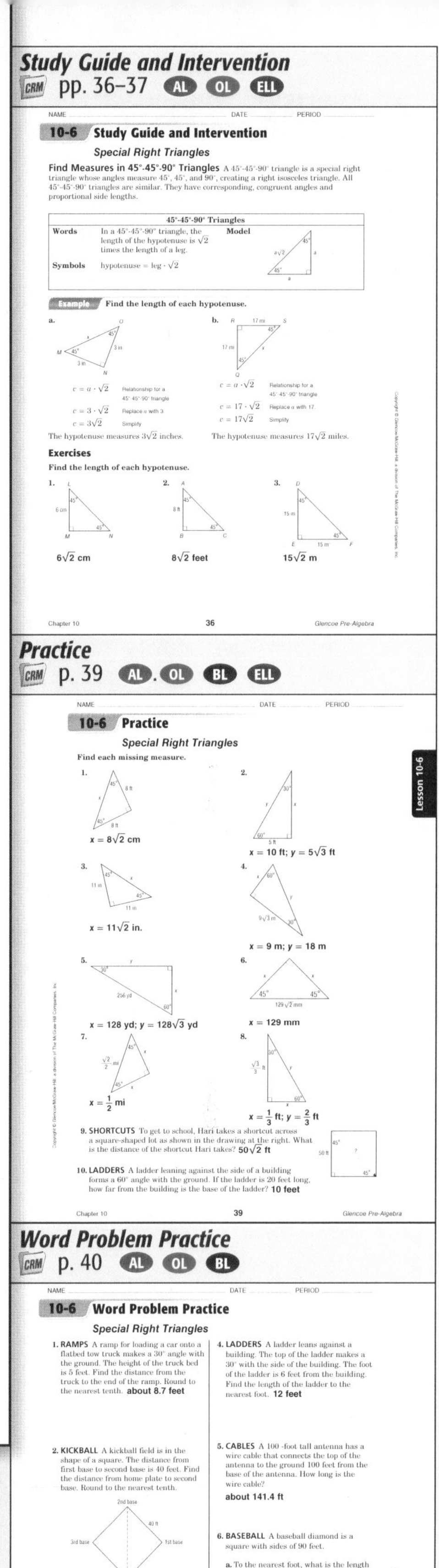

Study Guide and Intervention
CRM pp. 36–37 AL OL ELL

NAME ______ DATE ______ PERIOD ______

10-6 Study Guide and Intervention

Special Right Triangles

Find Measures in 45°-45°-90° Triangles A 45°-45°-90° triangle is a special right triangle whose angles measure 45°, 45°, and 90°, creating a right isosceles triangle. All 45°-45°-90° triangles are similar. They have corresponding, congruent angles and proportional side lengths.

45°-45°-90° Triangles		
Words	In a 45°-45°-90° triangle, the length of the hypotenuse is $\sqrt{2}$ times the length of a leg.	**Model**
Symbols	hypotenuse = leg · $\sqrt{2}$	

Example Find the length of each hypotenuse.

a. $c = a \cdot \sqrt{2}$ Relationship for a 45°-45°-90° triangle
$c = 3 \cdot \sqrt{2}$ Replace a with 3
$c = 3\sqrt{2}$ Simplify
The hypotenuse measures $3\sqrt{2}$ inches.

b. $c = a \cdot \sqrt{2}$ Relationship for a 45°-45°-90° triangle
$c = 17 \cdot \sqrt{2}$ Replace a with 17
$c = 17\sqrt{2}$ Simplify
The hypotenuse measures $17\sqrt{2}$ miles.

Exercises

Find the length of each hypotenuse.

1. $6\sqrt{2}$ cm
2. $8\sqrt{2}$ feet
3. $15\sqrt{2}$ m

Chapter 10 36 Glencoe Pre-Algebra

Practice
CRM p. 39 AL. OL BL ELL

NAME ______ DATE ______ PERIOD ______

10-6 Practice

Special Right Triangles

Find each missing measure.

1. $x = 8\sqrt{2}$ cm
2. $x = 10$ ft; $y = 5\sqrt{3}$ ft
3. $x = 11\sqrt{2}$ in.
4. $x = 9$ m; $y = 18$ m
5. $x = 128$ yd; $y = 128\sqrt{3}$ yd
6. $x = 129$ mm
7. $x = \frac{1}{2}$ mi
8. $x = \frac{1}{3}$ ft; $y = \frac{2}{3}$ ft

9. **SHORTCUTS** To get to school, Hari takes a shortcut across a square-shaped lot as shown in the drawing at the right. What is the distance of the shortcut Hari takes? $50\sqrt{2}$ **ft**

10. **LADDERS** A ladder leaning against the side of a building forms a 60° angle with the ground. If the ladder is 20 feet long, how far from the building is the base of the ladder? **10 feet**

Chapter 10 39 Glencoe Pre-Algebra

Word Problem Practice
CRM p. 40 AL OL BL

NAME ______ DATE ______ PERIOD ______

10-6 Word Problem Practice

Special Right Triangles

1. **RAMPS** A ramp for loading a car onto a flatbed tow truck makes a 30° angle with the ground. The height of the truck bed is 5 feet. Find the distance from the truck to the end of the ramp. Round to the nearest tenth. **about 8.7 feet**

2. **KICKBALL** A kickball field is in the shape of a square. The distance from first base to second base is 40 feet. Find the distance from home plate to second base. Round to the nearest tenth. **56.6 feet**

3. **BARNS** From the top of a barn 25 feet tall, you see a cat on the ground. The angle between your line of sight and the barn is 60°. How many feet, to the nearest foot, must the cat walk to reach the barn? **43 feet**

4. **LADDERS** A ladder leans against a building. The top of the ladder makes a 30° with the side of the building. The foot of the ladder is 6 feet from the building. Find the length of the ladder to the nearest foot. **12 feet**

5. **CABLES** A 100 -foot tall antenna has a wire cable that connects the top of the antenna to the ground 100 feet from the base of the antenna. How long is the wire cable? **about 141.4 ft**

6. **BASEBALL** A baseball diamond is a square with sides of 90 feet.

a. To the nearest foot, what is the length of a throw from home to second base? **127 ft**

b. During warm ups, a baseball is thrown between first and third base 20 times. What is the distance traveled by the baseball? **2,540 ft**

Chapter 10 40 Glencoe Pre-Algebra

Lesson 10-6

Multiple Representations In Exercise 19, students create a table of values, plot the resulting points on the coordinate plane, and write an equation to describe the proportions of an isosceles right triangle.

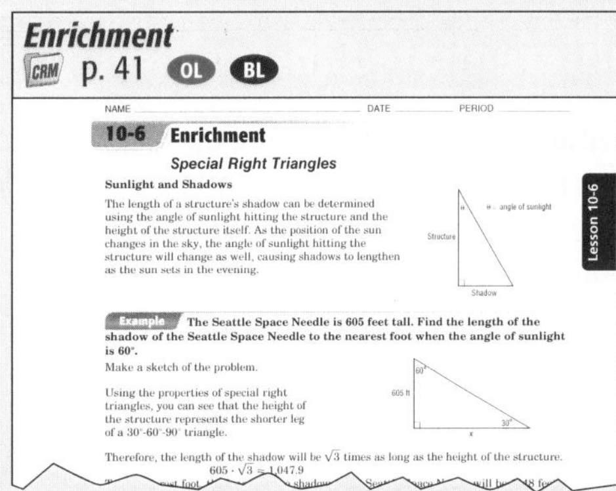

Enrichment
CRM p. 41 OL BL

NAME ______ DATE ______ PERIOD ______

10-6 Enrichment

Special Right Triangles

Sunlight and Shadows

The length of a structure's shadow can be determined using the angle of sunlight hitting the structure and the height of the structure itself. As the position of the sun changes in the sky, the angle of sunlight hitting the structure will change as well, causing shadows to lengthen as the sun sets in the evening.

Example The Seattle Space Needle is 605 feet tall. Find the length of the shadow of the Seattle Space Needle to the nearest foot when the angle of sunlight is 60°.

Make a sketch of the problem.

Using the properties of special right triangles, you can see that the height of the structure represents the shorter leg of a 30°-60°-90° triangle.

Therefore, the length of the shadow will be $\sqrt{3}$ times as long as the height of the structure.

$605 \cdot \sqrt{3} \approx 1{,}047.9$

4 ASSESS

Yesterday's News Have students write a sentence on how the previous lessons on right triangles helped with today's lesson on special right triangles.

Formative Assessment

Check for student understanding of concepts in Lesson 10-6.

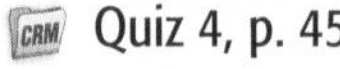 Quiz 4, p. 45

Additional Answer

31b. First solve for y to determine the triangle is an isosceles triangle. Since the triangle is isosceles, both legs are congruent so find x. Use the properties of 45-45-90 triangles to find z.

Standardized Test Practice

28. Mr. Govin installed the gate in his backyard. What is the value of x? **C**

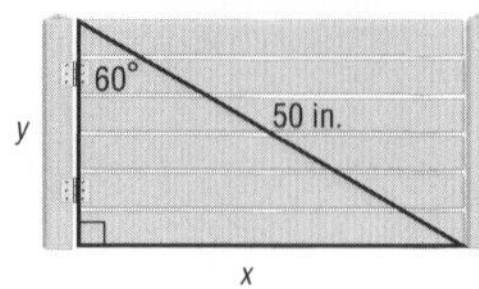

A 25 in.
B $25\sqrt{2}$ in.
C $25\sqrt{3}$ in.
D $50\sqrt{3}$ in.

29. Each leg of a 45°-45°-90° triangle has a length of 18 feet. What is the length of the hypotenuse? **H**

F $\frac{\sqrt{2}}{18}$ ft
G 18 ft
H $18\sqrt{2}$ ft
J $18\sqrt{3}$ ft

30. Which of the following is *not* true about 30°-60°-90° triangles? **A**

A The length of the hypotenuse is the product of the length of the leg and $\sqrt{2}$.

B The length of the hypotenuse is the product of the length of the shorter length and 2.

C The length of the longer leg is the product of the length of the shorter length and $\sqrt{3}$.

D The length of shorter leg is equal to half the length of the hypotenuse.

31. EXTENDED RESPONSE Use the triangle shown at the right.

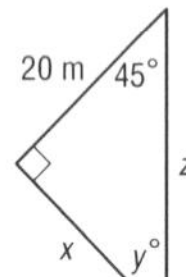

a. Find each missing measure. **$x = 20$, $y = 45$, $z = 20\sqrt{2}$**

b. Explain how you found each value. **b. See margin.**

Spiral Review

Find the distance between each pair of points. Round to the nearest tenth, if necessary. (Lesson 10-5)

32. $J(5, -4)$, $K(-1, 3)$ **9.2**

33. $C(-7, 2)$, $D(6, -4)$ **14.3**

34. $S(-9, 0)$, $T(6, -7)$ **16.6**

35. $M(0, 0)$, $N(-7, -8)$ **10.6**

If c is the measure of the hypotenuse, find each missing measure. Round to the nearest tenth, if necessary. (Lesson 10-4)

36. $a = 9, b = ?, c = 41$ **40**

37. $a = ?, b = 35, c = 37$ **12**

38. $a = ?, b = 12, c = 19$ **14.7**

39. $a = 7, b = ?, c = 14$ **12.1**

40. GEOMETRY If each side of the figures below has a length of 1 foot, find the perimeter of a figure with 9 pentagons. (Lesson 3-8) **29 ft**

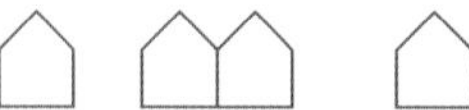

Skills Review

Solve each equation. (Lessons 4-3 and 4-4)

41. $2x = 180$ **90**

42. $x + 72 = 90$ **18**

43. $2x = 90$ **45**

44. $95 + x = 180$ **85**

45. $x + 55 = 90$ **35**

46. $3x = 180$ **60**

47. $x + 79 = 180$ **101**

48. $50 + x = 90$ **40**

Differentiated Instruction

 BL

Extension Ask students to solve the following problem: An equilateral triangle has a height of $4\sqrt{3}$ cm. What is the perimeter of the triangle? *Hint: Draw and label a diagram of the triangle before solving the problem.* 24 cm

576 Chapter 10 Real Numbers and Right Triangles

Math Online glencoe.com
- STUDY TO GO
- Vocabulary Review

Chapter Summary

Key Concepts

Squares and Square Roots (Lesson 10-1)

- Perfect squares are squares of integers.
- A square root of a number is one of two equal factors of the number.

The Real Number System (Lesson 10-2)

- Numbers that cannot be written as terminating or repeating decimals are called irrational numbers.
- The set of rational and irrational numbers together make up the set of real numbers.

Triangles (Lesson 10-3)

- An acute angle measures less than 90°, a right angle measures 90°, and an obtuse angle has a measure between 90° and 180°.
- Triangles can be classified by their angles as acute, obtuse, or right and by their sides as scalene, isosceles, or equilateral.

The Pythagorean Theorem (Lesson 10-4)

- In a right triangle with legs a and b and hypotenuse c, $c^2 = a^2 + b^2$.
- If you know the lengths of two sides of a right triangle, you can use the Pythagorean Theorem to find the length of the third side.

The Distance Formula (Lesson 10-5)

- The distance d between two points with coordinates (x_1, y_1) and (x_2, y_2) is given by $d = \sqrt{(x_2 - x_1)^2 + (y_2 - y_1)^2}$.

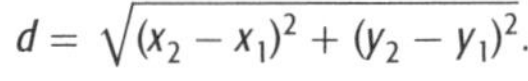

FOLDABLES® Study Organizer

Be sure the Key Concepts are noted in your Foldable.

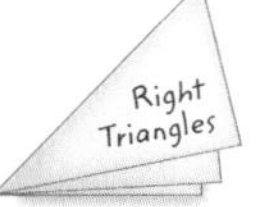

Key Vocabulary

congruent (p. 552)
converse (p. 560)
Distance Formula (p. 565)
hypotenuse (p. 558)
irrational numbers (p. 543)
legs (p. 558)
line segment (p. 550)
perfect square (p. 537)
Pythagorean Theorem (p. 558)
radical sign (p. 537)
real numbers (p. 543)
solving a right triangle (p. 559)
square root (p. 537)
triangle (p 550)
vertex (p. 550)

Vocabulary Check

Choose the term that best matches each statement or phrase.

1. a square of a whole number **perfect square**
2. a triangle with no congruent sides **scalene**
3. decimals that do not repeat or terminate **irrational numbers**
4. the sides of a right triangle that are adjacent to the right angle **legs**
5. a triangle with angle measures 73°, 30°, and 77° **scalene or acute triangle**
6. the side opposite the right angle in a triangle **hypotenuse**
7. sides of a figure that have the same length **congruent**
8. the point at which two sides of a triangle intersect **vertex**
9. used to indicate a positive square root **radical sign**
10. part of a line containing two endpoints and all the points between them **line segment**

CHAPTER 10 Study Guide and Review

Formative Assessment

Key Vocabulary The page references after each word denote where that term was first introduced. If students have difficulty answering questions 1–10, remind them that they can use these page references to refresh their memories about the vocabulary.

Summative Assessment

CRM Vocabulary Test, p. 47

Math Online glencoe.com

Vocabulary PuzzleMaker improves students' mathematics vocabulary using four puzzle formats–crossword, scramble, word search using a word list, and word search using clues. Students can work online or from a printed worksheet.

FOLDABLES® Study Organizer

Dinah Zike's Foldables®

Have students look through the chapter to make sure they have included examples in their Foldables.

Suggest that students keep their Foldables handy while completing the Study Guide and Review pages. Point out that their Foldables can serve as a quick review tool when studying for the Chapter Test.

Lesson-by-Lesson Review

Intervention If the given examples are not sufficient to review the topics covered by the questions, remind students that the page references tell them where to review that topic in their textbook.

Two-Day Option Have students complete the Lesson-by-Lesson Review on pp. 578–580. Then you can use ExamView® Assessment Suite to customize another review worksheet that practices all the objectives of this chapter or only the objectives on which your students need more help.

Differentiated Instruction

Super DVD: MindJogger Videoquizzes Use this DVD as an alternative format of review for the test.

Additional Answers

20. whole, integer, rational
21. rational
22. irrational
23. rational

CHAPTER 10 Study Guide and Review

Lesson-by-Lesson Review

10-1 Squares and Square Roots (pp. 537–542)

Find each square root.

11. $\sqrt{169}$ **13** **12.** $-\sqrt{25}$ **−5**

13. $\pm\sqrt{1}$ **±1** **14.** $\sqrt{484}$ **22**

Estimate each square root to the nearest integer. Do not use a calculator.

15. $\sqrt{15}$ **4** **16.** $-\sqrt{52}$ **−7**

17. $-\sqrt{90}$ **−9** **18.** $\sqrt{415}$ **20**

19. CLOCKS The *period* of a pendulum is the time it takes to make one complete swing. The period P of a pendulum is given by the formula $P = 2\pi\sqrt{\frac{\ell}{32}}$, where ℓ is the length of the pendulum. If a clock's pendulum is 8 feet long, find the period. Use 3.14 for π. **3.14 s**

EXAMPLE 1

Find $\pm\sqrt{256}$.

$\pm\sqrt{256} = \pm 16$ **Find both square roots of 256; $16^2 = 256$.**

EXAMPLE 2

Estimate $\sqrt{70}$ to the nearest integer.

The first perfect square less than 70 is 64.

$\sqrt{64} = 8$

The first perfect square greater than 70 is 81.

$\sqrt{81} = 9$

Since 70 is closer to 64 than 81, $\sqrt{70}$ is closer to 8 than 9.

10-2 The Real Number System (pp. 543–548)

Name all of the sets of numbers to which each real number belongs. Write *whole, integer, rational,* or *irrational.* **20–23. See margin.**

20. 18 **21.** $\frac{6}{11}$ **22.** $\sqrt{74}$ **23.** $4.\overline{5}$

Replace each ● with <, >, or = to make a true statement.

24. $6.\overline{25}$ ● $\sqrt{39}$ **>** **25.** $-\sqrt{70}$ ● $-8\frac{1}{5}$ **<**

26. $-11\frac{1}{9}$ ● $-\sqrt{124}$ **>** **27.** $\sqrt{68}$ ● $8.\overline{4}$ **<**

Solve each equation. Round to the nearest tenth, if necessary.

28. $d^2 = 100$ **10, −10** **29.** $4y^2 = 5.76$ **1.2, −1.2**

30. GARDENS The formula $A \approx 3.14\,r^2$ can be used to determine the area of a circle where A is the area and r is the distance from the center of the circle to the outside edge. If the area of a circular garden is 700 square feet, about how far is the distance from the center of the garden to the outside edge? Round to the nearest tenth. **14.9 ft**

EXAMPLE 3

Replace ● with <, >, or = to make $\sqrt{12}$ ● $\frac{10}{3}$ a true statement.

$\sqrt{12} = 3.46410162\ldots$ $\frac{10}{3} = 3.333\ldots$

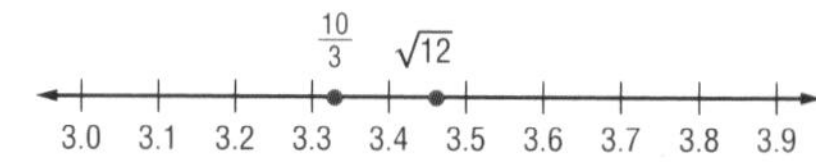

Since $\sqrt{12}$ is to the right of $\frac{10}{3}$, $\sqrt{12} > \frac{10}{3}$.

EXAMPLE 4

Solve $4n^2 = 44$.

$4n^2 = 44$	**Write the equation.**
$n^2 = 11$	**Divide each side by 4.**
$n = \pm\sqrt{11}$	**Definition of square root**
$n \approx 3.3$ and -3.3	**Use a calculator.**

The solutions are approximately 3.3 and −3.3.

MIXED PROBLEM SOLVING
For mixed problem-solving practice, see page 852.

10-3 Triangles (pp. 550–555)

Find the value of x in each triangle. Then classify each triangle by its angles and by its sides.

31. 45; acute scalene

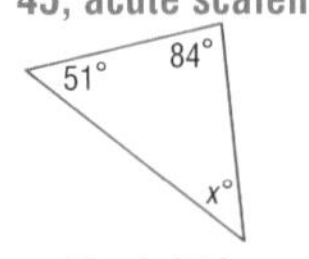

32. 54; acute isosceles

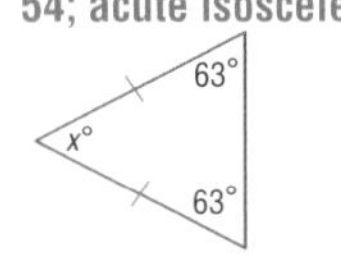

33. 45; right isosceles

45°
x°

34. 95; obtuse scalene

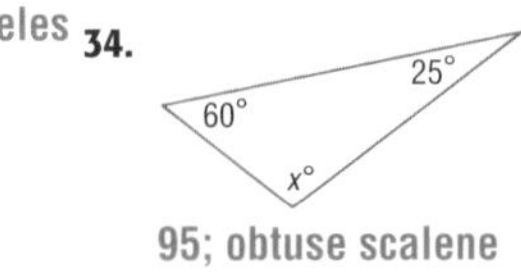

35. SIGNS Classify the yield sign by its angles and by its sides. acute equilateral

EXAMPLE 5

Find the value of x in the triangle. Then classify the triangle by its angles and by its sides.

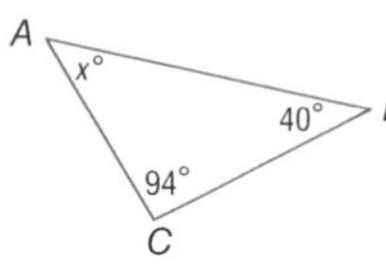

Step 1 Find the missing angle measure.

$x + 40 + 94 = 180$	**Write an equation.**
$x + 134 = 180$	**Simplify.**
$x + 134 - 134 = 180 - 134$	**Subtract 134 from each side.**
$x = 46$	**Simplify.**

Step 2 Classify the triangle.

Angles: The triangle has an obtuse angle.

Sides: The triangle has no congruent sides.

So, the triangle is obtuse scalene.

10-4 The Pythagorean Theorem (pp. 558–563)

Find the missing length of each triangle. Round to the nearest tenth, if necessary.

36.

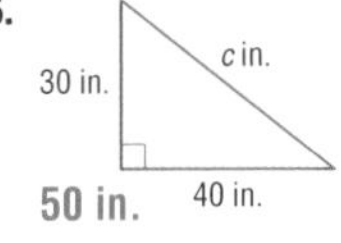

50 in.

37.

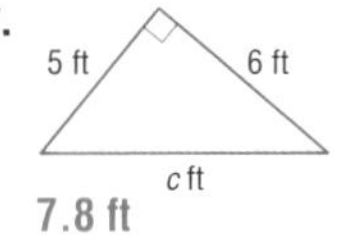

7.8 ft

38.

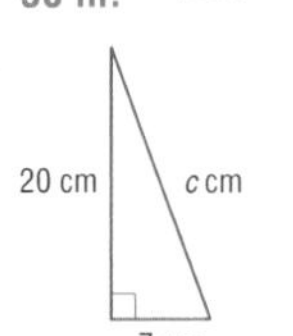

21.2 cm

39.

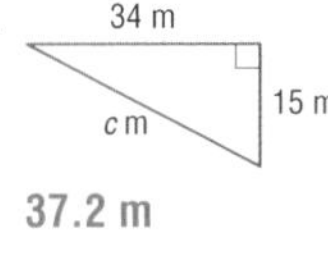

37.2 m

40. SOFTBALL On a fast pitch softball diamond, the bases are 60 feet apart. What is the distance from home plate to second base in a straight line to the nearest tenth of a foot? 84.9 ft

EXAMPLE 6

Find the missing measure of the right triangle. Round to the nearest tenth, if necessary.

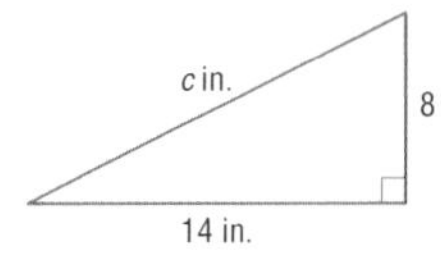

$a^2 + b^2 = c^2$	**Pythagorean Theorem**
$8^2 + 14^2 = c^2$	**Replace *a* with 8 and *b* with 14.**
$64 + 196 = c^2$	**Evaluate 8^2 and 14^2.**
$260 = c^2$	**Add 64 and 196.**
$\pm\sqrt{260} = c$	**Definition of square root**
$16.1 \approx c$	**Use the principal square root.**

So, c is about 16.1 inches.

Chapter 10 Study Guide and Review 579

Problem Solving Review

For additional practice in problem solving for Chapter 10, see the Mixed Problem Solving Appendix, p. 852, in the Student Handbook section.

Anticipation Guide

Have students complete the Chapter 10 Anticipation Guide and discuss how their responses have changed now that they have completed Chapter 10.

CHAPTER 10 Study Guide and Review

10-5 The Distance Formula (pp. 565–570)

Find the distance between each pair of points. Round to the nearest tenth, if necessary.

41. $G(0, 0)$, $H(3, 4)$ **5**
42. $B(-2, 7)$, $C(-5, 7)$ **3**
43. $J(9, -5)$, $K(0, 4)$ **12.7**
44. $M(-8, 1)$, $N(7, -6)$ **16.6**
45. **GEOMETRY** Find the perimeter of $\triangle DEF$. Round to the nearest tenth. **15.4**

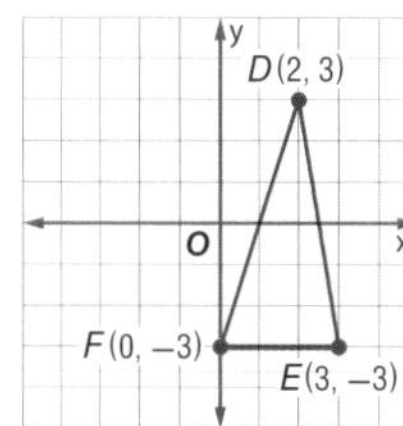

46. **LAKES** A distance of 2 units on a coordinate plane equals an actual distance of 1 mile. Suppose the locations of two lakes on a map are at (26, 15) and (9, 20). Find the actual distance between these lakes to the nearest mile. **9 mi**

EXAMPLE 7

Find the distance between $S(5, -3)$ and $T(-1, 2)$.

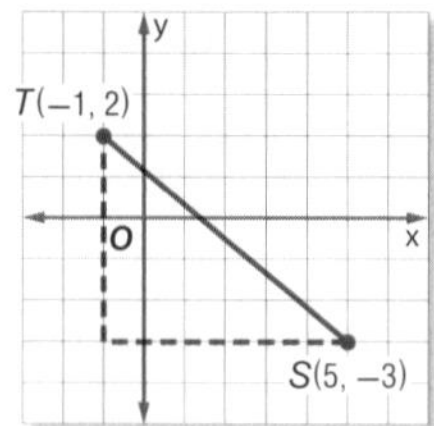

$d = \sqrt{(x_2 - x_1)^2 + (y_2 - y_1)^2}$	**Distance Formula**
$ST = \sqrt{(-1 - 5)^2 + [2 - (-3)]^2}$	**$(x_1, y_1) = (5, -3)$, $(x_2, y_2) = (-1, 2)$**
$ST = \sqrt{(-6)^2 + 5^2}$	**Simplify.**
$ST = \sqrt{36 + 25}$	**Evaluate 6^2 and 5^2.**
$ST = \sqrt{61}$	**Add 36 and 25.**
$ST \approx 7.8$	**Simplify.**

The distance between S and T is about 7.8 units.

10-6 Special Right Triangles (pp. 571–576)

Find each missing measure.

47. 48.

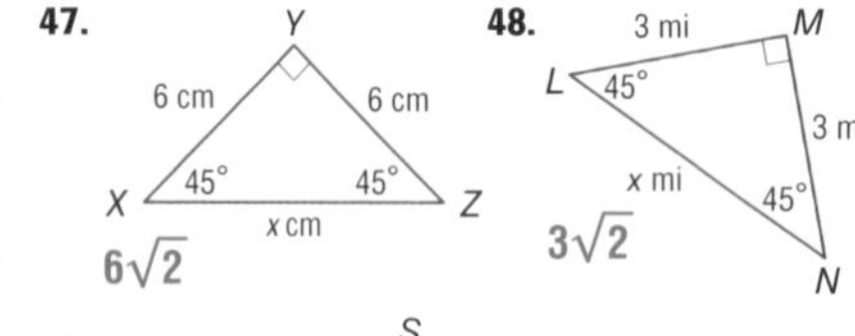

47. **$6\sqrt{2}$**
48. **$3\sqrt{2}$**

49. S, 60°, x in., 15 in., R, 30°, 45°, T, y in.
$x = 30$; $y = 15\sqrt{3}$

50. E, y m, F, 30°, x m, 60°, 22 m, D
$x = 11$; $y = 11\sqrt{3}$

51. **BAKERY** A 9-inch square cake is cut in half along the diagonal. What is the length of the cut? **$9\sqrt{2}$ in.**

EXAMPLE 8

$\triangle ABC$ and $\triangle DEF$ are 45°-45°-90° triangles. Find the missing measure.

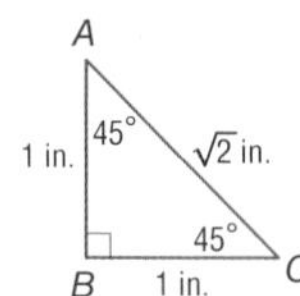

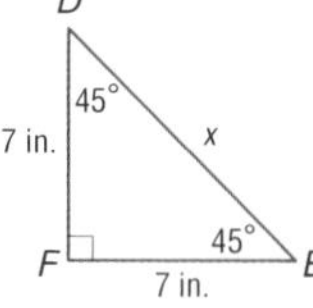

The scale factor from $\triangle ABC$ to $\triangle DEF$ is $\frac{7}{1}$ or 7. Use the scale factor to find the hypotenuse.

$x = 7 \cdot \sqrt{2}$ or $7\sqrt{2}$

So, the hypotenuse is $7\sqrt{2}$ inches.

Math Online glencoe.com
Chapter Test

Find each square root.

1. $\sqrt{256}$ 16
2. $-\sqrt{400}$ −20
3. Without using a calculator, estimate $-\sqrt{102}$ to the nearest integer. −10

Replace each ● with <, >, or = to make a true statement.

4. $4.\overline{9}$ ● $4\frac{9}{10}$ >
5. −6.8 ● $-\sqrt{45}$ <

ALGEBRA Solve each equation. Round to the nearest tenth, if necessary.

6. $t^2 = 49$ 7, −7
7. $72 = 6p^2$ 3.5, −3.5

8. **SPORTS** The formula $h = 16t^2$ describes the time t in seconds that it takes for an object to fall from a height of h feet. How long would it take a baseball dropped out of a window from a height of 50 feet to hit the ground? 1.8 s

9. **MULTIPLE CHOICE** The area of the square at the right is 256 square units. Which of the following is the value of x? A

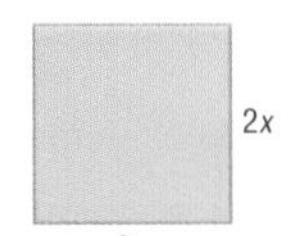

A 8
B 11.3
C 16
D 64

Classify each angle as *acute, obtuse, right,* or *straight.*

10. 45° acute
11. 95° obtuse
12. 180° straight

Find the value of x in each triangle. Then classify each triangle by its angles and by its sides.

13.

124; obtuse isosceles

14.
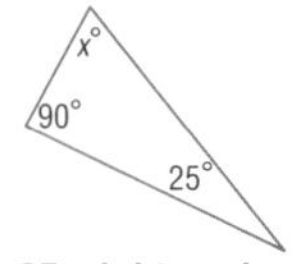

65; right scalene

The lengths of three sides of a triangle are given. Determine whether each triangle is a right triangle.

15. $a = 15, b = 36, c = 39$ yes
16. $a = 9, b = 15, c = 17$ no

Find each missing measure. Round to the nearest tenth, if necessary.

17.
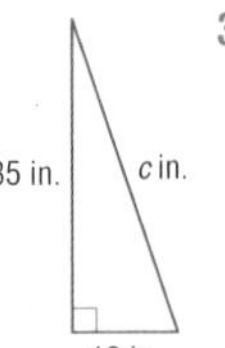

37

18.
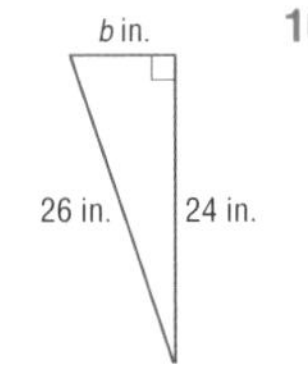

10

19. **LADDER** A building has a 12-foot-high window. If the bottom of a ladder is 5 feet away from the building, will a 15-foot ladder reach the window? Explain. Yes; a ladder that is at least 13 ft is needed to reach the window.

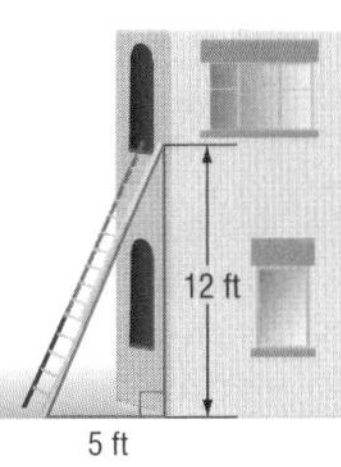

Find the distance between each pair of points. Round to the nearest tenth, if necessary.

20. $Q(-6, 4), R(6, -8)$ 17.0
21. $C(5, 9), D(-7, 3)$ 13.4

22. **MULTIPLE CHOICE** What is the perimeter of $\triangle GHJ$ shown? G

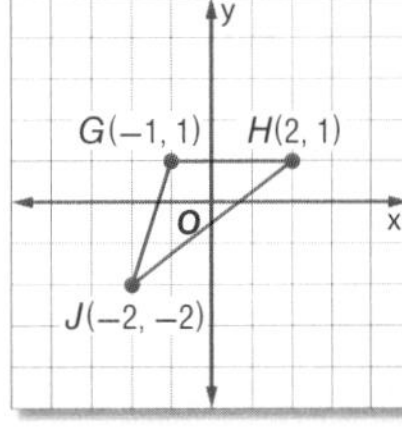

F 7.2 units
G 11.2 units
H 15.7 units
J 16.7 units

Find each missing measure.

23.
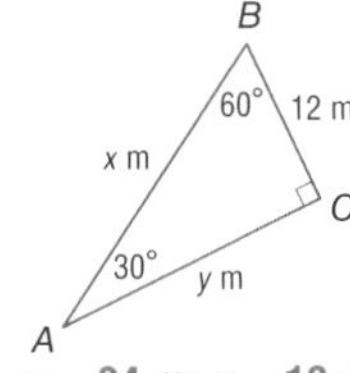

$x = 24$ m; $y = 12\sqrt{3}$ m

24.
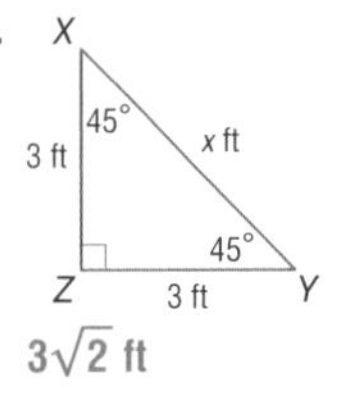

$3\sqrt{2}$ ft

25. **CRAFTS** A square piece of fabric 8 inches on each side is folded in half diagonally. What is the length of the fold? $8\sqrt{2}$ in.

ExamView Assessment Suite Customize and create multiple versions of your chapter test and their answer keys. All of the questions from the leveled chapter tests in the *Chapter 10 Resource Masters* are also available on ExamView® Assessment Suite.

Intervention Planner

Tier 1 On Level	Tier 2 Strategic Intervention approaching grade level	Tier 3 Intensive Intervention 2 or more grades below level
If students miss about 25% of the exercises or less,	**If** students miss about 50% of the exercises,	**If** students miss about 75% of the exercises,
Then choose a resource: **SE** Lessons 10-1 through 10-6 **CRM** Skills Practice, pp. 7, 13, 20, 26, 32, and 38 **TE** Chapter Project, p. 532	**Then** choose a resource: **CRM** Study Guide and Intervention, Chapter 10, pp. 5, 11, 18, 24, 30, and 36 *Quick Review Math Handbook*	**Then** use *Math Triumphs, Grade 8,* Ch. 4, 6
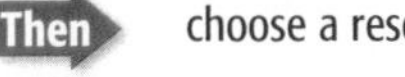 Math Online Self-Check Quiz	Math Online Extra Examples, Personal Tutor, Homework Help	Math Online Extra Examples, Personal Tutor, Homework Help, Review Vocabulary

1 FOCUS

Objective Use the strategy of using a formula to solve standardized test problems.

2 TEACH

Scaffolding Questions

Ask:

- What formulas do you already know? Answers will vary. What formulas do you think it would be useful to know? Answers will vary.
- Do you think it would be possible to solve a problem that uses a formula, but you do not know the formula? Explain. Sample answer: If the problem involves something such as perimeter, you could probably solve the problem without the formula, but if the problem involves the volume of a cone or finding the hypotenuse of a right triangle, you would need to know the formula.

CHAPTER 10 Preparing for Standardized Tests

Use a Formula

A *formula* is an equation that shows a relationship among certain quantities. Many standardized test problems will require using a formula to solve them.

Strategies for Using a Formula

Step 1

Become familiar with common formulas and their uses. You may or may not be given access to a formula sheet to use during the test.

- **If you are given a formula sheet,** be sure to practice with the formulas before taking the test so you know how to apply them.
- **If you are not given a formula sheet,** study and practice with common formulas. Your teacher can provide you with the formulas you need to know. The list may include the perimeter, circumference, area, and volume formulas, the distance formula, the Pythagorean Theorem, the midpoint formula, and others.

Formulas and Measures

Midpoint on a coordinate plane		$M = \left(\frac{x_1 + x_2}{2}, \frac{y_1 + y_2}{2}\right)$
Distance on a coordinate plane		$d = \sqrt{(x_2 - x_1)^2 + (y_2 - y_1)^2}$
Perimeter of a rectangle		$P = 2\ell + 2w$ or $P = 2(\ell + w)$
Circumference of a circle		$C = 2\pi r$ or $C = \pi d$
Area	rectangle	$A = \ell w$
	parallelogram	$A = bh$
	triangle	$A = \frac{1}{2}bh$
	trapezoid	$A = \frac{1}{2}h(b_1 + b_2)$
	circle	$A = \pi r^2$
Surface Area	cube	$S = 6s^2$
	prism	$S = Ph + 2B$
	cylinder	$S = 2\pi rh + 2\pi r^2$
	regular pyramid	$S = \frac{1}{2}P\ell + B$
	cone	$S = \pi r\ell + \pi r^2$
	cube	$V = s^3$

Step 2

Choose the appropriate formula and solve.

- **Ask Yourself:** What quantities are given in the problem statement?
- **Ask Yourself:** Is there a formula I know that relates these quantities?
- **Solve:** Substitute known quantities into the formula and solve for the unknown quantity.
- **Check:** Check your answer if time permits.

EXAMPLE

Read the problem. Identify what you need to know. Then use the information in the problem to solve.

Carla is making a map of her hometown on a coordinate grid. She plots her school at (6, 2) and the zoo at (−4, −5) as shown. If each unit on the map represents 1 mile, what is the distance between the school and the zoo? Round to the nearest tenth.

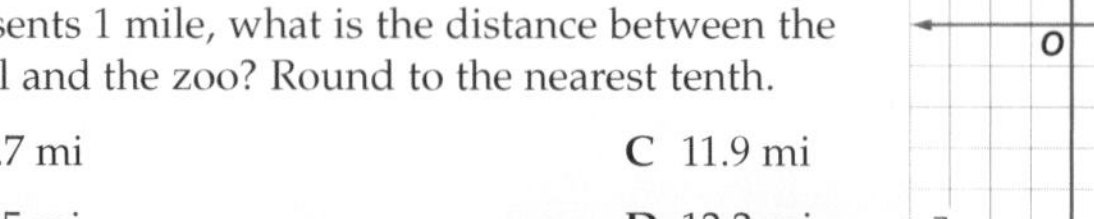

A 10.7 mi C 11.9 mi

B 11.5 mi D 12.2 mi

Read the problem carefully. You are given the coordinates of two points on a map and asked to find the distance between them. The Distance Formula relates the distance between two points on a coordinate grid.

Use the Distance Formula to find the distance between the school and the zoo.

$d = \sqrt{(x_2 - x_1)^2 + (y_2 - y_1)^2}$ **Write the Distance Formula.**

$d = \sqrt{((-4) - 6)^2 + ((-5) - 2)^2}$ **Replace x_1 with −4, 6 for x_2, −5 for y_1, and 2 for y_2.**

$d = \sqrt{(-10)^2 + (-7)^2}$ **Simplify.**

$d = \sqrt{100 + 49}$ **Simplify.**

$d = \sqrt{149} \approx 12.2$ **Use a calculator.**

Each unit on Carla's map represents 1 mile. So, the distance from the school to the zoo is about 12.2 miles.

The correct answer is D.

Exercises

Read each question. Identify what you need to know. Then use a formula to solve the questions.

1. Triangle XYZ has the vertices shown below. What is the perimeter of the triangle? Round to the nearest tenth. B

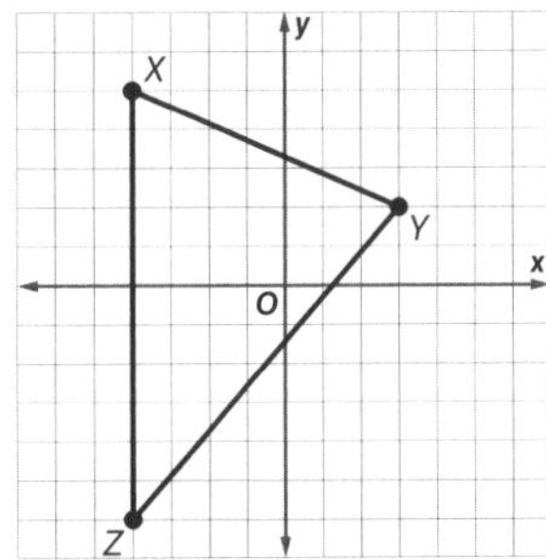

A 26.7 units

B 29.2 units

C 34.5 units

D 48.6 units

2. Alejandro is flying a kite on a breezy day. The kite is attached to the end of a piece of string that is 120 feet long. Using the diagram below, what is the current height of the kite? Round to the nearest foot. H

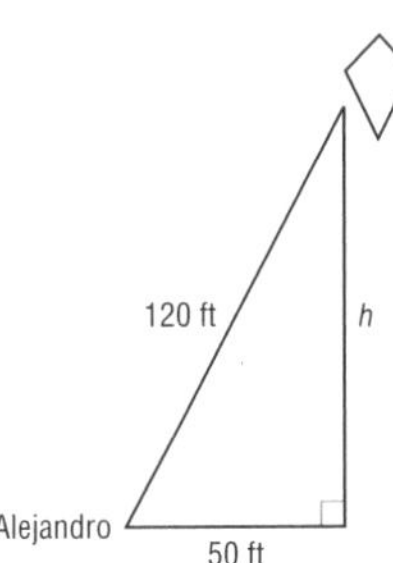

F 90 ft

G 98 ft

H 109 ft

J 130 ft

Additional Example

Hayden drew the parallelogram *STWZ* on the coordinate grid to represent the dimensions of a compost pit he is constructing in his backyard. If each unit on the grid represents 1 foot, what is the perimeter of the pit? Round to the nearest tenth. C

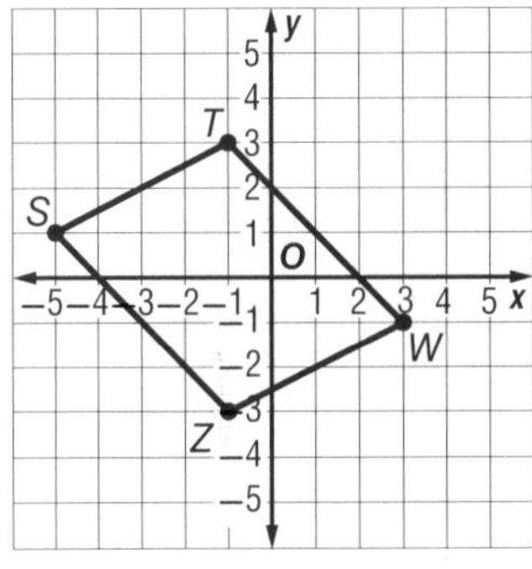

A 10.2 ft

B 14.5 ft

C 20.3 ft

D 25.7 ft

3 ASSESS

Use Exercise 1–2 to assess understanding.

Diagnose Student Errors

Survey students' responses for each item. Class trends may indicate common errors and misconceptions.

1. A correct
B misunderstood concept of estimating square roots
C misunderstood concept of estimating square roots
D misunderstood concept of estimating square roots

2. F misunderstood meaning of rational and irrational numbers
G misunderstood meaning of rational and irrational numbers
H misunderstood meaning of rational and irrational numbers
J correct

3. A calculation error or guess
B calculation error or guess
C calculation error or rounding error
D correct

4. F calculation error
G correct
H calculation error
J calculation error

5. A confused side relationships of 30°-60°-90° triangle and 45°-45°-90° triangle
B confused triangle area formula and side relationships of 30°-60°-90° triangle and 45°-45°-90° triangle
C correct
D confused triangle area formula with side relationships of 45°-45°-90° triangle

6. F correct
G used wrong conversion factor and/or calculation error
H used wrong conversion factor
J used wrong conversion factor and/or calculation error

CHAPTER 10 Standardized Test Practice

Cumulative, Chapters 1 through 10

Multiple Choice

Read each question. Then fill in the correct answer on the answer document provided by your teacher or on a sheet of paper.

1. Between which two consecutive whole numbers on a number line does $\sqrt{52}$ lie? **A**

A 7 and 8

B 8 and 9

C 9 and 10

D 10 and 11

2. Which of the following numbers is *not* rational? **J**

F $-\frac{1}{40}$

G $40.\overline{40}$

H 40.1

J $\sqrt{40}$

3. What is the length of the diagonal of the rectangular picture frame below? Round to the nearest tenth. **D**

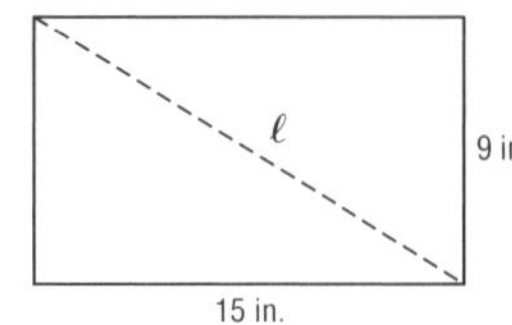

A 16.3 in.

B 16.7 in.

C 17.2 in.

D 17.5 in.

Test-Taking Tip

Question 3 Many standardized tests provide a Formula Sheet. Find and use the Pythagorean Theorem if this sheet is available.

4. Tyrone earns a 6.5% commission on his weekly sales. How much commission will he earn for his sales for the week shown in the table? Round to the nearest cent. **G**

Weekly Sales	
Day	**Sales**
Monday	$1,520
Tuesday	$1,945
Wednesday	$0
Thursday	$2,010
Friday	$2,485
Saturday	$0
Sunday	$1,625

F $574.14

G $623.03

H $655.49

J $703.68

5. Solve for x in the triangle below. **C**

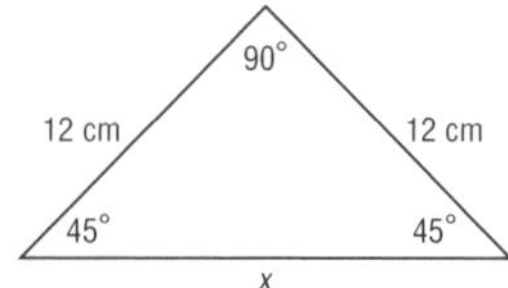

A $12\sqrt{3}$ cm

B $6\sqrt{3}$ cm

C $12\sqrt{2}$ cm

D $6\sqrt{2}$ cm

6. The average speed of the 2007 Tour de France winner was about 39 kilometers per hour. That is about the same rate as which of the following? **F**

F 24 mph

G 45 mph

H 63 mph

J 71 mph

584 Chapter 10 Real Numbers and Right Triangles

Math Online glencoe.com
Standardized Test Practice

Short Response/Gridded Response

Record your answers on the answer sheet provided by your teacher or on a sheet of paper.

7. Classify the triangle by its angles and its sides. **obtuse scalene triangle**

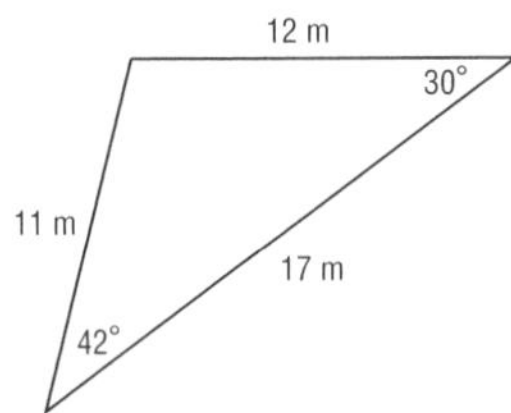

8. The table shows the approximate diameters of Mars and Neptune. About how many times as great is the diameter of Neptune than the diameter of Mars? **about 2^3 or 8 times greater**

Planet	Approximate Diameter (mi)
Mars	2^{12}
Neptune	2^{15}

9. GRIDDED RESPONSE Reggie has a square tarp with an area of 196 square feet. What are the lengths of the sides of the tarp in feet? **14**

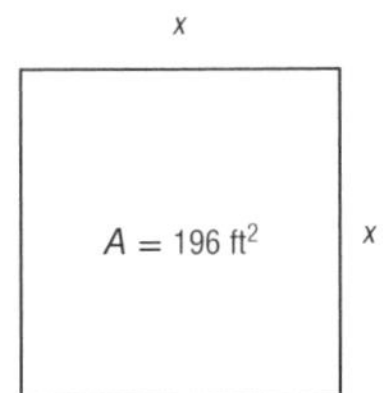

10. GRIDDED RESPONSE All of the coats in a clothing store were on sale for 30% off the original price. Carmen paid $41.30 for a coat after the discount. What was the original price of the coat in dollars? **59**

Extended Response

Record your answers on a sheet of paper. Show your work.

11. Triangle *RST* has the vertices shown on the coordinate grid. Use the triangle to answer each question.

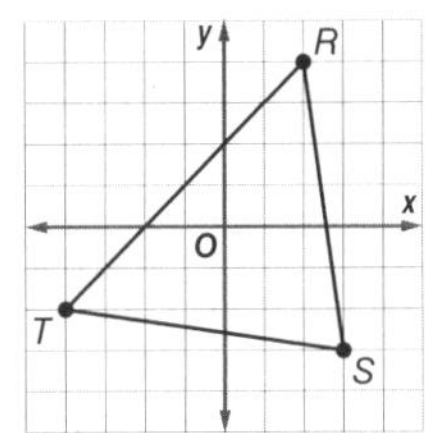

a. What are the lengths of $\overline{RS}$, $\overline{ST}$, and $\overline{RT}$? Round to the nearest hundredth.

b. Classify the triangle by its angles and sides.

c. What is the perimeter of the triangle? Round to the nearest tenth. **about 22.6 units**

11a. $RS \approx 7.07$ **units,** $ST \approx 7.07$ **units,** $RT \approx 8.49$ **units**

11b. acute isosceles

Need Extra Help?											
If you missed Question...	1	2	3	4	5	6	7	8	9	10	11
Go to Lesson or Page...	10-1	10-2	10-4	7-5	10-6	6-3	10-3	9-3	10-1	7-6	10-5

Formative Assessment

You can use these two pages to benchmark student progress.

CRM Standardized Test Practice, pp. 61–63

Answer Sheet Practice

Have students simulate taking a standardized test by recording their answers on practice recording sheets.

CRM Student Recording Sheet, p. 42

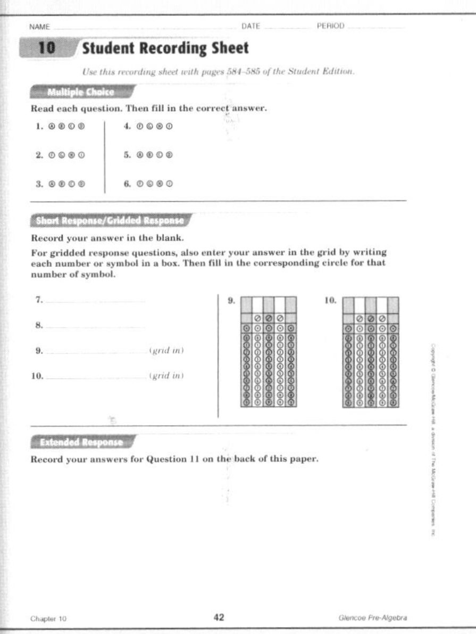

NAME ______ DATE ______ PERIOD ______

10 Student Recording Sheet

Use this recording sheet with pages 584–585 of the Student Edition.

Multiple Choice

Read each question. Then fill in the correct answer.

1. Ⓐ Ⓑ Ⓒ Ⓓ
2. Ⓕ Ⓖ Ⓗ Ⓘ
3. Ⓐ Ⓑ Ⓒ Ⓓ
4. Ⓕ Ⓖ Ⓗ Ⓘ
5. Ⓐ Ⓑ Ⓒ Ⓓ
6. Ⓕ Ⓖ Ⓗ Ⓘ

Short Response/Gridded Response

Record your answer in the blank.

For gridded response questions, also enter your answer in the grid by writing each number or symbol in a box. Then fill in the corresponding circle for that number of symbol.

7. ______
8. ______
9. ______ (grid in)
10. ______ (grid in)

Extended Response

Record your answers for Question 11 on the back of this paper.

Copyright © Glencoe/McGraw-Hill, a division of The McGraw-Hill Companies, Inc.

Chapter 10 42 Glencoe Pre-Algebra

Create practice worksheets or tests that align to your state's standards, as well as TIMSS and NAEP tests.

Homework Option

Get Ready for Chapter 11 Assign students the exercises on p. 587 as homework to assess whether they possess the prerequisite skills needed for the next chapter.

Pages 535–536 Explore 10-1

1. 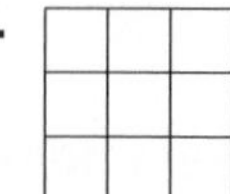

2. 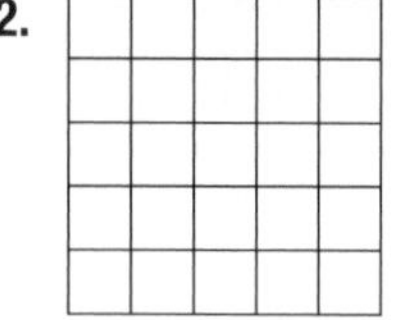

3. 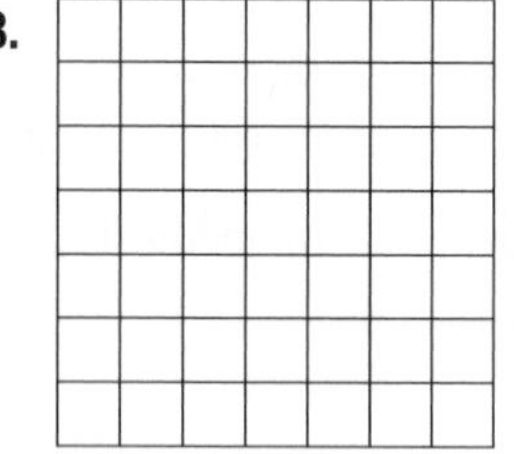

4. 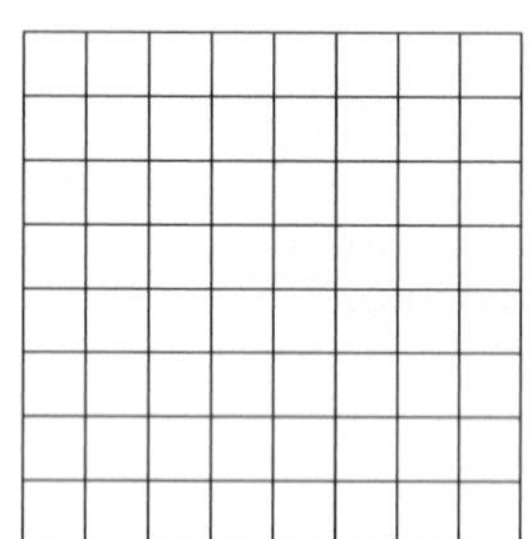

5. 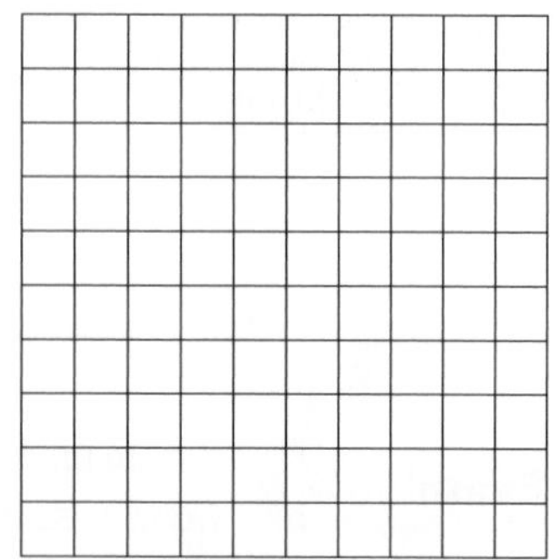

6. 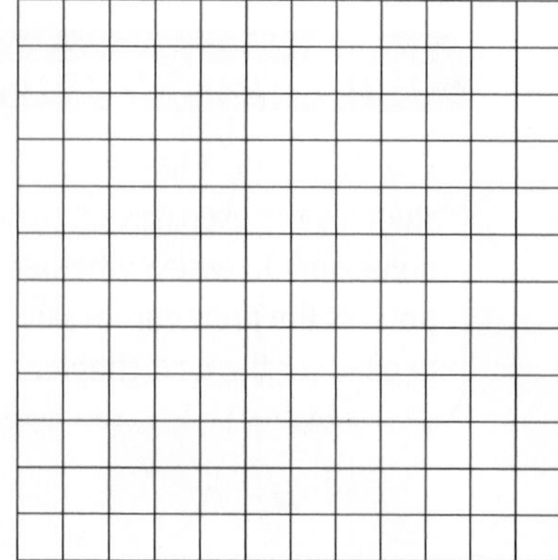

8. 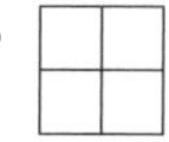

9. 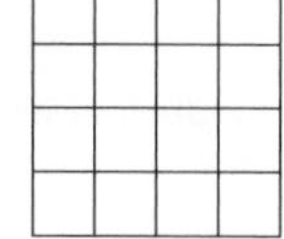

10. 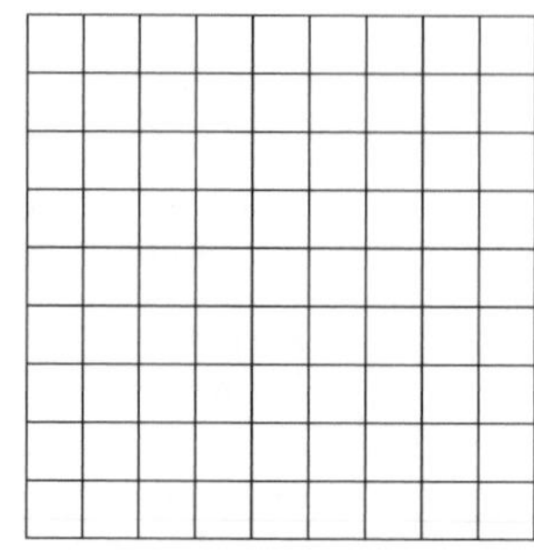

11. 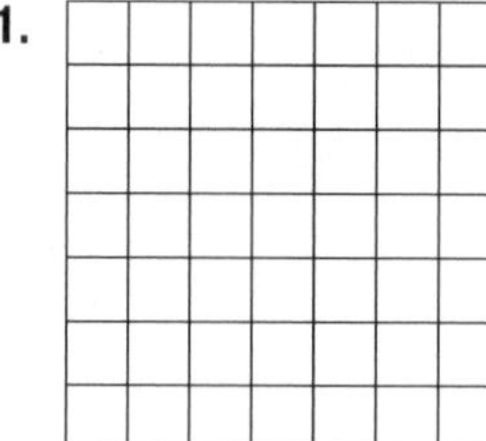

12. 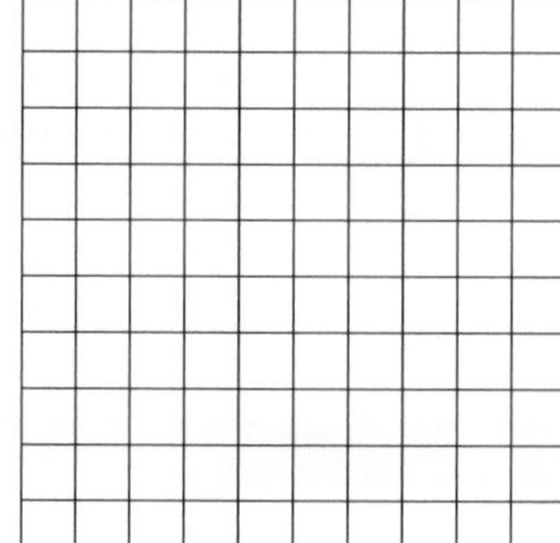

13. 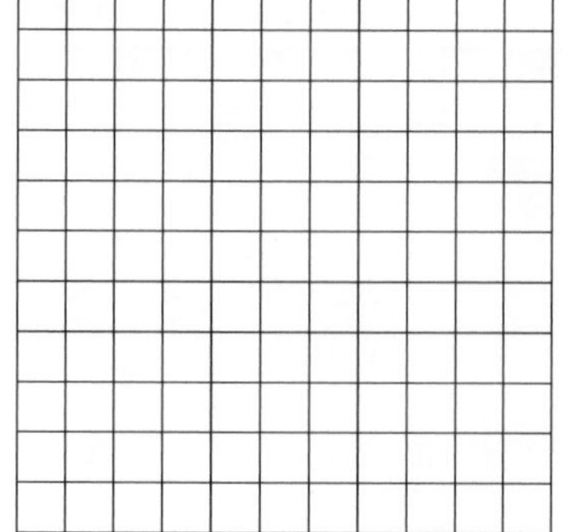

15. 4

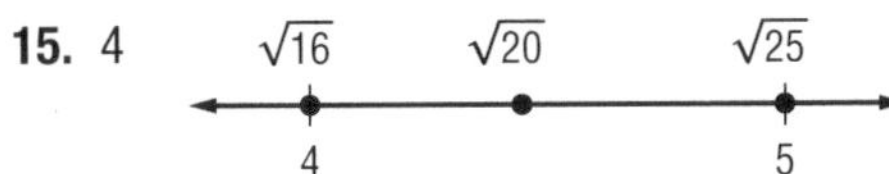

16. 7

17. 8

$\sqrt{49}$ $\sqrt{58}$ $\sqrt{64}$

7 8

18. 8

$\sqrt{64}$ $\sqrt{69}$ $\sqrt{81}$

8 9

19. 10

$\sqrt{81}$ $\sqrt{91}$ $\sqrt{100}$

9 10

20. 11

$\sqrt{100}$ $\sqrt{111}$ $\sqrt{121}$

10 11

Pages 541–542 Lesson 10-1

39a

x	x^2
−2	4
−1	1
0	0
1	1
2	4

x	$\sqrt{x}$
4	2
2.25	1.5
1	1
0.25	0.5
0	0

39b.

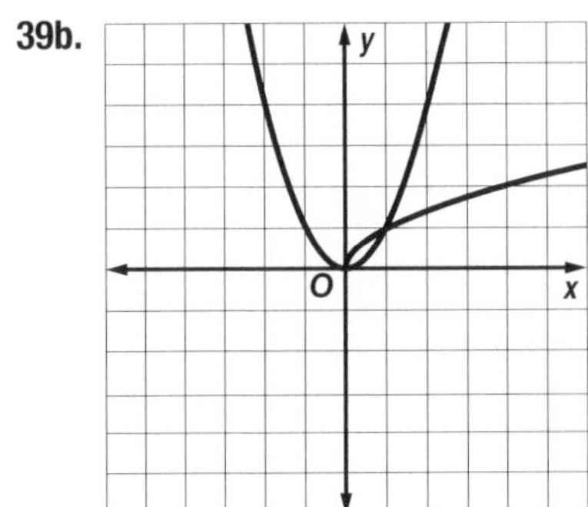

Pages 562–563 Lesson 10-4

37. $c^2 = a^2 + b^2$ Pythagorean Theorem

$10^2 = x^2 + x^2$ Replace c with 10, a with x and b with x.

$100 = 2x^2$ Simplify.

$50 = x^2$ Divide each side by 2.

$\sqrt{50} = x$ Take the square root of each side.

So, the length of the legs is $\sqrt{50}$ or about 7.1 in.

38. Sample answer: Use the converse of the Pythagorean Theorem. Find the square of the greatest measure. Then find the sum of the squares of the other two measures. If the two values are equal, then the measures are side lengths of a right triangle. Check to see if a triangle with side measures of 6 cm, 7 cm, and 11 cm is a right triangle. $11^2 = 121, 6^2 = 36, 7^2 = 49$; $36 + 49 = 85$ and $85 \neq 121$, so the triangle is not a right triangle.

42b. $a^2 + b^2 = c^2$ Pythagorean Theorem

$90^2 + 90^2 = c^2$ Replace a with 90 and b with 90.

$8100 + 8100 = c^2$ Evaluate 90^2.

$16{,}200 = c^2$ Simplify.

$\pm\sqrt{16{,}200} = c$ Definition of square root.

$127.28 \approx c$ Use the principal square root.

The distance from home plate to second base is about 127 feet.

Page 564, Extend 10-4

1.

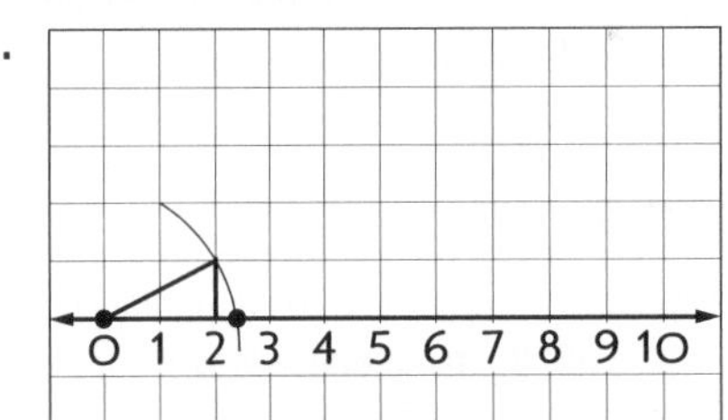

2.

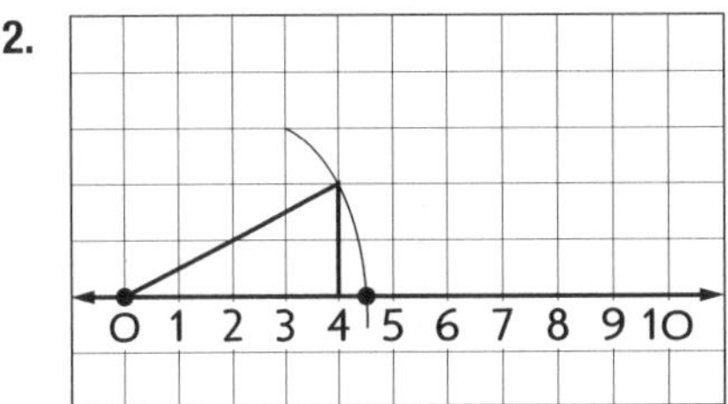

Chapter 10 Answer Appendix

3.

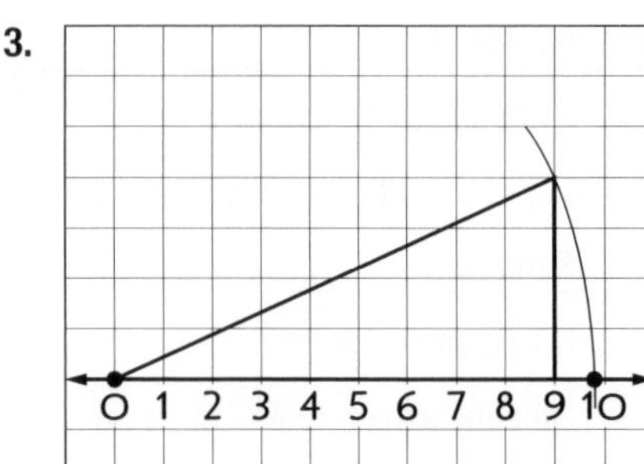

4.

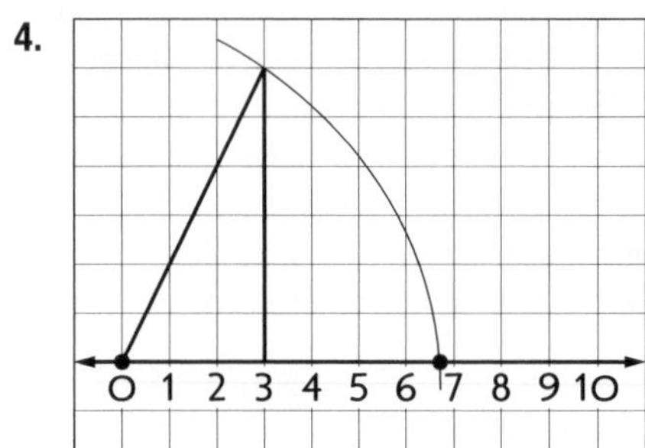

5. Sample answer: First, find two numbers whose squares have a sum of 61. Since $5^2 + 6^2 = 61$, draw a right triangle with length 5 units and height 6 units. Or, draw a right triangle with length 6 units and height 5 units. Then, open the compass to the length of the hypotenuse. With the tip of the compass at 0, draw an arc that intersects the number line.

6. Sample answer: Since $(\sqrt{2})^2 + 1^2 = 3$, use $\sqrt{2}$ as one leg of a right triangle and 1 unit as the other leg. Then follow the procedure in the activity to locate the graph of $\sqrt{3}$.

Page 575, Lesson 10-6

25. Yes; the legs are 21 cm and 36.4 cm and the hypotenuse is 42 cm. Since $21 \cdot 2 = 42$, the hypotenuse is twice the shorter leg. Since $21 \cdot \sqrt{3} \approx 36.4$, the longer leg is $\sqrt{3}$ times the length of the shorter leg.

Notes

CHAPTER 11 Chapter Planner

Diagnostic Assessment
Quick Check, p. 587

	Lesson 11-1 Pacing: 1 day	Explore 11-2 Pacing: 1 day	Lesson 11-2 Pacing: 1 day
Title	**Angle and Line Relationships**	**Geometry Lab: Investigating Congruent Triangles**	**Congruent Triangles**
Objectives	• Examine relationships of angles formed by parallel lines and a transversal. • Examine relationships between pairs of angles.	• Investigate the measures sufficient to show that two triangles are congruent.	• Identify corresponding parts of congruent triangles. • Identify congruent triangles.
Key Vocabulary	parallel lines transversal alternate interior angles alternate exterior angles corresponding angles perpendicular lines vertical angles adjacent angles complementary angles supplementary angles		congruent corresponding parts
NCTM Focal Points	G7–FP2. G8–FP4C For the complete wording of the Focal Points for Grades 7 and 8, please see pages iv, v, FP0 and FP1		
Multiple Representations	p. 594		
Lesson Resources	**Chapter 11 Resource Masters** • Study Guide and Intervention, pp. 5–6 AL OL BL • Skills Practice, p. 7 AL OL BL • Practice, p. 8 AL OL BL ELL • Word Problem Practice, p. 9 AL OL BL **Transparencies** • 5-Minute Check Transparency 11-1 AL OL BL ELL **Additional Print Resources** • *Study Notebook* AL OL BL ELL	**Materials:** • patty paper (20 pieces) • tape • ruler	**Chapter 11 Resource Masters** • Study Guide and Intervention, pp. 11–12 AL OL BL • Skills Practice, p. 13 AL OL BL • Practice, p. 14 AL OL BL ELL • Word Problem Practice, p. 15 AL OL BL • Enrichment, p. 16 OL BL **Transparencies** • 5-Minute Check Transparency 11-2 AL OL BL ELL **Additional Print Resources** • *Study Notebook* AL OL BL ELL
Technology for Every Lesson	Math Online glencoe.com • Extra Examples • Self-Check Quizzes • Personal Tutor	**CD/DVD Resources** IWB INTERACTIVE WHITEBOARD READY IWB StudentWorks Plus IWB Interactive Classroom IWB Diagnostic and Assessment Planner	• TeacherWorks Plus • eSolutions Manual Plus • ExamView Assessment Suite
Math in Motion		p. 596	
Differentiated Instruction	pp. 591, 595		pp. 599, 604

KEY: 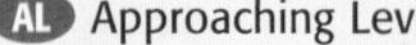 AL Approaching Level 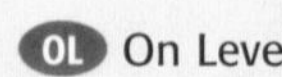 OL On Level 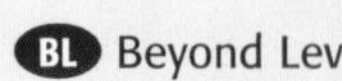 BL Beyond Level 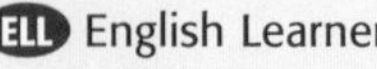 ELL English Learners

Distance and Angle

Suggested Pacing			
Time Periods	Instruction	Review& Asessment	Total
45-minute	12	2	14
90-minute	6	1	7

Lesson 11-3 Pacing: 1 day	Explore 11-4 Pacing: 1 day	Lesson 11-4 Pacing: 1 day	Lesson 11-5 Pacing: 1 day
Rotations	**Geometry Lab: Angles in Polygons**	**Quadrilaterals**	**Polygons**
• Define, identify, and draw rotations. • Determine if a figure has rotational symmetry.	• Use parallel lines to investigate the sum of the measures of the angles in a triangle and similar triangles.	• Find missing angle measures of a quadrilateral. • Classify quadrilaterals.	• Classify polygons. • Determine the sum of the measures of the interior angles of a polygon.
rotation center of rotation rotational symmetry		quadrilateral	polygon diagonal interior angle regular polygon tessellation
p. 609		p. 615	
Chapter 11 Resource Masters • Study Guide and Intervention, pp. 17–18 AL OL BL • Skills Practice, p. 19 AL OL BL • Practice, p. 20 AL OL BL ELL • Word Problem Practice, p. 21 AL OL BL • Enrichment, p. 22 OL BL • Quiz 1, p. 62 AL OL BL ELL **Transparencies** • 5-Minute Check Transparency 11-3 AL OL BL ELL **Additional Print Resources** • *Study Notebook* AL OL BL ELL	**Materials:** • straightedge or ruler	**Chapter 11 Resource Masters** • Study Guide and Intervention, pp. 23–24 AL OL BL • Skills Practice, p. 25 AL OL BL • Practice, p. 26 AL OL BL ELL • Word Problem Practice, p. 27 AL OL BL • Enrichment, p. 28 OL BL **Transparencies** • 5-Minute Check Transparency 11-4 AL OL BL ELL **Additional Print Resources** • *Study Notebook* AL OL BL ELL	**Chapter 11 Resource Masters** • Study Guide and Intervention, pp. 29–30 AL OL BL • Skills Practice, p. 31 AL OL BL • Practice, p. 32 AL OL BL ELL • Word Problem Practice, p. 33 AL OL BL • Enrichment, p. 34 OL BL • Quiz 2, p. 62 AL OL BL ELL **Transparencies** • 5-Minute Check Transparency 11-5 AL OL BL ELL **Additional Print Resources** • *Study Notebook* AL OL BL ELL

Math Online glencoe.com
- Extra Examples
- Self-Check Quizzes
- Personal Tutor

CD/DVD Resources IWB INTERACTIVE WHITEBOARD READY
- IWB StudentWorks Plus
- IWB Interactive Classroom
- IWB Diagnostic and Assessment Planner
- TeacherWorks Plus
- eSolutions Manual Plus
- ExamView Assessment Suite

	p. 611	p. 613	
pp. 607, 610		pp. 613, 616	pp. 618, 622

Formative Assessment
Mid Chapter Quiz, p. 623

CHAPTER 11

Chapter Planner

	Lesson 11-6 Pacing: 1 day	Lesson 11-7 Pacing: 1 day	Lesson 11-8 Pacing: 1 day
Title	**Area of Parallelograms, Triangles, and Trapezoids**	**Circles and Circumference**	**Area of Circles**
Objectives	• Find areas of parallelograms. • Find areas of triangles and trapezoids	• Find the circumference of circles. • Solve problems involving circumference.	• Find areas of circles. • Find areas of sectors.
Key Vocabulary	base altitude	circle; center radius; diameter chord; circumference π (pi)	sector central angle
NCTM Focal Points			
Multiple Representations	p. 629	p. 634	p. 640
Lesson Resources	**Chapter 11 Resource Masters** • Study Guide and Intervention, pp. 35–36 AL OL BL • Skills Practice, p. 37 AL OL BL • Practice, p. 38 AL OL BL ELL • Word Problem Practice, p. 39 AL OL BL • Enrichment, p. 40 OL BL • Spreadsheet, p. 41 AL OL BL ELL **Transparencies** • 5-Minute Check Transparency 11-6 AL OL BL ELL **Additional Print Resources** • *Study Notebook* AL OL BL ELL	**Chapter 11 Resource Masters** • Study Guide and Intervention, pp. 42–43 AL OL BL • Skills Practice, p. 44 AL OL BL • Practice, p. 45 AL OL BL ELL • Word Problem Practice, p. 46 AL OL BL • Enrichment, p. 47 OL BL • Quiz 3, p. 63 AL OL BL ELL **Transparencies** • 5-Minute Check Transparency 11-7 AL OL BL ELL **Additional Print Resources** • *Study Notebook* AL OL BL ELL	**Chapter 11 Resource Masters** • Study Guide and Intervention, pp. 48–49 AL OL BL • Skills Practice, p. 50 AL OL BL • Practice, p. 51 AL OL BL ELL • Word Problem Practice, p. 52 AL OL BL • Enrichment, p. 53 OL BL **Transparencies** • 5-Minute Check Transparency 11-8 AL OL BL ELL **Additional Print Resources** • *Study Notebook* AL OL BL ELL
Technology for Every Lesson	Math Online glencoe.com • Extra Examples • Self-Check Quizzes • Personal Tutor	**CD/DVD Resources** IWB INTERACTIVE WHITEBOARD READY IWB StudentWorks Plus IWB Interactive Classroom IWB Diagnostic and Assessment Planner	• TeacherWorks Plus • eSolutions Manual Plus • ExamView Assessment Suite
Math in Motion			
Differentiated Instruction	pp. 625, 630	pp. 632, 635	pp. 638, 641

KEY: AL Approaching Level OL On Level BL Beyond Level ELL English Learners

Lesson 11-9 Pacing: 1 day	Extend 11-9 Pacing: 1 day
Area of Composite Figures	**Spreadsheet Lab: Changes in Scale**
• Find the area of composite figures. • Solve problems involving the area of composite figures.	• Investigate scale factors with perimeter and area.
composite figure	
p. 646	
Chapter 11 Resource Masters • Study Guide and Intervention, pp. 54–55 AL OL BL • Skills Practice, p. 56 AL OL BL • Practice, p. 57 AL OL BL ELL • Word Problem Practice, p. 58 AL OL BL • Enrichment, p. 59 OL BL • Quiz 4, p. 63 AL OL BL ELL **Transparencies** • 5-Minute Check Transparency 11-9 AL OL BL ELL **Additional Print Resources** • *Study Notebook* AL OL BL ELL	**Materials:** • spreadsheet software

Math Online glencoe.com

- Extra Examples
- Self-Check Quizzes
- Personal Tutor

CD/DVD Resources IWB INTERACTIVE WHITEBOARD READY

- IWB StudentWorks Plus
- IWB Interactive Classroom
- IWB Diagnostic and Assessment Planner
- TeacherWorks Plus
- eSolutions Manual Plus
- ExamView Assessment Suite

pp. 643, 647	

Summative Assessment

- Study Guide and Review, pp. 650–654
- Practice Test, p. 655

CHAPTER 11

Assessment and Intervention

SE = Student Edition, **TE** = Teacher Edition, **CRM** = Chapter Resource Masters

	Diagnosis	Prescription
Diagnostic Assessment	**Beginning Chapter 11**	
	Get Ready for Chapter 11 **SE,** p. 587	Response to Intervention **TE,** p. 587
	Beginning Every Lesson	
	Then, Now, Why? **SE** 5-Minute Check Transparencies	Chapter 0 **SE,** pp. P1–P22 Concepts and Skills Bank **SE** pp. 856–887 *Quick Review Math Handbook*
Formative Assessment	**During/After Every Lesson**	
	Check Your Progress **SE,** every example Check Your Understanding **SE** H.O.T. Problems **SE** Spiral Review **SE** Additional Examples **TE** Watch Out! **TE** Step 4, Assess **TE** Chapter 11 Quizzes **CRM,** pp. 62–63 Self-Check Quizzes glencoe.com	Tier 1 Intervention Concepts and Skills Bank **SE,** pp. 856–887 Skills Practice **CRM,** Ch. 1–11 glencoe.com Tier 2 Intervention Differentiated Instruction **TE** Study Guide and Intervention Masters **CRM,** Ch. 1–11 *Quick Review Math Handbook* Tier 3 Intervention *Math Triumphs, Grade 8,* Ch. 4
	Mid-Chapter	
	Mid-Chapter Quiz **SE,** p. 623 Mid-Chapter Test **CRM,** p. 64 ExamView Assessment Suite	Tier 1 Intervention Concepts and Skills Bank **SE,** pp. 856–887 Skills Practice **CRM,** Ch. 1–11 glencoe.com Tier 2 Intervention Study Guide and Intervention Masters **CRM,** Ch. 1–11 *Quick Review Math Handbook* Tier 3 Intervention *Math Triumphs, Grade 8,* Ch. 4
	Before Chapter Test	
	Chapter Study Guide and Review **SE,** pp. 650–654 Practice Test **SE,** p. 655 Standardized Test Practice **SE,** pp. 656–659 Chapter Test glencoe.com Standardized Test Practice glencoe.com Vocabulary Review glencoe.com ExamView Assessment Suite	Tier 1 Intervention Concepts and Skills Bank **SE,** pp. 856–887 Skills Practice **CRM,** Ch. 1–11 glencoe.com Tier 2 Intervention Study Guide and Intervention Masters **CRM,** Ch. 1–11 *Quick Review Math Handbook* Tier 3 Intervention *Math Triumphs, Grade 8,* Ch. 4
Summative Assessment	**After Chapter 11**	
	Multiple-Choice Tests, Forms 1, 2A, 2B, **CRM,** pp. 66–71 Free-Response Tests, Forms 2C, 2D, 3, **CRM,** pp. 72–77 Vocabulary Test **CRM,** p. 65 Extended Response Test **CRM,** p. 78 Standardized Test Practice **CRM,** pp. 79–81 ExamView Assessment Suite	Study Guide and Intervention Masters **CRM,** Ch. 1–11 *Quick Review Math Handbook* glencoe.com

Differentiated Instruction

Option 1 Reaching All Learners AL OL BL ELL

INTRAPERSONAL Ask students to choose a favorite hobby or sport. They should then find a circle related to that activity and determine the circumference, area, diameter, and/or radius of the circle. For example, a basketball player might calculate the diameter of a basketball. He or she could then compare the diameter of the ball to the diameter of the hoop. A student who enjoys music could find the properties of a compact disc and relate the area of the CD to how many bytes it stores. Ask students to record any insights into their activity.

VISUAL/SPATIAL Have students explore the properties of polygons by creating a tessellation that uses one or more polygons. Ask students to choose a polygon(s) and determine whether it can be used to make a tessellation. Then have them create a tessellation. Encourage them to color their tessellations to create different designs. Ask them to describe the measures of the angles at a vertex of the tessellation and explain why the polygon(s) tessellates. For example, 3 hexagons surround a vertex of the tessellation below, and since each angle measures 120° and 3(120°) = 360°, the hexagon tessellates.

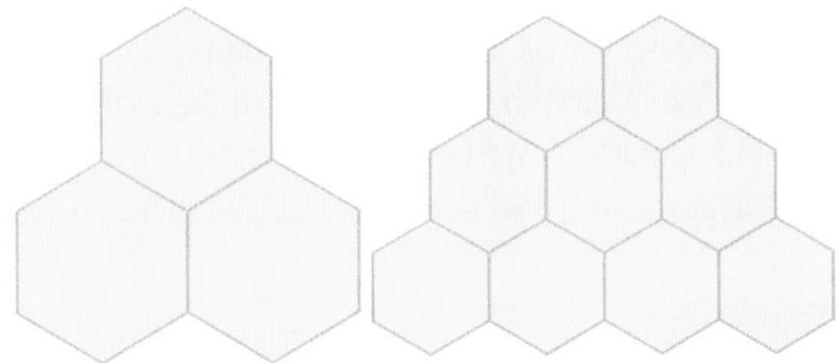

Option 2 Approaching Level AL

Have students bring to class pictures that show geometric shapes. Suggest that they use magazines, newspapers, and books on architecture, interior design, and paintings. Have students work in groups to identify and classify the polygons in their group's pictures. Then have them find the sum of the measures of the interior angles of two of the polygons.

Option 3 English Learners ELL

Several words in the chapter appear in different contexts including *alternate*, in alternate interior and alternate exterior angles; *center*, in center of rotation and central angle; *congruent*, in congruent triangles and angles; *corresponding*, in corresponding angles, corresponding parts, and corresponding sides; *interior*, in interior angles and alternate interior angles; and *rotation*, in center of rotation and rotational symmetry.

Have students make a chart with the six italicized words as the headings. Ask them to look up the meanings of the words and write a definition under the heading. As they encounter new vocabulary, have them add the word to the chart and relate the definition of the heading to the word. Remind students that some words, such as alternate interior angles, will appear in more than one section of the chart.

Option 4 Beyond Level BL

Allow students to examine objects that rotate in real life. Pose questions for them to consider:

- How many degrees does a door knob in your house turn? Clockwise or counter-clockwise? How did you get your estimation? Is it the same in both directions?
- How far does a car travel if its tires have rotated 360°? How many rotational degrees do the car's tires cover from your home to the school? Provide evidence and mathematical support for your responses to both questions.
- Can you think of a situation where over-rotation of an object might cause harm? Explain your thinking.

CHAPTER 11 Focus on Mathematical Content

Vertical Alignment

Before Chapter 11

Related Topics before Pre-Algebra

- use angle measurement to classify pairs of angles
- use properties to classify triangles

Previous Topics from Pre-Algebra

- predict, find, and justify solutions
- locate and name points on a coordinate plane

Chapter 11

Related Topics from Pre-Algebra

- use geometric concepts and properties to solve problems in fields such as art and architecture
- graph rotations on a coordinate plane
- use properties to classify quadrilaterals and other polygons

After Chapter 11

Preparation for Geometry

- make conjectures about angles and lines and determine the validity of the conjectures
- justify and apply triangle congruence relationships

Lesson-by-Lesson Preview

11-1 Angle and Line Relationships

Two lines in a plane that never intersect are called parallel lines. When two parallel lines intersect a third line, called a transversal, eight angles are formed.

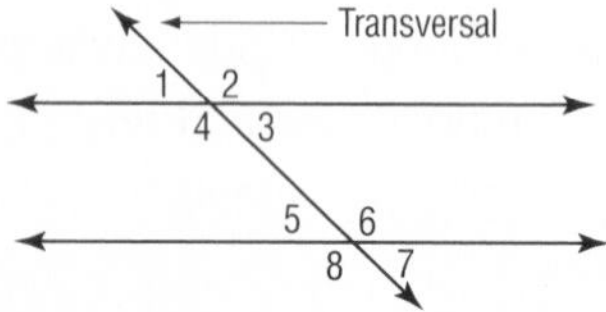

- interior angles: $\angle 3$, $\angle 4$, $\angle 5$, and $\angle 6$
- exterior angles: $\angle 1$, $\angle 2$, $\angle 7$, and $\angle 8$
- alternate interior angles: $\angle 3$ and $\angle 5$, $\angle 4$ and $\angle 6$
- alternate exterior angles: $\angle 1$ and $\angle 7$, $\angle 2$ and $\angle 8$
- corresponding angles: $\angle 1$ and $\angle 5$, $\angle 2$ and $\angle 6$, $\angle 3$ and $\angle 7$, $\angle 4$ and $\angle 8$

Pairs of corresponding angles, alternate interior angles, and alternate exterior angles are congruent.

11-2 Congruent Triangles

Congruent triangles have the same size and the same shape. The parts of congruent triangles that match are called corresponding parts. Congruent triangles have corresponding angles and corresponding sides that are congruent.

11-3 Rotations

A rotation, or a turn, is a transformation in which a figure is rotated around a fixed point called the center of rotation. A rotated image has the same size and shape as the original figure. The images below show a clockwise rotation of an arrow with a center of rotation at point *B*.

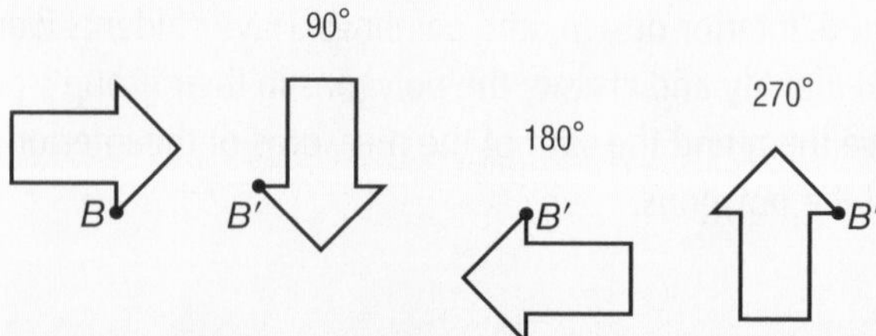

A figure has rotational symmetry if it can be rotated less than 360° about its center so that the image matches the original.

11-4 Quadrilaterals

A quadrilateral is a closed figure with four sides and four angles. The sum of the measures of the interior angles of a quadrilateral is 360°. Quadrilaterals are classified according to their characteristics:

- trapezoid: exactly one pair of parallel sides
- parallelogram: both pairs of opposite sides parallel and congruent
- rectangle: parallelogram with 4 right angles
- square: parallelogram with 4 right angles and 4 congruent sides
- rhombus: parallelogram with 4 congruent sides

11-5 Polygons

A polygon is a simple, closed figure formed by three or more line segments called sides. The line segments meet only at their endpoints. Polygons are classified by the number of sides they have: triangle (3), quadrilateral (4), pentagon (5), hexagon (6), heptagon (7), octagon (8), nonagon (9), and decagon (10).

The sum of the measures of the interior angles of any polygon is equal to $(n - 2)180$, where n is the number of sides of a polygon. For example, a decagon has 10 sides, so the sum of the measure of the interior angles is $(10 - 2)180 = 8(180)$ or 1440°.

11-6 Area of Parallelograms, Triangles, and Trapezoids

You can use formulas to find the areas of parallelograms, triangles, and trapezoids.

- parallelogram: Use $A = bh$ to find the area A of a parallelogram with base b and height h.
- triangle: $A = \frac{1}{2}bh$ to find the area A of a triangle with base b and height h
- trapezoid: $A = \frac{1}{2}h(b_1 + b_2)$ to find the area A of a trapezoid with height h and bases b_1 and b_2

11-7 Circles and Circumference

A circle is the set of all points in a plane that are the same distance from a given point, the center. The ratio of the circumference of a circle to its diameter is π (pi) or 3.1415926.... To find the circumference of a circle, use the formulas $C = \pi d$ or $C = 2\pi r$.

11-8 Area of Circles

The area A of a circle is equal to π times the square of its radius. In symbols, this is written as $A = \pi r^2$. To find the area of a sector of a circle, use the formula $A = \frac{N}{360}(\pi r^2)$, where N is the degree measure of the central angle of the circle and r is the radius of the circle.

11-9 Area of Composite Figures

Composite figures are figures that are composed of two or more shapes. The following steps can be used to find the area of a composite figure:

- Decompose the figure into figures with areas you know how to find. There may be more than one way to decompose the figure.
- Use formulas to find the area of each shape.
- Find the sum of the areas.

Mc Graw Hill Professional Development

Targeted professional development has been articulated throughout McGraw-Hill's mathematics program. The **McGraw-Hill Professional Development Video Library** provides short videos that support key topics. For more information, visit glencoe.com.

Model Lessons

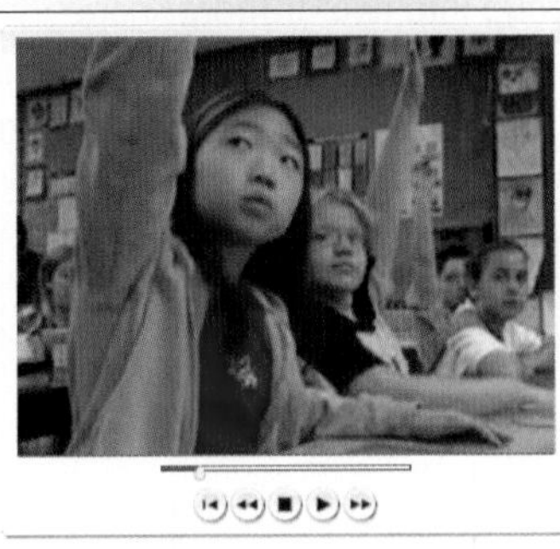

Instructional Strategies

CHAPTER 11 Notes

Chapter Project

Real World: The Geometry of a Park

Students use what they have learned about shapes, rotations and rotational symmetry, and finding areas of composite figures to work with concepts related to nature.

- Ask students to bring to class a drawing or map of a local or state park that shows its shape, and have them add approximate lengths of each side of the park to the drawing or map. Also have them bring a picture or photograph of an object that could be found in the park, such as a rock, flower, leaf, bird, or starfish.
- Have groups examine each of the park objects and then sort them into shapes that are polygons or not polygons. Ask them to classify the polygon shapes of the objects and explain why the other objects cannot be classified as polygons.
- Ask groups to sketch each of the objects and then rotate them 90°, 180°, and 270° clockwise about a point. If necessary, rotate a point on the figure. Which objects have rotational symmetry? What is the angle of rotation?
- Have groups divide each park in their group into two or more shapes. In how many ways can they divide the park into shapes? Ask them to choose one of the ways and then find the approximate area of the park.

CHAPTER 11 Distance and Angle

Then
In Chapter 10 you worked with angles, triangles, and the Pythagorean Theorem.

Now
In Chapter 11, you will:

- Identify the relationship of parallel and intersecting lines.
- Identify properties of congruent triangles.
- Find the area of polygons, irregular figures, and circles.

Why?
NATURE There are about 24,000 different species of butterflies in the world. They range in size from an $\frac{1}{8}$ inch up to 12 inches. Did you know that butterflies taste with their feet? Their taste sensors are located in the feet. By standing on their food, they can taste it!

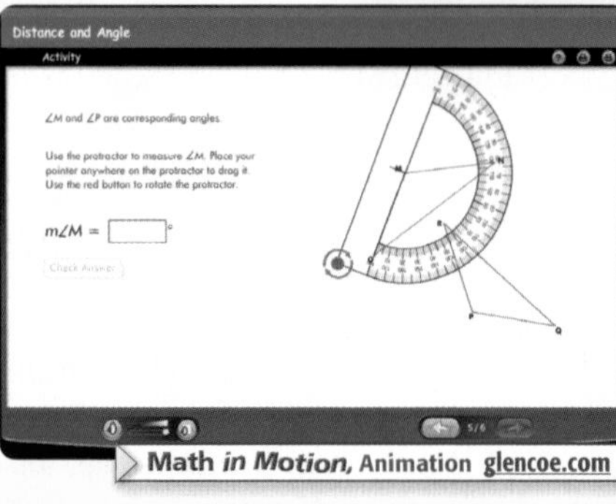

Math in Motion, Animation glencoe.com

Key Vocabulary Introduce the key vocabulary in the chapter using the routine below.

Define: The radius of a circle is the distance from the center to any point on the circle.

Example: In the circle shown, the radius equals 5 inches.

5 in.

Ask: On a given circle, if $\overline{AB}$ and $\overline{AD}$ are both radii, what does that tell you about both line segments? They are the same length.

Get Ready for Chapter 11

Diagnose Readiness You have two options for checking Prerequisite Skills.

Text Option Take the Quick Check below. Refer to the Quick Review for help.

QuickCheck

(Used in Lessons 11-1 and 11-4)

Solve each equation. (Lesson 5-5)

1. $x + 25 = -67$ **−92**
2. $x + 18 = 106$ **88**
3. $3x - 22 = 83$ **35**
4. $2x - 16 = -128$ **−56**
5. $4x + 140 = 420$ **70**
6. $5x + 160 = 220$ **12**
7. **RUNNING** Darius ran the same number of miles each day from Monday through Friday, and 2 miles on Saturday. If he ran a total of 27 miles during the week, how many miles did he run each weekday? **5 mi**

(Used in Lessons 11-6 through 11-8)

Find each product. Round to the nearest tenth, if necessary. (Lesson 0-3)

8. $2.7(5)$ **13.5**
9. $9.2(1.8)$ **16.6**
10. $2.5(16.7)$ **41.8**
11. $\frac{1}{2}(6)(3.2)$ **9.6**
12. $3(7.17)(5.1)$ **109.7**
13. $2(1.7)(2.62)$ **8.9**
14. **FOOD** Nicole poured 32 bowls of soup volunteering in a soup kitchen. If each bowl contained 16.5 ounces of soup, how much soup did Nicole pour? **528 oz**

(Used in Lesson 11-5)

Find each sum. (Lesson 3-6)

15. $3\frac{2}{3} + 5\frac{4}{5}$ **$9\frac{7}{15}$**
16. $6\frac{3}{8} + 2\frac{1}{2}$ **$8\frac{7}{8}$**
17. $3\frac{1}{3} + 2\frac{3}{4}$ **$6\frac{1}{12}$**
18. $3\frac{2}{3} + 2\frac{5}{9}$ **$6\frac{2}{9}$**
19. $5\frac{1}{4} + 2\frac{5}{6}$ **$8\frac{1}{12}$**
20. $4\frac{1}{2} + 2\frac{2}{3}$ **$7\frac{1}{6}$**
21. **RECYCLING** The class collected $12\frac{5}{6}$ pounds of bottles and $8\frac{1}{8}$ pounds of aluminum cans. How many pounds of bottles and aluminum cans did the class collect? **$20\frac{23}{24}$ lb**

QuickReview

EXAMPLE 1

Solve $7x - 2 = -72$.

$7x - 2 = -72$	Write the equation.
$7x - 2 + 2 = -72 + 2$	Add 2 to each side.
$7x = -70$	Simplify.
$\frac{7x}{7} = \frac{-70}{7}$	Divide each side by 7.
$x = -10$	

EXAMPLE 2

Find 0.5(3)(6.25). Round to the nearest tenth.

0.5(3)(6.25)

$= [0.5(3)](6.25)$	Order of operations
$= (1.5)(6.25)$	$0.5 \times 3 = 1.5$
$= 9.375$	Multiply.
≈ 9.4	Round to the nearest tenth.

EXAMPLE 3

Find $1\frac{3}{4} + 4\frac{5}{6}$.

$1\frac{3}{4} + 4\frac{5}{6} = \frac{7}{4} + \frac{29}{6}$	Write the mixed numbers as improper fractions.
$= \frac{7}{4} \cdot \frac{3}{3} + \frac{29}{6} \cdot \frac{2}{2}$	Rename each fraction using the LCD.
$= \frac{21}{12} + \frac{58}{12}$	Simplify.
$= \frac{79}{12}$ or $6\frac{7}{12}$	Add the numerators.

Online Option Math Online Take a self-check Chapter Readiness Quiz at glencoe.com.

Get Ready for Chapter 11

Response to Intervention (RtI)

Use the *Quick Check* results and the Intervention Planner to help you determine your Response to Intervention. The If-Then statements in the chart help you decide the appropriate tier of RtI and suggest intervention resources for each tier.

Intervention Planner

Tier 1 On Level

If students miss about 25% of the exercises or less,

Then choose a resource:

- **SE** Lessons 0-3, 3-6, 5-5
- **CRM** Skills Practice, Chapter 3, p. 38; Chapter 5, p. 33
- **TE** Chapter Project, p. 586

Math Online Self-Check Quiz

Tier 2 Strategic Intervention approaching grade level

If students miss about 50% of the exercises,

Then choose a resource:

- **CRM** Study Guide and Intervention, Chapter 3, p. 36; Chapter 5, p. 31

Quick Review Math Handbook

Math Online Extra Examples, Personal Tutor, Homework Help

Tier 3 Intensive Intervention 2 or more grades below level

If students miss about 75% of the exercises,

Then use *Math Triumphs, Grade 8,* Ch. 4

Math Online Extra Examples, Personal Tutor, Homework Help, Review Vocabulary

CHAPTER 11 Notes

FOLDABLES® Study Organizer

Dinah Zike's Foldables®

Focus Students write notes about what they learn about three-dimensional figures in this chapter.

Teach Have students make and label the tabs for each lesson of their Foldables as illustrated. Have students use the appropriate tabs as they cover lessons on prisms, cylinders, pyramids, and cones in this chapter.

When to Use It Encourage students to add to their Foldable as they work through the chapter, and use them to review for the chapter test. A completed Foldable is shown on p. 650.

Differentiated Instruction

CRM Student-Built Glossary, pp. 1–2 Students should complete the chart by providing a definition of each term and an example as they progress through Chapter 11. This study tool can also be used to review for the chapter test.

Get Started on Chapter 11

You will learn several new concepts, skills, and vocabulary terms as you study Chapter 11. To get ready, identify important terms and organize your resources. You may wish to refer to **Chapter 0** to review prerequisite skills.

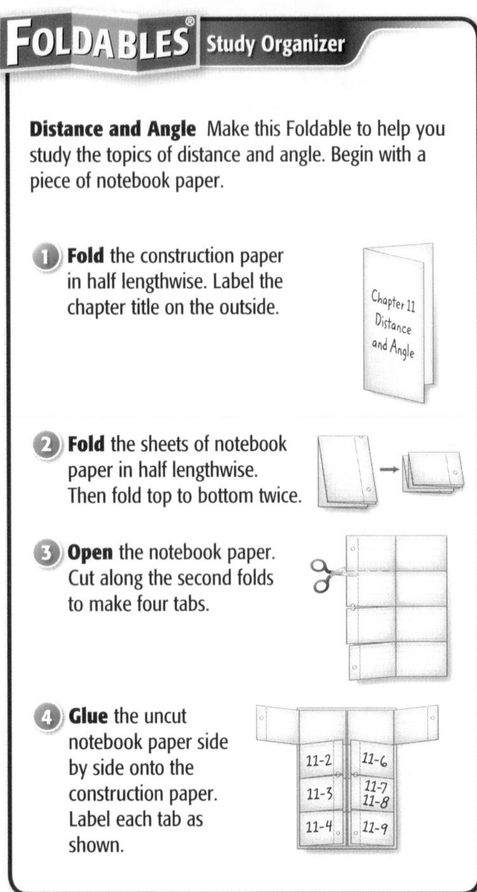

FOLDABLES® Study Organizer

Distance and Angle Make this Foldable to help you study the topics of distance and angle. Begin with a piece of notebook paper.

1. **Fold** the construction paper in half lengthwise. Label the chapter title on the outside.
2. **Fold** the sheets of notebook paper in half lengthwise. Then fold top to bottom twice.
3. **Open** the notebook paper. Cut along the second folds to make four tabs.
4. **Glue** the uncut notebook paper side by side onto the construction paper. Label each tab as shown.

Math Online glencoe.com

- Study the chapter online
- Explore **Math in Motion**
- Get extra help from your own **Personal Tutor**
- Use **Extra Examples** for additional help
- Take a **Self-Check Quiz**
- **Review Vocabulary** in fun ways

New Vocabulary

English		Español
adjacent angles	p. 589	ángulos adyacentes
complementary angles	p. 589	ángulos complementarios
supplementary angles	p. 589	ángulos supplementarios
perpendicular lines	p. 589	rectas perpendiculars
parallel lines	p. 590	rectas paralelas
transversal	p. 590	transversal
congruent	p. 598	congruentes
quadrilateral	p. 611	cuadrilateral
polygon	p. 617	polígono
interior angle	p. 618	ángulo interiors
radius	p. 631	radio
diameter	p. 631	diámetro
circumference	p. 631	circunferencia
π (pi)	p. 631	pi

Review Vocabulary

exponents • p. 471 • exponente in a power, the exponent is the number of times the base is used as a factor

$5^3 \leftarrow$ exponent

ray • rayo a ray extends indefinitely in one direction

A B

Multilingual eGlossary glencoe.com

11-1 Angle and Line Relationships

Why?

Step 1 Draw two different pairs of intersecting lines and label the angles formed as shown.

Step 2 Find and record the measure of each angle.

Step 3 Color angles that have the same measure.

a. For each set of intersecting lines, identify the pairs of angles that have the same measure. **∠1 and ∠3, ∠2 and ∠4**

b. What is true about the sum of the measures sharing a side? **Their sum is 180°.**

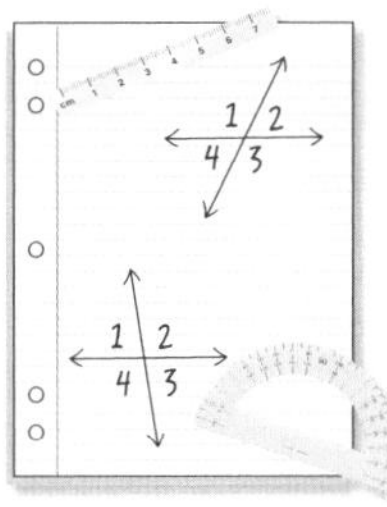

Then
You have already found the missing angle measure of a triangle. (Lesson 10-3)

Now
- Examine relationships between pairs of angles.
- Examine relationships of angles formed by parallel lines and a transversal.

New Vocabulary
perpendicular lines
vertical angles
adjacent angles
complementary angles
supplementary angles
parallel lines
transversal
alternate interior angles
alternate exterior angles
corresponding angles

Math Online
glencoe.com
- Extra Examples
- Personal Tutor
- Self-Check Quiz
- Homework Help

Angle Relationships Pairs of angles can be classified by their relationship to each other.

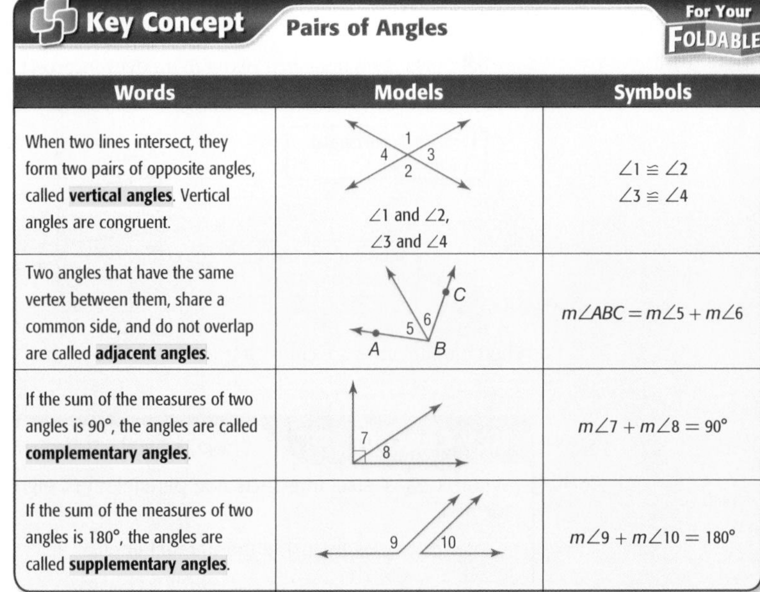

Key Concept Pairs of Angles — For Your FOLDABLE

Words	Models	Symbols
When two lines intersect, they form two pairs of opposite angles, called **vertical angles**. Vertical angles are congruent.	∠1 and ∠2, ∠3 and ∠4	$\angle 1 \cong \angle 2$ $\angle 3 \cong \angle 4$
Two angles that have the same vertex between them, share a common side, and do not overlap are called **adjacent angles**.		$m\angle ABC = m\angle 5 + m\angle 6$
If the sum of the measures of two angles is 90°, the angles are called **complementary angles**.		$m\angle 7 + m\angle 8 = 90°$
If the sum of the measures of two angles is 180°, the angles are called **supplementary angles**.		$m\angle 9 + m\angle 10 = 180°$

A special case occurs when two lines intersect to form a right angle. These lines are **perpendicular lines**.

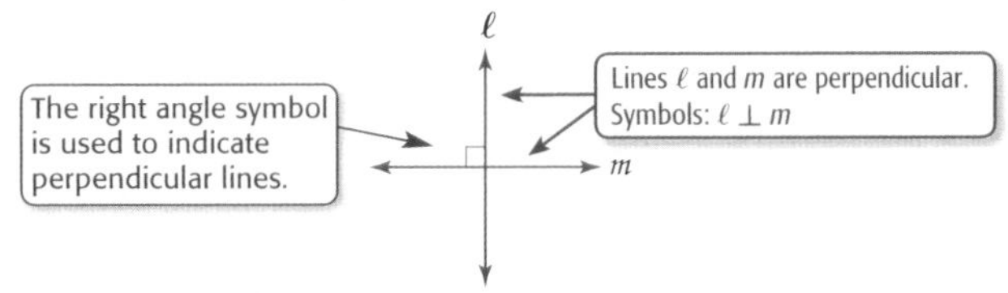

The right angle symbol is used to indicate perpendicular lines.
Lines ℓ and m are perpendicular.
Symbols: ℓ ⊥ m
ℓ
m

11-1 Lesson Notes

1 FOCUS

Vertical Alignment

Before Lesson 11-1
Find the missing angle measure of a triangle.

Lesson 11-1
Examine the relationships between pairs of angles.
Examine the relationships of angles formed by parallel lines and a transversal.

After Lesson 11-1
Make conjectures about angles and lines and determine the validity of the conjectures.

2 TEACH

Scaffolding Questions

Have students read the *Why?* section of the lesson and answer the questions.

Ask:
- Without measuring, how can you know the sum of the measures of ∠2 and ∠3? The angles share a side and form a straight line, which measures 180°.

(continued on next page)

Lesson 11-1 Resources

Resource	Approaching-Level	On-Level	Beyond-Level	English Learners
Teacher Edition	• Differentiated Instruction, p. 591		• Differentiated Instruction, p. 595	
Chapter Resource Masters	• Study Guide and Intervention, pp. 5–6 • Skills Practice, p. 7 • Practice, p. 8 • Word Problem Practice, p. 9	• Study Guide and Intervention, pp. 5–6 • Skills Practice, p. 7 • Practice, p. 8 • Word Problem Practice, p. 9 • Enrichment, p. 10	• Practice, p. 8 • Word Problem Practice, p. 9 • Enrichment, p. 10	• Study Guide and Intervention, pp. 5–6 • Skills Practice, p. 7 • Practice, p. 8
Transparencies	• 5-Minute Check Transparency 11-1	• 5-Minute Check Transparency 11-1	• 5-Minute Check Transparency 11-1	• 5-Minute Check Transparency 11-1
Other	• Study Notebook • Teaching Pre-Algebra with Manipulatives	• Study Notebook • Teaching Pre-Algebra with Manipulatives	• Study Notebook	• Study Notebook • Teaching Pre-Algebra with Manipulatives

- Can you find the measures of each of the angles if you know the measure of $\angle 1$? Explain. Yes; if you know the measure of $\angle 1$, you can find the measure of $\angle 2$ since they share a side, and the measure of $\angle 3$ is the same as $\angle 1$ and the measure of $\angle 4$ is the same as $\angle 2$.

Parallel Lines and a Transversal

Example 1 shows how to find unknown angle measures of vertical, adjacent, complementary, and supplementary angles.

Formative Assessment

Use the Check Your Progress exercises after each example to determine students' understanding of concepts.

Additional Example

1 Jun is cutting another tile.

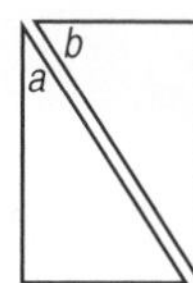

a. Classify the relationship of $\angle a$ and $\angle b$. complementary angles

b. If $m\angle a = 53°$, what is the measure of $\angle b$? $m\angle b = 37°$

Additional Examples also in Interactive Classroom PowerPoint® Presentations

Real-World EXAMPLE 1 Find a Missing Angle Measure

TILING Jun is cutting a piece of tile.

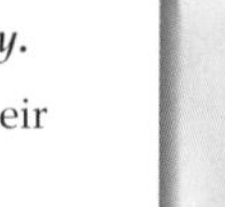

a. Classify the relationship between $\angle x$ and $\angle y$.

The angles are supplementary. The sum of their measures is 180°.

b. If $m\angle y = 135°$, what is the measure of $\angle x$?

$m\angle x + 135 = 180$	**Write the equation.**
$m\angle x + 135 - 135 = 180 - 135$	**Subtract 135 from each side.**
$m\angle x = 45$	**Simplify.**

So, $m\angle x = 45°$.

StudyTip

Angles Complementary angles and supplementary angles can either be adjacent angles or separate angles.

Check Your Progress

1. Angles R and S are complementary. If $m\angle R = 65.3°$, what is the measure of $\angle S$? **24.7°**

Personal Tutor glencoe.com

Parallel Lines Two lines in a plane that never intersect are called **parallel lines**. A line that intersects two or more other lines in a plane is called a **transversal**.

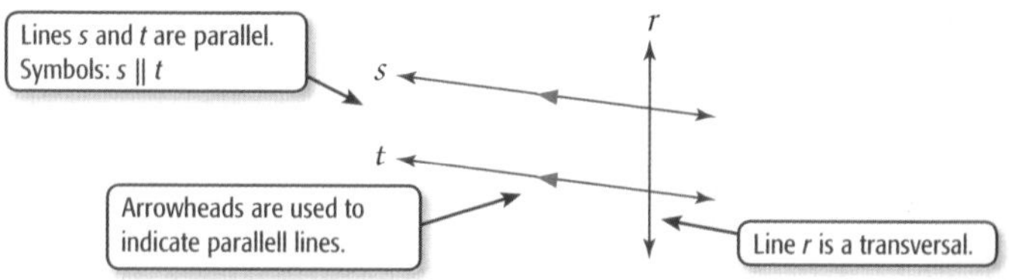

When parallel lines are cut by a transversal, special pairs of angles are congruent.

Key Concept Special Angle Relationships

For Your FOLDABLE

When a transversal intersects two parallel lines, eight angles are formed.

- *Interior angles* lie inside the parallel lines. $\angle 3$, $\angle 4$, $\angle 5$, $\angle 6$
- *Exterior angles* lie outside the parallel lines. $\angle 1$, $\angle 2$, $\angle 7$, $\angle 8$

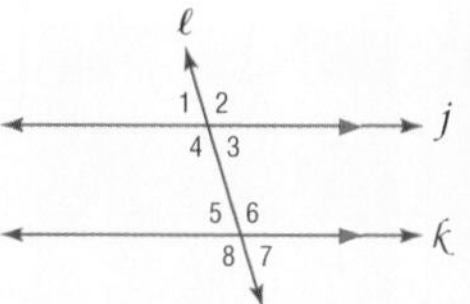

The following pairs of angles are congruent.

- **Alternate interior angles** are on opposite sides of the transversal and inside the parallel lines. $\angle 3 \cong \angle 5$, $\angle 4 \cong \angle 6$
- **Alternate exterior angles** are on opposite sides of the transversal and outside the parallel lines. $\angle 1 \cong \angle 7$, $\angle 2 \cong \angle 8$
- **Corresponding angles** are in the same position on the parallel lines in relation to the transversal. $\angle 1 \cong \angle 5$, $\angle 2 \cong \angle 6$, $\angle 3 \cong \angle 7$, $\angle 4 \cong \angle 8$

ReadingMath

Symbols The symbol for *is congruent to* is $\cong$. So, *angle 3 is congruent to angle 5* is written as $\angle 3 \cong \angle 5$.

TEACH with TECH

STUDENT RESPONSE SYSTEM Create a presentation consisting of a diagram of two parallel lines with a transversal and number the angles 1 through 8. Choose an angle and have students respond with the number of an alternate interior angle. Repeat this activity with additional slides asking students to identify alternate exterior angles, vertical angles, or supplementary angles. Provide students with a numerical key for how to respond.

EXAMPLE 2 Find Measures of Angles Formed by Parallel Lines

In the figure at the right, $a \parallel b$ and q and r are transversals.

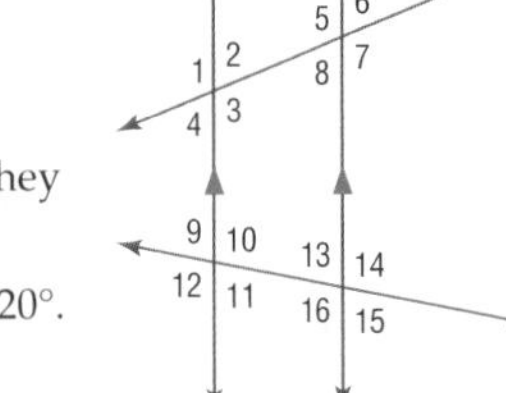

a. Classify the relationship between ∠3 and ∠5.

Since ∠3 and ∠5 are alternate interior angles, they are congruent.

b. If $m\angle 1 = 120°$, find $m\angle 5$ and $m\angle 3$.

Since ∠1 and ∠5 are corresponding angles, they are congruent. So, $m\angle 5 = 120°$.

Since $m\angle 5$ and $m\angle 3$ are congruent, $m\angle 3 = 120°$.

Check Your Progress

2. Classify the relationship between ∠11 and ∠15. If $m\angle 15 = 78.5°$, find $m\angle 11$ and $m\angle 9$.

Personal Tutor glencoe.com

ReadingMath

Symbols The symbol $\parallel$ means *is parallel to.*

2. ∠11 and ∠15 are corresponding angles, so they are congruent. $m\angle 11 = 78.5°$, $m\angle 9 = 78.5°$; ∠9 and ∠15 are alternate exterior angles, so they are congruent.

EXAMPLE 3 Use Algebra to Find Missing Angle Measures

ALGEBRA In the figure at the right, $m\angle ABD = 164°$. Find the measures of ∠ABC and ∠CBD.

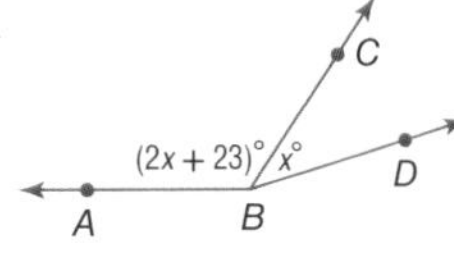

Angles ABC and CBD are adjacent angles that have a total measure of 164°.

Step 1 Find the value of x.

$m\angle ABC + m\angle CBD = 164$	**Adjacent angles**
$(2x + 23) + x = 164$	**Replace $m\angle ABC$ with $2x + 23$ and replace $m\angle CBD$ with x.**
$3x + 23 = 164$	**Combine like terms.**
$-23 = -23$	**Subtract 23 from each side.**
$3x = 141$	**Simplify.**
$\frac{3x}{3} = \frac{141}{3}$	**Divide each side by 3.**
$x = 47$	**Simplify.**

Step 2 Replace x with 47 to find the measure of each angle.

$m\angle ABC = 2x + 23 = 2(47) + 23$ or 117 $\qquad$ $m\angle CBD = x = 47$

So, $m\angle ABC = 117°$ and $m\angle CBD = 47°$.

Check Your Progress

ALGEBRA Angles RVT and UVW are vertical angles, with $m\angle RVT = 3x$ and $m\angle UVW = 5x - 36$.

3A. Find the value of x. 18

3B. Find $m\angle UVW$. 54°

Personal Tutor glencoe.com

Vocabulary Review

Ray A ray is a part of a line that extends indefinitely in one direction. In the figure at the right, $\overrightarrow{BA}$, $\overrightarrow{BC}$, and $\overrightarrow{BD}$ are rays.

Intersecting Lines and Angles

Example 2 shows how to find measures of angles formed by parallel lines and a transversal. **Example 3** shows how to use algebra to find missing angle measures.

Additional Examples

2 Refer to Example 2 of the Student Edition.

a. Classify the relationship between ∠9 and ∠13. ∠9 and ∠13 are corresponding and congruent angles

b. If $m\angle 13$ is 75°, find $m\angle 11$ and $m\angle 15$. Since ∠13 and ∠11 are alternate interior angles, they are congruent, so $m\angle 11 = 75°$; ∠11 and ∠15 are corresponding angles, so $m\angle 15 = 75°$.

3 **ALGEBRA** Angles DEF and WXY are complementary angles, with $m\angle DEF = 2x$ and $m\angle WXY = 3x - 20$. Find the measures of ∠DEF and ∠WXY. ∠DEF = 44°; $m\angle WXY = 46°$.

Differentiated Instruction AL

If students could use hands-on practice identifying and understanding angle relationships,

Then use masking tape to set up two parallel lines and a transversal on the floor in a large open space. Separate the class into eight groups and have each group stand in one of the eight angles. Give angle 1 a measure. Have the other seven groups determine their angle measure and what relationship it has to angle 1. Repeat for all eight angles.

Focus on Mathematical Content

Finding Angle Measures When a transversal intersects parallel lines, you can find other angle measures if one angle measurement is known. Using a protractor to find unknown angle measurements is not sufficient because measurements are not exact and drawings are not exact.

3 PRACTICE

Formative Assessment

Use Exercises 1–9 to check for understanding.

Use the chart at the bottom of this page to customize assignments for your students.

Tips for New Teachers

Angle Positions Remind students that congruent angles are angles that have the same measure. Angles can be congruent even if their orientation and position differ.

Additional Answers

14. 52.6°; ∠6 and ∠3 are alternate interior angles, so they are congruent.
15. 52.6°; ∠6 and ∠5 are corresponding angles, so they are congruent.
16. 127.4°; ∠6 and ∠2 are supplementary angles, so the sum of their measures is 180°.
17. 127.4°; ∠6 and ∠8 are supplementary angles, so the sum of their measures is 180°.
18. 52.6°; ∠6 and ∠4 are vertical angles, so they are congruent.
19. 127.4°; Sample answer: ∠6 and ∠8 are supplementary angles, so m∠8 = 127.4. ∠8 and ∠1 are alternate exterior angles, so m∠1 = 127.4.

Check Your Understanding

Example 1 p. 590

Classify the pairs of angles shown. Then find the value of x in each figure.

1. 146°, $x°$ — supplementary angles; 34

2. 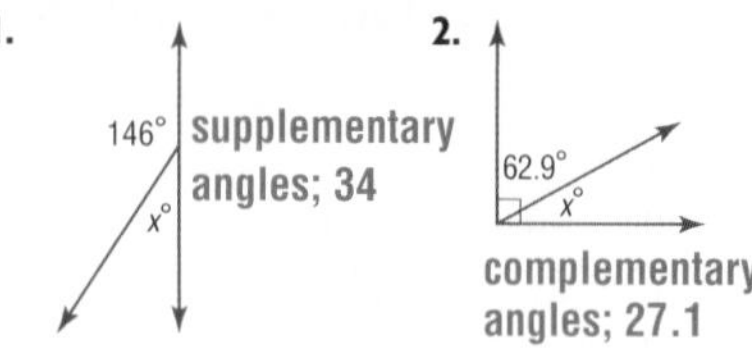

complementary angles; 27.1

3. 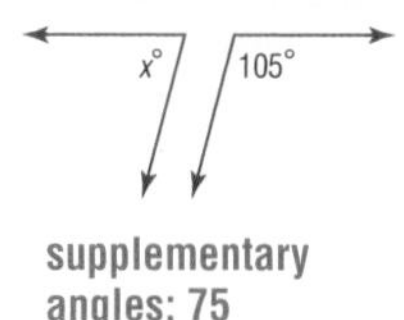

supplementary angles; 75

Example 2 p. 591

In the figure at the right, $r \parallel s$ and w is a transversal. If $m\angle 1 = 128°$, find the measure of each angle. Explain your reasoning.

4. ∠5
5. ∠8
6. ∠2

(Figure: transversal w with angles 1–8.)

4. 128°; ∠1 and ∠5 are corresponding angles, so they are congruent.
5. 128°; ∠1 and ∠8 are alternate exterior angles, so they are congruent.
6. 52°; ∠1 and ∠2 are supplementary angles, so the sum of their measures is 180°.

7. **GYMNASTICS** The balance beam shown below is parallel to the floor.
   a. Classify the relationship between ∠x and ∠y. **the angles are alternate interior angles**
   b. If $m\angle y = 117°$, find the value of x. **117**

Example 3 p. 591

ALGEBRA The measure of ∠Q is $6x + 16.8$ and the measure of ∠R is $2x$.

8. If ∠Q and ∠R are supplementary, what is the value of x? What is the measure of each angle? **$x = 20.4$, $m\angle Q = 139.2°$, $m\angle R = 40.8°$**

9. If ∠Q and ∠R are complementary, what is the value of x? What is the measure of each angle? **$x = 9.15$, $m\angle Q = 71.7°$, $m\angle R = 18.3°$**

Practice and Problem Solving

= **Step-by-Step Solutions** begin on page R11. **Extra Practice** begins on page 810.

Example 1 p. 590

Classify the pairs of angles shown. Then find the value of x in each figure.

10. 152°, $x°$ — vertical angles; 152

11. 58.9°, $x°$ — supplementary angles; 121.1

12. 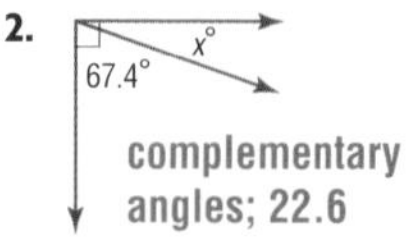

complementary angles; 22.6

13. **ARCHITECTURE** Look at the semicircular window.
    a. Classify the relationship between ∠1 and ∠2. **complementary angles**
    b. If $m\angle 2$ is 24°, find $m\angle 1$. **66°**

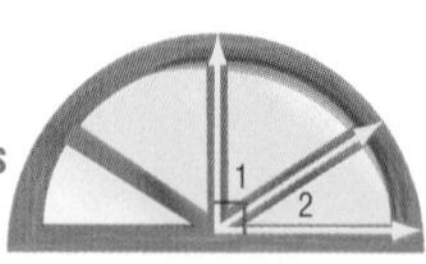

Differentiated Homework Options

Level	Assignment	Two-Day Option	
AL Basic	10–23, 33, 34, 36–51	11–23 odd, 37–40	10–22 even, 33, 34, 36, 41–51
OL Core	11–23 odd, 24–34, 36–51	10–23, 37–40	24–34, 36, 41–51
BL Advanced	24–46 (optional: 47–51)		

Example 2 p. 591

In the figure at the right, $f \parallel g$ and t is a transversal. If $m\angle 6 = 52.6°$, find the measure of each angle. Explain your reasoning. 14–19. See margin.

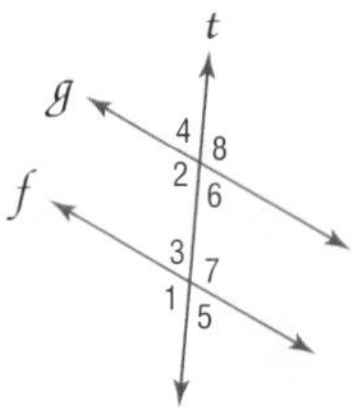

14. $\angle 3$
15. $\angle 5$
16. $\angle 2$
17. $\angle 8$
18. $\angle 4$
19. $\angle 1$

Example 3 p. 591

20. If $m\angle FGH = 165°$, find $m\angle 1$. **75°**

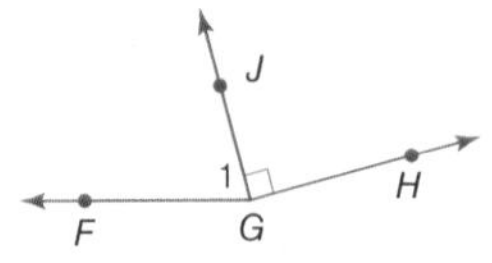

21. If $m\angle QRS = 158°$, find $m\angle TRS$. **30°**

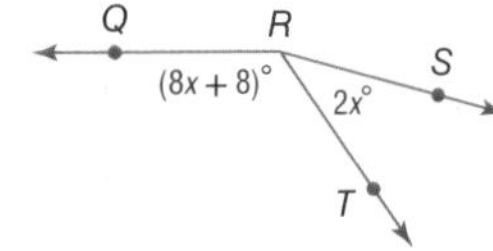

22. **ALGEBRA** Angles M and P are complementary. If $m\angle M = 3x - 45$ and $m\angle P = 2x + 15$, what is the value of x? What is the measure of each angle? **$x = 24$, $m\angle M = 27°$, $m\angle P = 63°$**

23. **ALGEBRA** The measure of $\angle C$ is $4x - 24.6$ and the measure of $\angle D$ is $x + 11.3$. If the angles are supplementary, find the value of x and $m\angle D$. **$x = 38.66$; $m\angle D = 49.96°$**

ALGEBRA In the figure below, $a \parallel b$ and z is a transversal.

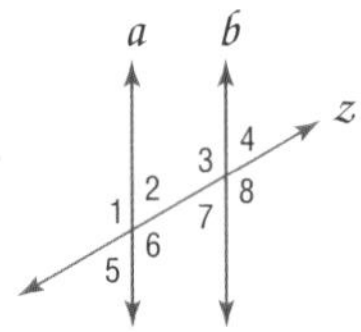

24. If $m\angle 1 = 5x$ and $m\angle 5 = 2x - 2$, find the value of x, $m\angle 1$, and $m\angle 5$. **$x = 26$, $m\angle 1 = 130°$, $m\angle 5 = 50°$**

25. If $m\angle 4 = 15x$ and $m\angle 2 = 11x + 20$, find the value of x, $m\angle 4$, and $m\angle 2$. **$x = 5$, $m\angle 4 = 75°$, $m\angle 2 = 75°$**

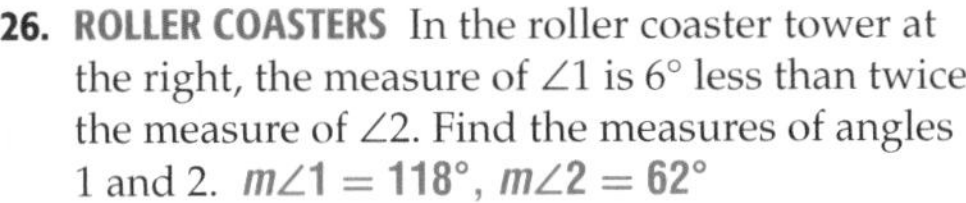

26. **ROLLER COASTERS** In the roller coaster tower at the right, the measure of $\angle 1$ is 6° less than twice the measure of $\angle 2$. Find the measures of angles 1 and 2. **$m\angle 1 = 118°$, $m\angle 2 = 62°$**

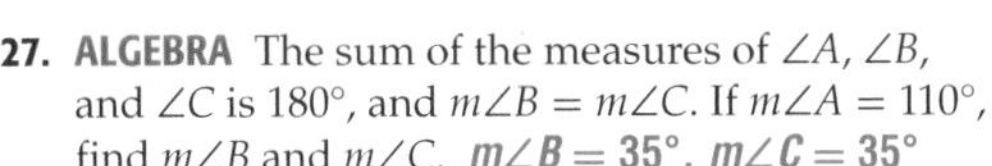

27. **ALGEBRA** The sum of the measures of $\angle A$, $\angle B$, and $\angle C$ is 180°, and $m\angle B = m\angle C$. If $m\angle A = 110°$, find $m\angle B$ and $m\angle C$. **$m\angle B = 35°$, $m\angle C = 35°$**

28. **ALGEBRA** Angles U and V are supplementary angles. The ratio of their measures is 7:13. Find the measure of each angle. **$m\angle U = 63°$, $m\angle V = 117°$**

29. **ALGEBRA** Use the pair of angles shown.

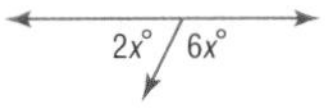

a. Write an equation to find the value of x. Then find the value of x. **$2x + 6x = 180$; 22.5**

b. What are the measures of the two angles? **45°; 135°**

Real-World Link

Cedar Point in Sandusky, Ohio, is known as "America's Roller Coast" because it has more roller coasters than any other amusement park.

Source: Cedar Point

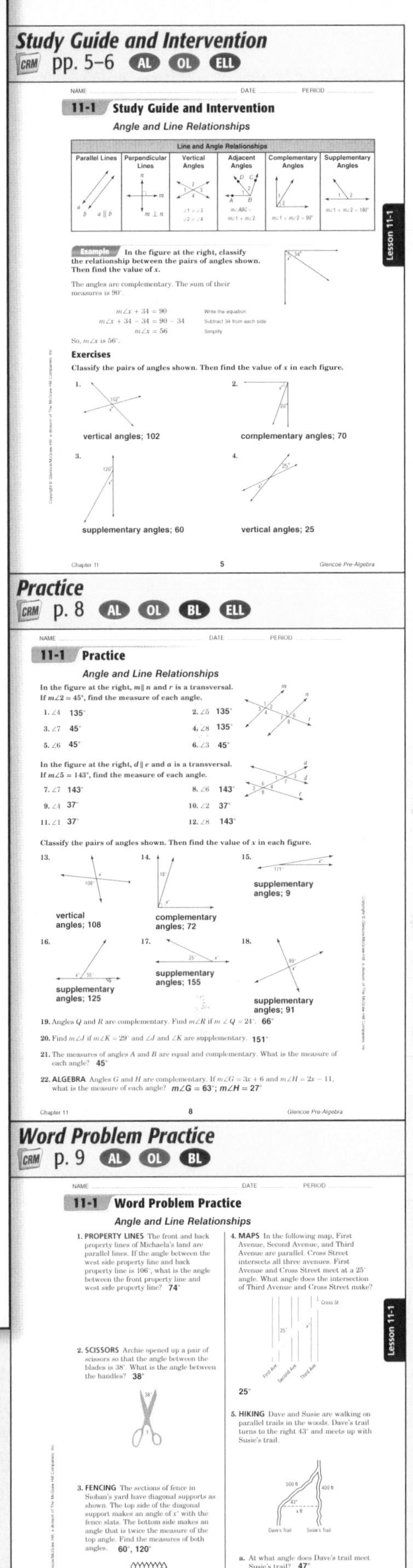

Study Guide and Intervention

CRM pp. 5–6 AL OL ELL

NAME ____ DATE ____ PERIOD ____

11-1 Study Guide and Intervention

Angle and Line Relationships

Line and Angle Relationships					
Parallel Lines	Perpendicular Lines	Vertical Angles	Adjacent Angles	Complementary Angles	Supplementary Angles
$a \parallel b$	$m \perp n$	$\angle 1 \cong \angle 3$; $\angle 2 \cong \angle 4$	$m\angle ABC = m\angle 1 + m\angle 2$	$m\angle 1 + m\angle 2 = 90°$	$m\angle 1 + m\angle 2 = 180°$

Example In the figure at the right, classify the relationship between the pairs of angles shown. Then find the value of x.

The angles are complementary. The sum of their measures is 90°.

$m\angle x + 34 = 90$ Write the equation.
$m\angle x + 34 - 34 = 90 - 34$ Subtract 34 from each side.
$m\angle x = 56$ Simplify.

So, $m\angle x$ is 56°.

Exercises

Classify the pairs of angles shown. Then find the value of x in each figure.

1. vertical angles; 102
2. complementary angles; 70
3. supplementary angles; 60
4. vertical angles; 25

Chapter 11 5 Glencoe Pre-Algebra

Practice

CRM p. 8 AL OL BL ELL

NAME ____ DATE ____ PERIOD ____

11-1 Practice

Angle and Line Relationships

In the figure at the right, $m \parallel n$ and r is a transversal. If $m\angle 2 = 45°$, find the measure of each angle.

1. $\angle 4$ 135°
2. $\angle 5$ 135°
3. $\angle 7$ 45°
4. $\angle 8$ 135°
5. $\angle 6$ 45°
6. $\angle 3$ 45°

In the figure at the right, $d \parallel e$ and a is a transversal. If $m\angle 5 = 143°$, find the measure of each angle.

7. $\angle 7$ 143°
8. $\angle 6$ 143°
9. $\angle 4$ 37°
10. $\angle 2$ 37°
11. $\angle 1$ 37°
12. $\angle 8$ 143°

Classify the pairs of angles shown. Then find the value of x in each figure.

13. vertical angles; 108
14. complementary angles; 72
15. supplementary angles; 9
16. supplementary angles; 125
17. supplementary angles; 155
18. supplementary angles; 91

19. Angles Q and R are complementary. Find $m\angle R$ if $m\angle Q = 24°$. **66°**

20. Find $m\angle J$ if $m\angle K = 29°$ and $\angle J$ and $\angle K$ are supplementary. **151°**

21. The measures of angles A and B are equal and complementary. What is the measure of each angle? **45°**

22. **ALGEBRA** Angles G and H are complementary. If $m\angle G = 3x + 6$ and $m\angle H = 2x - 11$, what is the measure of each angle? **$m\angle G = 63°$; $m\angle H = 27°$**

Chapter 11 8 Glencoe Pre-Algebra

Word Problem Practice

CRM p. 9 AL OL BL

NAME ____ DATE ____ PERIOD ____

11-1 Word Problem Practice

Angle and Line Relationships

1. **PROPERTY LINES** The front and back property lines of Michaela's land are parallel lines. If the angle between the west side property line and back property line is 106°, what is the angle between the front property line and west side property line? **74°**

2. **SCISSORS** Archie opened up a pair of scissors so that the angle between the blades is 38°. What is the angle between the handles? **38°**

3. **FENCING** The sections of fence in Sioban's yard have diagonal supports as shown. The top side of the diagonal support makes an angle of $x°$ with the fence slats. The bottom side makes an angle that is twice the measure of the top angle. Find the measures of both angles. **60°, 120°**

4. **MAPS** In the following map, First Avenue, Second Avenue, and Third Avenue are parallel. Cross Street intersects all three avenues. First Avenue and Cross Street meet at a 25° angle. What angle does the intersection of Third Avenue and Cross Street make?

25°

5. **HIKING** Dave and Susie are walking on parallel trails in the woods. Dave's trail turns to the right 43° and meets up with Susie's trail.

a. At what angle does Dave's trail meet Susie's trail? **47°**

b. How far apart were Dave and Susie's trails originally? **300 ft**

Chapter 11 9 Glencoe Pre-Algebra

Lesson 11-1

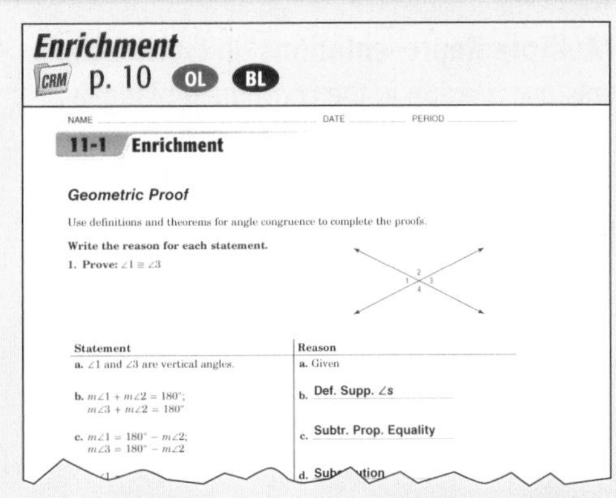

Enrichment

CRM p. 10 OL BL

NAME ____ DATE ____ PERIOD ____

11-1 Enrichment

Geometric Proof

Use definitions and theorems for angle congruence to complete the proofs.

Write the reason for each statement.

1. **Prove:** $\angle 1 \cong \angle 3$

Statement	Reason
a. $\angle 1$ and $\angle 3$ are vertical angles.	a. Given
b. $m\angle 1 + m\angle 2 = 180°$; $m\angle 3 + m\angle 2 = 180°$	b. Def. Supp. $\angle$s
c. $m\angle 1 = 180° - m\angle 2$; $m\angle 3 = 180° - m\angle 2$	c. Subtr. Prop. Equality
	d. Substitution

Watch Out!

Find the Error For Exercise 34, suggest that students first determine the relationship between the angles. Then have them analyze the methods Elias and Taylor used to find the value of x.

Additional Answers

32a.

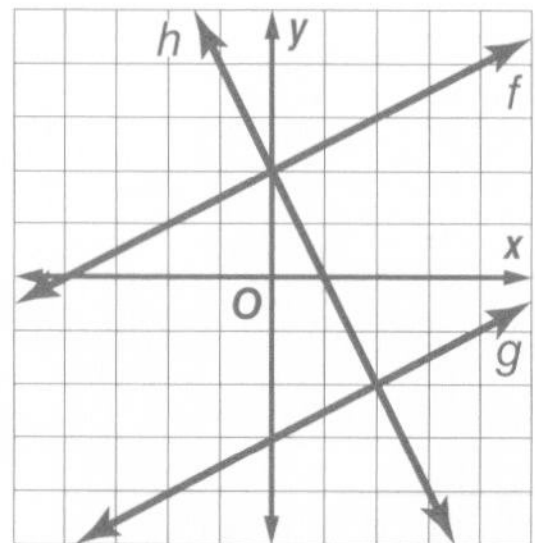

33. Sample answer:

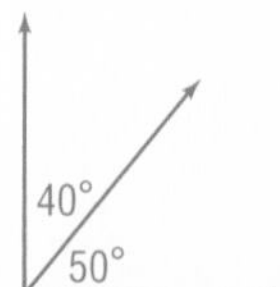

Real-World Link

Every second lightning strikes somewhere on the surface of Earth about 100 times.

30. No; r and s are not parallel since the corresponding angles of 60° and 62° are not congruent. p and q are parallel because the angle that is supplementary to the 60° has a measure of 120°, so the corresponding angles are congruent.

34. Taylor; the angles are complementary, but Elias used the definition of supplementary angles to calculate the value of x.

35. The sum of their measures is 180°. The interior angles on the same side of a transversal are supplementary.

36. All the other angles measure 90°. Since an exterior angle measures 90°, the angles that are vertical, adjacent, and corresponding to that angle also measure 90°.

30. GEOMETRY Lines p, q, r, and s form the quadrilateral shown at the right. Can you conclude that opposite sides of the quadrilateral are parallel? Explain your reasoning.

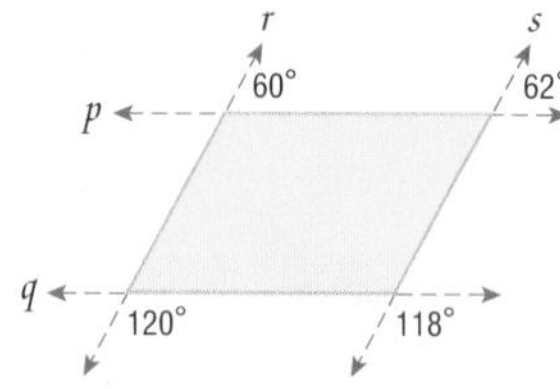

31. TIME Use the clock at the right that shows 6 o'clock and 10 seconds.

a. Find $m\angle WXY$ and $m\angle YXZ$. **$m\angle WXY = 60°$, $m\angle YXZ = 120°$**

b. Find the time that will show when $m\angle WXY = m\angle YXZ = 90°$. **Sample answer: 6:00, 15 s**

32. MULTIPLE REPRESENTATIONS In this problem, you will investigate parallel lines on the coordinate plane. Line f passes through points at (0, 2) and (2, 3). Line g passes through points at (0, −3) and (2, −2). Line h passes through points at (1, 0) and (2, −2).

a. GRAPHICAL Graph the three lines on the same coordinate plane. Label each line. **See margin.**

b. VERBAL Describe the angles that are formed by the lines. **The angles appear to be right angles.**

c. ANALYTICAL Describe the relationship between the slopes of parallel lines. **Sample answer: The slopes of parallel lines are equivalent.**

H.O.T. Problems Use Higher-Order Thinking Skills

33. OPEN ENDED Draw a pair of complementary adjacent angles. Label the measures of the angles. **See margin.**

34. FIND THE ERROR Elias and Taylor calculated the value of x for the missing angle shown at the right. Is either of them correct? Explain your reasoning.

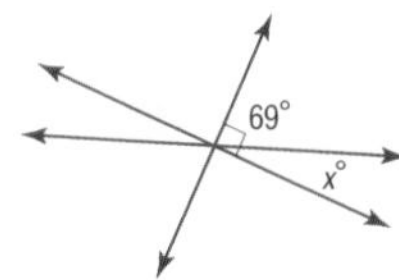

Elias	Taylor
$69 + x = 180$	$69 + x = 90$
$x = 111$	$x = 21$

35. CHALLENGE Lines ℓ and m shown at the right are parallel and are cut by transversals j and k. Describe how the following pairs of angles are related: 1 and 2, 3 and 4, 5 and 6. Then make a conjecture about how the interior angles on the same side of a transversal are related.

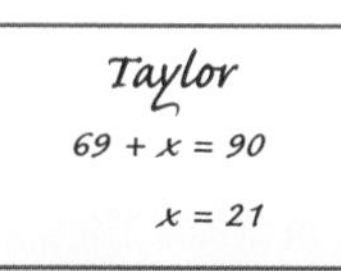

36. WRITING IN MATH Suppose two parallel lines are cut by a transversal and an exterior angle measures 90°. What can you conclude about the measures of the other seven angles that are formed? Explain your reasoning.

Multiple Representations In Exercise 32, students use a graph in the coordinate plane, a verbal description, and geometric analysis to describe the slopes of lines and the angles formed by their intersection.

Standardized Test Practice

37. Lines a and b are parallel in the figure below. Find the value of x. **C**

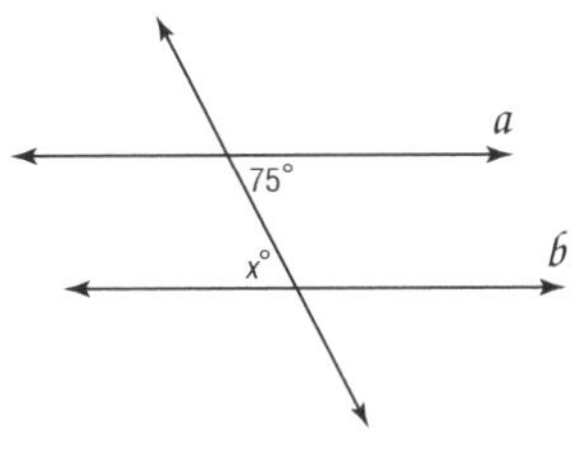

A 110   C 75
B 105   D 15

38. Which angles are *not* supplementary? **G**

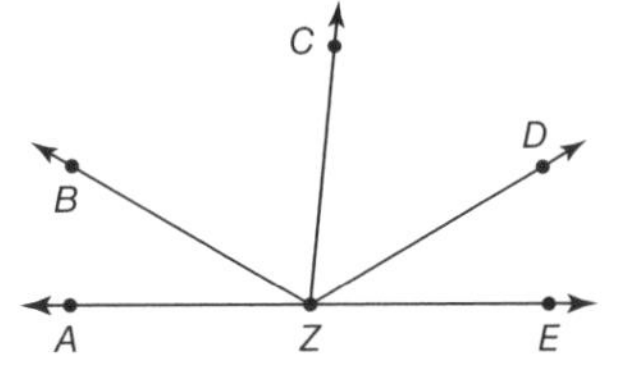

F $\angle EZC$ and $\angle CZA$ H $\angle AZB$ and $\angle BZE$
G $\angle BZC$ and $\angle CZD$ J $\angle DZE$ and $\angle AZD$

39. In the figure below, the two angles are congruent. Find the value of x. **A**

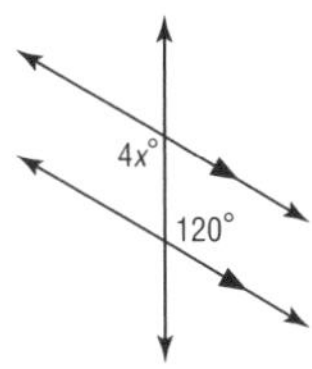

A 30   C 116
B 40   D 124

40. **EXTENDED RESPONSE** The hedge shears have two different angles shown. Find the value of x. Explain your reasoning. **148; Since the angles are supplementary, the sum of the measures is 180°. So, $m\angle x = 180° - 32°$ or 148°.**

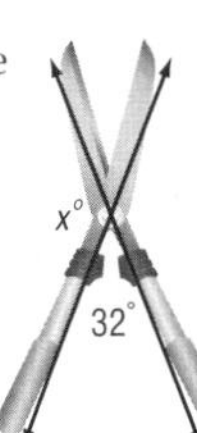

Spiral Review

41. **GEOMETRY** In a 30°-60°-90° triangle, the shorter leg is 12 feet long. Find the length of the hypotenuse and the length of the longer leg. (Lesson 10-6) **hypotenuse: 24 ft, leg: $12\sqrt{3}$**

42. **ARCHAEOLOGY** Two artifacts are found at a dig. A coordinate plane was set up. One artifact was found at (1, 5), and the other artifact was found at (3, 1). How far apart were the two artifacts? Round to the nearest tenth of a unit if necessary. (Lesson 10-5) **4.5 units**

43. **ANIMALS** In 2000, there were 356 endangered species in the U.S. Five years later, 389 species were considered endangered. What was the percent of change? Then state whether the percent of change is an *increase* or *decrease*. Round to the nearest tenth. (Lesson 7-6) **9.3%; increase**

ALGEBRA Solve each inequality. (Lesson 5-4)

44. $5m < 5$ **$m < 1$**   **45.** $\frac{a}{-2} > 3$ **$a < -6$**   **46.** $-4x \geq -16$ **$x \leq 4$**

Skills Review

Use a protractor to draw an angle having each measure. (Previous Course) **47–51. See margin.**

47. 35°   **48.** 65°   **49.** 85°   **50.** 155°   **51.** 180°

Differentiated Instruction

Extension Present students with the following problem: Angles P and Q are supplementary. Angles T and S are also supplementary. If angles P and T are vertical angles and $m\angle P = 5x - 14$, what is $m\angle S$? $194 - 5x$ If $x = 7$, what are the measures of angles P, Q, T, and S? $m\angle P$ and $m\angle T = 21°$, $m\angle Q$ and $m\angle S = 159°$

4 ASSESS

Ticket Out the Door Have students draw two parallel lines and a transversal. Give them one angle measure and have them fill in the measures of the other angles. Have students hand in their work as they exit.

Additional Answers

47.

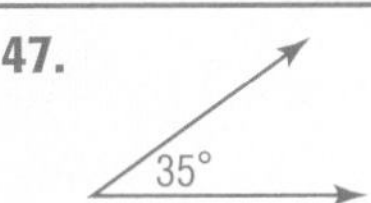

48.

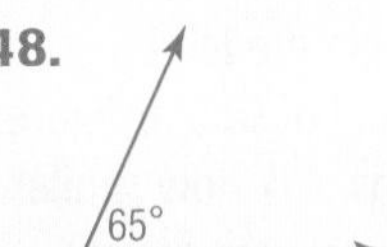

49.

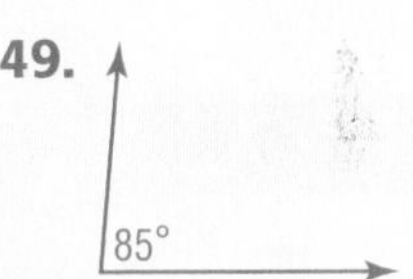

50. 155°

51. 180°

EXPLORE 11-2

Lesson Notes

FOCUS

Objective Investigate which three pairs of corresponding parts can be used to show that two triangles are congruent.

Materials for Each Group

- patty paper (20 pieces)
- tape
- ruler

Teaching Tip

You may want to begin the lab by reviewing the meaning of similar figures from previous lessons. Ask how similar figures differ from congruent figures.

TEACH

Working in Cooperative Groups

Have students work in pairs or groups of three to complete Activities 1–3 and Exercises 1–3 after Activity 1, Exercises 4–6 after Activity 2, and Exercises 7–9 after Activity 3.

Alternative Teaching Strategy: Constructions

Activities 1, 2, and 3 could be performed as a construction activity.

Ask:

- In Activity 1, does the order in which you tape the sides of the triangle together matter? Explain. No; the lengths of the sides of the triangle determine its shape and size, so the triangle will have the same side lengths and angle measures no matter how you put it together.
- In Activity 2, why are the results different from the results in Activity 1? Sample answer: In Activity 1, the lengths of the three sides determine the angle measures, so the triangles are congruent, but in Activity 2, the angle measures do not determine the lengths of the sides, so the triangles are similar but not congruent.

EXPLORE 11-2

Geometry Lab

Investigating Congruent Triangles

Math Online glencoe.com

Math *in Motion*, Animation

In this lab, you will investigate whether it is possible to show that two triangles are congruent without showing that all six pairs of corresponding parts are congruent.

ACTIVITY 1

Step 1 Draw a triangle on a piece of patty paper. Copy the sides of the triangle onto another piece of patty paper and cut them out.

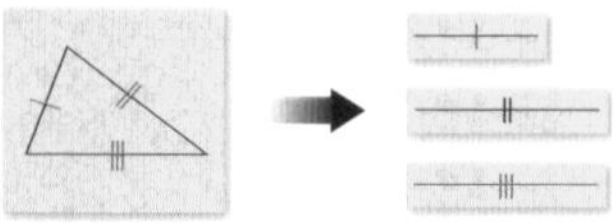

Step 2 Arrange and tape the pieces together so that they form a triangle.

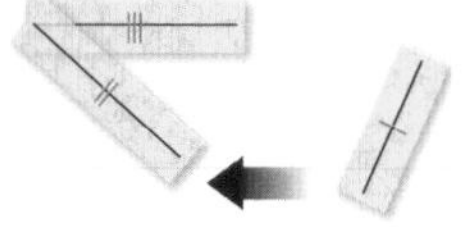

Analyze the Results

1. Is the triangle you formed congruent to the original triangle? Explain. Yes; the corresponding sides and angles are congruent to the original triangle.
2. Repeat Activity 1 and try to form another triangle. Is it congruent to the original triangle? yes
3. **MAKE A CONJECTURE** Based on this activity, can three pairs of congruent sides be used to show that two triangles are congruent? yes

ACTIVITY 2

Step 1 Draw a triangle on a piece of patty paper. Copy each angle of the triangle onto separate pieces of patty paper. Extend each ray of each angle to the edge of the patty paper.

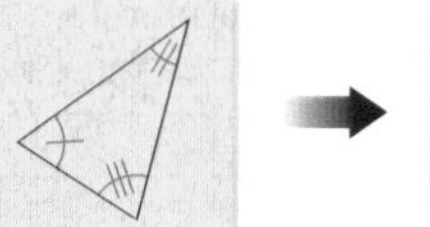

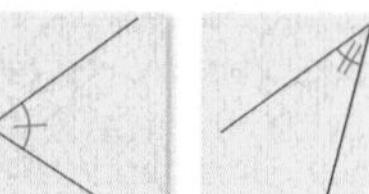

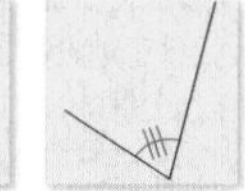

Step 2 Arrange and tape the pieces together so that they form a triangle.

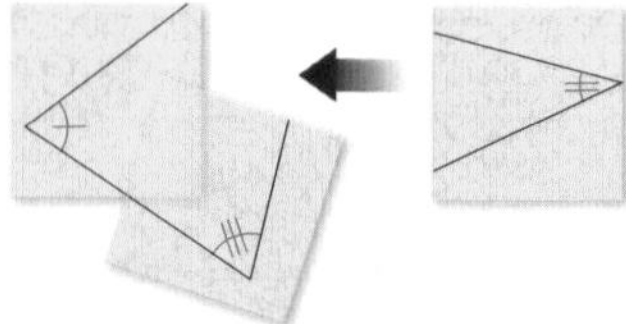

4. See student's work. Most students' triangles will be similar, but not congruent to the original triangle. Sample answer: The triangle is similar to the original triangle since corresponding angles are congruent, but it is larger than the original, so it is not congruent to the original triangle.

Analyze the Results

4. Is the triangle you formed congruent to the original triangle? Explain.
5. Repeat Activity 2 and try to form another triangle. Is it congruent to the original triangle? Sample answer: The triangle is similar, but not congruent to the original triangle.
6. **MAKE A CONJECTURE** Based on this activity, can three pairs of congruent angles be used to show that two triangles are congruent? no

ACTIVITY 3

Step 1 Draw a triangle on a piece of patty paper. Copy two sides of the triangle and the angle between them onto separate pieces of patty paper and cut them out.

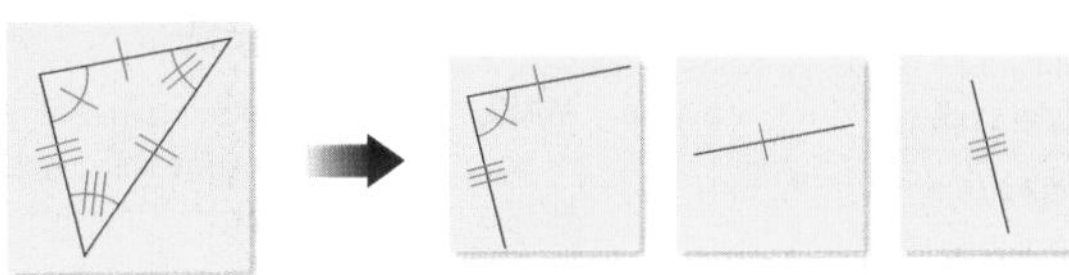

Step 2 Arrange and tape the pieces together so that the two sides are joined to form the rays of the angle. Then tape these joined pieces onto a piece of construction paper and connect the two rays to form a triangle.

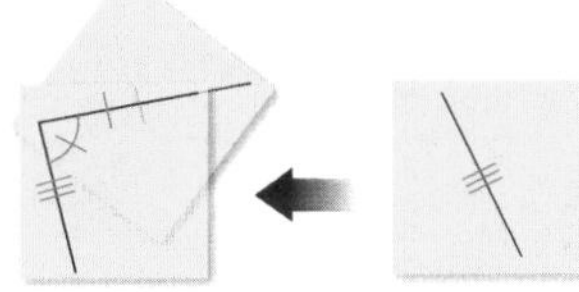

Analyze the Results

7. Is the triangle you formed congruent to the original triangle? Explain. Yes; the corresponding sides and angles are congruent to the original triangle.
8. Repeat Activity 3 and try to form another triangle. Is it congruent to the original triangle? yes
9. **MAKE A CONJECTURE** Based on this activity, can two pairs of congruent sides and the pair of congruent angles between them be used to show that two triangles are congruent? yes
10. **EXTENSION** Use patty paper to investigate and determine whether each of the following can be used to show that two triangles are congruent.
    - two pairs of congruent sides and a pair of congruent angles *not* between them no
    - two pairs of congruent angles and the pair of congruent sides between them yes
    - two pairs of congruent angles and a pair of congruent sides *not* between them yes

- In Activity 3, Step 1, why is it necessary that the two sides that you copy be the same length as the original triangle? Sample answer: If the sides are shorter or longer than the original triangle, the second triangle will be smaller or larger than the original triangle.

Practice Have students complete Exercise 10 after the Activities.

3 ASSESS

Formative Assessment

Use Exercises 3, 6, and 9 to assess whether students understand which measures they need to know to determine whether two triangles are congruent.

From Concrete to Abstract

What needs to be true for you to show that two triangles are congruent? Sample answers: If three sides of one triangle are congruent to three sides of a second triangle, the two triangles are congruent; if two sides of a triangle and the angle between them are congruent to two sides of a second triangle and the angle between them, the triangles are congruent.

11-2 Lesson Notes

1 FOCUS

Vertical Alignment

Before Lesson 11-2
Identify triangles with congruent sides.

Lesson 11-2
Identify corresponding parts of congruent triangles.
Identify congruent triangles.

After Lesson 11-2
Justify and apply triangle congruence relationships.

2 TEACH

Scaffolding Questions

Have students read the *Why?* section of the lesson and answer the questions.

Ask:

- In part **c**, why is it important to match up the parts of the triangles with the same measures? It is the only way to tell whether the triangles are the same size and shape.
- Two triangles are the same size and shape. You know the angle measures and side lengths of one triangle. How can you find the angle measures and side lengths of the other triangle? Since the triangles are the same size and shape, line up the parts to find the measures of the second triangle.

11-2 Congruent Triangles

Then
You identified triangles with congruent sides. (Lesson 9-3)

Now
- Identify corresponding parts of congruent triangles.
- Identify congruent triangles.

New Vocabulary
congruent
corresponding parts

Math Online
glencoe.com
- Extra Examples
- Personal Tutor
- Self-Check Quiz
- Homework Help

Why?

The flag of the United Kingdom is shown below. Consider the four large triangles appearing on the top and the bottom of the flag.

a. The lengths of the corresponding sides are equal.
b. The measures of the corresponding angles are equal.

a. Measure the sides of the four triangles. What is true about the lengths?

b. Use a protractor to measure the angles of the four triangles. What is true about the measures?

c. **MAKE A CONJECTURE** Suppose the triangles were cut out and laid on top of one another so that the parts with the same measures were matched up. What is true about the triangles? **The triangles have the same size and shape.**

Corresponding Parts of Congruent Triangles Figures that have the same size and shape are **congruent**. In the figure below, triangle *ABC* is congruent to triangle *DEF*.

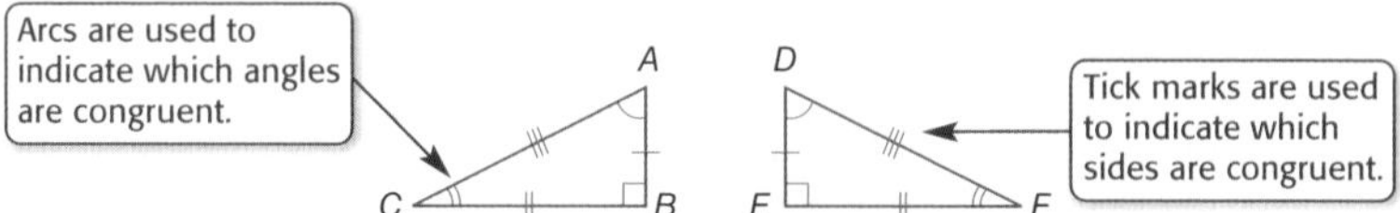

The parts of congruent triangles that *match* or correspond, are called **corresponding parts**.

Key Concept: Corresponding Parts of Congruent Triangles

For Your FOLDABLE

Words If two triangles are congruent, their corresponding sides are congruent and their corresponding angles are congruent.

Model

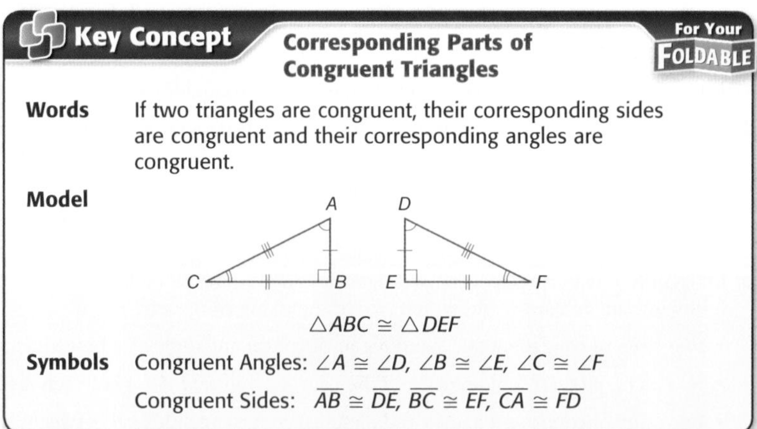

$\triangle ABC \cong \triangle DEF$

Symbols Congruent Angles: $\angle A \cong \angle D$, $\angle B \cong \angle E$, $\angle C \cong \angle F$

Congruent Sides: $\overline{AB} \cong \overline{DE}$, $\overline{BC} \cong \overline{EF}$, $\overline{CA} \cong \overline{FD}$

Lesson 11-2 Resources

Resource	Approaching-Level	On-Level	Beyond-Level	English Learners
Teacher Edition	• Differentiated Instruction, p. 599		• Differentiated Instruction, p. 604	
Chapter Resource Masters	• Study Guide and Intervention, pp. 11–12 • Skills Practice, p. 13 • Practice, p. 14 • Word Problem Practice, p. 15	• Study Guide and Intervention, pp. 11–12 • Skills Practice, p. 13 • Practice, p. 14 • Word Problem Practice, p. 15 • Enrichment, p. 16	• Practice, p. 14 • Word Problem Practice, p. 15 • Enrichment, p. 16	• Study Guide and Intervention, pp. 11–12 • Skills Practice, p. 13 • Practice, p. 14
Transparencies	• 5-Minute Check Transparency 11-2	• 5-Minute Check Transparency 11-2	• 5-Minute Check Transparency 11-2	• 5-Minute Check Transparency 11-2
Other	• Study Notebook • Teaching Pre-Algebra with Manipulatives	• Study Notebook • Teaching Pre-Algebra with Manipulatives	• Study Notebook	• Study Notebook • Teaching Pre-Algebra with Manipulatives

StudyTip

Congruence Statements You can write the following congruence statements for the congruent triangles at the right.

$\triangle RSQ \cong \triangle UVT$
$\triangle SQR \cong \triangle VTU$
$\triangle SRQ \cong \triangle VUT$
$\triangle RQS \cong \triangle UTV$
$\triangle QSR \cong \triangle TVU$
$\triangle QRS \cong \triangle TUV$

In a *congruence statement*, the letters are written so that corresponding vertices appear in the same order.

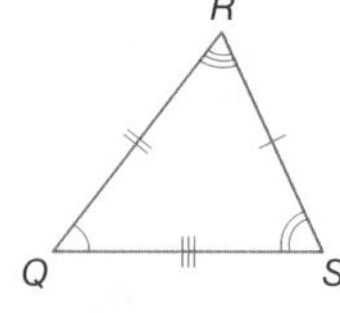

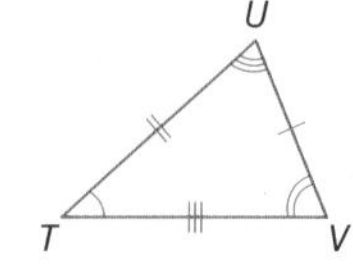

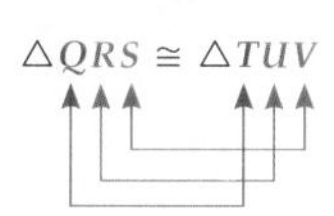

Vertex *Q* corresponds to vertex *T*.
Vertex *R* corresponds to vertex *U*.
Vertex *S* corresponds to vertex *V*.

EXAMPLE 1 Name Corresponding Parts

a. Name the corresponding parts in the congruent triangles below. Then complete the congruence statement $\triangle JKL \cong \triangle$ __?__.

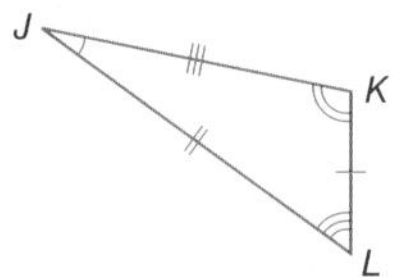

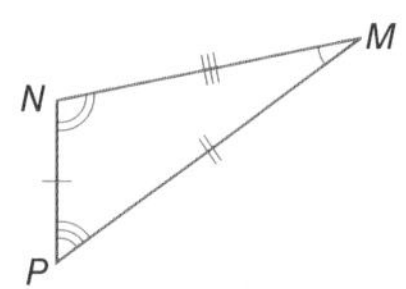

Use the matching arcs and tick marks to identify the corresponding parts.

Corresponding angles: $\angle J \cong \angle M$, $\angle K \cong \angle N$, $\angle L \cong \angle P$

Corresponding sides: $\overline{JK} \cong \overline{MN}$, $\overline{KL} \cong \overline{NP}$, $\overline{LJ} \cong \overline{PM}$

The congruence statement is $\triangle JKL \cong \triangle MNP$.

b. If $\triangle ABC \cong \triangle HGF$, name the corresponding parts. Then complete the congruence statement $\triangle BAC \cong \triangle$ __?__.

Use the order of the vertices in the congruence statement $\triangle ABC \cong \triangle HGF$ to identify the corresponding parts.

Corresponding angles: $\angle A \cong \angle H$, $\angle B \cong \angle G$, $\angle C \cong \angle F$

Corresponding sides: $\overline{AB} \cong \overline{HG}$, $\overline{BC} \cong \overline{GF}$, $\overline{CA} \cong \overline{FH}$

The congruence statement is $\triangle BAC \cong \triangle GHF$.

StudyTip

Draw a Figure When given only a congruence statement, it is helpful to draw the two triangles in the same position. Then it will be easier to visualize and confirm the corresponding angles and sides.

A B C   H G F

Check Your Progress

Name the corresponding parts in each pair of congruent triangles. Then complete the congruence statement.

1A.

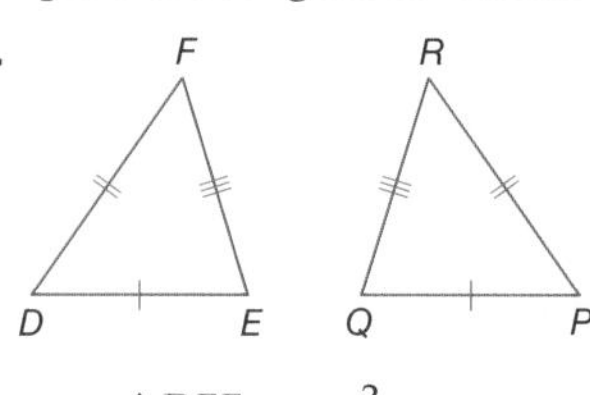

$\triangle DEF \cong$ __?__

1B. $\triangle TUV \cong \triangle CDE$

$\triangle VTU \cong$ __?__

1A. $\angle D \cong \angle P$, $\angle E \cong \angle Q$, $\angle F \cong \angle R$, $\overline{DE} \cong \overline{PQ}$, $\overline{EF} \cong \overline{QR}$, $\overline{DF} \cong \overline{PR}$; $\triangle PQR$

1B. $\angle T \cong \angle C$, $\angle U \cong \angle D$, $\angle V \cong \angle E$, $\overline{TU} \cong \overline{CD}$, $\overline{UV} \cong \overline{DE}$, $\overline{VT} \cong \overline{EC}$; $\triangle ECD$

Personal Tutor glencoe.com

Corresponding Parts of Congruent Triangles

Example 1 shows how to name corresponding parts of triangles. **Example 2** shows how to find missing measures in congruent triangles.

Formative Assessment

Use the Check Your Progress exercises after each example to determine students' understanding of concepts.

Additional Example

1 **a.** Name the corresponding parts in the congruent triangles below. Then complete the congruence statement $\triangle DEF \cong \triangle$ __?__.

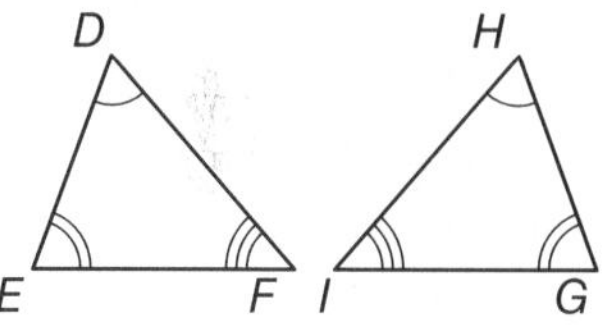

$\angle D \cong \angle H$, $\angle E \cong \angle G$, $\angle F \cong \angle I$; $\overline{DE} \cong \overline{HG}$, $\overline{DF} \cong \overline{HI}$, $\overline{EF} \cong \overline{GI}$; HGI

b. If $\triangle STU \cong \triangle VWZ$, name the corresponding parts. Then complete the congruence statement $\triangle TSU \cong \triangle$?. $\angle S \cong \angle V$; $\angle T \cong \angle W$; $\angle U \cong \angle Z$; $\overline{ST} \cong \overline{VW}$; $\overline{TU} \cong \overline{WZ}$; $\overline{US} \cong \overline{ZV}$; WVZ.

Additional Examples also in Interactive Classroom PowerPoint® Presentations

IWB INTERACTIVE WHITEBOARD READY

Differentiated Instruction AL

If students have difficulty identifying congruent triangles,

Then they may benefit from working with models. Have them draw several pairs of congruent triangles, using tick marks and arcs to identify corresponding parts. Then have them cut out, mix up, and then match the congruent triangles. Encourage them to explain why they know the triangles are congruent.

Tips for New Teachers

Congruence Do not assume congruence based on the art alone. Figures and parts of figures are only congruent when it is stated to be fact.

TEACH with TECH

INTERACTIVE WHITEBOARD Display two congruent triangles on the board. Drag one of the triangles to show your students that it fits exactly on top of the other triangle.

Additional Example

2 **CONSTRUCTION** A brace is used to support a tabletop. In the figure, $\triangle ABC \cong \triangle DEF$.

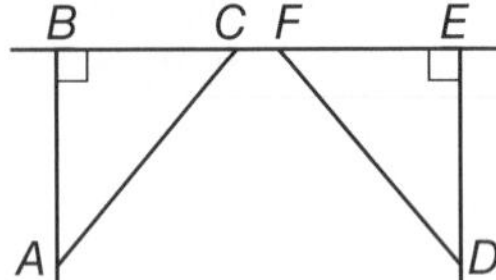

a. If $m\angle C = 50°$, what is the measure of $\angle F$? 50°

b. The length of $\overline{AC}$ is 2 feet. What is the length of $\overline{DF}$? 2 ft

Identify Congruent Triangles

Example 3 shows how to identify congruent triangles.

Additional Example

3 Determine whether the triangles shown are congruent. If so, name the corresponding parts and write a congruence statement.

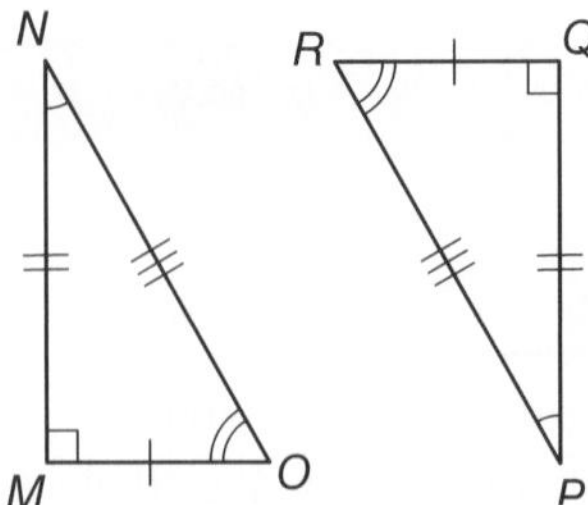

yes; $\angle M \cong \angle Q$, $\angle N \cong \angle P$, $\angle O \cong \angle R$; $\overline{MN} \cong \overline{QP}$, $\overline{NO} \cong \overline{PR}$, $\overline{MO} \cong \overline{QR}$; $\triangle MNO \cong \triangle QPR$

You can use corresponding parts to find the measures of angles and sides in a figure that is congruent to a figure with known measures.

Real-World EXAMPLE 2 Find Missing Measures

SIGNS In the signs below, $\triangle RST \cong \triangle VWX$.

a. If $m\angle W = 60°$, what is the measure of $\angle S$?

$\angle W$ and $\angle S$ are corresponding angles, so they are congruent.

$m\angle S = 60°$ — **Congruent angles have equal measures.**

b. The length of $\overline{ST}$ is 30 inches. What is the length of $\overline{WX}$?

$\overline{ST}$ and $\overline{WX}$ are corresponding sides, so they are congruent.

$WX = 30$ inches — **Congruent sides have equal lengths.**

Check Your Progress

2. QUILTING In the quilt design shown, $\triangle ABC \cong \triangle ADE$. What is the measure of $\angle BCA$? What is the length of AD? **59°; 18 cm**

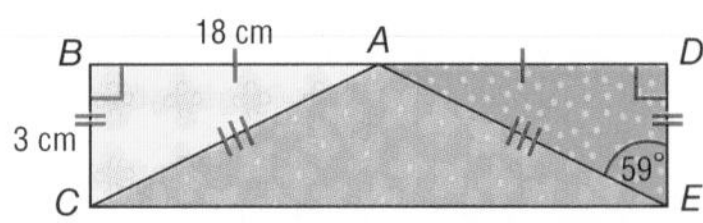

Personal Tutor glencoe.com

Identify Congruent Triangles In congruent triangles, all corresponding angles are congruent and all corresponding sides are congruent.

StudyTip

Identify Congruent Parts To write a congruence statement, note which angles are congruent and which segments have the same length. Then write corresponding vertices in the same order.

EXAMPLE 3 Identify Congruent Triangles

Determine whether the triangles shown at the right are congruent. If so, name the corresponding parts and write a congruence statement.

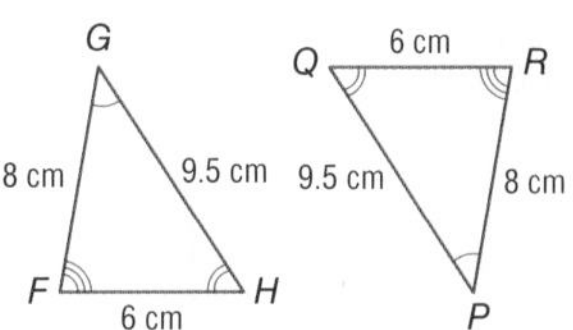

The arcs indicate that $\angle G \cong \angle P$, $\angle H \cong \angle Q$, and $\angle F \cong \angle R$.

The side measures indicate that $\overline{GH} \cong \overline{PQ}$, $\overline{HF} \cong \overline{QR}$, and $\overline{FG} \cong \overline{RP}$.

Since all pairs of corresponding angles and sides are congruent, the triangles are congruent. One congruence statement is $\triangle GHF \cong \triangle PQR$.

Check Your Progress

3. Determine whether the triangles shown are congruent. If so, name the corresponding parts and write a congruence statement. **no**

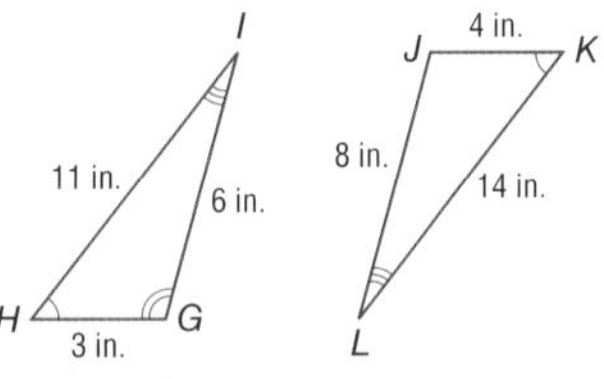

Personal Tutor glencoe.com

Tips for New Teachers

Congruence Statements Although triangles are usually named with the letters in alphabetical order, this practice is not required. The letters can be in any order and still designate the same triangle. However, when writing congruence statements, the order of the two sets of vertices *must* follow the order of the corresponding congruent angles.

Check Your Understanding

Example 1 p. 599 — Name the corresponding parts in each pair of congruent triangles. Then complete the congruence statement.

1. 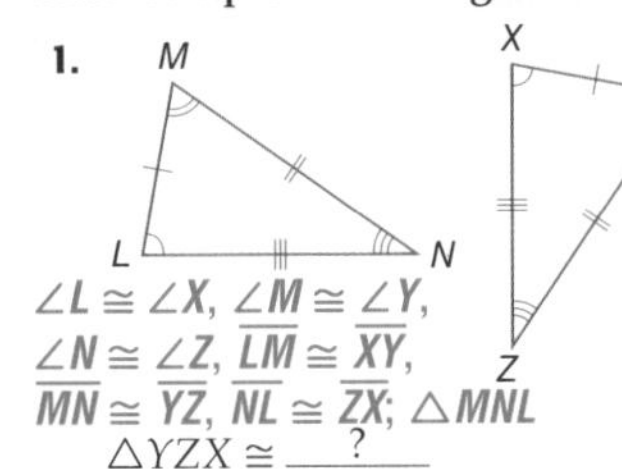

$\angle L \cong \angle X$, $\angle M \cong \angle Y$, $\angle N \cong \angle Z$, $\overline{LM} \cong \overline{XY}$, $\overline{MN} \cong \overline{YZ}$, $\overline{NL} \cong \overline{ZX}$; $\triangle MNL$

$\triangle YZX \cong$ ___?___

2. $\triangle RST \cong \triangle GJK$

$\triangle STR \cong$ ___?___

$\angle R \cong \angle G$, $\angle S \cong \angle J$, $\angle T \cong \angle K$, $\overline{RS} \cong \overline{GJ}$, $\overline{ST} \cong \overline{JK}$, $\overline{TR} \cong \overline{KG}$; $\triangle JKG$

Example 2 p. 600

3. **KITES** In the umbrella kite shown at the right, $\triangle JLK \cong \triangle NLM$.

   a. If $m\angle JKL = 67.5°$, what is $m\angle NML$? 67.5°

   b. If $NL = 14$ inches and $MN = 12$ inches, what is JK? 12 in.

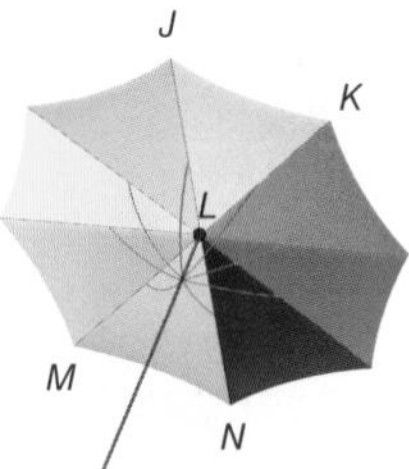

Example 3 p. 600 — Determine whether the triangles shown are congruent. If so, name the corresponding parts and write a congruence statement.

6. $\angle A \cong \angle F$, $\angle B \cong \angle G$, $\angle C \cong \angle J$, $\overline{AB} \cong \overline{FG}$, $\overline{BC} \cong \overline{GJ}$, $\overline{CA} \cong \overline{JF}$; $\triangle BCA$

7. $\angle S \cong \angle Y$, $\angle STZ \cong \angle YTW$, $\angle Z \cong \angle W$, $\overline{ST} \cong \overline{YT}$, $\overline{TZ} \cong \overline{TW}$, $\overline{ZS} \cong \overline{WY}$; $\triangle YTW$

4. 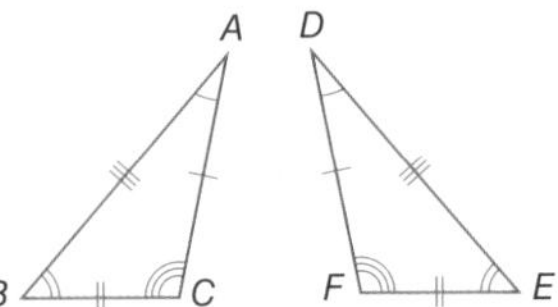

yes; $\angle A \cong \angle D$, $\angle B \cong \angle E$, $\angle C \cong \angle F$, $\overline{AB} \cong \overline{DE}$, $\overline{BC} \cong \overline{EF}$, $\overline{AC} \cong \overline{DF}$; Sample answer: $\triangle ABC \cong \triangle DEF$

5. 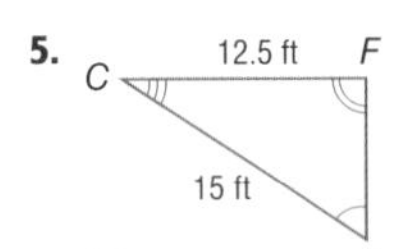

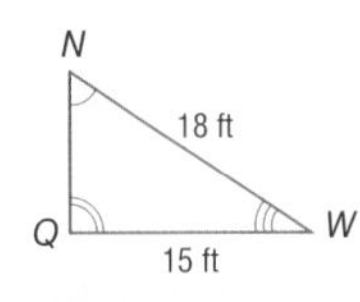

no

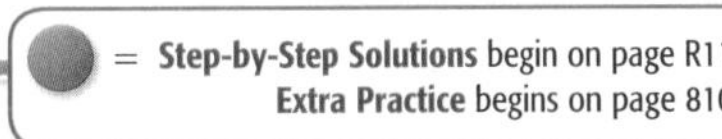

Practice and Problem Solving

Example 1 p. 599 — Name the corresponding parts in each pair of congruent triangles. Then complete the congruence statement.

6. 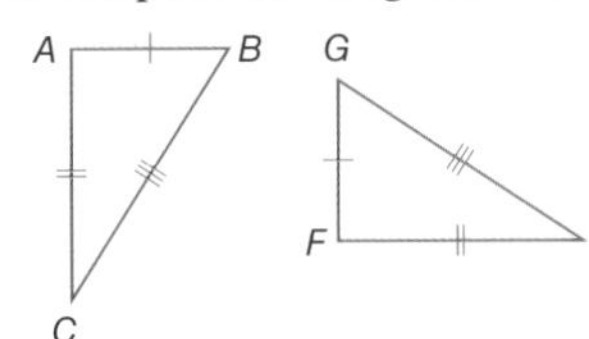

$\triangle GJF \cong$ ___?___

7. 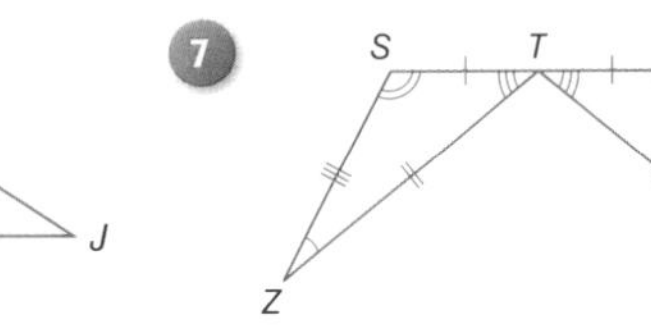

$\triangle STZ \cong$ ___?___

8. $\triangle KLM \cong \triangle WXY$

$\triangle LKM \cong$ ___?___

9. $\triangle NPQ \cong \triangle DEF$

$\triangle EFD \cong$ ___?___

8. $\angle K \cong \angle W$, $\angle L \cong \angle X$, $\angle M \cong \angle Y$, $\overline{KL} \cong \overline{WX}$, $\overline{LM} \cong \overline{XY}$, $\overline{MK} \cong \overline{YW}$; $\triangle XWY$

9. $\angle N \cong \angle D$, $\angle P \cong \angle E$, $\angle Q \cong \angle F$, $\overline{NP} \cong \overline{DE}$, $\overline{PQ} \cong \overline{EF}$, $\overline{QN} \cong \overline{FD}$; $\triangle PQN$

Focus on Mathematical Content

Congruent Triangles If two triangles are congruent, their corresponding sides and angles will be congruent. If the corresponding angles of two triangles are congruent with sides that are not congruent, but are proportional, the triangles are *similar*, and not congruent.

3 PRACTICE

Formative Assessment

Use Exercises 1–5 to check for understanding.

Use the chart at the bottom of this page to customize assignments for your students.

Differentiated Homework Options

Level	Assignment	Two-Day Option	
AL Basic	6–16, 24, 25, 28–40	7–15 odd, 29–32	6–16 even, 24, 25, 28, 33–40
OL Core	7–15 odd, 16, 17–21, 23–25, 28–40	6–16, 29–32	17–25, 28, 33–40
BL Advanced	17–36 (optional: 37–40)		

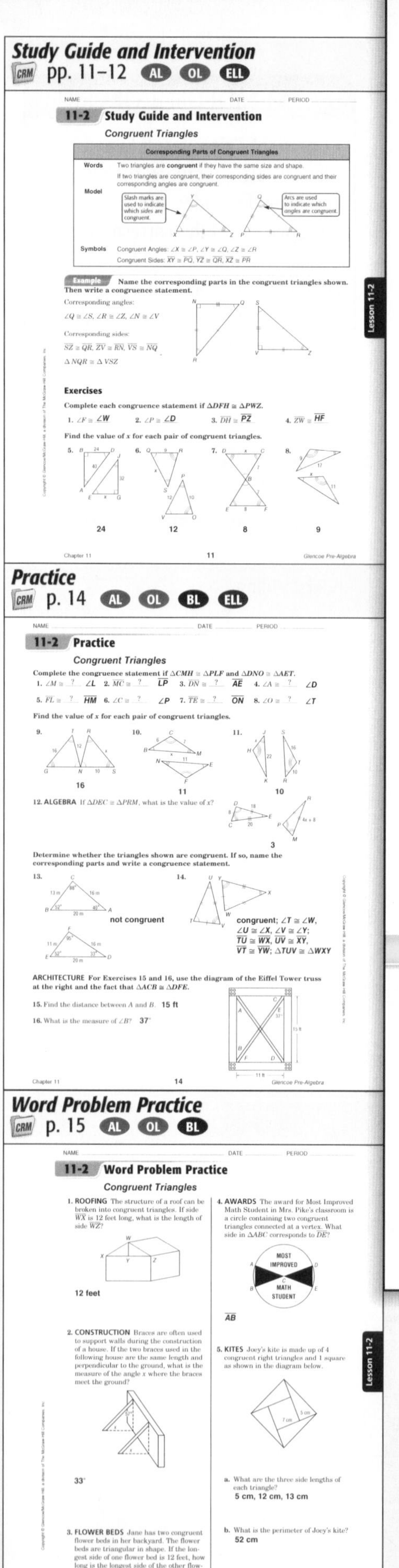

Study Guide and Intervention
CRM pp. 11–12 AL OL ELL

NAME ____ DATE ____ PERIOD ____

11-2 Study Guide and Intervention

Congruent Triangles

Corresponding Parts of Congruent Triangles

Words	Two triangles are **congruent** if they have the same size and shape. If two triangles are congruent, their corresponding sides are congruent and their corresponding angles are congruent.
Model	Slash marks are used to indicate which sides are congruent. Arcs are used to indicate which angles are congruent.
Symbols	Congruent Angles: $\angle X \cong \angle P$, $\angle Y \cong \angle Q$, $\angle Z \cong \angle R$ Congruent Sides: $\overline{XY} \cong \overline{PQ}$, $\overline{YZ} \cong \overline{QR}$, $\overline{XZ} \cong \overline{PR}$

Example Name the corresponding parts in the congruent triangles shown. Then write a congruence statement.

Corresponding angles:
$\angle Q \cong \angle S$, $\angle R \cong \angle Z$, $\angle N \cong \angle V$

Corresponding sides:
$\overline{SZ} \cong \overline{QR}$, $\overline{ZV} \cong \overline{RN}$, $\overline{VS} \cong \overline{NQ}$

$\triangle NQR \cong \triangle VSZ$

Exercises

Complete each congruence statement if $\triangle DFH \cong \triangle PWZ$.

1. $\angle F \cong$ $\angle W$
2. $\angle P \cong$ $\angle D$
3. $\overline{DH} \cong$ $\overline{PZ}$
4. $\overline{ZW} \cong$ $\overline{HF}$

Find the value of x for each pair of congruent triangles.

5. 24
6. 12
7. 8
8. 9

Chapter 11 — 11 — Glencoe Pre-Algebra

Practice
CRM p. 14 AL OL BL ELL

NAME ____ DATE ____ PERIOD ____

11-2 Practice

Congruent Triangles

Complete the congruence statement if $\triangle CMH \cong \triangle PLF$ and $\triangle DNO \cong \triangle AET$.

1. $\angle M \cong$? $\angle L$
2. $\overline{MC} \cong$? $\overline{LP}$
3. $\overline{DN} \cong$? $\overline{AE}$
4. $\angle A \cong$? $\angle D$
5. $\overline{FL} \cong$? $\overline{HM}$
6. $\angle C \cong$? $\angle P$
7. $\overline{TE} \cong$? $\overline{ON}$
8. $\angle O \cong$? $\angle T$

Find the value of x for each pair of congruent triangles.

9. 16
10. 11
11. 10

12. ALGEBRA If $\triangle DEC \cong \triangle PRM$, what is the value of x? 3

Determine whether the triangles shown are congruent. If so, name the corresponding parts and write a congruence statement.

13. not congruent

14. congruent; $\angle T \cong \angle W$, $\angle U \cong \angle X$, $\angle V \cong \angle Y$; $\overline{TU} \cong \overline{WX}$, $\overline{UV} \cong \overline{XY}$, $\overline{VT} \cong \overline{YW}$; $\triangle TUV \cong \triangle WXY$

ARCHITECTURE For Exercises 15 and 16, use the diagram of the Eiffel Tower truss at the right and the fact that $\triangle ACB \cong \triangle DFE$.

15. Find the distance between A and B. 15 ft
16. What is the measure of $\angle B$? 37°

Chapter 11 — 14 — Glencoe Pre-Algebra

Word Problem Practice
CRM p. 15 AL OL BL

NAME ____ DATE ____ PERIOD ____

11-2 Word Problem Practice

Congruent Triangles

1. ROOFING The structure of a roof can be broken into congruent triangles. If side $\overline{WX}$ is 12 feet long, what is the length of side $\overline{WZ}$? 12 feet

2. CONSTRUCTION Braces are often used to support walls during the construction of a house. If the two braces used in the following house are the same length and perpendicular to the ground, what is the measure of the angle x where the braces meet the ground? 33°

3. FLOWER BEDS Jane has two congruent flower beds in her backyard. The flower beds are triangular in shape. If the longest side of one flower bed is 12 feet, how long is the longest side of the other flower bed? 12 feet

4. AWARDS The award for Most Improved Math Student in Mrs. Pike's classroom is a circle containing two congruent triangles connected at a vertex. What side in $\triangle ABC$ corresponds to $\overline{DE}$? $\overline{AB}$

5. KITES Joey's kite is made up of 4 congruent right triangles and 1 square as shown in the diagram below.

a. What are the three side lengths of each triangle? 5 cm, 12 cm, 13 cm

b. What is the perimeter of Joey's kite? 52 cm

Chapter 11 — 15 — Glencoe Pre-Algebra

Example 2 p. 600

10. **STAINED GLASS** In the stained glass window at the right, $\triangle ABC \cong \triangle ADC$.

 a. If $BC = 26$ centimeters, what is DC? **26 cm**

 b. If $m\angle ADC = 90°$, and $m\angle DCA = 45°$, what is $m\angle BAC$? **45°**

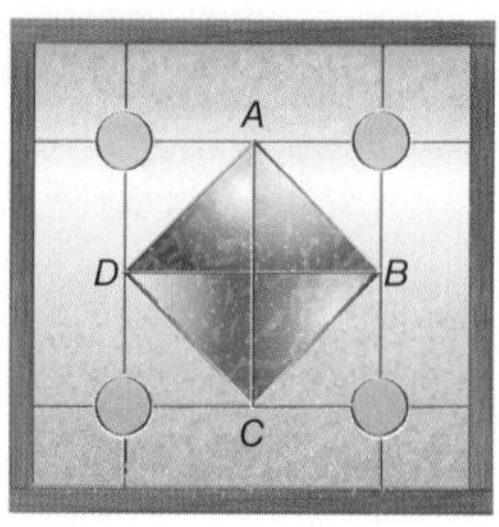

11. **ALGEBRA** Triangle STU is congruent to triangle MNP. In the figures, $TU = 15.4$ millimeters, $US = 13$ millimeters, and $ST = 18.1$ millimeters. If $MN = 2x + 1$, what is the value of x? **8.55 mm**

Example 3 p. 600

Determine whether the triangles shown are congruent. If so, name the corresponding parts and write a congruence statement.

12. yes; $\angle P \cong \angle V$, $\angle W \cong \angle Q$, $\angle Z \cong \angle S$, $\overline{WZ} \cong \overline{QS}$, $\overline{WP} \cong \overline{QV}$, $\overline{PZ} \cong \overline{VS}$; Sample answer: $\triangle ZWP \cong \triangle SQV$

15. yes; $\angle J \cong \angle P$, $\angle L \cong \angle R$, $\angle K \cong \angle Q$, $\overline{JL} \cong \overline{PR}$, $\overline{JK} \cong \overline{PQ}$, $\overline{LK} \cong \overline{RQ}$; Sample answer: $\triangle JLK \cong \triangle PRQ$

12.

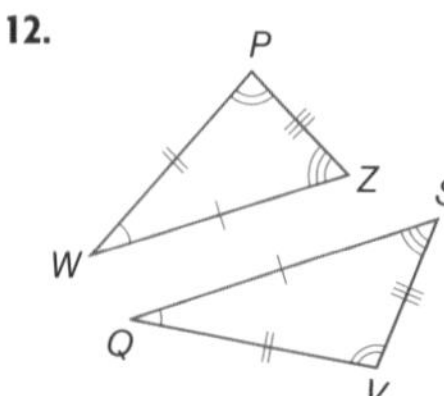

13. no

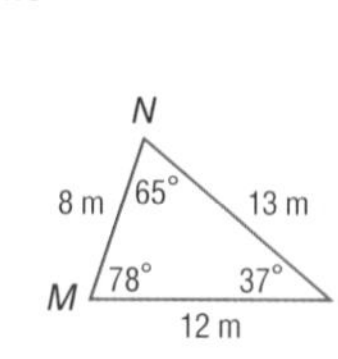

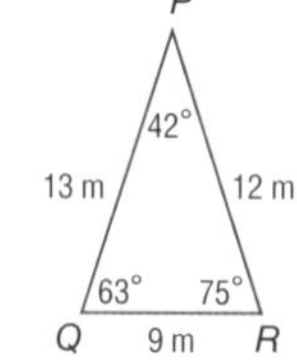

14. no

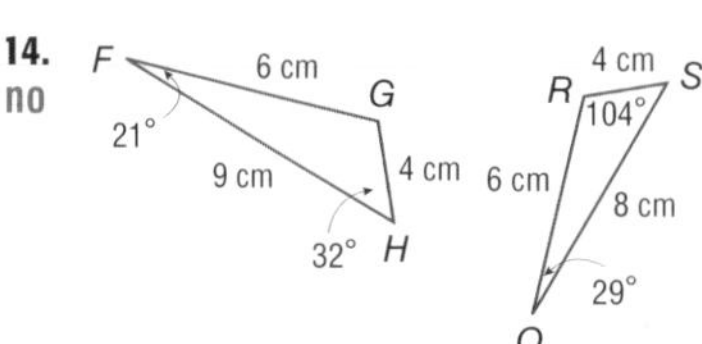

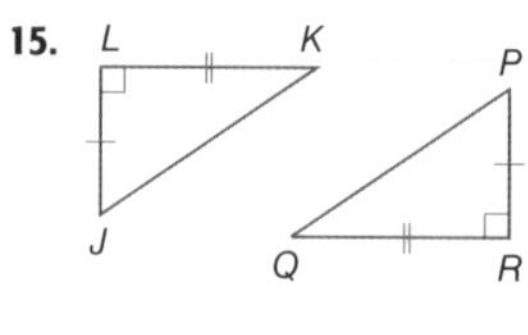

15.

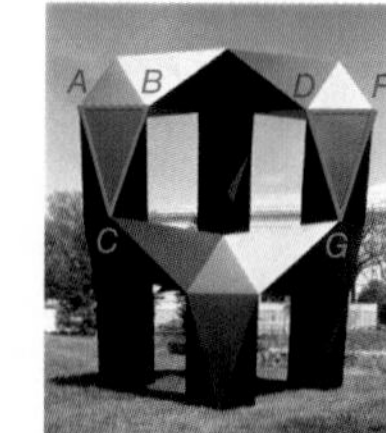

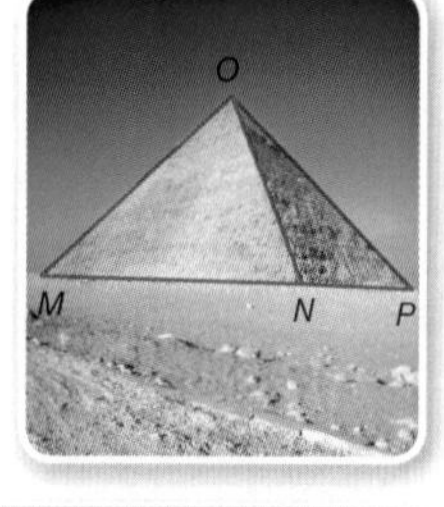

Real-World Link

The average weight of an individual block of stone that makes up the Khafre pyramid in Egypt is 2.5 tons. Some of the outside stones weigh up to 7 tons.

Source: PBS

18. Triangles CBA and CDE are congruent. Triangles CAF and CEF are congruent.

16. **ART** The structure shown at the right, *Moondog*, created by Tony Smith, is located at the Hirshhorn Museum and Sculpture Garden in Washington, D.C. If $\triangle ABC \cong \triangle DFG$, name all corresponding sides. $\overline{AC} \cong \overline{DG}$, $\overline{AB} \cong \overline{DF}$; $\overline{BC} \cong \overline{FG}$

17. **SOCIAL STUDIES** The Khafre pyramid shown at the left is composed of triangles. If $\triangle MNO \cong \triangle NPO$, $m\angle M = 60°$, and $m\angle OPN = 50°$, find $m\angle O$. **70°**

18. **GEOMETRY** Hexagon $ABCDEF$ has six congruent sides. Segments $\overline{CA}$, $\overline{CF}$, and $\overline{CE}$ are drawn on the hexagon, forming four triangles. Make a conjecture about which triangles are congruent. Test your conjecture by measuring the sides and angles of the triangles.

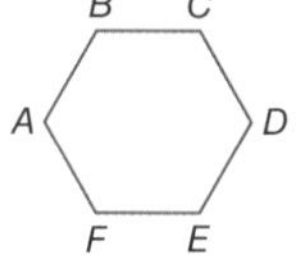

19. In the figure below, $\triangle FGI \cong \triangle LKM$. Find the value of x. Round to the nearest tenth. **3.6 cm**

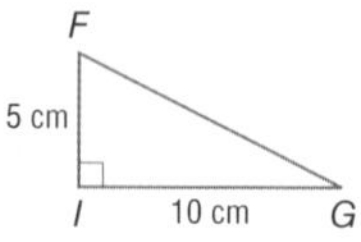

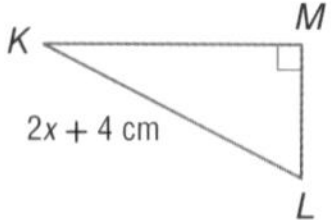

Enrichment
CRM p. 16 OL BL

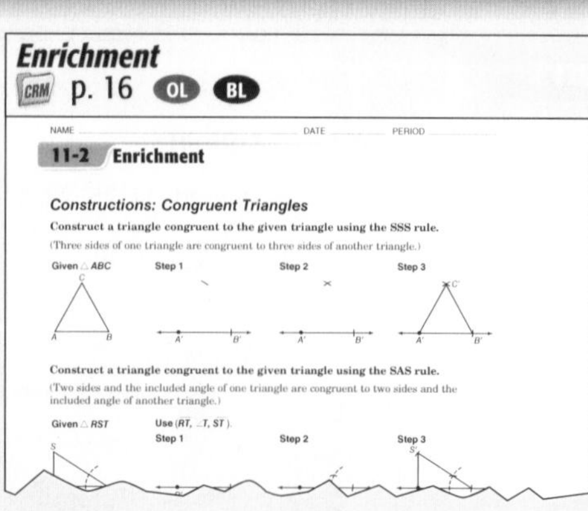

NAME ____ DATE ____ PERIOD ____

11-2 Enrichment

Constructions: Congruent Triangles

Construct a triangle congruent to the given triangle using the SSS rule.
(Three sides of one triangle are congruent to three sides of another triangle.)

Given $\triangle ABC$ — Step 1 — Step 2 — Step 3

Construct a triangle congruent to the given triangle using the SAS rule.
(Two sides and the included angle of one triangle are congruent to two sides and the included angle of another triangle.)

Given $\triangle RST$ — Use $\overline{RT}$, $\angle T$, $\overline{ST}$. Step 1 — Step 2 — Step 3

Real-World Career

Biological Scientists Biological scientists study the behavior, genetics, and diseases of living things. Since the job requires collecting and analyzing data, knowledge of arithmetic, algebra and statistics are important.

A four-year degree in a biological field is the minimum level of education required for this career.

20. **CONSTRUCTION** The roof at the right contains two congruent triangles.

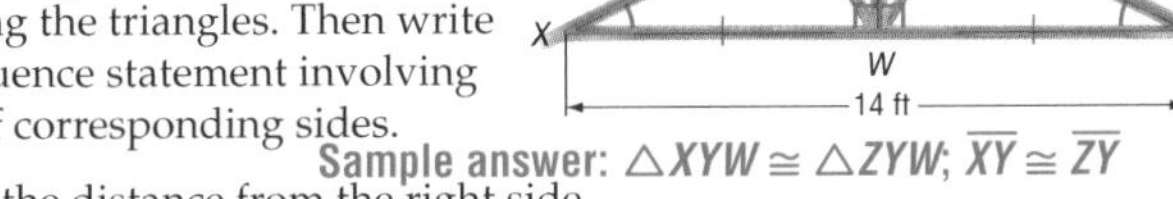

a. Write a congruence statement involving the triangles. Then write a congruence statement involving a pair of corresponding sides. **Sample answer: $\triangle XYW \cong \triangle ZYW$; $\overline{XY} \cong \overline{ZY}$**

b. What is the distance from the right side of the roof at the base to the center? Name the side. **7 ft; $\overline{ZW}$**

c. If the length of $\overline{XW}$ is 4 feet longer than $\overline{WY}$, what is the length of $\overline{WY}$? **3 ft**

21. **BUTTERFLIES** Butterfly wings are triangular in shape. Using the art of the butterfly as a model, draw two sets of congruent triangles, label the vertices, and write a congruence statement for each. **See margin.**

ALGEBRA Find the value of x for each pair of congruent triangles.

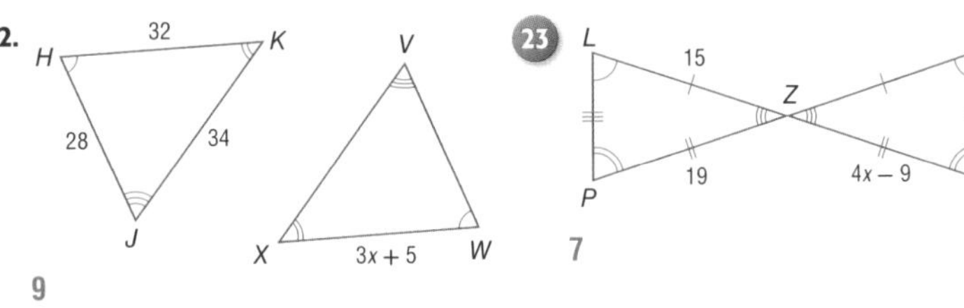

22. **9**

23. **7**

H.O.T. Problems Use Higher-Order Thinking Skills

24. **OPEN ENDED** Find a real-world example of congruent triangles. Explain how you know the triangles are congruent. **See students' work.**

25. **FIND THE ERROR** Jade and Fernando are writing a congruence statement for the congruent triangles at the right. Is either of them correct? Justify your reasoning.

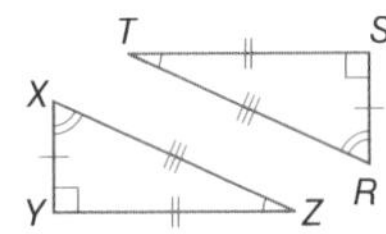

Jade	Fernando
$\angle YXZ \cong \angle STR$	$\overline{ST} \cong \overline{ZY}$

26. **CHALLENGE** Determine whether each statement is *true* or *false*. If true, explain your reasoning. If false, give a counterexample. **See margin.**

a. Triangles *EFG* and *KLM* are congruent. So, their perimeters are equal.

b. Triangles *WXY* and *HJK* are congruent. So, their areas are equal.

c. The perimeter of $\triangle ABC$ is 24 millimeters and the perimeter of $\triangle RST$ is 24 millimeters. So, triangles *ABC* and *RST* are congruent.

27. **CHALLENGE** Describe the scale factor of two congruent triangles. **The scale factor is 1:1 or 1.**

28. **WRITING IN MATH** Describe structures that are built using congruent triangles. Explain why you think congruent triangles are used.

25. **No; corresponding vertices must be written in the same order, so $\angle YXZ \cong \angle SRT$, not $\angle STR$ and $\overline{ST} \cong \overline{YZ}$, not $\overline{ZY}$**

28. **Sample answer: Congruent triangles are used in bridges and roofs. Congruent triangles help balance and support structures.**

Watch Out!

Find the Error For Exercise 25, have students write angle congruence statements so they recognize how to match up the vertices when the original angle is not named in alphabetical order.

Additional Answers

21. Sample answer:

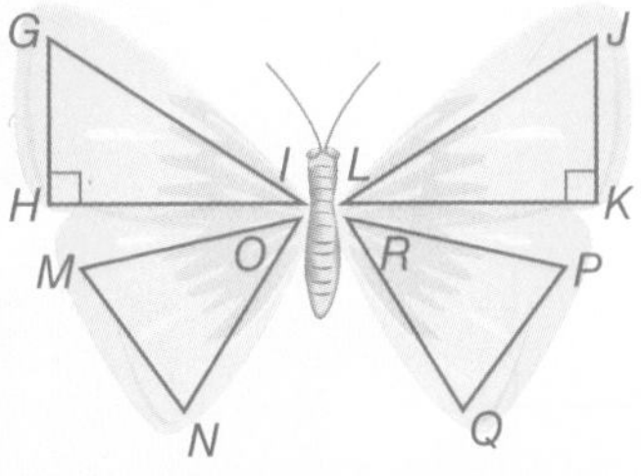

$\triangle GHI \cong \triangle JKL$, $\triangle MNO \cong \triangle PQR$

26a. True; If the triangles are congruent, then the corresponding sides have equal lengths. Therefore, the sums of the lengths, or the perimeters, are equal.

26b. True; If the triangles are congruent, then the corresponding sides have equal lengths and the corresponding bases and heights are equal. Therefore, the products $\frac{1}{2} \cdot$ base $\cdot$ height, or the areas, are equal.

26c. False; Sample answer: the sides of $\triangle ABC$ measure 8 mm, 8mm, and 8 mm. The sides of RST measure 6 mm, 8 mm, and 10 mm.

4 ASSESS

Yesterday's News Have students write about how yesterday's concepts on congruent angles helped them with today's new material about congruent triangles.

Additional Answers

37–40.

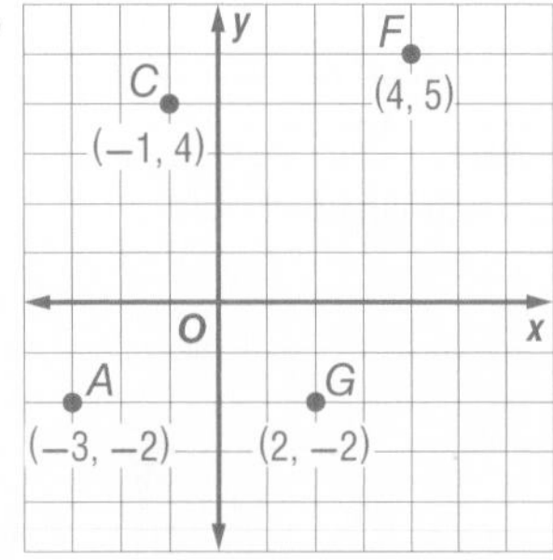

Standardized Test Practice

29. In the road sign below, $\triangle ABC \cong \triangle DCB$, AC is 2.5 meters long, BC is 1 meter long, and AB is 2.7 meters long. What is the length of $\overline{BD}$? **B**

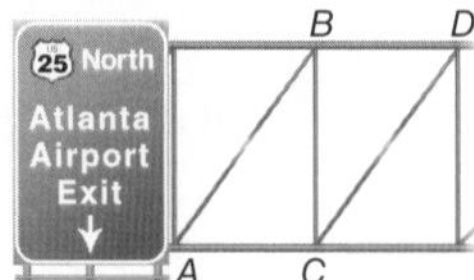

A 1 meter
B 2.5 meters
C 2.7 meters
D 2 meters

30. Guy–wires connected to a telephone pole create two congruent triangles $\triangle PQR$ and $\triangle SQR$. Find the length of $\overline{QS}$. **F**

F 12 ft
G 24 ft
H 48 ft
J 65 ft

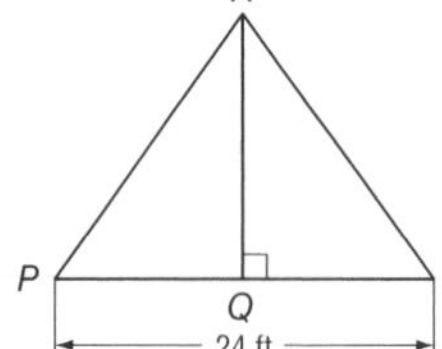

31. Which of the following statements is *not* true if $\triangle FGH \cong \triangle LMN$? **D**

A $\overline{FH} \cong \overline{LN}$
B $\overline{GH} \cong \overline{MN}$
C $\angle G \cong \angle M$
D $\angle F \cong \angle N$

32. EXTENDED RESPONSE Determine whether the triangles shown below are congruent. If so, name the corresponding parts and write a congruence statement.

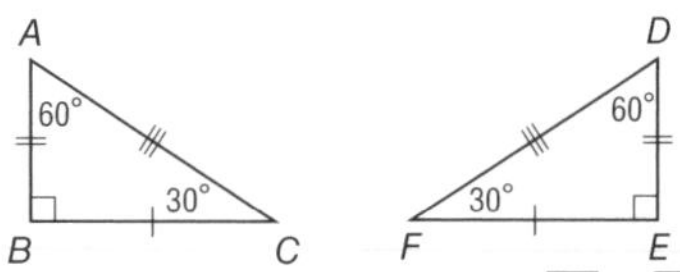

yes; $\angle A \cong \angle D$, $\angle B \cong \angle E$, $\angle C \cong \angle F$, $\overline{AB} \cong \overline{DE}$, $\overline{BC} \cong \overline{EF}$, $\overline{AC} \cong \overline{DF}$; Sample answer: $\triangle ABC \cong \triangle DEF$

Spiral Review

33. Angles R and S are complementary. Find $m\angle R$ if $m\angle S = 65.7°$ (Lesson 11-1) **24.3°**

34. In a 45°-45°-90° triangle, a leg is 4 centimeters long. Find the length of the hypotenuse to the nearest tenth. (Lesson 10-6) **5.7 cm**

35. BIRDS A mockingbird uses about 5^{-4} Joules of energy to sing a song. Write the amount of energy the bird uses as an expression using a positive exponent. (Lesson 9-4) $\frac{1}{5^4}$

36. CAR RENTAL The costs for renting a car from Able Car Rental and from Baker Car Rental are shown in the table. For what mileage does Baker have the better deal? Use the inequality $30 + 0.05x > 20 + 0.10x$. Explain why this inequality works. (Lesson 5-5)
$x < 200$; Sample answer: The inequality finds at what mileage Able's charge is greater than Baker's charge.

Rental Car Costs

	Cost per Day	Cost per Mile
Able Car Rental	$30	$0.05
Baker Car Rental	$20	$0.10

Skills Review

Graph each ordered pair on a coordinate plane. (Lesson 2-6) **37–40. See margin.**

37. F (4, 5) **38.** G (2, −2) **39.** C (−1, 4) **40.** A (−3, −2)

Differentiated Instruction BL

Extension Tell students that another way to prove two triangles are congruent is to show that two angles, and the side of the triangle between them, are congruent to corresponding parts of another triangle. Another way is to prove that two sides, and the angle between them, are congruent. These are the Angle-Side-Angle (ASA) and Side-Angle-Side (SAS) Postulates. Prove that $\triangle ABD \cong \triangle CDB$ if $\overline{AB} \parallel \overline{DC}$.
See students' work.

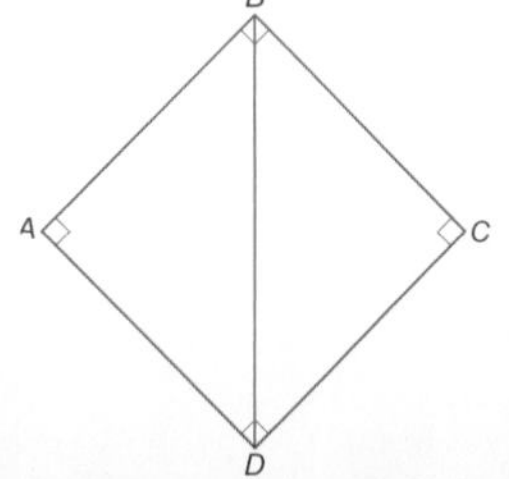

11-3 Rotations

Why?

Jasmine gets on the Ferris wheel at point *A*. The Ferris wheel stops when she is at point *B* to let more people get on the ride.

a. Does the size and shape of the Ferris wheel change as the wheel spins? **no**

b. Describe the movement involved as Jasmine travels from point *A* to point *B*. **Sample answer: She travels halfway around the Ferris wheel. She is 180° from her starting position.**

Then
You drew translations and reflections on the coordinate plane. (Lesson 2-7)

Now
- Define, identify, and draw rotations.
- Determine if a figure has rotational symmetry.

New Vocabulary
rotation
center of rotation
rotational symmetry

Math Online
glencoe.com
- Extra Examples
- Personal Tutor
- Self-Check Quiz
- Homework Help

Rotations A **rotation** is a transformation in which a figure is turned around a fixed point. This point is called the **center of rotation**. Rotations are also called *turns*. A rotated image has the same size and shape as the original figure.

The images below show clockwise rotations of a figure with a center of rotation at point *A*.

Original Figure	Angle of Rotation		
	90°	180°	270°
A, center of rotation	A′	A′	A′

EXAMPLE 1 Rotate a Figure about a Point

Draw the figure at the right after a 90° clockwise rotation about point *C*.

Since point *C* is the center of rotation, it remains in the same position. The figure moves one quarter turn clockwise.

Check Your Progress

Draw the figure in Example 1 after each rotation. **1A–1B. See Chapter 11 Answer Appendix.**

1A. 270° clockwise rotation about point *C*.

1B. 180° counterclockwise about point *C*.

Personal Tutor glencoe.com

11-3 Lesson Notes

1 FOCUS

Vertical Alignment

Before Lesson 11-3
Draw translations and reflections on the coordinate plane.

Lesson 11-3
Define, identify, and draw rotations. Determine if a figure has rotational symmetry.

After Lesson 11-3
Use rotations to create tessellations.

2 TEACH

Scaffolding Questions

Have students read the *Why?* section of the lesson and answer the questions.

Ask:
- Can you tell from looking at points A and B whether the Ferris wheel moved in a clockwise or counterclockwise direction? Explain. No; Jasmine will arrive at point B whether the Ferris wheel moves in a clockwise or counterclockwise direction.
- Suppose the Ferris wheel moves 90° clockwise after Jasmine's car has reached point B. Describe the location of Jasmine's car. It will be to the right of point B, half of the way between points B and A.

Lesson 11-3 Resources

Resource	Approaching-Level	On-Level	Beyond-Level	English Learners
Teacher Edition	• Differentiated Instruction, p. 607		• Differentiated Instruction, p. 610	
Chapter Resource Masters	• Study Guide and Intervention, pp. 17–18 • Skills Practice, p. 19 • Practice, p. 20 • Word Problem Practice, p. 21	• Study Guide and Intervention, pp. 17–18 • Skills Practice, p. 19 • Practice, p. 20 • Word Problem Practice, p. 21 • Enrichment, p. 22	• Practice, p. 20 • Word Problem Practice, p. 21 • Enrichment, p. 22	• Study Guide and Intervention, pp. 17–18 • Skills Practice, p. 19 • Practice, p. 20
Transparencies	• 5-Minute Check Transparency 11-3	• 5-Minute Check Transparency 11-3	• 5-Minute Check Transparency 11-3	• 5-Minute Check Transparency 11-3
Other	• Study Notebook • Teaching Pre-Algebra with Manipulatives	• Study Notebook • Teaching Pre-Algebra with Manipulatives	• Study Notebook	• Study Notebook • Teaching Pre-Algebra with Manipulatives

Rotations

Example 1 shows how to rotate a figure clockwise about a point. **Example 2** shows how to rotate a figure clockwise about a point on a coordinate plane. **Example 3** shows how to rotate a figure clockwise about the origin.

Formative Assessment

Use the Check Your Progress exercises after each example to determine students' understanding of concepts.

Additional Examples

1 Draw the figure shown after a 90° clockwise rotation about point A.

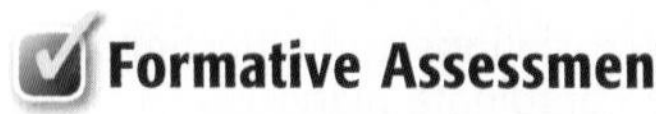

2 Triangle *EFG* has vertices *E*(2, 1), *F*(1, −1), and *G*(4, −1). Graph the figure and its image after a clockwise rotation of 90° about vertex *F*. Then give the coordinates of the vertices for triangle *E'F'G'*.

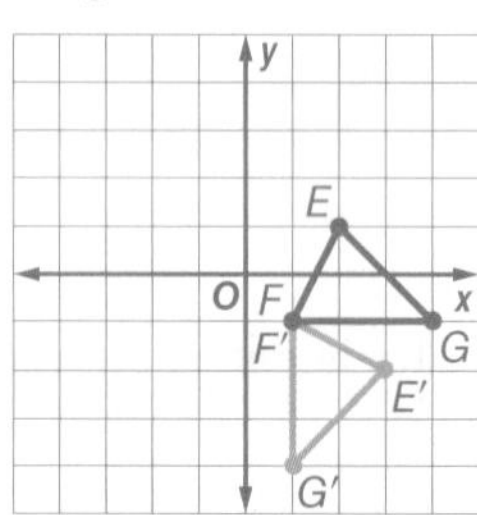

E'(3, −2), *F'*(1, −1), and *G'*(1, −4)

Additional Examples also in Interactive Classroom PowerPoint® Presentations

IWB INTERACTIVE WHITEBOARD READY

Tips for New Teachers

Clockwise and Counterclockwise Tell students that the word *clockwise* refers to the direction in which the hands of a clock rotate. The word *counterclockwise* refers to the opposite direction.

ReadingMath

Notation The notation *W'* is read *W prime.* It represents the point *W* after the rotation.

EXAMPLE 2 Rotate a Figure about a Point

Quadrilateral *WXYZ* has vertices *W*(−4, −1), *X*(−2, 0), *Y*(−1, −3), and *Z*(−2, −4). Graph the figure and its image after a clockwise rotation of 180° about vertex *X*. Then give the coordinates of the vertices for quadrilateral *W'X'Y'Z'*.

Step 1 Graph the original figure. Then graph vertex *W'* after a 180° rotation about vertex *X*. Note that $m\angle WXW' = 180°$ and $WX = XW'$.

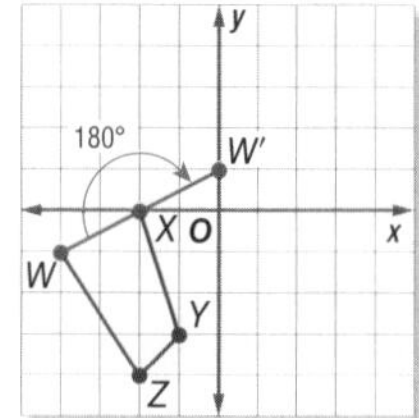

Step 2 Graph the remaining vertices after 180° rotations about vertex *X*. Connect the vertices to form quadrilateral *W'X'Y'Z'*.

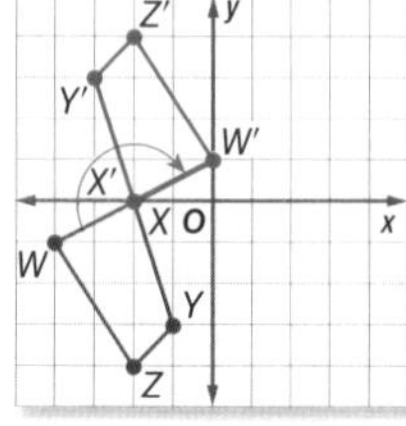

So, the coordinates of the vertices of quadrilateral *W'X'Y'Z'* are *W'*(0, 1), *X'*(−2, 0), *Y'*(−3, 3), and *Z'*(−2, 4).

Check Your Progress

2. Graph quadrilateral *WXYZ* and its image after a counterclockwise rotation of 270° about vertex *Y*. Then give the coordinates of the vertices for quadrilateral *W'X'Y'Z'*. **See margin.**

Personal Tutor glencoe.com

Vocabulary Link

Rotate
Everyday Use to take turns
Math Use to turn around a fixed point

The diagrams below show three clockwise rotations of a figure about the origin.

90° Rotation

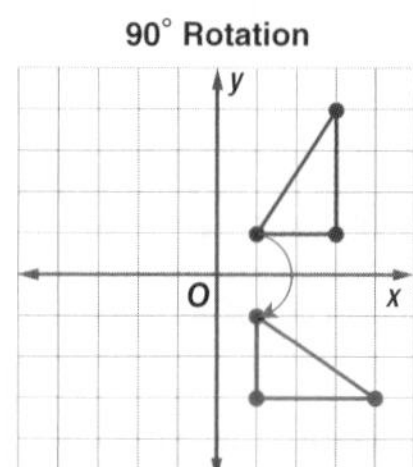

180° Rotation

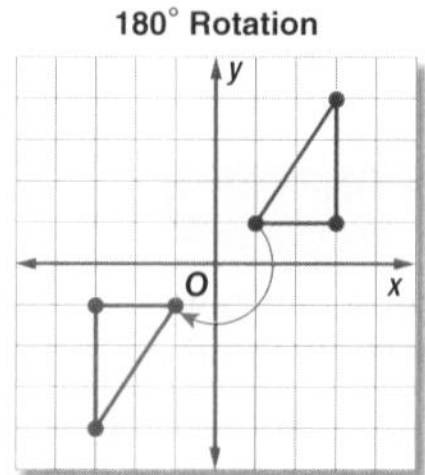

270° Rotation

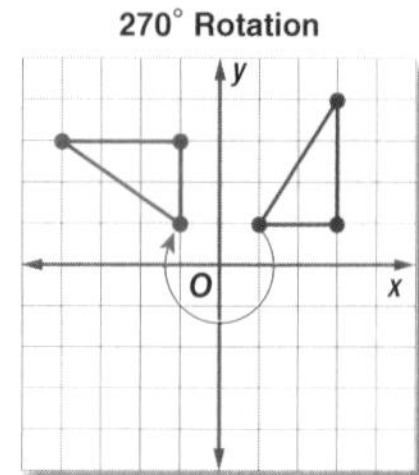

The following diagrams show three counterclockwise rotations about the origin.

270° Rotation

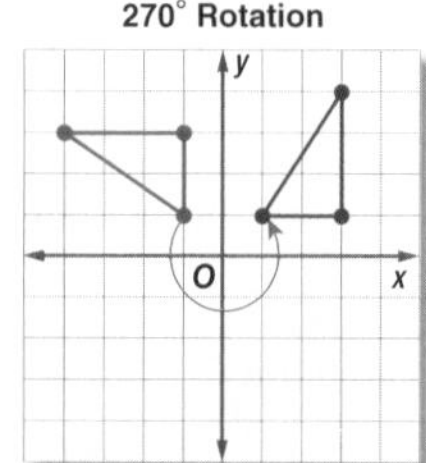

180° Rotation

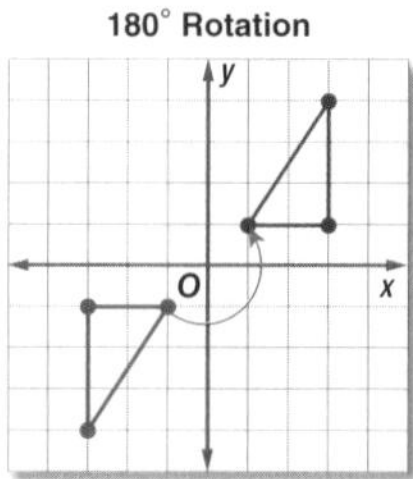

90° Rotation

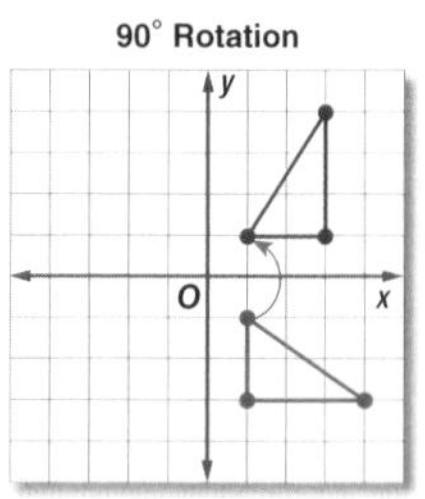

Focus on Mathematical Content

Rotations A rotation is a transformation in which a figure is turned or rotated about a point. Rotations are usually described in degrees and direction, such as 90° counterclockwise or 90° clockwise. Sometimes they are described as half turns or quarter turns.

Additional Answer

2. W'(1, 0), X'(2,−2), Y'(−1,−3) Z'(−2,−2)

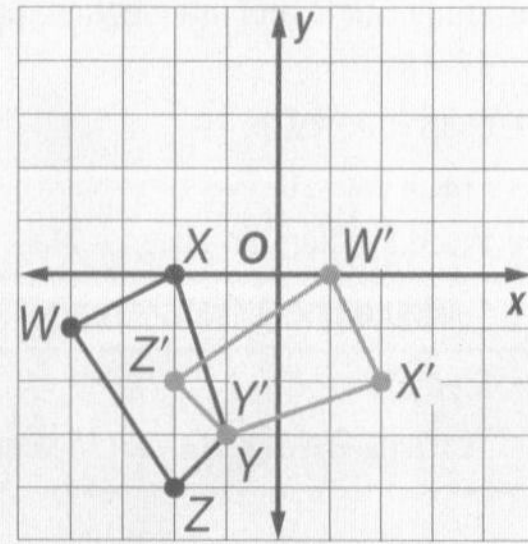

EXAMPLE 3 Rotations about the Origin

A triangle has vertices $A(2, -5)$, $B(4, -4)$, and $C(2, -1)$. Graph the triangle and its image after a rotation of 270° clockwise about the origin.

Step 1 Graph $\triangle ABC$ on a coordinate plane. A 270° degree rotation is the same as three 90° rotations or $\frac{3}{4}$ of a complete circle. Then graph vertex C' after a 270° clockwise rotation about the origin.

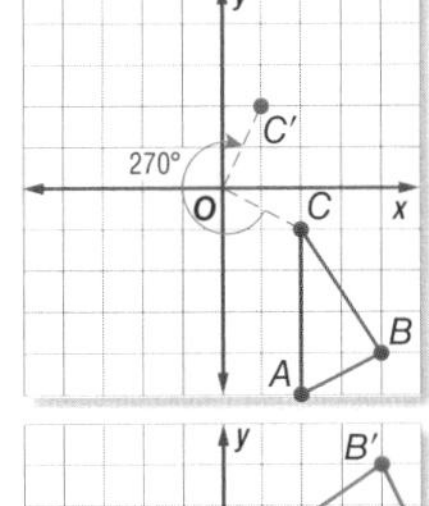

Step 2 Graph the remaining vertices after 270° rotations about the origin. Then connect the vertices to form $\triangle A'B'C'$.

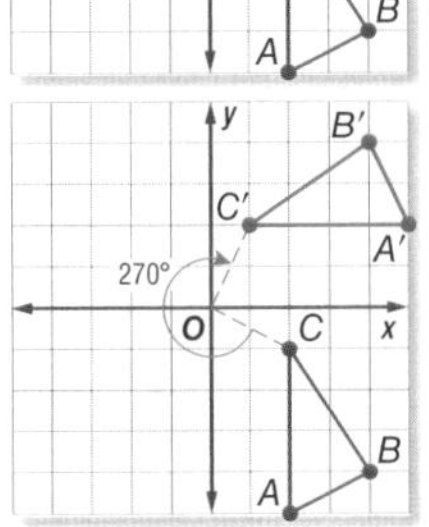

So, the coordinates of the vertices of $\triangle A'B'C'$ are $A'(5, 2)$, $B'(4, 4)$, and $C'(1, 2)$.

Check Your Progress

See margin.

3. A figure has vertices $J(3, 2)$, $K(6, 4)$, $M(6, 7)$, and $N(3, 7)$. Graph the figure and its image after a rotation of 90° clockwise about the origin.

Personal Tutor glencoe.com

Rotational Symmetry If a figure can be rotated less than 360° about its center so that the image matches the original figure, the figure has **rotational symmetry.**

StudyTip

Rotational Symmetry One complete turn of a figure measures 360° because there are 360° in a circle. A figure that matches itself only after a 360° turn does not have rotational symmetry.

Real-World EXAMPLE 4 Rotational Symmetry

NATURE Determine whether the snowflake shown has rotational symmetry. If it does, describe the angle of rotation.

The snowflake can match itself in six positions.

The pattern repeats in 6 even intervals.

So, the angle of rotation is 360° ÷ 6 or 60°.

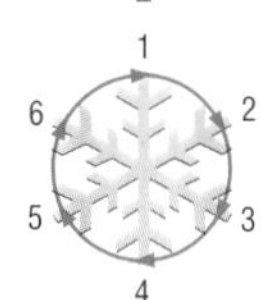

Check Your Progress

4. **NATURE** Determine whether the flower has rotational symmetry. If it does, describe the angle of rotation. yes; 120°

Personal Tutor glencoe.com

Additional Example

3 Parallelogram *ABCD* has vertices $A(-3, -1)$, $B(1, -2)$, $C(-1, -4)$, and $D(-5, -3)$. Graph the parallelogram and its image after a rotation of 180° around the origin.

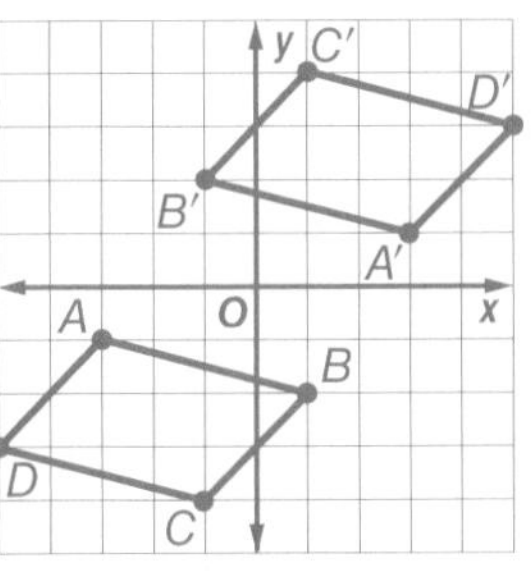

Rotational Symmetry

Example 4 shows how to determine whether a figure has rotational symmetry.

Additional Example

4 **STAR** Determine whether the star shown has rotational symmetry. If it does, describe the angle of rotation.

yes; angle of rotation is 72°

Differentiated Instruction

If students have trouble with rotations,

Then they may find it helpful to first use models. Have students copy, label, and cut out the figure in Example 3 to rotate on a grid. Suggest that they graph the points on the grid as they manipulate the model. Encourage students to use models until they are comfortable with the concepts in the lesson.

Additional Answer

3.

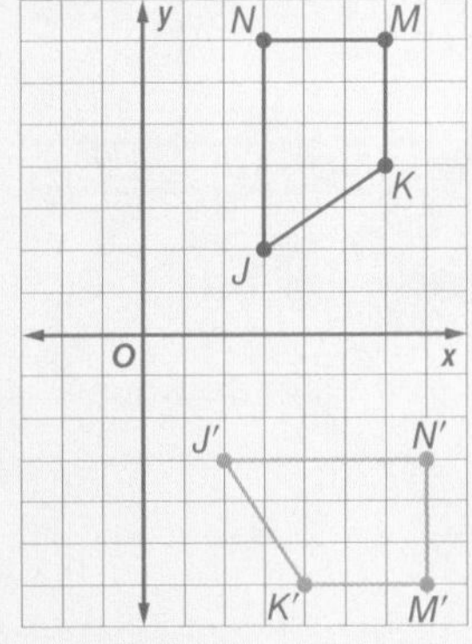

3 PRACTICE

Formative Assessment

Use Exercises 1–4 to check for understanding.

Use the chart at the bottom of this page to customize assignments for your students.

Additional Answers

1.

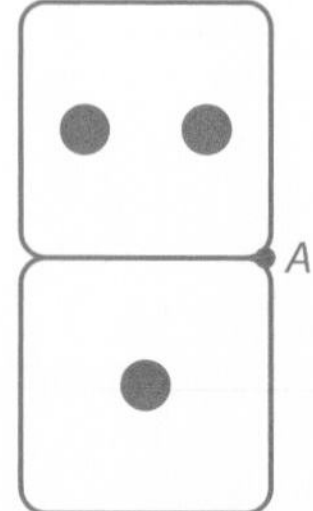

2a.

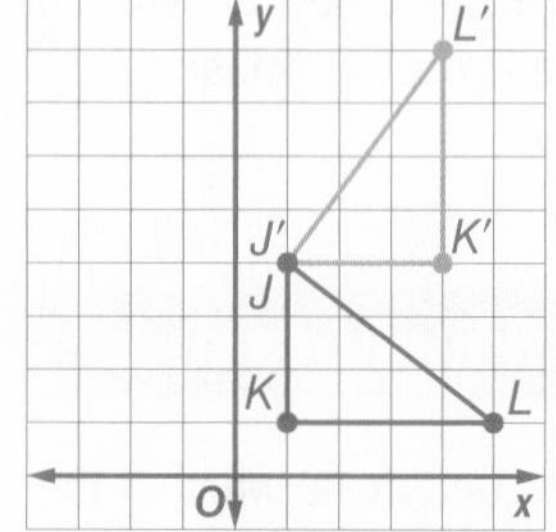

3.

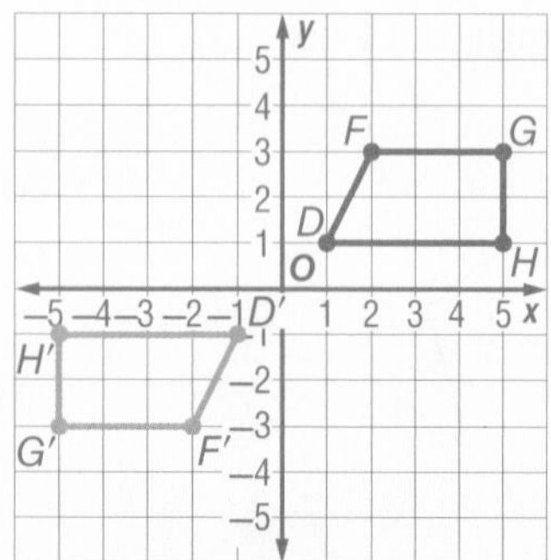

5.

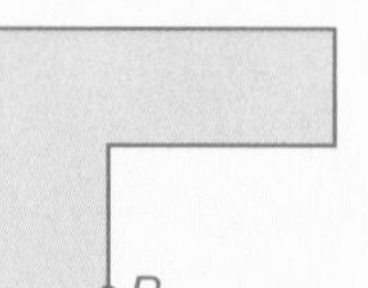

6.

Check Your Understanding

Example 1 p. 605

1. Draw the figure at the right after a 270° clockwise rotation about point A. **See margin.**

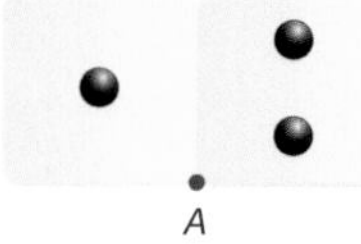

Example 2 p. 606

2. Triangle JKL has vertices $J(1, 4)$, $K(1, 1)$, and $L(5, 1)$.
   a. Graph the figure and its image after a clockwise rotation of 270° about vertex J. **See margin.**
   b. Give the coordinates of the vertices for triangle $J'K'L'$. **$J'(1, 4)$, $K'(4, 4)$, $L'(4, 8)$**

Example 3 p. 607

3. A figure has vertices $D(1, 1)$, $F(2, 3)$, $G(5, 3)$, and $H(5, 1)$. Graph the figure and its image after a rotation of 180° around the origin. **See margin.**

Example 4 p. 607

4. **WINDMILL** Determine whether the blades of the windmill shown at the right have rotational symmetry. If they do, describe the angle of rotation. **yes; 90°**

Practice and Problem Solving

● = **Step-by-Step Solutions** begin on page R11.
Extra Practice begins on page 810.

Example 1 p. 605

Draw each figure after the rotation described.

5. 90° clockwise rotation about point R **See margin.**

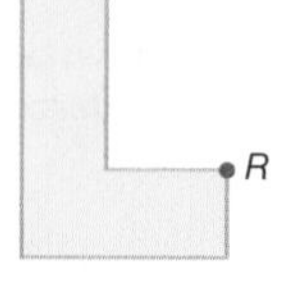

6. 180° clockwise rotation about point S **See margin.**

Example 2 p. 606

7. Triangle GHJ is shown at the right.
   a. Graph the figure after a clockwise rotation of 90° about vertex G. **See Chapter 11 Answer Appendix.**
   b. Give the coordinates of the vertices for $\triangle G'H'J'$. **$G'(1, 1)$, $H'(-3, -1)$, $J'(-3, 1)$**

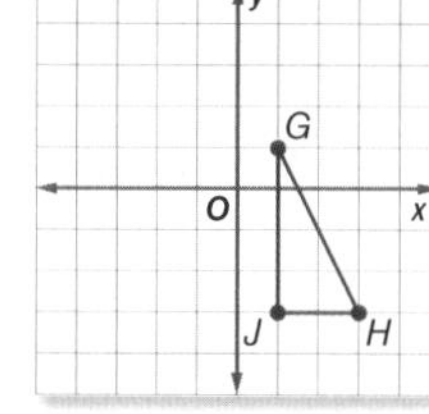

8. Trapezoid $ABCD$ has vertices $A(-3, 1)$, $B(-3, 4)$, $C(1, 4)$, and $D(-1, 1)$.
   a. Graph the figure and its image after a clockwise rotation of 180° about vertex D. **See Chapter 11 Answer Appendix.**
   b. Give the coordinates of the vertices for trapezoid $A'B'C'D'$. **$A'(1, 1)$, $B'(1, -2)$, $C'(-3, -2)$, $D'(-1, 1)$**

Differentiated Homework Options

Level	Assignment	Two-Day Option	
AL Basic	5–14, 17, 18, 20–31	5–13 odd, 22–25	6–14 even, 17, 18, 20, 21, 26–31
OL Core	5–13 odd, 15–18, 20–31	5–14, 22–25	15–18, 20, 21, 26–31
BL Advanced	15–28 (optional: 29–31)		

Example 3
p. 607

9. A figure has vertices $K(1, -1)$, $L(3, -4)$, $M(1, -5)$, and $N(-1, -4)$. Graph the figure and its image after a rotation of 270° counterclockwise about the origin. **9–10. See Chapter 11 Answer Appendix.**

10. A triangle has vertices $P(-3, 1)$, $Q(0, 4)$, and $R(1, -1)$. Graph the triangle and its image after a rotation of 180° about the origin.

Example 4
p. 607

11. **SHAPES** Describe the rotational symmetry of the star in Exercise 6. **72°**

SWIMMING Determine whether each synchronized swimming formation has rotational symmetry. If it does, describe the angle of rotation.

12. 
yes; 45°

13. 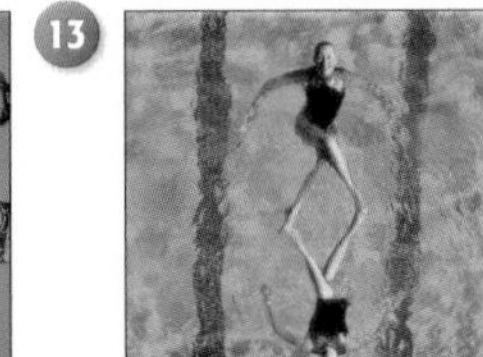
yes; 180°

14. 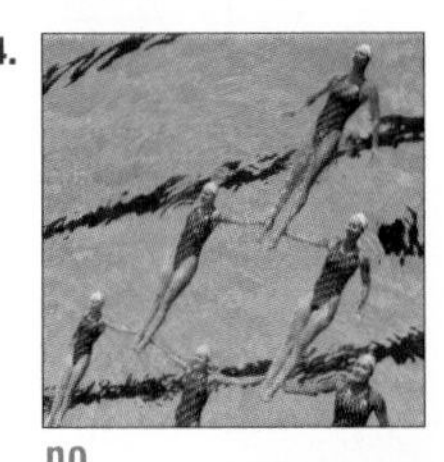
no

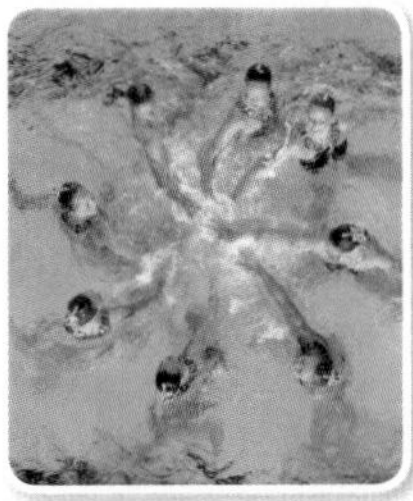

15. **DECORATING** Pat is placing the tile at the right in different orientations on a wall. Describe three rotations that would change the orientation of the tile. Use drawings to show what the tile looks like after each rotation. **See Chapter 11 Answer Appendix.**

16. **MULTIPLE REPRESENTATIONS** In this problem, you will investigate rotations. A figure is graphed on the coordinate plane. One of its vertices has coordinates (x, y).

a. **SYMBOLIC** Write the coordinates of the vertex after each rotation.
- 90° clockwise about the origin $(y, -x)$
- 180° about the origin $(-x, -y)$
- 270° clockwise about the origin $(-y, x)$

b. **ANALYTICAL** The vertex of the figure is located in Quadrant II. If the figure is rotated 180° about the origin, in which quadrant will the corresponding vertex of the image be located? **Quadrant IV**

Real-World Link

Sixty percent of a synchronized swimming routine is underwater. Synchronized swimmers at the highest level can swim up to 75 meters underwater without coming up for air.

Source: Meredith College

H.O.T. Problems

Use Higher-Order Thinking Skills

17. **OPEN ENDED** Sketch a figure that has rotational symmetry. Describe the angle of rotation. **See Chapter 11 Answer Appendix.**

18. **REASONING** If two polygons are similar, could they also be congruent? Explain your reasoning. **See margin.**

19. **CHALLENGE** Triangle RST is rotated 270° clockwise around the origin. Its rotated image has vertices $R'(-5, 1)$, $S'(2, 0)$, and $T'(-3, -6)$. What are the coordinates of triangle RST? **$R(1, 5)$, $S(0, -2)$, $T(-6, 3)$**

20. **REASONING** Will a geometric figure and its rotated image *sometimes*, *always*, or *never* have the same perimeter? Explain your reasoning.

21. **WRITING IN MATH** Describe the similarities and differences between reflections and rotations.

20. Always; the original figure and the rotated image are congruent. Since the corresponding side lengths are equal, the perimeters are the same.

21. With both transformations, the original figure and the image are congruent. In a reflection, a figure is reflected across a line. In a rotation, a figure is rotated around a point.

Multiple Representations In Exercise 16, students use mathematical symbols, a verbal description, and algebraic analysis to describe the appearance of a figure rotated about the origin.

Additional Answer

18. Yes; Sample answer: If the scale factor between the 2 figures is 1, then the lengths of the corresponding sides would be the same. So, the polygons would be congruent.

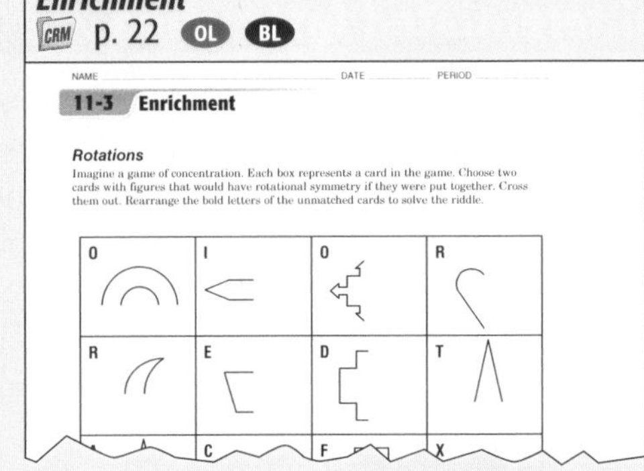
Enrichment
CRM p. 22 OL BL

NAME ______ DATE ______ PERIOD ______

11-3 Enrichment

Rotations

Imagine a game of concentration. Each box represents a card in the game. Choose two cards with figures that would have rotational symmetry if they were put together. Cross them out. Rearrange the bold letters of the unmatched cards to solve the riddle.

O	I	O	R
R	E	D	T
	C	F	X

Study Guide and Intervention
CRM pp. 17–18 AL OL ELL

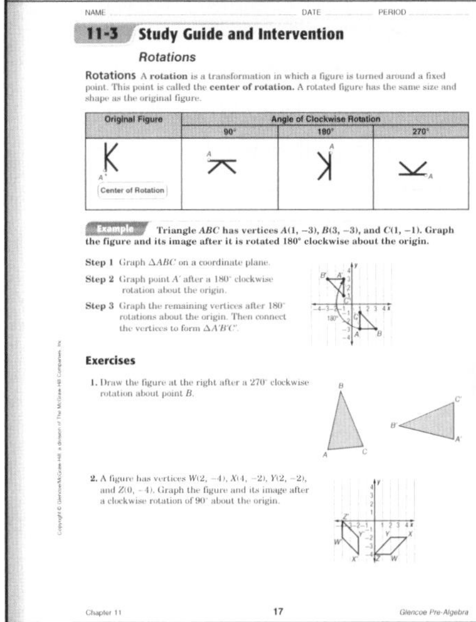

NAME ______ DATE ______ PERIOD ______

11-3 Study Guide and Intervention

Rotations

Rotations A **rotation** is a transformation in which a figure is turned around a fixed point. This point is called the **center of rotation.** A rotated figure has the same size and shape as the original figure.

Original Figure	Angle of Clockwise Rotation		
	90°	180°	270°
Center of Rotation			

Example **Triangle ABC has vertices $A(1, -3)$, $B(3, -3)$, and $C(1, -1)$. Graph the figure and its image after it is rotated 180° clockwise about the origin.**

Step 1 Graph $\triangle ABC$ on a coordinate plane.

Step 2 Graph point A' after a 180° clockwise rotation about the origin.

Step 3 Graph the remaining vertices after 180° rotations about the origin. Then connect the vertices to form $\triangle A'B'C'$.

Exercises

1. Draw the figure at the right after a 270° clockwise rotation about point B.

2. A figure has vertices $W(2, -4)$, $X(4, -2)$, $Y(2, -2)$, and $Z(0, -4)$. Graph the figure and its image after a clockwise rotation of 90° about the origin.

Chapter 11 17 Glencoe Pre-Algebra

Practice
CRM p. 20 AL OL BL ELL

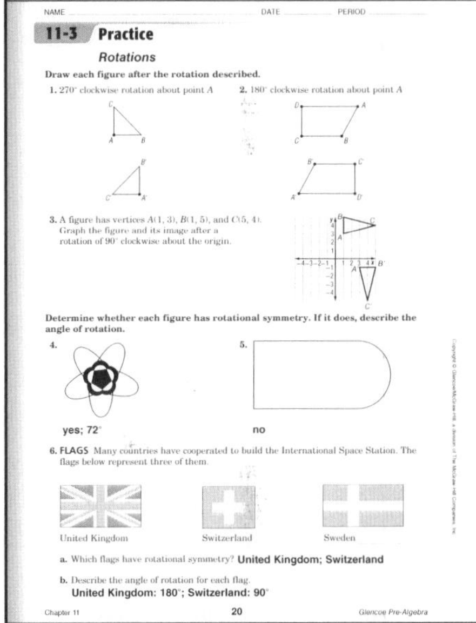

NAME ______ DATE ______ PERIOD ______

11-3 Practice

Rotations

Draw each figure after the rotation described.

1. 270° clockwise rotation about point A

2. 180° clockwise rotation about point A

3. A figure has vertices $A(1, 3)$, $B(1, 5)$, and $C(5, 4)$. Graph the figure and its image after a rotation of 90° clockwise about the origin.

Determine whether each figure has rotational symmetry. If it does, describe the angle of rotation.

4. **yes; 72°**

5. **no**

6. **FLAGS** Many countries have cooperated to build the International Space Station. The flags below represent three of them.

United Kingdom Switzerland Sweden

a. Which flags have rotational symmetry? **United Kingdom; Switzerland**

b. Describe the angle of rotation for each flag.
United Kingdom: 180°; Switzerland: 90°

Chapter 11 20 Glencoe Pre-Algebra

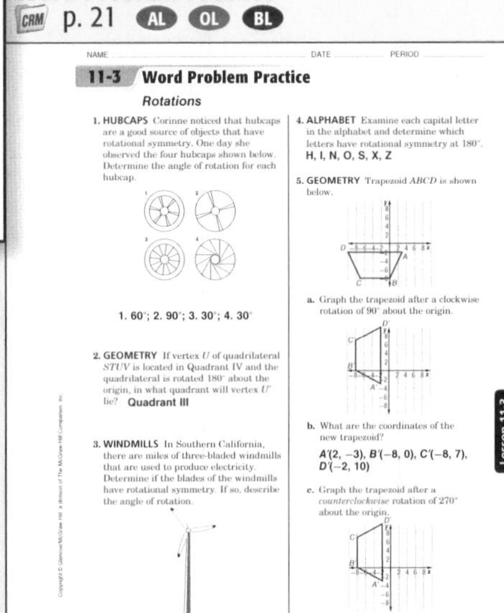
Word Problem Practice
CRM p. 21 AL OL BL

NAME ______ DATE ______ PERIOD ______

11-3 Word Problem Practice

Rotations

1. **HUBCAPS** Corinne noticed that hubcaps are a good source of objects that have rotational symmetry. One day she observed the four hubcaps shown below. Determine the angle of rotation for each hubcap.
1. 60°; 2. 90°; 3. 30°; 4. 30°

2. **GEOMETRY** If vertex U of quadrilateral $STUV$ is located in Quadrant IV and the quadrilateral is rotated 180° about the origin, in what quadrant will vertex U' lie? **Quadrant III**

3. **WINDMILLS** In Southern California, there are miles of three-bladed windmills that are used to produce electricity. Determine if the blades of the windmills have rotational symmetry. If so, describe the angle of rotation.
yes; 120°

4. **ALPHABET** Examine each capital letter in the alphabet and determine which letters have rotational symmetry at 180°.
H, I, N, O, S, X, Z

5. **GEOMETRY** Trapezoid $ABCD$ is shown below.

a. Graph the trapezoid after a clockwise rotation of 90° about the origin.

b. What are the coordinates of the new trapezoid?
$A'(2, -3)$, $B'(-8, 0)$, $C'(-8, 7)$, $D'(-2, 10)$

c. Graph the trapezoid after a *counterclockwise* rotation of 270° about the origin.

d. What do you notice about the two images graphed in parts a and c?
They are the same image.

Chapter 11 21 Glencoe Pre-Algebra

Lesson 11-3 Rotations 609

ASSESS

Name the Math Give students the coordinates of a triangle. Ask them to name the steps they would use to write the coordinates of the image after a 90° clockwise rotation about the origin. Then have students write the coordinates of the rotated triangle.

Formative Assessment

Check for student understanding of concepts in Lessons 11-1, 11-2, and 11-3.

CRM Quiz 1, p. 62

Additional Answer

24a.

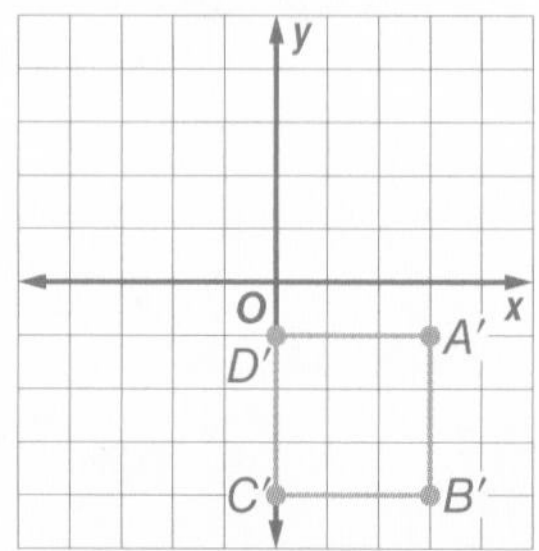

TEACH with TECH

PHOTO EDITING SOFTWARE Give students several digital pictures that are upside down and sideways. Have them use a photo editing program to rotate the pictures to make them right-side up. Have them make connections between the image they see and the angle and direction of rotation they used.

Standardized Test Practice

22. Triangle *XYZ* was rotated about the origin to $\triangle X'Y'Z'$. Which of the following describes the rotation? **C**

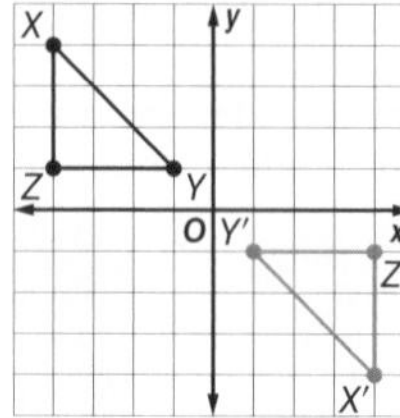

A 90° clockwise about the origin
B 90° counterclockwise about the origin
C 180° clockwise about the origin
D 270° clockwise about the origin

23. Triangle *ABC* has vertices $A(1, 2)$, $B(-1, -1)$, and $C(2, 0)$. If the triangle is rotated clockwise 90° about the origin, which of the following would be the vertices of $\triangle A'B'C'$? **J**

F $A'(2, 1)$, $B'(-1, -1)$, $C'(0, 2)$
G $A'(-1, 2)$, $B'(1, 1)$, $C'(-2, 0)$
H $A'(-2, 1)$, $B'(1, -1)$, $C'(0, 2)$
J $A'(2, -1)$, $B'(-1, 1)$, $C'(0, -2)$

24. EXTENDED RESPONSE Figure *ABCD* is shown. **a. See margin.**

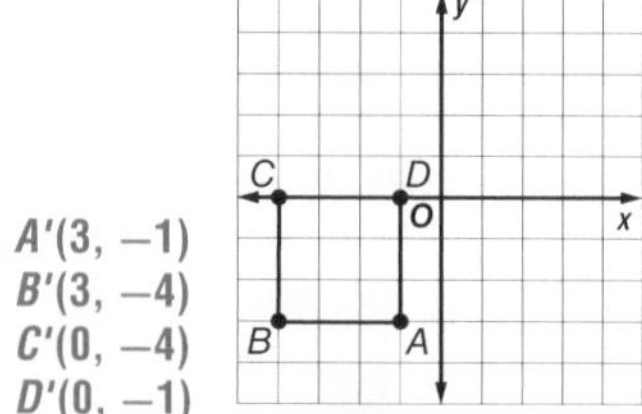

b. $A'(3, -1)$
$B'(3, -4)$
$C'(0, -4)$
$D'(0, -1)$

a. Graph the figure after a clockwise rotation of 270° about the origin.
b. Give the coordinates of the vertices for square $A'B'C'D'$.

25. Which of the following is true about the image shown below? **C**

A The figure does not have rotational symmetry.
B The figure has angle of rotation of 90°.
C The figure has angle of rotation of 180°.
D The figure has angle of rotation of 270°.

Spiral Review

26. ARCHITECTURE Refer to the diagram of the roof truss. In the diagram, $\triangle TRU \cong \triangle SRU$. (Lesson 11-2)

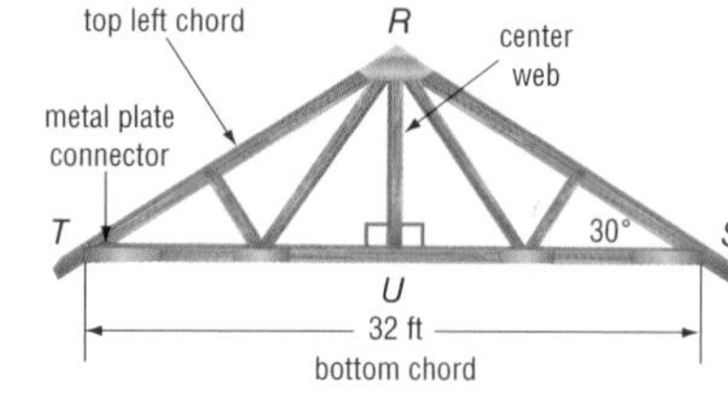

a. Find the distance from the right metal plate connector to the center web. **16 ft**
b. What is the measure of the angle formed by the top left chord and the bottom chord? **30°**

27. If $m\angle B = 17°$ and $\angle A$ and $\angle B$ are complementary, find $m\angle A$. (Lesson 11-1) **73°**

28. Find the distance between $F(-3, -6)$ and $G(4, 1)$. Round to the nearest tenth, if necessary. (Lesson 10-5) **9.9**

Skills Review

Solve each equation. (Lesson 4-5)

29. $4x + 157 = 243$ **21.5**

30. $2x + 89 = 351$ **131**

31. $6x - 72 = 138$ **35**

Differentiated Instruction

Extension Explain how you can use the rules for writing the coordinates of clockwise rotations about the origin to write the coordinates of counterclockwise rotations. Then use (x, y) to write the coordinates after a 90°, 180°, and 270° counterclockwise rotation about the origin. Because the results are the same for the following pairs of rotations, you can use the same rules for the pair: 90° clockwise and 270° counterclockwise; 270° clockwise and 90° counterclockwise; and 180° clockwise or counterclockwise; $(-y, x)$; $(-x, -y)$; $(y, -x)$

Geometry Lab
Angles in Polygons

Math Online glencoe.com
Math *in Motion*, Animation

Objective
Use parallel lines to investigate the sum of the measures of the angles in a triangle and similar triangles.

In Lesson 11-1, you identified special pairs of angles that are formed when parallel lines are cut by a transversal. In this lab, you will use the angle relationships of those angles to discover the sum of the measures of the angles in a triangle.

ACTIVITY Angles in a Triangle

Step 1 Draw a pair of parallel lines.

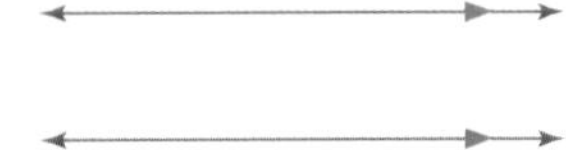

Step 2 Draw a transversal as shown. Label ∠1 and ∠2.

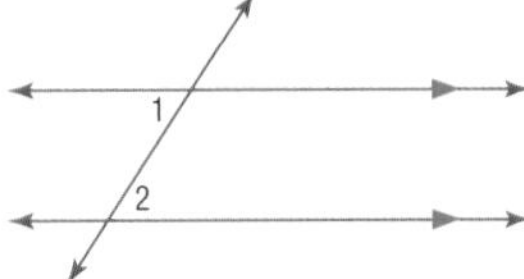

Step 3 Draw a second transversal as shown. Label ∠3 and ∠4. Label the triangle formed by these lines *ABC*.

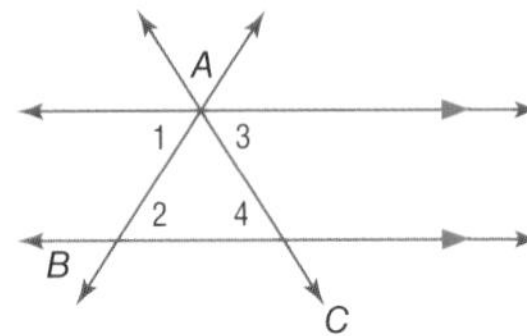

Analyze the Results

1. Classify the relationship between ∠1 and ∠2. What is true about these pairs of angles? Classify the relationship between ∠3 and ∠4. What is true about these pairs of angles? **∠1 and ∠2 are alternate interior angles; they are congruent; ∠3 and ∠4 are alternate interior angles; they are congruent**
2. What type of angle is formed by ∠1, ∠3, and ∠*BAC*? What is the sum of the measures of ∠1, ∠3, and ∠*BAC*? **straight angle; 180°**
3. What can you conclude about the sum of the measures of the angles in △*ABC*? Explain your reasoning.
4. **MAKE A CONJECTURE** Based on this activity, what is the sum of the measures of the angles of any triangle? **180°**
5. **MAKE A CONJECTURE** The quadrilateral at the right is separated into two triangles. Based on the activity above, what do you think is the sum of the angle measures of this quadrilateral? Explain.

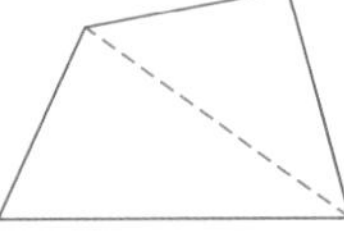

3. **The sum of the measures of the angles in △*ABC* is 180°. We know ∠1 ≅ ∠2, ∠3 ≅ ∠4, and $m\angle 1 + m\angle BAC + m\angle 3 = 180°$. Therefore, we can conclude that $m\angle 2 + m\angle BAC + m\angle 4 = 180°$.**

5. **360°; Sample answer: Since a quadrilateral can be split into 2 triangles, the sum of the angles in a quadrilateral is equal to 2 • 180° or 360°.**

1 FOCUS

Objective Use parallel lines to investigate the sum of the measures of the angles in a triangle and similar triangles.

Materials for Each Student
- straightedge or ruler

Teaching Tip
You may want to review from Lesson 11-1 the angles that are formed when a transversal intersects parallel lines. Have students indicate the pairs of angles that are congruent.

2 TEACH

Working in Cooperative Groups
Have students work in pairs to complete the Activity and Exercises 1–3.
- Emphasize that the angles and triangle must be labeled as shown to analyze results.
- It may be helpful to analyze the results as students perform each step. Pair Exercise 1 with Step 1 and Exercises 2 and 3 with Step 2.
- After Step 3, have students list what they know about the relationships between the angles. Remind them that they want to use what they know to make a conclusion.

Practice Have students complete Exercises 4–5.

3 ASSESS

Formative Assessment
Use Exercises 1–3 to assess whether students understand the angle relationships in the diagram.

From Concrete to Abstract
Use Exercise 4 to assess whether students can use angle relationships to draw a conclusion about the sum of the measures of a triangle.

11-4 Lesson Notes

1 FOCUS

Vertical Alignment

Before Lesson 11-4
Find missing angle measures of a triangle.

Lesson 11-4
Find missing angle measures of a quadrilateral. Classify quadrilaterals.

After Lesson 11-4
Find the area of quadrilaterals.

2 TEACH

Scaffolding Questions

Have students read the *Why?* section of the lesson and answer the questions.

Ask:

- What do the shapes of the panels and dance pad have in common? They are all four-sided figures with 4 corners or vertices and 4 angles.
- How are the shapes of the panels and the dance pad different from the arrows and circle on the dance pad? The shapes have straight sides while the circle is curved, and the arrows have more than 4 sides.

11-4 Quadrilaterals

Then
You found missing angle measures of a triangle. (Lesson 10-3)

Now
- Find missing angle measures of a quadrilateral.
- Classify quadrilaterals.

New Vocabulary
quadrilateral

Math Online
glencoe.com
- Extra Examples
- Personal Tutor
- Self-Check Quiz
- Homework Help
- Math in Motion

Why?

The *dance pad* shown is an electronic mat used in a video game. In the game, a player must move his or her feet to a set pattern, stepping on the panels of the mat according to the beat of a song.

a. Describe the shapes of the panels that have arrows on them. **squares, rectangles**

b. Describe the shape of the entire dance pad. **rectangle**

Find Angle Measures A **quadrilateral** is a closed figure with four sides and four angles. The segments that form a quadrilateral intersect only at their endpoints. Squares, rectangles, and trapezoids are examples of quadrilaterals.

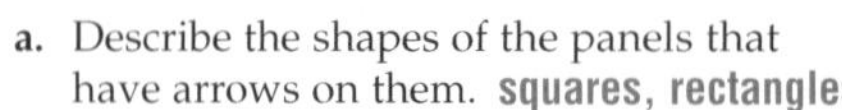

As with triangles, a quadrilateral can be named by its vertices. When you name a quadrilateral, begin at any vertex and name the vertices in order. Quadrilateral *ABCD* is shown below.

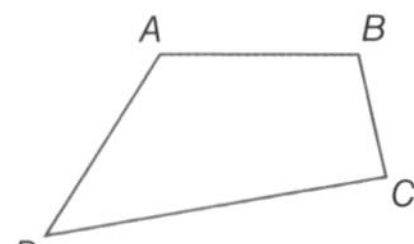

- sides: $\overline{AB}, \overline{BC}, \overline{CD}, \overline{DA}$
- vertices: A, B, C, D
- angles: $\angle A, \angle B, \angle C, \angle D$

Notice how a quadrilateral can be separated into two triangles. The sum of the measures of the angles of a triangle is 180°. So, the sum of the measures of the angles of a quadrilateral is 2(180°) or 360°.

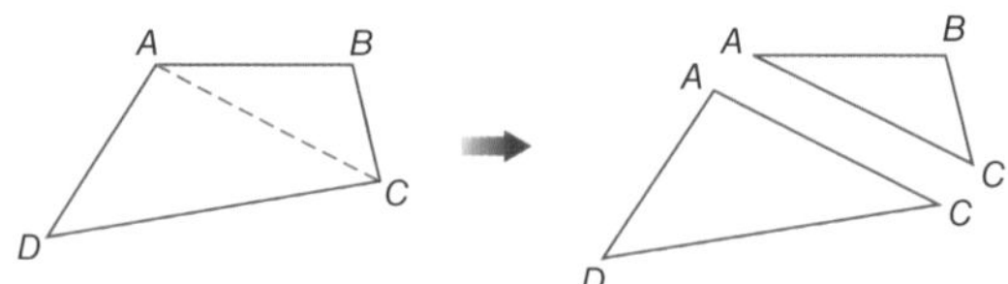

Key Concept Angles of a Quadrilateral — For Your FOLDABLE

Words The sum of the measures of the angles of a quadrilateral is 360°.

Symbols $a + b + c + d = 360$

Model

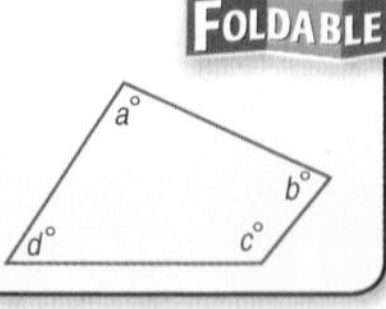

Lesson 11-4 Resources

Resource	Approaching-Level	On-Level	Beyond-Level	English Learners
Teacher Edition	• Differentiated Instruction, p. 613		• Differentiated Instruction, p. 616	
Chapter Resource Masters	• Study Guide and Intervention, pp. 23–24 • Skills Practice, p. 25 • Practice, p. 26 • Word Problem Practice, p. 27	• Study Guide and Intervention, pp. 23–24 • Skills Practice, p. 25 • Practice, p. 26 • Word Problem Practice, p. 27 • Enrichment, p. 28	• Practice, p. 26 • Word Problem Practice, p. 27 • Enrichment, p. 28	• Study Guide and Intervention, pp. 23–24 • Skills Practice, p. 25 • Practice, p. 26
Transparencies	• 5-Minute Check Transparency 11-4	• 5-Minute Check Transparency 11-4	• 5-Minute Check Transparency 11-4	• 5-Minute Check Transparency 11-4
Other	• Study Notebook • Teaching Pre-Algebra with Manipulatives	• Study Notebook • Teaching Pre-Algebra with Manipulatives	• Study Notebook	• Study Notebook • Teaching Pre-Algebra with Manipulatives

EXAMPLE 1 Find Angle Measures

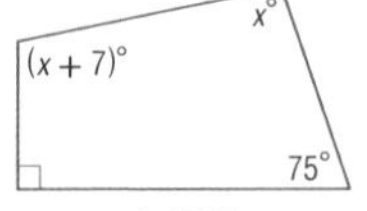

Find the value of x in the quadrilateral. Then find each missing angle measure.

$(x + 7) + x + 75 + 90 = 360$	The sum of the angle measures is 360°.
$2x + 172 = 360$	Combine like terms.
$2x + 172 - 172 = 360 - 172$	Subtract 172 from each side.
$2x = 188$	Simplify.
$x = 94$	Divide each side by 2.

So, the missing angle measures are 94° and 94 + 7 or 101°.

StudyTip

Check Your Work To check the answer, find the sum of the measures of the angles. Since 75 + 90 + 101 + 94 = 360, the answer is correct.

Check Your Progress

52; $m\angle G = 52°$; $m\angle E = 156°$

1. In quadrilateral $EFGH$, $m\angle E = 3x°$, $m\angle F = 70°$, $m\angle G = x°$, and $m\angle H = 82°$. Find the value of x. Then find each missing angle measure.

Personal Tutor glencoe.com

Math *in Motion,* Animation glencoe.com

Classify Quadrilaterals Quadrilaterals can be classified by the relationship of their sides and angles, as shown in the diagram below.

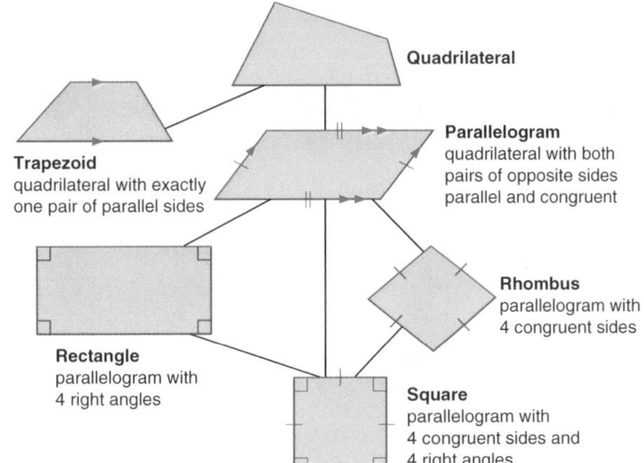

StudyTip

Classifying Quadrilaterals The diagram at the right begins with the most general quadrilaterals and ends with the most specific. The name that *best* describes the quadrilateral is the one that is most specific.

Real-World EXAMPLE 2 Classify Quadrilaterals

BASKETBALL The free-throw lane used during International Basketball Federation competitions is shown. Classify the quadrilateral using the name that *best* describes it.

The quadrilateral has exactly one pair of opposite sides that are parallel. It is a trapezoid.

Check Your Progress

2. Classify the quadrilateral in Example 1 using the name that *best* describes it. quadrilateral

Personal Tutor glencoe.com

Find Angle Measures

Example 1 shows how to find missing angle measures in a quadrilateral.

Formative Assessment

Use the Check Your Progress exercises after each example to determine students' understanding of concepts.

Additional Example

1 **ALGEBRA** Find the value of x in the quadrilateral. Then find each missing angle measure.

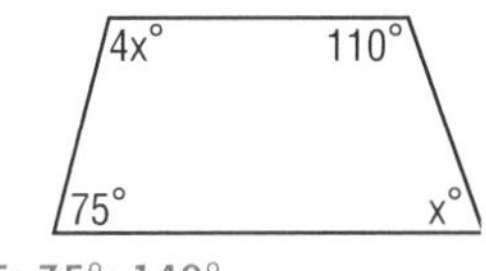

35; 35°; 140°

Additional Examples also in Interactive Classroom PowerPoint® Presentations

Classify Quadrilaterals

Example 2 shows how to classify quadrilaterals.

Additional Example

2 Classify the quadrilateral below using the name that *best* describes it.

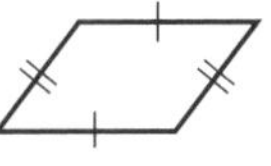

parallelogram

Differentiated Instruction

Auditory/Musical Have students write raps, rhymes, songs, or poems describing the various quadrilaterals. Students' work should explain how the various quadrilaterals relate to one another (a square is a form of parallelogram) and may include real-life examples of objects with the various shapes (the classroom window is a rectangle).

Focus on Mathematical Content

Classify Quadrilaterals When classifying quadrilaterals, different polygons will fit into more than one category. For example, a square is a parallelogram, a rectangle, and a rhombus. When choosing a single classification, the best one is the most specific.

3 PRACTICE

Formative Assessment

Use Exercises 1–5 to check for understanding.

Use the chart at the bottom of this page to customize assignments for your students.

Additional Answers

25b. Sample answer:

parallelogram

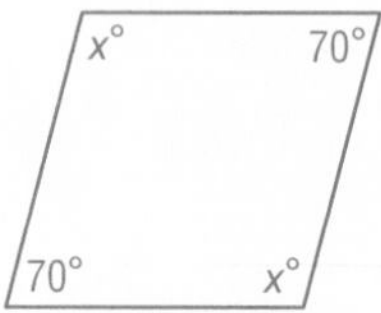

trapezoid

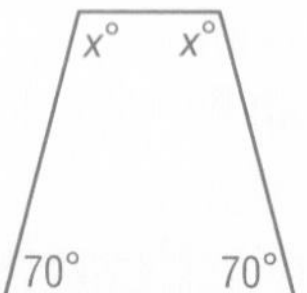

Check Your Understanding

Example 1 p. 613

Find the value of x in each quadrilateral. Then find the missing angle measures.

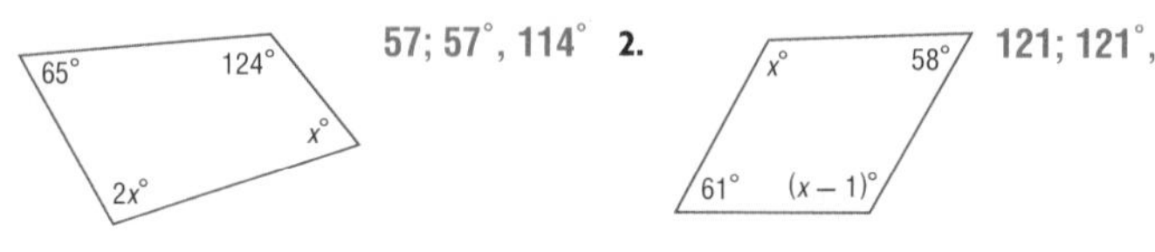

Example 2 p. 613

Classify each quadrilateral using the name that *best* describes it.

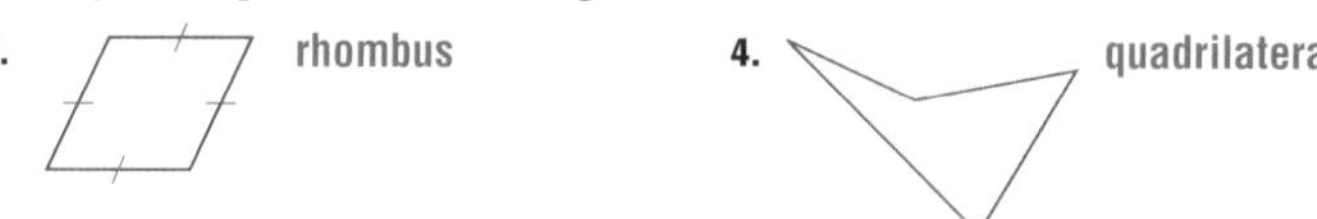

5. **SOCCER** Classify the quadrilaterals that are found on the soccer field. rectangles

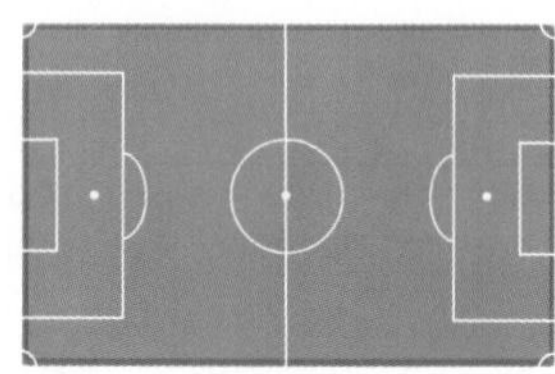

Practice and Problem Solving

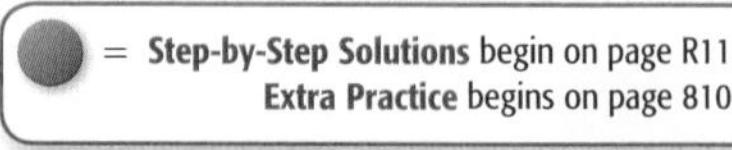

Example 1 p. 613

Find the value of x in each quadrilateral. Then find the missing angle measures.

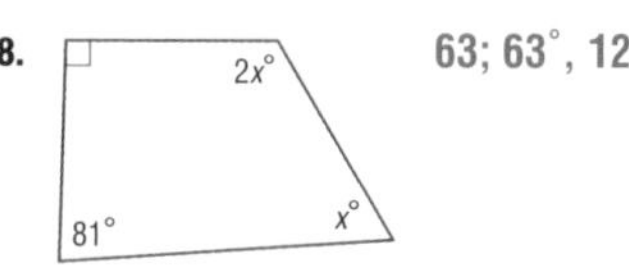

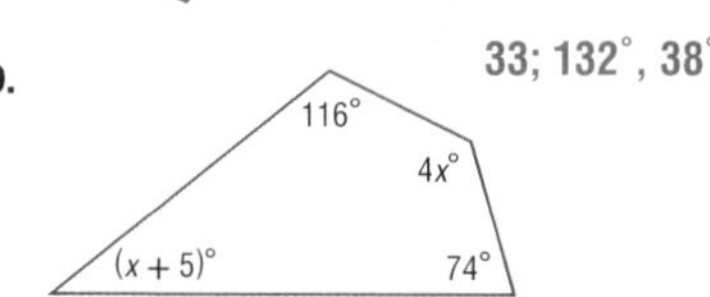

Example 2 p. 613

10. **CLOCK** Classify the quadrilateral that forms the face of the clock. Use the name that *best* describes it.

trapezoid

11. **PICTURE FRAMES** Classify the quadrilaterals that are found in the picture frames.

square, rectangles

Differentiated Homework Options

Level	Assignment	Two-Day Option	
AL Basic	6–17, 26, 28–45	7–17 odd, 30–33	6–16 even, 26, 28, 29, 34–45
OL Core	7–17 odd, 18–26, 28–45	6–17, 30–33	18–26, 28, 29, 34–45
BL Advanced	18–41 (optional: 42–45)		

18. Sample answer: trapezoids

19. Sample answer: The top of a coffee table is shaped like a rectangle or square.

Classify each quadrilateral using the name that *best* describes it.

12. 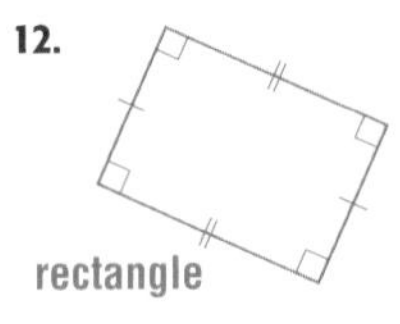 rectangle

13. 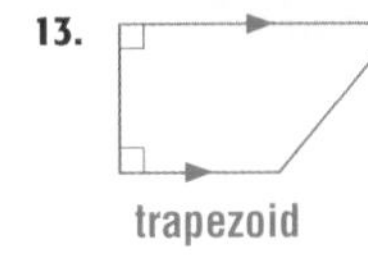 trapezoid

14. 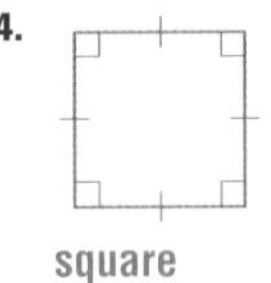 square

15. 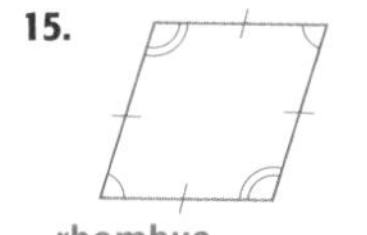 rhombus

16. 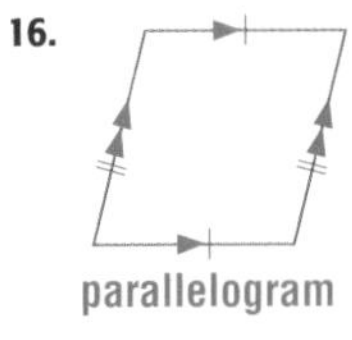 parallelogram

17. 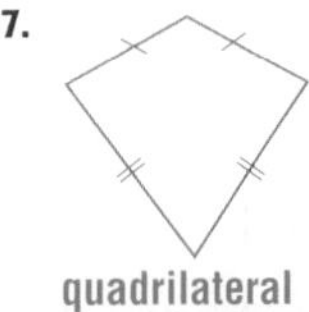 quadrilateral

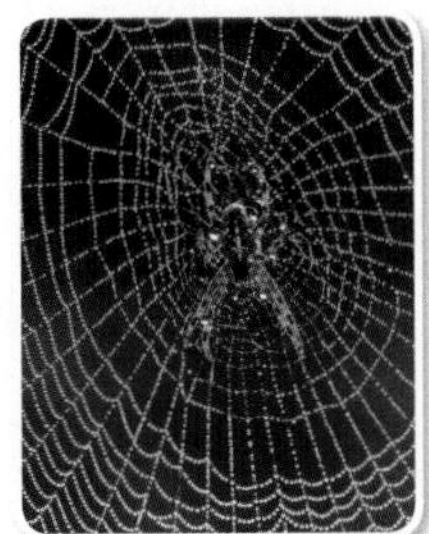

18. **SPIDER WEB** Classify the quadrilaterals that are found in the spider web at the right.

19. **LIVING ROOM** Name an object that is commonly found in a living room that has the shape of a quadrilateral. Classify the quadrilateral.

20. **SCHOOL SUPPLIES** Identify a school supply that is shaped like a quadrilateral. What characteristics did you use to identify the item?

Real-World Link

The combined length of thread in a spider's web is about 20 to 60 meters. On an equal weight basis, spider silk is twice as strong as steel.

Source: Belleza Spiders

20. Sample answer: A piece of paper is shaped like a rectangle. It has four right angles.

Determine whether each statement is *sometimes, always,* or *never* true.

21. A square is a rectangle. always

22. A trapezoid is a rhombus. never

23. A parallelogram is a square. sometimes

24. A rhombus is a square. sometimes

25. **MULTIPLE REPRESENTATIONS** In this problem, you will use algebra to help you draw a figure. A quadrilateral has angle measures $x°$, $x°$, 70°, and 70°.

a. **ALGEBRAIC** Write an equation that can be used to find the missing angle measures. Then find the measures. $x + x + 70 + 70 = 360$; 110°; 110°

b. **GEOMETRIC** Sketch and label two different quadrilaterals that fit the description above. What types of quadrilaterals did you draw? See margin.

H.O.T. Problems

Use Higher-Order Thinking Skills

26. **OPEN ENDED** Use a map of the United States to find two states that appear to be shaped like quadrilaterals. Classify the quadrilaterals.
Sample answer: Wyoming and Colorado, rectangles

27. **CHALLENGE** Can a quadrilateral have two angles that are twice as large as the other two angles? Explain your reasoning or give an example.
Yes; sample answer: quadrilateral with angles that measure 60°, 60°, 120°, and 120°.

28. **WHICH ONE DOESN'T BELONG?** Which quadrilateral does not belong with the other three? Explain your reasoning.

trapezoid	square	parallelogram	rectangle

29. **WRITING IN MATH** Describe the characteristics that a square shares with a rectangle and with a rhombus.

28. Trapezoid; it is the only quadrilateral that does not have two pairs of parallel sides or two pairs of congruent sides.

29. A square and a rectangle both have four right angles. A square and a rhombus both have four congruent sides.

Multiple Representations In Exercise 25, students use an algebraic equation and a sketch to create quadrilaterals with specified angle measures.

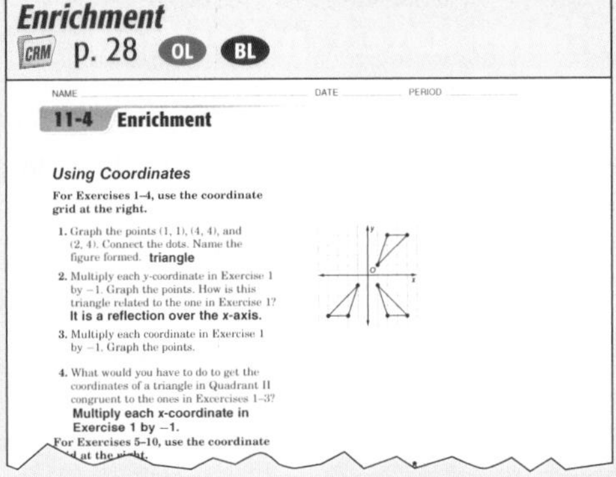

Enrichment CRM p. 28 OL BL

11-4 Enrichment

Using Coordinates

For Exercises 1–4, use the coordinate grid at the right.

1. Graph the points (1, 1), (4, 4), and (2, 4). Connect the dots. Name the figure formed. triangle
2. Multiply each y-coordinate in Exercise 1 by −1. Graph the points. How is this triangle related to the one in Exercise 1? It is a reflection over the x-axis.
3. Multiply each coordinate in Exercise 1 by −1. Graph the points.
4. What would you have to do to get the coordinates of a triangle in Quadrant II congruent to the ones in Exercises 1–3? Multiply each x-coordinate in Exercise 1 by −1.

For Exercises 5–10, use the coordinate ...

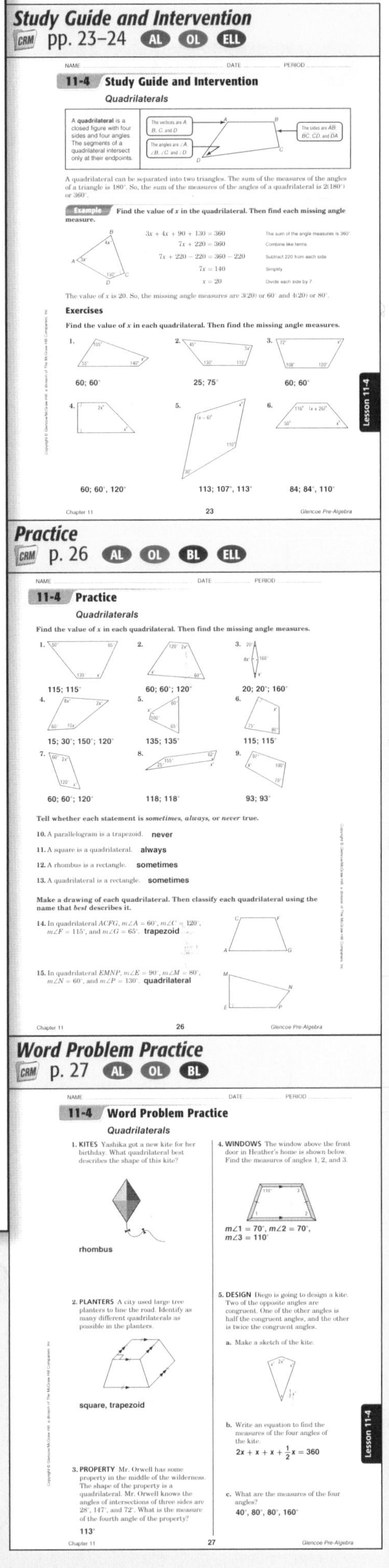

Study Guide and Intervention CRM pp. 23–24 AL OL ELL

11-4 Study Guide and Intervention

Quadrilaterals

A **quadrilateral** is a closed figure with four sides and four angles. The segments of a quadrilateral intersect only at their endpoints.

A quadrilateral can be separated into two triangles. The sum of the measures of the angles of a triangle is 180°. So, the sum of the measures of the angles of a quadrilateral is 2(180°) or 360°.

Example: Find the value of x in the quadrilateral. Then find each missing angle measure.

$3x + 4x + 90 + 130 = 360$
$7x + 220 = 360$
$7x + 220 - 220 = 360 - 220$
$7x = 140$
$x = 20$

The value of x is 20. So, the missing angle measures are 3(20) or 60° and 4(20) or 80°.

Exercises

Find the value of x in each quadrilateral. Then find the missing angle measures.

1. 60; 60°
2. 25; 75°
3. 60; 60°
4. 60; 60°, 120°
5. 113; 107°, 113°
6. 84; 84°, 110°

Chapter 11 23 Glencoe Pre-Algebra

Practice CRM p. 26 AL OL BL ELL

11-4 Practice

Quadrilaterals

Find the value of x in each quadrilateral. Then find the missing angle measures.

1. 115; 115°
2. 60; 60°; 120°
3. 20; 20°; 160°
4. 15; 30°; 150°; 120°
5. 135; 135°
6. 115; 115°
7. 60; 60°; 120°
8. 118; 118°
9. 93; 93°

Tell whether each statement is *sometimes, always,* or *never* true.

10. A parallelogram is a trapezoid. never
11. A square is a quadrilateral. always
12. A rhombus is a rectangle. sometimes
13. A quadrilateral is a rectangle. sometimes

Make a drawing of each quadrilateral. Then classify each quadrilateral using the name that *best* describes it.

14. In quadrilateral $ACFG$, $m\angle A = 60°$, $m\angle C = 120°$, $m\angle F = 115°$, and $m\angle G = 65°$. trapezoid
15. In quadrilateral $EMNP$, $m\angle E = 90°$, $m\angle M = 80°$, $m\angle N = 60°$, and $m\angle P = 130°$. quadrilateral

Chapter 11 26 Glencoe Pre-Algebra

Word Problem Practice CRM p. 27 AL OL BL

11-4 Word Problem Practice

Quadrilaterals

1. KITES Yashika got a new kite for her birthday. What quadrilateral best describes the shape of this kite? rhombus
2. PLANTERS A city used large tree planters to line the road. Identify as many different quadrilaterals as possible in the planters. square, trapezoid
3. PROPERTY Mr. Orwell has some property in the middle of the wilderness. The shape of the property is a quadrilateral. Mr. Orwell knows the angles of intersections of three sides are 28°, 147°, and 72°. What is the measure of the fourth angle of the property? 113°
4. WINDOWS The window above the front door in Heather's home is shown below. Find the measures of angles 1, 2, and 3. $m\angle1 = 70°$, $m\angle2 = 70°$, $m\angle3 = 110°$
5. DESIGN Diego is going to design a kite. Two of the opposite angles are congruent. One of the other angles is half the congruent angles, and the other is twice the congruent angles.
a. Make a sketch of the kite.
b. Write an equation to find the measures of the four angles of the kite. $2x + x + x + \frac{1}{2}x = 360$
c. What are the measures of the four angles? 40°, 80°, 80°, 160°

Chapter 11 27 Glencoe Pre-Algebra

4 ASSESS

Ticket Out the Door Hand each student a sheet of quadrilateral figures that includes trapezoids, rhombuses, rectangles, parallelograms, and so on. Ask students to classify each figure using as many categories as possible, underlining the classification that is the most specific and "best" describes the figure. Have them hand in their papers as they exit.

Additional Answer

34.

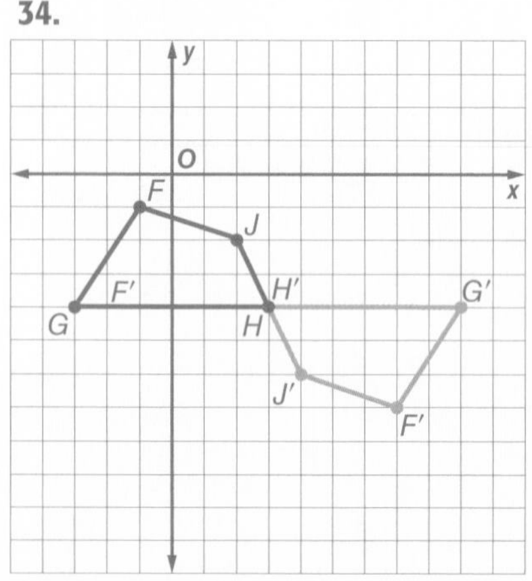

Standardized Test Practice

30. Find the value of x in the figure below. **C**

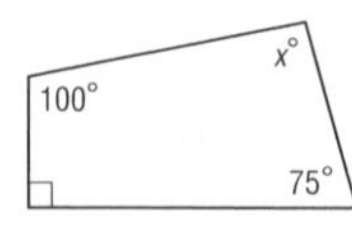

A 75°
B 90°
C 95°
D 105°

31. GRIDDED RESPONSE Mrs. Farias used the parallelogram below to design a pattern for a paving stone. She will use the paving stone for a sidewalk. Find x. **50**

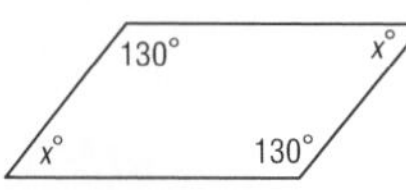

32. Which figure is *best* described as a square? **G**

F 

H

G

J 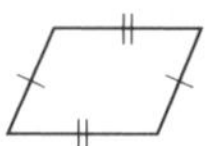

33. Find the value of x in the parallelogram below. **C**

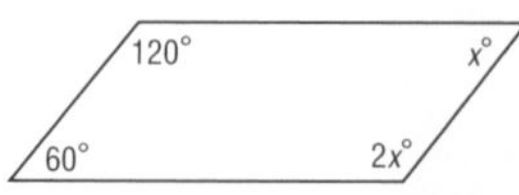

A 50°
B 55°
C 60°
D 65°

Spiral Review

34. Quadrilateral $FGHJ$ has vertices $F(-1, -1)$, $G(-3, -4)$, $H(3, -4)$, $J(2, -2)$. Graph the figure and its image after a 180° counterclockwise rotation about point H. (Lesson 11-3)

Complete each congruence statement if $\triangle LMN \cong \triangle QRS$. (Lesson 11-2)

35. $\angle Q \cong$? $\angle L$

36. $\overline{QS} \cong$? $\overline{LN}$

37. $\overline{LM} \cong$? $\overline{QR}$

38. $\angle M \cong$? $\angle R$

39. ALGEBRA Angles P and Q are complementary. If $m\angle P = (x + 3)°$ and $m\angle Q$ is twice $m\angle P$, write an equation that can be used to find the value of x. (Lesson 11-1) **$2(x + 3) + (x + 3) = 90$**

40. SKYSCRAPERS On a clear day, the number of miles a person can see to the horizon can be found using the formula $d = 1.22 \cdot \sqrt{h}$ where d is the distance to the horizon in miles and h is the person's distance from the ground in feet. Suppose you are standing in the observation area of the Willis Tower in Chicago. About how far can a person see if the deck is 1353 feet above the ground? Round to the nearest tenth. (Lesson 9-1) **44.9 mi**

41. Evaluate $|25.3| - |-3.7|$. (Lesson 2-1) **21.6**

Skills Review

Solve each equation. (Lesson 4-5)

42. $3x + 60 = 120$ **20**

43. $4x + 24 = 36$ **3**

44. $10x + 100 = 300$ **20**

45. $2x + 25 = 79$ **27**

Differentiated Instruction

BL

Extension Present the following to students: A quadrilateral has four angles. The sum of the measures of those angles equals 360°. How can you prove this? Take a quadrilateral and run a diagonal from one vertex across to the opposite vertex. The diagonal divides the quadrilateral into two triangles. Since the sum of the angles of a triangle is 180° and 2 × 180° = 360°, the sum of the angles of the quadrilateral is 360°. If the sum of the angle measures in a quadrilateral is 360°, what is the sum of the angle measures of a pentagon? Explain. A pentagon can be divided into 3 triangles; 3 times 180° is 540°.

11-5 Polygons

Why?

Puzzles pieces from two advanced level puzzles were accidentally mixed together.

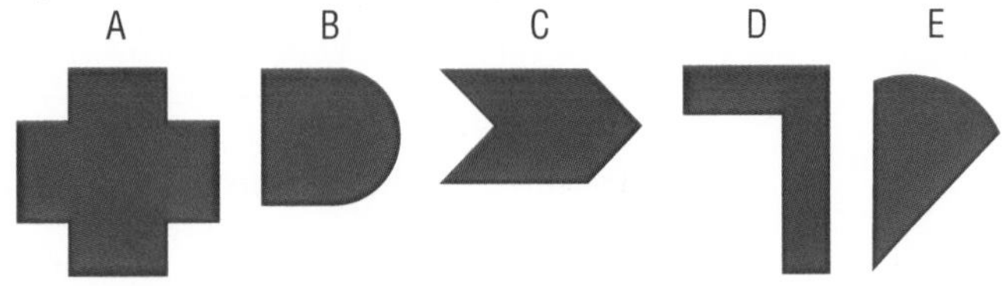

a. Pieces A, C, and D were from puzzle one. The other two pieces were from puzzle two. Describe a difference between the shapes of the two groups of puzzle pieces. **Sample answer: The pieces from puzzle one all have straight edges and the pieces from puzzle two have rounded edges.**

b. Draw a sample of another puzzle piece that could be a part of each puzzle. **See Chapter 11 Answer Appendix.**

Then
You have already classified quadrilaterals. (Lesson 11-4)

Now
- Classify polygons.
- Determine the sum of the measures of the interior angles of a polygon.

New Vocabulary
polygon
diagonal
interior angle
regular polygon
tessellation

Math Online
glencoe.com
- Extra Examples
- Personal Tutor
- Self-Check Quiz
- Homework Help

Classify Polygons A **polygon** is a simple, closed figure formed by three or more line segments called *sides*. The segments that form a polygon intersect only at their endpoints. The figures below are *not* polygons.

Non Polygons

The figure has a curve.

The sides overlap.

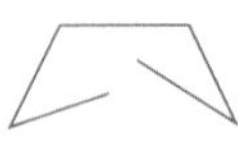
The figure is not closed.

Polygons can be classified by the number of sides they have, as shown in the table.

Polygon	Number of Sides	Polygon	Number of Sides
triangle	3	heptagon	7
quadrilateral	4	octagon	8
pentagon	5	nonagon	9
hexagon	6	decagon	10

EXAMPLE 1 Classify Polygons

Determine whether the figure is a polygon. If it is, classify the polygon. If it is not a polygon, explain why.

The figure has 7 sides that only intersect at their endpoints. It is a heptagon.

Check Your Progress

1A. 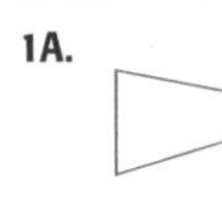 **The figure has 6 sides that only intersect at their endpoints. It is a hexagon.**

1B. 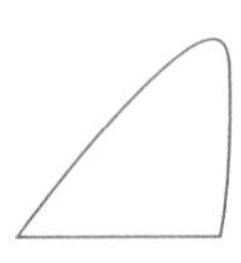 **The figure is not a polygon because it has a curved side.**

Personal Tutor glencoe.com

11-5 Lesson Notes

1 FOCUS

Vertical Alignment

Before Lesson 11-5
Classify quadrilaterals.

Lessson 11-5
Classify polygons. Determine the sum of the measures of the interior angles of a polygon.

After Lesson 11-5
Find the area of composite figures.

2 TEACH

Scaffolding Questions

Have students read the *Why?* section of the lesson and answer the questions.

Ask:

- How are the pieces in puzzle one different? Pieces A, C, and D are different shapes. A has 12 sides, C and D both have 6 sides.
- Suppose you measure the interior angles of pieces A, C, and D. Would you expect the sum of their angle measures to be the same or different? Explain. Sample answer: The same for C and D since they have the same number of sides, and different for A since it has a greater number of sides.

Lesson 11-5 Resources

Resource	Approaching-Level	On-Level	Beyond-Level	English Learners
Teacher Edition		• Differentiated Instruction, p. 618	• Differentiated Instruction, p. 622	
Chapter Resource Masters	• Study Guide and Intervention, pp. 29–30 • Skills Practice, p. 31 • Practice, p. 32 • Word Problem Practice, p. 33	• Study Guide and Intervention, pp. 29–30 • Skills Practice, p. 31 • Practice, p. 32 • Word Problem Practice, p. 33 • Enrichment, p. 34	• Practice, p. 32 • Word Problem Practice, p. 33 • Enrichment, p. 34	• Study Guide and Intervention, pp. 29–30 • Skills Practice, p. 31 • Practice, p. 32
Transparencies	• 5-Minute Check Transparency 11-5	• 5-Minute Check Transparency 11-5	• 5-Minute Check Transparency 11-5	• 5-Minute Check Transparency 11-5
Other	• Study Notebook • Teaching Pre-Algebra with Manipulatives	• Study Notebook • Teaching Pre-Algebra with Manipulatives	• Study Notebook	• Study Notebook • Teaching Pre-Algebra with Manipulatives

Classify Polygons

Example 1 shows how to classify polygons.

Formative Assessment

Use the Check Your Progress exercises after each example to determine students' understanding of concepts.

Additional Example

1 Determine whether the figure is a polygon. If it is, classify the polygon. If it is not a polygon, explain why. The figure has 5 sides that only intersect at their endpoints. It is a pentagon.

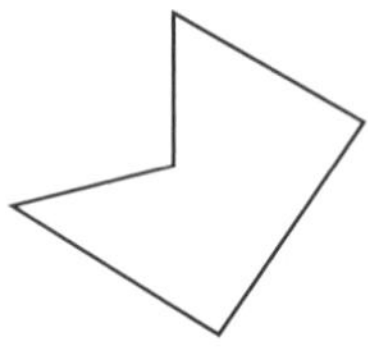

Additional Examples also in Interactive Classroom PowerPoint® Presentations

IWB INTERACTIVE WHITEBOARD READY

Find Angle Measures of a Polygon

Example 2 shows how to find the sum of the interior angle measures in a polygon. **Example 3** shows how to find the measure of an interior angle of a regular polygon.

Additional Example

2 **STANDARDIZED TEST PRACTICE** Find the sum of the measures of the interior angles of a heptagon. C

A 1260° **C** 900°

B 1080° **D** 1620°

StudyTip

***n*-gon** A polygon with *n* sides is called an *n*-gon. For example, an octagon can also be called an 8-gon.

Find Angle Measures of a Polygon A **diagonal** is a line segment that joins two nonconsecutive vertices in a polygon. In the figures below, all possible diagonals from one vertex are shown.

quadrilateral	pentagon	hexagon	octagon
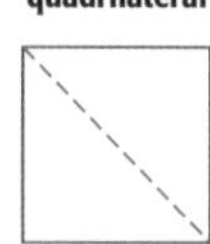			
4 sides 2 triangles	5 sides 3 triangles	6 sides 4 triangles	8 sides 6 triangles

Notice that the number of triangles is 2 less than the number of sides. You can use this relationship to find the sum of the interior angle measures of a polygon. An **interior angle** is an angle formed at a vertex of a polygon.

Key Concept — Interior Angles of a Polygon

For Your FOLDABLE

Words The sum of the degree measures of the interior angles of the polygon is $(n - 2)180$.

Symbols $(n - 2)180$

Model

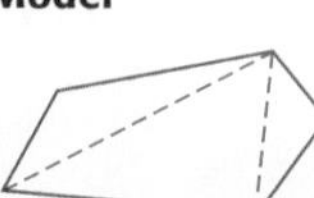

STANDARDIZED TEST EXAMPLE 2

Find the sum of the measures of the interior angles of a nonagon.

A 540° **B** 810° **C** 1260° **D** 1620°

Read the Test Item

The sum of the measures of the interior angles is $(n - 2)180$. Since a nonagon has 9 sides, $n = 9$.

Solve the Test Item

$(n - 2)180 = (9 - 2)180$ **Replace *n* with 9.**

$= 7(180)$ or 1260 **Simplify.**

The sum of the measures of the interior angles of a nonagon is 1260°. The answer is C.

Check

All possible diagonals from one vertex of a nonagon are shown at the right. You can see that 7 triangles are formed. So, $7 \cdot 180 = 1260$ is correct. ✓

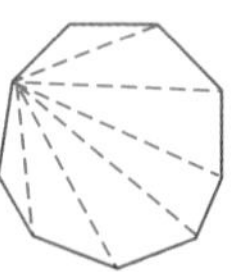

Check Your Progress

2. Find the sum of the measures of the interior angles of a 13-gon. H

F 990° **G** 1170° **H** 1980° **J** 2340°

Personal Tutor glencoe.com

Differentiated Instruction

Visual/Spatial Give students copies of various polygons and ask them to determine the diagonals from one vertex and the number of triangles formed before presenting the information in the student text. Remind them when drawing their diagonals that the sum of the interior angle measures in a triangle is 180°.

Real-World Link

The modern soccer ball is made of hexagonal and pentagonal panels because when they are sewn together and inflated, they make a near perfect sphere.

Source: SoccerBallWorld

A **regular polygon** is a polygon that has all sides congruent and all angles congruent. Since the angles are congruent, their measures are equal.

Real-World EXAMPLE 3 Measure of One Interior Angle

SOCCER The surface of the soccer ball contains 12 regular pentagons and 20 regular hexagons. What is the measure of one interior angle of a hexagon?

Step 1 Find the sum of the measures of the interior angles of a hexagon.

$(n - 2)180 = (6 - 2)180$ — **A hexagon has 6 sides. Replace n with 6.**

$= 4(180)$ or 720 — **Simplify.**

The sum of the measures of the interior angles is 720°.

Step 2 Divide the sum of the measures by 6 to find the measure of one angle.

$720 \div 6 = 120$

The measure of one interior angle of a hexagon is 120°.

Check Your Progress

3. What is the measure of an interior angle of one of the pentagonal panels in the soccer ball? **108°**

Personal Tutor glencoe.com

Tessellations A repetitive pattern of polygons that fit together with no overlaps or holes is called a **tessellation**. The sum of the measures of the angles where the vertices meet in a tessellation is 360°.

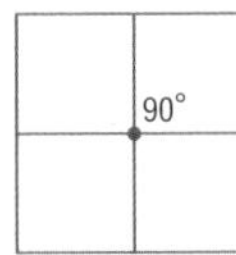

$4 \times 90° = 360°$

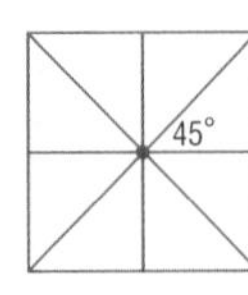

$8 \times 45° = 360°$

EXAMPLE 4 Find Tessellations

Determine whether or not a tessellation can be created using only regular hexagons. If not, explain.

The measure of each angle in a regular hexagon is 120°.

The sum of the measures of the angles where the vertices meet must be 360°. So, solve $120°n = 360$.

$120n = 360$ — **Write the equation.**

$\frac{120n}{120} = \frac{360}{120}$ — **Divide each side by 120.**

$n = 3$ — **Simplify.**

Since 120° divides evenly into 360°, a regular hexagon can be used to make a tessellation.

Check Your Progress

Determine whether or not a tessellation can be created using each regular polygon. If not, explain.

4A. pentagon

4B. octagon

Personal Tutor glencoe.com

4A. no; Each interior angle of a regular pentagon measures 108° and 360° is not evenly divisible by 108°.

4B. no; Each interior angle of a regular octagon measures 135° and 360° is not evenly divisible by 135°.

Focus on Mathematical Content

Angle Measures in a Polygon To find the measures of the angles in a regular polygon, count the number of sides and subtract 2. Multiply that number by 180 and divide it by the number of interior angles. Each interior angle will have that measure.

Additional Example

3 TRAFFIC SIGNS A stop sign is a regular octagon. What is the measure of one interior angle in a stop sign? 135°

Tessellations

Example 4 shows how to determine whether a regular polygon can be used to make a tessellation.

Additional Example

4 Determine whether or not a tessellation can be created using only regular decagons. If not, explain. No; each interior angle of a decagon measures 144° and 360° is not evenly divisible by 144°.

Tips for New Teachers

Formulas Students may have difficulty recalling the formula in the Key Concept box. Remind them that they can "discover" the formula by drawing all the diagonals from one vertex and counting the triangles formed.

TEACH with TECH

DOCUMENT CAMERA Students can work independently or in pairs to create tessellations using regular polygons. They should shade each different polygon with a different color. Take pictures of the work to post on the classroom Web site.

3 PRACTICE

Formative Assessment

Use Exercises 1–6 to check for understanding.

Use the chart at the bottom of this page to customize assignments for your students.

Additional Answers

1. The figure is not a polygon because it is an open figure. Two of the sides are not connected.
2. The figure has 8 sides that only intersect at their endpoints. It is an octagon.
3. The figure has 5 sides that only intersect at their endpoints. It is a pentagon.
7. The figure has 5 sides that only intersect at their endpoints. It is a pentagon.
8. The figure has 8 sides that only intersect at their endpoints. It is an octagon.
9. The figure has 6 sides that only intersect at their endpoints. It is a hexagon.
10. The figure is not a polygon because it has sides that cross each other.
11. The figure has 9 sides that only intersect at their endpoints. It is a nonagon.
12. The figure is not a polygon because it has a curved side.
19. yes
20. no; Each interior angle of a regular 12-gon measures 150° and 360° is not evenly divisible by 150°.
21. no; Each interior angle of a regular 15-gon measures 156° and 360° is not evenly divisible by 156°.
22. no; Each interior angle of a regular 20-gon measures 162° and 360° is not evenly divisible by 162°.

Check Your Understanding

Example 1 p. 617

Determine whether the figure is a polygon. If it is, classify the polygon. If it is not a polygon, explain why. 1–3. See margin.

1. 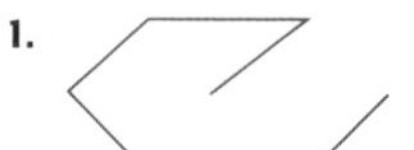
2. 
3. 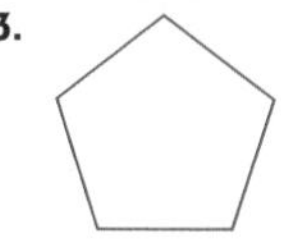

Example 2 p. 618

4. **MULTIPLE CHOICE** The sum of the measures of the interior angles of a certain regular polygon is 1800°. How many sides does this polygon have? D

A 9 sides **B** 10 sides **C** 11 sides **D** 12 sides

Example 3 p. 619

5. **KALEIDOSCOPE** The kaleidoscope image at the right is a regular polygon with 14 sides. What is the measure of one interior angle of the polygon? Round to the nearest tenth. 154.3°

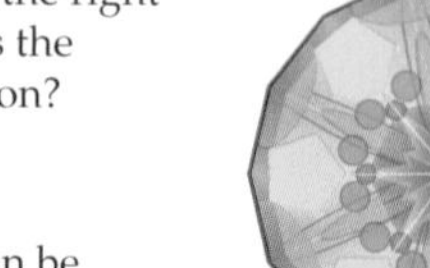
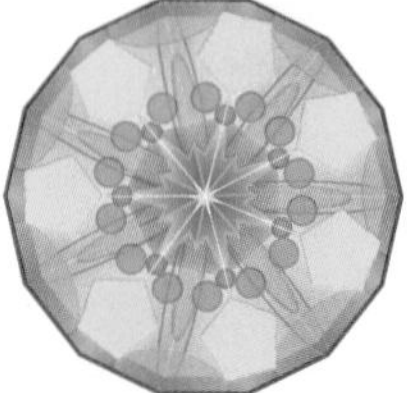

Example 4 p. 619

6. Determine whether or not a tessellation can be created using only equilateral triangles. If not, explain. yes

Practice and Problem Solving

● = **Step-by-Step Solutions** begin on page R11.
Extra Practice begins on page 810.

Example 1 p. 617

Determine whether the figure is a polygon. If it is, classify the polygon. If it is not a polygon, explain why. 7–12. See margin.

7. 
8. 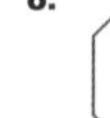
9. 
10. 
11. 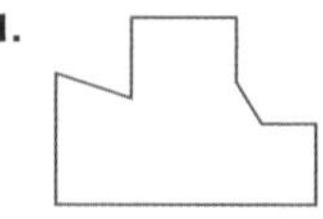
12. 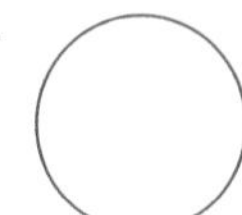

Example 2 p. 618

Find the sum of the measures of the interior angles of each polygon.

13. decagon 1440° 14. 11-gon 1620° 15. 16-gon 2520° 16. 24-gon 3960°

Example 3 p. 619

17. **NATURE** The individual cells of a honeycomb are hexagons. What is the measure of an interior angle of a honeycomb? 120°

18. **ARCHITECTURE** The dome in a state capitol building is octagonal. What is the measure of an interior angle of an octagon? 135°

Example 4 p. 619

Determine whether or not a tessellation can be created using each regular polygon. If not, explain. 19–22. See margin.

19. quadrilateral 20. 12-gon 21. 15-gon 22. 20-gon

Differentiated Homework Options

Level	Assignment	Two-Day Option	
AL Basic	7–22, 35–37, 39–59	7–21 odd, 40–43	8–22 even, 35–37, 39, 44–59
OL Core	7–21 odd, 23–33 odd, 35–37, 39–59	7–22, 40–43	23–37, 39, 44–59
BL Advanced	23–55 (optional: 56–59)		

Real-World Link

M.C. Escher was an artist who often used tessellations to create fabulous works of art. The painting above was created using this method.

M.C. Escher "SKY AND WATER I"©2008 The M.C. Escher Company-Holland. All rights reserved. www.mcescher.com/Granger Collection, New York

27. He used translations of the image of the bird and fish to make the tessellating pattern.

37. Jacinta; the interior angles of a polygon do not have to be congruent in order to create a tessellation. The sum of their measures at a vertex must equal 360°.

39. Sample answer: A regular polygon has all sides congruent and all angles congruent. A polygon that is not regular has different side lengths, different angle measures, or both. To find the interior angle measure of a regular polygon, subtract 2 from the number of sides, multiply the result by 180, then divide that result by the number of angles.

B **Identify the polygon given the sum of the interior angle measures.**

23. 1080° **octagon** **24.** 2340° **15-gon** **25.** 3240° **20-gon** **26.** 5040° **30-gon**

27. ART Refer to the painting at the left. How did the artist use tessellations to create the image?

TESSELLATIONS You can create a tessellation using a translation.

a. Draw a square. Then draw a triangle inside the top of the square.
b. Translate or slide the triangle from the top to the bottom of the square.
c. Repeat this pattern unit to create a tessellation.

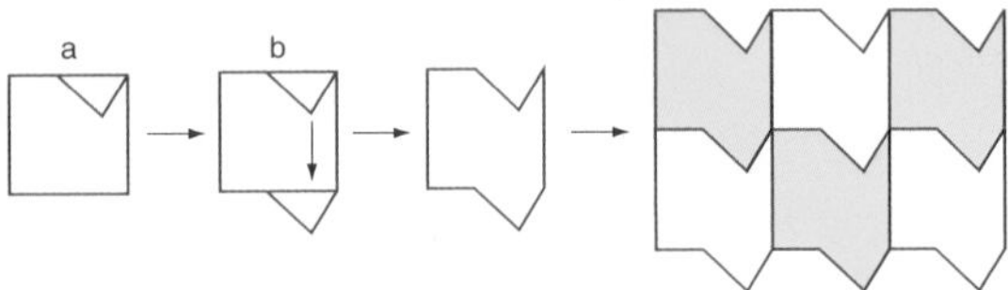

28–30. See Chapter 11 Answer Appendix.

Use a translation to create a tessellation for each pattern shown.

28. 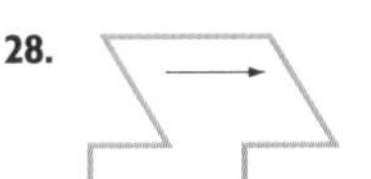 **29.** 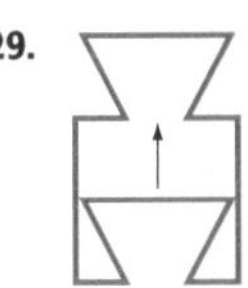 **30.** 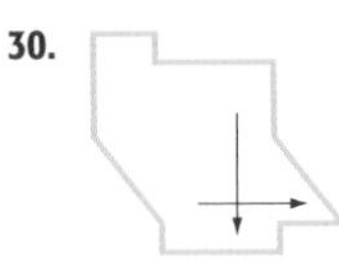

When a side of a polygon is extended, an *exterior angle* is formed. In any polygon, the sum of the measures of the exterior angles, one at each vertex, is 360°. Find the measure of an exterior angle of each regular polygon.

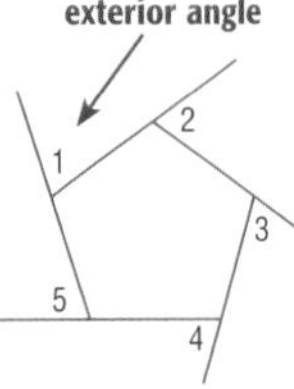

31. triangle **120°** **32.** octagon **45°**
33. decagon **36°** **34.** 15-gon **24°**

H.O.T. Problems Use Higher-Order Thinking Skills

35. OPEN ENDED Use two types of polygons to create a tessellation that is **C** different from the tessellations shown in this lesson. Describe the polygons and the transformation that you used. **See Chapter 11 Answer Appendix.**

36. REASONING If the number of sides of a regular polygon increases by 1, what happens to the sum of the measures of the interior angles? **It increases by 180°.**

37. FIND THE ERROR Jacinta says that it is possible to use a trapezoid to create a tessellation. Robert says this is impossible because the interior angles of a trapezoid are not congruent. Is either of them correct? Explain your reasoning.

38. CHALLENGE Create a tessellation using regular octagons and squares. **See Chapter 11 Answer Appendix.**

39. WRITING IN MATH Describe the difference between a regular polygon and a polygon that is irregular. Then explain the process used to find the interior angle measure of a regular polygon.

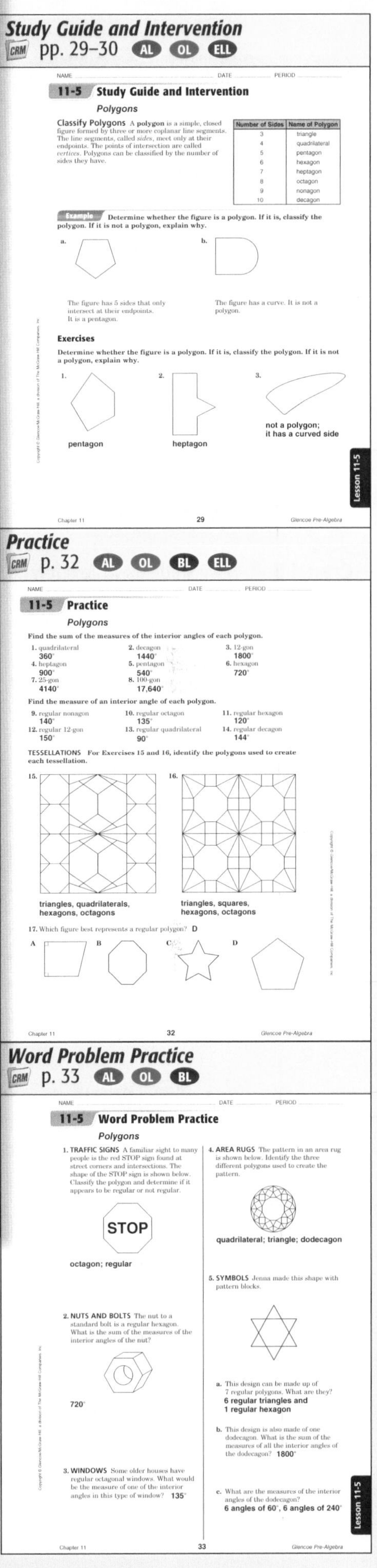

Study Guide and Intervention
CRM pp. 29–30 AL OL ELL

NAME ______ DATE ______ PERIOD ______

11-5 Study Guide and Intervention

Polygons

Classify Polygons A **polygon** is a simple, closed figure formed by three or more coplanar line segments. The line segments, called *sides*, meet only at their endpoints. The points of intersection are called *vertices*. Polygons can be classified by the number of sides they have.

Number of Sides	Name of Polygon
3	triangle
4	quadrilateral
5	pentagon
6	hexagon
7	heptagon
8	octagon
9	nonagon
10	decagon

Example Determine whether the figure is a polygon. If it is, classify the polygon. If it is not a polygon, explain why.

a. The figure has 5 sides that only intersect at their endpoints. It is a pentagon.

b. The figure has a curve. It is not a polygon.

Exercises

Determine whether the figure is a polygon. If it is, classify the polygon. If it is not a polygon, explain why.

1. **pentagon** 2. **heptagon** 3. **not a polygon; it has a curved side**

Chapter 11 29 Glencoe Pre-Algebra

Practice
CRM p. 32 AL OL BL ELL

NAME ______ DATE ______ PERIOD ______

11-5 Practice

Polygons

Find the sum of the measures of the interior angles of each polygon.

1. quadrilateral **360°** 2. decagon **1440°** 3. 12-gon **1800°**
4. heptagon **900°** 5. pentagon **540°** 6. hexagon **720°**
7. 25-gon **4140°** 8. 100-gon **17,640°**

Find the measure of an interior angle of each polygon.

9. regular nonagon **140°** 10. regular octagon **135°** 11. regular hexagon **120°**
12. regular 12-gon **150°** 13. regular quadrilateral **90°** 14. regular decagon **144°**

TESSELLATIONS **For Exercises 15 and 16, identify the polygons used to create each tessellation.**

15. **triangles, quadrilaterals, hexagons, octagons** 16. **triangles, squares, hexagons, octagons**

17. Which figure best represents a regular polygon? **D**

A B C D

Chapter 11 32 Glencoe Pre-Algebra

Word Problem Practice
CRM p. 33 AL OL BL

NAME ______ DATE ______ PERIOD ______

11-5 Word Problem Practice

Polygons

1. **TRAFFIC SIGNS** A familiar sight to many people is the red STOP sign found at street corners and intersections. The shape of the STOP sign is shown below. Classify the polygon and determine if it appears to be regular or not regular.

STOP

octagon; regular

2. **NUTS AND BOLTS** The nut to a standard bolt is a regular hexagon. What is the sum of the measures of the interior angles of the nut?

720°

3. **WINDOWS** Some older houses have regular octagonal windows. What would be the measure of one of the interior angles in this type of window? **135°**

4. **AREA RUGS** The pattern in an area rug is shown below. Identify the three different polygons used to create the pattern.

quadrilateral; triangle; dodecagon

5. **SYMBOLS** Jenna made this shape with pattern blocks.

a. This design can be made up of 7 regular polygons. What are they? **6 regular triangles and 1 regular hexagon**

b. This design is also made of one dodecagon. What is the sum of the measures of all the interior angles of the dodecagon? **1800°**

c. What are the measures of the interior angles of the dodecagon? **6 angles of 60°, 6 angles of 240°**

Chapter 11 33 Glencoe Pre-Algebra

Lesson 11-5

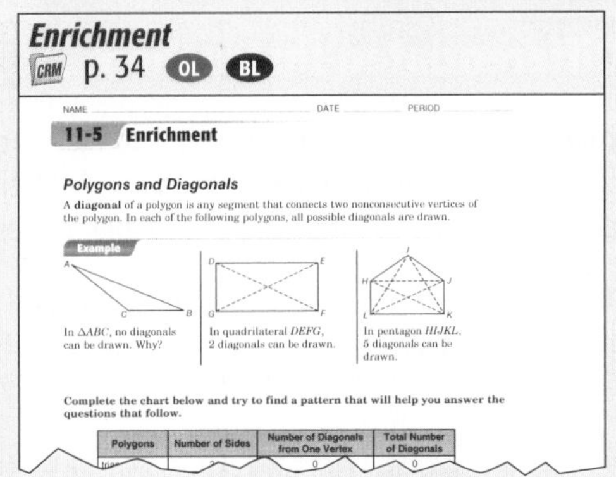

Enrichment
CRM p. 34 OL BL

NAME ______ DATE ______ PERIOD ______

11-5 Enrichment

Polygons and Diagonals

A **diagonal** of a polygon is any segment that connects two nonconsecutive vertices of the polygon. In each of the following polygons, all possible diagonals are drawn.

Example

In $\triangle ABC$, no diagonals can be drawn. Why?

In quadrilateral $DEFG$, 2 diagonals can be drawn.

In pentagon $HIJKL$, 5 diagonals can be drawn.

Complete the chart below and try to find a pattern that will help you answer the questions that follow.

Polygons	Number of Sides	Number of Diagonals from One Vertex	Total Number of Diagonals
[illegible]	[illegible]	0	0

Watch Out!

Find the Error In Exercise 37, students may think polygons must have congruent angle measures to tessellate because Example 4 in the lesson focused on using angle measures to determine whether regular polygons tessellate. Have students use a trapezoid to test whether it can tessellate. Then have them find the sum of the angle measures where the vertices meet. Remind students that the latter determines whether a polygon will tessellate.

ASSESS

Crystal Ball Have students write a few sentences on how they think today's lesson on polygons will help them with tomorrow's lesson on the area of parallelograms, triangles, and trapezoids.

Formative Assessment

Check for student understanding of concepts in Lessons 11-4 and 11-5.

 Quiz 2, p. 62

Additional Answers

48.

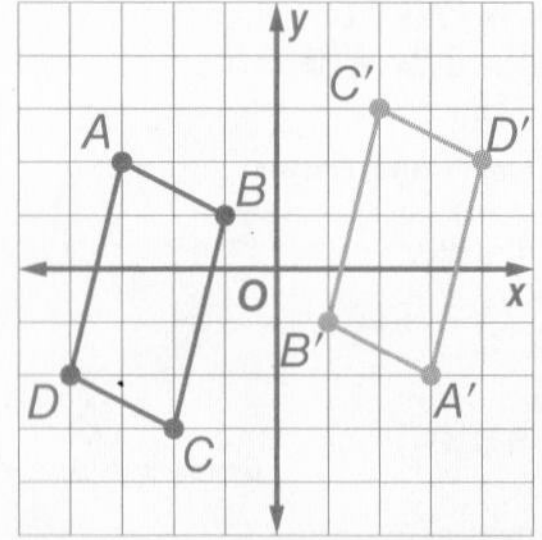

51. $x \geq 9.6$

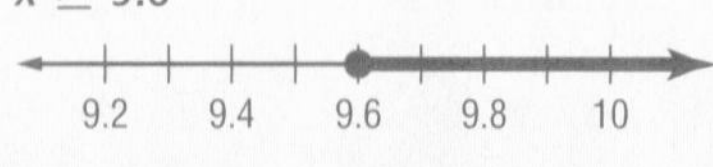

Standardized Test Practice

40. Which term identifies the shaded part of the design shown? **B**

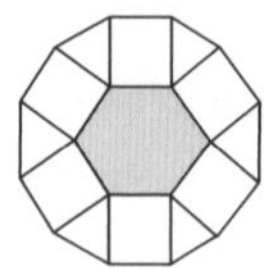

A heptagon
B hexagon
C octagon
D pentagon

41. The sum of the measures of the interior angles of a polygon is 2160°. Find the number of sides of the polygon. **G**

F 10
G 14
H 16
J 18

42. A landscape architect is looking for a brick paver shape that will tessellate. Which shape by itself will allow her to tessellate a patio area? **A**

A 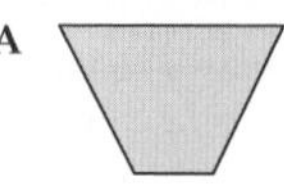

C 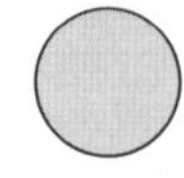

B 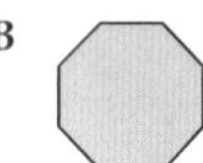

D

43. GRIDDED RESPONSE What is the measure in degrees of an interior angle of a regular polygon with 20 sides? **162°**

Spiral Review

Determine whether each statement is *always, sometimes* or *never* true. (Lesson 11-4)

44. A square is a rhombus. **always**

45. A parallelogram is a rectangle. **sometimes**

46. A rectangle is a square. **sometimes**

47. A parallelogram is a quadrilateral. **always**

48. A figure has vertices $A(-3, 2)$, $B(-1, 1)$, $C(-2, -3)$, and $D(-4, -2)$. Graph the figure and its image after a rotation of 180° around the origin. (Lesson 11-3) **See margin.**

49. yes; $\angle M \cong \angle O$, $\angle L \cong \angle PNO$, $\angle LNM \cong \angle P$, $\overline{ML} \cong \overline{ON}$, $\overline{LN} \cong \overline{NP}$, $\overline{NM} \cong \overline{PO}$, $\triangle LMN \cong \triangle NOP$

49. Determine whether the triangles shown are congruent. If so, name the corresponding parts and write a congruence statement. (Lesson 11-2)

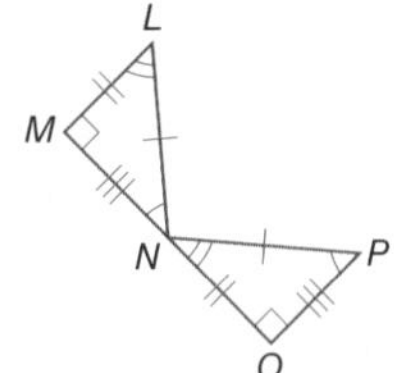

50. GARDENING Suppose you plant a square garden with an area of 300 square feet. What is the minimum amount of fencing needed to enclose the garden if the fencing only comes in whole-foot sections? (Lesson 5-1) **70 ft of fencing**

51. ALGEBRA Solve $x - 3.4 \geq 6.2$. Graph the solution on a number line. (Lesson 5-4) **See margin.**

Find each quotient. (Lesson 2-5)

52. $-69 \div 23$ **−3**

53. $48 \div (-8)$ **−6**

54. $-24 \div (-12)$ **2**

55. $-50 \div 5$ **−10**

Skills Review

Simplify each expression. (Lesson 1-2)

56. $(5 - 2)180$ **540**

57. $(7 - 2)180$ **900**

58. $(10 - 2)180$ **1440**

59. $(9 - 2)180$ **1260**

Differentiated Instruction

Extension You can introduce students to the concept of informal proof using Exercises 31–34. If you use the pentagon on p. 621, the sum of $\angle 1$ and its interior angle is 180°. So, if a polygon has n sides, the sum of n exterior angles and their corresponding interior angles is $180 \bullet n$ or $180n$.

The sum of the exterior angles and interior angles minus the sum of the interior angles equals the sum of the exterior angles. So, $180n - 180(n - 2)$ or $180n - 180n + 360 = 360$.

622 Chapter 11 Distance and Angle

1. If $m\angle Y = 23°$ and $\angle Y$ and $\angle Z$ are complementary, what is $m\angle Z$? (Lesson 11-1) **67°**

2. Angles G and H are supplementary. If $m\angle G = x + 11$ and $m\angle H = x - 13$, what is x, $m\angle G$, and $m\angle H$? (Lesson 11-1)
$x = 91$, $m\angle G = 102°$, $m\angle H = 78°$

In the figure, $m \parallel \ell$ and t is a transversal. If $m\angle 3 = 140°$, find the measure of each angle. Explain your reasoning. (Lesson 11-1)

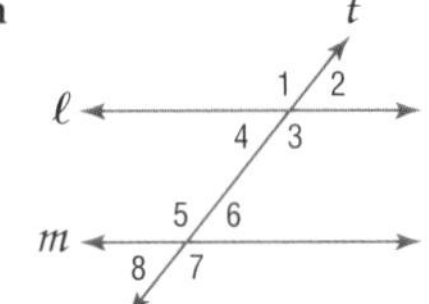

3. $m\angle 5$ 4. $m\angle 7$
3–4. See margin.

5. **UMBRELLAS** Each of the eight sections in the umbrella at the right is congruent, with the spokes having equal length. (Lesson 11-2)

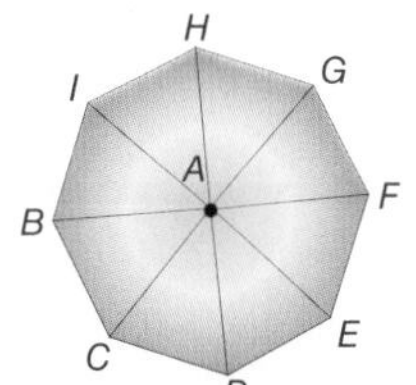

a. If $EF = 11$ inches and $EA = 14$ inches, what is CD? **11 in.**

b. Write a congruence statement involving $\triangle ABI$ and another triangle.
Sample answer: $\triangle ABI \cong \triangle AGF$

6. **MULTIPLE CHOICE** Which is *not* a true congruence statement for the congruent triangles shown below? (Lesson 11-2) **C**

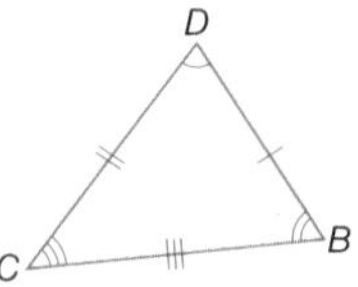

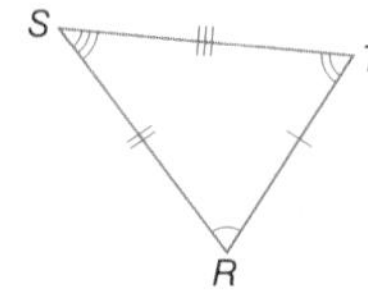

A $\triangle BCD \cong \triangle TSR$
B $\overline{CD} \cong \overline{SR}$
C $\angle DBC \cong \angle RST$
D $\triangle BDC \cong \triangle TRS$

7. Triangle GHJ has vertices $G(-2, 4)$, $H(-3, 0)$, and $J(-4, 3)$. Graph the figure and its image after a clockwise rotation of 90° about vertex H. Give the coordinates of the vertices for $\triangle G'H'J'$. (Lesson 11-3) **See margin.**

8. Determine whether the hubcap shown at the right has rotational symmetry. If it does, describe the angle of rotation. (Lesson 11-3)
yes; 72°

9. **ALGEBRA** Find the value of x in the quadrilateral at the right. Then find the missing angle measures. (Lesson 11-4) **70; 70°, 85°**

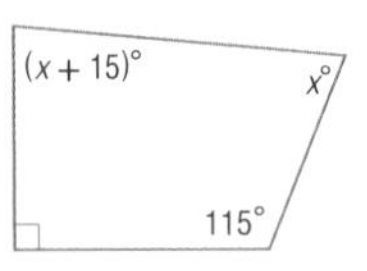

10. **MULTIPLE CHOICE** Which figure is a parallelogram? (Lesson 11-4) **J**

F
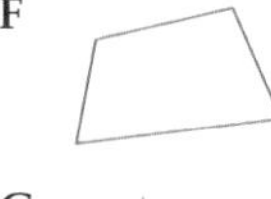

H
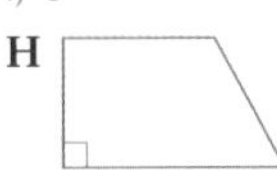

G

J
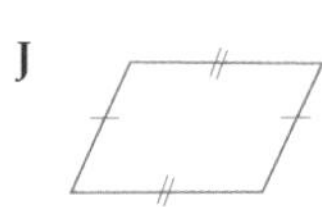

PARKING SPACES **Classify each quadrilateral using the name that *best* describes it.** (Lesson 11-4)

11.  **rectangle**

12.  **parallelogram**

13. **GRIDDED RESPONSE** The outline of the star in the Houston Astros' logo is a regular pentagon. What is the measure in degrees of one interior angle in the pentagon? (Lesson 11-5)
108

Find the sum of the measures of the interior angles of each polygon. (Lesson 11-5)

14. octagon **1080°**
15. 14-gon **2160°**

16. Find the measure of one interior angle of a regular nonagon. (Lesson 11-5) **140°**

CHAPTER 11 Mid-Chapter Quiz

Formative Assessment

Use the Mid-Chapter Quiz to assess students' progress in the first half of the chapter.

For problems answered incorrectly, have students review the lessons indicated in parentheses.

Customize and create multiple versions of your Mid-Chapter Quiz and their answer keys.

FOLDABLES Follow-Up

Before students complete the Mid-Chapter Quiz, encourage them to review the information for Lessons 11-1 through 11-5 in their Foldables.

Additional Answers

3. 140°; $\angle 3$ and $\angle 5$ are alternate interior angles.
4. 140°; $\angle 3$ and $\angle 7$ are corresponding angles.
7.

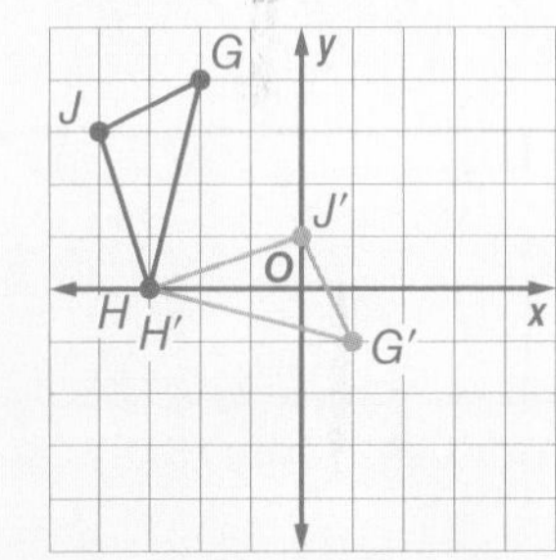

$G'(1, -1)$, $H'(-3, 0)$, $J'(0, 1)$

Intervention Planner

Tier 1 On Level	Tier 2 Strategic Intervention approaching grade level	Tier 3 Intensive Intervention 2 or more grades below level
If students miss about 25% of the exercises or less,	**If** students miss about 50% of the exercises,	**If** students miss about 75% of the exercises,
Then choose a resource: **SE** Lessons 11-1 through 11-5 **CRM** Skills Practice, pp. 7, 13, 19, 25, and 31 **TE** Chapter Project, p. 586 **Math Online** Self-Check Quiz	**Then** choose a resource: **CRM** Study Guide and Intervention, Chapter 11, pp. 5, 11, 17, 23, and 29 *Quick Review Math Handbook* **Math Online** Extra Examples, Personal Tutor, Homework Help	 **Then** use *Math Triumphs, Grade 8*, Ch. 4 **Math Online** Extra Examples, Personal Tutor, Homework Help, Review Vocabulary

11-6 Lesson Notes

1 FOCUS

Vertical Alignment

Before Lesson 11-6
Find areas of rectangles.

Lesson 11-6
Find areas of parallelograms, triangles, and trapezoids.

After Lesson 11-6
Find areas of regular polygons.

2 TEACH

Scaffolding Questions

Have students read the *Why?* section of the lesson and answer the questions.

Ask:

- Suppose Maya cut a diagonal across the rectangle. What shapes would be created? two congruent triangles
- What is the area of one of those triangles? half of the area of the rectangle or 4 units^2

11-6 Area of Parallelograms, Triangles, and Trapezoids

Then
You found the area of rectangles. (Lesson 5-1)

Now
- Find areas of parallelograms.
- Find areas of triangles and trapezoids.

New Vocabulary
base
altitude

Math Online
glencoe.com
- Extra Examples
- Personal Tutor
- Self-Check Quiz
- Homework Help

Why?

Maya draws a rectangle on grid paper. She cuts off a triangle from the left and moves it to the right side of the figure.

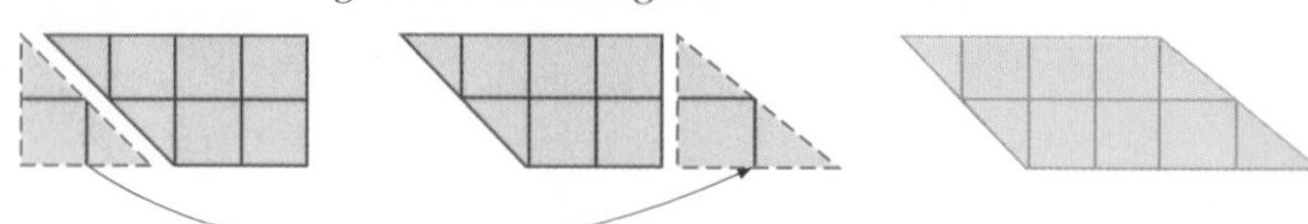

a. What is the area of the original rectangle? 8 units^2

b. Describe the new figure. What is its area? parallelogram; 8 units^2

c. What parts of a parallelogram could you use to find its area? length of the base and height

Area of Parallelograms The **base** of a parallelogram is any side of the parallelogram. The *height* is the length of an **altitude**, a line segment perpendicular to the base with endpoints on the base and the side opposite the base.

Key Concept: Area of Parallelogram

For Your FOLDABLE

Words The area A of a parallelogram in square units is $A = bh$, where b is the base of the parallelogram and h is the height.

Symbols $A = bh$

h
b

EXAMPLE 1 Find Areas of Parallelograms

Find the area of each parallelogram.

a.

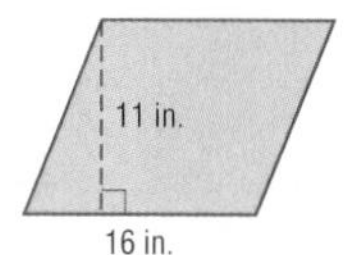

$A = bh$	Area of a parallelogram
$= 16 \cdot 11$	$b = 16$ and $h = 11$
$= 176$	Multiply.

The area is 176 square inches.

b.

7.5 cm
6.2 cm

$A = bh$	Area of a parallelogram
$= 6.2 \cdot 7.5$	$b = 6.2$ and $h = 7.5$
$= 46.5$	Multiply.

The area is 46.5 square centimeters.

Check Your Progress

1A.

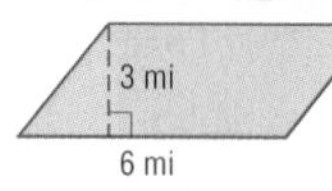

18 mi^2

1B.

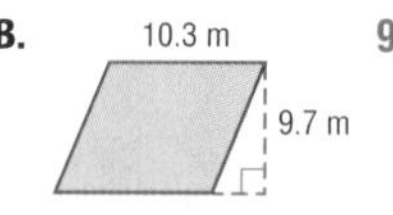

99.91 m^2

Personal Tutor glencoe.com

Lesson 11-6 Resources

Resource	Approaching-Level	On-Level	Beyond-Level	English Learners
Teacher Edition	• Differentiated Instruction, p. 625		• Differentiated Instruction, p. 630	
Chapter Resource Masters	• Study Guide and Intervention, pp. 35–36 • Skills Practice, p. 37 • Practice, p. 38 • Word Problem Practice, p. 39 • Spreadsheet Activity, p. 41	• Study Guide and Intervention, pp. 35–36 • Skills Practice, p. 37 • Practice, p. 38 • Word Problem Practice, p. 39 • Enrichment, p. 40 • Spreadsheet Activity, p. 41	• Practice, p. 38 • Word Problem Practice, p. 39 • Enrichment, p. 40 • Spreadsheet Activity, p. 41	• Study Guide and Intervention, pp. 35–36 • Skills Practice, p. 37 • Practice, p. 38 • Spreadsheet Activity, p. 41
Transparencies	• 5-Minute Check Transparency 11-6	• 5-Minute Check Transparency 11-6	• 5-Minute Check Transparency 11-6	• 5-Minute Check Transparency 11-6
Other	• Study Notebook • Teaching Pre-Algebra with Manipulatives	• Study Notebook • Teaching Pre-Algebra with Manipulatives	• Study Notebook	• Study Notebook • Teaching Pre-Algebra with Manipulatives

StudyTip

Altitudes An altitude can be outside a parallelogram or triangle.

Area of Triangles and Trapezoids The parallelogram below is separated into two congruent triangles by a diagonal.

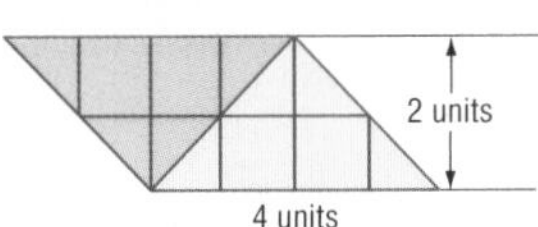
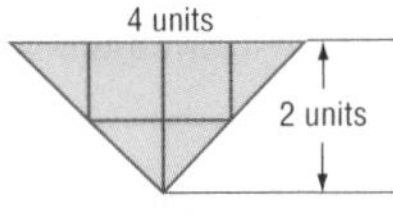
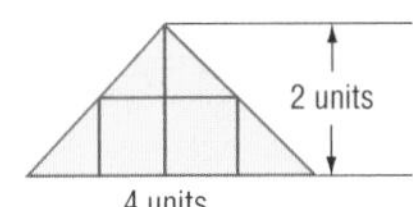

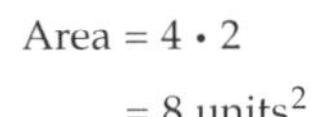

Area = 4 • 2
= 8 units^2

Area = $\frac{1}{2}$ • (4 • 2)
= 4 units^2

Area = $\frac{1}{2}$ • (4 • 2)
= 4 units^2

The area of each triangle is one-half the area of the parallelogram.

Key Concept Area of Triangle — For Your FOLDABLE

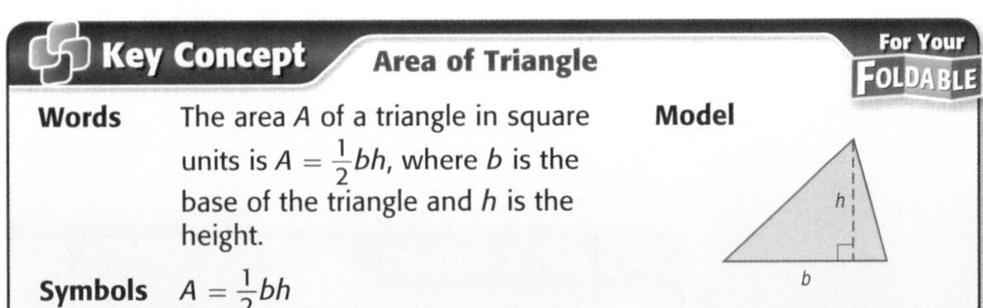

Words The area A of a triangle in square units is $A = \frac{1}{2}bh$, where b is the base of the triangle and h is the height.

Symbols $A = \frac{1}{2}bh$

Model

EXAMPLE 2 Find Areas of Triangles

Find the area of each triangle.

a.

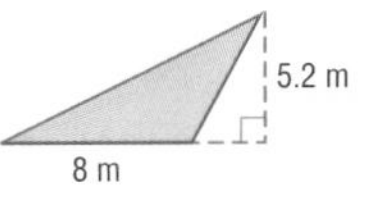

Estimate $\frac{1}{2} \cdot 8 \cdot 5 = 4 \cdot 5$ or 20

$A = \frac{1}{2}bh$	Area of a triangle
$= \frac{1}{2}(8)(5.2)$	$b = 8$ and $h = 5.2$
$= \frac{1}{2}(41.6)$	Multiply 8 • 5.2.
$= 20.8$	Simplify.

Check $20.8 \approx 20$ ✓

The area is 20.8 square meters.

b.

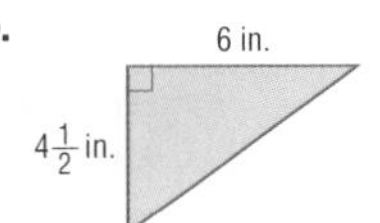

Estimate $\frac{1}{2} \cdot 6 \cdot 5 = 3 \cdot 5$ or 15

$A = \frac{1}{2}bh$	Area of a triangle
$= \frac{1}{2}(6)\left(4\frac{1}{2}\right)$	$b = 6$ and $h = 4\frac{1}{2}$
$= \frac{1}{2}\left(\frac{6}{1}\right)\left(\frac{9}{2}\right)$	Rewrite terms as improper fractions.
$= \frac{54}{4}$ or $13\frac{1}{2}$	Multiply.

Check $13\frac{1}{2} \approx 15$ ✓

The area is $13\frac{1}{2}$ square inches.

StudyTip

Alternative Method Multiplication is commutative and associative. So, you can also find $\frac{1}{2}(8)(5.2)$ by first multiplying $\frac{1}{2} \cdot 8$ and then multiplying the result by 5.2.

Check Your Progress

2A. 10 cm^2

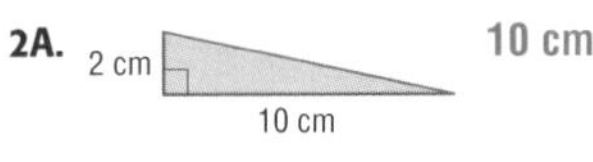

2B. 8 ft^2

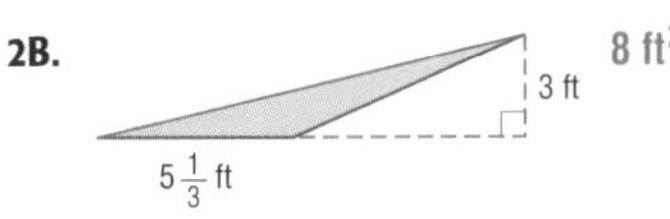

Personal Tutor glencoe.com

Differentiated Instruction AL

If students would benefit from hands-on practice with finding the area of given figures,

Then have students model a rectangle on grid paper using toothpicks with a small amount of modeling clay at the vertices. Have them determine the area of the figure. Then modify the rectangle to form a parallelogram with the same base lengths and height. Determine the area of the figure. Repeat for other sizes of rectangles.

Area of Parallelograms

Example 1 shows how to find the area of a parallelogram.

Formative Assessment

Use the Check Your Progress exercises after each example to determine students' understanding of concepts.

Additional Example

1 Find the area of each parallelogram.

a. 9 m^2

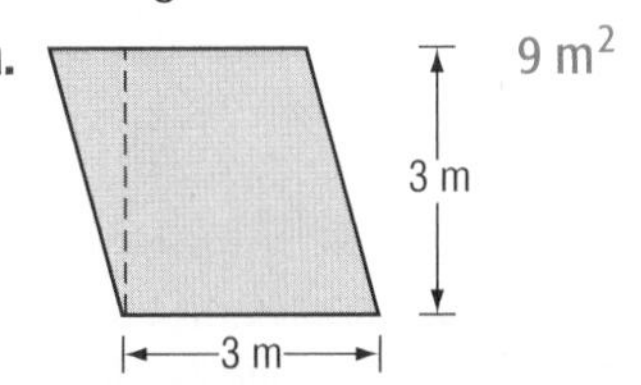

b. 26.66 in^2

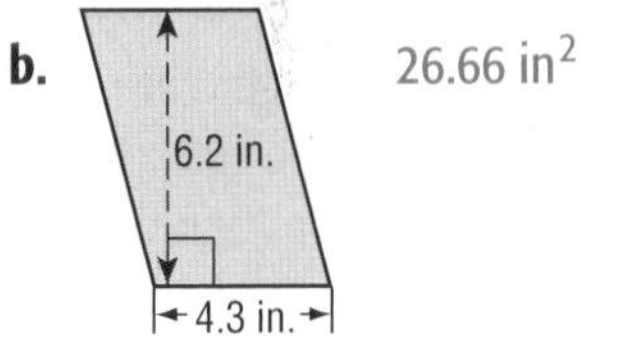

Additional Examples also in Interactive Classroom PowerPoint® Presentations

IWB INTERACTIVE WHITEBOARD READY

Area of Triangles and Trapezoids

Example 2 shows how to find the area of a triangle. **Example 3** shows how to use area to solve a real-world problem.

Additional Example

2 Find the area of each triangle.

a. 6 m^2

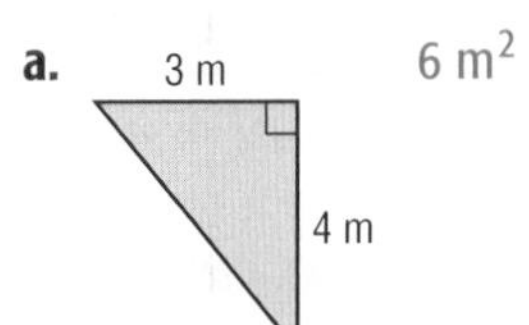

b. 12.48 ft^2

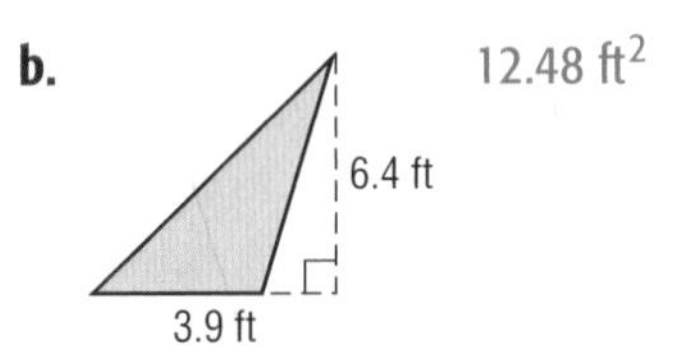

Focus on Mathematical Content

Area Just as the area for a figure can be found by dividing it into shapes of known areas, area formulas can be derived from other area formulas. Ask students how the area formula of a trapezoid, $A = \frac{1}{2}h(a + b)$, can be used to find the area formula for a triangle. A triangle is a 3-sided polygon, one "base" is equal to 0, so $\frac{1}{2}h(0 + b)$ or $\frac{1}{2}hb$.

TEACH with TECH

INTERACTIVE WHITEBOARD Draw two triangles on the board and drag them together to form a trapezoid. Drag them apart to show students that the area of the trapezoid is the sum of the areas of these two triangles.

Additional Example

3 **PLAYROOM** The floor of a playroom is shaped like a trapezoid. Use the figure below to find the area of the playroom. $38\frac{1}{4}$ m^2

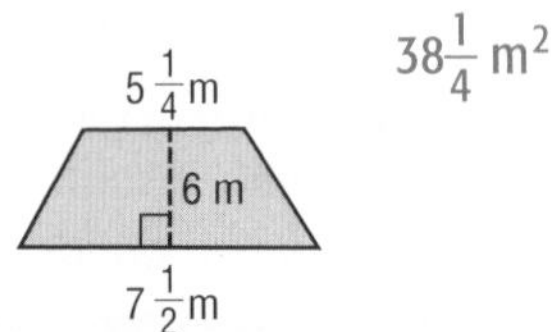

Tips for New Teachers

Alternative Teaching Strategy Sometimes a trapezoid is defined as a quadrilateral having **at least** one pair of parallel sides rather than exactly one pair. Ask students how this definition would change the classifications of certain quadrilaterals. How would the flow chart on p. 612 look different?

A trapezoid has two bases. The height of a trapezoid h is the distance between the bases. Notice that diagonal $\overline{HK}$ separates the trapezoid below into two triangles, $\triangle GHK$ and $\triangle HJK$. The area of the trapezoid is the sum of the areas of the two triangles.

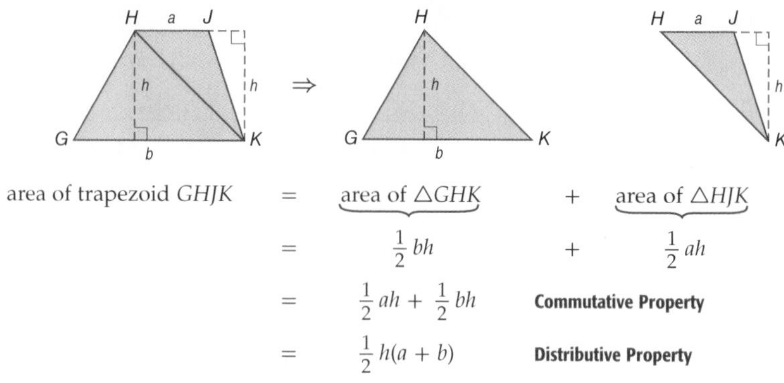

$$\begin{aligned}
\text{area of trapezoid } GHJK &= \underbrace{\text{area of } \triangle GHK} + \underbrace{\text{area of } \triangle HJK} \\
&= \tfrac{1}{2}bh + \tfrac{1}{2}ah \\
&= \tfrac{1}{2}ah + \tfrac{1}{2}bh && \textbf{Commutative Property} \\
&= \tfrac{1}{2}h(a + b) && \textbf{Distributive Property}
\end{aligned}$$

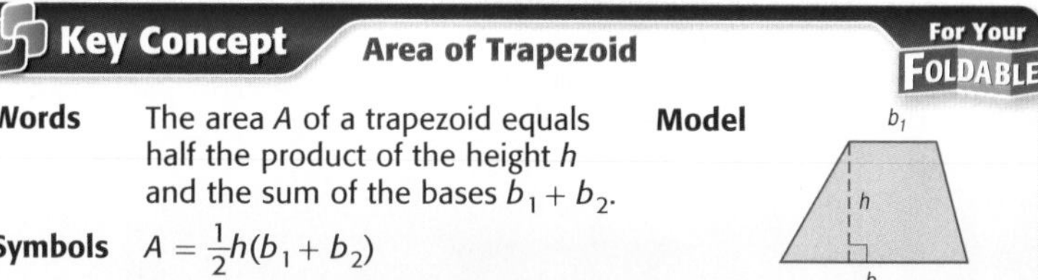

Key Concept — Area of Trapezoid

For Your FOLDABLE

Words The area A of a trapezoid equals half the product of the height h and the sum of the bases $b_1 + b_2$.

Symbols $A = \frac{1}{2}h(b_1 + b_2)$

Model

Watch Out!

Do not assume that the bases of a trapezoid are always the "top" and "bottom" sides of the figure.

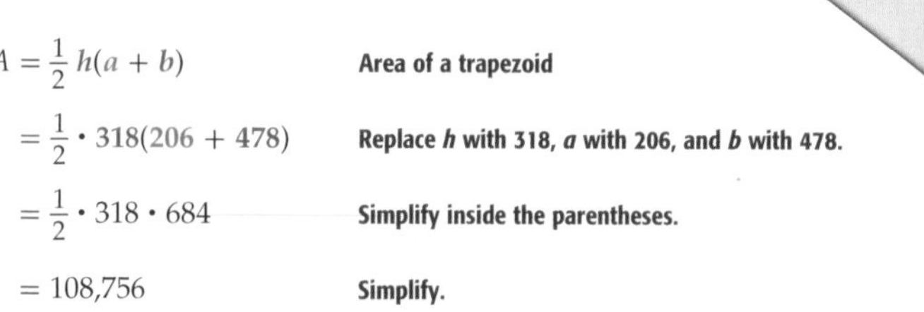

Real-World EXAMPLE 3 — Find Areas of Trapezoids

GEOGRAPHY The state of Nevada is shaped like a trapezoid as shown. Estimate the area of Nevada.

The height is 318 miles, and the bases are 206 miles and 478 miles.

$A = \frac{1}{2}h(a + b)$ **Area of a trapezoid**

$= \frac{1}{2} \cdot 318(206 + 478)$ **Replace h with 318, a with 206, and b with 478.**

$= \frac{1}{2} \cdot 318 \cdot 684$ **Simplify inside the parentheses.**

$= 108{,}756$ **Simplify.**

The area of Nevada is approximately 108,756 square miles.

Check Your Progress

3. Find the area of a trapezoid that has a height of 12.4 centimeters and bases of 10.5 centimeters and 7 centimeters. **108.5 cm^2**

Personal Tutor glencoe.com

626 Chapter 11 Distance and Angle

Check Your Understanding

Examples 1–3 pp. 624–626

Find the area of each figure.

1. 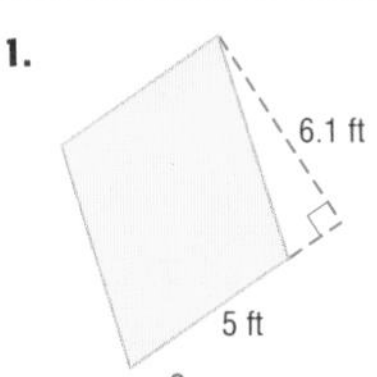

30.5 ft²

2. 3 m, 3.2 m, 5.8 m
14.08 m²

3. 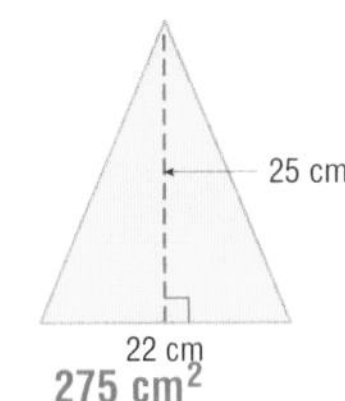

275 cm²

4. parallelogram: base = 9.4 m, height = 7.6 m 71.44 m²

5. trapezoid: height = 16 in., bases = 3.1 in., 7.6 in. 85.6 in²

6. **LACROSSE** A lacrosse goal with net is shown at the right. The goal is 6 feet wide, 6 feet high, and 7 feet deep. What is the area of the triangular region of the ground inside the net? 21 ft²

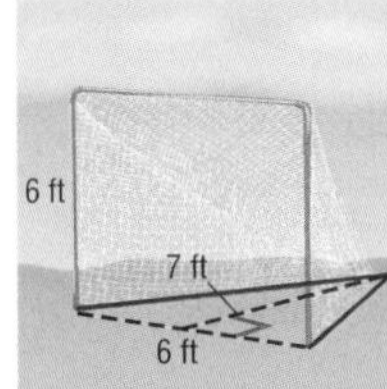

Practice and Problem Solving

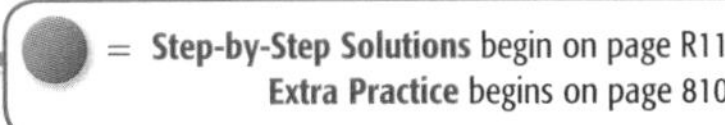
= **Step-by-Step Solutions** begin on page R11.
Extra Practice begins on page 810.

Examples 1–3 pp. 624–626

Find the area of each figure.

7. 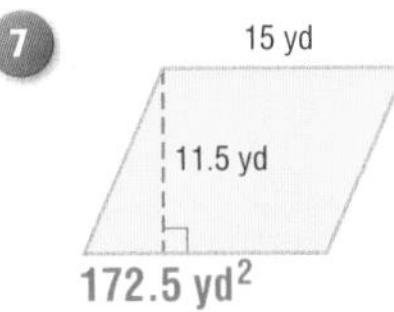

172.5 yd²

8. 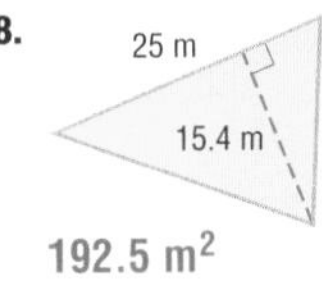

192.5 m²

9. 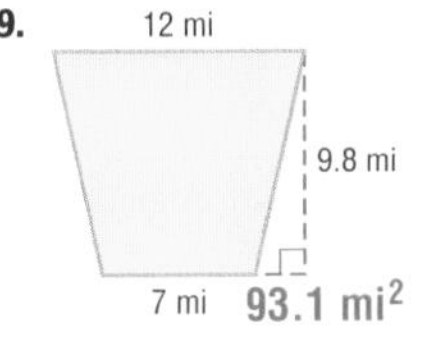

93.1 mi²

10. 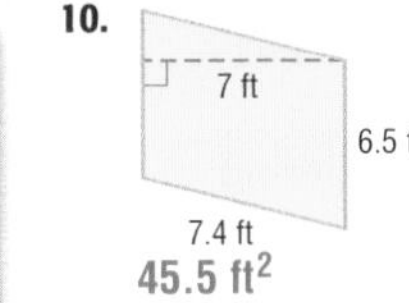

45.5 ft²

11. 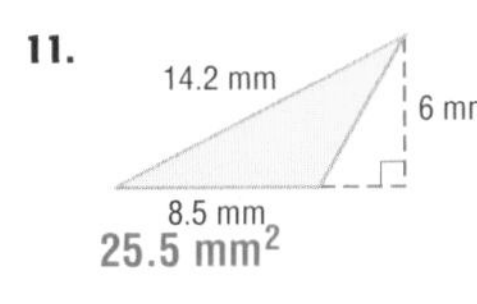

25.5 mm²

12. 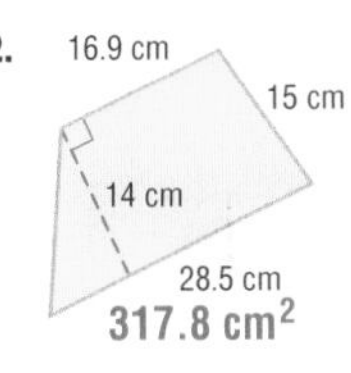

317.8 cm²

Real-World Link

The Mayan Pyramid of Kukulkan in the Yucatan Peninsula, Mexico, was built around 800 A.D. Each face of the pyramid has a stairway with ninety-one steps.

Source: World-Mysteries

13. **HISTORY** Each face of the Mayan Pyramid of Kukulkan is a trapezoid with the approximate dimensions shown at the left. What is the approximate area of one face of the structure? 972.4 m²

Find the area of each figure.

14. parallelogram: height = 9 mm, base = 5 mm 45 mm²

15. trapezoid: height = 6 cm, bases = 4 cm, 7 cm 33 cm²

16. triangle: base = 12 ft, height = 4.4 ft 26.4 ft²

Tips for New Teachers

Trapezoids The formula for a trapezoid can also be written as $A = \frac{1}{2}(b_1 + b_2)h$ or $A = \frac{(b_1 + b_2)h}{2}$.

3 PRACTICE

Formative Assessment

Use Exercises 1–6 to check for understanding.

Use the chart at the bottom of this page to customize assignments for your students.

Tips for New Teachers

Area If students are having difficulty remembering the formula for the area of a trapezoid, show students how the formula reflects the sum of the areas of the two triangles formed by drawing a diagonal.

$$A = \frac{1}{2}(b_1 + b_2)$$
$$= \frac{1}{2}b_1 h + \frac{1}{2}b_2 h$$

b_2, b_1

Differentiated Homework Options

Level	Assignment	Two-Day Option	
AL Basic	7–19, 35–36, 38–57	7–19 odd, 40–43	8–18 even, 35–36, 38–39, 44–57
OL Core	7–19 odd, 20–23, 25–31 odd, 32–36, 38–57	7–19, 40–43	20–36, 38, 39, 44–57
BL Advanced	20–52 (optional: 53–57)		

17. **HOPSCOTCH** The first six steps of a hopscotch pattern are shown at the right.

a. What is the area of triangle 5? **6.25 ft^2**

b. What is the area formed by triangles 3 and 4? **12.5 ft^2**

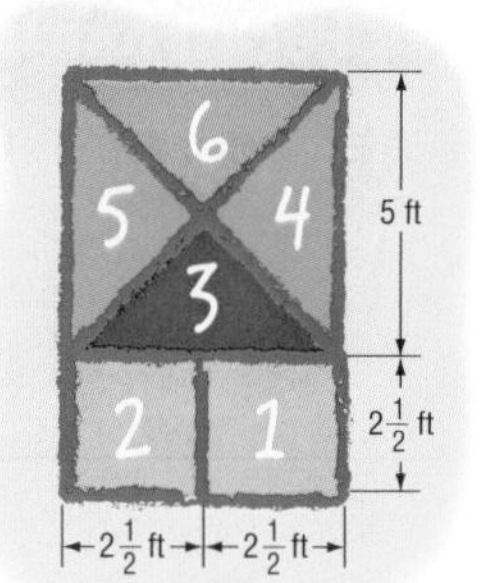

Find the area of each figure.

18. parallelogram: base = 8.2 km, height = 5.2 km **42.64 km^2**

19. trapezoid: height = 2.4 m, bases = 7.9 m, 8.1 m **19.2 m^2**

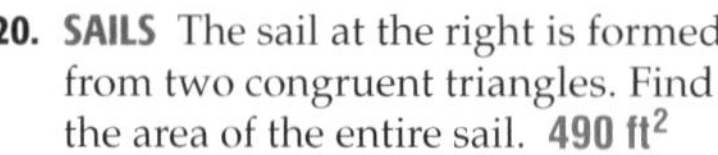

B

20. **SAILS** The sail at the right is formed from two congruent triangles. Find the area of the entire sail. **490 ft^2**

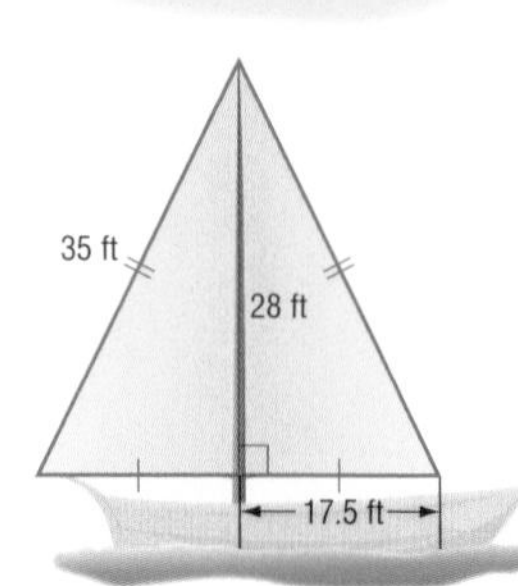

21. Find the base of a parallelogram with a height of 14.3 centimeters and an area of 128.7 square centimeters. **9 cm**

22. Suppose a triangle has an area of 32 square kilometers and a base of 12.8 kilometers. What is the height? **5 km**

23. A trapezoid has an area of 26 square feet. What is the measure of the height if the bases measure 1.3 feet and 3.2 feet? Round to the nearest tenth. **11.6 ft**

Find the area of each figure.

24. **121 cm^2**

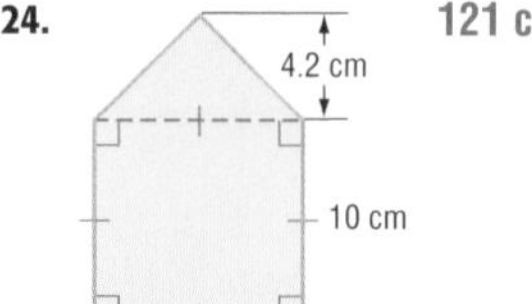

25. **81 mm^2**

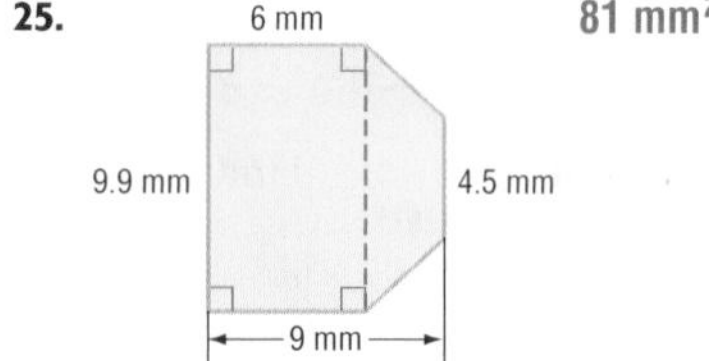

Find the area of each figure with the vertices shown.

26. rectangle: $A(-3, 4)$, $B(5, 4)$, $C(5, -1)$, $D(-3, -1)$ **40 units^2**

27. parallelogram: $H(-2, -1)$, $I(0, 2)$, $J(5, 2)$, $K(3, -1)$ **15 units^2**

28. triangle: $E(-2.5, 2)$, $F(3, -2.5)$, $G(3, 2)$ **12.375 units^2**

Find the perimeter and area of each trapezoid.

29. 30.

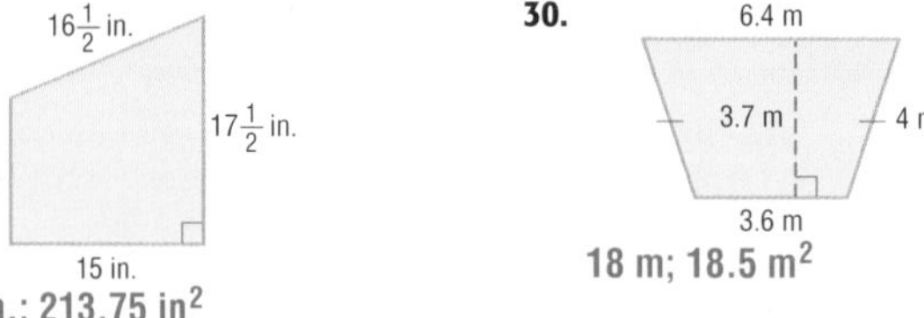

29. **60 in.; 213.75 in^2**

30. **18 m; 18.5 m^2**

C

31. **PAINTING** One wall of Tyve's room is in the shape of a trapezoid. The base of the wall is 12 feet wide. The top is 8 feet wide. The wall is 9 feet high. There is a rectangular window 2 feet by 3 feet. If she wants to paint the wall, what is the area that she needs to paint? **84 ft^2**

StudyTip

Estimation When finding areas of polygons, it is helpful to use estimation to determine whether your answer is reasonable.

Vocabulary Review

Perimeter the distance around a geometric figure (Lesson 5-1)

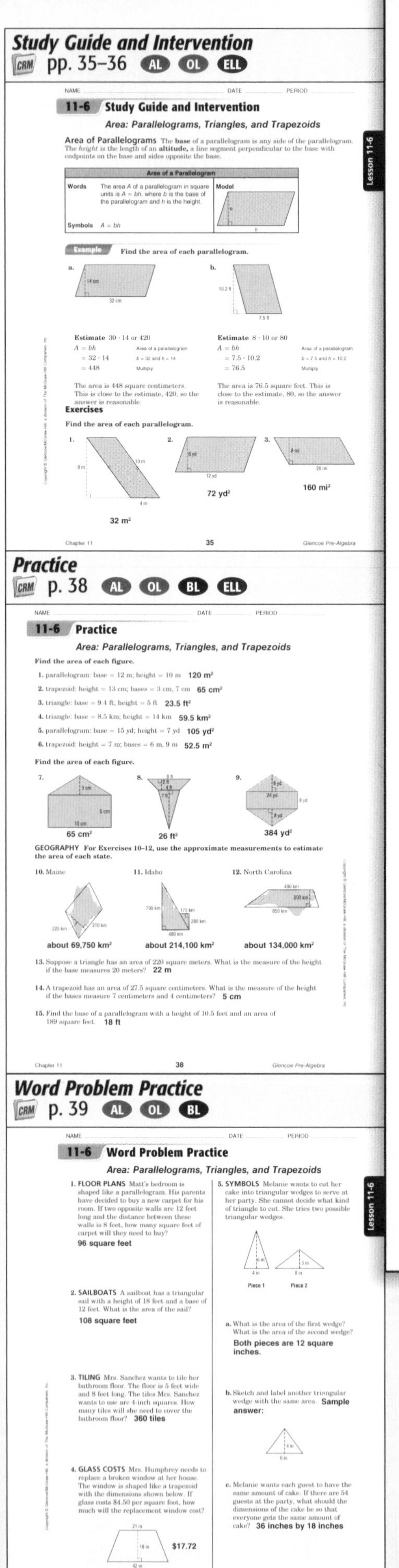

Study Guide and Intervention

CRM pp. 35–36 AL OL ELL

NAME ______ DATE ______ PERIOD ______

11-6 Study Guide and Intervention

Area: Parallelograms, Triangles, and Trapezoids

Area of Parallelograms The **base** of a parallelogram is any side of the parallelogram. The *height* is the length of an **altitude,** a line segment perpendicular to the base with endpoints on the base and sides opposite the base.

Area of a Parallelogram		
Words	The area A of a parallelogram in square units is $A = bh$, where b is the base of the parallelogram and h is the height.	**Model**
Symbols	$A = bh$	

Example Find the area of each parallelogram.

a. 14 cm, 32 cm

b. 10.2 ft, 7.5 ft

Estimate $30 \cdot 14$ or 420

$A = bh$ Area of a parallelogram

$= 32 \cdot 14$ $b = 32$ and $h = 14$

$= 448$ Multiply

The area is 448 square centimeters. This is close to the estimate, 420, so the answer is reasonable.

Estimate $8 \cdot 10$ or 80

$A = bh$ Area of a parallelogram

$= 7.5 \cdot 10.2$ $b = 7.5$ and $h = 10.2$

$= 76.5$ Multiply

The area is 76.5 square feet. This is close to the estimate, 80, so the answer is reasonable.

Exercises

Find the area of each parallelogram.

1. 8 m, 10 m, 4 m **32 m²**

2. 6 yd, 12 yd **72 yd²**

3. 8 mi, 20 mi **160 mi²**

Chapter 11 35 Glencoe Pre-Algebra

Practice

CRM p. 38 AL OL BL ELL

NAME ______ DATE ______ PERIOD ______

11-6 Practice

Area: Parallelograms, Triangles, and Trapezoids

Find the area of each figure.

1. parallelogram: base = 12 m; height = 10 m **120 m²**
2. trapezoid: height = 13 cm; bases = 3 cm, 7 cm **65 cm²**
3. triangle: base = 9.4 ft; height = 5 ft **23.5 ft²**
4. triangle: base = 8.5 km; height = 14 km **59.5 km²**
5. parallelogram: base = 15 yd; height = 7 yd **105 yd²**
6. trapezoid: height = 7 m; bases = 6 m, 9 m **52.5 m²**

Find the area of each figure.

7. 3 cm, 5 cm, 10 cm **65 cm²**

8. 6 ft, 2 ft, 4 ft, 7 ft **26 ft²**

9. 8 yd, 24 yd, 8 yd, 8 yd **384 yd²**

GEOGRAPHY For Exercises 10–12, use the approximate measurements to estimate the area of each state.

10. Maine — 225 km, 310 km **about 69,750 km²**

11. Idaho — 790 km, 175 km, 280 km, 480 km **about 214,100 km²**

12. North Carolina — 490 km, 200 km, 850 km **about 134,000 km²**

13. Suppose a triangle has an area of 220 square meters. What is the measure of the height if the base measures 20 meters? **22 m**

14. A trapezoid has an area of 27.5 square centimeters. What is the measure of the height if the bases measure 7 centimeters and 4 centimeters? **5 cm**

15. Find the base of a parallelogram with a height of 10.5 feet and an area of 189 square feet. **18 ft**

Chapter 11 38 Glencoe Pre-Algebra

Word Problem Practice

CRM p. 39 AL OL BL

NAME ______ DATE ______ PERIOD ______

11-6 Word Problem Practice

Area: Parallelograms, Triangles, and Trapezoids

1. **FLOOR PLANS** Matt's bedroom is shaped like a parallelogram. His parents have decided to buy a new carpet for his room. If two opposite walls are 12 feet long and the distance between these walls is 8 feet, how many square feet of carpet will they need to buy?
96 square feet

2. **SAILBOATS** A sailboat has a triangular sail with a height of 18 feet and a base of 12 feet. What is the area of the sail?
108 square feet

3. **TILING** Mrs. Sanchez wants to tile her bathroom floor. The floor is 5 feet wide and 8 feet long. The tiles Mrs. Sanchez wants to use are 4-inch squares. How many tiles will she need to cover the bathroom floor? **360 tiles**

4. **GLASS COSTS** Mrs. Humphrey needs to replace a broken window at her house. The window is shaped like a trapezoid with the dimensions shown below. If glass costs $4.50 per square foot, how much will the replacement window cost?
21 in, 18 in, 42 in **$17.72**

5. **SYMBOLS** Melanie wants to cut her cake into triangular wedges to serve at her party. She cannot decide what kind of triangle to cut. She tries two possible triangular wedges.
Piece 1: 6 in, 4 in — Piece 2: 3 in, 8 in

a. What is the area of the first wedge? What is the area of the second wedge?
Both pieces are 12 square inches.

b. Sketch and label another triangular wedge with the same area. **Sample answer:** 4 in, 6 in

c. Melanie wants each guest to have the same amount of cake. If there are 54 guests at the party, what should the dimensions of the cake be so that everyone gets the same amount of cake? **36 inches by 18 inches**

Chapter 11 39 Glencoe Pre-Algebra

628 Chapter 11 Distance and Angle

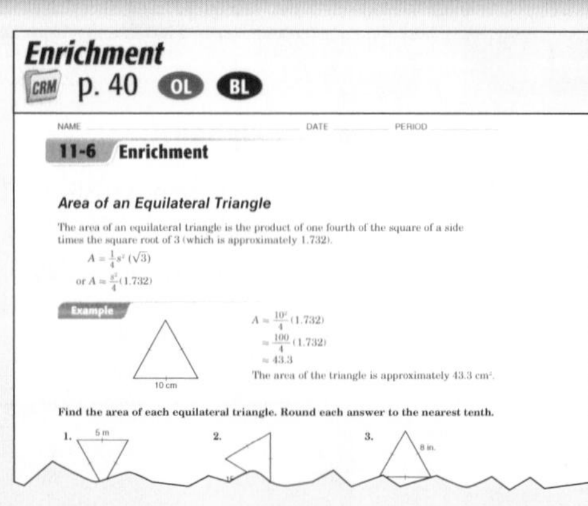

Enrichment

CRM p. 40 OL BL

NAME ______ DATE ______ PERIOD ______

11-6 Enrichment

Area of an Equilateral Triangle

The area of an equilateral triangle is the product of one fourth of the square of a side times the square root of 3 (which is approximately 1.732).

$A = \frac{1}{4}s^2(\sqrt{3})$

or $A = \frac{s^2}{4}(1.732)$

Example 10 cm

$A = \frac{10^2}{4}(1.732)$

$= \frac{100}{4}(1.732)$

≈ 43.3

The area of the triangle is approximately 43.3 cm².

Find the area of each equilateral triangle. Round each answer to the nearest tenth.

1. 5 m

2.

3. 8 in.

StudyTip

Measurement When converting measurements, remember that there will be a greater number of smaller units than larger units.

35. Sample answer: a triangle with a base of 8 units and a height of 3 units has the same area as a parallelogram with a base of 4 units and a height of 3 units, 12 units^2.

36. Lydia; Cameron incorrectly multiplied the bases rather than adding them.

37a. Sample answer: a parallelogram with base 10 in., height 12 in., and sides 13 in.; 46 in., 120 in^2

37b. Sample answer: a parallelogram with base 11 in., height 11 in., and sides 13 in.; 48 in., 121 in^2

39. In the formula for the area of a triangle, $\frac{1}{2}$ is multiplied by the base and the height. The formula for the area of a trapezoid is the same, except that the sum of the bases is multiplied rather than a single base.

32. **MEASUREMENT** Find the area of the parallelogram at the right in square centimeters. Round to the nearest tenth. (*Hint*: 1 in. ≈ 2.54 cm) **838.7 cm^2**

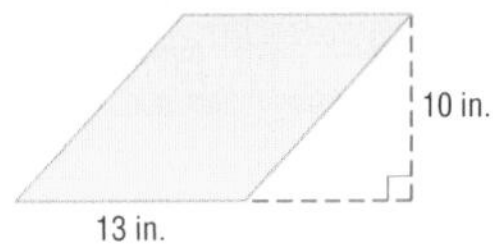

33. **MEASUREMENT** Find the area of the trapezoid at the right in square yards. Round to the nearest tenth. (*Hint*: 1 yd^2 = 9 ft^2) **23.6 yd^2**

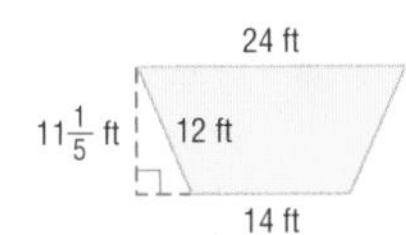

34. **MULTIPLE REPRESENTATIONS** In this problem, you will explore the area of a figure when a dilation occurs.

   a. **GEOMETRIC** Sketch and label a triangle with a base of 6 units and a height of 3 units. **a–c. See margin.**

   b. **TABULAR** Make a table like the one shown at the right. Find the area of each triangle.

   c. **ANALYTICAL** Describe how the area of a triangle changes if the dimensions are doubled and if the dimensions are tripled.

Triangle	Base (in.)	Height (in.)	Area (in^2)
1	6	3	■
2	12	6	■
3	18	9	■

H.O.T. Problems
Use Higher-Order Thinking Skills

35. **OPEN ENDED** Give an example of a triangle and a parallelogram that have the same area. Describe the bases and heights of each figure. State the area.

36. **FIND THE ERROR** Cameron and Lydia found the area of the trapezoid shown at the right. Is either of them correct? Explain your reasoning.

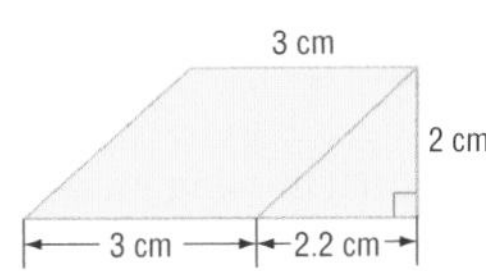

Cameron

$A = \frac{1}{2} \times 2 \times (3 \times 5.2)$
$= 15.6\ m^2$

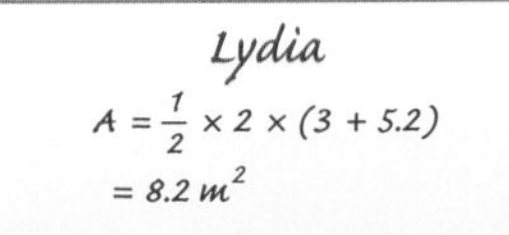

37. **CHALLENGE** Refer to the parallelogram *QRST* shown at the right.

   a. Describe a parallelogram that has the same area but a different perimeter than *QRST*. State the perimeter and area of the new parallelogram.

   b. Describe a parallelogram that has the same perimeter but a different area than *QRST*. State the perimeter and area of the new parallelogram.

Q R 14 in. 12 in. T S 10 in.

38. **REASONING** Describe another method for finding the area of the trapezoid in Exercise 36. **See margin.**

39. **WRITING IN MATH** Describe how the formula for the area of a trapezoid is related to the formula for the area of a triangle.

Watch Out!

Find the Error In Exercise 36, explain to students that one way to avoid errors when using formulas is to first write the formula and then substitute the given values for the variables. Ask whether this strategy might have helped either Cameron or Lydia.

Additional Answers

34a.

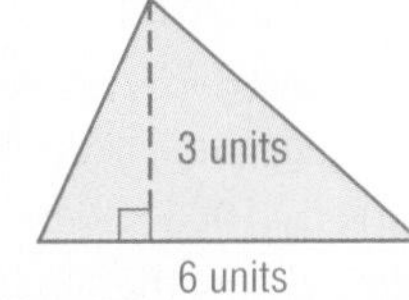

34b.

Triangle	Base (in.)	Height (in.)	Area (in^2)
1	6	3	9
2	12	6	36
3	18	9	81

34c. If the dimensions are doubled, the area is multiplied by $2 \cdot 2$ or 4. If the dimensions are tripled, the area is multiplied by $3 \cdot 3$ or 9.

38. Sample answer: Find the area of the parallelogram and the area of the triangle and add: $A = (3)(2) + \frac{1}{2}(2.2)(2) = 8.2$ cm^2.

Multiple Representations In Exercise 34, students use a drawing and a table to show how the area of a triangle changes when the dimensions are changed.

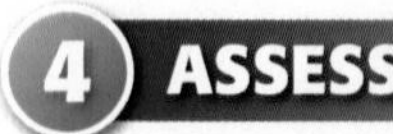

4 ASSESS

Yesterday's News Have students write how the previous lessons on triangles and quadrilaterals have helped them with today's lesson on finding the area of parallelograms, triangles, and trapezoids.

Additional Answer

41a. She would need to determine the area of the lawn that she is going to fertilize. After finding the total area, she will then divide that by 1000 square feet to determine how many bags she needs to buy.

41b. $90 \cdot 150 = 13{,}500$. $13{,}500 \div 1000 = 13.5$ so she would need to buy 14 bags of fertilizer.

Standardized Test Practice

40. Find the area of the figure below. **C**

A $17\ m^2$
B $25\ m^2$
C $30\ m^2$
D $60\ m^2$

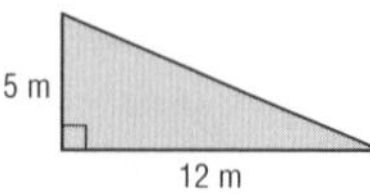

41. **EXTENDED RESPONSE** Mrs. Watts wants to fertilize her lawn for spring. The fertilizer that she wants to buy indicates one bag will fertilize 1000 square feet.

a. List the steps that Mrs. Watts will need to follow to determine the number of bags she will need to purchase. **See margin.**

b. Suppose Mrs. Watts' lawn measures 90 feet by 150 feet. Calculate the number of bags of fertilizer she will need. **See margin.**

42. Square X has an area of 9 square feet. The sides of square Y are twice as long as the sides of square X. Find the area of square Y. **G**

F $18\ ft^2$
G $36\ ft^2$
H $9\ ft^2$
J $6\ ft^2$

43. An architect designed a room that was in the shape of a trapezoid. She wants to figure the amount of carpet that will be needed for the room. Use the room's dimensions below to determine the amount of carpet needed. **B**

A $432.5\ ft^2$
B $487.5\ ft^2$
C $585\ ft^2$
D $607.5\ ft^2$

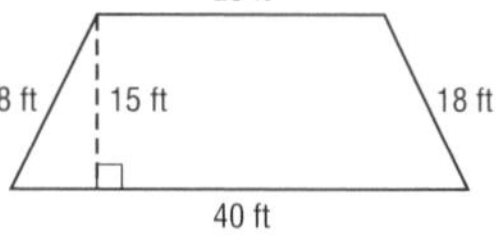

Spiral Review

Find the measure of an interior angle of each polygon to the nearest tenth. (Lesson 11-4)

44. regular pentagon **108°**

45. regular heptagon **about 128.6°**

46. regular quadrilateral **90°**

47. regular 12-gon **150°**

Find each missing measure. (Lesson 11-4)

48. 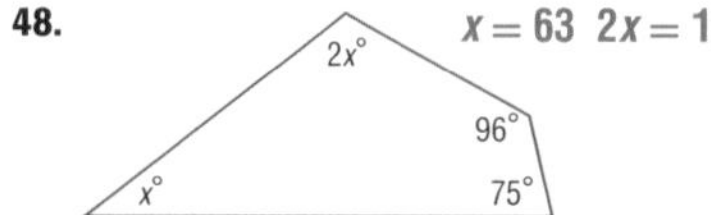

$x = 63$ $2x = 126$

49. 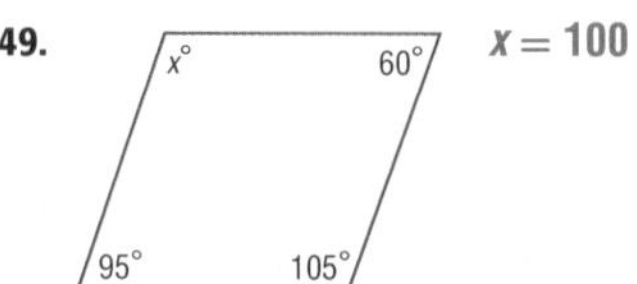
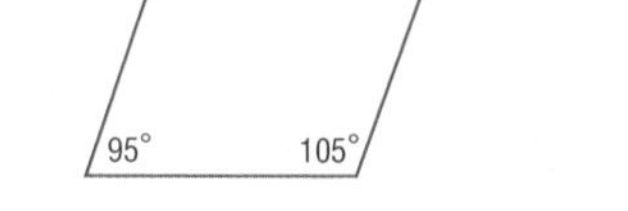

$x = 100$

Find the discount to the nearest cent. (Lesson 7-5)

50. \$85 cordless phone, 20% off **\$17**

51. \$489 stereo, 15% off **\$73.35**

52. 25% off a \$74 baseball glove **\$18.50**

53. 

\$16.25

Skills Review

Use a calculator to find each product. Round to the nearest tenth. (Previous Course)

54. $3.14 \cdot 6$ **18.8**

55. $2 \cdot 3.14 \cdot 5.4$ **33.9**

56. $3.14 \cdot 2.2$ **6.9**

57. $3.14 \cdot 4.3$ **13.5**

Differentiated Instruction

Extension Tell students that one way to compare areas in the United States is to find out how many people live there per square mile. This is called the population density. If the population of Texas is about 22,490,022 people and the area is 268,581 square miles, what is the population density of Texas? about 83.74 people per square mile

11-7

Circles and Circumference

Then

You have already found the perimeter of rectangles. (Lesson 5-1)

Now

- Find the circumference of circles.
- Solve problems involving circumference.

New Vocabulary

circle
center
radius
diameter
chord
circumference
π (pi)

Math Online

glencoe.com

- Extra Examples
- Personal Tutor
- Self-Check Quiz
- Homework Help
- Math in Motion

Why?

Collect three different large circular objects. a–b. See students' work.

a. Use a tape measure to find d, the distance across each object through its center and C, the distance around each object. Round to the nearest millimeter. Record your measures in a table.

b. For each object, find the ratio $\frac{C}{d}$.

c. Write an equation showing the relationship between C and d. Sample answer: $\frac{C}{d} \approx 3$ or $C \approx 3d$

Circumference of Circles A **circle** is the set of all points in a plane that are the same distance from a given point in the plane.

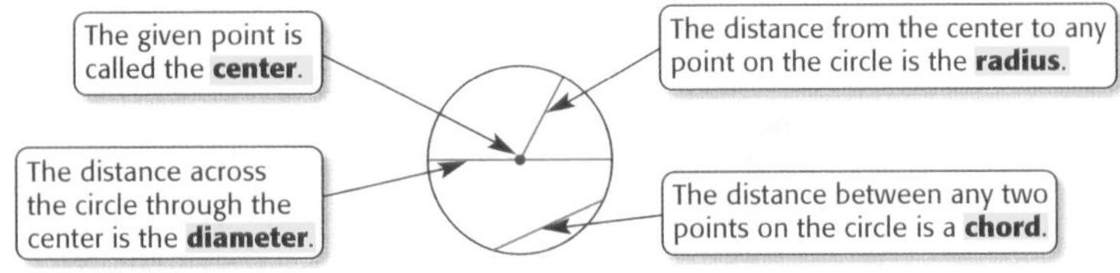

The **circumference** of a circle is the distance around the circle. In every circle, the ratio of the circumference to the diameter is equal to 3.1415926… . The Greek letter **π (pi)** stands for this number. So, $\frac{C}{d} = \pi$ or $C = \pi d$.

Key Concept Circumference of a Circle — For Your FOLDABLE

Words The circumference C of a circle is equal to its diameter times π, or 2 times its radius times π.

Symbols $C = \pi d$ or $C = 2\pi r$

Model (circle with d, r, C)

Math *in Motion*, Interactive Lab glencoe.com

EXAMPLE 1 Find the Circumference of a Circle

Find the circumference of the circle. Round to the nearest tenth. (circle: 3 in.)

$C = \pi d$ — Circumference of a circle

$= \pi \cdot 3$ — Replace d with 3.

$= 3\pi$ — Simplify. This is the *exact* circumference.

3 [×] [2nd] [π] [ENTER] 9.424777961 — Use a calculator.

The circumference is about 9.4 inches.

Check Your Progress

1. Find the circumference of a circle with a diameter of $3\frac{3}{4}$ feet. Round to the nearest tenth. 11.8 ft

Personal Tutor glencoe.com

11-7 Lesson Notes

1 FOCUS

Vertical Alignment

Before Lesson 11-7
Find the perimeter of rectangles.

Lesson 11-7
Find the circumference of circles. Solve problems involving circumference.

After Lesson 11-7
Find areas of circles.

2 TEACH

Scaffolding Questions

Have students read the *Why?* section of the lesson and answer the questions.

Ask:

- Suppose the distance around an orange is about 6.5 cm. The orange is cut in half and the distance across the center is about 2.1 cm; what is the ratio $\frac{C}{d}$? about 3.1
- Suppose a U.S. regulation basketball is 30 inches around; what is its diameter? about 10 inches

Lesson 11-7 Resources

Resource	Approaching-Level	On-Level	Beyond-Level	English Learners
Teacher Edition	• Differentiated Instruction, p. 632		• Differentiated Instruction, p. 635	
Chapter Resource Masters	• Study Guide and Intervention, pp. 42–43 • Skills Practice, p. 44 • Practice, p. 45 • Word Problem Practice, p. 46	• Study Guide and Intervention, pp. 42–43 • Skills Practice, p. 44 • Practice, p. 45 • Word Problem Practice, p. 46 • Enrichment, p. 47	• Practice, p. 45 • Word Problem Practice, p. 46 • Enrichment, p. 47	• Study Guide and Intervention, pp. 42–43 • Skills Practice, p. 44 • Practice, p. 45
Transparencies	• 5-Minute Check Transparency 11-7	• 5-Minute Check Transparency 11-7	• 5-Minute Check Transparency 11-7	• 5-Minute Check Transparency 11-7
Other	• Study Notebook • Teaching Pre-Algebra with Manipulatives	• Study Notebook • Teaching Pre-Algebra with Manipulatives	• Study Notebook	• Study Notebook • Teaching Pre-Algebra with Manipulatives

TEACH with TECH

INTERACTIVE WHITEBOARD
Display a circle on the board to use as a template on which you can draw radii, diameters, and chords.

Circumference of Circles

Examples 1 and 2 show how to find the circumference of a circle.

Formative Assessment

Use the Check Your Progress exercises after each example to determine students' understanding of concepts.

Additional Examples

1 Find the circumference of the circle. Round to the nearest tenth.

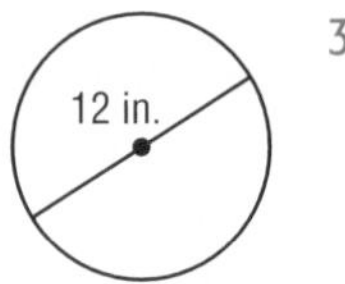

37.7 in.

2 Find the circumference of the circle. Round to the nearest tenth.

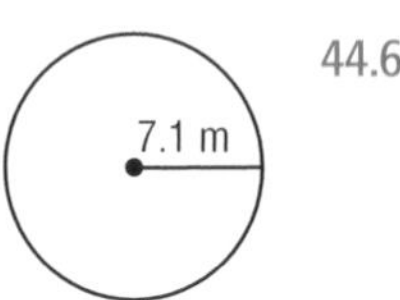

44.6 m

Additional Examples also in Interactive Classroom PowerPoint® Presentations

StudyTip

Estimating If an exact answer is needed, leave the answer in terms of π. The exact answer to Example 2 is 10.6π. If an estimate is sufficient, use a calculator to find a decimal approximation. Round to the indicated place value.

EXAMPLE 2 Find the Circumference of a Circle

Find the circumference of the circle. Round to the nearest tenth.

$C = 2\pi r$	**Circumference of a circle**
$= 2 \cdot \pi \cdot 5.3$	**Replace *r* with 5.3.**
≈ 33.3	**Simplify. Use a calculator.**

The circumference is about 33.3 centimeters.

Check Your Progress

2. Find the circumference of the circle with a radius of 7 millimeters. Round to the nearest tenth. 44.0 mm

Personal Tutor glencoe.com

Use Circumference to Solve Problems You can use the circumference of a circle to find the diameter or the radius.

π

Math History Link

π (pi)
Approximations for pi have been around for over 4000 years. One Babylonian tablet c.1900 B.C. used 3.125 as an estimate. One of the latest estimates was published in a book, *π to Five Million Places*. The book is 558 pages long and consists of the number pi computed to 5 million decimal places.

3. Sample answer: The circumference of a CD ≈ 377.0 mm and the circumference of a UMD ≈ 188.5 mm. So, the circumference of the CD is twice the circumference of the UMD.

Real-World EXAMPLE 3 Solve Problems

POOLS **Bernard works at a community center that has a circular swimming pool with a circumference of 40 meters. He would like to use a rope to divide the pool down the center. What should be the length of the rope?**

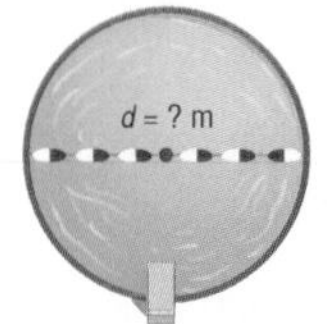

Understand You know the circumference of the pool. You need to find the diameter of the pool.

Plan Use the formula for the circumference of a circle to find the diameter.

Solve

$C = \pi d$	**Circumference of a circle**
$40 = \pi \cdot d$	**Replace *C* with 40.**
$\frac{40}{\pi} = d$	**Divide each side by π.**
$12.7 \approx d$	**Simplify. Use a calculator.**

So, the length of the rope should be about 12.7 meters.

Check Check the reasonableness of the solution by replacing d with 12.7 in $C = \pi d$.

$C = \pi d$	**Circumference of a circle**
$= \pi \cdot 12.7$	**Replace *d* with 12.7.**
≈ 39.9	**Simplify. Use a calculator.**

Since this circumference is close to the original circumference, 40 meters, the solution is reasonable.

Check Your Progress

3. **MUSIC** A CD has a diameter of 120 millimeters. A Universal Media Disc (UMD) has a diameter of 60 millimeters. Compare the circumferences of the discs.

Personal Tutor glencoe.com

Differentiated Instruction

AL

If students have trouble understanding the relationship between *C* and *d*,

Then have students look for additional circular objects to measure either inside or outside the classroom. Then have them repeat Steps a and b in the *Why?* section of the lesson. In Step b, have students round to the nearest hundredth. Then have them explain why the ratio $\frac{C}{d}$ is called a constant.

Check Your Understanding

Examples 1 and 2 pp. 631–632

Find the circumference of each circle. Round to the nearest tenth.

1. 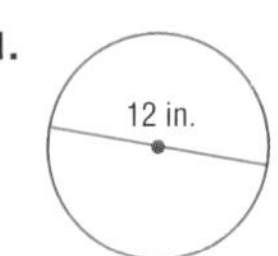

37.7 in.

2. 4 ft
25.1 ft

3. 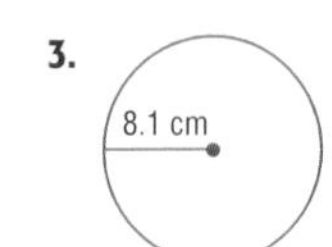

50.9 cm

4. diameter = 10.5 centimeters 33.0 cm

5. radius = 3.6 kilometers 22.6 km

Example 3 p. 632

6. **HISTORY** An ancient *timber circle* discovered in the United Kingdom was thought to have been built more than 4000 years ago. Known as "Seahenge," this ancient circle has a circumference of about 21.3 meters. What is the radius of the circle to the nearest tenth? 3.4 m

Answers were computed using the π key on a calculator.

Practice and Problem Solving

= **Step-by-Step Solutions** begin on page R11. **Extra Practice** begins on page 810.

Examples 1–3 pp. 631–632

Find the circumference of each circle. Round to the nearest tenth.

7. 

22.0 m

8. 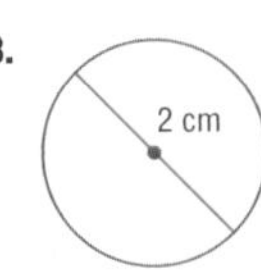

6.3 cm

9. 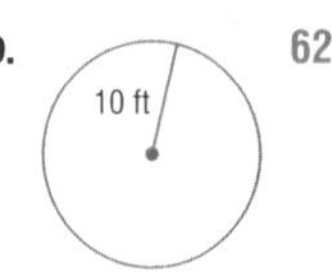

62.8 ft

10. 8 in.
50.3 in.

11. 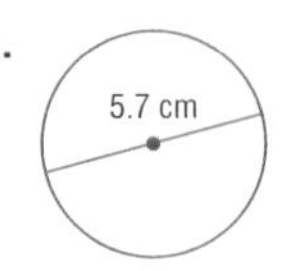

17.9 cm

12. 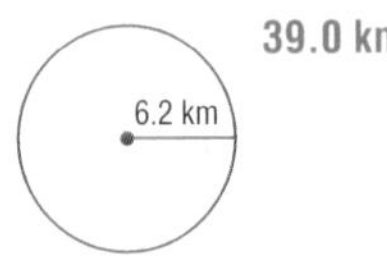

39.0 km

13. diameter = 9.4 meters 29.5 m

14. radius = 13.7 millimeters 86.1 mm

15. radius = $11\frac{1}{4}$ feet 70.7 ft

16. diameter = $14\frac{3}{5}$ yards 45.9 yd

17. **SAND DOLLARS** Compare the circumferences of the two sand dollars shown below.

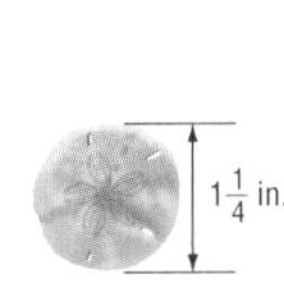

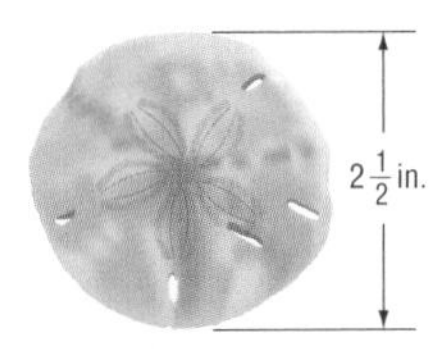

17. Sample answer: Small sand dollar: $C \approx 3.9$ in., large sand dollar: $C \approx 7.9$ in.; the circumference of the small sand dollar is half the circumference of the large sand dollar.

Real-World Link

The life span of a sand dollar ranges from 1 to 15 years. Sand dollars cannot survive if exposed to air for more than 2 or 3 hours.

Source: San Francisco State University

18. **SCIENCE** The circumference of the Moon is about 6790 miles. What is the distance to the center of the Moon in kilometers? Round to the nearest kilometer. (*Hint*: 1 mile ≈ 1.6 kilometers) 1729 km

B 19. **CLOCKS** The tower at Philadelphia City Hall contains four clocks that have a radius of about 3.96 meters. Find how far the minute hand travels after each number of rotations around the clock face. Round to the nearest hundredth.

a. 2 rotations 49.76 m **b.** $\frac{1}{2}$ rotation 12.44 m **c.** $5\frac{3}{4}$ rotations 143.07 m

Use Circumference to Solve Problems

Example 3 shows how to use circumference to find the diameter of a circle.

Additional Example

LANDSCAPING A landscaper has a tree whose roots form a ball-shaped bulb with a circumference of 110 inches. What is the minimum diameter of the hole that the landscaper will have to dig in order to plant the tree? 35 in.

Focus on Mathematical Content

Circles The radius is any line that extends out from the center, touching a point on the circle. The ratio of circumference to diameter equals the value π. The three values *d*, *r*, and π can be used to determine the circumference of a circle, but since π is constant, only the diameter or radius need to be known.

3 PRACTICE

Formative Assessment

Use Exercises 1–6 to check for understanding.

Use the chart at the bottom of this page to customize assignments for your students.

Differentiated Homework Options

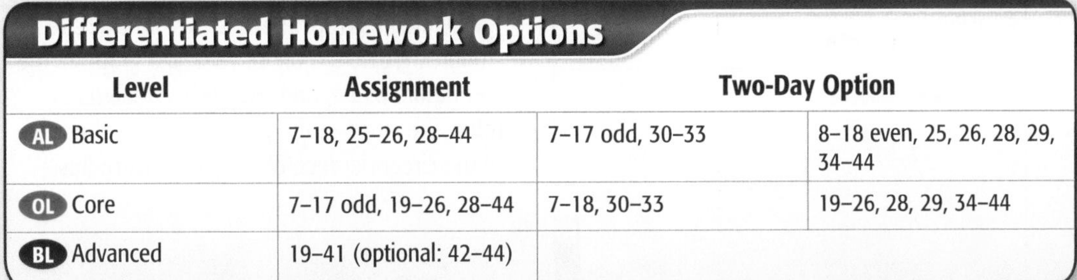

Level	Assignment	Two-Day Option	
AL Basic	7–18, 25–26, 28–44	7–17 odd, 30–33	8–18 even, 25, 26, 28, 29, 34–44
OL Core	7–17 odd, 19–26, 28–44	7–18, 30–33	19–26, 28, 29, 34–44
BL Advanced	19–41 (optional: 42–44)		

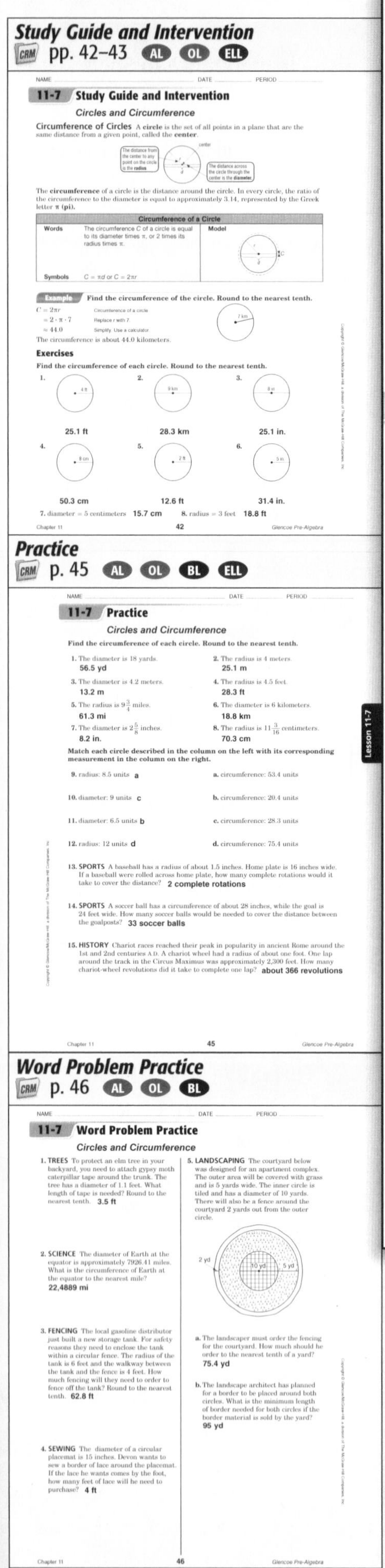
Study Guide and Intervention
CRM pp. 42–43 AL OL ELL

NAME ______ DATE ______ PERIOD ______

11-7 Study Guide and Intervention

Circles and Circumference

Circumference of Circles A **circle** is the set of all points in a plane that are the same distance from a given point, called the **center**.

The distance from the center to any point on the circle is the **radius**. The distance across the circle through the center is the **diameter**.

The **circumference** of a circle is the distance around the circle. In every circle, the ratio of the circumference to the diameter is equal to approximately 3.14, represented by the Greek letter π (**pi**).

Circumference of a Circle	
Words: The circumference C of a circle is equal to its diameter times π, or 2 times its radius times π.	Model
Symbols: $C = \pi d$ or $C = 2\pi r$	

Example Find the circumference of the circle. Round to the nearest tenth.

$C = 2\pi r$ Circumference of a circle
$= 2 \cdot \pi \cdot 7$ Replace r with 7
≈ 44.0 Simplify. Use a calculator.

The circumference is about 44.0 kilometers.

Exercises

Find the circumference of each circle. Round to the nearest tenth.

1. 25.1 ft 2. 28.3 km 3. 25.1 in.
4. 50.3 cm 5. 12.6 ft 6. 31.4 in.
7. diameter = 5 centimeters 15.7 cm 8. radius = 3 feet 18.8 ft

Chapter 11 42 Glencoe Pre-Algebra

Practice
CRM p. 45 AL OL BL ELL

NAME ______ DATE ______ PERIOD ______

11-7 Practice

Circles and Circumference

Find the circumference of each circle. Round to the nearest tenth.

1. The diameter is 18 yards. 56.5 yd
2. The radius is 4 meters. 25.1 m
3. The diameter is 4.2 meters. 13.2 m
4. The radius is 4.5 feet. 28.3 ft
5. The radius is $9\frac{3}{4}$ miles. 61.3 mi
6. The diameter is 6 kilometers. 18.8 km
7. The diameter is $2\frac{5}{8}$ inches. 8.2 in.
8. The radius is $11\frac{3}{16}$ centimeters. 70.3 cm

Match each circle described in the column on the left with its corresponding measurement in the column on the right.

9. radius: 8.5 units a — a. circumference: 53.4 units
10. diameter: 9 units c — b. circumference: 20.4 units
11. diameter: 6.5 units b — c. circumference: 28.3 units
12. radius: 12 units d — d. circumference: 75.4 units

13. SPORTS A baseball has a radius of about 1.5 inches. Home plate is 16 inches wide. If a baseball were rolled across home plate, how many complete rotations would it take to cover the distance? 2 complete rotations

14. SPORTS A soccer ball has a circumference of about 28 inches, while the goal is 24 feet wide. How many soccer balls would be needed to cover the distance between the goalposts? 33 soccer balls

15. HISTORY Chariot races reached their peak in popularity in ancient Rome around the 1st and 2nd centuries A.D. A chariot wheel had a radius of about one foot. One lap around the track in the Circus Maximus was approximately 2,300 feet. How many chariot-wheel revolutions did it take to complete one lap? about 366 revolutions

Chapter 11 45 Glencoe Pre-Algebra

Word Problem Practice
CRM p. 46 AL OL BL

NAME ______ DATE ______ PERIOD ______

11-7 Word Problem Practice

Circles and Circumference

1. TREES To protect an elm tree in your backyard, you need to attach gypsy moth caterpillar tape around the trunk. The tree has a diameter of 1.1 feet. What length of tape is needed? Round to the nearest tenth. 3.5 ft

2. SCIENCE The diameter of Earth at the equator is approximately 7926.41 miles. What is the circumference of Earth at the equator to the nearest mile? 24,901 mi

3. FENCING The local gasoline distributor just built a new storage tank. For safety reasons they need to enclose the tank within a circular fence. The radius of the tank is 6 feet and the walkway between the tank and the fence is 4 feet. How much fencing will they need to order to fence off the tank? Round to the nearest tenth. 62.8 ft

4. SEWING The diameter of a circular placemat is 15 inches. Devon wants to sew a border of lace around the placemat. If the lace he wants comes by the foot, how many feet of lace will he need to purchase? 4 ft

5. LANDSCAPING The courtyard below was designed for an apartment complex. The outer area will be covered with grass and is 5 yards wide. The inner circle is tiled and has a diameter of 10 yards. There will also be a fence around the courtyard 2 yards out from the outer circle.

a. The landscaper must order the fencing for the courtyard. How much should he order to the nearest tenth of a yard? 75.4 yd

b. The landscape architect has planned for a border to be placed around both circles. What is the minimum length of border needed for both circles if the border material is sold by the yard? 95 yd

Chapter 11 46 Glencoe Pre-Algebra

20. **CAROUSELS** The world's largest carousel in Spring Green, Wisconsin, has a diameter of 80 feet. How far does a rider travel on an outside horse after 10 revolutions? Round to the nearest foot. **2513 ft**

21. **FOUNTAINS** A circular fountain at a park has a radius of 4 feet. The mayor wants to build a fountain that is quadruple the radius of the current fountain. Find the circumference of the new fountain. Round to the nearest tenth. **100.5 ft**

22. **MOTORCYCLES** The world's largest rideable motorcycle travels one mile after about 272.5 rotations of a tire.

a. To the nearest tenth, how many feet does the motorcycle travel after one rotation of a tire? What does this measure represent? (*Hint*: 1 mile = 5280 feet) **19.4 ft; the circumference of the tire**

b. To the nearest tenth, how many feet tall are the tires? **6.2 ft**

Real-World Link

The world's largest rideable motorcycle is 20 feet 4 inches long and weighs 6500 pounds.

Source: *Guinness World Records*

23. **MULTIPLE REPRESENTATIONS** In this problem, you will investigate the relationship between the radius and circumference of a circle.

a. **TABULAR** Make a table of values like the one at the right. Find the circumference of a circle having each radius. Round to the nearest tenth.

Radius (in.)	Circumference (in.)
1	6.3 ■
2	12.6 ■
3	18.8 ■
4	25.1 ■
5	31.4 ■

b. **GRAPHICAL** Use your table to graph the circumference C of a circle as a function of the radius r. **See margin.**

c. **ANALYTICAL** Describe the slope of the graph. How is the slope related to the formula for finding circumference? **2π; Since the formula for the circumference of a circle, $C = 2\pi r$, is in the form of $y = mx$, 2π is the slope.**

24. **GEOLOGY** The Beaverhead Crater is the largest impact crater in the United States. If the circumference of the crater is about 188.5 kilometers, what is the diameter of the crater? **60 km**

25. **Sample answer: A glass with a diameter of 7 centimeters has a circumference of about 22.0 centimeters.**

H.O.T. Problems
Use **H**igher-**O**rder **T**hinking Skills

25. **OPEN ENDED** Find a circular object in your home. Measure the diameter and use that value to calculate the circumference. Use a tape measure to check your calculation.

26. **REASONING** A *variable* is a quantity with a value that changes. In the formula for the circumference of a circle, identify any variables. **Both C and d.**

27. **CHALLENGE** Three congruent circles are inside a rectangle as shown at the right. Which is greater, the length of the rectangle ℓ, or the circumference of one circle? Explain your reasoning.

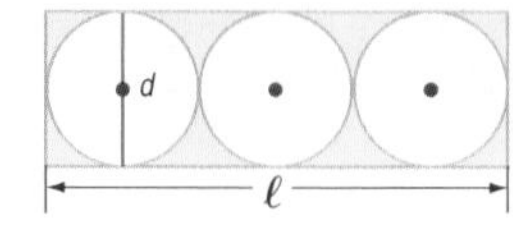

28. **REASONING** Explain why the formula $C = \pi d$ can be used to calculate the length of a circular bracelet. If the bracelet is opened up and laid out flat, can the same formula be used to find the length? Explain.

29. **WRITING IN MATH** Describe the relationship between circumference and radius. How does the circumference change if the radius is increased? How does the radius change if the circumference is decreased?

27. **Circumference of one circle; ℓ equals $3d$ and the circumference of one circle is approximately $3.14d$**

28. **As a circle, the bracelet has a diameter. So, its length is the circumference of the circle. When the bracelet is laid out flat, it has no diameter. So, the formula for the circumference of a circle cannot be used.**

29. **Circumference is 2π or about 6.3 times the radius. The circumference increases as the radius increases. The radius decreases as the circumference decreases.**

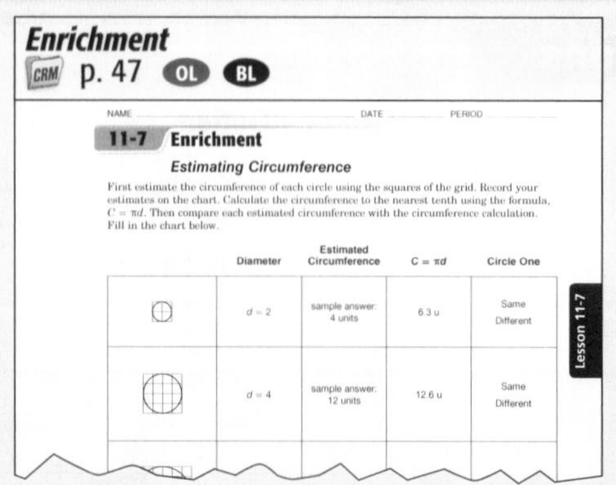
Enrichment
CRM p. 47 OL BL

NAME ______ DATE ______ PERIOD ______

11-7 Enrichment

Estimating Circumference

First estimate the circumference of each circle using the squares of the grid. Record your estimates on the chart. Calculate the circumference to the nearest tenth using the formula, $C = \pi d$. Then compare each estimated circumference with the circumference calculation. Fill in the chart below.

	Diameter	Estimated Circumference	$C = \pi d$	Circle One
	d = 2	sample answer: 4 units	6.3 u	Same Different
	d = 4	sample answer: 12 units	12.6 u	Same Different

Multiple Representations In Exercise 23, students create a table of values, a graph in the coordinate plane, and use verbal analysis to relate the slope of the graphed line to the ratio of the circumference of a circle to its radius.

Standardized Test Practice

30. A plate has a radius of 5 inches. Which equation could be used to find the circumference of the plate in inches? **C**

A $C = 2(10\pi)$
B $C = 5\pi$
C $C = 10\pi$
D $C = 2\pi$

31. A bicycle tire has a diameter of 24 inches. Find the circumference of the tire to the nearest tenth of an inch. **F**

F 75.4 in.
G 83.5 in.
H 87.9 in.
J 91.5 in.

32. A planter has a circumference of 37.6 inches. Which measure is *closest* to the diameter of the planter? **C**

A 10 in.
B 11 in.
C 12 in.
D 14 in.

33. EXTENDED RESPONSE The circle shown below has a diameter of 15 feet.

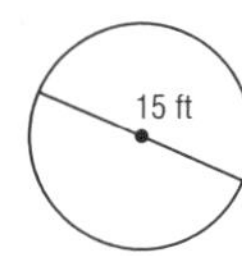

a. Write an expression to find the circumference of the circle. **15π**
b. What is the circumference to the nearest foot? **47 ft**

Spiral Review

Find the area of each figure described. (Lesson 11-6)

34. parallelogram: base, 10 yd; height 5 yd **50 yd^2**

35. trapezoid: height 3 ft; bases, 15 ft and 20 ft **52.5 ft^2**

Find the sum of the measures of the interior angles of each polygon. (Lesson 11-5)

36. triangle **180°** **37.** hexagon **720°** **38.** pentagon **540°**

39. INTERNET SHOPPING For every order submitted, an online bookstore charges a $5 shipping fee plus a charge of $2 per pound on the weight of the items being shipped. The total shipping charges y can be represented by $y = 2x + 5$, where x represents the weight of the order in pounds. Graph the equation. (Lesson 8-3) **See margin.**

40. ALGEBRA Solve $2x - 7 > 5x + 14$. (Lesson 5-5) **$x < -7$**

41. TOURS It costs $15 per person to take a tour of an underground cave. (Lesson 4-6)

a. Write an equation to determine the total cost for any number of people to take the tour. **$C = 15n$**

b. What is the total cost if 12 people take the tour? **$180**

Skills Review

Find each product. (Lesson 9-1)

42. $3.14 \cdot 4^2$ **50.24** **43.** $3.14 \cdot \left(\frac{14}{2}\right)^2$ **153.86** **44.** $3.14 \cdot (4.3)^2$ **58.0586**

4 ASSESS

Name the Math Have students tell what mathematical procedures they use to find the circumference of a circle with $r = 8$ cm, to the nearest tenth. 50.3 cm

Formative Assessment

Check for student understanding of Lessons 11-6 and 11-7.

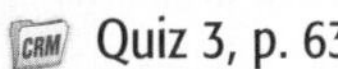

Additional Answers

23b. Sample answer:

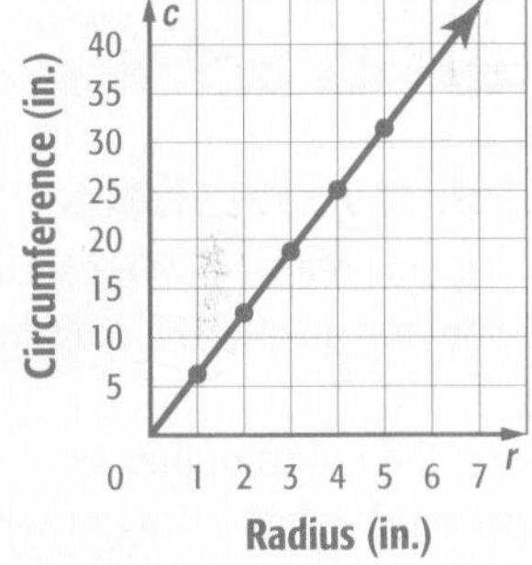

39.

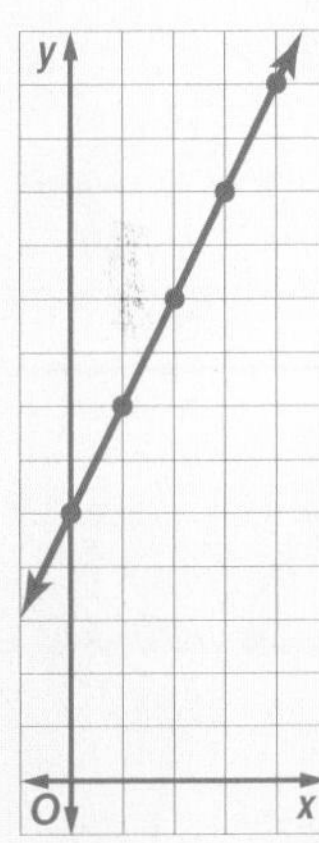

Differentiated Instruction

Extension Present students with the following problem: A landscape architect installed a 3-foot wide path around a circular garden. The radius of the garden is 4 feet. What is the outermost circumference of the path? Round to the nearest whole number. *Hint:* Draw and label a diagram to solve. 44 ft

11-8 Lesson Notes

1 FOCUS

Vertical Alignment

Before Lesson 11-8
Find the circumference of a circle.

Lesson 11-8
Find areas of circles. Find areas of sectors.

After Lesson 11-8
Find areas of composite figures.

2 TEACH

Scaffolding Questions

Have students read the *Why?* section of the lesson and answer the questions.

Ask:

- What is the radius of the trampoline? 8 feet
- What would be the area of one-fourth of the trampoline? about 50 square feet

11-8 Area of Circles

Then
You have already found the circumference of a circle. (Lesson 11-7)

Now
- Find areas of circles.
- Find areas of sectors.

New Vocabulary
sector
central angle

Math Online
glencoe.com
- Extra Examples
- Personal Tutor
- Self-Check Quiz
- Homework Help

Why?

The trampoline at the right has a diameter of 16 feet. The circular area is shown on the grid paper below.

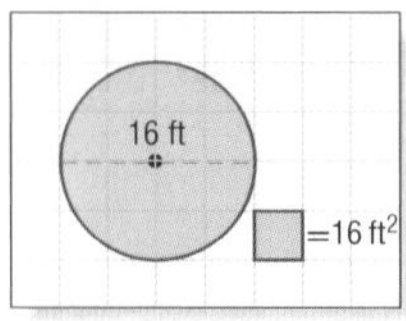

a. Approximately how many squares are shaded? **about 14 squares**

b. If one grid square represents 16 square feet, what is the approximate area of the trampoline? **about 224 ft^2**

Area of Circles A circle can be separated into parts and be arranged to form a figure that looks like a parallelogram.

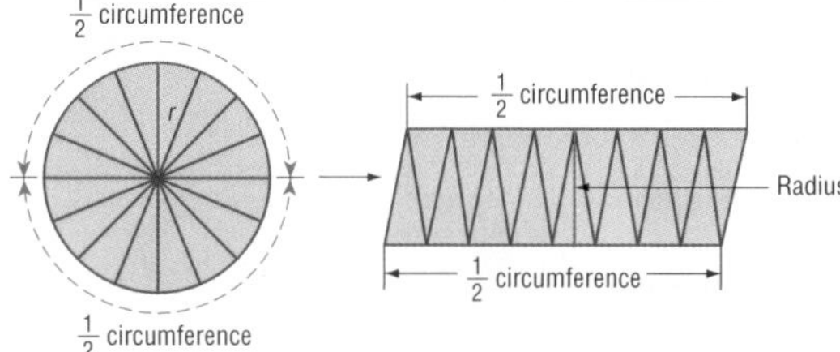

Since the areas of both figures are approximately the same, you can use the formula for the area of a parallelogram to find the area of a circle.

$A = bh$	**Area of a parallelogram**
$A = \left(\frac{1}{2} \times C\right)r$	**The base equals half the circumference of the circle; the height equals the radius of the circle.**
$A = \left(\frac{1}{2} \times 2\pi r\right)r$	**Replace C with $2\pi r$.**
$A = \pi \times r \times r$	**Simplify.**
$A = \pi r^2$	**Replace $r \times r$ with r^2.**

Key Concept — Area of a Circle *For Your FOLDABLE*

Words The area A of a circle in square units is $A = \pi r^2$, where r is the length of the radius.

Symbols $A = \pi r^2$

Model

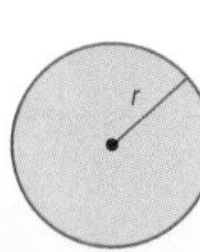

Lesson 11-8 Resources

Resource	Approaching-Level	On-Level	Beyond-Level	English Learners
Teacher Edition	• Differentiated Instruction, p. 638	• Differentiated Instruction, p. 638	• Differentiated Instruction, p. 641	
Chapter Resource Masters	• Study Guide and Intervention, pp. 48–49 • Skills Practice, p. 50 • Practice, p. 51 • Word Problem Practice, p. 52	• Study Guide and Intervention, pp. 48–49 • Skills Practice, p. 50 • Practice, p. 51 • Word Problem Practice, p. 52 • Enrichment, p. 53	• Practice, p. 51 • Word Problem Practice, p. 52 • Enrichment, p. 53	• Study Guide and Intervention, pp. 48–49 • Skills Practice, p. 50 • Practice, p. 51
Transparencies	• 5-Minute Check Transparency 11-8	• 5-Minute Check Transparency 11-8	• 5-Minute Check Transparency 11-8	• 5-Minute Check Transparency 11-8
Other	• Study Notebook • Teaching Pre-Algebra with Manipulatives	• Study Notebook • Teaching Pre-Algebra with Manipulatives	• Study Notebook	• Study Notebook • Teaching Pre-Algebra with Manipulatives

EXAMPLE 1 Find Areas of Circles

Find the area of each circle. Round to the nearest tenth.

a.

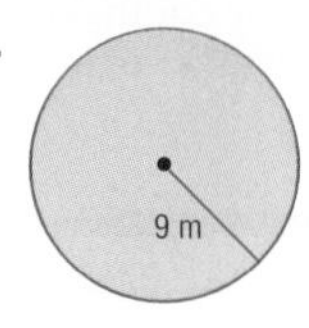

Estimate $A \approx 3 \cdot 9^2$ or 243

$A = \pi r^2$	Area of a circle
$= \pi \cdot 9^2$	Replace r with 9.
$= \pi \cdot 81$	Evaluate 9^2.
≈ 254.5	Use a calculator.

Check $254.5 \approx 243$ ✓

The area is about 254.5 m^2.

b.

15 ft

Estimate $A \approx 3 \cdot 8^2$ or 192

$A = \pi r^2$	Area of a circle
$= \pi \cdot 7.5^2$	$r = \frac{15}{2}$ or 7.5
$= \pi \cdot 56.25$	Evaluate 7.5^2.
≈ 176.7	Use a calculator.

Check $176.7 \approx 192$ ✓

The area is about 176.7 ft^2.

StudyTip

Estimation To estimate the area of a circle, multiply the square of the radius by 3.

Check Your Progress

1A.

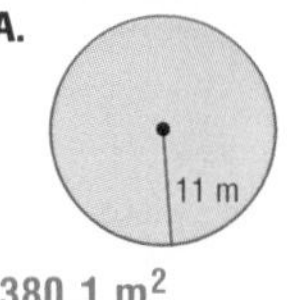

380.1 m^2

1B.

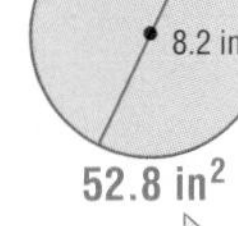

52.8 in^2

Personal Tutor glencoe.com

Real-World Link

The National Collegiate Athletic Association added women's hockey as a sanctioned sport in 1993. Women's ice hockey became an Olympic event in 1998. The U.S. team won the first gold medal.

Source: SportsKnowHow

Real-World EXAMPLE 2 Use Area of Circles to Solve Problems

HOCKEY A hockey rink is divided into three parts. The center part, called the *neutral zone*, is a rectangle with a center circle, as shown at the right. What is the area of the neutral zone around the center circle?

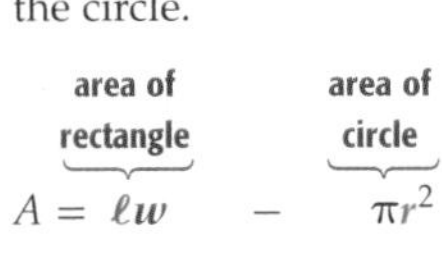

Find the area of the rectangle minus the area of the circle.

$$A = \underbrace{\ell w}_{\text{area of rectangle}} - \underbrace{\pi r^2}_{\text{area of circle}}$$

$= 85(54) - \pi(15)^2$	Replace ℓ with 85, w with 54, and r with 15.
$= 4590 - 225\pi$	Simplify.
≈ 3883.1	Use a calculator.

So, the area of the neutral zone around the circle is about 3883.1 square feet.

Check Your Progress

2. **HOCKEY** A *face-off circle* on a hockey rink is 30 feet across. At its center is a red spot 2 feet in diameter. What is the area of the face-off circle that is *not* red? Round to the nearest tenth. 703.7 ft^2

Personal Tutor glencoe.com

Area of Circles

Example 1 shows how to find the area of a circle. **Example 2** shows how to use the area of a circle to solve a real-world problem.

Formative Assessment

Use the Check Your Progress exercises after each example to determine students' understanding of concepts.

Additional Examples

1 Find the area of each circle. Round to the nearest tenth.

a.

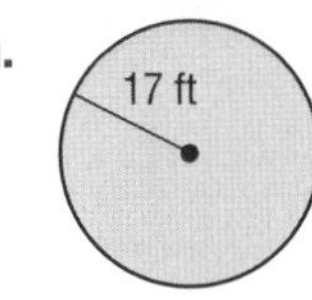

907.9 ft^2

b.

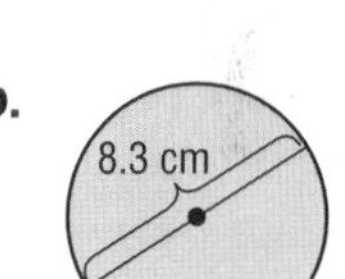

54.1 cm^2

2 **PICTURE FRAMES** The rectangular matting for a picture frame has a circular cutout for the photograph, as shown in the figure. What is the area of the mat? Round to the nearest tenth.

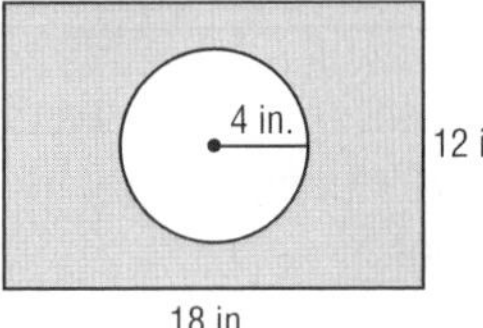

about 165.7 in^2

Additional Examples also in Interactive Classroom PowerPoint® Presentations

Focus on Mathematical Content

Units Students will often forget to write the units with their answers. Area is a product of two linear measurements, and the answer is in units squared. Circumference is a linear measurement, and the answer is a unit to the first power. Volume is a product of three linear measurements, and the answer is in units cubed.

Area of Sectors

Example 3 shows how to find the area of a sector.

Additional Example

3 Find the area of the shaded sector in the circle below. Round to the nearest tenth.

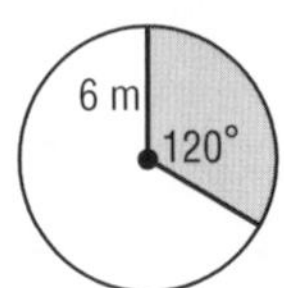

about 37.7 m^2

Tips for New Teachers

Explain to students that a sector is part of a circle. The formula for area is arranged to calculate the portion of the circle that the sector occupies, hence $\frac{N}{360}$ appears before πr^2.

TEACH with TECH

INTERACTIVE WHITEBOARD Have different students work through the same example using different approximations of π. Then have students share their solutions and discuss the differences in their answers. Save the students' work to hand out.

Tips for New Teachers

Proportions You can find the formula for the area of a sector by using a proportion.

$$\frac{\text{Degree measure of sector}}{\text{Degree measure of circle}} = \frac{\text{Area of sector}}{\text{Area of circle}}$$

$$\frac{N°}{360°} = \frac{A}{\pi r^2}$$

$$N° \cdot \pi r^2 = A \cdot 360°$$

$$\frac{N° \cdot \pi r^2}{360°} = A$$

So, $A = \frac{N°}{360°}(\pi r^2)$.

Area of Sectors The shaded region in the circle at the right is called a **sector**. Its area depends on the radius of the circle and on the measure of the central angle. A **central angle** is an angle with a vertex at the center of a circle and with sides that intersect the circle.

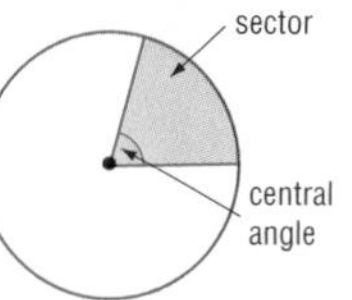

StudyTip

Units As with areas of circles, the area of a sector is given in square units.

Key Concept — Area of a Sector

For Your FOLDABLE

Words The area A of a sector is $\frac{N}{360}(\pi r^2)$, where N is the degree measure of the central angle of the circle and r is the radius.

Symbols $A = \frac{N}{360}(\pi r^2)$

EXAMPLE 3 Find the Area of a Sector

Find the area of the shaded sector in the circle at the right. Round to the nearest tenth.

$A = \frac{N}{360}(\pi r^2)$ — **Area of a sector**

$= \frac{90}{360}(\pi)(5^2)$ — **Replace N with 90 and r with 5.**

$= \frac{1}{4}(\pi)(25)$ — **Simplify.**

$\approx 19.6 \text{ cm}^2$ — **Use a calculator.**

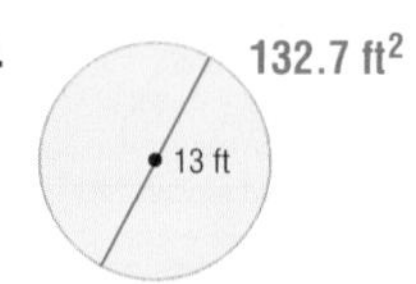

Check Your Progress

3. The diameter of a circle is 16 inches. It has a sector with a central angle of 120°. What is the area of the sector to the nearest tenth? **67.0 in^2**

Personal Tutor glencoe.com

Answers were computed using the π key on a calculator.

Check Your Understanding

Example 1 p. 637 — Find the area of each circle. Round to the nearest tenth.

1. **153.9 m^2** **2.** **12.6 yd^2** **3.** **132.7 ft^2**

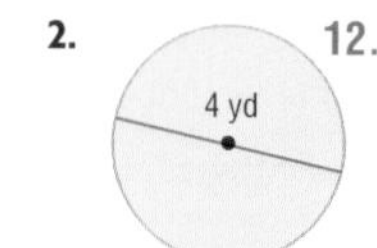

4. radius = 3.6 kilometers **40.7 km^2**

5. diameter = 10.5 centimeters **86.6 cm^2**

Example 2 p. 637

6. TRAMPOLINES Refer to the trampoline at the beginning of the lesson.

a. Find the area of the trampoline. Compare to the estimate. **201.1 ft^2**

b. The safety padding around the jumping surface is 1 foot wide. What is the area of the jumping surface? (*Hint*: Draw and label a diagram.) **153.9 ft^2**

Differentiated Instruction

AL OL

If students need more practice with finding the area of a sector of a circle,

Then have students draw a circle on grid paper to estimate the area of the sector in Example 3. Suggest that students use a compass set to the width of 5 units on the grid paper to draw the circle. Ask students how they might use this strategy to estimate the area of the sector in *Check Your Progress*.

Example 3 p. 638

Find the area of each shaded sector. Round to the nearest tenth.

7. 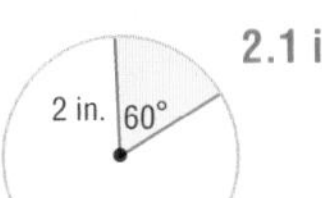

$2.1\ \text{in}^2$

8. 8 m, 270° $150.8\ \text{m}^2$

Practice and Problem Solving

= **Step-by-Step Solutions** begin on page R11.
Extra Practice begins on page 810.

Example 1 p. 637

Find the area of each circle. Round to the nearest tenth.

9. 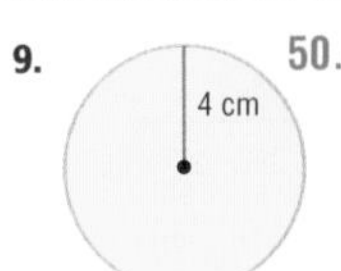

$50.3\ \text{cm}^2$

10. 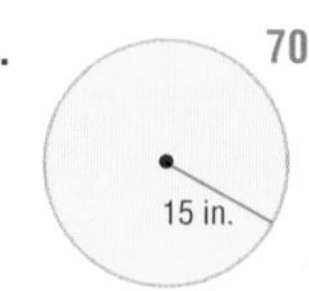

$706.9\ \text{in}^2$

11. 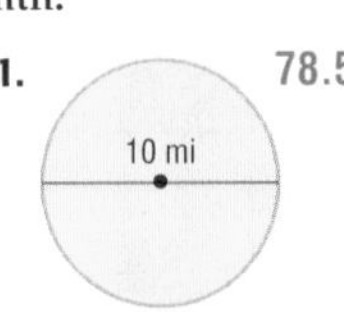

$78.5\ \text{mi}^2$

12. 17 ft $227.0\ \text{ft}^2$

13. 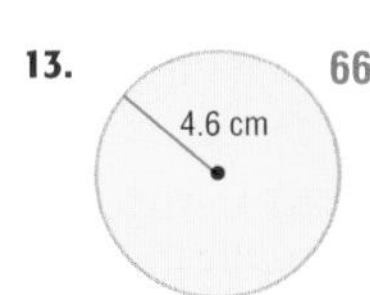

$66.5\ \text{cm}^2$

14. 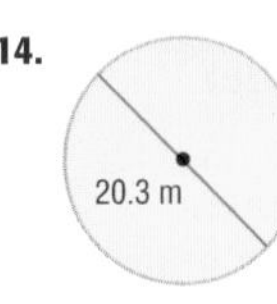

$323.7\ \text{m}^2$

15. radius = 9.6 feet $289.5\ \text{ft}^2$

16. diameter = 24.8 meters $483.1\ \text{m}^2$

17. diameter = $11\frac{1}{2}$ yards $103.9\ \text{yd}^2$

18. radius = $3\frac{2}{3}$ miles $42.2\ \text{mi}^2$

Example 2 p. 637

19. **LAWN CARE** Lauren has a sprinkler positioned in her lawn that directs a 12-foot spray in a circular pattern. About how much of the lawn does the sprinkler water if there is a rectangular flower bed 3 feet by 6 feet that is also in the path of the spray? Round to the nearest tenth. $434.4\ \text{ft}^2$

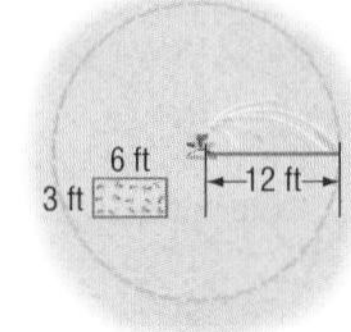

20. **CDS** What is the area of the CD shown at the right? Round to the nearest tenth. $111.3\ \text{cm}^2$

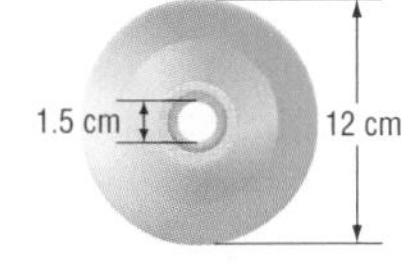

Example 3 p. 638

Find the area of each shaded sector. Round to the nearest tenth.

21. 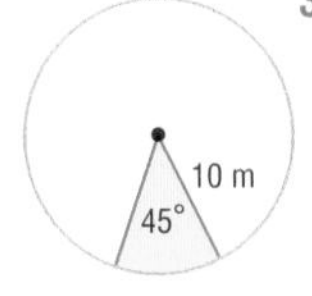

$39.3\ \text{m}^2$

22. 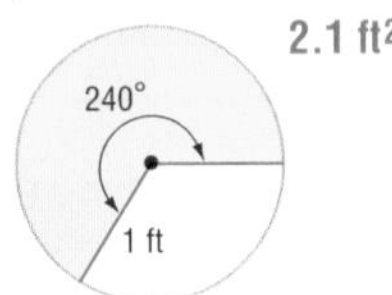

$2.1\ \text{ft}^2$

23. The diameter of a circle is 6 millimeters. It has a sector with a central angle of 72°. What is the area of the sector to the nearest tenth? $5.7\ \text{mm}^2$

24. The diameter of a circle is 11 yards. It has a sector with a central angle of 20°. What is the area of the sector to the nearest tenth? $5.3\ \text{yd}^2$

3 PRACTICE

Formative Assessment

Use Exercises 1–8 to check for understanding.

Use the chart at the bottom of this page to customize assignments for your students.

Differentiated Homework Options

Level	Assignment	Two-Day Option	
AL Basic	9–24, 32–33, 35–51	9–23 odd, 37–40	10–24 even, 32–33, 35–36, 41–51
OL Core	9–25 odd, 26, 27–31 odd, 35–51	9–24, 37–40	25–33, 35–36, 41–51
BL Advanced	25–47 (optional: 48–51)		

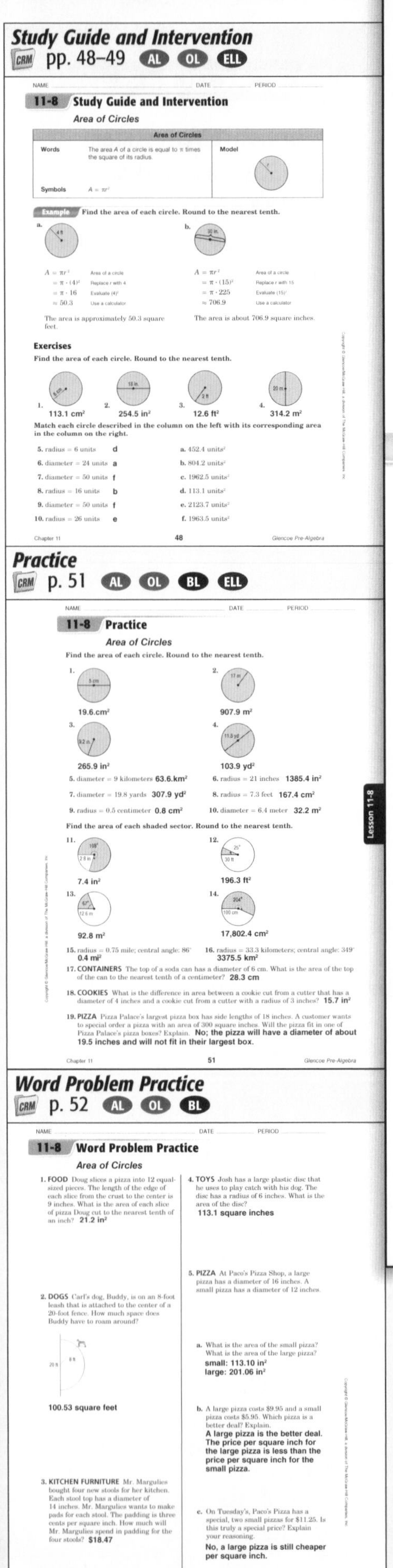
Study Guide and Intervention
CRM pp. 48–49 AL OL ELL

NAME ______ DATE ______ PERIOD ______

11-8 Study Guide and Intervention

Area of Circles

Area of Circles		
Words	The area A of a circle is equal to π times the square of its radius.	Model
Symbols	$A = \pi r^2$	

Example Find the area of each circle. Round to the nearest tenth.

a. (4 ft)

$A = \pi r^2$ Area of a circle
$= \pi \cdot (4)^2$ Replace r with 4
$= \pi \cdot 16$ Evaluate $(4)^2$
≈ 50.3 Use a calculator

The area is approximately 50.3 square feet.

b. (30 in.)

$A = \pi r^2$ Area of a circle
$= \pi \cdot (15)^2$ Replace r with 15
$= \pi \cdot 225$ Evaluate $(15)^2$
≈ 706.9 Use a calculator

The area is about 706.9 square inches.

Exercises

Find the area of each circle. Round to the nearest tenth.

1. (6 cm) **113.1 cm²**
2. (18 in.) **254.5 in²**
3. (2 ft) **12.6 ft²**
4. (20 m) **314.2 m²**

Match each circle described in the column on the left with its corresponding area in the column on the right.

5. radius = 6 units **d** — a. 452.4 units²
6. diameter = 24 units **a** — b. 804.2 units²
7. diameter = 50 units **f** — c. 1962.5 units²
8. radius = 16 units **b** — d. 113.1 units²
9. diameter = 50 units **f** — e. 2123.7 units²
10. radius = 26 units **e** — f. 1963.5 units²

Chapter 11 48 Glencoe Pre-Algebra

Practice
CRM p. 51 AL OL BL ELL

NAME ______ DATE ______ PERIOD ______

11-8 Practice

Area of Circles

Find the area of each circle. Round to the nearest tenth.

1. (5 cm) **19.6.cm²**
2. (17 m) **907.9 m²**
3. (9.2 in.) **265.9 in²**
4. (11.5 yd) **103.9 yd²**
5. diameter = 9 kilometers **63.6.km²**
6. radius = 21 inches **1385.4 in²**
7. diameter = 19.8 yards **307.9 yd²**
8. radius = 7.3 feet **167.4 cm²**
9. radius = 0.5 centimeter **0.8 cm²**
10. diameter = 6.4 meter **32.2 m²**

Find the area of each shaded sector. Round to the nearest tenth.

11. (108°, 2.8 in.) **7.4 in²**
12. (25°, 30 ft) **196.3 ft²**
13. (67°, 12.6 m) **92.8 m²**
14. (204°, 100 cm) **17,802.4 cm²**
15. radius = 0.75 mile; central angle: 86° **0.4 mi²**
16. radius = 33.3 kilometers; central angle: 349° **3375.5 km²**
17. CONTAINERS The top of a soda can has a diameter of 6 cm. What is the area of the top of the can to the nearest tenth of a centimeter? **28.3 cm**
18. COOKIES What is the difference in area between a cookie cut from a cutter that has a diameter of 4 inches and a cookie cut from a cutter with a radius of 3 inches? **15.7 in²**
19. PIZZA Pizza Palace's largest pizza box has side lengths of 18 inches. A customer wants to special order a pizza with an area of 300 square inches. Will the pizza fit in one of Pizza Palace's pizza boxes? Explain. **No; the pizza will have a diameter of about 19.5 inches and will not fit in their largest box.**

Chapter 11 51 Glencoe Pre-Algebra

Word Problem Practice
CRM p. 52 AL OL BL

NAME ______ DATE ______ PERIOD ______

11-8 Word Problem Practice

Area of Circles

1. FOOD Doug slices a pizza into 12 equal-sized pieces. The length of the edge of each slice from the crust to the center is 9 inches. What is the area of each slice of pizza Doug cut to the nearest tenth of an inch? **21.2 in²**
2. DOGS Carl's dog, Buddy, is on an 8-foot leash that is attached to the center of a 20-foot fence. How much space does Buddy have to roam around? (20 ft, 8 ft) **100.53 square feet**
3. KITCHEN FURNITURE Mr. Margulies bought four new stools for her kitchen. Each stool top has a diameter of 14 inches. Mr. Margulies wants to make pads for each stool. The padding is three cents per square inch. How much will Mr. Margulies spend in padding for the four stools? **$18.47**
4. TOYS Josh has a large plastic disc that he uses to play catch with his dog. The disc has a radius of 6 inches. What is the area of the disc? **113.1 square inches**
5. PIZZA At Paco's Pizza Shop, a large pizza has a diameter of 16 inches. A small pizza has a diameter of 12 inches.
   a. What is the area of the small pizza? What is the area of the large pizza? **small: 113.10 in² large: 201.06 in²**
   b. A large pizza costs $9.95 and a small pizza costs $5.95. Which pizza is a better deal? Explain. **A large pizza is the better deal. The price per square inch for the large pizza is less than the price per square inch for the small pizza.**
   c. On Tuesday's, Paco's Pizza has a special, two small pizzas for $11.25. Is this truly a special price? Explain your reasoning. **No, a large pizza is still cheaper per square inch.**

Chapter 11 52 Glencoe Pre-Algebra

Lesson 11-8

B 25. Find the radius of a circle if its area is 50 square inches. Round to the nearest inch. **4 in.**

26. What is the diameter of a circle if its area is 35.6 square centimeters? Round to the nearest tenth. **6.7 cm**

27. **NATURE** The trunk of the General Sherman Tree in Sequoia National Park has a circumference of 102.6 feet. If the tree were cut down at the base, what would be the area of the cross section? **837.7 ft²**

Real-World Link

The General Sherman Tree in Sequoia National Park is nearly 275 feet tall and is estimated to be 2500 to 3000 years old.

Source: Illinois State University's Fell Arboretum

Find the distance around and the area of each figure. Round to the nearest tenth.

28. semicircle 29. semicircle 30. quarter circle

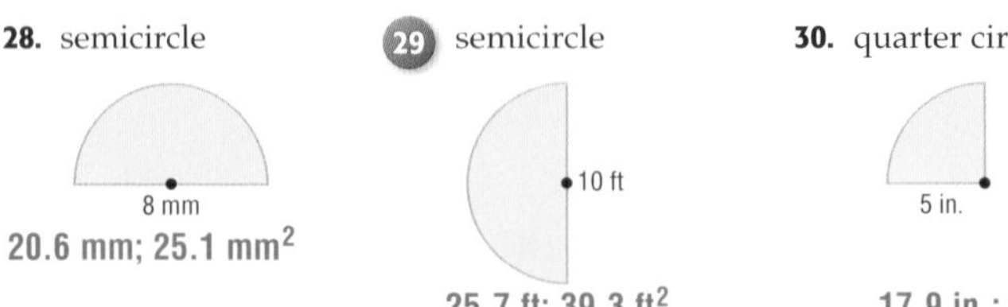

28. **20.6 mm; 25.1 mm²** 29. **25.7 ft; 39.3 ft²** 30. **17.9 in.; 19.6 in²**

31. **MULTIPLE REPRESENTATIONS** In this problem, you will investigate the area of a circle as the radius changes.

C

a. **TABULAR** Make a table like the one at the right. Find the area of each circle to the nearest tenth. **See margin.**

Radius (cm)	Area (cm²)
3	■
6	■
12	■
24	■
48	■

b. **ANALYTICAL** Describe how the area of a circle changes when the radius is doubled. **The area is multiplied by 4.**

c. **LOGICAL** Predict the area of a circle that has a radius of 96 centimeters. Explain your reasoning. Then verify your prediction by finding the area. **Sample answer: Since $96 = 48 \cdot 2$, the area should be $4 \cdot 7238.2$ or about 28,952.8 cm²; actual area ≈ 28,952.9 cm².**

H.O.T. Problems
Use Higher-Order Thinking Skills

32. **OPEN ENDED** Draw and label a circle that has an area between 800 square centimeters and 820 square centimeters. Label the length of the radius and state the area of the circle to the nearest tenth. **See margin.**

33. **WRITING IN MATH** Describe the difference between the circumference and area of a circle and explain how the formulas for circumference and area of a circle are related.

33. Circumference measures the distance around a circle and is given in units. Area measures the surface enclosed by the circle and is given in square units. The formulas for both measures involve π and the radius. The formula for circumference is $C = 2\pi r$ and the formula for area is $A = \pi r^2$.

34. **CHALLENGE** The radius of circle B is 2.5 times the radius of circle A. If the area of circle A is 8 square yards, what is the area of circle B? **50 yd²**

35. **REASONING** If the measures of the area and circumference of a circle have the same numerical values, what is the radius of the circle? Explain. **See margin.**

36. **WRITING IN MATH** Describe how you can find the area of a circle given the radius, diameter, or circumference. **See margin.**

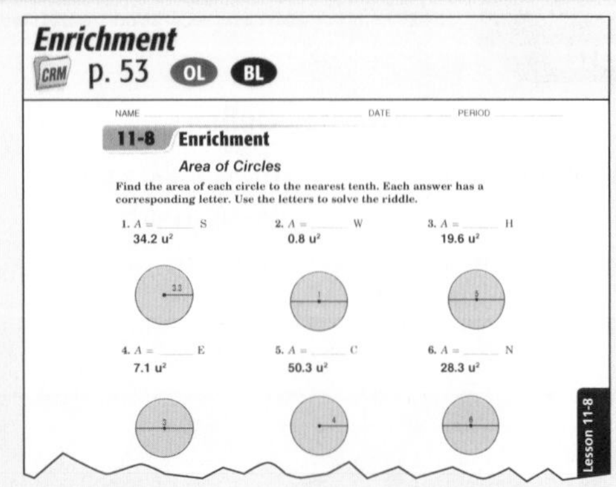
Enrichment
CRM p. 53 OL BL

NAME ______ DATE ______ PERIOD ______

11-8 Enrichment

Area of Circles

Find the area of each circle to the nearest tenth. Each answer has a corresponding letter. Use the letters to solve the riddle.

1. A = ____ S **34.2 u²** (3.3)
2. A = ____ W **0.8 u²** (1)
3. A = ____ H **19.6 u²** (5)
4. A = ____ E **7.1 u²** (3)
5. A = ____ C **50.3 u²** (4)
6. A = ____ N **28.3 u²** (6)

Lesson 11-8

Multiple Representations In Exercise 31, students use a table to show how the area of a circle changes when the radius is changed.

640 Chapter 11 Distance and Angle

Standardized Test Practice

37. Find the area of a circle with a diameter of 22 millimeters. Round to the nearest tenth. **A**

A 380.1 mm^2
B 319.5 mm^2
C 189.9 mm^2
D 69.1 mm^2

38. A sprinkler is set to cover the area shown. Find the area of the grass being watered if the sprinkler reaches a distance of 20 feet. **H**

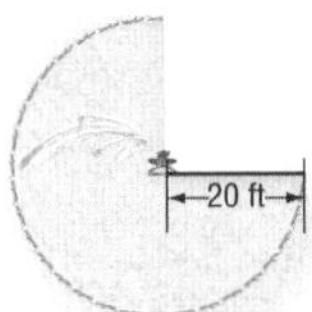

F 78.5 ft^2
G 314.2 ft^2
H 942.5 ft^2
J 1256.6 ft^2

39. The Blackwells have a circular pool with a radius of 10 feet. They want to install a 3–foot sidewalk around the pool. What will be the area of the walkway? **A**

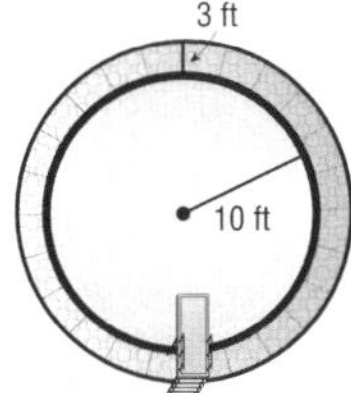

A 216.8 ft^2
B 285.9 ft^2
C 314.2 ft^2
D 442.2 ft^2

40. **EXTENDED RESPONSE** The area of a circle is 327.6 square centimeters.

a. Write an algebraic expression in terms of r that could be used to find the radius of the circle. $r = \sqrt{\frac{A}{\pi}}$

b. Find the radius to the nearest tenth. **10.2 cm**

Spiral Review

Find the circumference of each circle. Round to the nearest tenth. (Lesson 11-7)

41. radius: 8 in. **50.3 in.**

42. radius: 12.5 ft **78.5 ft**

43. diameter: 21 cm **66.0 cm**

Find the area of each figure. (Lesson 11-6)

44. **11 m^2**

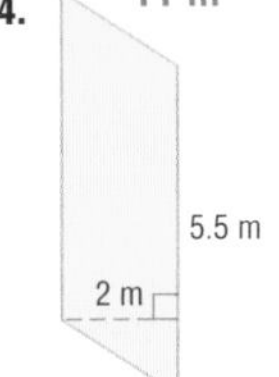

45. **90 cm^2**

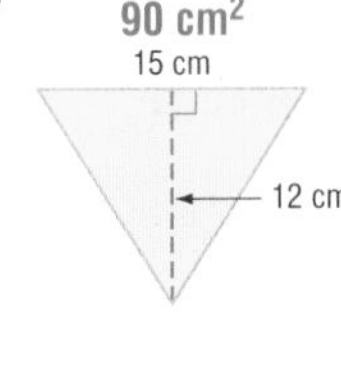

46. **25.9 in^2**

47. Find the product of $\frac{5}{9}$ and $\frac{8}{25}$. (Lesson 3-3) $\frac{8}{45}$

Skills Review

Find each sum. (Previous Course)

48. 211 + 23.9 **234.9**

49. 512.41 + 21.3 **533.71**

50. 587 + 65.9 **652.9**

51. 52.89 + 85.56 **138.45**

Differentiated Instruction

BL

Extension Give students the following problem: A sidewalk is in the shape of a half circle. It is 2 feet wide and 6 feet from one end to another. Find the area of the sidewalk. The total area of the circle is about 28.3 ft^2, so the area of the half circle is about 14.15 ft^2. The area of the cut-out circle is about 3.14 ft^2, because the radius is 1 ft, so the area of half the cut-out circle is about 1.57 ft^2. 14.15 ft^2 – 1.57 ft^2 = 12.58 ft^2

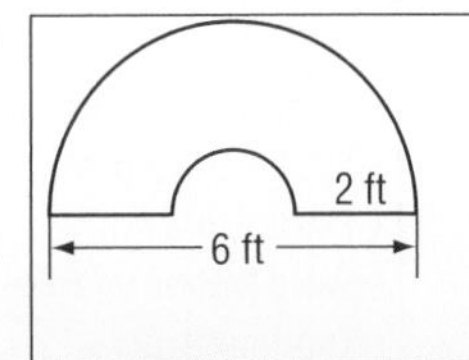

4 ASSESS

Crystal Ball Have students write how they think the concepts that they learned in this lesson will help with the next lesson on area of composite figures.

Additional Answers

31a.

Radius (cm)	Area (cm^2)
3	28.3
6	113.1
12	452.4
24	1809.6
48	7238.2

32. Sample answer:

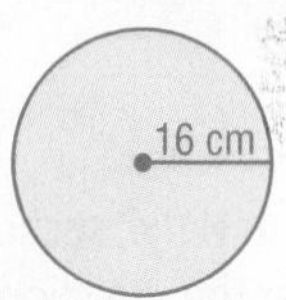

804.2 cm^2

35. 2 units; if $r = 2$, then $C = 2\pi(2)$ or 4π units and $A = \pi(2)^2$ or 4π units^2.

36. If you know the radius, substitute the value for r in $A = \pi r^2$. If you know the diameter, first divide by 2 to find the radius. Then substitute the value for r in $A = \pi r^2$. If you know the circumference, substitute the value for C in $C = 2\pi r$ and solve for r to find the radius. Then substitute the value for r in $A = \pi r^2$.

11-9 Lesson Notes

1 FOCUS

Vertical Alignment

Before Lesson 11-9
Find the areas of parallelograms, triangles, and trapezoids.

Lesson 11-9
Find the area of composite figures.
Solve problems involving the area of composite figures.

After Lesson 11-9
Find surface areas of regular polygons and composite figures.

2 TEACH

Scaffolding Questions

Have students read the *Why?* section of the lesson and answer the questions.

Ask:

- Can the flag be separated into different numbers of polygons? Explain. Yes; it could be separated into one triangle and two trapezoids or one triangle, two trapezoids, and one hexagon, for example.
- Would the area be the same if the figure was separated differently? Yes; the sum of the parts should be the same regardless of the number of the parts.

11-9 Area of Composite Figures

Then
You found the areas of parallelograms, triangles, and trapezoids. (Lesson 11-6)

Now
- Find the area of composite figures.
- Solve problems involving the area of composite figures.

New Vocabulary
composite figure

Math Online
glencoe.com
- Extra Examples
- Personal Tutor
- Self-Check Quiz
- Homework Help

Why?

The flag of Ohio is the only state flag that is not in the shape of a rectangle.

a. Name different polygons that make up the flag.

b. Describe how these polygons could be used to find the total area of the flag.

a–b. See Chapter 11 Answer Appendix.

Area of Composite Figures A **composite figure** is made up of two or more shapes. To find the area of a composite figure, decompose the figure into shapes with areas you know how to find. Then find the sum of those areas.

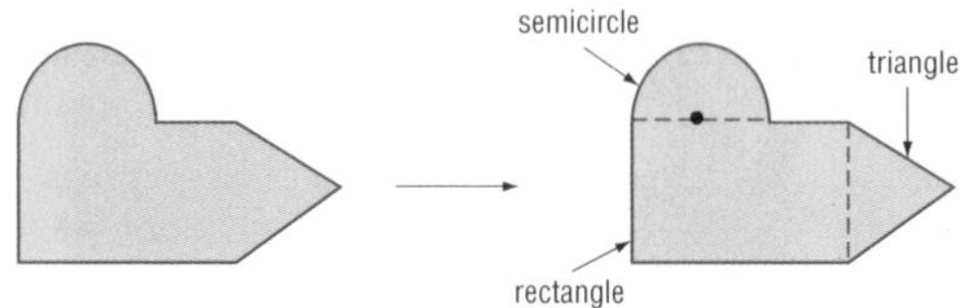

EXAMPLE 1 Find the Area of Composite Figures

Find the area of the composite figure.

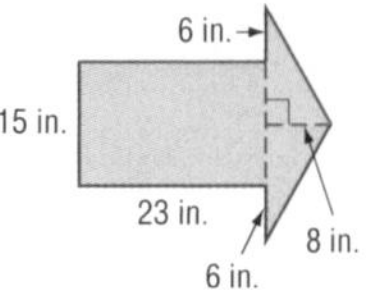

Separate the figure into a rectangle and a triangle. Find the sum of the areas of the figures.

$A = bh$	**Area of a rectangle**	$A = \frac{1}{2}bh$	**Area of a triangle**
$= 15 \cdot 23$	**$b = 15$ and $h = 23$**	$= \frac{1}{2} \cdot 27 \cdot 8$	**$b = 6 + 15 + 6$ or 27 and $h = 8$**
$= 345$	**Simplify.**	$= 108$	**Simplify.**

The area of the composite figure is 345 + 108 or 453 square inches.

Check Your Progress

Find the area of each composite figure. Round to the nearest tenth, if necessary.

1A. 6 mm, 16 mm — 62.1 mm^2

1B. 17 ft, 9 ft, 8 ft, 10 ft — 193 ft^2

Personal Tutor glencoe.com

Lesson 11-9 Resources

Resource	Approaching-Level	On-Level	Beyond-Level	English Learners
Teacher Edition		• Differentiated Instruction, p. 643	• Differentiated Instruction, p. 647	
Chapter Resource Masters	• Study Guide and Intervention, pp. 54–55 • Skills Practice, p. 56 • Practice, p. 57 • Word Problem Practice, p. 58	• Study Guide and Intervention, pp. 54–55 • Skills Practice, p. 56 • Practice, p. 57 • Word Problem Practice, p. 58 • Enrichment, p. 59	• Practice, p. 57 • Word Problem Practice, p. 58 • Enrichment, p. 59	• Study Guide and Intervention, pp. 54–55 • Skills Practice, p. 56 • Practice, p. 57
Transparencies	• 5-Minute Check Transparency 11-9	• 5-Minute Check Transparency 11-9	• 5-Minute Check Transparency 11-9	• 5-Minute Check Transparency 11-9
Other	• Study Notebook • Teaching Pre-Algebra with Manipulatives	• Study Notebook • Teaching Pre-Algebra with Manipulatives	• Study Notebook	• Study Notebook • Teaching Pre-Algebra with Manipulatives

Concept Summary — Area Formulas

For Your FOLDABLE

Parallelogram	Triangle	Trapezoid	Circle
$A = bh$	$A = \frac{1}{2}bh$	$A = \frac{1}{2}h(a + b)$	$A = \pi r^2$

Problem-Solving Tip

Solve a Simpler Problem Sometimes it is necessary to break a problem into parts. You can use colored pencils to shade each separate figure that makes up the composite figure a different color. Find the area of each part, then combine the solutions of the parts.

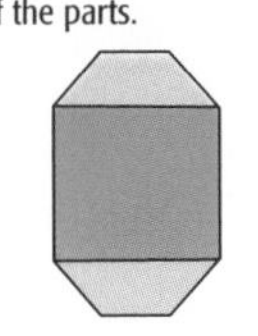

Solve Problems Involving Area Often the first step in a multi-step problem is to find the area of a composite figure.

Real-World EXAMPLE 2 Solve Multi-Step Problems

CONSTRUCTION A ceiling tile covers 3 square feet. How many tiles are needed to cover the octagonal ceiling shown at the right?

Understand You know the area of one ceiling tile and the dimensions of the ceiling.

Plan First, find the area of the ceiling by separating the figure into a rectangle and two trapezoids. Then, find the number of ceiling tiles.

Solve

$A = \frac{1}{2}h(a + b)$ — **Area of a trapezoid**

$= \frac{1}{2}(5)(10 + 18)$ — **$h = 5, a = 10, b = 18$**

$= 70$ — **Simplify.**

The area of both trapezoids is $70 \cdot 2$ or 140 square feet.

$A = bh$ — **Area of a rectangle**

$= 18 \cdot 20$ — **$b = 18, h = 20$**

$= 360$ — **Simplify.**

The total area of the ceiling is 360 + 140 or 500 square feet.

Each ceiling tile covers 3 square feet, so the total number of tiles needed is $500 \div 3 \approx 166.7$, or about 167 tiles.

Check The area of the figure should be a little less than the area of a rectangle that is 30 feet by 18 feet. Since the area of a 30-by-18-foot rectangle is 540 square feet, the answer of 500 square feet is reasonable.

StudyTip

Estimate Area One way to estimate the area of a composite figure is to draw a rectangle around the figure, as shown below. The area of the figure should be slightly less than the area of the rectangle.

Check Your Progress

2. **REMODELING** The L-shaped counter shown is to be replaced with a new countertop that costs \$52 per square foot. What will be the cost of the new countertop? **\$2340**

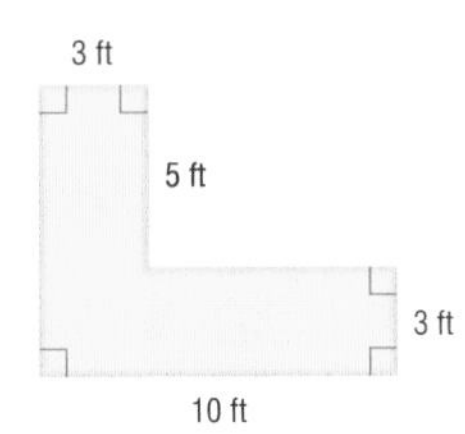

Personal Tutor glencoe.com

Area of Composite Figures

Example 1 shows how to find the area of composite figures.

Formative Assessment

Use the Check Your Progress exercises after each example to determine students' understanding of concepts.

Additional Example

1. Find the area of the composite figure. Round to the nearest tenth if necessary. 11.1 in²

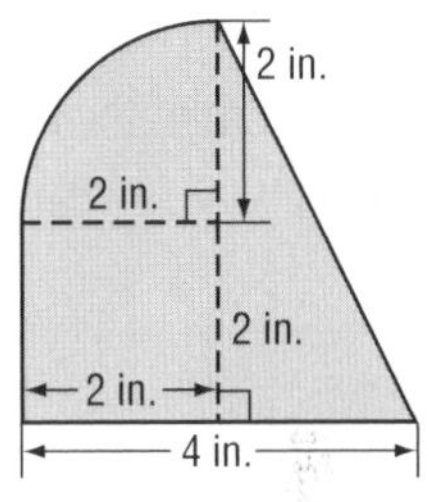

Additional Examples also in Interactive Classroom PowerPoint® Presentations

IWB INTERACTIVE WHITEBOARD READY

Solve Problems

Example 2 shows how to use the area of a composite figure to solve a real-world problem.

Additional Example

2. **CARPETING** Carpeting costs \$2 per square foot. How much will it cost to carpet the area shown? \$466

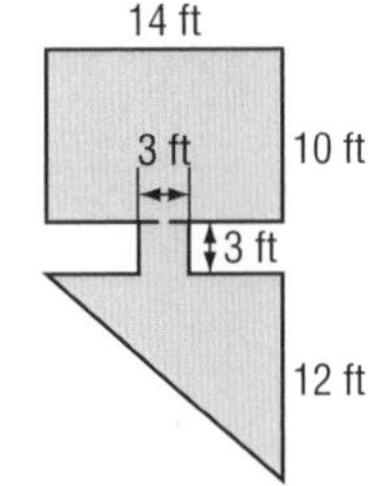

Differentiated Instruction

Interpersonal Have students work in pairs or teams to separate one of the fifty states or a Canadian province into polygons to estimate the area of the state or province. Team members should decide what polygons they might use to estimate the area. Have simple outline maps with scales or have students get the information from the Internet. Students can estimate the area and check against real totals. Have teams share their strategies with the class.

TEACH with TECH

VIDEO RECORDING Have students, working in groups, create a video of how to find the area of a composite figure. Show videos to the class and discuss the different approaches used.

3 PRACTICE

Formative Assessment

Use Exercises 1–5 to check for understanding.

Use the chart at the bottom of the next page to customize assignments for your students.

Check Your Understanding

Example 1 p. 642

Find the area of each figure. Round to the nearest tenth, if necessary.

1. 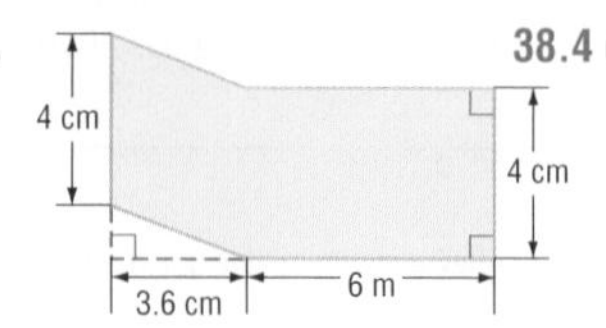

38.4 cm²

2. 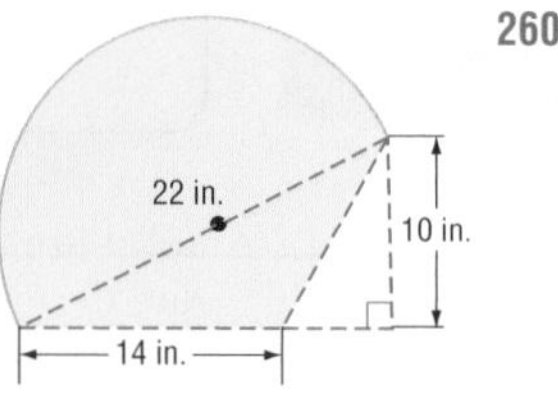

260.1 in²

3. 5 cm, 5.7 cm, 3 cm, 2.8 cm
18.9 cm²

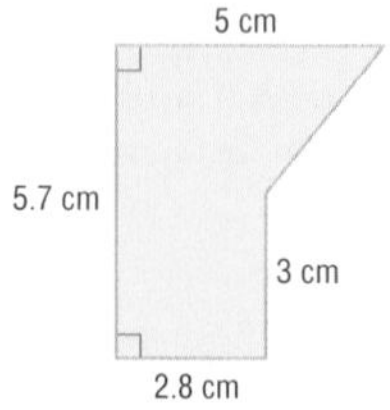

4. 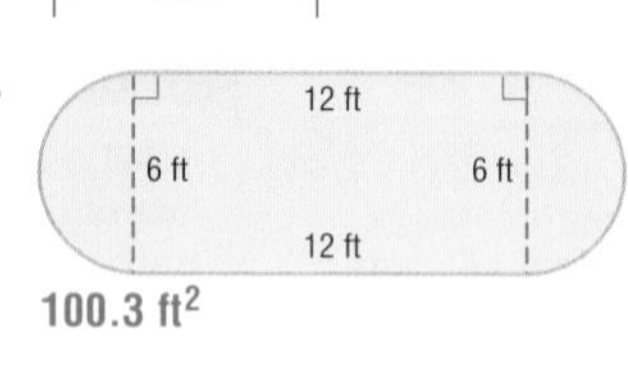

100.3 ft²

Example 2 p. 643

5. **LANDSCAPING** The Jamesons hired a landscaper to brick their walkway. One case of bricks costs $25 and covers 6 square feet.

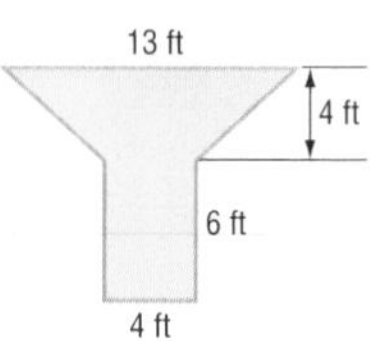

   a. What is the area of the walkway? 58 ft²

   b. How many cases are needed to cover the walkway with bricks? What would be the cost? 10 cases; $250

Answers were computed using the π key on a calculator.

Practice and Problem Solving

= **Step-by-Step Solutions** begin on page R11.
Extra Practice begins on page 810.

Example 1 p. 642

Find the area of each figure. Round to the nearest tenth, if necessary.

6. 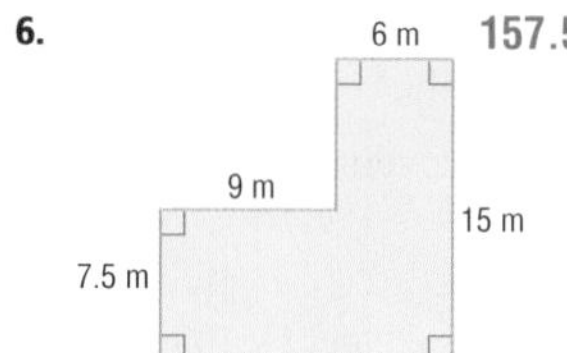

157.5 m²

7. 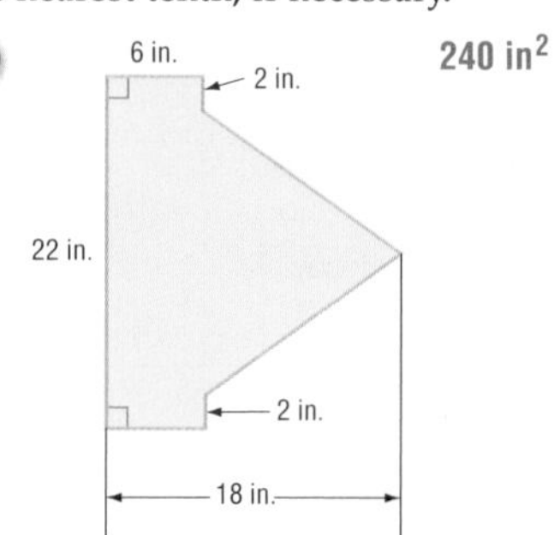

240 in²

8. 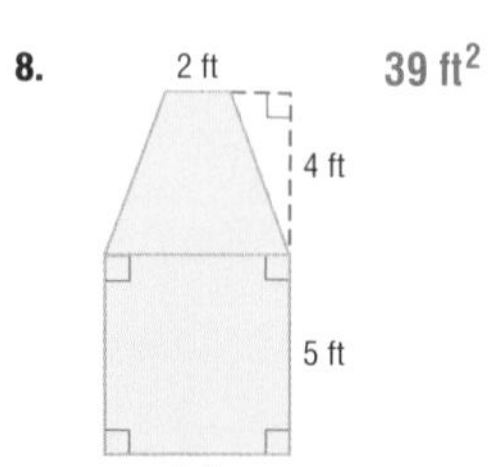

39 ft²

9. 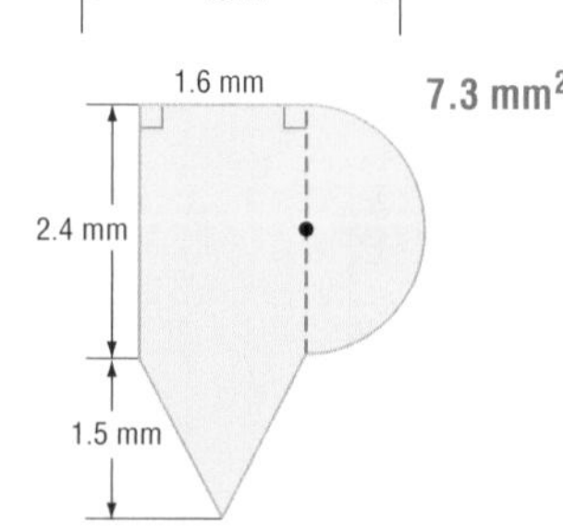

7.3 mm²

ReadingMath

Composite Figures Composite figures are also sometimes called *complex figures* or *irregular figures*.

Find the area of each figure. Round to the nearest tenth, if necessary.

10. **153.3 in²**

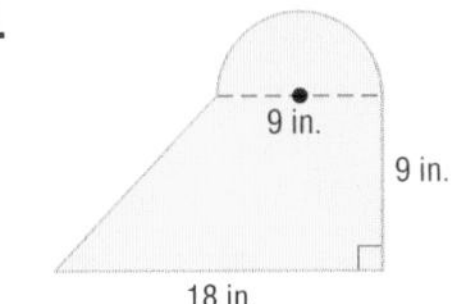

11. **257.1 ft²**

20 ft
20 ft

Example 2 p. 643

12. **POOLS** Refer to the swimming pool shown at the right.

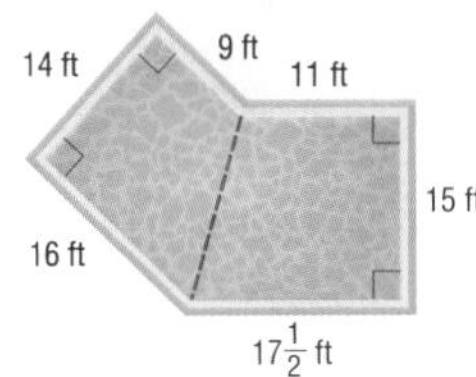

a. What is the area of the pool's floor? **388.75 ft²**

b. A pool cover costs $1.70 per square foot. How much would a cover for the pool cost? **$660.88**

13. **FINANCIAL LITERACY** Mr. Reyes wants to carpet his family room.

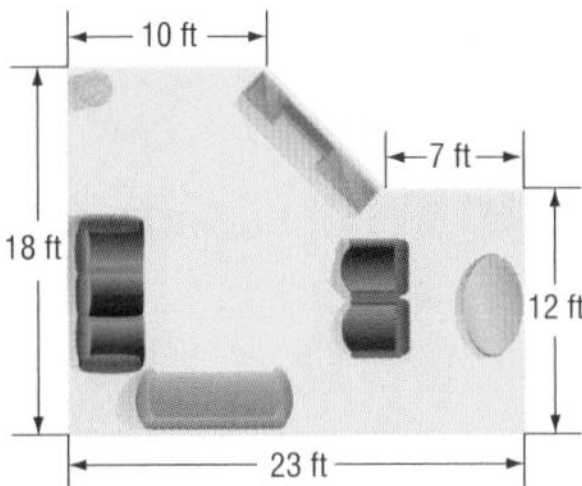

a. What is the area of the space to be carpeted? **354 ft²**

b. If carpet costs $2.25 per square foot, how much would it cost to carpet Mr. Reyes' family room if there is no leftover carpet? **$796.50**

14. What is the area, to the nearest tenth, of a figure that is formed using a rectangle 10 feet long and 7 feet wide and a semicircle with a diameter of 7 feet? **89.2 ft²**

15. A figure is formed using a semicircle and a triangle that has a base of 8 inches and a height of 12 inches. Find the area of each figure to the nearest tenth.

a. The diameter of the semicircle equals the base of the triangle. **73.1 in²**

b. The diameter of the semicircle equals the height of the triangle. **104.5 in²**

16. **CARPENTRY** Mr. Reyes wants to put ceiling molding in the room described in Exercise 13. How many feet of molding will he need? Round to the nearest tenth. **78.5 ft**

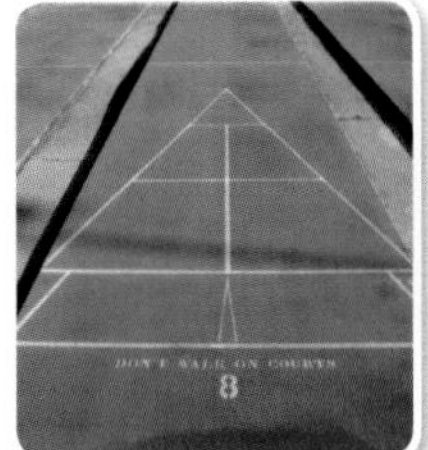

Real-World Link

A shuffleboard court is 52 feet long and 6 feet wide. Each player uses four discs to try to get 50, 75, or 100 points.

Source: Yahoo! Education

17 **SHUFFLEBOARD** Find the area of the part of the shuffleboard court shown. **35.25 ft²**

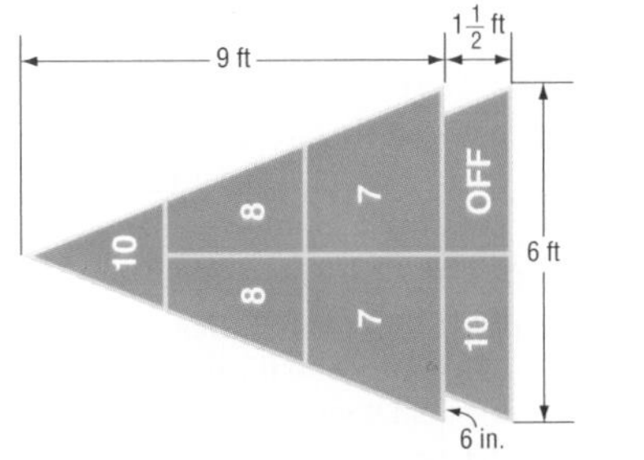

Focus on Mathematical Content

Area of Composite Shapes The area of a composite shape is the sum of its parts. A composite shape can be separated into polygons or other shapes whose areas can be calculated. The areas of the parts are then added together.

Differentiated Homework Options

Level	Assignment	Two-Day Option	
AL Basic	6–13, 23, 25–40	7–13 odd, 27–30	6–12 even, 23, 25, 26, 31–40
OL Core	7–13 odd, 14–19, 21–23, 25–40	6–13, 27–30	14–23, 25, 26, 31–40
BL Advanced	14–36 (optional: 37–40)		

Lesson 11-9 Area of Composite Figures 645

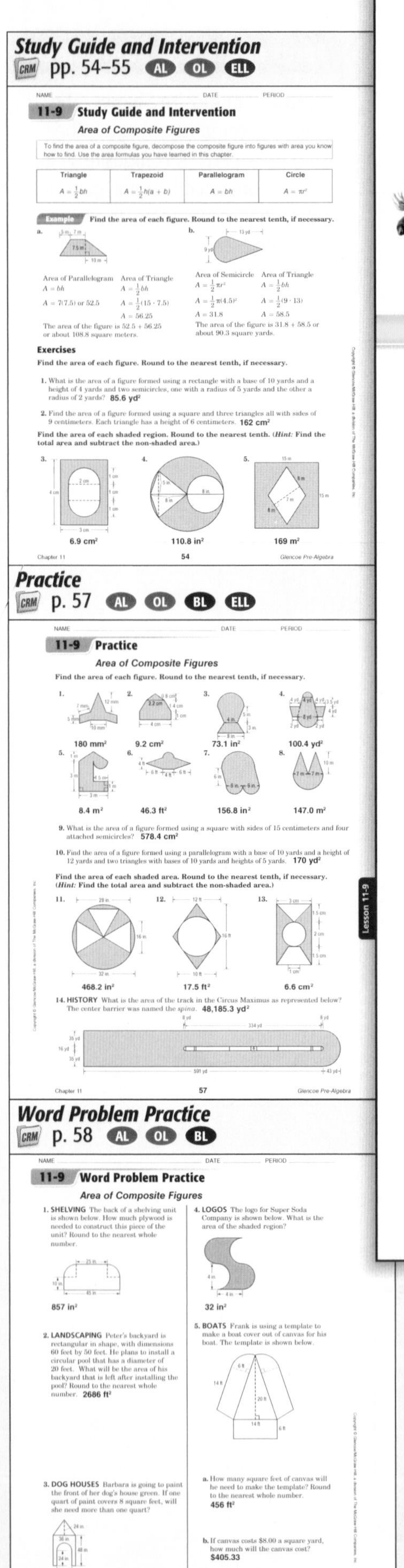
Study Guide and Intervention
CRM pp. 54–55 AL OL ELL

NAME DATE PERIOD

11-9 Study Guide and Intervention

Area of Composite Figures

To find the area of a composite figure, decompose the composite figure into figures with area you know how to find. Use the area formulas you have learned in this chapter.

Triangle	Trapezoid	Parallelogram	Circle
$A = \frac{1}{2}bh$	$A = \frac{1}{2}h(a + b)$	$A = bh$	$A = \pi r^2$

Example Find the area of each figure. Round to the nearest tenth, if necessary.

a. Area of Parallelogram $A = bh$, $A = 7(7.5)$ or 52.5; Area of Triangle $A = \frac{1}{2}bh$, $A = \frac{1}{2}(15 \cdot 7.5)$, $A = 56.25$. The area of the figure is 52.5 + 56.25 or about 108.8 square meters.

b. Area of Semicircle $A = \frac{1}{2}\pi r^2$, $A = \frac{1}{2}\pi(4.5)^2$, $A = 31.8$; Area of Triangle $A = \frac{1}{2}bh$, $A = \frac{1}{2}(9 \cdot 13)$, $A = 58.5$. The area of the figure is 31.8 + 58.5 or about 90.3 square yards.

Exercises

Find the area of each figure. Round to the nearest tenth, if necessary.

1. What is the area of a figure formed using a rectangle with a base of 10 yards and a height of 4 yards and two semicircles, one with a radius of 5 yards and the other a radius of 2 yards? **85.6 yd²**

2. Find the area of a figure formed using a square and three triangles all with sides of 9 centimeters. Each triangle has a height of 6 centimeters. **162 cm²**

Find the area of each shaded region. Round to the nearest tenth. (*Hint:* Find the total area and subtract the non-shaded area.)

3. **6.9 cm²** 4. **110.8 in²** 5. **169 m²**

Chapter 11 54 Glencoe Pre-Algebra

Practice
CRM p. 57 AL OL BL ELL

11-9 Practice

Area of Composite Figures

Find the area of each figure. Round to the nearest tenth, if necessary.

1. **180 mm²** 2. **9.2 cm²** 3. **73.1 in²** 4. **100.4 yd²**
5. **8.4 m²** 6. **46.3 ft²** 7. **156.8 in²** 8. **147.0 m²**

9. What is the area of a figure formed using a square with sides of 15 centimeters and four attached semicircles? **578.4 cm²**

10. Find the area of a figure formed using a parallelogram with a base of 10 yards and a height of 12 yards and two triangles with bases of 10 yards and heights of 5 yards. **170 yd²**

Find the area of each shaded region. Round to the nearest tenth, if necessary. (*Hint:* Find the total area and subtract the non-shaded area.)

11. **468.2 in²** 12. **17.5 ft²** 13. **6.6 cm²**

14. HISTORY What is the area of the track in the Circus Maximus as represented below? The center barrier was named the *spina*. **48,185.3 yd²**

Chapter 11 57 Glencoe Pre-Algebra

Word Problem Practice
CRM p. 58 AL OL BL

11-9 Word Problem Practice

Area of Composite Figures

1. SHELVING The back of a shelving unit is shown below. How much plywood is needed to construct this piece of the unit? Round to the nearest whole number. **857 in²**

2. LANDSCAPING Peter's backyard is rectangular in shape, with dimensions 60 feet by 50 feet. He plans to install a circular pool that has a diameter of 20 feet. What will be the area of his backyard that is left after installing the pool? Round to the nearest whole number. **2686 ft²**

3. DOG HOUSES Barbara is going to paint the front of her dog's house green. If one quart of paint covers 8 square feet, will she need more than one quart? **Yes; the area of front is 9.43 ft²**

4. LOGOS The logo for Super Soda Company is shown below. What is the area of the shaded region? **32 in²**

5. BOATS Frank is using a template to make a boat cover out of canvas for his boat. The template is shown below.

a. How many square feet of canvas will he need to make the template? Round to the nearest whole number. **456 ft²**

b. If canvas costs $8.00 a square yard, how much will the canvas cost? **$405.33**

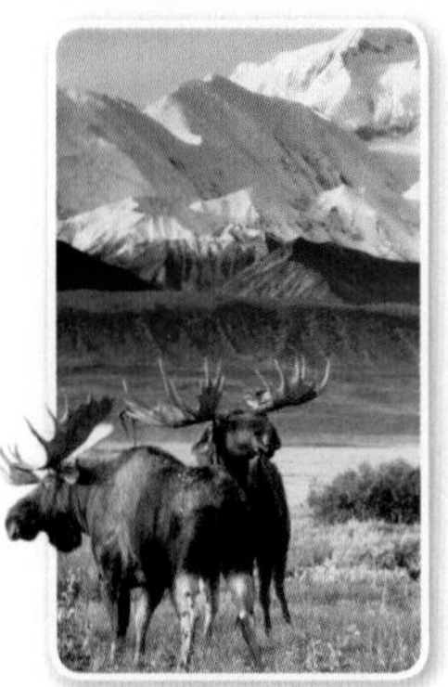

Real-World Link

The Denali National Park covers 6 million acres and contains Mt. McKinley, the highest mountain on the North American Continent. The park was originally named Mt. McKinley National Park in 1917.

18. NATURE A diagram of the Denali National Park Wilderness area in Alaska is shown at the right.

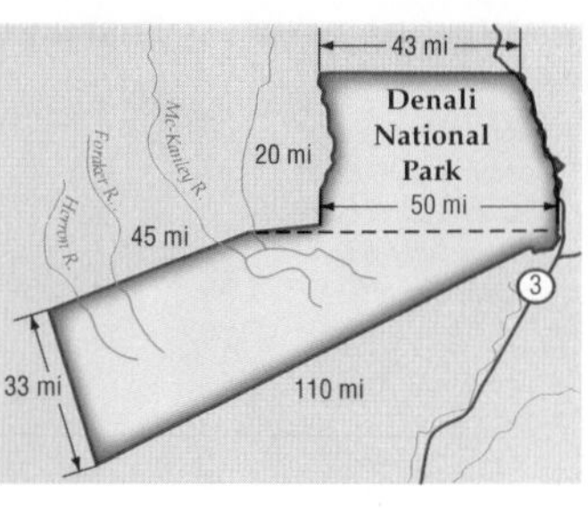

a. Describe how the irregular shape can be separated into polygons to find its area. **It can be separated into two trapezoids.**

b. Estimate the number of square miles contained in the Denali National Park Wilderness area. **3487.5 mi²**

c. Estimate the perimeter of the Wilderness area. **Sample answer: 271 mi**

C

Find the area of each shaded region. Round to the nearest tenth, if necessary.

19.

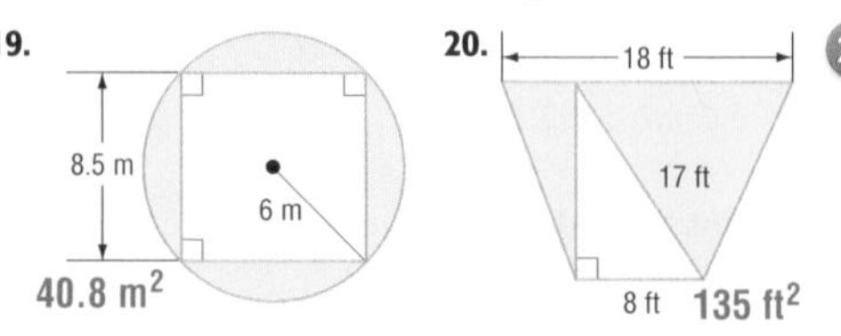

40.8 m²

20. **135 ft²**

21.

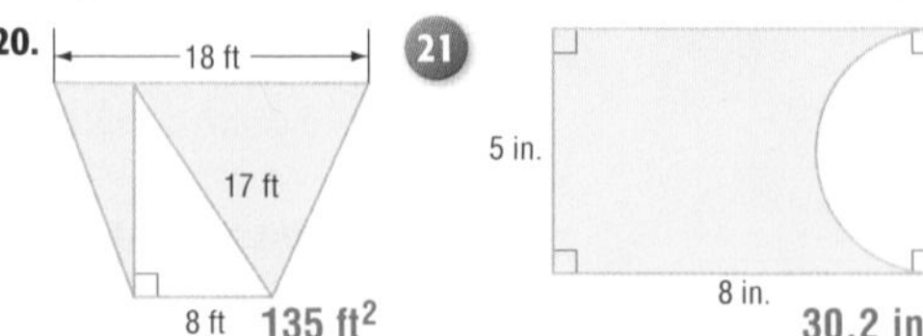

30.2 in²

22. MULTIPLE REPRESENTATIONS In this problem, you will investigate areas of composite figures.

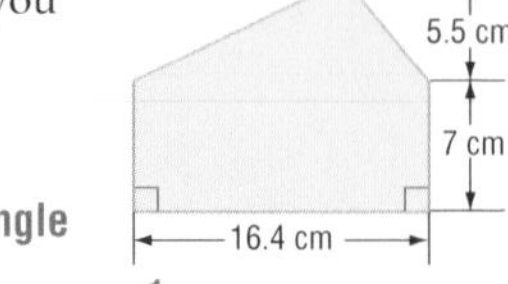

a. **VERBAL** Describe the figure using names of geometric figures whose areas you can find. **rectangle, triangle**

b. **SYMBOLIC** List the formulas that you can use to find the area of the composite figure. $A = \ell w$, $A = \frac{1}{2}bh$

c. **ANALYTICAL** Make a conjecture about how the area of the composite figure changes if each dimension given is doubled. Then test your conjecture by doubling the dimensions and finding the area. **The area is multiplied by 4. Original area: 159.9 cm²; New area: 639.6 cm²**

H.O.T. Problems
Use Higher-Order Thinking Skills

23. OPEN ENDED Describe real-life composite figures whose areas can be found by separating the figures into geometric figures that have area formulas. **Sample answer: states, parks, shopping malls**

24. CHALLENGE Reena created the flower at the right by placing semicircles around a regular pentagon. Using the measurements shown, find the area of the flower. Round to the nearest tenth. **Sample answer: 58.8 in²**

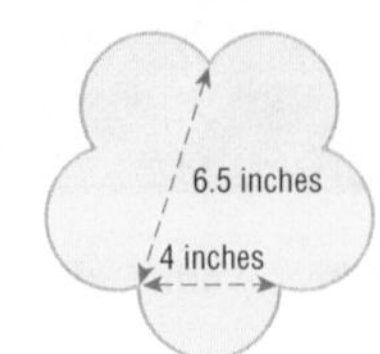

25. REASONING Suppose a composite figure has a curved side that is not a semicircle. Describe how you could estimate the area. **Sample answer: Use polygons to approximate the shape of the curved side.**

26. WRITING IN MATH Describe how circles and polygons help you find the area of a composite figure. Give an example by drawing and labeling a composite figure. Describe the figures that can be used to find the area and then find the area. **See margin.**

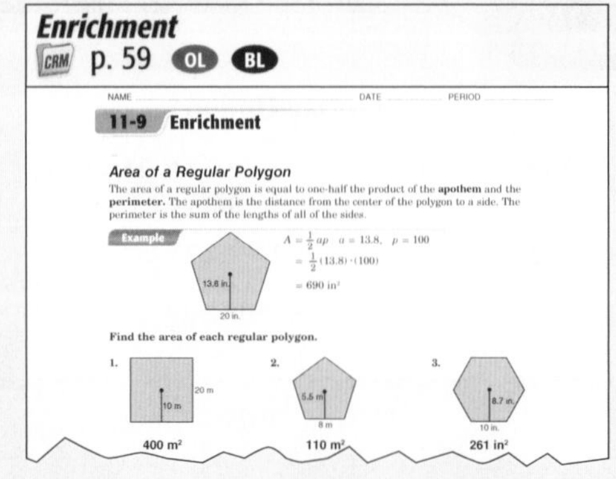
Enrichment
CRM p. 59 OL BL

11-9 Enrichment

Area of a Regular Polygon

The area of a regular polygon is equal to one-half the product of the **apothem** and the **perimeter**. The apothem is the distance from the center of the polygon to a side. The perimeter is the sum of the lengths of all of the sides.

Example $A = \frac{1}{2}ap$, $a = 13.8$, $p = 100$; $= \frac{1}{2}(13.8)\cdot(100)$; $= 690$ in²

Find the area of each regular polygon.

1. **400 m²** 2. **110 m²** 3. **261 in²**

Multiple Representations In Exercise 22, students describe a composite figure by identifying its component shapes verbally, listing the area formulas for the component shapes in mathematical symbols, and testing a conjecture about how the area of the figure will change with a change in the scale of the dimensions.

Standardized Test Practice

27. **GRIDDED RESPONSE** In the diagram, a patio that is 4 feet wide surrounds a swimming pool. What is the area of the patio in square feet? Round to the nearest tenth. **429.7**

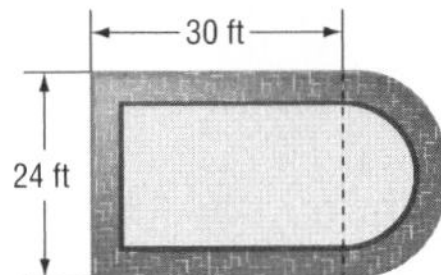

28. Find the area of the shaded region. Use 3.14 for π. Round to the nearest hundredth. **C**

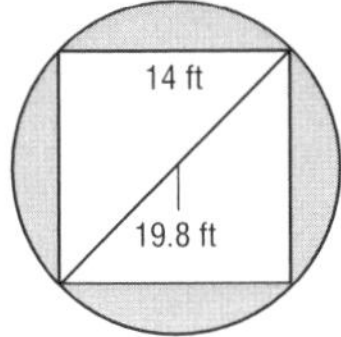

A 392.04 ft^2 C 111.75 ft^2
B 503.75 ft^2 D 258.17 ft^2

29. The Lin family is buying a cover for their swimming pool shown below. The cover costs \$3.19 per square foot. How much will the cover cost? **J**

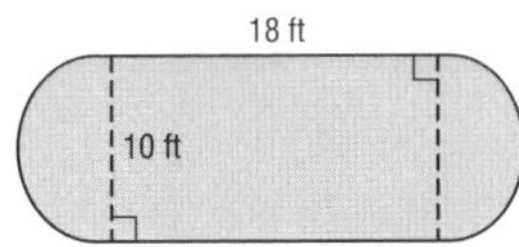

F \$219.27 H \$699.47
G \$258.54 J \$824.74

30. Using the floor plan below, find the difference between the areas of each bedroom. **B**

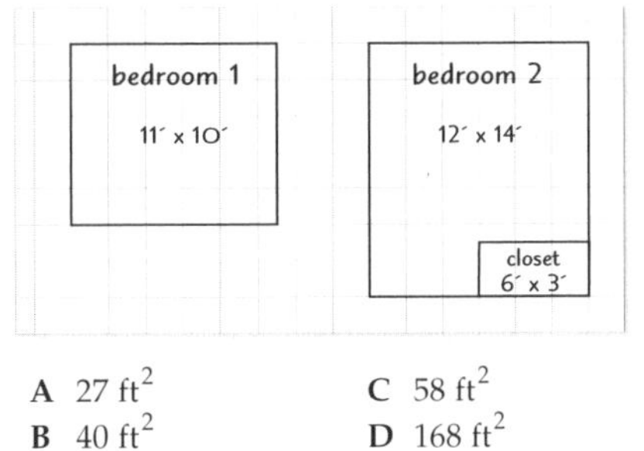

A 27 ft^2 C 58 ft^2
B 40 ft^2 D 168 ft^2

Spiral Review

Find the circumference and area of each circle. Round to the nearest tenth. (Lessons 11-7 and 11-8)

31. radius 6 cm **37.7 cm; 113.1 cm²** 32. diameter $9\frac{1}{2}$ ft **29.8 ft; 70.9 ft²** 33. radius 20 in. **125.7 in.; 1256.6 in²**

Find the area of each figure described. (Lesson 11-6)

34. triangle: base, 9 in.; height, 6 in. **27 in²** 35. trapezoid: height, 3 cm; bases, 4 cm, 8 cm **18 cm²**

36. **CROSS COUNTRY** Jeremy can run $3\frac{1}{3}$ miles in 25 minutes. How many minutes would it take him to run 5 miles at this same rate? (Lesson 6-5) **37 min 30 s**

Skills Review

Classify each polygon according to its number of sides. (Lessons 11-5)

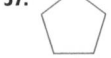

37.  **pentagon**

38. 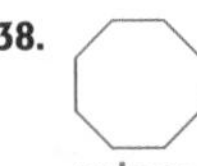 **octagon**

39. 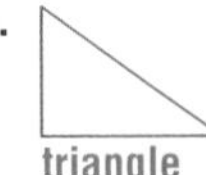 **triangle**

40.  **quadrilateral**

4 ASSESS

Yesterday's News Have students write a few sentences on how yesterday's lesson on finding the area of a circle helped them in today's lesson on finding the area of composite shapes.

Formative Assessment

Check for student understanding of concepts in Lessons 11-8 and 11-9.

CRM Quiz 4, p. 63

Additional Answer

26. You can use polygons and circles to find the area of a composite figure by finding the area of each individual figure and then adding the areas. Sample answer:

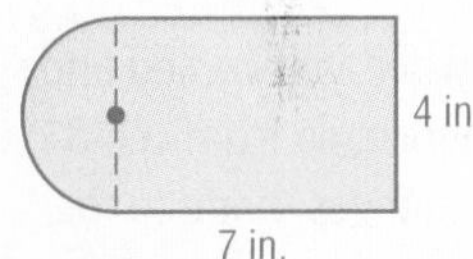

semicircle, rectangle; 34.3 in²

Differentiated Instruction

Extension Find the area of the shaded region in the figure shown. Round to the nearest tenth, if necessary.
10.3 m²

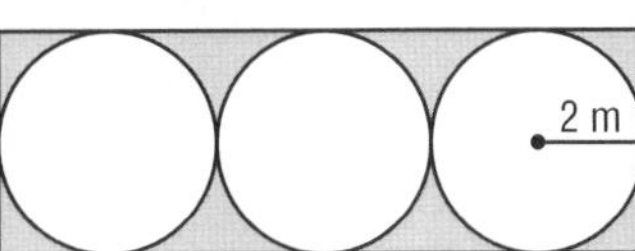

FOCUS

Objective Investigate scale factors with perimeter and area.

Materials for Each Group

- computer with spreadsheet software

TEACH

Working in Cooperative Groups

Have students of mixed abilities work in groups of two or three to complete steps 1–9 of the Activity.

Ask:

- In Step 3, when you copied and pasted the formula from cell B3, were there any changes made to the formulas placed in columns C– F? Explain any changes. Yes; the cells named in the formula changed to correspond with the column into which the formula was pasted.

Additional Answers

1. If the number in row 5 is a, then row 6 contains a, and row 7 contains a^2.
2. The perimeter is doubled. The perimeter is multiplied by 4. The perimeter is multiplied by n.
3. The area is quadrupled. The area is multiplied by 16. The area is multiplied by n^2.
4. The ratio of the perimeters to areas is $a:b$, the same as the scale factor. The ratio of the areas is $a^2:b^2$, the square of the scale factor.
5. If the dimensions are changed proportionally by multiplying by n, the new dimensions are $n\ell$ and nw. The perimeter of the new figure is $P = 2(n\ell + nw)$ or $n \cdot 2(\ell + w)$. The area of the new figure is $A = (n\ell)(nw)$ or $n^2 \ell w$. Thus, the perimeter is multiplied by the scale factor and the area is multiplied by the square of the scale factor.

Spreadsheet Lab: Changes in Scale

Math Online glencoe.com
- Graphing Calculator Personal Tutor

In Lesson 6-6, you learned that when measurements have the same units the *scale factor* is the ratio of the length on a scale drawing or model to the corresponding length on the real figure. You can use a spreadsheet to investigate how the perimeter and area are affected when dimensions of a figure are changed by a scale factor.

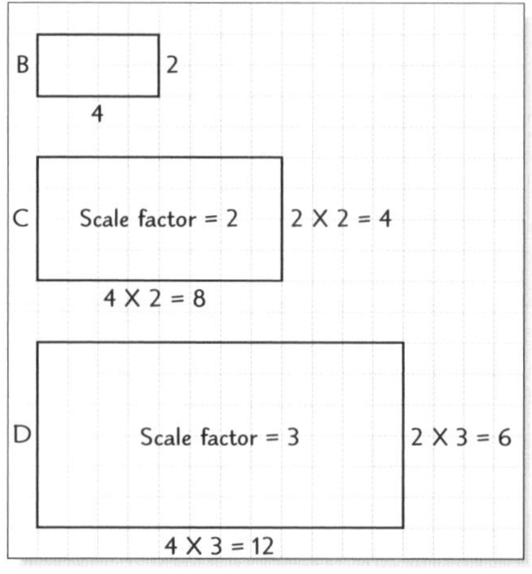

ACTIVITY

Step 1 In cells A1 through A7, enter the labels *Width, Length, Perimeter, Area, Scale Factor, Ratio of Perimeters,* and *Ratio of Areas*. Columns B, C, D, E, and F will be used for five similar rectangles.

Step 2 Enter a 2 in cell B1 and a 4 in cell B2 to represent the width and length of a rectangle.

Step 3 Enter the formula = 2*(B1 + B2) for the perimeter of the rectangle in cell B3. Copy the formula into the other cells in row 3.

Step 4 Write a formula to find the area of the rectangle. Copy the formula in the cells in row 4.

Step 5 Enter a scale factor of 2 in cell C5.

Perimeter, Area, and ....

◇	A	B	C
1	Width	2	4
2	Length	4	8
3	Perimeter	12	24
4	Area	8	32
5	Scale Factor		2
6	Ratio of Perimeters		
7	Ratio of Areas		

Sheet 1 / Sheet 2

648 Chapter 11 Distance and Angle

Step 6 Enter the formula = B1*C5 in cell C1 and enter = B2*C5 in cell C2. These formulas find the dimensions of rectangle C based on the dimensions of rectangle B and the scale factor you entered. Enter similar formulas in the cells for columns D, E, and F.

Step 7 Type the formula = C3/B3 in cell C6, type = D3/B3 in cell D6, and so on. This formula will find the ratio of the perimeter of each of the other rectangles to the perimeter of rectangle B.

Step 8 Write a formula for the ratio of the area of rectangle C to the area of rectangle B. Enter the formula in cell C7. Enter similar formulas in the cells in row 7.

Step 9 Use Columns D, E, and F to find the perimeters, areas, and ratios for rectangles with scale factors of 3, 4, and 5.

Perimeter, Area, and Changes in Scale.xls

◇	A	B	C	D	E	F
1	Width	2	4	6	8	10
2	Length	4	8	12	16	20
3	Perimeter	12	24	36	48	60
4	Area	8	32	72	128	200
5	Scale Factor		2	3	4	5
6	Ratio of Perimeters		2	3	4	5
7	Ratio of Areas		4	9	16	25
8						

Sheet 1 Sheet 2 Sheet 3

Analyze the Results

1. Compare the ratios in rows 5, 6, and 7 of columns C, D, and E. What do you observe? **1–5. See margin.**
2. What happens to the perimeter of a rectangle if the dimensions are doubled? multiplied by 4? multiplied by n? Change the original dimensions of the rectangle and the scale factors in the spreadsheet to verify your conclusion.
3. Describe the effect on the area of a rectangle if its dimensions are doubled. multiplied by 4? multiplied by n? Change the original dimensions of the rectangle and the scale factors in the spreadsheet to verify your conclusion.
4. Change the scale factors in cells C5, D5, E5, and F5 to 0.1, 0.2, 0.3 and 0.5. Describe the ratios of the perimeters and areas for these reductions.
5. Use the perimeter formula $P = 2(\ell + w)$ and the area formula $A = \ell w$ to explain the effects of changing the dimensions of a rectangle proportionally.

- In Steps 6 and 7, can you copy and paste the formulas in cells C6 and C7 into rows 6 and 7 in columns C–F, as you did in Steps 2 and 3? Explain your answer. No; the cells named in the formulas will change with each column into which it is pasted and B3 and B4 should remain the same in the formulas for columns C–F.

Practice Have students complete Exercises 1–5.

3 ASSESS

Formative Assessment

Use Exercises 2 and 3 to assess whether students comprehend how the perimeter and area of a rectangle are affected when its dimensions are changed by a scale factor.

From Concrete to Abstract

Use Exercise 5 to assess whether students can explain algebraically what occurs to perimeter and area when a scale factor is applied to the dimensions of a rectangle.

Extending the Concept Have students investigate how the area and circumference of a circle change as its radius is scaled. Determine if the generalizations made regarding the ratios of perimeters and areas of rectangles are also true for ratios of circumferences and areas of circles.

Key Vocabulary The page references after each word denote where that term was first introduced. If students have difficulty answering questions 1–9, remind them that they can use these page references to refresh their memories about the vocabulary.

Summative Assessment

Vocabulary Test, p. 65

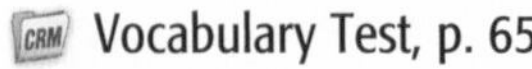

Vocabulary PuzzleMaker improves students' mathematics vocabulary using four puzzle formats–crossword, scramble, word search using a word list, and word search using clues. Students can work online or from a printed worksheet.

CHAPTER 11 Study Guide and Review

- STUDY TO GO
- Vocabulary Review

Chapter Summary

Key Concepts

Angle and Line Relationships (Lesson 11-1)

- Two angles are complementary if the sum of their measures is 90°.
- Two angles are supplementary if the sum of their measures is 180°.
- If two parallel lines are cut by a transversal, the following pairs of angles are congruent: corresponding angles, alternate interior angles, alternate exterior angles.

Congruent Triangles and Rotations (Lessons 11-2 and 11-3)

- Figures that have the same size and shape are congruent.
- A rotation is a transformation in which a figure is turned around a fixed point.

Polygons (Lesson 11-5)

- Polygons are classified by their sides.
- If a polygon has n sides, then the sum of the interior angle measures is $(n - 2)180$.

Formulas (Lessons 11-6 through 11-9)

- Area of a parallelogram: $A = bh$
- Area of a triangle: $A = \frac{1}{2}bh$
- Area of a trapezoid: $A = \frac{1}{2}h(b_1 + b_2)$
- Circumference of a circle: $C = 2\pi r$
- Area of a circle: $A = \pi r^2$

FOLDABLES® Study Organizer

Be sure the Key Concepts are noted in your Foldable.

11-2 11-3 11-4 11-6 11-7 11-8 11-9

Key Vocabulary

adjacent angles (p. 589)
alternate exterior angles (p. 590)
alternate interior angles (p. 590)
center of rotation (p. 605)
central angle (p. 638)
circumference (p. 631)
complementary angles (p. 589)
composite figure (p. 642)
corresponding angles (p. 590)
corresponding parts (p. 598)
diameter (p. 631)
interior angle (p. 618)
parallel lines (p. 590)
perpendicular lines (p. 589)
quadrilateral (p. 612)
radius (p. 631)
regular polygon (p. 619)
rotation (p. 605)
rotational symmetry (p. 607)
sector (p. 638)
supplementary angles (p. 589)
transversal (p. 590)
vertical angles (p. 589)

Vocabulary Check

Determine whether each statement is *true* or *false*. If false, replace the underlined word or phrase to make a true statement.

1. Two lines in a plane that never intersect are called <u>parallel lines</u>. **true**
2. A <u>composite figure</u> has congruent sides and congruent angles. **false; regular polygon**
3. The <u>altitude</u> can be any side of a parallelogram. **false; base**
4. An <u>interior angle</u> is an angle formed at a vertex of a polygon. **true**
5. A <u>rhombus</u> is an example of a quadrilateral. **true**
6. The <u>radius</u> of a circle is the section formed by a central angle. **false; sector**
7. <u>Complementary angles</u> are two angles with a sum of 180°. **false; supplementary angles**
8. If two parallel lines are cut by a transversal, corresponding angles are <u>equal</u>. **true**
9. A <u>tessellation</u> is a transformation in which a figure is turned around a fixed point. **false; rotation**

FOLDABLES® Study Organizer

Dinah Zike's Foldables®

Have students look through the chapter to make sure they have included examples in their Foldables.

Suggest that students keep their Foldables handy while completing the Study Guide and Review pages. Point out that their Foldables can serve as a quick review tool when studying for the Chapter Test.

Lesson-by-Lesson Review

11-1 Angle and Line Relationships (pp. 589–595)

In the figure below, $m \parallel n$ and r is a transversal. If $m\angle 4 = 112°$, find the measure of each angle. Explain your reasoning. 10–13. See margin.

10. $\angle 6$
11. $\angle 2$
12. $\angle 8$
13. $\angle 1$

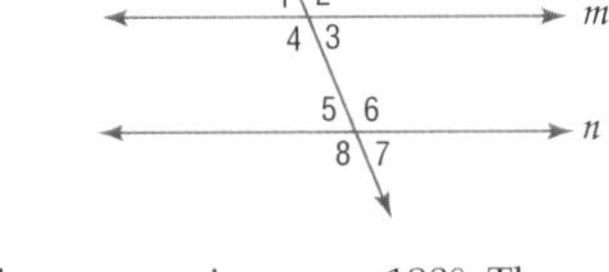

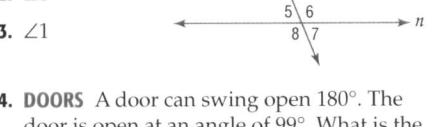

14. **DOORS** A door can swing open 180°. The door is open at an angle of 99°. What is the measure of the angle between the door and the door jam? 81°

EXAMPLE 1

In the figure below, $a \parallel b$ and g is a transversal. If $m\angle 2 = 61°$, find $m\angle 7$ and $m\angle 4$. Explain your reasoning.

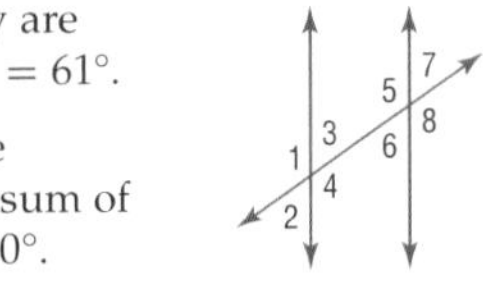

Since $\angle 2$ and $\angle 7$ are alternate exterior angles, they are congruent. So, $m\angle 7 = 61°$.

Since $\angle 2$ and $\angle 4$ are supplementary, the sum of their measures is 180°.

$m\angle 2 + m\angle 4 = 180$	**Supplementary angles**
$61 + m\angle 4 = 180$	**Replace $m\angle 2$ with 61.**
$m\angle 4 = 119$	**Subtract 61 from each side.**

So, $m\angle 4 = 119°$.

11-2 Congruent Triangles (pp. 598–604)

15. Name the corresponding parts in the congruent triangles below. Then complete the congruence statement $\triangle FGH \cong$ __?__. See margin.

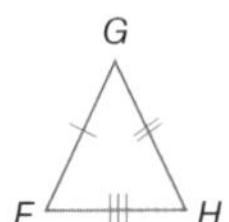

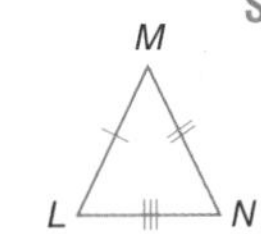

16. **SOFTBALL** On a softball diamond, the triangle formed by home plate, first base, and second base is congruent to the triangle formed by home plate, third base, and second base. If it is 65 feet from home plate to first base, how far is it from third base to home plate? 65 ft

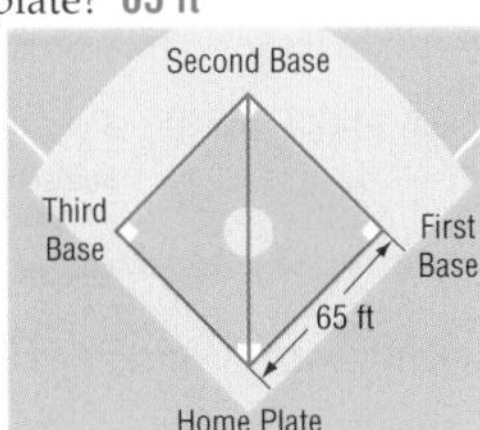

EXAMPLE 2

Name the corresponding parts in the congruent triangles shown below. Then complete the congruence statement $\triangle STU \cong \triangle$ __?__.

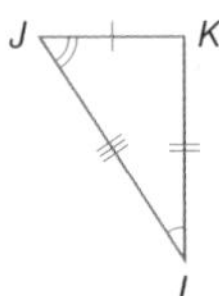

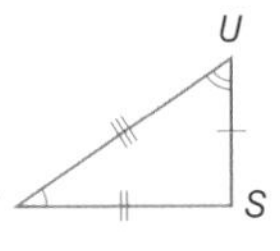

Use the matching arcs and tick marks to identify the corresponding parts.

Corresponding angles:

$\angle J \cong \angle U$, $\angle K \cong \angle S$, $\angle L \cong \angle T$

Corresponding sides:

$\angle\overline{JK} \cong \angle\overline{US}$, $\angle\overline{KL} \cong \angle\overline{ST}$, $\angle\overline{LJ} \cong \angle\overline{TU}$

The congruence statement is $\triangle STU \cong \triangle KLJ$.

Lesson-by-Lesson Review

Intervention If the given examples are not sufficient to review the topics covered by the questions, remind students that the page references tell them where to review that topic in their textbook.

Two-Day Option Have students complete the Lesson-by-Lesson Review on pp. 651–654. Then you can use ExamView® Assessment Suite to customize another review worksheet that practices all the objectives of this chapter or only the objectives on which your students need more help.

Differentiated Instruction

Super DVD: MindJogger Videoquizzes Use this DVD as an alternative format of review for the test.

Additional Answers

10. 112°; $\angle 4$ and $\angle 6$ are alternate interior angles, so they are congruent.
11. 112°; $\angle 4$ and $\angle 2$ are vertical angles, so they are congruent.
12. 112°; $\angle 4$ and $\angle 8$ are corresponding angles, so they are congruent.
13. 68°; $\angle 4$ and $\angle 1$ are supplementary angles, so the sum of their measures is 180°.
15. $\angle F \cong \angle L$, $\angle G \cong \angle M$, $\angle H \cong \angle N$; $\overline{FG} \cong \overline{LM}$, $\overline{GH} \cong \overline{MN}$, $\overline{HF} \cong \overline{NL}$; $\triangle LMN$

CHAPTER 11 Study Guide and Review

Additional Answers

17.

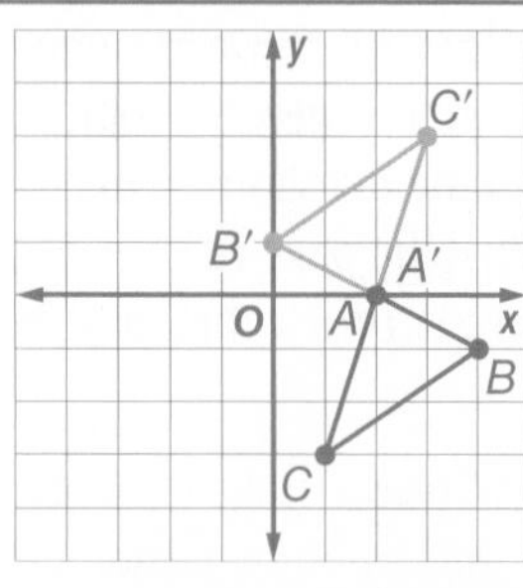

$A'(2, 0)$, $B'(0, 1)$, $C'(3, 3)$

18.

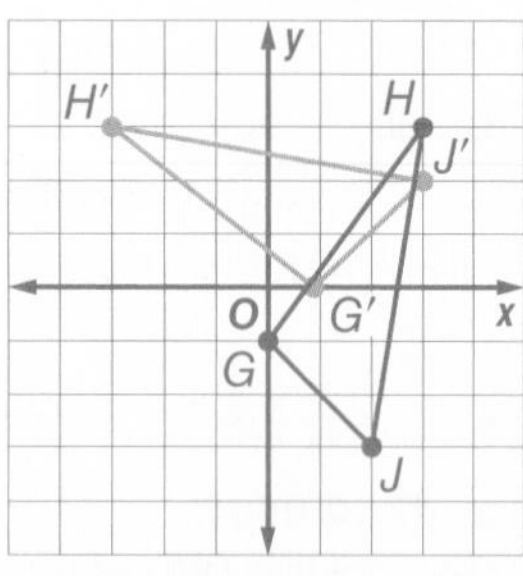

19.

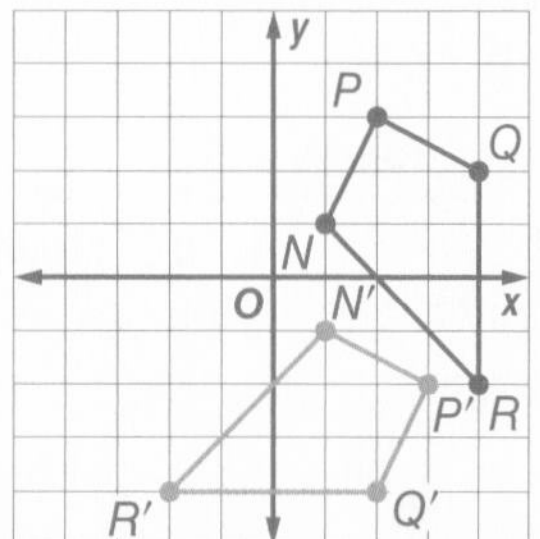

CHAPTER 11 Study Guide and Review

11-3 Rotations (pp. 605–610)

17. Triangle ABC has vertices $A(2, 0)$, $B(4, -1)$, and $C(1, -3)$. Graph the figure and its image after a clockwise rotation of 180° about vertex A. Give the coordinates of the vertices for triangle $A'B'C'$. **17–19. See margin.**

Graph each figure and its image after a clockwise rotation about the origin.

18. triangle GHJ with vertices $G(0, -1)$, $H(3, 3)$, and $J(2, -3)$; 270° clockwise rotation

19. quadrilateral $NPQR$ with vertices $N(1, 1)$, $P(2, 3)$, $Q(4, 2)$, and $R(4, -2)$; 90° clockwise rotation

20. **SIGNS** Determine whether the shape of the sign shown at the right has rotational symmetry. If it does, describe the angle of rotation. **yes; 120°**

EXAMPLE 3

Triangle TVW has vertices $T(-1, 0)$, $V(0, 3)$, and $W(2, 2)$. Graph the figure and its image after a clockwise rotation of 270° about vertex T. Give the coordinates of the vertices for triangle $T'V'W'$.

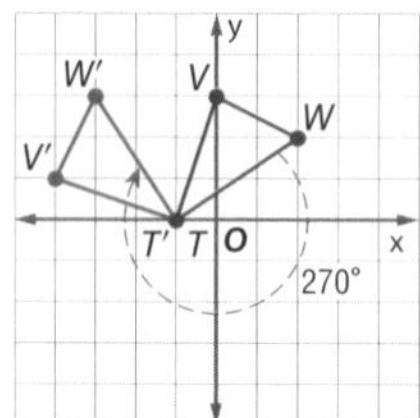

The coordinates of the vertices are $T'(-1, 0)$, $V'(-4, 1)$, and $W'(-3, 3)$.

11-4 Quadrilaterals (pp. 612–616)

Find the value of x in each quadrilateral. Then find the missing angle measures.

21. 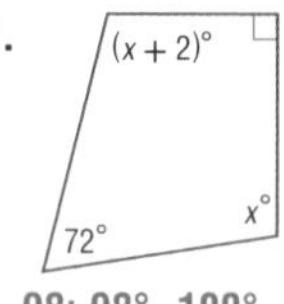 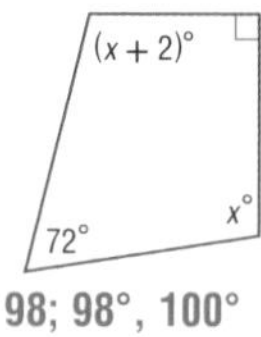

98; 98°, 100°

22. 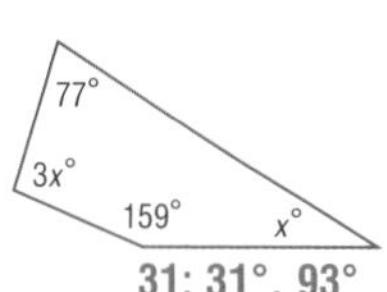

31; 31°, 93°

23. **WINDOWS** Classify the quadrilaterals shown in the window at the right. Use the name that *best* describes it. **rhombus**

EXAMPLE 4

Find the value of x in the quadrilateral below. Then find the missing angle measures.

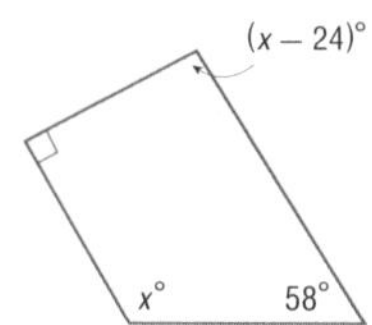

$x + 90 + (x - 24) + 58 = 360$	**Write an equation.**
$2x + 124 = 360$	**Simplify.**
$2x = 236$	**Subtract 124 from each side.**
$x = 118$	**Simplify.**

So, the missing angle measures are 118° and 118 − 24 or 94°.

MIXED PROBLEM SOLVING
For mixed problem-solving practice, see page 843.

11-5 Polygons (pp. 617–622)

Determine whether the figure is a polygon. If it is, classify the polygon and state whether it is regular. If it is not a polygon, explain why.

24. 

25.  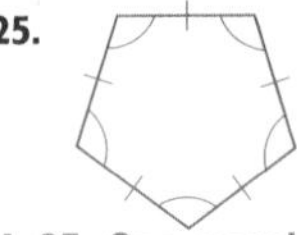

24–25. See margin.

Find the measure of an interior angle of each regular polygon.

26. hexagon 120°

27. 18-gon 160°

28. **STREET SIGNS** What is the measure of each interior angle of the stop sign? 135°

EXAMPLE 5

Find the measure of one interior angle in a regular heptagon.

Step 1 Find the sum of the measures of the angles. A heptagon has 7 sides. So, $n = 7$.

$(n - 2)180 = (7 - 2)180$ **Replace n with 7.**

$= 5(180)$ or $900°$ **Simplify.**

The sum of the measures of the interior angles is 900°.

Step 2 Divide the sum by 7 to find the measure of one angle.

$900 \div 7 \approx 128.6$

So, the measure of one interior angle in a heptagon is about 128.6°.

11-6 Area of Parallelograms, Triangles, and Trapezoids (pp. 624–630)

Find the area of each figure.

29. 120 ft² 30.

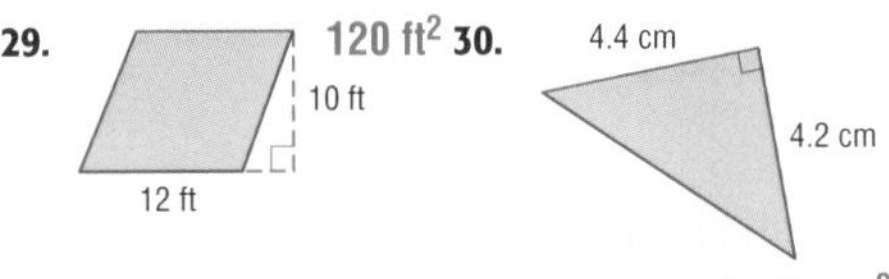

9.24 cm²

31. **DECORATING** Mrs. Jackson wants to lay tile in the area in front of her fireplace, as shown in the diagram. The tile costs $2.99 per square foot. About how much will it cost Mrs. Jackson to tile the area? about $76.25

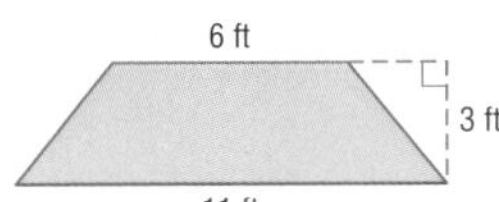

EXAMPLE 6

Find the area of the triangle.

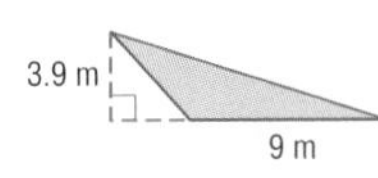

$A = \frac{1}{2}bh$ **Area of a triangle**

$= \frac{1}{2}(9)(3.9)$ **Replace b with 9 and h with 3.9.**

$= 17.55 \text{ m}^2$ **Simplify.**

EXAMPLE 7

Find the area of a trapezoid that has bases that measure 3 centimeters and 10.5 centimeters and a height that measures 5.2 centimeters.

$A = \frac{1}{2}h(a + b)$ **Area of a trapezoid**

$= \frac{1}{2}(5.2)(3 + 10.5)$ **Substitution**

$= 35.1 \text{ cm}^2$ **Simplify.**

Additional Answers

24. The figure has 4 sides that only intersect at their endpoints. It is a quadrilateral that is not regular.

25. The figure has 5 sides that only intersect at their endpoints. It is a regular pentagon.

Chapter 11 Study Guide and Review **653**

Problem Solving Review

For additional practice in problem solving for Chapter 11, see the Mixed Problem Solving Appendix, p. 853, in the Student Handbook section.

Anticipation Guide

Have students complete the Chapter 11 Anticipation Guide and discuss how their responses have changed now that they have completed Chapter 11.

CHAPTER 11 Study Guide and Review

11-7 Circles and Circumference (pp. 631–635)

Find the circumference of each circle. Round to the nearest tenth.

32. 

125.7 km

33. 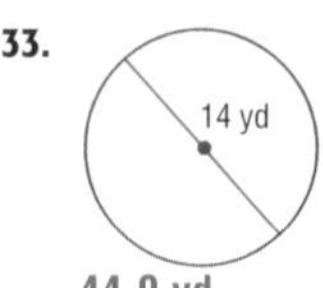

44.0 yd

34. diameter = $5\frac{1}{3}$ ft **16.8 ft**

35. radius = 13.5 mm **84.8 mm**

36. **FERRIS WHEEL** The first Ferris wheel had a diameter of 250 feet. What was the distance, to the nearest whole foot, that riders traveled if they stayed on the ride for 15 rotations? **about 11,781 ft**

EXAMPLE 8

Find the circumference of the circle. Round to the nearest tenth.

$C = 2\pi r$ — **Circumference of a circle**

$= 2 \cdot \pi \cdot 9.2$ — **Replace *r* with 9.2.**

≈ 57.8 — **Simplify.**

So, the circumference of the circle is about 57.8 meters.

11-8 Area of Circles (pp. 636–641)

Find the area of each circle. Round to the nearest tenth.

37. 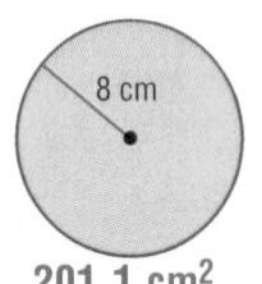

201.1 cm²

38. 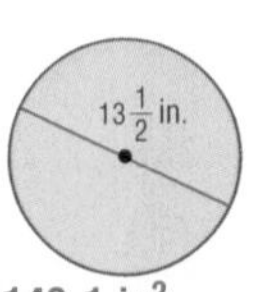

143.1 in²

39. **BAKERY** A blueberry pie has a diameter of 9 inches. What is the area of the top crust? Round to the nearest tenth. **63.6 in²**

EXAMPLE 9

Find the area of the circle. Round to the nearest tenth.

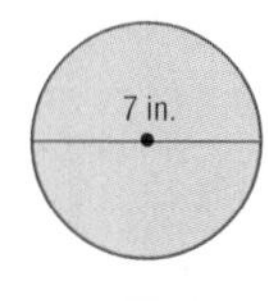

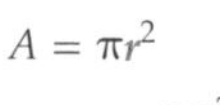
$A = \pi r^2$ — **Area of a circle**

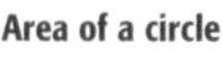
$= \pi \cdot 3.5^2$ — **$d = 7$, so $r = 3.5$**

≈ 38.5 — **Simplify.**

So, the area of the circle is about 38.5 square inches.

11-9 Area of Composite Figures (pp. 642–647)

40. Find the area of the composite figure. **8.25 in²**
(figure labels: 3 in., 2 in., $1\frac{1}{2}$ in.)

41. **MUSEUM** The floor plan of a new museum is shown. What is the area of the museum rounded to the nearest whole foot? **about 14,055 ft²**

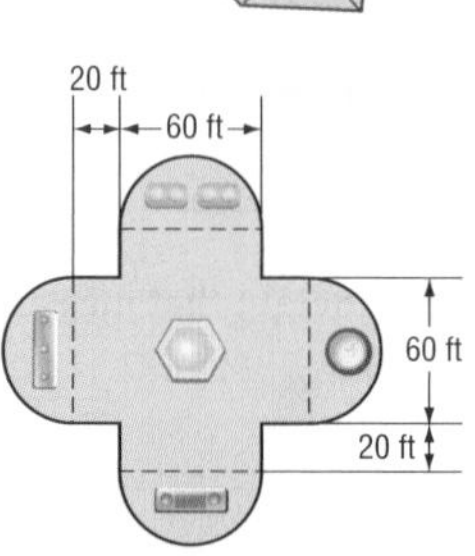

EXAMPLE 10

Find the area of the composite figure.

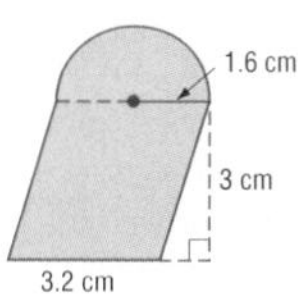

Find the areas of the semicircle and of the parallelogram. Then add.

Area of Semicircle	Area of Parallelogram
$A = \frac{1}{2}\pi r^2$	$A = bh$
$= \frac{1}{2}\pi(1.6)^2$	$= (3.2)(3)$
$\approx 4.0\ \text{cm}^2$	$= 9.6\ \text{cm}^2$

So, the area of the figure is 4.0 + 9.6 or about 13.6 square centimeters.

654 Chapter 11 Distance and Angle

Math Online glencoe.com
Chapter Test

Find the value of x in each figure.

1. 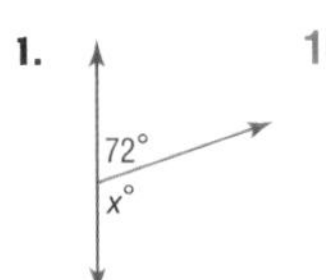

108

2. 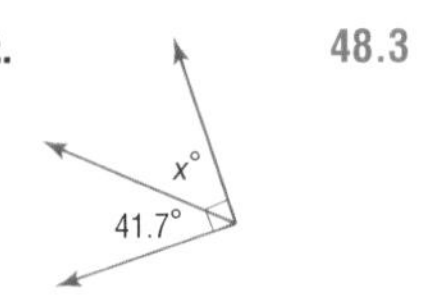

48.3

3. Name the corresponding parts in the congruent triangles. Then complete the congruence statement.

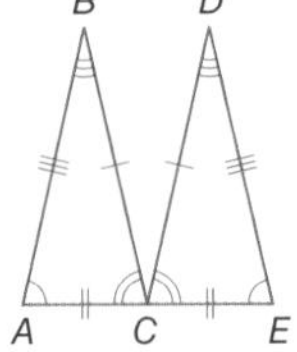

$\triangle CAB \cong$ __?__ See margin.

4. A figure has vertices $G(1, -1)$, $H(3, -4)$, $J(1, -5)$, and $K(-1, -4)$. Graph the figure and its image after a clockwise rotation of 90° about vertex J. See margin.

5. **MULTIPLE CHOICE** What are the coordinates of point R after a clockwise rotation of 270° about the origin? C

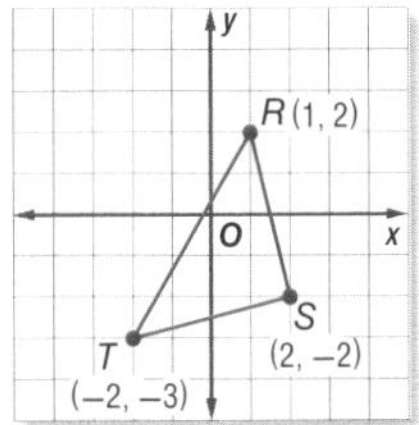

A $R'(-1, -2)$
B $R'(2, 1)$
C $R'(-2, 1)$
D $R'(2, -1)$

6. Find the value of x in the quadrilateral at the right. Then find the missing angle measures. 34; 90°, 68°

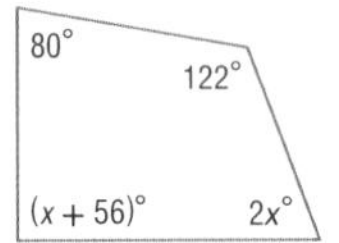

7. **MULTIPLE CHOICE** What is the measure of each interior angle of a regular 16-gon? F

F 157.5°
G 205.7°
H 2520°
J 2880°

Classify each polygon. Then determine whether it is *regular* or *not regular.*

8. 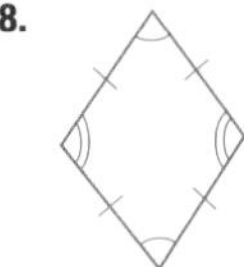
quadrilateral; not regular

9. 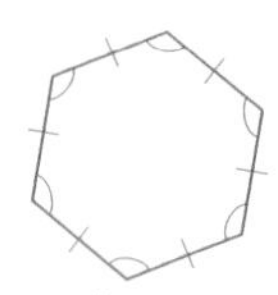
hexagon; regular

Find the area of each figure.

10. 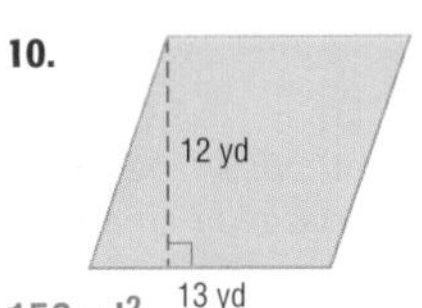

156 yd^2

11. 10.3 cm, 6 cm, 6.4 cm
50.1 cm^2

12. **BANNERS** A triangular banner has a base of 1 foot and a height of $1\frac{1}{2}$ feet. What is the area of the banner? $\frac{3}{4}$ ft^2

Find the circumference and area of each circle. Round to the nearest tenth.

13. 12 ft
75.4 ft; 452.4 ft^2

14. 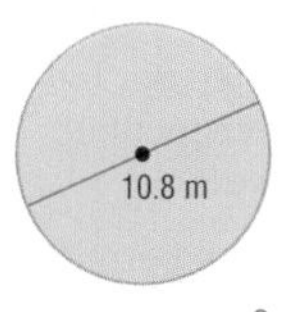

33.9 m; 91.6 m^2

15. **PIZZA** The pizza at the right has a diameter of 15 inches. If one eighth of the pizza is eaten, what is the area of the pizza that is left? Round to the nearest tenth. about 154.6 in^2

16. In the diagram, 1 square unit equals 5 square feet. What is the area of the shaded figure? 132.5 ft^2

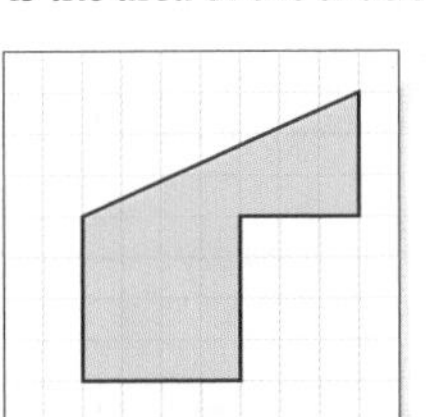

CHAPTER 11 Practice Test

ExamView Assessment Suite Customize and create multiple versions of your Chapter Test and their answer keys. All of the questions from the leveled Chapter Tests in the *Chapter 11 Resource Masters* are also available on ExamView® Assessment Suite.

Additional Answers

3. $\angle A \cong \angle E$, $\angle B \cong \angle D$, $\angle BCA \cong \angle DCE$, $\overline{AB} \cong \overline{ED}$, $\overline{BC} \cong \overline{DC}$, $\overline{AC} \cong \overline{EC}$; $\triangle CED$

4. 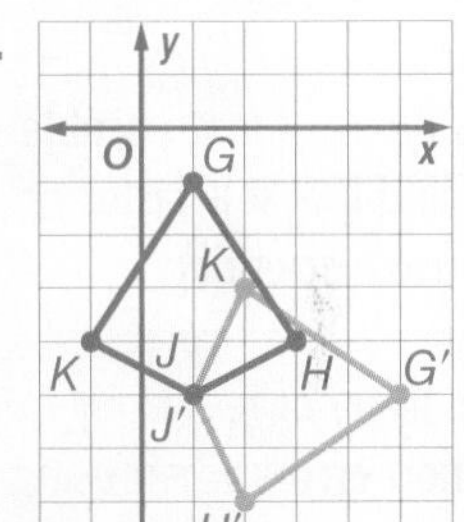

Intervention Planner

Tier 1 On Level	Tier 2 Strategic Intervention approaching grade level	Tier 3 Intensive Intervention 2 or more grades below level
 If students miss about 25% of the exercises or less,	 If students miss about 50% of the exercises,	 If students miss about 75% of the exercises,
Then choose a resource: **SE** Lessons 11-1 through 11-9 **CRM** Skills Practice, pp. 7, 13, 19, 25, 31, 37, 44, 50, and 56 **TE** Chapter Project, p. 586 Math Online Self-Check Quiz	 Then choose a resource:  **CRM** Study Guide and Intervention, Chapter 11, pp. 5, 11, 17, 23, 29, 35, 42, 48, and 54 *Quick Review Math Handbook* Math Online Extra Examples, Personal Tutor, Homework Help	 Then use *Math Triumphs, Grade 8,* Ch. 4 Math Online Extra Examples, Personal Tutor, Homework Help, Review Vocabulary

1 FOCUS

Objective Use the strategy of using a scientific calculator to solve standardized test problems.

2 TEACH

Scaffolding Questions

Ask:

- For which types of math problems have you used a scientific calculator? Answers will vary.
- Are there any types of math problems in which you find that it is faster or easier to *not* use a scientific calculator? Answers will vary.
- Are you more likely or less likely to make calculation errors when using a scientific calculator? Explain. Sample answer: You are less likely to make a calculation error, but you could still make errors if you enter the numbers incorrectly, or use formulas incorrectly, or round incorrectly.

CHAPTER 11 Preparing for Standardized Tests

Using a Scientific Calculator

Scientific calculators are powerful problem-solving tools. Some problems can be solved faster or easier using a scientific calculator. Other problems that you encounter may have steps or computations that require the use of a scientific calculator.

Strategies for Using a Scientific Calculator

Step 1

Familiarize yourself with the various functions of a scientific calculator as well as when they should be used:

- **Exponents**—Used to solve problems involving scientific notation or calculations with large or small numbers.
- **Pi**—used to solve circle problems involving circumference and area.
- **Square roots**—Used to solve problems involving distance on a coordinate plane or the Pythagorean theorem.

Step 2

Use your calculator to solve the problem.

- Remember to work as efficiently as possible. Some steps may be done faster mentally or by hand, while others should be completed using your calculator.
- If time permits, check your answer.

EXAMPLE

Solve the problem below. Responses will be graded using the short-response scoring rubric shown.

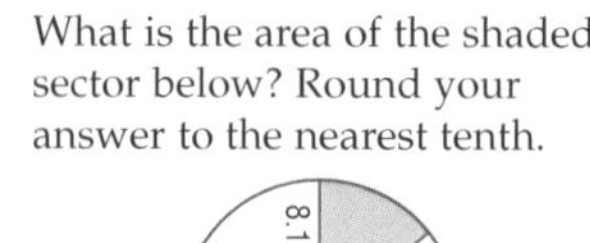

What is the area of the shaded sector below? Round your answer to the nearest tenth.

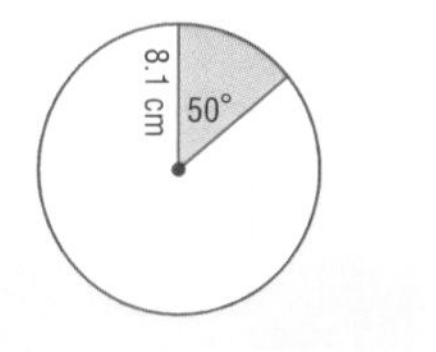

Scoring Rubric	
Criteria	**Score**
Full Credit: The answer is correct and a full explanation is provided that shows each step.	2
Partial Credit: • The answer is correct, but the explanation is incomplete. • The answer is incorrect, but the explanation is correct.	1
No Credit: Either an answer is not provided or the answer does not make sense.	0

Read the problem carefully. You are given the radius of a circle and the central angle of a sector and asked to find the area of the sector. Use the formula $A = \frac{N}{360}(\pi r^2)$ to find the area of the sector. Show your work to receive full credit.

Example of a 2-point response:

The formula $A = \frac{N}{360}(\pi r^2)$ gives the area of a sector with radius r and central angle N.

$$A = \frac{N}{360}(\pi r^2)$$

$$A = \frac{50}{360}[\pi(8.1)^2]$$

$$A = \frac{5}{36}[\pi(65.61)]$$

$$A = 9.1125\pi$$

$$A \approx 28.6$$

The area of the sector is about 28.6 square centimeters.

The steps, calculations, and reasoning are clearly stated. The student also arrives at the correct answer. So, this response is worth the full 2 points.

Exercises

Solve each problem. Show your work. Responses will be graded using the short-response scoring rubric given on page 656.

1. Heather's bicycle tire has a diameter of 22 inches. How far will she travel if the tire completes 50 revolutions? Round your answer to the nearest inch and to the nearest foot. **about 3,456 in. or 288 ft**

2. Find the area of the shaded region. Use 3.14 for π. Round to the nearest hundredth. **7.74 ft²**

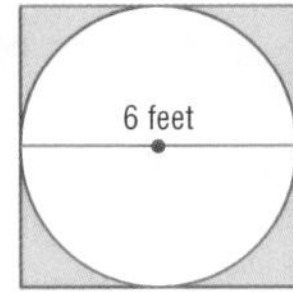

3. A metal washer is made by cutting a circular disk from the center of a larger disk. What is the area of the metal washer below? Round to the nearest tenth. **250.5 mm²**

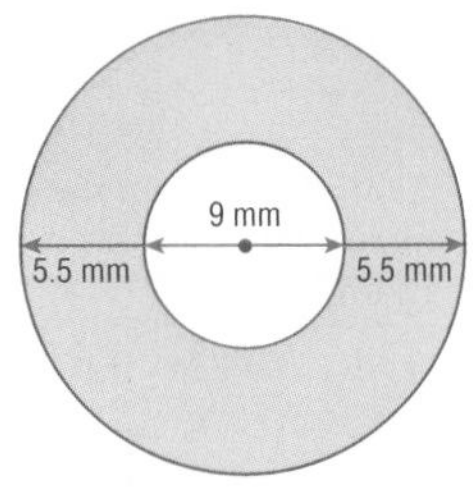

4. The diameter of a circle is 12 inches. Find the area of a sector of the circle with a central angle that measures 110°. Use 3.14 for π. Round to the nearest hundredth. **34.54 in²**

Additional Example

SHORT RESPONSE A circular fountain has a 2-foot wide concrete bench around its circumference. What is the area of the circular bench? Round your answer to the nearest tenth.

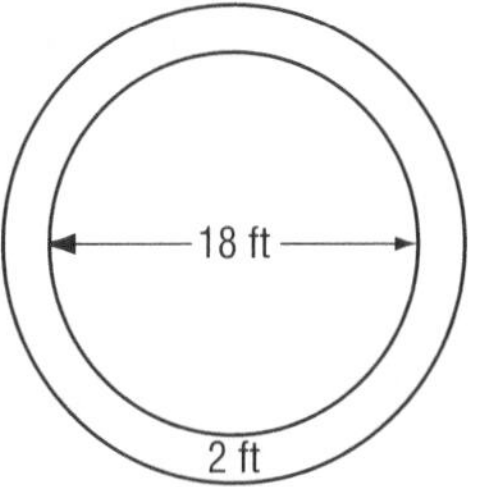

Sample 2-point response: The formula for the area of a circle is $A = \pi r^2$. To find the area of the circular bench, subtract the area of the inner circle from the area of the outer circle.

The radius is half the diameter, so the radius of the inner circle is $18 \div 2 = 9$ and the radius of the outer circle is $18 + 2 + 2$ or $22 \div 2 = 11$.

$$A = \pi(11)^2 - \pi(9)^2$$

$$A = 121\pi - 81\pi$$

$$A = 40\pi$$

$$A \approx 125.7$$

The area of the circular bench is about 125.7 square feet.

3 ASSESS

Use Exercises 1–4 to assess students' understanding.

Chapter 11 Preparing for Standardized Tests 657

CHAPTER 11 Standardized Test Practice

Diagnose Student Errors

Survey student responses for each item. Class trends may indicate common errors and misconceptions.

1. A guess
B correct
C mistakenly found only the value of $(3x)^\circ$
D mistakenly found only the value of $(5x)^\circ$

2. F correct
G chose complementary angle instead of congruent angle
H misunderstood concept of congruent angles
J misunderstood concept of congruent angles

3. A misunderstood concept of function
B misunderstood concept of function
C correct
D misunderstood concept of function

4. F misread instructions or misunderstood how to find the angles of a triangle using ratios
G misread instructions or misunderstood how to find the angles of a triangle using ratios
H misread instructions or misunderstood how to find the angles of a triangle using ratios
J correct

5. A misread instructions or guess
B misread instructions or guess
C misread instructions or guess
D correct

6. F correct
G did not choose the most specific quadrilateral
H did not choose the most specific quadrilateral
J did not choose the most specific quadrilateral

7. A found the sum of the interior angles of a hexagon
B found the sum of the interior angles of a heptagon
C guess
D correct

8. F found circumference instead of area
G guess or calculation error
H guess or calculation error
J correct

9. A correct
B used wrong conversion factors or calculation error
C used wrong conversion factors or calculation error
D used wrong conversion factors or calculation error

CHAPTER 11 Standardized Test Practice

Cumulative, Chapters 1 through 11

Multiple Choice

Read each question. Then fill in the correct answer on the answer document provided by your teacher or on a sheet of paper.

1. What is the value of x in the figure below? **B**

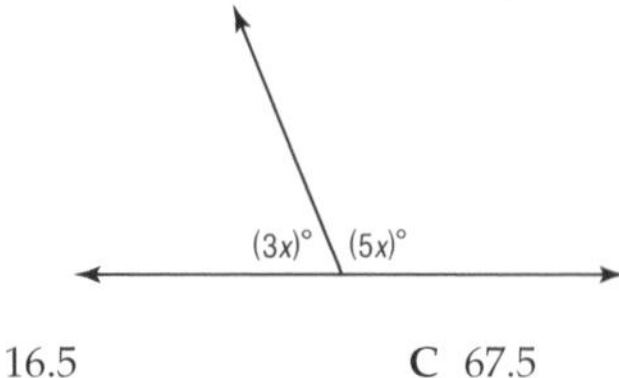

A 16.5
B 22.5
C 67.5
D 112.5

2. If right triangle *DEF* is congruent to right triangle *LMN* and $m\angle EDF = 42^\circ$, what is $m\angle MLN$? **F**

F 42°
G 48°
H 60°
J 90°

3. Which missing value for x would result in the relation shown in the table being a function? **C**

x	2	5	1	■
y	11	4	8	10

A 1
B 2
C 3
D 5

4. The angles of a triangle are in the ratio 5 : 6 : 19. Which of the following measures is *not* an angle of the triangle? **J**

F 30°
G 36°
H 114°
J 118°

5. Which of the following is *not* a factor of 3,003? **D**

A 7
B 11
C 13
D 17

6. What is the sum of the interior angles of the figure below? **J**

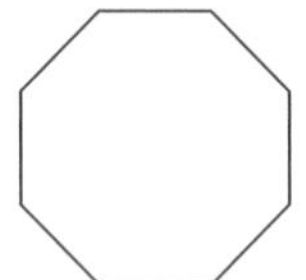

F 720°
G 900°
H 940°
J 1080°

7. Which of the following terms *best* describes a quadrilateral with opposite sides parallel and congruent? **A**

A parallelogram
B rectangle
C rhombus
D square

8. Find the area of the circle below. **J**

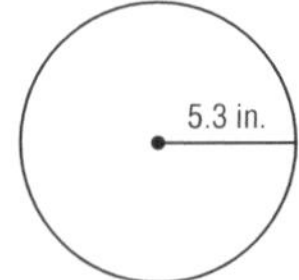

F 33.3 in^2
G 57.6 in^2
H 71.4 in^2
J 88.2 in^2

9. Lisa is going on a 2-week camping trip this summer. How many seconds are there in 2 weeks? **A**

A 1,209,600 s
B 1,420,500 s
C 1,516,100 s
D 1,812,300 s

Test-TakingTip

Question 7 Sometimes a multiple choice item may have more than one *reasonable* answer, but you need to choose the *best* one.

CHAPTER 11 Standardized Test Practice

Short Response/Gridded Response

Record your answers on the answer sheet provided by your teacher or on a sheet of paper.

10. GRIDDED RESPONSE Find the area of the composite figure below. Express your answer in square centimeters and round to the nearest tenth if necessary. **91**

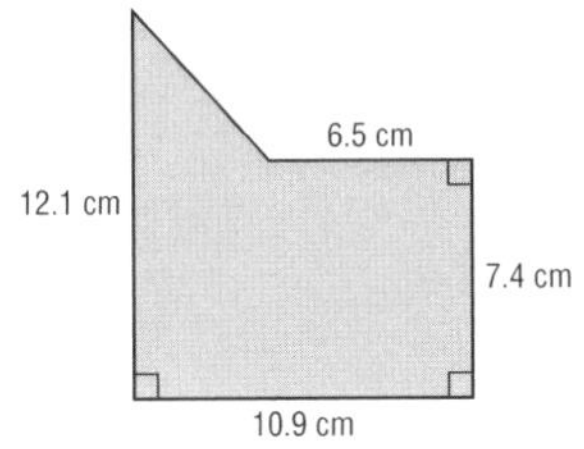

11. Triangle *EFG* is shown on the coordinate grid below.

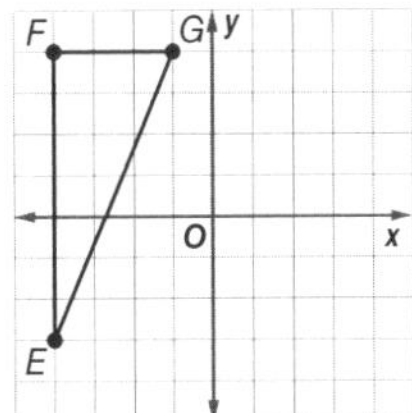

What are the coordinates of the vertices after a clockwise rotation of 90° about vertex *E*? **$E'(-4, -3)$, $F'(3, -3)$, $G'(3, -6)$**

12. What is the distance between points $M(2, 4)$ and $N(-5, -3)$ on a coordinate plane? Round to the nearest tenth. **9.9 units**

13. GRIDDED RESPONSE What is the angle of rotational symmetry in degrees for the figure shown below? **72**

Extended Response

Record your answers on a sheet of paper. Show your work.

14. A large pizza from Santa Ana's Pizzeria has a 14-inch diameter as shown below.

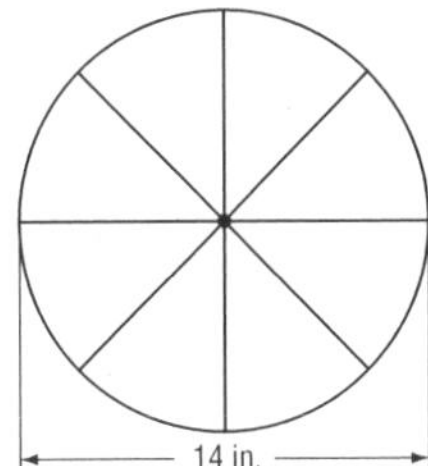

a. How many square inches of dough are needed to make a large pizza? Round to the nearest tenth. **153.9 in^2**

b. What is the circumference, to the nearest tenth, of a large pizza? **44.0 in.**

c. Suppose the large pizza is cut into 8 equal slices. What is the central angle of each slice? **45°**

Need Extra Help?														
If you missed Question...	1	2	3	4	5	6	7	8	9	10	11	12	13	14
Go to Lesson or Page...	11-1	11-2	8-1	10-3	9-2	11-4	11-5	11-8	6-3	11-9	11-3	10-5	11-3	11-5,7,8

Formative Assessment

You can use these two pages to benchmark student progress.

CRM Standardized Test Practice, pp. 79–81

Answer Sheet Practice

Have students simulate taking a standardized test by recording their answers on practice recording sheets.

CRM Student Recording Sheet, p. 60

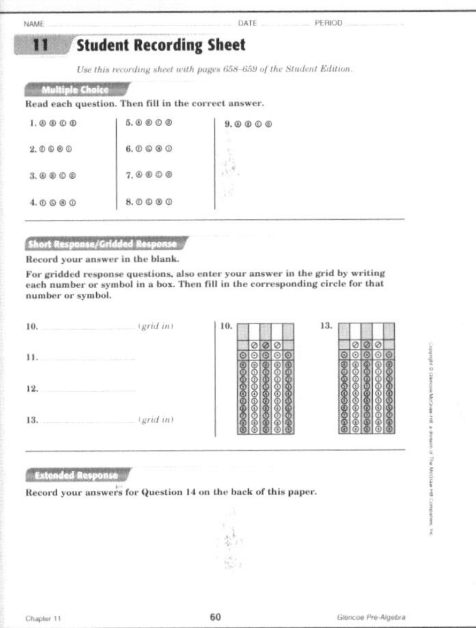
NAME DATE PERIOD

11 Student Recording Sheet

Use this recording sheet with pages 658–659 of the Student Edition.

Multiple Choice

Read each question. Then fill in the correct answer.

1. Ⓐ Ⓑ Ⓒ Ⓓ
2. Ⓕ Ⓖ Ⓗ Ⓘ
3. Ⓐ Ⓑ Ⓒ Ⓓ
4. Ⓕ Ⓖ Ⓗ Ⓘ
5. Ⓐ Ⓑ Ⓒ Ⓓ
6. Ⓕ Ⓖ Ⓗ Ⓘ
7. Ⓐ Ⓑ Ⓒ Ⓓ
8. Ⓕ Ⓖ Ⓗ Ⓘ
9. Ⓐ Ⓑ Ⓒ Ⓓ

Short Response/Gridded Response

Record your answer in the blank.

For gridded response questions, also enter your answer in the grid by writing each number or symbol in a box. Then fill in the corresponding circle for that number or symbol.

10. ______ (grid in)
11. ______
12. ______
13. ______ (grid in)

10. 13.

Extended Response

Record your answers for Question 14 on the back of this paper.

Chapter 11 60 Glencoe Pre-Algebra

Create practice worksheets or tests that align to your state's standards as well as TIMSS and NAEP tests.

Homework Option

Get Ready for Chapter 12 Assign students the exercises on p. 661 as homework to assess whether they possess the prerequisite skills needed for the next chapter.

Page 605, Lesson 11-3, Check Your Progress

1A.

1B.

Pages 608–609, Lesson 11-3

7a.

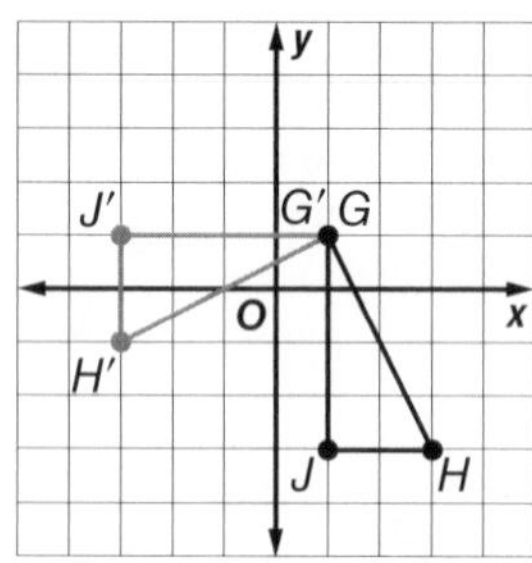

8a.

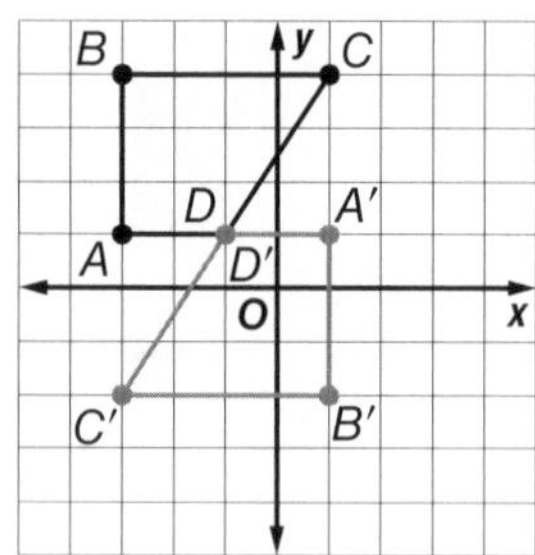

9.

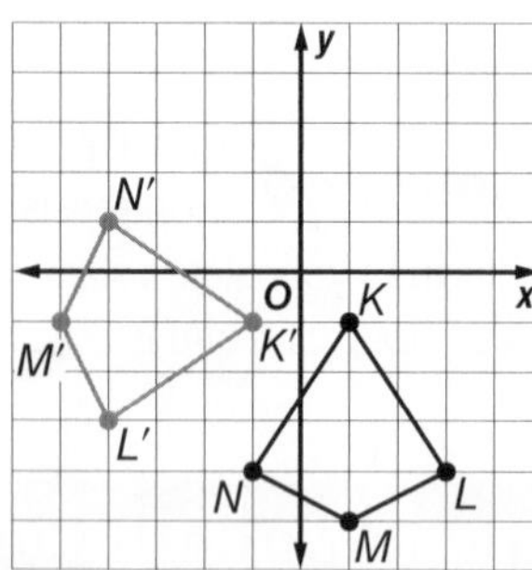

10.

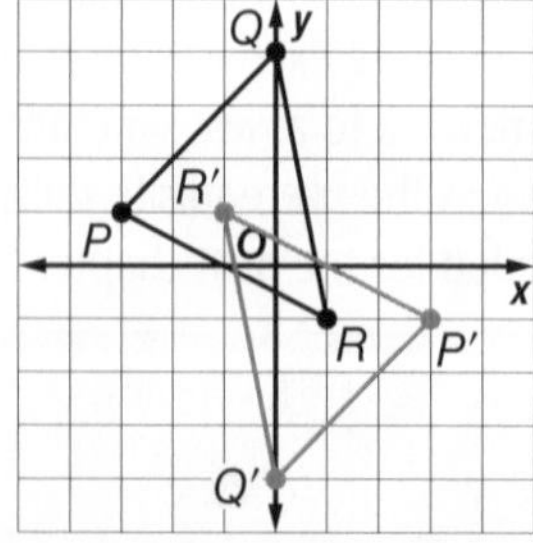

15. Sample answer: 90° clockwise

270° clockwise

180°

17. Sample answer: 90°

Page 617, Lesson 11-5, Why?

b. Sample answer:

Puzzle One

Puzzle Two

Page 621, Lesson 11-5

28.

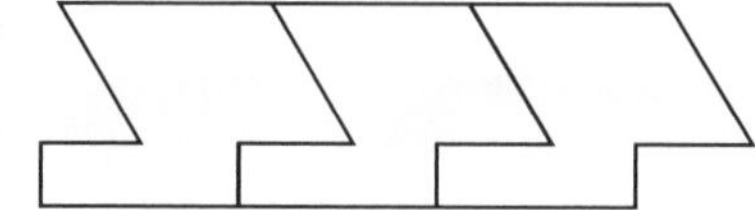

29.

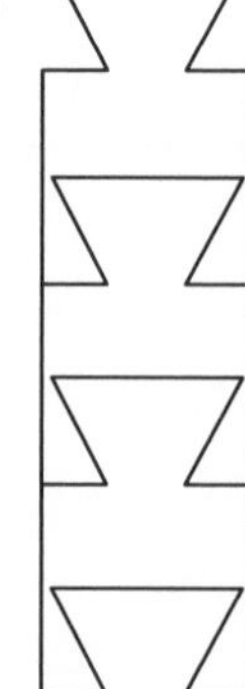

30. 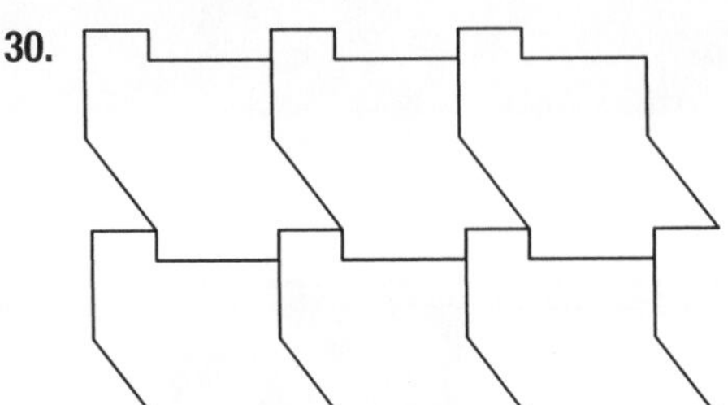

35. Sample answer: 

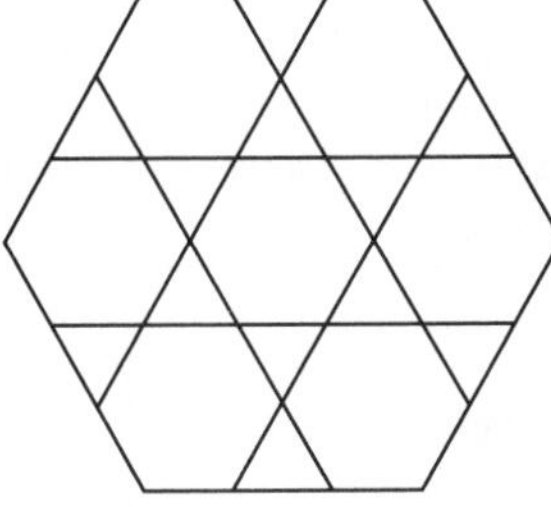

regular hexagons, equilateral triangles; translations, reflections, or rotations

38. 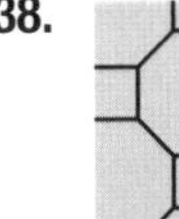 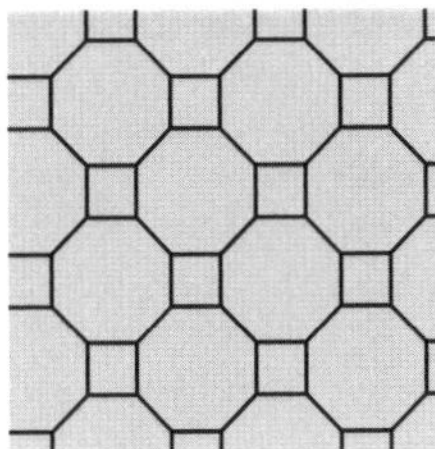

Page 642, Lesson 11-9, Why?

a. Sample answer: triangle, trapezoids, non-regular quadrilaterals, non-regular hexagon, non-regular decagons

b. Find the area of each polygon and then add the areas.

CHAPTER 12

Chapter Planner

Diagnostic Assessment
Quick Check, p. 661

	Explore 12-1 Pacing: 1 day	Lesson 12-1 Pacing: 1 day	Explore 12-2 Pacing: 1 day
Title	**Geometry Lab: Drawing Three-Dimensional Figures**	**Three-Dimensional Figures**	**Geometry Lab: Volume**
Objectives	• Draw three-dimensional figures using different perspectives.	• Identify three-dimensional figures. • Describe and draw vertical, horizontal, and angled cross sections of three-dimensional figures.	• Investigate volume by creating and comparing containers of various shapes.
Key Vocabulary		plane; solid polyhedron; edge vertex; face; prism; base pyramid; cylinder cone; cross section	
NCTM Focal Points	G7-FP2, G7-FP7C For the complete wording of the Focal Points for Grades 7 and 8, please see pages iv, v, FP0, and FP1.		
Multiple Representations		p. 668	
Lesson Resources	**Materials:** • cubes • isometric dot paper	**Chapter 12 Resource Masters** • Study Guide and Intervention, pp. 5–6 AL OL ELL • Skills Practice, p. 7 AL OL ELL • Practice, p. 8 AL OL BL ELL • Word Problem Practice, p. 9 AL OL ELL • Enrichment, p. 10 OL BL **Transparencies** • 5-Minute Check Transparency 12-1 AL OL BL ELL **Additional Print Resources** • *Study Notebook* AL OL BL ELL	**Materials:** • index cards • tape • rice
Technology for Every Lesson	Math Online glencoe.com • Extra Examples • Self-Check Quizzes • Personal Tutor	**CD/DVD Resources** IWB INTERACTIVE WHITEBOARD READY IWB StudentWorks Plus IWB Interactive Classroom IWB Diagnostic and Assessment Planner	• TeacherWorks Plus • eSolutions Manual Plus • ExamView Assessment Suite
Math in Motion	p. 663		p. 670
Differentiated Instruction		pp. 665, 669	

KEY: AL Approaching Level OL On Level BL Beyond Level ELL English Learners

Surface Area and Volume

Suggested Pacing			
Time Periods	Instruction	Review & Assessment	Total
45-minute	14	2	16
90-minute	7	1	8

Lesson 12-2 Pacing: 1 day	Lesson 12-3 Pacing: 1 day	Explore 12-4 Pacing: 1 day	Lesson 12-4 Pacing: 1 day
Volume of Prisms	**Volume of Cylinders**	**Geometry Lab: Volume of a Pyramid**	**Volume of Pyramids, Cones, and Spheres**
• Find volumes of prisms. • Find volumes of composite figures.	• Find the volumes of circular cylinders. • Find the volumes of composite figures involving circular cylinders.	• Develop a method to find the volume of a pyramid.	• Find the volumes of pyramids and cones. • Find the volumes of spheres.
volume			sphere
	p. 680		
Chapter 12 Resource Masters • Study Guide and Intervention, pp. 11–12 AL OL ELL • Skills Practice, p. 13 AL OL ELL • Practice, p. 14 AL OL BL ELL • Word Problem Practice, p. 15 AL OL ELL • Enrichment, p. 16 OL BL • Graphing Calculator, p. 17 AL OL BL ELL • Quiz 1, p. 58 AL OL BL ELL **Transparencies** • 5-Minute Check Transparency 12-2 AL OL BL ELL **Additional Print Resources** • *Study Notebook* AL OL BL ELL	**Chapter 12 Resource Masters** • Study Guide and Intervention, pp. 18–19 AL OL ELL • Skills Practice, p. 20 AL OL ELL • Practice, p. 21 AL OL BL ELL • Word Problem Practice, p. 22 AL OL ELL • Enrichment, p. 23 OL BL **Transparencies** • 5-Minute Check Transparency 12-3 AL OL BL ELL **Additional Print Resources** • *Study Notebook* AL OL BL ELL	**Materials:** • ruler • tape • rice • scissors	**Chapter 12 Resource Masters** • Study Guide and Intervention, pp. 24–25 AL OL ELL • Skills Practice, p. 26 AL OL ELL • Practice, p. 27 AL OL BL ELL • Word Problem Practice, p. 28 AL OL ELL • Enrichment, p. 29 OL BL • Quiz 2, p. 58 AL OL BL ELL **Transparencies** • 5-Minute Check Transparency 12-4 AL OL BL ELL **Additional Print Resources** • *Study Notebook* AL OL BL ELL

Math Online glencoe.com
- Extra Examples
- Self-Check Quizzes
- Personal Tutor

CD/DVD Resources IWB INTERACTIVE WHITEBOARD READY
- IWB StudentWorks Plus
- IWB Interactive Classroom
- IWB Diagnostic and Assessment Planner
- TeacherWorks Plus
- eSolutions Manual Plus
- ExamView Assessment Suite

		p. 682	p. 685
pp. 672, 676	pp. 678, 681		pp. 684, 688

Formative Assessment
Mid-Chapter Quiz, p. 689

CHAPTER 12

Chapter Planner

	Explore 12-5 Pacing: 1 day	Lesson 12-5 Pacing: 1 day	Explore 12-6 Pacing: 1 day
Title	**Geometry Lab: Surface Area of Prisms**	**Surface Area of Prisms**	**Geometry Lab: Surface Area of Cylinders**
Objectives	• Find the surface area of prisms.	• Find lateral area and surface area of prisms. • Find surface area of real-world objects shaped like prisms.	• Use a net to find the surface area of a cylinder.
Key Vocabulary		lateral face lateral area surface area	
NCTM Focal Points			
Multiple Representations		p. 694	
Lesson Resources	**Materials:** • empty box with a tuck lid • ruler • marker	**Chapter 12 Resource Masters** • Study Guide and Intervention, pp. 30–31 AL OL ELL • Skills Practice, p. 32 AL OL ELL • Practice, p. 33 AL OL BL ELL • Word Problem Practice, p. 34 AL OL ELL • Enrichment, p. 35 OL BL • Spreadsheet, p. 36 AL OL BL ELL • Quiz 3, p. 59 AL OL BL ELL **Transparencies** • 5-Minute Check Transparency 12-5 AL OL BL ELL **Additional Print Resources** • *Study Notebook* AL OL BL ELL	**Materials:** • cylinder-shaped container with lid • ruler • tape • scissors
Technology for Every Lesson	Math Online glencoe.com • Extra Examples • Self-Check Quizzes • Personal Tutor	**CD/DVD Resources** IWB INTERACTIVE WHITEBOARD READY IWB StudentWorks Plus IWB Interactive Classroom IWB Diagnostic and Assessment Planner	• TeacherWorks Plus • eSolutions Manual Plus • ExamView Assessment Suite
Math in Motion	p. 690		p. 696
Differentiated Instruction		pp. 692, 695	

KEY: AL Approaching Level OL On Level BL Beyond Level ELL English Learners

Lesson 12-6 Pacing: 1 day	Lesson 12-7 Pacing: 1 day	Explore 12-8 Pacing: 1 day	Lesson 12-8 Pacing: 1 day
Surface Area of Cylinders	**Surface Area of Pyramids and Cones**	**Geometry Lab: Similar Solids**	**Similar Solids**
• Find lateral and surface areas of cylinders. • Compare surface areas of cylinders.	• Find lateral areas and surface areas of pyramids. • Find lateral areas and surface areas of cones.	• Investigate similar solids.	• Identify similar solids. • Examine properties of similar solids.
	regular pyramid slant height		similar solids
	p. 706		
Chapter 12 Resource Masters • Study Guide and Intervention, pp. 37–38 AL OL ELL • Skills Practice, p. 39 AL OL ELL • Practice, p. 40 AL OL BL ELL • Word Problem Practice, p. 41 AL OL ELL • Enrichment, p. 42 OL BL • Quiz 3, p. 59 AL OL BL ELL **Transparencies** • 5-Minute Check Transparency 12-6 AL OL BL ELL **Additional Print Resources** • *Study Notebook* AL OL BL ELL	**Chapter 12 Resource Masters** • Study Guide and Intervention, pp. 43–44 AL OL ELL • Skills Practice, p. 45 AL OL ELL • Practice, p. 46 AL OL BL ELL • Word Problem Practice, p. 47 AL OL ELL • Enrichment, p. 48 OL BL **Transparencies** • 5-Minute Check Transparency 12-7 AL OL BL ELL **Additional Print Resources** • *Study Notebook* AL OL BL ELL	**Materials:** • sugar cubes or centimeter blocks	**Chapter 12 Resource Masters** • Study Guide and Intervention, pp. 49–50 AL OL ELL • Skills Practice, p. 51 AL OL ELL • Practice, p. 52 AL OL BL ELL • Word Problem Practice, p. 53 AL OL ELL • Enrichment, p. 54 OL BL • Quiz 4, p. 59 AL OL BL ELL **Transparencies** • 5-Minute Check Transparency 12-8 AL OL BL ELL **Additional Print Resources** • *Study Notebook* AL OL BL ELL
Math Online glencoe.com • Extra Examples • Self-Check Quizzes • Personal Tutor	**CD/DVD Resources** IWB INTERACTIVE WHITEBOARD READY IWB StudentWorks Plus IWB Interactive Classroom IWB Diagnostic and Assessment Planner	• TeacherWorks Plus • eSolutions Manual Plus • ExamView Assessment Suite	
p. 697		p. 708	
pp. 698, 701	pp. 703, 707		pp. 710, 715

Summative Assessment
- Study Guide and Review, pp. 716–720
- Practice Test, p. 721

CHAPTER 12

Assessment and Intervention

SE = Student Edition, **TE** = Teacher Edition, **CRM** = Chapter Resource Masters

	Diagnosis	Prescription
Diagnostic Assessment	**Beginning Chapter 12**	
	Get Ready for Chapter 12 **SE,** p. 661	Response to Intervention **TE,** p. 661
	Beginning Every Lesson	
	Then, Now, Why? **SE** 5-Minute Check Transparencies	Chapter 0 **SE,** pp. P1–P22 Concepts and Skills Bank **SE,** pp. 856–887 *Quick Review Math Handbook*
Formative Assessment	**During/After Every Lesson**	
	Check Your Progress **SE,** every example Check Your Understanding **SE** H.O.T. Problems **SE** Spiral Review **SE** Additional Examples **TE** Watch Out! **TE** Step 4, Assess **TE** Chapter 12 Quizzes **CRM,** pp. 58–59 Self-Check Quizzes **glencoe.com**	**Tier 1 Intervention** Concepts and Skills Bank **SE,** pp. 856–887 Skills Practice **CRM,** Ch. 1–12 **glencoe.com** **Tier 2 Intervention** Differentiated Instruction **TE** Study Guide and Intervention Masters **CRM,** Ch. 1–12 *Quick Review Math Handbook* **Tier 3 Intervention** *Math Triumphs, Grade 7,* Ch. 5–6
	Mid-Chapter	
	Mid-Chapter Quiz **SE,** p. 689 Mid-Chapter Test **CRM,** p. 60 ExamView Assessment Suite	**Tier 1 Intervention** Concepts and Skills Bank **SE,** pp. 856–887 Skills Practice **CRM,** Ch. 1–12 **glencoe.com** **Tier 2 Intervention** Study Guide and Intervention Masters **CRM,** Ch. 1–12 *Quick Review Math Handbook* **Tier 3 Intervention** *Math Triumphs, Grade 7,* Ch. 5–6
	Before Chapter Test	
	Chapter Study Guide and Review **SE,** pp. 716–720 Practice Test **SE,** p. 721 Standardized Test Practice **SE,** pp. 722–725 Chapter Test **glencoe.com** Standardized Test Practice **glencoe.com** Vocabulary Review **glencoe.com** ExamView Assessment Suite	**Tier 1 Intervention** Concepts and Skills Bank **SE,** pp. 856–887 Skills Practice **CRM,** Ch. 1–12 **glencoe.com** **Tier 2 Intervention** Study Guide and Intervention Masters **CRM,** Ch. 1–12 *Quick Review Math Handbook* **Tier 3 Intervention** *Math Triumphs, Grade 7,* Ch. 5–6
Summative Assessment	**After Chapter 12**	
	Multiple-Choice Tests, Forms 1, 2A, 2B, **CRM,** pp. 62–67 Free-Response Tests, Forms 2C, 2D, 3, **CRM,** pp. 68–73 Vocabulary Test **CRM,** p. 61 Extended Response Test **CRM,** p. 74 Standardized Test Practice **CRM,** pp. 75–77 ExamView Assessment Suite	Study Guide and Intervention Masters **CRM,** Ch. 1–12 *Quick Review Math Handbook* **glencoe.com**

CHAPTER 12 Differentiated Instruction

Option 1 Reaching All Learners AL OL BL ELL

INTERPERSONAL Have students use nets to explore lateral area and surface area. Have pairs follow these steps:

- Create a net of any solid of choice.
- Measure the dimensions of the net and record them on a separate sheet of paper.
- Find the lateral area and surface area of the solid and record it on the same sheet of paper with the measurements.
- Write on an index card three possible measures for lateral area and surface area, including the correct measures.

Have student pairs trade solids and index cards. Ask pairs to estimate and circle the two areas they believe are correct. Then have them measure the solids and find the lateral area and surface area. Have them discuss any differences between their estimated choices of areas and the actual areas.

VISUAL/SPATIAL Have students work in small groups. Ask each group to make several clay models of a polyhedron. Then have them use string, floss, or plastic wedges to make horizontal, vertical, and angled slices through the models. Have students make at least two angled slices through different parts of the polyhedron. For example, one slice might be through a corner, while another might be through all of the faces of the solid. Ask students to make a sketch of each cross section and include a description of the type of slice and its angle. Then have them discuss whether a relationship exists between the shape of the cross section, type of slice, and the solid.

Option 2 Approaching Level AL

Have small groups use centimeter cubes or other cubes to build as many rectangular prisms as they can with the same volume, such as 24 cm^3, 36 cm^3, or 48 cm^3. As students build the prisms, have them record the base, the height, and the volume in a chart.

Base	Height	Volume

Have groups compare the base and height of the prisms to the volumes of the prisms, and then make a conjecture about the relationship.

Option 3 English Learners ELL

Use solids to demonstrate the different parts of each solid. Placing the item on an overhead projector will help them visualize the shapes of each part. For example, if you place a cylinder on its base on an overhead you will see a circle as the base. When you place the cylinder on its side on the overhead, students will be able to see the shape is a rectangle.

As students work through the chapter, encourage them to compare and contrast the words they tend to confuse, such as *prism* and *pyramid*, *cone* and *cylinder*, *lateral area* and *surface area*, *base* and *face*. Suggest that students use graphic organizers such as Venn diagrams or T-charts to record similarities and differences between the words.

Option 4 Beyond Level BL

Have students work in groups to design a box for an object in the classroom, such as a map, globe, or pencil holder. Remind students that box designs do not have to be rectangular prisms and that objects may require additional space for cushioning. Have groups present the following with their designs:

- A net that shows the dimensions of the box.
- Calculations that show the object will fit in the box, including any additional space that may be necessary.
- Calculations to show how much paper they would need to wrap the box.

CHAPTER 12

Focus on Mathematical Content

Vertical Alignment

Before Chapter 12

Related Topics before Pre-Algebra
- use properties to classify three-dimensional figures
- connect models to formulas

Previous Topics from Pre-Algebra
- communicate mathematical ideas
- use geometric concepts and properties

Chapter 12

Related Topics from Pre-Algebra
- draw three-dimensional figures from different perspectives
- connect models of prisms, cylinders, pyramids, spheres, and cones to formulas for volume of these objects
- estimate measurements and use formulas to solve application problems involving lateral and surface area
- use proportional relationships in similar three-dimensional figures to find missing measurements

After Chapter 12

Preparation for Geometry
- find surface area and volume of prisms, pyramids, spheres, cones, cylinders, and composites of these figures in problem situations
- analyze the characteristics of polyhedra and other three-dimensional figures
- use and extend similarity properties to explore and justify conjectures

Lesson-by-Lesson Preview

12-1 Three-Dimensional Figures

A plane is a two-dimensional flat surface that extends in all directions. Intersecting planes can form the edges and vertices of three-dimensional figures or solids. An edge is where two planes intersect in a line, and a vertex is where three or more planes intersect in a point.

A polyhedron is a solid with flat surfaces that are polygons. Polyhedrons are composed of faces, edges, and vertices and are differentiated by the shape and number of their bases.

- Prisms and pyramids are named by the shape of their bases, such as rectangular prisms and pentagonal pyramids.
- Prisms have two parallel, congruent faces called bases. Pyramids have one base.

Solids that are not polyhedrons include cylinders and cones. Vertical, angled, and horizontal slices through solid figures produce various shapes called cross sections.

12-2 Volume of Prisms

Volume is the measure of space occupied by a solid region. To find the volume of a prism, use the formula $V = Bh$, where B is the area of the base of the prism and h is height.

A solid containing several prisms can be broken into its component prisms. Then the volume of each component can be found and the volumes added.

12-3 Volume of Cylinders

To find the volume of a cylinder, find the area of its circular base and then multiply by the height: $V = Bh$, or $V = \pi r^2 h$, where r is radius of the circular base and h is height. For example, use the formula to find the volume of the cylinder shown below:

- $V = Bh$
  $V = \pi r^2 h$
  $= \pi \cdot 3^2 \cdot 10$
  282.7 cubic units

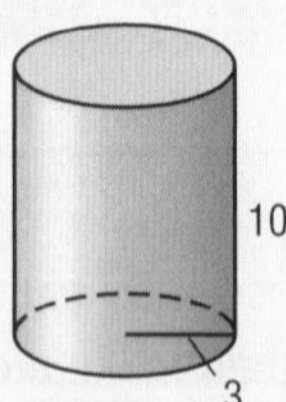

Surface Area and Volume

12-4 Volume of Pyramids, Cones, and Spheres

The volume of a pyramid is one-third the volume of a prism with the same base and height. To find the volume of a pyramid, use the formula $V = \frac{1}{3}Bh$.

The volume of a cone is one-third the volume of a cylinder with the same base and height. To find the volume of a cone, use the formula $V = \frac{1}{3}Bh$, where $B = \pi r^2$ or $V = \frac{1}{3}\pi r^2 h$.

A sphere is a set of points in space that are a given distance r from a given point called the center. If a sphere with radius r is placed inside a cylinder with the same radius r and height $2r$, the volume of the sphere is $\frac{2}{3}$ the volume of the cylinder. So the volume of a sphere is $V = \left(\frac{2}{3}\right)(\pi r^2)(2r)$ or $V = \frac{4}{3}\pi r^3$.

12-5 Surface Area of Prisms

A prism has two bases, which are parallel, and faces that are not bases, which are called lateral faces.

- The lateral area L of a prism is the sum of the areas of the lateral faces. The formula for the lateral area is $L = Ph$, where P is the perimeter of the base and h is height.
- The surface area of a prism is the sum of the lateral area plus the area of the bases. The formula for surface area is $S = L + 2B$ or $S = Ph + 2B$, where B is the area of a base.

12-6 Surface Area of Cylinders

The net of a cylinder is a rectangle (lateral face) and two circles (bases).

- The lateral area L of a cylinder with radius r and height h is the circumference of the base $(2\pi r)$ times the height h or $L = 2\pi rh$.
- The surface area S is the lateral area L plus the area of the two bases or $S = L + 2B$ or $S = 2\pi rh + 2\pi r^2$.

12-7 Surface Area of Pyramids and Cones

The base of a regular pyramid is a regular polygon. The lateral faces of a regular pyramid are congruent isosceles triangles that intersect at the vertex. The altitude or height of each lateral face is the slant height.

- The lateral area L of a regular pyramid is $L = \frac{1}{2}P\ell$, where P is the perimeter of the base and ℓ is the slant height.
- The total surface area S is the lateral area L plus the area of the base B or $S = L + B$ or $S = \frac{1}{2}P\ell + B$.

A cone consists of a lateral area and a base area.

- The lateral area L of a cone is π times the radius r times the slant height ℓ or $L = \pi r\ell$.
- The surface area S of a cone with slant height ℓ and radius r is the lateral area plus the area of the base or $S = L + \pi r^2$.

12-8 Similar Solids

Solid figures are similar if they have the same shape and their corresponding linear measures are proportional.

- If two solids are similar with a scale factor of $\frac{a}{b}$, then the ratio of the surface areas of the two solids is $\frac{a^2}{b^2}$.
- If two solids are similar with a scale factor of $\frac{a}{b}$, then the ratio of the volumes of the two solids is $\frac{a^3}{b^3}$.

Professional Development

Targeted professional development has been articulated throughout McGraw-Hill's mathematics program. The **McGraw-Hill Professional Development Video Library** provides short videos that support key topics. For more information, visit glencoe.com.

Model Lessons

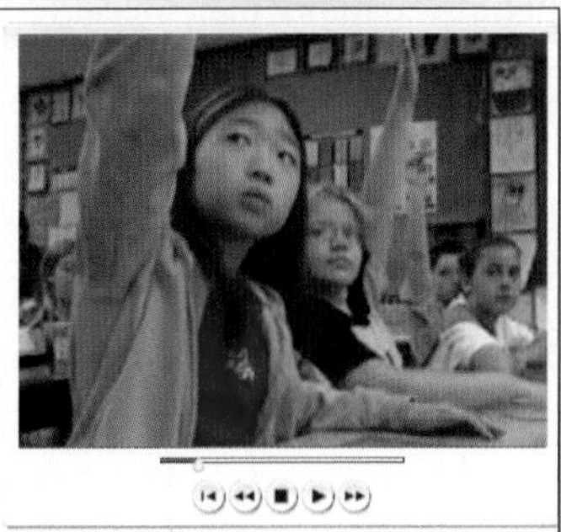

Instructional Strategies

CHAPTER 12 Notes

Chapter Project

The Measure of a Sculpture or Building

Students use what they have learned about three-dimensional figures, volume, lateral and surface area, and similar solids to work with concepts related to sculptures or buildings.

- Ask students to bring to class a photograph or drawing of a sculpture or building.
- Divide students into groups. Ask them to identify the geometric figures in the sculpture or building for each photograph or drawing in their group. Then have them draw the top view, the side view, and the shape that results from a vertical slice of each sculpture or building. What best describes each of the cross sections?
- Have groups design and draw their own sculpture or building using at least two of the following figures: cone, cylinder, rectangular or triangular prism, or rectangular, pentagonal, or hexagonal pyramid. Ask them to describe the faces, bases, edges, and vertices of the figures they use.
- Ask groups to add appropriate dimensions to their sculptures or buildings, and then find the volume and surface area of their designs. For which figures should they find the lateral area rather than the surface area?

CHAPTER 12 Surface Area and Volume

Then
In Chapter 11, you explored the properties of two-dimensional figures.

Now
In Chapter 12, you will:

- Describe three-dimensional figures.
- Find volumes and surface areas of three-dimensional figures.
- Examine properties of similar solids.

Why?
ART The world of art and design relies heavily on the use of three-dimensional figures. Artist Dale Chihuly uses blown glass to construct sculptures. His designs are geometric masterpieces!

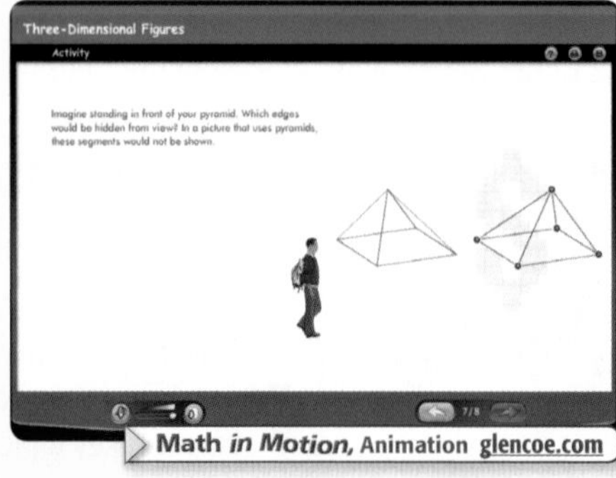

Math in Motion, Animation glencoe.com

Key Vocabulary Introduce the key vocabulary in the chapter using the routine below.

Define: Similar solids are solids that have the same shape and their corresponding linear measures are proportional.

Example: The two cylinders shown are similar. They have the same shape and their corresponding measures are proportional.

Ask: Choose two solid objects in the classroom that have the same shape. Measure the objects. Are they similar? Explain. Answers will vary but should indicate an understanding of similar solids.

Get Ready for Chapter 12

Diagnose Readiness You have two options for checking Prerequisite Skills.

Text Option Take the Quick Check below. Refer to the Quick Review for help.

QuickCheck

(Used in Lesson 12-1)

Determine whether each figure is a polygon. If it is, classify the polygon. (Lesson 11-5)

1.  yes; parallelogram

2.  no

3. **SIGNS** Classify the shape of the sign shown. octagon

(Used in Lessons 12-2 through 12-7)

Find each product. (Lesson 3-3)

4. 3(6)(12) 216
5. $\frac{1}{3}(21)(5)$ 35
6. $\frac{4}{3}(16)(3)$ 64
7. $\frac{5}{4}(24)(11)$ 330
8. **MUSIC** Suppose you practice the cello for $\frac{2}{3}$ hour every day. How many hours do you practice every week? $4\frac{2}{3}$ hr

(Used in Lesson 12-8)

Determine whether each pair of ratios forms a proportion. (Lesson 6-4)

9. $\frac{1}{3}$ and $\frac{2}{3}$ no
10. $\frac{2}{5}$ and $\frac{10}{25}$ yes
11. $\frac{2}{9}$ and $\frac{3}{18}$ no
12. $\frac{3}{4}$ and $\frac{39}{52}$ yes
13. **WATER** Determine whether the set of numbers in the table are proportional. Explain your reasoning.

Bottles	1	2	3	4
Cost ($)	1.25	2.50	3.75	5.00

yes; $\frac{1}{1.25} = \frac{2}{2.5} = \frac{3}{3.75} = \frac{4}{5}$

QuickReview

EXAMPLE 1

Determine whether the figure is a polygon. If it is, classify the polygon.

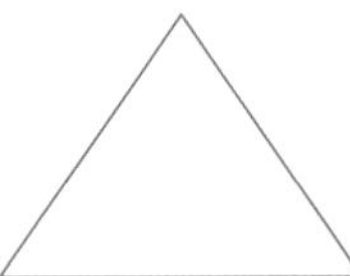

The polygon has 3 sides. It is a triangle.

EXAMPLE 2

Find $\frac{1}{3}(24)(5.8)$.

$\frac{1}{3}(24)(5.8) = \left[\frac{1}{3}(24)\right](5.8)$ Associative Property

$= (8)(5.8)$ Simplify.

$= 46.4$ Simplify.

EXAMPLE 3

Determine whether $\frac{2}{7}$ and $\frac{12}{42}$ form a proportion.

$\frac{2}{7} = \frac{12}{42}$ Write a proportion.

$2(42) = (7)12$ Find the cross products.

$84 = 84$ Simplify.

Since $\frac{2}{7} = \frac{12}{42}$, $\frac{2}{7}$ and $\frac{12}{42}$ form a proportion.

Online Option Math Online Take a self-check Chapter Readiness Quiz at glencoe.com.

Get Ready for Chapter 12

Response to Intervention (RtI)

Use the *Quick Check* results and the Intervention Planner chart to help you determine your Response to Intervention. The If-Then statements in the chart help you decide the appropriate tier of RtI and suggest intervention resources for each tier.

Intervention Planner

Tier 1 On Level

 students miss about 25% of the exercises or less,

 choose a resource:

- **SE** Lessons 3-3, 6-4, 11-5
- **CRM** Skills Practice, Chapter 3, p20; Chapter 6, p. 25; Chapter 11, p. 31
- **TE** Chapter Project, p. 660

Math Online Self-Check Quiz

Tier 2 Strategic Intervention approaching grade level

 students miss about 50% of the exercises,

Then choose a resource:

- **CRM** Study Guide and Intervention, Chapter 3, p. 18; Chapter 6, p. 23; Chapter 11, p. 29

Quick Review Math Handbook

Math Online Extra Examples, Personal Tutor, Homework Help

Tier 3 Intensive Intervention 2 or more grades below level

students miss about 75% of the exercises,

use *Math Triumphs, Grade 7*, Ch. 5–6

Math Online Extra Examples, Personal Tutor, Homework Help, Review Vocabulary

CHAPTER 12 Notes

FOLDABLES® Study Organizer

Dinah Zike's Foldables®

Focus Students write notes about surface area and volume as they work through this chapter.

Teach Have students make and label the tabs for each lesson of their Foldables as illustrated. Students should write concepts on the front of each tab and definitions on the back. Have students use the appropriate tabs as they cover each lesson in this chapter and include their own statistical examples for each.

When to Use It Encourage students to add to their Foldable as they work through the chapter and use it as a self-checking study guide as they prepare for the chapter test.

Differentiated Instruction

CRM Student-Built Glossary, pp. 1–2 Students should complete the chart by providing a definition of each term and an example as they progress through Chapter 12. This study tool can also be used to review for the chapter test.

Get Started on Chapter 12

You will learn several new concepts, skills, and vocabulary terms as you study Chapter 12. To get ready, identify important terms and organize your resources. You may wish to refer to **Chapter 0** to review prerequisite skills.

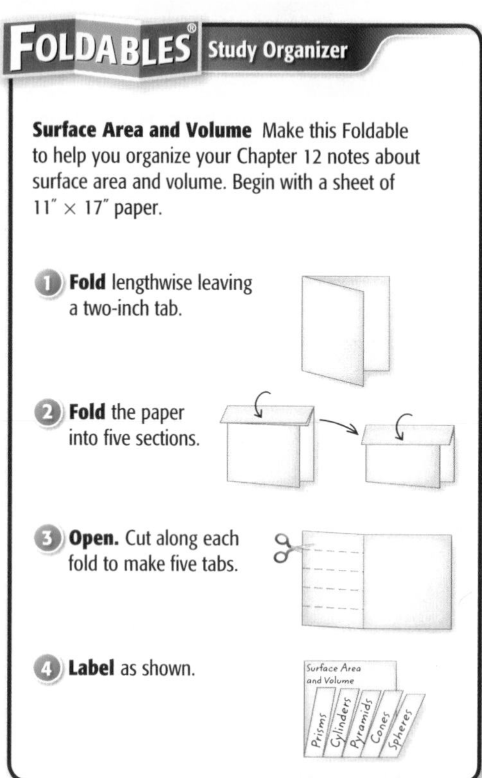

FOLDABLES® Study Organizer
Surface Area and Volume Make this Foldable to help you organize your Chapter 12 notes about surface area and volume. Begin with a sheet of 11″ × 17″ paper.
1 **Fold** lengthwise leaving a two-inch tab.
2 **Fold** the paper into five sections.
3 **Open.** Cut along each fold to make five tabs.
4 **Label** as shown.
Surface Area and Volume
Prisms
Cylinders
Pyramids
Cones
Spheres

New Vocabulary

English		Español
plane	• p. 664 •	plano
solid	• p. 664 •	sólido
edge	• p. 664 •	arista
vertex	• p. 664 •	vértice
face	• p. 664 •	cara
prism	• p. 665 •	prisma
base	• p. 665 •	base
pyramid	• p. 665 •	pirámide
cylinder	• p. 665 •	cilindro
cone	• p. 665 •	cono sección
cross section	• p. 666 •	transversal
volume	• p. 671 •	volumen
sphere	• p. 684 •	esfera
nets	• p. 690 •	redes
lateral face	• p. 691 •	cara lateral
lateral area	• p. 691 •	área lateral
surface area	• p. 691 •	área
slant height	• p. 702 •	altura oblicua
similar solids	• p. 709 •	sólidos semejantes

Review Vocabulary

dilation • p. 307 • homotecia a transformation that alters the size of a figure by a scale factor, but not its shape

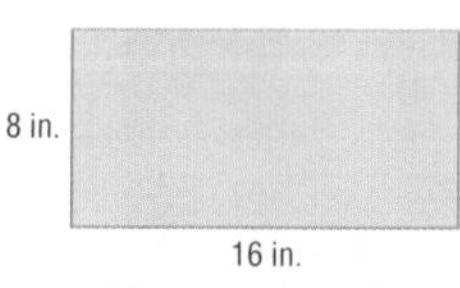

Multilingual eGlossary glencoe.com

Math Online glencoe.com

- Study the chapter online
- Explore **Math in Motion**
- Get extra help from your own **Personal Tutor**
- Use **Extra Examples** for additional help
- Take a **Self-Check Quiz**
- **Review Vocabulary** in fun ways

EXPLORE 12-1 Geometry Lab
Drawing Three-Dimensional Figures

Math Online glencoe.com
Math *in Motion*, Animation

Different views of a stack of cubes are shown. A point of view is called a **perspective.** You can build or draw three-dimensional figures using different perspectives.

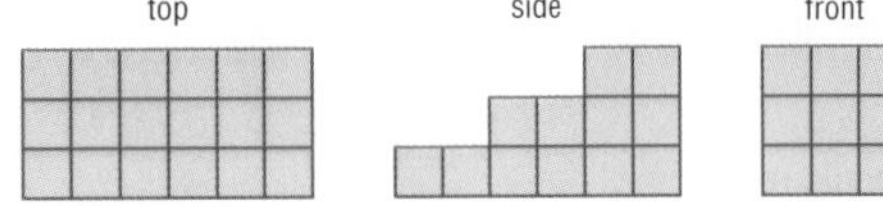

ACTIVITY

Build the figure that has the views shown above. Then use isometric dot paper to draw the model.

Step 1 Use the top view. The top view shows the shape of the base. It is a 3-by-6 rectangle.

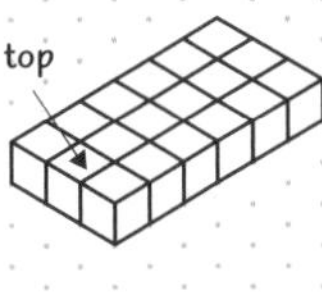

Step 2 The front view is a 3-by-3 square. This shows that the overall height and width of the figure is 3 units. The side view shows that the height increases in steps from 1 unit to 3 units.

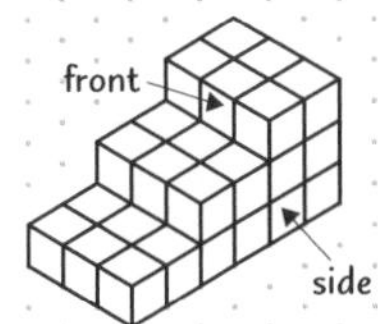

Exercises

The top view, a side view, and the front view of a three-dimensional figure are shown. Use cubes to build each figure. Then draw your model on isometric dot paper. 1–6. See Chapter 12 Answer Appendix.

1. 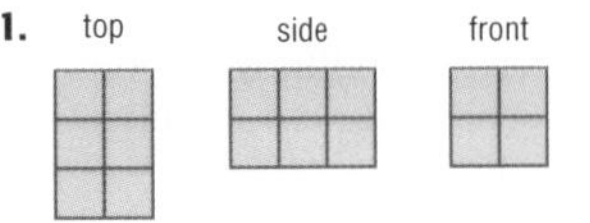

2. 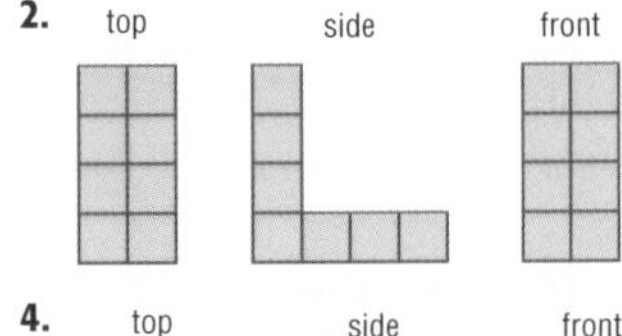

3. 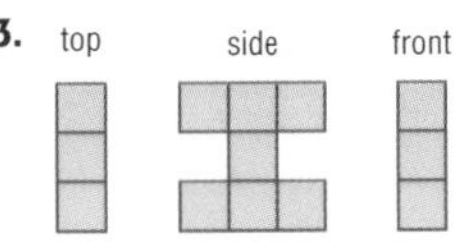

4. 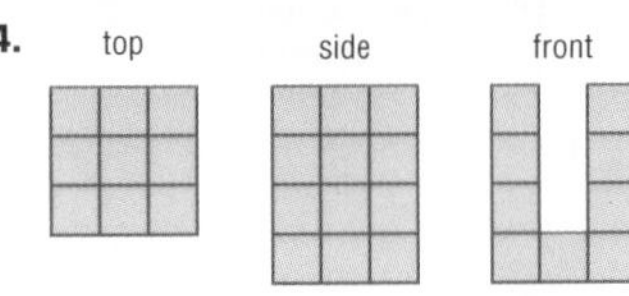

Draw and label the top view, a side view, and the front view for each figure.

5. 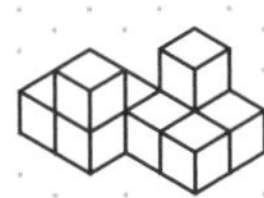

6.

From Concrete to Abstract

Have students work in pairs to create figures with cubes. Have partners trade figures and draw the three perspectives of their figure on isometric dot paper.

EXPLORE 12-1 Lesson Notes

1 FOCUS

Objective Draw three-dimensional figures using different perspectives.

Materials for Each Student

- cubes
- isometric dot paper

Easy to Make Manipulatives

Teaching Pre-Algebra with Manipulatives, template for

- isometric dot paper, p. 16

Teaching Tip

Use square building blocks to create a figure to demonstrate different perspectives.

2 TEACH

Working in Cooperative Groups

Arrange students in groups of two or three, mixing abilities. Have students try to determine the number of blocks they need to build each figure before they begin.

Ask:

- What perspective gives the most complete view of the shape of the figure? None; each perspective adds a different, but limited, dimension to the figure.
- Is there a figure that would have the same shape in all three perspectives? yes; a cube

Practice Have students complete Exercises 1–6.

3 ASSESS

Formative Assessment

Use Exercises 1–6 to assess whether students comprehend how to draw different perspectives of three-dimensional figures.

12-1 Lesson Notes

1 FOCUS

Vertical Alignment

Before Lesson 12-1
Model three-dimensional figures.

Lesson 12-1
Identify three-dimensional figures. Describe and draw vertical, horizontal, and angled cross sections of three-dimensional figures.

After Lesson 12-1
Analyze the characteristics of polyhedra and other three-dimensional figures and their component parts based on explorations and concrete models.

2 TEACH

Scaffolding Questions

Have students read the *Why?* section of the lesson and answer the questions.

Ask:

- How does the top view, or perspective, of the cylinder differ from the front view? The top of the cylinder is a circle, the front view is rectangular.
- How could you make a model of the glass with paper? Take a rectangle and tape the two short sides together and then tape a circle to the bottom.

12-1 Three-Dimensional Figures

Then
You have already modeled three-dimensional figures. (Lesson 12-1a)

Now
- Identify three-dimensional figures.
- Describe and draw vertical, horizontal, and angled cross sections of three-dimensional figures.

New Vocabulary
plane
solid
polyhedron
edge
vertex
face
prism
base
pyramid
cylinder
cone
cross section

Math Online
glencoe.com
- Extra Examples
- Personal Tutor
- Self-Check Quiz
- Homework Help

Why?

a. If you observe the figures from directly above, what geometric figure(s) do you see? ice cream: circle; glass: circle; silo: circle

b. If you view the figures directly from the front, what geometric figure(s) do you see? b–c. See margin.

c. Explain how you can see different two-dimensional figures when looking at a three-dimensional figure.

Identify Three-Dimensional Figures A two-dimensional figure has two dimensions—length and width. A **plane** is a two-dimensional flat surface that extends in all directions. There are different ways that planes may be related in space.

Intersect in a Line

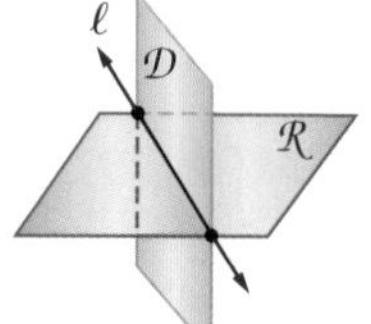

ℓ
D
R

Intersect in a Point

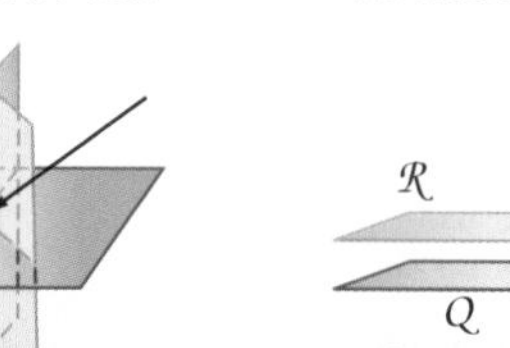

Q
A
R
P

No Intersection

R

Q

These are called parallel planes.

A three-dimensional figure has three dimensions—length, width, and depth (or height). Intersecting planes can form three-dimensional figures or **solids**. A **polyhedron** is a solid with flat surfaces that are polygons.

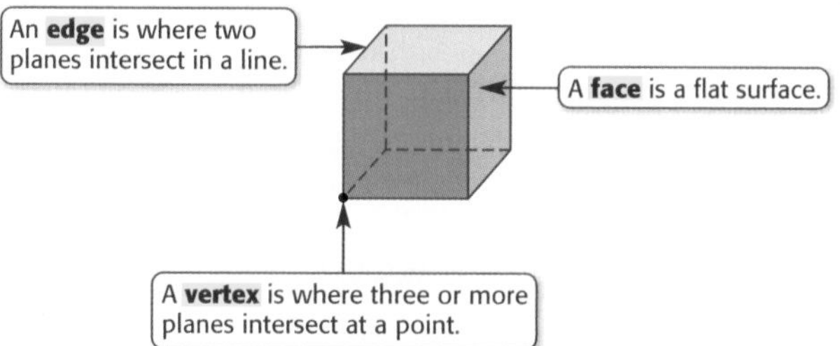

An edge is where two planes intersect in a line.
A face is a flat surface.
A vertex is where three or more planes intersect at a point.

Lesson 12-1 Resources

Resource	Approaching-Level	On-Level	Beyond-Level	English Learners
Teacher Edition	• Differentiated Instruction, p. 665		• Differentiated Instruction, p. 669	• Differentiated Instruction, p. 665
Chapter Resource Masters	• Study Guide and Intervention, pp. 5–6 • Skills Practice, p. 7 • Practive, p. 8 • Word Problem Practice, p. 9	• Study Guide and Intervention, pp. 5–6 • Skills Practice, p. 7 • Practice, p. 8 • Word Problem Practice, p. 9 • Enrichment, p. 10	• Practice, p. 8 • Word Problem Practice, p. 9 • Enrichment, p. 10	• Study Guide and Intervention, pp. 5–6 • Skills Practice, p. 7 • Practice, p. 8
Transparencies	• 5-Minute Check Transparency 12-1	• 5-Minute Check Transparency 12-1	• 5-Minute Check Transparency 12-1	• 5-Minute Check Transparency 12-1
Other	• Study Notebook • Teaching Pre-Algebra with Manipulatives	• Study Notebook • Teaching Pre-Algebra with Manipulatives	• Study Notebook	• Study Notebook • Teaching Pre-Algebra with Manipulatives

Watch Out!

Bases In a *rectangular* prism, the bases do not have to be the top and bottom. Any two parallel rectangles are bases. In a *triangular* pyramid, any face is a base.

A **prism** is a polyhedron with two parallel, congruent faces called **bases** that are polygons. A **pyramid** is a polyhedron with one base that is any polygon. Its other faces are triangles. Prisms and pyramids are named by the shape of their bases.

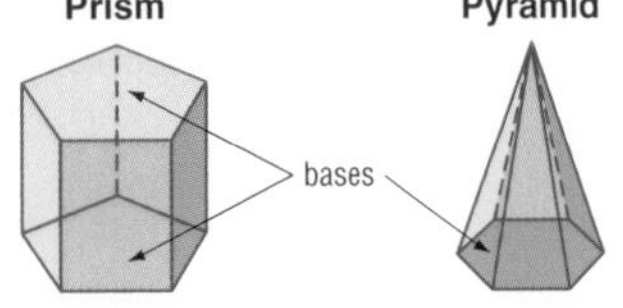

Concept Summary Polyhedrons — For Your FOLDABLE

Polyhedron	triangular prism	rectangular prism	triangular pyramid	rectangular pyramid
Number of Bases	2	2	1	1
Polygon Base	triangle	rectangle	triangle	rectangle
Figure				

Vocabulary Link

Cone
Everyday Use Lupe had an ice cream *cone* for dessert.
Math Use A solid with one base that is a circle connected to a vertex by a curved side is a *cone*.

There are solids that are *not* polyhedrons. A **cylinder** is a three-dimensional figure with congruent, parallel bases that are circles connected with a curved side. A **cone** has one circular base and a vertex connected by a curved side.

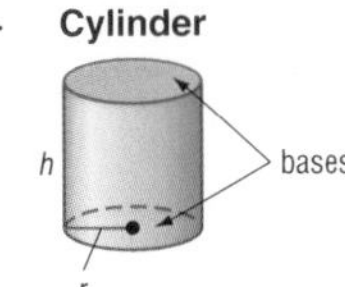

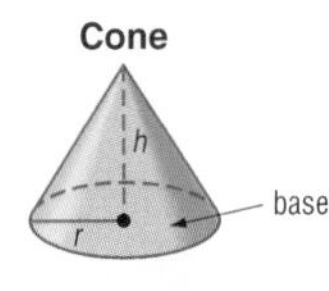

EXAMPLE 1 Identify Three-Dimensional Figures

Identify the figure. Name the bases, faces, edges, and vertices.

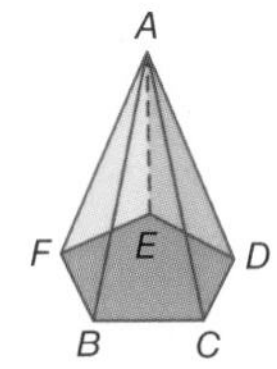

This figure has one pentagonal base, *BCDEF*, so it is a pentagonal pyramid.

faces: *ABF, AFE, AED, ADC, ACB, BCDEF*

edges: $\overline{AB}, \overline{AC}, \overline{AD}, \overline{AE}, \overline{AF}, \overline{BC}, \overline{CD}, \overline{DE}, \overline{EF}, \overline{FB}$

vertices: *A, B, C, D, E, F*

Check Your Progress

1A.

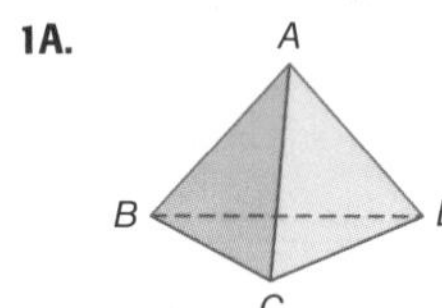

1B.

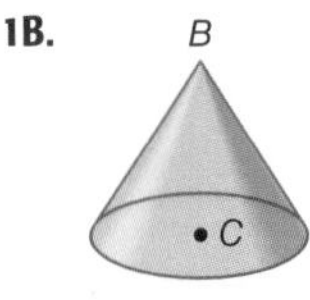

Personal Tutor glencoe.com

1A. triangular pyramid; base *BCD*; faces: *ABD*, *ABC*, *ACD*, *BCD*; edges: $\overline{AB}$, $\overline{AC}$, $\overline{AD}$, $\overline{BC}$, $\overline{CD}$, $\overline{DB}$; vertices; *A*, *B*, *C*, *D*

1B. cone; base circle *C*; vertex: *B*; no faces or edges.

Identify Three-Dimensional Figures

Example 1 shows how to identify a three-dimensional figure and its bases, faces, edges, and vertices.

Formative Assessment

Use the Check Your Progress exercises after each example to determine students' understanding of concepts.

Additional Example

1 Identify the figure. Name the bases, faces, edges, and vertices.

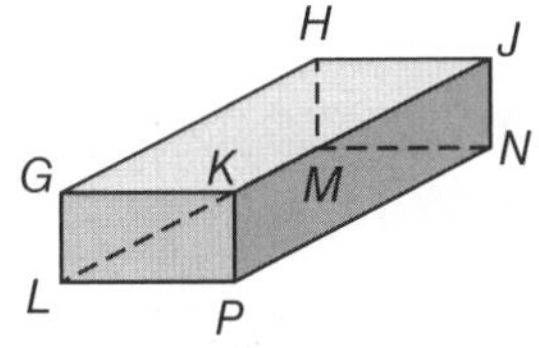

rectangular prism; bases: *GHJK*, *LMNP* or *GHML*, *KJNP* or *HJNM*, *GKPL*; faces: *GHJK*, *LMNP*, *GHML*, *HJNM*, *JKPN*, *GKPL*; edges: $\overline{GH}$, $\overline{HJ}$, $\overline{JK}$, $\overline{GK}$, $\overline{LM}$, $\overline{MN}$, $\overline{NP}$, $\overline{LP}$, $\overline{GL}$, $\overline{HM}$, $\overline{JN}$, $\overline{KP}$; vertices: *G, H, J, K, L, M, N, P*

Additional Examples also in Interactive Classroom PowerPoint® Presentations

Additional Answers

b. ice cream: triangle with a circle on top; glass of juice: rectangle; silo: rectangle with a triangle on top

c. Sample answer: When a three-dimensional figure has faces that are different polygons, the polygon you see depends on your point of view.

Differentiated Instruction

AL ELL

If students are struggling to identify three-dimensional figures,

Then provide students with scissors, cardboard or heavy paper, and tape. Assign students a three-dimensional figure such as a rectangular prism, square pyramid, triangular prism, triangular pyramid, or intersecting planes. Tell them to begin by drawing the base or bases of their figure and cutting it out. Have them draw and cut one face of the figure, and then use that shape as a guide to cut the other faces. Have students assign letters to various points on the figures and identify the bases, edges, and vertices.

Focus on Mathematical Content

Three-Dimensional Figures Three-dimensional figures differ from two-dimensional figures in that they have depth (or height). An example of a two-dimensional figure is a square. An example of a three-dimensional figure is a cube.

Cross Sections

Example 2 shows how to draw and describe cross sections of a cone. **Example 3** shows how to describe and draw a real-world figure.

Additional Examples

2 Draw and describe the shape resulting from a vertical, angled, and horizontal cross section of a rectangular pyramid. triangle or trapezoid; triangle or trapezoid; rectangle

3 **GIFT BOX** A gift box is shown below. Draw the top view and side view. Then draw and describe the shape resulting from a vertical cross section of the figure.

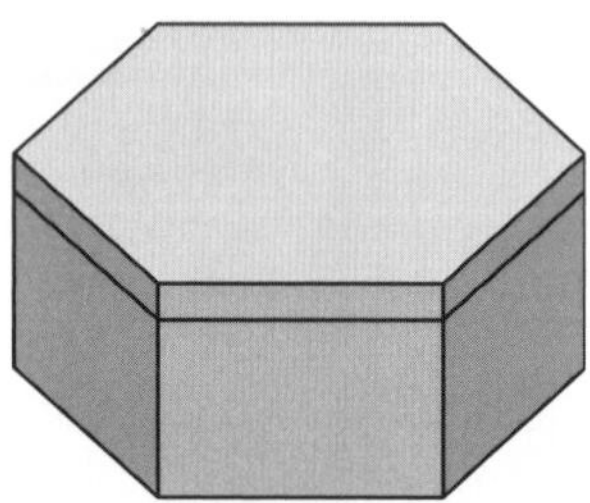

A vertical cross section results in the shape of a rectangle.

Cross Sections Interesting shapes can occur when a plane intersects, or slices, a three-dimensional figure. The intersection of the figure and the plane is called a **cross section** of the figure.

StudyTip

Parabola The shape that results from the angled slice through a cone is called a *parabola*. You learned about parabolas in Chapter 9.

EXAMPLE 2 Cross Section of a Cone

Draw and describe the shape resulting from the following vertical, angled, and horizontal cross sections of a cone.

Vertical Slice

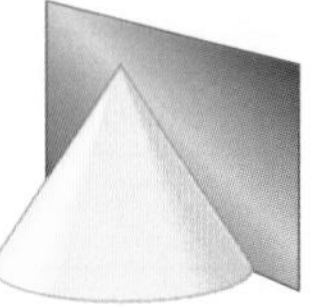

The cross section is a triangle.

Angled Slice

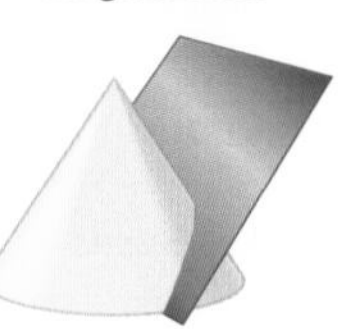

The cross section is a parabola.

Horizontal Slice

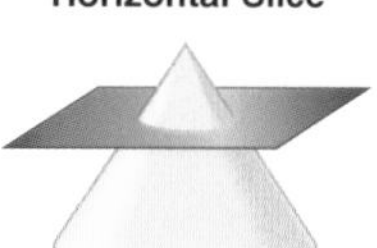

The cross section is a circle.

Check Your Progress

2. Draw and describe the shape resulting from a vertical, angled, and horizontal cross section of a triangular pyramid. See margin.

Personal Tutor glencoe.com

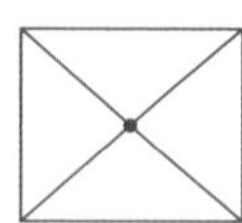

Math History Link

Euclid (c. 325–283 B.C.) The kind of solid geometry presented here is part of *Euclidean geometry.* Euclid was a Greek mathematician best known for his series of 13 books called *Elements*.

Real-World EXAMPLE 3 Describe and Draw

CRYSTALS A fluorite crystal is shown at the right. Draw the top view and side view. Then draw and describe the shape resulting from a vertical cross section of the figure.

The crystal is a rectangular prism with two square pyramids attached. The vertical cross sections will look similar to the side view.

Top View

Side View

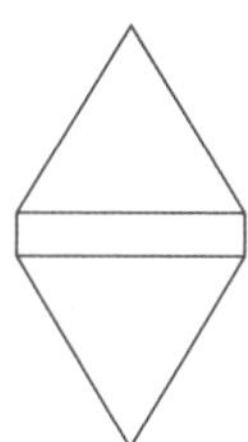

Vertical Cross Section

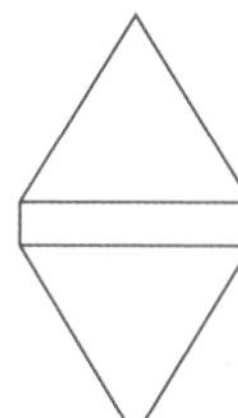

Check Your Progress

3. **CAMPING** Lemar and his brother went camping for the weekend. They set up the tent at the right. Draw the top view and side view. Then draw and describe the shape resulting from a vertical cross section of the figure. See Chapter 12 Answer Appendix

Personal Tutor glencoe.com

Additional Answers

CYP 2. triangle; triangle or trapezoid; triangle; See students work for drawings.

Additional Example 3

Top

Side

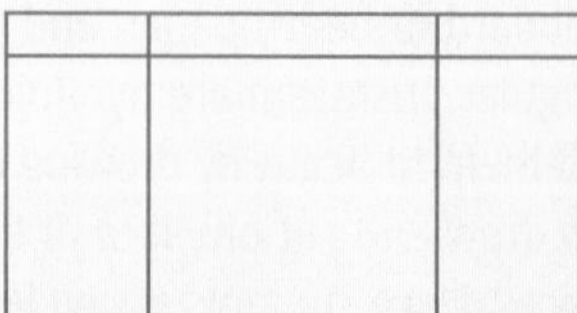

Cross Section

666 Chapter 12 Surface Area and Volume

Check Your Understanding

Example 1 p. 665 Identify each figure. Name the bases, faces, edges, and vertices.

1–5. See margin.

1. 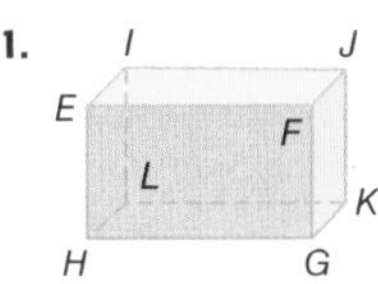

2. 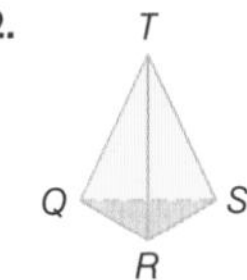

Example 2 p. 666 Draw and describe the shape resulting from each cross section.

3. 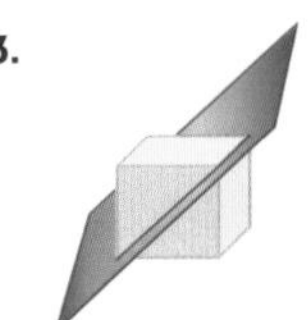

4. 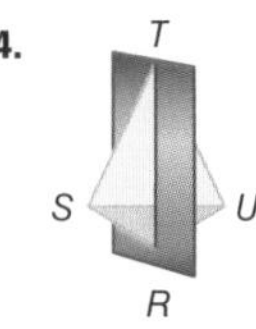

5. 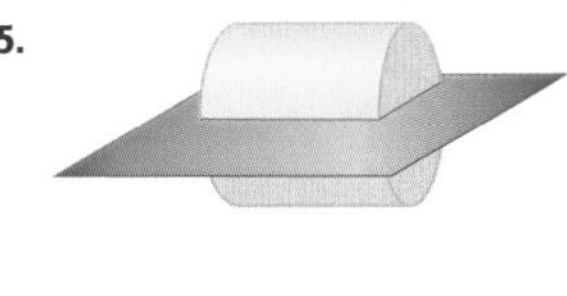

Example 3 p. 666

6. See Chapter 12 Answer Appendix.

6. **PAPERWEIGHT** A glass paperweight in the shape of a pyramid is placed on a desk. Draw the top view and side view. Then draw and describe the shape resulting from a vertical cross section of the figure.

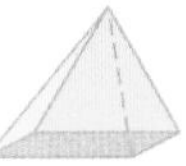

Practice and Problem Solving

● = **Step-by-Step Solutions** begin on page R11. **Extra Practice** begins on page 810.

Example 1 p. 665 Identify each figure. Name the bases, faces, edges, and vertices.

7–16. See Chapter 12 Answer Appendix.

7. 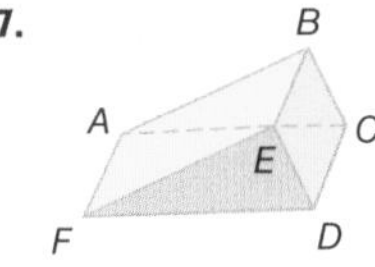

8. 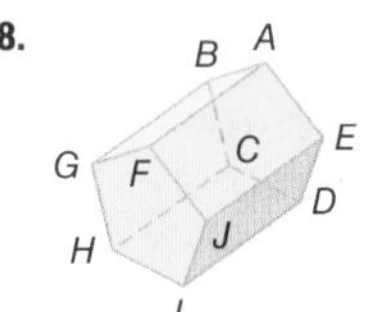

9. 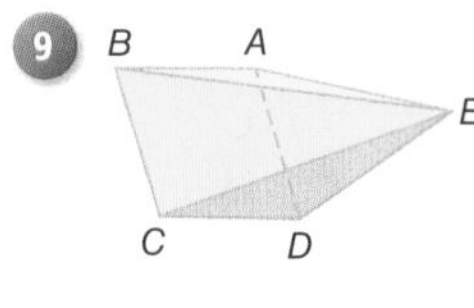

10. 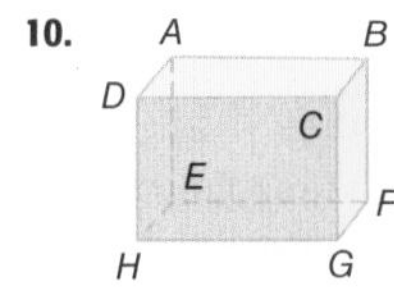

11. 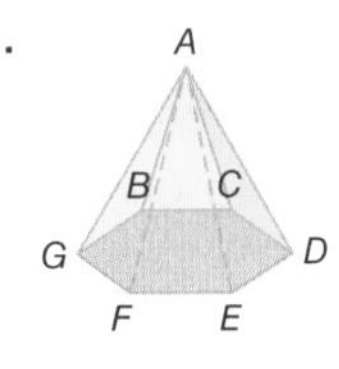

12. 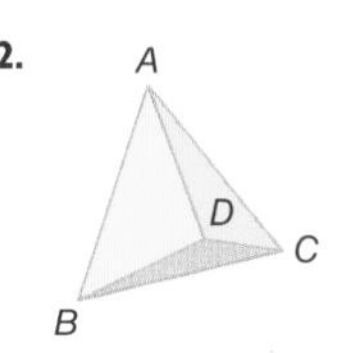

Example 2 p. 666 Draw and describe the shape resulting from each cross section.

13. 

14. 

15. 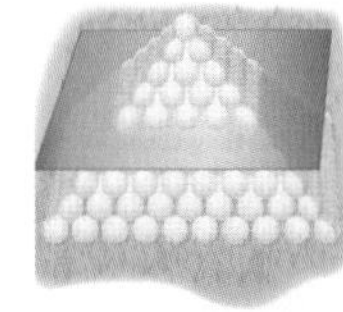

Example 3 p. 666

16. **BOXES** For an art project, Jorge is using the box shown at the right. Draw the top view and side view. Then draw and describe the shape resulting from an angled cross section of the figure.

Differentiated Homework Options

Level	Assignment	Two-Day Option	
AL Basic	7–16, 22–25, 27–39	7–15 odd, 29–32	8–16 even, 22–25, 27, 28, 33–39
OL Core	7–15 odd, 16–25, 27–39	7–16, 29–32	17–25, 27, 28, 33–39
BL Advanced	17–36 (optional: 37–39)		

TEACH with TECH

INTERACTIVE WHITEBOARD Display moveable graphics of three-dimensional figures on the board. Find the numbers of faces, edges, and vertices of the figures.

Tips for New Teachers

Cross Sections of Solids You may want to have models available to show the cross sections of various solids. Models can also be made from Styrofoam.

3 PRACTICE

Formative Assessment

Use Exercises 1–6 to check for understanding.

Use the chart at the bottom of this page to customize assignments for your students.

Additional Answers

1. rectangular prism; bases: *EIJF* and *HLKG*, *EILH* and *FGKJ*, *IJKL* and *EFGH*; faces: *EFGH*, *EFJI*, *GHLK*, *JFGK*, *EHLI*, *IJKL*; edges: $\overline{EF}$, $\overline{FJ}$, $\overline{JI}$, $\overline{IE}$, $\overline{HG}$, $\overline{GK}$, $\overline{KL}$, $\overline{LH}$, $\overline{EH}$, $\overline{IL}$, $\overline{FG}$, $\overline{JK}$; vertices: *E*, *F*, *G*, *H*, *I*, *J*, *K*, *L*
2. triangular pyramid; bases: *QRS*, *RST*, *RTQ* or *STQ*; faces: *QRS*, *RST*, *RTQ* or *STQ*; edges: $\overline{TQ}$, $\overline{TR}$, $\overline{TS}$, $\overline{RS}$, $\overline{RQ}$, $\overline{SQ}$; vertices: *R*, *S*, *T*, *Q*
3. parallelogram; 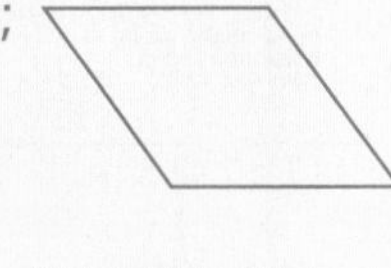
4. triangle; 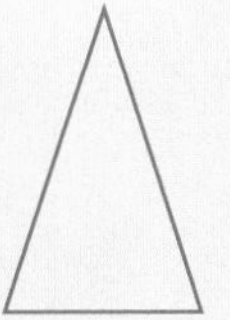
5. rectangle; 

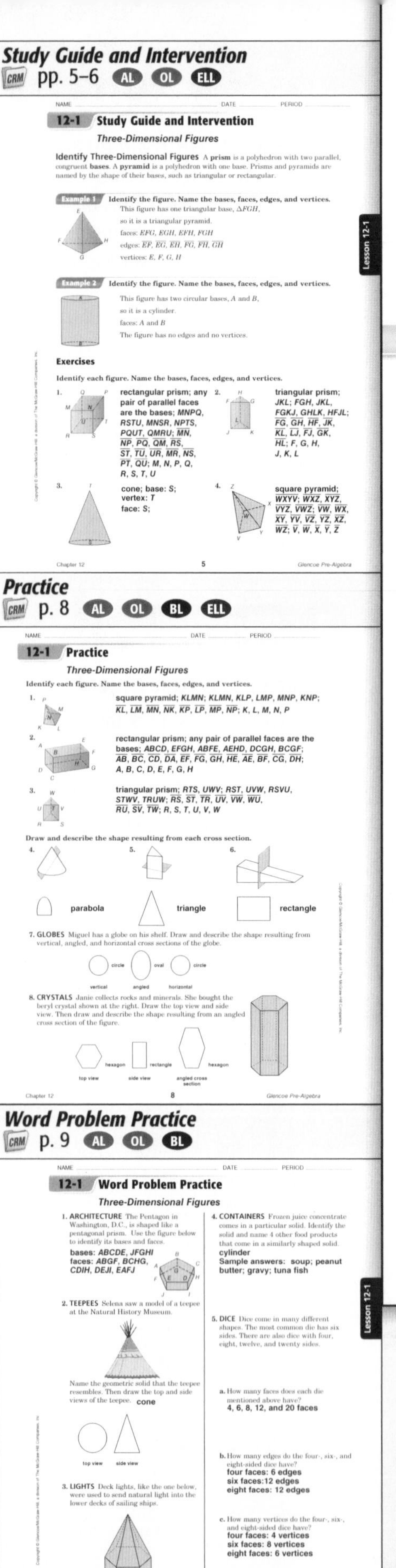
Study Guide and Intervention
CRM pp. 5–6 AL OL ELL

NAME ______ DATE ______ PERIOD ______

12-1 Study Guide and Intervention
Three-Dimensional Figures

Identify Three-Dimensional Figures A **prism** is a polyhedron with two parallel, congruent **bases**. A **pyramid** is a polyhedron with one base. Prisms and pyramids are named by the shape of their bases, such as triangular or rectangular.

Example 1 Identify the figure. Name the bases, faces, edges, and vertices.
This figure has one triangular base, $\triangle FGH$, so it is a triangular pyramid.
faces: EFG, EGH, EFH, FGH
edges: $\overline{EF}$, $\overline{EG}$, $\overline{EH}$, $\overline{FG}$, $\overline{FH}$, $\overline{GH}$
vertices: E, F, G, H

Example 2 Identify the figure. Name the bases, faces, edges, and vertices.
This figure has two circular bases, A and B, so it is a cylinder.
faces: A and B
The figure has no edges and no vertices.

Exercises
Identify each figure. Name the bases, faces, edges, and vertices.
1. rectangular prism; any pair of parallel faces are the bases: $MNPQ$, $RSTU$, $MNSR$, $NPTS$, $PQUT$, $QMRU$; $\overline{MN}$, $\overline{NP}$, $\overline{PQ}$, $\overline{QM}$, $\overline{RS}$, $\overline{ST}$, $\overline{TU}$, $\overline{UR}$, $\overline{MR}$, $\overline{NS}$, $\overline{PT}$, $\overline{QU}$; M, N, P, Q, R, S, T, U
2. triangular prism; JKL; FGH, JKL, $FGKJ$, $GHLK$, $HFJL$; $\overline{FG}$, $\overline{GH}$, $\overline{HF}$, $\overline{JK}$, $\overline{KL}$, $\overline{LJ}$, $\overline{FJ}$, $\overline{GK}$, $\overline{HL}$; F, G, H, J, K, L
3. cone; base: S; vertex: T face: S;
4. square pyramid; $WXYV$; WXZ, XYZ, VYZ, VWZ; $\overline{VW}$, $\overline{WX}$, $\overline{XY}$, $\overline{YV}$, $\overline{VZ}$, $\overline{YZ}$, $\overline{XZ}$, $\overline{WZ}$; V, W, X, Y, Z

Chapter 12 5 Glencoe Pre-Algebra

Practice
CRM p. 8 AL OL BL ELL

NAME ______ DATE ______ PERIOD ______

12-1 Practice
Three-Dimensional Figures

Identify each figure. Name the bases, faces, edges, and vertices.
1. square pyramid; $KLMN$; $KLMN$, KLP, LMP, MNP, KNP; $\overline{KL}$, $\overline{LM}$, $\overline{MN}$, $\overline{NK}$, $\overline{KP}$, $\overline{LP}$, $\overline{MP}$, $\overline{NP}$; K, L, M, N, P
2. rectangular prism; any pair of parallel faces are the bases; $ABCD$, $EFGH$, $ABFE$, $AEHD$, $DCGH$, $BCGF$; $\overline{AB}$, $\overline{BC}$, $\overline{CD}$, $\overline{DA}$, $\overline{EF}$, $\overline{FG}$, $\overline{GH}$, $\overline{HE}$, $\overline{AE}$, $\overline{BF}$, $\overline{CG}$, $\overline{DH}$; A, B, C, D, E, F, G, H
3. triangular prism; RTS, UWV; RST, UVW, $RSVU$, $STWV$, $TRUW$; $\overline{RS}$, $\overline{ST}$, $\overline{TR}$, $\overline{UV}$, $\overline{VW}$, $\overline{WU}$, $\overline{RU}$, $\overline{SV}$, $\overline{TW}$; R, S, T, U, V, W

Draw and describe the shape resulting from each cross section.
4. parabola 5. triangle 6. rectangle

7. **GLOBES** Miguel has a globe on his shelf. Draw and describe the shape resulting from vertical, angled, and horizontal cross sections of the globe.
circle (vertical) oval (angled) circle (horizontal)

8. **CRYSTALS** Janie collects rocks and minerals. She bought the beryl crystal shown at the right. Draw the top view and side view. Then draw and describe the shape resulting from an angled cross section of the figure.
hexagon (top view) rectangle (side view) hexagon (angled cross section)

Chapter 12 8 Glencoe Pre-Algebra

Word Problem Practice
CRM p. 9 AL OL BL

NAME ______ DATE ______ PERIOD ______

12-1 Word Problem Practice
Three-Dimensional Figures

1. **ARCHITECTURE** The Pentagon in Washington, D.C., is shaped like a pentagonal prism. Use the figure below to identify its bases and faces.
bases: $ABCDE$, $JFGHI$
faces: $ABGF$, $BCHG$, $CDIH$, $DEJI$, $EAFJ$

2. **TEEPEES** Selena saw a model of a teepee at the Natural History Museum.
Name the geometric solid that the teepee resembles. Then draw the top and side views of the teepee. cone
top view side view

3. **LIGHTS** Deck lights, like the one below, were used to send natural light into the lower decks of sailing ships.
Identify the solid figure that forms the base of the light.
hexagonal prism

4. **CONTAINERS** Frozen juice concentrate comes in a particular solid. Identify the solid and name 4 other food products that come in a similarly shaped solid.
cylinder
Sample answers: soup; peanut butter; gravy; tuna fish

5. **DICE** Dice come in many different shapes. The most common die has six sides. There are also dice with four, eight, twelve, and twenty sides.
a. How many faces does each die mentioned above have?
4, 6, 8, 12, and 20 faces
b. How many edges do the four-, six-, and eight-sided dice have?
four faces: 6 edges
six faces: 12 edges
eight faces: 12 edges
c. How many vertices do the four-, six-, and eight-sided dice have?
four faces: 4 vertices
six faces: 8 vertices
eight faces: 6 vertices

Chapter 12 9 Glencoe Pre-Algebra

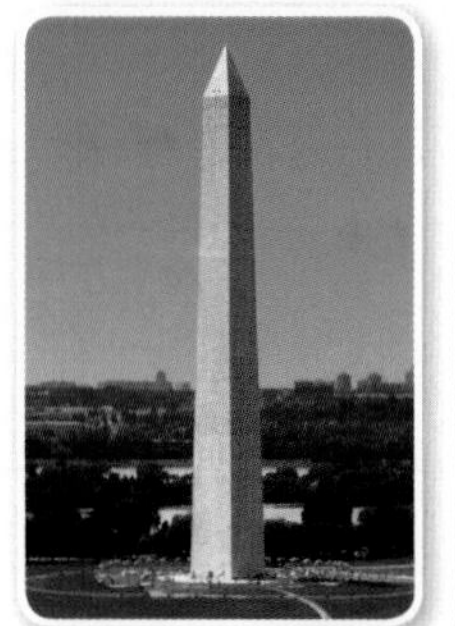

Real-World Link

The Washington Monument is in the shape of an *obelisk*. An obelisk is a four-sided tapered shaft that has a pyramid at the top.

17. **MONUMENTS** Use the information about the Washington Monument shown at the left. **a–d. See margin.**
   a. Sketch the pyramid shaped top of the monument and label the vertices.
   b. Identify the bases, faces, and edges.
   c. Describe the shapes that result from vertical, angled, and horizontal cross sections of the pyramid top of the monument.
   d. Draw and describe the shape that would result from an angled cross section through the top and base of the monument.

ART For each sculpture shown below, draw the top view and side view. Then draw and describe the shape resulting from a vertical cross section of the figure. **18–21. See Chapter 12 Answer Appendix.**

18. 
19. 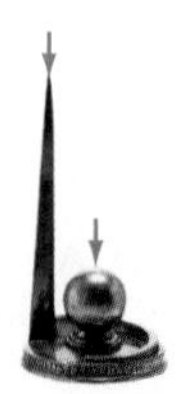
20. 

21. **MULTIPLE REPRESENTATIONS** In this problem, you will investigate Euler's Formula on polyhedra.
   a. **TABULAR** Draw each figure. Then, copy and complete the table shown.

Name	Triangular Pyramid	Square Pyramid	Pentagonal Pyramid
Vertices	4	5	■
Faces	■	■	6
Edges	■	8	■

   b. **ANALYTICAL** What do you notice about the number of vertices, faces, and edges?
   c. **ALGEBRAIC** Write an equation that compares the sum of the number of vertices V and the number of faces F to the number of edges E.

H.O.T. Problems Use Higher-Order Thinking Skills

22. **OPEN ENDED** Choose a solid object from your home. Draw and describe the shape resulting from a vertical, angled, and horizontal cross section of it. **See students' work.**

REASONING For Exercises 23–25, determine whether each statement is *always*, *sometimes*, or *never true*.

23. The bases of cylinders have different radii. **never**
24. Two planes intersect in a single point. **never**
25. Three planes do not intersect in a point. **sometimes**
26. **CHALLENGE** A triangular pyramid has 6 edges. A square pyramid has 8 edges. Write a formula that gives the number of edges e for a pyramid with an n-sided base. $e = 2n$
27. **REASONING** Explain how you would classify the polyhedron shown at the right.
28. **WRITING IN MATH** Are cylinders polyhedrons? Explain. **No. They are not made up of polygons.**

27. Sample answer: Examine the base of the object; it is a hexagon. Since it has two parallel, congruent bases, it is also a prism. The figure is a hexagonal prism.

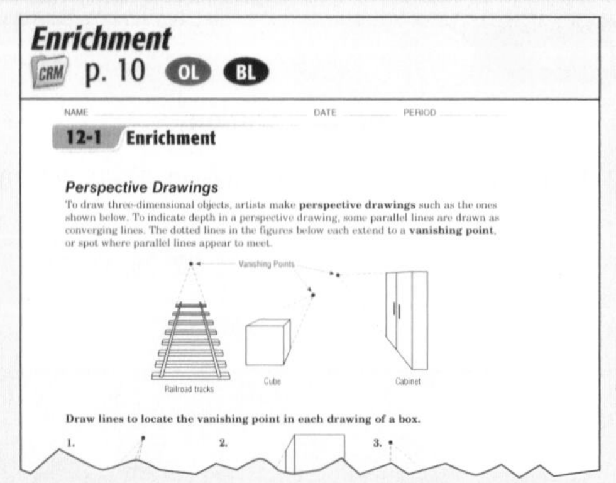
Enrichment
CRM p. 10 OL BL

NAME ______ DATE ______ PERIOD ______

12-1 Enrichment

Perspective Drawings
To draw three-dimensional objects, artists make **perspective drawings** such as the ones shown below. To indicate depth in a perspective drawing, some parallel lines are drawn as converging lines. The dotted lines in the figures below each extend to a **vanishing point**, or spot where parallel lines appear to meet.

Draw lines to locate the vanishing point in each drawing of a box.
1. 2. 3.

Multiple Representations In Exercise 21, students use a table of values and numerical analysis to write an equation relating vertices, faces, and edges of polyhedral figures.

Standardized Test Practice

29. Which of the following is *not* considered an edge of the triangular prism? **D**

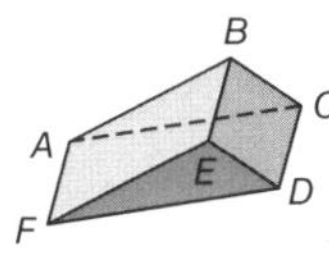

A $\overline{AF}$
B $\overline{BE}$
C $\overline{DE}$
D $\overline{AE}$

30. What three-dimensional figure has one vertex? **F**

F cone
G cylinder
H triangular prism
J triangular pyramid

31. **EXTENDED RESPONSE** Draw and describe the shape resulting from a vertical cross section of the figure shown. **See margin.**

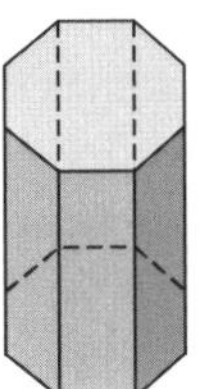

32. Which of the following real-world objects resembles a rectangular prism? **B**

A bowl
B box
C soup can
D stop sign

Spiral Review

Find the area of each figure. Round to the nearest tenth, if necessary. (Lesson 11-9)

33. 4 ft, 6 ft, 4 ft, 12 ft **72 ft^2**

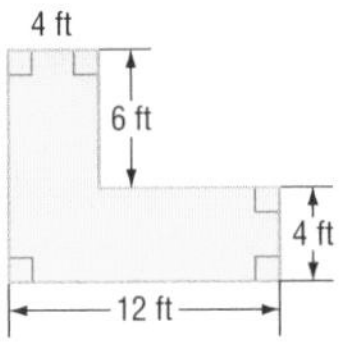

34. 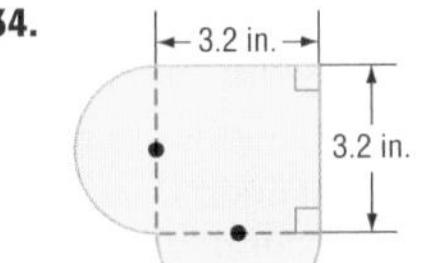

18.3 in^2

35. 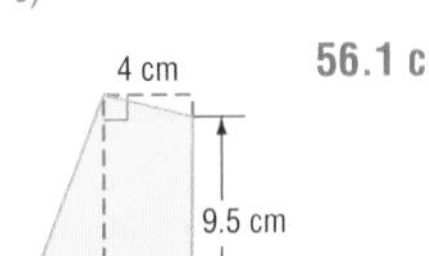

56.1 cm^2

36. **BAND** During a football game, a marching band can be heard within a radius of 1.7 miles. What is the area that can hear the band? Round to the nearest tenth. (Lesson 11-8) **about 9.1 mi^2**

Skills Review

Find the area of each figure. (Lesson 11-6)

37. 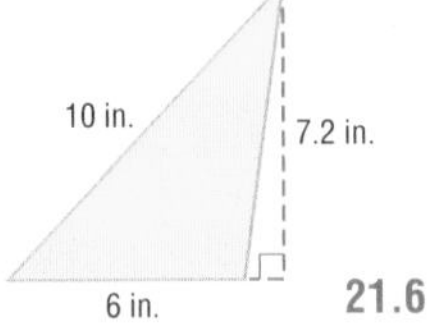

21.6 in^2

38. 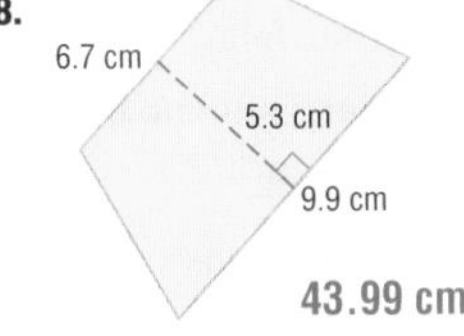

43.99 cm^2

39. 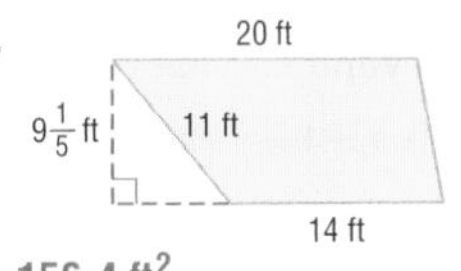

156.4 ft^2

4 ASSESS

Name the Math Ask students to give the name of three-dimensional figures that have faces or bases that are square, triangular, rectangular, and circular. Students can include a sketch of the figure to illustrate.

Additional Answers

17a.

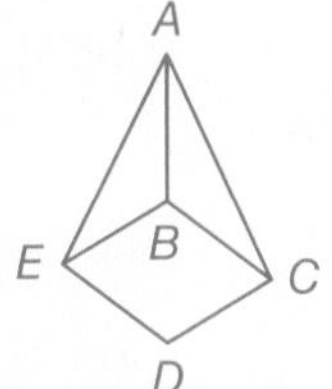

17b. base: *BCDE*; faces *ABC, ABE, BCDE, ACD, ADE*; edges: $\overline{AB}$, $\overline{AC}$, $\overline{AD}$, $\overline{AE}$, $\overline{BC}$, $\overline{CD}$, $\overline{DE}$, $\overline{EB}$

17c. triangle, triangle or trapezoid, square

17d. top: triangle, base: trapezoid

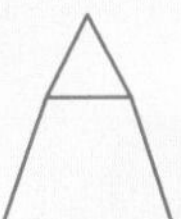

31.

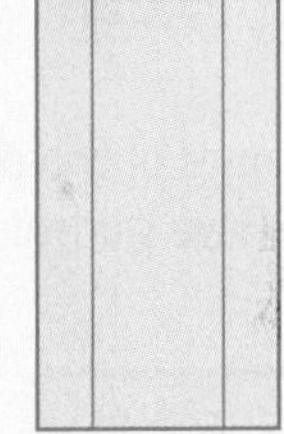

The shape resulting from a vertical cross section is a rectangle.

Differentiated Instruction

Extension Lines that are neither intersecting nor parallel are called skew lines. These lines lie in different planes. Identify the skew lines in the drawing of the triangular pyramid below. $\overleftrightarrow{AD}$ and $\overleftrightarrow{BC}$; $\overleftrightarrow{BD}$ and $\overleftrightarrow{AC}$; $\overleftrightarrow{CD}$ and $\overleftrightarrow{AB}$

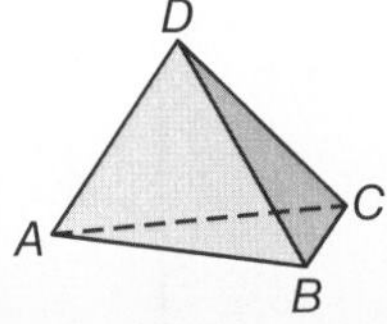

FOCUS

Objective Investigate volume by creating and comparing containers of various shapes.

Materials for Each Student

- 5 x 8 index cards
- tape
- rice
- grid paper
- ruler

Teaching Tip

Tell students to mark off the indicated base lengths along the 8-inch side of a card. Then draw a line to the opposite side of the card to form a fold line for sides of two of the figures.

TEACH

Working in Cooperative Groups

Arrange students in groups of two or three, mixing abilities. Have students complete the Activity.

Ask:

- What types of storage containers have you seen at home? Sample answers: plastic containers, boxes, and bottles
- If you wanted to make a container for maximum volume, what shape would you make it? cylinder

Practice Have students complete Exercises 1–6.

ASSESS

Formative Assessment

Use Exercises 1–6 to assess whether students comprehend how the base area affects the volume.

EXPLORE 12-2 Geometry Lab Volume

Math Online glencoe.com
Math *in Motion,* Animation

ACTIVITY

Step 1 Use three 5 × 8 index cards to make three containers each with a height of 5 inches as shown.

- Make one with a square base that has 2-inch sides.
- Make one with a triangular base that has sides of 2 inches, 3 inches, and 3 inches.
- Make one with a circular base that has an 8-inch circumference.

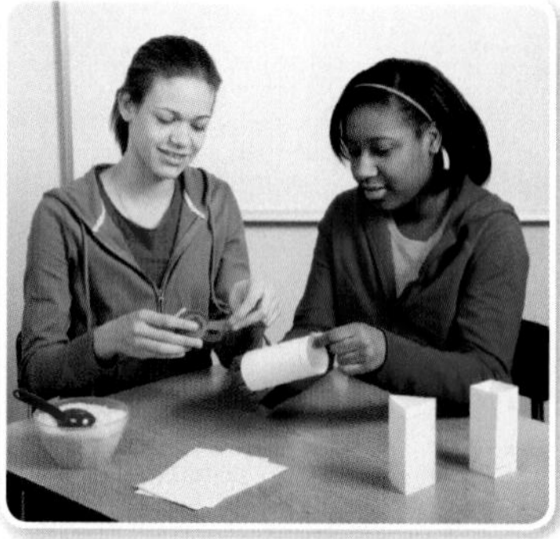

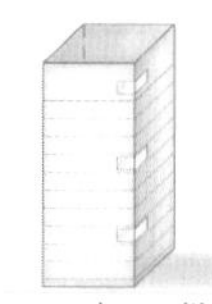

square base with 2-inch sides

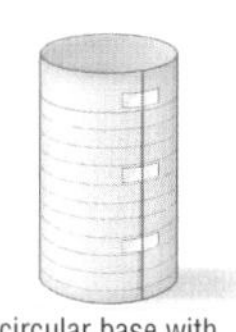

circular base with 8-inch circumference

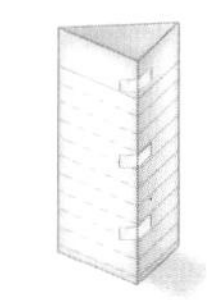

triangular base with sides 2 inches, 3 inches, and 3 inches

Step 2 Tape one end of each container to another card as a bottom, but leave the top open.

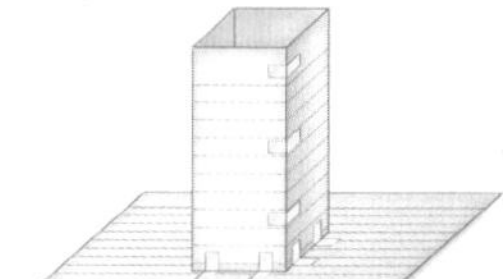

Step 3 Estimate which container holds the most (has the greatest volume) and which holds the least (has the least volume), or whether each container holds the same amount.

Step 4 Use rice to fill the container that you believe holds the least amount. Then put the rice into another container. Does the rice fill this container? Continue the process until you find which, if any, container has the least volume and which has the greatest.

Analyze the Results

1. Which container holds the most? the least? **cylinder; triangular prism**
2. How do the heights of the three containers compare? What is each height? **same height; 5 in.**
3. Compare the perimeters of the bases of each container with the circumference of the cylinder. What is each base perimeter? **same; 8 in.**
4. Trace the base of each container onto grid paper. Estimate the area of each base. **circular: ≈ 5 in^2; triangular: ≈ 3 in^2; square: 4 in^2**
5. Which container has the greatest base area? **cylinder**
6. **MAKE A CONJECTURE** Does there appear to be a relationship between the area of the base and the volume? Explain. **Yes; the greater the base area, the greater the volume.**

From Concrete to Abstract

Have students draw the three containers, labelling their dimensions and including their estimations of the base areas. Tell them to include notes of the relative volumes of the three containers.

12-2 Volume of Prisms

Then
You have already found the areas of rectangles and triangles. (Lesson 5-1)

Now
- Find volumes of prisms.
- Find volumes of composite figures.

New Vocabulary
volume

Math Online
glencoe.com
- Extra Examples
- Personal Tutor
- Self-Check Quiz
- Homework Help

Why?

You can investigate the amount of space a prism occupies by examining its cross sections. Look at the block of pottery clay at the right. It measures 4 inches long by 2 inches wide by 10 inches tall.

a. If the piece of clay is cut into 5 equal pieces horizontally, what are the dimensions of each piece? **4 in. × 2 in. × 2 in.**

b. How many one-inch cubes could be cut from each piece? from the entire piece of clay? **16 cubes; 80 cubes**

c. **MAKE A CONJECTURE** How are the area of the base and the height of each piece related to the number of one-inch cubes that can be cut from the clay? **See margin.**

Volumes of Prisms **Volume** is the measure of space occupied by a three-dimensional region. It is measured in cubic units. In the example above, the *volume* of the block of clay is 80 cubic inches.

Key Concept Volume of a Prism — For Your FOLDABLE

Words The volume V of a prism is the area of the base B times the height h.

Symbols $V = Bh$

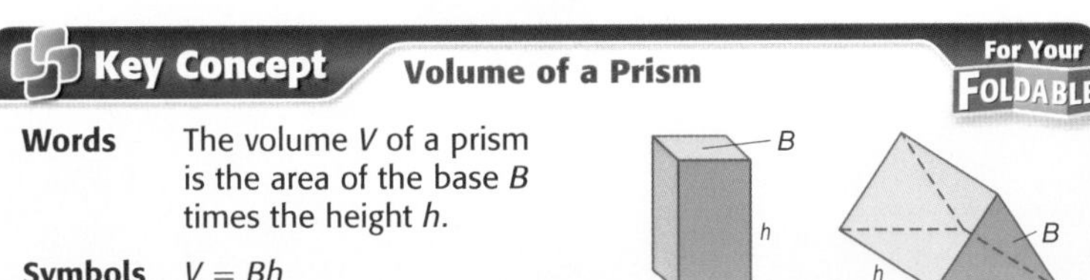

EXAMPLE 1 Find the Volume of a Rectangular Prism

Find the volume of the rectangular prism.

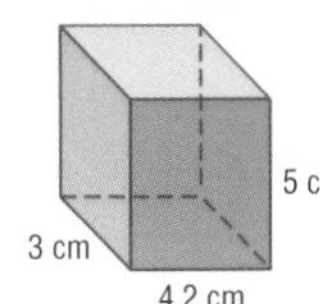

$V = Bh$	Write the formula for volume of a prism.
$= (\ell w)h$	The base is a rectangle, so $B = \ell w$.
$= (4.2 \cdot 3) \cdot 5$ or 63	Replace ℓ with 4.2 cm, w with 3 cm, and h with 5 cm.
	Simplify.

The volume is 63 cubic centimeters.

Check Your Progress

1. Find the volume of a rectangular prism with a length of 10 feet, a width of 13 feet, and a height of 21 feet. **2730 ft^3**

Personal Tutor glencoe.com

12-2 Lesson Notes

1 FOCUS

Vertical Alignment

Before Lesson 12-2
Find the areas of rectangles and triangles.

Lesson 12-2
Find the volumes of prisms and composite figures.

After Lesson 12-2
Find surface areas and volumes of three-dimensional figures.

2 TEACH

Scaffolding Questions

Have students read the *Why?* section of the lesson and answer the questions.

- What units are used to find the area of the base? square units
- Since the area of the bottom is multiplied times the height to give the total number of cubes, what unit would be used to denote the number of cubes? cubic units
- How many one-inch cubes are in the block of clay? Explain. 80; multiply the number of cubes in one piece times 5: $16 \cdot 5 = 80$.

Additional Answer

c. They are multiplied together.

Lesson 12-2 Resources

Resource	Approaching-Level	On-Level	Beyond-Level	English Learners
Teacher Edition	• Differentiated Instruction, p. 672		• Differentiated Instruction, p. 676	• Differentiated Instruction, p. 672
Chapter Resource Masters	• Study Guide and Intervention, pp. 11–12 • Skills Practice, p. 13 • Practice, p. 14 • Word Problem Practice, p. 15 • Graphing Calculator, p. 17	• Study Guide and Intervention, pp. 11–12 • Skills Practice, p. 13 • Practice, p. 14 • Word Problem Practice, p. 15 • Enrichment, p. 16 • Graphing Calculator, p. 17	• Practice, p. 14 • Word Problem Practice, p. 15 • Enrichment, p. 16 • Graphing Calculator, p. 17	• Study Guide and Intervention, pp. 11–12 • Skills Practice, p. 13 • Practice, p. 14 • Graphing Calculator, p. 17
Transparencies	• 5-Minute Check Transparency 12-2	• 5-Minute Check Transparency 12-2	• 5-Minute Check Transparency 12-2	• 5-Minute Check Transparency 12-2
Other	• Study Notebook • Teaching Pre-Algebra with Manipulatives	• Study Notebook • Teaching Pre-Algebra with Manipulatives	• Study Notebook	• Study Notebook • Teaching Pre-Algebra with Manipulatives

Volumes of Prisms

Examples 1 and 2 show how to find the volume of a prism. **Example 3** shows how to find a missing length of a prism, using a known volume.

Formative Assessment

Use the Check Your Progress exercises after each example to determine students' understanding of concepts.

Additional Examples

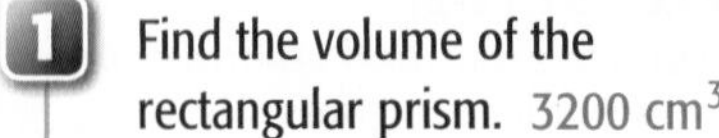

1 Find the volume of the rectangular prism. $3200\ \text{cm}^3$

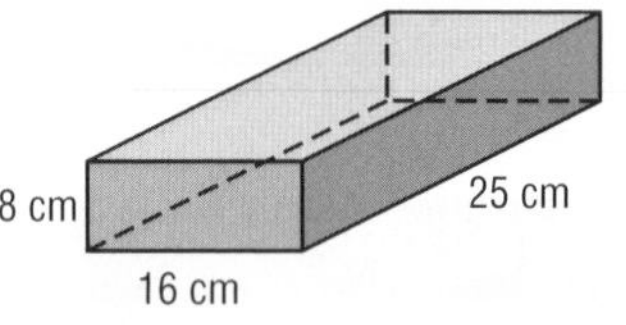

2 Find the volume of the triangular prism. $15\ \text{in}^3$

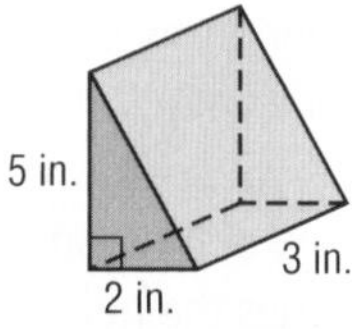

3 **BAKING** Cake batter is poured into a pan that is a rectangular prism with an 8-inch square base. If the cake batter occupies 192 cubic inches, what will be the height of the batter? 3 in.

Additional Examples also in Interactive Classroom PowerPoint® Presentations

EXAMPLE 2 Volume of a Triangular Prism

Find the volume of the triangular prism.

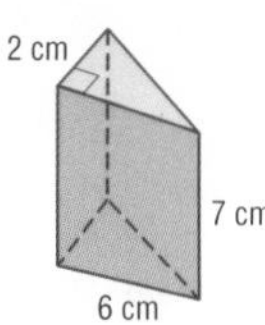

$V = Bh$	**Write the formula for volume of a prism.**
$= \left(\frac{1}{2} \cdot 6 \cdot 2\right)h$	**The base is a triangle, so $B = \frac{1}{2}bh$, $b = 6$ and $h = 2$.**
$= 6 \cdot 7$	**The height of the prism is 7 cm.**
$= 42$	**Simplify.**

The volume is 42 cubic centimeters.

Watch Out!

Height Be sure not to confuse the height of the triangle with the height of the prism.

Check Your Progress

Find the volume of each triangular prism.

2A. $390\ \text{in}^3$

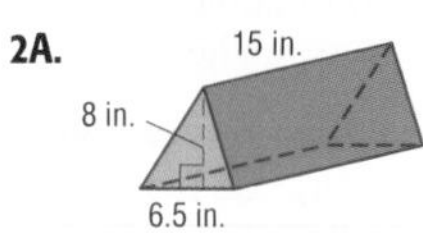

2B. $118.3\ \text{mm}^3$

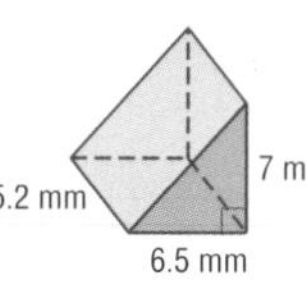

Personal Tutor glencoe.com

Real-World Link

Air conditioners have earned the energy star rating from the Department of Energy. In 2006, Americans avoided producing greenhouse gas emissions equal to those made by 25 million cars.

Source: U.S. Department of Energy

Real-World EXAMPLE 3 Find the Missing Length

HOME IMPROVEMENT **A room air conditioner can cool a room with a volume of 1600 cubic feet. If a room has a height of 8 feet and a length of 16 feet, what is the maximum width of the room?**

Estimate $1600 \div (10 \times 16) = 10$

$V = Bh$	**Write the formula for the volume of a prism.**
$V = \ell wh$	**Replace B with ℓw.**
$1600 = 16 \cdot w \cdot 8$	**Replace V with 1600, ℓ with 16, and h with 8.**
$1600 = 16 \cdot 8 \cdot w$	**Commutative Property**
$1600 = 128w$	**Simplify.**
$12.5 = w$	**Divide each side by 128.**

The room is 12.5 feet wide.

Check for Reasonableness $12.5 \approx 10$ ✓

Check Your Progress

3. POOLS A children's rectangular pool holds 17.5 cubic feet of water. What is the width of the pool if its length is 3.5 feet and its height is 1 foot? 5 ft

Personal Tutor glencoe.com

Tips for New Teachers

base vs. Base In Example 2, the variables b and B are used. Point out to students that B refers to the area of the base of a three-dimensional figure and b refers to the length of the base of a two-dimensional figure.

Differentiated Instruction

students have trouble keeping track of the measurements of the base of a solid,

have these students sketch the solid on their papers, shade the base a color, and write its measurements in the same color. They could even color-code the measurements as they substitute them into the volume formula.

Volumes of Composite Figures You can find the area of composite three-dimensional figures by breaking them into smaller pieces.

Problem-SolvingTip

Eliminating Choices You can eliminate A and B as answers because the volume of the rectangular prism is 36 ft^3, so the volume of the whole figure must be greater.

STANDARDIZED TEST EXAMPLE 4

Find the volume of the ramp.

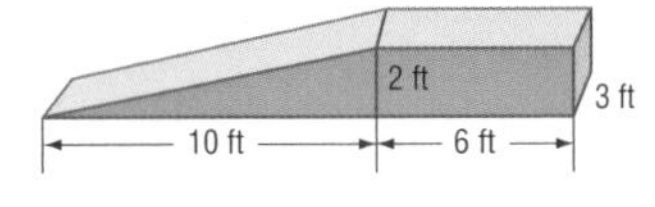

A 30 ft^3 C 66 ft^3

B 36 ft^3 D 96 ft^3

Read the Test Item

The solid is made up of a triangular prism and a rectangular prism. The volume of the solid is the sum of both volumes.

Solve the Test Item

Triangular Prism	Rectangular Prism
$V = Bh$	$V = \ell wh$
$V = \frac{1}{2} \cdot 10 \cdot 2 \cdot 3$	$V = 6 \cdot 3 \cdot 2$
$V = 30$	$V = 36$

The volume of the figure is 30 + 36 or 66 cubic feet. The answer is C.

Check Your Progress

4. Find the volume of the figure at the right. G

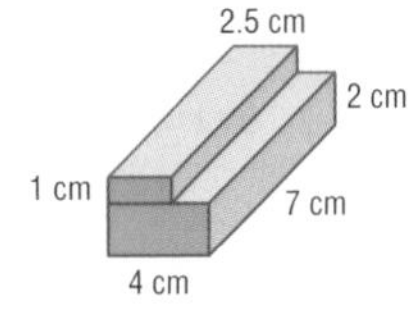

F 60 cm^3 H 98 cm^3

G 73.5 cm^3 J 107.5 cm^3

Personal Tutor glencoe.com

Check Your Understanding

Examples 1 and 2 pp. 671–672

Find the volume of each figure.

1. 36 mm^3 (4 mm, 3 mm, 3 mm)

2. 90 yd^3 (3 yd, 6 yd, 10 yd)

3. 1000 in^3 (10 in., 10 in., 10 in.)

Example 3 p. 672

4. **GARDENING** A window box has a length of 8.5 inches and a height of 9 inches. If the volume of the box is 2295 cubic inches, what is the width of the box? 30 in.

Example 4 p. 673

5. **MULTIPLE CHOICE** Find the volume of the figure at the right. B

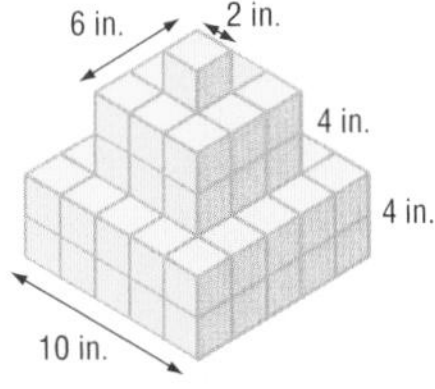

A 400 in^3 C 56 in^3

B 552 in^3 D 840 in^3

Focus on Mathematical Content

Volume of a Prism To find the volume of *any* prism, use the formula $V = Bh$. B is the area of the base, and is capitalized. The formula or method used to find the value of B will be different for different prisms, depending on the shape of its base.

Volumes of Composite Solids

Example 4 is a Standardized Test practice for finding the volume of a composite solid.

Additional Example

4 **STANDARDIZED TEST PRACTICE** Find the volume of the solid. D

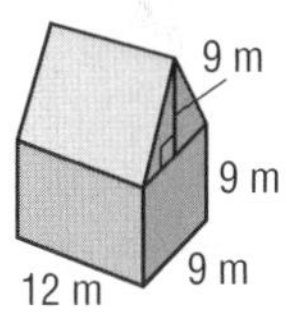

A 262 m^3 C 918 m^3

B 972 m^3 D 1458 m^3

3 PRACTICE

Formative Assessment

Use Exercises 1–5 to check for understanding.

Use the chart at the bottom of the next page to customize assignments for your students.

TEACH with TECH

WEB PAGE Create a class Web page about volume and surface area of three-dimensional figures. After each class period, update the page with information from the most recent lesson.

Tips for New Teachers

Study Tip Stress that the measure of volume is in cubic units, or units to the third power.

Additional Answers

26. small: \$0.03 per in^3, medium: \$0.02 per in^3, large: \$0.01 per in^3; The large popcorn is the best buy per cubic inch.

27b. The volume is multiplied by 2 because $V = \ell w(2h) = 2(\ell wh)$; The original volume is multiplied by 2^2 or 4 because $V = \ell(2w)(2h) = 4(\ell wh)$; The original volume is multiplied by 2^3 or 8 because $V = (2\ell)(2w)(2h) = 8(\ell wh)$.

27c. When one dimension is tripled, the volume is multiplied by 3. When two dimensions are tripled, the original volume is multiplied by 3^2. When three dimensions are tripled, the original volume is multiplied by 3^3.

28. Sample answer: The volumes are equal. The length of each figure is the same. The width of the first figure is twice the width of the second figure and the height of the first figure is half the height of the second figure. So, the volumes are the same.

29. Sample answer: base length 4 in., base height 2 in., prism height 11 in.

33. Sample answer: The volume of the box is changed by 2^3 or 8.

Practice and Problem Solving

● = **Step-by-Step Solutions** begin on page R11. **Extra Practice** begins on page 810.

Examples 1 and 2 pp. 671–672

Find the volume of each figure.

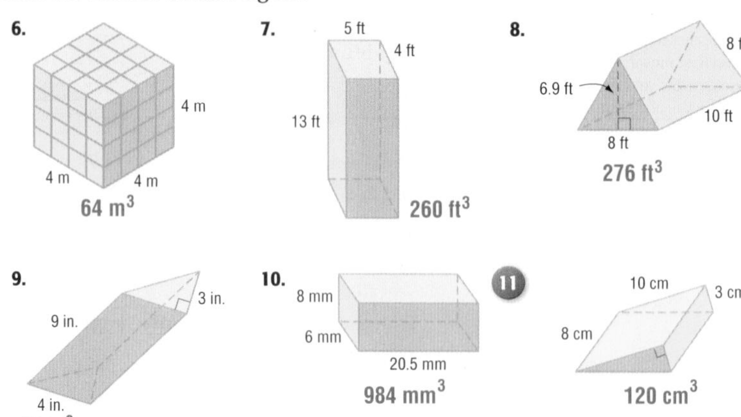

9. 9 in., 3 in., 4 in. **54 in³**

10. 8 mm, 6 mm, 20.5 mm **984 mm³**

11. 10 cm, 3 cm, 8 cm **120 cm³**

12. triangular prism: base of triangle 6.2 yards, height of triangle 20 yards, height of prism 14 yards **868 yd³**

13. rectangular prism: height 4 inches, width $1\frac{1}{2}$ inches, length $\frac{1}{4}$ inch **$1\frac{1}{2}$ in³**

Example 3 p. 672

14. Find the length of a rectangular prism with a width of 4 feet, a height of 6 feet, and a volume of 84 cubic feet. **3.5 ft**

15. Find the height of a triangular prism with a base length of 10 yards, a base height of 20 yards, and a volume of 600 cubic yards. **6 yd**

Example 4 p. 673

16. DOG HOUSES Josh and his mom are building the dog house shown below. Find the volume of the dog house. **27,300 in³**

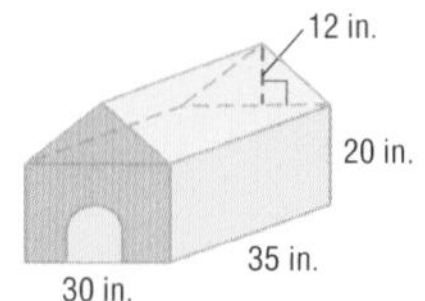

17. STEPS Morgan is building a model of some steps with 6 inch foam blocks. What is the total volume of the blocks? **3888 in³**

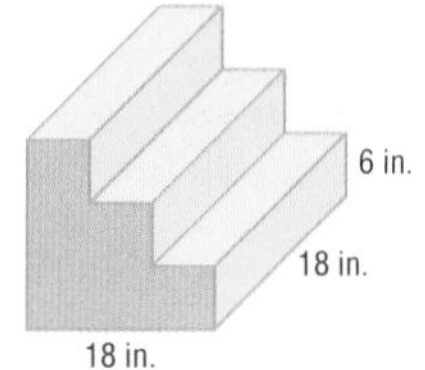

18. CRAFTS Jill is mailing a candle that is in the shape of a triangular prism as shown. She put the candle in a rectangular box that measures 3 inches by 5 inches by 7 inches and places foam pieces around the candle. Find the volume of the foam pieces needed to fill the space between the candle and the box. **85.5 in³**

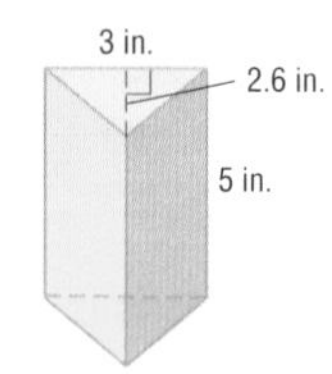

19. The height of a triangular prism is 8 feet and it has a volume of 200 cubic feet. If the base has a length of 5 feet, what is the height of the base? **10 ft**

20. PLANTING Ben wants to buy enough potting soil to fill a window box that is 42 inches long, 8 inches wide, and 6 inches high. If one bag of potting soil contains 576 cubic inches, how many bags should he buy? **4 bags**

Differentiated Homework Options

Level	Assignment	Two-Day Option	
AL Basic	6–17, 28, 29, 33–45	7–17 odd, 34–37	6–16 even, 28, 29, 33, 38–45
OL Core	7–17 odd, 18–20, 21–25 odd, 26–29, 33–45	6–17, 34–37	18–29, 33, 38–45
BL Advanced	18–42 (optional: 43–45)		

Find the volume of each figure.

21. $972\ m^3$

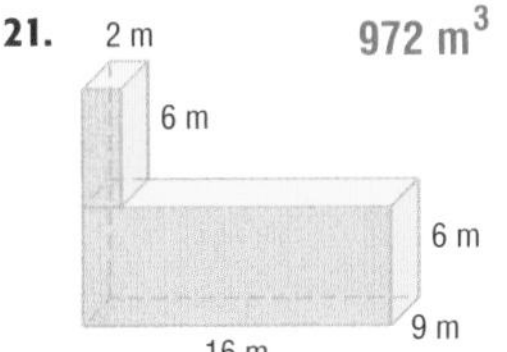

22. $168\ cm^3$

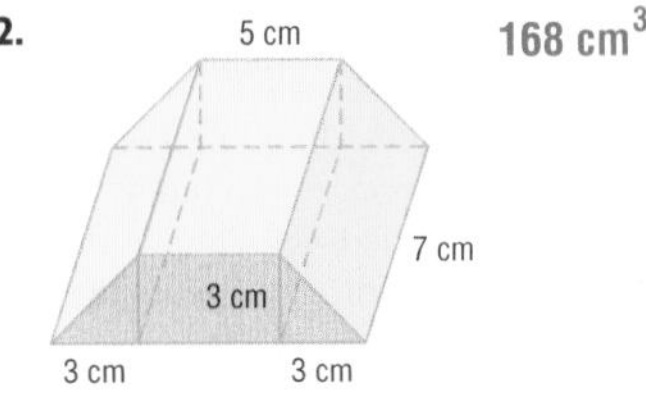

23. $180\ ft^3$

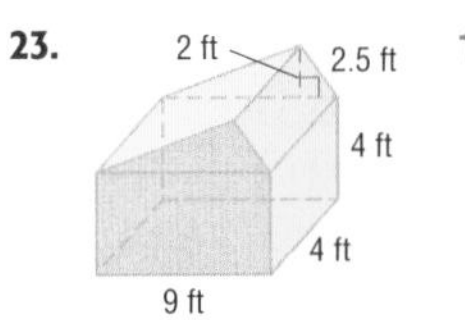

24. $513\ ft^3$

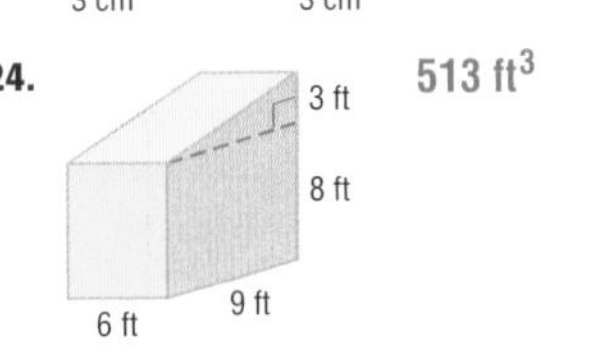

Real-World Link

In the United States, 16 billion quarts of popcorn are consumed each year. That's about 16 gallons per person per year. Most popcorn is grown in Indiana, Nebraska, Ohio, Illinois, Iowa, Kentucky and Missouri.

Source: The Popcorn Board

25. CANDY A chocolate bar is in the shape of a trapezoidal prism as shown at the right. Find the volume of the chocolate bar. $1.875\ in^3$

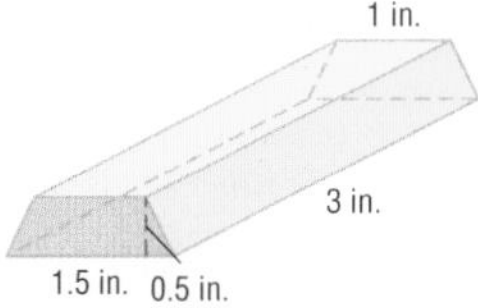

26. FINANCIAL LITERACY A movie theater sells different sizes of popcorn as shown in the table. If the containers are rectangular prisms, find the ratio of cost to the volume of each bag of popcorn. Which size of popcorn is the best buy? See margin.

Popcorn Sizes Available

Size	Length (in.)	Width (in.)	Height (in.)	Price ($)
Small	5	4	8	4.50
Medium	7	5	10	5.75
Large	10	6	12	6.50

27. GEOMETRY Refer to the figure at the right.

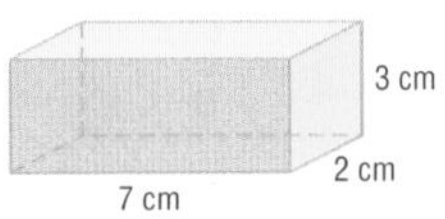

a. What is the volume of the figure? $42\ cm^3$

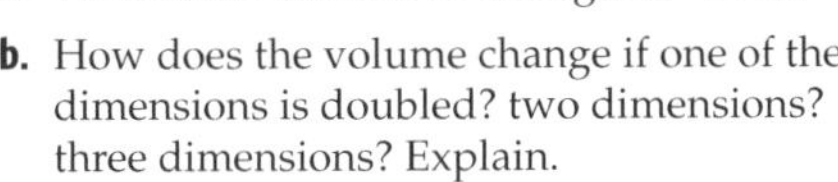

b. How does the volume change if one of the dimensions is doubled? two dimensions? three dimensions? Explain.

c. Repeat the above steps and triple each dimension. What do you notice?

d. Without calculating, find the volume of the prism if each of the dimensions is multiplied by 6. $9072\ cm^3$

27b–c. See margin.

H.O.T. Problems

Use Higher-Order Thinking Skills

28. REASONING Without calculating, compare the volumes of the prisms shown. Explain.

28–29. See margin.

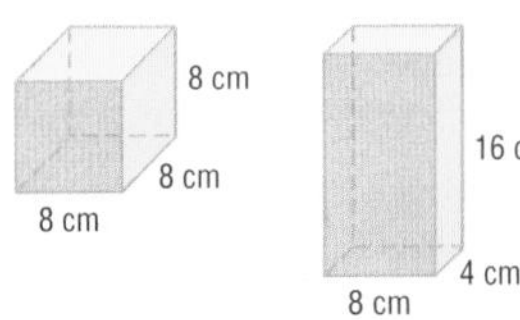

29. OPEN ENDED Find the dimensions of any triangular prism that has a volume of 44 cubic inches.

CHALLENGE Use dimensional analysis to make each conversion.

30. $5\ yd^3 = \blacksquare\ ft^3$ 135 **31.** $945\ ft^3 = \blacksquare\ yd^3$ 35 **32.** $2\ m^3 = \blacksquare\ cm^3$ 2,000,000

33. WRITING IN MATH Explain how doubling the length, width, and height of a box changes the volume of the box. See margin.

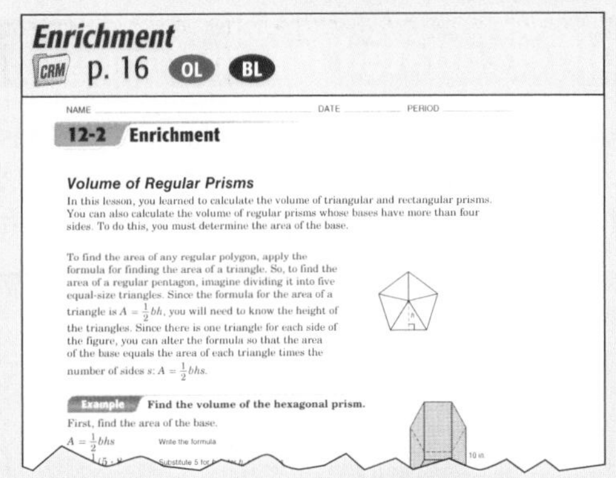

Enrichment
CRM p. 16 OL BL

NAME DATE PERIOD

12-2 Enrichment

Volume of Regular Prisms

In this lesson, you learned to calculate the volume of triangular and rectangular prisms. You can also calculate the volume of regular prisms whose bases have more than four sides. To do this, you must determine the area of the base.

To find the area of any regular polygon, apply the formula for finding the area of a triangle. So, to find the area of a regular pentagon, imagine dividing it into five equal-size triangles. Since the formula for the area of a triangle is $A = \frac{1}{2}bh$, you will need to know the height of the triangles. Since there is one triangle for each side of the figure, you can alter the formula so that the area of the base equals the area of each triangle times the number of sides s: $A = \frac{1}{2}bhs$.

Example Find the volume of the hexagonal prism.

First, find the area of the base.

$A = \frac{1}{2}bhs$ Write the formula

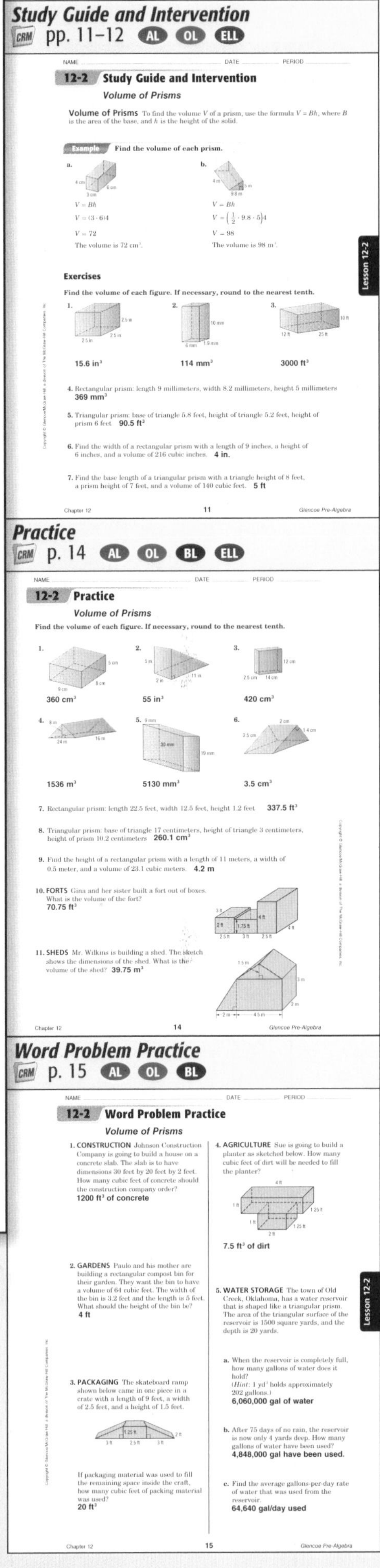

Study Guide and Intervention
CRM pp. 11–12 AL OL ELL

NAME DATE PERIOD

12-2 Study Guide and Intervention

Volume of Prisms

Volume of Prisms To find the volume V of a prism, use the formula $V = Bh$, where B is the area of the base, and h is the height of the solid.

Example Find the volume of each prism.

a. $V = Bh$; $V = (3 \cdot 6)4$; $V = 72$; The volume is 72 cm³.

b. $V = Bh$; $V = \left(\frac{1}{2} \cdot 9.8 \cdot 5\right)4$; $V = 98$; The volume is 98 m³.

Exercises

Find the volume of each figure. If necessary, round to the nearest tenth.

1. 15.6 in³ 2. 114 mm³ 3. 3000 ft³

4. Rectangular prism: length 9 millimeters, width 8.2 millimeters, height 5 millimeters 369 mm³

5. Triangular prism: base of triangle 5.8 feet, height of triangle 5.2 feet, height of prism 6 feet 90.5 ft³

6. Find the width of a rectangular prism with a length of 9 inches, a height of 6 inches, and a volume of 216 cubic inches. 4 in.

7. Find the base length of a triangular prism with a triangle height of 8 feet, a prism height of 7 feet, and a volume of 140 cubic feet. 5 ft

Chapter 12 11 Glencoe Pre-Algebra

Practice
CRM p. 14 AL OL BL ELL

NAME DATE PERIOD

12-2 Practice

Volume of Prisms

Find the volume of each figure. If necessary, round to the nearest tenth.

1. 360 cm³ 2. 55 in³ 3. 420 cm³

4. 1536 m³ 5. 5130 mm³ 6. 3.5 cm³

7. Rectangular prism: length 22.5 feet, width 12.5 feet, height 1.2 feet 337.5 ft³

8. Triangular prism: base of triangle 17 centimeters, height of triangle 3 centimeters, height of prism 10.2 centimeters 260.1 cm³

9. Find the height of a rectangular prism with a length of 11 meters, a width of 0.5 meter, and a volume of 23.1 cubic meters. 4.2 m

10. FORTS Gina and her sister built a fort out of boxes. What is the volume of the fort? 70.75 ft³

11. SHEDS Mr. Wilkins is building a shed. The sketch shows the dimensions of the shed. What is the volume of the shed? 39.75 m³

Chapter 12 14 Glencoe Pre-Algebra

Word Problem Practice
CRM p. 15 AL OL BL

NAME DATE PERIOD

12-2 Word Problem Practice

Volume of Prisms

1. CONSTRUCTION Johnson Construction Company is going to build a house on a concrete slab. The slab is to have dimensions 30 feet by 20 feet by 2 feet. How many cubic feet of concrete should the construction company order? 1200 ft³ of concrete

2. GARDENS Paulo and his mother are building a rectangular compost bin for their garden. They want the bin to have a volume of 64 cubic feet. The width of the bin is 3.2 feet and the length is 5 feet. What should the height of the bin be? 4 ft

3. PACKAGING The skateboard ramp shown below came in one piece in a crate with a length of 9 feet, a width of 2.5 feet, and a height of 1.5 feet. If packaging material was used to fill the remaining space inside the craft, how many cubic feet of packing material was used? 20 ft³

4. AGRICULTURE Sue is going to build a planter as sketched below. How many cubic feet of dirt will be needed to fill the planter? 7.5 ft³ of dirt

5. WATER STORAGE The town of Old Creek, Oklahoma, has a water reservoir that is shaped like a triangular prism. The area of the triangular surface of the reservoir is 1500 square yards, and the depth is 20 yards.

a. When the reservoir is completely full, how many gallons of water does it hold? (Hint: 1 yd³ holds approximately 202 gallons.) 6,060,000 gal of water

b. After 75 days of no rain, the reservoir is now only 4 yards deep. How many gallons of water have been used? 4,848,000 gal have been used.

c. Find the average gallons-per-day rate of water that was used from the reservoir. 64,640 gal/day used

Chapter 12 15 Glencoe Pre-Algebra

4 ASSESS

Yesterday's News Tell students to write about how yesterday's lesson on three-dimensional figures helped them with today's lesson on finding the volume of prisms.

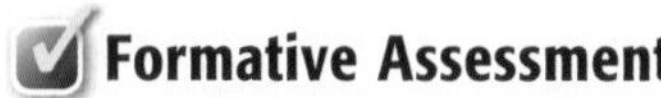

Formative Assessment

Check for student understanding of concepts in Lessons 12-1 and 12-2.

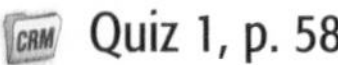 Quiz 1, p. 58

Additional Answers

38. rectangular pyramid; base: *BCDE;* faces: *ABC, ACD, ADE, AEB, BCDE;* edges: $\overline{AB}$, $\overline{AC}$, $\overline{AD}$, $\overline{AE}$, $\overline{BC}$, $\overline{CD}$, $\overline{DE}$, $\overline{EB}$; vertices: *A, B, C, D, E*

39. rectangular prism; bases: *ABCD* and *EFGH,* or *BCGF* and *ADHE,* or *ABFE* and *DCGH;* faces: *ABCD, EFGH, BCGF, ADHE, ABFE, DCGH;* edges: $\overline{AB}$, $\overline{DC}$, $\overline{HG}$, $\overline{EF}$, $\overline{AD}$, $\overline{BC}$, $\overline{EH}$, $\overline{FG}$, $\overline{AE}$, $\overline{BF}$, $\overline{DH}$, $\overline{CG}$; vertices: *A, B, C, D, E, F, G, H*

Standardized Test Practice

34. Mr. Toshio is filling a 20-foot by 35-foot garden framed by two levels of bricks with topsoil. If the topsoil costs $9 per cubic foot, what other information is needed to find *s*, the cost of the soil? **D**

A The area of the garden.
B The perimeter of the garden.
C The price per cubic yard of soil.
D The height of the bricks.

35. GRIDDED RESPONSE How many centimeters tall is a rectangular prism with a length of 8 centimeters, width of 10 centimeters, and a volume of 960 cubic centimeters? **12**

36. What is the volume of the prism below? **H**

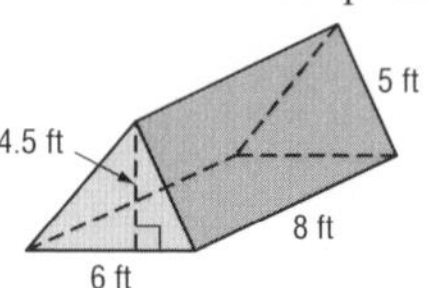

F 67.5 ft^3 H 108 ft^3
G 90 ft^3 J 216 ft^3

37. Which of the following is the best estimate for the volume of a shoe box with sides that measure 15.75 inches, 9.25 inches, and 8 inches? **C**

A 10 in^3 C 1000 in^3
B 100 in^3 D 10,000 in^3

Spiral Review

Identify each figure. Name the bases, faces, edges, and vertices. (Lesson 12-1) **38–39. See margin.**

38.

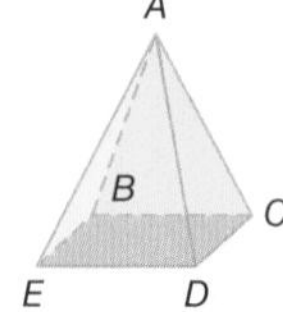

39.

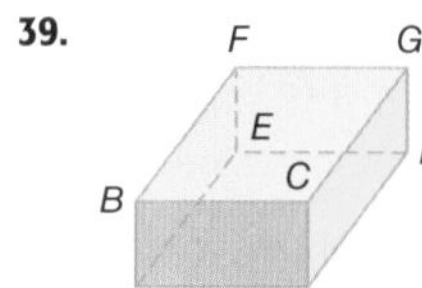

Find the area of each figure. Round to the nearest tenth. (Lesson 11-9)

40. **12.9 yd^2**

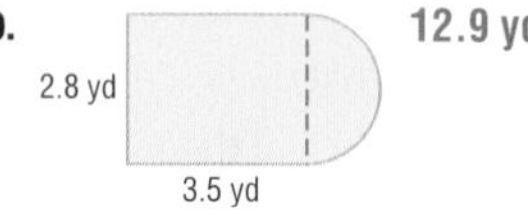

41. **228.5 mm^2**

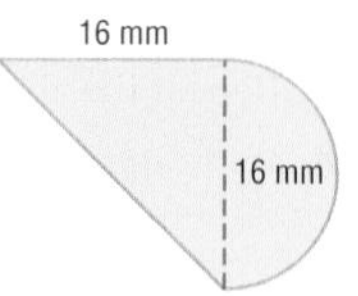

42. SOCCER Tomás wants to spend less than $100 for a new soccer ball and shoes. The ball costs $24. Write and solve an inequality that gives the amount that Tomás can spend on shoes. (Lesson 5-4) **$24 + s < 100$; less than $76**

Skills Review

Find the area of each circle. Round to the nearest tenth. (Lesson 11-8)

43. **12.6 in^2**

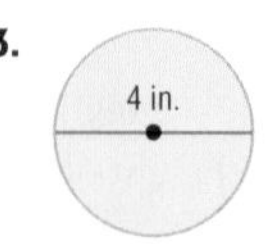

44. 8 m **201.1 m^2**

45. 5 mi **78.5 mi^2**

Differentiated Instruction

BL

Extension Pose the following problem to students: A refrigerator has an interior volume of 15.2 cubic feet and measures 19.5 inches wide and 20.5 inches deep. To the nearest tenth of an inch, what is the interior height of the refrigerator? ($1 \text{ ft}^3 = 1728 \text{ in}^3$) 65.7 inches

12-3 Volume of Cylinders

Why?

Marisol has a stack of dimes and another stack of quarters.

a. How would you find the value in dollars of the dimes? the quarters? **$0.10 • the number of dimes; $0.25 • the number of quarters**

b. How much money would Marisol have if she had 30 dimes and 25 quarters? **$9.25**

c. **MAKE A CONJECTURE** How do the answers to part **a** and part **b** relate to finding the volume of a cylinder? **The value of the stack of coins is similar to finding the volume of the cylinder.**

Then

You have already found the areas of circles. (Lesson 11-8)

Now

- Find the volumes of circular cylinders.
- Find the volumes of composite figures involving circular cylinders.

Math Online

glencoe.com

- Extra Examples
- Personal Tutor
- Self-Check Quiz
- Homework Help

Volumes of Cylinders Like prisms, the volume of a cylinder is the product of the area of the base and the height.

Key Concept — Volume of a Cylinder

For Your FOLDABLE

Words The volume V of a circular cylinder with radius r is the area of the base B times the height h.

Model

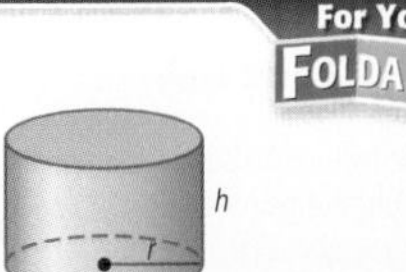

Symbols $V = Bh$, where $B = \pi r^2$ or $V = \pi r^2 h$

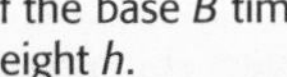

EXAMPLE 1 Volume of a Cylinder

Find the volume of each cylinder. Round to the nearest tenth.

a. radius of base 3 in., height 12 in.

$V = Bh$	Volume of a cylinder
$V = \pi r^2 h$	Replace B with πr^2.
$\approx \pi \cdot 3^2 \cdot 12$	Replace r with 3 and h with 12.
$\approx 339.1 \text{ in}^3$	Use a calculator.

3 in.

12 in.

b. diameter of base 14 cm, height 20 cm

$V = Bh$	Volume of a cylinder
$V = \pi r^2 h$	Replace B with πr^2.
$\approx \pi \cdot 7^2 \cdot 20$	Replace r with 7 and h with 20.
$\approx 3078.8 \text{ cm}^3$	Use a calculator.

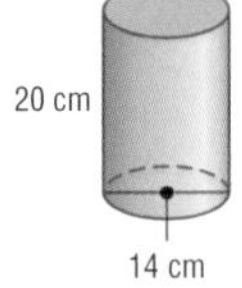

Check Your Progress

1A. **1402.8 ft^3**

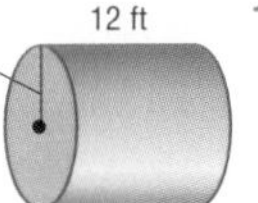

1B. **510.4 m^3**

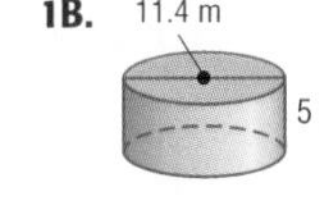

Personal Tutor glencoe.com

12-3 Lesson Notes

1 FOCUS

Vertical Alignment

Before Lesson 12-3
Find the area of circles.

Lesson 12-3
Find the volumes of circular cylinders.
Find the volumes of composite figures involving circular cylinders.

After Lesson 12-3
Find surface areas and volumes of prisms, pyramids, spheres, cones, cylinders, and composites of these figures in problem situations.

2 TEACH

Scaffolding Questions

Have students read the *Why?* section of the lesson and answer the questions.

- In the formula $V = Bh$, the B represents the area of the base. If the solid is a prism, the base is a polygon. What does B represent if the figure is a cylinder? area of a circle
- What is the formula for the area of a circle? $A = \pi r^2$
- What formula could you use for the volume of a cylinder, if you substitute the formula for area for b? $V = \pi r^2 h$

Lesson 12-3 Resources

Resource	Approaching-Level	On-Level	Beyond-Level	English Learners
Teacher Edition	• Differentiated Instruction, p. 678	• Differentiated Instruction, p. 678	• Differentiated Instruction, pp. 678, 681	
Chapter Resource Masters	• Study Guide and Intervention, pp. 18–19 • Skills Practice, p. 20 • Practice, p. 21 • Word Problem Practice, p. 22	• Study Guide and Intervention, pp. 18–19 • Skills Practice, p. 20 • Practice, p. 21 • Word Problem Practice, p. 22 • Enrichment, p. 23	• Practice, p. 21 • Word Problem Practice, p. 22 • Enrichment, p. 23	• Study Guide and Intervention, pp. 18–19 • Skills Practice, p. 20 • Practice, p. 21
Transparencies	• 5-Minute Check Transparency 12-3	• 5-Minute Check Transparency 12-3	• 5-Minute Check Transparency 12-3	• 5-Minute Check Transparency 12-3
Other	• Study Notebook • Teaching Pre-Algebra with Manipulatives	• Study Notebook • Teaching Pre-Algebra with Manipulatives	• Study Notebook	• Study Notebook • Teaching Pre-Algebra with Manipulatives

Volumes of Cylinders

Example 1 shows how to find the volume of a cylinder. **Example 2** shows how to find the height of a cylinder when the volume and radius are given.

Formative Assessment

Use the Check Your Progress exercises after each example to determine students' understanding of concepts.

Additional Examples

1 Find the volume of each cylinder. Round to the nearest tenth.

a. 2154.0 ft^3

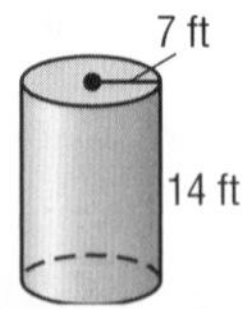

b. diameter of base 10 m, height 2 m 157 m^3

2 The volume of the cylinder is 99 cubic inches. Find the height of the cylinder. Round to the nearest tenth. 3.5 inches

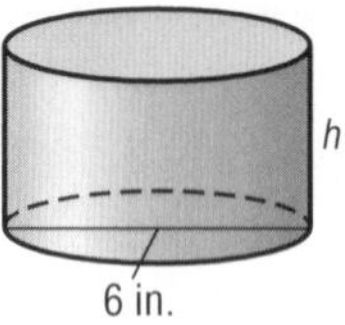

Additional Examples also in Interactive Classroom PowerPoint® Presentations

IWB INTERACTIVE WHITEBOARD READY

EXAMPLE 2 Height of a Cylinder

The volume of the cylinder is 618 cubic meters. Find the height of the cylinder. Round to the nearest tenth.

$V = Bh$	**Volume of a cylinder**
$V = \pi r^2 h$	**Replace B with πr^2.**
$618 = \pi \cdot 4^2 \cdot h$	**Replace V with 618 and r with 4.**
$618 = 16\pi h$	**Simplify.**
$12.3 \approx h$	**Divide each side by 16π. Round to the nearest tenth.**

The height of the cylinder is about 12.3 meters.

Check Your Progress

2. Find the height of a cylinder with a diameter of 10 yards and a volume of 549.5 cubic yards. Round to the nearest tenth. 7.0 yd

Personal Tutor glencoe.com

Real-World Link

The Hirshshorn Museum and Sculpture Garden is part of the National Smithsonian Museum. It opened in 1974 and displays modern and contemporary art. It is located on the National Mall in Washington, D.C.

Volumes of Composite Figures When a composite figure includes cylinders, you can find the volume by separating it into the different pieces.

Real-World EXAMPLE 3 Volume of a Composite Figure

SCULPTURE An art museum is placing a sculpture on the stone pedestal shown at the right. Find the volume of the pedestal.

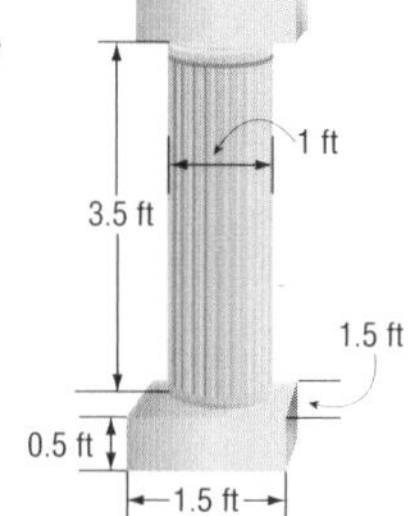

Find the volume. The volume of the pedestal is the sum of two rectangular prisms and a cylinder.

Step 1 Find the volume of the prisms.

$V = Bh$	**Volume of a prism**
$V = 1.5 \cdot 1.5 \cdot 0.5$	**The length and width are each 1.5 ft. The height is 0.5 ft.**
$= 1.125 \text{ ft}^3$	**Simplify.**

So, the volume of the two square bases is $2 \cdot 1.125$ or 2.25 ft^3.

Step 2 Find the volume of the cylinder.

$V = \pi r^2 h$	**Volume of a cylinder**
$= \pi \cdot (0.5)^2 \cdot 3.5$	**Replace r with 0.5 and h with 3.5.**
$\approx 2.75 \text{ ft}^3$	**Use a calculator.**

Step 3 Find the volume of the composite figure.

$2.25 + 2.75 = 5$	**Add the volumes.**

So, the total volume of the pedestal is 5 ft^3.

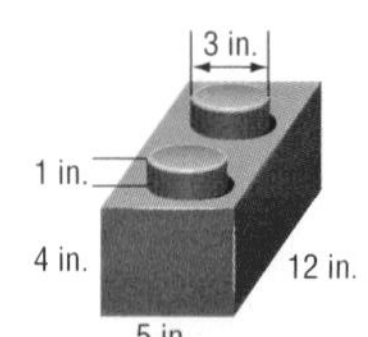

Check Your Progress 3. 254.1 in^3

3. Find the volume of the plastic building brick shown at the right. Round to the nearest tenth.

Personal Tutor glencoe.com

678 Chapter 12 Surface Area and Volume

TEACH with TECH

INTERACTIVE WHITEBOARD Save your notes as you work through each example of finding the volume of a cylinder. E-mail the notes to your students or post to your classroom Web site so they can use them as a reference outside of class.

Differentiated Instruction

Auditory/Musical Let students experiment with five identical glass or ceramic cylinders to find how the volume of water in each cylinder affects its tone when struck with a pen or stick. Identical coffee mugs will work for this. Students should be able to develop a partial musical scale based on the volume of water.

Check Your Understanding

Answers were computed using the π key on a calculator.

Example 1 p. 677

Find the volume of each cylinder. Round to the nearest tenth.

1. 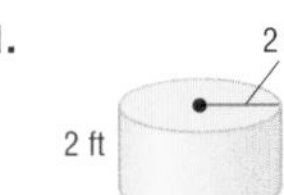

25.1 ft³

2. diameter of base: 33.2 mm
height: 60 mm 51,941.8 mm³

Example 2 p. 678

Find the height of each cylinder. Round to the nearest tenth.

3. volume = 283 in³ 10.0 in.

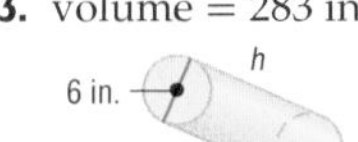

4. volume: 5700 m³
diameter of base: 22 m 15.0 m

Example 3 p. 678

5. CRAFTS An oak peg like the one shown at the right was used in a toy truck. Find the volume of the peg. Round to the nearest tenth. 22.0 cm³

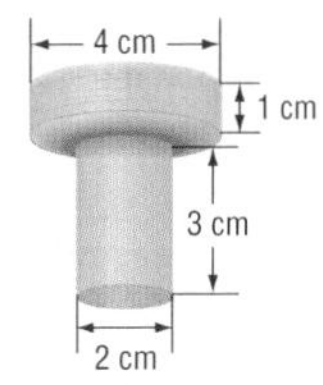

Practice and Problem Solving

Examples 1 and 2 pp. 677 and 678

Find the volume of each figure. Round to the nearest tenth.

6. 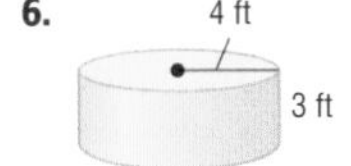

150.8 ft³

7. 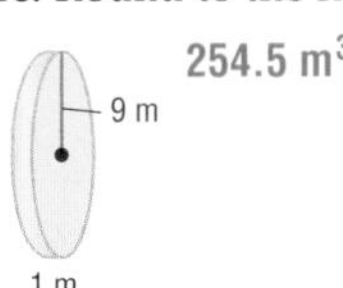

254.5 m³

8. 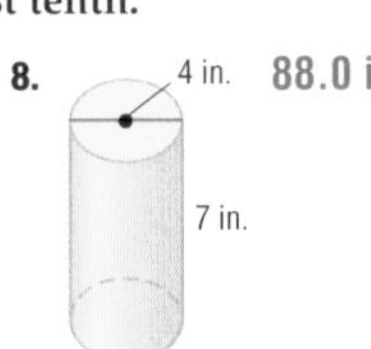

88.0 in³

9. radius: 2.2 cm
height: 3 cm 45.6 cm³

10. diameter: 5 yd
height: 11 yd
216.0 yd³

11. diameter: 4.6 m
height: 6.1 m 101.4 m³

Find the height of each cylinder. Round to the nearest tenth.

12. volume: 41.5 yd³ 3.3 yd

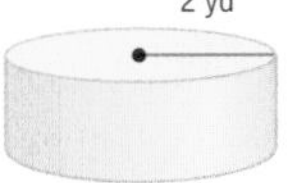

13. volume: 9.7 m³
diameter: 1.5 m 5.5 m

A size 303 can measures $3\frac{3}{16}$ inches in diameter. The can number indicates the measure of the diameter.

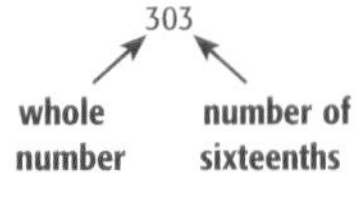

14. CANDLES A scented candle is in the shape of a cylinder that is 8 inches tall. The diameter of the candle is 3.5 inches. Find the volume of the candle. Round to the nearest tenth. 77.0 in³

15. FOOD Use the information at the left to find the volume of soup in a size 400 can that is 5.5 inches tall. 69.1 in³

Example 3 p. 678

Find the volume of each figure. Round to the nearest tenth.

16. 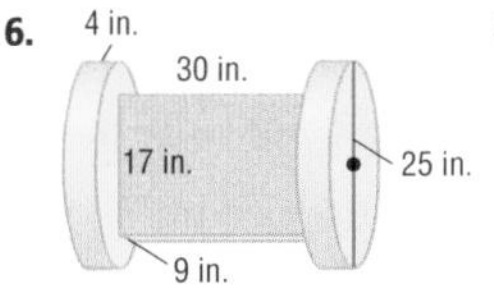

8517.0 in³

17. 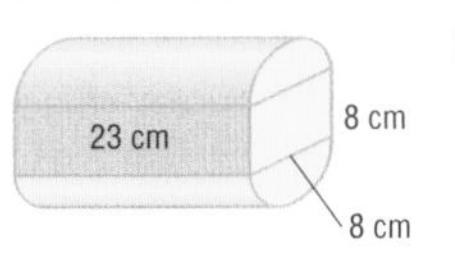

2628.1 cm³

Focus on Mathematical Content

Volume of a Cylinder The volume of a cylinder, just like a prism, is the area of its base times its height. In the case of a cylinder, the base is a circle whose area is $A = \pi r^2 h$.

Volumes of Composite Figures

Example 3 shows how to find the volume of a composite figure that involves cylinders.

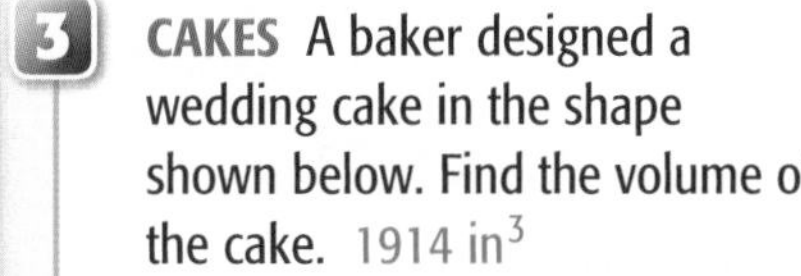

Additional Example

3 **CAKES** A baker designed a wedding cake in the shape shown below. Find the volume of the cake. 1914 in³

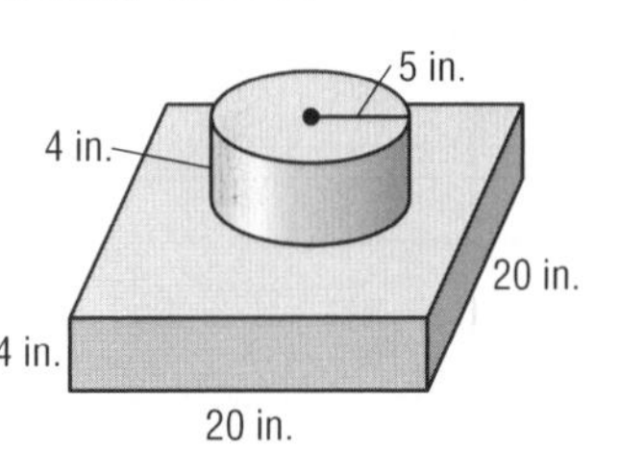

3 PRACTICE

Formative Assessment

Use Exercises 1–5 to check for understanding.

Use the chart at the bottom of this page to customize assignments for your students.

Differentiated Homework Options

Level	Assignment	Two-Day Option	
AL Basic	6–17, 23, 25–41	7–17 odd, 27–30	6–16 even, 23, 25–26, 31–41
OL Core	7–17 odd, 18–23, 25–41	6–17, 27–30	18–23, 25–26, 31–41
BL Advanced	18–38 (optional: 39–41)		

Lesson 12-3 Volume of Cylinders 679

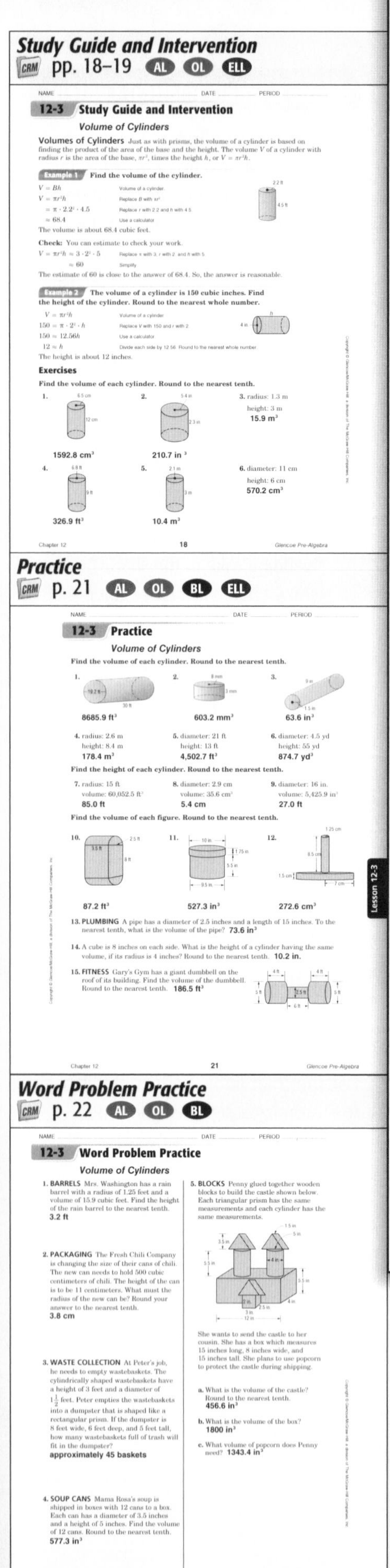

Study Guide and Intervention
CRM pp. 18–19 AL OL ELL

12-3 Study Guide and Intervention

Volume of Cylinders

Volumes of Cylinders Just as with prisms, the volume of a cylinder is based on finding the product of the area of the base and the height. The volume V of a cylinder with radius r is the area of the base, πr^2, times the height h, or $V = \pi r^2 h$.

Example 1 Find the volume of the cylinder.

$V = Bh$ Volume of a cylinder
$V = \pi r^2 h$ Replace B with πr^2
$= \pi \cdot 2.2^2 \cdot 4.5$ Replace r with 2.2 and h with 4.5
≈ 68.4 Use a calculator

The volume is about 68.4 cubic feet.

Check: You can estimate to check your work.
$V = \pi r^2 h \approx 3 \cdot 2^2 \cdot 5$
≈ 60 Simplify

The estimate of 60 is close to the answer of 68.4. So, the answer is reasonable.

Example 2 The volume of a cylinder is 150 cubic inches. Find the height of the cylinder. Round to the nearest whole number.

$V = \pi r^2 h$ Volume of a cylinder
$150 = \pi \cdot 2^2 \cdot h$ Replace V with 150 and r with 2
$150 = 12.56h$ Use a calculator
$12 \approx h$ Divide each side by 12.56. Round to the nearest whole number.

The height is about 12 inches.

Exercises

Find the volume of each cylinder. Round to the nearest tenth.

1. 1592.8 cm³
2. 210.7 in³
3. radius: 1.3 m, height: 3 m — 15.9 m³
4. 326.9 ft³
5. 10.4 m³
6. diameter: 11 cm, height: 6 cm — 570.2 cm³

Chapter 12 | 18 | Glencoe Pre-Algebra

Practice
CRM p. 21 AL OL BL ELL

12-3 Practice

Volume of Cylinders

Find the volume of each cylinder. Round to the nearest tenth.

1. 8685.9 ft³
2. 603.2 mm³
3. 63.6 in³
4. radius: 2.6 m, height: 8.4 m — 178.4 m³
5. diameter: 21 ft, height: 13 ft — 4,502.7 ft³
6. diameter: 4.5 yd, height: 55 yd — 874.7 yd³

Find the height of each cylinder. Round to the nearest tenth.

7. radius: 15 ft, volume: 60,052.5 ft³ — 85.0 ft
8. diameter: 2.9 cm, volume: 35.6 cm³ — 5.4 cm
9. diameter: 16 in., volume: 5,425.9 in³ — 27.0 ft

Find the volume of each figure. Round to the nearest tenth.

10. 87.2 ft³
11. 527.3 in³
12. 272.6 cm³

13. PLUMBING A pipe has a diameter of 2.5 inches and a length of 15 inches. To the nearest tenth, what is the volume of the pipe? 73.6 in³

14. A cube is 8 inches on each side. What is the height of a cylinder having the same volume, if its radius is 4 inches? Round to the nearest tenth. 10.2 in.

15. FITNESS Gary's Gym has a giant dumbbell on the roof of its building. Find the volume of the dumbbell. Round to the nearest tenth. 186.5 ft³

Chapter 12 | 21 | Glencoe Pre-Algebra

Word Problem Practice
CRM p. 22 AL OL BL

12-3 Word Problem Practice

Volume of Cylinders

1. BARRELS Mrs. Washington has a rain barrel with a radius of 1.25 feet and a volume of 15.9 cubic feet. Find the height of the rain barrel to the nearest tenth. 3.2 ft

2. PACKAGING The Fresh Chili Company is changing the size of their cans of chili. The new can needs to hold 500 cubic centimeters of chili. The height of the can is to be 11 centimeters. What must the radius of the new can be? Round your answer to the nearest tenth. 3.8 cm

3. WASTE COLLECTION At Peter's job, he needs to empty wastebaskets. The cylindrically shaped wastebaskets have a height of 3 feet and a diameter of $1\frac{1}{2}$ feet. Peter empties the wastebaskets into a dumpster that is shaped like a rectangular prism. If the dumpster is 8 feet wide, 6 feet deep, and 5 feet tall, how many wastebaskets full of trash will fit in the dumpster? approximately 45 baskets

4. SOUP CANS Mama Rosa's soup is shipped in boxes with 12 cans to a box. Each can has a diameter of 3.5 inches and a height of 5 inches. Find the volume of 12 cans. Round to the nearest tenth. 577.3 in³

5. BLOCKS Penny glued together wooden blocks to build the castle shown below. Each triangular prism has the same measurements and each cylinder has the same measurements.

She wants to send the castle to her cousin. She has a box which measures 15 inches long, 8 inches wide, and 15 inches tall. She plans to use popcorn to protect the castle during shipping.

a. What is the volume of the castle? Round to the nearest tenth. 456.6 in³

b. What is the volume of the box? 1800 in³

c. What volume of popcorn does Penny need? 1343.4 in³

Chapter 12 | 22 | Glencoe Pre-Algebra

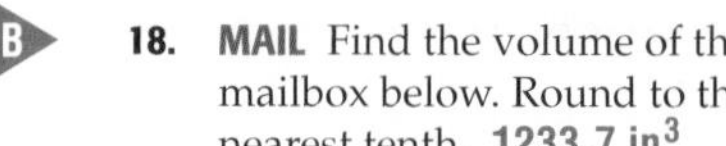

18. MAIL Find the volume of the mailbox below. Round to the nearest tenth. **1233.7 in³**

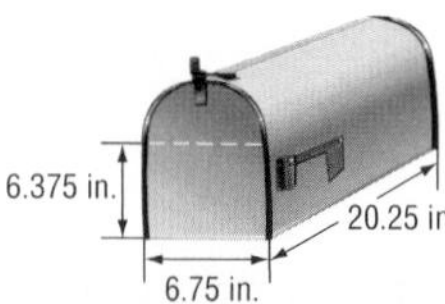

19. TOWELS A roll of paper towels has the dimensions shown. Find the volume of the roll. Round to the nearest tenth. **3271.2 cm³**

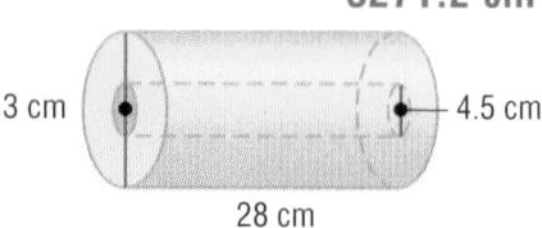

Watch Out!

In Exercise 19 do not subtract the diameter of the small tube from the roll of paper towels. You need to find the volume of each before you subtract.

20. MULTIPLE REPRESENTATIONS In this problem, you will examine how changing the size of a cylinder affects its volume. Round to the nearest tenth, if necessary.

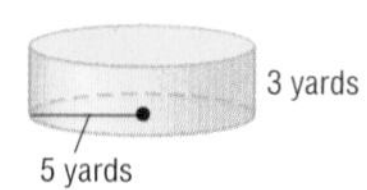

a. TABULAR Copy and complete the table for the cylinder shown. **a–b. See margin.**

Cylinder	Radius	Height	Volume (yd³)
Original	5	3	■
Multiply radius by 3	5 • 3 = ■	3	■
Multiply height by 3	5	3 • 3 = ■	■
Multiply both by 3	■	■	■

b. ANALYTICAL Compare the original volume to the other volumes.

c. ALGEBRAIC Write an equation to find the volume of a cylinder after a dilation d. **Sample answer: If $V = \pi r^2 h$, after a dilation of d, $V = d^3 \cdot \pi r^2 h$**

21. CONSERVATION A cylindrical rain barrel is 38 inches tall and has a diameter of 28 inches. If the volume of one gallon of water is 231 cubic inches, how many gallons of water will the rain barrel hold? Round to the nearest tenth. **101.3 gal**

22. FIREFIGHTING Kamilah's uncle, a fire captain, said the diameters of fire hoses range from 1.5 inches to 6 inches and the hoses are 50 feet long. Find the approximate minimum and maximum volumes of a fire hose in cubic feet. **approximately 0.6 ft³ to 9.8 ft³**

H.O.T. Problems
Use Higher-Order Thinking Skills

23. OPEN ENDED Write two real-world examples where you would want to change the dimensions of cylinders, but maintain the volume.

24. CHALLENGE Two equal-sized sheets of paper are rolled along the length and along the width, as shown. Which cylinder do you think has the greater volume? Explain.

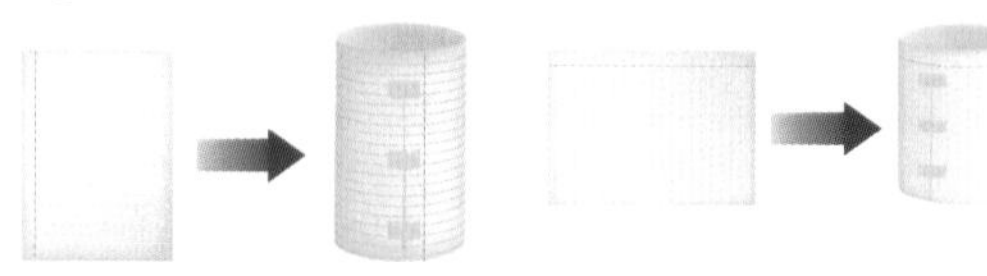

25. NUMBER SENSE Find the ratios of the volume of cylinder A to cylinder B.

a. Cylinder A has the same radius but twice the height of cylinder B. **2:1**

b. Cylinder A has the same height but twice the radius of cylinder B. **4:1**

26. WRITING IN MATH Explain how the formula for the volume of a cylinder is similar to the formula for the volume of a rectangular prism.

23. Sample answer: Changing the packaging size of a drink; changing the size of a garbage can to fit in a narrower but taller space.

24. Sample answer: The shorter cylinder, because the radius is larger and that is the squared value in the formula.

26. Sample answer: In both formulas, you multiply the area of the base by the height of the solid.

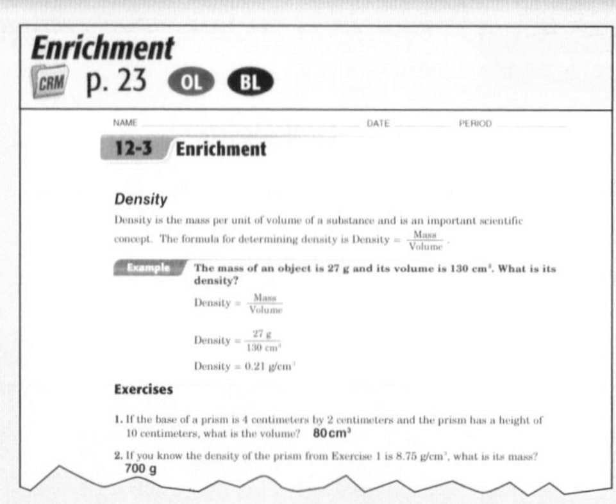

Enrichment
CRM p. 23 OL BL

12-3 Enrichment

Density

Density is the mass per unit of volume of a substance and is an important scientific concept. The formula for determining density is Density = $\frac{\text{Mass}}{\text{Volume}}$.

Example The mass of an object is 27 g and its volume is 130 cm³. What is its density?

Density = $\frac{\text{Mass}}{\text{Volume}}$

Density = $\frac{27 \text{ g}}{130 \text{ cm}^3}$

Density = 0.21 g/cm³

Exercises

1. If the base of a prism is 4 centimeters by 2 centimeters and the prism has a height of 10 centimeters, what is the volume? 80cm³

2. If you know the density of the prism from Exercise 1 is 8.75 g/cm³, what is its mass? 700 g

Multiple Representations In Exercise 20, students use a table of values and geometric analysis to write an equation comparing volumes of cylinders after a specified change in dimensions.

Standardized Test Practice

27. Find the maximum amount of water that can fill the trough shown. B

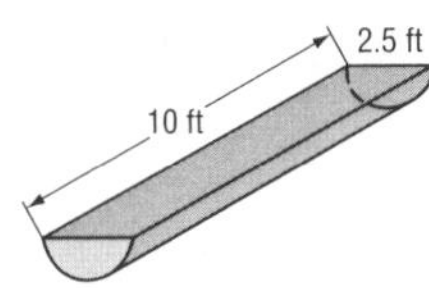

A 20.5 ft^3 C 48 ft^3
B 24.5 ft^3 D 49 ft^3

28. What is the volume of a cylinder with a radius of 8 inches and a height of 1 foot? Round to the nearest tenth. J

F 25.1 in^3 H 301.6 in^3
G 201.1 in^3 J 2412.7 in^3

29. **EXTENDED RESPONSE** The smallest canister in a set of cylindrical canisters has a height of 11 inches and a radius of 1.5 inches.
   a. Find the volume of the smallest canister. 77.8 in^3
   b. The medium canister has the same height as the smallest but the radius is tripled. What is the volume of the medium canister? 699.8 in^3

30. A cylindrical diesel tank is 1.25 meters high and has a radius of 0.60 meter. If the tank can only be filled to an 85% capacity to allow for expansion and contraction of the fuel, what is the maximum volume of fuel? Round to the nearest hundredth. D

A 4.71 m^3 C 1.41 m^3
B 2.01 m^3 D 1.20 m^3

Spiral Review

Find the volume of each figure. (Lesson 12-2)

31.

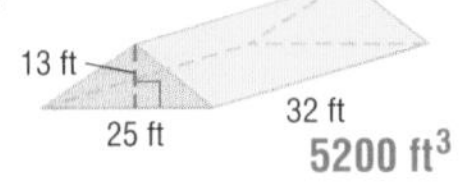

5200 ft^3

32.

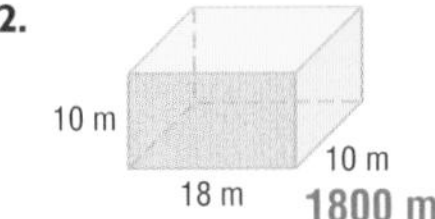

1800 m^3

33.

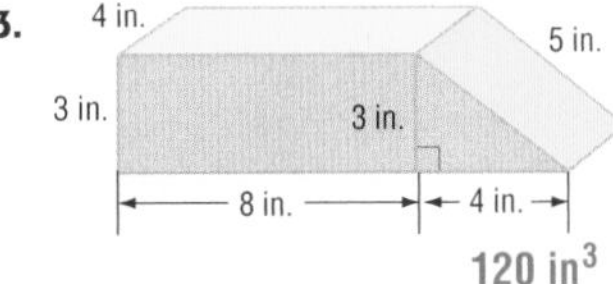

120 in^3

Identify each figure. Name the bases, faces, edges, and vertices. (Lesson 12-1) 34–35. See margin.

34.

35.

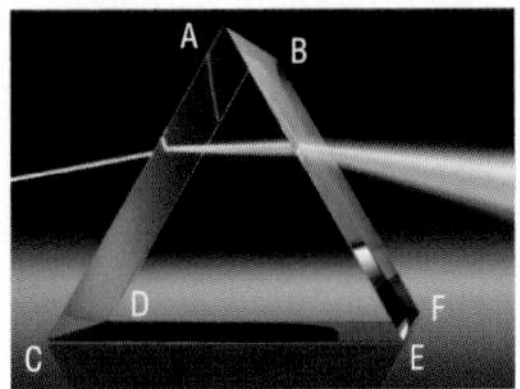

Solve each problem using the percent equation. Round to the nearest tenth. (Lesson 7-5)

36. 12 is what percent of 78? 15.4%
37. 5% of what number is 8? 160
38. What is 42% of 45? 18.9

Skills Review

Find each product. (Lesson 3-3)

39. $\frac{1}{3} \cdot 7 \cdot 15$ 35
40. $\frac{4}{3} \cdot 2 \cdot 5 \cdot 20$ $266\frac{2}{3}$
41. $\frac{1}{3} \cdot \frac{5}{6} \cdot 12$ $3\frac{1}{3}$

4 ASSESS

Crystal Ball Tell students to write about how they think today's lesson on the volume of cylinders will help them with tomorrow's lesson on the volumes of pyramids, cones, and spheres.

Additional Answers

20a.

	Radius	Height	Volume (yd^3)
Original	5	3	235.6
Multiply radius by 3	$5 \cdot 3 = 15$	3	2120.6
Multiply height by 3	5	$3 \cdot 3 = 9$	706.9
Multiply both by 3	15	9	6361.7

20b. Sample answer: The volume when the radius is multiplied by 3 is 9 times the original. The volume when the height is multiplied by 3 is 3 times the original. The volume when both are multiplied by 3 is 27 times the original.

34. Rectangular pyramid; base: *BCED;* faces: *BCED, ABC, ADE, AEC, ADB;* edges: $\overline{AB}, \overline{AC}, \overline{AD}, \overline{AE}, \overline{BC}, \overline{BD}, \overline{DE}, \overline{EC}$; vertices: *A, B, C, D, E*

35. triangular prism: bases: *ACE* and *BDF;* faces: *ABFE, EFDC, ABCD, ACE, BDF;* edges: $\overline{AB}, \overline{EF}, \overline{CD}, \overline{AC}, \overline{CE}, \overline{EA}, \overline{BF}, \overline{FD}, \overline{DB}$; vertices: *A, B, C, D, E, F*

Differentiated Instruction

Extension Give students the following problem: A company wants to package a sports drink in a cylindrical can with a volume of 0.35 liter. This is equivalent to 350 milliliters, which is about 12 fluid ounces. Using metric units, what approximate height and radius would the can need to be to hold this volume? ($1 \ mL = 1 \text{ cm}^3$) Sample answer: The radius would be about 4 centimeters and the height about 7 centimeters.

EXPLORE 12-4 Lesson Notes

FOCUS

Objective Develop a method to find the volume of a pyramid.

Materials for Each Student

- ruler
- tape
- rice
- scissors

Teaching Tip

Give students an old file folder or some other kind of stiff paper to use in building the models. Make sure they tape the edges of the models securely.

TEACH

Working in Cooperative Groups

Arrange students in groups of two or three, mixing abilities. Have students complete the Activity and Exercise 1.

Ask:

- How will the volume of the cube compare with the volume of the square pyramid? The cube's volume will be greater than the pyramid's volume.

Practice Have students complete Exercises 2–6.

ASSESS

Formative Assessment

Use Exercises 4–6 to assess whether students found a method for finding the volume of a pyramid.

EXPLORE 12-4 Geometry Lab Volume of a Pyramid

Math Online glencoe.com
Math *in Motion*, Animation

In Lesson 12-2, you learned how to find the volume of a prism. You can use this idea to develop a method to find the volume of a pyramid.

ACTIVITY

Step 1 Draw and cut out five 2-inch squares. Then tape them together as shown.

2 cm

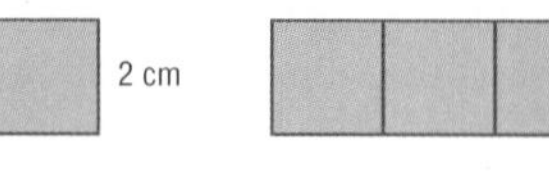

Step 2 Fold and tape to form a cube with an open top.

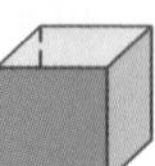

Step 3 Draw and cut out 4 isosceles triangles with the measurements shown. Then tape them together.

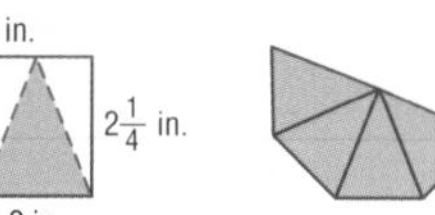

Step 4 Fold and tape to form an open square pyramid.

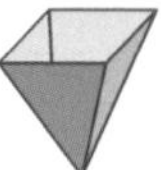

Analyze the Results

1. The areas of the bases and the heights of both solids are the same.

1. Compare the base areas and the heights of the prism and the pyramid.
2. Fill the pyramid with rice, sliding a ruler across the top to level the amount. Pour the rice into the cube. Repeat until the prism is filled. How many times did you fill the pyramid in order to fill the cube? **3 times**
3. What fraction of the prism volume does one pyramid fill? $\frac{1}{3}$
4. If the results of the activity apply to all pyramids, write a formula that relates the volume V of one pyramid to the dimensions of the prism. $V = \frac{1}{3}lwh$

Find the volume of each pyramid.

5. **50 in^3**

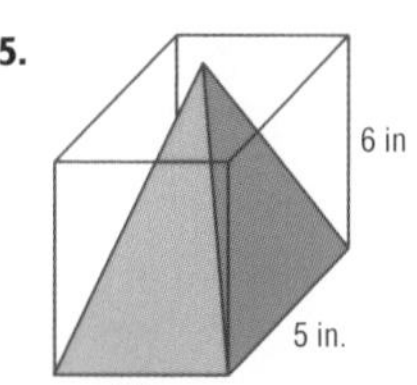

6. **297 cm^3**

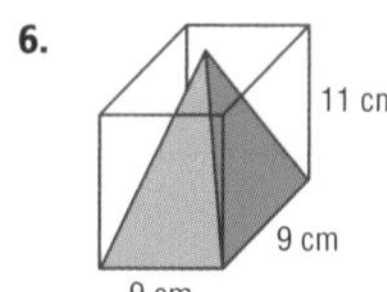

From Concrete to Abstract

Have students draw their own pyramids including the dimensions. Tell them to find the volumes and trade with other students to check their work.

12-4 Volume of Pyramids, Cones and Spheres

Then

You have already found the volume of prisms and cylinders. (Lessons 12-2 and 12-3)

Now

- Find the volumes of pyramids and cones.
- Find the volumes of spheres.

New Vocabulary

sphere

Math Online

glencoe.com

- Extra Examples
- Personal Tutor
- Self-Check Quiz
- Homework Help

Why?

An ice cream shop serves ice cream in cones and cups. Both the cone and the cup have a height of 6 inches and a radius of 2 inches.

a. Do the cone and the cup hold the same amount of ice cream? **no**

b. If the ice cream in the containers were to melt, would each container have the same amount of melted ice cream? Why or why not? Explain. **no; Sample answer: The cone holds less ice cream because it has a smaller volume.**

Volume of Pyramids A pyramid has one-third the volume of a prism with the same base and height. The height of a pyramid is the perpendicular distance from the vertex to the base.

Key Concept — Volume of a Pyramid

For Your FOLDABLE

Words The volume V of a pyramid is one-third the area of the base B times the height h.

Symbols $V = \frac{1}{3}Bh$

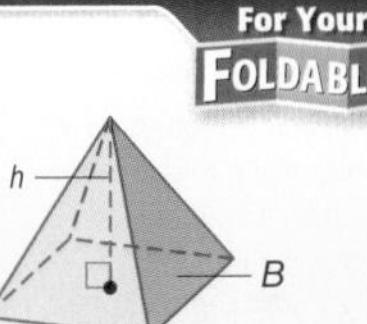

EXAMPLE 1 Volume of a Pyramid

Find the volume of the pyramid. Round to the nearest tenth, if necessary.

5 cm
8 cm
6 cm

$V = \frac{1}{3}Bh$	Volume of a pyramid
$V = \frac{1}{3}\left(\frac{1}{2} \cdot 8 \cdot 6\right) h$	The base is a triangle so $B = \frac{1}{2} \cdot 8 \cdot 6$.
$= \frac{1}{3} \cdot 24 \cdot 5$	The height of the pyramid is 5 cm.
$= 40$	Simplify.

The volume of the pyramid is 40 cubic centimeters.

Check Your Progress

1. Find the volume of a pyramid with a base area of 90 square feet and a height of 12 feet. **360 ft^3**

Personal Tutor glencoe.com

12-4 Lesson Notes

FOCUS

Vertical Alignment

Before Lesson 12-4
Find the volumes of prisms and cylinders.

Lesson 12-4
Find the volumes of pyramids, cones, and spheres.

After Lesson 12-4
Find surface areas and volumes of three-dimensional figures.

TEACH

Scaffolding Questions

Have students read the *Why?* section of the lesson and answer the questions.

Ask:

- What is the volume of the cup? 75.4 in^3
- What is one-third of the volume of the cup? ≈ 25.1 in^3

Tips for New Teachers

Use Models Bring in a cylindrical can and make a paper cone roughly the same height and diameter as the can. Ask students how many cones of rice would it take to fill the can. Then test their hypotheses by performing the activity.

Lesson 12-4 Resources

Resource	Approaching-Level	On-Level	Beyond-Level	English Learners
Teacher Edition		• Differentiated Instruction, p. 684	• Differentiated Instruction, pp. 684, 688	
Chapter Resource Masters	• Study Guide and Intervention, pp. 24–25 • Skills Practice, p. 26 • Practice, p. 27 • Word Problem Practice, p. 28	• Study Guide and Intervention, pp. 24–25 • Skills Practice, p. 26 • Practice, p. 27 • Word Problem Practice, p. 28 • Enrichment, p. 29	• Practice, p. 27 • Word Problem Practice, p. 28 • Enrichment, p. 29	• Study Guide and Intervention, pp. 24–25 • Skills Practice, p. 26 • Practice, p. 27
Transparencies	• 5-Minute Check Transparency 12-4	• 5-Minute Check Transparency 12-4	• 5-Minute Check Transparency 12-4	• 5-Minute Check Transparency 12-4
Other	• Study Notebook • Teaching Pre-Algebra with Manipulatives	• Study Notebook • Teaching Pre-Algebra with Manipulatives	• Study Notebook	• Study Notebook • Teaching Pre-Algebra with Manipulatives

Lesson 12-4 Volume of Pyramids, Cones, and Spheres 683

Volume of Pyramids

Example 1 shows how to find the volume of pyramids. **Example 2** shows how to find the volume of cones.

Formative Assessment

Use the Check Your Progress exercises after each example to determine students' understanding of concepts.

Additional Examples

1. Find the volume of the pyramid. Round to the nearest tenth, if necessary. 900 in^3

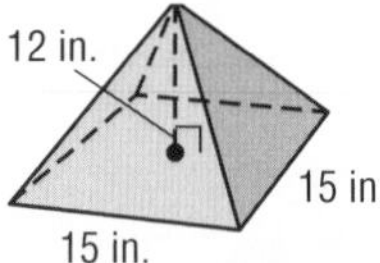

2. Find the volume of the cone. Round to the nearest tenth.

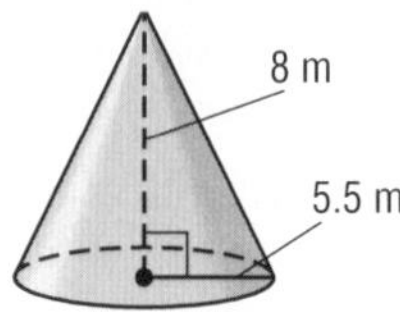

253.4 m^3

Additional Examples also in Interactive Classroom PowerPoint® Presentations

The volumes of a cone and a cylinder are related in the same way as the volumes of a pyramid and a prism are related.

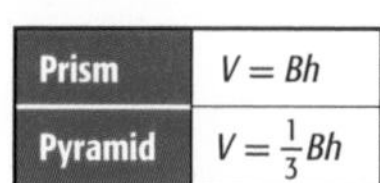

Prism	$V = Bh$
Pyramid	$V = \frac{1}{3}Bh$

Cylinder	$V = \pi r^2 h$
Cone	$V = \frac{1}{3}\pi r^2 h$

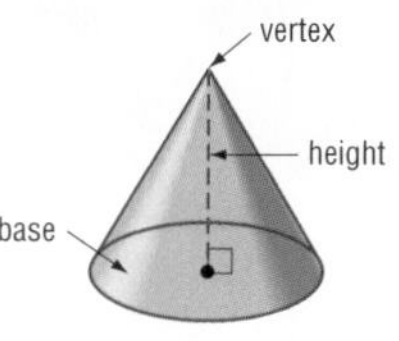

The volume of a cone is $\frac{1}{3}$ the volume of a cylinder with the same base and height.

Key Concept — Volume of a Cone

For Your FOLDABLE

Words The volume V of a cone with radius r is one third the area of the base πr^2 times the height h.

Symbols $V = \frac{1}{3}Bh$, where $B = \pi r^2$ or

$V = \frac{1}{3}\pi r^2 h$

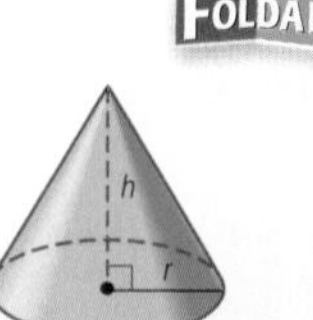

EXAMPLE 2 Volume of a Cone

Find the volume of the cone. Round to the nearest tenth.

$V = \frac{1}{3}\pi r^2 h$	**Volume of a cone**
$V = \frac{1}{3} \cdot \pi \cdot 5^2 \cdot 7$	**Replace r with 5 and h with 7.**
≈ 183.3 mm^3	**Simplify. Round to the nearest tenth.**

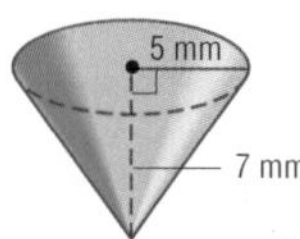

StudyTip

Estimating Since $\frac{1}{3} \cdot \pi$ is about 1, you can use estimation to determine whether your solution is reasonable.

$V \approx r^2 h$
$\approx 5^2 \cdot 7$
$\approx 25 \cdot 7$ or 175

Check Your Progress

2A. radius 6 ft, height 20 ft **754.0 ft^3**
2B. radius $1\frac{1}{2}$ yd, height 9 yd **21.2 yd^3**

Personal Tutor glencoe.com

Volume of a Sphere A **sphere** is a set of points in space that are a given distance r from the center. Suppose a sphere with radius r is placed inside a cylinder with the same radius r and height $2r$. The volume of the sphere is $\frac{2}{3}$ of the volume of the cylinder. The volume of the cylinder is shown below.

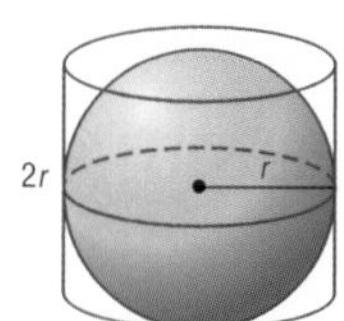

$V = \pi r^2 h$	**Volume of a cylinder**
$= \pi r^2(2r)$	**Replace h with $2r$.**
$= 2\pi r^3$	**Simplify.**

Since the sphere is $\frac{2}{3}$ the size of the cylinder, you can find the volume of the sphere.

$V = \left(\frac{2}{3}\right)2\pi r^3$	**The sphere is $\frac{2}{3}$ the size of the cylinder.**
$= \frac{4}{3}\pi r^3$	**Simplify.**

Differentiated Instruction

If students would benefit from extra practice comparing and contrasting the volumes of different solids,

Then have groups of students use modeling clay to make a cube and a cylinder. Have them measure and record the height and volume of each solid. Then, without adding or removing any clay, have them reform the cube into a square pyramid and the cylinder into a cone, maintaining the same base areas. Have students record the height and volume of their pyramids and cones. Compare the volumes and changes in the models.

Key Concept — Volume of a Sphere

For Your FOLDABLE

Words The volume V of a sphere with radius r is four-thirds times π times the radius cubed.

Symbols $V = \frac{4}{3}\pi r^3$

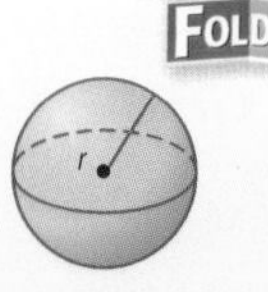

Math *in Motion*, Animation glencoe.com

EXAMPLE 3 Volume of a Sphere

Find the volume of the sphere. Round to the nearest tenth.

$V = \frac{4}{3}\pi r^3$ — Write the formula for the volume of a sphere.

$= \frac{4}{3} \cdot \pi \cdot 8^3$ — Replace r with 8.

$\approx 2144.7 \text{ in}^3$ — Simplify.

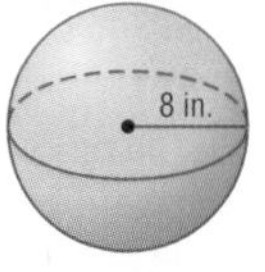

Check Your Progress

3. Find the volume of a sphere with a radius of 10 feet. Round to the nearest tenth. 4188.8 ft^3

Personal Tutor glencoe.com

Real-World EXAMPLE 4 Volume of a Sphere

Real-World Link

Ice cream and related frozen desserts are consumed by more than 90% of households in the United States.

Source: Mintel

ICE CREAM A spherical scoop of ice cream with a diameter of 6.3 centimeters is placed in a bowl. Find the volume of the ice cream. Then find how long it would take the ice cream to melt if it melts at a rate of 2.1 cubic centimeters every minute.

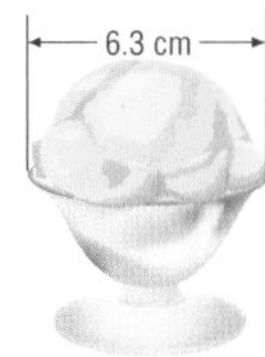

Understand You know the scoop of ice cream has a diameter of 6.3 centimeters and melts at a rate of 2.1 cubic centimeters per minute.

Plan Find the volume of the ice cream and how long it will take to melt.

Solve $V = \frac{4}{3}\pi r^3$ — Write the formula for volume of a sphere.

$= \frac{4}{3}\pi \cdot 3.15^3$ — Since $d = 6.3$, replace r with 3.15.

$\approx 130.9 \text{ cm}^3$ — Simplify.

Estimate $130 \div 2 = 65$

Use a proportion.

$\frac{2.1 \text{ cm}^3}{1 \text{ min}} = \frac{130.9 \text{ cm}^3}{x \text{ min}}$

$2.1x = 130.9$

$x \approx 62.3$

So, it will take approximately 62 minutes or about 1 hour for the ice cream to melt.

Check 62.3 is close to the estimate of 65. The answer is correct. ✓

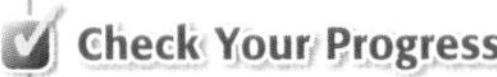

Check Your Progress

4. **TOYS** A beachball has a diameter of 18 inches. A hand pump will inflate the ball at a rate of 325 cubic inches per minute. How long will it take to inflate the ball? Round to the nearest tenth. 9.4 min

Personal Tutor glencoe.com

Focus on Mathematical Content

Volume of Pyramids, Cones, and Spheres The volumes of a pyramid and a cone are one-third of the volume of a cube with the same base and height. The volume of a sphere is two-thirds the volume of a cylinder with the same radius and height of $2r$.

Volume of Spheres

Example 3 shows how to find the volume of a sphere. **Example 4** shows how to find the volume of a sphere in a real-world problem.

Additional Examples

3 Find the volume of the sphere. Round to the nearest tenth. 523.6 ft^3

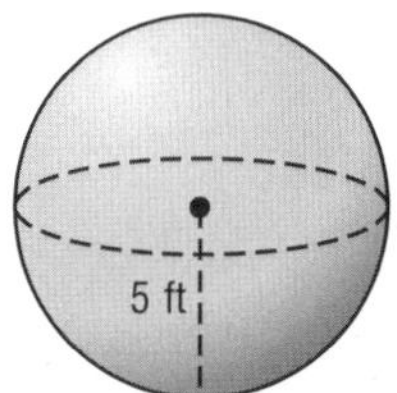

4 **BEACH BALL** A spherical beach ball has a diameter of 12 inches. Find the volume of the beach ball. Then find how long it would take to deflate the beach ball from a slow leak, if the leak lets air escape at the rate of 1.5 cubic inches per minute. Round answers to the nearest tenth. 904.8 in^3; 603.2 minutes or about 10 hr

TEACH with TECH

PORTABLE MEDIA PLAYER Create image files of pyramids, cones, and spheres, and the formulas for their volumes. Place them on your class Web page for students to load into their portable media players. They can use these as "flashcards" to help remember the formulas.

Tips for New Teachers

Spheres To help students remember the radius is cubed in the formula for the volume of a sphere, remind them that volume is in cubic units.

3 PRACTICE

Formative Assessment

Use Exercises 1–5 to check for understanding.

Use the chart at the bottom of this page to customize assignments for your students.

Additional Answer

31. Changing the shape of packaging. If the volumes remained the same and they have congruent bases, the cone's height would be 3 times the height of the cylinder.

Check Your Understanding

Answers were computed using the π key on a calculator

Examples 1–3 pp. 683–685

Find the volume of each figure. Round to the nearest tenth, if necessary.

1. 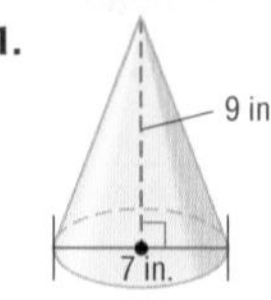

115.5 in^3

2. 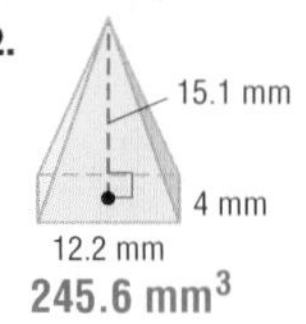

245.6 mm^3

3. 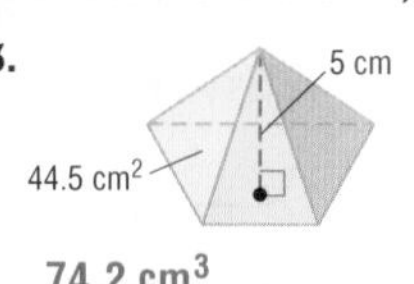

74.2 cm^3

4. 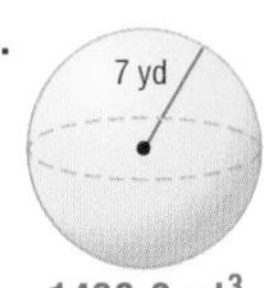

1436.8 yd^3

Example 4 p. 685

5. **JEWELRY** Amber purchased a necklace that contained an 8 millimeter diameter round pearl. Find the volume of the pearl to the nearest tenth. 268.1 mm^3

Practice and Problem Solving

● = **Step-by-Step Solutions** begin on page R11. **Extra Practice** begins on page 810.

Examples 1–3 pp. 683–685

Find the volume of each figure. Round to the nearest tenth, if necessary.

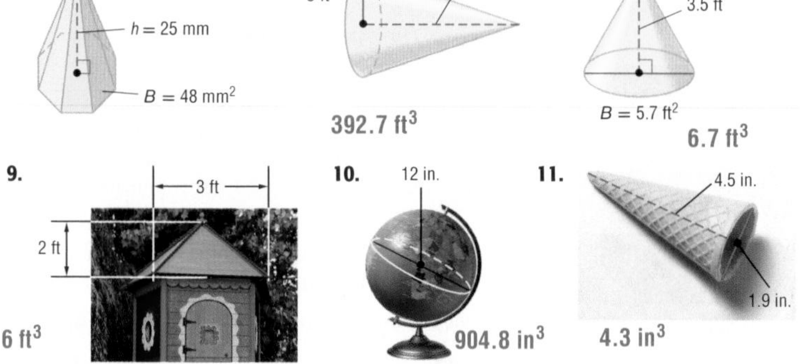

6. 400 mm^3 **7.** 392.7 ft^3 **8.** 6.7 ft^3

9. 6 ft^3 **10.** 904.8 in^3 **11.** 4.3 in^3

12. pentagonal pyramid: base area 52 in^2, height 12 in. 208 in^3

13. rectangular pyramid: length 3.5 feet, width 2 feet, height 4.5 feet 10.5 ft^3

14. cone: diameter 6.7 mm, height 2.1 mm 24.7 mm^3

15. sphere: radius 7.2 km 1563.5 km^3

16. sphere: diameter 1.8 mm 3.1 mm^3

Example 4 p. 685

17 **WEATHER** A cone-shaped icicle 2.5 feet long with a diameter of 1.5 feet has formed at the edge of a roof.

a. Find the amount of ice in the icicle to the nearest tenth of a cubic foot. 1.5 ft^3

b. The icicle melts at a rate of 0.1 cubic foot every 5 minutes. How long will it take for the icicle to melt? about 75 min or 1 h 15 min

Find the height of each figure. Round to the nearest tenth, if necessary.

18. square pyramid: volume 873.18 m^3, length 12.6 m 16.5 m

19. cone: volume 306.464 ft^3, diameter 8 ft 18.3 ft

Differentiated Homework Options

Level	Assignment	Two-Day Option	
AL Basic	6–17, 26, 28–44	7–17 odd, 32–35	6–16 even, 26, 28–31, 36–44
OL Core	7–17 odd, 19, 21, 23–26, 28–44	6–17, 32–35	18–26, 28–31, 36–44
BL Advanced	18–41 (optional: 42–44)		

Find the volume of each figure. Round to the nearest tenth, if necessary.

20. 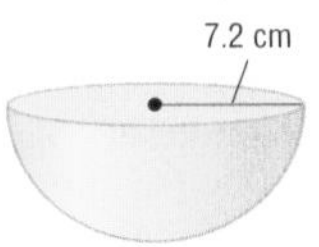

781.7 cm³

21. 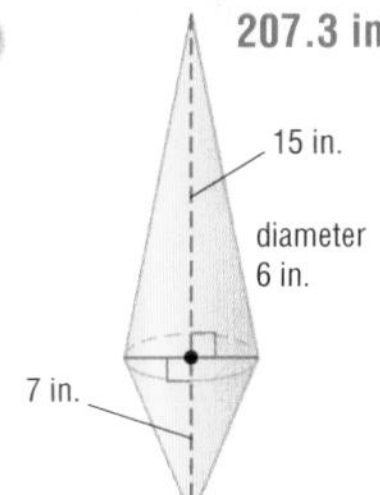

207.3 in³

22. 

230,907.1 ft³

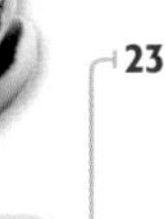

Real-World Link

Pure silver's weight is about 10.5 grams per cubic centimeter. Its chemical symbol is Ag and it has a melting point over 1700°F.

Source: Silver Users Association

23. SILVER The solid silver bead shown at the left is made of two cones. It measures 11 centimeters in diameter and is 10 centimeters from top to bottom. The center portion is 2 centimeters tall. Use the information at the left to find the approximate mass in grams of the bead. Round to the nearest tenth. **4656.8 g**

24. BASKETBALL The volume of a mini-basketball is about 230 cubic inches. What is its radius? Round to the nearest inch. **4 in.**

25. PACKAGING Three golf balls are packaged in a box 13.1 centimeters long, 4.5 centimeters wide, and 4.5 centimeters tall. If each ball is 4.3 centimeters in diameter, find the volume of the empty space in the box, rounded to the nearest tenth. **140.4 cm³**

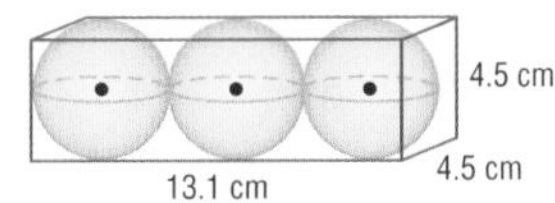

H.O.T. Problems Use Higher-Order Thinking Skills

26. OPEN ENDED Name the dimensions of a cone whose volume is between 45 cubic units and 55 cubic units.

27. CHALLENGE A cone contains 93 cubic units of water. All the water is poured equally into three congruent cylindrical containers to a level of 4.5 units. What is the diameter of each container? Round to the nearest tenth. **3 units**

28. WHICH ONE DOESN'T BELONG? Find the expression that does not represent the height of a three-dimensional figure. Explain your reasoning.

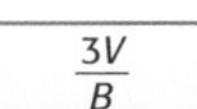
$\frac{3V}{B}$

$\frac{Vr^2}{3\pi}$

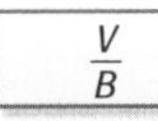
$\frac{V}{B}$

29. REASONING *True* or *false*? The volume of a rectangular-based pyramid and a cone with the same height and equal areas of the base are equal. Explain your reasoning.

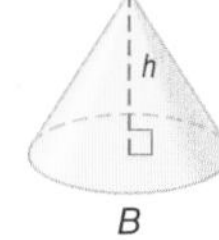

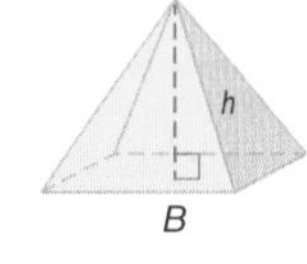

30. CHALLENGE Which has a greater effect on the volume of a cone: changing the radius or changing the height? Explain.

31. WRITING IN MATH Write a real-world example where you would want to change a cylinder to a cone. Describe how the dimensions of the cone would be affected if the volumes remain the same. **See margin.**

26. Sample answer: $r = 5$, $h = 2$; $r = 4$, $h = 3$; $r = 3$, $h = 5$

28. $\frac{Vr^2}{3\pi}$; Sample answer: When finding the height of a cone, the formula should be $\frac{3V}{\pi r^2} = h$.

29. True. The volumes are equal if both heights and both bases are equal. Changing the shape of the base will not affect the volume.

30. Sample answer: Changing the radius has a greater effect on the volume. If you double the radius, the volume is multiplied by 4. If you double the height, the volume is doubled.

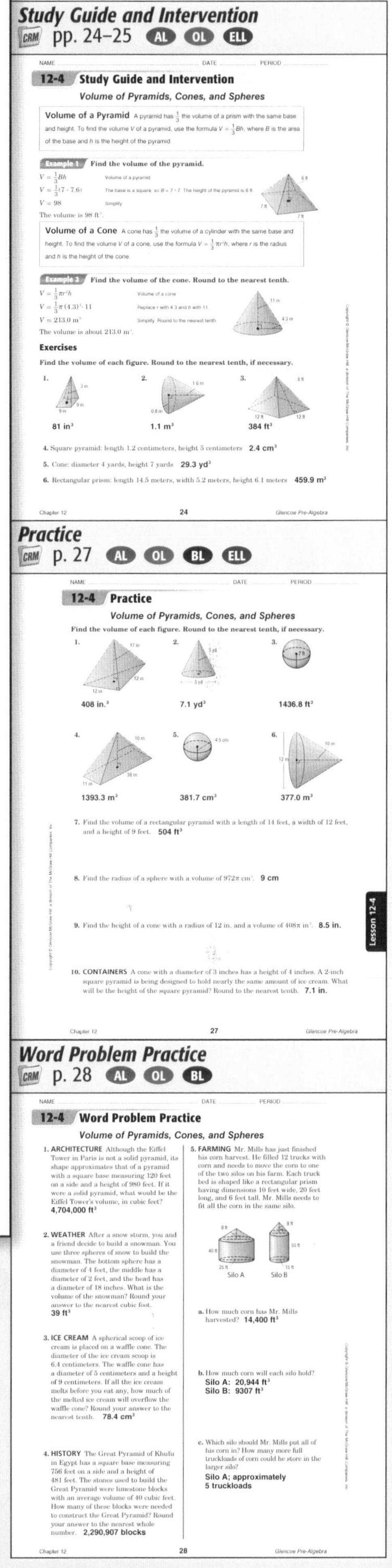

Study Guide and Intervention CRM pp. 24–25 AL OL ELL

NAME ______ DATE ______ PERIOD ______

12-4 Study Guide and Intervention

Volume of Pyramids, Cones, and Spheres

Volume of a Pyramid A pyramid has $\frac{1}{3}$ the volume of a prism with the same base and height. To find the volume V of a pyramid, use the formula $V = \frac{1}{3}Bh$, where B is the area of the base and h is the height of the pyramid.

Example 1 Find the volume of the pyramid.

$V = \frac{1}{3}Bh$ Volume of a pyramid

$V = \frac{1}{3}(7 \cdot 7)6$ The base is a square, so $B = 7 \cdot 7$. The height of the pyramid is 6 ft.

$V = 98$ Simplify

The volume is 98 ft³.

Volume of a Cone A cone has $\frac{1}{3}$ the volume of a cylinder with the same base and height. To find the volume V of a cone, use the formula $V = \frac{1}{3}\pi r^2h$, where r is the radius and h is the height of the cone.

Example 2 Find the volume of the cone. Round to the nearest tenth.

$V = \frac{1}{3}\pi r^2h$ Volume of a cone

$V = \frac{1}{3}\pi(4.3)^2 \cdot 11$ Replace r with 4.3 and h with 11.

$V \approx 213.0$ m³ Simplify. Round to the nearest tenth.

The volume is about 213.0 m³.

Exercises

Find the volume of each figure. Round to the nearest tenth, if necessary.

1. 81 in³
2. 1.1 m³
3. 384 ft³
4. Square pyramid: length 1.2 centimeters, height 5 centimeters **2.4 cm³**
5. Cone: diameter 4 yards, height 7 yards **29.3 yd³**
6. Rectangular prism: length 14.5 meters, width 5.2 meters, height 6.1 meters **459.9 m³**

Chapter 12 24 Glencoe Pre-Algebra

Practice CRM p. 27 AL OL BL ELL

NAME ______ DATE ______ PERIOD ______

12-4 Practice

Volume of Pyramids, Cones, and Spheres

Find the volume of each figure. Round to the nearest tenth, if necessary.

1. 408 in.³
2. 7.1 yd³
3. 1436.8 ft³
4. 1393.3 m³
5. 381.7 cm³
6. 377.0 m³
7. Find the volume of a rectangular pyramid with a length of 14 feet, a width of 12 feet, and a height of 9 feet. **504 ft³**
8. Find the radius of a sphere with a volume of 972π cm³. **9 cm**
9. Find the height of a cone with a radius of 12 in. and a volume of 408π in³. **8.5 in.**
10. **CONTAINERS** A cone with a diameter of 3 inches has a height of 4 inches. A 2-inch square pyramid is being designed to hold nearly the same amount of ice cream. What will be the height of the square pyramid? Round to the nearest tenth. **7.1 in.**

Chapter 12 27 Glencoe Pre-Algebra

Lesson 12-4

Word Problem Practice CRM p. 28 AL OL BL

NAME ______ DATE ______ PERIOD ______

12-4 Word Problem Practice

Volume of Pyramids, Cones, and Spheres

1. **ARCHITECTURE** Although the Eiffel Tower in Paris is not a solid pyramid, its shape approximates that of a pyramid with a square base measuring 120 feet on a side and a height of 980 feet. If it were a solid pyramid, what would be the Eiffel Tower's volume, in cubic feet? **4,704,000 ft³**
2. **WEATHER** After a snow storm, you and a friend decide to build a snowman. You use three spheres of snow to build the snowman. The bottom sphere has a diameter of 4 feet, the middle has a diameter of 2 feet, and the head has a diameter of 18 inches. What is the volume of the snowman? Round your answer to the nearest cubic foot. **39 ft³**
3. **ICE CREAM** A spherical scoop of ice cream is placed on a waffle cone. The diameter of the ice cream scoop is 6.4 centimeters. The waffle cone has a diameter of 5 centimeters and a height of 9 centimeters. If all the ice cream melts before you eat any, how much of the melted ice cream will overflow the waffle cone? Round your answer to the nearest tenth. **78.4 cm³**
4. **HISTORY** The Great Pyramid of Khufu in Egypt has a square base measuring 756 feet on a side and a height of 481 feet. The stones used to build the Great Pyramid were limestone blocks with an average volume of 40 cubic feet. How many of these blocks were needed to construct the Great Pyramid? Round your answer to the nearest whole number. **2,290,907 blocks**
5. **FARMING** Mr. Mills has just finished his corn harvest. He filled 12 trucks with corn and needs to move the corn to one of the two silos on his farm. Each truck bed is shaped like a rectangular prism having dimensions 10 feet wide, 20 feet long, and 6 feet tall. Mr. Mills needs to fit all the corn in the same silo.

   Silo A Silo B

   a. How much corn has Mr. Mills harvested? **14,400 ft³**

   b. How much corn will each silo hold? **Silo A: 20,944 ft³ Silo B: 9307 ft³**

   c. Which silo should Mr. Mills put all of his corn in? How many more full truckloads of corn could he store in the larger silo? **Silo A; approximately 5 truckloads**

Chapter 12 28 Glencoe Pre-Algebra

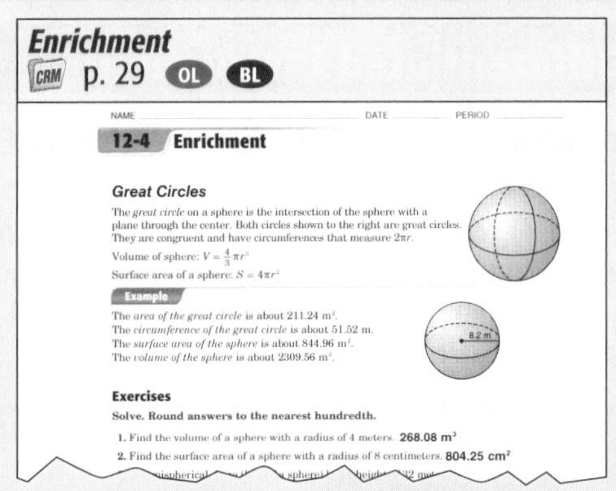

Enrichment CRM p. 29 OL BL

NAME ______ DATE ______ PERIOD ______

12-4 Enrichment

Great Circles

The *great circle* on a sphere is the intersection of the sphere with a plane through the center. Both circles shown to the right are great circles. They are congruent and have circumferences that measure $2\pi r$.

Volume of sphere: $V = \frac{4}{3}\pi r^3$

Surface area of a sphere: $S = 4\pi r^2$

Example

The *area of the great circle* is about 211.24 m².
The *circumference of the great circle* is about 51.52 m.
The *surface area of the sphere* is about 844.96 m².
The *volume of the sphere* is about 2309.56 m³.

Exercises

Solve. Round answers to the nearest hundredth.

1. Find the volume of a sphere with a radius of 4 meters. **268.08 m³**
2. Find the surface area of a sphere with a radius of 8 centimeters. **804.25 cm²**

4 ASSESS

Ticket Out the Door Have students write problems that involve a number of differently-shaped, but similarly-sized, solids. Students can exchange problems with each other and solve to find which solids have the greatest and least volumes. Students will hand in their papers as they exit.

Formative Assessment

Check for student understanding of concepts in Lessons 12-3 and 12-4.

CRM Quiz 2, p. 58

Additional Answer

40.

x	$x + 5$	y
−3	−3 + 5	2
−1	−1 + 5	4
0	0 + 5	5
1	1 + 5	6

(−3, 2), (−1, 4), (0, 5), (1, 6)

Standardized Test Practice

32. What is the volume of a square pyramid with a height of 12 centimeters and base edges of 4 centimeters? **B**

A 48 cm^3 C 96 cm^3
B 64 cm^3 D 192 cm^3

33. Find the volume of the cone. Use 3.14 for π. Round to the nearest hundredth. **H**

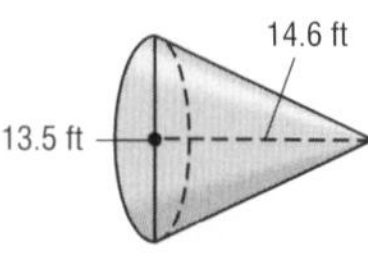

F 8355.07 ft^3 H 696. 26 ft^3
G 2785.02 ft^3 J 618.89 ft^3

34. SHORT RESPONSE The volume of a cone is 3768 cubic millimeters. The radius of the base is 5 millimeters Find the height of the cone. **143.9 mm**

35. A sphere has a radius of 5 meters. Which of the following is closest to the volume of the sphere in cubic meters? **D**

A 65.4 m^3 C 130.8 m^3
B 104.7 m^3 D 523.3 m^3

Spiral Review

Find the volume of each figure. Round to the nearest tenth, if necessary. (Lessons 12-2 and 12-3)

36. **512 in^3**

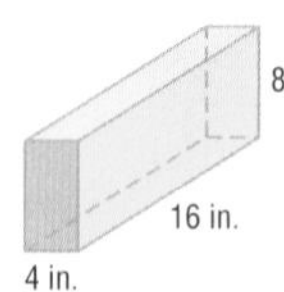

37. **748 cm^3**

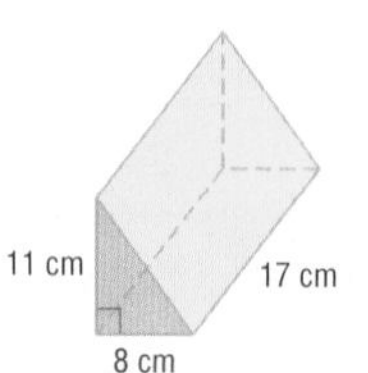

38. **88.0 ft^3**

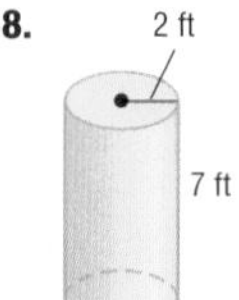

39. TRAVEL Loretta drives due north for 22 miles and then east for 11 miles. How far is Loretta from her starting point? Round to the nearest tenth of a mile. (Lesson 10-4) **24.6 mi**

40. FUNCTIONS Copy and complete the table. Use the results to write four solutions of $y = x + 5$. Write the solutions as ordered pairs. (Lesson 8-1) **See margin.**

x	$x + 5$	y
−3	−3 + 5	■
−1	■	■
0	■	■
1	■	■

41. SNACKS Manuel has $15 to buy snack mix that costs $5.75 per pound. Write and solve an equation to find the amount of snack mix he can buy if he spends all $15. Round to the nearest tenth. (Lesson 4-6) **$5.75p = 15$; 2.6 lb**

Skills Review

Find the area of each figure. Round to the nearest tenth, if necessary. (Lessons 11-6 and 11-8)

42. **572.6 ft^2**

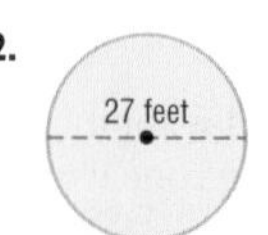

43. **3772 m^2**

44. **724.5 cm^2**

Differentiated Instruction

BL

Extension Give students the following problem: Ethan wants to increase his serving of ice cream by increasing the cone size that he chooses at the ice cream shop. The regular-sized cone has a 4 centimeter radius and a height of 7 centimeters. Which would increase his serving size more: increasing the radius and height of his cone by one centimeter each, or increasing the height of his cone by 2 centimeters? Increasing the radius and height by 1 centimeter each would increase his volume more substantially.

688 Chapter 12 Surface Area and Volume

Mid-Chapter Quiz

Lessons 12-1 through 12-4

Identify each figure. Name the bases, faces, edges, and vertices. (Lesson 12-1) **1–2. See margin.**

1.

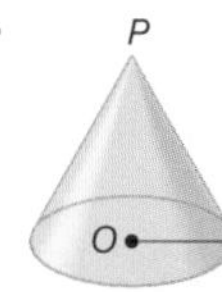

2.

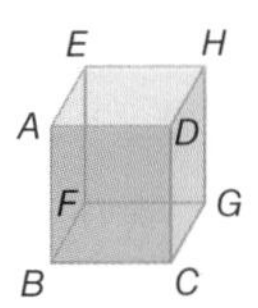

3.

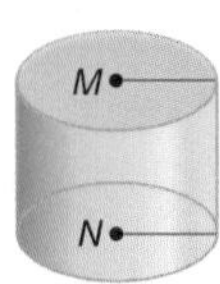

4.

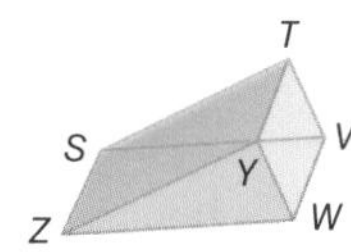

3–6. See Chapter 12 Answer Appendix.

Draw and describe the shape resulting from each cross section. (Lesson 12-1)

5.

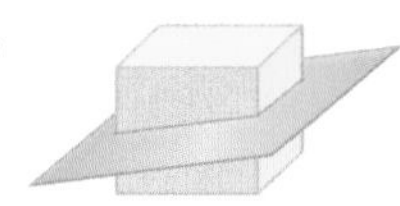

6.

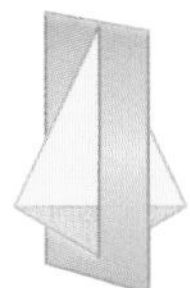

7. **MULTIPLE CHOICE** How much water can fit into an aquarium with a length 15 inches, width 12 inches, and height 16 inches? (Lesson 12-2) **A**

A $1\frac{2}{3}$ ft^3

C 2400 ft^3

B $2\frac{2}{5}$ ft^3

D 2880 ft^3

8. What is the volume of the prism shown at the right? (Lesson 12-2) **38.5 cm^3**

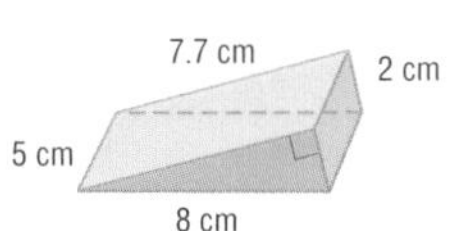

9. **MULTIPLE CHOICE** A can of lemonade concentrate has a diameter of 3 inches and a height of $4\frac{1}{2}$ inches. If the concentrate dissolves in $3\frac{1}{2}$ cans of water, how much water must be added? (Lesson 12-3) **G**

F 31.8 in^3

H 127.2 in^3

G 111.3 in^3

J 381.7 in^3

Find the volume of each figure. Round to the nearest tenth, if necessary. (Lessons 12-2 and 12-3)

10.

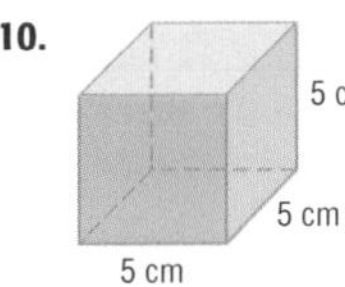

125 cm^3

11.

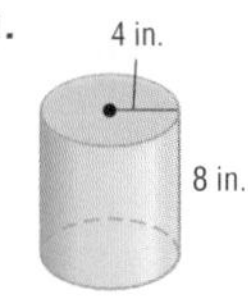

402.1 in^3

12. **HIGHWAY MAINTENANCE** Salt and sand mixtures are often used on icy roads. When the mixture is dumped from a truck into the staging area, it forms a cone-shaped mound with a diameter of 10 feet and a height of 6 feet. (Lesson 12-4)

   a. What is the volume of the salt-sand mixture to the nearest cubic foot? **157 ft^3**

   b. How many square feet of roadway can be salted using the mixture in part **a** if 500 square feet can be covered by 1 cubic foot of salt? **78,500 ft^2**

13. **MULTIPLE CHOICE** Mrs. McCullough is purchasing balloons for a party. Each spherical balloon is inflated with helium. How much helium is in the balloon if the balloon has a radius of 9 centimeters? (Lesson 12-4) **D**

A 339.3 cm^3

C 1357.2 cm^3

B 381.7 cm^3

D 3053.6 cm^3

Find the volume of each figure. Round to the nearest tenth, if necessary. (Lesson 12-4)

14.

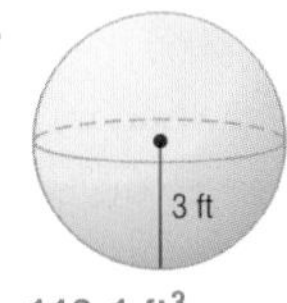

113.1 ft^3

15.

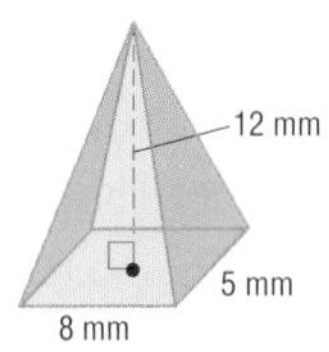

160 mm^3

16. **FOOD** A baker is using a cake-decorating bag in the shape of a cone. How much frosting can fit in the bag if its diameter is 4 inches and height is 9 inches? Round to the nearest tenth. (Lesson 12-4) **37.7 in^3**

CHAPTER 12 Mid-Chapter Quiz

Formative Assessment

Use the Mid-Chapter Quiz to assess students' progress in the first half of the chapter.

For problems answered incorrectly, have students review the lessons indicated in parentheses.

ExamView Assessment Suite Customize and create multiple versions of your Mid-Chapter Quiz and their answer keys.

FOLDABLES® Follow-Up

Before students complete the Mid-Chapter Quiz, encourage them to review the information for Lessons 12-1 through 12-4 in their Foldables.

Additional Answers

1. cone; base: circle O, vertex *P*; no faces or edges
2. rectangular prism; bases: *ABCD* and *EFGH,* or *BCGF* and *ADHE,* or *CDHG* and *BAEF;* faces: *ABCD, EFGH, BCGF, ADHE, CDHG, BAEF;* edges: $\overline{AB}, \overline{AD}, \overline{AE}, \overline{BC}, \overline{BF}, \overline{CD}, \overline{CG}, \overline{DH}, \overline{EF}, \overline{EH}, \overline{FG}, \overline{GH}$; vertices: *A, B, C, D, E, F, G, H*

Intervention Planner

Tier 1 **On Level**	Tier 2 **Strategic Intervention** approaching grade level	Tier 3 **Intensive Intervention** 2 or more grades below level
If students miss about 25% of the exercises or less,	 students miss about 50% of the exercises,	 students miss about 75% of the exercises,
Then choose a resource: **SE** Lessons 12-1 through 12-4 **CRM** Skills Practice, pp. 7, 13, 20, and 26 **TE** Chapter Project, p. 660 **Math Online** Self-Check Quiz	 choose a resource: **CRM** Study Guide and Intervention, Chapter 12, pp. 5, 11, 18, and 24 *Quick Review Math Handbook* **Math Online** Extra Examples, Personal Tutor	 use *Math Triumphs, Grade 7,* Ch. 5–6 **Math Online** Extra Examples, Personal Tutor, Homework Help, Review Vocabulary

1 FOCUS

Objective Find the surface area of prisms.

Materials for Each Student

- empty box with a tuck-in lid
- ruler
- marker

Easy to Make Manipulatives

Teaching Pre-Algebra with Manipulatives, template for
- rectangular prism pattern, p. 28

Teaching Tip

Have students measure the length and width of each face to the nearest half-inch or inch.

2 TEACH

Working in Cooperative Groups

Arrange students in pairs, mixing abilities. Have students complete the Activity.

Ask:

- Suppose you had a rectangular prism with faces that all had the same area. Which faces would be the bases? A rectangular prism with faces that were all the same area would have square faces. Any two parallel faces could be marked as bases.

Practice Have students complete Exercises 1–8.

3 ASSESS

Formative Assessment

Use Exercises 1–8 to assess whether students understand the concept of surface area.

Surface Area of Prisms

Math Online glencoe.com
Math *in Motion,* Animation

Nets are two-dimensional patterns of three-dimensional figures. When you construct a net, you are decomposing the three-dimensional figure into separate shapes. You can use a net to find the area of each surface of a three-dimensional figure such as the prism at the right.

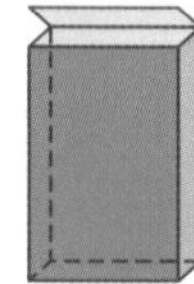

ACTIVITY

Find the surface area of a rectangular prism.

Step 1 Use an empty box with a tuck-in lid. Label the top, bottom, front, back, and side faces using a marker.

Step 2 Measure each face. Copy the table. Record the results in it. Then find and record the area of each face.

Face	Length	Width	Area
top	■	■	■
bottom	■	■	■
front	■	■	■
back	■	■	■
left	■	■	■
right	■	■	■

Step 3 Open the lid. Cut each of the 4 vertical edges. Open the box and lay it flat to form a net.

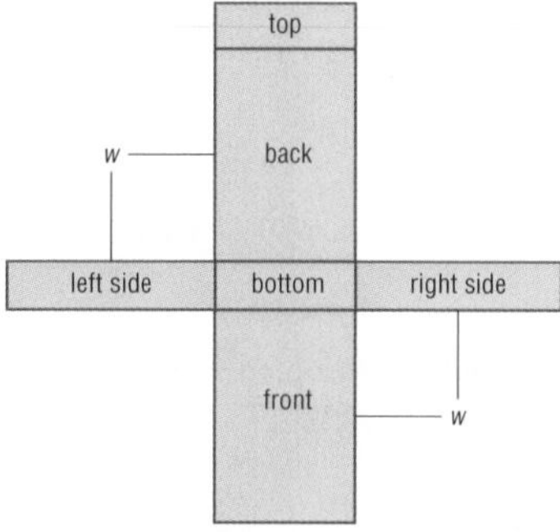

Step 4 Find the sum of the areas of the faces. This is the *surface area* of the prism.

Exercises

1. Classify the two-dimensional shape(s) that make up the net of the prism. **rectangles**
2. Find the perimeter of the top or the bottom base. **2–4. See students' work.**
3. Multiply the perimeter of the base by the height of the box.
4. Add the product from Exercise 3 to the sum of the areas of the two bases.
5. Compare your answer from Exercise 4 to the answer in Step 4. **They are equal.**
6. What do you observe about the areas of opposite faces? **They are equal.**
7. **MAKE A CONJECTURE** Write a formula for the surface area S of a rectangular prism with length ℓ, width w, and height h. $S = 2(\ell w + \ell h + wh)$
8. Find several objects that are rectangular prisms. Measure the dimensions of the objects. Find the surface area of the objects using the formula from Exercise 7. **See students' work.**

From Concrete to Abstract

Have students sketch a net for a rectangular prism on paper. Tell them to label the dimensions and trade with another student. Tell students to find the surface area of the prism.

Extending the Concept

- Ask students to sketch a net for a triangular prism.
- Ask students to label the dimensions.
- Ask students to find the surface area.

12-5 Surface Area of Prisms

Why?

The dimensions of a fish tank are given.

a. How many faces does the tank have? 6

b. Find the area of each face and the sum of the areas. See Chapter 12 Answer Appendix.

c. Find the volume of the fish tank. 6912 in^3

d. Is the sum of the areas the same as the volume? no

Then
You have already found the area of two-dimensional figures. (Lesson 11-6)

Now
- Find lateral area and surface area of prisms.
- Find surface area of real-world objects shaped like prisms.

New Vocabulary
lateral face
lateral area
surface area

Math Online
glencoe.com
- Extra Examples
- Personal Tutor
- Self-Check Quiz
- Homework Help

Prisms If you open up a box or prism and lay it flat, the result is a net. A net allows you to see all the surfaces. The surfaces of prisms have two characteristics.

- A prism has two parallel bases.
- Faces that are *not* bases are called **lateral faces**.

The **lateral area** is the sum of the areas of the lateral faces. The **surface area** is the sum of the lateral area plus the area of the bases. In the figures below, the lateral faces are shown in blue. The bases are shown in yellow.

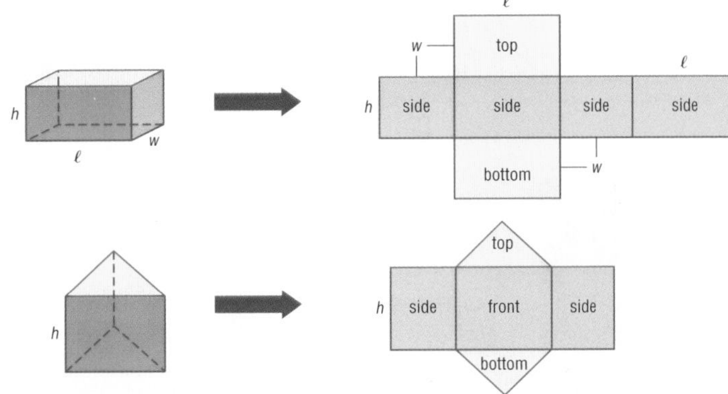

Key Concept

For Your FOLDABLE

Lateral Area of Prisms

Words The lateral area L of a prism is the perimeter of the base P times the height h.

Symbols $L = Ph$

Surface Area of Prisms

Words The surface area S of a prism is the lateral area L plus the area of the two bases $2B$.

Symbols $S = L + 2B$ or $S = Ph + 2B$

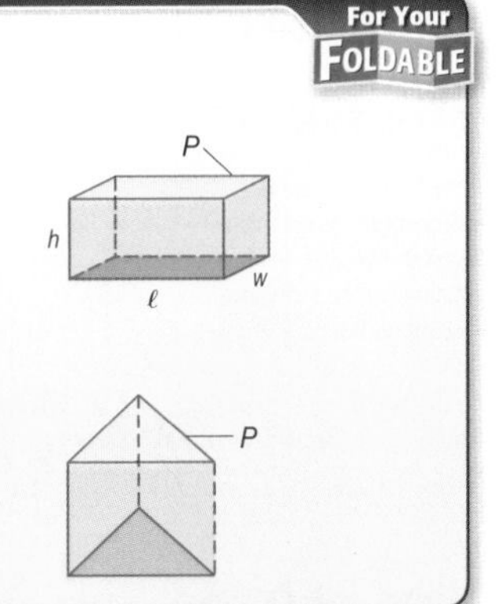

12-5 Lesson Notes

1 FOCUS

Vertical Alignment

Before Lesson 12-5
Find the area of two-dimensional figures.

Lesson 12-5
Find lateral area and surface area of prisms.
Find surface area of real-world objects shaped like prisms.

After Lesson 12-5
Find surface areas and volumes of prisms, pyramids, spheres, cones, cylinders, and composites of these figures in problem situations.

2 TEACH

Scaffolding Questions

Have students read the *Why?* section of the lesson and answer the questions.

Ask:
- Why isn't the sum of the areas the same as the volume? The areas are in square units, and the volume is in cubic units. Square units and cubic units are not the same thing.
- What are the shapes of the faces of the fish tank? rectangular
- Suppose you were given the dimensions of a triangular prism. What are the shapes of the faces? triangles and rectangles

Lesson 12-5 Resources

Resource	Approaching-Level	On-Level	Beyond-Level	English Learners
Teacher Edition	• Differentiated Instruction, p. 692		• Differentiated Instruction, p. 695	• Differentiated Instruction, p. 692
Chapter Resource Masters	• Study Guide and Intervention, pp. 30–31 • Skills Practice, p. 32 • Practice, p. 33 • Word Problem Practice, p. 34 • Spreadsheet Activity, p. 36	• Study Guide and Intervention, pp. 30–31 • Skills Practice, p. 32 • Practice, p. 33 • Word Problem Practice, p. 34 • Enrichment, p. 35 • Spreadsheet Activity, p. 36	• Practice, p. 33 • Word Problem Practice, p. 34 • Enrichment, p. 35 • Spreadsheet Activity, p. 36	• Study Guide and Intervention, pp. 30–31 • Skills Practice, p. 32 • Practice, p. 33 • Spreadsheet Activity, p. 36
Transparencies	• 5-Minute Check Transparency 12-5	• 5-Minute Check Transparency 12-5	• 5-Minute Check Transparency 12-5	• 5-Minute Check Transparency 12-5
Other	• Study Notebook • Teaching Pre-Algebra with Manipulatives	• Study Notebook • Teaching Pre-Algebra with Manipulatives	• Study Notebook	• Study Notebook • Teaching Pre-Algebra with Manipulatives

Lesson 12-5 Surface Area of Prisms 691

Prisms

Example 1 shows how to find the lateral and surface areas of rectangular and triangular prisms. **Example 2** shows how to solve a real-world problem that involves surface area of prisms.

Formative Assessment

Use the Check Your Progress exercises after each example to determine students' understanding of concepts.

Additional Examples

1 Find the lateral and surface areas of each prism.

a.

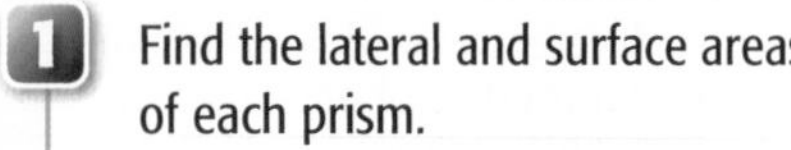

440 cm^2; 1868 cm^2

b.

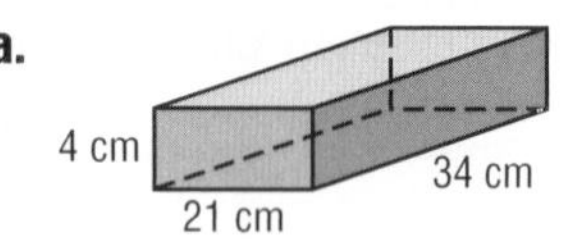

144 m^2; 336 m^2

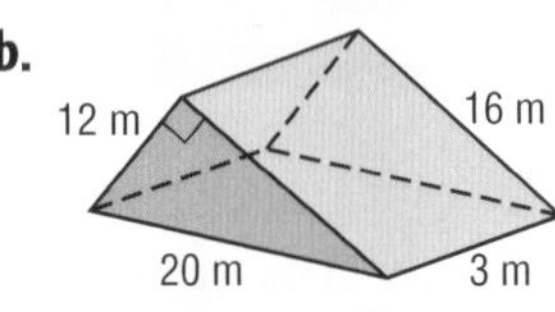

2 **CARPENTRY** Alex is building a large storage box out of plywood. The box is a rectangular prism measuring 5 feet long, 3 feet wide, and 2 feet high. Find the number of sheets of plywood he would need to buy to build the box if 1 sheet covers 32 square feet. at least 2 sheets

Additional Examples also in Interactive Classroom PowerPoint® Presentations

StudyTip

Nets Another way to find the surface area of any prism is to draw its net on grid paper and find the area of each face.

EXAMPLE 1 Surface Area of Prisms

Find the lateral and surface area of each prism.

a. Find the lateral area.

$L = Ph$

$L = (2\ell + 2w)h$

$= (2 \cdot 5.5 + 2 \cdot 3)15.1$

$= 256.7 \text{ in}^2$

Find the surface area.

$S = L + 2B$

$S = L + 2\ell w$

$= 256.7 \text{ in}^2 + 2 \cdot 5.5 \text{ in.} \cdot 3 \text{ in.}$

$= 256.7 + 33 \text{ or } 289.7 \text{ in}^2$

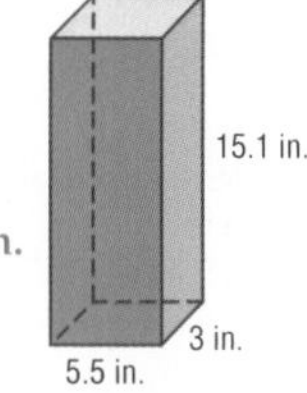

b. Find the lateral area. The lateral area is made up of faces that are *not* parallel.

$L = Ph$ **Formula for the lateral area**

$L = (8 + 15 + 17)20$ ***P* is the perimeter of the triangular base.**

$= 40 \cdot 20 \text{ or } 800 \text{ m}^2$ **Simplify.**

8 m, 17 m, 20 m, 15 m

Find the surface area.

$S = L + 2B$ **Formula for the surface area**

$= 800 + 2\left(\frac{1}{2} \cdot 15 \cdot 8\right)$ $B = \frac{1}{2}bh$

$= 800 + 120 \text{ or } 920 \text{ m}^2$ **Simplify.**

Check Your Progress

1A.

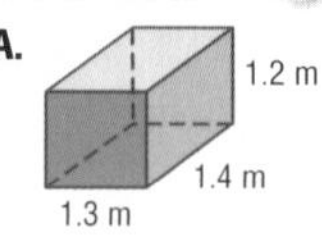

6.48 m^2; 10.12 m^2

1B.

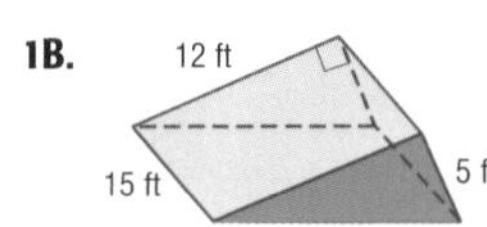

450 ft^2; 510 ft^2

Personal Tutor glencoe.com

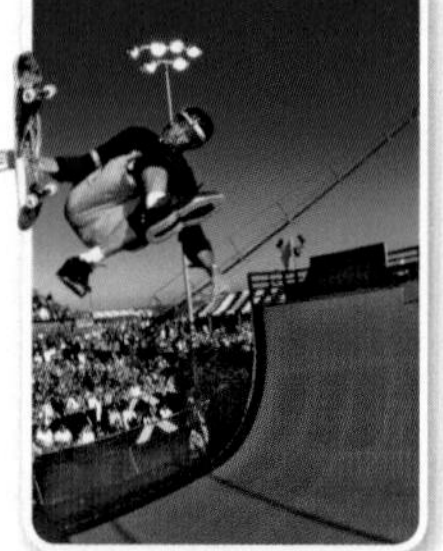

Real-World Link

Tony Hawk was the first skateboarder to complete the *900*—two and one-half rotations in the air before landing on the pipe.

Real-World EXAMPLE 2 Surface Area of Prisms

PAINT Marcus wants to paint a skateboard launch ramp like the one shown at the right. Find the amount of paint he will need if 1 quart covers 100 square feet.

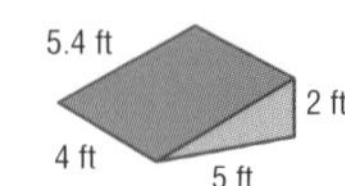

Find the lateral area.

$L = Ph$

$= (5.4 + 2 + 5)4$

$= 49.6 \text{ ft}^2$

Find the surface area.

$S = L + 2B$

$= 49.6 + 2\left(\frac{1}{2} \cdot 2 \cdot 5\right)$

$= 49.6 + 10$

$= 59.6 \text{ ft}^2$

Since $55 < 100$, Marcus will use less than 1 quart of paint.

Check Your Progress 2. 520 in^2

2. CRAFTS Lucia is covering boxes with fabric to sell at a craft fair. The boxes are rectangular prisms and measure 10 inches wide, 14 inches long, and 5 inches high. Find the amount of fabric she will need to cover 1 box.

Personal Tutor glencoe.com

692 Chapter 12 Surface Area and Volume

Differentiated Instruction

If students need help finding the surface areas of prisms,

Then create the surface regions for a number of rectangular and triangular prisms. Cut apart or separate the surface regions for each figure, then shuffle all the pieces together. Have students, working in groups, fit the pieces together again and re-create the figures or nets for the figures. Finally, have students find the surface areas for the figures they have put together.

Check Your Understanding

Example 1 p. 692 — Find the lateral and surface area of each prism.

1. 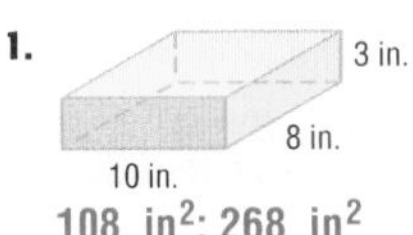

108 in^2; 268 in^2

2. 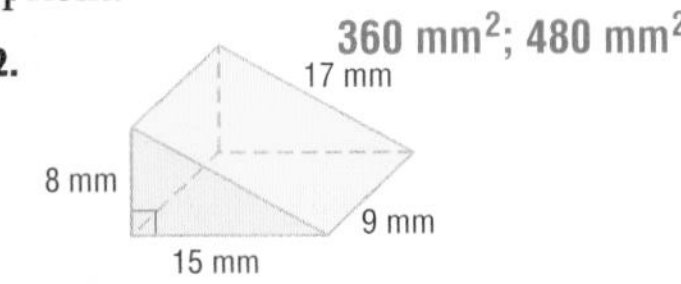

360 mm^2; 480 mm^2

3. rectangular prism: length $5\frac{1}{2}$ yd, width $9\frac{1}{2}$ yd, height 12 yd 360 yd^2; 464.5 yd^2

Example 2 p. 692

4. **PACKAGING** Find the amount of cardboard needed to make a box for a single slice of pizza. The box is in the shape of a triangular prism as shown. 116 in^2

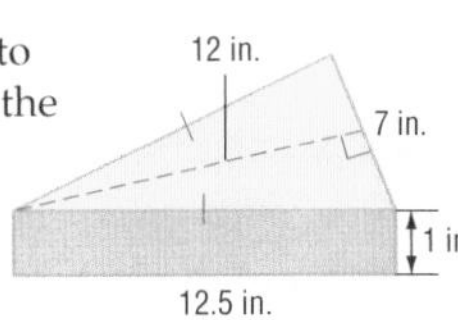

Practice and Problem Solving

= Step-by-Step Solutions begin on page R11.
Extra Practice begins on page 810.

Example 1 p. 692 — Find the lateral and surface area of each prism.

5. 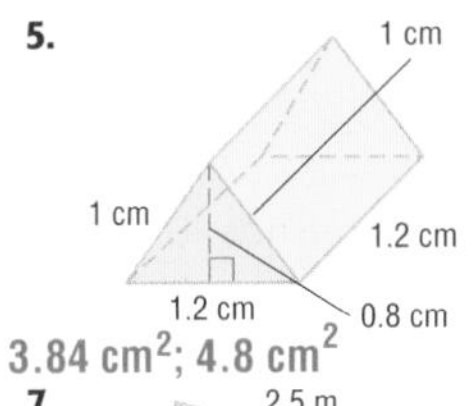

3.84 cm^2; 4.8 cm^2

6. 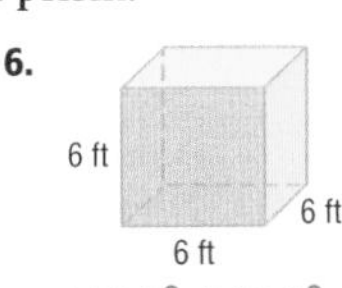

144 ft^2; 216 ft^2

7. 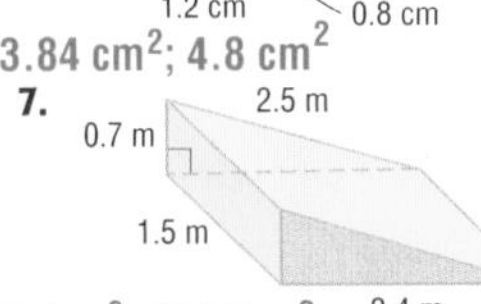

8.4 m^2; 10.08 m^2

8. 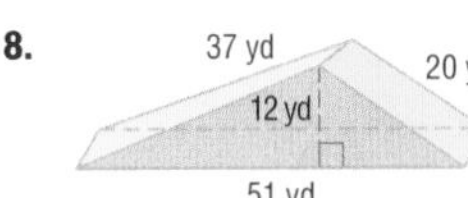

540 yd^2; 1152 yd^2

9. rectangular prism: length 2.2 cm, width 1.4 cm, height 9 cm

10. rectangular prism: length $6\frac{1}{2}$ in., width $8\frac{3}{4}$ in., height 10 in.

9. 64.8 cm^2; 70.96 cm^2
10. 305 in^2; $418\frac{3}{4}$ in^2

11. **JUICE** Find the amount of paper used to cover the juice box at the right. 334 in^2

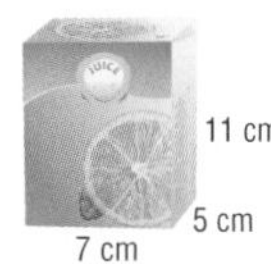

Example 2 p. 692

12. **PAINTING** Hinto is planning to paint the walls of a bedroom that is 20 feet long, 15 feet wide, and 8 feet high. If Hinto has 1 gallon of paint that covers 400 square feet, how many additional gallons of paint does he need? 1 gal

Find the surface area of each prism.

13. 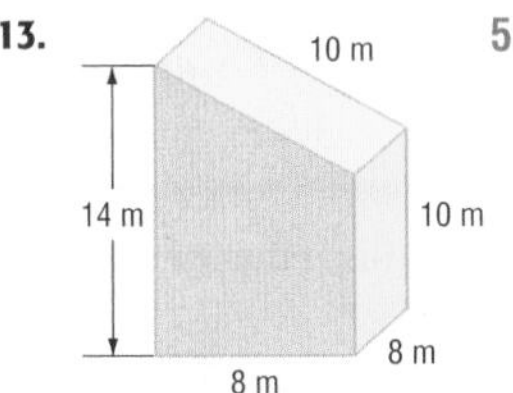

528 m^2

14. 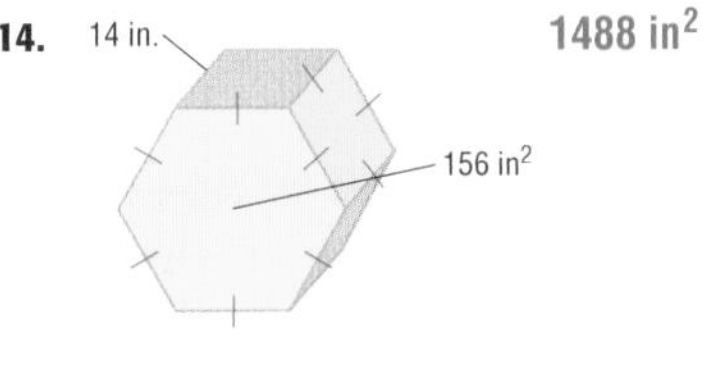

1488 in^2

Differentiated Homework Options

Level	Assignment	Two-Day Option	
AL Basic	5–12, 18–22 even, 23–37	5–11 odd, 23–26	6–12 even, 18–22 even, 27–37
OL Core	5–11 odd, 12, 13, 15–18, 20, 22–37	5–12, 23–26	13–18, 20, 22, 27–37
BL Advanced	13–34 (optional: 35–37)		

Focus on Mathematical Content

Surface Area of Prisms The surface area of any three-dimensional figure is the sum of the areas of its faces, including the bases. The areas for the lateral surfaces and the bases are calculated separately and then added because the faces are usually different polygons.

Tips for New Teachers

Alternative Formula The surface area for a rectangular prism can also be found using $S = 2\ell w + 2\ell h + 2wh$ or $S = 2(\ell w + \ell h + wh)$.

3 PRACTICE

Formative Assessment

Use Exercises 1–4 to check for understanding.

Use the chart at the bottom of this page to customize assignments for your students.

Multiple Representations In Exercise 15, students use a table of values, a geometric sketch, and numerical analysis to compare the surface areas of cubes after a specified change in dimension.

TEACH with TECH

BLOG Have students write a blog entry on your secure classroom blog describing the difference between the surface area and volume of a prism. Make sure they use physical descriptions and units in their entry.

Study Guide and Intervention

CRM pp. 30–31 AL OL ELL

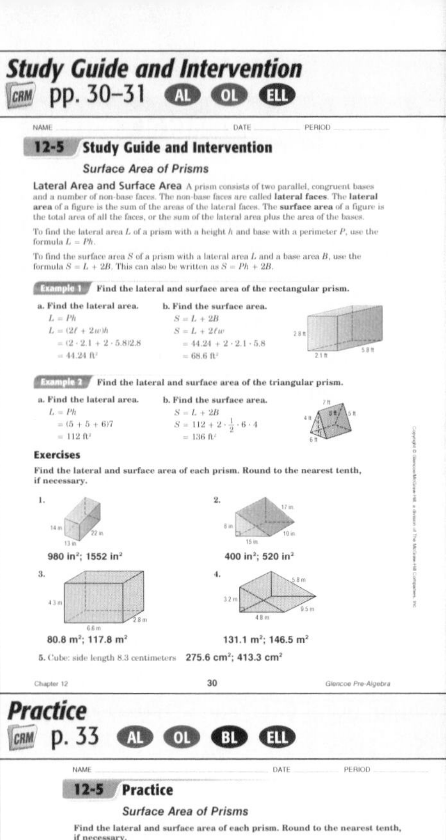
NAME ______ DATE ______ PERIOD ______

12-5 Study Guide and Intervention

Surface Area of Prisms

Lateral Area and Surface Area A prism consists of two parallel, congruent bases and a number of non-base faces. The non-base faces are called **lateral faces**. The **lateral area** of a figure is the sum of the areas of the lateral faces. The **surface area** of a figure is the total area of all the faces, or the sum of the lateral area plus the area of the bases.

To find the lateral area L of a prism with a height h and base with a perimeter P, use the formula $L = Ph$.

To find the surface area S of a prism with a lateral area L and a base area B, use the formula $S = L + 2B$. This can also be written as $S = Ph + 2B$.

Example 1 Find the lateral and surface area of the rectangular prism.

a. Find the lateral area.
$L = Ph$
$L = (2\ell + 2w)h$
$= (2 \cdot 2.1 + 2 \cdot 5.8)2.8$
$= 44.24$ ft²

b. Find the surface area.
$S = L + 2B$
$S = L + 2\ell w$
$= 44.24 + 2 \cdot 2.1 \cdot 5.8$
$= 68.6$ ft²

Example 2 Find the lateral and surface area of the triangular prism.

a. Find the lateral area.
$L = Ph$
$= (5 + 5 + 6)7$
$= 112$ ft²

b. Find the surface area.
$S = L + 2B$
$S = 112 + 2 \cdot \frac{1}{2} \cdot 6 \cdot 4$
$= 136$ ft²

Exercises

Find the lateral and surface area of each prism. Round to the nearest tenth, if necessary.

1. 14 in., 13 in., 22 in. **980 in²; 1552 in²**

2. 8 in., 15 in., 17 in., 10 in. **400 in²; 520 in²**

3. 4.3 m, 6.6 m, 2.8 m **80.8 m²; 117.8 m²**

4. 3.2 m, 4.8 m, 5.8 m, 9.5 m **131.1 m²; 146.5 m²**

5. Cube: side length 8.3 centimeters **275.6 cm²; 413.3 cm²**

Chapter 12 30 Glencoe Pre-Algebra

Practice

CRM p. 33 AL OL BL ELL

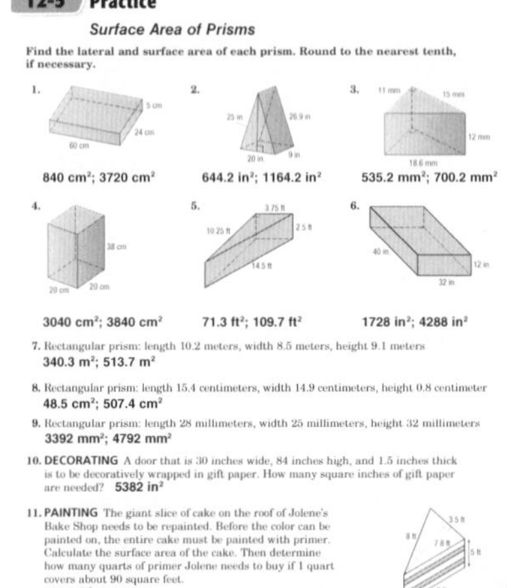
NAME ______ DATE ______ PERIOD ______

12-5 Practice

Surface Area of Prisms

Find the lateral and surface area of each prism. Round to the nearest tenth, if necessary.

1. 5 cm, 24 cm, 60 cm **840 cm²; 3720 cm²**

2. 25 in., 26.9 in., 20 in., 9 in. **644.2 in²; 1164.2 in²**

3. 11 mm, 15 mm, 12 mm, 18.6 mm **535.2 mm²; 700.2 mm²**

4. 38 cm, 20 cm, 20 cm **3040 cm²; 3840 cm²**

5. 3.75 ft, 10.25 ft, 2.5 ft, 14.5 ft **71.3 ft²; 109.7 ft²**

6. 40 in., 12 in., 32 in. **1728 in²; 4288 in²**

7. Rectangular prism: length 10.2 meters, width 8.5 meters, height 9.1 meters **340.3 m²; 513.7 m²**

8. Rectangular prism: length 15.4 centimeters, width 14.9 centimeters, height 0.8 centimeter **48.5 cm²; 507.4 cm²**

9. Rectangular prism: length 28 millimeters, width 25 millimeters, height 32 millimeters **3392 mm²; 4792 mm²**

10. **DECORATING** A door that is 30 inches wide, 84 inches high, and 1.5 inches thick is to be decoratively wrapped in gift paper. How many square inches of gift paper are needed? **5382 in²**

11. **PAINTING** The giant slice of cake on the roof of Jolene's Bake Shop needs to be repainted. Before the color can be painted on, the entire cake must be painted with primer. Calculate the surface area of the cake. Then determine how many quarts of primer Jolene needs to buy if 1 quart covers about 90 square feet. **124.8 ft²; 2 quarts**

Chapter 12 33 Glencoe Pre-Algebra

Word Problem Practice

CRM p. 34 AL OL BL

NAME ______ DATE ______ PERIOD ______

12-5 Word Problem Practice

Surface Area of Prisms

1. **DECORATING** Ms. Frank is going to wallpaper a living room with dimensions 24 feet long, 18 feet wide, and 8 feet high. What surface area does Ms. Frank plan to wallpaper? **672 ft²**

2. **GAMES** The sixth grade is holding a carnival. One class built the beanbag toss game shown below.

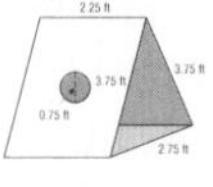

The game is a triangular prism with open sides. The class wants to paint the game with glow-in-the-dark paint. Each bottle of paint covers about 10 square feet and costs \$1.99. To the nearest tenth, what is the area that needs to be painted? How much will it cost to paint? **22.6 ft²; \$5.97**

3. **SIDING** The Ramirez family is going to put vinyl siding on a shed. They will cover all four walls completely, except for the door. The siding costs \$3 per square foot. How much will the siding cost for their shed?

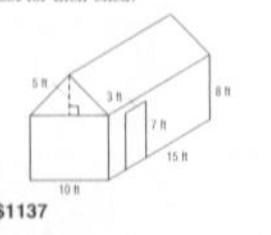

\$1137

4. **MUSEUM** A museum curator needs to order a display case for a small artifact. The case needs to be a rectangular prism and made entirely of clear plastic. The bases must each measure $1\frac{1}{2}$ feet by $1\frac{3}{4}$ feet and the sides each 3 feet high. Find the cost of the case if the clear plastic costs \$10 per square foot. **\$247.50**

5. **MUSEUMS** The diagram below shows the floor plan of a museum.

65 ft, Hall B, 105 ft, Great Hall, 40 ft, 42 ft, Hall A, 85 ft, 25 ft

The museum wants to repaint each of the three halls shown. The walls in each hall are 15 feet high. Each wall will receive a coat of primer and 2 coats of paint.

a. What is the area that will be painted? **10,860 ft²**

b. One gallon covers about 400 square feet. About how many total gallons of primer and paint will need to be purchased? **82**

c. The crew of painters can paint about 500 square feet an hour. About how many hours should it take them to completely paint each hall? **Great Hall: 26 hours; Hall A: 20 hours; Hall B: 19 hours**

Chapter 12 34 Glencoe Pre-Algebra

Lesson 12-5

16b. The surface area of the second box is 488 in², so the second box has a greater surface area.

Real-World Link

In 2007, the world's cardboard manufacturers produced over 150 billion square meters of cardboard, enough to cover the state of Louisiana, and then some.

18. Sample answer: cube with sides measuring 1.5 in.

20. Rhianna is correct. Serena found the volume.

21. See students' work. Sample answer: Prism A with dimensions 3 by 3 by 3 and Prism B with dimensions 10 by 2 by 1. Prism A has the larger volume while Prism B has the larger surface area.

15. **MULTIPLE REPRESENTATIONS** In this problem, you will explore how dilations affect surface area. Use the cube at the right.

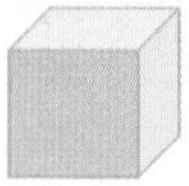

5 in.

a. **NUMERICAL** Find the surface area of the cube. **150 in²**

b. **TABULAR** Copy and complete the table shown.

Scale Factor of Dilation	Original	× 2	× 3
Length of Side	5 ■	10 ■	15 ■
Surface Area	150 ■	600 ■	1350 ■

c. **ANALYTICAL** Compare the original surface area to the surface area after a dilation by a scale factor of 2, then by a scale factor of 3. **See margin.**

d. **VERBAL** Does this same relationship exist with any rectangular prism? Explain your reasoning. **See margin.**

16. **SHIPPING** A shipping box in the shape of a rectangular prism can hold 576 cubic inches of material. The length of the box is 12 inches and the width of the box is 8 inches.

a. Find the surface area of the box. **432 in²**

b. Another box with the same volume has dimensions of 16 inches by 9 inches by 4 inches. Which box has the greater surface area? Explain.

c. Predict the shape of a rectangular prism with the same volume but with a greater surface area than either of the boxes above. Then, test your prediction. **See students' work.**

17. **FINANCIAL LITERACY** The boxes shown below are puzzle boxes that are made from wood. If the wood to make the boxes costs \$1.30 per square inch, which box would cost more to make? Explain. **See margin.**

Box 1

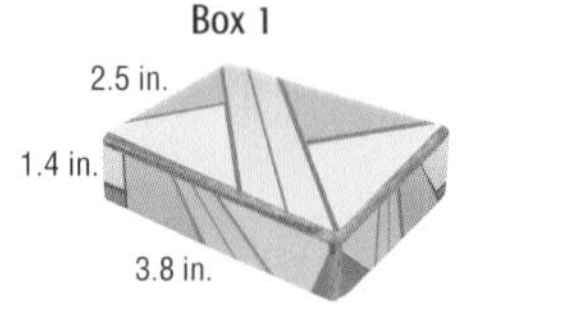

Box 2

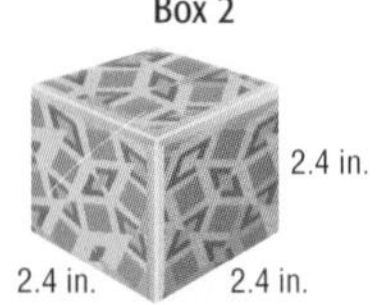

H.O.T. Problems

Use **H**igher-**O**rder **T**hinking Skills

18. **OPEN ENDED** Name the dimensions of a cube with a surface area between 10 and 20 square inches.

19. **CHALLENGE** A box manufacturer wants to make a box that has a volume of 216 cm³ and uses the least amount of cardboard possible. Find the dimensions of that box. **The box is a cube that measures 6 cm on each side.**

20. **FIND THE ERROR** Serena and Rhianna want to find the surface area of the cube shown. Is either of them correct? Explain.

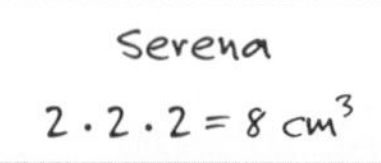

Rhianna
$8 \cdot 2 + 2 \cdot 2 \cdot 2 = 24\ cm^2$

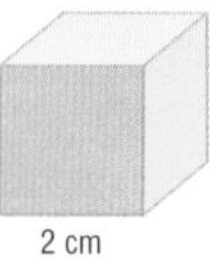

21. **CHALLENGE** Sketch two prisms such that one has a greater volume and the other has a greater surface area.

22. **WRITING IN MATH** Explain the difference between surface area and volume. **See margin.**

Enrichment

CRM p. 35 OL BL

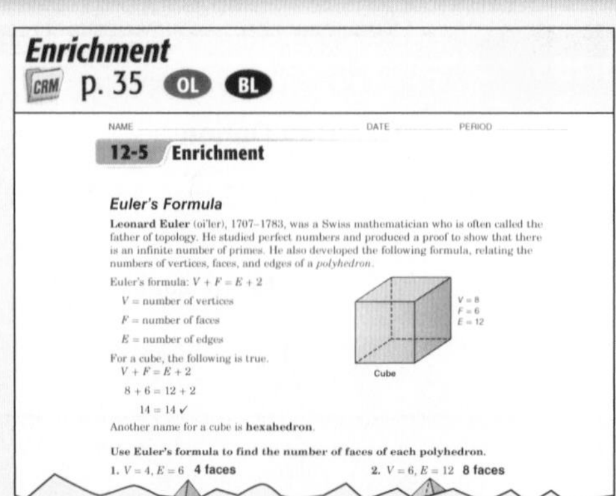
NAME ______ DATE ______ PERIOD ______

12-5 Enrichment

Euler's Formula

Leonard Euler (oi'ler), 1707–1783, was a Swiss mathematician who is often called the father of topology. He studied perfect numbers and produced a proof to show that there is an infinite number of primes. He also developed the following formula, relating the numbers of vertices, faces, and edges of a *polyhedron*.

Euler's formula: $V + F = E + 2$

V = number of vertices
F = number of faces
E = number of edges

For a cube, the following is true.
$V + F = E + 2$
$8 + 6 = 12 + 2$
$14 = 14$ ✓

Another name for a cube is **hexahedron**.

Use Euler's formula to find the number of faces of each polyhedron.

1. $V = 4, E = 6$ **4 faces**

2. $V = 6, E = 12$ **8 faces**

Watch Out!

Find the Error For Exercise 20, remind students that the surface area is the sum of the lateral areas and the area of the two bases. Surface area is measured in square, not cubic, units.

Standardized Test Practice

23. A rectangular cardboard box has the same volume as another rectangular box that measures 6 inches by 14 inches by 20 inches, but with less surface area. Which size box would *not* meet those requirements? **D**

A 7 in. by 10 in. by 24 in.

B 7 in. by 12 in. by 20 in.

C 10 in. by 12 in. by 14 in.

D 5 in. by 16 in. by 21 in.

24. SHORT RESPONSE The side measures of a rectangular prism are tripled. What is the ratio, written as a fraction, of the surface area of the original prism to the surface area of the larger prism? $\frac{1}{9}$

25. Find the surface area of the figure below to the nearest whole number. **J**

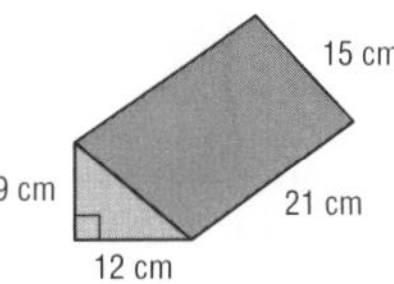

F 1065 cm^2 H 777 cm^2

G 945 cm^2 J 864 cm^2

26. How much cardboard is needed to make a rectangular box of cereal that measures 10 inches by 8 inches by 2 inches? **C**

A 116 in^2 C 232 in^2

B 160 in^2 D 248 in^2

Spiral Review

Find the volume of each figure. Round to the nearest tenth. (Lesson 12-4)

27.  268.1 cm^3

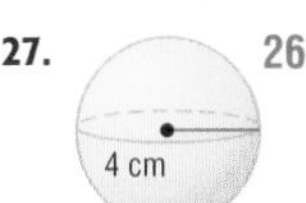

28. 24 ft^3

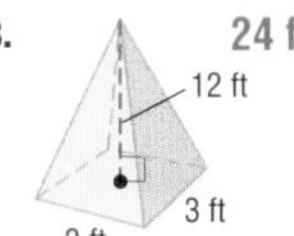

29. 251.3 m^3

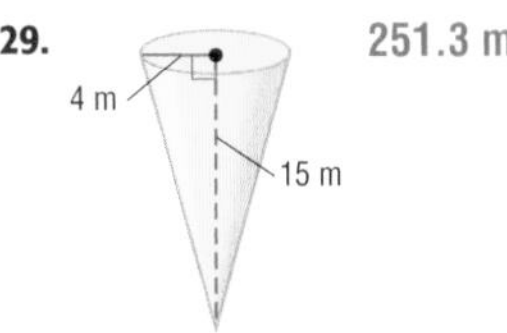

30. ANIMALS A water trough as shown at the right is used to provide water for farm animals. Find the volume of the trough. Round to the nearest tenth. (Lesson 12-3) 117.8 ft^3

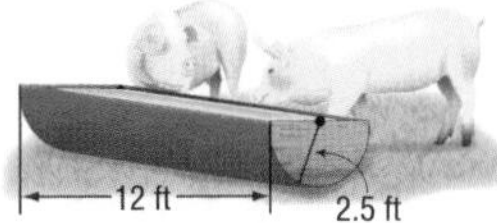

Evaluate each expression if $a = 3$, $b = 5$, and $c = 4$. (Lesson 9-1)

31. b^4 625

32. c^3 64

33. $2(3c + 7)^2$ 722

34. $4(2a - c^3)^2$ 13,456

Skills Review

Find the area of each figure. Round to the nearest tenth. (Lesson 11-9)

35. 153.9 yd^2

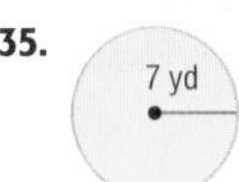

36. 31.8 ft^2

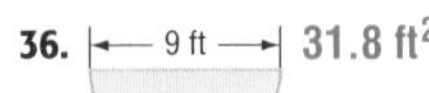

37. 1240.9 m^2

25 m

30 m

4 ASSESS

Name the Math Have students draw a prism. Ask them to create a net of their figure. Tell them to name the figure, each surface or face of the net, and the steps necessary to find the lateral and surface areas of the figure. Then have students find the dimensions of their figure using a ruler. Students should then find the lateral area and the surface area.

Additional Answers

15c. Sample answer: The surface area after a dilation of scale factor of 2 is four times the original; 9 times the original.

15d. Yes. The original formula for surface area is $S = Ph + 2B$. After doubling the sides, the new formula would be $S = (2P)(2h) + 2(4B)$ which simplifies to $S = 4(Ph + 2B)$. Remember, the B is four times as much because both base and height are doubled.

17. The rectangular prism would be more expensive to make. The surface area of the rectangular prism is 36.64 in^2, which would cost $47.63 to make. The surface area of the cube is 34.56 in^2, which would cost $44.93 to make.

22. Surface area involves the amount of area needed to cover a 3-D shape. Volume is the amount of space contained in the 3-D shape. Surface area is measured in square units, while volume is measured in cubic units.

Differentiated Instruction

Extension Give students the following problem: Nick has a triangular prism whose bases are equilateral triangles with sides each measuring 8 inches. The area of each base is about 27.7 square inches. He uses about 199.4 square inches of paper to cover the prism. What is the height of the prism? What is the volume of the prism? about 6 inches; 166.2 in^3

Lesson 12-5 Surface Area of Prisms 695

EXPLORE 12-6 Lesson Notes

1 FOCUS

Objective Use a net to find the surface area of a cylinder.

Materials for Each Student

- cylinder-shaped container with lid
- ruler
- tape
- scissors

Teaching Tip

Make sure the paper the students use to wrap around the container is long enough to go around the container. You may want them to tape two pieces of paper together before they begin.

2 TEACH

Working in Cooperative Groups

Have students work in groups of two or three, mixing abilities. Have groups complete Steps 1–4 of the Activity.

Ask:

- Will the circumference of the top and bottom of the container be the same? Explain. Not necessarily; if the top goes over the container, it would have to be slightly larger.

Practice Have students complete Exercises 1–7.

3 ASSESS

Formative Assessment

Use Exercise 7 to assess whether students can determine the surface area of a cylinder given its diameter and height.

EXPLORE 12-6 Geometry Lab: Surface Area of Cylinders

Math Online glencoe.com
Math *in Motion*, Animation

In Lesson 12-5, you used nets to decompose prisms to find surface areas. You can also use nets to help find the surface area of cylinders.

ACTIVITY

Step 1 Use an empty cylinder-shaped container that has a lid. Measure and record the height of the container. Outline the bases on blank paper and cut them out.

Step 2 Wrap paper around the curved surface of the cylinder and tape it in place. Draw a line from the bottom of the cylinder to the top along the edge of the paper. Draw a line around the circumference of the cylinder.

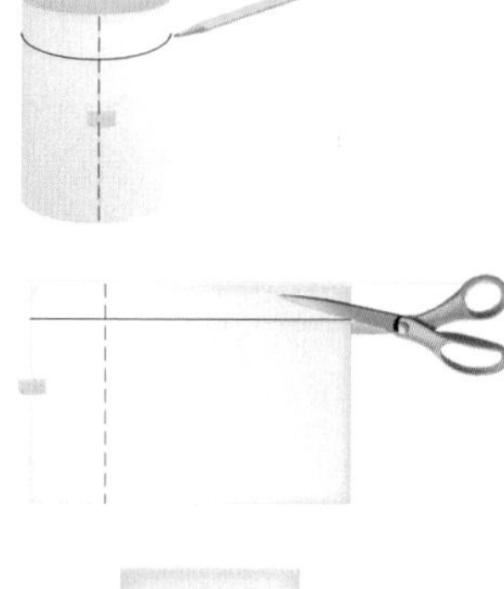

Step 3 Unroll the paper. Cut the paper along the lines marked.

Step 4 Tape the bases and the side together so that they can be re-folded to make the original cylinder. This figure is the net of the cylinder.

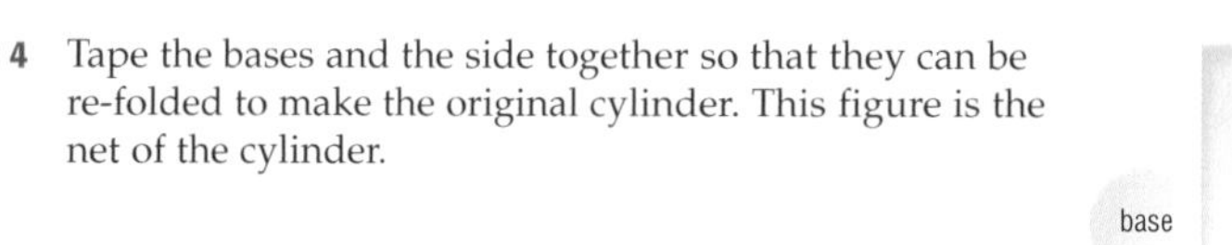

Analyze the Results

1. Classify the two-dimensional shapes that make up the net of the container. **Two circles and one rectangle.**
2. Find the area of each shape. Then find the sum of these areas. **See students' work.**
3. Find the diameter of the top of the container and use it to find the perimeter or circumference of that face. **See students' work.**
4. Multiply the circumference by the height of the container. What does this product represent? **See students' work; The product represents the area of the curved side.**
5. Add the product from Exercise 4 to the sum of the areas of the two circular bases. **See students' work.**
6. Compare your answers from Exercises 2 and 5. **They are the same.**
7. **MAKE A CONJECTURE** Describe a method for finding the area of all the surfaces of a cylinder given the diameter of one of its bases and its height. **See margin.**

From Concrete to Abstract

Have students sketch a net for a cylinder. Label the dimensions for the height and diameter. Have them trade papers with another student and find the surface area of the cylinder.

Additional Answer

7. Sample answer: Calculate the area of one circular base using the radius, which is half the diameter, and multiply this by 2 since there are two bases. Add to this the area of the curved side, which is the product of the circumference of one base and the height of the cylinder.

12-6 Surface Area of Cylinders

Then
You have already found the lateral areas and surface areas of prisms. (Lesson 12-5)

Now
- Find lateral and surface areas of cylinders.
- Compare surface areas of cylinders.

Math Online
glencoe.com
- Extra Examples
- Personal Tutor
- Self-Check Quiz
- Homework Help
- Math in Motion

Why?

Seki is working in the craft room as a counselor at day camp this summer. She is planning a project to make storage containers out of used tin cans. She uses the label of each can as a template for the decorative wrap.

a. What shape is the label if Seki makes a vertical cut through the label and unrolls it? rectangle

b. What is the height of the label? 5 inches

c. What is the length of the label? about 12.6 inches

d. What is the area of the label? about 63 in^2

Surface Area of Cylinders You found the surface areas of prisms by adding the lateral area and the area of the two bases, $S = L + 2B$. You can find surface areas of cylinders in the same way. If you unroll a cylinder, its net is a rectangle (lateral area) and two circles (bases).

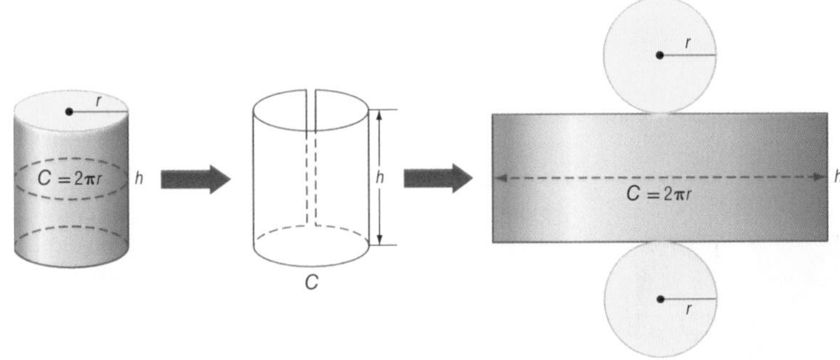

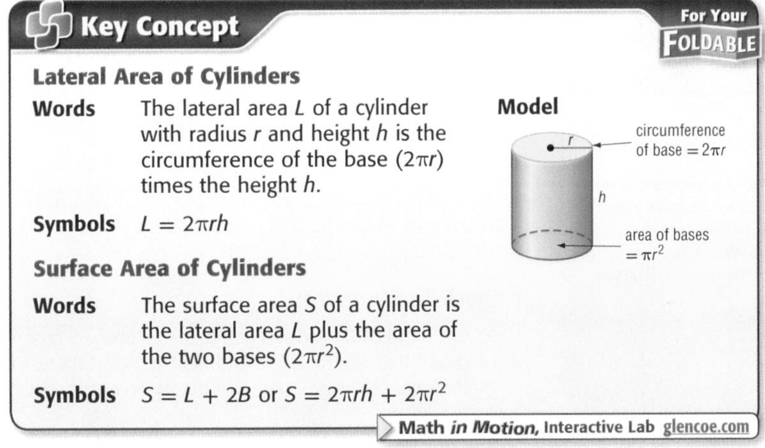

Key Concept For Your FOLDABLE

Lateral Area of Cylinders

Words The lateral area L of a cylinder with radius r and height h is the circumference of the base ($2\pi r$) times the height h.

Symbols $L = 2\pi rh$

Model

Surface Area of Cylinders

Words The surface area S of a cylinder is the lateral area L plus the area of the two bases ($2\pi r^2$).

Symbols $S = L + 2B$ or $S = 2\pi rh + 2\pi r^2$

Math *in Motion*, Interactive Lab glencoe.com

12-6 Lesson Notes

1 FOCUS

Vertical Alignment

Before Lesson 12-6
Find lateral area and surface area of prisms.

Lesson 12-6
Find lateral and surface areas of cylinders. Compare surface areas of cylinders.

After Lesson 12-6
Find surface areas and volumes of three-dimensional figures.

2 TEACH

Scaffolding Questions

Have students read the *Why?* section of the lesson and answer the questions.

Ask:
- How does the length of the label compare to the circumference of the can? Explain. The length of the label is the circumference of the can. They are the same thing.
- What is the area of one of the circular bases of the can? 12.6 in^2
- What is the sum of the area of both bases and the area of the label? 88 in^2

Lesson 12-6 Resources

Resource	Approaching-Level	On-Level	Beyond-Level	English Learners
Teacher Edition	• Differentiated Instruction, p. 698	• Differentiated Instruction, p. 698	• Differentiated Instruction, p. 701	
Chapter Resource Masters	• Study Guide and Intervention, pp. 37–38 • Skills Practice, p. 39 • Practice, p. 40 • Word Problem Practice, p. 41	• Study Guide and Intervention, pp. 37–38 • Skills Practice, p. 39 • Practice, p. 40 • Word Problem Practice, p. 41 • Enrichment, p. 42	• Practice, p. 40 • Word Problem Practice, p. 41 • Enrichment, p. 42	• Study Guide and Intervention, pp. 37–38 • Skills Practice, p. 39 • Practice, p. 40
Transparencies	• 5-Minute Check Transparency 12-6	• 5-Minute Check Transparency 12-6	• 5-Minute Check Transparency 12-6	• 5-Minute Check Transparency 12-6
Other	• Study Notebook • Teaching Pre-Algebra with Manipulatives	• Study Notebook • Teaching Pre-Algebra with Manipulatives	• Study Notebook	• Study Notebook • Teaching Pre-Algebra with Manipulatives

Surface Area of Cylinders

Example 1 shows how to find the lateral and surface areas of a cylinder. **Example 2** shows how to compare the surface areas in a real-world problem situation.

Formative Assessment

Use the Check Your Progress exercises after each example to determine students' understanding of concepts.

Additional Examples

1 Find the lateral and surface area of the cylinder. Round to the nearest tenth.

a.

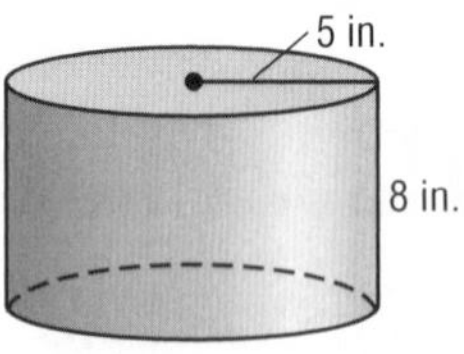

$L = 251.3$ in^2; $S = 408.4$ in^2

b. diameter of 18 feet and height of 9.5 feet $L = 537.2$ ft^2, $S = 1046.2$ ft^2

2 **MANUFACTURING** A company manufactures dowel rods. Rod A has a diameter of 3 inches and a height of 12 inches. Rod B has a diameter of 1 inch and a height of 36 inches. Which rod has the larger surface area? Rod A

Additional Examples also in Interactive Classroom PowerPoint® Presentations

EXAMPLE 1 Surface Area of a Cylinder

Find the lateral area and the surface area of each cylinder. Round to the nearest tenth.

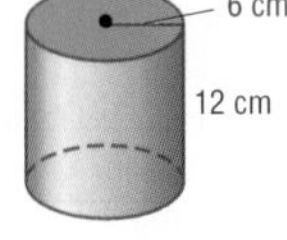

a. Lateral Area

$L = 2\pi rh$

$= 2 \cdot \pi \cdot 6 \cdot 12$

$= 144\pi$ m^2 **exact**

≈ 452.4 m^2 **approximate**

Surface Area

$S = L + 2\pi r^2$

$= 144\pi + 2\pi(6)^2$

$= 216\pi$ m^2 **exact**

≈ 678.6 m^2 **approximate**

b. diameter of 20 inches and height of 5.6 inches

The diameter is 20 inches so the radius r is $\frac{20}{2}$ or 10 inches.

Lateral Area

$L = 2\pi rh$

$= 2 \cdot \pi \cdot 10 \cdot 5.6$

$= 112\pi$ in^2

≈ 351.9 in^2

Surface Area

$S = L + 2\pi r^2$

$= 112\pi + 2\pi(10)^2$

$= 112\pi$ in^2 $+ 200\pi$ in^2

≈ 980.2 in^2

StudyTip

Exact vs. Approximate Answers Leave your answers in terms of π if exact answers are required. If approximate answers are sufficient, find a decimal approximation.

Check Your Progress

1. Find the lateral area and surface area of a cylinder with a radius of 7 centimeters and a height of 12 centimeters. Round to the nearest tenth.

1. 527.8 cm^2; 835.7 cm^2

Personal Tutor glencoe.com

Real-World EXAMPLE 2 Compare Surface Areas of Cylinders

CRAFTS Isabel is making two candles, each with a radius of 1.5 inches. One candle is 4 inches tall and the other is 8 inches tall. Is the surface area of the larger candle twice that of the smaller candle? Explain.

Find the surface areas of both candles.

Surface Area of Candle A

$S = L + 2\pi r^2$

$S = 2\pi rh + 2\pi r^2$

$= 2\pi \cdot 1.5 \cdot 4 + 2\pi \cdot (1.5)^2$

$= 12\pi + 4.5\pi$

$= 16.5\pi$

Surface Area of Candle B

$S = L + 2\pi r^2$

$S = 2\pi rh + 2\pi r^2$

$= 2\pi \cdot 1.5 \cdot 8 + 2\pi \cdot (1.5)^2$

$= 24\pi + 4.5\pi$

$= 28.5\pi$

The surface area of candle B is *not* twice the surface area of candle A. The lateral area of candle B is twice the lateral area of candle A, but the base areas are equal.

Real-World Link

Archaeologists have found remains of candles from as far back as 3000 B.C. Paraffin wax began to be popular in the 19th century.

Check Your Progress

2. **CANNED FOODS** Which can has a greater surface area: a tuna fish can with diameter 8 centimeters and height 4 centimeters or a soup can with a diameter 4 centimeters and height 8 centimeters? tuna fish can

Personal Tutor glencoe.com

Tips for New Teachers

Remind students that bases can be on opposite faces in a rectangular prism.

Differentiated Instruction

students struggle to understand the relationship between the circumference of the base and the length of the rectangle,

draw nets for several different cylinders. Mark the center of each circle. Pass the nets out to pairs of students. Have them find the diameter of each circle and then its circumference. Then have them measure the length and height of the rectangle. Ask them to compare the circumference to the rectangle's measured length. Finally, have them find the surface area of the net.

Check Your Understanding

Answers were computed using the π key on a calculator.

Example 1 p. 698

Find the lateral and surface area of each cylinder. Round to the nearest tenth.

3. 102.9 m^2; 130.6 m^2

1. 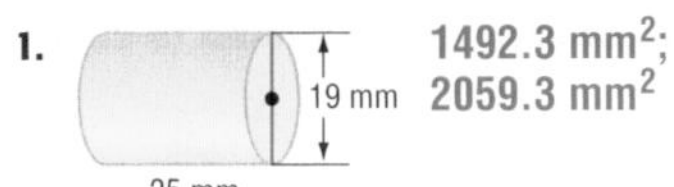

1492.3 mm^2; 2059.3 mm^2

2. 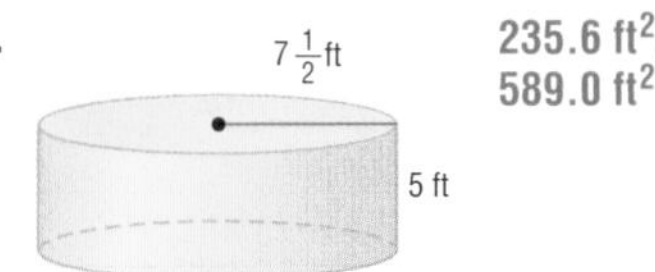

235.6 ft^2; 589.0 ft^2

3. diameter of 4.2 meters and a height of 7.8 meters

Example 2 p. 698

4. **LABELS** A case of frozen juice contains 12 cans like the one shown at the right. Find the area of the labels for one case of canned juice to the nearest tenth. 471.2 in^2

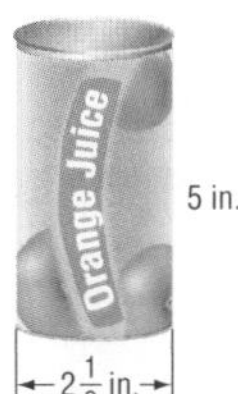

Practice and Problem Solving

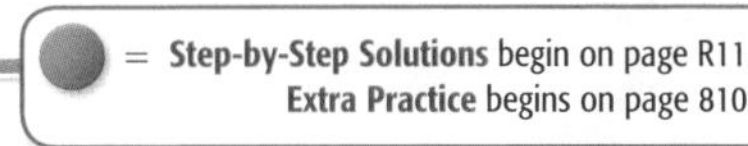

= **Step-by-Step Solutions** begin on page R11.
Extra Practice begins on page 810.

Example 1 p. 698

Find the lateral and surface area of each cylinder. Round to the nearest tenth.

5. 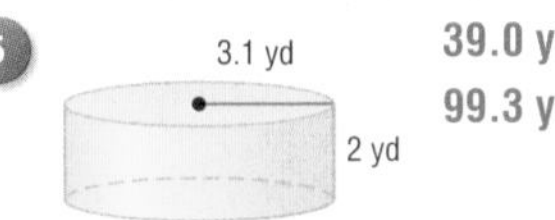

39.0 yd^2; 99.3 yd^2

6. 

166.5 mm^2 1269.6 mm^2

7. 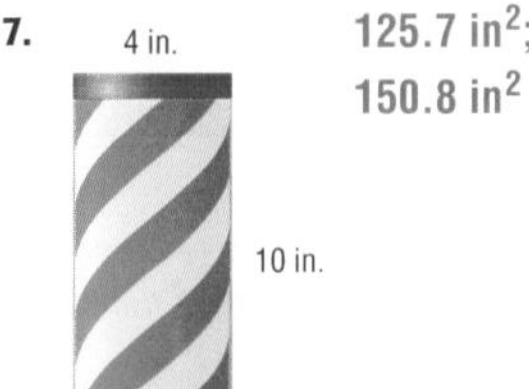

125.7 in^2; 150.8 in^2

8. 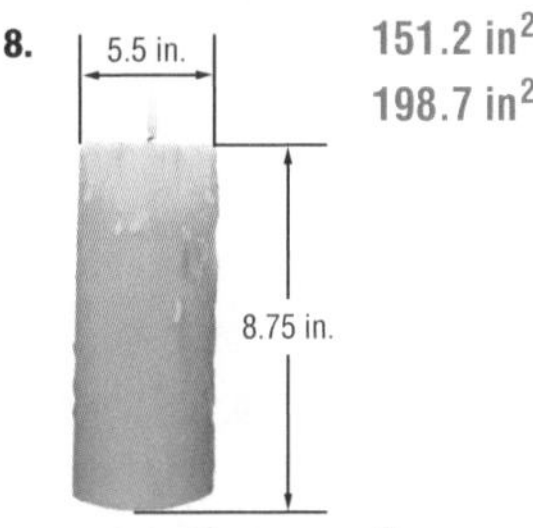

151.2 in^2; 198.7 in^2

11. The box has surface area of 1296 in^2 and the tube has a surface area of 1288.1 in^2. So the tube has a smaller surface area.

9. radius of $3\frac{2}{3}$ feet and a height of $5\frac{1}{4}$ feet 121.0 ft^2; 205.4 ft^2

10. diameter of 9 meters and a height of 7.3 meters 206.4 m^2; 333.6 m^2

Example 2 p. 698

11. **MAIL** The mailing box and mailing tube shown at the right have about the same volume. Which one has a smaller surface area? Explain.

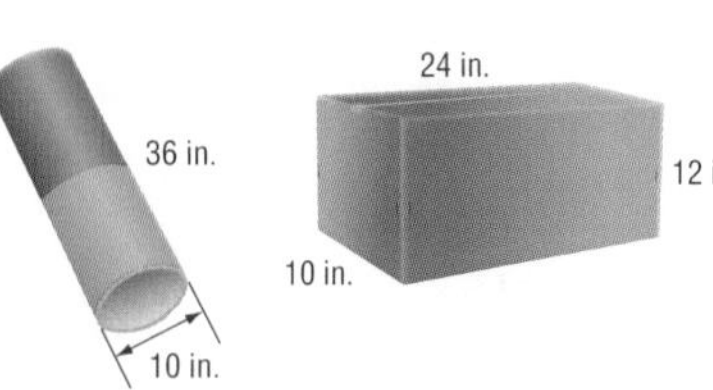

12. **HOME DECOR** Taryn is painting pillars. One pillar is 0.75 meter tall and 0.15 meter in diameter. Another pillar is 0.30 meter in diameter and 0.38 meter tall. Which pillar needs more paint?

12. The pillar that is 0.3 m in diameter and 0.38 m tall.

Focus on Mathematical Content

Surface Area of Cylinders Imagine a cylinder unrolled to show two circles and a rectangle. Its surface area would be the sum of the areas of the circles, πr^2, and the area of the rectangle, $2\pi rh$ (the length of the rectangle is the circumference of one of the circles), or $S = 2\pi r^2 + 2\pi rh$.

Tips for New Teachers

Preventing Errors Some students may confuse volume with surface area. Keep reminding them that volume fills the inside of a figure, whereas the surface area covers the outside of the figure.

3 PRACTICE

Formative Assessment

Use Exercises 1–4 to check for understanding.

Use the chart at the bottom of this page to customize assignments for your students.

TEACH with TECH

AUDIO RECORDING Have each student work with a partner to make an audio recording explaining how to find the height of a cylinder if the surface area and radius are known.

Differentiated Homework Options

Level	Assignment	Two-Day Option	
AL Basic	5–12, 19, 21–43	5–11 odd, 22–25	6–12 even, 19, 21, 26–43
OL Core	5–11 odd, 13, 15–19, 21–43	5–12, 22–25	13–19, 21, 26–43
BL Advanced	12–37 (optional: 38–43)		

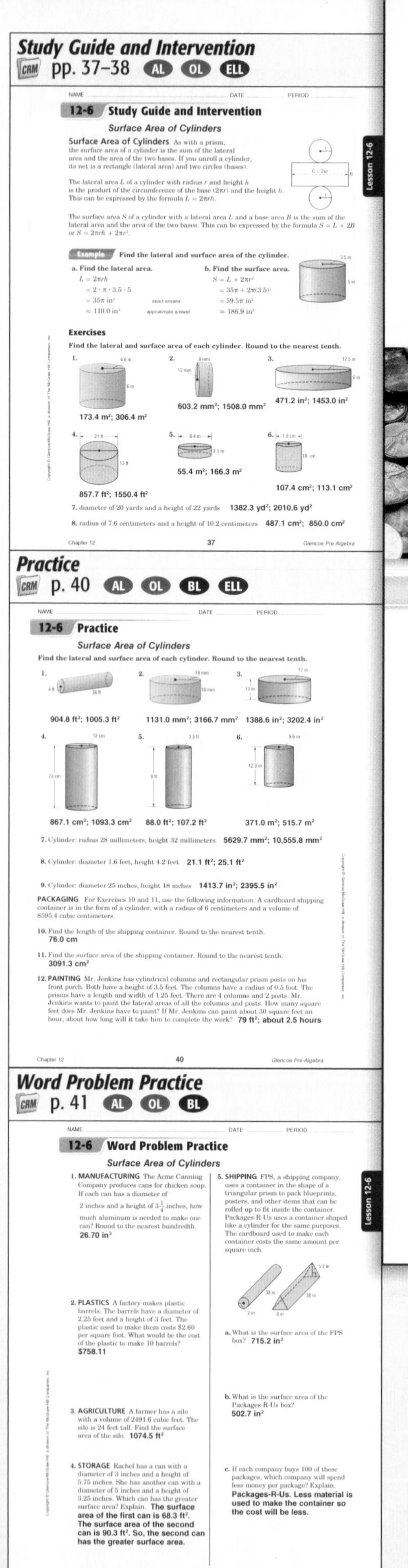

Study Guide and Intervention
CRM pp. 37–38 AL OL ELL

NAME ________ DATE ________ PERIOD ________

12-6 Study Guide and Intervention
Surface Area of Cylinders

Surface Area of Cylinders As with a prism, the surface area of a cylinder is the sum of the lateral area and the area of the two bases. If you unroll a cylinder, its net is a rectangle (lateral area) and two circles (bases).

The lateral area L of a cylinder with radius r and height h is the product of the circumference of the base $(2\pi r)$ and the height h. This can be expressed by the formula $L = 2\pi rh$.

The surface area S of a cylinder with a lateral area L and a base area B is the sum of the lateral area and the area of the two bases. This can be expressed by the formula $S = L + 2B$ or $S = 2\pi rh + 2\pi r^2$.

Example Find the lateral and surface area of the cylinder.

a. Find the lateral area.

$L = 2\pi rh$
$= 2 \cdot \pi \cdot 3.5 \cdot 5$
$= 35\pi \text{ in}^2$ exact answer
$\approx 110.0 \text{ in}^2$ approximate answer

b. Find the surface area.

$S = L + 2\pi r^2$
$= 35\pi + 2\pi(3.5)^2$
$= 59.5\pi \text{ in}^2$
$\approx 186.9 \text{ in}^2$

Exercises

Find the lateral and surface area of each cylinder. Round to the nearest tenth.

1. (4.6 m, 6 m) **173.4 m²; 306.4 m²**
2. (8 mm, 12 mm) **603.2 mm²; 1508.0 mm²**
3. (12.5 in., 6 in.) **471.2 in²; 1453.0 in²**
4. (21 ft, 13 ft) **857.7 ft²; 1550.4 ft²**
5. (8.4 m, 2.1 m) **55.4 m²; 166.3 m²**
6. (1.9 cm, 18 cm) **107.4 cm²; 113.1 cm²**
7. diameter of 20 yards and a height of 22 yards **1382.3 yd²; 2010.6 yd²**
8. radius of 7.6 centimeters and a height of 10.2 centimeters **487.1 cm²; 850.0 cm²**

Chapter 12 37 Glencoe Pre-Algebra

Practice
CRM p. 40 AL OL BL ELL

NAME ________ DATE ________ PERIOD ________

12-6 Practice
Surface Area of Cylinders

Find the lateral and surface area of each cylinder. Round to the nearest tenth.

1. (4 ft, 36 ft) **904.8 ft²; 1005.3 ft²**
2. (18 mm, 10 mm) **1131.0 mm²; 3166.7 mm²**
3. (17 in., 13 in.) **1388.6 in²; 3202.4 in²**
4. (12 cm, 23 cm) **867.1 cm²; 1093.3 cm²**
5. (3.5 ft, 8 ft) **88.0 ft²; 107.2 ft²**
6. (9.6 m, 12.3 m) **371.0 m²; 515.7 m²**
7. Cylinder: radius 28 millimeters, height 32 millimeters **5629.7 mm²; 10,555.8 mm²**
8. Cylinder: diameter 1.6 feet, height 4.2 feet **21.1 ft²; 25.1 ft²**
9. Cylinder: diameter 25 inches, height 18 inches **1413.7 in²; 2395.5 in²**

PACKAGING For Exercises 10 and 11, use the following information. A cardboard shipping container is in the form of a cylinder, with a radius of 6 centimeters and a volume of 8595.4 cubic centimeters.

10. Find the length of the shipping container. Round to the nearest tenth. **76.0 cm**
11. Find the surface area of the shipping container. Round to the nearest tenth. **3091.3 cm²**
12. **PAINTING** Mr. Jenkins has cylindrical columns and rectangular prism posts on his front porch. Both have a height of 3.5 feet. The columns have a radius of 0.5 foot. The prisms have a length and width of 1.25 feet. There are 4 columns and 2 posts. Mr. Jenkins wants to paint the lateral areas of all the columns and posts. How many square feet does Mr. Jenkins have to paint? If Mr. Jenkins can paint about 30 square feet an hour, about how long will it take him to complete the work? **79 ft²; about 2.5 hours**

Chapter 12 40 Glencoe Pre-Algebra

Word Problem Practice
CRM p. 41 AL OL BL

NAME ________ DATE ________ PERIOD ________

12-6 Word Problem Practice
Surface Area of Cylinders

1. **MANUFACTURING** The Acme Canning Company produces cans for chicken soup. If each can has a diameter of 2 inches and a height of $3\frac{1}{4}$ inches, how much aluminum is needed to make one can? Round to the nearest hundredth. **26.70 in²**

2. **PLASTICS** A factory makes plastic barrels. The barrels have a diameter of 2.25 feet and a height of 3 feet. The plastic used to make them costs $2.60 per square foot. What would be the cost of the plastic to make 10 barrels? **$758.11**

3. **AGRICULTURE** A farmer has a silo with a volume of 2491.6 cubic feet. The silo is 24 feet tall. Find the surface area of the silo. **1074.5 ft²**

4. **STORAGE** Rachel has a can with a diameter of 3 inches and a height of 5.75 inches. She has another can with a diameter of 5 inches and a height of 3.25 inches. Which can has the greater surface area? Explain. **The surface area of the first can is 68.3 ft². The surface area of the second can is 90.3 ft². So, the second can has the greater surface area.**

5. **SHIPPING** FPS, a shipping company, uses a container in the shape of a triangular prism to pack blueprints, posters, and other items that can be rolled up to fit inside the container. Packages-R-Us uses a container shaped like a cylinder for the same purposes. The cardboard used to make each container costs the same amount per square inch.

a. What is the surface area of the FPS box? **715.2 in²**

b. What is the surface area of the Packages-R-Us box? **502.7 in²**

c. If each company buys 100 of these packages, which company will spend less money per package? Explain. **Packages-R-Us. Less material is used to make the container so the cost will be less.**

Chapter 12 41 Glencoe Pre-Algebra

13. **PLUMBING** Find the surface area (exterior and interior) of the pipe shown. Round to the nearest tenth of a square inch. **194.7 in²**

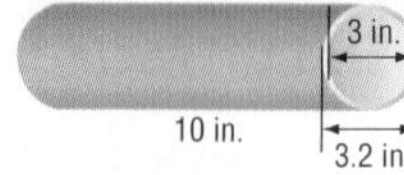

Find the surface area of each figure. Round to the nearest tenth.

14. **374.5 in²**

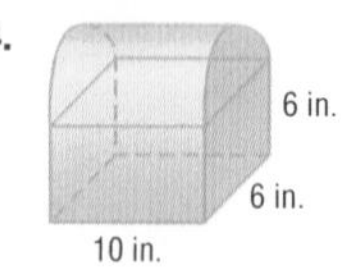

15. **6121.0 cm²**

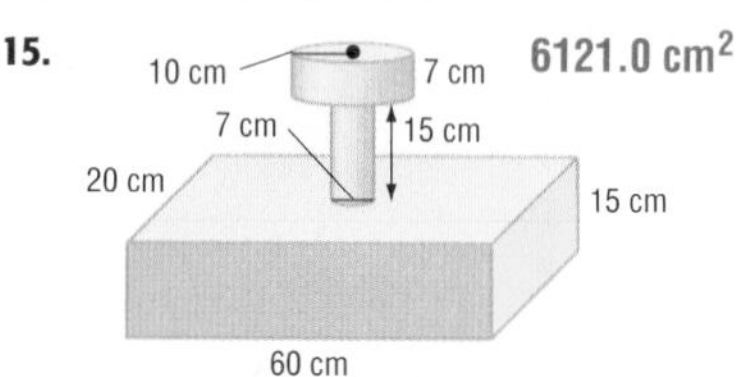

16. **MONEY** A penny's mass is exactly half the mass of a nickel. Using the information below, determine the ratio between their surface areas. Round to the nearest tenth. **8 : 10**

Coin	Penny	Nickel
Weight	2.5 g	5.0 g
Diameter	19.05 mm	21.21 mm
Thickness	1.55 mm	1.95 mm

Real-World Link

The average life span of a coin is 30 years. Coins that are found to be too old or damaged for circulation are melted down to create new coins.

Source: U.S. Mint

17. **FINANCIAL LITERACY** The Student Council is planning a movie night. They will sell popcorn in one of the open-top containers shown. The cost depends on the amount of cardboard used to make each container. Which container should they buy? Use volume and surface area measurements to explain your choice. **See margin.**

18. Find the height of a cylinder if the surface area is 402 square centimeters and the radius is 4 centimeters. Round to the nearest tenth. **12.0 cm**

H.O.T. Problems
Use **H**igher-**O**rder **T**hinking Skills

19–21. See margin.

19. **OPEN ENDED** Create a prism that has approximately the same surface area as the cylinder shown at the right.

10.2 ft
14.6 ft

20. **CHALLENGE** A cylinder has a radius of 10 centimeters and a height of 6 centimeters. Without calculating, explain whether multiplying the radius or the height by a scale factor of 0.5 would have a greater effect on the surface area of the cylinder.

21. **WRITING IN MATH** Both ice cubes have a volume of about 22.5 cubic centimeters. Which ice cube would you expect to melt faster? Find the total surface areas to explain your reasoning.

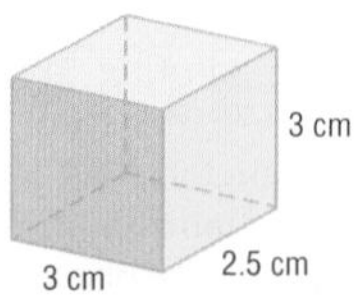

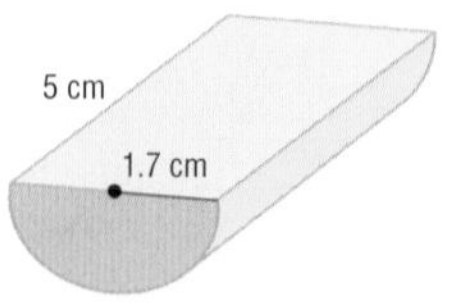

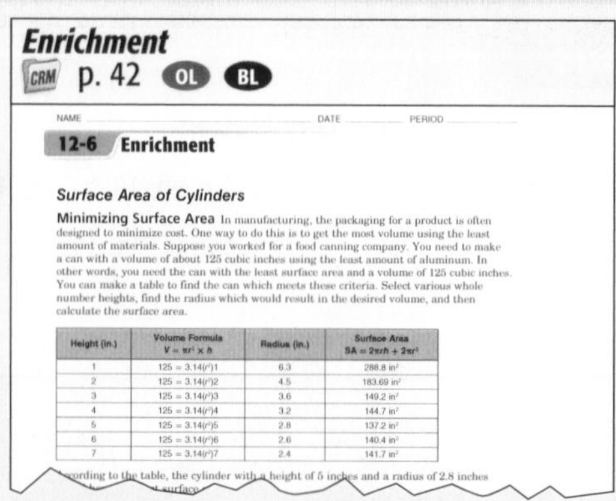

Enrichment
CRM p. 42 OL BL

NAME ________ DATE ________ PERIOD ________

12-6 Enrichment

Surface Area of Cylinders

Minimizing Surface Area In manufacturing, the packaging for a product is often designed to minimize cost. One way to do this is to get the most volume using the least amount of materials. Suppose you worked for a food canning company. You need to make a can with a volume of about 125 cubic inches using the least amount of aluminum. In other words, you need the can with the least surface area and a volume of 125 cubic inches. You can make a table to find the can which meets these criteria. Select various whole number heights, find the radius which would result in the desired volume, and then calculate the surface area.

Height (in.)	Volume Formula $V = \pi r^2 \times h$	Radius (in.)	Surface Area $SA = 2\pi rh + 2\pi r^2$
1	$125 = 3.14(r^2)1$	6.3	288.8 in²
2	$125 = 3.14(r^2)2$	4.5	183.69 in²
3	$125 = 3.14(r^2)3$	3.6	149.2 in²
4	$125 = 3.14(r^2)4$	3.2	144.7 in²
5	$125 = 3.14(r^2)5$	2.8	137.2 in²
6	$125 = 3.14(r^2)6$	2.6	140.4 in²
7	$125 = 3.14(r^2)7$	2.4	141.7 in²

According to the table, the cylinder with a height of 5 inches and a radius of 2.8 inches

Standardized Test Practice

22. Find the amount of paper needed for the label on the can. Use 3.14 for π. **A**

A 21.2 in^2
B 25.5 in^2
C 29.1 in^2
D 42.4 in^2

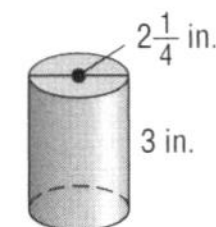

23. A cylinder has a surface area of 5652 square millimeters. If the diameter of the cylinder is 30 millimeters, what is the height? Use 3.14 for π. **G**

F 10 mm
G 45 mm
H 59 mm
J 105 mm

24. GRIDDED RESPONSE What is the surface area in square meters of a cylinder with a radius of 3.4 meters and a height of 2.8 meters? Round to the nearest hundredth. Use 3.14 for π. **132.38**

25. A cylindrical plastic bar is to have the same surface area as a cylindrical metal bar with a radius of 1 inch and a height of 4 inches. Which of the following dimensions meet these requirements? Use 3.14 for π. **D**

A radius: 4 in., height: 2 in.
B radius: 2 in., height: 2 in.
C radius: 2 in., height: 4 in.
D radius: 2 in., height: 0.5 in.

Spiral Review

Find the lateral and surface area of each figure. (Lesson 12-5)

26. 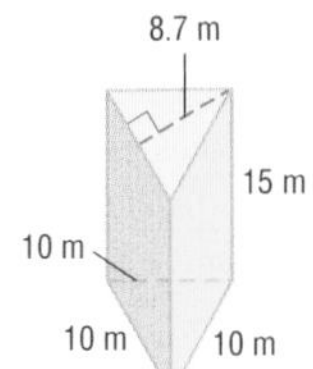

450 m^2; 537 m^2

27. 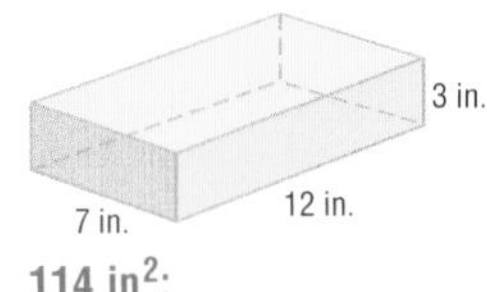

114 in^2; 282 in^2

28. 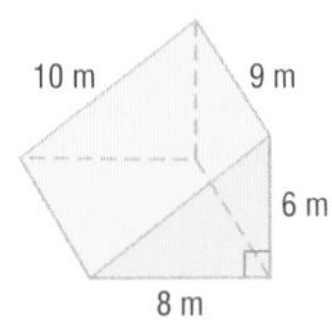

216 m^2; 264 m^2

29. HISTORY The Pyramid of Cestius in Rome, Italy, is 27 meters high and has a square base 22 meters on a side. What is its volume? Use an estimate to check your answer. (Lesson 12-4) **4356 m^3**

Classify each angle as *acute, obtuse, right,* or *straight*. (Lesson 11-1)

30. 50° **acute** **31.** 180° **straight** **32.** 43° **acute** **33.** 114° **obtuse**

Find the simple interest earned to the nearest cent. (Lesson 7-7)

34. $1500 at 7.5% for 5 years **$562.50**
35. $750 at 12.25% for 10 years **$918.75**
36. $625 at 5.75% for 8 years **$287.50**
37. $10,150 at 4.5% for 20 years **$9135**

Skills Review

Find each product. (Lesson 3-3)

38. 2.45^2 **6.0025**
39. $4 \cdot \frac{1}{2} \cdot 3 \cdot 8$ **48**
40. $3.14(5.4)^2$ **91.5624**
41. $7.5 \cdot \frac{1}{2} \cdot 15\frac{2}{3}$ **58.75**
42. $3.14\left(1\frac{1}{4}\right)^2$ **4.90625**
43. $\frac{2}{5} \cdot 2\frac{1}{3}$ **$\frac{14}{15}$**

4 ASSESS

Yesterday's News Have students write about how they think yesterday's lesson on surface area of prisms helped them with today's lesson on surface area of cylinders.

Formative Assessment

Check for student understanding of concepts in Lessons 12-5 and 12-6.

CRM Quiz 3, p. 59

Additional Answers

17. The cylindrical popcorn container because it uses less material (surface area) and holds about the same amount of popcorn (volume). Rectangular Prism: $V = 275\text{ in}^3$, $S.A. = 237.5\text{ in}^2$; Cylinder: $V = 274.3\text{ in}^3$, $S.A. = 211.1\text{ in}^2$

19. See students' work.

20. Multiplying by the radius; Sample answer: Multiplying by the radius or the height would both reduce the surface area, but multiplying by the radius would have a greater effect because it both reduces the area of the bases as well as the lateral area. Multiplying only the height by the scale factor does not change the area of the base.

21. The ice cube in the shape of a half cylinder would melt at a faster rate because it has a greater total surface area exposed to the air.

Differentiated Instruction

Extension Give the following problem to students: Elena made a scarecrow head using paper maché. She covered an inflated spherical balloon with rectangular pieces of newspaper that were saturated with a glue mixture. If the pieces of newspaper were cut into 1-in. by 6-in. strips, how many pieces did she use if the circumference of the balloon was 30 inches? The formula for the surface area of a sphere is $S = 4\pi r^2$. The surface area of the balloon is 286.48 in^2, so she will need 47.75 or 48 pieces of the paper.

Lesson 12-6 Surface Area of Cylinders 701

12-7 Lesson Notes

1 FOCUS

Vertical Alignment

Before Lesson 12-7
Find the surface area of prisms and cylinders.

Lesson 12-7
Find lateral area and surface area of pyramids and cones.

After Lesson 12-7
Find surface areas and volumes of three-dimensional figures.

2 TEACH

Scaffolding Questions

Have students read the *Why?* section of the lesson and answer the questions.

Ask:

- Which face is the base of the pyramid? the rectangle
- What formula would you use to find the area of the base? $A = lw$
- What formula would you use to find the area of each triangle? $A = \frac{1}{2}bh$

Additional Answers

b. The bottom is a rectangle and the four sides are triangles.

c. The triangles opposite each other are congruent.

d. Find the sum of the areas of the four triangles.

12-7 Surface Area of Pyramids and Cones

Then
You have already found the surface areas of prisms and cylinders. (Lessons 12-5 and 12-6)

Now
- Find lateral areas and surface areas of pyramids.
- Find lateral areas and surface areas of cones.

New Vocabulary
regular pyramid
slant height

Math Online
glencoe.com
- Extra Examples
- Personal Tutor
- Self-Check Quiz
- Homework Help

Why? b–d. See margin.

On a recent trip to Paris, Michelle visited the Louvre Museum.

a. How many faces are on the pyramid? 5
b. What are the shapes of the faces?
c. Do any of the shapes appear congruent?
d. How would you find the amount of glass needed to make the pyramid?

Surface Areas of Pyramids A **regular pyramid** is a pyramid whose base is a regular polygon. The lateral faces of a regular pyramid are congruent isosceles triangles that intersect at the vertex. The altitude or height of each lateral face is called the **slant height** of the pyramid.

Regular Pyramid

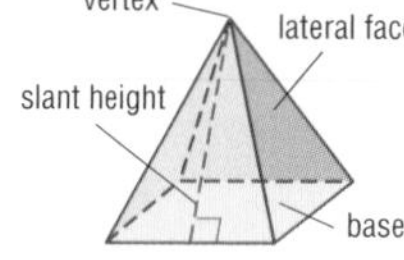

Net of Regular Pyramid

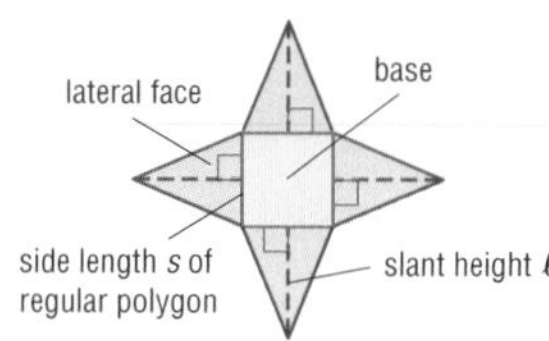

The lateral area of a pyramid is the sum of the areas of its lateral faces, which are all triangles.

$L = 4\left(\frac{1}{2}s\ell\right)$ **Area of the lateral faces**

$L = \frac{1}{2}(4s)\ell$ **Commutative Property of Multiplication**

$L = \frac{1}{2}P\ell$ **Replace 4*s* with *P*, the perimeter of the base.**

The total surface area is the lateral surface area plus the area of the base.

Key Concept — For Your FOLDABLE

Lateral Area of Pyramids

Words The lateral area L of a regular pyramid is half the perimeter P of the base times the slant height ℓ.

Symbols $L = \frac{1}{2}P\ell$

Surface Area of Pyramids

Words The total surface area S of a regular pyramid is the lateral area L plus the area of the base B.

Symbols $S = L + B$ or $S = \frac{1}{2}P\ell + B$

slant height ℓ
area of the base B
perimeter of the base P

Lesson 12-7 Resources

Resource	Approaching-Level	On-Level	Beyond-Level	English Learners
Teacher Edition	• Differentiated Instruction, p. 703	• Differentiated Instruction, p. 703	• Differentiated Instruction, pp. 703, 707	• Differentiated Instruction, p. 703
Chapter Resource Masters	• Study Guide and Intervention, pp. 43–44 • Skills Practice, p. 45 • Practice, p. 46 • Word Problem Practice, p. 47	• Study Guide and Intervention, pp. 43–44 • Skills Practice, p. 45 • Practice, p. 46 • Word Problem Practice, p. 47 • Enrichment, p. 48	Practice, p. 46 • Word Problem Practice, p. 47 • Enrichment, p. 48	• Study Guide and Intervention, pp. 43–44 • Skills Practice, p. 45 • Practice, p. 46
Transparencies	• 5-Minute Check Transparency 12-7	• 5-Minute Check Transparency 12-7	• 5-Minute Check Transparency 12-7	• 5-Minute Check Transparency 12-7
Other	• Study Notebook • Teaching Pre-Algebra with Manipulatives	• Study Notebook • Teaching Pre-Algebra with Manipulatives	• Study Notebook	• Study Notebook • Teaching Pre-Algebra with Manipulatives

StudyTip

Height of a Pyramid and Slant Height The height of a pyramid is the perpendicular distance from the top point to the base of the pyramid. The slant height of the pyramid is the altitude of one of the triangles that forms the sides of the pyramid.

EXAMPLE 1 Surface Area of a Pyramid

Find the lateral and total surface area of the regular pentagonal pyramid.

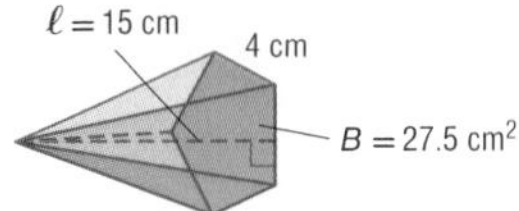

Find the lateral area.

$L = \frac{1}{2}P\ell$ **Write the formula.**

$L = \frac{1}{2}(4 \cdot 5)15$ **Replace P with $4 \cdot 5$ and ℓ with 15.**

$= 150 \text{ cm}^2$ **Simplify.**

Find the surface area.

$S = L + B$ **Write the formula.**

$S = 150 + 27.5$ **Replace L with 150 and B with 27.5.**

$= 177.5 \text{ cm}^2$ **Simplify.**

The lateral surface area is 150 cm² and the total surface area is 177.5 cm².

Check Your Progress

1. Find the lateral and surface area of a square pyramid with a base side length of 6 centimeters and a slant height of 18.4 centimeters. **220.8 cm²; 256.8 cm²**

Personal Tutor glencoe.com

Real-World EXAMPLE 2 Lateral Area of a Pyramid

HISTORY If the length of each side of the parachute shown at the left is 12 yards and the height of the pyramid is 12 yards, find the amount of cloth needed to make the parachute.

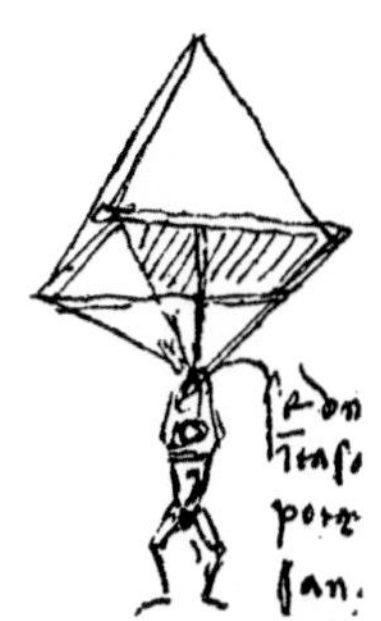

Real-World Link

In 1483, Leonardo Da Vinci sketched the first design for a parachute in the margin of a notebook. In 2000, Adrian Nicholas constructed and tested the parachute using Da Vinci's plans. It weighed 187 pounds, and it safely carried him down from an altitude of 8000 feet.

Step 1 Find the slant height ℓ of the square pyramid. The slant height of the pyramid is the hypotenuse of a right triangle with one leg the height of the pyramid and the other leg half the measure of one of the base sides.

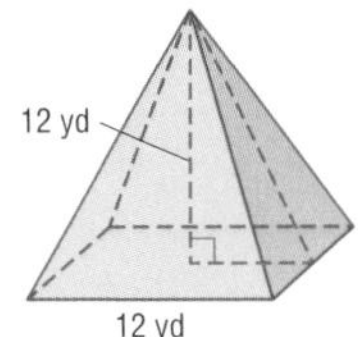

$a^2 + b^2 = c^2$ **Use the Pythagorean Theorem.**

$12^2 + 6^2 = \ell^2$ **Replace a with 12, b with 6, and c with ℓ.**

$180 = \ell^2$ **Simplify.**

$13.4 \approx \ell$ **Definition of square root**

Step 2 Since the parachute is open on the bottom, to find the amount of cloth needed for the parachute, find the lateral area of the pyramid.

$L = \frac{1}{2}P\ell$ **Write the formula for the lateral area.**

$L = \frac{1}{2}(12 \cdot 4)13.4$ **Replace P with $12 \cdot 4$ and ℓ with 13.4.**

$= 321.6 \text{ yd}^2$ **Simplify.**

So, 321.6 square yards of cloth are needed for the parachute.

Check Your Progress

2. MUSEUMS The pyramid at the Louvre Museum is a square pyramid with a height of 20.5 meters and sides of 35 meters. Find the amount of glass on the pyramid. **1890 m²**

Personal Tutor glencoe.com

Differentiated Instruction

AL OL BL ELL

Interpersonal Divide the class into small mixed groups. Have them draw different types of solid figures with similar measures and find their surface areas, for example, a square pyramid with a slant height of 6 units and a base length of 6 units. After working several problems with measurements similar to those just given, have students discuss whether different types of solid figures with similar measures will have equal surface areas.

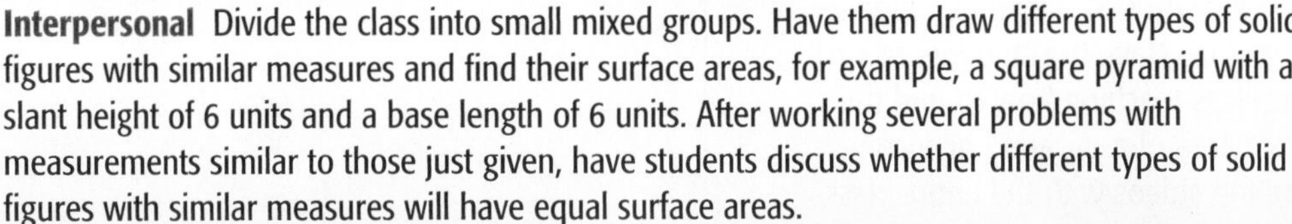

Surface Areas of Pyramids

Example 1 shows how to find the lateral and total surface area of a regular pyramid. **Example 2** shows how to use the lateral area of a pyramid to solve a real-world problem.

Formative Assessment

Use the Check Your Progress exercises after each example to determine students' understanding of concepts.

Additional Examples

1 Find the lateral and total surface area of the square pyramid. 142.4 ft²; 206.4 ft²

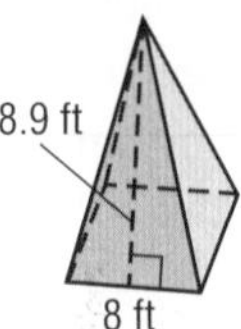

2 **CANOPIES** A canopy is in the shape of a square pyramid. If the length of each side is 3.4 meters and the slant height is 2 meters, how much canvas is needed for the canopy? 13.6 m²

Additional Examples also in Interactive Classroom PowerPoint® Presentations

IWB INTERACTIVE WHITEBOARD READY

Focus on Mathematical Content

Surface Area The surface area of a pyramid or cone is the sum of the lateral area plus the area of the base. These areas are often used separately in real-world problems that do not require total surface area. Ask students what formula they would use to calculate the area of a cone-shaped roof. The base of the roof is not covered, only the lateral area is calculated. This is the $\pi r\ell$ portion of the formula, $S = \pi r\ell + \pi r^2$.

Surface Area of Cones

Example 3 shows how to find the lateral and surface areas of a cone.

Additional Example

3 Find the lateral and surface areas of the cone. Round to the nearest tenth. 110.0 ft^2; 148.4 ft^2

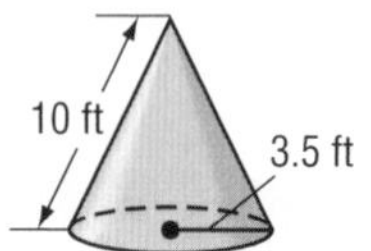

Tips for New Teachers

Modeling Have students explain the difference between the height and the slant height of a pyramid and a cone. Demonstrate with a model.

Surface Area of Cones You can also find surface areas of cones. The net of a cone shows the regions that make up the cone.

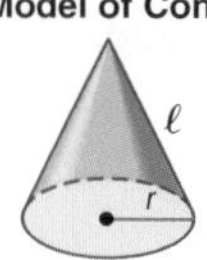

Net of Cone

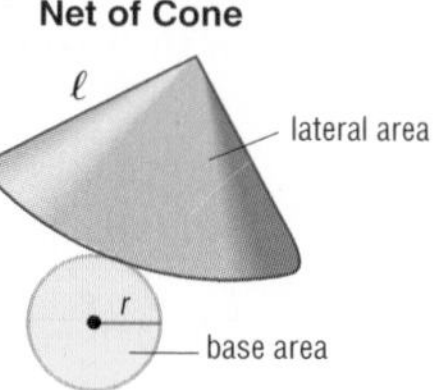

StudyTip

Slant Height of a Cone If you are not given the slant height of a cone, you can find it by using the Pythagorean Theorem. You need to know the radius and the height of the cone.

$a^2 + b^2 = c^2$

$\ell^2 = h^2 + r^2$

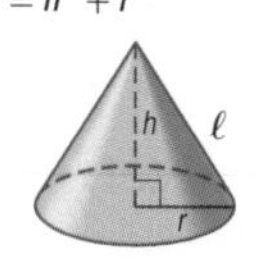

The lateral area of a cone with slant height ℓ is one-half the circumference of the base, $2\pi r$, times ℓ. So, $L = \frac{1}{2} \cdot 2\pi r \cdot \ell$ or $L = \pi r\ell$. The base of the cone is a circle with area πr^2.

Key Concept

For Your FOLDABLE

Lateral Area of Cones

Words The lateral area L of a cone is π times the radius times the slant height ℓ.

Symbols $L = \pi r\ell$

Surface Area of Cones

Words The surface area S of a cone with slant height ℓ and radius r is the lateral area plus the area of the base.

Symbols $S = L + \pi r^2$

slant height

area of the base B

EXAMPLE 3 Surface Area of a Cone

Find the lateral and surface area of the cone. Round to the nearest tenth.

11.6 ft

7.3 ft

Find the lateral area.

$L = \pi r\ell$	**Lateral area of a cone**
$L = \pi(7.3)(11.6)$	**Replace r with 7.3 and ℓ with 11.6.**
≈ 266.0	**Simplify.**

Find the surface area.

$S = L + \pi r^2$	**Surface area of a cone**
$S = 266 + \pi(7.3)^2$	**Replace r with 7.3.**
≈ 433.4 ft^2	**Simplify.**

The surface area of the cone is about 433.4 square feet.

Check Your Progress **110.0 yd^2; 148.4 yd^2**

3. Find the lateral and surface areas of a cone with a radius of $3\frac{1}{2}$ yards and a slant height of 10 yards. Round to the nearest tenth.

Personal Tutor glencoe.com

TEACH with TECH

VIDEO RECORDING Separate students into groups. Have the students record themselves teaching how to find the surface area of a pyramid or a cone. Share the videos with the entire class.

704 Chapter 12 Surface Area and Volume

Check Your Understanding

Answers were computed using the π key on a calculator.

Examples 1 and 3 pp. 703–704

Find the lateral and surface area of each figure. Round to the nearest tenth.

1. 14 m; 13 m
364 m^2; 533 m^2

2. 9 in.; 8 in.
113.1 in^2; 163.4 in^2

3. 8 mm; 12 mm
192 mm^2; 336 mm^2

Example 2 p. 703

4. **GLASS** The Luxor Hotel in Las Vegas, Nevada, is a square pyramid made from glass with a base length of 646 feet and a height of 350 feet. Find the surface area of the glass on the Luxor. 615,379.6 ft^2

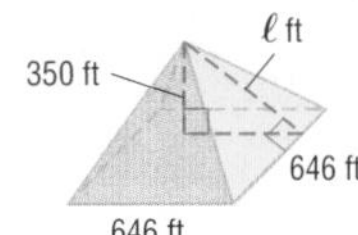

Practice and Problem Solving

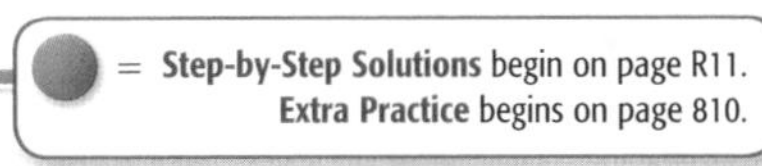
= **Step-by-Step Solutions** begin on page R11.
Extra Practice begins on page 810.

Example 1 p. 703

Find the lateral and surface area of each figure. Round to the nearest tenth.

5. 240 in^2; 340 in^2
6. 360 yd^2; 620 yd^2
7. 105.3 mm^2; 140.4 mm^2

5.

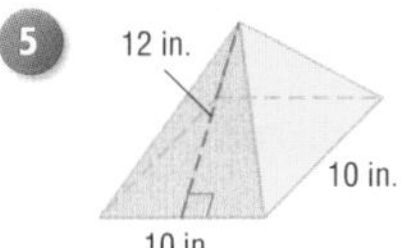

6.

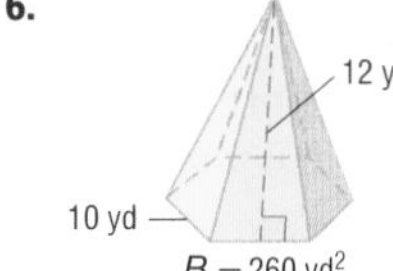

7.

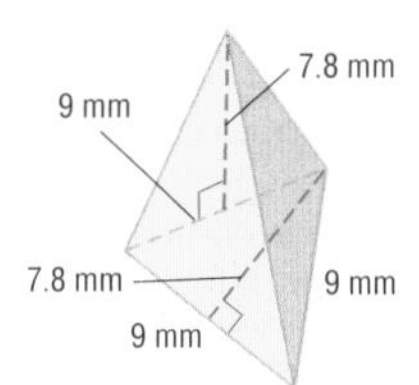

8. triangular pyramid: base side length 6 in., base area $15\frac{3}{5}$ in^2, slant height 8 in. 72 in^2; 87.6 in^2

Example 2 p. 703

9. **JEWELRY** Brianne is making a necklace using the bead shown at the right. Find the approximate surface area of the silver bead. 339.3 mm^2

10. **ARCHITECTURE** The Transamerica Building in San Francisco is shaped like a square pyramid. It has a slant height of about 856 feet, and each side of its base is 145 feet. Find the lateral area of the building. 248,240 ft^2

Example 3 p. 704

Find the lateral and surface area of each figure. Round to the nearest tenth.

11.

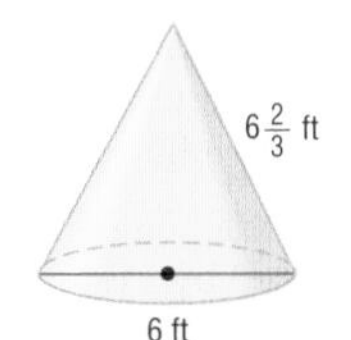

125.7 cm^2; 175.9 cm^2

12. $6\frac{2}{3}$ ft; 6 ft
62.8 ft^2; 91.1 ft^2

13.

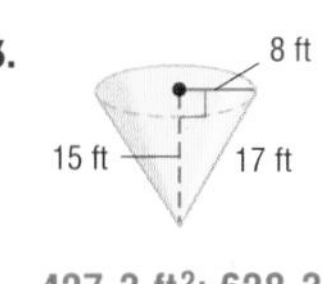

427.3 ft^2; 628.3 ft^2

14. cone: diameter 19 cm, slant height 30 cm 895.4 cm^2; 1178.9 cm^2

3 PRACTICE

Formative Assessment

Use Exercises 1–4 to check for understanding.

Use the chart at the bottom of this page to customize assignments for your students.

Differentiated Homework Options

Level	Assignment	Two-Day Option	
AL Basic	5–14, 23, 27–42	5–13 odd, 27–30	6–14 even, 23, 31–42
OL Core	5–21 odd, 22, 23, 26–42	5–14, 27–30	15–23, 26, 31–42
BL Advanced	17–36 (optional: 37–42)		

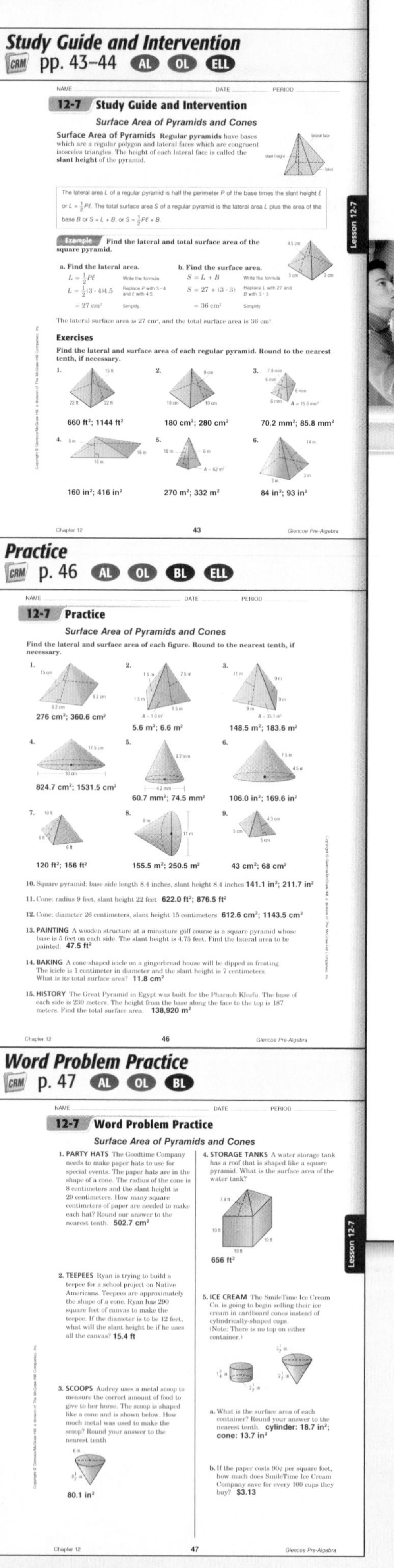

Study Guide and Intervention
CRM pp. 43–44 AL OL ELL

NAME ______ DATE ______ PERIOD ______

12-7 Study Guide and Intervention

Surface Area of Pyramids and Cones

Surface Area of Pyramids **Regular pyramids** have bases which are a regular polygon and lateral faces which are congruent isosceles triangles. The height of each lateral face is called the **slant height** of the pyramid.

The lateral area L of a regular pyramid is half the perimeter P of the base times the slant height ℓ or $L = \frac{1}{2}P\ell$. The total surface area S of a regular pyramid is the lateral area L plus the area of the base B or $S = L + B$, or $S = \frac{1}{2}P\ell + B$.

Example Find the lateral and total surface area of the square pyramid.

a. Find the lateral area.

$L = \frac{1}{2}P\ell$ Write the formula.
$L = \frac{1}{2}(3 \cdot 4)4.5$ Replace P with $3 \cdot 4$ and ℓ with 4.5.
$= 27 \text{ cm}^2$ Simplify.

b. Find the surface area.

$S = L + B$ Write the formula.
$S = 27 + (3 \cdot 3)$ Replace L with 27 and B with $3 \cdot 3$.
$= 36 \text{ cm}^2$ Simplify.

The lateral surface area is 27 cm², and the total surface area is 36 cm².

Exercises

Find the lateral and surface area of each regular pyramid. Round to the nearest tenth, if necessary.

1. 660 ft²; 1144 ft²
2. 180 cm²; 280 cm²
3. 70.2 mm²; 85.8 mm²
4. 160 in²; 416 in²
5. 270 m²; 332 m²
6. 84 in²; 93 in²

Chapter 12 43 Glencoe Pre-Algebra

Practice
CRM p. 46 AL OL BL ELL

NAME ______ DATE ______ PERIOD ______

12-7 Practice

Surface Area of Pyramids and Cones

Find the lateral and surface area of each figure. Round to the nearest tenth, if necessary.

1. 276 cm²; 360.6 cm²
2. 5.6 m²; 6.6 m²
3. 148.5 m²; 183.6 m²
4. 824.7 cm²; 1531.5 cm²
5. 60.7 mm²; 74.5 mm²
6. 106.0 in²; 169.6 in²
7. 120 ft²; 156 ft²
8. 155.5 m²; 250.5 m²
9. 43 cm²; 68 cm²

10. Square pyramid: base side length 8.4 inches, slant height 8.4 inches **141.1 in²; 211.7 in²**

11. Cone: radius 9 feet, slant height 22 feet **622.0 ft²; 876.5 ft²**

12. Cone: diameter 26 centimeters, slant height 15 centimeters **612.6 cm²; 1143.5 cm²**

13. **PAINTING** A wooden structure at a miniature golf course is a square pyramid whose base is 5 feet on each side. The slant height is 4.75 feet. Find the lateral area to be painted. **47.5 ft²**

14. **BAKING** A cone-shaped icicle on a gingerbread house will be dipped in frosting. The icicle is 1 centimeter in diameter and the slant height is 7 centimeters. What is its total surface area? **11.8 cm²**

15. **HISTORY** The Great Pyramid in Egypt was built for the Pharaoh Khufu. The base of each side is 230 meters. The height from the base along the face to the top is 187 meters. Find the total surface area. **138,920 m²**

Chapter 12 46 Glencoe Pre-Algebra

Word Problem Practice
CRM p. 47 AL OL BL

NAME ______ DATE ______ PERIOD ______

12-7 Word Problem Practice

Surface Area of Pyramids and Cones

1. **PARTY HATS** The Goodtime Company needs to make paper hats to use for special events. The paper hats are in the shape of a cone. The radius of the cone is 8 centimeters and the slant height is 20 centimeters. How many square centimeters of paper are needed to make each hat? Round our answer to the nearest tenth. **502.7 cm²**

2. **TEEPEES** Ryan is trying to build a teepee for a school project on Native Americans. Teepees are approximately the shape of a cone. Ryan has 290 square feet of canvas to make the teepee. If the diameter is to be 12 feet, what will the slant height be if he uses all the canvas? **15.4 ft**

3. **SCOOPS** Audrey uses a metal scoop to measure the correct amount of food to give to her horse. The scoop is shaped like a cone and is shown below. How much metal was used to make the scoop? Round your answer to the nearest tenth **80.1 in²**

4. **STORAGE TANKS** A water storage tank has a roof that is shaped like a square pyramid. What is the surface area of the water tank? **656 ft²**

5. **ICE CREAM** The SmileTime Ice Cream Co. is going to begin selling their ice cream in cardboard cones instead of cylindrically-shaped cups. (Note: There is no top on either container.)

a. What is the surface area of each container? Round your answer to the nearest tenth. **cylinder: 18.7 in²; cone: 13.7 in²**

b. If the paper costs 90¢ per square foot, how much does SmileTime Ice Cream Company save for every 100 cups they buy? **$3.13**

Chapter 12 47 Glencoe Pre-Algebra

Find the surface area of each figure. Round to the nearest tenth.

B

15. 5 cm, 15 cm **471.2 cm²**

16. 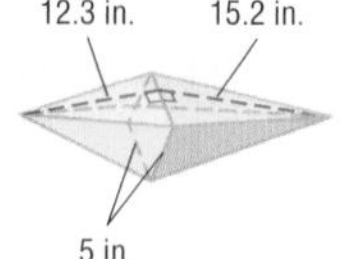

275 in²

17. **COSTUMES** Adrienne is making costumes for the school play. She needs to make eight conical medieval hats. She wants each hat to be 18 inches tall and the bases of each to be 22 inches in circumference. How much material will she use to make the hats? **1609.8 in²**

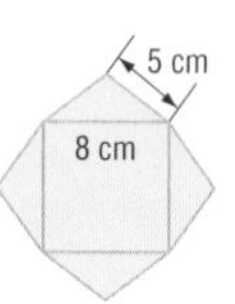

Real-World Career

Fabric Designers
There are many opportunities in the field of fashion, including fabric design. Fabric designers may develop fabrics for clothing or interior home design.

Fabric designers focus on art and design in high school and college. Some fashion institutes have two-year programs primarily for fabric designers.

Draw the figure represented by each net. Then find the lateral and total surface area of each figure. **18–20. See margin.**

18. 5 cm, 8 cm

19. 10 m, 8.7 m

20. 20 in., 15 in.

21. **TENTS** A rectangular piece of canvas is 50 feet by 60 feet. Delsin wants to make a tent in the shape of a cone that has a diameter of 30 feet. Find the slant height of the largest tent with a floor he can build using the canvas. **48.7 feet**

C

22. **MULTIPLE REPRESENTATIONS** In this problem, you will examine surface areas of pyramids.

a. **TABULAR** Find the surface area of a square pyramid with a side length of 1 and a slant height of 10. Then complete the table.

side length	1	2	3	4
slant height	10	20	30	40
surface area	■	■	■	■

21 84 189 336

b. **ANALYTICAL** What happens to the surface area if the base length and slant height are doubled, tripled, or multiplied by 4?

c. **VERBAL** Predict the surface area of a pyramid with the side length of 5 and slant height of 50. Then check your prediction. **525 square units**

22b. Sample answer: The original surface area is multiplied by the square of the scale factor.

H.O.T. Problems Use **H**igher-**O**rder **T**hinking Skills

23. **OPEN ENDED** Draw a cone with a surface area that is between 100 and 150 square units. **See students' work.**

24. **CHALLENGE** Which has a greater surface area: a square pyramid with a base of x units and a slant height of ℓ units or a cone with a diameter of x units and a slant height of ℓ units? Explain your reasoning. **See margin.**

25. **CHALLENGE** The dimensions of the prism shown are increased by a scale factor and the total surface area of the new prism is 240,000 square meters. What was the scale factor used to create the new prism? **4**

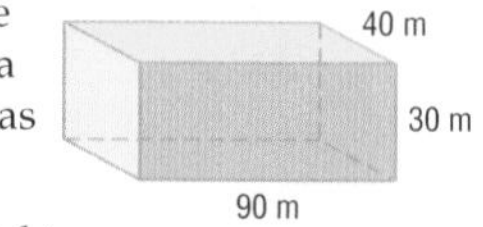

26. **WRITING IN MATH** Explain how to find the slant height of a cone if you are given the radius and the height of the cone.

26. Sample answer: Draw a right triangle using the radius and the height as the two legs. The slant height will be the hypotenuse of the triangle.

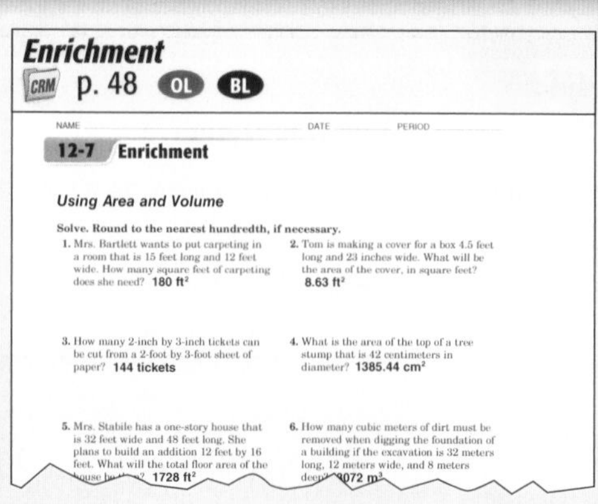

Enrichment
CRM p. 48 OL BL

NAME ______ DATE ______ PERIOD ______

12-7 Enrichment

Using Area and Volume

Solve. Round to the nearest hundredth, if necessary.

1. Mrs. Bartlett wants to put carpeting in a room that is 15 feet long and 12 feet wide. How many square feet of carpeting does she need? **180 ft²**

2. Tom is making a cover for a box 4.5 feet long and 23 inches wide. What will be the area of the cover, in square feet? **8.63 ft²**

3. How many 2-inch by 3-inch tickets can be cut from a 2-foot by 3-foot sheet of paper? **144 tickets**

4. What is the area of the top of a tree stump that is 42 centimeters in diameter? **1385.44 cm²**

5. Mrs. Stabile has a one-story house that is 32 feet wide and 48 feet long. She plans to build an addition 12 feet by 16 feet. What will the total floor area of the house be then? **1728 ft²**

6. How many cubic meters of dirt must be removed when digging the foundation of a building if the excavation is 32 meters long, 12 meters wide, and 8 meters deep? **3072 m³**

Multiple Representations In Exercise 22, students use a table to investigate surface area pyramids and predict the effects of changing dimensions.

Standardized Test Practice

27. Find the surface area of a cone with a radius of 6 centimeters and slant height of 15 centimeters. Round to the nearest tenth. **C**

A 141.3 cm^2
B 264.4 cm^2
C 395.8 cm^2
D 565.2 cm^2

28. Find the area of the ice cream cone covered by the wrapper. **F**

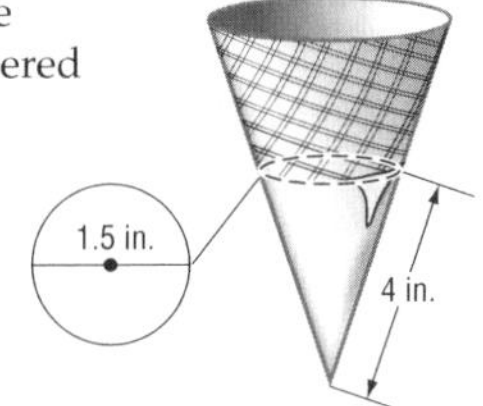

F 9.4 in^2
G 11.2 in^2
H 15.5 in^2
J 20.0 in^2

29. A square pyramid has a base with sides measuring 7 meters. If the surface area of the pyramid is 189 square meters, which of the following is the slant height of the pyramid? **B**

A 8 m
B 10 m
C 14 m
D 16 m

30. GRIDDED RESPONSE A square pyramid has a surface area of 39 square feet. After a dilation, the surface area is 351 square feet. What was the scale factor of the dilation? **3**

Spiral Review

Find the lateral and surface area of each three-dimensional figure. Round to the nearest tenth. (Lessons 12-5 and 12-6)

31. cylinder: radius 6 inches, height $10\frac{1}{4}$ inches **386.4 in²; 612.6 in²**

32. cylinder: diameter 5.7 meters, height 2.3 meters **41.2 m²; 92.2 m²**

33. equilateral triangular prism: base height 10.4 feet, base length 12 feet, prism height $3\frac{1}{3}$ feet **120 ft²; 244.8 ft²**

34. DESSERTS Find the volume of an ice cream cone that has a radius of 28 mm and a height of 117 mm. (Lesson 12-4) **96,057.3 mm³**

35. GEOMETRY Mrs. Morales used the parallelogram at the right as a pattern for a paving stone for her sidewalk. If $m\angle 1$ is 130°, find $m\angle 2$. (Lesson 11-5) **50°**

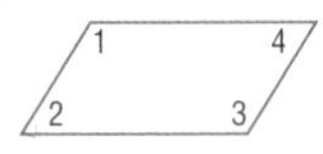

36. RETAIL Find the discount for a $45 shirt that is on sale for 20% off. (Lesson 7-4) **$9**

Skills Review

Solve each proportion. (Lesson 6-5)

37. $\frac{x}{4} = \frac{3}{5.6}$ **$2\frac{1}{7}$**

38. $\frac{2}{3} = \frac{14}{n}$ **21**

39. $\frac{n}{20} = \frac{15}{50}$ **6**

40. $\frac{14}{32} = \frac{x}{8}$ **3.5**

41. $\frac{3}{2.2} = \frac{7.5}{y}$ **5.5**

42. $\frac{30}{14} = \frac{m}{1.54}$ **3.3**

Differentiated Instruction

Extension A teepee is a large, cone-shaped structure with a frame of wooden poles that support a stiff fabric exterior. Alejandro and Natalie are going to build a teepee for a school production. The structure should have a slant height of about 10 feet, and a diameter of 8 feet. They plan to make the structure using a canvas tarp. If the tarp has a width of 12 feet, what length do they need to cut to make sure the tarp is large enough? They need a tarp with an area of about 125.7 feet, so a piece of tarp that is 12 by 10.5 would be just enough. Remind students that they are only covering the lateral portion of the teepee, not the base.

4 ASSESS

Ticket Out the Door Display a model of a square pyramid. Have students draw a net of the model. Then give students the dimensions of the pyramid and have them label the figure. Next, have them find the lateral area and surface area of the square pyramid. Students will hand in their work as they exit.

Additional Answers

18.

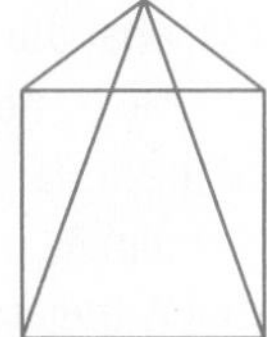

48 cm^2; 112 cm^2

19.

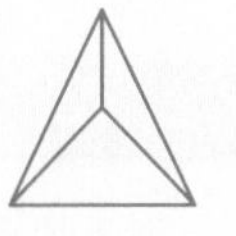

130.5 m^2; 174 m^2

20.

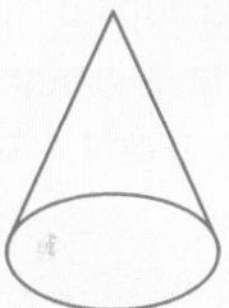

942.5 in^2; 1649.3 in^2

24. The square pyramid; Sample answer: The surface area of the pyramid is $x^2 + 2xl$. If you use $\pi \approx 3.14$, the surface area of the cone is $0.785x^2 + 1.57xl$. For all positive values of x and l, the surface area of the pyramid is greater than the surface area of the cone.

EXPLORE 12-8 Lesson Notes

1 FOCUS

Objective Investigate similar solids.

Materials for Each Student

- sugar cubes or centimeter blocks

Teaching Tip

Have four students with outstretched arms form a square. Ask what the area of the square is. 1 unit^2 Place another student on each side of the square and four students inside to complete the single unit squares. What is the area now? 4 unit^2 Discuss how the two squares are similar.

2 TEACH

Working in Cooperative Groups

Have students work in groups of two or three, mixing abilities. Have groups complete both Activities, along with Exercises 1–5.

Ask:

- How does the volume of the first cube you made compare to the volume of one cube? 8 times as large How does the volume of the second cube you made compare to the volume of one cube? 27 times as large

Practice Have students complete Exercises 6–11.

3 ASSESS

Formative Assessment

Use Exercise 11 to assess if students understand the concept of similar solids.

EXPLORE 12-8

Geometry Lab
Similar Solids

Math Online glencoe.com
Math *in Motion,* Animation

Objective
Investigate similar solids.

A model train is an exact replica of a real train, but much smaller. The dimensions of the model and the original are proportional. Therefore, these two objects are *similar solids.*

You can use sugar cubes or centimeter blocks to investigate similar solids.

ACTIVITY 1

- If each edge of a cube is 1 unit long, then each face is 1 square unit and the volume of the cube is 1 cubic unit.
- Make a cube that has sides twice as long as the first cube.

1 unit
1 unit
1 unit
First Cube

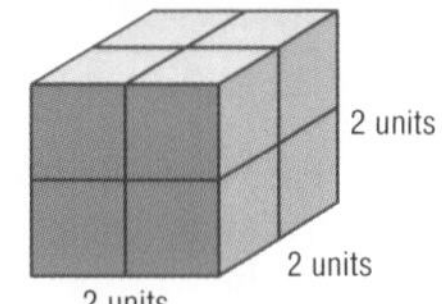

Second Cube

Analyze the Results

1. What is the area of one face of the first cube? second cube? **1 unit^2; 4 units^2**
2. What is the volume of the first cube? second cube? **1 unit^3; 8 units^3**

Vocabulary Review

Scale Factor number of times you increase or decrease linear dimensions

ACTIVITY 2

Build a cube that has sides three times as long as the first cube.

Analyze the Results

3. How many small cubes did you use? **27**
4. What is the area of one face of the cube? **9 units^2**
5. What is the volume of the cube? **27 units^3**
6. Copy and complete the tables below. **See Chapter 7 Answer Appendix.**

Scale Factor	Side Length	Volume
1	■	■
2	■	■
3	■	■

Scale Factor	Side Length	Area of a Face	Surface Area
1	■	■	■
2	■	■	■
3	■	■	■

7. What happens to the area of a face when the length of a side is doubled? tripled? **See margin.**
8. Consider the unit cube. If the scale factor is x, what is the area of one face? the surface area? **x^2; $6x^2$**
9. What happens to the volume of a cube when the length of a side is doubled? tripled? **See margin.**
10. Consider a unit cube with side length s. Let the scale factor be x. Write an equation for the cube's volume V. **$V = (sx)^3$**
11. **MAKE A CONJECTURE** What are the surface area and the volume of a cube if the sides are 4 times as long as the original cube? Check your conjecture. **96 units^2; 64 units^3**

From Concrete to Abstract

Use Exercise 10 to assess whether students can represent algebraically what they have learned about the volume of similar cubes using models.

Additional Answers

7. 4 times greater; 9 times greater
9. 2^3 or 8 times greater; 3^3 or 27 times greater.

Similar Solids

Why?

Then
You have already learned about similarity and two-dimensional figures. (Lesson 6-7)

Now
- Identify similar solids.
- Examine properties of similar solids.

New Vocabulary
similar solids

Math Online
glencoe.com
- Extra Examples
- Personal Tutor
- Self-Check Quiz
- Homework Help

ART In the 1800s, Edgar Degas created a wax sculpture of a young ballet dancer. The approximate height of the sculpture is 39 inches. Donise wants to purchase a model of the sculpture that is 13 inches tall.

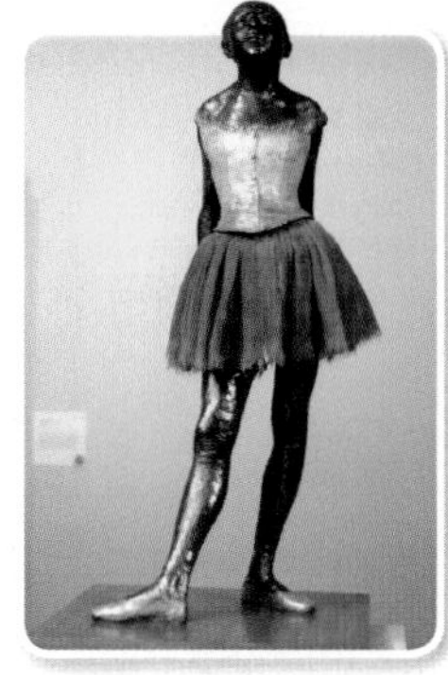

a. Find the scale of the model. 1 : 3

b. If the base of the model is a rectangle that measures $4\frac{1}{2}$ inches by $4\frac{5}{8}$ inches, what would you expect the base measurements to be for the actual sculpture? $13\frac{1}{2}$ in. by $13\frac{7}{8}$ in.

Identify Similar Solids The model and the sculpture have the same shape but are different sizes. The ratio of their corresponding parts is 1 : 3. Two figures are **similar solids** if they have the same shape and their corresponding linear measures are proportional.

EXAMPLE 1 Identify Similar Solids

Determine whether the pair of solids is similar.

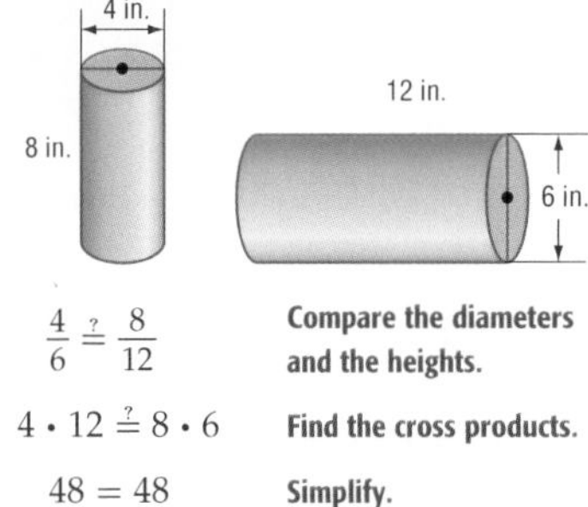

$\frac{4}{6} \stackrel{?}{=} \frac{8}{12}$ **Compare the diameters and the heights.**

$4 \cdot 12 \stackrel{?}{=} 8 \cdot 6$ **Find the cross products.**

$48 = 48$ **Simplify.**

The corresponding measurements are proportional. So, the cylinders are similar.

Check Your Progress

Determine whether each pair of solids is similar.

1A. no

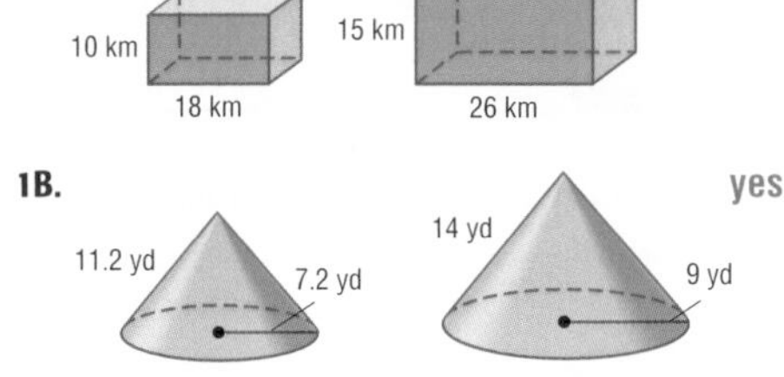

1B. yes

11.2 yd, 7.2 yd; 14 yd, 9 yd

Personal Tutor glencoe.com

12-8 Lesson Notes

1 FOCUS

Vertical Alignment

Before Lesson 12-8
Learn about similarity and two-dimensional figures.

Lesson 12-8
Identify and examine properties of similar solids.

After Lesson 12-8
Use and extend similarity properties to explore and justify conjectures about geometric figures.

2 TEACH

Scaffolding Questions

Have students read the *Why?* section of the lesson and answer the questions.

Ask:
- How did you find the measures of the base of the sculpture? multiplied the measures of the base by the scale
- Suppose instead of $\frac{1}{3}$ the size of the original sculpture, the model is $\frac{1}{4}$ the size of the original. How tall would the model be? $9\frac{3}{4}$ inches
- What would be the measures of the base if the model is $\frac{1}{4}$ the size of the original? $3\frac{3}{8}$ in. by $3\frac{15}{32}$ in.

Lesson 12-8 Resources

Resource	Approaching-Level	On-Level	Beyond-Level	English Learners
Teacher Edition	• Differentiated Instruction, p. 710	• Differentiated Instruction, p. 710	• Differentiated Instruction, pp. 710, 715	• Differentiated Instruction, p. 710
Chapter Resource Masters	• Study Guide and Intervention, pp. 49–50 • Skills Practice, p. 51 • Practice, p. 52 • Word Problem Practice, p. 53	• Study Guide and Intervention, pp. 49–50 • Skills Practice, p. 51 • Practice, p. 52 • Word Problem Practice, p. 53 • Enrichment, p. 54	• Practice, p. 52 • Word Problem Practice, p. 53 • Enrichment, p. 54	• Study Guide and Intervention, pp. 49–50 • Skills Practice, p. 51 • Practice, p. 52
Transparencies	• 5-Minute Check Transparency 12-8	• 5-Minute Check Transparency 12-8	• 5-Minute Check Transparency 12-8	• 5-Minute Check Transparency 12-8
Other	• Study Notebook • Teaching Pre-Algebra with Manipulatives	• Study Notebook • Teaching Pre-Algebra with Manipulatives	• Study Notebook	• Study Notebook • Teaching Pre-Algebra with Manipulatives

Identify Similar Solids

Example 1 shows how to determine whether two solids are similar.
Example 2 shows how to use similar solids to find missing measures.

Formative Assessment

Use the Check Your Progress exercises after each example to determine students' understanding of concepts.

Additional Examples

1 Determine whether the pair of solids is similar.

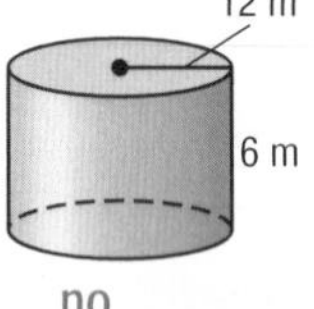

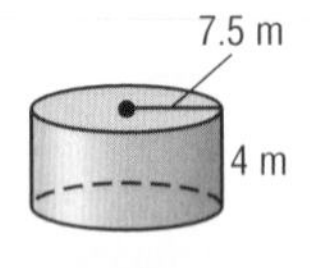

no

2 The pyramids are similar. Find the side length of pyramid B. 1.5 in.

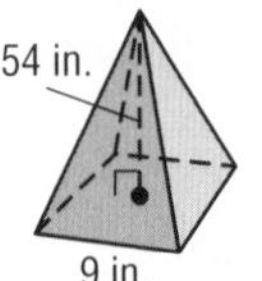

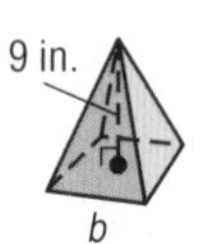

Additional Examples also in Interactive Classroom PowerPoint® Presentations

IWB INTERACTIVE WHITEBOARD READY

If you know solids are similar, you can find missing measures.

> **StudyTip**
>
> **Scale Factor and Dilation** The characteristics of scale factors that applied to two-dimensional figures also apply to three-dimensional solids.
>
> - If the scale factor > 1, the model is an enlargement.
> - If the scale factor = 1, the figure is congruent to the original figure.
> - If the scale factor < 1, the model is a reduction.

EXAMPLE 2 Find Missing Measures

The triangular pyramids at the right are similar. Find the side length of pyramid A.

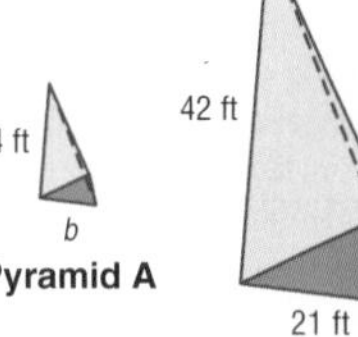

Since the two pyramids are similar, the ratios of their corresponding linear measures are proportional.

$$\frac{\text{side length of pyramid A}}{\text{side length of pyramid B}} = \frac{\text{side length of pyramid A}}{\text{side length of pyramid B}}$$

$\frac{14}{42} = \frac{b}{21}$ **Substitute the known values.**

$14 \cdot 21 = 42b$ **Find the cross products.**

$294 = 42b$ **Simplify.**

$7 = b$ **Divide each side by 42.**

The side length of pyramid A is 7 feet.

Check Your Progress

2. The triangular prisms are similar. Find the height of prism A. **30 ft**

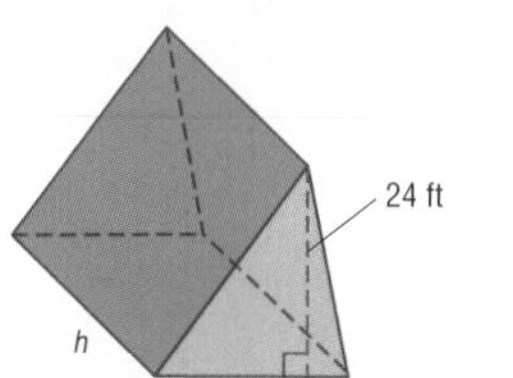

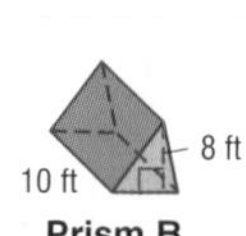

Personal Tutor glencoe.com

Properties of Similar Solids Corresponding linear measures of similar figures are proportional. Are corresponding surface areas and volumes also proportional? The two prisms below are similar with a scale factor of $\frac{1}{3}$.

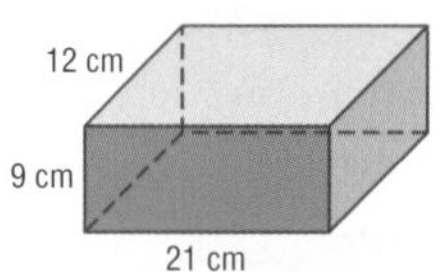

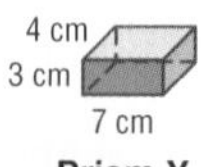

Scale Factor: $\frac{1}{3}$	Surface Area	Volume
Prism X	$(2 \cdot 21 + 2 \cdot 12)\,9 + 2 \cdot 21 \cdot 12$ or 1098 cm^2	$21 \cdot 9 \cdot 12$ or 2268 cm^3
Prism Y	$(2 \cdot 7 + 2 \cdot 4)\,3 + 2 \cdot 7 \cdot 4$ or 122 cm^2	$7 \cdot 3 \cdot 4$ or 84 cm^3

Notice the pattern in the following ratios.

$$\frac{\text{surface area of Prism Y}}{\text{surface area of Prism X}} = \frac{122}{1098} \text{ or } \frac{1}{9} \qquad \frac{1}{9} = \left(\frac{1}{3}\right)^2$$

$$\frac{\text{volume of Prism Y}}{\text{volume of Prism X}} = \frac{84}{2268} \text{ or } \frac{1}{27} \qquad \frac{1}{27} = \left(\frac{1}{3}\right)^3$$

Differentiated Instruction

students need additional practice comparing the volume and surface area of similar solids,

divide the class into small mixed groups. Have each group draw a pair of similar solids with the appropriate dimensions labeled. The group should determine the surface areas and volumes of their solids. Then have each group present their pair of similar solids to the class. Have the other groups compete to see who can be the first to correctly give both the surface area and volume of each. Repeat several times.

This and similar examples suggest the following relationships about the surface area and volume of similar solids.

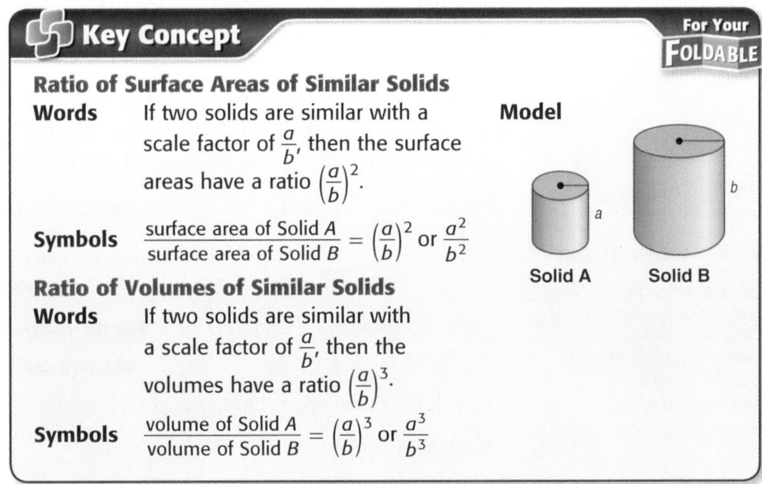

Key Concept — For Your FOLDABLE

Ratio of Surface Areas of Similar Solids

Words If two solids are similar with a scale factor of $\frac{a}{b}$, then the surface areas have a ratio $\left(\frac{a}{b}\right)^2$.

Symbols $\frac{\text{surface area of Solid } A}{\text{surface area of Solid } B} = \left(\frac{a}{b}\right)^2$ or $\frac{a^2}{b^2}$

Model

Ratio of Volumes of Similar Solids

Words If two solids are similar with a scale factor of $\frac{a}{b}$, then the volumes have a ratio $\left(\frac{a}{b}\right)^3$.

Symbols $\frac{\text{volume of Solid } A}{\text{volume of Solid } B} = \left(\frac{a}{b}\right)^3$ or $\frac{a^3}{b^3}$

EXAMPLE 3 Find Surface Areas of Similar Solids

A cube has a surface area of 600 square centimeters. If the dimensions are doubled, what is the surface area of the new cube?

Understand You know that the cubes are similar and the scale factor of the side lengths $\frac{a}{b}$ is $\frac{1}{2}$. You need to find the surface area of the new cube.

Plan Set up a proportion to find the surface area of the new cube.

Solve The surface areas of the cubes have a ratio of $\frac{a^2}{b^2}$ or $\frac{1^2}{2^2}$.

$$\frac{\text{surface area of original cube}}{\text{surface area of new cube}} = \frac{a^2}{b^2}$$ **Write a proportion.**

$$\frac{600}{S} = \frac{1^2}{2^2}$$ **Substitute the known values. Let S = the surface area of the new cube.**

$$\frac{600}{S} = \frac{1}{4}$$ **$\frac{1^2}{2^2} = \frac{1}{2} \cdot \frac{1}{2}$ or $\frac{1}{4}$**

$$600 \cdot 4 = S \cdot 1$$ **Find the cross products.**

$$2400 = S$$ **Multiply.**

The surface area of the new cube is 2400 square centimeters.

Check If the surface area of the first cube is 600 square centimeters, the measure of each side is 600 ÷ 6 or 10 centimeters. The new cube measures 20 centimeters on each side and has a surface area of 2400 square centimeters. The answer is correct. ✓

StudyTip

Scale Factor When the lengths of all dimensions of a solid are multiplied by a scale factor x, then the surface area is multiplied by x^2 and the volume is multiplied by x^3.

Check Your Progress

3. A cone has a surface area of 160 square inches. If the dimensions are reduced by a factor of $\frac{1}{2}$, what is the surface area of the new cone? **40 in^2**

Personal Tutor glencoe.com

Focus on Mathematical Content

Similar Solids If two solids are similar, their corresponding parts are proportional. Cross multiplying is a way to find if the ratios are equivalent. It is also a way to isolate the variable, when one exists, to find missing measures.

Properties of Similar Solids

Example 3 shows how to find surface areas of similar solids. **Example 4** shows how to find the volumes of similar solids in a real-world problem.

Additional Example

3 A cylinder has a surface area of 245 square inches. If the dimensions are doubled, what is the surface area of the new cylinder? 980 in^2

Additional Example

4 **DOLLHOUSE** A small model of a fish tank for Eva's dollhouse is built on a scale of 1 centimeter to 5 inches and has a volume of 24 cubic centimeters. What is the volume of the actual fish tank? 3000 in^3

3 PRACTICE

Formative Assessment

Use Exercises 1–6 to check for understanding.

Use the chart at the bottom of the next page to customize assignments for your students.

Real-World Link

Spaceship Earth at Epcot Center in Orlando, Florida, is a geosphere with a diameter of 165 feet. The volume of the sphere is about 2,400,000 cubic feet.

Real-World EXAMPLE 4 Volumes of Similar Solids

BUILDINGS A model of the Spaceship Earth building has a diameter of 3 feet. Use the information at the left to find the volume of the model to the nearest tenth.

The model and the actual building are similar and the scale factor of the diameters is $\frac{3}{165}$ or $\frac{1}{55}$. The volumes of the spheres have a ratio of $\left(\frac{a}{b}\right)^3$ or $\left(\frac{1}{55}\right)^3$. Set up a proportion to find the volume of the model.

$\frac{\text{volume of model}}{\text{volume of geosphere}} = \frac{a^3}{b^3}$ — **Write the ratio of volumes.**

$\frac{m}{2{,}400{,}000} = \frac{1^3}{55^3}$ — **Replace a with 1, b with 55, and volume of geosphere with 2,400,000.**

$m \cdot 55^3 = 2{,}400{,}000 \cdot 1^3$ — **Find the cross products.**

$m \approx 14.4$ — **Divide each side by 55^3.**

The volume of the Spaceship Earth model is about 14.4 cubic feet.

Check Your Progress

4. SPORTS Baseballs and softballs are similar in shape. The scale between a baseball and a softball is 1 inch : 1.3 inches. The volume of a baseball is about 12.8 in^3. What is the volume of a softball to the nearest tenth? 28.1 in^3

Personal Tutor glencoe.com

Check Your Understanding

Example 1 p. 709 — **Determine whether each pair of solids is similar.**

1.

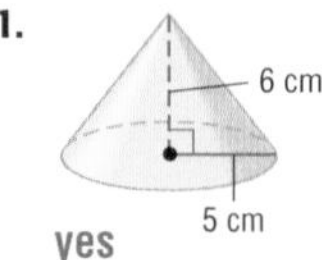

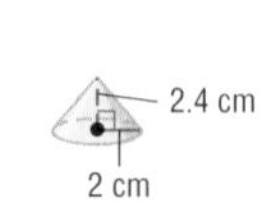

yes

2.

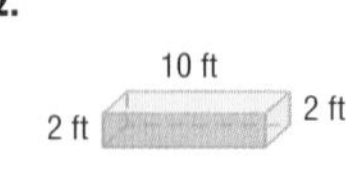

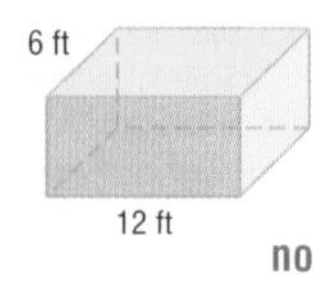

no

Example 2 p. 710 — **Find the missing measure for each pair of similar solids.**

3.

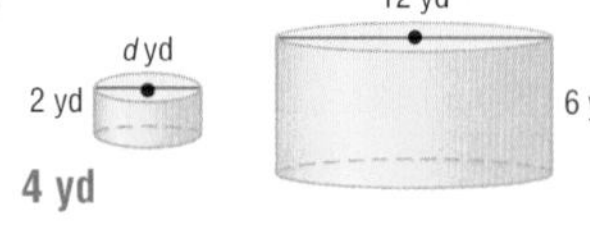

4 yd

4.

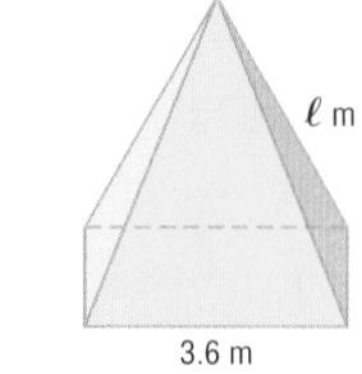

4.8 m

Example 3 p. 711

5. A pyramid has a surface area of 50 square feet. If the dimensions are tripled, what is the surface area of the new pyramid? 450 ft^2

Example 4 p. 712

6. CEREAL A prototype for a new cereal box is 10 centimeters tall, 3 centimeters long, and 2 centimeters wide. The actual box will be 28 centimeters tall.

a. What is the scale factor between the prototype and the actual box? 1: 2.8

b. What is the width of the actual box? 5.6 cm

c. Find the volume of the actual box. 1317.12 cm^3

Practice and Problem Solving

= **Step-by-Step Solutions** begin on page R11.
Extra Practice begins on page 810.

Example 1 p. 709

Determine whether each pair of solids is similar.

7. no **8.** yes **9.** no **10.** no

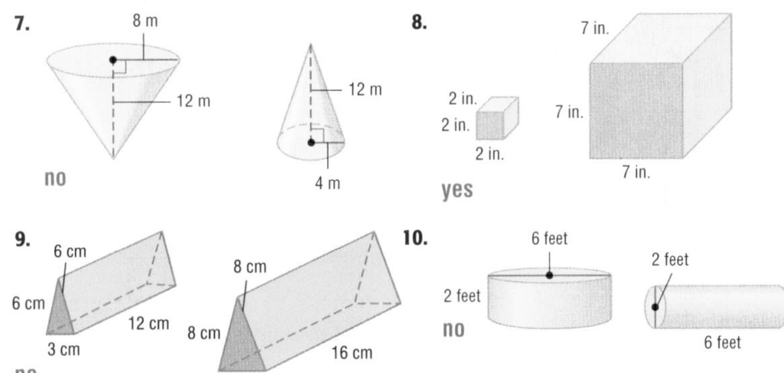

Example 2 p. 710

Find the missing measure for each pair of similar solids.

11. 4.8 in. **12.** 60 yd

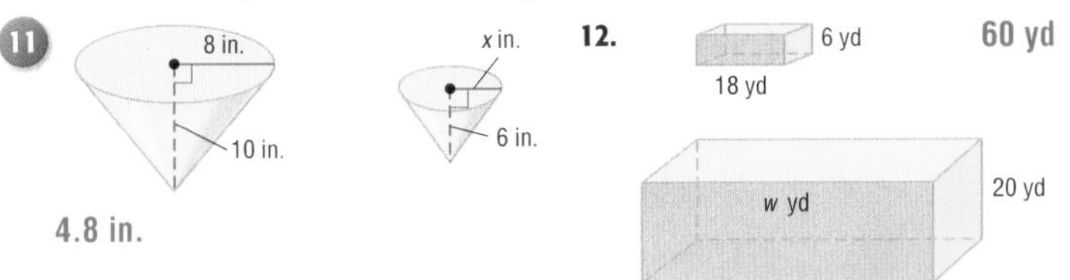

Example 3 p. 711

13. A rectangular prism has a surface area of 300 square millimeters. If the dimensions are quadrupled, what is the surface area of the new pyramid? 4800 mm^2

14. A pyramid has a surface area of 6400 square yards. If the new dimensions are $\frac{1}{8}$ the original size, what is the surface area of the new pyramid? 100 yd^2

Example 4 p. 712

15. FOOD A wheel of cheese given to Thomas Jefferson in 1802 measured 48 inches in diameter and 17 inches in height and was similar to the cheese wheel pictured at the right.

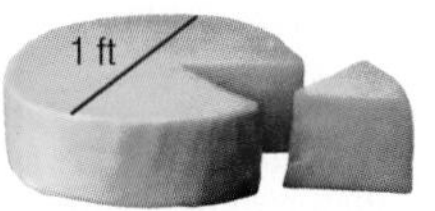

a. What is the scale factor between the large and small cheese wheels? 4:1

b. Find the height of the smaller cheese wheel. 4.25 inches

c. Find the volume of each wheel of cheese. Round to the nearest tenth. large wheel volume = $30{,}762.5 \text{ in}^3$; small wheel volume 480.7 in^3

d. How much greater is the volume of the large cheese wheel than the smaller cheese wheel? 64 times greater

16. The two cylinders are similar. What is the surface area of cylinder B if the volume of the cylinder A is 75 cubic meters? Round to the nearest tenth. 887.8 m^2

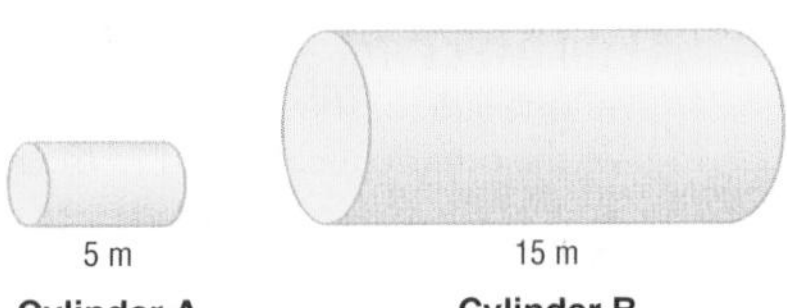

Tips for New Teachers

Similar Solids Another way to look at similar solids is that the ratio of their surface areas is proportional to the square of the scale factor between them, and the ratio of their volumes is proportional to the cube of the scale factors between them.

Differentiated Homework Options

Level	Assignment	Two-Day Option	
AL Basic	7–15, 22–25, 27–38	7–15 odd, 28–31	8–14 even, 22–25, 27, 32–38
OL Core	7–15 odd, 16–17, 19–25, 27–38	7–15, 28–31	16–25, 27, 32–38
BL Advanced	16–35 (optional: 36–38)		

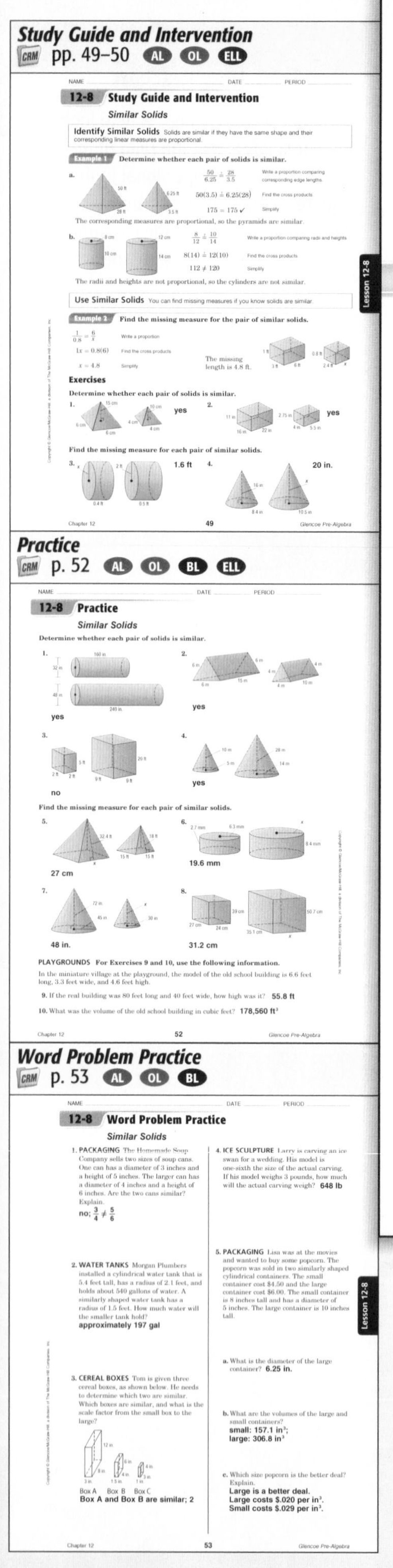

Study Guide and Intervention
CRM pp. 49–50 AL OL ELL

12-8 Study Guide and Intervention
Similar Solids

Identify Similar Solids Solids are similar if they have the same shape and their corresponding linear measures are proportional.

Example 1 Determine whether each pair of solids is similar.

a. $\frac{50}{6.25} \stackrel{?}{=} \frac{28}{3.5}$ Write a proportion comparing corresponding edge lengths.
$50(3.5) \stackrel{?}{=} 6.25(28)$ Find the cross products.
$175 = 175$ ✓ Simplify.
The corresponding measures are proportional, so the pyramids are similar.

b. $\frac{8}{12} \stackrel{?}{=} \frac{10}{14}$ Write a proportion comparing radii and heights.
$8(14) \stackrel{?}{=} 12(10)$ Find the cross products.
$112 \neq 120$ Simplify.
The radii and heights are not proportional, so the cylinders are not similar.

Use Similar Solids You can find missing measures if you know solids are similar.

Example 2 Find the missing measure for the pair of similar solids.
$\frac{1}{0.8} = \frac{6}{x}$ Write a proportion.
$1x = 0.8(6)$ Find the cross products.
$x = 4.8$ Simplify.
The missing length is 4.8 ft.

Exercises
Determine whether each pair of solids is similar.
1. yes 2. yes
Find the missing measure for each pair of similar solids.
3. 1.6 ft 4. 20 in.

Chapter 12 49 Glencoe Pre-Algebra

Practice
CRM p. 52 AL OL BL ELL

12-8 Practice
Similar Solids

Determine whether each pair of solids is similar.
1. yes 2. yes
3. no 4. yes
Find the missing measure for each pair of similar solids.
5. 27 cm 6. 19.6 mm
7. 48 in. 8. 31.2 cm

PLAYGROUNDS For Exercises 9 and 10, use the following information.
In the miniature village at the playground, the model of the old school building is 6.6 feet long, 3.3 feet wide, and 4.6 feet high.
9. If the real building was 80 feet long and 40 feet wide, how high was it? 55.8 ft
10. What was the volume of the old school building in cubic feet? 178,560 ft³

Chapter 12 52 Glencoe Pre-Algebra

Word Problem Practice
CRM p. 53 AL OL BL

12-8 Word Problem Practice
Similar Solids

1. PACKAGING The Homemade Soup Company sells two sizes of soup cans. One can has a diameter of 3 inches and a height of 5 inches. The larger can has a diameter of 4 inches and a height of 6 inches. Are the two cans similar? Explain.
no; $\frac{3}{4} \neq \frac{5}{6}$

2. WATER TANKS Morgan Plumbers installed a cylindrical water tank that is 5.4 feet tall, has a radius of 2.1 feet, and holds about 540 gallons of water. A similarly shaped water tank has a radius of 1.5 feet. How much water will the smaller tank hold?
approximately 197 gal

3. CEREAL BOXES Tom is given three cereal boxes, as shown below. He needs to determine which two are similar. Which boxes are similar, and what is the scale factor from the small box to the large?
Box A Box B Box C
Box A and Box B are similar; 2

4. ICE SCULPTURE Larry is carving an ice swan for a wedding. His model is one-sixth the size of the actual carving. If his model weighs 3 pounds, how much will the actual carving weigh? 648 lb

5. PACKAGING Lisa was at the movies and wanted to buy some popcorn. The popcorn was sold in two similarly shaped cylindrical containers. The small container cost $4.50 and the large container cost $6.00. The small container is 8 inches tall and has a diameter of 5 inches. The large container is 10 inches tall.

a. What is the diameter of the large container? 6.25 in.

b. What are the volumes of the large and small containers?
small: 157.1 in³; large: 306.8 in³

c. Which size popcorn is the better deal? Explain.
Large is a better deal. Large costs $.020 per in³. Small costs $.029 per in³.

Chapter 12 53 Glencoe Pre-Algebra

Real-World Link

A giant soccer ball pavilion greeted visitors to the 2006 Soccer World Cup semifinals in Dortmund, Germany. It housed exhibits on different aspects of soccer. The pavilion is 66 feet in diameter.

17. **SOCCER** Refer to the information at the left. The diameter of a regulation soccer ball is about 8.7 inches. If the volume of a regulation soccer ball is about 344.8 cubic inches, find the volume of the pavilion. **150,536.3 ft³**

Find the missing measure for each pair of similar solids. Round to the nearest tenth if necessary

18. **9 cm**

19. **3.3 in.**

20. **FISH** An aquarium has three cylindrical tanks. The dimensions of the largest are $1\frac{1}{2}$ the size of the one shown, while the dimensions of the smallest are $\frac{3}{4}$ the size. Determine the volumes of the three aquariums. Round to the nearest tenth. **58,679.1 cm³, 139,091.2 cm³, 469,432.8 cm³**

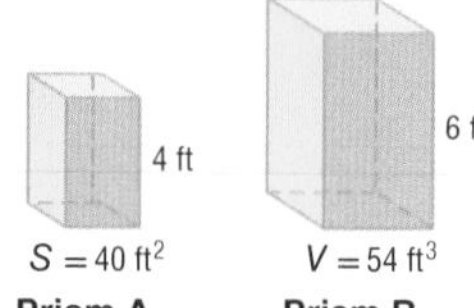

C

21. Use the two similar prisms at the right.
 a. Write the ratio of the surface areas and the ratio of the volumes. $\frac{4}{9}, \frac{8}{27}$
 b. Find the surface area of prism B. **90 ft²**
 c. Find the volume of prism A. **16 ft³**

4 ft
6 ft
$S = 40$ ft²
$V = 54$ ft³
Prism A **Prism B**

H.O.T. Problems

Use **H**igher-**O**rder **T**hinking Skills

22. **OPEN ENDED** Find a scale for a model plane or car. Then determine the ratio of their surface areas and volumes.

23. **REASONING** True or false? *All spheres are similar.* If false, provide a counter example. Explain your reasoning.

24. **FIND THE ERROR** Fred and Cassandra are finding the ratio of the surface areas of a building given that the model of the building was built on a scale of 1 centimeter to 5 meters. Is either of them correct? Explain your reasoning.

Fred	Cassandra
$\frac{a^2}{b^2} = \frac{1^2}{500^2} = \frac{1}{250{,}000}$	$\frac{a^2}{b^2} = \frac{1^2}{5^2} = \frac{1}{25}$

25. **NUMBER SENSE** Describe what happens to the surface area of a cone if its radius and slant height are doubled.

26. **CHALLENGE** The ratio of the surface areas of two cubes is 1:12. The length of one side of the smaller cube is 7 centimeters. Find the length of the side of the other cube. Round to the nearest tenth, if necessary. **24.2 cm**

27. **WRITING IN MATH** Write a real-world problem about similar solids that involves the purchase of a souvenir of a building. Then solve.

22. Sample answer: scale 1:12. Ratio of surface areas 1:144, ratio of volumes 1:1728

23. True; Spheres have only one measurement, the radius.

24. Fred; Cassandra did not convert 5 meters to centimeters.

25. The surface area quadruples.

27. See students' work.

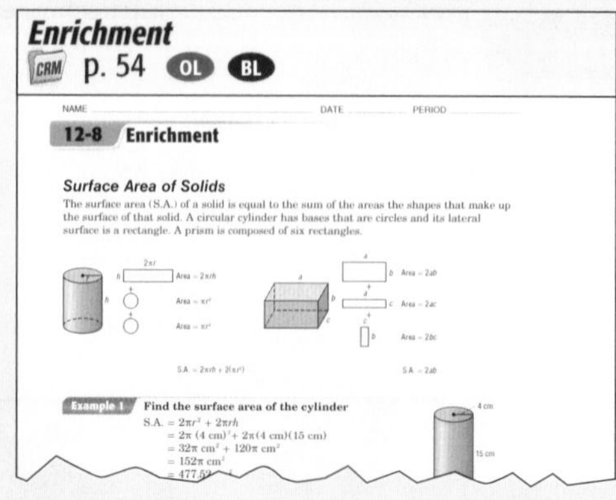

Enrichment
CRM p. 54 OL BL

12-8 Enrichment

Surface Area of Solids
The surface area (S.A.) of a solid is equal to the sum of the areas the shapes that make up the surface of that solid. A circular cylinder has bases that are circles and its lateral surface is a rectangle. A prism is composed of six rectangles.

Example 1 Find the surface area of the cylinder
S.A. $= 2\pi r^2 + 2\pi rh$
$= 2\pi(4\text{ cm})^2 + 2\pi(4\text{ cm})(15\text{ cm})$
$= 32\pi\text{ cm}^2 + 120\pi\text{ cm}^2$
$= 152\pi\text{ cm}^2$

Standardized Test Practice

28. The two prisms below are similar. What is the ratio of the volume of the smaller prism to the larger prism? **A**

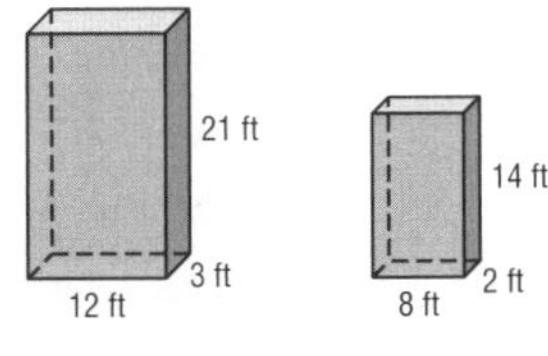

A 8 : 27
B 4 : 9
C 2 : 3
D 1 : 2

29. Which prism in the table is *not* similar to the other three? **G**

Prism	Length	Width	Height
A	7.5	6	5
B	10.5	9.8	7
C	15	12	10
D	4.5	3.6	3

F A
G B
H C
J D

30. Find the missing measure in the two similar solids. **B**

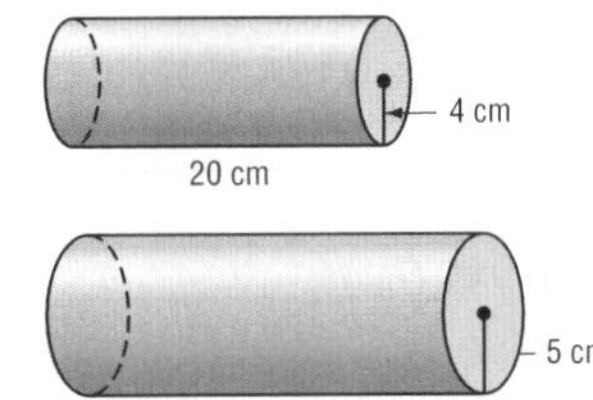

A 16 cm
B 25 cm
C 30 cm
D 35 cm

31. GRIDDED RESPONSE A prism has a surface area of 220 square feet. If the dimensions of a second prism are $\frac{1}{4}$ the original prism, what is the surface area in square feet of the second prism? **13.75**

Spiral Review

Find the lateral and surface area of each figure. Round to the nearest tenth. (Lessons 12-6 and 12-7)

32. 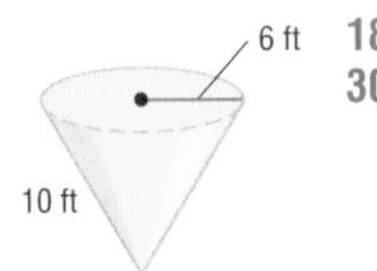

188.5 ft^2; 301.6 ft^2

33. 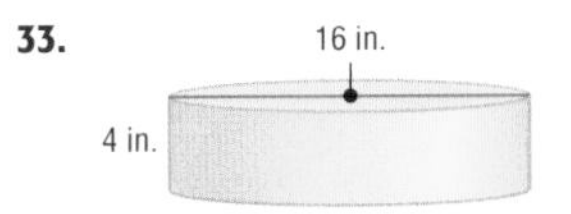

201.1 in^2; 603.2 in^2

34. SCIENCE A standard funnel is shaped like a cone, and a buchner funnel is shaped like a cone with a cylinder attached to the base. Which funnel has the greater volume? (Lesson 12-4) **standard funnel**

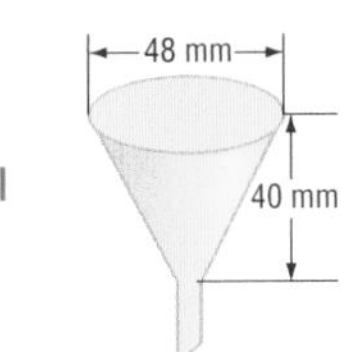

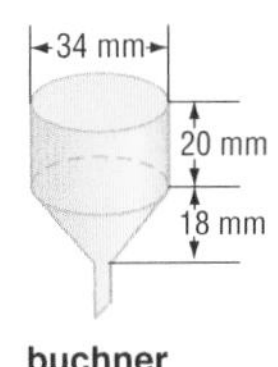

35. GARDENS Marty is designing two flower beds shaped like equilateral triangles. The lengths of each side of the flower beds are 8 feet and 20 feet, respectively. What is the ratio of the area of the larger flower bed to the smaller flower bed? (Lesson 10-6) $\frac{25}{4}$

Skills Review

Evaluate each expression. (Lesson 1-1)

36. $\frac{21 + 43 + 59}{3}$ **41**

37. $\frac{11(96) + 219 + 10(15)}{3}$ **475**

38. $\frac{478 - 136 + 12 - 18}{4}$ **84**

Watch Out!

Find the Error If students are having difficulty with Exercise 24, remind them that units must be the same before performing operations. Have students include the units beside every value when computing as a reminder.

4 ASSESS

Name the Math Have students explain the steps they would use to solve the following question: A student makes a model of the school building. The actual school building is rectangular in shape and is 220 feet wide, 340 feet long, and 40 feet tall. The scale of the model is 1 inch to 10 feet. What is the surface area of the model? 1,196 in^2; See students' work.

Formative Assessment

Check for student understanding of the concepts in Lessons 12-7 and 12-8.

CRM Quiz 4, p. 59

Differentiated Instruction

BL

Extension Give students the following problem: Nadia and Tess are building a model of the Alamo. Their model of the Alamo front is 10 inches long. The height is 5.3 inches. The actual length of the Alamo front is about 63.9 feet and the height is about 33.6 feet. What is the scale of their model to the actual building? about 1 in. to 76.7 in. (6.4 ft)

Formative Assessment

Key Vocabulary The page references after each word denote where that term was first introduced. If students have difficulty answering questions 1–8, remind them that they can use these page references to refresh their memories about the vocabulary.

Summative Assessment

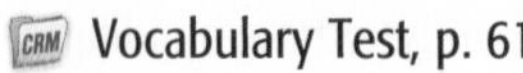

Vocabulary Test, p. 61

Math Online glencoe.com

Vocabulary PuzzleMaker improves students' mathematics vocabulary using four puzzle formats–crossword, scramble, word search using a word list, and word search using clues. Students can work online or from a printed worksheet.

CHAPTER 12 Study Guide and Review

Math Online glencoe.com
- STUDY TO GO
- Vocabulary Review

Chapter Summary

Key Concepts

Three-Dimensional Figures (Lesson 12-1)

- Prisms, pyramids, cylinders, cones, and spheres are three-dimensional figures.
- Prisms and pyramids are polyhedrons and are named by the shape of their bases.
- Cylinders, cones, and spheres are not polyhedrons.

Volume (Lessons 12-2 through 12-4)

- rectangular prism: $V = Bh$ or lwh
- cylinder: $V = \pi r^2 h$
- pyramid: $V = \frac{1}{3}Bh$
- cone: $V = \frac{1}{3}\pi r^2 h$
- sphere: $V = \frac{4}{3}\pi r^3$

Surface Area (Lessons 12-5 through 12-7)

- The surface area of a three-dimensional figure is the sum of the lateral area plus the area of the base(s).
- rectangular prism: $S = Ph + 2B$
- cylinder: $S = 2\pi r^2 + 2\pi rh$
- pyramid: $S = L + B$
- cone: $S = \pi rl + \pi r^2$

Similar Solids (Lesson 12-8)

- Solids are similar if they have the same shape and their corresponding linear measures are proportional.

FOLDABLES® Study Organizer

Be sure the Key Concepts are noted in your Foldable.

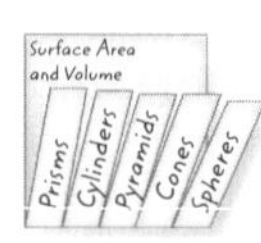

Key Vocabulary

base (p. 665)
cone (p. 665)
cross section (p. 666)
cylinder (p. 665)
edge (p. 664)
face (p. 664)
lateral area (p. 691)
lateral face (p. 691)
net (p. 690)
perspective (p. 663)
plane (p. 664)
polyhedron (p. 664)
prism (p. 665)
pyramid (p. 665)
regular pyramid (p. 702)
similar solids (p. 709)
slant height (p. 702)
solid (p. 664)
sphere (p. 684)
surface area (p. 691)
vertex (p. 664)
volume (p. 671)

Vocabulary Check

State whether each sentence is *true* or *false*. If *false,* replace the underlined term to make a true sentence.

1. A three-dimensional figure with two bases that are parallel circles is called a cylinder. **true**
2. The volume of a prism is the sum of the areas of its lateral faces. **false; lateral area**
3. Figures that have the same shape and corresponding linear measures that are proportional are called similar solids. **true**
4. An edge is where two planes intersect in a line. **true**
5. A cone is a polyhedron with one base that is any polygon. **false; pyramid**
6. The intersection of a solid and a plane is called a cross section of the solid. **true**
7. A cone has two bases. **false; cylinder or prism**
8. The surface area of a rectangular prism is the sum of the areas of its faces. **true**

FOLDABLES® Study Organizer

Dinah Zike's Foldables®

Have students look through the chapter to make sure they have included examples in their Foldables.

Suggest that students keep their Foldables handy while completing the Study Guide and Review pages. Point out that their Foldables can serve as a quick review tool when studying for the Chapter Test.

Lesson-by-Lesson Review

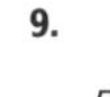

12-1 Three-Dimensional Figures (pp. 664–669)

Identify each figure. Name the bases, faces, edges, and vertices. 9–13. See margin.

9.

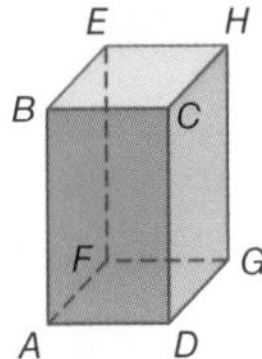

10.

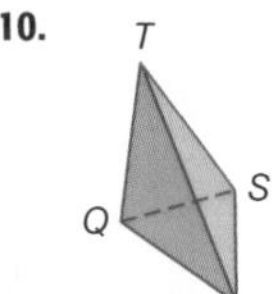

11.

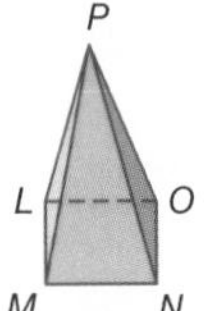

12.

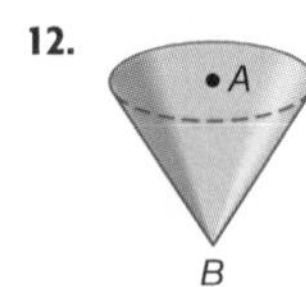

13. INSTRUMENTS Draw the top view and side view of the drum. Then draw and describe the shape resulting from a vertical cross section of the figure.

EXAMPLE 1

Identify the figure. Name the bases, faces, edges, and vertices.

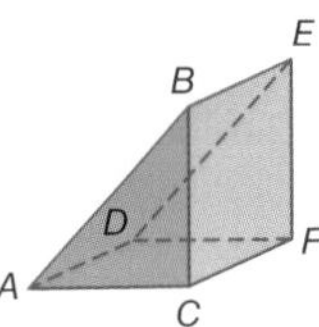

There are two triangular bases, so the solid is a triangular prism.

bases: *ABC, DEF*

faces: *ABED, BCFE, ACFD, ABC, DEF*

edges: $\overline{AB}$, $\overline{BC}$, $\overline{AC}$, $\overline{DE}$, $\overline{EF}$, $\overline{DF}$, $\overline{AD}$, $\overline{BE}$, $\overline{CF}$

vertices: *A, B, C, D, E, F*

12-2 Volume of Prisms (pp. 671–676)

Find the volume of each prism.

14. 60 in^3

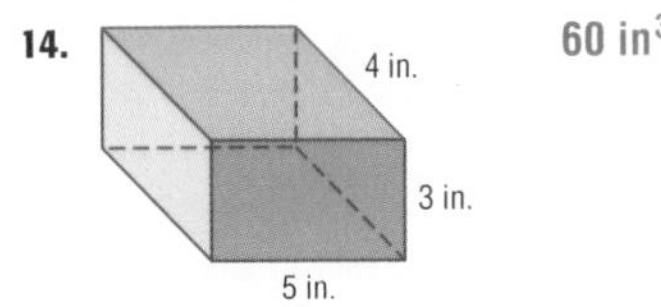

15. 60 cm^3

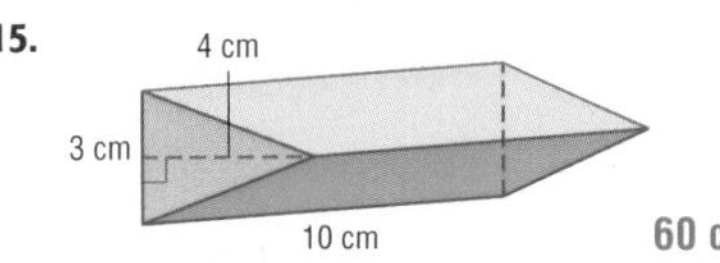

16. BOXES A shipping box is 11 inches long, 8.5 inches wide, and 5.5 inches high. What is the volume of the box? 514.25 in^3

EXAMPLE 2

Find the volume of the rectangular prism.

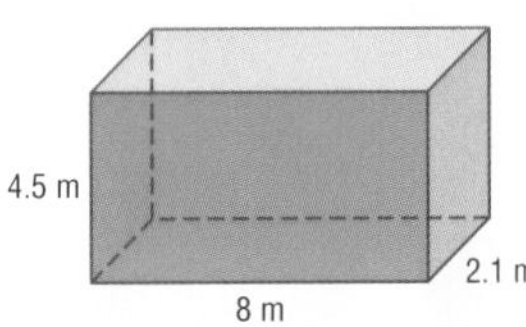

$V = \ell wh$	**Volume of a prism**
$V = 8 \cdot 2.1 \cdot 4.5$	**Replace ℓ with 8, w with 2.1, and h with 4.5.**
$V = 75.6$ m^3	**Simplify.**

The volume of the prism is 75.6 cubic meters.

Lesson-by-Lesson Review

Intervention If the given examples are not sufficient to review the topics covered by the questions, remind students that the page references tell them where to review that topic in their textbook.

Two-Day Option Have students complete the Lesson-by-Lesson Review on pp. 717–720. Then you can use ExamView® Assessment Suite to customize another review worksheet that practices all the objectives of this chapter or only the objectives on which your students need more help.

Differentiated Instruction

Super DVD: MindJogger Videoquizzes Use this DVD as an alternative format of review for the test.

Additional Answers

9. rectangular prism; bases: *AFGD, BEHC*; faces: *ABCD, EFGH, BEFA, ADGF, BCHE, CHGD*; edges: $\overline{AB}$, $\overline{BC}$, $\overline{CD}$, $\overline{AD}$, $\overline{EF}$, $\overline{EH}$, $\overline{FG}$, $\overline{GH}$, $\overline{EB}$, $\overline{HC}$, $\overline{AF}$, $\overline{GD}$; vertices: *A, B, C, D, E, F, G, H*

10. triangular pyramid; base: *QRS*; faces: *QRT, QST, TSR, QRS*; edges: $\overline{QT}$, $\overline{QR}$, $\overline{QS}$, $\overline{TS}$, $\overline{TR}$, $\overline{SR}$; vertices: *Q, R, S, T*

11. square pyramid; bases: *LMNO* faces: *LPM, LPO, NPO, NPM, LMNO*; edges: $\overline{LM}$, $\overline{MN}$, $\overline{NO}$, $\overline{OL}$, $\overline{LP}$, $\overline{MP}$, $\overline{NP}$, $\overline{OP}$; vertices: *L, M, N, O, P*

12. cone; base: circle *A*; vertex: *B*; no faces or edges

13.

Top View | Side View | Cross Section

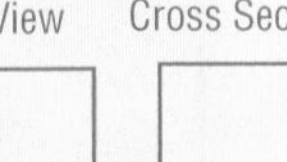

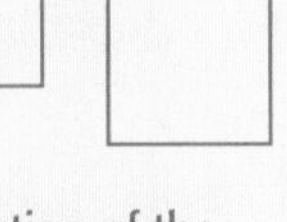

A vertical cross section of the drum is a rectangle.

Additional Answers

25. 68 cm^2; 101 cm^2
26. 720 in^2; 810 in^2
27. 143.6 m^2; 166.4 m^2
28. 348 ft^2; 428.1 ft^2
30. 378.9 ft^2; 506.1 ft^2
31. 298.5 ft^2; 865.5 ft^2
32. 131.9 m^2; 188.5 m^2
33. 202.3 mm^2; 335.3 mm^2

CHAPTER 12 Study Guide and Review

12-3 Volume of Cylinders (pp. 677–681)

Find the volume of each cylinder. Round to the nearest tenth, if necessary.

17. 445.3 cm^3

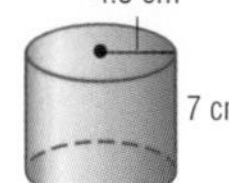

18. 282.7 in^3

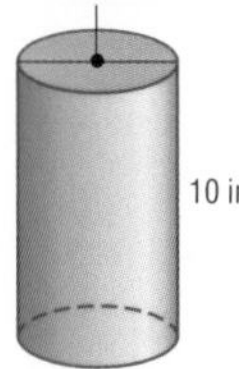

19. BEVERAGES A 12-ounce can of soda measures $4\frac{3}{4}$ inches high with a radius of $1\frac{1}{8}$ inches. Find the amount of soda that can fit in the can. Round to the nearest tenth. 18.9 in^3

EXAMPLE 3

Find the volume of the cylinder. Round to the nearest tenth, if necessary.

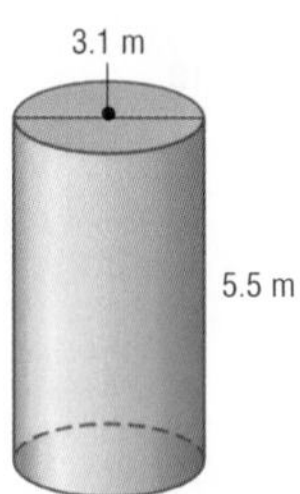

$V = \pi r^2 h$ — **Volume of a cylinder**

$V = \pi(1.55)^2(5.5)$ — **Replace *r* with 1.55 and *h* with 5.5.**

$V \approx 41.5 \text{ m}^3$ — **Simplify.**

12-4 Volume of Pyramids, Cones, and Spheres (pp. 683–688)

Find the volume of each figure. Round to the nearest tenth, if necessary.

20. 84.8 in^3

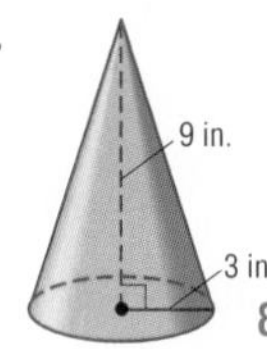

21. 8 in^3

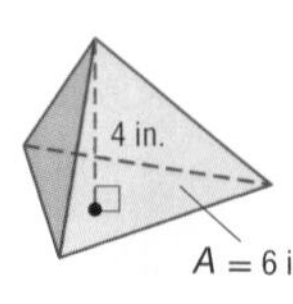

22. 1436.8 m^3

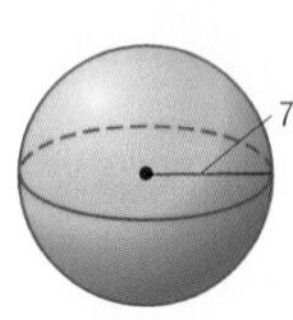

23. 15 ft^3

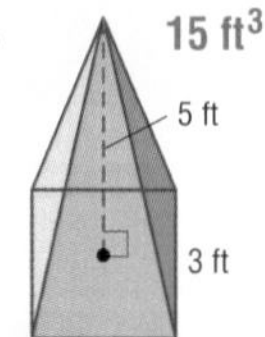

24. STORAGE Mr. Owens built a conical storage shed with a base 14 feet in diameter and a height of 11 feet. What is the volume of the shed? 564.4 ft^3

EXAMPLE 4

Find the volume of the cone. Round to the nearest tenth, if necessary.

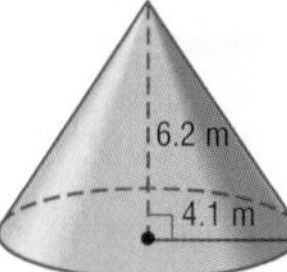

$V = \frac{1}{3}\pi r^2 h$ — **Volume of a cone**

$= \frac{1}{3}\pi(4.1)^2(6.2)$ — **Replace *r* with 4.1 and *h* with 6.2.**

$\approx 109.1 \text{ m}^3$ — **Simplify.**

MIXED PROBLEM SOLVING
For mixed problem-solving practice, see page 843.

12-5 Surface Area of Prisms (pp. 691–695)

Find the lateral and surface area of each prism. Round to the nearest tenth, if necessary.

25.

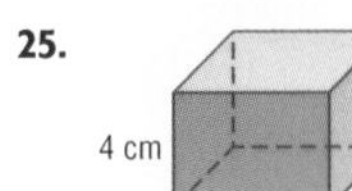

26.

25–28. See margin.

27.

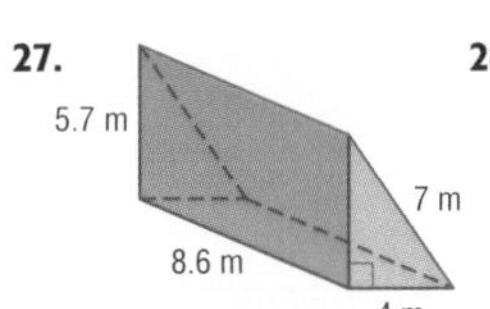

28.

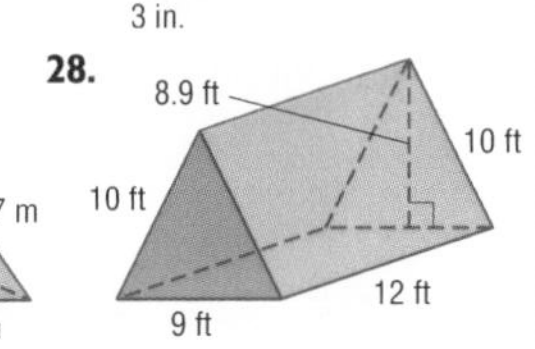

29. GIFTS Sarah is wrapping a gift that is 12 inches long, 6 inches wide, and 4 inches high. How many square inches of paper are needed to cover the gift? **288 in^2**

EXAMPLE 5

Find the lateral and surface area of the prism.

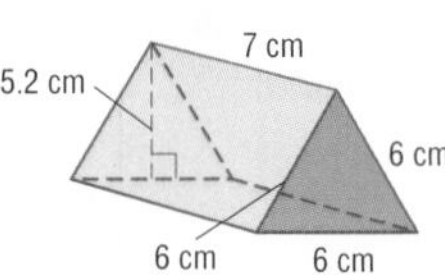

$L = Ph$	**Lateral area of a prism**
$= (6 + 6 + 6)7$	**P = the perimeter of the base.**
$= 126 \text{ cm}^2$	**Simplify.**
$S = L + 2B$	**Surface area of a prism**
$= 126 + 2\left(\frac{1}{2} \cdot 6 \cdot 5.2\right)$	**$B = \frac{1}{2}bh$**
$= 157.2 \text{ cm}^2$	**Simplify.**

12-6 Surface Area of Cylinders (pp. 697–701)

Find the lateral and surface area of each cylinder. Round to the nearest tenth, if necessary. 30–33. See margin.

30.

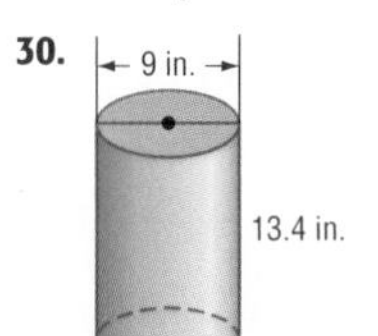

31.

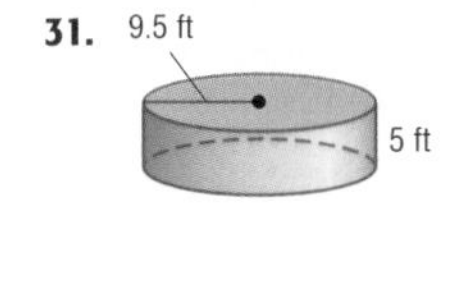

32.

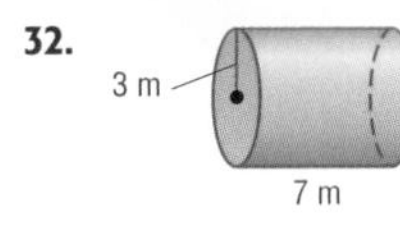

33.

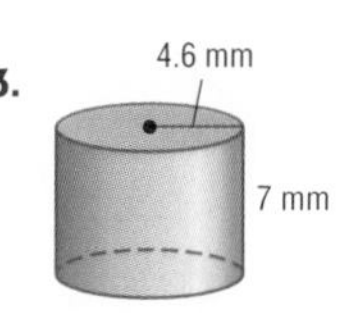

34. TELEVISION Coaxial cable is used to transmit cable television programming. The cable is covered by rubber sheathing. A typical coaxial cable has a diameter of 3 inches. How much rubber sheathing is there in 100 feet of cable? **78.5 ft^2**

EXAMPLE 6

Find the lateral and surface areas of the cylinder below. Round to the nearest tenth, if necessary.

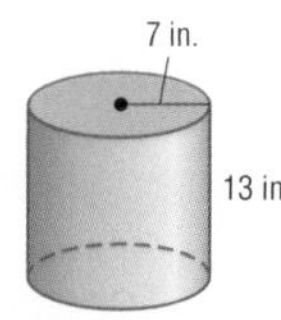

Lateral Area

$L = 2\pi rh$	**Lateral area of a cylinder**
$= 2 \cdot \pi \cdot 7 \cdot 13$	**Replace r with 7 and h with 13.**
$\approx 571.8 \text{ in}^2$	**Simplify.**

Surface Area

$S = L + 2\pi r^2$	**Surface area of a cylinder**
$= 571.8 + 2\pi(7)^2$	**Replace L with 571.8 and r with 7.**
$\approx 879.7 \text{ m}^2$	**Simplify.**

Chapter 12 Study Guide and Review **719**

Problem Solving Review

For additional practice in problem solving for Chapter 12, see the Mixed Problem Solving Appendix, p. 854, in the Student Handbook section.

Anticipation Guide

Have students complete the Chapter 12 Anticipation Guide and discuss how their responses have changed now that they have completed Chapter 12.

Additional Answers

35. 244.8 cm^2; 308.8 cm^2

36. 263.9 ft^2; 417.8 ft^2

37. 131.9 in^2; 182.2 in^2

38. 36 cm^2; 42 cm^2

12-7 Surface Area of Pyramids and Cones (pp. 702–707)

Find the lateral and surface areas of each figure. Round to the nearest tenth, if necessary. **35–38. See margin.**

35.

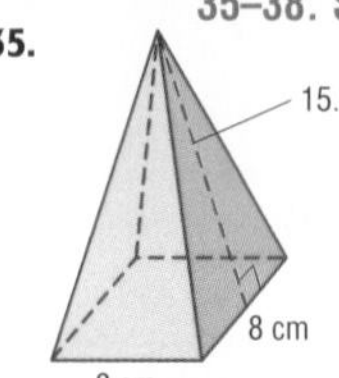

36.

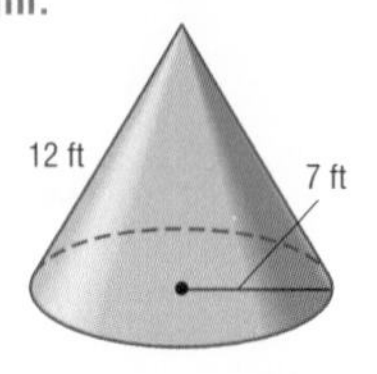

37.

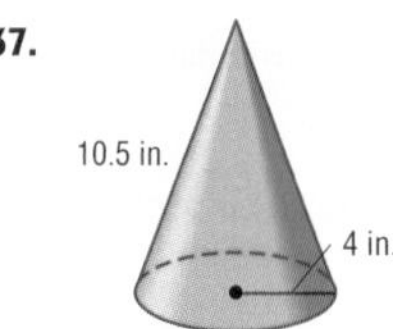

38.

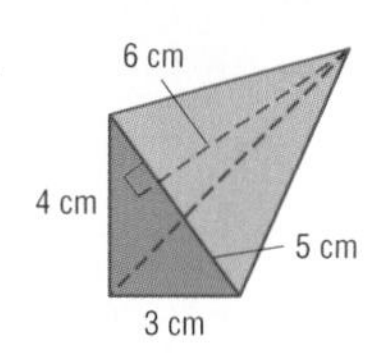

39. ROOFS A pyramid-shaped roof has a slant height of 18 feet and its square base is 55 feet wide. How many square feet of roofing material is needed to cover the roof? **1980 ft²**

EXAMPLE 7

Find the lateral and surface area of the square pyramid. Round to the nearest tenth, if necessary.

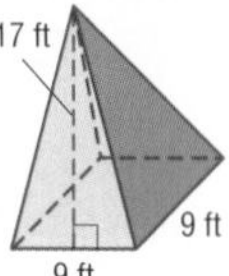

Lateral Area

$L = \frac{1}{2}Pl$ **Lateral area of a pyramid**

$= \frac{1}{2}(4 \cdot 9)(17)$ **Substitute.**

$= 306 \text{ ft}^2$ **Simplify.**

Surface Area

$S = L + B$ **Surface area of a pyramid**

$= 306 + 9^2$ **Substitute.**

$= 387 \text{ ft}^2$ **Simplify.**

12-8 Similar Solids (pp. 709–715)

Find the missing measure for each pair of similar solids.

40. **12 cm**

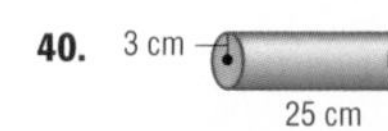

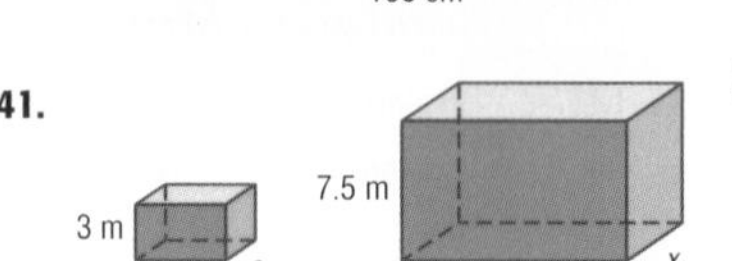

41. **5 m**

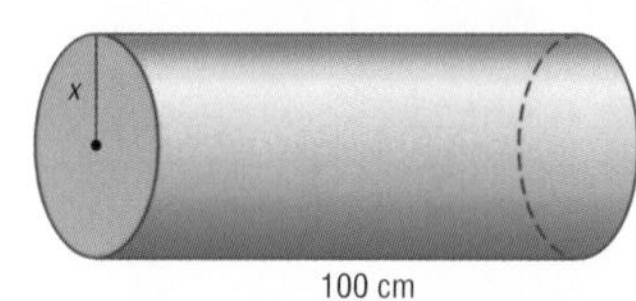

42. A prism has a surface area of 160 square feet. If the dimensions are reduced by a factor of $\frac{1}{4}$, what is the surface area of the new prism? **10 ft²**

EXAMPLE 8

Find the missing measure for the pair of similar solids.

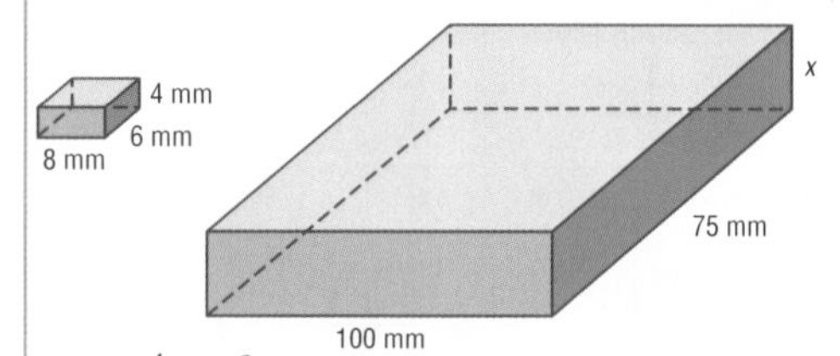

$\frac{4}{x} = \frac{8}{100}$ **Write the proportion.**

$4 \cdot 100 = 8x$ **Find the cross products.**

$400 = 8x$ **Simplify.**

$\frac{400}{8} = \frac{8x}{8}$ **Divide each side by 8.**

$50 = x$ **Simplify.**

720 Chapter 12 Surface Area and Volume

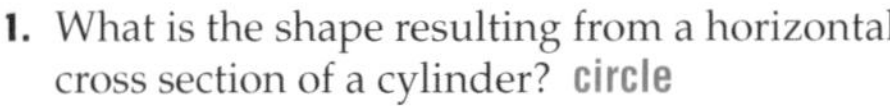

CHAPTER 12 Practice Test

Math Online glencoe.com
Chapter Test

1. What is the shape resulting from a horizontal cross section of a cylinder? **circle**

Find the volume of each solid. Round to the nearest tenth, if necessary.

2. cube: length 2.5 in. **15.6 in^3**
3. triangular prism: base of triangle 12 cm, altitude of triangle 8 cm, height of prism 4 cm **192 cm^3**
4. cone: radius 6 m, height 8 m **301.6 m^3**
5. cylinder: radius 6.5 ft, height 9.6 ft **1274.2 ft^3**

6. **MULTIPLE CHOICE** A rectangular prism has a volume of 32 cubic centimeters. If the length is 2 centimeters and the width is 2 centimeters, what is the height of the prism? **C**

   A 2 cm C 8 cm
   B 4 cm D 18 cm

7. **BREAKFAST** The inside of the cereal bowl is in the shape of a hemisphere (half of a sphere). Find the maximum amount of milk that can fit in the bowl. Round to the nearest hundredth. **134.04 in^3**

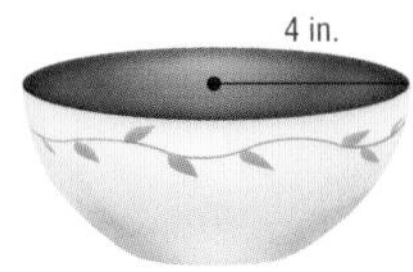

8. **COOKING** Sara is pouring 10 cartons of chicken broth into a large pot that holds 250 cubic inches. If each carton is 6 inches tall, 4 inches wide, and 1 inch thick, will all 10 cartons of broth fit in the pot? Explain. **See margin.**

9. **FURNITURE** Find the surface area of the ottoman that will be reupholstered, not including the bottom. Round to the nearest tenth. **19.3 ft^3**

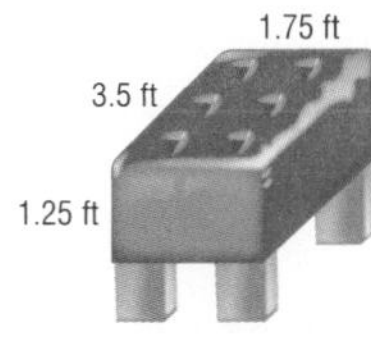

Find the lateral and surface area of each solid. Round to the nearest tenth, if necessary.

10. 11.

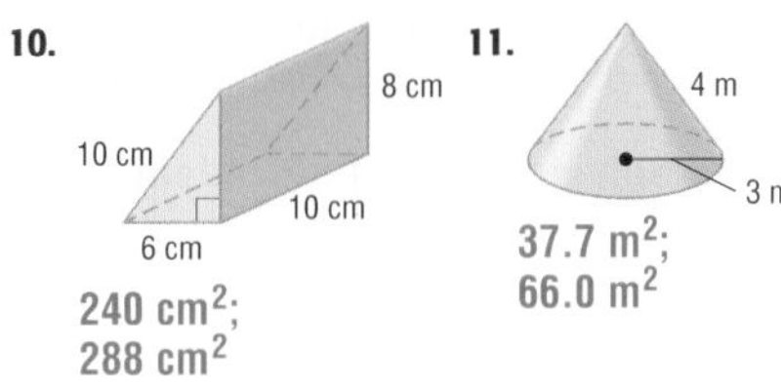

240 cm^2; 288 cm^2

37.7 m^2; 66.0 m^2

12. 13.

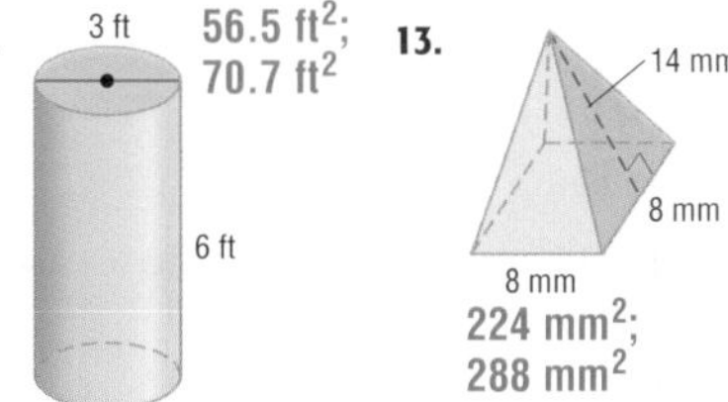

56.5 ft^2; 70.7 ft^2

224 mm^2; 288 mm^2

14. **MULTIPLE CHOICE** Chen is creating a model of a building. The building is in the shape of a pyramid. The model has a square base with sides of 10 inches and a slant height of 12 inches. What is the surface area of his model? **G**

   F 100 in^2 H 580 in^2
   G 340 in^2 J 1200 in^2

15. A cube has a volume of 8 cubic inches. If the dimensions are doubled, what is the volume of the new cube? **64 in^3**

16. Are the rectangular prisms described in the table similar? Explain your reasoning.

Prism	Length (m)	Width (m)	Height (m)
A	2	5	7
B	3	7.5	10.5

Yes, the ratio of the sides is the same (3:2)

17. The model of Duane's room is 6 inches long, 5 inches wide, and 4 inches high. The scale is 2 feet to 1 inch. Find the length of his actual room. **12 ft**

18. **CAMPING** The sides and the floor of a pyramid tent are made of a water resistant fabric. The slant height of the tent is about 14 feet. Its square base is 15 feet on each side. How much fabric was used in making the tent? **645 ft^2**

CHAPTER 12 Practice Test

ExamView Assessment Suite Customize and create multiple versions of your chapter test and their answer keys. All of the questions from the leveled chapter tests in the *Chapter 12 Resource Masters* are also available on ExamView® Assessment Suite.

Additional Answers

8. yes; Sample answer: The volume of one carton is 24 in^3. So the volume of 10 of the same carton is 10 • 24 or 240 in^3. Since 240 < 250, all 10 cartons will fit in the pot.

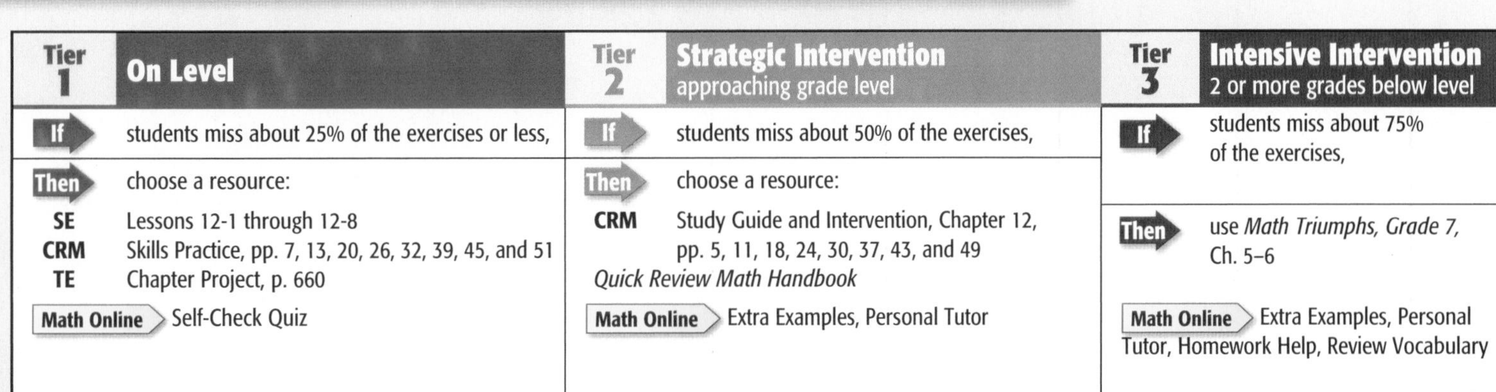

Tier 1 On Level	Tier 2 Strategic Intervention approaching grade level	Tier 3 Intensive Intervention 2 or more grades below level
If students miss about 25% of the exercises or less,	**If** students miss about 50% of the exercises,	**If** students miss about 75% of the exercises,
Then choose a resource: **SE** Lessons 12-1 through 12-8 **CRM** Skills Practice, pp. 7, 13, 20, 26, 32, 39, 45, and 51 **TE** Chapter Project, p. 660 Math Online Self-Check Quiz	**Then** choose a resource: **CRM** Study Guide and Intervention, Chapter 12, pp. 5, 11, 18, 24, 30, 37, 43, and 49 *Quick Review Math Handbook* Math Online Extra Examples, Personal Tutor	**Then** use *Math Triumphs, Grade 7,* Ch. 5–6 Math Online Extra Examples, Personal Tutor, Homework Help, Review Vocabulary

1 FOCUS

Objective Use the strategy of solving a simpler problem to solve standardized test problems.

TEACH

Scaffolding Questions

Ask:

- Have you ever had to complete a long research paper or other big school project? Answers will vary.
- Did you complete the entire paper or project in one work session? Or did you complete a number of smaller steps to complete the job? Answers will vary.

CHAPTER 12 Preparing for Standardized Tests

Solve a Simpler Problem

There is often more than one way to solve a problem. Two different methods can both result in the correct answer, but one method may be more efficient.

Strategies for Solving a Simpler Problem

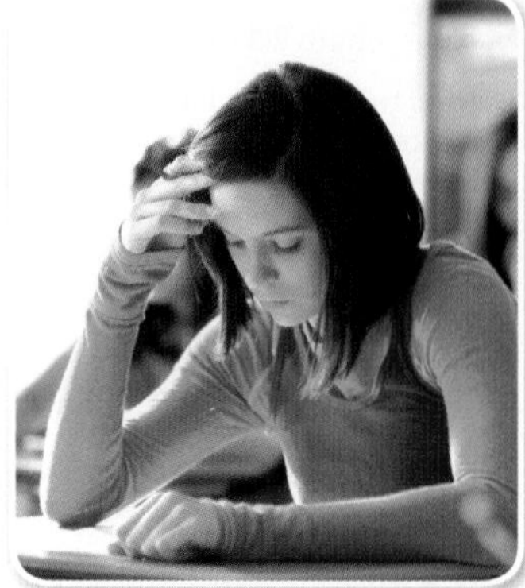

Step 1

Read the problem statement carefully.

Ask yourself:

- What information am I given?
- What am I being asked to solve?
- If the problem is a multi-step problem, can it be broken up into smaller, more manageable parts?

Step 2

Think of the most efficient way to solve the problem.

- If a calculator is allowed, it may speed up the process.
- Are there any shortcuts you can use to solve the problem?

Step 3

Solve the problem. Check your answer.

EXAMPLE

Read the problem. Identify what you need to know. Then use the information in the problem to solve.

Angela is using 2-centimeter blocks to build steps in a model. What is the total volume of the steps shown at the right?

A 120 cm^3

B 180 cm^3

C 220 cm^3

D 240 cm^3

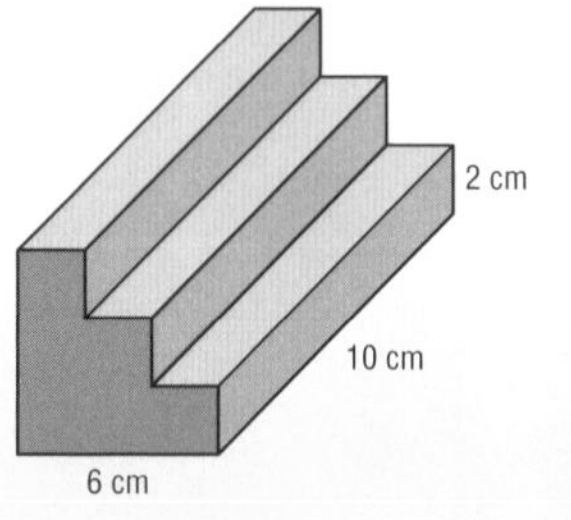

722 Chapter 12 Surface Area and Volume

Read the problem carefully. It looks like a challenging volume problem. If you recognize that the steps are formed by stacking 6 square prisms on top of each other, it becomes much simpler to solve.

Divide the figure into 6 square prisms by drawing dashed lines. Then find the volume of one prism. Multiply by 6 to find the total volume.

Volume of one prism:

$V = 2 \times 2 \times 10$

$V = 40 \text{ cm}^3$

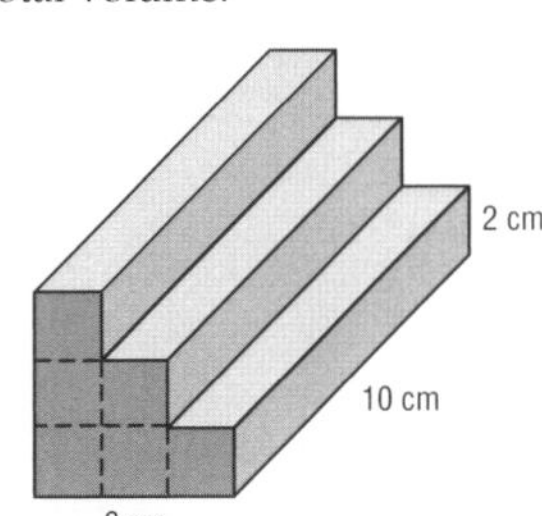

Total volume of steps:

$V = 6 \times 40$

$V = 240 \text{ cm}^3$

So, the total volume of the steps is 240 cubic centimeters. The correct answer is D.

Exercises

Read each problem. Identify what you need to know. Then use the information in the problem to solve.

1. What is the volume of the figure when a 10-millimeter diameter cylinder is removed? B

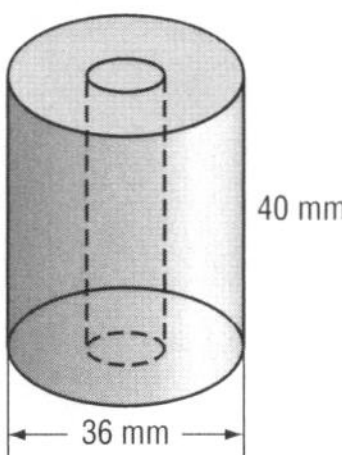

A 26,712.8 mm^3

B 37,573.4 mm^3

C 43,661.2 mm^3

D 48,985.3 mm^3

2. Neil and his father are building a tool shed against the side of a barn in the shape of the model shown below. What is the total volume of the shed? C

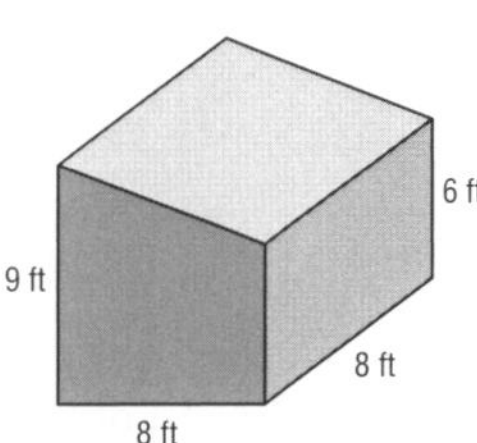

A 425 ft^3

B 464 ft^3

C 480 ft^3

D 512 ft^3

Additional Example

Jessie is building a dollhouse for her sister. What is the volume of the dollhouse? C

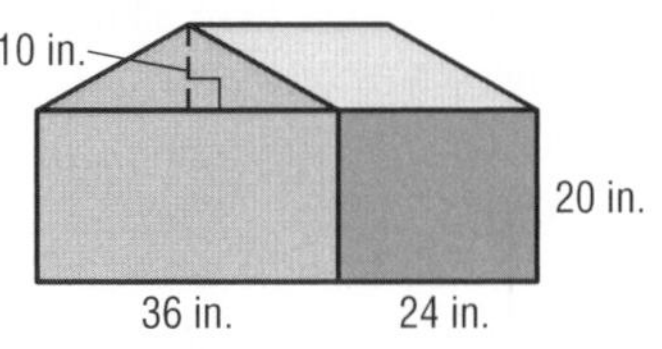

A 12,240 in^3

B 20,880 in^3

C 21,600 in^3

D 25,920 in^3

3 ASSESS

Use Exercises 1–2 to assess students' understanding.

Chapter 12 Preparing for Standardized Tests 723

CHAPTER 12 Standardized Test Practice

Diagnose Student Errors

Survey student responses for each item. Class trends may indicate common errors and misconceptions.

1. A used two given angles to classify triangle rather than all three angles
B guess
C correct
D classified triangle according to sides instead of angles

2. F guess or calculation error
G guess or calculation error
H correct
J guess or calculation error

3. A correct
B guess or calculation error
C forgot to multiply by $\frac{1}{3}$
D guess or calculation error and forgot to multiply by $\frac{1}{3}$

4. F guess
G used height instead of slant height
H correct
J guess

5. A guess
B correct
C guess
D confused relationship between tickets and dollars

6. F used half of 65 for radius
G guessed half of answer choice for J
H correct
J guess

7. A found volume instead of surface area
B guess
C guess
D correct

CHAPTER 12 Standardized Test Practice

Cumulative, Chapters 1 through 12

Multiple Choice

Read each question. Then fill in the correct answer on the answer document provided by your teacher or on a sheet of paper.

1. Classify the triangle below by its angles. C

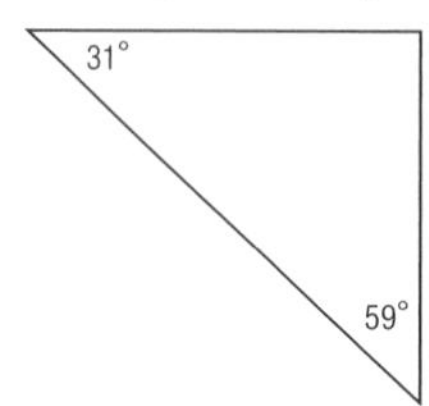

A acute
B obtuse
C right
D scalene

2. A water garden hose is shaped like a cylinder with a diameter of 1.25 inches and a length of 22 feet. What is the volume of the hose? Round your answer to the nearest tenth. H

F 300 in^3
G 318 in^3
H 324 in^3
J 350 in^3

3. What is the volume of a hexagonal pyramid that has a base area of 42 square meters and a height of 5.4 meters? A

A 75.6 m^3
B 78.4 m^3
C 226.8 m^3
D 234.9 m^3

4. A paper cup is shaped like a cone with a height of 12 centimeters, a diameter of 10 centimeters, and a slant height of 13 centimeters. How much paper is needed to make each cup? H

F 162.2 cm^2
G 188.5 cm^2
H 204.2 cm^2
J 211.9 cm^2

5 cm
12 cm
13 cm

5. What is the constant rate of change shown in the graph below? B

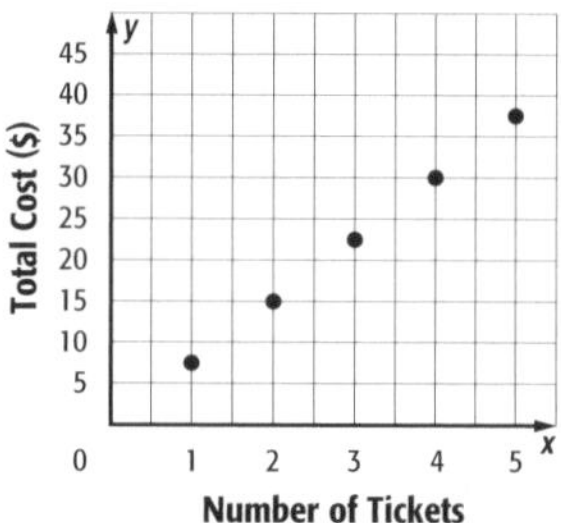

A $6.75 per ticket
B $7.50 per ticket
C $8.00 per ticket
D 7.5 tickets per dollar

6. A circular ice-skating rink has a radius of 65 feet. What is the circumference of the rink, rounded to the nearest tenth? H

F 204.2 ft
G 261.3 ft
H 408.4 ft
J 522.6 ft

7. How much wrapping paper would Nicole need to completely cover the gift box shown below? D

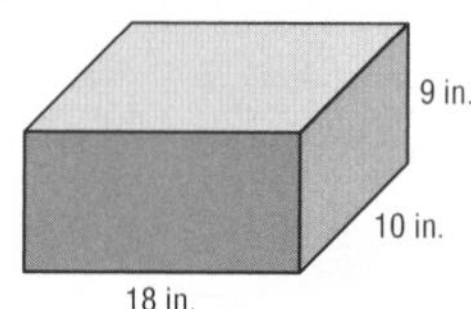

A 1620 in^2
B 1240 in^2
C 978 in^2
D 864 in^2

Test-TakingTip

Question 7 Remember to read each test item carefully. In this question you will need to find the surface area, not the volume of the prism.

CHAPTER 12 Standardized Test Practice

Short Response/Gridded Response

Record your answers on the answer sheet provided by your teacher or on a sheet of paper.

8. GRIDDED RESPONSE The two triangular prisms below are similar solids. What is the value of x? **23.8**

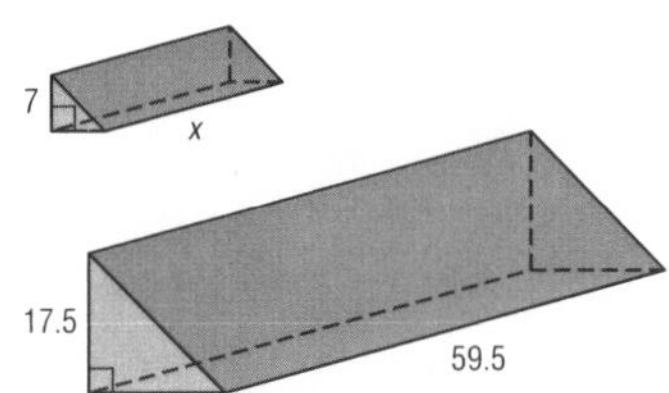

9. A plumber has two drainpipes shaped like cylinders. The first pipe is 8 inches long and has a diameter of 1.25 inches. The second pipe is 10 inches long and has a diameter of 1 inch. Which pipe has the greater outer surface area? **The pipes have the same surface area.**

10. Find the volume of the rectangular prism shown below. **945 ft³**

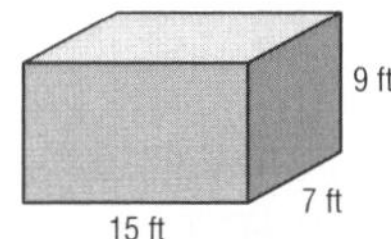

11. GRIDDED RESPONSE Terrance placed a 12-ft ladder against the side of his house to paint the shutters. The base of the ladder is 4 feet from the house. How high up the side of the house does the ladder reach? Round to the nearest tenth of a foot. **11.3**

12. GRIDDED RESPONSE Estimate $\sqrt{125}$ to the nearest integer without using a calculator. **11**

Extended Response

Record your answers on a sheet of paper. Show your work.

13. Use the rectangular prism below to answer each question.

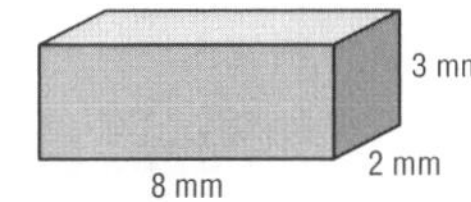

a. What is the volume of the rectangular prism? **48 mm^3**

b. What is the surface area of the rectangular prism? **92 mm^2**

c. Double the dimensions of the prism. What is the new volume? **384 mm^3**

d. What is the new surface area of the rectangular prism when the dimensions are doubled? **368 mm^2**

e. What effect does doubling the dimensions have on the volume and surface area of a prism? **Sample answer: The volume increases by a factor of 8, the surface area by a factor of 4**

Need Extra Help?													
If you missed Question...	1	2	3	4	5	6	7	8	9	10	11	12	13
Go to Lesson or Page...	10-3	12-3	12-4	12-7	8-5	11-7	12-5	12-8	12-6	12-2	10-4	10-1	12-2, 12-5

Formative Assessment

You can use these two pages to benchmark student progress.

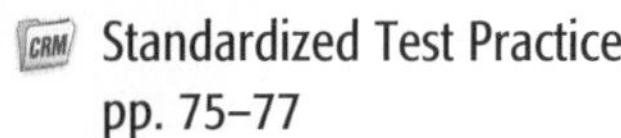

CRM Standardized Test Practice, pp. 75–77

Answer Sheet Practice

Have students simulate taking a standardized test by recording their answers on practice recording sheets.

CRM Student Recording Sheet, p. 56

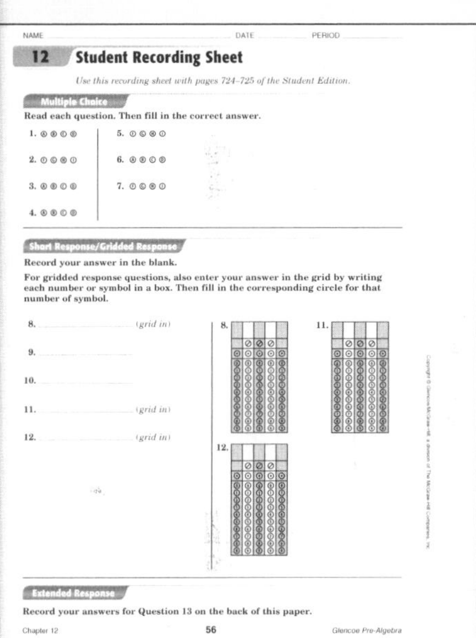

NAME DATE PERIOD

12 Student Recording Sheet

Use this recording sheet with pages 724–725 of the Student Edition.

Multiple Choice

Read each question. Then fill in the correct answer.

1. Ⓐ Ⓑ Ⓒ Ⓓ
2. Ⓕ Ⓖ Ⓗ Ⓙ
3. Ⓐ Ⓑ Ⓒ Ⓓ
4. Ⓐ Ⓑ Ⓒ Ⓓ
5. Ⓕ Ⓖ Ⓗ Ⓙ
6. Ⓐ Ⓑ Ⓒ Ⓓ
7. Ⓕ Ⓖ Ⓗ Ⓙ

Short Response/Gridded Response

Record your answer in the blank.

For gridded response questions, also enter your answer in the grid by writing each number or symbol in a box. Then fill in the corresponding circle for that number of symbol.

8. ______ (grid in)
9. ______
10. ______
11. ______ (grid in)
12. ______ (grid in)

8. 11. 12.

Extended Response

Record your answers for Question 13 on the back of this paper.

Chapter 12 56 Glencoe Pre-Algebra

Copyright © Glencoe/McGraw-Hill, a division of The McGraw-Hill Companies, Inc.

Create practice worksheets or tests that align to your state's standards as well as TIMSS and NAEP tests.

Homework Option

Get Ready for Chapter 13 Assign students the exercises on p. 727 as homework to assess whether they possess the prerequisite skills needed for the next chapter.

Page 663, Explore 12-1

1. 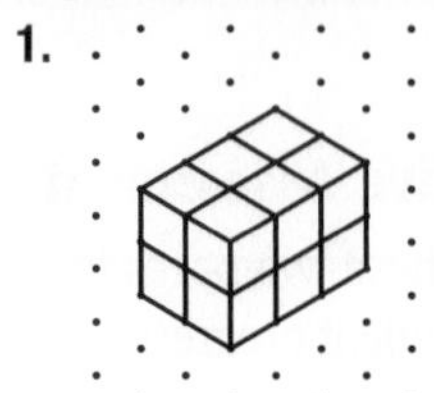

2. 

3. 

4. 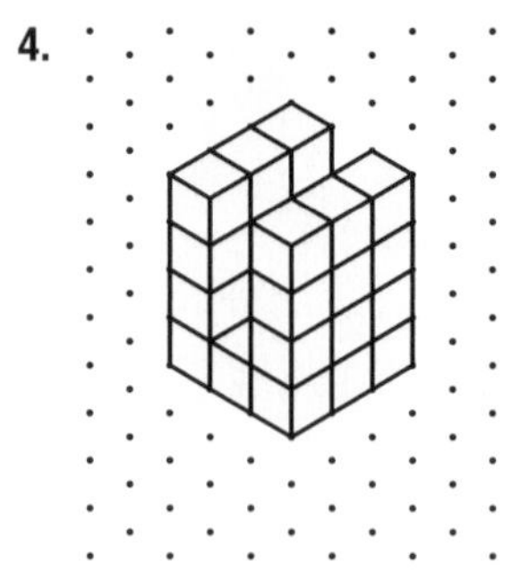

5. 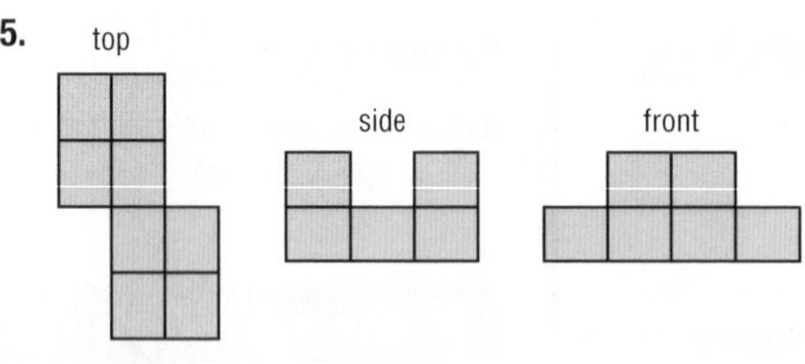

6. 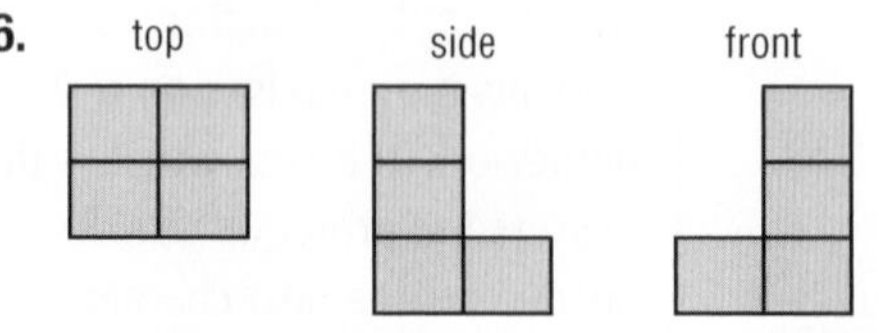

Pages 666, Lesson 12-1 (Check Your Progress

3. 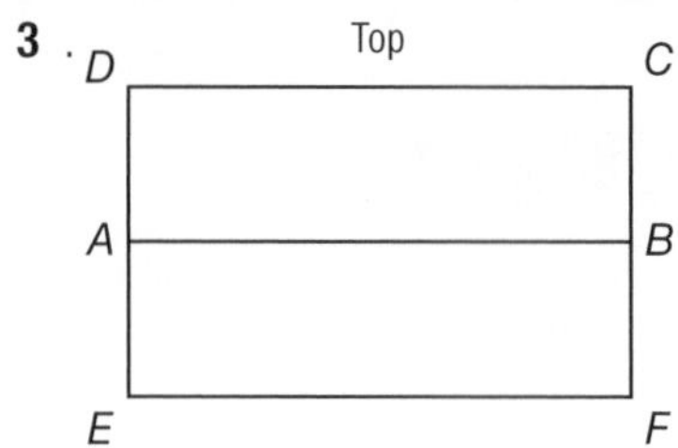

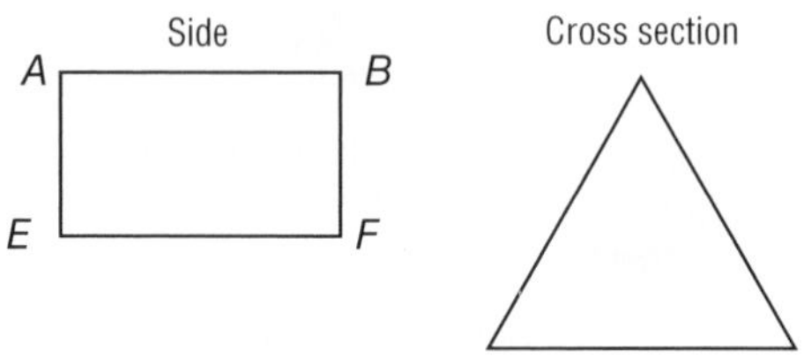

Pages 667–668, Lesson 12-1

6. 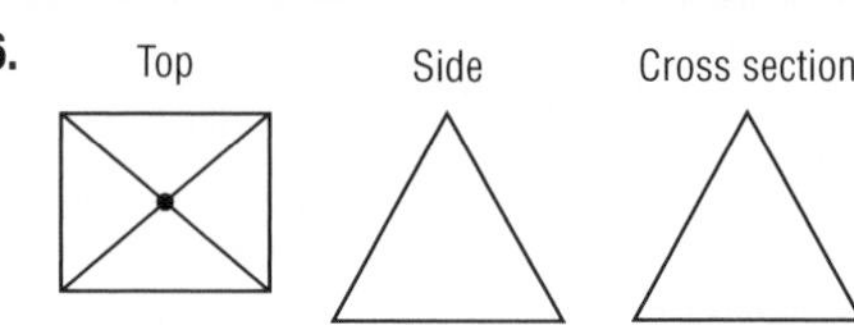

isosceles triangle

7. triangular prism, bases: *DEF, ABC;* faces: *ABEF, BCDE, ACDF, FED, ABC;* edges: $\overline{AB}$, $\overline{AC}$, $\overline{AF}$, $\overline{BC}$, $\overline{BE}$, $\overline{DF}$, $\overline{CD}$, $\overline{ED}$, $\overline{EF}$; vertices: *A, B, C, D, E, F*

8. pentagonal prism; bases: *ABCDE, FGHIJ;* faces: *ABGF, BGHC, ABCDE, FGHIJ; CHID, DEJI, EAFJ;* edges: $\overline{AB}$, $\overline{AE}$, $\overline{AF}$, $\overline{BC}$, $\overline{BG}$, $\overline{CD}$, $\overline{CH}$, $\overline{DE}$, $\overline{DI}$, $\overline{EJ}$, $\overline{FG}$, $\overline{FJ}$, $\overline{GH}$, $\overline{HI}$, $\overline{IJ}$; vertices: *A, B, C, D, E, F, G, H, I, J*

9. rectangular pyramid; base: *ABCD;* faces: *EAB, EBC, EDC, EDA, ABCD;* edges: $\overline{EA}$, $\overline{EB}$, $\overline{EC}$, $\overline{ED}$, $\overline{AB}$, $\overline{BC}$, $\overline{CD}$, $\overline{DA}$; vertices: *A, B, C, D, E*

10. rectangular prism; bases: *ABCD* and *EFGH,* or *BCGF* and *ADHE,* or *CDHG* and *BAEF;* faces; *ABCD, EFGH, BCGF, ADHE, CDHG, BAEF;* edges: $\overline{AB}$, $\overline{AD}$, $\overline{AE}$, $\overline{BC}$, $\overline{BF}$, $\overline{CD}$, $\overline{CG}$, $\overline{DH}$, $\overline{EF}$, $\overline{EH}$, $\overline{FG}$, $\overline{GH}$; vertices: *A, B, C, D, E, F, G, H*

11. hexagonal pyramid; base: *BCDEFG;* faces: *ABC, ACD, ADE, AEF, BCDEFG, AFG, AGB;* edges: $\overline{AB}$, $\overline{AC}$, $\overline{AD}$, $\overline{AE}$, $\overline{AF}$, $\overline{AG}$, $\overline{BC}$, $\overline{CD}$, $\overline{DE}$, $\overline{EF}$, $\overline{FG}$, $\overline{GB}$; vertices: *A, B, C, D, E, F, G*

12. triangular pyramid; base: *BCD;* faces: *ABD, ABC, ACD, BCD;* edges: $\overline{AB}$, $\overline{AC}$, $\overline{AD}$, $\overline{BC}$, $\overline{CD}$, $\overline{DB}$; vertices; *A, B, C, D*

13. circle; 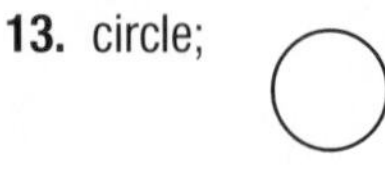

14. oval; 

15. square; 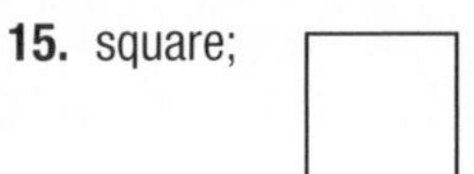

16.

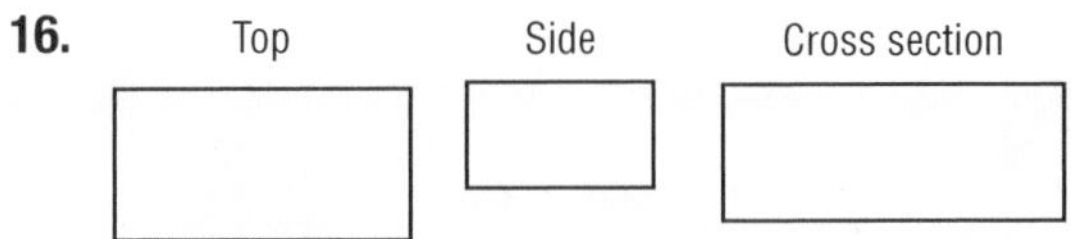

18.

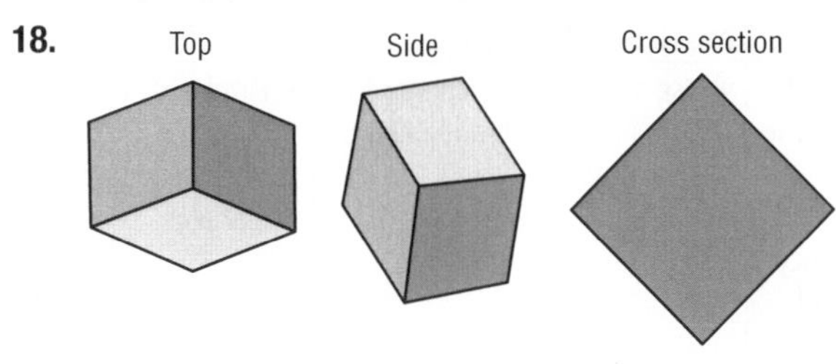

parallelogram

19.

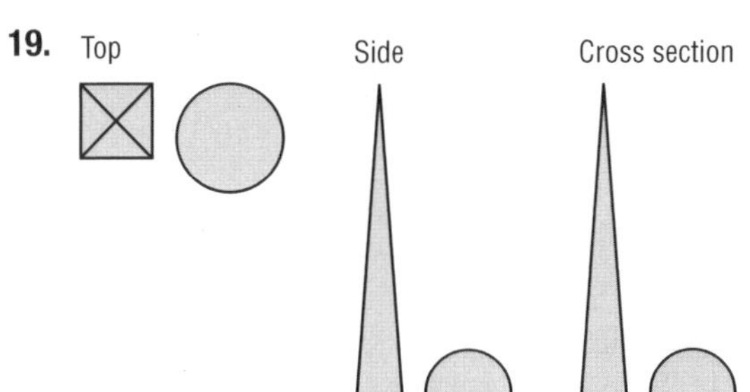

triangle and circle

20.

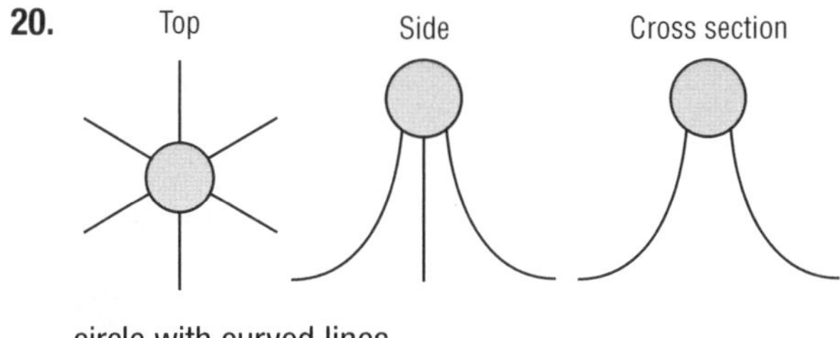

circle with curved lines

21a.

Name	Triangular pyramid	Square pyramid	Pentagonal pyramid
Figure			
Vertices	4	5	6
Faces	4	5	6
Edges	6	8	10

21b. Sample answer: The number of vertices is equal to the number of faces. The number of edges increases by 2 as the number of vertices of the pyramid increases by 1.

21c. $V + F = E + 2$

Page 689, Mid-Chapter Quiz

3. cylinder; bases: circle *M* and circle *N;* no faces, edges, or vertices

4. triangular prism; bases: *STV, ZYW;* faces: *STYZ, TVWY, SVWZ, STV, ZYW;* edges: $\overline{ST}$, $\overline{TV}$, $\overline{VW}$, $\overline{WZ}$, $\overline{ZS}$, $\overline{SV}$, $\overline{ZY}$, $\overline{YW}$, $\overline{TY}$; vertices: *S, T, V, W, Y, Z*

5. parallelogram 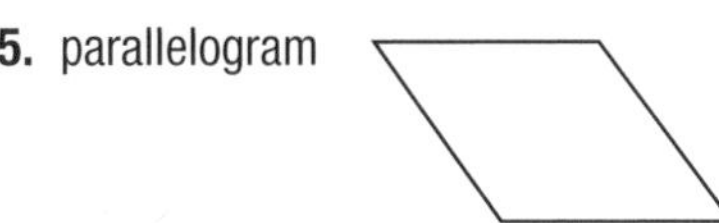

6. triangle 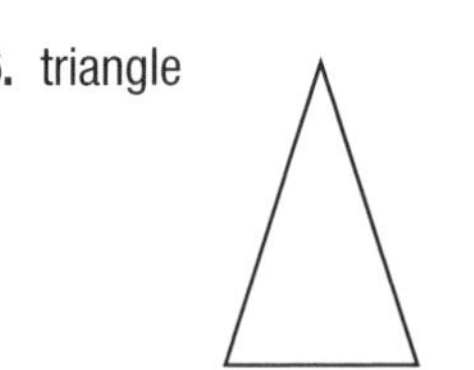

Page 691, Lesson 12-5, Why?

b. Area of faces: 576 in^2, 576 in^2, 192 in^2, 192 in^2, 432 in^2, 432 in^2; sum = 2400 in^2

Page 708, Explore 12-8

6.

Scale Factor	Side Length	Volume
1	1	1
2	2	8
3	3	27

Scale Factor	Side Length	Area of a Face	Surface Area
1	1	1	6
2	2	4	24
3	3	9	54

CHAPTER 13 Chapter Planner

Diagnostic Assessment
Quick Check, p. 727

	Explore 13-1 Pacing: $\frac{1}{2}$ day	**Lesson 13-1** Pacing: 1 day	**Extend 13-1** Pacing: $\frac{1}{2}$ day	**Lesson 13-2** Pacing: 1 day
Title	**Algebra Lab: Analyzing Data**	**Measures of Central Tendency**	**Graphing Technology Lab: Mean and Median**	**Stem and Leaf Plots**
Objectives	• Examine data and find a number to describe them.	• Use the mean, median, and mode as measures of central tendency. • Choose an appropriate measure of central tendency and recognize measures of statistics.	• Use a graphing calculator to find the mean and median of a set of data.	• Display data in stem-and-leaf plots. • Interpret data in a stem-and-leaf plot.
Key Vocabulary		measures of central tendency mean; median; mode		stem-and-leaf plot stems leaves
NCTM Focal Points	G7-FP6C, G7-FP7C, G8-FP3, G8-FP6C For the complete wording of the Focal Points for Grades 7 and 8, please see pages iv, v, FP0, and FP1.			
Multiple Representations				p. 741
Lesson Resources	**Materials:** • local sports data from a newspaper or Internet • graph or data table from newspaper or magazine • small boxes of raisins	**Chapter 13 Resource Masters** • Study Guide and Intervention, pp. 5–6 AL OL ELL • Skills Practice, p. 7 AL OL ELL • Practice, p. 8 AL OL BL ELL • Word Problem Practice, p. 9 AL OL ELL • Enrichment, p. 10 OL BL **Transparencies** • 5-Minute Check Transparency 13-1 AL OL BL ELL **Additional Print Resources** • *Study Notebook* AL OL BL ELL	**Materials:** • TI-83/84 Plus graphing calculator	**Chapter 13 Resource Masters** • Study Guide and Intervention, pp. 11–12 AL OL ELL • Skills Practice, p. 13 AL OL ELL • Practice, p. 14 AL OL BL ELL • Word Problem Practice, p. 15 AL OL ELL • Enrichment, p. 16 OL BL • Graphing Calculator, p. 17 AL OL BL ELL **Transparencies** • 5-Minute Check Transparency 13-2 AL OL BL ELL **Additional Print Resources** • *Study Notebook* AL OL BL ELL
Technology for Every Lesson	**Math Online** glencoe.com • Extra Examples • Self-Check Quizzes • Personal Tutor	**CD/DVD Resources** IWB INTERACTIVE WHITEBOARD READY IWB StudentWorks Plus IWB Interactive Classroom IWB Diagnostic and Assessment Planner	• TeacherWorks Plus • eSolutions Manual Plus • ExamView Assessment Suite	
Math in Motion	p. 729			
Differentiated Instruction		pp. 732, 735		pp. 738, 742

KEY: 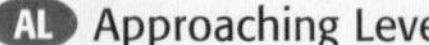

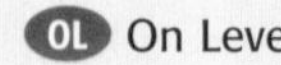

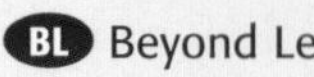

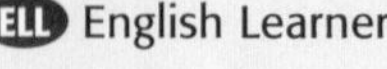

Statistics and Probability

Suggested Pacing			
Time Periods	Instruction	Review & Assessment	Total
45-minute	14	2	16
90-minute	7	1	8

Lesson 13-3 Pacing: 1 day	Lesson 13-4 Pacing: 1 day	Extend 13-4 Pacing: $\frac{1}{2}$ day	Lesson 13-5 Pacing: 1 day	Extend 13-5 Pacing: $\frac{1}{2}$ day
Measures of Variation	**Box-and-Whisker Plots**	**Graphing Technology Lab: Box-and-Whisker Plots**	**Histograms**	**Graphing Technology Lab: Histograms**
• Find measures of variation. • Use measures of variation to interpret and analyze data.	• Display data in a box-and-whisker plot. • Interpret data in a box-and-whisker plot.	• Use a graphing calculator to create box-and-whisker plots.	• Display data in a histogram. • Interpret data in a histogram.	• Use a graphing calculator to create histograms.
measures of variation range; quartiles outlier	box-and-whisker plot		histogram	
Chapter 13 Resource Masters • Study Guide and Intervention, pp. 18–19 AL OL ELL • Skills Practice, p. 20 AL OL ELL • Practice, p. 21 AL OL BL ELL • Word Problem Practice, p. 22 AL OL ELL • Enrichment, p. 23 OL BL • Quiz 1, p. 70 AL OL BL ELL **Transparencies** • 5-Minute Check Transparency 13-3 AL OL BL ELL **Additional Print Resources** • *Study Notebook* AL OL BL ELL	**Chapter 13 Resource Masters** • Study Guide and Intervention, pp. 24–25 AL OL ELL • Skills Practice, p. 26 AL OL ELL • Practice, p. 27 AL OL BL ELL • Word Problem Practice, p. 28 AL OL ELL • Enrichment, p. 29 OL BL **Transparencies** • 5-Minute Check Transparency 13-4 AL OL BL ELL **Additional Print Resources** • *Study Notebook* AL OL BL ELL	**Materials:** • TI-83/84 Plus graphing calculator	**Chapter 13 Resource Masters** • Study Guide and Intervention, pp. 30–31 AL OL ELL • Skills Practice, p. 32 AL OL ELL • Practice, p. 33 AL OL BL ELL • Word Problem Practice, p. 34 AL OL ELL • Enrichment, p. 35 OL BL • Spreadsheet Activity, p. 36 AL OL BL ELL • Quiz 2, p. 70 AL OL BL ELL **Transparencies** • 5-Minute Check Transparency 13-5 AL OL BL ELL **Additional Print Resources** • *Study Notebook* AL OL BL ELL	**Materials:** • TI-83/84 Plus graphing calculator

Math Online glencoe.com

- Extra Examples
- Self-Check Quizzes
- Personal Tutor

CD/DVD Resources IWB INTERACTIVE WHITEBOARD READY

- IWB StudentWorks Plus
- IWB Interactive Classroom
- IWB Diagnostic and Assessment Planner
- TeacherWorks Plus
- eSolutions Manual Plus
- ExamView Assessment Suite

pp. 744, 749	pp. 752, 755		pp. 759, 762	

Formative Assessment
Mid-Chapter Quiz, p. 764

Chapter 13 Chapter Planner

	Lesson 13-6 Pacing: 1 day	Lesson 13-7 Pacing: 1 day	Lesson 13-8 Pacing: 1 day	Extend 13-8 Pacing: $\frac{1}{2}$ day
Title	**Theoretical and Experimental Probability**	**Using Sampling to Predict**	**Counting Outcomes**	**Algebra Lab: Probability and Pascal's Triangle**
Objectives	• Find the probability of simple events. • Predict the actions of a larger group.	• Identify various sampling techniques. • Determine the validity of a sample.	• Use tree diagrams or the Fundamental Counting Principle to count outcomes. • Use tree diagrams or the Fundamental Counting Principle to find the probability of an event.	• Find the probability of events.
Key Vocabulary	outcomes theoretical probability experimental probability	sample; population unbiased sample biased sample	tree diagrams Fundamental Counting Principle	
NCTM Focal Points				
Multiple Representations				
Lesson Resources	**Chapter 13 Resource Masters** • Study Guide and Intervention, pp. 37–38 AL OL ELL • Skills Practice, p. 39 AL OL ELL • Practice, p. 40 AL OL BL ELL • Word Problem Practice, p. 41 AL OL ELL • Enrichment, p. 42 OL BL **Transparencies** • 5-Minute Check Transparency 13-6 AL OL BL ELL **Additional Print Resources** • *Study Notebook* AL OL BL ELL	**Chapter 13 Resource Masters** • Study Guide and Intervention, pp. 43–44 AL OL ELL • Skills Practice, p. 45 AL OL ELL • Practice, p. 46 AL OL BL ELL • Word Problem Practice, p. 47 AL OL ELL • Enrichment, p. 48 OL BL **Transparencies** • 5-Minute Check Transparency 13-7 AL OL BL ELL **Additional Print Resources** • *Study Notebook* AL OL BL ELL	**Chapter 13 Resource Masters** • Study Guide and Intervention, pp. 49–50 AL OL ELL • Skills Practice, p. 51 AL OL ELL • Practice, p. 52 AL OL BL ELL • Word Problem Practice, p. 53 AL OL ELL • Enrichment, p. 54 OL BL • Quiz 3, p. 71 AL OL BL ELL **Transparencies** • 5-Minute Check Transparency 13-8 AL OL BL ELL **Additional Print Resources** • *Study Notebook* AL OL BL ELL	**Materials:**
Technology for Every Lesson	Math Online glencoe.com • Extra Examples • Self-Check Quizzes • Personal Tutor	**CD/DVD Resources** IWB INTERACTIVE WHITEBOARD READY IWB StudentWorks Plus IWB Interactive Classroom IWB Diagnostic and Assessment Planner	• TeacherWorks Plus • eSolutions Manual Plus • ExamView Assessment Suite	
Math in Motion	p. 765			p. 782
Differentiated Instruction	pp. 766, 770	pp. 772, 776	pp. 778, 783	

Lesson 13-9 Pacing: 1 day	**Explore 13-10** Pacing: $\frac{1}{2}$ day	**Lesson 13-10** Pacing: 1 day	**Extend 13-10** Pacing: 1 day
Permutations and Combinations	**Graphing Technology Lab: Probability Simulation**	**Probability of Compound Events**	**Algebra Lab: Simulations**
• Use permutations. • Use combinations.	• Use a graphing calculator to simulate a probability experiment.	• Find the probability of independent and dependent events. • Find the probability of mutually exclusive events.	• Use simulations to examine outcomes.
permutations combinations		independent events dependent events mutually exclusive events	
p. 787			
Chapter 13 Resource Masters • Study Guide and Intervention, pp. 55–56 AL OL ELL • Skills Practice, p. 57 AL OL ELL • Practice, p. 58 AL OL BL ELL • Word Problem Practice, p. 59 AL OL ELL • Enrichment, p. 60 OL BL **Transparencies** • 5-Minute Check Transparency 13-9 AL OL BL ELL **Additional Print Resources** • *Study Notebook* AL OL BL ELL	**Materials:** • TI-83/84 Plus graphing calculator	**Chapter 13 Resource Masters** • Study Guide and Intervention, pp. 61–62 AL OL ELL • Skills Practice, p. 63 AL OL ELL • Practice, p. 64 AL OL BL ELL • Word Problem Practice, p. 65 AL OL ELL • Enrichment, p. 66 OL BL • Spreadsheet Activity, p. 67 AL OL BL ELL • Quiz 4, p. 71 AL OL BL ELL **Transparencies** • 5-Minute Check Transparency 13-10 AL OL BL ELL **Additional Print Resources** • *Study Notebook* AL OL BL ELL	**Materials:** • spinner • die • red and white counters • blue and red marbles
Math Online glencoe.com • Extra Examples • Self-Check Quizzes • Personal Tutor	**CD/DVD Resources** IWB INTERACTIVE WHITEBOARD READY IWB StudentWorks Plus IWB Interactive Classroom IWB Diagnostic and Assessment Planner	• TeacherWorks Plus • eSolutions Manual Plus • ExamView Assessment Suite	
		p. 791	p. 796
pp. 784, 788		pp. 791, 795	

Summative Assessment
- Study Guide and Review, pp. 798–802
- Practice Test, p. 803

CHAPTER 13

Assessment and Intervention

SE = Student Edition, **TE** = Teacher Edition, **CRM** = Chapter Resource Masters

	Diagnosis	Prescription
Diagnostic Assessment	**Beginning Chapter 13**	
	Get Ready for Chapter 13 **SE**, p. 727	Response to Intervention **TE**, p. 727
	Beginning Every Lesson	
	Then, Now, Why? **SE** 5-Minute Check Transparencies	Chapter 0 **SE**, P1–P22 Concepts and Skills Bank **SE**, pp. 856–887 *Quick Review Math Handbook*
Formative Assessment	**During/After Every Lesson**	
	Check Your Progress **SE**, every example Check Your Understanding **SE** H.O.T. Problems **SE** Spiral Review **SE** Additional Examples **TE** Watch Out! **TE** Step 4, Assess **TE** Chapter 13 Quizzes **CRM**, pp. 70–71 Self-Check Quizzes glencoe.com	**Tier 1 Intervention** Concepts and Skills Bank **SE**, pp. 856–887 Skills Practice **CRM**, Ch. 1–13 glencoe.com **Tier 2 Intervention** Differentiated Instruction **TE** Study Guide and Intervention Masters **CRM**, Ch. 1–13 *Quick Review Math Handbook* **Tier 3 Intervention** *Math Triumphs, Grade 8,* Ch. 7, 9
	Mid-Chapter	
	Mid-Chapter Quiz **SE**, p. 764 Mid-Chapter Test **CRM**, p. 72 ExamView Assessment Suite	**Tier 1 Intervention** Concepts and Skills Bank **SE**, pp. 856–887 Skills Practice **CRM**, Ch. 1–13 glencoe.com **Tier 2 Intervention** Study Guide and Intervention Masters **CRM**, Ch. 1–13 *Quick Review Math Handbook* **Tier 3 Intervention** *Math Triumphs, Grade 8,* Ch. 7, 9
	Before Chapter Test	
	Chapter Study Guide and Review **SE**, pp. 798–802 Practice Test **SE**, p. 803 Standardized Test Practice **SE**, pp. 804–807 Chapter Test glencoe.com Standardized Test Practice glencoe.com Vocabulary Review glencoe.com ExamView Assessment Suite	**Tier 1 Intervention** Concepts and Skills Bank **SE**, pp. 856–887 Skills Practice **CRM**, Ch. 1–13 glencoe.com **Tier 2 Intervention** Study Guide and Intervention Masters **CRM**, Ch. 1–13 *Quick Review Math Handbook* **Tier 3 Intervention** *Math Triumphs, Grade 8,* Ch. 7, 9
Summative Assessment	**After Chapter 13**	
	Multiple-Choice Tests, Forms 1, 2A, 2B **CRM**, pp. 74–79 Free-Response Tests, Forms 2C, 2D, 3 **CRM**, pp. 80–86 Vocabulary Test **CRM**, p. 73 Extended Response Test **CRM**, p. 86 Standardized Test Practice **CRM**, pp. 87–89 ExamView Assessment Suite	Study Guide and Intervention Masters **CRM**, Ch. 1–13 *Quick Review Math Handbook* glencoe.com

Differentiated Instruction

Option 1 Reaching All Learners AL OL BL ELL

INTERPERSONAL Have students work in small groups. Tell them they will design a survey for the following: *You own a company that makes playground equipment. You want to know what equipment is best liked by the children who play on it.*

The survey should produce valid results and include the following:

- how they will conduct the survey,
- who will complete the survey,
- the size of the sample and why it is representative of the larger population,
- the type of sample(s) used for the survey, and
- the question(s) asked in the survey.

Have groups discuss how they might display the results and how they might use them as a business owner.

VISUAL/SPATIAL Have small groups of students make spinners. The spinners should have equal sections, and could have letters, colors, numbers, or designs. Ask groups to use their spinners to model and explain:

- theoretical and experimental probability, and
- the probability of compound events, including independent events and mutually exclusive events.

Option 2 Approaching Level AL

Place 19 counters side-by-side in a row. Have a student locate the middle counter and slide it upward. Have two more students locate the middle counters of the two smaller groups and slide them downward.

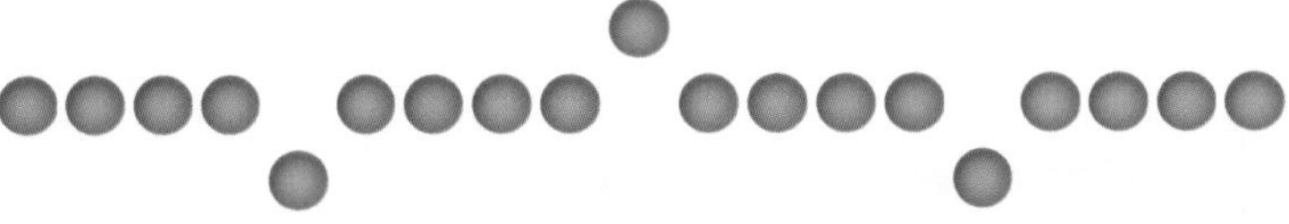

Explain that the interquartile range is the difference between the two lower counters. Tell them the middle counter of the larger set is called the median, while the middle counter or medians of the upper and lower half are called the upper and lower quartile, respectively.

Repeat the activity using 18 counters. Lead students to realize that although there is an even number of counters, the medians of the quartiles can be modeled with counters.

Option 3 English Learners ELL

Have students discuss the differences between biased and unbiased samples. Then give them a survey question, such as *should the school build a new gymnasium* and have them work in groups to write an example for each of the types of biased and unbiased samples: *simple random sample, stratified random sample, systematic random sample, convenience sample,* and *voluntary response sample.*

Option 4 Beyond Level BL

Students can explore the concept of geometric probability while designing a game. Tell them that geometric probability uses the area of figures to find the probability. They can use the formula

$$P(\text{specific region}) = \frac{\text{area of specific region}}{\text{area of the target}}$$

to find the geometric probability, or you can have them discover it on their own. Their game could be about tossing a beanbag or ball through holes in a target. Ask them to design a game that is fair and one that is unfair. Then they should explain why one is fair and the other is not.

Focus on Mathematical Content

Vertical Alignment

Before Chapter 13

Related Topics before Pre-Algebra

- construct sample spaces for simple or composite experiments
- select and use an appropriate representation for presenting and displaying relationships among collected data, including line plot, line graph, bar graph, stem-and-leaf plot, circle graph, and Venn diagrams, and justify the selection
- make inferences and convincing arguments based on an analysis of given or collected data

Previous Topics from Pre-Algebra

- select and use appropriate forms of rational numbers to solve real-world problems
- draw conclusions and make predictions by analyzing trends in scatter plots

Chapter 13

Related Topics from Pre-Algebra

- select and use an appropriate representation for presenting and displaying relationships among collected data, including line plots, line graphs, stem-and-leaf plots, circle graphs, bar graphs, box-and-whisker plots, histograms, and Venn diagrams, with and without the use of technology
- find the probabilities of dependent and independent events
- evaluate methods of sampling to determine validity of an inference made from a set of data

After Chapter 13

Preparation for Algebra 1

- represent relationships among quantities using concrete models, tables, graphs, diagrams, verbal descriptions, equations, and inequalities
- look for patterns and represent generalizations algebraically
- generate a different representation of data given another representation of data

Lesson-by-Lesson Preview

13-1 Measures of Central Tendency

Measures of central tendency describe the center of a set of data and include mean, median, and mode. The mean is the sum of the data divided by the number of items in the data set. The median is the middle number of the data ordered from least to greatest, or the mean of the two middle numbers. The mode is the number or numbers that occur most often.

These measures help you to analyze data.

Number of Days in a Month (2010)
31, 28, 31, 30, 31, 30, 31, 31, 30, 31, 30, 31

The mean is $\frac{\text{sum of data}}{\text{number of data}} = \frac{365}{12} = 30.42$. The median is 31. The mode is 31.

13-2 Stem-and-Leaf Plots

Stem-and-leaf plots list numerical data in ascending or descending order. The greatest place value of the data is used for the stems. The next greatest place value forms the leaves. List the stems from least to greatest in the *Stem* column. Write the leaves in the corresponding *Leaf* column. Order leaves from least to greatest and write a key that explains how to read the stems and leaves. For example, the data set 41, 53, 39, 48, and 32 is displayed in a stem-and-leaf plot:

Stem	Leaf
3	2 9
4	1 8
5	3

$3 \mid 2 = 32$

13-3 Measures of Variation

Measures of variation describe the distribution of data. The range is the difference between the greatest and least values of the set. The quartiles divide the data into four equal parts. The median separates the data set in half. The interquartile range is the difference between the upper quartile and the lower quartile. Outliers are values that are more than 1.5 times the value of the interquartile range beyond the quartiles.

13-4 Box-and-Whisker Plots

A box-and-whisker plot uses a number line to show the distribution of a data set. It divides a data set into four parts using the median and quartiles. A box is drawn around the quartile values and whiskers extend from each quartile to the extreme data points that are not outliers.

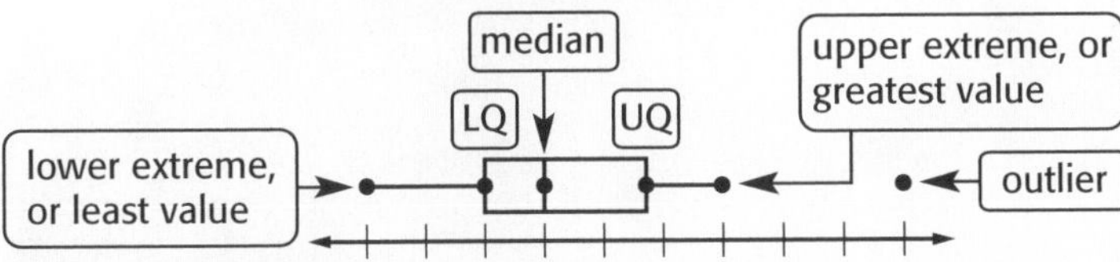

13-5 Histograms

A histogram displays numerical data that has been organized into equal intervals with bars that have the same width and no space between them. While a histogram does not show exact data points, its shape shows the distribution of the data. Histograms can be used to compare data although the mean, median, mode, and range cannot be determined.

13-6 Theoretical and Experimental Probability

Theoretical probability is what *should* occur in an experiment. Experimental probability is what *actually* occurs when repeating a probability experiment many times.

- The probability of an event is a ratio that compares the number of favorable outcomes to the number of possible outcomes:

  $P(\text{event}) = \dfrac{\text{number of favorable outcomes}}{\text{number of possible outcomes}}$.

- The probability of an event is between 0 and 1, inclusive. The closer a probability is to 1, the more likely it is to occur.
- The set of all possible outcomes is called the sample space.

13-7 Using Sampling to Predict

A sample is a smaller group of people or items chosen to represent a larger population. The best sample is one that is unbiased. An unbiased sample is representative of the larger population, selected at random or without preference, and large enough to provide accurate data.

13-8 Counting Outcomes

The Fundamental Counting Principle states that if event M can occur in m ways and is followed by event N that can occur in n ways, then the event M followed by N can occur in $m \cdot n$ ways. For example, if a shirt comes in 3 colors and 4 sizes, then there are $3 \cdot 4$ or 12 possible outcomes.

13-9 Permutations and Combinations

A permutation is an arrangement or listing in which order is important, such as finding the possible ways to arrange a line of 3 out of 6 photographs. The symbol $P(6, 3)$ represents the number of permutations of 6 things taken 3 at a time.

A combination is an arrangement or listing in which order is not important, such as choosing 5 colors of pencils from 10 colors. The symbol $C(10, 5)$ represents the number of combinations of 10 things taken 5 at a time.

13-10 Probability of Compound Events

Compound events consist of two or more simple events. Events are *independent* if the outcome of one event does not affect the outcome of a second event. Events are *dependent* if the outcome of one event does affect the outcome of a second event.

Professional Development

Targeted professional development has been articulated throughout McGraw-Hill's mathematics program. The **McGraw-Hill Professional Development Video Library** provides short videos that support key topics. For more information, visit glencoe.com.

Model Lessons

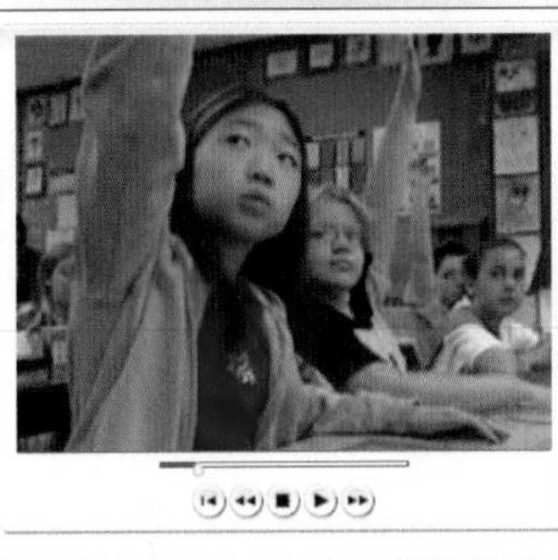

Instructional Strategies

13 Notes

Chapter Project

Games and Statistics

Students use what they have learned about measures of central tendency and variation, displaying data, and finding probabilities to work with data related to games.

- Divide students into groups. Have groups research and bring to class two sets of statistics related to the Olympics, such as the number of gold, silver, or bronze medals in the Summer Games, Winter Games, or a combination of games, for one country, or records in an event. Each data set should include 10 items or more.
- Have each group find the measures of central tendency for one of the sets of data. Which measure best represents the data? Why?
- Ask each group to display the second set of data using a stem-and-leaf plot, box-and-whisker plot, or histogram. Why is their display appropriate for the data? Would the others be appropriate or not? What can they infer from the data?
- Have students look for articles in newspapers or magazines that talk about probability and sports. Have students use their articles to create an interesting bulletin board or poster.

CHAPTER 13 Statistics and Probability

Then

In Chapter 2, you found the mean, or average, of a data set.

In Chapter 6, you have displayed data in circle graphs.

Now

In Chapter 13, you will:

- Find and use measures of central tendency and measures of variation.
- Display and interpret data.
- Find probabilities of simple events and independent and dependent events.

Why?

GAMES Statistics and statistical displays are frequently used to describe the results of the Olympic Games. In the 2006 Winter Olympics, the U.S. won 9 gold medals, 9 silver medals, and 7 bronze medals.

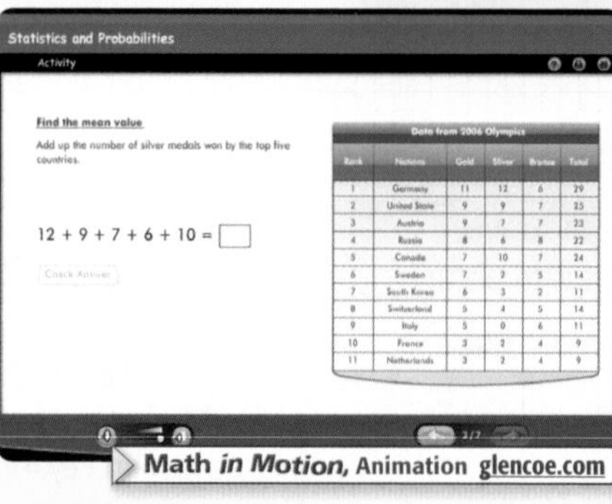

Math *in Motion,* Animation glencoe.com

Key Vocabulary Introduce the key vocabulary in the chapter using the routine below.

Define: The mode of a set of data is the number or numbers that occur(s) most often.

Example: In the data set 2, 5, 7, 3, 2, 5, 6, 5, the mode is 5.

Ask: What is the mode of the following data set: 15, 27, 19, 23, 27, 25, 15, 29, 21? The modes are 15 and 27.

726 Chapter 13 Statistics and Probability

Get Ready for Chapter 13

Diagnose Readiness You have two options for checking Prerequisite Skills.

Text Option Take the Quick Check below. Refer to the Quick Review for help.

QuickCheck

(Used in Lessons 13-1 through 13-3)
Find the mean for each data set. (Lesson 2-5)

1. \$8, \$22, \$16 **\$15.33**
2. 12.5 cm, 13 cm, 15.9 cm, 9.6 cm, 17.5 cm **13.7 cm**
3. **AQUARIUM** The table shows the number of visitors to the aquarium each month. Find the mean number of visitors. **5000 visitors**

Visitors to the Aquarium (thousands)			
3	11	5	4
5	3	6	3
12	2	2	4

(Used in Lesson 13-9)
Simplify. (Previous Course)

4. $\frac{6 \cdot 5}{5 \cdot 7}$ **$\frac{6}{7}$**
5. $\frac{9 \cdot 4}{2 \cdot 3}$ **6**
6. $\frac{7 \cdot 10 \cdot 9}{18 \cdot 15 \cdot 1}$ **$2\frac{1}{3}$**
7. $\frac{8 \cdot 9 \cdot 10}{3 \cdot 4 \cdot 5}$ **12**
8. **SURVEYS** Seven-eighths of students surveyed said they drink one glass of milk per day. Three-fourths of these drink a glass of milk with dinner. What fraction of students drink their glass of milk with dinner?

(Used in Lesson 13-10)
Find each sum, difference, or product. (Lessons 3-3 and 3-6)

9. $\frac{2}{3} \times \frac{9}{10} \times \frac{4}{5}$ **$\frac{12}{25}$**
10. $\frac{7}{8} \times \frac{2}{3} \times \frac{9}{14}$ **$\frac{3}{8}$**
11. $\frac{9}{10} + \frac{2}{5} - \frac{3}{10}$ **1**
12. $\frac{1}{3} + \frac{1}{6} - \frac{1}{9}$ **$\frac{7}{18}$**
13. **GARDENING** Hannah finished filling a $\frac{7}{8}$ gallon watering can by pouring $\frac{1}{4}$ of a gallon of water into the can. How much water was already in the can? **$\frac{5}{8}$**

QuickReview

EXAMPLE 1

Find the mean temperature of 65°, 70°, 75°, 70°, and 65°.

$$\frac{65 + 70 + 75 + 70 + 65}{5} = \frac{345}{5}$$
$$= 69 \quad \text{Simplify.}$$

The average temperature is 69°.

EXAMPLE 2

Simplify $\frac{9 \cdot 8 \cdot 7}{3 \cdot 2 \cdot 1}$.

$$\frac{9 \cdot 8 \cdot 7}{3 \cdot 2 \cdot 1} = \frac{\overset{3}{\cancel{9}} \cdot \overset{4}{\cancel{8}} \cdot 7}{\underset{1}{\cancel{3}} \cdot \underset{1}{\cancel{2}} \cdot 1} \quad \text{Divide out common factors.}$$
$$= 3 \cdot 4 \cdot 7 \text{ or } 84 \quad \text{Simplify.}$$

8. **$\frac{21}{32}$**

EXAMPLE 3

Find $\frac{7}{12} + \frac{5}{8} - \frac{1}{12}$.

$$\frac{7}{12} + \frac{5}{8} - \frac{1}{12}$$
$$= \left(\frac{7}{12} \cdot \frac{2}{2}\right) + \left(\frac{5}{8} \cdot \frac{3}{3}\right) - \left(\frac{1}{12} \cdot \frac{2}{2}\right) \quad \text{Rename using the LCD, 24.}$$
$$= \frac{14}{24} + \frac{15}{24} - \frac{2}{24} \quad \text{Simplify.}$$
$$= \frac{27}{24} \quad \text{Simplify the numerators.}$$
$$= 1\frac{3}{24} \text{ or } 1\frac{1}{8} \quad \text{Simplify.}$$

Online Option Math Online Take a self-check Chapter Readiness Quiz at glencoe.com.

Get Ready for Chapter 13

Response to Intervention (RtI)

Use the *Quick Check* results and the Intervention Planner to help you determine your Response to Intervention. The If-Then statements in the chart help you decide the appropriate tier of RtI and suggest intervention resources for each tier.

Intervention Planner

Tier 1 On Level

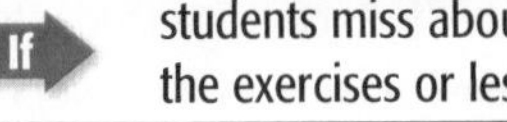
If students miss about 25% of the exercises or less,

Then choose a resource:

SE Lessons 2-5, 3-3, and 3-6
CRM Skills Practice, Chapter 2, p. 31; Chapter 3, pp. 20, 38
TE Chapter Project, p. 726

Math Online Self-Check Quiz

Tier 2 Strategic Intervention approaching grade level

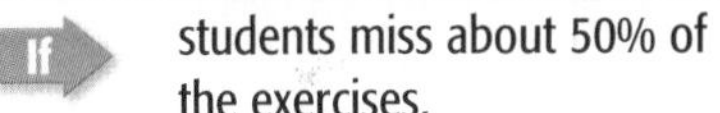
If students miss about 50% of the exercises,

Then choose a resource:

CRM Study Guide and Intervention, Chapter 2, p. 29; Chapter 3, pp. 18, 36
Quick Review Math Handbook

Math Online Extra Examples, Personal Tutor, Homework Help

Tier 3 Intensive Intervention 2 or more years below grade level

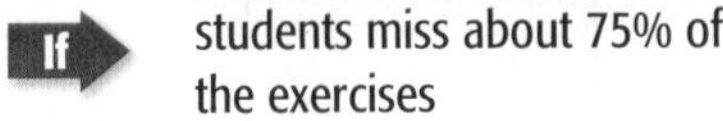
If students miss about 75% of the exercises

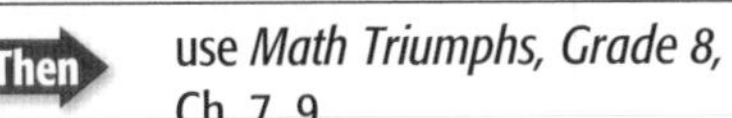
Then use *Math Triumphs, Grade 8,* Ch. 7, 9

Math Online Extra Examples, Personal Tutor, Homework Help, Review Vocabulary

CHAPTER 13 Notes

FOLDABLES® Study Organizer

Dinah Zike's Foldables®

Focus Students write notes on what they learn about statistics and probability.

Teach Have students make and label the pages for each lesson of their Foldables as illustrated. Have students use the appropriate pages to find measures of central tendency and variation, use different statistical displays, and find probabilities.

When to Use It Encourage students to add to their Foldable as they work through the chapter, and use them to review for the chapter test.

Differentiated Instruction

CRM Student-Built Glossary, p. 1–2 Students should complete the chart by providing a definition of each term and an example as they progress through Chapter 13. This study tool can also be used to review for the chapter test.

Get Started on Chapter 13

You will learn several new concepts, skills, and vocabulary terms as you study Chapter 13. To get ready, identify important terms and organize your resources. You may wish to refer to **Chapter 0** to review prerequisite skills.

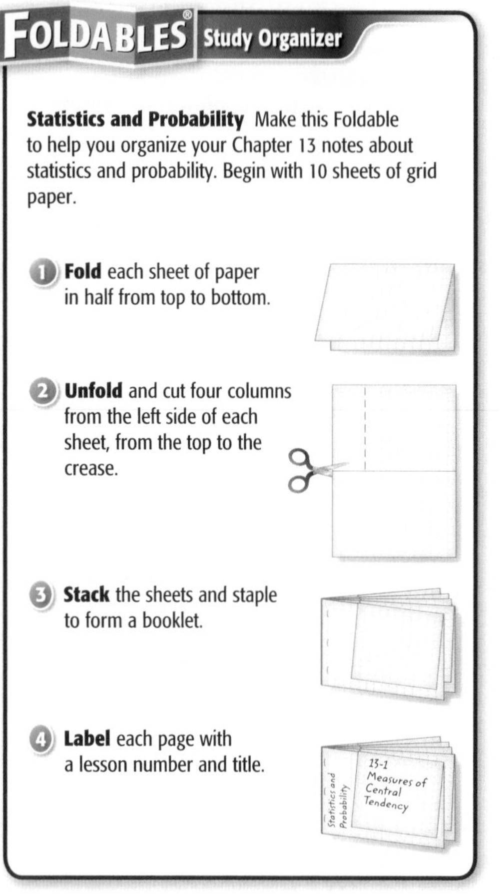

FOLDABLES® Study Organizer
Statistics and Probability Make this Foldable to help you organize your Chapter 13 notes about statistics and probability. Begin with 10 sheets of grid paper.
1 Fold each sheet of paper in half from top to bottom.
2 Unfold and cut four columns from the left side of each sheet, from the top to the crease.
3 Stack the sheets and staple to form a booklet.
4 Label each page with a lesson number and title.
Statistics and Probability
13-1 Measures of Central Tendency

Math Online glencoe.com

- Study the chapter online
- Explore **Math in Motion**
- Get extra help from your own **Personal Tutor**
- Use **Extra Examples** for additional help
- Take a **Self-Check Quiz**
- **Review Vocabulary** in fun ways

New Vocabulary

English		Español
measures of central tendency	• p. 730 •	medidas de tendencia central
median	• p. 730 •	mediana
mode	• p. 730 •	moda
stem-and-leaf plot	• p. 737 •	diagrama de tallo y hojas
measures of variation	• p. 743 •	medidas de varación
range	• p. 743 •	amplitud
outlier	• p. 745 •	valor atípico
box-and-whisker plot	• p. 750 •	diagrama de caja y patillas
histogram	• p. 757 •	histograma
probability	• p. 765 •	probabilidad
sample	• p. 771 •	muestra

Review Vocabulary

circle graph • p. 367 • gráfica circular type of statistical graph used to compare parts to a whole

Favorite Pets

Hamsters 13%
Hen 12%
Cats 25%
Dogs 50%

mean • p. 92 • media the sum of the data divided by the number of items in the data set, also called the average

Multilingual eGlossary glencoe.com

728 Chapter 13 Statistics and Probability

Analyzing Data

Math Online glencoe.com
Math *in Motion*, Animation

Objective
Examine data and find a number to describe it.

Often, it is useful to describe or represent a set of data by using a single number. The table shows the speeds in miles per hour of first serves in a tennis match.

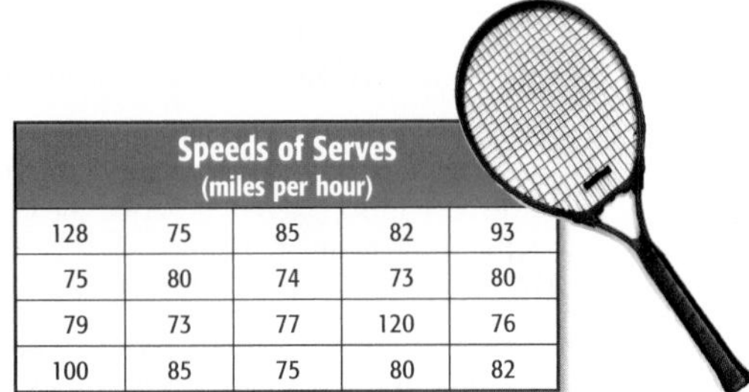

Speeds of Serves (miles per hour)				
128	75	85	82	93
75	80	74	73	80
79	73	77	120	76
100	85	75	80	82

The average of the data set is 84.6. This number is much higher than most of the data, so it is not a good number to describe the data.

A number that could be used to describe this data set is 80. Some reasons for choosing this number are listed below.

- It occurs three times. Only one other number appears as many times.
- If the numbers are arranged from least to greatest, 80 falls in the center of the data set.

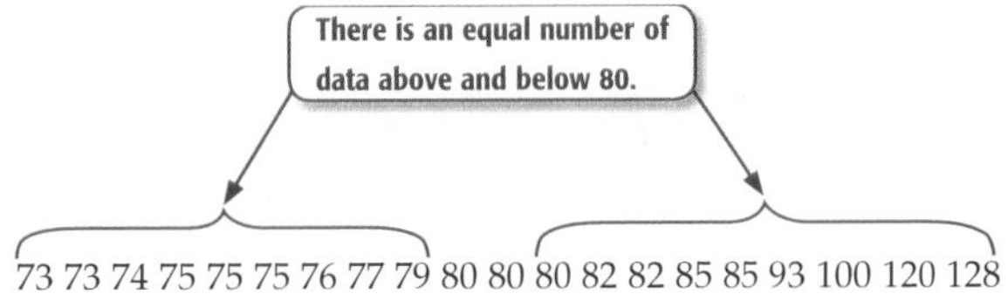
There is an equal number of data above and below 80.
73 73 74 75 75 75 76 77 79 80 80 80 82 82 85 85 93 100 120 128

Collect the Data

Collect a group of data. Use one of the suggestions below, or use your own method. Display your data in a table.

- Research data about a sports team in your area, such as batting averages, number of wins per season, or number of goals per game.
- Find a graph or table of data in the newspaper or a magazine. Some examples include weather data and population data.
- Conduct a survey to gather some data about your classmates.
- Count the number of raisins in a number of small boxes.

Analyze the Results 1–3. See students' work.

1. Choose a number that best describes all of the data in the set.
2. Explain what your number means, and explain which method you used to choose your number.
3. Describe how your number might be useful in real life.

EXPLORE 13-1 Lesson Notes

1 FOCUS

Objective Examine data and find a number to describe it.

Materials for Each Group

- local sports data from a newspaper or the Internet
- graph or data table from newspaper or magazine
- small boxes of raisins

2 TEACH

Working in Cooperative Groups

Have students work in groups of two or three, mixing abilities, to collect the data and complete Exercise 1.

Ask:

- Why would it be desirable to have a single number to describe a whole set of data? It would be more concise and take into account all the numbers.
- Who would use such a number? Someone who can use general, typical information, without specifics.

Practice Have students complete Exercises 2 and 3.

3 ASSESS

Formative Assessment

Use Exercises 1 and 2 to assess whether students understand how to organize data and identify the middle and repeated values. Students should be able to explain why a particular number represents their data best.

From Concrete to Abstract

Use Exercise 3 to determine whether students can apply what they have learned to analyze and interpret real-world data.

13-1 Lesson Notes

1 FOCUS

Vertical Alignment

Before Lesson 13-1
Find the mean or average of a data set.

Lesson 13-1
Use the mean, median, and mode as measures of central tendency. Choose an appropriate measure of central tendency and recognize measures of statistics.

After Lesson 13-1
Recognize and find measures of variation.

2 TEACH

Scaffolding Questions

Have students read the *Why?* section of the lesson and answer the questions.

Ask:

- If the players line up from least to greatest height, will the height of the middle player be closer to the overall height of the team? Explain. Yes; Sample answer: Most of the players seem to be about the height of the player in the middle of the heights.
- How would you describe the overall height of the team? Sample answer: Most players seem to be about the same height.

13-1 Measures of Central Tendency

Then
You have already found the mean or average of a data set. (Lesson 2-5)

Now
- Use the mean, median, and mode as measures of central tendency.
- Choose an appropriate measure of central tendency and recognize measures of statistics.

New Vocabulary
measures of central tendency
mean
median
mode

Math Online
glencoe.com
- Extra Examples
- Personal Tutor
- Self-Check Quiz
- Homework Help

Why?

The cartoon shows a basketball team getting ready to play a game.

a. Does the average of the heights of the players describe the overall height of the team? Explain.

b. If the player with the number 8 jersey was not on the team, would the average of the heights of the remaining players describe the overall height of the team? Explain.
a–b. See Chapter 13 Answer Appendix.

Measures of Central Tendency When you have a list of numerical data, it is often helpful to use one or more numbers to describe the whole data set. **Measures of central tendency** describe the center of the data.

Key Concept — Measures of Central Tendency (For Your FOLDABLE)

mean	sum of the data divided by the number of items in the data set
median	middle number of the data ordered from least to greatest, or the mean of the middle two numbers
mode	number or numbers that occur most often

Real-World EXAMPLE 1 Find Measures of Central Tendency

GOVERNMENT Find the mean, median, and mode of the data in the table.

House of Representatives

California	53	New York	29
Florida	25	North Carolina	13
Illinois	19	Ohio	18
Michigan	15	Pennsylvania	19
New Jersey	13	Texas	32

$$\text{mean} = \frac{\text{total number of representatives}}{\text{number of states}}$$

$$= \frac{53 + 25 + \ldots + 32}{10}$$

$$= \frac{236}{10} \text{ or } 23.6$$

The mean number of representatives is 23.6.

To find the median, order the numbers from least to greatest.

13, 13, 15, 18, 19, 19, 25, 29, 32,53

$$\frac{19 + 19}{2} = 19$$ **There is an even number of items. Find the mean of the two middle numbers.**

The median number of representatives is 19.

Since both 13 and 19 appear twice, the modes are 13 and 19 representatives.

Check Your Progress

1. **SNAKES** The reptile collection at a local zoo has snakes that measure 62, 48, 37, 45, 50, 65 , 48, 54, 48, 52, 40, and 51 centimeters long. Find the mean, median, and mode of the data. **50; 49; 48**

Personal Tutor glencoe.com

Lesson 13-1 Resources

Resource	Approaching-Level	On-Level	Beyond-Level	English Learners
Teacher Edition			• Differentiated Instruction, pp. 732, 735	
Chapter Resource Masters	• Study Guide and Intervention, pp. 5–6 • Skills Practice, p. 7 • Practice, p. 8 • Word Problem Practice, p. 9	• Study Guide and Intervention, pp. 5–6 • Skills Practice, p. 7 • Practice, p. 8 • Word Problem Practice, p. 9 • Enrichment, p. 10	• Practice, p. 8 • Word Problem Practice, p. 9 • Enrichment, p. 10	• Study Guide and Intervention, pp. 5–6 • Skills Practice, p. 7 • Practice, p. 8
Transparencies	• 5-Minute Check Transparency 13-1	• 5-Minute Check Transparency 13-1	• 5-Minute Check Transparency 13-1	• 5-Minute Check Transparency 13-1
Other	• Study Notebook • Teaching Pre-Algebra with Manipulatives	• Study Notebook • Teaching Pre-Algebra with Manipulatives	• Study Notebook	• Study Notebook • Teaching Pre-Algebra with Manipulatives

STANDARDIZED TEST EXAMPLE 2

Karen talked on the phone for 25 minutes, 39 minutes, 28 minutes, and 20 minutes over the last 4 days. If she talks for 34 minutes on the next day, which of the following statements would be true?

A The mean increases and the median decreases.

B The median is unchanged and the mean increases.

C Both the mean and the median decrease.

D Both the mean and the median increase.

Read the Test Item

You need to determine which statement would be true if Karen talks for 34 minutes on the fifth day.

Solve the Test Item

The mean of the four days is $\frac{25 + 39 + 28 + 20}{4}$ or 28. The mean of the five days is $\frac{25 + 39 + 28 + 20 + 34}{5}$ or 29.2. Since the mean increased, you can eliminate answer choice C.

Find the median to check the other answer choices. Arrange the numbers from least to greatest, first with four days and then with five days.

20, 25, 28, 39 **The median is 26.5.**

20, 25, 28, 34, 39 **The median is 28.**

The median also increased. The answer is D.

Test-TakingTip

Number Sense Eliminate possibilities using number sense. Since the new data value is greater than the least value in the data set, the mean will *not* decrease. So, you can eliminate choice C.

Check Your Progress

2. Nikko earned the following amounts raking leaves: \$15, \$10, \$12, \$8, and \$17. If he drops the lowest amount he has earned raking leaves, which of the following statements would be true? G

F The mean decreases and the median increases.

G The mean and the median both increase.

H The mean is unchanged and the median increases.

J The mean and the median both decrease.

Personal Tutor glencoe.com

Choose Appropriate Measures Different circumstances determine which measures of central tendency are most appropriate.

Concept Summary Using Mean, Median, and Mode — For Your FOLDABLE

Measure	Most Useful When...
mean	• the data have no extreme values (values that are much greater or much less than the rest of the data)
median	• the data have extreme values • there are no big gaps in the middle of the data
mode	• data have many repeated numbers

Measures of Central Tendency

Example 1 shows how to find measures of central tendency. **Example 2** shows how to solve a test example that compares measures.

Formative Assessment

Use the Check Your Progress exercises after each example to determine students' understanding of concepts.

Additional Examples

1 **MOVIES** Find the mean, median, and mode of the data in the table.

Ten Highest Grossing Movies as of 2007 (millions)				
601	461	436	435	431
423	404	380	377	373

mean, \$432.1 million; median, \$427 million; no mode

2 **STANDARDIZED TEST PRACTICE** Nabuko has test scores of 80, 85, 72, and 91. If her next score is 82, which of the following statements would be true? B

A The mean increases and the median decreases.

B The mean is unchanged and the median decreases.

C Both mean and median increase.

D Both mean and median decrease.

Additional Examples also in Interactive Classroom PowerPoint® Presentations

IWB INTERACTIVE WHITEBOARD READY

Focus on Mathematical Content

Extreme Values Extreme values in a set of data are also called outliers because they lie outside the overall pattern of distribution. Extreme values affect the mean because the mean is sensitive to each value in the set. The median and mode are affected little by an individual number. Therefore, the median and mode are not greatly affected by extreme values.

Tips for New Teachers

Remind students that measures of central tendency must fall within the range of data, between the minimum and maximum.

Choose Appropriate Measures

Examples 3 and 4 show how to choose appropriate measures of central tendency to represent data.

Additional Examples

3 **SURVEYS** Mai took a poll in her class to see how many times her classmates visited the local amusement park during summer vacation: 4, 0, 2, 3, 2, 4, 1, 2, 1, 2, 3, 2, 2, 0. What measure of central tendency best represents the data? Then find the measure of central tendency. Mode; there are many repeated values; 2.

4 **SALARIES** The weekly salaries for the employees at Bob's Book Store are: \$600, \$600, \$625, \$1250, \$1800. Which measure of data should Bob's Book Store's manager use to show new employees that the salaries are high? Mean; Sample answer: The mean (\$975) results in a higher salary than the median (\$625) or the mode (\$600).

Focus on Mathematical Content

Mode In a set of data, there can be more than one mode. A set with two modes is bi-modal. A set with three modes is tri-modal, and more. There can also be a data set with no mode.

Tips for New Teachers

Measures of Central Tendency Emphasize to students that mean, median, and mode are all appropriate averages that can be used to describe a data set. The fact that one measure may best describe a particular data set does not invalidate the other measures.

Real-World EXAMPLE 3 Choose an Appropriate Measure

WEATHER The table shows daytime high temperatures for the previous week. Which measure of central tendency best represents the data? Then find the measure of central tendency.

Day	Temperature (°F)
Sun.	84
Mon.	83
Tues.	89
Wed.	90
Thurs.	91
Fri.	85
Sat.	80

Since the set of data has no extreme values or numbers that are identical, the mean would best represent the data.

Mean: $\frac{84 + 83 + \ldots + 80}{7} = \frac{602}{7}$ or 86

The temperature 86°F is the measure of central tendency that best represents the data.

Check Your Progress

3. **EXERCISE** The table shows the number of sit-ups Pablo had done in one minute for the past 7 days. Which measure of central tendency best represents the data? Justify your selection and then find the measure of central tendency.
Median; There is an extreme value of 19 and no numbers repeat.

Day	Number of Situps
Sun.	40
Mon.	37
Tues.	45
Wed.	19
Thurs.	49
Fri.	50
Sat.	46

Personal Tutor glencoe.com

You can also use measures of central tendency to show different points of view.

Real-World EXAMPLE 4 Different Points of View

RIDES The average wait times for 10 different rides at an amusement park are 65, 21, 17, 52, 25, 17, 11, 22, 60, and 44 minutes. Which measure of central tendency would the amusement park advertise to show that the wait times for its rides are short? Explain.

Mean: $\frac{65 + 21 + \ldots + 44}{10} = \frac{334}{10}$ or 33.4

Median: 11, 17, 17, 21, 22, 25, 44, 52, 60, 65

$\frac{22 + 25}{2}$ or 23.5

Mode: 17

The amusement park would want to advertise a short wait time. So, the amusement park would want to use the mode, 17 minutes.

Real-World Link

There are more than 400 amusement parks around the world. The park with the greatest annual attendance is Magic Kingdom in Orlando, Florida. It averages almost 17 million visitors per year.

Source: Coaster Grotto

Check Your Progress

4. **SCORES** Maggie had the following times on her runs in the 100-meter dash: 11.6, 11.8, 12.7, 12.6, 11.9, and 12.0. Which measure of data would she want to use to describe her performance?

4. median; Sample answer: The median results in the best time.

Personal Tutor glencoe.com

Differentiated Instruction BL

 students enjoy challenges,

 have students analyze the mean, median, and mode in Example 4. Have them explain which measure is most misleading and why. Ask them to explain why they might want to use the mean or median wait time rather than the mode.

732 Chapter 13 Statistics and Probability

Check Your Understanding

Example 1 p. 730

1. mean: 151.4; median: 157; mode: 157
2. mean: 35 min; median: 35 min; mode: 30 min

Example 2 p. 731

1. RACING The table shows the winning speeds of the Indianapolis 500 in recent years. Find the mean, median, and mode of the data. Round to the nearest tenth.

Year	Driver	Speed (mph)
2001	Helio Castroneves	131
2002	Helio Castroneves	166
2003	Gil de Ferran	157
2004	Buddy Rice	139
2005	Dan Wheldon	158
2006	Sam Hornish Jr	157
2007	Dario Franchitti	152

Source: Indianapolis 500

2. EXERCISE Last week, Sarah spent 35, 30, 45, 30, 40, 37, and 28 minutes exercising. Find the mean, median, and mode. Round to the nearest whole number.

3. MULTIPLE CHOICE One week, a store sold 53, 61, 46, 59, 61, 55, and 49 board games. Suppose the store sells 83 board games on the eighth day. Which measure of central tendency would change the most? **A**

A mean
B median
C mode
D all measures were affected equally

Example 3 p. 732

4. BOOKS The different eighth grade homerooms read 38, 45, 26, 51, 42, 38, 50, and 58 books for a reading competition. Which measure of central tendency best represents the data? Justify your selection and then find the measure of central tendency. **Mean; the data has no extreme values. 43.5**

Example 4 p. 732

5. EXERCISE Refer to the data in Exercise 2. Which measure of central tendency could Sarah use to show that she exercises for large amounts of time each day? Explain. **mean or median; Sample answer: The mean and median both show longer amounts of time.**

Practice and Problem Solving

= **Step-by-Step Solutions** begin on page R11.
Extra Practice begins on page 810.

Example 1 p. 730

Find the mean, median, and mode for each set of data. If necessary, round to the nearest whole number.

6. the minutes spent biking each day in one week: 45, 30, 65, 90, 74, 60, 35
7. the price, in dollars, of digital cameras: 250, 200, 320, 235, 265, 200

6–7. See margin.

Example 2 p. 731

8a. median; mean goes from 15 to 16.2 while the median goes from 15 to 16.5.

8b. median; Sample answer: The mean decreases to 14.75 and the median decreases to 14.5.

9. median; 869 is an extreme value that shifts the mean upward; 820

8. BASKETBALL Sasha scored the following point totals in 7 games this basketball season: 12, 18, 20, 8, 15, 18, and 14.

a. If she drops her lowest score, which measure of central tendency would increase more, the mean or median? Explain.

b. In her next basketball game, Sasha scores 13 points. Which measure of central tendency would decrease more, the mean or median? Explain.

Example 3 p. 732

9. The table shows the football teams with the most all-time wins. Which measure of central tendency best represents the data? Justify your selection and then find the measure of central tendency.

University	All-Time Football Wins*
Michigan	869
Notre Dame	824
Texas	820
Nebraska	817
Ohio State	798

Source: College Football Data Warehouse
*As of 2007.

TEACH with TECH

Interactive Whiteboard Write a data set on the board. Set up a fraction to find the mean, and drag each data value to the numerator of the fraction.

3 PRACTICE

Formative Assessment

Use Exercises 1–5 to check for understanding.

Use the chart at the bottom of this page to customize assignments for your students.

Additional Answers

6. mean: 57 min; median: 60 min; mode: none
7. mean: $245; median: $243; mode: $200

Differentiated Homework Options

Level	Assignment	Two-Day Option	
AL Basic	6–11, 16–17, 20–29	7–11 odd, 22–25	6–10 even, 16–17, 20–21, 26–29
OL Core	7–11 odd, 12–17, 20–29	6–11, 22–25	12–17, 20–21, 26–29
BL Advanced	12–28 (optional: 29)		

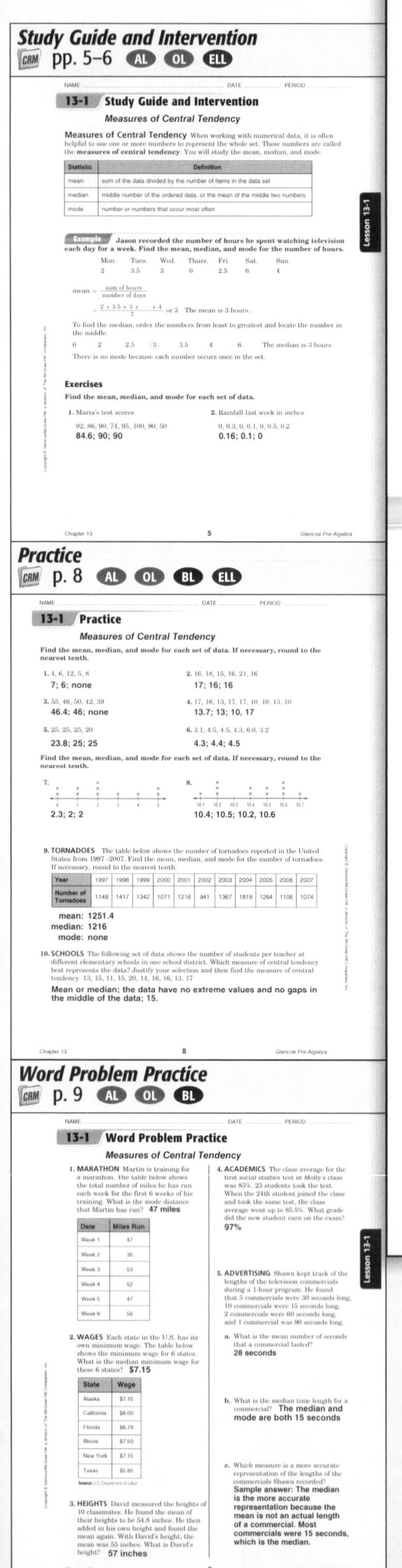

Study Guide and Intervention

CRM pp. 5–6 AL OL ELL

NAME ______ DATE ______ PERIOD ______

13-1 Study Guide and Intervention

Measures of Central Tendency

Measures of Central Tendency When working with numerical data, it is often helpful to use one or more numbers to represent the whole set. These numbers are called the **measures of central tendency**. You will study the mean, median, and mode.

Statistic	Definition
mean	sum of the data divided by the number of items in the data set
median	middle number of the ordered data, or the mean of the middle two numbers
mode	number or numbers that occur most often

Example **Jason recorded the number of hours he spent watching television each day for a week. Find the mean, median, and mode for the number of hours.**

Mon.	Tues.	Wed.	Thurs.	Fri.	Sat.	Sun.
2	3.5	3	0	2.5	6	4

$\text{mean} = \frac{\text{sum of hours}}{\text{number of days}}$

$= \frac{2 + 3.5 + 3 + \ldots + 4}{7}$ or 3 The mean is 3 hours.

To find the median, order the numbers from least to greatest and locate the number in the middle.

0 2 2.5 (3) 3.5 4 6 The median is 3 hours.

There is no mode because each number occurs once in the set.

Exercises

Find the mean, median, and mode for each set of data.

1. Maria's test scores
92, 86, 90, 74, 95, 100, 90, 50
84.6; 90; 90

2. Rainfall last week in inches
0, 0.3, 0, 0.1, 0, 0.5, 0.2
0.16; 0.1; 0

Chapter 13 5 Glencoe Pre-Algebra

Practice

CRM p. 8 AL OL BL ELL

NAME ______ DATE ______ PERIOD ______

13-1 Practice

Measures of Central Tendency

Find the mean, median, and mode for each set of data. If necessary, round to the nearest tenth.

1. 4, 6, 12, 5, 8
7; 6; none

2. 16, 18, 15, 16, 21, 16
17; 16; 16

3. 55, 46, 50, 42, 39
46.4; 46; none

4. 17, 16, 13, 17, 17, 10, 10, 13, 10
13.7; 13; 10, 17

5. 25, 25, 25, 20
23.8; 25; 25

6. 3.1, 4.5, 4.5, 4.3, 6.0, 3.2
4.3; 4.4; 4.5

Find the mean, median, and mode for each set of data. If necessary, round to the nearest tenth.

7. (line plot 0–5)
2.3; 2; 2

8. (line plot 10.1–10.7)
10.4; 10.5; 10.2, 10.6

9. **TORNADOES** The table below shows the number of tornadoes reported in the United States from 1997–2007. Find the mean, median, and mode for the number of tornadoes. If necessary, round to the nearest tenth.

Year	1997	1998	1999	2000	2001	2002	2003	2004	2005	2006	2007
Number of Tornadoes	1148	1417	1342	1071	1216	941	1367	1819	1264	1106	1074

mean: 1251.4
median: 1216
mode: none

10. **SCHOOLS** The following set of data shows the number of students per teacher at different elementary schools in one school district. Which measure of central tendency best represents the data? Justify your selection and then find the measure of central tendency. 13, 15, 11, 15, 20, 14, 16, 16, 13, 17
Mean or median; the data have no extreme values and no gaps in the middle of the data; 15.

Chapter 13 8 Glencoe Pre-Algebra

Word Problem Practice

CRM p. 9 AL OL BL

NAME ______ DATE ______ PERIOD ______

13-1 Word Problem Practice

Measures of Central Tendency

1. **MARATHON** Martin is training for a marathon. The table below shows the total number of miles he has run each week for the first 6 weeks of his training. What is the mode distance that Martin has run? **47 miles**

Date	Miles Run
Week 1	47
Week 2	35
Week 3	53
Week 4	52
Week 5	47
Week 6	56

2. **WAGES** Each state in the U.S. has its own minimum wage. The table below shows the minimum wage for 6 states. What is the median minimum wage for these 6 states? **$7.15**

State	Wage
Alaska	$7.15
California	$8.00
Florida	$6.79
Illinois	$7.50
New York	$7.15
Texas	$5.85

Source: U.S. Department of Labor

3. **HEIGHTS** David measured the heights of 10 classmates. He found the mean of their heights to be 54.8 inches. He then added in his own height and found the mean again. With David's height, the mean was 55 inches. What is David's height? **57 inches**

4. **ACADEMICS** The class average for the first social studies test in Molly's class was 85%. 23 students took the test. When the 24th student joined the class and took the same test, the class average went up to 85.5%. What grade did the new student earn on the exam? **97%**

5. **ADVERTISING** Shawn kept track of the lengths of the television commercials during a 1-hour program. He found that 5 commercials were 30 seconds long, 10 commercials were 15 seconds long, 2 commercials were 60 seconds long, and 1 commercial was 90 seconds long.

a. What is the mean number of seconds that a commercial lasted? **28 seconds**

b. What is the median time length for a commercial? **The median and mode are both 15 seconds**

c. Which measure is a more accurate representation of the lengths of the commercials Shawn recorded? **Sample answer: The median is the more accurate representation because the mean is not an actual length of a commercial. Most commercials were 15 seconds, which is the median.**

Chapter 13 9 Glencoe Pre-Algebra

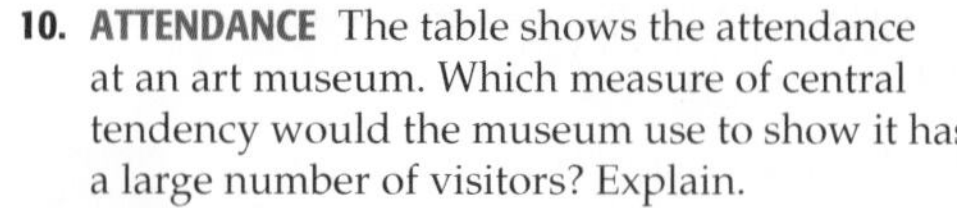

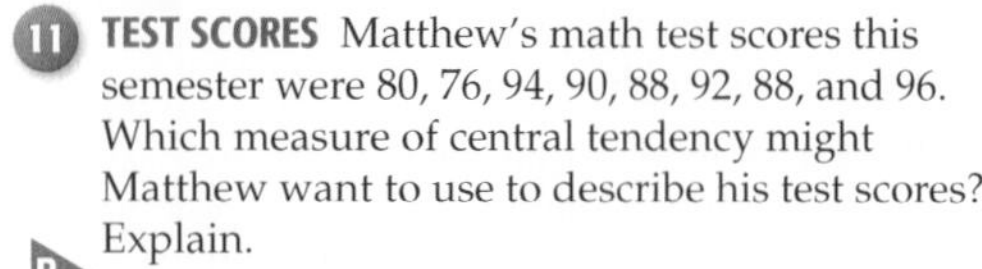

Example 4 p. 732

10–13. See margin.

10. **ATTENDANCE** The table shows the attendance at an art museum. Which measure of central tendency would the museum use to show it has a large number of visitors? Explain.

Day	Attendance
Tuesday	214
Wednesday	189
Thursday	214
Friday	248
Saturday	220
Sunday	253

11. **TEST SCORES** Matthew's math test scores this semester were 80, 76, 94, 90, 88, 92, 88, and 96. Which measure of central tendency might Matthew want to use to describe his test scores? Explain.

B

12. **FINANCIAL LITERACY** The hourly wages of employees in a small store are $7, $24, $8, $10, $6, $8, and $8. Which measure of central tendency might the store use to attract people to work there? Explain.

13. **SIBLINGS** The graph shows the number of siblings that Ms. Delgado's students have. Which measure of central tendency best represents the data? Explain.

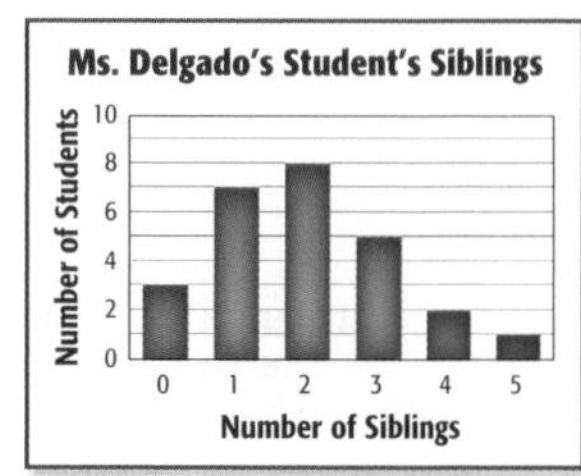

14. **ICE SKATING** Winona needs to average 5.8 points from 14 judges to win the competition. The mean score of 13 judges was 5.9. What is the lowest score she can receive from the 14th judge and still win? **4.5**

Real-World Link

In the women's individual Olympic figure skating competitions, the United States has won gold medals 7 times since 1924. Sarah Hughes was 16 when she won the gold medal in 2002.

15. **COLLECT DATA** Survey your classmates to find their height. Display the results of your survey in a line plot. Then find the mean, median, and mode of your data. Which measure of central tendency would you use to represent the overall height? **See margin.**

C

H.O.T. Problems

Use Higher-Order Thinking Skills

16. **OPEN ENDED** Construct a data set with a mean of 4 and a median that is *not* 4. **Sample answer: 2, 2, 8, 4**

17. **REASONING** Is it *always*, *sometimes*, or *never* possible for the mean, median, and mode to be equal? Justify your reasoning.

17. Sometimes; For example, the data set: $3, $5, $5, $5, and $7. The mean is $5, the median is $5, and the mode is $5.

18. **CHALLENGE** The ages of the players on an intramural volleyball team are 29, 25, 26, 31, 28, 23, 21, and 25.

a. Suppose another player joins the team. What must the age of the new player be so that the mean age is 27? Explain your reasoning.

b. What must the age of the new player be so that the median age is 25? Explain your reasoning.

18–21. See Chapter 13 Answer Appendix.

19. **CHALLENGE** A real estate guide lists the "average" home prices for counties in your state. Do you think the mean, median, or mode would be the most useful average for homebuyers? Explain.

20. **REASONING** Can a data set have more than one mode? median? Explain.

21. **WRITING IN MATH** Use the Internet to find some real-world data. Which measure of central tendency best represents the data you found? Justify your selection and then find the measure of central tendency.

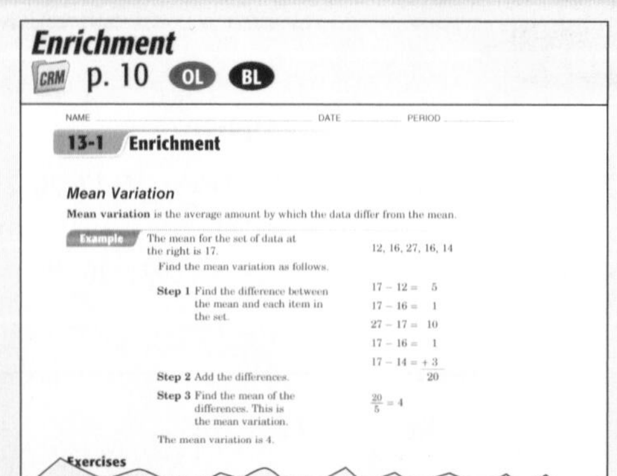

Enrichment

CRM p. 10 OL BL

NAME ______ DATE ______ PERIOD ______

13-1 Enrichment

Mean Variation

Mean variation is the average amount by which the data differ from the mean.

Example The mean for the set of data at the right is 17. 12, 16, 27, 16, 14

Find the mean variation as follows.

Step 1 Find the difference between the mean and each item in the set.
17 − 12 = 5
17 − 16 = 1
27 − 17 = 10
17 − 16 = 1
17 − 14 = + 3

Step 2 Add the differences. 20

Step 3 Find the mean of the differences. This is the mean variation. $\frac{20}{5} = 4$

The mean variation is 4.

Exercises

Exercise Alert

Internet Exercise 21 requires the use of the Internet or other reference materials to find real-world data.

Standardized Test Practice

22. The number of books read by the students in each reading class this year are shown in the table. Which measure of central tendency would the school use to show they read lots of books? **C**

104	90
162	134
110	97
145	126

A mode
B median
C mean
D cannot be determined

23. The high temperatures, in degrees Fahrenheit, for one week are 79°, 81°, 77°, 81°, 82°, 75°, and 76°. If the temperature on the eighth day is 80°, which of the following would be true? **J**

F The mode will change.
G The mean will increase and the median will remain the same.
H The median will increase and the mean will remain the same.
J Both the mean and the median will increase.

24. Jamal said that the number that best represented the following set of data is 27. Which measure of central tendency is he referring to? **B**

28, 32, 21, 25, 33, 32, 20, 26

A mean
B median
C mode
D all of the above

25. EXTENDED RESPONSE Shane and Chien have the bowling scores shown.

Game #	Shane	Chien
1	124	125
2	135	132
3	109	128
4	116	130
5	141	125

a. After the sixth game, the mean of Shane's scores is 130. What was Shane's score for his sixth game? **155**

b. What must Chien bowl in the sixth game in order to have the same average as Shane? **140**

Spiral Review

Determine whether each pair of solids is similar. (Lesson 12-8)

26. **no**

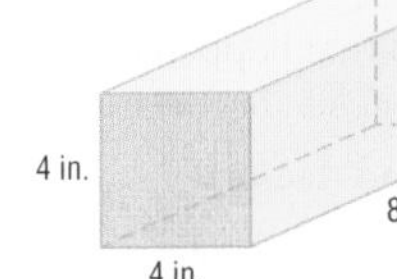

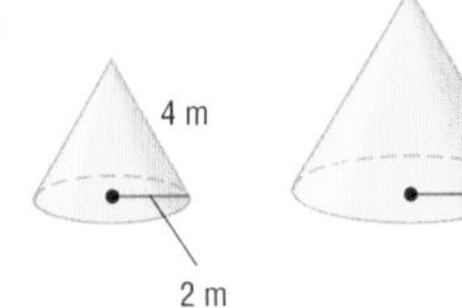

27. **yes**

28. ARCHITECTURE The small tower of a historic house is shaped like a regular hexagonal pyramid as shown at the right. How much roofing will be needed to cover this tower? (*Hint*: Do not include the base of the pyramid.) (Lesson 12-7) **336 ft^2**

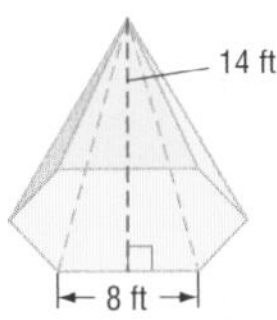

Skills Review

Make a line plot for the data set. (Previous Course) **See Chapter 13 Answer Appendix.**

29. ages of basketball players: 21, 20, 19, 16, 16, 18, 17, 19, 18, 20, 16, 18, and 20

4 ASSESS

Ticket Out the Door Give students a data set to analyze. Have them write on index cards the mean, median, and mode of the data set. As they leave the class, they should turn in their index cards.

Additional Answers

10. mean; Sample answer: The mean is the greatest value. Since the museum wants to show a large number of visitors, the mean value should be used.

11. median; Sample answer: The median is the greatest value. Since he wants to show a high score, he would use the median.

12. mean; Sample answer: The mean is the greatest value. The store wants to show they pay a lot, so they would advertise the mean value.

13. mode; Sample answer: More students have 2 siblings than any other number. It is the best representation of the data.

15. Sample answer: mean: 60.45; median: 60; mode: 60; Any of them. Each measure is around 60 inches.

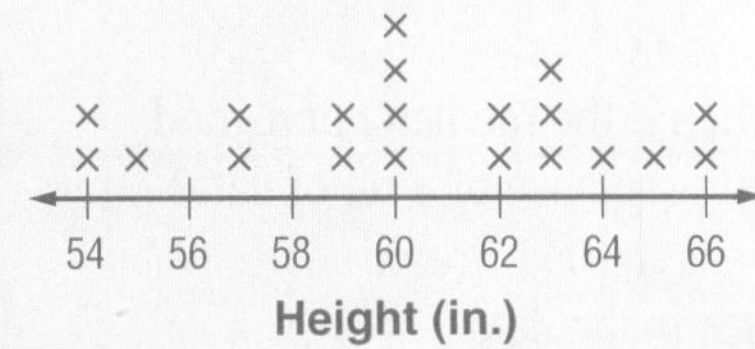

Differentiated Instruction

BL

Extension Have students create a data set consisting of nine numbers that has a mean of 19, a median of 25, and a mode of both 31 and 33. Sample data set: 1, 2, 7, 8, 25, 31, 31, 33, 33

EXTEND 13-1 Lesson Notes

FOCUS

Objective Use a graphing calculator to find the mean and median of a set of data.

Materials for Each Group

- TI 83/84 Plus graphing calculator

Teaching Tip

- To find the mean or the median individually, have students use the following keystrokes: 2nd LIST. Scroll over to the MATH menu. Press 3 ENTER to find the mean or 4 ENTER to find the median of the data set.

TEACH

Working in Cooperative Groups

Have students work in pairs to complete the Activity and Exercises 1–4.

Ask:

- Is the mean always a member of the set? No. The median? No, only if there is an odd number of members in the set. The mode? Yes, but there is not always a mode or there can be more than one mode.
- When is the median *not* a good representative of a set of data? when there are no extreme values or big gaps in the data

Practice Have students complete Exercises 5 and 6.

EXTEND 13-1 Graphing Technology Lab: Mean and Median

Math Online glencoe.com
- Other Calculator Keystrokes
- Graphing Calculator Personal Tutor

A graphing calculator can quickly and accurately determine measures of central tendency for large data sets. You can use a graphing calculator to find the mean and median of a set of data.

ACTIVITY

SPORTS The number of wins for the last 15 seasons for the local soccer team is shown at the right.

12	9	13	11	12
7	8	7	11	14
8	6	2	10	13

Find the mean and median number of wins.

Step 1 Enter the data.

- Clear any existing lists.

KEYSTROKES: STAT ENTER ▲ CLEAR ENTER

- Enter the number of wins as L1.

KEYSTROKES: 12 ENTER 9 ENTER ... 13 ENTER

Step 2 Find the mean and median.

- Display a list of statistics for the data.

KEYSTROKES: STAT ▶ ENTER ENTER

Use the down arrow key to locate Med. The median number of wins is 10 and the mean number of wins is about 9.5.

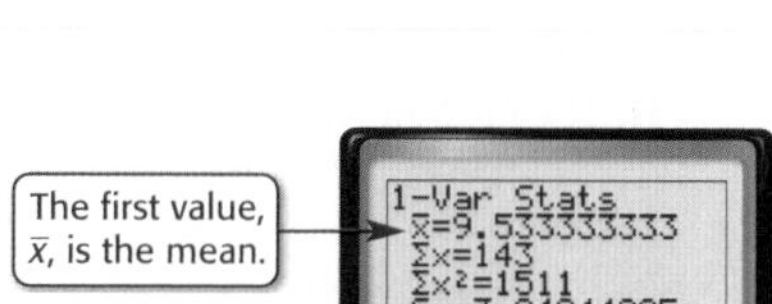

Analyze the Results

1. In the opening Activity, remove the number 2 from the data set. What happens to the mean and median of the data set? **The mean becomes 10.07 and the median becomes 10.5.**

Clear list L1 and find the mean and median of each data set. Round decimal answers to the nearest hundredth if necessary.

2. 7.6, 6.3, 8.9, 2.4, 6.1, 9.5 **mean = 6.8, median = 6.95**
3. −54, −47, −42, −59, −46, −68, −52 **mean = −52.57, median = −52**
4. 3.8, −3.4, −5.8, 7.6, −6.9, 8.7, 4.3, 2.5, 1.8, 7.2, −2.7, 5.9, −1.7, 54 **mean = 5.38, median = 3.15**
5. Look back at the medians found. When is the median a member of the data set? **The median is a term when the number of terms is odd.**
6. Refer to Exercise 4. **a–c. See margin.**
   a. Which statistic better represents the data, the mean or the median? Explain.
   b. Suppose the number 54 should have been 5.4. Recalculate the mean and median. Is there a significant difference between the first pair of values and the second?
   c. When there is an error in one of the data values, which statistic is less likely to be affected? Why?

ASSESS

Formative Assessment

Use Exercise 3 to assess whether students understand how to use a graphing calculator to find the mean and median of a set of data.

From Concrete to Abstract

Use Exercise 6 to assess whether students understand how data values can affect mean and median and whether students can recognize which statistic best represents the data.

Additional Answers

6a. Median; 54 in the data set increases the mean so that it does not best represent the data.

6b. 1.91; 3.15; There is a significant difference between the pair of means. The second mean is 3.47 less than the first mean. The median remains the same.

6c. Median; an error can change mean significantly because it affects the sum of the data. However, the median could remain the same.

13-2 Stem-and-Leaf Plots

Then
You have already displayed data in circle graphs. (Lesson 7-8)

Now
- Display data using stem-and-leaf plots.
- Interpret data in a stem-and-leaf plot.

New Vocabulary
stem-and-leaf plot
stems
leaves
back-to-back stem-and-leaf plot

Math Online

glencoe.com
- Extra Examples
- Personal Tutor
- Self-Check Quiz
- Homework Help

Why?

The average winning speeds, in miles per hour, for the Daytona 500 are shown. Write each number on a sticky note. Then group the numbers using the intervals: 130–139, 140–149, 150–159, 160–169, and 170–179.

DAYTONA 500 Winning Speeds (mph), 1979–2008

142	134	156	151	160	148
156	162	148	143	135	154
177	156	148	149	173	162
143	157	138	154	170	148
149	144	155	172	166	176

Source: Daytona International Speedway

a. Is there an equal number of speeds in each group? Explain.

b. What is an advantage of displaying data in groups?
a–b. See Chapter 13 Answer Appendix.

Display Data In a **stem-and-leaf plot**, numerical data are listed in ascending or descending order. The greatest place values of the data are used for the **stems**. The least place value forms the **leaves**.

EXAMPLE 1 Draw a Stem-and-Leaf Plot

DOGS The table shows the average weight in pounds of different breeds of adult dogs. Display the data in a stem-and-leaf plot.

Adult Dog Weight (lb)			
10	21	15	9
17	6	4	18
9	26	20	24
11	13	8	25

Step 1 The stems are the greatest place values of the data. List the stems 0, 1, and 2 in order in the *Stem* column. Write the ones digits to the right of the corresponding stems in the *Leaf* column.

Stem	Leaf
0	9 6 4 9 8
1	0 5 7 8 1 3
2	1 6 0 4 5

Step 2 Order the leaves from least to greatest and write a *key* that explains how to read the stems and leaves. Include a title.

Adult Dog Weight (lb)

Stem	Leaf
0	4 6 8 9 9
1	0 1 3 5 7 8
2	0 1 4 5 6

2|6 = 26 lb

Write each data leaf as many times as it appears.

Check Your Progress

1. **EXERCISE** The numbers of minutes Will spent exercising are shown. Display the data in a stem-and-leaf plot.
See Chapter 13 Answer Appendix.

Exercising Time (min)				
42	15	65	30	45
40	20	28	45	60
38	23	39	30	10

Personal Tutor glencoe.com

13-2 Lesson Notes

1 FOCUS

Vertical Alignment

Before Lesson 13-2
Display data in circle graphs.

Lesson 13-2
Display and interpret data using stem-and-leaf plots.

After Lesson 13-2
Recognize and interpret measures of variation in stem-and-leaf plots.

2 TEACH

Scaffolding Questions

Have students read the *Why?* section of the lesson and answer the questions.

Ask:
- Which values do you think were used to create the intervals? the least value, 134, and the greatest value, 177
- Why would you use these values to create intervals? By using the least and greatest values, you cover all of the values in the table.
- Once the data values are grouped, what do you need to do if you want to find the median of the data? order the data from least to greatest value

Lesson 13-2 Resources

Resource	Approaching-Level	On-Level	Beyond-Level	English Learners
Teacher Edition	• Differentiated Instruction, p. 738		• Differentiated Instruction, p. 742	
Chapter Resource Masters	• Study Guide and Intervention, pp. 11–12 • Skills Practice, p. 13 • Practice, p. 14 • Word Problem Practice, p. 15	• Study Guide and Intervention, pp. 11–12 • Skills Practice, p. 13 • Practice, p. 14 • Word Problem Practice, p. 15 • Enrichment, p. 16	• Practice, p. 14 • Word Problem Practice, p. 15 • Enrichment, p. 16 • Graphing Calculator, p. 17	• Study Guide and Intervention, pp. 11–12 • Skills Practice, p. 13 • Practice, p. 14 • Graphing Calculator, p. 17
Transparencies	• 5-Minute Check Transparency 13-2	• 5-Minute Check Transparency 13-2	• 5-Minute Check Transparency 13-2	• 5-Minute Check Transparency 13-2
Other	• Study Notebook • Teaching Pre-Algebra with Manipulatives	• Study Notebook • Teaching Pre-Algebra with Manipulatives	• Study Notebook	• Study Notebook • Teaching Pre-Algebra with Manipulatives

Display Data

Example 1 shows how to draw a stem-and-leaf plot.

Formative Assessment

Use the Check Your Progress exercises after each example to determine students' understanding of concepts.

Additional Example

1 **FOOD** Display the data in a stem-and-leaf plot.

Peanuts Harvested, 2007	
State	**Amount (hundred lb./acre)**
Alabama	24
Florida	25
Georgia	31
New Mexico	35
North Carolina	26
Oklahoma	32
South Carolina	29
Texas	34
Virginia	19

Stem	Leaf
1	9
2	4 5 6 9
3	1 2 4 5

2 | 4 = 2400 lb/acre

Additional Examples also in Interactive Classroom PowerPoint® Presentations

IWB INTERACTIVE WHITEBOARD READY

Interpret Data

Example 2 shows how to interpret data in a stem-and-leaf plot. **Example 3** shows how to compare data in a back-to-back stem-and-leaf plot.

Additional Answers

3A. Chicago; Sample answer: All but one of the daily high temperatures for Chicago were 70° or higher, while all but three of the temperatures for Portland were below 70°.

3B. Chicago; Sample answer: The temperatures for Chicago are mostly between 70° and 90°, while the majority of the temperatures for Portland are between 60° and 68°.

Interpret Data Stem-and-leaf plots are useful in analyzing data because you can see all the data values, including the least, greatest, median, and mode.

StudyTip

Median The data values are already ordered in a stem-and-leaf plot. There are 21 data values in Example 2. The middle value is data value #11 or 38.

EXAMPLE 2 Interpret Data

SOFTBALL The stem-and-leaf plot shows the number of wins for various softball teams in one season.

Softball Wins

Stem	Leaf
1	8
2	2 3 4 4 4 7
3	1 5 6 8 9 9
4	0 4 7 7 9
5	0 0 1

2|3 = 23 wins

a. Find the median and mode.
The median, the middle value, is 38. The most frequent value is 24.

b. What is the difference between the least and greatest number of wins?
The difference is 51 − 18 or 33.

Check Your Progress

DOGS Refer to the stem-and-leaf plot of adult dog weight in Example 1.

2A. Find the median and mode. **14 lb; 9 lb**

2B. What is the difference between the least weight and greatest weight? **22 lb**

Personal Tutor glencoe.com

A **back-to-back stem-and-leaf plot** can be used to compare two sets of data. The back-to-back stem-and-leaf plot below compares daily high temperatures.

Daily High Temperatures in June

Portland, OR	Stem	Chicago, IL
9 9 8 7 7	5	
2 2 2 1 1 1 1 1 1 0 0	6	7
8 8 7 6 6 6 6 6 5 5 4		
1 0 0	7	0 0 1 1 5 5 6 7 7 7 9 9
	8	1 2 2 3 3 4 4 4 5 5 5 5 5 7 7 9
	9	0

1|7 = 71°F *7|9 = 79°F*

The leaves for one set of data are on one side of the stem.

The leaves for the other set of data are on the other side of the stem.

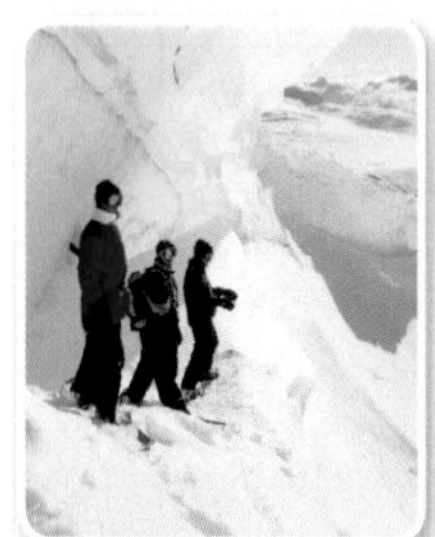

Real-World Link

Thompson Pass, Alaska, holds the record for the greatest August–July snowfall total. From August 1952 to July 1953, 974.1 inches of snow fell there.

Source: National Climatic Data Center

Real-World EXAMPLE 3 Back to Back Stem-and-Leaf Plots

SNOWFALL The monthly snowfall accumulations for nine months in Syracuse and Buffalo, New York, are shown.

Snowfall Accumulations

Syracuse	Stem	Buffalo
9 4 1	0	1 1 3 9
7	1	2 2 8
7 6	2	3 7
5 4	3	
0	4	

7|1 = 17 in. *1|2 = 12 in.*

a. In general, which city has the lower amount of monthly snowfall? Explain.
Buffalo; it experiences lower numbers and does not have snowfall over 27 inches.

b. Which city has more varied amounts of snowfall? Explain.
The data for Syracuse is more spread out, while the data for Buffalo is clustered. So, Syracuse has the more varied amount of snowfall.

Check Your Progress

TEMPERATURES Refer to the stem-and-leaf plot about temperatures.

3A. In general, which city had the higher daily temperatures? Explain.

3B. Which city has more varied temperatures? Explain. **3a–b. See margin.**

Personal Tutor glencoe.com

Differentiated Instruction AL

If students need more practice creating stem-and-leaf plots,

Then have groups of two or three students find the average daily temperatures of a city, rounded to the nearest degree. Have them write the last digit of each temperature on one side of an index card and the first digit(s) on the other in a different color. Ask students to sort cards by stem and then write each stem on the board. Have students complete the stem-and-leaf plot by taping each leaf into place.

Check Your Understanding

Example 1 p. 737 — **Display each set of data in a stem-and-leaf plot.**

1.

Science Test Scores				
99	80	84	72	79
73	76	80	81	76

2.

Height of Plants (in.)				
40	51	68	57	55
50	57	51	67	41
67	57	48	58	67

1–2. See Chapter 13 Answer Appendix.

Example 2 p. 738

3. **NUTRITION** The average amount of pasta that people in different countries consume each year is shown in the stem-and-leaf plot below.

Pasta Consumption (lb)

Stem	Leaf
0	3 4 5 8 8 9 9
1	0 1 4 5 5 5 5 5 9
2	0 0 8
3	
4	
5	9

2 | 8 = 28 lb

a. Find the median of the data. 14.5 lb

b. Find the mode of the data. 15 lb

c. What is the difference between the greatest amount of pasta and least amount of pasta consumed? 56 lb

Example 3 p. 738

4. **STATES** The maximum allowable speed limits in various western and eastern states are shown in the back-to-back stem-and-leaf plot below.

Western States	Stem	Eastern States
5	5	
5 5	6	5 5 5 5 5 5 5 5 5
5 5 5 5 5 5 5 5 5 0 0	7	0 0 0

0 | 7 = 70 mph   *6 | 5 = 65 mph*

a. In general, which region has higher maximum speed limits? Explain. Western; the west has 8 states with speed limits of 75 mph.

b. Which region has more varied speed limits? Explain. Western; the data is more spread out. While, the eastern is more clustered.

Practice and Problem Solving

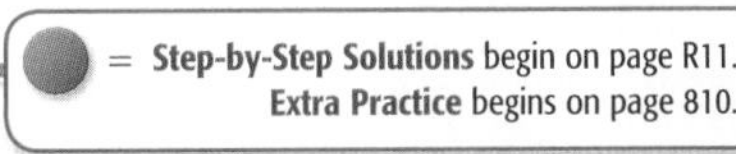
= **Step-by-Step Solutions** begin on page R11. **Extra Practice** begins on page 810.

Example 1 p. 737 — **Display each set of data in a stem-and-leaf plot.** 5–8. See Chapter 13 Answer Appendix.

5. The ages of people attending a spinning class: 18, 27, 35, 22, 23, 30, 21, 40, 26, 33, 49, 55, 27, 22, 20, 39, and 42.

6. The number of students in each class in an elementary school that own a video game system: 20, 22, 18, 29, 30, 24, 19, 32, 27, 28, 30, 21, and 25.

7. The cost of a new pair of tennis shoes: \$50, \$65, \$80, \$96, \$65, \$70, \$76, \$80, \$60, \$75, \$78, and \$59.

8. Number of applicants at annual talent shows: 88, 90, 102, 104, 67, 109, 97, 98, 86, 88, 86, 100, 103, 99, 90, and 106.

Additional Examples

2 **PETS** The stem-and-leaf plot lists the number of students in each class in a middle school that own pets.

Stem	Leaf
1	1 3 4 7 7 9
2	1 1 5 6 8 9
3	0 1 2 2 3

3 | 1 = 31%

a. Find the median and mode. 25; 17, 21, and 32

b. What is the difference between the least and the greatest number of students who own pets? 22

3 **AGRICULTURE** The yearly production of honey in California and Florida is shown for the years 2000 to 2006, in millions of pounds.

California		Florida
7	1	4 4 4
8 4 0	2	0 0 2 4
2 1 0	3	

2 | 3 = 32 million lb   *2 | 0 = 20 million lb*

a. What state produces more honey? Explain. California; it produces greater numbers of pounds.

b. Which state has the more varied production? Explain. California; the data are more spread out.

Focus on Mathematical Content

Stem-and-Leaf Plots A stem-and-leaf plot displays a set of data so that the distribution of the data is visually represented. A stem-and-leaf plot places the values in order, ascending or descending, making their distribution obvious.

3 PRACTICE

Formative Assessment

Use Exercises 1–4 to check for understanding.

Use the chart at the bottom of this page to customize assignments for your students.

Tips for New Teachers

Explain Your Reasoning Students can explain their reasoning by:

- Think-Pair-Share
- Writing
- Small Groups
- Panel Discussions.

These offer students with different learning modalities alternative approaches to success.

Additional Answers

13. Sample answer: The person who came in first beat the other runners by almost 2 s. An average time is about 17.8 s.

100 Meter Times

Stem	Leaf
14	3
15	
16	2 5
17	4 7 9
18	0 7
19	2 9

18 | 0 = 18.0s

17. Sample Answer:

Stem	Leaf
1	0 0 2 3 6 7 8
2	2 5 6 9 9
3	1 2 8

2 | 6 = 26

18. Sample Answer:

Stem	Leaf
1	9
2	2 6
3	4 5 6 7
4	3
5	4 5 6 7
6	3 4 5

2 | 6 = 26

Example 2 p. 738

12a. mode; The Rams mode is 24. The Stallions mode is 10. 24 > 10

12b. Mean and median; The Stallions have a median of 20.5 and the Rams have median of 16.5. 20.5 > 16.5; the mean of Stallions is 20.1. The Rams have a mean of 15.8.

9 **SCHOOL** The stem-and-leaf plot at the right shows the number of pages of a novel each student in Mrs. Switlick's class has read.

a. Find the median of the data. **50 pages**

b. Find the mode of the data. **50 pages**

c. What is the difference between the greatest number of pages read and the least number of pages read? **57 pages**

Pages Read by Students

Stem	Leaf
3	1 5 5 7 7 9
4	2 4 4 6 6 8 8
5	0 0 0 3 4 6 6 7
6	1 6 7 8 8
7	
8	8

6 | 1 = 61 pages

10. **NUTRITION** The stem-and-leaf plot shows the number of Calories per servings of various dry cereals.

a. Find the median of the data. **108.5 Calories**

b. Find the mode of the data. **100 Calories, 101 Calories, 102 Calories**

c. What is the difference between the greatest number of Calories and the least number of Calories for these cereals? **71 Calories**

Calories in Cereal

Stem	Leaf
7	0 2
8	1 5
9	0 3
10	0 0 0 1 1 1 2 2 2 8 8 9
11	0 0 1 1 2 3 4 4 5
12	0 5 6 6
13	0
14	0 1

11 | 0 = 110 Calories

Example 3 p. 738

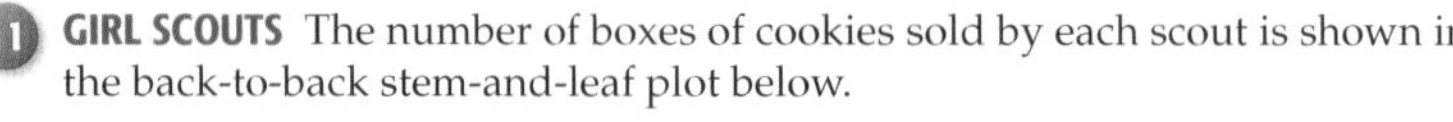

11 **GIRL SCOUTS** The number of boxes of cookies sold by each scout is shown in the back-to-back stem-and-leaf plot below.

Cookie Sales

Troop 60	Stem	Troop 122
9 9 5 4 3 2 0	3	0 1 3 5 8 9
5 5 4 4 2	4	4
3 0	5	0 4 5 7
	6	0 1 8

0 | 5 = 50 boxes *6 | 0 = 60 boxes*

a. Overall, which troop sold more cookies? Explain. **Troop 122; they had more members sell over 45 boxes.**

b. Which troop has more varied sales? Explain. **Troop 122; troop 122 sales are more spread out. Troop 60 are more clustered.**

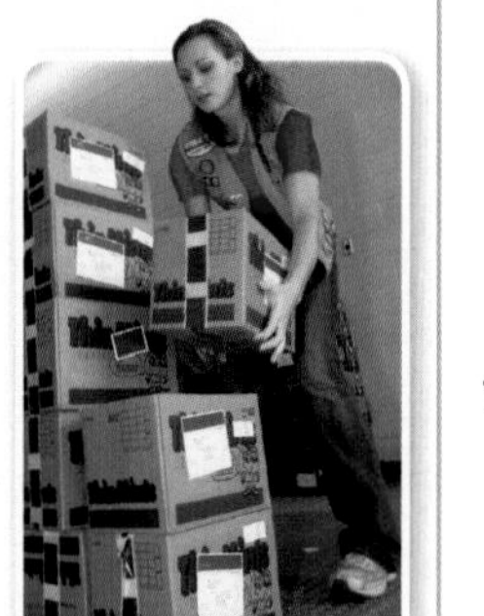

Real-World Link

Girl Scout cookies have been a part of the American culture for over 80 years. Individual troops receive about 17% of the purchase price of each box of cookie sold.

Source: Girl Scout

12. **FOOTBALL** The back-to-back stem-and-leaf plot at the right shows the points scored by two high school football teams in their games this season.

a. Which measure of central tendency would the Rams want to use to show they have a greater number of points scored than the Stallions? Explain.

b. Which measure(s) of central tendency would the Stallions want to use to show they have a greater number of points scored than the Rams? Explain.

High School Football Points

Rams	Stem	Stallions
9 8 7	0	
9 8 5 4	1	0 0 5 9
4 4 0	2	0 1 2 5 8
	3	1

9 | 0 = 9 points *1 | 9 = 19 points*

13. **TRACK** The times in seconds of the top 10 finishers of the 100-meter race are 14.3, 18.0, 19.9, 18.7, 16.2, 17.7, 16.5, 19.2, 17.9 and 17.4. Make and analyze a stem-and-leaf plot of the data. Draw two conclusions about the times. **See margin.**

740 Chapter 13 Statistics and Probability

Differentiated Homework Options

Level	Assignment	Two-Day Option	
AL Basic	5–12, 17, 19, 21–33	5–11 odd, 22–25	6–12 even, 17, 19, 21, 26–33
OL Core	5–11 odd, 13–17, 19, 21–33	5–12, 22–25	13–17, 19, 21, 26–33
BL Advanced	13–29 (optional: 30–33)		

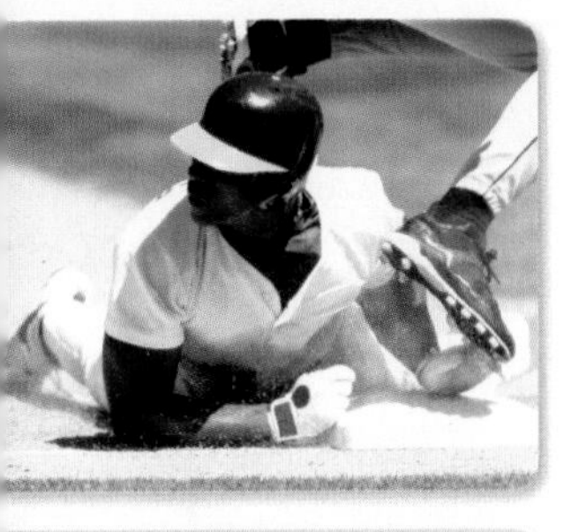

Real-World Link

Ricky Henderson played professional baseball from 1979 to 2003. He holds the career record for the greatest number of stolen bases, 1,406.

Source: MLB

14. BASEBALL The table below shows the number of stolen bases by team for each league during a recent season of professional baseball.

American League	139	144	96	78	72	103	78	
	112	123	52	81	131	88	57	
National League	96	200	138	68	55	56	69	119
	109	64	86	97	100	105	65	137

Display the data in a back-to-back stem-and-leaf plot. Then analyze and compare the data. **See Chapter 13 Answer Appendix.**

15. MULTIPLE REPRESENTATIONS In this problem, you will use a stem-and-leaf plot to analyze data. The test scores of 36 students are shown in the table at the right. **a–e. See Chapter 13 Answer Appendix.**

Test Scores (total score of 80)					
80	13	23	34	56	56
73	79	6	19	73	62
68	20	78	78	32	59
36	48	75	79	39	62
46	59	76	49	64	76
78	63	59	67	80	38

a. **TABULAR** Display the data in a stem-and-leaf plot.

b. **NUMERICAL** Find the mean, median, and mode of the data.

c. **GRAPHICAL** Turn the stem-and-leaf plot 90° counterclockwise. Sketch the graph that is formed by the peaks of the stem-and-leaf plot.

d. **ANALYTICAL** Describe the data by the number of peaks in the graph. Is it symmetric? Explain your reasoning.

e. **VERBAL** A set of data can be described as being *skewed* if a graph of the data is not symmetric. Is this set of data skewed? Explain your reasoning.

16. COLLECT DATA Display the hand lengths, in inches, of the students in your class in a frequency table.

a. Make a stem-and-leaf plot of the data.

b. Analyze the data. Then write a summary explaining your data. **See students' work.**

H.O.T. Problems

Use Higher-Order Thinking Skills

17–18. See margin.

17. OPEN ENDED Create a stem-and-leaf plot that has a median of 22.

18. CHALLENGE Create a stem-and-leaf plot that has at least 15 pieces of data in which the minimum value is 19 and the median is 43.

19. FIND THE ERROR Paolo and J'vonté are finding the median plant height from the stem-and-leaf plot at the right. Paolo says the median is 64. J'vonté says the median is 31. Is either of them correct? Explain your reasoning.

Plant Heights (cm)

Stem	Leaf
0	6 8
1	1
2	8
3	6 8
4	0 9

$2|8 = 28$ cm

20. CHALLENGE Use the stem-and-leaf plot about plant heights at the right. Add two data values that do not affect the median but add 3 to the mean.

21. WRITING IN MATH Refer to the information on page 737 about Daytona 500 winning speeds. Explain how a stem-and-leaf plot can help you analyze the data.

19. Sample answer: Neither; Sample answer: The median is 32. J'vonté divided wrong, and Paolo forgot to divide 64 by 2.

20. Sample answer: 27 and 57

21. Sample answer: Stem-and-leaf plots can help you see how the winning speeds are distributed. You can identify the fastest and slowest winning speeds, the mean speed, the mode speed, and the median speed.

Watch Out!

Find the Error For Exercise 19, suggest that students base their explanation of the error(s) on their own calculations. For example, did Paolo or J'vonté miss a step in calculating the median? You may want to discuss how students can avoid similar errors in their own work.

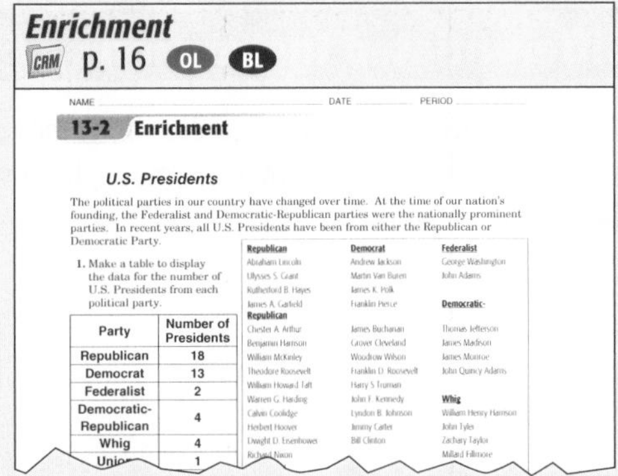

Enrichment CRM p. 16 OL BL

13-2 Enrichment

U.S. Presidents

The political parties in our country have changed over time. At the time of our nation's founding, the Federalist and Democratic-Republican parties were the nationally prominent parties. In recent years, all U.S. Presidents have been from either the Republican or Democratic Party.

1. Make a table to display the data for the number of U.S. Presidents from each political party.

Party	Number of Presidents
Republican	18
Democrat	13
Federalist	2
Democratic-Republican	4
Whig	4
Union	1

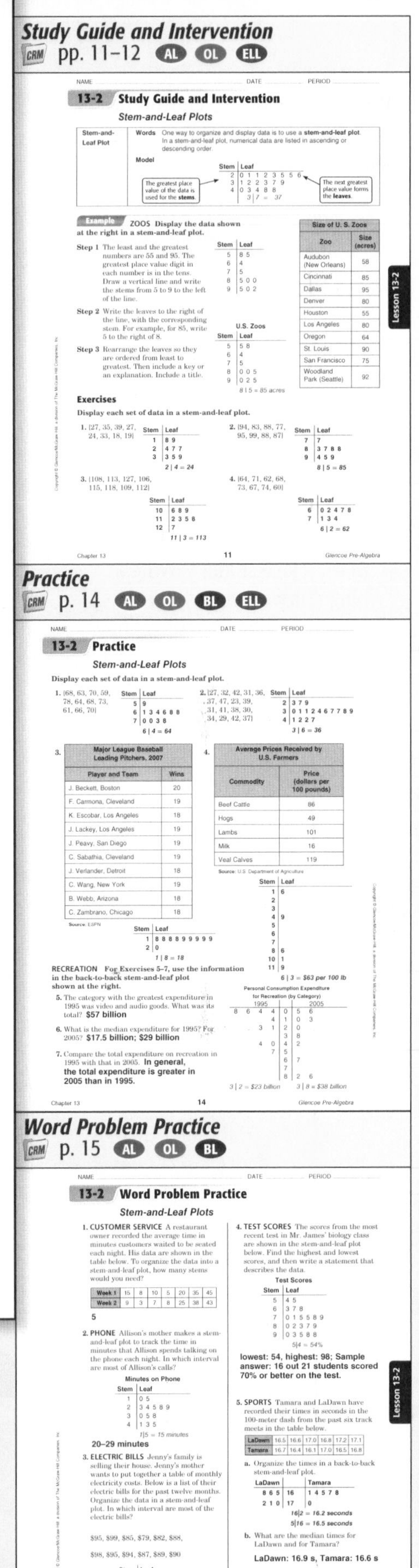

Study Guide and Intervention CRM pp. 11–12 AL OL ELL

13-2 Study Guide and Intervention

Stem-and-Leaf Plots

Stem-and-Leaf Plot — Words: One way to organize and display data is to use a stem-and-leaf plot. In a stem-and-leaf plot, numerical data are listed in ascending or descending order.

Practice CRM p. 14 AL OL BL ELL

13-2 Practice

Stem-and-Leaf Plots

Word Problem Practice CRM p. 15 AL OL BL

13-2 Word Problem Practice

Stem-and-Leaf Plots

Exercise Alert

Ruler In Exercise 16, students need a customary ruler to measure hand lengths.

ASSESS

Name the Math Give students a small set of data and tell them to make a stem-and-leaf plot. Have them name the reasons why a stem-and-leaf plot can be useful. Remind them to include a key with their plot.

TEACH with TECH

BLOG Have students write a blog entry on your secure classroom blog describing how stem-and-leaf plots are useful for displaying some sets of data.

Standardized Test Practice

22. **GRIDDED RESPONSE** What is the median number of hours shown in the stem-and-leaf plot below? **3.1**

Marathon Times (h)

Stem	Leaf
1	3 4 4
2	0 5 7 7
3	1 1 1 2 8
4	0 0 1

$2|8 = 2.8\ h$

23. What are the stems for the following data?
22, 67, 43, 45, 7, 33, 29 **D**

A {2, 3, 4, 6}
B {1, 2, 3, 4, 5, 6, 7}
C {0, 2, 3, 4, 6}
D {0, 1, 2, 3, 4, 5, 6}

24. What is the mode of the set of data shown in the stem-and-leaf plot below? **H**

Package Weights (oz)

Stem	Leaf
10	0 3 5 7 7
11	0 0 2 2
12	4 6 6 6 6
13	0 0 0 1
14	0

$11|2 = 11.2\ h$

F 0
G 10 and 12
H 12.6
J 13.0

25. Which of the following statements is true about the stem-and-leaf plot in Exercise 24? **B**

A The mode is 1.40.
B The mean is about 11.9.
C The median is 12.3.
D Twice as many packages weigh between 10 and 13 pounds than 13 to 14 pounds.

Spiral Review

26. Sample answer: the median, 95, because most students scored higher than the mean, which is 91.

26. **TESTS** Which measure of central tendency best summarizes the test scores shown below? Explain. (Lesson 13-1)
97, 99, 95, 89, 99, 100, 87, 85, 89, 92, 96, 95, 60, 97, 85

Find the missing measure for each pair of similar solids. (Lesson 12-8)

27. $33\frac{1}{3}$ ft

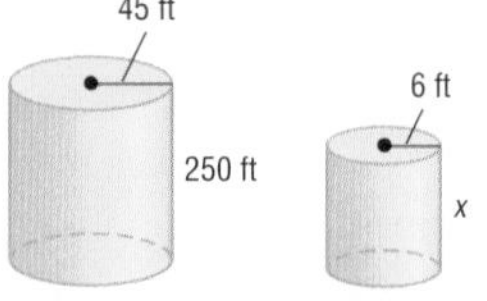

28.

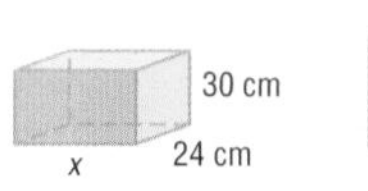

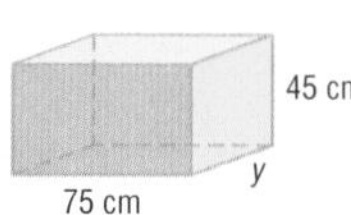

$x = 50$ cm, $y = 36$ cm

29. **FLOORING** A square room has a floor area of 324 square feet. The homeowners plan to cover the floor with 6-inch square tiles. How many tiles will be in each row on the floor? (Lesson 10-2) **36**

Skills Review

Find the median of each set of data. Round to the nearest tenth, if necessary. (Lesson 13-1)

30. 41, 37, 43, 43, 36 **41**
31. 2, 8, 16, 21, 3, 8, 9, 7, 6 **8**
32. 14, 6, 8, 10, 9, 5, 7, 13 **8.5**
33. 7.5, 7.1, 7.4, 7.6, 7.4, 9.0, 7.9, 7.1 **7.5**

Differentiated Instruction

BL

Extension Have students use the data from the table in the *Why?* section of the lesson to make a stem-and-leaf plot. Find the median, mode, least speed, and greatest speed. 154.5, 148, 134, 177

Measures of Variation

Why?

One of the main reasons people attend amusement parks is to ride roller coasters. The maximum speeds of ten of the world's fastest steel roller coasters are shown.

a. Find the difference between the fastest and slowest speeds. **44 mph**

b. Graph the data on a line plot. **See Chapter 13 Answer Appendix.**

c. Write a sentence describing how the data are distributed on the line plot. **Sample answer: A majority of the speeds are between 84 and 108 miles per hour.**

Roller Coaster	Speed (mph)
American Eagle	66
Dodonpa	107
Furious Baco	84
Goliath	85
Kingda Ka	128
Millennium Force	93
Steel Dragon 2000	95
Titan	85
Top Thrill Dragster	120
Tower of Terror	100

Then
You have already found measures of central tendency. (Lesson 13-2)

Now
- Find measures of variation.
- Uses measures of variation to interpret and analyze data.

New Vocabulary
measures of variation
range
quartiles
lower quartile
upper quartile
interquartile range
outlier

Math Online

glencoe.com
- Extra Examples
- Personal Tutor
- Self-Check Quiz
- Homework Help

Measures of Variation **Measures of variation** are used to describe the distribution of the data. One measure of variation is the range. The **range** of a set of data is the difference between the greatest and the least values of the set. It describes whether the data are spread out or clustered together.

EXAMPLE 1 Find Range

Find the range for each set of data.

a. Study Time

Stem	Leaf
1	0 0 2 3 6 7 8
2	2 5 6 9 9
3	1 2 8

2|6 = 26 minutes

The greatest value is 38 minutes, and the least value is 10 minutes. So, the range is 38 − 10 or 28 minutes.

b. The age in years of Mrs. Tyznik's grandchildren: 27, 8, 5, 19, 21, 10, 4, and 21.

The greatest value is 27 years and the least value is 4 years. So, the range is 27 − 4 or 23 years.

Check Your Progress

1A. The cost in dollars of DVDs: 20, 25, 15, 16, 10, and 9 **$16**

1B. Weight of Letters **25 g**

Stem	Leaf
3	3 8 9 7 8
4	4 4 6 6 8 9
5	0 2 6 8

3|3 = 33 grams

Personal Tutor glencoe.com

13-3 Lesson Notes

1 FOCUS

Vertical Alignment

Before Lesson 13-3
Find measures of central tendency.

Lesson 13-3
Find and use measures of variation to interpret and analyze data.

After Lesson 13-3
Analyze measures of variation in various displays, including box-and-whisker plots.

2 TEACH

Scaffolding Questions

Have students read the *Why?* section of the lesson and answer the questions.

Ask:
- Would you describe the majority of the speeds as clustered or spread out? spread out
- From looking at the line plot, which values, if any, appear to be extreme? least and greatest speeds
- What does the large difference between the least and greatest speeds suggest about the data? It is spread out.

Lesson 13-3 Resources

Resource	Approaching-Level	On-Level	Beyond-Level	English Learners
Teacher Edition	• Differentiated Instruction, p. 744		• Differentiated Instruction, p. 749	
Chapter Resource Masters	• Study Guide and Intervention, pp. 18–19 • Skills Practice, p. 20 • Practice, p. 21 • Word Problem Practice, p. 22	• Study Guide and Intervention, pp. 18–19 • Skills Practice, p. 20 • Practice, p. 21 • Word Problem Practice, p. 22 • Enrichment, p. 23	• Practice, p. 21 • Word Problem Practice, p. 22 • Enrichment, p. 23	• Study Guide and Intervention, pp. 18–19 • Skills Practice, p. 20 • Practice, p. 21
Transparencies	• 5-Minute Check Transparency 13-3	• 5-Minute Check Transparency 13-3	• 5-Minute Check Transparency 13-3	• 5-Minute Check Transparency 13-3
Other	• Study Notebook • Teaching Pre-Algebra with Manipulatives	• Study Notebook • Teaching Pre-Algebra with Manipulatives	• Study Notebook	• Study Notebook • Teaching Pre-Algebra with Manipulatives

Measures of Variation

Example 1 shows how to find the range for sets of data. **Example 2** shows how to find the quartiles and the interquartile range for a set of real-world data. **Example 3** shows how to find the outliers for a data set.

Formative Assessment

Use the Check Your Progress exercises after each example to determine students' understanding of concepts.

Additional Examples

1 Find the range for each set of data.

a. Work Time

Stem	Leaf
3	3 3 5 7 7 8
4	0 3 3 4 9
5	4 9

3 | 5 = 35 hours 26

b. The cost of jeans at a department store: $79, $42, $38, $51, $63, $91 $53

2 **OLYMPICS** Find the measures of variation for the data in the table.

Torino Winter Olympics 2006 Total Medals for Top 8 Countries			
29	25	14	24
23	14	22	19

Source: Torino 2006

range: 15; median: 22.5; LQ: 16.5; UQ: 24.5; IR: 8

Additional Examples also in Interactive Classroom PowerPoint® Presentations

IWB INTERACTIVE WHITEBOARD READY

In a set of data, the **quartiles** are the values that divide the data into four equal parts. Recall that the median of a set of data separates the set in half.

StudyTip

Quartiles One half of the data lies between the lower quartile and the upper quartile.

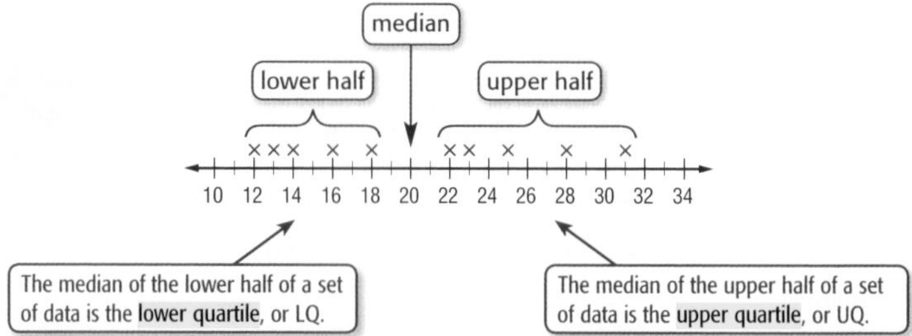

The upper and lower quartiles can be used to find another measure of variation called the **interquartile range**.

Key Concept — Interquartile Range

For Your FOLDABLE

Words The interquartile range is the range of the middle half of a set of data. It is the difference between the upper quartile and the lower quartile.

Symbols Interquartile range = UQ − LQ

EXAMPLE 2 Identify Measures of Variation

OLYMPICS Find the measures of variation for the data in the table.

U.S. Summer Olympic Silver Medals 1972–2004		
34	32	31
31	35	0
39	24	61

Step 1 **Range:** 61 − 0 or 61 medals

Step 2 **Median, Upper Quartile, and Lower Quartile:**
Order the data from least to greatest.

lower quartile **median** **upper quartile**

0 24 31 31 32 34 35 39 61

$\frac{24 + 31}{2} = 27.5$ $\frac{35 + 39}{2} = 37$

The interquartile range is 37 – 27.5 or 9.5. The median is 32, the lower quartile is 27.5, and the upper quartile is 37.

StudyTip

Statistics A small interquartile range means that the data in the middle of the set are close in value. A large interquartile range means that the data in the middle are spread out, or vary.

Check Your Progress

2. CONTESTS Find the measures of variation for the data in the table. **Range: 28 feet; median: 42; LQ: 38.5; UQ:47; IR: 8.5**

Marley's Paper Airplane Tosses (ft)			
40	45	49	25
44	39	53	38

Personal Tutor glencoe.com

Differentiated Instruction

AL

If students are confused and mistakenly try to find the quartiles by dividing the range into four equal sections,

Then pair these students with students who understand the concepts of quartiles and interquartile range, and have them work through Example 2 and Check Your Progress together.

StudyTip

Outliers A data value that is much larger or much smaller than the median is an outlier.

Data that are more than 1.5 times the value of the interquartile range beyond the quartiles are called **outliers**.

EXAMPLE 3 Find Outliers

ANIMAL Find any outliers in the data set.

Animal Speeds	
Animal	Speed (mph)
Squirrel	12
Turkey (lower quartile)	15
Elephant	25
Cat (median)	30
Reindeer	32
Rabbit (upper quartile)	35
Cheetah	70

Step 1 Find the interquartile range.
$35 - 15 = 20$

Step 2 Multiply the interquartile range, 20, by 1.5.
$20 \times 1.5 = 30$

Step 3 Subtract 30 from the lower quartile and add 30 to the upper quartile.
$15 - 30 = -15$ $35 + 30 = 65$

The only outlier is 70 because it is greater than 65.

Real-World Link

The cheetah is the fastest land animal in the world. It can sprint 70 miles per hour for only 200 to 300 yards at a time. It can run 3–4 miles at about 45 miles per hour.

Check Your Progress

3. **MOVIES** Find any outliers in the data set. 155

Movie Running Time (min)			
105	120	155	115
96	100	110	120

Personal Tutor glencoe.com

Use Measures of Variation Measures of variation can be used to interpret and compare data.

EXAMPLE 4 Use Measures of Variation

EXERCISE The table shows the number of Calories burned for 30 minutes of each activity. Use measures of variation to describe the data at the right.

Number of Calories Burned for 30 Minutes	
Swimming (fast crawl)	261
Soccer	234
Racquetball	228
Football	222
Basketball	210
Tennis	183
Downhill Skiing	150
Volleyball	84

Find the measures of variation.
The range is 261 − 84 or 177.
The median is $\frac{222 + 210}{2}$ or 216.
The upper quartile is 231.
The lower quartile is 166.5.
The interquartile range is 231 − 166.5 or 64.5.

In one fourth of the activities, you will burn 166.5 Calories or less. In one fourth of the activities, you will burn 231 Calories or more. The number of Calories burned for half of the activities is in the interval 166.5 to 231.

Check Your Progress

4. **VIDEO GAMES** Use measures of variation to describe the data at the right.

Cost of Video Games ($)			
22.79	49.99	34.00	59.99
44.76	32.50	29.25	24.95

4. The spread of the data is $37.20. The median is $33.25. One fourth of the games cost $27.10 or less. One fourth of the games cost $47.38 or more. The price for half of the games is in the interval $27.10 – $47.38.

Personal Tutor glencoe.com

Additional Example

3 **NUTRITION** Find any outliers in the data set. 14

Number of Grams of Fat in Granola Bars		
5	2.5	6
4.5	3	8
3	14	5

Use Measures of Variation

Examples 4 and 5 show how to interpret and compare data in real-world examples.

Additional Example

4 **SOCCER** The table shows the number of tickets sold to soccer games at a local stadium. Use the measures of variation to describe the data.

Number of Tickets			
144	245	98	224
237	262	301	286

The spread of the data is 203 tickets. The median number of tickets is 241. The least fourth of ticket sales is 184 tickets or less. The greatest fourth of ticket sales is 274 tickets or more. The number of tickets sold for half of the games was between 184 and 274.

TEACH with TECH

INTERACTIVE WHITEBOARD Write data values on the board and drag them to rearrange them in order from least to greatest. Group and drag the lower half of the data to separate it from the upper half of the data. If there are an odd number of data values, do not move the middle value and identify it as the median. Repeat the process to find the lower and upper quartiles.

Additional Example

5 **LAND USE** The urban land in certain Western and Eastern states is listed below as the percent of each state's total land, rounded to the nearest percent.

Western States		Eastern States
4 3 2 2 2 2 1	0	
5 4	0	6 6 7 8
	1	0 3 4 5
	2	7

2 | 0 = 2% *2 | 7 = 27%*

a. Compare the western states' range with the eastern states' range. Western: 4%; Eastern: 24%; The percents of urban land use in the East vary more.

b. Does the data for either region contain an outlier? Yes; Eastern States: 27

c. How does the outlier affect the measures of central tendency for the Eastern States? The mean and median increase with the outlier, while the mode does not change.

Focus on Mathematical Content

Measures of Variation Data can be interpreted and compared with the range and interquartile range of a set of data. The range is affected by extreme values. The interquartile range is the range of the middle 50% of the data and is not affected by extreme values.

5A. The range for Homeroom 102 is 38 and the range for Homeroom 104 is 50. So, the number of magazines sold varied more in Homeroom 104 than in Homeroom 102. Yes, Homeroom 104

5B. The range with the outlier is 50, while without the outlier the range is 25. So, the outlier increases the range by 25.

Real-World EXAMPLE 5 Measures of Variation

COUNTIES The number of counties for certain western and northeastern states are shown.

Number of Counties by Region

Western States		Northeastern States
	0	3 5 8
7 5	1	0 4 4 6
9 3	2	1 4
9 6 3	3	
4	4	
6 3	5	
	6	2

3 | 2 = 23 counties *2 | 4 = 24 counties*

a. Compare the western states' range with the northeastern states' range.

The range for the western region is 56 − 15, or 41 counties and the range for the northeastern region is 62 − 3, or 59. So, the number of counties in the northeast vary more than in the west.

b. Do the data for either region contain an outlier?

	Western States	Northeastern States
Lower Quartile:	23	8
Upper Quartile:	44	21
Interquartile Range:	44 − 23 = 21	21 − 8 = 13
Multiply by 1.5:	21 • 1.5 = 31.5	13 • 1.5 = 19.5
Determine Outliers:	23 − 31.5 = −8.5 ✗ 44 + 31.5 = 75.5 ✗	8 − 19.5 = −11.5 ✗ 21 + 19.5 = 40.5 ✓

Since 62 is greater than 40.5, 62 is an outlier for the northeastern states' data.

c. How does the outlier affect the measures of central tendency for the northeast region?

Calculate the mean, median, and mode without the outlier, 62.

	without the outlier	with the outlier
Mean:	$\frac{3+5+\ldots+24}{9} \approx 12.78$	$\frac{3+5+\ldots+62}{10} = 17.7$
Median:	14	14
Mode:	14	14

When the outlier is not included, the mean increased by 17.7 − 12.78, or 4.92, while the median and mode did not change.

Real-World Link

Each year about 33 million 12- to 19-year-olds spend around 175 billion dollars on magazines.

Source: Study of Entertainment and Health

Check Your Progress

5. MAGAZINES The number of magazines sold by each student in Homeroom 102 and Homeroom 104 is shown in the stem-and-leaf plot.

Magazines Sold

Homeroom 102	Stem	Homeroom 104
9 8 7 7 5 2	0	1 2 4 8 9 9
6 6 4 4 3	1	0 0 1 1 2 5 6 6
8 4 3	2	0 5 6
5 5 3	3	
0	4	
	5	1

3 | 2 = 23 magazines *2 | 5 = 25 magazines*

A. Compare Homeroom 104's range with Homeroom 102's range. Does either homeroom have an outlier in the data set?

B. How does the outlier affect the range for the number of magazines sold in that homeroom?

Personal Tutor glencoe.com

Check Your Understanding

Examples 1–3 pp. 743–745

Find the measures of variation and any outliers for each set of data.

1. The number of minutes spent bike riding are: 120, 80, 170, 100, 120, 110, 180, and 35. R: 145; UQ: 145; LQ: 90; M: 115; IR 55; none

2. R: 14; UQ: 16; LQ: 7; M: 15; IR 9; none

2. **Animal Life Span**

Stem	Leaf
0	6 7
1	2 5 5 6
2	0

2 | 0 = 20 years

Examples 4 and 5 pp. 745–746

3. **FOOD** The number of Calories in a serving of certain fruits and vegetables is shown at the right.
   a. Compare the fruits' range with the vegetables' range.
   b. Determine any outliers. How do the outliers affect the measures of central tendency for the number of Calories in fruits?

3a. The fruits' range is 30. The vegetables' range is 20. So, the number of Calories in fruits varies more than the number of Calories in vegetables.

3b. 80; With the outliers, the mean increased by 57.5 – 54.3 or 3.2, the median increased by 55–50 or 5, and the mode did not change.

Calories Per Serving

Fruits	Stem	Vegetables
	3	0 5 5
	4	0 0 0 5
0 0 0 0	5	0
0 0 0	6	
	7	
0	8	

0 | 6 = 60 Calories *3 | 5 = 35 Calories*

Practice and Problem Solving

= **Step-by-Step Solutions** begin on page R11. **Extra Practice** begins on page 810.

Examples 1–3 pp. 743–745

Find the measures of variation and any outliers for each set of data.

4.

Computer Game Sales	
Day	**Number Sold**
Monday	89
Tuesday	90
Wednesday	80
Thursday	100
Friday	92
Saturday	104
Sunday	150

R: 70; UQ: 104; LQ: 89; M: 92; IR: 15; 150

5. **Number of Sunny Days Per Month**

Stem	Leaf
0	
1	5 7 8 8
2	0 1 2 3 5 5 7
3	0

2 | 2 = 22 days

R: 15; UQ: 25; LQ: 18; M: 21.5; IR 7; no outlier

6.

Popcorn Sales at Movie Time Theatre								
Year	2003	2004	2005	2006	2007	2008	2009	2010
Sales (thousands)	0.66	0.43	1.25	0.2	0.53	0.6	0.58	0.48

R: 1.05; UQ: 0.63; LQ: 0.455; M: 0.555; IR: 0.175; 1.25

Examples 4 and 5 pp. 745–746

7. **SCIENCE** The table shows the top scores on a science test.
   a. What is the median score for each room?
   b. Which room has a greater range of scores? Room 100
   c. Of the top scores shown, does either set of data have an outlier? If so, how does the outlier affect the range?

7a. Room 110: 91; Room 100: 94

7c. Room 100 has an outlier, 64. The outlier makes the range greater by 24 points.

Science Scores

Room 100	Room 110
94	82
64	79
88	85
100	91
91	97
106	109
97	103
88	100
97	82

3 PRACTICE

Formative Assessment

Use Exercises 1–3 to check for understanding.

Use the chart at the bottom of this page to customize assignments for your students.

Tips for New Teachers

Median Point out to students that with an odd number of data, the median is the middle number and should be excluded from both halves. With an even number of data, the median falls between the two middle values and no data point is eliminated.

Differentiated Homework Options

Level	Assignment	Two-Day Option	
AL Basic	4–8, 12–29	5, 7, 17–20	4–8 even, 12–16, 21–29
OL Core	5, 7, 9–29	4–8, 17–20	9–16, 21–29
BL Advanced	9–27 (optional: 28, 29)		

Study Guide and Intervention
CRM pp. 18–19 AL OL ELL

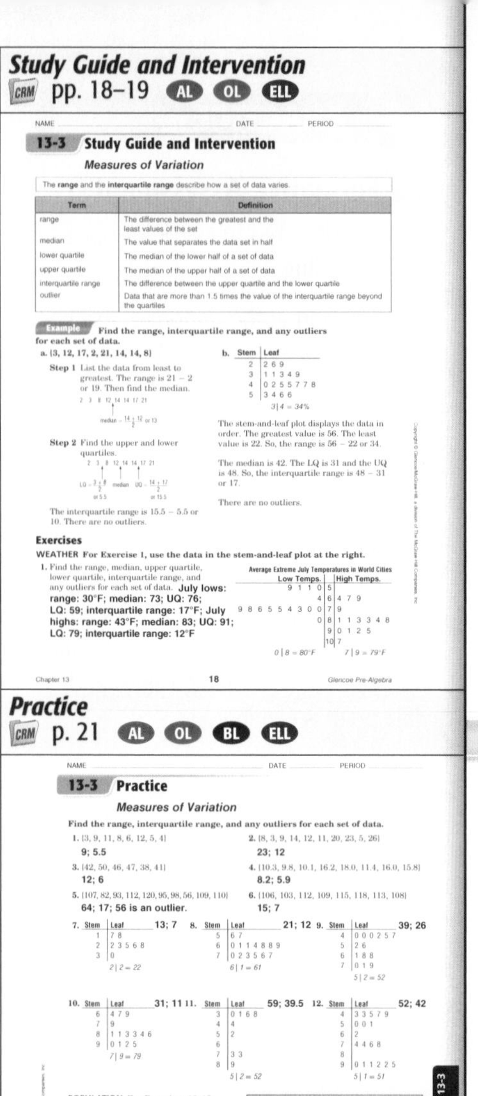

NAME ______ DATE ______ PERIOD ______

13-3 Study Guide and Intervention

Measures of Variation

The **range** and the **interquartile range** describe how a set of data varies.

Term	Definition
range	The difference between the greatest and the least values of the set
median	The value that separates the data set in half
lower quartile	The median of the lower half of a set of data
upper quartile	The median of the upper half of a set of data
interquartile range	The difference between the upper quartile and the lower quartile
outlier	Data that are more than 1.5 times the value of the interquartile range beyond the quartiles

Example Find the range, interquartile range, and any outliers for each set of data.

a. {3, 12, 17, 2, 21, 14, 14, 8}

Step 1 List the data from least to greatest. The range is 21 − 2 or 19. Then find the median.

Step 2 Find the upper and lower quartiles.

The interquartile range is 15.5 − 5.5 or 10. There are no outliers.

b.

Stem	Leaf
2	2 6 9
3	1 1 3 4 9
4	0 2 5 5 7 7 8
5	3 4 6 6

3 | 4 = 34%

The stem-and-leaf plot displays the data in order. The greatest value is 56. The least value is 22. So, the range is 56 − 22 or 34.

The median is 42. The LQ is 31 and the UQ is 48. So, the interquartile range is 48 − 31 or 17.

There are no outliers.

Exercises

WEATHER For Exercise 1, use the data in the stem-and-leaf plot at the right.

1. Find the range, median, upper quartile, lower quartile, interquartile range, and any outliers for each set of data. **July lows: range: 30°F; median: 73; UQ: 76; LQ: 59; interquartile range: 17°F; July highs: range: 43°F; median: 83; UQ: 91; LQ: 79; interquartile range: 12°F**

Average Extreme July Temperatures in World Cities

Low Temps.		High Temps.
9 1 1 0	5	
4	6	4 7 9
9 8 6 5 5 4 3 0 0	7	9
0	8	1 1 3 3 4 8
	9	0 1 2 5
	10	7

0 | 8 = 80°F 7 | 9 = 79°F

Chapter 13 18 Glencoe Pre-Algebra

Practice
CRM p. 21 AL OL BL ELL

NAME ______ DATE ______ PERIOD ______

13-3 Practice

Measures of Variation

Find the range, interquartile range, and any outliers for each set of data.

1. {3, 9, 11, 8, 6, 12, 5, 4} **9; 5.5**
2. {8, 3, 9, 14, 12, 11, 20, 23, 5, 26} **23; 12**
3. {42, 50, 46, 47, 38, 41} **12; 6**
4. {10.3, 9.8, 10.1, 16.2, 18.0, 11.4, 16.0, 15.8} **8.2; 5.9**
5. {107, 82, 93, 112, 120, 95, 98, 56, 109, 110} **64; 17; 56 is an outlier.**
6. {106, 103, 112, 109, 115, 118, 113, 108} **15; 7**
7. **13; 7**
8. **21; 12**
9. **39; 26**
10. **31; 11**
11. **59; 39.5**
12. **52; 42**

POPULATION For Exercises 13–15, use the data in the table at the right.

13. What is the range of populations shown? **13.8 million**
14. What is the interquartile range for the annual growth rate? **1.3%**
15. Where does the city with the fastest growth rate fall in terms of population? The city with the slowest growth rate? **near the median; at the LQ**

Populations of the World's Largest Cities 2000

City	Population millions	Annual Growth Rate (%)
Tokyo, Japan	26.4	0.51
Mexico City, Mexico	18.1	1.81
Mumbai, India	18.1	3.54
Sao Paulo, Brazil	17.8	1.43
New York City, U.S.	16.6	0.37
Lagos, Nigeria	13.4	5.33
Los Angeles, U.S.	13.1	1.15
Calcutta, India	12.9	1.60
Shanghai, China	12.9	−0.35
Buenos Aires, Argentina	12.6	1.14

Source: World Almanac

Chapter 13 21 Glencoe Pre-Algebra

Word Problem Practice
CRM p. 22 AL OL BL

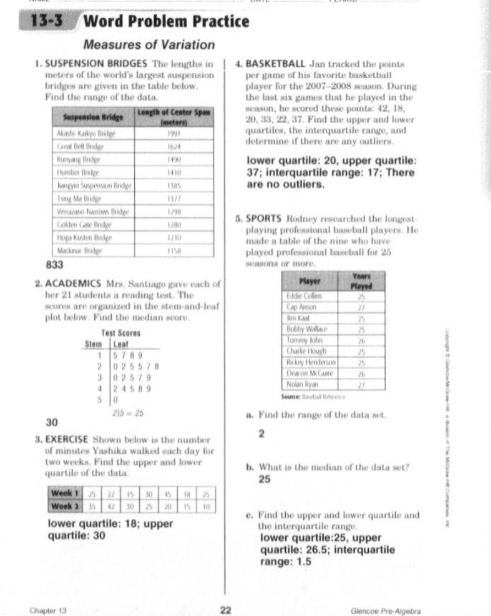

NAME ______ DATE ______ PERIOD ______

13-3 Word Problem Practice

Measures of Variation

1. SUSPENSION BRIDGES The lengths in meters of the world's largest suspension bridges are given in the table below. Find the range of the data. **833**

2. ACADEMICS Mrs. Santiago gave each of her 21 students a reading test. The scores are organized in the stem-and-leaf plot below. Find the median score. **30**

Test Scores

Stem	Leaf
1	5 7 8 9
2	0 2 5 5 7 8
3	0 2 5 7 9
4	2 4 5 8 9
5	0

2|5 = 25

3. EXERCISE Shown below is the number of minutes Yashika walked each day for two weeks. Find the upper and lower quartile of the data. **lower quartile: 18; upper quartile: 30**

4. BASKETBALL Jan tracked the points per game of his favorite basketball player for the 2007–2008 season. During the last six games that he played in the season, he scored these points: 42, 18, 20, 33, 22, 37. Find the upper and lower quartiles, the interquartile range, and determine if there are any outliers. **lower quartile: 20, upper quartile: 37; interquartile range: 17; There are no outliers.**

5. SPORTS Rodney researched the longest-playing professional baseball players. He made a table of the nine who have played professional baseball for 25 seasons or more.

a. Find the range of the data set. **2**

b. What is the median of the data set? **25**

c. Find the upper and lower quartile and the interquartile range. **lower quartile: 25, upper quartile: 26.5; interquartile range: 1.5**

Chapter 13 22 Glencoe Pre-Algebra

Examples 4 and 5
pp. 745–746

8. **SCORES** The table shows the number of points Cami scored per basketball game.
   a. In which season did Cami have a greater range of points? **2008**
   b. Select the appropriate measure of central tendency to describe the number of points she scored each season. Justify your response. **See margin.**
   c. The score 40 is considered an outlier. How does the inclusion of the outlier for the number of points scored in the 2008 season affect the range? **See margin.**

Cami's Basketball Stats

2008	Stem	2007
	0	6 7 8 9 9
8 8 6 6 4 4 4	1	0 0 2 4 6 7 8
6 6 4 4 2 2	2	1 7
	3	
0	4	

4 | 2 = 24 points 2 | 1 = 21 points

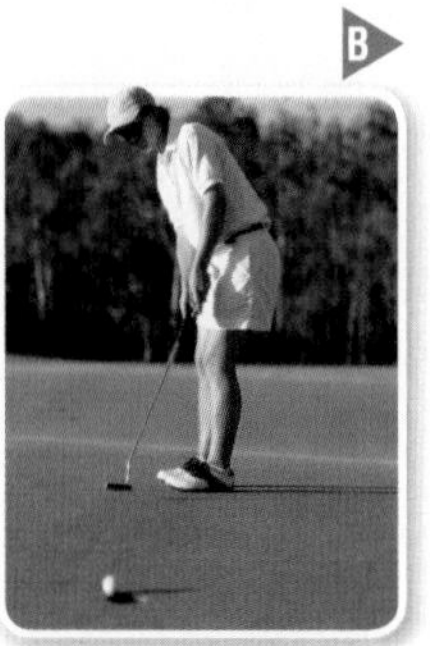

Real-World Link

In golf, the difficulty of a particular hole is given by its par, the number of strokes expected to reach the hole. A score of +3, read as 3 above par, means it took 3 additional tries to put the ball in the hole. A score of −2, read as 2 below par, means it took 2 less tries than expected to reach the hole.

9. **WEATHER** The table shows average monthly temperatures. **b–c. See margin.**
   a. Which city has a greater range of temperatures? **Antelope**
   b. Find the measures of variation for each city.
   c. Compare the medians and the interquartile ranges of the average temperatures.
   d. Select the appropriate measure of central tendency to describe the average high temperature for Augusta. Justify your response.
   e. Describe the average temperatures of Antelope and Augusta, using both the measures of central tendency and variation. **d–e. See Chapter 13 Answer Appendix.**

Average Monthly Highs

Month	Antelope, MT	Augusta, ME
January	21	28
February	30	32
March	42	41
April	58	53
May	70	66
June	79	75
July	84	80
August	84	79
September	72	70
October	58	58
November	37	46
December	24	34

10. **GOLF** Rondell's golf scores at the end of the high school golf tournament were −1, −2, 4, −6, 3, −1, and −3. Find the measures of variation of his golf scores. Explain what the measures of variation tell you about the data. **10–11. See Chapter 13 Answer Appendix.**

11. **ANALYZE DATA** Find a real-world data set with at least eight values that include one or more outliers. Display the data in a table. Find the mean and the interquartile range of the data set. Then remove the outlier(s) from the data set and find the mean and the interquartile range. Describe any differences in the values.

12. **Sample answer: 1, 2, 3, 4, 5, 6, 7, 10, 20, 21, 22, 23, 24, 25, 26; 8, 8, 8, 8, 9, 9, 9, 10, 11, 11, 11, 12, 12, 13, 14**

13. **Always; the range is the difference between the greatest and least value. An outlier is an extreme value, therefore will always affect the range.**

H.O.T. Problems
Use Higher-Order Thinking Skills

12. **OPEN ENDED** Write two lists of data that each have at least 15 values and a median of 10. One should have a range of 25 and the other a range of 6.
13. **REASONING** The range is *always, sometimes,* or *never* affected by outliers. Justify your reasoning.
14. **REASONING** *True or false.* The interquartile range is affected by high and low values of a data set. Explain your reasoning. **See Chapter 13 Answer Appendix.**
15. **REASONING** *True or false.* Of mean, median, and mode, the mean will always be most affected by the outliers. If false, give a counterexample. **True**
16. **WRITING IN MATH** Explain how outliers affect the calculation of measures of variation in a data set. **See Chapter 13 Answer Appendix.**

748 Chapter 13 Statistics and Probability

Enrichment
CRM p. 23 OL BL

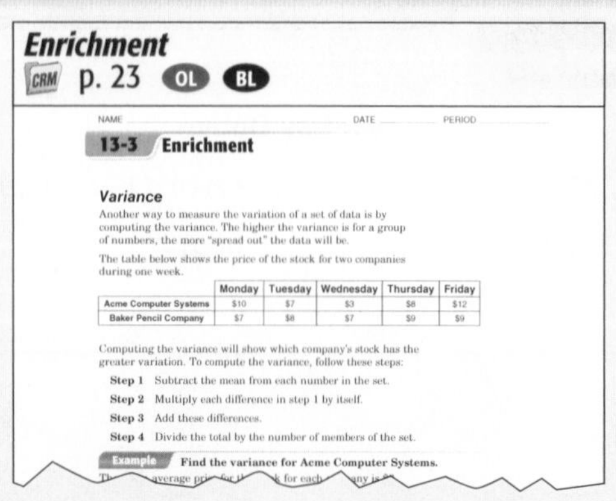

NAME ______ DATE ______ PERIOD ______

13-3 Enrichment

Variance

Another way to measure the variation of a set of data is by computing the variance. The higher the variance is for a group of numbers, the more "spread out" the data will be.

The table below shows the price of the stock for two companies during one week.

	Monday	Tuesday	Wednesday	Thursday	Friday
Acme Computer Systems	$10	$7	$3	$8	$12
Baker Pencil Company	$7	$8	$7	$9	$9

Computing the variance will show which company's stock has the greater variation. To compute the variance, follow these steps:

Step 1 Subtract the mean from each number in the set.
Step 2 Multiply each difference in step 1 by itself.
Step 3 Add these differences.
Step 4 Divide the total by the number of members of the set.

Example Find the variance for Acme Computer Systems.

Exercise Alert

Internet Exercise 11 requires the use of the Internet or other reference materials to find a real-world data set.

Standardized Test Practice

17. The table shows the total number of wins by the team that won the women's NCAA basketball tournament for the past 15 years. **D**

Total Wins				
34	39	29	31	34
34	34	32	37	39
33	36	35	33	31

Which of the following statements is *not* supported by these data?

A Less than half of the teams won more than 34 games and half won less than 34 games.

B The range of the data is 10 games.

C About one fourth of the teams won 32 or fewer games.

D An outlier of the data is 29 games.

18. Refer to the table in Exercise 17. What is the interquartile range of the data? **F**

F 4 H 8

G 5 J 10

19. What is the lower quartile of the following set of data? **A**

37, 12, 7, 8, 10, 5, 14, 19, 7, 15, 11

A 7 C 11

B 7.5 D 15

20. **SHORT RESPONSE** Find the measures of variation and any outliers for the set of data.

30, 62, 35, 80, 12, 24, 30, 39, 53, 38

R: 68; UQ: 53; LQ: 30; M: 36.5; IR: 23; outlier: none

Spiral Review

21. **MONEY** Display the data representing the cost of DVDs $12, $15, $18, $21, $14, $37, $27, $9 in a stem-and-leaf plot. (Lesson 13-2) **See Chapter 13 Answer Appendix.**

Find the mean, median, and mode for each set of data. Round to the nearest tenth. (Lesson 13-1)

22. 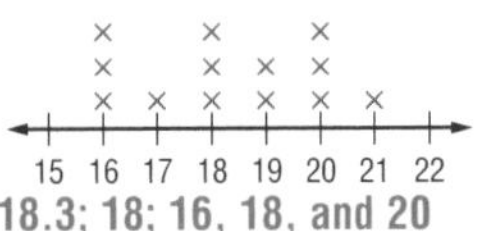

18.3; 18; 16, 18, and 20

23. 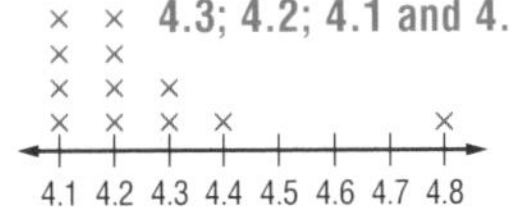

4.3; 4.2; 4.1 and 4.2

Determine whether each pair of solids is similar. (Lesson 12-8)

24. 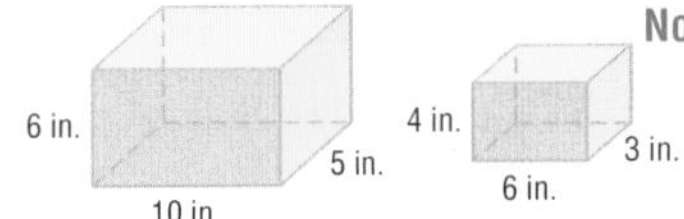

No

25. 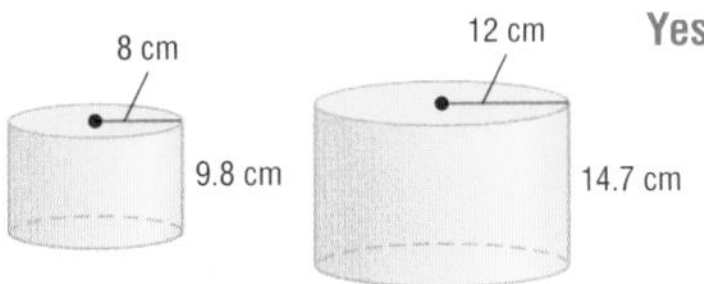

Yes

Find the volume of each cone. Round to the nearest tenth. (Lesson 12-4)

26. radius, 7 cm; height, 9 cm **461.8 cm^3**

27. diameter, 8.4 yd; height, 6.5 yd **120.1 yd^3**

Skills Review

Order each set of decimals from least to greatest. (Previous Course)

28. 1.0, 1.1, 0.9, 0.5, 1.9, 10.9, 0.1
0.1, 0.5, 0.9, 1.0, 1.1, 1.9, 10.9

29. 7.8, 8.7, 6.7, 6.8, 7.0, 6.9
6.7, 6.8, 6.9, 7.0, 7.8, 8.7

Differentiated Instruction

Extension Have students create a set of data with an interquartile range of 8 and 2 outliers. Sample data set: 2, 15, 16, 18, 20, 23, 36

4 ASSESS

Crystal Ball Tell students to write how they think today's lesson on measures of variation will connect with tomorrow's lesson on box-and-whisker plots.

Formative Assessment

Check for student understanding of concepts in Lessons 13-1, 13-2, and 13-3.

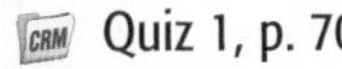

Quiz 1, p. 70

Additional Answers

8b. Sample answer: For the 2008 season, the mean was 21, the median was 20, and the mode was 14. So, the mean would be used since it is the greatest value. For the 2007 season, the mean was 13.1, the median was 11, and the modes were 9 and 10. So, the mean would be used since it is the greatest value.

8c. Without the outlier, 40, the range is 12 points. The inclusion of the outlier, 40, makes the range 26 points. So, the range is increased by 14 points.

9b. Antelope: range: 63; median: 58; upper quartile: 75.5; lower quartile: 33.5; interquartile range: 42; Augusta: range: 52; median: 55.5; upper quartile: 72.5; lower quartile: 37.5; interquartile range: 35

9c. Sample answer: The median average high temperature of Antelope is only slightly greater than the median average high temperature of Augusta. The interquartile range for Antelope is only 42°, while the interquartile range for Augusta is 35°.

13-4 Lesson Notes

1 FOCUS

Vertical Alignment

Before Lesson 13-4
Interpret and analyze data.

Lesson 13-4
Display and interpret data in a box-and-whisker plot.

After Lesson 13-4
Recognize misuses of graphical information and evaluate predictions and conclusions based on data analysis.

2 TEACH

Scaffolding Questions

Have students read the *Why?* section of the lesson and answer the questions.

Ask:

- What is the range of the number of wins for Boston? 20 wins for Florida? 38 wins
- What do the differences between these two ranges indicate? There is more variance in the number of wins for Florida.
- Are there any outliers in the data for Boston? Explain. No; there are no data 1.5 times greater than the interquartile range beyond the quartiles for Boston (70, 110).

13-4 Box-and-Whisker Plots

Then
You have already interpreted and analyzed data. (Lessons 13-1 through 13-3)

Now
- Display data in a box-and-whisker plot.
- Interpret data in a box-and-whisker plot.

New Vocabulary
box-and-whisker plot

Math Online
glencoe.com
- Extra Examples
- Personal Tutor
- Self-Check Quiz
- Homework Help

Why?

The table shows the number of wins per season for the Boston Red Sox and the Florida Marlins.

NUMBER OF WINS	'96	'97	'98	'99	'00	'01	'02	'03	'04	'05	'06	'07
BOSTON	85	78	92	94	85	82	93	95	98	95	86	96
FLORIDA	80	92	54	64	79	76	79	91	83	83	78	71

Source: Major League Baseball

a. What is the least value in the data set for Boston? Florida? **78; 54**

b. What is the lower quartile of the data for Boston? Florida? **85; 73.5**

c. What is the median of the data for Boston? Florida? **92.5; 79**

d. What is the upper quartile of the data for Boston? Florida? **95; 83**

e. What is the greatest value in the data for Boston? Florida? **98; 92**

Display Data A **box-and-whisker plot**, or box plot, uses a number line to show the distribution of a set of data. It divides a set of data into four parts using the median and quartiles. A *box* is drawn around the quartile values, and *whiskers* extend from each quartile to the minimum and maximum values that are not outliers.

EXAMPLE 1 Draw a Box-and-Whisker Plot

BASEBALL Use the data in the table above to draw a box-and-whisker plot for Boston's number of wins.

Step 1 Draw a number line that includes the least and greatest numbers in the data.

Step 2 Mark the minimum and maximum values, the median, and the upper and lower quartile above the number line. Check for outliers. If an outlier exists, mark the greatest value that is not an outlier. Use an asterisk (*) to indicate an outlier. It is not connected to a whisker.

Step 3 Draw the box and the whiskers.

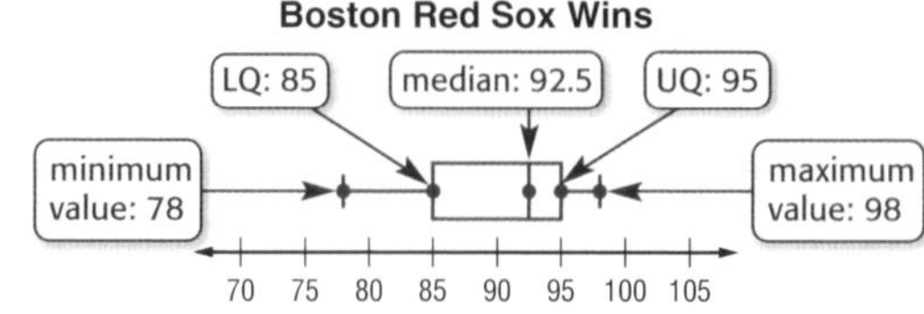

Check Your Progress

1. **BASEBALL** Use the data in the table above to draw a box-and-whisker plot for Florida's number of wins. **See margin.**

Personal Tutor glencoe.com

750 Chapter 13 Statistics and Probability

Lesson 13-4 Resources

Resource	Approaching-Level	On-Level	Beyond-Level	English Learners
Teacher Edition	• Differentiated Instruction, p. 752	• Differentiated Instruction, p. 752	• Differentiated Instruction, p. 755	
Chapter Resource Masters	• Study Guide and Intervention, pp. 24–25 • Skills Practice, p. 26 • Practice, p. 27 • Word Problem Practice, p. 28	• Study Guide and Intervention, pp. 24–25 • Skills Practice, p. 26 • Practice, p. 27 • Word Problem Practice, p. 28 • Enrichment, p. 29	• Practice, p. 27 • Word Problem Practice, p. 28 • Enrichment, p. 29	• Study Guide and Intervention, pp. 24–25 • Skills Practice, p. 26 • Practice, p. 27
Transparencies	• 5-Minute Check Transparency 13-4	• 5-Minute Check Transparency 13-4	• 5-Minute Check Transparency 13-4	• 5-Minute Check Transparency 13-4
Other	• Study Notebook • Teaching Pre-Algebra with Manipulatives	• Study Notebook • Teaching Pre-Algebra with Manipulatives	• Study Notebook	• Study Notebook • Teaching Pre-Algebra with Manipulatives

StudyTip

Five-number summary While the box-and-whisker plot separates data into four parts, it uses 5 numbers to do so: the minimum value, the lower quartile, the median, the upper quartile, and the maximum value.

Interpret Box-and-Whisker Plots Box-and-whisker plots separate data into four parts, excluding outliers. Even though the parts may differ in length, each part contains one-fourth or, 25%, of the data.

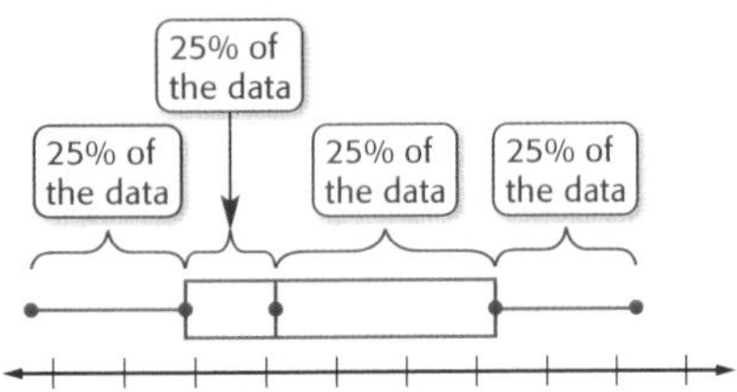

A long whisker or box indicates that the data have a greater range. The values of the data are spread out. A short whisker or box indicates the data have a lesser range. The values of the data in that part are concentrated.

Real-World EXAMPLE 2 **Interpret Data**

MUSIC The number of chart hits for the top female groups in the U.S. are displayed.

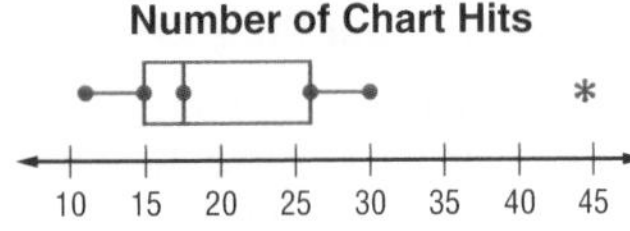

a. What percent of the groups had at least 18 chart hits?

Half of the groups, or 50%, had at least 18 chart hits.

b. What does the length of the box tell about the data? length of the whisker?

The median divides the data in the box into two unequal parts. The data between the lower quartile and the median are more clustered than the data between the median and the upper quartile.

The whiskers are the same length, so the data below the lower quartile and above the upper quartile have the same range.

Check Your Progress

2. CALORIES The number of Calories in one serving of various muffins are displayed in the box-and-whisker plot below.

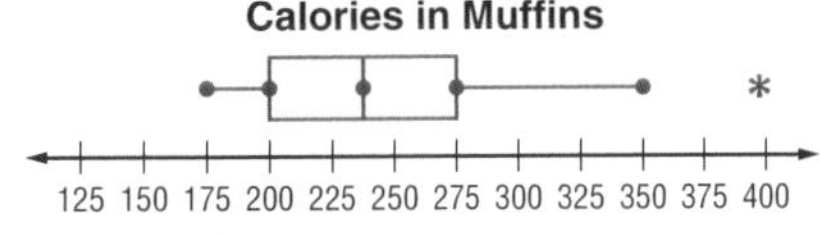

A. What percent of the muffins have more than 275 Calories per muffin? **25%**

B. What does the length of the box tell about the data? length of the whiskers?

Personal Tutor glencoe.com

2B. The median divides the data box into two approximately equal parts so, the data between the upper and lower quartile are similarly spread out. The whisker at the right is longer than any other parts of the plot, so the data above the upper quartile are more spread out.

Display Data

Example 1 shows how to draw a box-and-whisker plot.

Formative Assessment

Use the Check Your Progress exercises after each example to determine students' understanding of concepts.

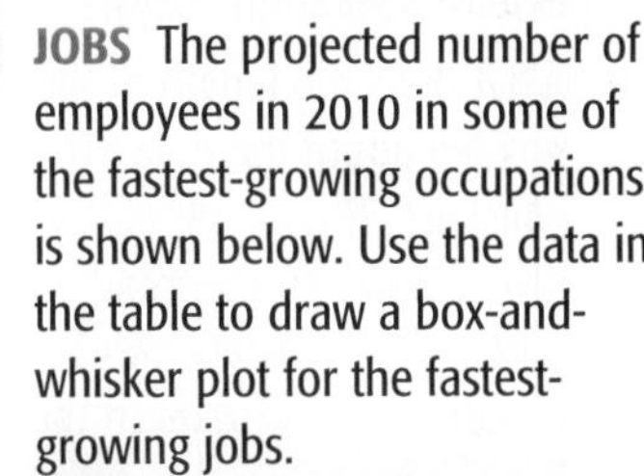

Additional Example

1 **JOBS** The projected number of employees in 2010 in some of the fastest-growing occupations is shown below. Use the data in the table to draw a box-and-whisker plot for the fastest-growing jobs.

Fastest-Growing Jobs

Occupation	Jobs (1000s)
Computer Engineer	760
Computer Support	996
Systems Engineer	601
Database Administrator	176
Network Analyst	211
Home Health Aide	672
Medical Assistant	516

See answer at bottom of page.

Additional Examples also in Interactive Classroom PowerPoint® Presentations

IWB INTERACTIVE WHITEBOARD READY

Tips for New Teachers

Explain to students that a data set can have more than one outlier. Each outlier must be graphed separately.

Interpret Box-and-Whisker Plots

Example 2 shows how to interpret the data from a box-and-whisker plot. **Example 3** shows how to compare sets of data in a real-world problem.

Additional Answer (Check Your Progress)

1.

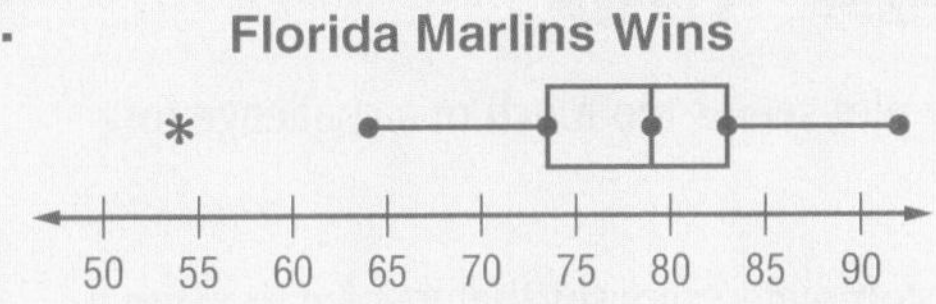

Additional Answer (Additional Example)

1.

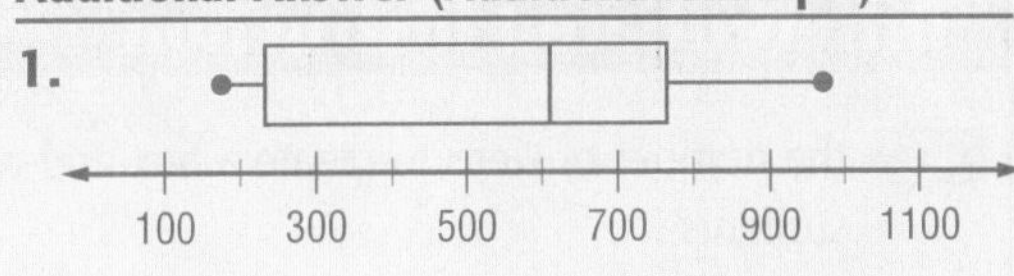

Additional Examples

2 **WEATHER** The box-and-whisker plot below shows the average percent of sunny days per year for selected cities in each state.

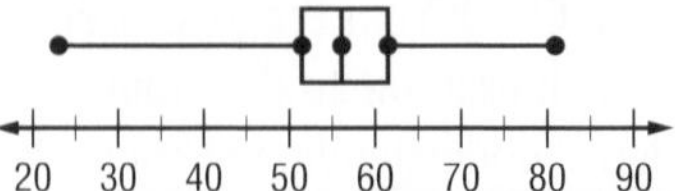

a. What percent of the cities had at least 56% sunny days? 50%

b. What does the length of the box tell about the data? The whisker? The length of the box is short, so the middle 50% of the data are clustered together. The whisker at the left is longer than other parts of the plot, so the data in the lower quartile are more spread out.

3 **TREES** The average maximum height, in feet, for selected evergreen trees and deciduous trees is shown. How do the heights of evergreen trees compare with the heights of deciduous trees? Most evergreen trees are taller than most deciduous trees.

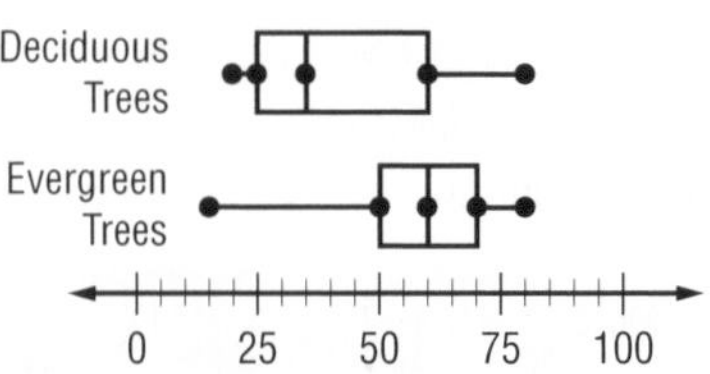

Additional Answer

3. Sample answer: The lower extreme and the lower quartile for each team is the same. The box for the Flyers is larger than the box for the Penguins so their middle 50% is more spread out. The upper quartile of the Penguins' scores is less than the median of the Flyers' scores. This means 75% of the Penguins' scores were less than 50% of the Flyers' scores.

Real-World EXAMPLE 3 Compare Data

FITNESS Two fitness clubs are analyzing their daily attendance for September. How does the daily attendance at the Athletic Club compare to the daily attendance at SuperFit?

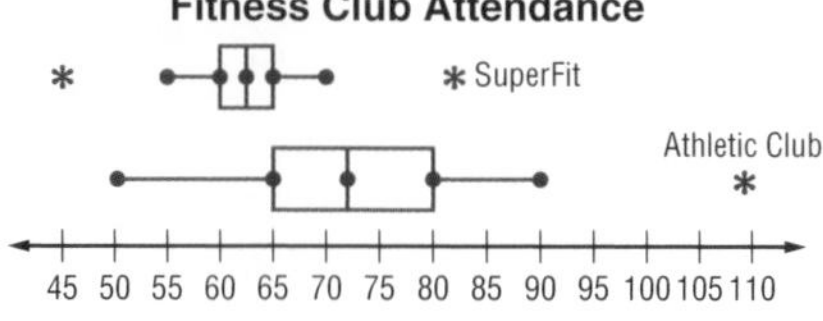

- The Athletic Club's highest and lowest daily attendance figures are both greater than SuperFit's corresponding attendance figures.
- The range of values from the Athletic Club is greater than the range of values from SuperFit.
- One fourth of the time, the attendance at The Athletic Club is greater than 80. The attendance at SuperFit is almost always less than 80.

These results suggest that the Athletic Club's daily attendance varies more than SuperFit's daily attendance. On average the Athletic Club has a higher daily attendance than SuperFit does.

Real-World Link

The National Hockey League began in Montreal in 1917. The league expanded into the United States in 1924 with the Boston Bruins.

Check Your Progress

3. **HOCKEY** The number of goals scored in a recent regular season for players on the Philadelphia Flyers and the Pittsburgh Penguins is displayed. How does the number of goals for Philadelphia compare to the number of goals for Pittsburgh? **See margin.**

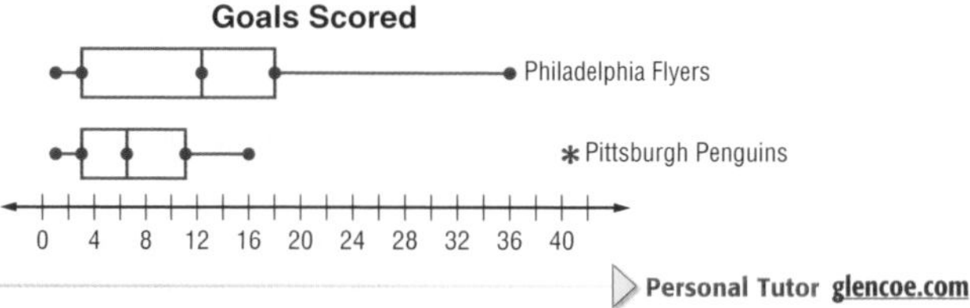

Personal Tutor glencoe.com

Check Your Understanding

Example 1 p. 750

1. **GEOGRAPHY** The heights in feet of several waterfalls in Africa and Asia are shown. Display the data in a box-and-whisker plot. **See Chapter 13 Answer Appendix.**

406	508	630	343	480	330	726
830	330	614	1100	885	1137	890

Source: *The World Almanac*

Example 2 p. 751

2. **EXERCISE** The number of Calories burned for 15 minutes of exercise for various activities is shown.

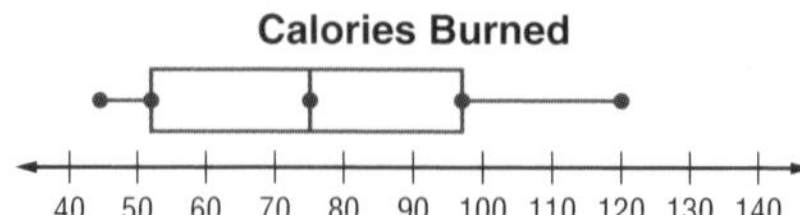

a. What percent of the activities burn fewer than 98 Calories? **75%**

b. What does the length of the box tell about the data? **See margin.**

Differentiated Instruction

If the number of steps to create a box-and-whisker plot seems too much of a challenge for students,

Then have students work in groups of two or three to complete exercises that involve drawing a box plot. Have members split tasks, such as finding the median, quartiles, and interquartile range, checking for outliers, and drawing the box plot. Encourage students to rotate tasks for different exercises.

Example 3 p. 752

3. Sample answer: Half the time the Cougars scored between 18 and 31 points. Half the time the Falcons scored between 14 and 21 points. So, the Cougars usually scored more points per game than the Falcons.

3. **FOOTBALL** Two football teams are analyzing the number of points they scored in each game this season. How does the number of points scored by the Falcons compare to the number of points scored by the Cougars?

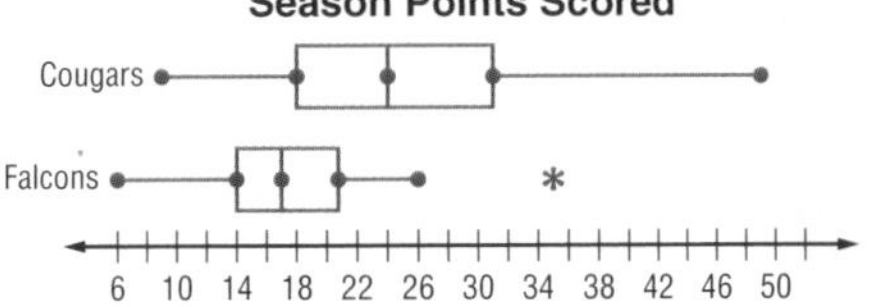

Practice and Problem Solving

= **Step-by-Step Solutions** begin on page R11. **Extra Practice** begins on page 810.

Example 1 p. 750

Construct a box-and-whisker plot for each set of data. 4–7. See Chapter 13 Answer Appendix.

4.

Number of Rainy Days Last Year for Various Cities		
173	176	185
182	172	120
190	173	182
182	180	173

5.

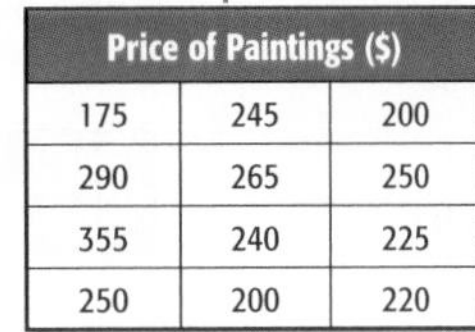

Price of Paintings ($)		
175	245	200
290	265	250
355	240	225
250	200	220

6. Miles per gallon, for city driving, of various automobiles: 28, 24, 23, 21, 27, 32, 19, 20, 18, 25, 25

7. Age of students in a pottery class: 23, 37, 34, 19, 28, 33, 26, 27, 35, 25, 21, 29, 28

Example 2 p. 751

8. **GAMES** The yearly games sales for a popular toy manufacturer are displayed.

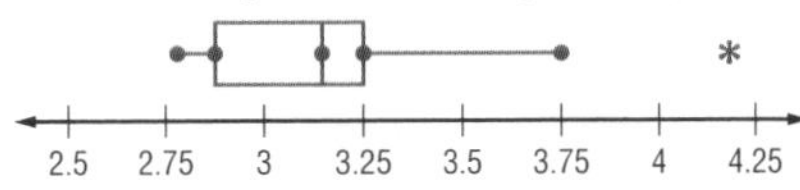

a. What percent of the years had sales that were more than $3.25 billion? 25%

b. What does the length of the box tell about the data? the whiskers? See Chapter 13 Answer Appendix.

9. **HURRICANES** The top wind speeds for hurricanes in a recent year are shown below.

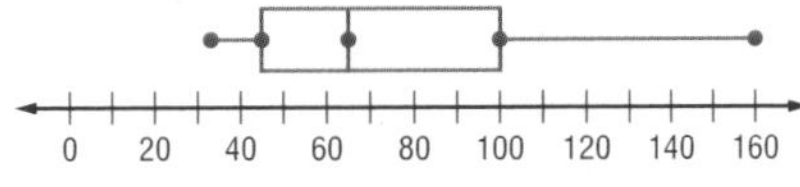

a. What percent of the hurricanes had top wind speeds less than 65 miles per hour? 50%

b. What does the length of the box tell about the data? the whiskers? See Chapter 13 Answer Appendix.

Real-World Link

The eye of a hurricane is a circular area that can range from 2–230 miles in diameter. Inside the eye, the wind is calm and the skies may be clear. The eyewall surrounds the eye and contains the most violent weather in a hurricane.

Tips for New Teachers

Explain to students that there are various types of outliers. Outliers may occur above maximum value or below minimum value. There can be multiple outliers. Sometimes an outlier can cause a whisker to be eliminated. This happens when the first or third interquartile occurs at the end point of the data set up to the outlier.

Focus on Mathematical Content

Outliers The whiskers of a box-and-whisker plot do not always extend to the extreme values of a data set. When extreme values are outliers–at least 1.5 times the interquartile range–they are shown with an asterisk or bullet. In the case of outliers, the minimum and maximum values of the box plot are the minimum and maximum values that are not outliers.

3 PRACTICE

Formative Assessment

Use Exercises 1–3 to check for understanding.

Use the chart at the bottom of this page to customize assignments for your students.

Additional Answer

2b. The median divides the data into two approximately equal parts so, the data between the upper and lower quartile are similarly spread out. The length of the box is significantly larger than the left whisker which indicates that the lower 25% of values are more concentrated between about 43 and 51 Calories.

Differentiated Homework Options

Level	Assignment	Two-Day Option	
AL Basic	4–10, 13, 14, 16–22	5–9 odd, 17–20	4–10 even, 13, 14, 16, 21, 22
OL Core	5–9 odd, 11–14, 16–22	4–10, 17–20	11–14, 16, 21, 22
BL Advanced	11–21 (optional: 22)		

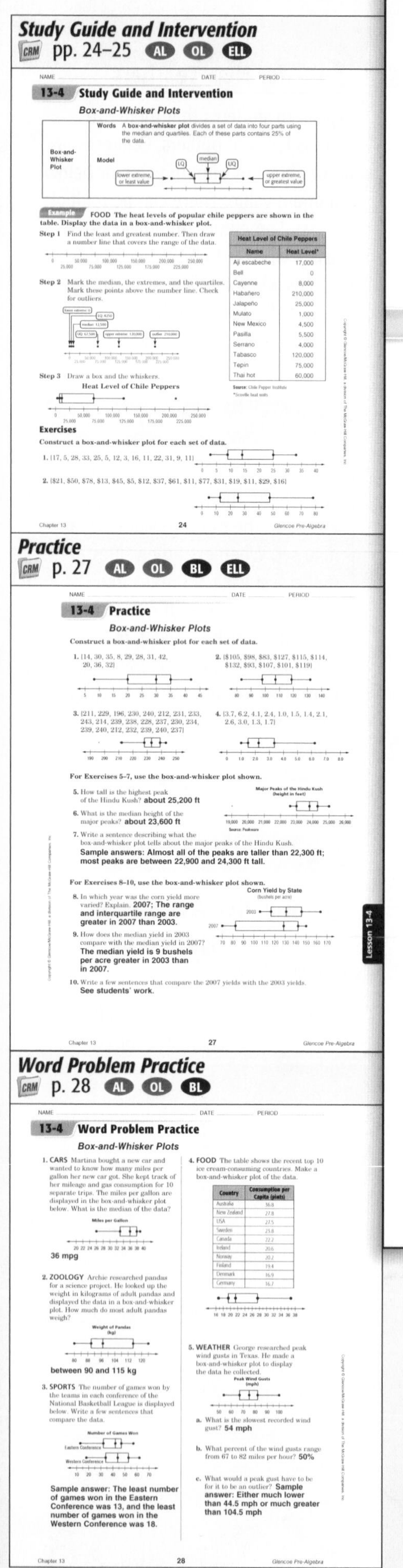

Study Guide and Intervention
CRM pp. 24–25 AL OL ELL

NAME ______ DATE ______ PERIOD ______

13-4 Study Guide and Intervention

Box-and-Whisker Plots

Box-and-Whisker Plot	Words	A box-and-whisker plot divides a set of data into four parts using the median and quartiles. Each of these parts contains 25% of the data.
	Model	lower extreme, or least value; LQ; median; UQ; upper extreme, or greatest value

Example FOOD The heat levels of popular chile peppers are shown in the table. Display the data in a box-and-whisker plot.

Step 1 Find the least and greatest number. Then draw a number line that covers the range of the data.

Step 2 Mark the median, the extremes, and the quartiles. Mark these points above the number line. Check for outliers.

Step 3 Draw a box and the whiskers.

Heat Level of Chile Peppers	
Name	Heat Level*
Aji escabeche	17,000
Bell	0
Cayenne	8,000
Habañero	210,000
Jalapeño	25,000
Mulato	1,000
New Mexico	4,500
Pasilla	5,500
Serrano	4,000
Tabasco	120,000
Tepin	75,000
Thai hot	60,000

Source: Chile Pepper Institute
*Scoville heat units

Heat Level of Chile Peppers

Exercises

Construct a box-and-whisker plot for each set of data.

1. {17, 5, 28, 33, 25, 5, 12, 3, 16, 11, 22, 31, 9, 11}

2. {$21, $50, $78, $13, $45, $5, $12, $37, $61, $11, $77, $31, $19, $11, $29, $16}

Chapter 13 24 Glencoe Pre-Algebra

Practice
CRM p. 27 AL OL BL ELL

NAME ______ DATE ______ PERIOD ______

13-4 Practice

Box-and-Whisker Plots

Construct a box-and-whisker plot for each set of data.

1. {14, 30, 35, 8, 29, 28, 31, 42, 20, 36, 32}

2. {$105, $98, $83, $127, $115, $114, $132, $93, $107, $101, $119}

3. {211, 229, 196, 230, 240, 212, 231, 233, 243, 214, 239, 238, 228, 237, 230, 234, 239, 240, 212, 232, 239, 240, 237}

4. {3.7, 6.2, 4.1, 2.4, 1.0, 1.5, 1.4, 2.1, 2.6, 3.0, 1.3, 1.7}

For Exercises 5–7, use the box-and-whisker plot shown.

5. How tall is the highest peak of the Hindu Kush? **about 25,200 ft**

6. What is the median height of the major peaks? **about 23,600 ft**

7. Write a sentence describing what the box-and-whisker plot tells about the major peaks of the Hindu Kush. **Sample answers: Almost all of the peaks are taller than 22,300 ft; most peaks are between 22,900 and 24,300 ft tall.**

For Exercises 8–10, use the box-and-whisker plot shown.

8. In which year was the corn yield more varied? Explain. **2007; The range and interquartile range are greater in 2007 than 2003.**

9. How does the median yield in 2003 compare with the median yield in 2007? **The median yield is 9 bushels per acre greater in 2003 than in 2007.**

10. Write a few sentences that compare the 2007 yields with the 2003 yields. **See students' work.**

Chapter 13 27 Glencoe Pre-Algebra

Word Problem Practice
CRM p. 28 AL OL BL

NAME ______ DATE ______ PERIOD ______

13-4 Word Problem Practice

Box-and-Whisker Plots

1. CARS Martina bought a new car and wanted to know how many miles per gallon her new car got. She kept track of her mileage and gas consumption for 10 separate trips. The miles per gallon are displayed in the box-and-whisker plot below. What is the median of the data? **36 mpg**

2. ZOOLOGY Archie researched pandas for a science project. He looked up the weight in kilograms of adult pandas and displayed the data in a box-and-whisker plot. How much do most adult pandas weigh? **between 90 and 115 kg**

3. SPORTS The number of games won by the teams in each conference of the National Basketball League is displayed below. Write a few sentences that compare the data. **Sample answer: The least number of games won in the Eastern Conference was 13, and the least number of games won in the Western Conference was 18.**

4. FOOD The table shows the recent top 10 ice cream-consuming countries. Make a box-and-whisker plot of the data.

5. WEATHER George researched peak wind gusts in Texas. He made a box-and-whisker plot to display the data he collected.

a. What is the slowest recorded wind gust? **54 mph**

b. What percent of the wind gusts range from 67 to 82 miles per hour? **50%**

c. What would a peak gust have to be for it to be an outlier? **Sample answer: Either much lower than 44.5 mph or much greater than 104.5 mph**

Chapter 13 28 Glencoe Pre-Algebra

Example 3 p. 752

10. **OLYMPICS** Refer to the double box-and-whisker plot shown that shows the ages of the 2004 U.S. Men's and Women's Olympic Swimming Team.

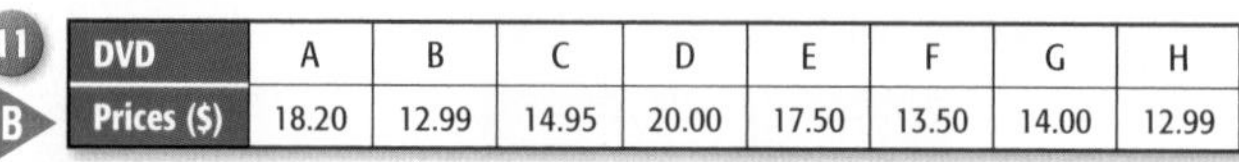

a. Which set of data has the greater range? **women's**

b. How many outliers are there in the data? **none**

c. What percent of the women's team is 22 years or younger? men's? **50%; 75%**

d. Describe the ages of the women compared to the men. **See margin.**

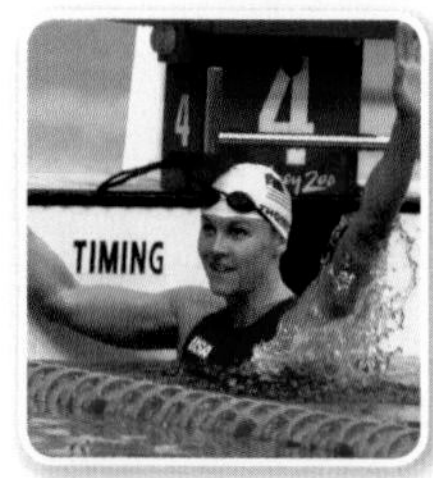

Real-World Link

Jenny Thompson competed in the 1992, 1996, 2000, and 2004 Olympics. She won a record total of 8 gold medals in swimming.

Construct a box-and-whisker plot for each set of data. **11–12. See margin.**

11. B

DVD	A	B	C	D	E	F	G	H
Prices ($)	18.20	12.99	14.95	20.00	17.50	13.50	14.00	12.99

12.

Song	1	2	3	4	5	6	7	8
Length (min)	4.5	3.75	5.25	4.0	5.75	3.75	3.5	5.0

H.O.T. Problems
Use Higher-Order Thinking Skills

13. **OPEN ENDED** C Create two data sets that contain from 10 to 20 values each that could have been used to generate the box-and-whisker plots shown below. Then write a few sentences that analyze the data.

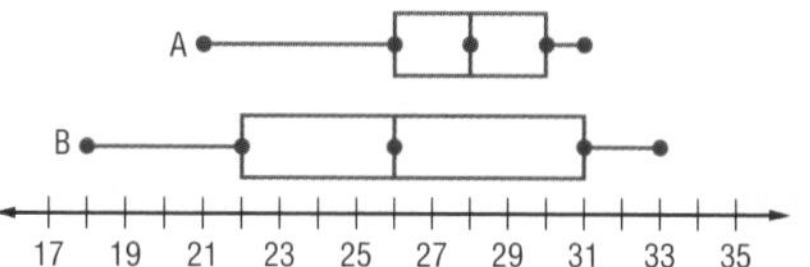

14. **FIND THE ERROR** Trina constructed a box-and-whisker plot showing her favorite NASCAR driver's yearly wins of 7, 14, 6, 1, 2, 2, 6, 3, 2, 8, 4, 7. Is she correct? Explain your reasoning.

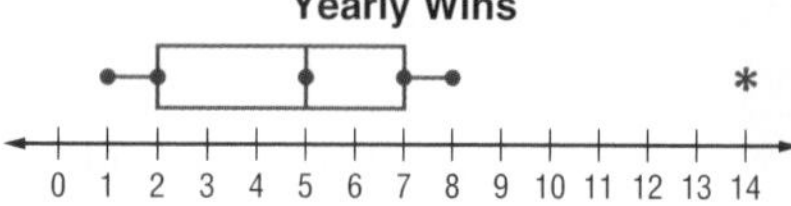

15. **CHALLENGE** The following data show the performance of a math class on a 50-point quiz: minimum: 28, lower quartile score: 30, median: 38, upper quartile score: 42, and maximum: 48. **a–b. See Chapter 13 Answer Appendix.**

a. Suppose there are 13 students in the class. Give a set of scores that would satisfy all the data shown.

b. Suppose six students have scores ranging from 38 to 42. How many students might there be in the class? Explain your reasoning.

16. **WRITING IN MATH** Explain how extending a whisker to include an outlier changes the look of a box-and-whisker plot. **See margin.**

13. Sample answer: Data set A: {21, 21, 22, 26, 26, 27, 28, 28, 28, 29, 30, 30, 30, 30, 31}; Data set B: {18, 18, 18, 22, 22, 22, 22, 26, 26, 26, 26, 31, 31, 31, 33}

14. No; Sample answer: 14 is not an outlier. $7 - 2 = 5$ and $5 \cdot 1.5 = 7.5$. An upper outlier would start at 14.5 so 14 is not an outlier.

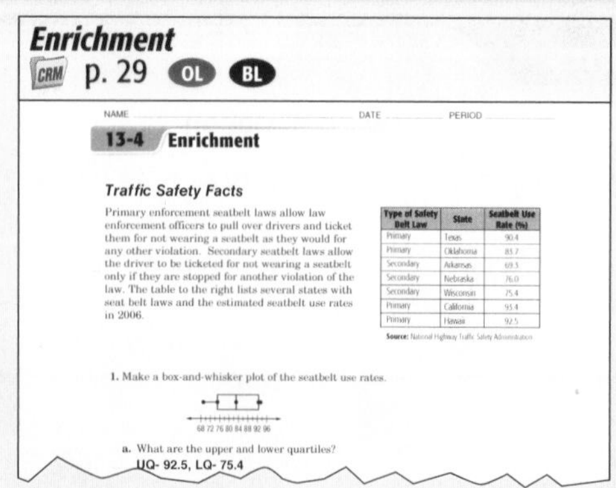

Enrichment
CRM p. 29 OL BL

NAME ______ DATE ______ PERIOD ______

13-4 Enrichment

Traffic Safety Facts

Primary enforcement seatbelt laws allow law enforcement officers to pull over drivers and ticket them for not wearing a seatbelt as they would for any other violation. Secondary seatbelt laws allow the driver to be ticketed for not wearing a seatbelt only if they are stopped for another violation of the law. The table to the right lists several states with seat belt laws and the estimated seatbelt use rates in 2006.

Type of Safety Belt Law	State	Seatbelt Use Rate (%)
Primary	Texas	90.4
Primary	Oklahoma	83.7
Secondary	Arkansas	69.3
Secondary	Nebraska	76.0
Secondary	Wisconsin	75.4
Primary	California	93.4
Primary	Hawaii	92.5

Source: National Highway Traffic Safety Administration

1. Make a box-and-whisker plot of the seatbelt use rates.

a. What are the upper and lower quartiles? **UQ- 92.5, LQ- 75.4**

Watch Out!

Find the Error In Exercise 14, have students check that Trina used the correct values for the lower and upper quartiles, the minimum and maximum values, and the median. Point out that the box plot shows an outlier and that it should be checked, too.

Standardized Test Practice

For Exercises 17–19, use the box-and-whisker plot below of the following quiz scores for 25 students. {3, 3, 4, 4, 5, 5, 5, 5, 5, 6, 6, 6, 6, 7, 8, 8, 9, 9, 9, 10, 10, 11, 11, 16}

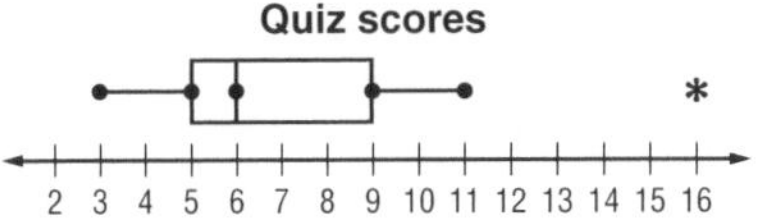

17. GRIDDED RESPONSE What is the interquartile range in the box-and-whisker plot? 4

18. Which of the following statements is *not* true about the box-and-whisker plot? D

A The outlier is 16.
B Seventy-five percent of the data is less than or equal to 9.
C The median is 6.
D There are more data values in the interval 6 to 11 than in the interval 3 to 6.

19. Kenko was absent the day the quiz was given. If she scored a 12 on her quiz, how will the box-and-whisker plot at the left change? H

F The lower quartile will change to 4.
G The median will change to 7.
H The right whisker will increase to 12.
J There will no longer be an outlier.

20. The five number summary required to make a box-and-whisker plot contains which of the following? D

A mean, median, mode, range, outliers
B lower extreme, lower quartile, median, upper quartile, outliers
C range, lower quartile, median, upper quartile, mode
D lower extreme, lower quartile, median, upper quartile, upper extreme

Spiral Review

21. SPORTS Use the data in the stem-and-leaf plot. (Lessons 13-1 through 13-3) a–b. See Chapter 13 Answer Appendix.

Total Points Scored by Winners 1960–2008

Rose Bowl		Cotton Bowl
	0	7 7
8 7 7 7 7 7 7 4 4 4 4 3 0	1	0 0 0 0 2 3 3 4 4 7 7 7 7 9 9
8 8 7 7 7 4 3 3 2 2 1 1 1 0 0 0	2	0 1 3 4 4 4 7 8 8 8 9
8 8 8 8 7 4 4 4 4 2	3	0 0 0 1 1 1 5 5 5 5 6 6 8 8 8 8 8
9 6 5 5 4 2 2 2 1 1	4	1 5 6
	5	5

7|1 = 17 Points *2|4 = 24 Points*

Source: *The World Almanac*

a. Find the range, median, upper quartile, lower quartile, interquartile range, and any outliers for each set of data.

b. Write a few sentences that compare the data.

Skills Review

22. PETS The table shows the number of pets owned by students in Mr. Hinkel's class. (Previous Course)

a. How many students were surveyed? 26

b. How many students have more than five pets? 6

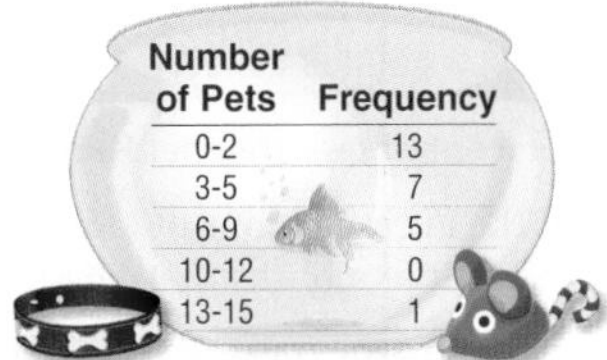

Number of Pets	Frequency
0-2	13
3-5	7
6-9	5
10-12	0
13-15	1

4 ASSESS

Name the Math Show students the plot below and ask them to name facts from the plot. For example, have them name the range (8), the median (7), the upper and lower quartiles (8 upper, 4 lower), and the extremes (2, 10). Ask them what percent of the values falls between 7 and 10 (50%). Tell them to label the plot.

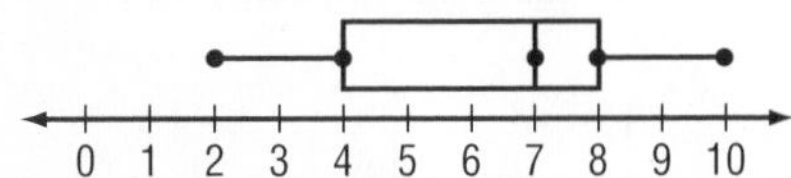

Additional Answers

10d. Sample answer: In general, most of the men are younger than the women. The upper quartile for the men is 22 years, meaning that 75% of the men are 22 years or younger. Only 50% of women are 22 years old or younger.

11.

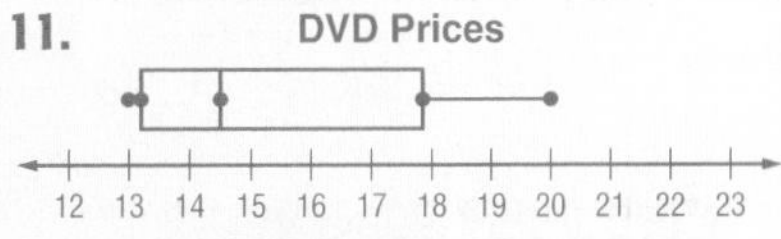

12.

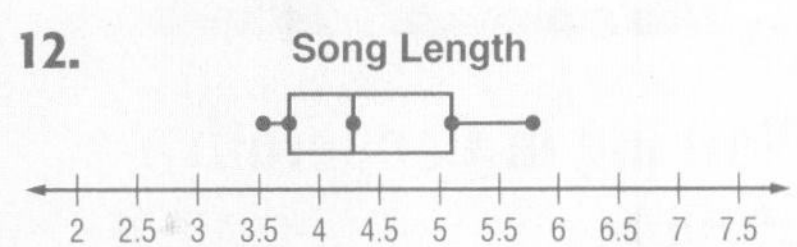

16. Sample answer: By including an outlier, the length of the whisker is greatly increased. By excluding an outlier, the length of the whisker is decreased.

Differentiated Instruction

Extension Present students with the following scenario: A sales manager at a car lot received the following data plot from the regional manager. It was based on average weekly sales. What can the sales manager learn from the plot? How can this help him with staffing and stock issues? Median weekly sales are 25 cars, interquartile range is 10. Extremes are 45 and 15 cars, and are not outliers. The manager should anticipate staff for 22–32 sales per week, although sales can be less or more.

0 10 20 30 40 50

FOCUS

Objective Use a graphing calculator to create box-and-whisker plots.

Materials for Each Group

- TI-83/84 Plus graphing calculator

Teaching Tip

There are two types of box-and-whisker plots. In Step 2, the keystrokes will select MODBOXPLOT (modified box plot) rather than BOXPLOT (regular box plot). MODBOXPLOT will show outliers while BOXPLOT will not.

If more than one column in students' calculators have data, have students enter the keystrokes STAT 4 to select ClrList function. Then enter list names.

TEACH

Working in Cooperative Groups

Have students work in groups of two or three, mixing abilities, to complete Steps 1–3.

Ask:

- Which point is an outlier for Missouri? How do you know it is an outlier? 0.56; it lies outside the data
- Suppose that precipitation for one month in Missouri is 6.05 inches. Would that value be an outlier? yes

Practice Have students complete Exercises 1–6.

ASSESS

Formative Assessment

Use Exercises 1–6 to assess whether students comprehend how to interpret data using medians, quartiles, and extreme values.

EXTEND 13-4 Graphing Technology Lab: Box-and-Whisker Plots

Math Online glencoe.com
Math *in Motion*, Animation

You can use a graphing calculator to create box-and-whisker plots.

EXAMPLE

The table shows the total precipitation (in inches) during each month in a recent year for two states.

State	J	F	M	A	M	J	J	A	S	O	N	D
Kentucky	5.72	2.22	3.69	4.63	4.44	4.24	4.61	4.63	8.55	5.05	3.17	3.01
Missouri	2.07	0.56	3.9	3.72	3.7	3.08	3.55	4.32	2.85	3.91	3.68	3.2

Source: NOAA

Make box-and-whisker plots for the precipitation levels in Kentucky and in Missouri.

Step 1 Enter the data.

- Clear any existing data.

KEYSTROKES: STAT ENTER ▲ CLEAR ENTER

- Enter the Kentucky data in L1 and the Missouri data in L2.

KEYSTROKES: *Review entering a list on page 47.*

Step 2 Format the graph.

- Turn on two statistical plots.

KEYSTROKES: *Review statistical plots on page 47.*

- For Plot 1, select the box-and-whisker plots and L1 as the Xlist.

KEYSTROKES: ▼ ▶ ▶ ▶ ENTER ▼ 2nd [L1] ENTER

- Repeat for Plot 2, using L2 as the Xlist, to make a box-and-whisker plot for Missouri.

Step 3 Graph the box-and-whisker plots.

- Display the graph.

KEYSTROKES: Zoom 9

Press TRACE. Move from one plot to the other using the up and down arrow keys. The right and left arrow keys allow you to find the least value, greatest value, and quartiles.

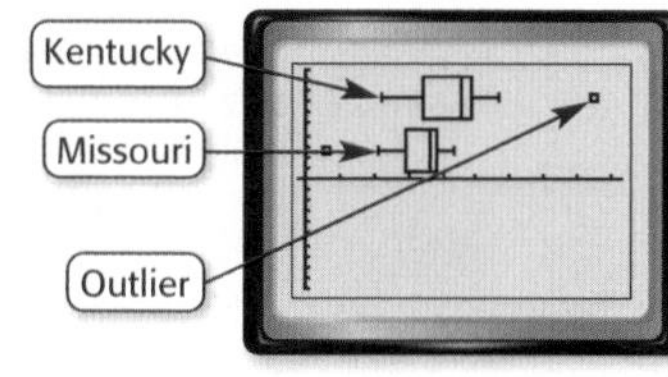

Exercises

Kentucky minimum: 2.22; Q1: 3.43; median: 4.525; Q3: 4.84; maximum: 8.55; Missouri minimum: 0.56; Q1: 2.965; median: 3.615; Q3: 3.81; maximum: 4.32

1. What are the least, greatest, quartile, and median values for Kentucky and Missouri?
2. What is the interquartile range for Kentucky? Missouri? **Kentucky: 1.41; Missouri: 0.845**
3. Are there any outliers? How does the graphing calculator show them? **Yes; a point is separated from the box-and-whisker plot.**
4. If the average monthly precipitation for Kentucky is 3.94 inches, estimate the percent of months that Kentucky had above average precipitation. **Sample answer: 70%**
5. If the average monthly precipitation for Missouri is 3.2 inches, estimate the percent of months that Missouri had above average precipitation. **Sample answer: 60%**
6. Based on the precipitation data, in which state would you prefer to live? Explain. **Sample answer: Missouri because there is less precipitation.**

From Concrete to Abstract

Have students reset Xmin and Xmax values to create greater range. Ask them how this change affects the appearance of the graph and how this might be misleading.

13-5 Histograms

Why?

A heliport pad is a landing and takeoff pad for helicopters. The number of heliports in each state in the United States are shown in a *frequency table.*

a. How many states have 151–200 heliports? more than 300 heliports? 2; 3

b. What do you notice about the intervals? They are equal in size.

Number of Heliports in Each State

Heliports	Tally	Frequency
1-50	卌 卌 卌 III	18
51-100	卌 卌 IIII	14
101-150	卌 III	8
151-200	II	2
201-250	II	2
251-300	III	3
301-350	I	1
351-400	I	1
401-450	I	1

Then
You have already displayed data in a stem-and-leaf plot.
(Lesson 13-2)

Now
- Display data in a histogram.
- Interpret data in a histogram.

New Vocabulary
histogram

Math Online
glencoe.com
- Extra Examples
- Personal Tutor
- Self-Check Quiz
- Homework Help

Display Data A **histogram** uses bars to display numerical data that have been organized into equal intervals.

EXAMPLE 1 Draw a Histogram

RETAIL The table shows the ages of people who entered a store. Display the data in a histogram.

Age	Tally	Frequency
1–10	卌	5
11–20	卌 III	8
21–30	卌 卌 IIII	14
31–40	卌 卌 卌 III	18
41–50	卌 卌 卌 卌	20
51–60	卌 卌 III	13
61–70	卌 I	6

Step 1 Draw and label a horizontal and vertical axis as shown. Include a title.

Step 2 Show the intervals from the frequency table on the horizontal axis and an interval of 2 on the vertical axis.

Step 3 For each interval, draw a bar whose height is given by the frequency.

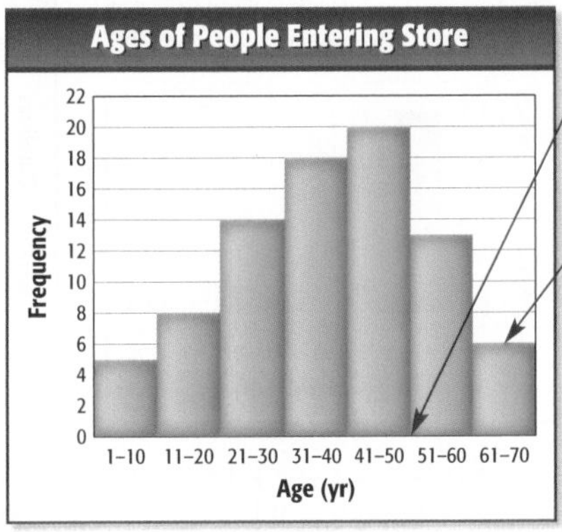

There is no space between bars.

Because the intervals are equal, all of the bars have the same width.

Check Your Progress

1. HELIPORTS Refer to the frequency table above about the number of heliports in each state. Display the data in a histogram.
See Chapter 13 Answer Appendix.

Personal Tutor glencoe.com

13-5 Lesson Notes

1 FOCUS

Vertical Alignment

Before Lesson 13-5
Display data in a stem-and-leaf plot.

Lesson 13-5
Display and interpret data in a histogram.

After Lesson 13-5
Use histograms to describe probability distributions.

2 TEACH

Scaffolding Questions

Have students read the *Why?* section of the lesson and answer the questions.

Ask:
- What does each tally mark represent? a state
- Are there any states that have no heliports? Explain. No; there are 50 tally marks and 50 states, so all states have a heliport.
- Which interval contains the greatest number of data? 1–50

Lesson 13-5 Resources

Resource	Approaching-Level	On-Level	Beyond-Level	English Learners
Teacher Edition		• Differentiated Instruction, p. 759	• Differentiated Instruction, pp. 759, 762	
Chapter Resource Masters	• Study Guide and Intervention, pp. 30–31 • Skills Practice, p. 32 • Practice, p. 33 • Word Problem Practice, p. 34 • Spreadsheet Activity, p. 36	• Study Guide and Intervention, pp. 30–31 • Skills Practice, p. 32 • Practice, p. 33 • Word Problem Practice, p. 34 • Enrichment, p. 35 • Spreadsheet Activity, p. 36	• Practice, p. 33 • Word Problem Practice, p. 34 • Enrichment, p. 35 • Spreadsheet Activity, p. 36	• Study Guide and Intervention, pp. 30–31 • Skills Practice, p. 32 • Practice, p. 33 • Spreadsheet Activity, p. 36
Transparencies	• 5-Minute Check Transparency 13-5	• 5-Minute Check Transparency 13-5	• 5-Minute Check Transparency 13-5	• 5-Minute Check Transparency 13-5
Other	• Study Notebook • Teaching Pre-Algebra with Manipulatives	• Study Notebook • Teaching Pre-Algebra with Manipulatives	• Study Notebook	• Study Notebook • Teaching Pre-Algebra with Manipulatives

Display Data

Example 1 shows how to draw a histogram in a real-world example.

Formative Assessment

Use the Check Your Progress exercises after each example to determine students' understanding of concepts.

Additional Example

1 **WATER PARKS** The frequency table shows certain water park admission costs. Display the data in a histogram. See margin.

Cost ($)	Tally	Frequency
8–15	𝍸	5
16–23	𝍸 ||	7
24–31	||||	4
32–39		0
40–47	||	2

Additional Examples also in Interactive Classroom PowerPoint® Presentations

IWB INTERACTIVE WHITEBOARD READY

Interpret Data

Example 2 shows how to interpret data from a histogram. **Example 3** shows how to compare two sets of data in a real-world example.

Additional Example

2 **ELEVATIONS** Refer to the histogram.

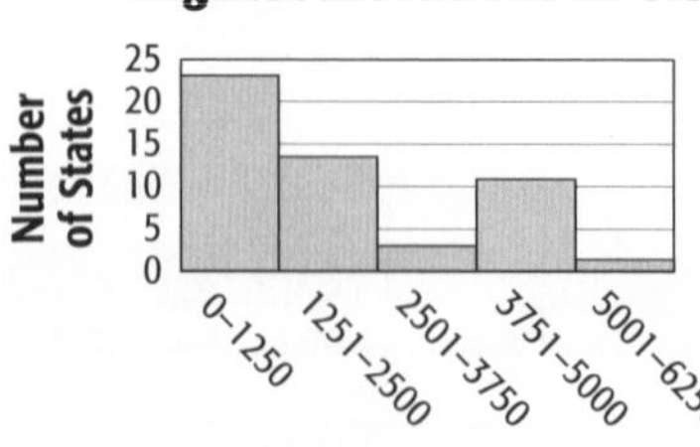

a. How many states have highest points with elevation at least 3,751 meters? 12 states

b. What percent of states contain elevations above 2,500 meters? 30%

Interpret Data A histogram gives a better visual display of data than a frequency table. Thus, it is easier to interpret data displayed in a histogram.

StudyTip

Break in Scale The symbol ⋀⁄ means there is a break in the scale. The scale from 0 to 59 has been omitted.

EXAMPLE 2 Interpret Data

SCHOOL Refer to the histogram.

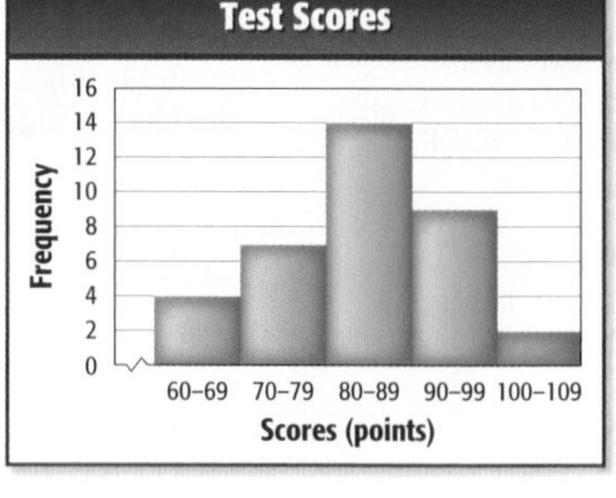

a. How many students scored at least 90 points on the test?

Since 9 students scored between 90 and 99 points and 2 received over one hundred points, 9 + 2 or 11 students scored at least 90 points on the test.

b. What percent of the students scored 79 points or lower?

There were 4 + 7 + 14 + 9 + 2 or 36 students who took the test. There were 4 + 7 or 11 total students who scored 79 points or less. Since $\frac{11}{36}$ is about 30.56%, about 31% of the students scored 79 points or lower on the test.

Check Your Progress

2. **SCHOOL** Refer to the histogram about test scores above.

A. Is it possible to tell the score of the highest test?

B. In what range is a student most likely to score on the test? between 80 and 89

Personal Tutor glencoe.com

2A. No, you can only tell that the highest score is between 100 points and 109 points.

3. Sample answer: Atlanta has nearly 3 times the number of buildings over 400 feet tall than Charlotte. Charlotte only has 2 buildings over 600 feet tall while Atlanta has 10 buildings over 600 feet tall.

Real-World EXAMPLE 3 Compare Data

BUILDINGS Use the histograms shown below. Which city has a greater number of buildings at least 600 feet tall?

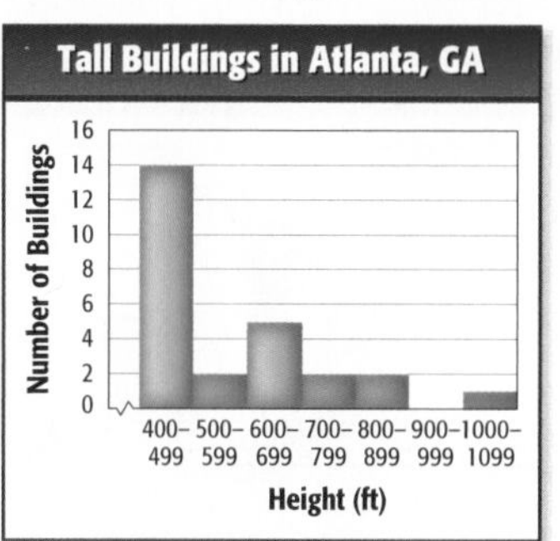

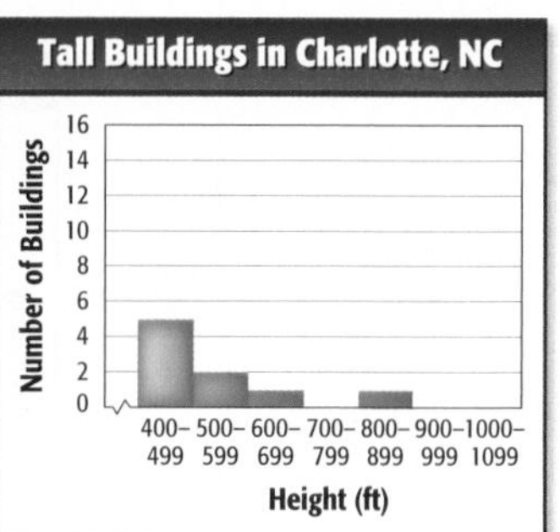

Atlanta has 5 + 2 + 2 + 1 or 10 buildings at least 600 feet tall. Charlotte has 1 + 1 or 2 buildings at least 600 feet tall. So, Atlanta has more buildings at least 600 feet tall.

StudyTip

No Data In both histograms, there is no bar for the 900–999 interval. When this happens, there is no data for that interval. In this situation, there are no buildings with a height of 900–999 feet in either city.

Check Your Progress

3. Compare the heights of the tall buildings in the two cities.

Personal Tutor glencoe.com

Focus on Mathematical Content

Histograms A histogram is a type of bar graph that shows the distribution of data organized into equal intervals. Since the intervals cover all possible data values, there are no gaps between the bars of the histogram. If most of the data occur on either the lower or upper end of the scale, the histogram is said to be skewed to the left or right, respectively.

TEACH with TECH

INTERACTIVE WHITEBOARD Display a blank frequency table and a blank grid on the screen. Use these as templates when creating the histogram.

Check Your Understanding

Example 1 p. 757

Display each set of data in a histogram. 1–2. See Chapter 13 Answer Appendix.

1.

Age of Indy 500 Winners		
Age	Tally	Frequency
21–25	||	2
26–30	~~||||~~ |	6
31–35	~~||||~~ |||	8
36–40	~~||||~~	5
41–45	||||	4
46–50	|||	3

2.

Weekly Time Spent Doing Chores		
Time (min)	Tally	Frequency
0–14	~~||||~~ |||	8
15–29	~~||||~~ ~~||||~~ |	11
30–44	~~||||~~ ~~||||~~ ||||	14
45–59	~~||||~~ |	6
60–74	||||	4

Example 2 p. 758

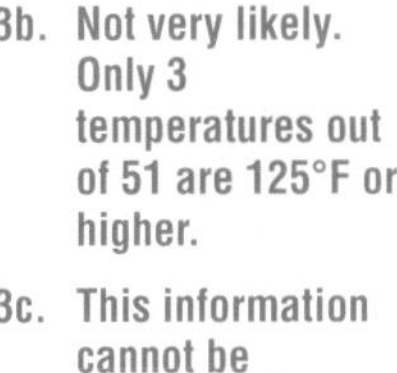

3b. Not very likely. Only 3 temperatures out of 51 are 125°F or higher.

3c. This information cannot be determined from the data presented in the graph. We only know the highest temperature is between 130–134 degrees Fahrenheit and the lowest is between 100–104.

3. **TEMPERATURE** The histogram shown below shows the record high temperatures for several U.S. cities.

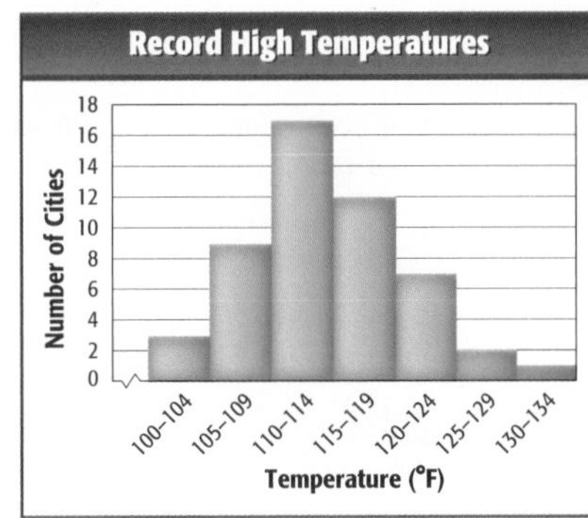

a. About what percent of U.S. cities had record high temperatures of 109° F or less? about 24%

b. How likely is it that a record high temperature is 125° F or higher?

c. What is the greatest temperature?

Example 3 p. 758

4. **ANALYZE GRAPHS** The histograms below show the winning times for two different women's swimming events from the summer Olympics.

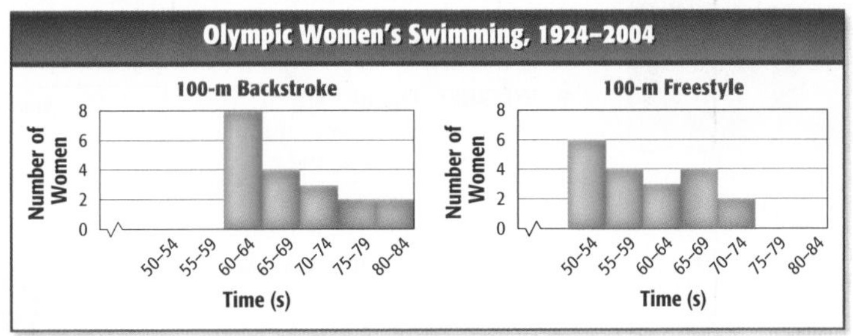

a. Which event has more winning times less than one minute? 100-m freestyle

b. How many Olympic Games were held from 1924 to 2004? 19

c. Compare the winning times of the two Olympic events.

4c. Sample answer: The winning times of the 100-m Freestyle are much lower than the 100-m Backstroke's winning times.

Differentiated Instruction

If students have a musical background,

Then have students work in groups of four to compose a short piece of music inspired by the histograms in Example 3. Ask them to imagine that each bar on the histograms represents a range of notes in a musical scale. Have them assign musical intervals to each interval on the histograms and then "play" the graphs, using the heights of the bars as a guide for volume. Instruments such as the flute and the voice, which can play all the notes in an interval sliding manner, lend themselves well to this activity.

Additional Answer (Additional Example 2)

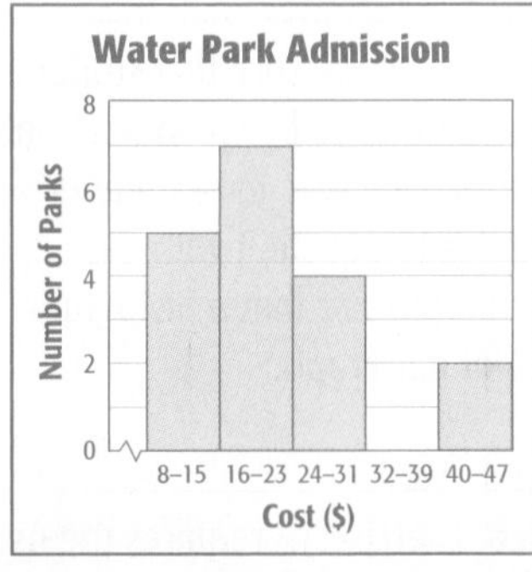

Additional Example

3 **EMPLOYMENT** Use the histograms shown below.

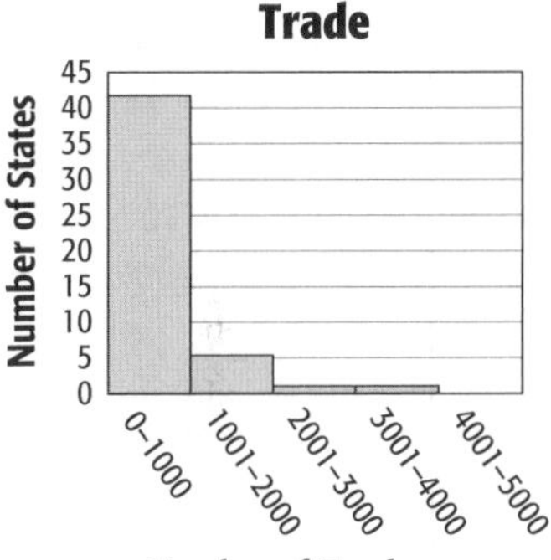

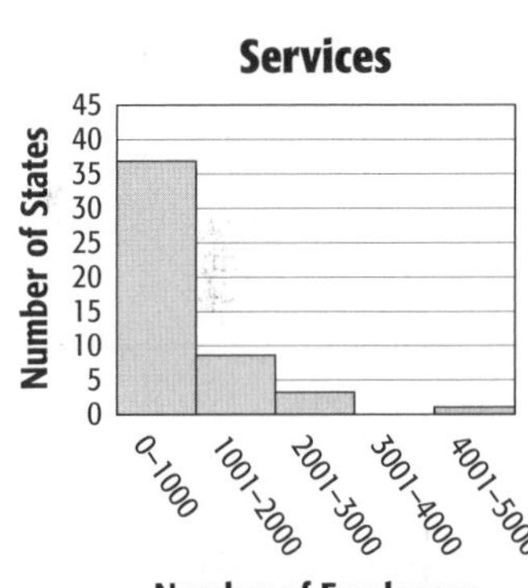

Which business sector has more states with the number of employees in the interval 1,001 to 3,000? services

3 PRACTICE

Formative Assessment

Use Exercises 1–4 to check for understanding.

Use the chart at the bottom of the next page to customize assignments for your students.

Tips for New Teachers

Connections Make sure that students know the difference between horizontal and vertical. One way to remember horizontal is to equate it with the horizon. Emphasize that a histogram is a type of bar graph.

Exercise Alert

Research Exercise 12 requires the use of the Internet or other research materials to construct a histogram using real-world data.

Additional Answers

9a. Sample answer: By counting the heights of the bars, there are 75 students represented in the graph. You can find the number of students in each 10-minute span. The students in the survey spent at least 11 minutes on the Internet. Eighty percent of students spent at least 31 minutes on the Internet.

9b. Since exact data values are not listed, you are not able to find any measure of central tendency. However, the median is located in the 41–50 minute time period by counting the number of students in each time period.

11c. Sample answer: The data could be rearranged into intervals of 50. Then the histogram would give a more accurate representation of the data.

Practice and Problem Solving

● = Step-by-Step Solutions begin on page R11. Extra Practice begins on page 810.

Example 1 p. 757

Display each set of data in a histogram. **5–6. See Chapter 13 Answer Appendix.**

5.

Calories of Fruit Bars		
Calories	Tally	Frequency
0–39	|||	3
40–79	~~||||~~ ||||	9
80–119	~~||||~~ |	6
120–159	||||	4
160–199	~~||||~~ ||	7

6.

Weekly Time Spent Reading		
Time (hr)	Tally	Frequency
0–1	~~||||~~ |	6
2–3	~~||||~~ ~~||||~~	10
4–5	~~||||~~ ||	7
6–7	|||	3
8–9	||||	4

Example 2 p. 758

8. Sample answer: The students in Room 120 are taller. Of the students in Room 120, 12 out of 25 or 48% are at least 65 inches tall. Of the students in Room 100, 9 out of 25 or 36% are at least 65 inches tall.

7. **ANALYZE GRAPHS** The histogram shows the cost of different shoes at a store.

a. How many pairs of shoes cost $59.99 or less? **20**

b. About what percent of the shoes cost $60 or more? **about 62%**

c. What price is a pair of shoes most likely to cost? **between $60.99–$69.99**

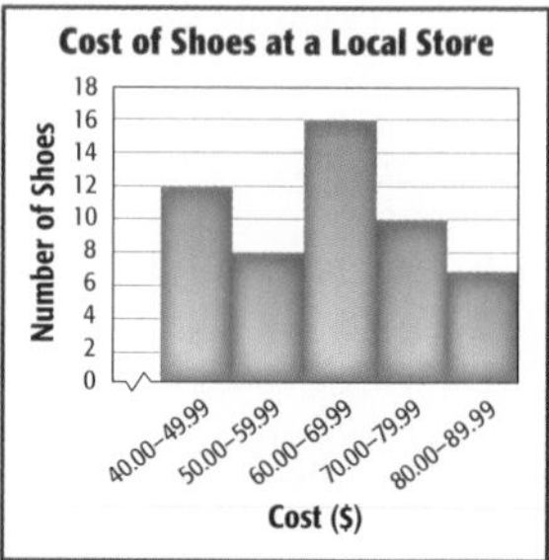

Example 3 p. 758

8. **HEIGHTS** The histograms below show the heights' of students in two homerooms. Compare the data in the histograms.

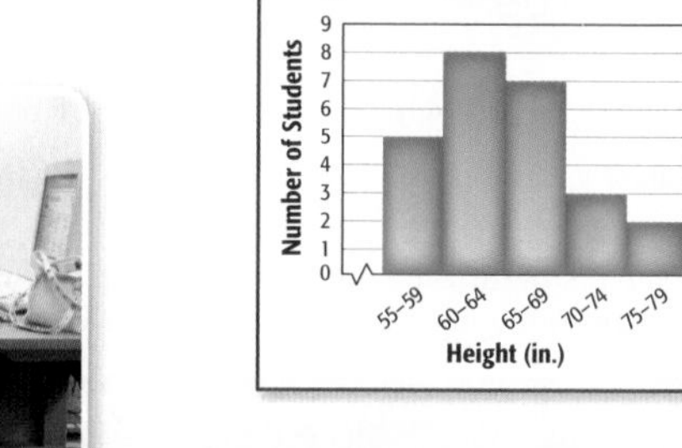

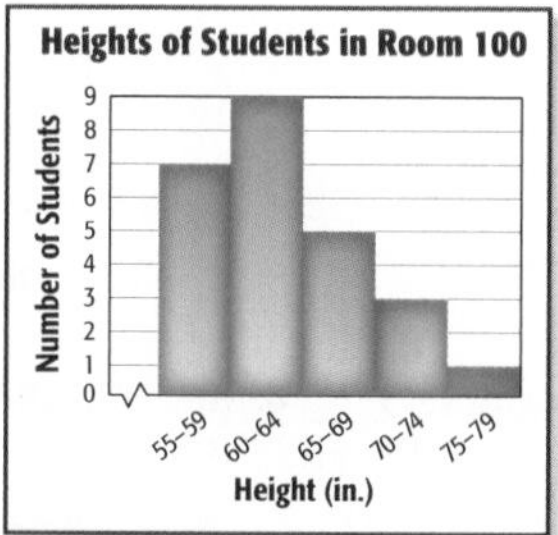

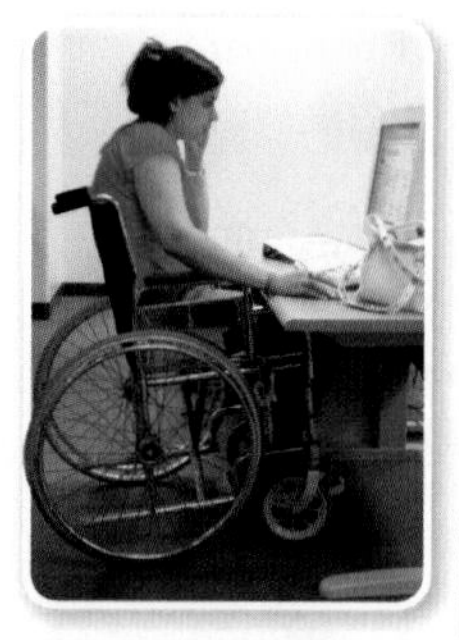

Real-World Link

According to a survey, 82% of teens age 12–14 and 92% of teens age 15–17 use the Internet, with approximately 11 million teens going online daily.

Source: Pew Internet & American Life Project

9. **INTERNET** The histogram shows the number of minutes students spend on the Internet in one day.

a. Discuss all of the information that you can collect from the histogram. **a–b. See margin.**

b. Are you able to find any measures of central tendency from the histogram? Explain your reasoning.

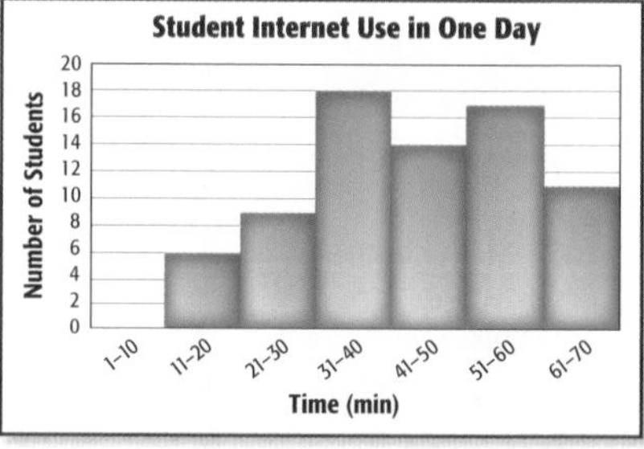

Differentiated Homework Options

Level	Assignment	Two-Day Option	
AL Basic	5–8, 12, 13, 15, 16–25	5, 7, 17–20	6, 8, 12, 13, 15, 16, 21–25
OL Core	5, 7, 9–13, 15–25	5–8, 17–20	9–13, 15, 16, 21–25
BL Advanced	9–22, (optional: 23–25)		

11a. Sample answer: There have been 25 summer Olympic games. In 52% of the games, the country that won the medal count won at least 100 total medals.

11b. Sample answer: The intervals along the x-axis are not equal. Because the intervals are not equal the data is distributed unevenly.

Real-World Link

Each individual Olympic city designs the medal for that year's competition. The medals must be at least 66 millimeters in diameter and at least 3 millimeters thick.

Source: Sports Illustrated

16. Sample answer: Line plots and histograms both give a visual representation of data. Line plots, unlike histograms, give you exact amounts for each category and are not separated into intervals. Histograms more easily allow you to compare frequencies between different intervals.

10. FINANCIAL LITERACY The table shows the average ticket prices to attend a game for each of the teams in the NHL.

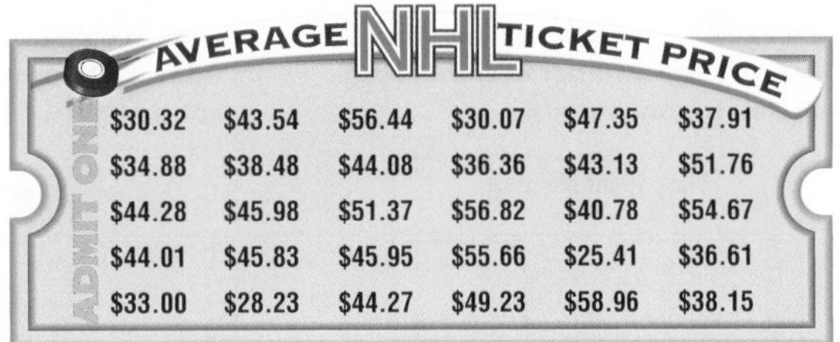

AVERAGE NHL TICKET PRICE

$30.32	$43.54	$56.44	$30.07	$47.35	$37.91
$34.88	$38.48	$44.08	$36.36	$43.13	$51.76
$44.28	$45.98	$51.37	$56.82	$40.78	$54.67
$44.01	$45.83	$45.95	$55.66	$25.41	$36.61
$33.00	$28.23	$44.27	$49.23	$58.96	$38.15

Source: Team Marketing Report

a. Select an appropriate interval for the data. Explain your reasoning. Then make a frequency table using the interval you selected.

b. Construct a histogram of the data.

a–b. See Chapter 13 Answer Appendix.

11. MEDALS The histogram at the right shows the total number of medals won by the top ranking country per year for the summer Olympics from 1896 to 2004.

a. Describe the data in the histogram.

b. Describe how the histogram was constructed incorrectly.

c. How could you change the histogram so that it is no longer constructed incorrectly?

See margin.

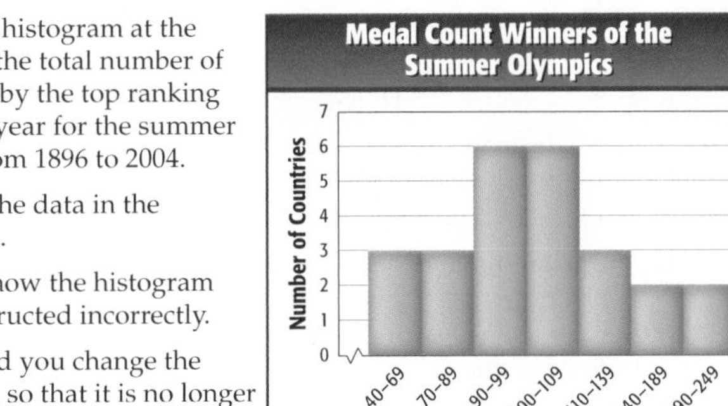

H.O.T. Problems

Use Higher-Order Thinking Skills

12. OPEN ENDED Construct a histogram from real-world data that has five intervals and exactly one gap. 12–14. See Chapter 13 Answer Appendix.

13. ANALYZE DATA Create a set of data that, when plotted on a histogram, has a gap between 40 and 50, three items in the 20–29 interval, and the median value in the 30–39 interval. Display your data in a histogram.

14. CHALLENGE Eighty people were surveyed about the number of times they exercise in a month. The results are shown in the table. Construct a histogram based on these percents.

Exercise Habits	
Days per Month	Percent of People
1–5	10%
6–10	20%
11–15	15%
16–20	30%
21–25	20%
26–30	5%

15. COLLECT THE DATA Conduct a survey of your classmates to determine the number of text messages each person sends or receives during a typical week. Then make a frequency table and construct a histogram to represent the data. Compare the data in your histogram with a classmate's data. See students' work.

16. WRITING IN MATH Compare a line plot and a histogram. What are the advantages? What are the disadvantages?

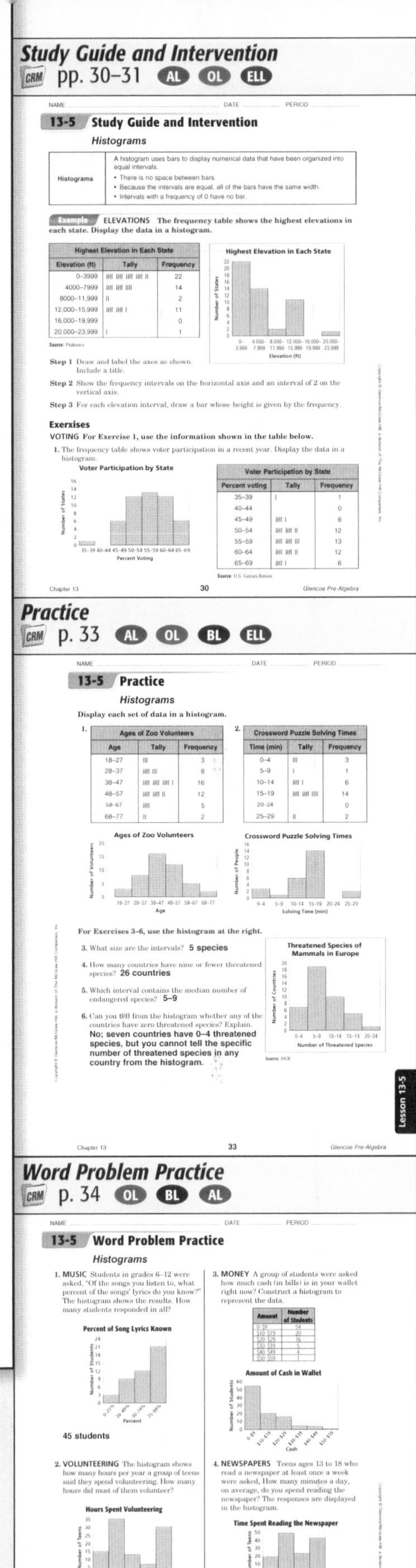

Study Guide and Intervention CRM pp. 30–31 AL OL ELL

13-5 Study Guide and Intervention

Histograms

Practice CRM p. 33 AL OL BL ELL

13-5 Practice

Histograms

Word Problem Practice CRM p. 34 OL BL AL

13-5 Word Problem Practice

Histograms

Enrichment CRM p. 35 OL BL

NAME ______ DATE ______ PERIOD ______

13-5 Enrichment

Displaying Real-World Data

The Big D Marathon is an annual event that takes place in Dallas, Texas, in the spring. Marathons are 26.2 miles in length and require intense preparation and endurance. Here are the results from the 50–54 age group from a recent Big D Marathon. 3:58:08 means 3 hours, 58 minutes, 8 seconds.

Place	Name	Age	Time (h:min:s)
1	Kathy Johnson	50	3:58:08
2	Lana Parks	51	4:17:16
3	Adrienne Gabriel	50	4:55:33
4	Sarah Gordon	50	5:07:45
5	Teresa Lynd	52	5:22:03
6	Margaret Darneille	53	5:25:56
7	Deborah Kerr-Leathem	51	5:34:36
8	Velena Cowsen	54	6:03:29
9	Kathy Davidson	50	6:15:50

Source: Texas Marathon

1. Use the data to complete the frequency table below. Then draw a histogram to display the data.

Number of Runners in Each Time Group

ASSESS

Ticket Out the Door Tell students to describe one way in which histograms are similar to stem-and-leaf plots, and one way in which they are different.

Formative Assessment

Check for student understanding of concepts in Lessons 13-4 and 13-5.

CRM Quiz 2, p. 70

Standardized Test Practice

For Exercises 17 and 18, use the histogram below. It shows the number of hours Hugo slept each day for one month.

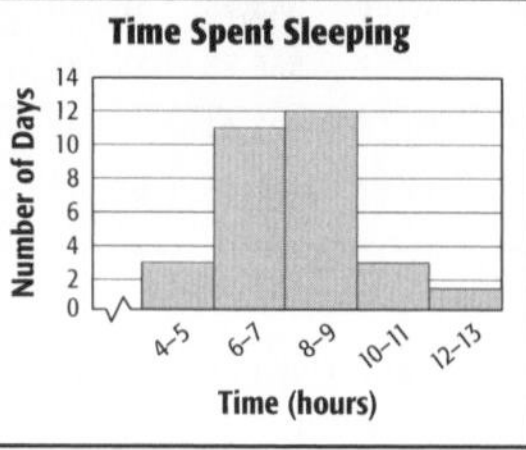

17. What percent of the nights did he sleep for 8 or more hours? D

A 40% C 50%
B 47% D 53%

18. Which of the following can be concluded from the histogram above? H

F The least number of hours Hugo slept is 4.
G The greatest number of hours Hugo slept is 13.
H Most of the nights Hugo slept for 8 or more hours.
J The mean number of hours he slept each night was 7.5.

For Exercises 19 and 20, use the data below that shows the amount of playing time (in minutes) of different CDs from Janet's CD collection.

Playing Time of CDs (min)				
59	68	56	55	62
48	44	63	47	49
42	61	51	45	61
65	48	58	64	57
54	59	69	55	45

19. **SHORT RESPONSE** Complete the histogram of the data. See Chapter 13 Answer Appendix.

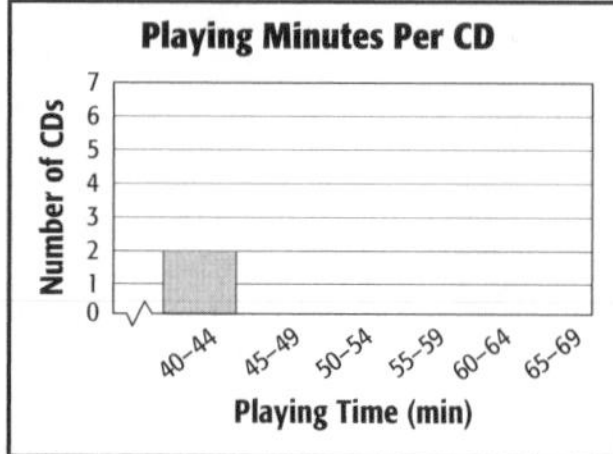

20. **GRIDDED RESPONSE** How many CDs have a playing time of at least 50 minutes? 17

Spiral Review

21. **DANCE** The ages of students in a dance class in years are 25, 30, 27, 35, 19, 23, 25, 22, 40, 34, and 20. Draw a box-and-whisker plot of the data. (Lesson 13-4) See Chapter 13 Answer Appendix.

22. **CALORIES** The stem-and-leaf plot shown shows the number of Calories found in a serving of yogurt. Find the range, interquartile range, and any outliers. (Lessons 13-3 and 13-2) 29; 11.5; no outliers

Calories in Yogurt

Stem	Leaf
4	0
5	0 1 1 5 7 7 7 8
6	7 7 9

5 | 7 = 57 Calories

Skills Review

Max surveyed his classmates to find the school activities they attended last weekend. The results are shown in the Venn diagram. (Lesson 4-3)

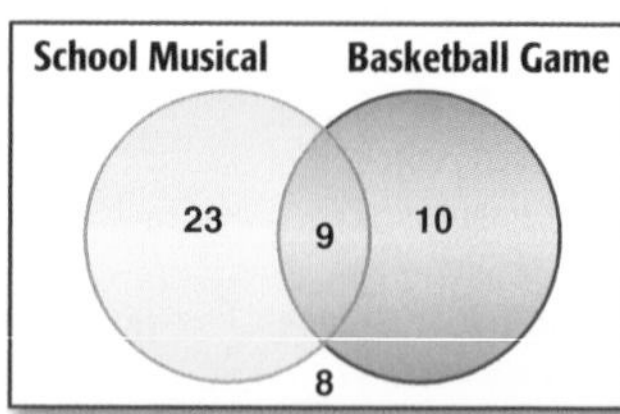

23. How many students attended the musical? the basketball game? 32; 19

24. How many students attended both? neither? 9; 8

25. How many students participated in the survey? 50

762 Chapter 13 Statistics and Probability

Differentiated Instruction

BL

Extension Pose the following situation to students: Another student collects data on the heights of the students in your class and creates a histogram. You have the histogram and you want to recreate the original data. You want to find the median of students' heights, and other measures of central tendency and variation. Can this be done? Why or why not? Sample answer: You cannot find exact measures such as median, mode, mean, range, and quartiles, but you can determine the intervals in which measures such as median and range occur, and you can tell whether the data are clustered or spread out.

Histograms

Math Online glencoe.com
- Math *in Motion*, Animation
- Other Calculator Keystrokes

You can use a graphing calculator to make a histogram.

ACTIVITY

FOOTBALL The table below shows the total number of points scored in each Super Bowl. Make a histogram to show the point distribution.

Total Number of Points Scored in Each Super Bowl						
45	47	23	30	29	27	21
31	22	38	46	37	66	50
37	47	44	47	54	56	59
52	36	65	39	61	69	43
75	44	56	55	53	39	41
37	69	61	45	31	46	

Step 1 Enter the data.

- Clear any existing data in list L1.

KEYSTROKES: STAT ENTER ▲ CLEAR ENTER

- Enter the data in L1.

KEYSTROKES: *Review entering a list on page 47.*

Step 2 Format the graph.

- Turn on the statistical plot.

KEYSTROKES: 2nd [STAT PLOT] ENTER ENTER

- Select the histogram and L1 as the Xlist.

KEYSTROKES: ▼ ▶ ▶ ENTER ▼ 2nd [L1] ENTER

Step 3 Graph the histogram.

- Set the viewing window so the x-axis goes from 20 to 80 in increments of 5, and the y-axis goes from -5 to 15 in increments of 1. So, [20, 80] scl: 5 by [-5, 15] scl: 1. Then graph.

KEYSTROKES: WINDOW 20 ENTER 80 ENTER 5 ENTER -5 ENTER 15 ENTER 1 ENTER GRAPH

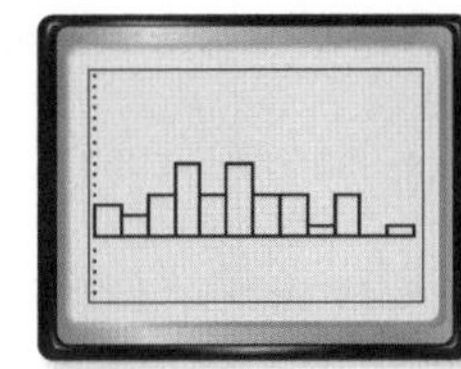

Analyze the Data

1. Press TRACE. Find the frequency of each interval using the right and left arrow keys. **1–3. See Chapter 13 Answer Appendix.**
2. Discuss why the domain is from 21 to 75 for this data set.
3. How does the graphing calculator determine the size of the intervals?
4. How many Super Bowls have had a point total of at least 35, but less than 60? **26**
5. What percent of point totals falls in the range of Exercise 4? **about 63%**
6. Can you tell from the histogram how many Super Bowls had point totals of 48? **6, 7. See Chapter 13 Answer Appendix.**
7. Make a stem-and-leaf plot of the data. How does the stem-and-leaf plot compare to the histogram you have graphed here? Which graph is easier to read?

EXTEND 13-5 Lesson Notes

1 FOCUS

Objective Use a graphing calculator to make histograms.

Materials for Each Group

- graphing calculator

2 TEACH

Working in Cooperative Groups

Have students work in pairs. When students have finished entering the numbers into the lists, have them check for accuracy.

Ask:

- Suppose you want to find out how many games are recorded on each bar. How is it done? Trace the bar; the screen shows $n =$ that number.
- What frequency has the most Super Bowl games? 35–40 and 45–50
- How can you verify that you have entered all the data? Add the number of data in each bar and match it up to the number of data from the table.

Practice Have students complete Exercises 1–7.

3 ASSESS

Formative Assessment

Have students use the data on NHL ticket prices from Exercise 10 of Lesson 13-5 to make a histogram on the calculator. Have them write down what numbers they used on the x-axis and how they determined the frequency.

Tips for New Teachers

When students are ready to format their graphs, some may receive error messages if PLOT 2 or PLOT 3 is turned on as well as PLOT 1. Have them use STAT PLOT to turn all off but 1. Alternatively, they can use the Y=, ENTER, and the arrow keys to turn off the extra graphs.

From Concrete to Abstract

In groups, have students measure each other's height. Post the class data and tell them to make a histogram of the data.

CHAPTER 13 Mid-Chapter Quiz

Formative Assessment

Use the Mid-Chapter Quiz to assess students' progress in the first half of the chapter.

For problems answered incorrectly, have students review the lessons indicated in parentheses.

ExamView Assessment Suite Customize and create multiple versions of your Mid-Chapter Quiz and their answer keys.

FOLDABLES® Follow-Up

Before students complete the Mid-Chapter Quiz, encourage them to review the information for Lessons 13-1 through 13-5 in their Foldables.

CHAPTER 13 Mid-Chapter Quiz

Lessons 13-1 through 13-5

Find the mean, median and mode for each set of data. Round to the nearest whole number. (Lesson 13-1)

1. The number of miles several students bike each weekend: 5, 8, 6, 10, 12 **8, 8, none**
2. The number of hours spent sleeping each week for several weeks: 45, 49, 41, 50, 53, 47, 45 **47, 47, 45**
3. The ages of people at a party: 2, 5, 7, 9, 10, 36, 37, 41, 42 **21, 10, none**
4. **SCHOOL** The stem-and-leaf plot shows the test scores on Mr. Lisy's social studies test.

Test Scores

Stem	Leaf
4	5 8
5	1 5 7 7
6	2
7	2 2 3 5 8 9
8	1 1 1 1 7 8
9	2 7 9 9
10	0

5|1 = 51

   a. Find the median and mode of the data. (Lesson 13-2) **78.5; 81**

   b. What is the range of the data? (Lesson 13-3) **55**

5. There are 22, 21, 24, 23, 26, 23, 28, 24, and 25 students in the homerooms at Morgan Middle School. Find the measures of variation for the data. (Lesson 13-3) **R: 7; UQ: 25.5; LQ: 22.5; M: 24; IR 3; none**
6. **MULTIPLE CHOICE** The number of minutes it took several students to complete a test are shown below. What is the interquartile range of the data? (Lesson 13-3) **A**

   45, 57, 55, 42, 48, 21, 39, 62, 45, 51

   A 13 C 42

   B 41 D 55

7. The total amount of monthly precipitation, in inches, for a city is 1.0, 1.2, 2.2, 3.6, 4.3, 4.6, 4.2, 4.5, 3.2, 2.6, 2.1, and 1.3. Display the data in a box-and-whisker plot. (Lesson 13-4) **See Chapter 13 Answer Appendix.**
8. **SKIING** The box-and-whisker-plot below shows the winning times for the women's downhill skiing event in the winter Olympics. (Lesson 13-4)

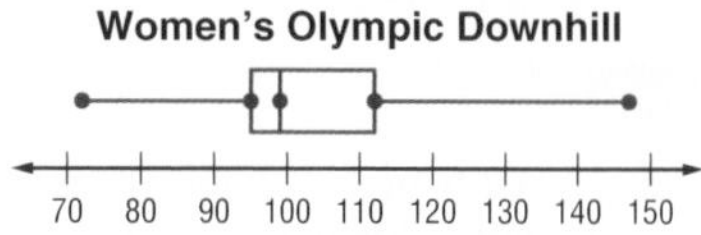

   a. What percent of the winning times are less than 99 seconds? **50%**

   b. What does the length of the box tell about the data? the whiskers? **8b, 9. See Chapter 13 Answer Appendix.**

9. **Display the data below in a histogram.** (Lesson 13-5)

# of Pets	Tally	Frequency
0–1	||||	4
2–3	𝍸 𝍸	10
4–5	|||	3
6–7	|	1

10. **MULTIPLE CHOICE** The histogram shows the prices for attending different sports activities at South High School. (Lesson 13-5)

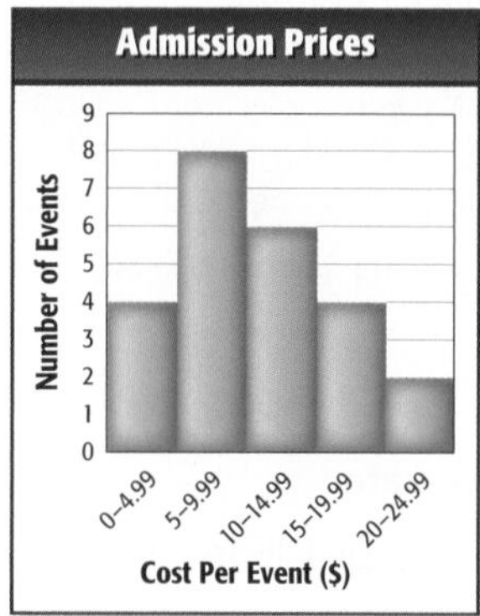

How many events cost $10 or more to attend? **J**

F 3 H 8

G 5 J 12

11. Refer to the histogram above. How many different activities were sampled? **24**
12. What fraction of events cost between $5 and $19.99 to attend? $\frac{3}{4}$

Intervention Planner

Tier 1 On Level	Tier 2 Strategic Intervention approaching grade level	Tier 3 Intensive Intervention 2 or more grades below level
If students miss about 25% of the exercises or less,	**If** students miss about 50% of the exercises,	**If** students miss about 75% of the exercises,
Then choose a resource: **SE** Lessons 13-1 through 13-5 **CRM** Skills Practice, pp. 7, 13, 20, 26, and 32 **TE** Chapter Project, p. 726 **Math Online** Self-Check Quiz	**Then** choose a resource: **CRM** Study Guide and Intervention, Chapter 13, pp. 5, 11, 18, 24, and 30 *Quick Review Math Handbook* **Math Online** Extra Examples, Personal Tutor, Homework Help	**Then** use *Math Triumphs, Grade 8*, Ch. 7, 9 **Math Online** Extra Examples, Personal Tutor, Homework Help, Review Vocabulary

13-6

Theoretical and Experimental Probability

Then
You have already simplified ratios. (Lesson 6-1)

Now
- Find the probability of simple events.
- Predict the actions of a larger group.

New Vocabulary
outcomes
simple event
probability
sample space
random
theoretical probability
experimental probability
odds in favor
odds against

Math Online
glencoe.com
- Extra Examples
- Personal Tutor
- Self-Check Quiz
- Homework Help
- Math in Motion

Why?

The table shows the number of gumballs of each flavor that is in a gumball machine.

Flavor	Number
blueberry	14
cherry	8
grape	18
lime	18
orange	16
strawberry	16

a. Write a ratio in simplest form that compares the number of grape gumballs to the total number of gumballs. $\frac{1}{5}$

b. What percent of gumballs are grape? 20%

c. Is there a better chance of getting a cherry or lime flavored gumball? Explain. There is a better chance of getting a lime flavored one because there are more of them

Probability of Simple Events In the activity above, there are 6 types of gumballs. These results are called **outcomes**. A **simple event** is one outcome or a collection of outcomes.

You can measure the chances of an event happening with probability. The **probability** of an event is a ratio that compares the number of favorable outcomes to the number of possible outcomes, assuming each outcome is equally likely to occur.

$$P(\text{event}) = \frac{\text{number of favorable outcomes}}{\text{number of possible outcomes}}$$

The probability of an event is always between 0 and 1, inclusive. The closer a probability is to 1, the more likely it is to occur.

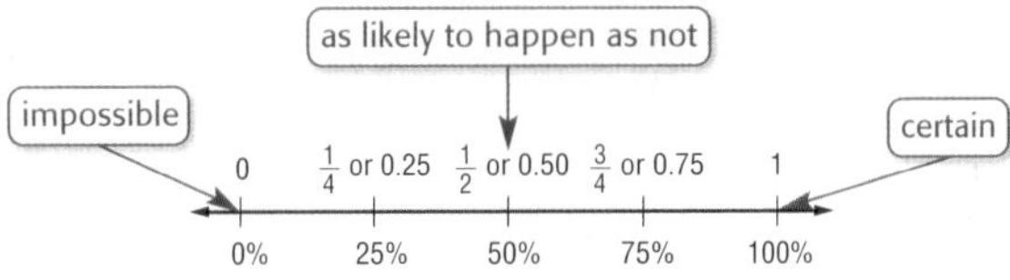

Math *in Motion*, Interactive Lab glencoe.com

EXAMPLE 1 Find Probability

A bag contains 7 pink, 2 white, and 5 blue marbles. A marble is selected without looking. Find the probability that a pink marble is chosen.

There are 14 marbles in all, and 7 of them are pink.

$$P(\text{pink}) = \frac{\text{number of pink marbles}}{\text{number of marbles in all}}$$

$$= \frac{7}{14} \text{ or } \frac{1}{2}$$

The probability of a pink marble being chosen is $\frac{1}{2}$ or 50%.

Check Your Progress

1. What is the probability of choosing a white marble? Express as a fraction and a percent. $\frac{1}{7}$ or 14.3%

Personal Tutor glencoe.com

13-6 Lesson Notes

1 FOCUS

Vertical Alignment

Before Lesson 13-6
Simplify ratios.

Lesson 13-6
Find the probability of simple events. Predict the actions of a larger group.

After Lesson 13-6
Select and use different models to simulate an event.

2 TEACH

Scaffolding Questions

Have students read the *Why?* section of the lesson and answer the questions.

Ask:
- How many cherry gumballs are there? 8
- What percent of gumballs are cherry-flavored? about 9%
- Suppose you insert a quarter into the machine. What flavor gumball are you most likely to get? grape or lime

Lesson 13-6 Resources

Resource	Approaching-Level	On-Level	Beyond-Level	English Learners
Teacher Edition	• Differentiated Instruction, p. 766	• Differentiated Instruction, p. 766	• Differentiated Instruction, p. 770	
Chapter Resource Masters	• Study Guide and Intervention, pp. 37–38 • Skills Practice, p. 39 • Practice, p. 40 • Word Problem Practice, p. 41	• Study Guide and Intervention, pp. 37–38 • Skills Practice, p. 39 • Practice, p. 40 • Word Problem Practice, p. 41 • Enrichment, p. 42	• Practice, p. 40 • Word Problem Practice, p. 41 • Enrichment, p. 42	• Study Guide and Intervention, pp. 37–38 • Skills Practice, p. 39 • Practice, p. 40
Transparencies	• 5-Minute Check Transparency 13-6	• 5-Minute Check Transparency 13-6	• 5-Minute Check Transparency 13-6	• 5-Minute Check Transparency 13-6
Other	• Study Notebook • Teaching Pre-Algebra with Manipulatives	• Study Notebook • Teaching Pre-Algebra with Manipulatives	• Study Notebook	• Study Notebook • Teaching Pre-Algebra with Manipulatives

Probability of Simple Events

Examples 1 and 2 show how to find theoretical probability. **Example 3** shows how to find experimental probability. **Example 4** shows how to find the odds related to an event.

Formative Assessment

Use the Check Your Progress exercises after each example to determine students' understanding of concepts.

Additional Examples

1 Suppose a number cube is rolled. What is the probability of rolling a 4 or a 5? $\frac{1}{3}$ or $33\frac{1}{3}\%$

2 Suppose two number cubes are rolled. Find the probability of rolling two identical numbers. $\frac{1}{6}$ or $16\frac{2}{3}\%$

3 A coin was tossed 40 times and heads came up 18 times. Find the experimental probability of getting tails for this experiment. Then compare the experimental probability with the theoretical probability. experimental probability: $\frac{22}{40}$ or 55%; theoretical probability: $\frac{1}{2}$ or 50%. So, getting heads in the experiment occurred more often than expected.

Additional Examples also in Interactive Classroom PowerPoint® Presentations

IWB INTERACTIVE WHITEBOARD READY

Additional Answer

3. $\frac{8}{29}$ or about 27.6%; Sample answer: The theoretical probability of rolling a four is $\frac{1}{6}$ or about 17%. So, rolling a four in the experiment occurred more often than expected.

The set of all possible outcomes is called the **sample space.** In Example 1, the sample space is {pink, white, blue}. When you roll a die, the sample space is {1, 2, 3, 4, 5, 6}. Outcomes occur at **random** if each outcome is equally likely to occur.

ReadingMath

P(prime) *is read as the probability of rolling a prime number.*

EXAMPLE 2 Find Probability

A die is rolled and a coin is tossed. Find *P*(even, heads).

Make a table showing the sample space when rolling a die and tossing a coin.

	H	T
1	(1, H)	(1, T)
2	(2, H)	(2, T)
3	(3, H)	(3, T)
4	(4, H)	(4, T)
5	(5, H)	(5, T)
6	(6, H)	(6, T)

There are 3 outcomes (shown in green) in which an even number is rolled and heads is tossed.

So, $P(\text{even, heads}) = \frac{3}{12}$ or $\frac{1}{4}$.

This means there is a 25% chance of rolling an even number and tossing heads.

Check Your Progress

2. Find *P*(even, heads or tails). $\frac{1}{2}$ **or 50%**

Personal Tutor glencoe.com

The probabilities in Examples 1 and 2 are called theoretical probabilities. **Theoretical probability** is what *should* occur in an experiment. **Experimental probability** is what *actually* occurs when repeating a probability experiment many times. If the number of trials is very small, there can be a wide variation in results.

Math History Link

Gerolamo Cardano (1501–1576) was a mathematician who developed the classical definition of probability. His model described probability as a comparison of favorable outcomes to the number of possible outcomes.

EXAMPLE 3 Find Experimental Probability

The table shows the results of an experiment in which a die was rolled. Find the experimental probability of rolling a six for this experiment. Then compare the experimental probability with the theoretical probability.

Outcome	Tally	Frequency
1	IIII	4
2	𝍸 I	6
3	II	2
4	𝍸 III	8
5	III	3
6	𝍸 I	6

$$\frac{\text{number of times six is rolled}}{\text{number of possible outcomes}} = \frac{6}{4 + 6 + 2 + 8 + 3 + 6} \text{ or } \frac{6}{29}$$

The experimental probability of rolling a six in this case is $\frac{6}{29}$ or about 21%. The theoretical probability of rolling a six is $\frac{1}{6}$ or about 17%. So, rolling a six in the experiment occurred more often than expected.

Check Your Progress

3. Find the experimental probability of rolling a four for the experiment above. Then compare it to the theoretical probability. **See margin.**

Personal Tutor glencoe.com

Differentiated Instruction

 students need additional practice finding experimental probability,

 have students determine the experimental probability of a thumbtack landing with its point up when tossed on a flat surface.

766 Chapter 13 Statistics and Probability

Another way to describe the chance of an event occurring is with odds. The **odds in favor** of an event is the ratio that compares the number of ways the event *can* occur to the number of ways that the event *cannot* occur. The **odds against** an event occurring is the ratio that compares the number of ways the event *cannot* occur to the number of ways that the event *can* occur.

StudyTip

Probability and Odds The probability of an event occurring can be written as a fraction or a percent.
$P(E) = \frac{3}{5}$ or 60%.
The odds in favor of the same event occurring is written as a ratio, 3:2.

EXAMPLE 4 Find the Odds

A die is rolled. Find the odds in favor of rolling a 1 or 2.

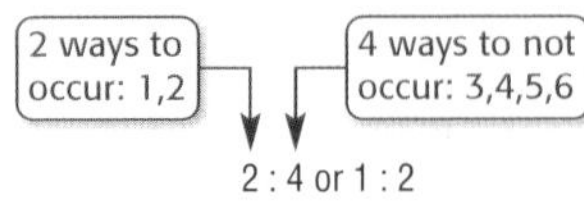
2 ways to occur: 1,2
4 ways to not occur: 3,4,5,6
2 : 4 or 1 : 2

So, the odds in favor of rolling a 1 or a 2 is 1:2.

Check Your Progress

4. A die is rolled. Find the odds against rolling an even number. 3:3 or 1:1

Personal Tutor glencoe.com

Focus on Mathematical Content

Probability The difference between theoretical and experimental probability is that theoretical probability is what *should* happen and experimental probability is what *does* happen. Events are affected by outside influences such as human error and environmental conditions. The more an experiment is performed, the closer the results will align with the theoretical results.

Use a Sample to Make Predictions You can use past performance or a survey to predict future events.

Real-World EXAMPLE 5 Make A Prediction

HOBBIES The circle graph shows the results of a survey that asked teens, ages 13 to 19, what they would be doing if they were not online. Out of a similar group of 450 teens, predict how many would listen to music.

Teen Hobbies (Other Than Internet)
Watching TV 25%
Listening to music 26%
Reading 9%
Physical activity/Sports 27%
Writing/Drawing 5%
Other 8%

Understand You know that 26% listen to music. You need to know how many teens out of 450 listen to music.

Plan Use the percent proportion to find 26% of 450.

Solve The percent is 26%, and 450 is the whole. Let n represent the part.

$$\text{part} \rightarrow \frac{n}{450} = \frac{26}{100} \Big\} \text{percent} \quad \text{whole} \rightarrow$$

$$100 \cdot n = 26 \cdot 450$$

$$100n = 11{,}700 \quad \text{Find the cross products.}$$

$$= 117 \quad \text{Mentally divide each side by 100.}$$

Check Estimate: 25% of 440 is 110. So, 117 is reasonable. ✓

Check Your Progress

5. **HOBBIES** Out of the 450 teens surveyed, how many would you expect to say they would be writing or drawing? Explain your reasoning.

Personal Tutor glencoe.com

Review Vocabulary

Percent Proportion compares *part* of a quantity to the *whole* quantity as a fraction. (Lesson 7-3)

5. about 23; Sample answer: Use the percent proportion to find 5% of 450.

$\frac{p}{450} = \frac{5}{100}$.

Additional Example

Three students have equal chances of getting a prize in a drawing. What are the odds against a particular student getting the prize? 2:1

Use a Sample to Make Predictions

Example 5 shows how to make a prediction in a real-world problem.

Additional Example

SPORTS Miss Newman surveyed her class to see which sports they preferred watching. Forty-four percent preferred football, 28% basketball, 20% soccer, and 8% tennis. Out of 560 students in the entire school, how many would you expect to say they preferred watching basketball? about 157 students

TEACH with TECH

INTERACTIVE WHITEBOARD Use the probability simulator that comes with your IWB software (using coins, spinners, etc.). Find the theoretical probability of an event, then use the simulator to obtain real experimental data.

Lesson 13-6 Theoretical and Experimental Probability 767

3 PRACTICE

Formative Assessment

Use Exercises 1–8 to check for understanding.

Use the chart at the bottom of this page to customize assignments for your students.

Additional Answers

6. $\frac{1}{5}$ or 20%; Sample answer: The theoretical probability of rolling a four is $\frac{1}{6}$ or about 17%. So, rolling a four in the experiment occurred about the same number of times.

15a.

(1, 1)	(1, 2)	(1, 3)	(1, 4)
(2, 1)	(2, 2)	(2, 3)	(2, 4)
(3, 1)	(3, 2)	(3, 3)	(3, 4)
(4, 1)	(4, 2)	(4, 3)	(4, 4)

16c. $\frac{1}{16}$ or 6%; Sample answer: Spinning a sum of 8 in the experiment occurred more than twice as often as expected.

25. Sample answer: The theoretical probability is $\frac{7}{35}$ or 20%. So, she would expect to select a navy pair of socks 4 out of 20 times. Since she selected a navy pair 6 times, her experimental probability of $\frac{6}{20}$ or 30%, exceeded her theoretical probability.

Check Your Understanding

Example 1 p. 765 — **The spinner shown at right is spun once. Determine the probability of each outcome. Express each probability as a fraction and as a percent.**

1. $P(6)$ $\frac{1}{10}$ or 10%
2. $P(\text{even})$ $\frac{1}{2}$ or 50%
3. $P(\text{greater than } 6)$ $\frac{2}{5}$ or 40%
4. $P(\text{less than } 5)$ [illegible]

Example 2 p. 766

5. Two coins are tossed. What is the probability of both coins landing on heads? $\frac{1}{4}$ or 25%

Example 3 p. 766

6. The table shows the results of an experiment in which a die was rolled. Find the experimental probability of rolling a 4. Then compare it to the theoretical probability. See margin.

Number	Frequency
1	II
2	I
3	IIII
4	III
5	III
6	II

Example 4 p. 767

7. A letter of the alphabet is chosen at random. Find the odds in favor of picking an A, E, I, O, or U. 5:21

Example 5 p. 767

8. **COLORS** Without looking, Delores took a handful of multi-colored candies from a bag and found that 40% of the candies were yellow. Suppose that there were 375 candies in the bag. How many can she expect to be yellow? 150; Sample answer: Use the percent proportion to find 40% of 375. $\frac{p}{375} = \frac{40}{100}$.

Practice and Problem Solving

● = **Step-by-Step Solutions** begin on page R11. **Extra Practice** begins on page 810.

Example 1 p. 765 — **A dartboard like the one shown is divided into 20 equal sections. Determine the probability of each outcome if a dart is equally likely to land anywhere on the dartboard. Express each probability as a fraction and as a percent.**

9. $P(20)$ $\frac{1}{20}$ or 5%
10. $P(\text{less than } 8)$ $\frac{7}{20}$ or 35%
11. $P(\text{odd})$ $\frac{1}{2}$ or 50%
12. $P(\text{even})$ $\frac{1}{2}$ or 50%
13. $P(\text{greater than } 16)$ — 13. $\frac{1}{5}$ or 20%
14. $P(\text{multiple of } 3)$ $\frac{3}{10}$ or 30%

Example 2 p. 766

15. The spinners shown are each spun once.
    a. Make a table showing the sample space. See margin.
    b. Find $P(\text{even sum})$. $\frac{1}{2}$ or 50%
    c. Find $P(\text{two even numbers})$. $\frac{1}{4}$ or 25%

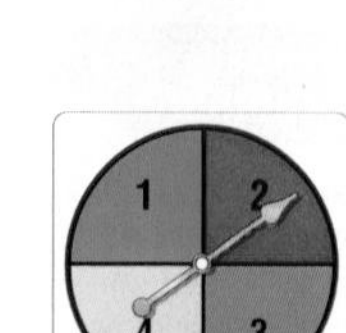

Example 3 p. 766

16. The table shows the results of an experiment in which the spinners shown above were each spun 50 times.
    a. What is the experimental probability of spinning a sum of 6? $\frac{3}{10}$ or 30%
    b. What is the experimental probability of spinning a sum of 8? $\frac{4}{25}$ or 16%
    c. What is the theoretical probability of spinning a sum of 8? Compare it to the experimental probability. See margin.

Sum	Frequency
2	II
3	III
4	𝍸 III
5	𝍸 I
6	𝍸 𝍸 𝍸
7	𝍸 III
8	𝍸 III

Differentiated Homework Options

Level	Assignment	Two-Day Option	
AL Basic	9–19, 22, 25–35	9–19 odd, 26–29	10–18 even, 22, 25, 30–35
OL Core	9–19 odd, 20–22, 25–35	9–19, 26–29	20–22, 25, 30–35
BL Advanced	20–31, (optional: 32–35)		

Example 4 p. 767

17. A jar contains 40 pennies, 18 nickels, 20 dimes, and 12 quarters. If a coin is selected at random, what are the odds in favor of picking a penny or dime? **2:1**

18. In an assembly line, 56 out of 60 randomly selected parts have no faults. What are the odds in favor of a randomly selected part having a fault? **1:14**

Example 5 p. 767

19. ANALYZE GRAPHS Refer to the graph that shows the results of a survey that asked youth about what is important to their personal success.

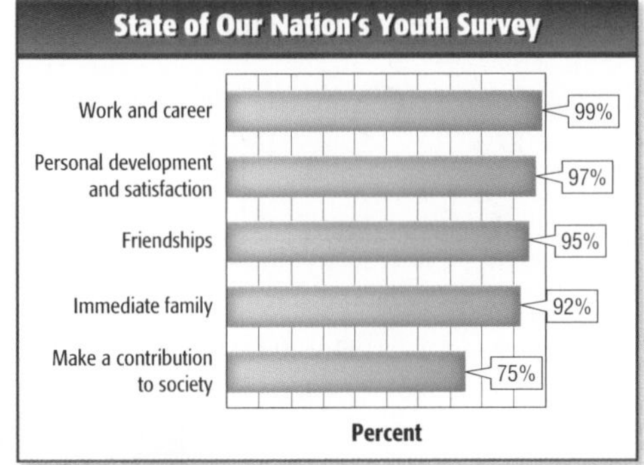

a. If 1200 youth were surveyed, how many would you expect to say friendships are a factor in their personal success? **1140**

b. Suppose 1500 youth were surveyed. How many would you expect to say immediate family is a factor in their personal success? **1380**

Real-World Link

The X games are held annually with an emphasis on action sports. The first X games were held in the summer of 1995 with competitions in Providence, Rhode Island, Newport, Rhode Island, and Mount Snow, Vermont.

B **20. RAFFLE** In a raffle, one ticket is randomly chosen from 80 tickets to receive free haircuts for a year. If Wakim entered 6 tickets, what is the probability that he is *not* chosen to receive the free haircuts? **$\frac{37}{40}$ or 92.5%**

21. X GAMES Use the graph that shows the results of a class survey about students' favorite X Game sport.

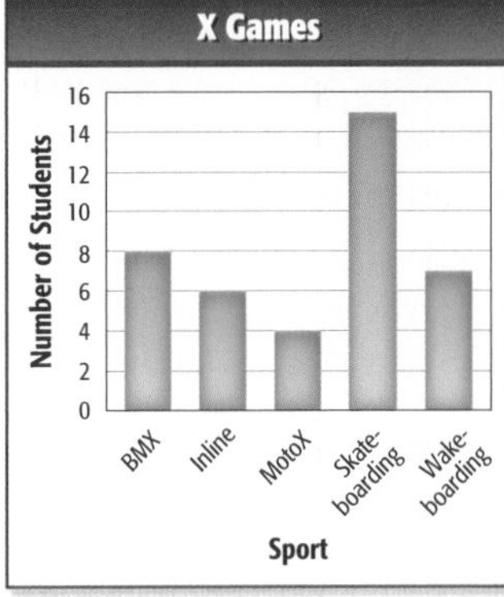

a. What is the probability of skateboarding being someone's favorite sport? **$\frac{3}{8}$ or 37.5%**

b. Suppose 800 students in the school are surveyed. At this rate, predict how many will choose inline skating as their favorite sport. **120 students**

c. Of the 800 surveyed, predict how many more students will prefer BMX than MotoX. Explain.

21c. 80 students; Sample answer: The number of students that prefer BMX is 20% of 800 or 160. The number of students that prefer MotoX is 10% of 800 or 80. So 160 − 80 or 80 students would prefer BMX to MotoX.

H.O.T. Problems Use Higher-Order Thinking Skills

22. OPEN ENDED Give an example of a real-world situation in which the C probability of an event is 25%.

22. Sample Answer: Choosing the correct answer on a 4 choice multiple-choice test by random guessing.

23. CHALLENGE The experimental probability of a penny landing on tails is $\frac{9}{16}$. If the penny landed on heads 21 times, how many times was the coin tossed? **48**

24. CHALLENGE A survey found that 95 households out of 150 have high speed internet and that 125 out of 200 have cable television. What is the probability that a household has both? **about 40%**

25. WRITING IN MATH Jasmine's sock drawer has 8 white pairs, 5 black pairs, 7 navy pairs, 3 khaki, and 12 other pairs. She randomly selected a pair of socks 20 times and selected a navy pair 6 times. Compare and contrast the theoretical and experimental probability. **See margin.**

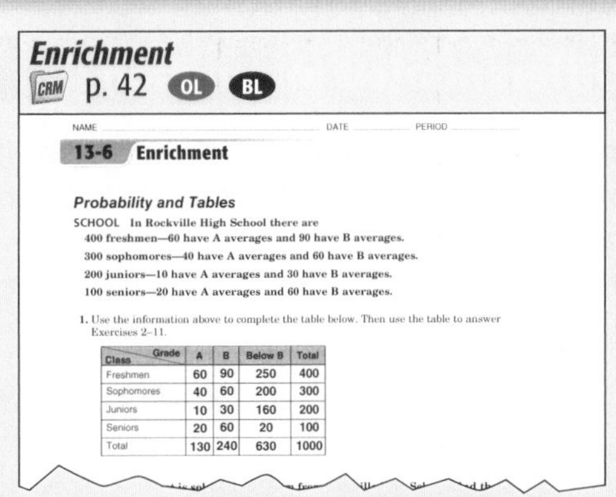

Enrichment
CRM p. 42 OL BL

NAME ______ DATE ______ PERIOD ______

13-6 Enrichment

Probability and Tables

SCHOOL In Rockville High School there are
400 freshmen—60 have A averages and 90 have B averages.
300 sophomores—40 have A averages and 60 have B averages.
200 juniors—10 have A averages and 30 have B averages.
100 seniors—20 have A averages and 60 have B averages.

1. Use the information above to complete the table below. Then use the table to answer Exercises 2–11.

Class \ Grade	A	B	Below B	Total
Freshmen	60	90	250	400
Sophomores	40	60	200	300
Juniors	10	30	160	200
Seniors	20	60	20	100
Total	130	240	630	1000

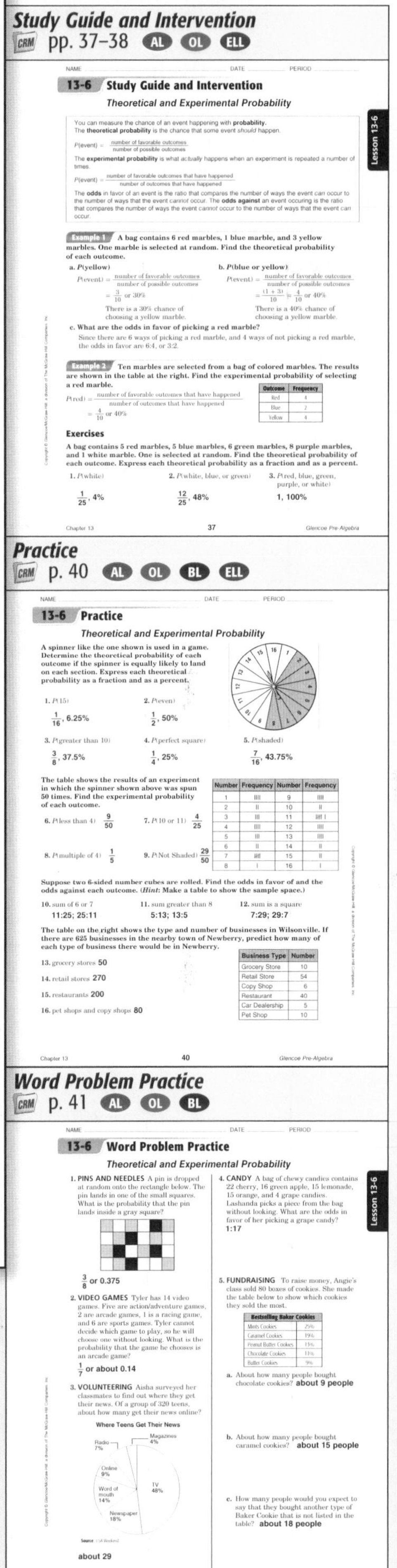

Study Guide and Intervention
CRM pp. 37–38 AL OL ELL

NAME ______ DATE ______ PERIOD ______

13-6 Study Guide and Intervention

Theoretical and Experimental Probability

You can measure the chance of an event happening with **probability.**
The **theoretical probability** is the chance that some event *should* happen.

$P(\text{event}) = \frac{\text{number of favorable outcomes}}{\text{number of possible outcomes}}$

The **experimental probability** is what *actually* happens when an experiment is repeated a number of times.

$P(\text{event}) = \frac{\text{number of favorable outcomes that have happened}}{\text{number of outcomes that have happened}}$

The **odds** in favor of an event is the ratio that compares the number of ways the event *can* occur to the number of ways that the event *cannot* occur. The **odds against** an event occuring is the ratio that compares the number of ways the event *cannot* occur to the number of ways that the event *can* occur.

Example 1 A bag contains 6 red marbles, 1 blue marble, and 3 yellow marbles. One marble is selected at random. Find the theoretical probability of each outcome.

a. P(yellow)
$P(\text{event}) = \frac{\text{number of favorable outcomes}}{\text{number of possible outcomes}} = \frac{3}{10}$ or 30%
There is a 30% chance of choosing a yellow marble.

b. P(blue or yellow)
$P(\text{event}) = \frac{\text{number of favorable outcomes}}{\text{number of possible outcomes}} = \frac{(1+3)}{10} = \frac{4}{10}$ or 40%
There is a 40% chance of choosing a yellow marble.

c. What are the odds in favor of picking a red marble?
Since there are 6 ways of picking a red marble, and 4 ways of not picking a red marble, the odds in favor are 6:4, or 3:2.

Example 2 Ten marbles are selected from a bag of colored marbles. The results are shown in the table at the right. Find the experimental probability of selecting a red marble.

$P(\text{red}) = \frac{\text{number of favorable outcomes that have happened}}{\text{number of outcomes that have happened}} = \frac{4}{10}$ or 40%

Outcome	Frequency
Red	4
Blue	2
Yellow	4

Exercises

A bag contains 5 red marbles, 5 blue marbles, 6 green marbles, 8 purple marbles, and 1 white marble. One is selected at random. Find the theoretical probability of each outcome. Express each theoretical probability as a fraction and as a percent.

1. P(white) **$\frac{1}{25}$, 4%**
2. P(white, blue, or green) **$\frac{12}{25}$, 48%**
3. P(red, blue, green, purple, or white) **1, 100%**

Chapter 13 37 Glencoe Pre-Algebra

Practice
CRM p. 40 AL OL BL ELL

NAME ______ DATE ______ PERIOD ______

13-6 Practice

Theoretical and Experimental Probability

A spinner like the one shown is used in a game. Determine the theoretical probability of each outcome if the spinner is equally likely to land on each section. Express each theoretical probability as a fraction and as a percent.

1. P(15) **$\frac{1}{16}$, 6.25%**
2. P(even) **$\frac{1}{2}$, 50%**
3. P(greater than 10) **$\frac{3}{8}$, 37.5%**
4. P(perfect square) **$\frac{1}{4}$, 25%**
5. P(shaded) **$\frac{7}{16}$, 43.75%**

The table shows the results of an experiment in which the spinner shown above was spun 50 times. Find the experimental probability of each outcome.

Number	Frequency	Number	Frequency
1	IIII	9	IIII
2	II	10	II
3	III	11	IIII I
4	IIII	12	IIII
5	III	13	IIII
6	II	14	II
7	IIII	15	II
8	I	16	I

6. P(less than 4) **$\frac{9}{50}$**
7. P(10 or 11) **$\frac{4}{25}$**
8. P(multiple of 4) **$\frac{1}{5}$**
9. P(Not Shaded) **$\frac{29}{50}$**

Suppose two 6-sided number cubes are rolled. Find the odds in favor of and the odds against each outcome. (*Hint*: Make a table to show the sample space.)

10. sum of 6 or 7 **11:25; 25:11**
11. sum greater than 8 **5:13; 13:5**
12. sum is a square **7:29; 29:7**

The table on the right shows the type and number of businesses in Wilsonville. If there are 625 businesses in the nearby town of Newberry, predict how many of each type of business there would be in Newberry.

Business Type	Number
Grocery Store	10
Retail Store	54
Copy Shop	6
Restaurant	40
Car Dealership	5
Pet Shop	10

13. grocery stores **50**
14. retail stores **270**
15. restaurants **200**
16. pet shops and copy shops **80**

Chapter 13 40 Glencoe Pre-Algebra

Word Problem Practice
CRM p. 41 AL OL BL

NAME ______ DATE ______ PERIOD ______

13-6 Word Problem Practice

Theoretical and Experimental Probability

1. **PINS AND NEEDLES** A pin is dropped at random onto the rectangle below. The pin lands in one of the small squares. What is the probability that the pin lands inside a gray square? **$\frac{3}{8}$ or 0.375**

2. **VIDEO GAMES** Tyler has 14 video games. Five are action/adventure games, 2 are arcade games, 1 is a racing game, and 6 are sports games. Tyler cannot decide which game to play, so he will choose one without looking. What is the probability that the game he chooses is an arcade game? **$\frac{1}{7}$ or about 0.14**

3. **VOLUNTEERING** Aisha surveyed her classmates to find out where they get their news. Of a group of 320 teens, about how many get their news online?

Where Teens Get Their News: Radio 7%; Magazines 4%; Online 9%; Word of mouth 14%; Newspaper 18%; TV 48%

about 29

4. **CANDY** A bag of chewy candies contains 22 cherry, 16 green apple, 15 lemonade, 15 orange, and 4 grape candies. Lashanda picks a piece from the bag without looking. What are the odds in favor of her picking a grape candy? **1:17**

5. **FUNDRAISING** To raise money, Angie's class sold 80 boxes of cookies. She made the table below to show which cookies they sold the most.

Bestselling Baker Cookies	
Mints Cookies	25%
Caramel Cookies	19%
Peanut Butter Cookies	13%
Chocolate Cookies	11%
Butter Cookies	9%

a. About how many people bought chocolate cookies? **about 9 people**

b. About how many people bought caramel cookies? **about 15 people**

c. How many people would you expect to say that they bought another type of Baker Cookie that is not listed in the table? **about 18 people**

Chapter 13 41 Glencoe Pre-Algebra

Tips for New Teachers

Making Connections Exercise 28 involves replacement. In Lesson 13-10, students will learn how to find the probability of two dependent events.

4 ASSESS

Crystal Ball Tell students to write how they think what they have learned today will connect with tomorrow's theme of using sampling to predict. Have them include ways that it might connect to life outside the classroom, as well.

Additional Answers

28b. $\frac{p}{250} = \frac{20}{100}$

$100p = 5000$

$p = 50$

You would expect Casey to pick a white marble 50 times.

30a. The number of states that have a certain number of roller coasters; most states have less than 10 roller coasters

30b. to show a break in the vertical scale

30c. The graph shows that 30 states have anywhere from 0 to 9 roller coasters, but it does not indicate how many states have none.

31a. Since SUVs average the least miles per gallon, they tend to be less fuel-efficient.

31b. The most fuel-efficient SUV and the least fuel-efficient sedan both average 22 miles per gallon.

Standardized Test Practice

26. The production records of a toy manufacturing company show that 5 out of every 75 toys have a defect. What is the probability that a randomly selected toy manufactured at the company will *not* have a defect? **D**

A 7% C 70%
B 27% D 93%

27. If Luke spins a spinner like the one shown 400 times, how many times should he expect it to land on the space with a triangle? **F**

F 100 H 300
G 200 J 400

28. EXTENDED RESPONSE Casey has a bag containing 3 white, 8 red, 2 blue, and 2 yellow marbles. She randomly picks a marble from the bag and replaces it. She repeats the experiment 250 times.

a. What is the probability that the marble Casey picks will be white? $\frac{1}{5}$ **or 20%**

b. Predict the number of times out of 250 Casey will pick a white marble. **See margin.**

29. The results of rolling a die are shown in the table. What is the experimental probability of rolling a 3? **D**

Roll	1	2	3	4	5	6
Frequency	13	9	20	8	10	15

A 13% C 20%
B 17% D 27%

Spiral Review

30. ROLLER COASTERS Use the histogram shown. (Lesson 13-5)

a. Describe the data. **a–c. See margin.**

b. Why is there a jagged line in the vertical axis?

c. How many states have no roller coasters? Explain.

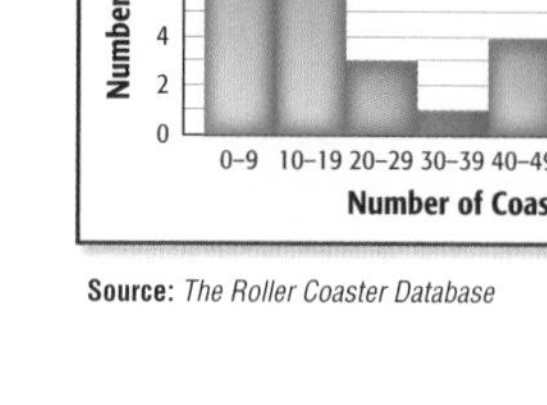

Source: *The Roller Coaster Database*

31. TRAVEL The box-and-whisker plots below show the average gas mileage for some cars. (Lesson 13-4)

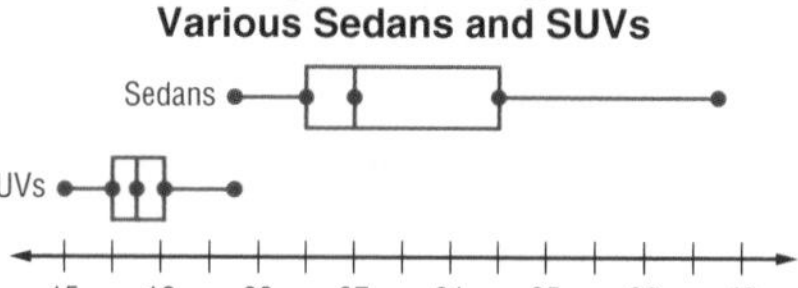

a. Which types of vehicles tend to be less fuel-efficient? **a–b. See margin.**

b. Compare the most fuel-efficient SUV to the least fuel-efficient sedan.

Skills Review

Find each product. (Previous Course)

32. $8 \times 2 \times 3$ **48**

33. $5 \times 10 \times 2 \times 9$ **900**

34. $20 \times 15 \times 20$ **6000**

35. $12 \times 9 \times 12 \times 10$ **12,960**

Differentiated Instruction BL

Extension Pose the following to students: Maria has a number cube and a coin. She tosses the coin with her right hand and rolls the die with her left. What is the chance that the coin will be tails and the number cube will be 6? There are 12 possible outcomes. The probability that the coin will be tails is $\frac{1}{2}$. The probability that the number cube will be 6 is $\frac{1}{6}$. The probability of tails and a 6 is $\frac{1}{12}$.

Suppose Maria has a number cube and 2 coins. What is the chance both coins will be tails and the number cube will be 6? $\frac{1}{24}$

770 Chapter 13 Statistics and Probability

13-7 Using Sampling to Predict

Then
You have already analyzed data in graphs. (Lessons 13-1 through 13-5)

Now
- Identify various sampling techniques.
- Determine the validity of a sample and predict the actions of a larger group.

New Vocabulary
sample
population
unbiased sample
simple random sample
stratified random sample
systemic random sample
biased sample
convenience sample
voluntary response sample

Math Online
glencoe.com
- Extra Examples
- Personal Tutor
- Self-Check Quiz
- Homework Help

Why?

The activities committee surveyed a group of students about a mascot for their new high school. The results are shown in the table.

Mascot	Number
Bisons	17
Cougars	4
Huskies	18
Knights	32
Other	3

a. About how many students would vote for the Huskies if the entire student body of 1600 voted? About how many would vote for the Knights? 389; 692

b. Suppose the students surveyed were in the Spanish club. Do you think the results of the survey would fairly represent the student body? Explain. b–c. See Chapter 13 Answer Appendix.

c. How could you survey a part of the student population that would fairly represent all students? Give two examples.

Identify Sampling Techniques The committee cannot survey every student in the school. So, a randomly selected smaller group called a **sample** is chosen from the larger group, or **population**. The best sample is an unbiased sample. An **unbiased sample** is a sample that is:

- representative of the larger population,
- selected at random or without preference, and
- large enough to provide accurate data. If a sample is too small, data accurately representing the larger population may not be available.

Concept Summary — Unbiased Samples — *For Your FOLDABLE*

Type	Definition	Example
Simple Random Sample	Each item or person in a population is as likely to be chosen as any other.	Thirty student ID numbers are randomly selected by a computer.
Stratified Random Sample	The population is divided into similar, nonoverlapping groups. A simple random sample is then selected from each group.	A population of election districts can be separated into urban, suburban, and rural strata.
Systematic Random Sample	The items or people are selected according to a specific time or item interval.	Every 20 minutes a customer is chosen, or every 10th customer in line is chosen.

A sample that is not representative of the population is called a **biased sample**. A biased sample usually favors certain parts of the population over others.

13-7 Lesson Notes

1 FOCUS

Vertical Alignment

Before Lesson 13-7
Analyze data.

Lesson 13-7
Identify various sampling techniques. Determine the validity of a sample.

After Lesson 13-7
Draw conclusions and make predictions by analyzing trends in scatter plots.

2 TEACH

Scaffolding Questions

Have students read the *Why?* section of the lesson and answer the questions.

Ask:
- How many students participated in this sample? 74
- About what percent of the students in the survey voted for the Huskies? the Knights? about 24.3%; about 43.2%
- Suppose the students surveyed are a crowd leaving a basketball game. Would the results fairly represent the student body? Explain. No; students attending a basketball game might prefer a mascot related to a sports theme.

Lesson 13-7 Resources

Resource	Approaching-Level	On-Level	Beyond-Level	English Learners
Teacher Edition	• Differentiated Instruction, p. 772	• Differentiated Instruction, p. 772	• Differentiated Instruction, p. 776	
Chapter Resource Masters	• Study Guide and Intervention, pp. 43–44 • Skills Practice, p. 45 • Practice, p. 46 • Word Problem Practice, p. 47	• Study Guide and Intervention, pp. 43–44 • Skills Practice, p. 45 • Practice, p. 46 • Word Problem Practice, p. 47 • Enrichment, p. 48	• Practice, p. 46 • Word Problem Practice, p. 47 • Enrichment, p. 48	• Study Guide and Intervention, pp. 43–44 • Skills Practice, p. 45 • Practice, p. 46
Transparencies	• 5-Minute Check Transparency 13-7	• 5-Minute Check Transparency 13-7	• 5-Minute Check Transparency 13-7	• 5-Minute Check Transparency 13-7
Other	• Study Notebook • Teaching Pre-Algebra with Manipulatives	• Study Notebook • Teaching Pre-Algebra with Manipulatives	• Study Notebook	• Study Notebook • Teaching Pre-Algebra with Manipulatives

Identify Sampling Techniques

Example 1 shows how to identify and describe samples by their types.

Formative Assessment

Use the Check Your Progress exercises after each example to determine students' understanding of concepts.

Additional Example

1 A hardware store wants feedback on its products and service. The store includes a telephone number on each receipt so customers can call and participate in a survey. Identify the sample as *biased* or *unbiased* and describe its type. Explain your reasoning. biased; voluntary response sample; the sample includes only those customers who choose to participate

Additional Examples also in Interactive Classroom PowerPoint® Presentations

IWB INTERACTIVE WHITEBOARD READY

Validating and Predicting Samples

Examples 2 and 3 show how to use sampling to predict amounts.

Additional Example

2 **VACATION** Mr. Stevens surveyed every tenth student in the hallway to see where they would prefer to go on a vacation. Forty-eight percent preferred the beach, 36% preferred an amusement park, and 16% preferred the mountains. Is this sampling method valid? If so, how many of the 560 students in the school would you expect to say they preferred the beach? Explain. Yes; this is a systematic random sample; about 269 students

Concept Summary — Biased Samples

For Your FOLDABLE

Type	Definition	Example
Convenience Sample	Includes members of the population that are easily accessed.	The first 10 students in the cafeteria line.
Voluntary Response Sample	Involves only those who want to or can participate in the sampling.	The principal sent an email to graduating seniors asking them where to hold commencement. Seniors are asked to vote through an online poll.

EXAMPLE 1 Identify and Describe Samples

To determine the types of music their customers like, all the people attending a concert of a country music singer are surveyed. Identify the sample as *biased* or *unbiased* and describe its type. Explain your reasoning.

Since the customers at a country concert probably prefer country music, the sample is biased. The sample is a convenience sample since all of the people surveyed are in one location.

Check Your Progress

1. To determine which passengers' carry-on bags are to be inspected, every eighth person to check in will have his or her bags inspected. Identify the sample as *biased* or *unbiased* and describe its type. Explain your reasoning.

Personal Tutor glencoe.com

Validating and Predicting Samples Depending on the sampling method used, you can make predictions about larger populations.

Real-World EXAMPLE 2 Using Sampling to Predict

PETS A pet store mailed a survey to residents to determine their favorite pets. Fifty people responded and the results are shown in the table. Is this sampling method valid? If so, how many people can you expect to choose dogs as their favorite pet in a city with 1585 people? Explain.

Pet	Number
dog	20
cat	16
fish	9
gerbil	5
no pets	0

This is a biased and voluntary response sample since it involves only those who want to participate in the survey. Therefore, this sampling method will not produce an accurate and valid prediction of the total number of dogs in the city.

Real-World Link

In the United States, there are approximately 73 million dogs that have owners.

Source: Humane Society

Check Your Progress

2. **WATCHES** Of the 2000 watches made, the manufacturer tests the first 15 watches produced for defects. Of the watches, 3 were defective. Is this sampling method valid? If so, about how many of the 2000 are defective? Explain.

Personal Tutor glencoe.com

1. unbiased; systematic random sample; people are selected according to an interval
2. No; this is a biased and convenience sample since it involves sampling only the first 15 watches. A greater or lesser number of watches could be defective later in the batch. This is not representative of the entire population of 2000 watches so this sampling method will not produce a valid prediction.

Differentiated Instruction

If students need additional practice in validating and predicting samples,

Then have students work in groups of four to create a survey question that can be asked of other students in their grade. Examples might be questions about favorite sports, food, number of pets, or favorite celebrities. Arrange to have students go to another classroom of their same grade to conduct their survey. Have students use their results to make predictions for the entire grade. Ask them to speculate whether their results might be valid for students of different grades.

Real-World EXAMPLE 3 Using Sampling to Predict

TECHNOLOGY From a batch of 7500 computer chips produced, the manufacturer sampled every 150th chip at random for defects and found that 2 were defective. Is this sampling method valid? If so, find how many of the 7500 computer chips you can expect to be defective. Explain.

This is a systematic random sample because the samples are selected according to a specific interval. So, this sampling method is reasonable and will produce a valid prediction.

Since every 150 chips were sampled, there were a total of 7500 ÷ 150 or 50 chips sampled and 2 were defective. Two out of 50, or 4%, were defective. So, find 4% of 7500.

StudyTip

Alternate Method Set up a proportion.

$$\frac{2}{50} = \frac{n}{7500}$$

$$2 \cdot 7500 = 50 \cdot n$$

$$300 = n$$

(Lesson 6-4)

Words	What number is 4% of 7500?
Variable	Let n = the number of defective chips.
Equation	$n = 0.04 \times 7500$

$n = 0.04 \times 7500$ **Write the equation.**

$= 300$ **Multiply.**

So, you would expect approximately 300 defective chips.

Check Your Progress

3. **FOOD** After finishing their meal, every fifth person that left the restaurant was surveyed about whether they ordered dessert after their meals. Out of 20 people, 12 said yes. Is this sampling method valid? If so, about how many of the 380 people who had dinner at the restaurant ate dessert?

3. Yes; this is a simple random sample because the diners are selected randomly throughout the night; 228 people

Personal Tutor glencoe.com

Check Your Understanding

Example 1 p. 772

Identify each sample as *biased* or *unbiased* and describe its type. Explain your reasoning. 1–4. See margin.

1. To determine how many students at a middle school bring their lunch from home, all the students on one school bus are surveyed.
2. To determine the theme for the homecoming dance, the homecoming committee surveys one classroom.
3. To determine shopping habits at a department store, one male and one female shopper are randomly selected and surveyed from each of their 75 stores.

Examples 2 and 3 pp. 772–773

4. **ANALYZE TABLES** The theater group took a survey about the type of popcorn they should sell during plays. They randomly surveyed 52 students at lunch. Their results are shown in the table. Is this sampling method valid? If so, how many of the boxes of popcorn should be caramel if they order 600 boxes?

Flavor	Number of Students
butter	18
cheese	14
caramel	13
plain	7

TEACH with TECH

STUDENT RESPONSE SYSTEM Create a presentation with several examples of types of surveys and ask students if the sample is biased or unbiased. Have them respond with 1 for biased and 2 for unbiased. If the sample is biased, ask students to name unbiased samples that could be used instead.

Additional Example

3. **MUSIC** A middle school planned to play music during lunch. To determine what type of music students preferred, 25 students with MP3 players in one lunch period were surveyed and asked what type of music they preferred. Sixteen said they preferred country music. Is this sampling method valid? If so, find how many of the 535 students in school you can expect to prefer country music. Explain. No; this is a biased, convenience sample since only students with MP3 players in one lunch period were surveyed. So, this sampling method will not produce a valid prediction.

3 PRACTICE

Formative Assessment

Use Exercises 1–4 to check for understanding.

Use the chart at the bottom of the next page to customize assignments for your students.

Additional Answers

1. biased, convenience sample; all the students on 1 school bus might come from the same neighborhood/economic status.
2. biased, convenience sample; the sample includes only students in one classroom
3. unbiased, stratified random sample; the shoppers are first divided into non-overlapping groups and then 1 male and 1 female is selected randomly from each group
4. This is a simple random sample since the students were randomly chosen during lunch. So, this sampling method will produce a valid prediction; 150

Focus on Mathematical Content

Sampling Sampling of a population can be biased or unbiased. Often a biased opinion is desired because a select group is targeted. Sometimes samplings are unintentionally biased.

Tips for New Teachers

A more detailed definition for a simple random sample is as follows: a sample of size n such that all samples of size n have the same probability of being selected.

Additional Answers

9. This sampling method is not valid because it will include students who do not attend your school. So, the results can not lead to a reasonable conclusion.
10. No; this is a biased sample. The flu may have been passed more easily between students in that class, so more of them may have the flu than compared to the entire school population.
11. Yes; this is a systematic random survey because the sample is selected according to an interval; 1225
12. No; The sample is unbiased, but preference does not necessarily indicate what will be bought. The store manager should review sales receipts to determine what types of milk have actually been bought.
13. No; only 80 out of 300 customers agree. From this random survey, you can predict that only about 27% of the customers would like a foreign movie section, so the store should not add such an area.

Practice and Problem Solving

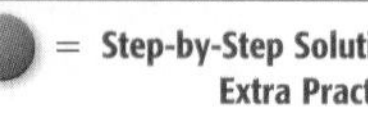
= **Step-by-Step Solutions** begin on page R11.
Extra Practice begins on page 810.

Example 1
p. 772

5. unbiased, simple random sample; the students are randomly selected
6. unbiased, systematic random sample; the cell phones are selected according to a time interval

Identify each sample as *biased* or *unbiased* and describe its type. Explain your reasoning.

5. To determine whether a new university library would be useful, all students whose student ID number ends in 2 are surveyed.
6. To determine the quality of cell phones coming off an assembly line, the manager chooses one cell phone every 20 minutes and checks it.
7. To determine the popularity of a musician, a magazine asks teenagers to log on to their website and participate in the survey.
8. To determine whether a candidate for governor is popular with the voters, 30% of citizens in each of the 254 counties are surveyed.

Examples 2 and 3
pp. 772–773

7. biased, voluntary response survey; those teenagers who are interested in participating in the survey are part of the sample
8. unbiased, stratified random sample; the population is first divided into the 254 counties, and then 30% of the citizens are surveyed from each of those counties

9. **ANALYZE GRAPHS** A school committee wanted to find out if students will recycle at school. The committee randomly surveyed 25% of the teenagers at a mall on a Saturday afternoon. The results are in the graph. Is this sampling method valid? If so, about how many of the 576 students at the school will participate in the program?
9–13. See margin.

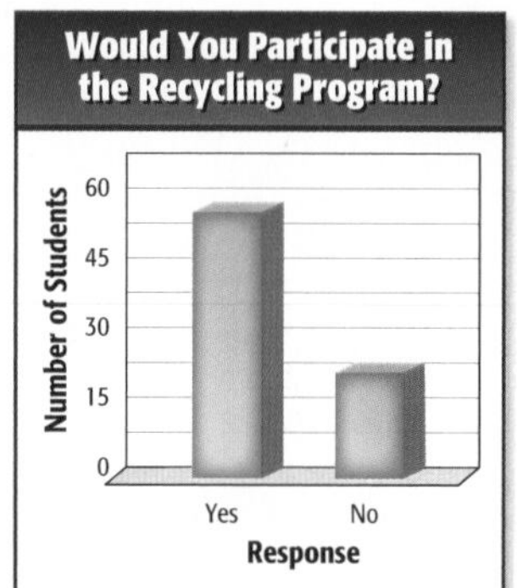

10. **HEALTH** Seven of the 28 students in math class have the flu. Is this sampling of the students who have the flu representative of the entire school? If so, how many of the 464 students who attend the school have the flu?

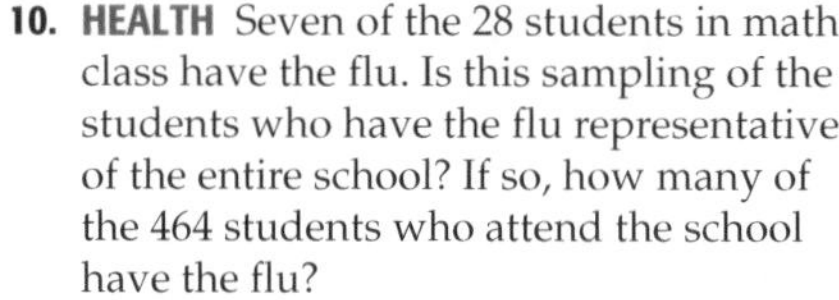

11. **CONCERT** As teenagers leave a concert, every 10th person is surveyed. They are asked if they would buy a T-shirt. One hundred forty of 800 people surveyed said yes. Is this sampling method valid? If so, how many people would you expect to buy T-shirts at the next concert if 7000 attend? Explain your reasoning.
12. **ANALYZE TABLES** Every hour, twenty customers in a grocery store are randomly selected and surveyed on their milk preference. The results are shown in the table. After reviewing the data, the store manager decided that 40% of his total milk stock should be low-fat milk. Is this a valid conclusion? If not, what information should the store manager review to make a better conclusion?

Milk Preference	
Milk	Number
skim	88
low-fat	92
whole	60

Real-World Link

Approximately 170 billion pounds of milk are produced annually in the United States.

Source: National Agriculture Statistics Service

13. **VIDEOS** A video store is considering adding an international movie section. They randomly selected 300 customers, and 80 customers agree the international movie section is a good idea. Should the store add this section? Explain.

Differentiated Homework Options

Level	Assignment	Two-Day Option	
AL Basic	5–10, 17, 19–34	5–9 odd, 21–24	6–10 even, 17, 19, 20, 25–34
OL Core	5–9 odd, 11–17, 19–34	5–10, 21–24	11–17, 19, 20, 25–34
BL Advanced	11–30 (optional: 31–34)		

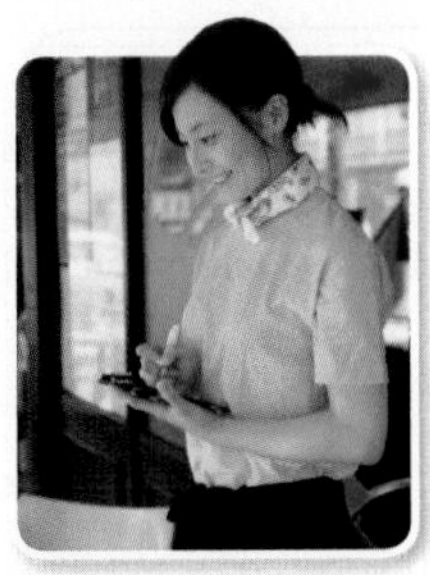

Real-World Link

The restaurant industry provides 12.8 million jobs nationally. This is the nation's second largest employer behind the government.

Source: National Restaurant Association

14a. Sample answer: He could survey one of every 10 people that exit the local grocery store.

14b. Sample answers: What types of restaurants do you visit most often? What is your favorite type of food?

14c. Sample answer: He could use the results to determine the type of food he serves or even the type of atmosphere people would like in the restaurant.

17. Sample answer: unbiased survey: Survey your classmates about their favorite sport.; See student's work.

18. Sample answer: Randomly pick 10 rows in your field. Then choose the 20th stalk in each of those 10 rows and pick an ear of corn.

14. FOOD Ellis is planning on opening a restaurant in his community. He is conducting a survey to determine what type of food people in the community like.

a. Describe an unbiased population sample that Ellis could survey to get unbiased results.

b. Write two questions that Ellis could ask.

c. After the survey is completed, how could Ellis use the results of the survey to determine what types of food he should serve in his restaurant?

15. CARNIVALS The student council is planning to have a school carnival. **a–c. See Chapter 13 Answer Appendix.**

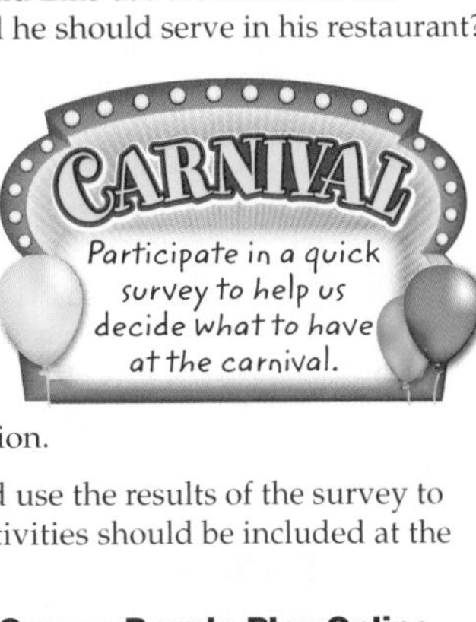

CARNIVAL
Participate in a quick survey to help us decide what to have at the carnival.

a. Describe an unbiased population sample they could survey to determine types of games and activities to have at the carnival.

b. Write three questions the student council could ask their sample population.

c. Describe how the student council could use the results of the survey to determine what types of games and activities should be included at the carnival.

16. GAMES An online gaming site conducted a survey to determine the types of games people play online. The results are shown in the circle graph.

Games People Play Online

Adventure Games 22%
Puzzles 28%
Card Games 30%
Board Games 11%
Arcade Games 9%

a. If 2500 people participated in the study, how many of them would play arcade or board games? **500**

b. An article said 30% of Americans play card games online. Is this statement valid? Explain your reasoning. **b–c. See Chapter 13 Answer Appendix.**

c. Describe how the study could have been conducted so that it represented all Americans and not just online gamers.

H.O.T. Problems Use Higher-Order Thinking Skills

17. OPEN ENDED Give an example of a unbiased survey. Then conduct the survey. Display the your results in a graph.

18. CHALLENGE Suppose you are a farmer and want to know if your corn crop is ready to be harvested. Describe an unbiased way to determine whether the crop is ready to harvest.

19. REASONING If someone were to conduct a survey in person, could the surveyor's tone of voice or how they ask the questions alter the response to the question? Explain. **19–20. See Chapter 13 Answer Appendix.**

20. WRITING IN MATH Why is sampling an important part of the manufacturing process? Illustrate your answer with an unbiased and biased sampling method you can use to check the quality of DVDs.

Enrichment CRM p. 48 OL BL

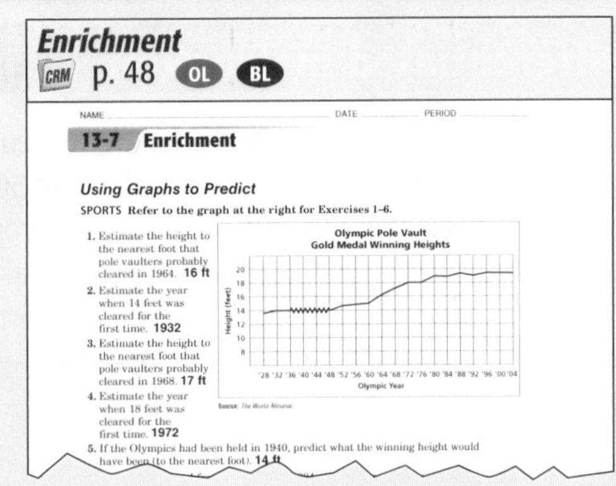

NAME ______ DATE ______ PERIOD ______

13-7 Enrichment

Using Graphs to Predict

SPORTS **Refer to the graph at the right for Exercises 1–6.**

1. Estimate the height to the nearest foot that pole vaulters probably cleared in 1964. **16 ft**
2. Estimate the year when 14 feet was cleared for the first time. **1932**
3. Estimate the height to the nearest foot that pole vaulters probably cleared in 1968. **17 ft**
4. Estimate the year when 18 feet was cleared for the first time. **1972**
5. If the Olympics had been held in 1940, predict what the winning height would have been (to the nearest foot). **14 ft**

Study Guide and Intervention CRM pp. 43–44 AL OL ELL

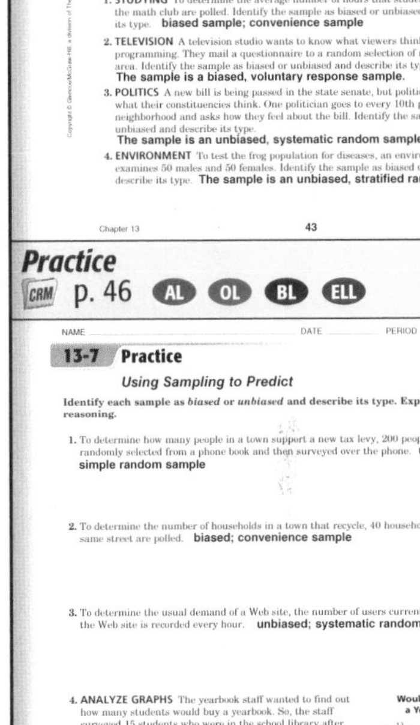

NAME ______ DATE ______ PERIOD ______

13-7 Study Guide and Intervention

Using Sampling to Predict

Identify Sampling Techniques A **sample** is a randomly selected smaller group chosen from the larger group, or **population**. An **unbiased sample** is representative of the larger population, selected without preference, and large enough to provide accurate data. A **biased sample** is not representative of the larger population.

Types of Unbiased Samples	
Type	**Definition**
Simple Random Sample	a sample where each item or person in a population is as likely to be chosen as any other
Stratified Random Sample	a sample in which the population is divided into similar, nonoverlapping groups. A simple random sample is then chosen from each group
Systematic Random Sample	a sample in which the items or people are selected according to a specific time or item interval

Types of Biased Samples	
Type	**Definition**
Convenience Sample	a sample that includes members of the population that are easily accessed
Voluntary Response Sample	a sample which involves only those who want to or can participate in the sampling

Example POLITICS **To determine the popularity of a political candidate, 5 people are randomly polled from 10 different age groups of eligible voters. Identify the sample as biased or unbiased and describe its type.**

Since all eligible voters are equally likely to be polled, it is an unbiased sample. Since eligible voters are randomly polled from similar, non-overlapping groups, the sample is a stratified random sample.

Exercises

1. **STUDYING** To determine the average number of hours that students study, members of the math club are polled. Identify the sample as biased or unbiased and describe its type. **biased sample; convenience sample**
2. **TELEVISION** A television studio wants to know what viewers think about their programming. They mail a questionnaire to a random selection of residents in their area. Identify the sample as biased or unbiased and describe its type. **The sample is a biased, voluntary response sample.**
3. **POLITICS** A new bill is being passed in the state senate, but politicians want to know what their constituencies think. One politician goes to every 10th person's house in a neighborhood and asks how they feel about the bill. Identify the sample as biased or unbiased and describe its type. **The sample is an unbiased, systematic random sample.**
4. **ENVIRONMENT** To test the frog population for diseases, an environmental group examines 50 males and 50 females. Identify the sample as biased or unbiased and describe its type. **The sample is an unbiased, stratified random sample.**

Chapter 13 43 Glencoe Pre-Algebra

Practice CRM p. 46 AL OL BL ELL

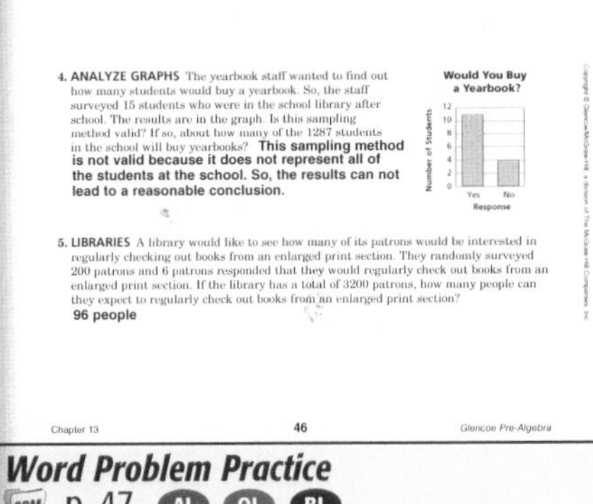

NAME ______ DATE ______ PERIOD ______

13-7 Practice

Using Sampling to Predict

Identify each sample as *biased* or *unbiased* and describe its type. Explain your reasoning.

1. To determine how many people in a town support a new tax levy, 200 people are randomly selected from a phone book and then surveyed over the phone. **unbiased; simple random sample**
2. To determine the number of households in a town that recycle, 40 households from the same street are polled. **biased; convenience sample**
3. To determine the usual demand of a Web site, the number of users currently visiting the Web site is recorded every hour. **unbiased; systematic random sample**
4. **ANALYZE GRAPHS** The yearbook staff wanted to find out how many students would buy a yearbook. So, the staff surveyed 15 students who were in the school library after school. The results are in the graph. Is this sampling method valid? If so, about how many of the 1287 students in the school will buy yearbooks? **This sampling method is not valid because it does not represent all of the students at the school. So, the results can not lead to a reasonable conclusion.**

5. **LIBRARIES** A library would like to see how many of its patrons would be interested in regularly checking out books from an enlarged print section. They randomly surveyed 200 patrons and 6 patrons responded that they would regularly check out books from an enlarged print section. If the library has a total of 3200 patrons, how many people can they expect to regularly check out books from an enlarged print section? **96 people**

Chapter 13 46 Glencoe Pre-Algebra

Word Problem Practice CRM p. 47 AL OL BL

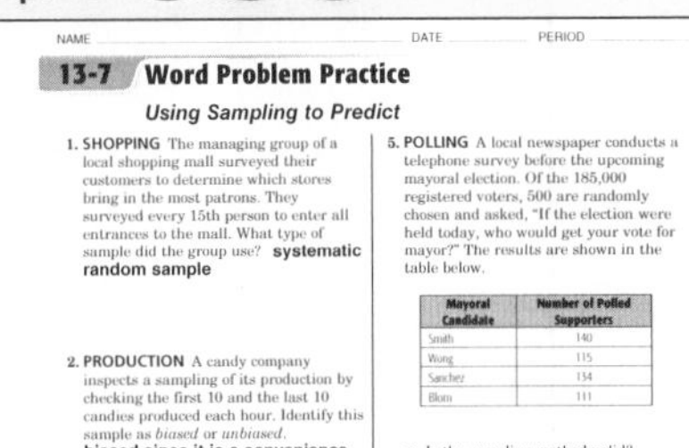

NAME ______ DATE ______ PERIOD ______

13-7 Word Problem Practice

Using Sampling to Predict

1. **SHOPPING** The managing group of a local shopping mall surveyed their customers to determine which stores bring in the most patrons. They surveyed every 15th person to enter all entrances to the mall. What type of sample did the group use? **systematic random sample**
2. **PRODUCTION** A candy company inspects a sampling of its production by checking the first 10 and the last 10 candies produced each hour. Identify this sample as *biased* or *unbiased*. **biased since it is a convenience sample**
3. **SCHOOL LUNCH** A survey of 50 randomly selected students showed that 38 students buy lunch at school and 12 students bring lunch from home each day. About how many of the school's 524 students buy lunch at school each day? **398 students**
4. **CUSTOMER SATISFACTION** Johnson's Hardware randomly selects 125 of its customers and questions them to determine their overall customer satisfaction rating. The poll indicates 100 were completely satisfied, 15 were satisfied, and 10 were not satisfied at all. What percent of customers were either satisfied or completely satisfied? About how many of the 5000 customers were not satisfied at all? **92%; 400**
5. **POLLING** A local newspaper conducts a telephone survey before the upcoming mayoral election. Of the 185,000 registered voters, 500 are randomly chosen and asked, "If the election were held today, who would get your vote for mayor?" The results are shown in the table below.

Mayoral Candidate	Number of Polled Supporters
Smith	140
Wong	115
Sanchez	134
Blom	111

a. Is the sampling method valid? Explain. **Yes, it is a simple random sample of all registered voters.**

b. How many votes can Sanchez expect to receive in the election? **49,580**

c. How many voters are not expected to vote for Smith? **133,200**

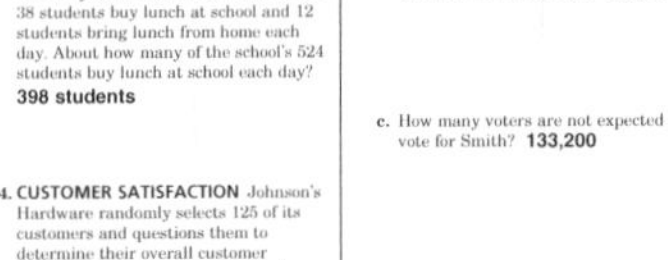

Chapter 13 47 Glencoe Pre-Algebra

4 ASSESS

Name the Math Tell students to name the sampling techniques they learned about today. Ask them to give examples to illustrate. Encourage them to use words like *random*, *biased*, *unbiased*, and so on.

Additional Answer

26.

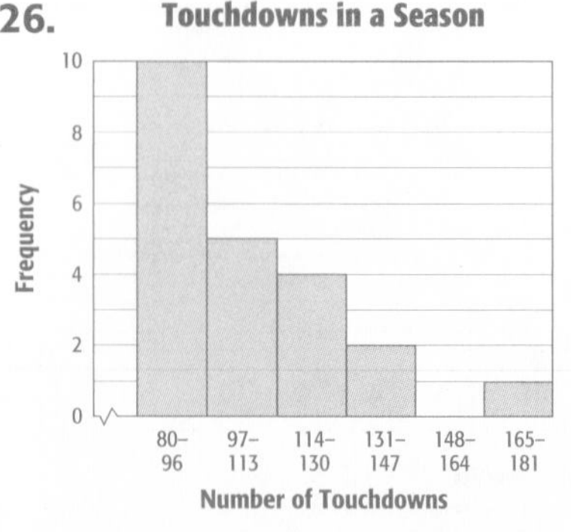

Standardized Test Practice

21. A real estate agent surveys people about their housing preferences at an open house for a luxury townhouse. Which is the best explanation for why the results of this survey might *not* be valid? **B**

A The survey is biased because the agent should have conducted the survey by telephone.

B The survey is biased because the sample consisted of only people who already are interested in townhouses.

C The survey is biased because the sample was a voluntary response sample.

D The survey is biased because the agent should have conducted the survey at a single-family home.

22. GRIDDED RESPONSE One hundred people in a music store were surveyed about what type of music they prefer. If 35% of them said they prefer rock music, how many people out of 1500 can be expected to prefer rock music? **525**

An online survey of about 38,000 children produced the results shown in the circle graph.

How Many Cans of Soda Do You Drink in a Day?

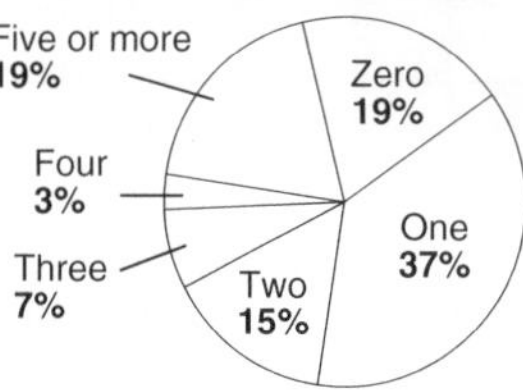

23. About how many of the children surveyed drink two cans of soda or less per day? **J**

F 5700 H 14,060
G 8993 J 26,980

24. Based on the results, about how many children in a class of 30 would drink two or more cans of soda per day? **C**

A 5 C 13
B 8 D 21

Spiral Review

25. What is the probability that a 12-month calendar is randomly turned to the month of January or April? (Lesson 13-6) **$\frac{1}{6}$; 16.7%**

26. FOOTBALL Display the data about touchdowns in a histogram. (Lesson 13-5) **See margin.**

Touchdowns in a Season		
Amount	Tally	Frequency
80–96	𝍸 𝍸	10
97–113	𝍸	5
114–130	||||	4
131–147	||	2
148–164		0
165–181	|	1

27. Find the percent of change from 32 feet to 79 feet. Round to the nearest tenth, if necessary. Then state whether the percent of change is a *percent of increase* or a *percent of decrease*. (Lesson 7-6) **146.9%; increase**

Solve each problem using the percent equation. Round to the nearest tenth. (Lesson 7-5)

28. 7 is what percent of 32? **21.9%**

29. What is 28.5% of 84? **23.9**

30. WEATHER During a 10-hour period, the temperature in Browning, Montana, changed at a rate of -10°F per hour, starting at 44°F. What was the ending temperature? (Lesson 2-4) **-56°F**

Skills Review

Express each fraction as a percent. (Lesson 7-1)

31. $\frac{3}{4}$ **75%**

32. $\frac{1}{5}$ **20%**

33. $\frac{2}{3}$ **$66\frac{2}{3}$%**

34. $\frac{5}{6}$ **$83\frac{1}{3}$%**

Differentiated Instruction

Extension Present students with the following scenario: Monish wanted to collect money for natural disaster victims. His goal was to collect $10 from 50% of the 100 houses he visited. He went door-to-door in his neighborhood. He received an average of $5 from 16% of the 100 houses. How much did Monish collect? $80 What strategies could Paki use to produce a better response? Sample answer: He could stand outside a busy store to increase his contacts.

Counting Outcomes

Why?

An online store sells fish tanks in 4 sizes and 3 shapes. The choices are shown at the right.

Size	Shape
small	hexagon
medium	pentagon
large	rectangle
x-large	

a. Make a list of all of the possible fish tanks. See Chapter 13 Answer Appendix.

b. How many different fish tank choices are possible? 12

Then
You have already found the probability of simple events. (Lesson 13-6)

Now
- Use tree diagrams or the Fundamental Counting Principle to count outcomes.
- Use tree diagrams or the Fundamental Counting Principle to find the probability of an event.

New Vocabulary
tree diagrams
Fundamental Counting Principle

Math Online
glencoe.com
- Extra Examples
- Personal Tutor
- Self-Check Quiz
- Homework Help

Counting Outcomes To solve the problem above, you can look at a simpler problem. Suppose there are only three size choices, small, medium, or large, and only two shape choices, pentagon or rectangle. You can draw a **tree diagram** to represent the possible outcomes.

EXAMPLE 1 Use a Tree Diagram to Count Outcomes

How many different fish tanks can be made from three size choices and two shape choices?

You can draw a diagram to find the number of possible fish tanks. List each size choice. Then pair each shape choice with each size.

Size	Shape	Outcome
small	pentagon	small, pentagon
	rectangle	small, rectangle
medium	pentagon	medium, pentagon
	rectangle	medium, rectangle
large	pentagon	large, pentagon
	rectangle	large, rectangle

There are 6 possible outcomes.

There are 6 possible outcomes.

Check Your Progress

1. Draw a tree diagram to find the number of different outfits that can be assembled using 5 shirts and 4 pairs of pants.
See Chapter 13 Answer Appendix.

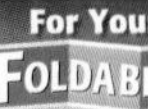
Personal Tutor glencoe.com

The **Fundamental Counting Principle** relates the number of outcomes to the number of choices.

Key Concept Fundamental Counting Principle — For Your FOLDABLE

Words If event *M* can occur in *m* ways and is followed by event *N* that can occur in *n* ways, then the event *M* followed by *N* can occur in $m \cdot n$ ways.

Example If there are 4 possible sizes for fish tanks and 3 possible shapes, then there are $4 \cdot 3$ or 12 possible fish tanks.

13-8 Lesson Notes

1 FOCUS

Vertical Alignment

Before Lesson 13-8
Find the probability of simple events.

Lesson 13-8
Use tree diagrams or the Fundamental Counting Principle to count outcomes.
Use tree diagrams or the Fundamental Counting Principle to find the probability of an event.

After Lesson 13-8
Use theoretical probabilities and experimental results to make predictions and decisions.

2 TEACH

Scaffolding Questions

Have students read the *Why?* section of the lesson and answer the questions.

Ask:
- If a tank is in the shape of a hexagon, what number of different sizes could it have? 4
- Suppose there are 5 choices of tank shapes instead of 3. How many different designs are possible? 20
- How did you determine the number of different designs that are possible? Sample answer: Made a list or multiplied 5 shapes times 4 sizes to give 20 designs.

Lesson 13-8 Resources

Resource	Approaching-Level	On-Level	Beyond-Level	English Learners
Teacher Edition	• Differentiated Instruction, p. 778	• Differentiated Instruction, p. 778	• Differentiated Instruction, p. 781	
Chapter Resource Masters	• Study Guide and Intervention, pp. 49–50 • Skills Practice, p. 51 • Practice, p. 52 • Word Problem Practice, p. 53	• Study Guide and Intervention, pp. 49–50 • Skills Practice, p. 51 • Practice, p. 52 • Word Problem Practice, p. 53 • Enrichment, p. 54	• Practice, p. 52 • Word Problem Practice, p. 53 • Enrichment, p. 54	• Study Guide and Intervention, pp. 49–50 • Skills Practice, p. 51 • Practice, p. 52
Transparencies	• 5-Minute Check Transparency 13-8	• 5-Minute Check Transparency 13-8	• 5-Minute Check Transparency 13-8	• 5-Minute Check Transparency 13-8
Other	• Study Notebook • Teaching Pre-Algebra with Manipulatives	• Study Notebook • Teaching Pre-Algebra with Manipulatives	• Study Notebook	• Study Notebook • Teaching Pre-Algebra with Manipulatives

Counting Outcomes

Example 1 shows how to use a tree diagram to count outcomes. **Example 2** shows how to use the Fundamental Counting Principle to calculate the number of outcomes when there are two or more events.

Formative Assessment

Use the Check Your Progress exercises after each example to determine students' understanding of concepts.

Additional Examples

1 A greeting card maker offers three birthday greetings in four possible colors, as shown below. Draw a tree diagram to find the number of cards that can be made from three greeting choices and four color choices. 12

Greeting	Color
Humorous	Blue
Traditional	Green
Romantic	Orange
	Red

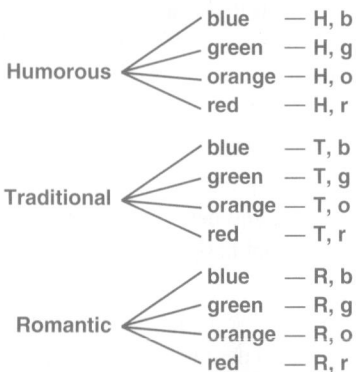

Humorous — blue — H, b; green — H, g; orange — H, o; red — H, r
Traditional — blue — T, b; green — T, g; orange — T, o; red — T, r
Romantic — blue — R, b; green — R, g; orange — R, o; red — R, r

2 **CELL PHONES** A cell phone company offers 3 payment plans, 4 styles of phones, and 6 decorative phone wraps. How many phone options are available? 72

Additional Examples also in Interactive Classroom PowerPoint® Presentations

IWB INTERACTIVE WHITEBOARD READY

You can also use the Fundamental Counting Principle when there are more than two events.

EXAMPLE 2 Use the Fundamental Counting Principle

FOOD **A pizza shop has regular, deep-dish, and thin pizza crusts, 2 different cheeses, and 5 toppings. How many different one-cheese and one-topping pizzas can be ordered?**

The number of crust types	times	the number of cheeses	times	the number of toppings	equals	the number of possible outcomes.
3	×	2	×	5	=	30

So, 30 different pizzas can be ordered.

StudyTip

Multiplying More than Two Factors Remember, when you multiply, you can change the order of the factors. For example, in 3 × 2 × 5 you can multiply 2 × 5 first, then multiply the product, 10, by 3 to get 30.

Check Your Progress

2. **ROUTES** When Shelly goes into her school, she can walk through 4 different doors. Once inside, she can go to her locker by using 4 different sets of stairs and then 3 different hallways. How many ways can Shelly get from outside the school to her locker? **48**

Personal Tutor glencoe.com

Find the Probability of an Event When you know the number of outcomes, you can find the probability that an event will occur.

Real-World EXAMPLE 3 Find Probabilities

GAMES **Emilio has 2 counters. Each counter has one side marked with an E and the other side marked with a J, for Jacob. Both counters are tossed. If one counter lands with E up and the other lands with J up, Emilio wins. Otherwise, Jacob wins. What is the probability that Emilio will win?**

First find the number of outcomes.

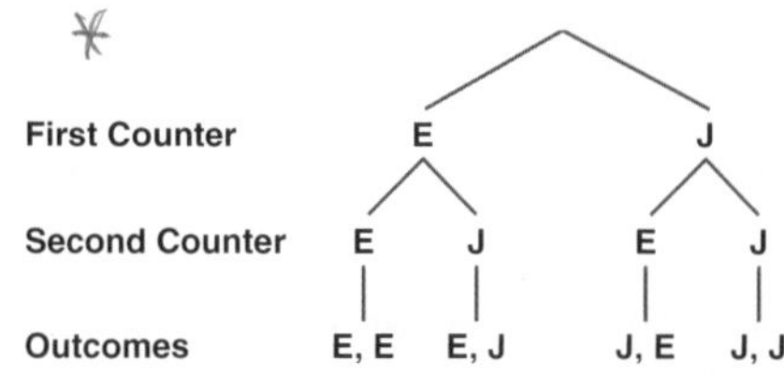

There are four equally likely outcomes with two favoring Emilio. So, the probability of Emilio winning is $\frac{1}{2}$ or 50%.

Real-World Link

Passwords Approximately 80% of passwords are alphanumeric, which means they are a combination of letters and words.

Check Your Progress

3. **PASSWORDS** What is the probability of randomly choosing a 5-letter password for an Internet Web site that consists of only vowels if each vowel can be used more than once? $\frac{1}{3125}$

Personal Tutor glencoe.com

Differentiated Instruction AL OL

If students need additional practice counting outcomes,

Then have students work in groups of four or five to act out the number of different ways the students in the group can be seated. Each student should have a chair. The students should keep a chart showing each of the arrangements of students and chairs. When each student in the group has sat in each of the chairs, the students should discuss their chart. They should then use the Fundamental Counting Principle to determine whether they recorded each possible arrangement only once.

EXAMPLE 4 Find Probabilities

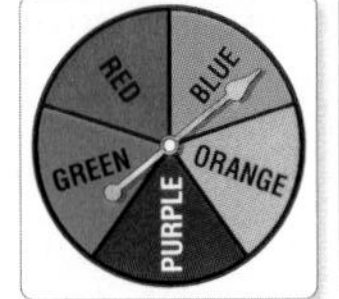

Lamar is going to spin each spinner once. What is the probability that he will spin red and the number 9?

Step 1 Find the number of possible outcomes.

Number of choices for first spinner	times	number of choices for second spinner	equals	the total number of outcomes.
5	×	10	=	50

There are 50 outcomes.

Step 2 Find the probability. There is one way to spin red and the number 9. So, the probability is $\frac{1}{50}$ or 2%.

Check Your Progress

4. Three dice are rolled. What is the probability of rolling three 5s? $\frac{1}{216}$

Personal Tutor glencoe.com

Check Your Understanding

Example 1 p. 777

1. Draw a tree diagram to find the number of tennis shoes available if they come in gray or white and are available in sizes 6, 7, or 8. See Chapter 13 Answer Appendix.

Example 2 p. 778

Use the Fundamental Counting Principle to find the total number of outcomes in each situation.

2. **CARS** The table shows the options a dealership offers for a model of a car. 24

Doors	Gears	Color
2-door	automatic	black
4-door	5-speed	tan
	4-speed	white
		red

3. **SCHOOL** Elisa can take 6 different classes first period, 4 different classes second period, 2 different classes third period, and 3 fourth period. 144

Examples 3 and 4 pp. 778–779

4. **ACCESSORIES** Amber has a denim and a black purse. Ebony has a black, a red, a denim, and a brown purse. Each girl picks a purse at random to bring to the mall. What is the probability the girls will bring the same color purse? $\frac{1}{4}$

5. A spinner with 8 equal sections labeled 1–8 is spun twice. What is the probability that it will land on 6 after the first spin and on 6 after the second spin? $\frac{1}{64}$

Practice and Problem Solving

● = **Step-by-Step Solutions** begin on page R11. **Extra Practice** begins on page 810.

Example 1 p. 777

6–8. See Chapter 13 Answer Appendix.

For each situation, draw a tree diagram to find the number of outcomes.

6. A pet store has male and female huskies with blue, green, and amber eyes.

7. There are 3 true-false questions on a quiz.

8. A coin is tossed and a die is rolled.

Find the Probability of an Event

Examples 3 and 4 show how to find the probability of an event.

Additional Examples

3 **TOYS** A toy robot moves straight ahead until it hits an obstacle. Then it turns, with equal chances of turning left or right. If the robot makes three turns, what is the probability that all three will be left turns? $\frac{1}{8}$

4 Henry rolls a number cube and tosses a coin. What is the probability that he will roll a 3 and toss heads? $\frac{1}{12}$

Focus on Mathematical Content

Counting Outcomes Tree diagrams and the Fundamental Counting Principle are two methods used for counting outcomes. Use tree diagrams when it is necessary to know the specific possible outcomes or when the number of choices is small. Use the Fundamental Counting Principle when there are many choices, the numbers are large, the number of possible outcomes are needed quickly, or a list of specific possible outcomes is not necessary.

3 PRACTICE

Formative Assessment

Use Exercises 1–5 to check for understanding.

Use the chart at the left to customize assignments for your students.

Differentiated Homework Options

Level	Assignment	Two-Day Option	
AL Basic	6–13, 16–18, 20–32	7–13 odd, 21–24	6–12 even, 16–18, 20, 25–32
OL Core	7–13 odd, 14–18, 20–32	6–13, 21–24	14–18, 20, 25–32
BL Advanced	14–28, (optional: 29–32)		

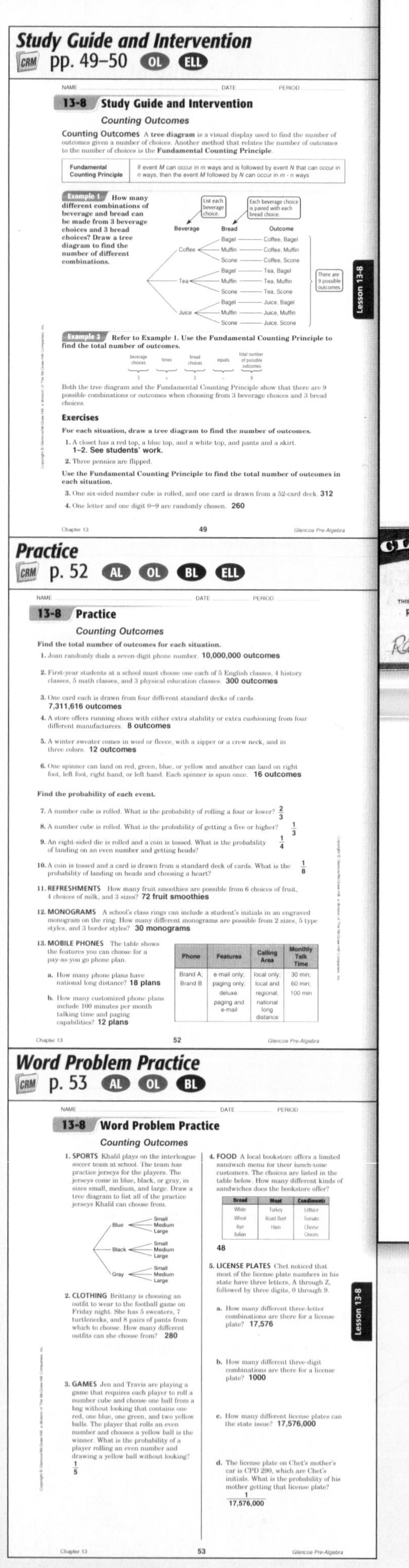
Study Guide and Intervention
CRM pp. 49–50 OL ELL

NAME ______ DATE ______ PERIOD ______

13-8 Study Guide and Intervention

Counting Outcomes

Counting Outcomes A **tree diagram** is a visual display used to find the number of outcomes given a number of choices. Another method that relates the number of outcomes to the number of choices is the **Fundamental Counting Principle**.

Fundamental Counting Principle	If event M can occur in m ways and is followed by event N that can occur in n ways, then the event M followed by N can occur in m · n ways.

Example 1 How many different combinations of beverage and bread can be made from 3 beverage choices and 3 bread choices? Draw a tree diagram to find the number of different combinations.

Example 2 Refer to Example 1. Use the Fundamental Counting Principle to find the total number of outcomes.

beverage choices × bread choices = total number of possible outcomes
3 · 3 = 9

Both the tree diagram and the Fundamental Counting Principle show that there are 9 possible combinations or outcomes when choosing from 3 beverage choices and 3 bread choices.

Exercises

For each situation, draw a tree diagram to find the number of outcomes.

1. A closet has a red top, a blue top, and a white top, and pants and a skirt. **1–2. See students' work.**
2. Three pennies are flipped.

Use the Fundamental Counting Principle to find the total number of outcomes in each situation.

3. One six-sided number cube is rolled, and one card is drawn from a 52-card deck. **312**
4. One letter and one digit 0–9 are randomly chosen. **260**

Chapter 13 49 Glencoe Pre-Algebra

Practice
CRM p. 52 AL OL BL ELL

NAME ______ DATE ______ PERIOD ______

13-8 Practice

Counting Outcomes

Find the total number of outcomes for each situation.

1. Joan randomly dials a seven-digit phone number. **10,000,000 outcomes**
2. First-year students at a school must choose one each of 5 English classes, 4 history classes, 5 math classes, and 3 physical education classes. **300 outcomes**
3. One card each is drawn from four different standard decks of cards. **7,311,616 outcomes**
4. A store offers running shoes with either extra stability or extra cushioning from four different manufacturers. **8 outcomes**
5. A winter sweater comes in wool or fleece, with a zipper or a crew neck, and in three colors. **12 outcomes**
6. One spinner can land on red, green, blue, or yellow and another can land on right foot, left foot, right hand, or left hand. Each spinner is spun once. **16 outcomes**

Find the probability of each event.

7. A number cube is rolled. What is the probability of rolling a four or lower? $\frac{2}{3}$
8. A number cube is rolled. What is the probability of getting a five or higher? $\frac{1}{3}$
9. An eight-sided die is rolled and a coin is tossed. What is the probability of landing on an even number and getting heads? $\frac{1}{4}$
10. A coin is tossed and a card is drawn from a standard deck of cards. What is the probability of landing on heads and choosing a heart? $\frac{1}{8}$
11. **REFRESHMENTS** How many fruit smoothies are possible from 6 choices of fruit, 4 choices of milk, and 3 sizes? **72 fruit smoothies**
12. **MONOGRAMS** A school's class rings can include a student's initials in an engraved monogram on the ring. How many different monograms are possible from 2 sizes, 5 type styles, and 3 border styles? **30 monograms**
13. **MOBILE PHONES** The table shows the features you can choose for a pay-as-you go phone plan.
    a. How many phone plans have national long distance? **18 plans**
    b. How many customized phone plans include 100 minutes per month talking time and paging capabilities? **12 plans**

Phone	Features	Calling Area	Monthly Talk Time
Brand A; Brand B	e-mail only; paging only; deluxe paging and e-mail	local only; local and regional; national long distance	30 min; 60 min; 100 min

Chapter 13 52 Glencoe Pre-Algebra

Word Problem Practice
CRM p. 53 AL OL BL

NAME ______ DATE ______ PERIOD ______

13-8 Word Problem Practice

Counting Outcomes

1. **SPORTS** Khalil plays on the interleague soccer team at school. The team has practice jerseys for the players. The jerseys come in blue, black, or gray, in sizes small, medium, and large. Draw a tree diagram to list all of the practice jerseys Khalil can choose from.

2. **CLOTHING** Brittany is choosing an outfit to wear to the football game on Friday night. She has 5 sweaters, 7 turtlenecks, and 8 pairs of pants from which to choose. How many different outfits can she choose from? **280**
3. **GAMES** Jen and Travis are playing a game that requires each player to roll a number cube and choose one ball from a bag without looking that contains one red, one blue, one green, and two yellow balls. The player that rolls an even number and chooses a yellow ball is the winner. What is the probability of a player rolling an even number and drawing a yellow ball without looking? $\frac{1}{5}$
4. **FOOD** A local bookstore offers a limited sandwich menu for their lunch-time customers. The choices are listed in the table below. How many different kinds of sandwiches does the bookstore offer?

Bread	Meat	Condiments
White	Turkey	Lettuce
Wheat	Roast Beef	Tomato
Rye	Ham	Cheese
Italian		Onions

48

5. **LICENSE PLATES** Chet noticed that most of the license plate numbers in his state have three letters, A through Z, followed by three digits, 0 through 9.
   a. How many different three-letter combinations are there for a license plate? **17,576**
   b. How many different three-digit combinations are there for a license plate? **1000**
   c. How many different license plates can the state issue? **17,576,000**
   d. The license plate on Chet's mother's car is CPD 290, which are Chet's initials. What is the probability of his mother getting that license plate? $\frac{1}{17{,}576{,}000}$

Chapter 13 53 Glencoe Pre-Algebra

Example 2 p. 778

Use the Fundamental Counting Principle to find the total number of outcomes in each situation.

9. A month of the year is picked at random and a coin is tossed. **24**
10. There are three choices for each of 5 multiple-choice questions on a science test. **243**
11. A 3-digit password is created. Digits can repeat. **1000**

Examples 3 and 4 pp. 778–779

12. **SANDWICHES** The table shows the sandwich choices for lunch at a cafe. If a one-bread, one-meat, one-cheese sandwich is chosen at random, what is the probability that it will be turkey and Swiss on wheat bread? $\frac{1}{36}$

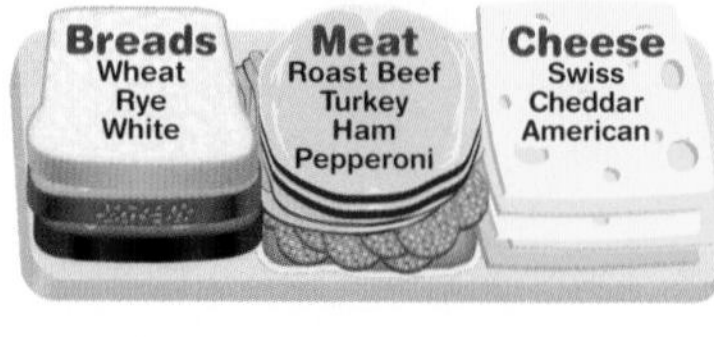

B

13. **GAMES** A game requires you to toss a 10-sided die and a 6-sided die to determine how to move on a game board. Find the following probabilities.
    a. P(same number on both dice) $\frac{1}{10}$
    b. P(odd, even) or P(even, odd) $\frac{1}{2}$
14. **GOVERNMENT** Use the information at the left about Social Security numbers. What is the probability that the last two numbers are your age? $\frac{1}{100}$
15. Each of the spinners at the right is spun once. Use a tree diagram to find the following probabilities.
    a. P(at least one 2) $\frac{7}{16}$
    b. P (at least one 3) $\frac{1}{4}$

C

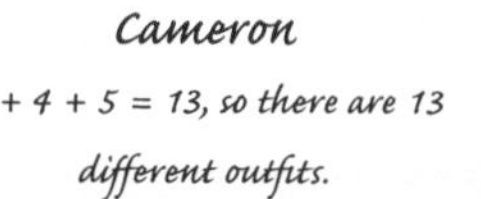

Real-World Link

The first three digits of a social security number are a geographic code. The next two digits are determined by the year and the state where the number is issued. The final four digits are random numbers.

H.O.T. Problems
Use Higher-Order Thinking Skills

16. **OPEN ENDED** Give an example of a real-world situation that has 16 outcomes. **See Chapter 13 Answer Appendix.**
17. **FIND THE ERROR** Cameron and Lisa are finding the number of different outfits they can make with 3 pairs of shoes, 4 pairs of pants, and 5 shirts. Is either of them correct? Explain your reasoning. **See margin.**

Cameron	Lisa
4 + 4 + 5 = 13, so there are 13 different outfits.	3 · 3 · 4 = 36, so there are 36 different outfits.

18. **NUMBER SENSE** Marcus has a choice of a white, grey, or black shirt to wear with a choice of tan, black, brown, or denim pants. Without calculating the number of possible outcomes, how many more outfits can he make if he buys a green shirt? Explain.

18. **4 more outfits; Sample answer. He will have four different pairs of pants that he can wear with that green shirt.**

19. **CHALLENGE** Write an algebraic expression for the number of possible outcomes if the spinner at the right is spun x number of times. 5^x

20. **WRITING IN MATH** Explain how a tree diagram might be more useful than the Fundamental Counting Principle when finding probability. **See margin.**

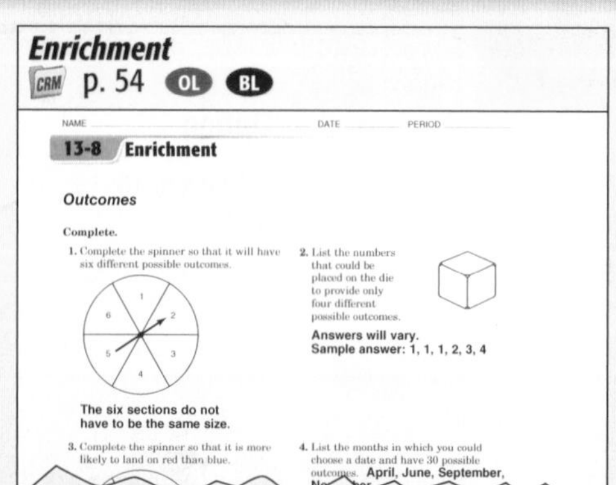
Enrichment
CRM p. 54 OL BL

NAME ______ DATE ______ PERIOD ______

13-8 Enrichment

Outcomes

Complete.

1. Complete the spinner so that it will have six different possible outcomes.
   The six sections do not have to be the same size.
2. List the numbers that could be placed on the die to provide only four different possible outcomes. **Answers will vary. Sample answer: 1, 1, 1, 2, 3, 4**
3. Complete the spinner so that it is more likely to land on red than blue.
4. List the months in which you could choose a date and have 30 possible outcomes. **April, June, September, November**

Watch Out!

Find the Error For Exercise 17, point out that the Fundamental Counting Principle involves multiplying the numbers of ways each event can occur.

Standardized Test Practice

21. The spinner is spun twice. What is the probability that it will land on 2 after the first spin and on 5 after the second spin? A

A $\frac{1}{64}$ C $\frac{1}{8}$

B $\frac{1}{16}$ D $\frac{5}{8}$

22. A bicycle lock has 4 rotating discs and each contains the digits 0–9. How many different lock combinations are possible? J

F 3024 H 6561

G 5040 J 10,000

23. A restaurant offers a combo special with 3 different sandwiches, 2 different salads, and 5 different drinks. From how many different combos could Keisha choose? C

A 10 C 30

B 11 D 50

24. **SHORT RESPONSE** Pilan can make outfits out of the clothes shown in the table. Draw a tree diagram to show all of the possible outcomes. See Chapter 13 Answer Appendix.

Shoes	Shirts	Pants
white	blue	tan
black	red	navy
	green	denim
	black	

Spiral Review

25. **MUSIC** Sixty-three of the 105 students in the band said that their favorite class was music. Is this sampling representative of the entire school? If so, how many of the 848 students who attend the school would say music is their favorite class? (Lesson 13-7) See margin.

26. **FOOD** Maresha took a random sample from a package of jellybeans without looking and found that 30% of the beans were red. Suppose there are 250 jellybeans in the package. How many can she expect to be red? (Lesson 13-6) 75 jellybeans

27. **NUTRITION** **Use the food data shown in the back-to-back stem-and-leaf plot.** (Lessons 13-2 and 13-3) b–c. See margin.

a. What is the greatest number of fat grams in each sandwich? 20; 36

b. In general, which type of sandwich has a lower amount of fat? Explain.

c. Find the measures of variation and any outliers for the data.

Fat (g) of Various Burgers and Chicken Sandwiches

Chicken		Burgers
8	0	
9 8 5 5 3 3	1	0 5 9
0	2	0 6
	3	0 3 6

$8|0 = 8$ g $\quad 2|6 = 26$ g

28. **POPULATION** Population density is a unit rate that gives the number of people per square mile. If the area of North Carolina is 48,711 square miles and its population is 8,856,505 people, what is the population density of North Carolina? Round to the nearest tenth. (Lesson 6-2) 181.8 people per square mile

Skills Review

Simplify. (Previous Course)

29. $\frac{4 \cdot 3}{2 \cdot 1}$ 6

30. $\frac{6 \cdot 5 \cdot 4}{3 \cdot 2 \cdot 1}$ 20

31. $\frac{9 \cdot 8}{3 \cdot 2}$ 12

32. $\frac{7 \cdot 6 \cdot 5 \cdot 4}{4 \cdot 3 \cdot 2}$ 35

Differentiated Instruction

BL

Extension In Japan, people greet one another by bowing. A group of five Japanese students gather to study. Each student bows to every other student exactly once. How many bows will take place? 10 bows

4 ASSESS

Crystal Ball Have students explain how they think today's lesson on counting outcomes will help them with tomorrow's lesson on permutations and combinations.

Formative Assessment

Check for student understanding of the concepts in Lessons 13-6 through 13-8.

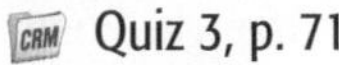

CRM Quiz 3, p. 71

Additional Answers

17. Neither girl is correct. Cameron added the possibilities and she should have multiplied them. Lisa multiplied the wrong possibilities.

20. Sample answer: The Fundamental Counting Principle gives only the total number of outcomes. While, a tree diagram lists all the possible outcomes. So, you can easily see the possible outcomes when determining probability.

25. No; this is a biased sample. The students who participate in band are more likely to enjoy music, so more of them may say music is their favorite class, than compared to the entire school population.

27b. Chicken; whereas chicken sandwiches have 8–20 grams of fat, burgers have 10–36 grams of fat

27c. Chicken: R: 12; UQ: 18.5; LQ: 13; M: 15; IR: 5.5; outliers: none; Burgers: R: 26; UQ: 31.5; LQ: 17; M: 23; IR: 14.5; outliers: none

EXTEND 13-8 Lesson Notes

1 FOCUS

Objective Find the probability of events.

Teaching Tip

If necessary, remind students about how to construct Pascal's triangle. Point out that you begin by writing only the number 1. Then, to construct each entry in the row below it, you add the two entries above it (the one above it and to the right and the one above it and to the left). If either of the numbers is not there, substitute a zero in its place.

2 TEACH

Working in Cooperative Groups

Arrange students in groups of two, mixing abilities. Have pairs complete Step 1 of the Activity and then switch their tree diagrams with another student pair that can quickly proof their diagrams before proceeding with Steps 2 and 3 of the Activity.

Ask:

- How does the number of possible outcomes increase as the number of questions asked increases? Each time a new question is added, the number of outcomes doubles.

Practice Have students complete Exercises 1–7.

3 ASSESS

Formative Assessment

Use Exercises 1–7 to assess whether students comprehend how to find the probability of an event.

EXTEND 13-8

Algebra Lab: Probability and Pascal's Triangle

Math Online > glencoe.com
Math *in Motion*, Animation

Objective
Find probability of events.

ACTIVITY

Step 1 Copy and complete the tree diagram shown below listing all possible outcomes if you have two true and false questions on a test.

1st Question	True		False	
2nd Question	True	False	True	?
Outcomes	T, T	?	?	?

Step 2 Make another tree diagram showing the possible outcomes if there are three true and false questions on a test. **Steps 2–3. See margin.**

Step 3 Make another tree diagram showing the possible outcomes if there are four true and false questions on a test.

Analyze the Results

1. For two questions, how many outcomes are there? How many have one true and one false? **4; 2**
2. Find P(two true), P(one true, one false), and P(two false). Do not simplify. **See margin.**
3. For three questions, how many outcomes are there? How many have two true and one false? one true and two false? **8; 3; 3**
4. Find P(three true), P(two true, one false), P(one true, two false), and P(three false). Do not simplify. $\frac{1}{8}, \frac{3}{8}, \frac{3}{8}, \frac{1}{8}$
5. For four questions, how many outcomes are there? How many have three true and one false? two true and two false? one true and three false? **16; 4; 6; 4**
6. Find P(four true), P(three true, one false), P(two true, two false), P(one true, three false), and P(four false). Do not simplify. **See margin.**

Pascal was a French mathematician who lived in the 1600s. He is known for the triangle of numbers at the right, called Pascal's Triangle.

7. Examine the rows of Pascal's Triangle. Explain how the numbers in each row are related to true and false questions. (*Hint*: Row 2 relates to answering two questions.) **See margin.**

1	Row 0
1 1	Row 1
1 2 1	Row 2
1 3 3 1	Row 3
1 4 6 4 1	Row 4

From Concrete to Abstract

Ask students to extend Pascal's triangle to 8 questions. Then have them transcribe each row into probabilities in fractional form for 6, 7, and 8 questions asked.

Additional Answers

2. $\frac{1}{4}, \frac{2}{4}, \frac{1}{4}$
6. $\frac{1}{16}, \frac{4}{16}, \frac{6}{16}, \frac{4}{16}, \frac{1}{16}$
7. The sum of the numbers in each row is the number of outcomes for a test with the number of questions equal to the row number. The numbers in each row are the numerators for the probabilities for outcomes for the number of questions connected with that row.

13-9 Permutations and Combinations

Why?

The list shows the classes you plan to take next year. You wonder how many different ways there are to arrange your schedule for the first three periods of the day.

a. Make a tree diagram that lists all of the possibilities for the three periods. Do not repeat any classes in each arrangement. **a–b. See Chapter 13 Answer Appendix.**

b. How many different choices did you have for the first period? the second period? the third period?

Scheduling Options
- Algebra
- Biology
- Language Arts
- Spanish
- World History

Then

You have already used tree diagrams or the Fundamental Counting Principle to find the probability of an event. (Lesson 13-8)

Now

- Use permutations.
- Use combinations.

New Vocabulary

permutations
combinations

Math Online

glencoe.com

- Extra Examples
- Personal Tutor
- Self-Check Quiz
- Homework Help

Use Permutations An arrangement or listing in which order is important is called a **permutation**. Algebra, Language Arts, and Biology is a permutation of Language Arts, Biology, and Algebra because the order is different.

You can use the Fundamental Counting Principle to find the number of possible permutations.

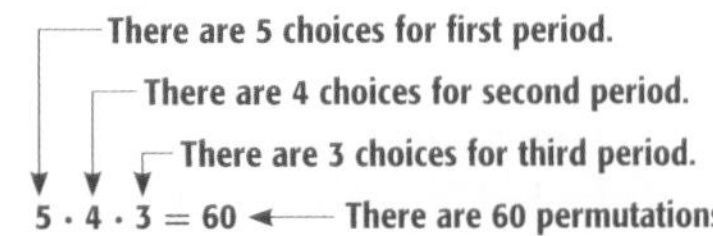

There are 5 choices for first period.
There are 4 choices for second period.
There are 3 choices for third period.
5 · 4 · 3 = 60
There are 60 permutations.

The notation $P(5, 3)$ represents the number of permutations of 5 things taken 3 at a time, as in 5 classes for 3 periods.

EXAMPLE 1 Use a Permutation

SOFTBALL How many ways can the first 3 batters of a batting order be arranged from a team of 12 players?

In a softball game, batting order is important. This arrangement is a permutation.

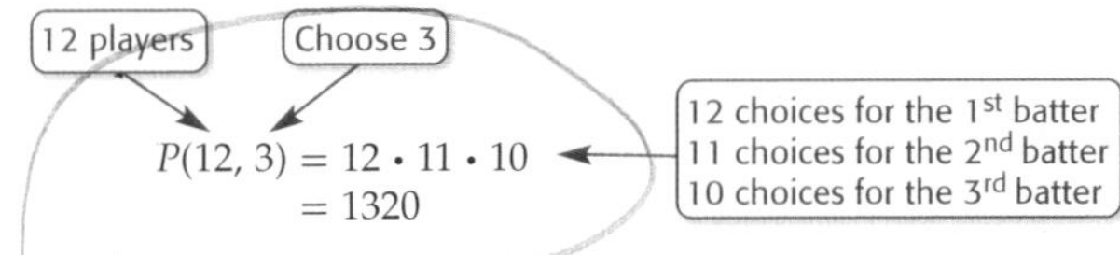

12 players
Choose 3
P(12, 3) = 12 • 11 • 10
= 1320
12 choices for the 1st batter
11 choices for the 2nd batter
10 choices for the 3rd batter

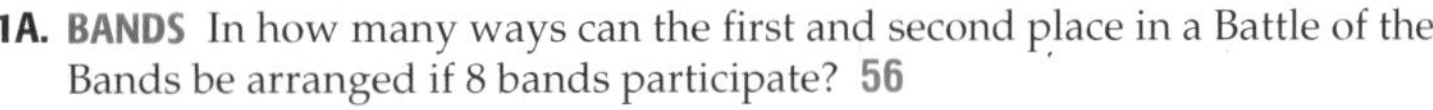

So, there are 1320 ways to arrange the first 3 batters.

Check Your Progress

1A. BANDS In how many ways can the first and second place in a Battle of the Bands be arranged if 8 bands participate? **56**

1B. FOOD Four of ten different fruits are being selected to be placed in a row in a display window. In how many ways can they be placed? **5040**

Personal Tutor glencoe.com

13-9 Lesson Notes

1 FOCUS

Vertical Alignment

Before Lesson 13-9
Use tree diagrams or the Fundamental Counting Principle to find the probability of an event.

Lesson 13-9
Use permutations.
Use combinations.

After Lesson 13-9
Use theoretical probabilities and experimental results to make predictions and decisions.

2 TEACH

Scaffolding Questions

Have students read the *Why?* section of the lesson and answer the questions.

Ask:

- Why are there 4 choices for second period when there are 5 choices for first period? Since there are 5 classes, there are 5 possibilities for the first period. When one class is assigned, there are 4 possibilities for the second.
- How many choices will there be for all three periods? 60
- Suppose you want to know how many different ways you can arrange your schedule for 4 periods. How many choices will there be for the fourth period? 2

Lesson 13-9 Resources

Resource	Approaching-Level	On-Level	Beyond-Level	English Learners
Teacher Edition	• Differentiated Instruction, p. 784	• Differentiated Instruction, p. 784	• Differentiated Instruction, p. 788	
Chapter Resource Masters	• Study Guide and Intervention, pp. 55–56 • Skills Practice, p. 57 • Practice, p. 58 • Word Problem Practice, p. 59	• Study Guide and Intervention, pp. 55–56 • Skills Practice, p. 57 • Practice, p. 58 • Word Problem Practice, p. 59 • Enrichment, p. 60	• Practice, p. 58 • Word Problem Practice, p. 59 • Enrichment, p. 60	• Study Guide and Intervention, pp. 55–56 • Skills Practice, p. 57 • Practice, p. 58
Transparencies	• 5-Minute Check Transparency 13-9	• 5-Minute Check Transparency 13-9	• 5-Minute Check Transparency 13-9	• 5-Minute Check Transparency 13-9
Other	• Study Notebook • Teaching Pre-Algebra with Manipulatives	• Study Notebook • Teaching Pre-Algebra with Manipulatives	• Study Notebook	• Study Notebook • Teaching Pre-Algebra with Manipulatives

Use Permutations

Examples 1 and 2 show how to use permutations in real-world examples.

Formative Assessment

Use the Check Your Progress exercises after each example to determine students' understanding of concepts.

Additional Examples

1 **TRAVEL** The Reyes family will visit a complex of theme parks during their summer vacation. They have a four-day pass good at one park per day. They can choose from seven parks. How many different ways can they arrange their vacation schedule? 840

2 How many six-digit numbers can be made from the digits 2, 3, 4, 5, 8, and 9 if each digit is used only once? 720

Additional Examples also in Interactive Classroom PowerPoint® Presentations

IWB INTERACTIVE WHITEBOARD READY

Use Combinations

Example 3 shows how to use a combination to count the number of arrangements. **Example 4** shows how to use a combination to solve a real-world problem.

Additional Example

3 **HATS** How many ways can a window dresser choose two hats out of a fedora, a bowler, and a sombrero? 3

ReadingMath

Permutation
Root Word: Permute
Permute means to change the order or arrangement of, especially to arrange the order in all possible ways.

EXAMPLE 2 Use a Permutation

How many zip codes can be made from the digits 2, 4, 5, 8, and 6 if each digit is used only once?

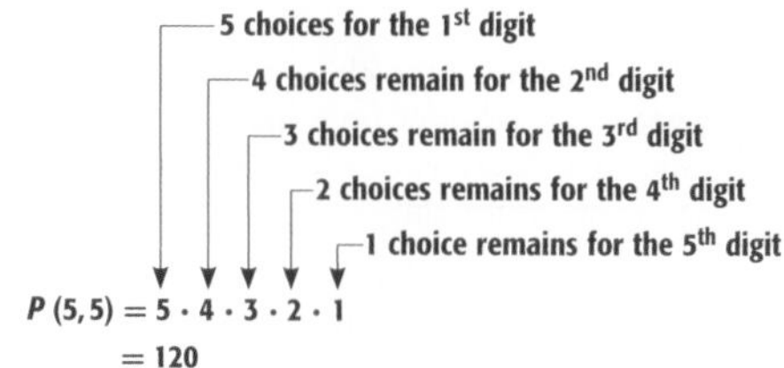
5 choices for the 1st digit
4 choices remain for the 2nd digit
3 choices remain for the 3rd digit
2 choices remains for the 4th digit
1 choice remains for the 5th digit

$$P(5, 5) = 5 \cdot 4 \cdot 3 \cdot 2 \cdot 1$$
$$= 120$$

Check Your Progress

2. How many 7-digit identification numbers can be made from the digits 1, 2, 3, 5, 6, 8, and 9 if each digit is used only once? **5040**

Personal Tutor glencoe.com

Use Combinations Sometimes order is not important. For example *chocolate, vanilla,* and *strawberry* is the same as *strawberry, chocolate,* and *vanilla* when you order ice cream. A **combination** is an arrangement or listing where order is *not* important.

Real-World EXAMPLE 3 Use a Combination

SHERBET **How many ways can students choose two flavors of sherbet from orange, lemon, strawberry, and raspberry?**

In choosing two flavors, order is not important. This arrangement is a combination.

Use the first letter of each flavor to list all of the permutations of the flavors taken two at a time. Then cross off arrangements that are the same as another one.

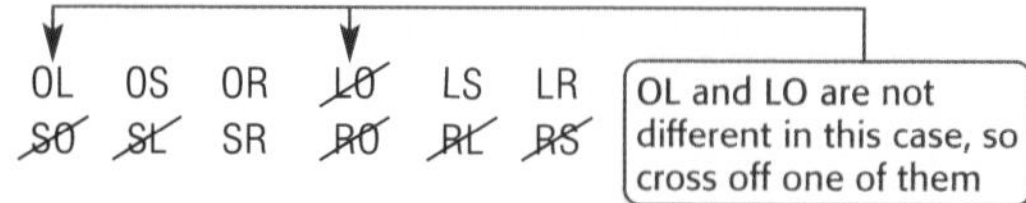
OL OS OR ~~LO~~ LS LR
~~SO~~ ~~SL~~ SR ~~RO~~ ~~RL~~ ~~RS~~
OL and LO are not different in this case, so cross off one of them

There are only six *different* arrangements. So, there are six ways to choose two flavors from a list of four flavors.

Real-World Link

Pizza Pepperoni is America's favorite pizza topping. 36% of all pizza orders contain pepperoni.

Check Your Progress

3A. **STUDENT COUNCIL** In how many ways can you choose two student council representatives from the students shown? **15**

Student Council Candidates		
Jimmy	Evita	Debra
Molly	Julián	Candace

3B. **PIZZA** How many ways can a customer choose 3 pizza toppings from pepperoni, onion, sausage, green pepper, and mushroom? **10**

Personal Tutor glencoe.com

Differentiated Instruction

AL OL

If students struggle to find the number of combinations of a given situation,

Then tell students that Pascal's triangle can be used to answer questions involving combinations. Show students this table and ask them to find the number of combinations of 6 things taken 4 at a time. 15

Number Taken at a Time	0	1	2	3	4	5	6
Row 6	1	6	15	20	15	6	1

You can find the number of combinations of items by dividing the number of permutations of the set of items by the number of ways each smaller set can be arranged.

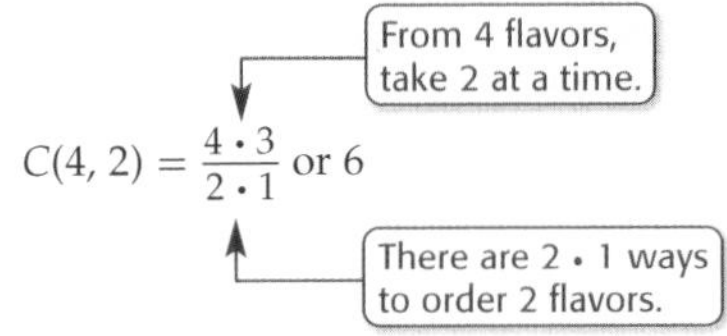

From 4 flavors, take 2 at a time.

$C(4, 2) = \frac{4 \cdot 3}{2 \cdot 1}$ or 6

There are $2 \cdot 1$ ways to order 2 flavors.

Real-World EXAMPLE 4 Find Probability

CHESS The students listed are playing in a chess tournament. If in the first round each player plays every other player once, what is the probability that the first match played involves Abigail?

Lorenzo	Yasu
Abigail	Rashid
Irene	Destiny
Booker	William
Mato	Mercedes

Understand Abigail playing Yasu is the same as Yasu playing Abigail, so this is a combination.

Plan Find the combination of 10 people taken 2 at a time. This will give you the number of matches that take place during the tournament. Then find how many of the matches involve Abigail.

Solve $C(10, 2) = \frac{10 \cdot 9}{2 \cdot 1}$ or 45 **There are 45 ways to choose 2 people to play.**

Abigail plays each person once during the tournament. If there are 9 other people, Abigail is involved in 9 games. So the probability that Abigail plays in the first match is $\frac{9}{45}$ or $\frac{1}{5}$.

Check List all of the 2-player matches in the tournament. Check to see if there are 45 matches.

Check Your Progress

4. **CHESS** Suppose Booker drops out of the chess tournament. What is the probability that the final first-round game involves Abigail and Mato? $\frac{1}{36}$

Personal Tutor glencoe.com

StudyTip

Checking Reasonableness of Results The number of combinations of 10 taken 2 at a time is less than the number of permutations of 10 taken 2 at a time because order does not matter in a combination. So, check that $C(10, 2) < P(10, 2)$.

Check Your Understanding

Examples 1 and 2 pp. 783–784

1. **MUSIC** A disc jockey has 12 songs he plans to play in the next hour. How many ways can he pick the next 3 songs if he does not repeat? 1320 ways

2. **CONSTRUCTION** A contractor can build 11 different model homes. She only has 4 lots. How many ways can she put a different house on each lot? 7920 ways

Example 3 p. 784

3. **BOOKS** Erica has to write 2 book reports this month. She has 6 books from which to choose. How many different ways can she pick 2 books? 15

Example 4 p. 785

4. **LOCKS** Omar knows the numbers to his locker combination are 24, 38, and 6. He cannot remember the correct order to the combination. What is the probability that Omar opens his locker on his first attempt? $\frac{1}{6}$

TEACH with TECH

INTERACTIVE WHITEBOARD Use the board to help show the factorial calculations and cancellations when computing permutations and combinations. Save these pages and distribute them to the class.

Focus on Mathematical Content

Permutations and Combinations A permutation and a combination are both arrangements, but in a permutation the number of arrangements includes all possible orders. For example, in a combination, arrangement *A–B* is the same as arrangement *B–A* and is only counted once. In a permutation, *A–B* and *B–A* count as two arrangements.

Additional Example

4 **TENNIS** The players listed are playing singles in a tennis tournament. If in the first round each player plays every other player once, what is the probability that Kyle plays in the first match? $\frac{1}{4}$

Thomas	Carl
Ager	Jack
Brian	Seth
Kyle	Pedro

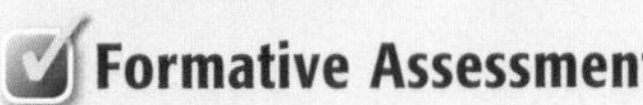

Tips for New Teachers

Combination Notation Tell students that $C(4, 2)$ is read as *the number of combinations of 4 things taken 2 at a time.*

3 PRACTICE

Formative Assessment

Use Exercises 1–4 to check for understanding.

Use the chart at the bottom of the next page to customize assignments for your students.

Watch Out!

Preventing Errors Before students begin the exercises, remind them that order matters for permutations and does not matter for combinations. Have students give several examples of each. Clarify any misconceptions that they might have about whether order matters or not.

Additional Answers

30b. Sample answer: find the number of combinations of the number of points

30c. $C(4, 2) = 6$; $C(5, 3) = 10$; $C(6, 4) = 15$; $C(7, 5) = 21$; Sample answer: The combination is the same as the number of segments for the different numbers of points.

30d. 10 points have 45 segments; 12 points have 66 segments; n points have $C(n, n-2)$ segments

37. Sample answer: A combination could be used to find 9 batters from a baseball team with 20 players. A permutation would be used if the 9 batters are to bat in a particular order. In the first situation, the batters would hit in any order, while in the second they would hit in a determined order.

Practice and Problem Solving

 = **Step-by-Step Solutions** begin on page R11. **Extra Practice** begins on page 810.

Examples 1 and 2 pp. 783–784

5. **PHOTOS** From among five photos, how can four of them be arranged on a shelf that holds four photographs? **120**

6. **RACES** In a race with 7 runners, how many ways can the runners finish in first, second, and third place? **210 ways**

7. **GAMES** In the game Tic Tac Toe, players take turns placing an X or an O in any of the locations that are empty. How many different ways can the first 3 moves of the game occur? **504 ways**

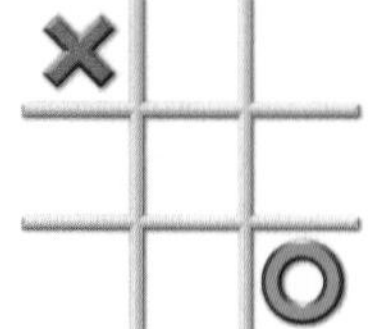

8. **SPELLING** There are 15 contestants in a spelling bee. How many different ways can the contestants finish first, second, third, and fourth? **32,760**

Example 3 p. 784

9. **CHESS** The chess team wants to have practice two different days next week, from Monday through Friday. How many schedules can be made? **10**

10. **FLAGS** A group of students are designing a new school flag using the colors blue, white, red, black, and gold. In how many ways can students choose 3 colors for the flag? **10**

Example 4 p. 785

11. **MUSIC** Out of 10 songs on a CD, 3 are randomly selected to play without repeating a song. What is the probability that the first 3 songs on the CD are selected to play in any order? $\frac{1}{120}$

12. **PHONE NUMBERS** Ivy knows that the last four digits of her friend's phone number contain the digits 0, 3, 5, and 6. She remembers that the first digit is 5. What is the probability that a randomly selected phone number with these digits will be her friend's? $\frac{1}{6}$

Find each value.

13. $P(6, 4)$ **360** 14. $P(5, 5)$ **120** 15. $C(7, 7)$ **1** 16. $C(12, 3)$ **220**

17. $P(14, 5)$ **240,240** 18. $P(12, 4)$ **11,880** 19. $C(25, 4)$ **12,650** 20. $C(20, 15)$ **15,504**

Tell whether each situation is a *permutation* or *combination*. Then solve.

21. At a business meeting, each of the 12 people attending shakes hands with every other person exactly once. How many distinct handshakes are given? **combination; 66**

22. A phone survey asks people to rank the activities shown according to how much time they spend listening to each activity on the radio. How many different rankings are possible? **permutation; 120**

Activities	
music	sports
weather	news
entertainment	

23. The school bus has 10 empty seats. At the next stop, 4 students get on the bus. How many ways can the 4 students arrange themselves in the empty seats, if each student takes one seat? **permutation; 5040**

24. How many ways can 3 different movies be picked from 15 different movie choices? **combination; 455**

LETTERS Each arrangement of the letters in the word *dream* is placed on a piece of paper. One paper is selected at random. Find each probability.

25. P(word begins with d) $\frac{1}{5}$

26. P(word ends with am) $\frac{1}{20}$

Differentiated Homework Options

Level	Assignment	Two-Day Option	
AL Basic	5–12, 33, 35, 37–52	5–11 odd, 38–41	6–12 even, 33, 35, 37, 42–52
OL Core	5–19 odd, 21–33, 35, 37–52	5–12, 38–41	13–33, 35, 37, 42–52
BL Advanced	13–48 (optional: 49–52)		

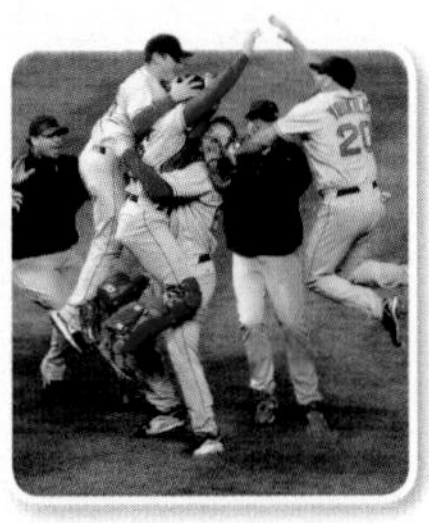

Real-World Link

The finals of the World Series is a best of seven series to determine the Major League Baseball champion. However, in 1903, 1919, 1920, and 1921, a best of nine series determined the winner.

Source: MLB

27. **SPORTS** In a best-of-three series, the first team to win 2 games wins the series. Two ways to win a best-of-three series are to win the first 2 games or lose the first game and win the next two games. How many ways are there to win a best-of-three series? a best-of-five series? a best-of-seven series? **3 ways; 10 ways; 35 ways**

28. **FOOD** At a restaurant, customers can choose three toppings for hamburgers from among ketchup, mustard, pickles, lettuce, onions, and cheese. Does ordering a hamburger with three toppings represent a combination or permutation? How many three-topping hamburgers are possible? **combination; 20 hamburgers**

29. **TECHNOLOGY** Your cell phone uses a 4-digit personal identification number (PIN) to lock it from use.

a. How many PINs can you choose to lock your cell phone? **10,000**

b. Use probability to explain how someone is unlikely to guess your PIN.

30. **MULTIPLE REPRESENTATIONS** In this problem, you will investigate points and line segments. In the figure at the right, each of the 4 non-collinear points are connected to every other point exactly once. There are a total of six line segments connecting the points. **b–d. See margin.**

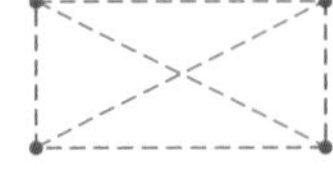

a. **TABULAR** Copy and complete the table.

Number of Points	Number of Segments
4	6
5	■ **10**
6	■ **15**
7	■ **21**

b. **ANALYTICAL** Explain how you can find the number of segments mathematically.

c. **NUMERICAL** Find $C(4, 2)$, $C(5, 3)$, $C(6, 4)$, and $C(7, 5)$. How do these results compare to the number of segments for 4, 5, 6, and 7 points?

d. **MAKE A PREDICTION** How many segments would be drawn between 10 points? 12 points? n points?

31. **BASKETBALL** There are 2730 ways for three teams to finish first, second, and third in their basketball league. How many teams are in the league? **15 teams**

32. **PARTIES** How many people were at a party if each person shook hands with every other person exactly once, and there were 300 handshakes? **25 people**

H.O.T. Problems

Use **H**igher-**O**rder **T**hinking Skills

33. **OPEN ENDED** Describe a situation that could be represented by the expression $C(15, 5)$.

34. **CHALLENGE** *True* or *false*? The number of combinations of items is always greater than 1. If false, provide a counterexample.

35. **SELECT A TECHNIQUE** If $P(9, 9) = 362{,}880$, which technique would you use to find $P(10, 10)$? Justify your selection. Then find $P(10, 10)$.

mental math	number sense	estimation

36. **CHALLENGE** Is the value of $P(x, y)$ *sometimes*, *always*, or *never* greater than the value of $C(x, y)$? Explain. Assume x and y are positive integers and $x \geq y$.

37. **WRITING IN MATH** Give an example of a situation in which you would use a combination. Then, change the situation so that you need to use a permutation. Explain the difference between the situations. **See margin.**

29b. Since there are 10,000 different PINs, there is only a $\frac{1}{10{,}000}$ chance that someone could guess the PIN.

33. Sample answer: the number of five-person committees that could be formed from a group of 15 people.

34. False; $C(x, y) = 1$ when $x = y$ or when $y = 0$.

35. mental math; $P(10, 10) = 10 \cdot P(9, 9)$ so $10 \cdot 362{,}880 = 3{,}628{,}800$.

36. Sometimes; they are equal if $y = 1$.

Multiple Representations In Exercise 30, students use geometric sketches, a table of values, and numerical analysis to relate the number of non-collinear points in a plane to the number of line segments that would connect them.

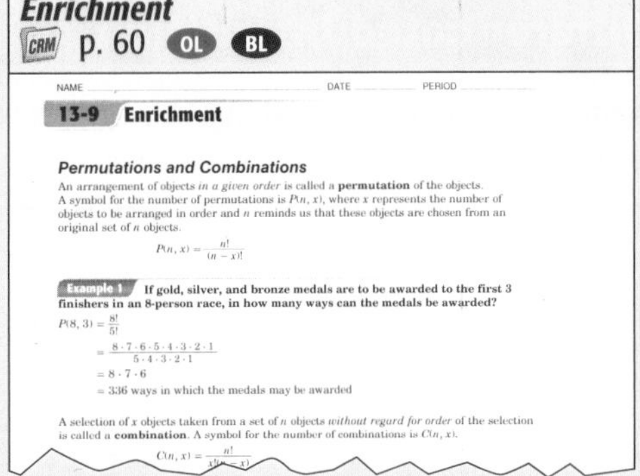

Enrichment

CRM p. 60 OL BL

NAME ______ DATE ______ PERIOD ______

13-9 Enrichment

Permutations and Combinations

An arrangement of objects *in a given order* is called a **permutation** of the objects. A symbol for the number of permutations is $P(n, x)$, where x represents the number of objects to be arranged in order and n reminds us that these objects are chosen from an original set of n objects.

$$P(n, x) = \frac{n!}{(n - x)!}$$

Example 1 If gold, silver, and bronze medals are to be awarded to the first 3 finishers in an 8-person race, in how many ways can the medals be awarded?

$$P(8, 3) = \frac{8!}{5!} = \frac{8 \cdot 7 \cdot 6 \cdot 5 \cdot 4 \cdot 3 \cdot 2 \cdot 1}{5 \cdot 4 \cdot 3 \cdot 2 \cdot 1} = 8 \cdot 7 \cdot 6$$

= 336 ways in which the medals may be awarded

A selection of x objects taken from a set of n objects *without regard for order* of the selection is called a **combination**. A symbol for the number of combinations is $C(n, x)$.

$$C(n, x) = \frac{n!}{x!(n - x)!}$$

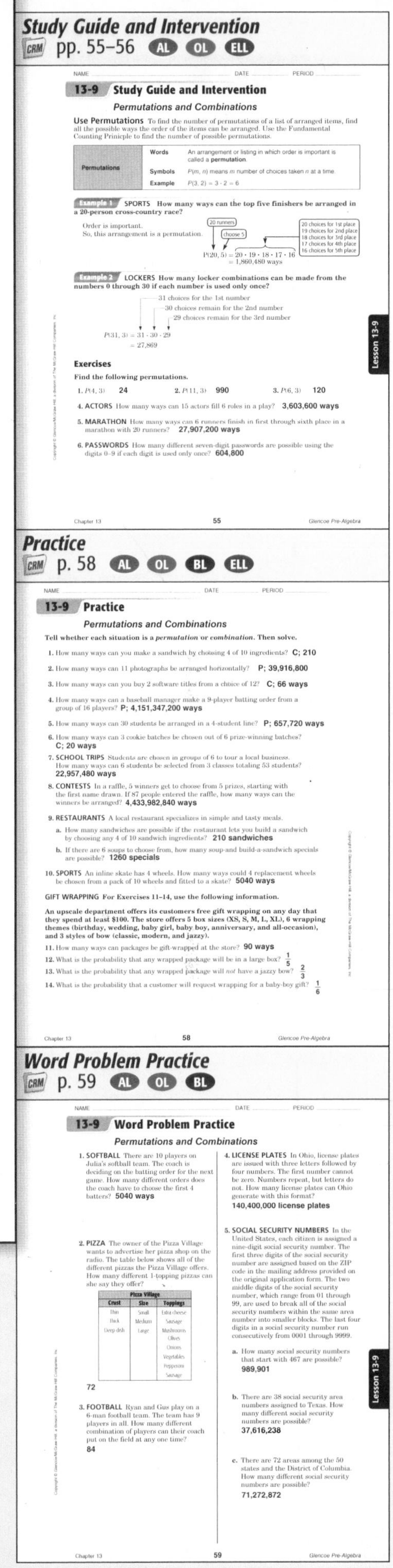

Study Guide and Intervention

CRM pp. 55–56 AL OL ELL

NAME ______ DATE ______ PERIOD ______

13-9 Study Guide and Intervention

Permutations and Combinations

Use Permutations To find the number of permutations of a list of arranged items, find all the possible ways the order of the items can be arranged. Use the Fundamental Counting Prinicple to find the number of possible permutations.

Permutations		
	Words	An arrangement or listing in which order is important is called a **permutation**.
	Symbols	$P(m, n)$ means m number of choices taken n at a time.
	Example	$P(3, 2) = 3 \cdot 2 = 6$

Example 1 SPORTS **How many ways can the top five finishers be arranged in a 20-person cross-country race?**

Order is important. So, this arrangement is a permutation.

20 runners; choose 5

20 choices for 1st place; 19 choices for 2nd place; 18 choices for 3rd place; 17 choices for 4th place; 16 choices for 5th place

$P(20, 5) = 20 \cdot 19 \cdot 18 \cdot 17 \cdot 16$
$= 1{,}860{,}480$ ways

Example 2 LOCKERS **How many locker combinations can be made from the numbers 0 through 30 if each number is used only once?**

31 choices for the 1st number
30 choices remain for the 2nd number
29 choices remain for the 3rd number

$P(31, 3) = 31 \cdot 30 \cdot 29$
$= 27{,}869$

Exercises

Find the following permutations.

1. $P(4, 3)$ **24**
2. $P(11, 3)$ **990**
3. $P(6, 3)$ **120**
4. **ACTORS** How many ways can 15 actors fill 6 roles in a play? **3,603,600 ways**
5. **MARATHON** How many ways can 6 runners finish in first through sixth place in a marathon with 20 runners? **27,907,200 ways**
6. **PASSWORDS** How many different seven-digit passwords are possible using the digits 0–9 if each digit is used only once? **604,800**

Chapter 13 55 Glencoe Pre-Algebra

Lesson 13-9

Practice

CRM p. 58 AL OL BL ELL

NAME ______ DATE ______ PERIOD ______

13-9 Practice

Permutations and Combinations

Tell whether each situation is a *permutation* or *combination*. Then solve.

1. How many ways can you make a sandwich by choosing 4 of 10 ingredients? **C; 210**
2. How many ways can 11 photographs be arranged horizontally? **P; 39,916,800**
3. How many ways can you buy 2 software titles from a choice of 12? **C; 66 ways**
4. How many ways can a baseball manager make a 9-player batting order from a group of 16 players? **P; 4,151,347,200 ways**
5. How many ways can 30 students be arranged in a 4-student line? **P; 657,720 ways**
6. How many ways can 3 cookie batches be chosen out of 6 prize-winning batches? **C; 20 ways**
7. **SCHOOL TRIPS** Students are chosen in groups of 6 to tour a local business. How many ways can 6 students be selected from 3 classes totaling 53 students? **22,957,480 ways**
8. **CONTESTS** In a raffle, 5 winners get to choose from 5 prizes, starting with the first name drawn. If 87 people entered the raffle, how many ways can the winners be arranged? **4,433,982,840 ways**
9. **RESTAURANTS** A local restaurant specializes in simple and tasty meals.
   a. How many sandwiches are possible if the restaurant lets you build a sandwich by choosing any 4 of 10 sandwich ingredients? **210 sandwiches**
   b. If there are 6 soups to choose from, how many soup-and build-a-sandwich specials are possible? **1260 specials**
10. **SPORTS** An inline skate has 4 wheels. How many ways could 4 replacement wheels be chosen from a pack of 10 wheels and fitted to a skate? **5040 ways**

GIFT WRAPPING For Exercises 11–14, use the following information.

An upscale department offers its customers free gift wrapping on any day that they spend at least $100. The store offers 5 box sizes (XS, S, M, L, XL), 6 wrapping themes (birthday, wedding, baby girl, baby boy, anniversary, and all-occasion), and 3 styles of bow (classic, modern, and jazzy).

11. How many ways can packages be gift-wrapped at the store? **90 ways**
12. What is the probability that any wrapped package will be in a large box? $\frac{1}{5}$
13. What is the probability that any wrapped package will *not* have a jazzy bow? $\frac{2}{3}$
14. What is the probability that a customer will request wrapping for a baby-boy gift? $\frac{1}{6}$

Chapter 13 58 Glencoe Pre-Algebra

Word Problem Practice

CRM p. 59 AL OL BL

NAME ______ DATE ______ PERIOD ______

13-9 Word Problem Practice

Permutations and Combinations

1. **SOFTBALL** There are 10 players on Julia's softball team. The coach is deciding on the batting order for the next game. How many different orders does the coach have to choose the first 4 batters? **5040 ways**

2. **PIZZA** The owner of the Pizza Village wants to advertise her pizza shop on the radio. The table below shows all of the different pizzas the Pizza Village offers. How many different 1-topping pizzas can she say they offer?

Pizza Village		
Crust	**Size**	**Toppings**
Thin	Small	Extra cheese
Thick	Medium	Sausage
Deep dish	Large	Mushrooms
		Olives
		Onions
		Vegetables
		Pepperoni
		Sausage

72

3. **FOOTBALL** Ryan and Gus play on a 6-man football team. The team has 9 players in all. How many different combination of players can their coach put on the field at any one time? **84**

4. **LICENSE PLATES** In Ohio, license plates are issued with three letters followed by four numbers. The first number cannot be zero. Numbers repeat, but letters do not. How many license plates can Ohio generate with this format? **140,400,000 license plates**

5. **SOCIAL SECURITY NUMBERS** In the United States, each citizen is assigned a nine-digit social security number. The first three digits of the social security number are assigned based on the ZIP code in the mailing address provided on the original application form. The two middle digits of the social security number, which range from 01 through 99, are used to break all of the social security numbers within the same area number into smaller blocks. The last four digits in a social security number run consecutively from 0001 through 9999.
   a. How many social security numbers that start with 467 are possible? **989,901**
   b. There are 38 social security area numbers assigned to Texas. How many different social security numbers are possible? **37,616,238**
   c. There are 72 areas among the 50 states and the District of Columbia. How many different social security numbers are possible? **71,272,872**

Chapter 13 59 Glencoe Pre-Algebra

4 ASSESS

Ticket Out the Door Have students compare and contrast permutations and combinations. Tell them to explain why order is sometimes important when determining outcomes. Have them illustrate with examples. Students will turn in their papers as they exit the classroom.

Additional Answers

43. biased, convenience sample; Sara is only surveying people who probably like chocolate and not other types of desserts

45. $a \geq 6$

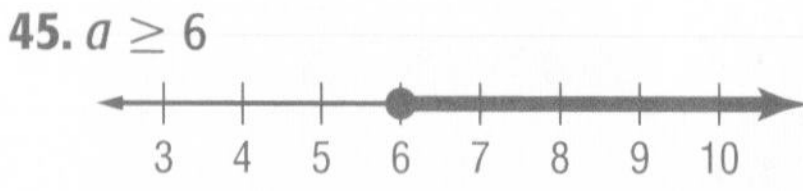

46. $c > 7$

47. $y > -3$

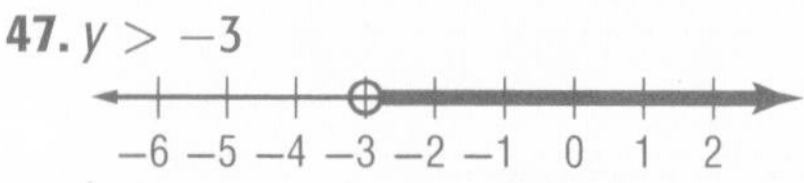

48. $m \geq -5$

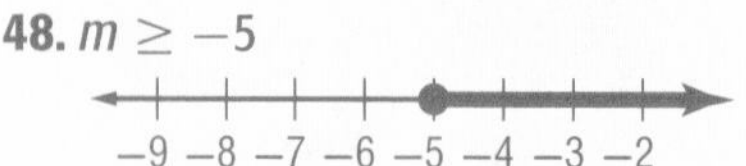

Standardized Test Practice

38. When the Rockets win a basketball game, the 12 players on the team give each other high-fives. How many distinct high-fives are given? **C**

A 24 C 66
B 36 D 96

39. Which situation is represented by $C(10, 5)$? **G**

F the number of arrangements of 10 people in a line
G the number of ways to pick 5 out of 10 students for a project
H the number of ways to pick 5 out of 10 students to be first through fifth place in a spelling bee
J the number of ways 10 people can sit in a row of 5 chairs

40. How many seven-digit phone numbers are available if a digit can be used only once and the first digit cannot be zero or one? **B**

A 40,320 C 1,209,600
B 483,840 D 2,097,152

41. SHORT RESPONSE Determine whether the following situation is a permutation or a combination. Then solve the problem.

There are 13 people running the 100-meter dash at a track meet. In how many ways can the runners finish in first, second, third, fourth, and fifth places? **permutation; 154,440**

Spiral Review

42. GAMES How many outcomes are possible for rolling three dice? (Lesson 13-8) **216**

43. To determine what type of dessert people in a community like, Sara surveys 20% of the people who enter 3 different chocolate shops. Identify the sample as *biased* or *unbiased* and describe its type. Explain your reasoning. (Lesson 13-7) **See margin.**

44. ANIMALS The histogram shows the life spans of different animals. (Lesson 13-5)

a. How many years are there in each interval? **10 years**

b. Which interval has the greatest number of animals? **11–20 years**

c. How many of the animals in the histogram have a life span of more than 20 years? **3 animals**

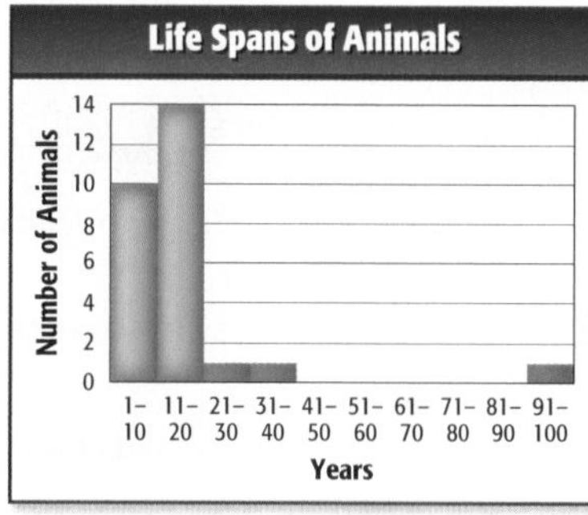

Source: *The World Almanac*

Solve each inequality. Then graph the solution on a number line. (Lesson 5-4) **45–48. See margin.**

45. $2a - 3 \geq 9$

46. $4c + 4 > 32$

47. $-2y + 3 < 9$

48. $-6m - 12 \leq 18$

Skills Review

Find each product. (Lesson 3-3)

49. $\frac{1}{6} \cdot \frac{1}{3}$ $\frac{1}{18}$

50. $\frac{2}{3} \cdot \frac{3}{6}$ $\frac{1}{3}$

51. $\frac{1}{3} \cdot \frac{1}{3} \cdot \frac{1}{3}$ $\frac{1}{27}$

52. $\frac{3}{8} \cdot \frac{2}{7} \cdot \frac{1}{6}$ $\frac{1}{56}$

Differentiated Instruction

BL

Extension The top three dogs in a dog competition of 50 dogs will win cash prizes. How many winning combinations are possible? 19,600

788 Chapter 13 Statistics and Probability

Graphing Technology Lab
Probability Simulation

Math Online > glencoe.com
• Other Calculator Keystrokes

A simulation is an experiment that is designed to act out a given situation. You can use a random number generator on a graphing calculator to create data for the experiment. Repeating a simulation may result in different probabilities since the numbers generated are different each time.

ACTIVITY

Generate 30 random numbers from 1 to 10, simulating selecting a card from cards numbered 1 through 10 and replacing a card after it is drawn.

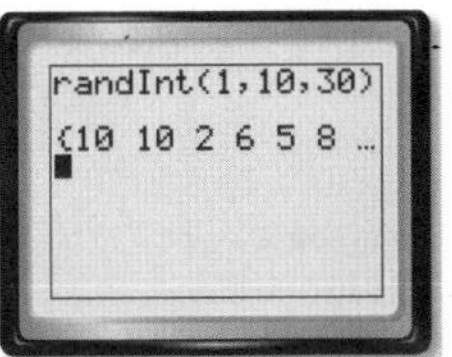

- Access the random number generator.
- Enter 1 as a lower bound and 10 as an upper bound for 30 trials.

KEYSTROKES: [MATH] [◄] 5 1 [,] 10 [,] 30 [)] [ENTER]

Record all 30 numbers in a column on a separate sheet of paper.

3. To use the random number generator, let A = 1, B = 2, C = 3, and D = 4.

Analyze the Results

1. Record how often each number from 1 to 10 appeared.
   a. Find the experimental probability of each number. See students' work.
   b. Compare the experimental probabilities with the theoretical probabilities. See students' work.
2. Repeat the simulation of selecting 30 cards. Record this second set of numbers in a column next to the first set of numbers. Each pair of 30 numbers represents selecting two numbers. Find the sum for each of the 30 pairs of cards.
   a. Find the experimental probability of each sum. See students' work.
   b. Compare the experimental probabilities with the theoretical probabilities. See students' work.
3. Design an experiment to simulate 30 spins of a spinner that has equal sections labeled A, B, C, and D.
   a. Find the experimental probability of each letter. See students' work.
   b. Compare the experimental probabilities with the theoretical probabilities. See students' work.
4. Suppose you play a game where there are three containers, each with ten balls numbered 0 to 9. Pick three numbers and then use the random number generator to simulate the game. Score 2 points if one number matches, 16 points if two numbers match, and 32 points if all three numbers match. (Note: numbers can appear more than once.)

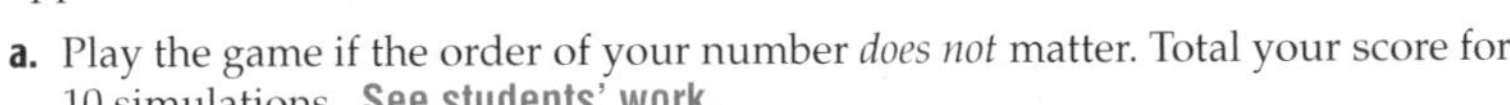

   a. Play the game if the order of your number *does not* matter. Total your score for 10 simulations. See students' work.
   b. Now play the game if the order of the numbers *does* matter. Total your score for 10 simulations. See students' work.
   c. With which game did you score more points? The game where order does not matter.

From Concrete to Abstract

Use Exercise 4 to assess whether students can apply what they have learned to a game situation in which order does and does not matter.

EXPLORE 13-10 Lesson Notes

1 FOCUS

Objective Use a graphing calculator to simulate a probability experiment.

Materials for Each Group

- graphing calculator

Teaching Tip

The graphing calculator has the capability of generating random numbers when given an upper limit, lower limit, and the quantity of numbers to generate.

2 TEACH

Working in Cooperative Groups

Arrange students in pairs, mixing abilities. Have students complete the Activity.

Ask:

- How does the calculator make simulating a probability an easier task? Many numbers can be quickly generated.
- Why are different numbers generated each time? Because the numbers are generated randomly.

Practice Have students complete Exercises 1–4.

To clarify Exercises 4a and 4b, point out to students that in 4a, if you choose the numbers 446 and the simulation shows 564, you score 16 points for picking one 4 and one 6. In 4b, where order does matter, 446 and 564 would be a score of 0 points.

3 ASSESS

Formative Assessment

Use Exercises 1–3 to assess whether students comprehend how to calculate experimental probability and use their calculator to generate random numbers.

13-10 Lesson Notes

1 FOCUS

Vertical Alignment

Before Lesson 13-10
Find simple probability.

Lesson 13-10
Find the probability of independent and dependent events. Find the probability of mutually exclusive events.

After Lesson 13-10
Validate conclusions using mathematical properties and relationships.

2 TEACH

Scaffolding Questions

Have students read the *Why?* section of the lesson and answer the questions.

Ask:

- Suppose 5 more teams are included so that a fifth heat is needed. How many different outcomes are possible? 25
- Find *P*(fifth heat) and find *P*(lane 3). $\frac{1}{5}, \frac{1}{5}$
- Find *P*(fifth heat, lane 3). $\frac{1}{25}$

13-10 Probability of Compound Events

Then
You have already found simple probability. (Lesson 13-6)

Now
- Find the probability of independent and dependent events.
- Find the probability of mutually exclusive events.

New Vocabulary
compound events
independent events
dependent events
mutually exclusive events

Math Online
glencoe.com
- Extra Examples
- Personal Tutor
- Self-Check Quiz
- Homework Help
- Math in Motion

Why?

The 800-meter relay features 20 teams competing in a preliminary round of competition. Before the race, each team chooses a number from jar 1 to determine the heat in which they swim and a number from jar 2 to determine one of five lanes they occupy.

The tree diagram shows all of the different possibilities for a team's heat and lane numbers.

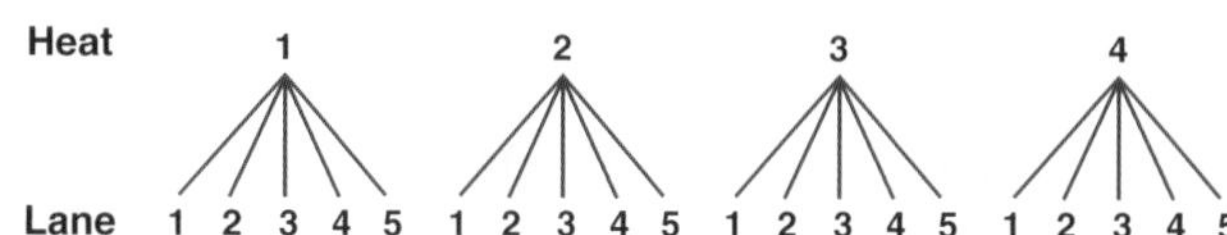

a. How many different outcomes are there for team placement in the competition? **20**

b. Suppose Sabrina's team is the first to choose from the jars. What is *P*(third heat, lane 2)? $\frac{1}{20}$

c. Find *P*(third heat) and *P*(lane 2). Multiply your answers and compare the product to your answer in part **b.** $\frac{1}{4} \cdot \frac{1}{5} = \frac{1}{20}$; **The answer is the same as part b.**

Probabilities of Independent and Dependent Events In the above example, choosing the heat and the lane is a compound event. A **compound event** consists of two or more simple events. Since choosing the heat number does not affect choosing the lane number, the events are called independent events. In **independent events**, the outcome of one event does *not* influence the outcome of a second event.

$P(\text{third heat}) = \frac{1}{4}$ $\qquad P(\text{lane } 2) = \frac{1}{5}$

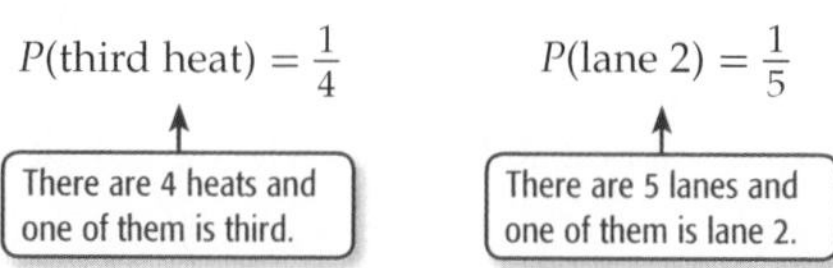

Key Concept **Probability of Two Independent Events** *For Your FOLDABLE*

Words The probability of two independent events is found by multiplying the probability of the first event by the probability of the second event.

Symbols $P(A \text{ and } B) = P(A) \cdot P(B)$

Example $P(\text{third heat, lane } 2) = \frac{1}{4} \cdot \frac{1}{5} \text{ or } \frac{1}{20}$

Lesson 13-10 Resources

Resource	Approaching-Level	On-Level	Beyond-Level	English Learners
Teacher Edition		• Differentiated Instruction, p. 791	• Differentiated Instruction, p. 795	
Chapter Resource Masters	• Study Guide and Intervention, pp. 61–62 • Skills Practice, p. 63 • Practice, p. 64 • Word Problem Practice, p. 65 • Spreadsheet Activity, p. 67	• Study Guide and Intervention, pp. 61–62 • Skills Practice, p. 63 • Practice, p. 64 • Word Problem Practice, p. 65 • Enrichment, p. 66 • Spreadsheet Activity, p. 67	• Practice, p. 64 • Word Problem Practice, p. 65 • Enrichment, p. 66 • Spreadsheet Activity, p. 67	• Study Guide and Intervention, pp. 61–62 • Skills Practice, p. 63 • Practice, p. 64 • Spreadsheet Activity, p. 67
Transparencies	• 5-Minute Check Transparency 13-10	• 5-Minute Check Transparency 13-10	• 5-Minute Check Transparency 13-10	• 5-Minute Check Transparency 13-10
Other	• Study Notebook • Teaching Pre-Algebra with Manipulatives	• Study Notebook • Teaching Pre-Algebra with Manipulatives	• Study Notebook	• Study Notebook • Teaching Pre-Algebra with Manipulatives

EXAMPLE 1 Probability of Independent Events

The two spinners are spun. What is the probability that both spinners will show an odd number?

The events are independent since each spin does not affect the outcome of the next spin.

$P(\text{first spinner is odd}) = \frac{3}{5}$

$P(\text{second spinner is odd}) = \frac{1}{2}$

$P(\text{both spinners are odd}) \frac{3}{5} \cdot \frac{1}{2} = \frac{3}{10}$

Check Your Progress

Use the spinners above to find each probability.

1A. $P(\text{both show a 2})$ $\frac{1}{30}$

1B. $P(\text{both are less than 4})$ $\frac{3}{10}$

Personal Tutor glencoe.com

Vocabulary Link

Dependent
Everyday Use Kayley's choice of coat was *dependent* on the weather.
Math Use Choosing two playing cards without replacement are *dependent* events.

If the outcome of one event affects the outcome of a second event, the events are called **dependent events**.

Key Concept — Probability of Two Dependent Events

For Your FOLDABLE

Words If two events, *A* and *B*, are dependent, then the probability of both events occurring is the product of the probability of *A* and the probability of *B* after *A* occurs.

Symbols $P(A \text{ and } B) = P(A) \cdot P(B \text{ following } A)$

Math *in Motion*, BrainPOP® glencoe.com

EXAMPLE 2 Probability of Dependent Events

In a bag, there are 3 blue, 7 red, and 5 white marbles. Once a marble is selected, it is not replaced. Find the probability that two blue marbles are chosen.

Since the first marble is not replaced, the first event affects the second event. These are dependent events.

$P(\text{first marble is blue}) = \frac{3}{15}$ ← number of blue marbles / ← total number of marbles

$P(\text{second marble is blue}) = \frac{2}{14}$ ← number of blue marbles after one blue marble is removed / ← total number of marbles after one blue marble is removed

$P(\text{two blue marbles}) = \frac{3}{15} \cdot \frac{2}{14} = \frac{6}{210}$ or $\frac{1}{35}$

StudyTip

Check for Reasonableness Since at least one possibility is eliminated in a second event, the probability of 2 dependent events is greater than the probability of 2 similar independent events.

Check Your Progress

2A. $P(\text{two white marbles})$ $\frac{2}{21}$

2B. $P(\text{a red marble and then a white marble})$ $\frac{1}{6}$

Personal Tutor glencoe.com

Differentiated Instruction

OL

If students confuse independent events, dependent events, and mutually exclusive events,

Then have each student give an example of each type of event. Ask students to include a description of how that example helps them understand each selected concept.

Probabilities of Independent and Dependent Events

Example 1 shows how to find the probability of independent events. **Example 2** shows how to find the probability of dependent events.

Formative Assessment

Use the Check Your Progress exercises after each example to determine students' understanding of concepts.

Additional Examples

1. Two number cubes are rolled. What is the probability that both numbers are less than 3? $\frac{1}{9}$
2. In a bag, there are 4 yellow pencils, 9 blue pencils, and 8 red pencils. Once a pencil is selected, it is not replaced. Find the probability that two blue pencils are chosen. $\frac{6}{35}$

Additional Examples also in Interactive Classroom PowerPoint® Presentations

TEACH with TECH

STUDENT RESPONSE SYSTEM Create a presentation of examples that represent dependent or independent events. Before working through each example, check for students' understanding by asking them if the problem uses dependent events or independent events. Have them respond with 1 for dependent and 2 for independent.

Focus on Mathematical Content

Probability of Compound Events The probability of dependent compound events is greater than the probability of independent compound events. This is because the probability of each subsequent event increases. Since the ratios are multiplied, the product ratio is larger.

Mutually Exclusive Events

Example 3 shows how to find the probability of mutually exclusive events.

Additional Example

3 CARDS You draw a card from a standard deck of playing cards. What is the probability that the card will be a black nine or any heart? $\frac{15}{52}$

Mutually Exclusive Events If two events cannot happen at the same time, they are said to be **mutually exclusive**. For example, when you spin two spinners like the one shown, you cannot spin a sum that is both 5 and even.

The probability of two mutually exclusive events is found by adding.

$P(5 \text{ or even}) = P(5) + P(\text{even})$

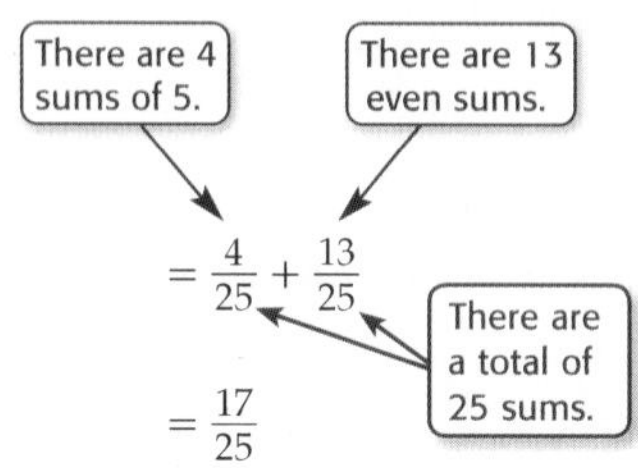

$= \frac{4}{25} + \frac{13}{25}$

$= \frac{17}{25}$

Second Spinner (columns); First Spinner (rows)

+	1	2	3	4	5
1	2	3	4	5	6
2	3	4	5	6	7
3	4	5	6	7	8
4	5	6	7	8	9
5	6	7	8	9	10

Key Concept — Probability of Mutually Exclusive Events

For Your FOLDABLE

Words The probability of one or the other of two mutually exclusive events can be found by adding the probability of the first event to the probability of the second event.

Symbols $P(A \text{ or } B) = P(A) + P(B)$

Example $P(5 \text{ or even}) = \frac{4}{25} + \frac{13}{25} \text{ or } \frac{17}{25}$

Real-World Career

Video Game Designer A video game designer works with a team to create the latest video games. This job requires creativity, superior problem-solving skills, and a passion for video games.

Video game designers complete a two-year degree in either Game Design and Simulation Programming or Game Art and Design.

Real-World EXAMPLE 3 Probability of Mutually Exclusive Events

GAMES Teresa is playing a video game that involves rolling two dice. What is the probability that she will roll a sum of 4 or a sum that is an odd number?

The events are mutually exclusive because the number cubes cannot add up to 4 and be odd at the same time.

$P(4 \text{ or odd}) = P(4) + P(\text{odd})$

$= \frac{3}{36} + \frac{18}{36}$

$= \frac{21}{36} \text{ or } \frac{7}{12}$

The probability that the sum of the number cubes is 4 or odd is $\frac{7}{12}$.

Check Your Progress

3. What is the probability of drawing a ten or two from a standard deck of 52 playing cards? $\frac{2}{13}$

Personal Tutor glencoe.com

792 Chapter 13 Statistics and Probability

Check Your Understanding

Example 1 p. 791

CARDS Two cards are drawn from a deck of cards numbered 1–10. After a card is selected, it is returned to the deck.

1. What is the probability of drawing an even-numbered card and then a card numbered greater than 8? $\frac{1}{10}$
2. What is the probability of drawing an odd-numbered card and then a card numbered less than or equal to 5? $\frac{1}{4}$

Example 2 p. 791

3. **FRUIT** A bowl of apples contains 6 red delicious, 7 granny smith, and 3 macintosh apples. After an apple is selected, it is not returned to the bowl. Find the probability of randomly choosing a macintosh and then a granny smith. $\frac{7}{80}$

Example 3 p. 792

4. **CONTESTS** Rocko is drawing the winning ball of a contest. What is the probability that he will pick a ball that is purple or the number 2? $\frac{2}{5}$

Practice and Problem Solving

● = **Step-by-Step Solutions** begin on page R11. **Extra Practice** begins on page 810.

Example 1 p. 791

A penny is tossed and the spinner is spun. Find each probability.

5. P(heads and 4) $\frac{1}{12}$
6. P(tails and odd) $\frac{1}{4}$
7. P(heads and a number greater than 2) $\frac{1}{3}$
8. P(tails and a number less than or equal to 5) $\frac{5}{12}$

Example 2 p. 791

A card is drawn from a deck of eight cards with letters A, B, C, D, E, F, G, H. The card is *not* replaced and a second card is drawn. Find each probability.

9. P(B and F) $\frac{1}{56}$
10. P(a vowel and D) $\frac{1}{28}$

A jar contains 6 blue, 3 red, 5 green, and 2 yellow candies. Once a candy is drawn, it is *not* replaced. Find the probability of each outcome.

11. P(two green candies) $\frac{1}{12}$
12. P(two red candies) $\frac{1}{40}$
13. P(a yellow then a blue candy) $\frac{1}{20}$
14. P(a blue then a green candy) $\frac{1}{8}$

Example 3 p. 792

A card is drawn from the cards shown. Find the probability of each outcome.

15. P(5 or even numbers) $\frac{4}{7}$
16. P(2 or greater than or equal to 5) $\frac{5}{7}$
17. P(3 or 7) $\frac{1}{7}$
18. P(composite or prime number) $\frac{6}{7}$

3 PRACTICE

Formative Assessment

Use Exercises 1–4 to check for understanding.

Use the chart at the bottom of this page to customize assignments for your students.

Differentiated Homework Options

Level	Assignment	Two-Day Option	
AL Basic	5–18, 26, 28–40	5–17 odd, 31–34	6–18 even, 26, 28–30, 35–40
OL Core	5–17 odd, 19–26, 28–40	5–18, 31–34	19–26, 28–30, 35–40
BL Advanced	19–40		

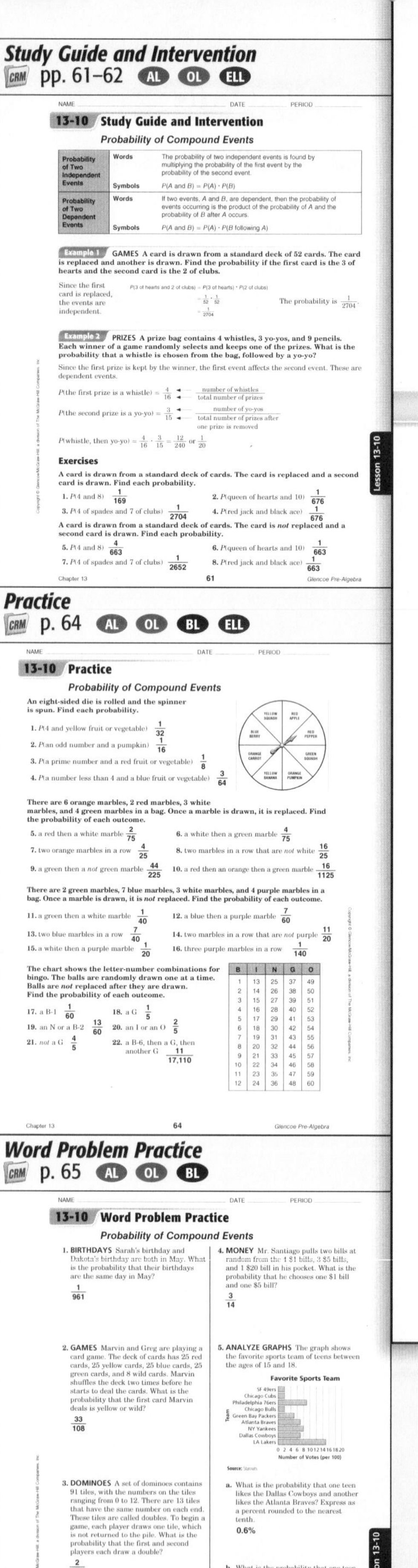

Study Guide and Intervention
CRM pp. 61–62 AL OL ELL

NAME ______ DATE ______ PERIOD ______

13-10 Study Guide and Intervention
Probability of Compound Events

Probability of Two Independent Events	Words	The probability of two independent events is found by multiplying the probability of the first event by the probability of the second event.
	Symbols	$P(A \text{ and } B) = P(A) \cdot P(B)$
Probability of Two Dependent Events	Words	If two events, A and B, are dependent, then the probability of events occurring is the product of the probability of A and the probability of B after A occurs.
	Symbols	$P(A \text{ and } B) = P(A) \cdot P(B \text{ following } A)$

Example 1 **GAMES A card is drawn from a standard deck of 52 cards. The card is replaced and another is drawn. Find the probability if the first card is the 3 of hearts and the second card is the 2 of clubs.**

Since the first card is replaced, the events are independent.

$P(\text{3 of hearts and 2 of clubs}) = P(\text{3 of hearts}) \cdot P(\text{2 of clubs})$
$= \frac{1}{52} \cdot \frac{1}{52}$
$= \frac{1}{2704}$

The probability is $\frac{1}{2704}$.

Example 2 **PRIZES A prize bag contains 4 whistles, 3 yo-yos, and 9 pencils. Each winner of a game randomly selects and keeps one of the prizes. What is the probability that a whistle is chosen from the bag, followed by a yo-yo?**

Since the first prize is kept by the winner, the first event affects the second event. These are dependent events.

$P(\text{the first prize is a whistle}) = \frac{4}{16}$ ← $\frac{\text{number of whistles}}{\text{total number of prizes}}$

$P(\text{the second prize is a yo-yo}) = \frac{3}{15}$ ← $\frac{\text{number of yo-yos}}{\text{total number of prizes after one prize is removed}}$

$P(\text{whistle, then yo-yo}) = \frac{4}{16} \cdot \frac{3}{15} = \frac{12}{240}$ or $\frac{1}{20}$

Exercises

A card is drawn from a standard deck of cards. The card is replaced and a second card is drawn. Find each probability.

1. $P(4 \text{ and } 8)$ $\frac{1}{169}$
2. $P(\text{queen of hearts and } 10)$ $\frac{1}{676}$
3. $P(\text{4 of spades and 7 of clubs})$ $\frac{1}{2704}$
4. $P(\text{red jack and black ace})$ $\frac{1}{676}$

A card is drawn from a standard deck of cards. The card is *not* replaced and a second card is drawn. Find each probability.

5. $P(4 \text{ and } 8)$ $\frac{4}{663}$
6. $P(\text{queen of hearts and } 10)$ $\frac{1}{663}$
7. $P(\text{4 of spades and 7 of clubs})$ $\frac{1}{2652}$
8. $P(\text{red jack and black ace})$ $\frac{1}{663}$

Chapter 13 61 Glencoe Pre-Algebra

Lesson 13-10

Practice
CRM p. 64 AL OL BL ELL

NAME ______ DATE ______ PERIOD ______

13-10 Practice
Probability of Compound Events

An eight-sided die is rolled and the spinner is spun. Find each probability.

1. $P(4 \text{ and yellow fruit or vegetable})$ $\frac{1}{32}$
2. $P(\text{an odd number and a pumpkin})$ $\frac{1}{16}$
3. $P(\text{a prime number and a red fruit or vegetable})$ $\frac{1}{8}$
4. $P(\text{a number less than 4 and a blue fruit or vegetable})$ $\frac{3}{64}$

There are 6 orange marbles, 2 red marbles, 3 white marbles, and 4 green marbles in a bag. Once a marble is drawn, it is replaced. Find the probability of each outcome.

5. a red then a white marble $\frac{2}{75}$
6. a white then a green marble $\frac{4}{75}$
7. two orange marbles in a row $\frac{4}{25}$
8. two marbles in a row that are *not* white $\frac{16}{25}$
9. a green then a *not* green marble $\frac{44}{225}$
10. a red then an orange then a green marble $\frac{16}{1125}$

There are 2 green marbles, 7 blue marbles, 3 white marbles, and 4 purple marbles in a bag. Once a marble is drawn, it is *not* replaced. Find the probability of each outcome.

11. a green then a white marble $\frac{1}{40}$
12. a blue then a purple marble $\frac{7}{60}$
13. two blue marbles in a row $\frac{7}{40}$
14. two marbles in a row that are *not* purple $\frac{11}{20}$
15. a white then a purple marble $\frac{1}{20}$
16. three purple marbles in a row $\frac{1}{140}$

The chart shows the letter-number combinations for bingo. The balls are randomly drawn one at a time. Balls are *not* replaced after they are drawn. Find the probability of each outcome.

B	I	N	G	O
1	13	25	37	49
2	14	26	38	50
3	15	27	39	51
4	16	28	40	52
5	17	29	41	53
6	18	30	42	54
7	19	31	43	55
8	20	32	44	56
9	21	33	45	57
10	22	34	46	58
11	23	35	47	59
12	24	36	48	60

17. a B-1 $\frac{1}{60}$
18. a G $\frac{1}{5}$
19. an N or a B-2 $\frac{13}{60}$
20. an I or an O $\frac{2}{5}$
21. *not* a G $\frac{4}{5}$
22. a B-6, then a G, then another G $\frac{11}{17{,}110}$

Chapter 13 64 Glencoe Pre-Algebra

Word Problem Practice
CRM p. 65 AL OL BL

NAME ______ DATE ______ PERIOD ______

13-10 Word Problem Practice
Probability of Compound Events

1. **BIRTHDAYS** Sarah's birthday and Dakota's birthday are both in May. What is the probability that their birthdays are the same day in May?
$\frac{1}{961}$

2. **GAMES** Marvin and Greg are playing a card game. The deck of cards has 25 red cards, 25 yellow cards, 25 blue cards, 25 green cards, and 8 wild cards. Marvin shuffles the deck two times before he starts to deal the cards. What is the probability that the first card Marvin deals is yellow or wild?
$\frac{33}{108}$

3. **DOMINOES** A set of dominoes contains 91 tiles, with the numbers on the tiles ranging from 0 to 12. There are 13 tiles that have the same number on each end. These tiles are called doubles. To begin a game, each player draws one tile, which is not returned to the pile. What is the probability that the first and second players each draw a double?
$\frac{2}{105}$

4. **MONEY** Mr. Santiago pulls two bills at random from the 4 $1 bills, 3 $5 bills, and 1 $20 bill in his pocket. What is the probability that he chooses one $1 bill and one $5 bill?
$\frac{3}{14}$

5. **ANALYZE GRAPHS** The graph shows the favorite sports team of teens between the ages of 15 and 18.

Source: Starnats

a. What is the probability that one teen likes the Dallas Cowboys and another likes the Atlanta Braves? Express as a percent rounded to the nearest tenth.
0.6%

b. What is the probability that one teen likes the L.A. Lakers and another likes the N.Y. Yankees? Express as a percent rounded to the nearest thousandth.
0.012

Chapter 13 65 Glencoe Pre-Algebra

Lesson 13-10

 **Real-World Link**

Sales of video games, game consoles, and accessories were more than $12 billion in 2006. One video game alone made more than $115 million in its first week of sales.

B **A bag contains 3 red marbles, 4 green marbles, 2 yellow marbles, and 5 blue marbles. Once a marble is drawn, it is *not* replaced. Find the probability of each outcome.**

19. three green marbles in a row $\frac{1}{91}$

20. a blue marble, a yellow marble, and then a red marble $\frac{5}{364}$

21. **CLOTHING** Your sock drawer contains 6 blue socks, 8 black socks, and 10 white socks. It is dark and you are getting dressed. What is the probability that you will randomly pick a pair of socks that match? $\frac{22}{69}$

22. **VIDEO GAMES** A company claims its video game players have a defective rate of 4%. What is the probability that you and a friend both receive a defective player? $\frac{1}{625}$

23. **SPORTS** A professional basketball player makes a field goal 49% of the time he shoots.
    a. What is the probability that he will score on his next two attempts? **0.2401**
    b. What is the probability that he will score on all of his next four attempts? **0.0576**
    c. Would you say shooting multiple field goals are independent, dependent, or mutually exclusive events? Explain your reasoning. **See margin.**

24. **FOOD** A box contains 6 apple cinnamon granola bars, 4 peanut granola bars, and 8 oatmeal raisin granola bars. Luis is first in line and Rashona is second in line. If they are given a granola bar at random, what is the probability that they will receive the same kind of bar? $\frac{49}{153}$

C 25. Draw a tree diagram to find the number of outcomes if the spinner at the right is spun twice. What is the probability of spinning red twice? Is this an independent event or dependent event? **See margin.**

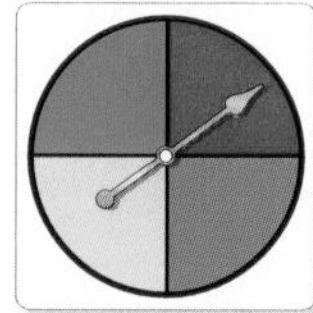

H.O.T. Problems
Use **H**igher-**O**rder **T**hinking Skills

26. **OPEN ENDED** Write a real-world example of two independent events.

27. **CHALLENGE** Seamus reaches into a box and randomly pulls out a marker. Without replacing it, he pulls out another marker. The probability that he first pulls out a red marker is 40%. If $P(\text{red, yellow})$ is 15%, find $P(\text{yellow})$. **37.5%**

28. **REASONING** Determine whether the following statement is *true* or *false*. If *false*, provide a counterexample.

If two events are dependent, then the probability of both events is less than 1.

29. **FIND THE ERROR** Dale and Shannon are finding the probability of rolling a difference of 0 or 1 on two number cubes. Is either of them correct? Explain. **See margin.**

Dale	Shannon
$\frac{10}{36} \cdot \frac{6}{36} = \frac{60}{1296}$ or $\frac{5}{108}$	$\frac{10}{36} + \frac{6}{36} = \frac{16}{36}$ or $\frac{4}{9}$

30. **WRITING IN MATH** Compare and contrast independent events and dependent events. **See margin.**

26. Sample answer: There are 4 movies about drama, 6 comedy movies and 2 movies about romance on a shelf. If a movie is chosen at random and replaced, then another movie is chosen, what is the probability of choosing a movie about romance or comedy?

28. Sample answer: false; For example, you have 2 red marbles. What is the probability of picking 2 red marbles? $\frac{2}{2} \cdot \frac{1}{1} = \frac{2}{2}$ or 1

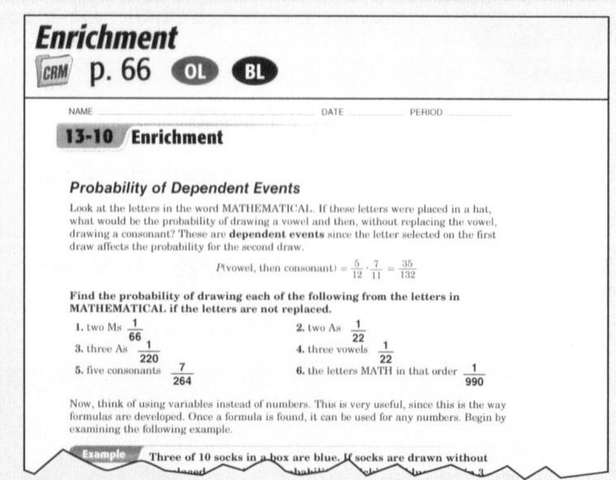

Enrichment
CRM p. 66 OL BL

NAME ______ DATE ______ PERIOD ______

13-10 Enrichment

Probability of Dependent Events

Look at the letters in the word MATHEMATICAL. If these letters were placed in a hat, what would be the probability of drawing a vowel and then, without replacing the vowel, drawing a consonant? These are **dependent events** since the letter selected on the first draw affects the probability for the second draw.

$P(\text{vowel, then consonant}) = \frac{5}{12} \cdot \frac{7}{11} = \frac{35}{132}$

Find the probability of drawing each of the following from the letters in MATHEMATICAL if the letters are not replaced.

1. two Ms $\frac{1}{66}$
2. two As $\frac{1}{22}$
3. three As $\frac{1}{220}$
4. three vowels $\frac{1}{22}$
5. five consonants $\frac{7}{264}$
6. the letters MATH in that order $\frac{1}{990}$

Now, think of using variables instead of numbers. This is very useful, since this is the way formulas are developed. Once a formula is found, it can be used for any numbers. Begin by examining the following example.

Example **Three of 10 socks in a box are blue. If socks are drawn without**

Watch Out!

Find the Error Students may confuse independent and mutually exclusive events in Exercise 29. Emphasize the definitions, model various situations, and ask whether the events can happen at the same time.

Standardized Test Practice

31. A quarter is tossed and the spinner shown is spun. How do you find the probability of tossing heads and spinning an odd number? **A**

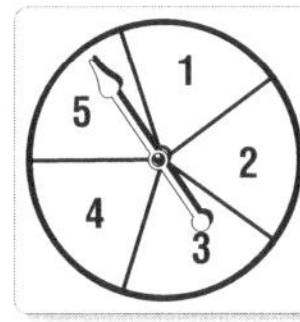

A $\frac{1}{2} \times \frac{3}{5}$ C $\frac{1}{2} \times \frac{2}{5}$

B $\frac{1}{2} + \frac{3}{5}$ D $\frac{1}{2} + \frac{2}{5}$

32. GRIDDED RESPONSE A jar contains 5 blue marbles, 4 red marbles, and 3 white marbles. Simone picks a marble at random. Without replacing it, she randomly chooses a second marble. Find *P*(red, white). $\frac{1}{11}$

33. What is the probability of rolling a number cube three times and getting numbers less than 3 each time? **G**

F $\frac{1}{216}$ H $\frac{1}{8}$

G $\frac{1}{27}$ J $\frac{27}{64}$

34. You buy a bag of assorted fruit that contains 3 apples, 5 oranges, and 2 bananas. You randomly choose a piece of fruit. Your friend then chooses a piece of fruit. What is the probability you both will get a banana? **A**

A $\frac{1}{45}$ C $\frac{20}{45}$

B $\frac{14}{45}$ D $\frac{40}{45}$

Spiral Review

Tell whether each situation is a *permutation* or *combination*. Then solve. (Lesson 13-9)

35. How many ways can 6 cars line up for a race? **P; 720 ways**

36. How many different flags can be made from the colors red, blue, green, and white if each flag has three vertical stripes and no colors can repeat? **P; 24 flags**

37. How many ways can 4 shirts be chosen from 10 shirts to take on a trip? **C; 210 ways**

38. How many ways can you buy 2 DVDs from a display of 15? **C; 105 ways**

39. FOOD SERVICE Hastings Cafeteria serves toast, a muffin, or a bagel with coffee, milk, or orange juice. (Lesson 13-8)

a. How many different breakfasts of one bread and one beverage are possible? **9**

b. What is the probability that a customer chooses a bagel with orange juice if a bread and beverage are equally likely to be chosen? $\frac{1}{9}$

40. SCIENCE Use the information in the table about the length of days on each planet. (Lesson 13-3)

a. What is the median length of day for the planets? **20.5 h**

b. Are there any outliers in the data? If so, name them. **yes; 5832**

c. Write a sentence describing how the lengths of days vary. Include a statement about any outliers in the data. **See margin.**

Planet	Length of Day* (Earth hours)
Mercury	1416
Venus	5832
Earth	24
Mars	25
Jupiter	10
Saturn	11
Uranus	17
Neptune	16

*The lengths are approximate
Source: *The World Almanac*

Differentiated Instruction

Extension Pose the following problem to students: A math class was given a pop quiz. There were ten true or false questions. What was the probability of a student who did not know any of the answers of getting all ten questions correct by guessing? A student has a $\frac{1}{1024}$ probability of getting all the answers correct, which is just under 0.1%.

4 ASSESS

Yesterday's News Ask students how yesterday's lesson on permutations and combinations helped them in learning today's lesson on the probability of compound events.

Formative Assessment

Check for student understanding of concepts in Lessons 13-9 and 13-10.

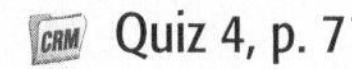

Quiz 4, p. 71

Additional Answers

23c. Independent; making one field goal does not typically affect making another one.

25.

R

R Y B G

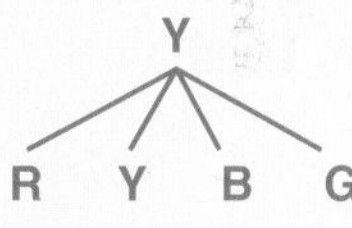

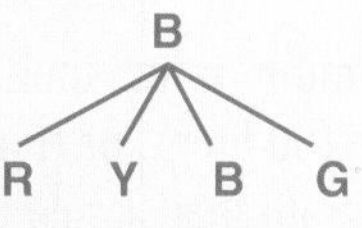

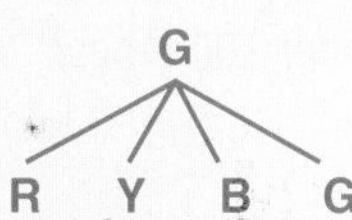

$\frac{1}{16}$; independent event

29. Shannon; rolling a difference of 0 or 1 are mutually exclusive events so the probability of rolling a difference of 0 must be added to the probability of rolling a difference of 1.

30. Both independent events and dependent events are compound events. Independent events do not affect each other. Dependent events affect each other.

40c. Sample answer: Since the length of a day ranges from 5832 − 10 or 5822 hours, the lengths of days for the planets vary greatly.

FOCUS

Objective Use simulations to examine outcomes.

Materials for Each Group

- spinner
- number cube
- red and white counters
- blue and red marbles

TEACH

Working in Cooperative Groups

Arrange students in groups of three or four, mixing abilities. Have students complete Activities 1 and 2.

Activity 1

Ask:

- Would it take more or less time to spin a spinner 100 times, or run a computer program that simulates spinning a spinner 100 times? A computer program would take less time.
- What is the probability that Logan will make four shots in a row? about 32%

Practice Have students complete Exercises 1 and 2.

Additional Answer

1. Sample answer: The theoretical probability of making a free throw is $\frac{3}{4}$. In his game, Logan attempted 12 free throws and made 8 free throws. The simulations are not accurate because they do not match the actual results.

EXTEND 13-10 Algebra Lab: Simulations

Math Online glencoe.com
Math *in Motion*, Animation

You can use items such as a die, a coin, or a spinner to simulate many real-world situations. The items or combination of items should have the same number of outcomes as the number of possible outcomes of the situation.

ACTIVITY 1

Logan usually makes three out of every four free throws he attempts during a basketball game. Is spinning a spinner that is divided into four equal sections a good strategy to determine how many free throws he will make in his next game?

Since the probability of Logan making a free throw are 3 in 4, spinning a spinner with four equal sections where 3 sections are red and one section is black is a reasonable activity to simulate made free throws. The red sections will represent made free throws and the black section will represent a missed free throw.

Step 1 Spin the spinner and record the results. Write a ● for a made free throw and an X for a missed free throw.

Step 2 Repeat the simulation three times. Record your results in a table like the one shown below.

Simulation 1	●	●	●	X	●	X	●	●	●	X	X	●
Simulation 2												
Simulation 3												

Analyze the Results

1. Compare the results of the simulations to the theoretical probability. Explain any differences. **See margin.**

Use a simulation to act out the situation.

2. At the grand opening of a store, every person that comes to the store receives a free sports bottle. The bottle comes in six different colors.
   a. Use a die to simulate this situation. Let each number represent one color of the sports bottles. Conduct a simulation until you have one of each number. **See students' work.**
   b. Based on your simulation, how many times must you enter the store in order to get all six colors of water bottles? **Sample answer: at least 6**

796 Chapter 13 Statistics and Probability

ACTIVITY 2

A student organization is selling raffle tickets to raise money for a trip. The odds in favor of winning an item in the raffle are 1 to 4. Conduct the following experiment to simulate the probability of two winning tickets being drawn in a row.

Step 1 Use red counters to represent a winning ticket and white counters to represent a losing ticket. There is one favorable outcome and four unfavorable outcomes. So, use 1 red counter and 4 white counters.

Step 2 Conduct a simulation for 30 tickets sold.

Step 3 Without looking, draw a counter from the bag and record its color. Replace the counter and draw a second counter.

Step 4 Repeat 30 times and record the results of the simulation in a table like the one shown below.

First ticket is a winner.	First ticket is a winner, second ticket is a loser.	Both tickets are winners.

Analyze the Results

3. Calculate the experimental probability that two tickets in a row will be winners. **See margin.**
4. How do the results in Activity 2 compare to the theoretical probability that two winners will be drawn in a row? (*Hint*: These are independent events.) **See students' work.**
5. The odds in favor of winning a different raffle are 3 to 4. Calculate the theoretical probability that two winning tickets will be drawn in a row. **18.4%**
6. Refer to Exercise 5. To simulate the probability of drawing two winning tickets in a row, Marcus puts 40 red and blue marbles in a bag. **a–b. See margin.**
   a. How many red and how many blue marbles should he use? Explain your reasoning.
   b. Conduct a simulation for this situation. Compare the theoretical probability with the experimental probability.
7. A test has 12 multiple choice questions with answer choices A, B, C, or D for each question. The correct answers are A, B, B, A, C, A, D, A, B, A, D, C. You need to correctly answer 9 or more questions to pass the test. **a–b. See margin.**
   a. Design a simulation that could be used to answer the questions on the test.
   b. Is your simulation a good strategy for taking the test? Explain.

Activity 2

Ask:

- What is the probability of winning an item in the raffle? $\frac{1}{4}$
- Are the events of drawing a winning ticket on the first draw and drawing a winning ticket on the second draw independent or dependent events? Explain. They are independent events because the counter from the first draw is replaced.

Practice Have students complete Exercises 3–7.

3 ASSESS

Formative Assessment

Use Exercises 2 and 6 to assess whether students comprehend how to use a simulation to find experimental probability.

From Concrete to Abstract

Have students write about the differences between experimental and theoretical probability.

Additional Answers

3. See students' work. The probability should be about 4%.

6a. 30 red marbles and 10 blue marbles; red represents a winning ticket and blue represents a losing ticket.

6b. See students' work. The theoretical probability and the experimental probability should be about the same.

7a. Sample answer: Use a spinner divided into four equal sections labeled A, B, C, and D. Spin the spinner and use the results of each spin to answer the questions on the test.

7b. No; Sample answer: It is very unlikely that spinning the spinner for test answers will result in a passing grade.

CHAPTER 13 Study Guide and Review

Formative Assessment

Key Vocabulary The page references after each word denote where that term was first introduced. If students have difficulty answering questions 1–8, remind them that they can use these page references to refresh their memories about the vocabulary.

Summative Assessment

CRM Vocabulary Test, p. 73

Math Online glencoe.com

Vocabulary PuzzleMaker improves students' mathematics vocabulary using four puzzle formats–crossword, scramble, word search using a word list, and word search using clues. Students can work online or from a printed worksheet.

CHAPTER 13 Study Guide and Review

Math Online glencoe.com
- STUDY TO GO
- Vocabulary Review

Chapter Summary

Key Concepts

Measures of Central Tendency (Lesson 13-1)

- Measures of central tendency describe the center of the data. The most common measures are mean, median, and mode.

Data Displays and Measures of Variation (Lessons 13-2 through 13-5)

- A stem-and-leaf plot is most often used when displaying data in a condensed form.
- The interquartile range is the range of the middle half of a set of data.
- A box-and-whisker plot separates data into four parts.
- A histogram displays data that have been organized into equal intervals.

Simple Probability and Probability of Compound Events (Lessons 13-6 and 13-10)

- The probability of an event is a ratio that compares the number of favorable outcomes to the number of possible outcomes.
- When the outcome of one event does not affect the outcome of a second event, these are called independent events.
- When the outcome of one event does affect the outcome of a second event, these are called dependent events.

Counting Outcomes and Permutations and Combinations (Lessons 13-7 and 13-8)

- The Fundamental Counting Principle states that an event M followed by an event N can occur in $m \times n$ ways if event M occurs in m ways and event N occurs in n ways
- Permutations: order is important
- Combinations: order is not important

FOLDABLES® Study Organizer

Be sure the Key Concepts are noted in your Foldable.

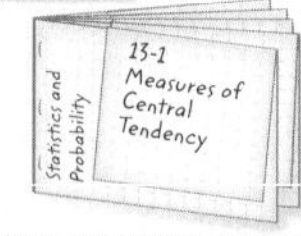

Key Vocabulary

box-and-whisker plot (p. 750)
compound events (p. 790)
dependent events (p. 791)
experimental probability (p. 766)
Fundamental Counting Principle (p. 777)
histogram (p. 757)
independent events (p. 790)
interquartile range (p. 744)
lower quartile (p. 744)
mean (p. 730)
measures of central tendency (p. 730)
measures of variation (p. 743)
median (p. 730)
mode (p. 730)
outcome (p. 765)
outlier (p. 745)
population (p. 771)
probability (p. 765)
quartile (p. 744)
range (p. 743)
sample (p. 771)
sample space (p. 766)
simple event (p. 765)
stem-and-leaf plot (p. 737)
theoretical probability (p. 766)
tree diagram (p. 777)
upper quartile (p. 744)

Vocabulary Check

Choose the term that best matches each statement or phrase. Choose from the list above.

1. sum of the data divided by the number of items in the data set **mean**
2. two or more simple events **compound events**
3. drawing to represent possible outcomes **tree diagram**
4. what should occur in an experiment **theoretical probability**
5. divides sets of data into four parts **box-and-whisker plot**
6. number or numbers that occur more often **mode**
7. the difference between the greatest and least values in a set of data **range**
8. uses bars to display numerical data that have been organized into equal intervals **histogram**

FOLDABLES® Study Organizer

Dinah Zike's Foldables®

Have students look through the chapter to make sure they have included examples in their Foldables.

Suggest that students keep their Foldables handy while completing the Study Guide and Review pages. Point out that their Foldables can serve as a quick review tool when studying for the Chapter Test.

CHAPTER 13 Study Guide and Review

Lesson-by-Lesson Review

13-1 Measures of Central Tendency (pp. 730–735)

Find the mean, median, and mode for each set of data. Round to the nearest tenth, if necessary.

9. number of students in each math class: 22, 23, 24, 22, 21 **22.4; 22; 22**
10. grams of fat per serving: 2, 7, 4, 5, 6, 4, 5, 6, 3, 5 **4.7; 5; 5**
11. inches of rain last week: 1.5, 2, 2.5, 2, 1.5, 2.5, 3 **2.1; 2; 1.5, 2, 2.5**
12. **MOVIES** At the movie theater, six movies are playing and their lengths are 138, 117, 158, 145, 135, and 120 minutes. Which measures of central tendency best represent the data? Justify your selections and then find the measure of central tendency. **See margin.**

EXAMPLE 1

Find the mean, median, and mode of 2, 3, 2, 4, 4, 6, 4, and 7.

Mean: $\frac{2+3+2+4+4+6+4+7}{8} = \frac{32}{8}$ or 4

Median:

2, 2, 3, 4, 4, 4, 6, 7 — **Arrange the numbers from least to greatest.**

$\frac{4+4}{2} = 4$ — **Find the middle number or the mean of the two middle numbers.**

Mode: 4 — **Find the data value(s) that occur most often.**

13-2 Stem-and-Leaf Plots (pp. 737–742)

Display each set of data in a stem-and-leaf plot. **13–15. See margin.**

13.

Heights of Football Players (in.)			
72	73	69	71
74	76	70	71
68	75	72	73

14.

Attendance at Key Club			
35	46	36	42
41	32	55	56
22	28	33	45
51	52	48	49

15. Frank's and Shandra's times for their last eight races are shown below.

Racing Times (min)

Frank	Stem	Shandra
9 8	0	
5 4 3 2 1	1	3 3 3 4 4 5
0	2	1 1

2 | 1 = 12 min *1 | 3 = 13 min*

In general, which runner has a faster time? Explain.

EXAMPLE 2

The table below shows the low temperatures for two weeks for a certain city.

Low Temperatures for Two Weeks (°F)						
47	48	51	48	55	57	40
39	57	42	37	48	55	42

a. Display the data in a stem-and-leaf plot. The least number is 37, and the greatest number is 57. So, the stems are 3, 4, and 5.

Low Temperatures

Stem	Leaf
3	7 9
4	0 2 2 7 8 8 8
5	1 5 5 7 7

3 | 7 = 37°F

b. What is the median temperature?

The median is the mean of the two middle numbers of the set of data.

The median temperature is $\frac{48+48}{2}$ or 48°F.

Lesson-by-Lesson Review

Intervention If the given examples are not sufficient to review the topics covered by the questions, remind students that the page references tell them where to review that topic in their textbook.

Two-Day Option Have students complete the Lesson-by-Lesson Review on pp. 799–802. Then you can use ExamView® Assessment Suite to customize another review worksheet that practices all the objectives of this chapter or only the objectives on which your students need more help.

Differentiated Instruction

Super DVD: Mindjogger Videoquizzes
Use this DVD as an alternative format of review for the test.

Additional Answers

12. Mean; there are no extreme values or numbers that are identical; 135.5 min

13. Heights of Football Players (in.)

Stem	Leaf
6	8 9
7	0 1 1 2 2 3 3 4 5 6

6 | 8 = 68 in.

14. Attendance at Key Club

Stem	Leaf
2	2 8
3	2 3 5 6
4	1 2 5 6 8 9
5	1 2 5 6

4 | 1 = 41 people

15. Frank; whereas Frank's times range from 0.8–2.0 minutes, Shandra's times range from 1.3–2.1 minutes.

Additional Answers

16. R: 4; UQ: 34; LQ: 32; M: 33; IR 2; none

17. R: 4; UQ: 8; LQ: 6; M: 6.5; IR 2; none

18. R: 5; UQ: 9; LQ: 5.5; M: 7; IR 3.5; none

19. The spread of the data is 41 points. The median is 82 points. One fourth of the students earned 76 points or less. One fourth of the students earned 87.5 points or more. Half of the students earned between 76 and 87.5 points.

20b. The median divides the men's marathon times in the box into two unequal parts. The times between the lower quartile and the median are more clustered and the times between the median and the upper quartiles are more spread out.

13-3 Measures of Variation (pp. 743–749)

Find the measures of variation and any outliers for each set of data. **16–19. See margin.**

16. The number of minutes spent reading each night: 31, 33, 32, 34, 35, 33

17. The number of fish in each fish tank: 6, 5, 7, 8, 5, 6, 7, 9, 8, 6

18. **GIFTS** Claire earned \$5, \$7, \$10, \$6, and \$8 doing errands for her neighbors. Find the measures of variation and any outliers for the set of data.

19. **GRADES** The scores Mr. Han's students earned on their last test are shown in the table. Use the measures of variations to describe the data in the table.

Test Scores			
99	88	81	89
77	58	92	80
83	82	74	84
76	73	99	74
82	87	82	74
86	76	85	92

EXAMPLE 4

During a baking contest, each baker had 26, 20, 21, 24, 23, 22, 21, 27, 23, 24, and 25 cookies to sample. Find the measures of variation and any outlier for the data.

Range: 27 - 20 or 7 cookies

Median, Upper Quartile, Lower Quartile:

List the data from the least to greatest.

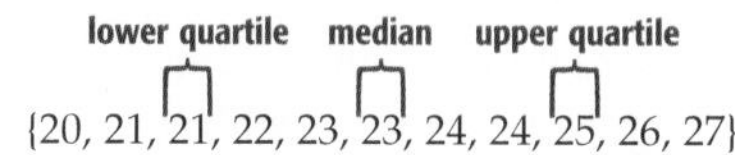

The median is 23, the lower quartile is 21, and the upper quartile is 25.

Interquartile Range: 25 - 21 or 4.

Outliers:

Multiply the interquartile range by 1.5.

$4 \times 1.5 = 6$

Subtract 6 from the lower quartile and add 6 to the upper quartile.

$21 - 6 = 15$ $\quad 25 + 6 = 31$

Since there are no values less than 15 or greater than 31, there are no outliers.

13-4 Box-and-Whisker Plots (pp. 750–755)

20. The box-and-whisker plot below shows the winning times in minutes for the men's marathon in the Summer Olympic Games from 1928 to 2004.

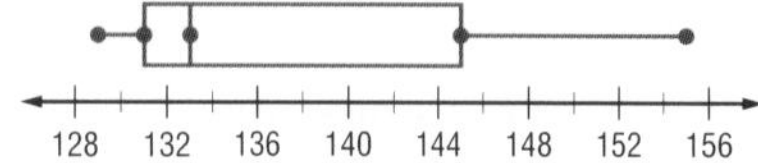

a. Find the percent of winning marathon times that were under 131. **25%**

b. Write a sentence describing what the length of the box-and-whisker plot tells about the winning times for the men's marathon. **See margin.**

EXAMPLE 5

Use the box-and-whisker plot shown to find the percent of New York City marathons that were held on days that had a high temperature greater than 72.5°F.

NYC Marathon High Temperatures (°F)

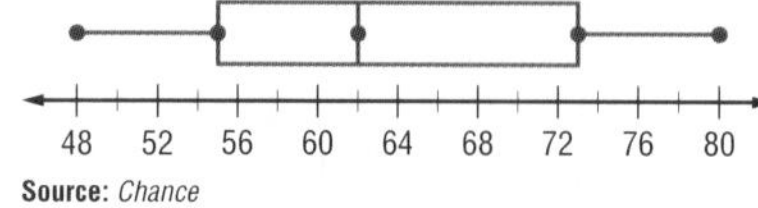

Each of the four parts represents 25% of the data, so 25% of the marathons had a high temperature greater than 72.5°F.

MIXED PROBLEM SOLVING
For mixed-problem-solving practice, see page 746.

13-5 Histograms (pp. 757–762)

21. The results of a class survey are shown in the table. Display the results in a histogram. See margin.

Number of Siblings		
Number of Siblings	Tally	Frequency
0–1	卌 卌 卌 III	18
2–3	卌	5
4–5	II	2

22. U.S. PRESIDENTS The frequency table shows the ages at which 43 U.S. Presidents began their terms in office. Display the data in a histogram. See margin.

Age	Frequency
42–51	14
52–61	23
62–71	6

EXAMPLE 6

Display the set of data in a histogram.

Times for 100-Meter Freestyle		
Times (S)	Tally	Frequency
0–29.9		0
30–59.9	卌 卌	10
60–89.9	卌 卌 卌 III	18
90–119.9	卌 II	7

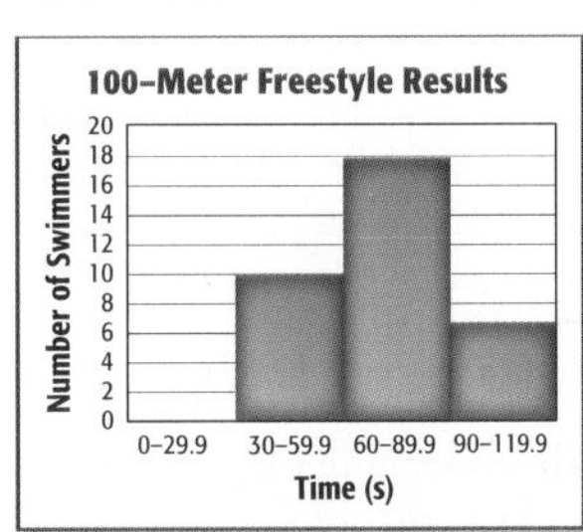

13-6 Theoretical and Experimental Probability (pp. 765–770)

MARBLES **There are 2 blue marbles, 5 red marbles, and 8 green marbles in one bag. One marble is selected at random. Find the probability of each outcome.**

23. $P(\text{red})$ $\frac{1}{3}$

24. $P(\text{blue or green})$ $\frac{2}{3}$

25. $P(\textit{not}\text{ blue})$ $\frac{13}{15}$

26. $P(\text{yellow})$ 0

EXAMPLE 7

Suppose a number cube is rolled. Find the probability of rolling an even number.

$$P(\text{even}) = \frac{\text{number of favorable outcomes}}{\text{number of possible outcomes}}$$

$$= \frac{3}{6} \text{ or } \frac{1}{2}$$

13-7 Using Sampling to Predict (pp. 771–776)

27. To determine the weekly top ten songs, the local radio station asks people to log onto their Web site and vote for their favorite song. Identify the sample as *biased* or *unbiased* and describe its type. Explain.

27–28. See margin.

28. FOOD Forty-five out of 60 people at a steakhouse said their favorite meal was steak. Is this sampling representative of the entire town? If so, how many of the 13,000 residents would say steak was their favorite meal?

EXAMPLE 8

Is polling students on the football team about their favorite sports a biased or unbiased sample? Then describe the type of sample.

Biased, convenience sample
Students who play football are more likely to choose football as their favorite sport.

Additional Answers

21.

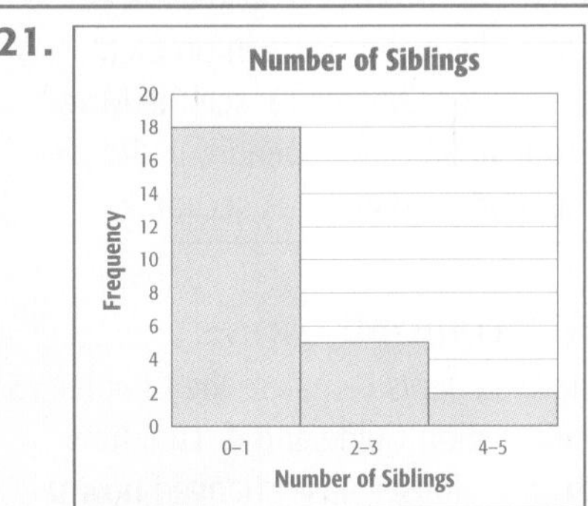

22.

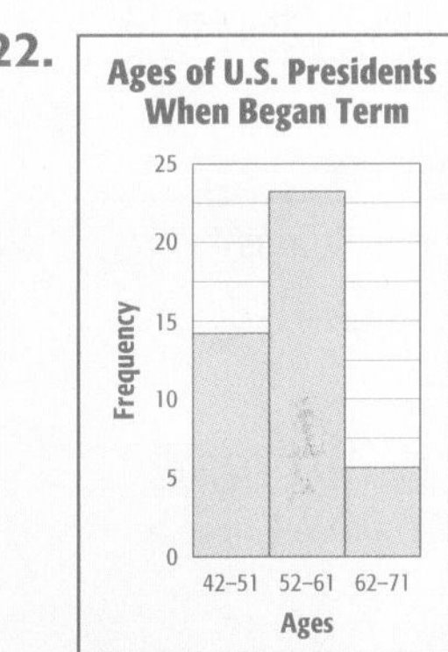

27. biased, voluntary response survey; only those people who are interested in participating in the survey are part of the sample.

28. No; the sample is biased. Diners at a steakhouse are more likely to choose steak as their favorite meal.

Problem Solving Review

For additional practice in problem solving for Chapter 13, see the Mixed Problem Solving Appendix, p. 855, in the Student Handbook section.

Anticipation Guide

Have students complete the Chapter 13 Anticipation Guide and discuss how their responses have changed now that they have completed Chapter 13.

Additional Answers

35. 59,280 combinations

36. 125,970 choices

CHAPTER 13 Study Guide and Review

13-8 Counting Outcomes (pp. 777–781)

Find the number of possible outcomes for each situation.

29. Two coins are tossed. **4**

30. Customers can choose vanilla or chocolate ice cream and strawberry, chocolate, or caramel topping. **6**

31. A number cube is rolled three times. **216**

32. A coin is tossed and a spinner with four equal sections is spun. **8**

33. James can choose blue or black socks, tan or black pants, and a red, blue, or green shirt. **12**

EXAMPLE 9

A die is rolled and a coin is tossed. Find the number of possible outcomes.

Outcomes of Die		Outcomes of Coin Toss		
6	×	2	=	12

There are 12 possible outcomes.

13-9 Permutations and Combinations (pp. 783–788)

34. RACES In how many ways can five runners come in first, second, or third place? **60 ways**

35. LOCKS How many different combinations can be made with three distinct numbers on a lock with 40 numbers? **See margin.**

36. PRIZES How many different ways can you select eight prizes out of twenty choices? **See margin.**

37. PARTIES How many different sets of people could you have if you chose five people out of the 22 people in your class to invite to your birthday party? **26,334**

EXAMPLE 10

How many ways can 8 runners place first, second, and third in a race?

The order is important, so this is a permutation.

$P(8, 3) = 8 \cdot 7 \cdot 6$

$= 336$

There are 336 ways for 8 runners to place first, second, and third.

13-10 Probability of Compound Events (pp. 790–795)

A box contains 8 red markers, 5 green markers, and 5 white markers. Once a marker is pulled from the box, it is not replaced. Find each probability.

38. P(red, then green) $\frac{20}{153}$

39. P(red, then red) $\frac{28}{153}$

40. P(white, then red) $\frac{20}{153}$

41. P(green, then green) $\frac{10}{153}$

42. P(white, then white) $\frac{10}{153}$

EXAMPLE 11

A card is drawn from a deck of eight cards numbered from 1 to 8 and not replaced. Find the probability of drawing a 3 and then a 6.

$P(3, 6) = P(3 \text{ on } 1^{st} \text{ draw}) \cdot P(6 \text{ on the } 2^{nd} \text{ draw})$

$= \frac{1}{8} \cdot \frac{1}{7}$

$= \frac{1}{56}$

The probability of drawing a 3 then a 6 is $\frac{1}{56}$.

802 Chapter 13 Statistics and Probability

Math Online glencoe.com
Chapter Test

Find the mean, median, and mode for the following data sets. Round to the nearest hundredth if necessary.

1. the ages of the students at a picnic: 8.375, 8, 7
 7, 8, 7, 9, 8, 10, 11, 7
2. shoe sizes: 5.29, 5; 4, 5, 6
 4, 5, 6, 5, 4, 7, 6
3. **TEST SCORES** Use the table that shows Ms. Fernandez' 1st period test grades.

Science Test Grades							
77	78	88	89	67	65	87	99
93	92	76	79	70	85	83	81

 a. Display the data in a stem-and-leaf plot. See margin.
 b. What is the median test grade? 82
 c. In which interval do most of the grades occur? 80 to 89
4. **MULTIPLE CHOICE** The data show times for a race at a track meet. Find the range. A

Track Times

Stem	Leaf
3	1 3 4 4 5 7
4	6 8 8 9 9
5	2 3 4

$4 \mid 6 = 46$ s

 A 23 C 25
 B 24 D 84
5. Refer to the stem-and-leaf plot above. Find the remaining measures of variation. See margin.
6. Display the following data in a box-and-whisker plot. See margin.

15	19	26	14	17
13	20	21	29	18

7. What percent of the data shown above is below 21? 75%
8. Display the data shown in a histogram. See margin.

Length of Time Spent Reading		
Time (min)	Tally	Frequency
0–14	𝍸𝍸 ǁ	12
15–29	𝍸 ǁ	7
30–44	ǁǁ	4
45–59	ǁ	2

A bowl contains 8 red apples, 4 green apples, and 8 yellow apples. Suppose one apple is selected at random. Find each probability as a fraction.

9. P(red) 2/5
10. P(green) 1/5
11. P(yellow) 2/5
12. P(red or green) 3/5
13. Identify each of the following as *biased* or *unbiased* and describe its type. a–b. See margin.
 a. To determine the quality of TVs coming off an assembly line, every 5th TV is checked.
 b. To determine if a new book store should be built, every tenth person exiting the library is surveyed.
14. **MULTIPLE CHOICE** Find the number of possible outcomes for a choice of bologna, salami, or ham and rye, wheat, sourdough, or white bread. H
 F 2 H 12
 G 7 J 37

Tell whether each situation is a *permutation* or a *combination*. Then solve.

15. The number of ways 6 notebooks can be arranged on a bookshelf. permutation; 720
16. An envelope contains 12 different names. The number of ways you can choose 3 of the names. combination; 220

A card is randomly drawn from the cards shown and not replaced. A second card is drawn. Find the probability of each outcome.

17. P(2, odd) $\frac{1}{14}$
18. P(even, odd) $\frac{2}{7}$
19. P(multiple of 3, multiple of 4) $\frac{1}{28}$
20. P(5, odd) $\frac{3}{56}$

CHAPTER 13 Practice Test

Customize and create multiple versions of your chapter test and their answer keys. All of the questions from the leveled chapter tests in the *Chapter 13 Resource Masters* are also available on ExamView® Assessment Suite.

Additional Answers

3a. Test Scores

Stem	Leaf
6	5 7
7	0 6 7 8 9
8	1 3 5 7 8 9
9	2 3 9

$9 \mid 2 = 92$ points

5. The median is 47. The upper quartile is 49. The lower quartile is 34.

6. 13 15 17 19 21 23 25 27 29 31

8.

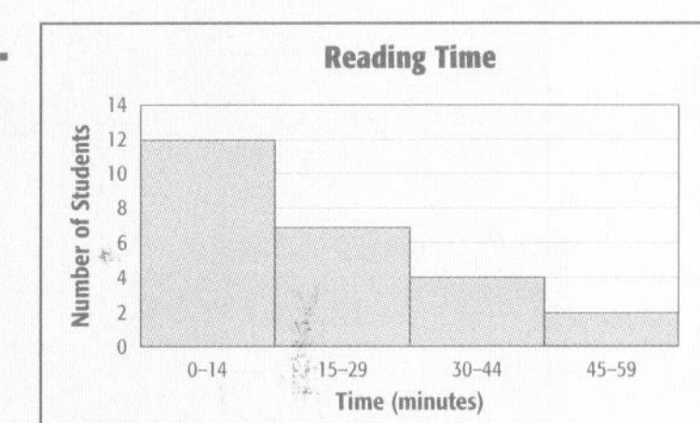

13a. unbiased; systematic random sample

13b. biased; convenience sample

Intervention Planner

Tier 1 On Level	Tier 2 Strategic Intervention approaching grade level	Tier 3 Intensive Intervention 2 or more grades below level
If students miss about 25% of the exercises or less,	**If** students miss about 50% of the exercises,	 students miss about 75% of the exercises,
Then choose a resource:	**Then** choose a resource:	 use *Math Triumphs, Grade 8*, Ch. 7, 9
SE Lessons 13-1 through 13-10 **CRM** Skills Practice, pp. 7, 13, 20, 26, 32, 39, 45, 51, 57, and 63 **TE** Chapter Project, p. 726	**CRM** Study Guide and Intervention, Chapter 13, pp. 5, 11, 18, 24, 30, 37, 43, 49, 55, and 61 *Quick Review Math Handbook*	
Math Online Self-Check Quiz	**Math Online** Extra Examples, Personal Tutor, Homework Help	**Math Online** Extra Examples, Personal Tutor, Homework Help, Review Vocabulary

Objective Use the strategy of making an organized list to solve standardized test problems.

2 TEACH

Scaffolding Questions

Ask:

- Can you think of some situation in your daily life or school work in which you used a list to organize information or data? Answers will vary.
- How did you use the list to organize the information or data? Answers will vary.
- What were the benefits of using the list? Answers will vary.

CHAPTER 13 Preparing for Standardized Tests

Make an Organized List

One strategy for solving problems on standardized tests is to organize data in a table or list. Organizing data in a table or list can make it is easier to analyze the data and answer questions about the data.

Strategies for Making an Organized List

Step 1

Read the problem quickly to gain a general understanding of it.

- **Ask yourself:** "What information or data is given in the problem?"
- **Ask yourself:** "Would the problem be easier to comprehend and solve if the data were organized in a table or list?"

Step 2

Create an organized list.

- Choose the best format for organizing and displaying the data given in the problem statement.
- Fill the list or table with the data.
- Be sure to include all of the data values.
- Label the list or table as appropriate.

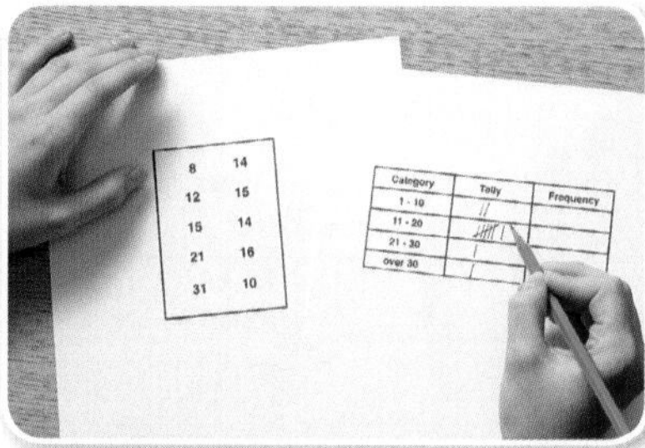

Step 3

Solve the problem.

- Use your organized list to solve the problem.
- If time permits, check your answer.

EXAMPLE

Read the problem. Identify what you need to know. Then use the information in the problem to solve.

A deli offers customers two choices of bread: white or wheat; two choices of cheese: cheddar or Swiss; and three types of meat: ham, turkey, or salami. If a sub sandwich with one type of bread, cheese, and meat is chosen at random, what is the probability that it contains ham or cheddar cheese?

A $\frac{3}{4}$ B $\frac{2}{3}$ C $\frac{1}{2}$ D $\frac{2}{5}$

Read the problem carefully. You are given the bread, cheese, and meat choices for sub sandwiches at a deli. You need to find the probability that a randomly selected sandwich contains ham or cheddar cheese. A *tree diagram* is a type of organized list that shows you all of the possible sandwich combinations.

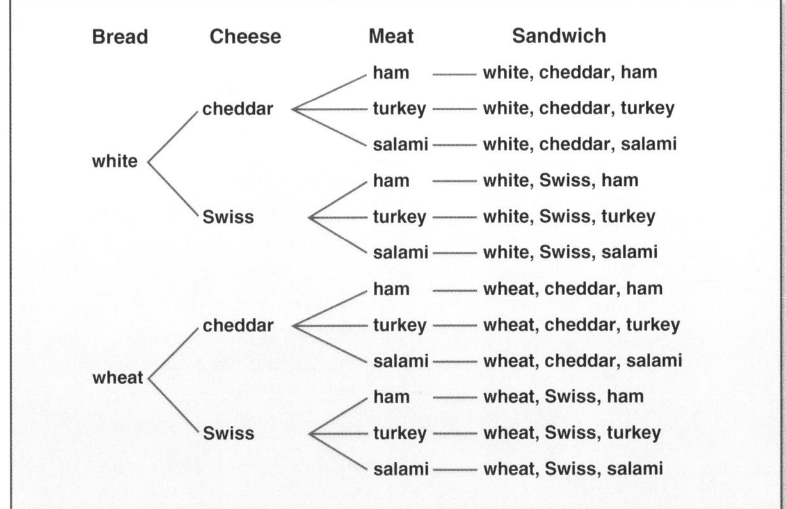

With the deli choices organized in the tree diagram, it is easy to see which sandwiches contain ham or cheddar cheese. There are 12 total sandwich combinations and 8 of them contain ham or cheddar cheese. So, the probability is $\frac{8}{12}$ or $\frac{2}{3}$. The correct answer is B.

Exercises

Read each problem. Identify what you need to know. Then use the information in the problem to solve.

1. A store has gray, white, or black shoes in sizes 8, 9, 10, 11, and 12. If a pair of shoes is chosen at random, what is the probability that the shoes are either gray, white, size 11 or size 12? **C**

   A $\frac{1}{12}$ C $\frac{4}{5}$

   B $\frac{3}{4}$ D $\frac{5}{6}$

2. A car manufacturer offers two kinds of transmissions: standard or automatic; two different interiors: leather or cloth; and six different colors: black, red, white, gray, yellow, or blue. If a car is chosen at random, what is the probability that it is red and has leather interior? **J**

   F $\frac{2}{3}$ H $\frac{3}{4}$

   G $\frac{5}{12}$ J $\frac{1}{12}$

Additional Example

A computer store is having a sale on laptop computers. The computer comes in black, blue, white, or red, with a 120GB, 160GB, or 200GB hard drive. You can also buy the computer with or without a case. If a laptop is chosen at random, what is the probability that the laptop is either red, white, or black, has a case, and has either a 160GB or 200GB hard drive? **B**

A $\frac{2}{3}$

B $\frac{1}{4}$

C $\frac{1}{8}$

D $\frac{1}{6}$

3 ASSESS

Use Exercises 1–2 to assess students' understanding.

Diagnose Student Errors

Survey student responses for each item. Class trends may indicate common errors and misconceptions.

1. A moved right instead of left
   B misread directions and moved 2 left and 4 down instead of 4 left and 2 down
   C correct
   D misread directions and moved 2 left and 4 up instead of 4 left and 2 down
2. F miscounted one less than median
   G correct
   H miscounted one more than median
   J used the number for the key as the median
3. A chose minimum number of years instead of range
   B guess
   C correct
   D chose maximum number of years instead of range
4. F guess
   G misunderstood concept of quartiles
   H misunderstood concept of quartiles
   J correct
5. A correct
   B guess
   C found volume instead of total surface area
   D guess
6. F correct
   G guess
   H guess
   J guess
7. A misunderstood concept of simple probability
   B chose the probability that the coin is a quarter
   C misunderstood concept of simple probability
   D correct

Multiple Choice

Read each question. Then fill in the correct answer on the answer document provided by your teacher or on a sheet of paper.

1. Which point is 4 units to the left and 2 units below the origin? **C**

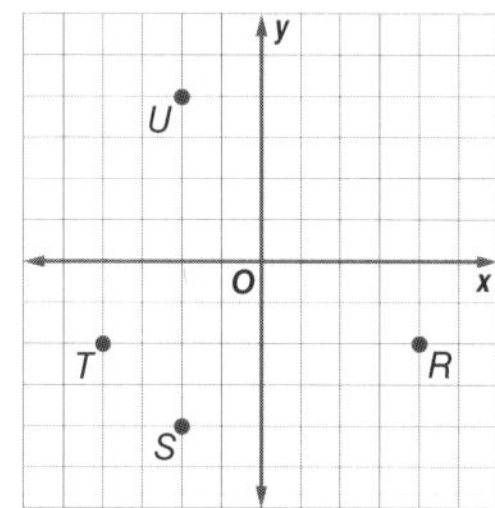

A *R* C *T*

B *S* D *U*

2. What is the median age shown in the stem-and-leaf plot below? **G**

Customer Ages (years)

Stem	Leaf
1	8 9 9
2	1 2 3 3 3 4 5 5 6 7 9
3	0 0 1 4 6 6 8
4	2 3 3 4 6 7 9
5	
6	0
7	1 4

3|4 = 34 years

F 29 years H 31 years

G 30 years J 34 years

3. What is the range of the ages shown in the stem-and-leaf plot in Exercise 2? **C**

A 18 years C 56 years

B 42 years D 74 years

4. In the box-and-whisker plot shown below, what percent of the cars get 24 miles per gallon or better? **J**

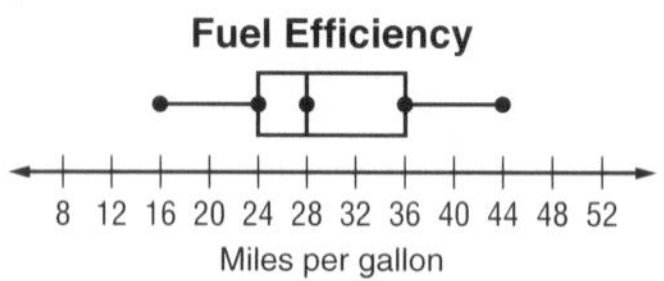

F 15% H 50%

G 25% J 75%

5. What is the total surface area of a cylinder that is 5.4 inches tall and has a diameter of 3.8 inches? **A**

A 87.1 in.^{2} C 61.2 in.^{2}

B 73.3 in.^{2} D 55.4 in.^{2}

6. A random sample of 120 shoppers is interviewed as they leave a shopping center. Twenty-four of them say that they used a store coupon for their purchase. If this sample is representative of the population, how many of 650 customers would you expect to use a coupon? **F**

F 130 H 135

G 140 J 150

7. Mickey has 3 pennies, 5 nickels, 2 dimes, and 8 quarters in her backpack. If she selects one coin at random, what is the probability that it is *not* a quarter? **D**

A $\frac{1}{3}$ C $\frac{1}{2}$

B $\frac{4}{9}$ D $\frac{5}{9}$

Test-TakingTip

Question 7 Compare the number of *successes* to the total number of possible outcomes. In this problem, the number of success would be 10, the number of coins that are not quarters.

CHAPTER 13 Standardized Test Practice

Short Response/Gridded Response

Record your answers on the answer sheet provided by your teacher or on a sheet of paper.

8. The table shows the pizza choices at Angelo's Pizzeria.

Angelo's Pizzeria	
Crust	**Toppings**
Hand-Tossed	Pepperoni
Deep Dish	Sausage
Pan	Green Peppers
	Mushrooms
	Olives

a. If a 1-topping pizza is selected at random from the menu, what is the probability that it will be a hand-tossed pizza with pepperoni? $\frac{1}{15}$

b. What is the probability that a randomly selected 1-topping pizza will be a deep dish pizza? $\frac{1}{3}$

9. Write a congruence statement for the triangles shown below.

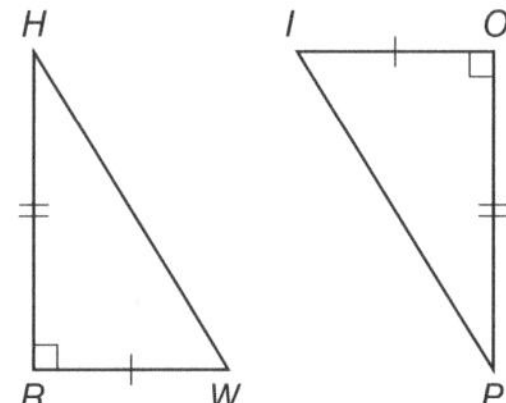

Sample answer: $\triangle HRW \cong \triangle POI$

10. **GRIDDED RESPONSE** Coach Gonzalez has 9 batters playing in today's softball game. How many ways can she arrange the first 3 batters of the lineup, assuming order is important? 504

11. **GRIDDED RESPONSE** Gina has a jar of marbles that contains 7 blue marbles, 5 red marbles, and 8 green marbles. Once a marble is selected, it is not replaced. If she selects 2 marbles at random, find the probability that two red marbles are chosen. $\frac{1}{19}$

12. This season, Antoine scored 13, 15, 9, 10, 14, and 11 points.

a. Calculate the mean, median, and mode for the set of data. Show your work. mean: 12, median: 12, no mode

b. Which measure of central tendency best describes Antoine's scoring production this season? Explain.

12b. Sample answer: Either the mean or median (both 12 points per game) describe Antoine's point production. There is no mode.

Extended Response

Record your answers on a sheet of paper. Show your work.

13. The table below shows the high temperatures over the past 20 days.

Daily High Temperatures (°F)				
72	74	76	76	75
79	81	84	83	76
73	72	67	69	70
74	76	78	79	80

a. Make a stem-and-leaf plot of the data. See margin.

b. What is the range of the daily high temperatures over the 20-day period? 17°F

c. Does there appear to be an outlier in the set of data? Explain.

13c. Sample answer: no outliers, the temperatures are all grouped fairly close together.

Need Extra Help?													
If you missed Question...	1	2	3	4	5	6	7	8	9	10	11	12	13
Go to Lesson or Page...	2-6	13-2	13-3	13-4	12-6	13-7	13-6	13-8	11-2	13-9	13-10	13-2	13-3

Formative Assessment

You can use these two pages to benchmark student progress.

CRM Standardized Test Practice, pp. 87–89

Answer Sheet Practice

Have students simulate taking a standardized test by recording their answers on practice recording sheets.

CRM Student Recording Sheet, p. 69

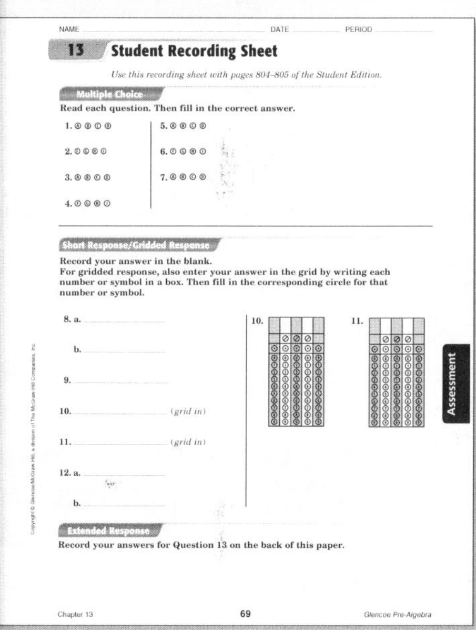
NAME DATE PERIOD

13 Student Recording Sheet

Use this recording sheet with pages 804–805 of the Student Edition.

Multiple Choice

Read each question. Then fill in the correct answer.

1. 2. 3. 4. 5. 6. 7.

Short Response/Gridded Response

Record your answer in the blank.
For gridded response, also enter your answer in the grid by writing each number or symbol in a box. Then fill in the corresponding circle for that number or symbol.

8. a. ______
b. ______
9. ______
10. ______ (grid in)
11. ______ (grid in)
12. a. ______
b. ______

Extended Response

Record your answers for Question 13 on the back of this paper.

Chapter 13 69 Glencoe Pre-Algebra

Create practice worksheets or tests that align to your state's standards as well as TIMSS and NAEP tests.

Additional Answer

13a.

Stem	Leaf
6	7 9
7	0 2 2 3 4 4 5 6 6 6 6 8 9 9
8	0 1 3 4

$6 | 7 = 67°F$

Page 730, Lesson 13-1 (Why?)

a. no; Sample answer: Because one player is much taller than the rest of the team, the average of the heights is actually much greater than most of the heights of the players on the team.

b. yes; Sample answer: The average would be much closer to the heights of the players because the tallest player is no longer on the team.

Pages 734–735, Lesson 13-1

18a. 35 years old; Sample answer:

$$\frac{29 + 25 + 26 + 31 + 28 + 23 + 21 + 25 + x}{9} = 27 \text{ or}$$

$$\frac{208 + x}{9} = 27 \text{ So, } x = 35.$$

18b. Sample answer: The new player must be 25 years or younger. When the ages are listed in order from least to greatest, any age added before the original median will make the median age 25.

19. Sample answer: The median home price would be useful because it is not affected by the cost of the very expensive homes. The cost of half the homes in the county would be greater than the median cost and half would be less.

20. A data set can have more than mode, but can only have one median. For example, the data set: 11, 12, 12, 14, 15, 15, 16 . The mode is 12 and 15. The median is 14.

21. Sample answer: The median; the mean is affected by the extreme value of 175, and there is no mode.

Completed Passes in the NFL

Player	Number of Passes
Jon Kitna	372
Peyton Manning	362
Carson Palmer	324
Steve McNair	295
Jake Plummer	175

Source: National Football League

The median is 324 passes.

29. **Ages of Basketball Players**

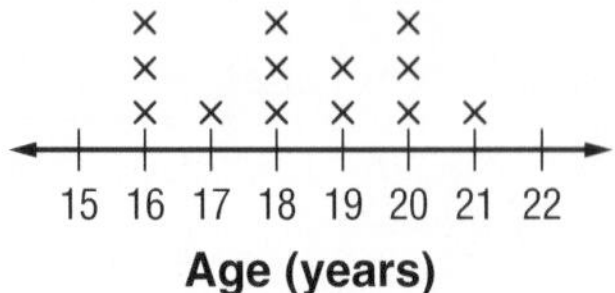

Page 737, Lesson 13-2 (Why?)

a. Sample answer: Even though the intervals are the same, the data is not distributed evenly because the number of pieces of data in each interval are not the same.

b. Sample answer: You can see how the data is distributed.

Page 737, Lesson 13-2 (Check Your Progress)

1. **Exercising Times**

Stem	Leaf
1	0 5
2	0 3 8
3	0 0 8 9
4	0 2 5 5
5	
6	0 5
	4|2 = 42 min

Page 739, Lesson 13-2

1. **Test Scores**

Stem	Leaf
7	2 3 6 6 9
8	0 0 1 4
9	9
	8|1 = 81 points

2. **Height of Plants**

Stem	Leaf
4	0 1 8
5	0 1 1 5 7 7 7 8
6	7 7 7 8
	5|7 = 57 in

5. **Ages of People in Spinning Class**

Stem	Leaf
1	8
2	0 1 2 2 3 6 7 7
3	0 3 5 9
4	0 2 9
5	5
	2|8 = 28 years

6. **Video Game Ownership**

Stem	Leaf
1	8 9
2	0 1 2 4 5 7 8 9
3	0 0 2
	2|8 = 28 students

7. **Tennis Shoe Cost**

Stem	Leaf
5	0 9
6	0 5 5
7	0 5 6 8
8	0 0
9	6
	5|9 = $59

8. **Number of Applicants**

Stem	Leaf
6	7
7	
8	6 6 8 8
9	0 0 7 8 9
10	0 2 3 4 6 9
	6|7 = 67 people

Page 741, Lesson 13-2

14. Sample answer: The NL is spread out more with an extreme value of 200. It also has a slightly higher median of 96.5 versus 92.

Baseball Stats

American League	Stem	National League
7 2	5	5 6
	6	4 5 8 9
8 8 2	7	
8 1	8	6
6	9	6 7
3	10	0 5 9
2	11	9
3	12	
9 1	13	7 8
4	14	
	15	
	16	
	17	
	18	
	19	
	20	0

2|5 = 52 bases *5|3 = 53 bases*

Sample answer: The NL is spread out more with an extreme value of 200. It also has a slightly higher median of 96.5 versus 92.

15a. **Test Scores**

Stem	Leaf
0	6
1	3 9
2	0 3
3	2 4 6 8 9
4	6 8 9
5	6 6 9 9 9
6	2 2 3 4 7 8
7	3 3 5 6 6 8 8 8 9 9
8	0 0
	8|0 = 80 points

15b. mean: 55.6; median 60.5; mode; 59 and 78

15c.

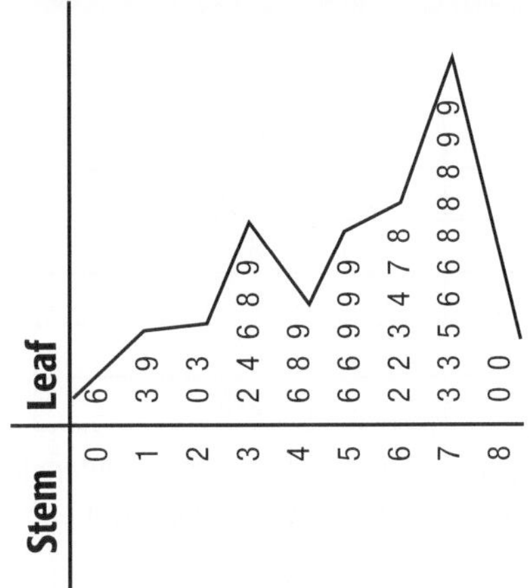

15d. Sample answer: There are two main peaks in the graph with one valley. The graph is not symmetric since the shape is not the same on each side of the graph.

15e. Sample answer: The data set is skewed. Most of the data is on the right side of the graph.

Page 743, Lesson 13-3 (Why?)

b. **Roller Coaster Speeds**

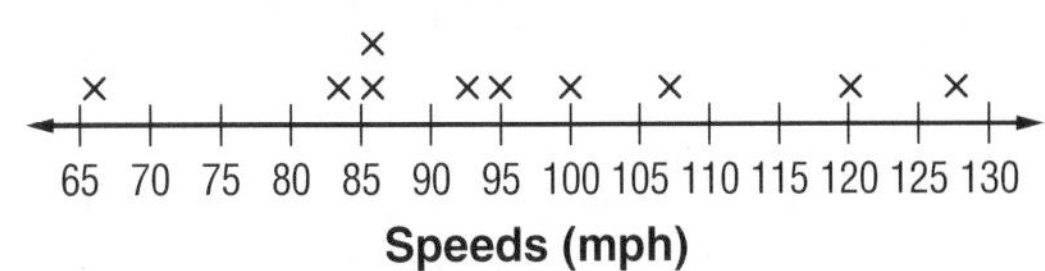

Pages 748–749, Lesson 13-3

9d. The appropriate measure of central tendency to describe the average temperature is the mean or median, since they are roughly about the same for Augusta. The mean is about 55.17; median: 55.5; mode: none

Chapter 13 Answer Appendix

9e. Sample answer: Antelope has a greater range, or spread, of temperatures than Augusta. Both cities have about the same mean average. Augusta has a mean of 55.17 and Antelope has a mean of 54.92. The median for Antelope is only slighter greater than median for Augusta. Since the upper quartile and the lower quartile for Antelope are higher and lower, respectively, than Augusta, it follows that Augusta's high temperatures do not fluctuate as much as Antelope's.

10. Range: 10; Median: −1; Lower Quartile: −3; Upper Quartile: 3; Sample answer: The spread of the data is 10 and the middle score is −1. About one-fourth of the data is below −3 and about one-fourth of the data is above 3.

11. Sample Answer:

Colorado 1-day Lift Ticket Prices for Kids	
Ski Area	**Child Price**
Arapahoe Basin	$24
Aspen Highlands	$52
Howelsen	$10
Loveland	$23
Monarch	$19
Ski Cooper	$18
SolVista	$24
Wolf Creek	$25

Mean: 24.38; Interquartile Range: 6; Mean: 20.43; Interquartile Range: 6; Without the outlier, the mean price is lower and the prices vary less.

14. false; Sample answer: The interquartile range deals with the middle values of a data set.

16. Sample answer: An outlier is a value that is either much larger or much smaller than the median. Therefore, an outlier greatly increases or decreases some of the measures of variation, specifically the range and mean.

21. **Cost of DVDs**

Stem	Leaf
0	9
1	2 4 5 8
2	1 7
3	7
	3|7 = $37

Pages 752–755, Lesson 13-4

1.

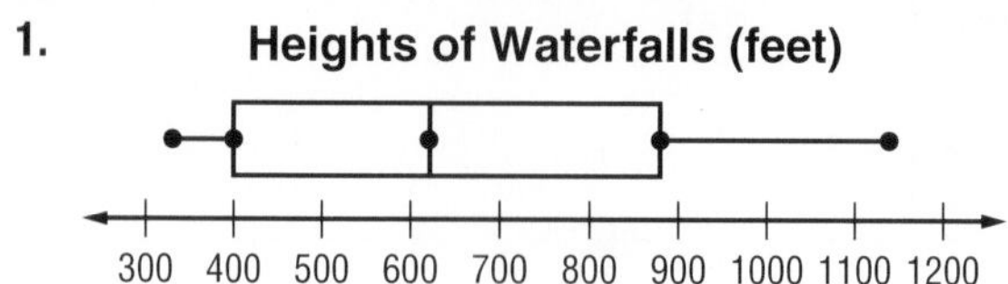

4.

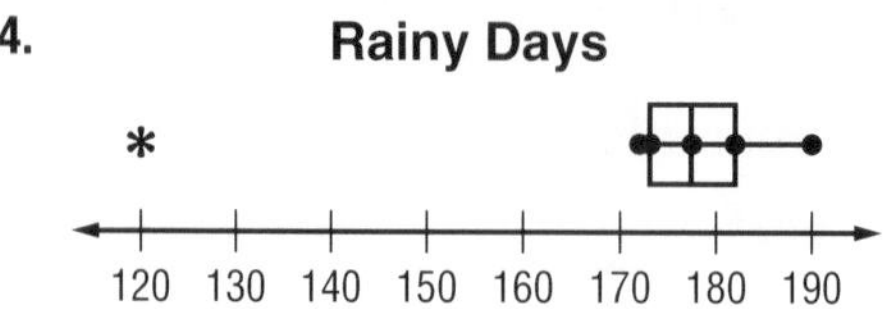

5.

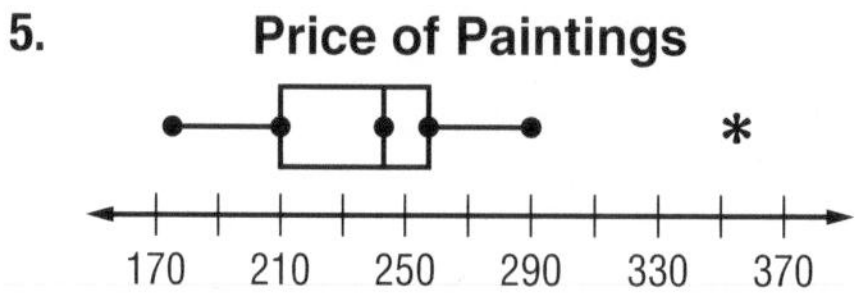

6.

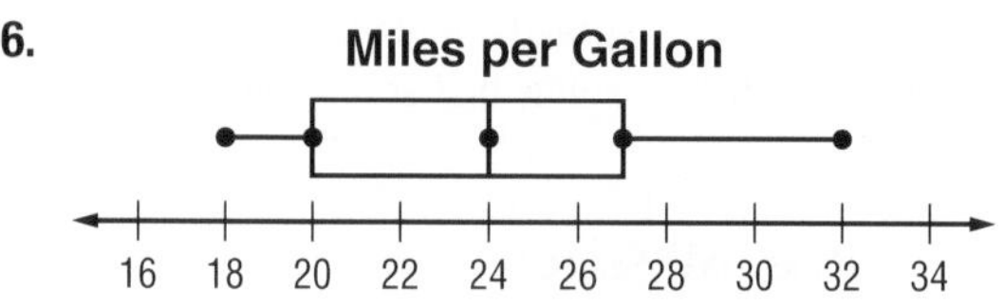

7.

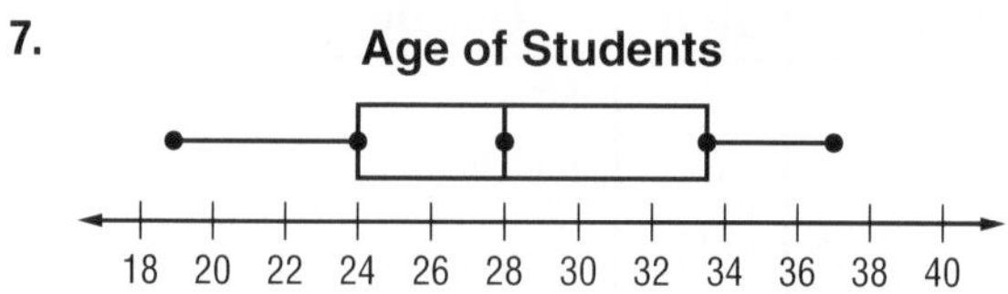

8b. Sample answer: The box indicates that 50% of the values lie between about 2.9 and 3.25. The lower 50% is more concentrated than the upper 50%.

9b. Sample answer: The median divides the data in the box into unequal parts. The left whisker is significantly shorter than the right whisker so the data below the lower quartile is more concentrated than the data above the upper quartile. The data below the upper quartile is more spread out.

15a. 28, 29, 30, 30, 31, 35, 38, 39, 41, 42, 42, 47, 48

15b. at least 21; Sample answer: since 6 students have scores ranging from 38 to 42, there are at most 4 students with scores between 38 and 42. If the measures of variation above are constant, there are at most 4 students with scores between 28 and 30, 30 and 38, 38 and 42, and 42 and 48. Therefore, 16 students are accounted for in these scores, plus the minimum, lower quartile, median, upper quartile, and maximum scores gives a minimum of 21 students.

21a. Rose Bowl: 39, 27, 38, 17.5, 20.5, no outliers; Cotton Bowl: 48, 28, 35, 17, 18, no outliers

21b. Sample answer: The winners of the Cotton Bowl scored more points on average than the winners of the Rose Bowl. The number of points scored by the Cotton Bowl winners varies more than the number of points scored by the Rose Bowl winners. The Rose Bowl data in the middle are more spread out than the Cotton Bowl data.

Page 757, Lesson 13-5 (Check Your Progress)

1.

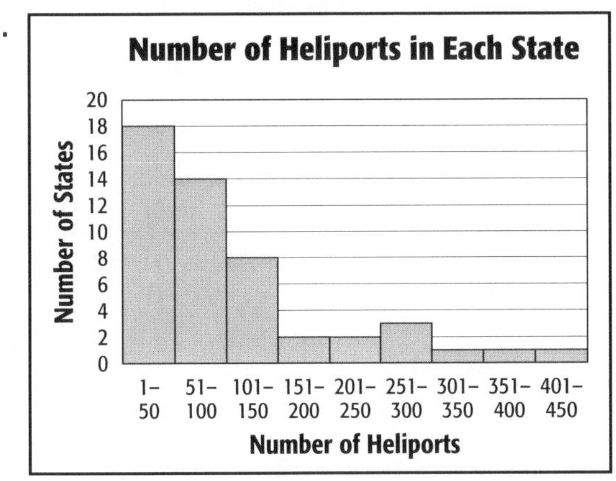

Pages 759–762, Lesson 13-5

1.

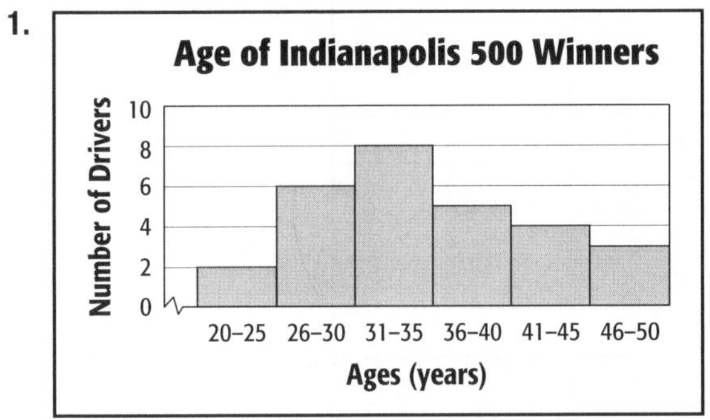

2.

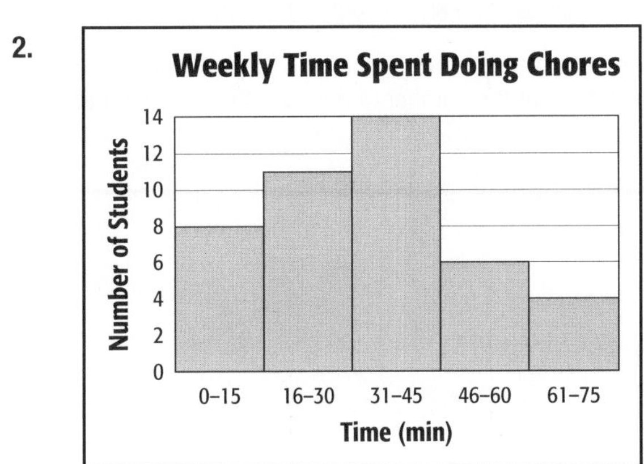

5.

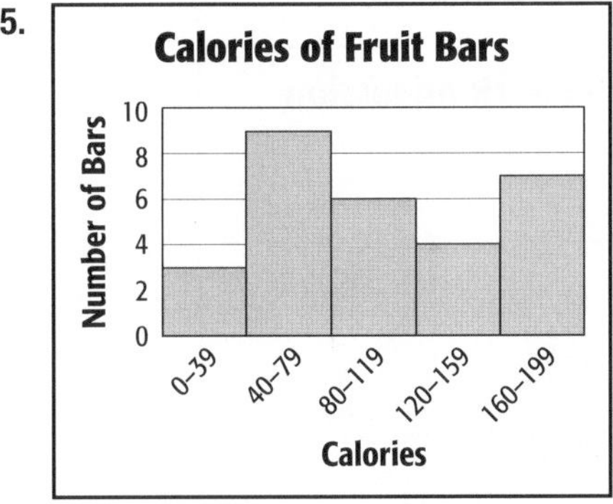

6.

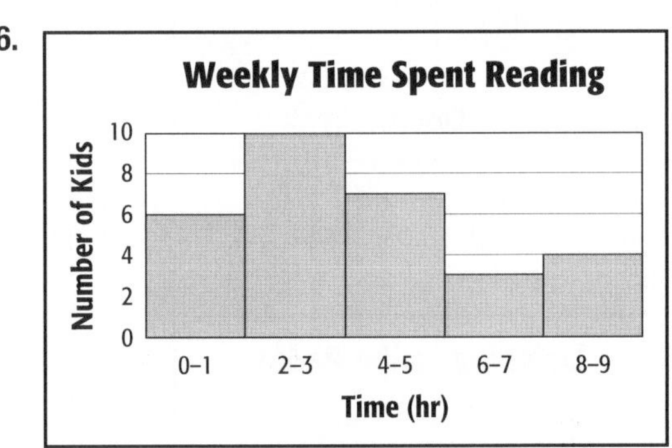

10a. interval size: $5; Sample answer: A five dollar interval range is a good range because the least value is about $25 and the greatest value is about $60.

Price of Ticket ($)	Tally	Frequency
25.00–29.99	II	2
30.00–34.99	IIII	4
35.00–39.99	𝍸	5
40.00–44.99	𝍸 II	7
45.00–49.99	𝍸	5
50.00–54.99	III	3
55.00–59.99	IIII	4

10b.

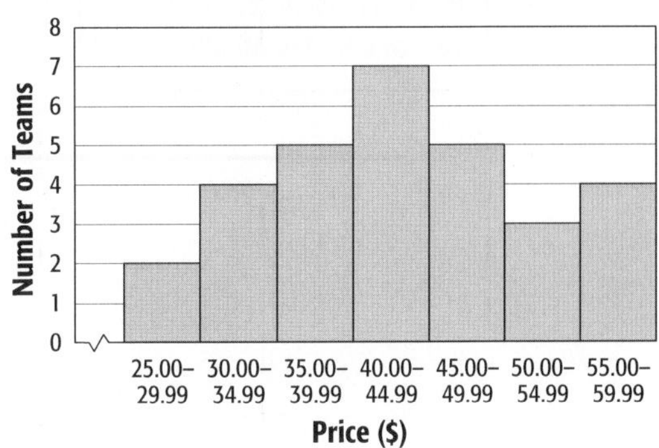

12. Sample answer:

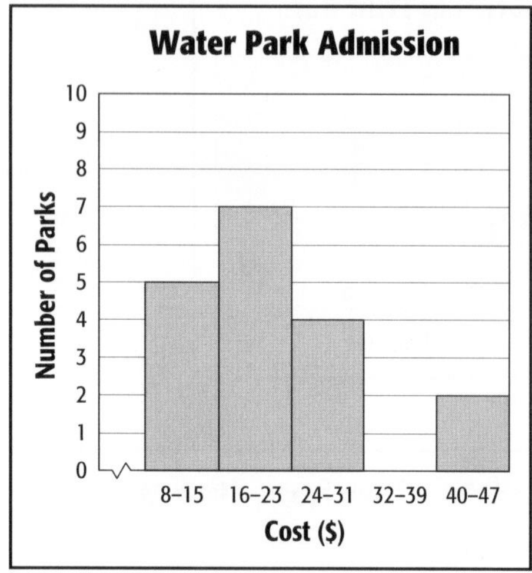

13. Sample answer: 10, 12, 15, 19, 20, 25, 26, 31, 31, 31, 33, 36, 50, 52, 55, 57, 58, 59

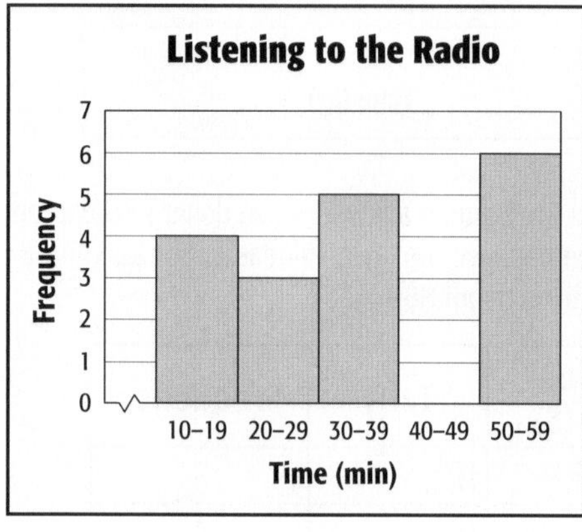

14.

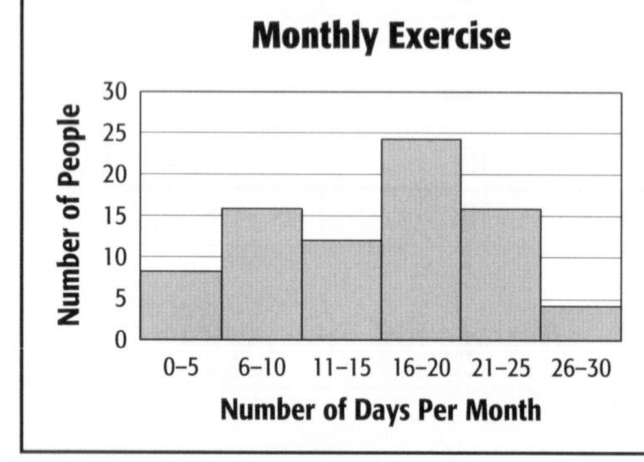

19.

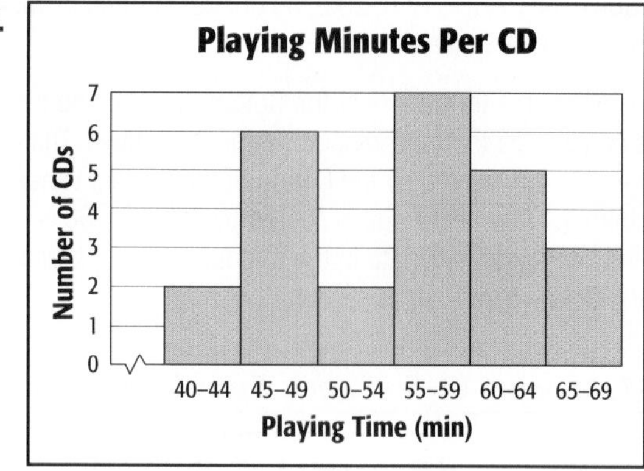

21.

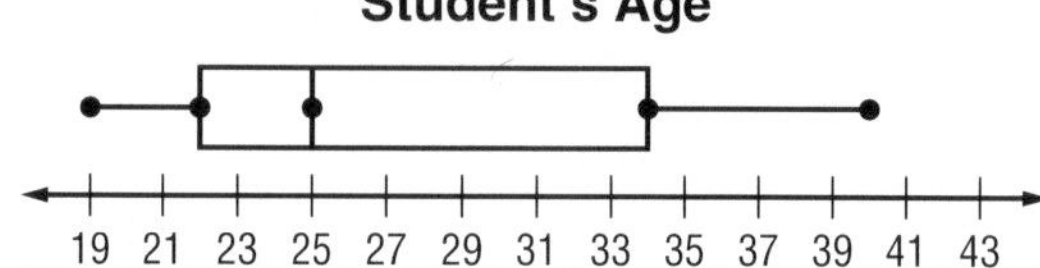

Page 763, Extend 13-5

1.

Interval	Frequency
20–24	3
25–29	2
30–34	3
35–39	7
40–44	4
45–49	7
50–54	4
55–59	4
60–64	2
65–69	4
70–74	0
75–79	1

2. It contains all the possible point totals.

3. It determines interval size by the scale factor x.

6. No; the histogram shows the number of games for a range of point totals, not the number of games with each point total.

7. Sample answer: The stem-and-leaf plot shows intervals of 10 instead of 5. The stem-and-leaf plot is easier to read because you can easily see the different data points.

Stem	Leaf
2	1 2 3 7 9
3	0 1 1 6 7 7 7 7 8 9 9
4	1 3 4 4 5 5 6 6 7 7 7
5	0 2 3 4 5 6 6 9
6	1 1 5 6 9 9
7	5
	5 ǀ 9 = 59 points

Page 764, Mid-Chapter Quiz

7.

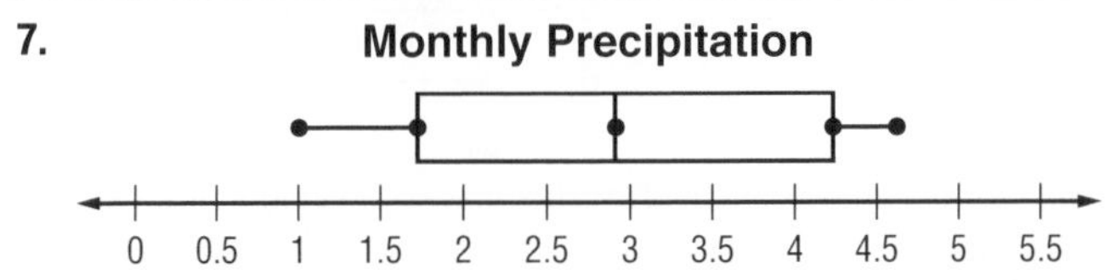

8b. The median divides the data in the box into two unequal parts. So, the data between the lower quartile and the median is more clustered and the data between the median and the upper quartile is more spread out. The whiskers are about the same length but longer than the box, so the data above the upper quartile and below the lower quartile are the most spread out.

9.

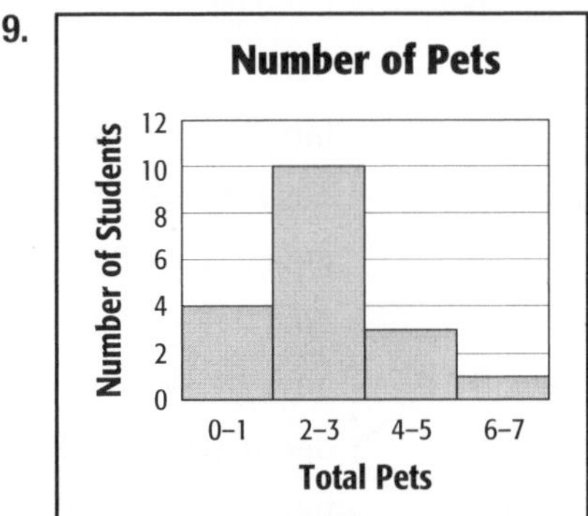

Page 771, Lesson 13-7 (Why?)

b. No; students in the Spanish club may like different types of mascots than other students in the school.

c. A survey must be representative of the entire student population; Survey every 25th student entering the school; Randomly sample 100 students from each grade.

Page 775, Lesson 13-7

15a. Sample answer: They could survey everyone in the school, including the students and staff.

15b. Sample answer: What types of food should we offer at the carnival?; How many and what types of games should we offer?; Would you attend the carnival?

15c. Sample answer: Most importantly, the results could show whether or not they should have the carnival. After that, the results could show what types of food and games they should offer.

16b. no; Sample answer: The statement is not valid because the study only included people that played games online. It isn't 30% of Americans, it's 30% of online gamers.

16c. Sample answer: The study could have been sent to 100,000 people from all over the United States. If most of them respond, a result that is representative of the population could be produced.

19. yes: Sample answer: If questions are asked in a neutral tone, then a more accurate answer can be expected. However, if the person asking the questions changes their tone of voice it can persuade someone to give an inaccurate response.

20. Random sampling of products allows companies to check whether the manufacturing process is running smoothly and producing products without defects. A large percent of defective products alerts the company that there is a problem in the manufacturing process. Answers should include the following: biased method: check the first 50 DVDs out of 1000 in a batch for defects; unbiased method: check every 25th DVD off of the assembly line for defects.

Page 777, Lesson 13-8 (Why?)

a. hexagonal-small, hexagonal-medium, hexagonal-large, hexagonal-x-large, pentagonal-small, pentagonal-medium, pentagonal-large, pentagonal-x-large, rectangular-small, rectangular-medium, rectangular-large, rectangular-x-large

Page 777, Lesson 13-8 (Check Your Progress)

1. 20 outfits

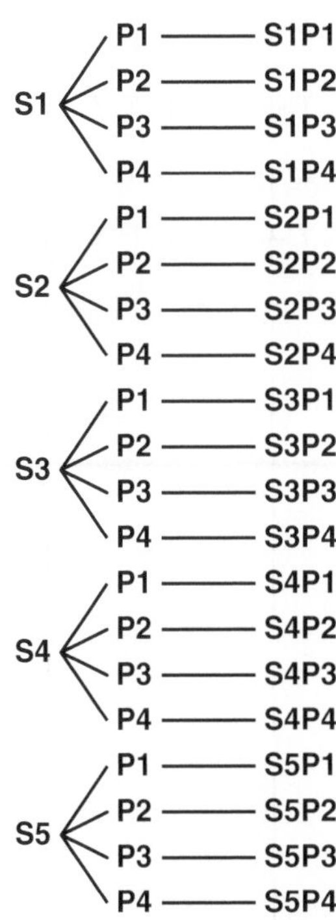

Pages 779–781, Lesson 13-8

1. 6 pairs

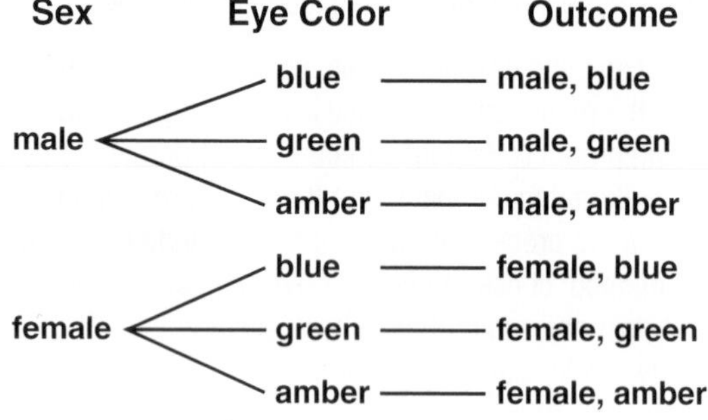

6. 6 outcomes

7. 8 outcomes

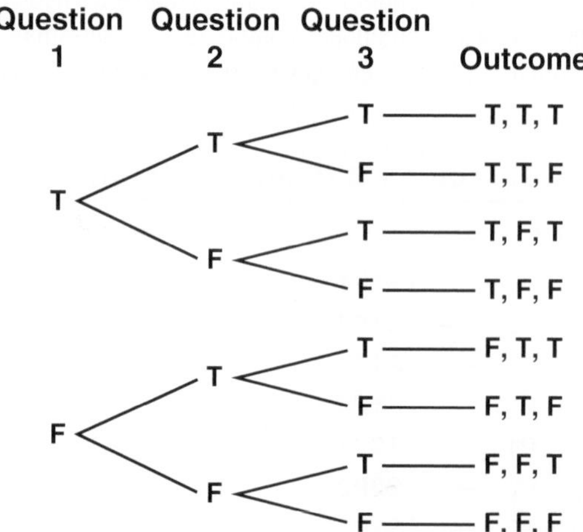

8. 12 outcomes

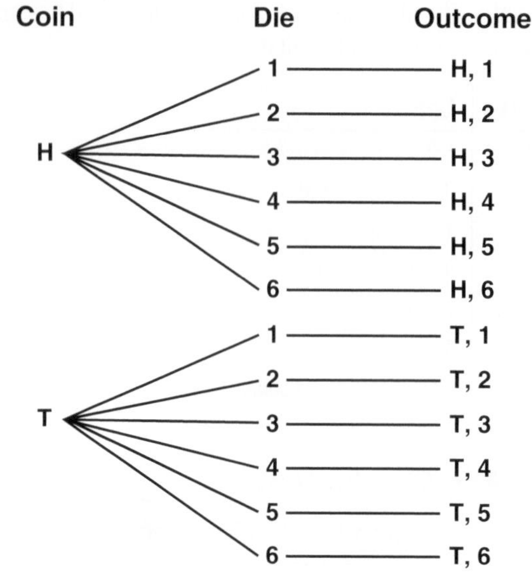

16. Sample answer: School sweatshirts come in four sizes and four colors.

24. 24 outcomes

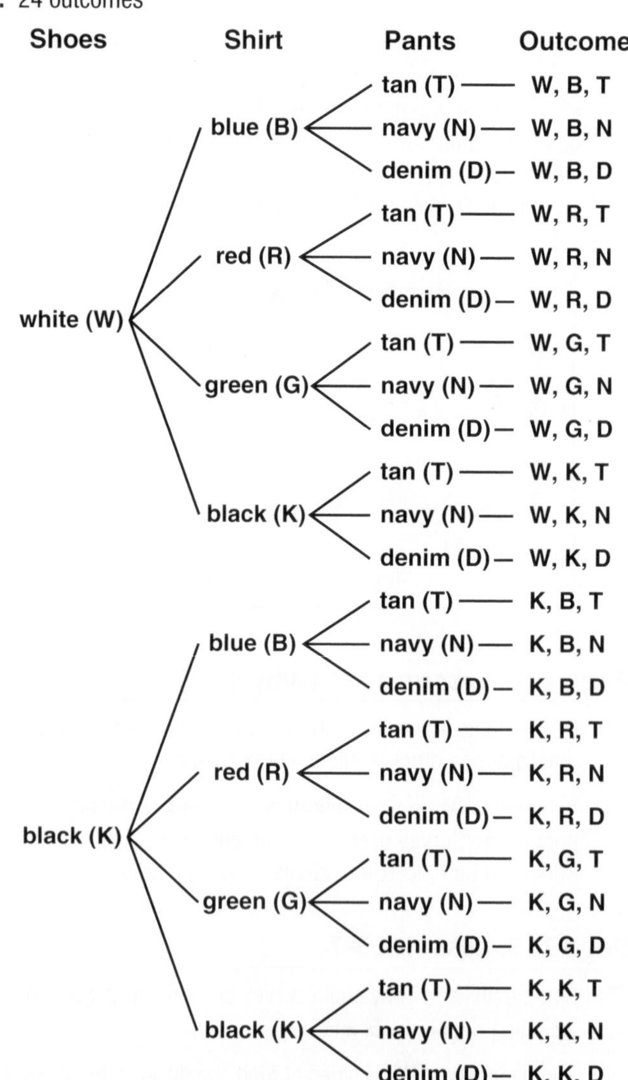

Page 783, Lesson 13-9 (Why?)

a.

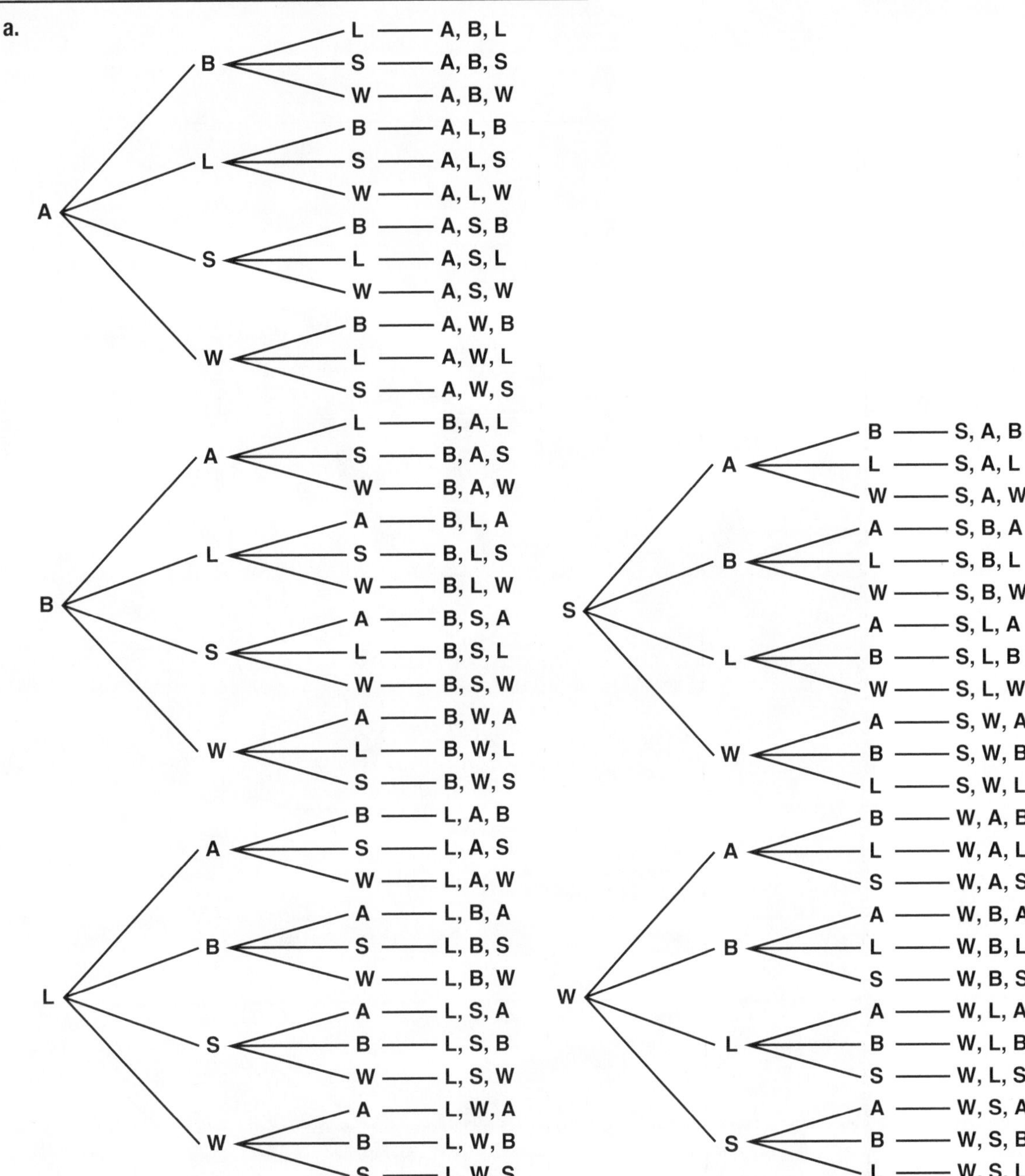

b. first period: 5 choices; second period: 4 choices; third period: 3 choices

Chapter 13 Answer Appendix

Looking Ahead to Algebra 1

The lessons in **Looking Ahead to Algebra 1** help students get ready for the next year by introducing key standards from algebra at a concrete level. In this chapter, students will investigate operations with polynomials using algebra tiles. By presenting these important concepts now, you can help students be better prepared for success in Algebra 1.

Looking Ahead to Algebra 1

Then

You have already multiplied and divided monomials. (Lesson 9-3)

Now

- Add, subtract, multiply, and divide polynomials.
- Use the GCF to factor polynomials.
- Use the FOIL method to factor trinomials.

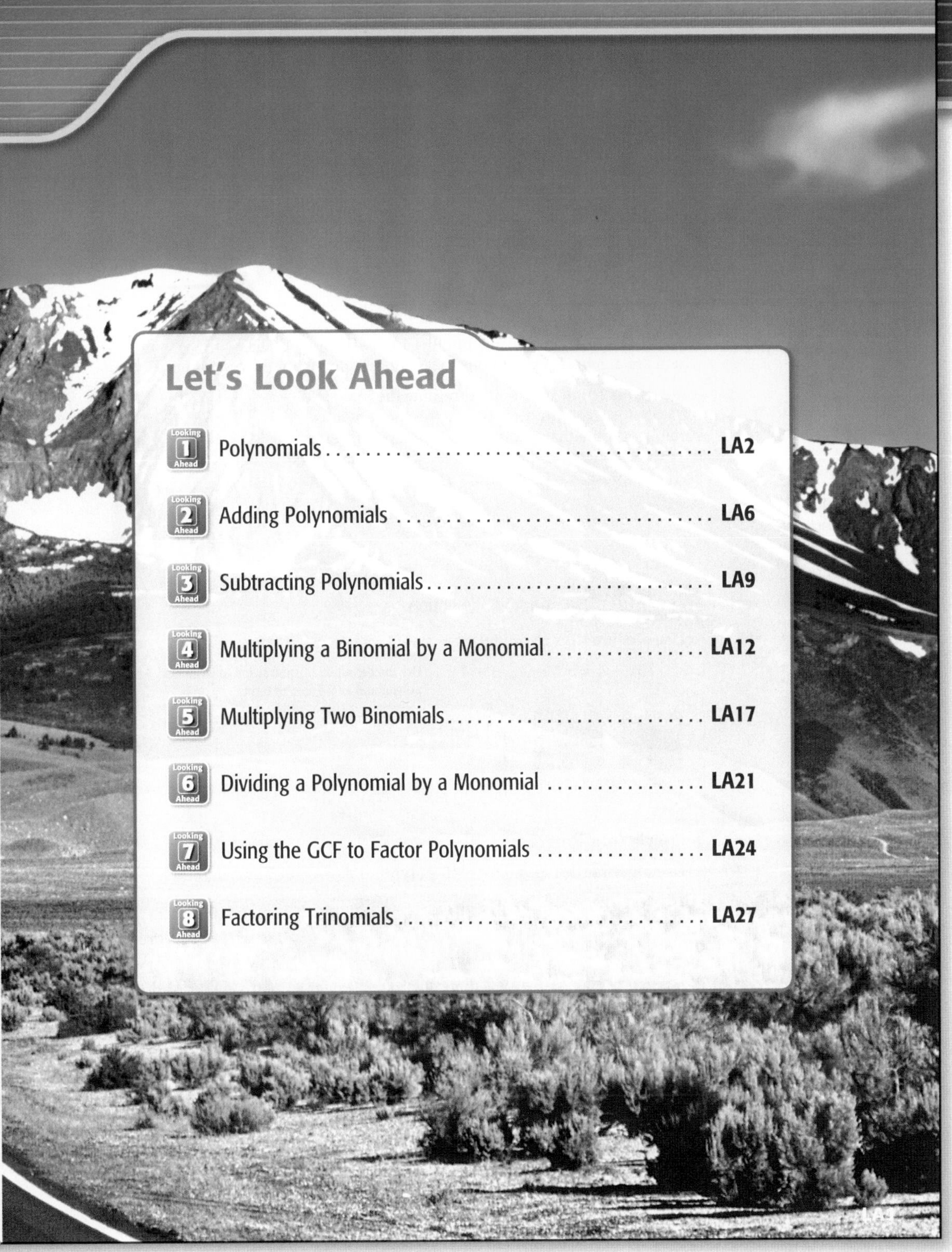

Let's Look Ahead

Lesson Notes

1 FOCUS

Vertical Alignment

Before Lesson LA-1
Simplify algebraic expressions.

Lesson LA-1
Use models to simplify polynomials.
Use polynomials to represent real-world problems.

After Lesson LA-1
Add and subtract polynomials.

2 TEACH

Scaffolding Questions

Have students read the *Why?* section of the lesson and answer the questions.

Ask:

- What does y represent? the number of notebooks
- Which two items cost the same? pencils and erasers
- What would it cost for 2 pencils, 1 notebook, and 1 eraser? 40 cents

Polynomials

Example 1 shows how to model polynomials using algebra tiles. **Examples 2 and 3** show how to use algebra tiles to simplify polynomials.

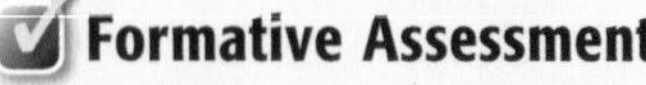

Formative Assessment

Use the Check Your Progress exercises after each example to determine students' understanding of concepts.

Additional Example

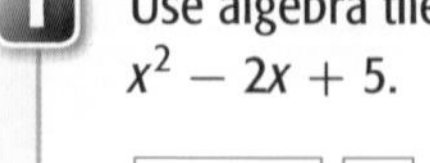

1 Use algebra tiles to model $x^2 - 2x + 5$.

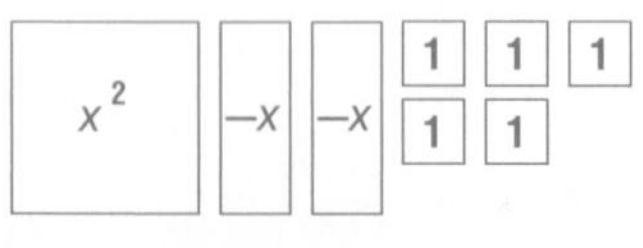

Then
You have already simplified algebraic expressions. (Lesson 4-2)

Now
- Use models to simplify polynomials.
- Use polynomials to represent real-world problems.

New Vocabulary
polynomial

Math Online
glencoe.com
- Extra Examples
- Personal Tutor
- Self-Check Quiz
- Homework Help

Polynomials

Why?

The value of x pencils that cost 5 cents is $5x$ cents.

a. Write an expression to represent the value in cents of y spiral notebooks that cost 25 cents each. $25y$

b. If erasers cost 5 cents each, write an expression to represent the total value of x pencils, y spiral notebooks, and z erasers. $5x + 25y + 5z$

Polynomials You can use algebra tiles to model monomials and **polynomials**, which are algebraic expressions that contain more than one monomial.

A tile that is 1 unit by 1 unit represents the integer 1. A tile that is 1 unit by x units is represented by the variable x. A tile that is x units by x units represents the expression x^2. Red tiles with the same shapes are used to represent -1, $-x$, and $-x^2$.

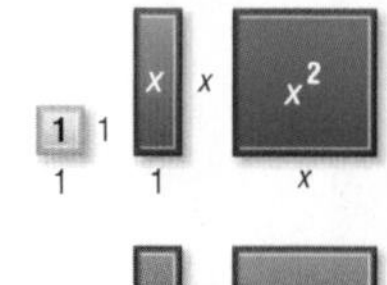

EXAMPLE 1 Model Polynomials

Use algebra tiles to model $x^2 - 3x + 4$.

$x^2 - 3x + 4 = x^2 + (-3x) + 4$ Use the definition of subtraction to write the polynomial as the sum of terms.

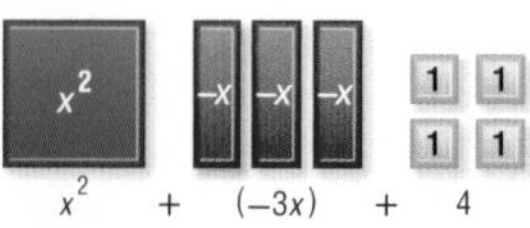

Check Your Progress

Use algebra tiles to model each polynomial. 1A–1B. See margin.

1A. $5x - 6$ **1B.** $2x^2 + 4x + 3$

Personal Tutor glencoe.com

Recall that *like terms* are terms that contain the same variable. When working with polynomials, like terms contain the same variable and exponent.

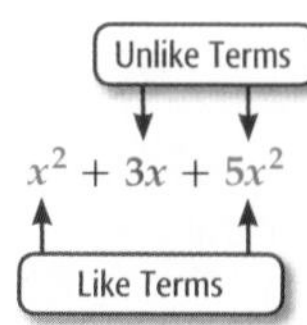

When simplifying polynomials, it is customary to write the result in *standard form*. That is, write the powers of the variable in decreasing order from left to right.

Standard form	Not standard form
$-3x^2 + 4x + 1$	$4x - 3x^2 + 1$

Additional Answers

1A.

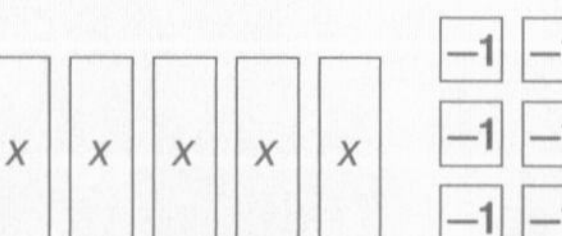

1B.

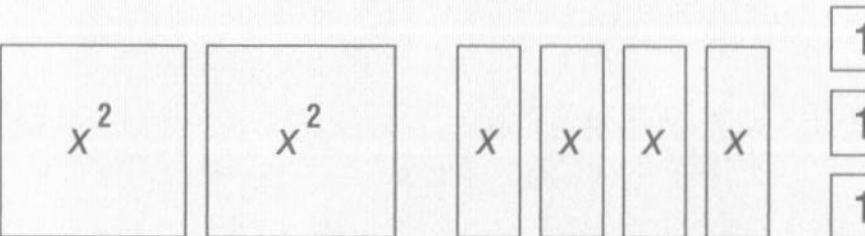

Vocabulary Review

Monomial An expression that is a number, a variable, or a product of numbers and/or variables. (Lesson 9–2)

EXAMPLE 2 Simplify Polynomials

Simplify $-3 + 4x + x^2 + x$.

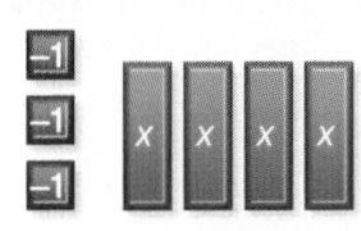

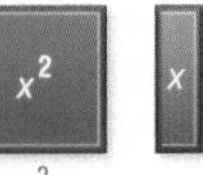

$-3 + 4x + x^2 + x$

Group tiles with the same shape. Then write a polynomial.

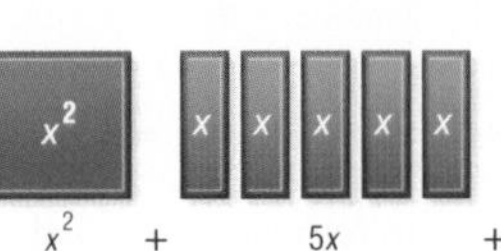
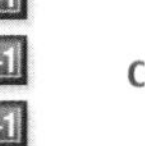

$x^2 + 5x + (-3)$

Combine like terms.

So, $-3 + 4x + x^2 + x = x^2 + 5x + (-3)$ or $x^2 + 5x - 3$.

Simplify each polynomial. Use models if needed.

2A. $-x + 1 - 2x + 5$ $\mathbf{-3x + 6}$

2B. $x^2 + 4 + 3x + x^2$ $\mathbf{2x^2 + 3x + 4}$

Personal Tutor glencoe.com

When a positive tile and a negative tile of the same shape are paired, the result is a *zero pair*. Remove any zero pairs when simplifying polynomials.

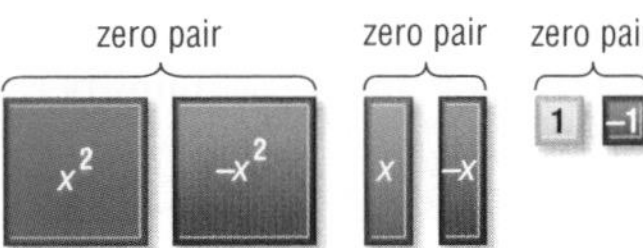

EXAMPLE 3 Remove Zero Pairs to Simplify Polynomials

Simplify $2x^2 - 3x - x^2$.

$2x^2 - 3x - x^2 = 2x^2 + (-3x) + (-x^2)$ Write the polynomial as the sum of terms.

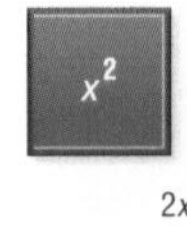

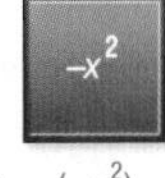

$2x^2 + (-3x) + (-x^2)$

Group tiles with the same shape. Then write a polynomial.

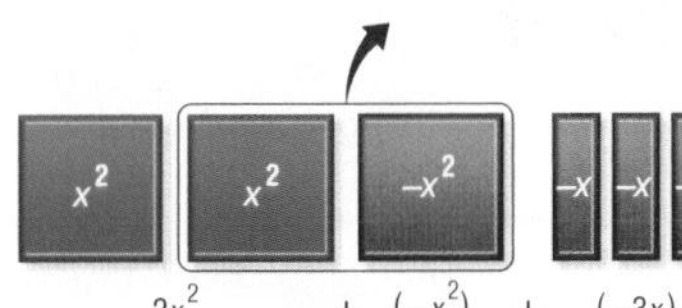

$2x^2 + (-x^2) + (-3x)$

Remove the zero pairs and combine like terms.

So, $2x^2 - 3x - x^2 = x^2 - 3x$.

Check Your Progress

Simplify each polynomial. Use models if needed.

3A. $6 - 2x^2 + 3x^2$ $\mathbf{x^2 + 6}$

3B. $-2x^2 + 5 - 1 + x^2$ $\mathbf{-x^2 + 4}$

Personal Tutor glencoe.com

Additional Examples

Simplify $-2 + 3x + 5x^2 + 4x$. $5x^2 + 7x - 2$

Simplify $2x^2 - 3x^2 + 2$. $-x^2 + 2$

Additional Examples also in Interactive Classroom PowerPoint® Presentations

IWB INTERACTIVE WHITEBOARD READY

Tips for New Teachers

Simplify Polynomials Students may think that $x + x = x^2$. Use algebra tiles to demonstrate that $x + x = 2x$. Then use the Distributive Property to show the sum.

$$x + x = 1x + 1x$$
$$= (1 + 1)x$$
$$= 2x$$

Focus on Mathematical Content

Naming Polynomials You can name polynomials according to how many terms are contained in the expression. A **monomial** such as $3x$ has one term, a **binomial** such as $2x + 1$ has two terms, and a **trinomial** such as $3x^2 + 2x - 1$ contains three terms.

Differentiated Instruction

students have difficulty modeling polynomials,

have students work in groups of three. Two students each use algebra tiles to model a two-term polynomial. The third student then combines the tiles, removes any zero pairs, and names the simplified polynomial modeled by the remaining tiles. Students should switch roles and repeat the activity several times.

Use Polynomials

Example 4 shows how to use a polynomial to represent a real-world problem.

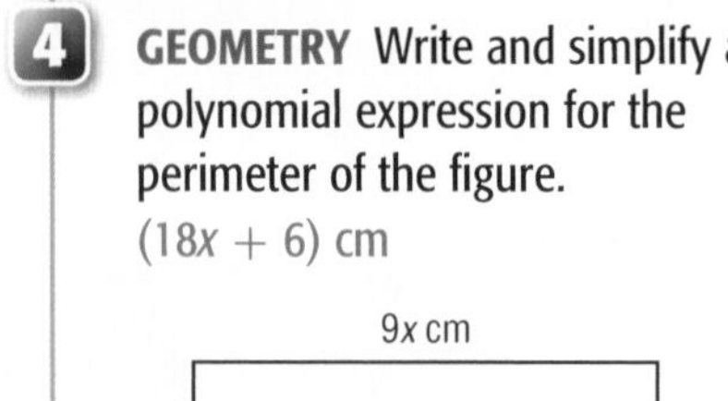

Additional Example

4 **GEOMETRY** Write and simplify a polynomial expression for the perimeter of the figure.
$(18x + 6)$ cm

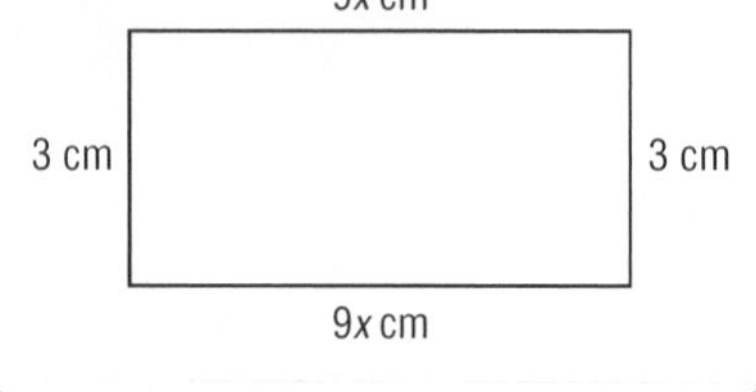

3 PRACTICE

Formative Assessment

Use Exercises 1–9 to check for understanding.

Use the chart at the bottom of this page to customize assignments for your students.

Additional Answers

1.

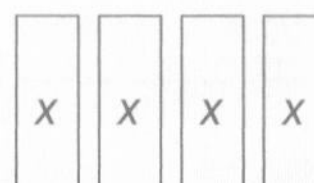

2.

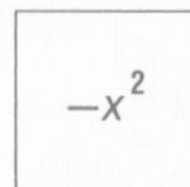
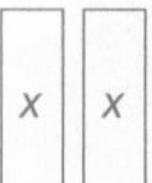

10.

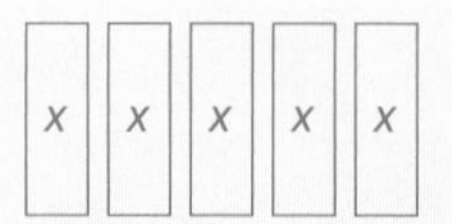

Use Polynomials Polynomials can represent real-world problems.

Real-World EXAMPLE 4 Use a Polynomial

GEOMETRY Write and simplify a polynomial expression for the perimeter of the rectangle.

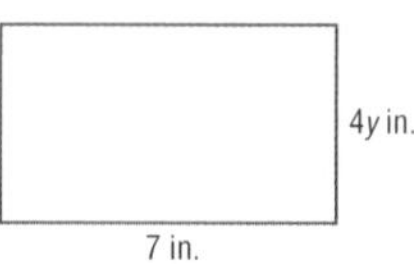

$P = 4y + 4y + 7 + 7$ **Definition of perimeter**

$= (8y + 14)$ in. **Combine like terms.**

Check Your Progress

4. CRAFTS Charlie bought a model airplane kit for \$5, three small jars of paint for \$$x$ each, and a bottle of glue for \$2. Write and simplify a polynomial expression to represent the total amount of money he spent. $5 + 3x + 2$; $3x + 7$

Personal Tutor glencoe.com

Check Your Understanding

Example 1 p. LA2

Use algebra tiles to model each polynomial. 1–2. See margin.

1. $3x^2 + 4x$ **2.** $-x^2 + 2x + 5$

Examples 2 and 3 p. LA3

Simplify each polynomial. Use models if needed.

3. $2x + 3 + 3x$ $5x + 3$ **4.** $x^2 - 3x + x$ $x^2 - 2x$

5. $1 + 2x + 4 + x$ $3x + 5$ **6.** $x^2 - 6x + 4x$ $x^2 - 2x$

7. $3x^2 + 5x - x^2 + 2x$ $2x^2 + 7x$ **8.** $-2x^2 + 7 + 3x - x^2 - 5x$

8. $-3x^2 - 2x + 7$

Example 4 p. LA4

9. GEOMETRY Write and simplify a polynomial expression for the perimeter of the parallelogram. $(6a + 16)$ cm

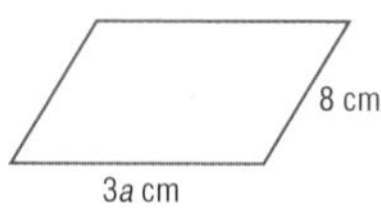

Practice and Problem Solving

Example 1 p. LA2

Use algebra tiles to model each polynomial. 10–13. See margin.

10. $5x - 1$ **11.** $x^2 + 6$

12. $2x^2 - x + 3$ **13.** $-x^2 + 6x - 4.$

Examples 2 and 3 p. LA3

Simplify each polynomial.

14. $5 + x + 2$ $x + 7$ **15.** $-x^2 + 4x - x^2$ $-2x^2 + 4x$

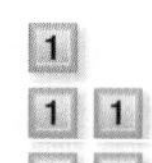

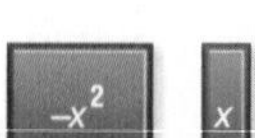

Differentiated Homework Options

Level	Assignment	Two-Day Option	
AL Basic	10–27, 34, 36, 37	11–27 odd	10–26 even, 34, 36, 37
OL Core	11–27 odd, 28, 29–33 odd, 34, 36, 37	10–27	28–34, 36, 37
BL Advanced	28–37		

Examples 2 and 3 p. LA3

Simplify each polynomial. Use models if needed.

16. $x^2 - x + 4 + 2x - 3$ $\mathbf{x^2 + x + 1}$

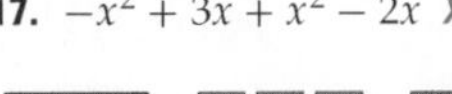

17. $-x^2 + 3x + x^2 - 2x$ $\mathbf{x}$

18. $x^2 + 7 + 3x^2$ $\mathbf{4x^2 + 7}$

19. $9 - 5x - 2x + 2$ $\mathbf{-7x + 11}$

20. $-2x^2 + x - 3x^2 - 6$ $\mathbf{-5x^2 + x - 6}$

21. $7x - 8 + 2x + 4x^2 + x^2$ $\mathbf{5x^2 + 9x - 8}$

22. $-6x + 4 + 2x + 7$ $\mathbf{-4x + 11}$

23. $5 - x^2 + 7x + 4x^2$ $\mathbf{3x^2 + 7x + 5}$

24. $4x^2 + 5x + 1 - 4x^2 - 6x$ $\mathbf{-x + 1}$

25. $6 + 2x^2 - 3x - 4x - x^2$ $\mathbf{x^2 - 7x + 6}$

Example 4 p. LA4

26. GEOMETRY Write and simplify a polynomial expression for the perimeter of the trapezoid. **(6k + 24) mm**

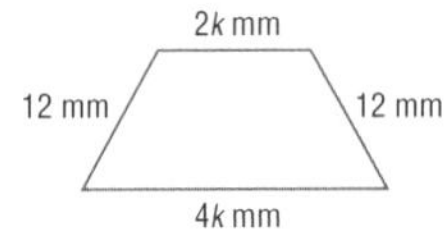

27. EXERCISE Taylor jogged x miles after school. Seth jogged twice the distance that Taylor jogged. Rashida jogged 4 miles. Write and simplify a polynomial expression to represent the total number of miles that the three students jogged. $\mathbf{x + 2x + 4; (3x + 4)}$ **mi**

28. PIZZA For a party, one classroom ordered 4 large pizzas, 2 medium pizzas, and 6 subs. Another classroom ordered 6 large pizzas and 8 subs. If ℓ represents the cost of a large pizza, m represents the cost of a medium pizza, and s represents the cost of a sub, write an expression in simplest form for the total amount of money that the two classrooms spent on food. $\mathbf{10\ell + 2m + 14s}$

29. JOBS Michael and Olivia each earn x dollars per lawn that they mow and y dollars per hour for babysitting. The table shows how many lawns each mowed and how many hours each babysat. Write an expression in simplest form for the total amount of money they earned together. $\mathbf{17x + 10y}$

	Number of Lawns	Number of Hours Babysitting
Michael	8	6
Olivia	9	4

Simplify each polynomial.

30. $1.5t^2 - 7.6 + 4t - 2t^2 + t - 5.1$

31. $10 + 6c^3 - c^2 - 2c^3 + 2c^2 - 4c^2$

32. $\frac{1}{2}n^2 - 6n - \frac{3}{4}n + 7n$ $\mathbf{\frac{1}{2}n^2 + \frac{1}{4}n}$

33. $4a^2 + 2b - b^2 - 6b + 3a^2 - 5a$ $\mathbf{7a^2 - b^2 - 5a - 4b}$

30. $\mathbf{-0.5t^2 + 5t - 12.7}$

31. $\mathbf{4c^3 - 3c^2 + 10}$

H.O.T. Problems

Use **H**igher-**O**rder **T**hinking Skills

34. OPEN ENDED Write a polynomial with four terms that simplifies to $x^2 + 3x$. **Sample answer:** $\mathbf{2x^2 - x^2 + 2x + x}$

35. CHALLENGE Determine whether $x^2 + 6x = 7x^2$ is *always*, *sometimes*, or *never* true. Explain your reasoning. **sometimes; true only if** $\mathbf{x = 0}$ **or** $\mathbf{x = 1}$

36. REASONING Explain how you can tell from a model whether a polynomial will have at most one term, two terms, or three terms when it is simplified. **36–37. See margin.**

37. WRITING IN MATH Describe how you can use models to simplify polynomial expressions.

Differentiated Instruction

Extension Using algebra tiles, have students write a polynomial expression for the perimeter of each figure. rectangle: $8x^2 + 6$; triangle: $2w^2 + 5w + 16$

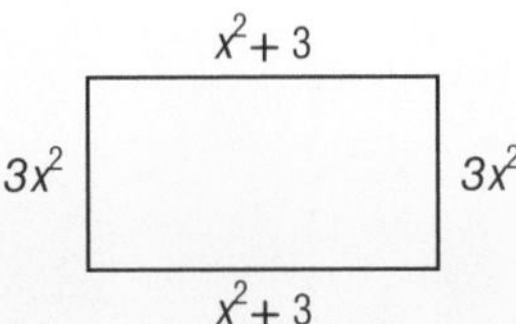

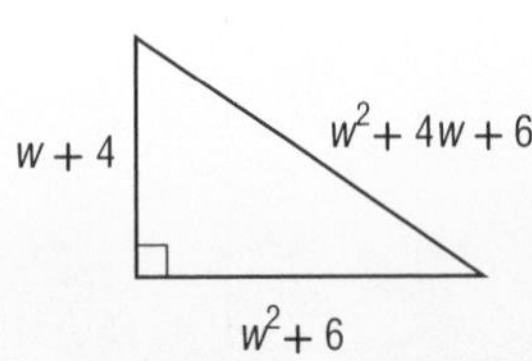

4 ASSESS

Name the Math Have students explain how zero pairs can be used to simplify polynomials with positive and negative terms. Suggest that they draw pictures to help with their explanation.

Tips for New Teachers

Simplifying Polynomials Remind students that the variable has to be the same power in order to be simplified. For example, $3r^2 + 2r^3 + r^2 = 4r^2 + 3r^3$.

Additional Answers

11.

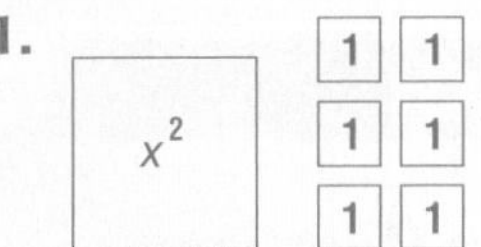

12.

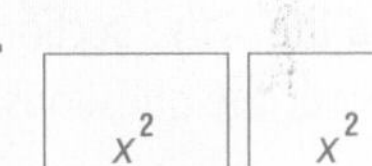
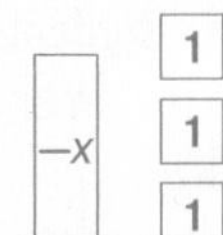

13.

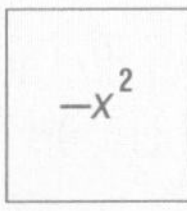
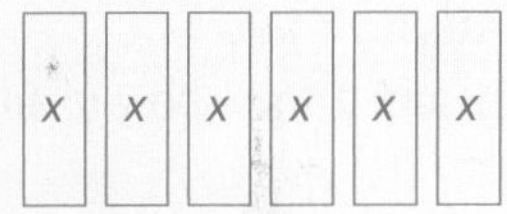
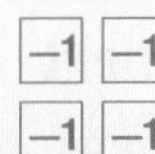

36. A polynomial that has tiles of one size will have one term when simplified. If it has tiles of two sizes, it will have two terms when simplified. If it has tiles of three sizes, it will have three terms when simplified.

37. Sample answer: First, model each term of the polynomial. Then group tiles with the same shape. Remove zero pairs if possible. The tiles remaining represent the simplified polynomial.

Lesson Notes

FOCUS

Vertical Alignment

Before Lesson LA-2
Solve equations by adding.

Lesson LA-2
Add polynomials. Find perimeter by adding polynomials.

After Lesson LA-2
Subtract polynomials.

TEACH

Scaffolding Questions

Have students read the *Why?* section of the lesson and answer the questions.

Ask:

- How many phone calls do Lauren and Javier have altogether? 63
- How many text messages do Lauren and Javier have altogether? 99

Adding Polynomials

Examples 1 and 2 show how to add polynomials.

Formative Assessment

Use the Check Your Progress exercises after each example to determine students' understanding of concepts.

Additional Example

Add. Use models if needed.

a. $(4x + 5) + (2x + 5)$
$6x + 10$

b. $(3x^2 - 2x + 1) + (-x + 3)$
$3x^2 - 3x + 4$

Adding Polynomials

Then
You have already solved equations by adding. (Lesson 4-3)

Now

- Add polynomials.
- Find perimeter by adding polynomials.

Math Online
glencoe.com

- Extra Examples
- Personal Tutor
- Self-Check Quiz
- Homework Help

Why?

Lauren has 38 phone calls and 47 text messages on her cell phone bill. Javier has 25 phone calls and 52 text messages on his cell phone bill.

a. The expression 38 calls + 47 texts represents the items on Lauren's phone bill. Write an expression for the items on Javier's phone bill. **25 calls + 52 text messages**

b. Write an expression for the total number of calls and text messages. **63 calls + 99 text messages**

Adding Polynomials You can use models to add polynomials.

EXAMPLE 1 Add Polynomials

Add. Use models if needed.

a. $(3x + 4) + (2x + 1)$

Step 1 Model each polynomial.

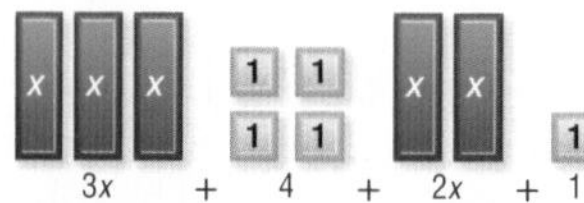

Step 2 Combine the tiles that have the same shape.

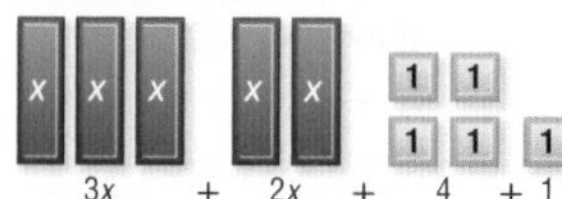

Step 3 Write the polynomial for the combined tiles.

$(3x + 4) + (2x + 1) = 5x + 5$

b. $(2x^2 - 4x + 2) + (-2x + 2)$

$$\begin{array}{rl} 2x^2 - 4x + 2 & \\ -2x + 2 & \text{Arrange like terms in columns.} \\ \hline 2x^2 - 6x + 4 & \text{Add.} \end{array}$$

So, $(2x^2 - 4x + 2) + (-2x + 2) = 2x^2 - 6x + 4$.

Check Your Progress

1A. $(x^2 + x - 3) + (3x^2 - 4)$ **1B.** $(-2x^2 - x + 1) + (-x^2 - 3x)$

1A. $4x^2 + x - 7$
1B. $-3x^2 - 4x + 1$

Personal Tutor glencoe.com

EXAMPLE 2 Use Zero Pairs to Add Polynomials

Add $(-2x^2 + 3x + 2) + (x^2 - x + 4)$.

Model the polynomials.

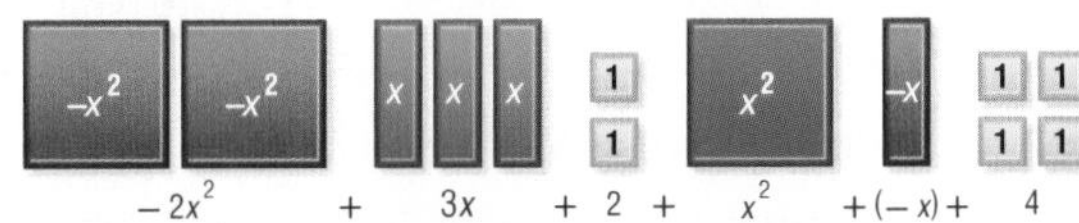

Group tiles with the same shape. Then remove any zero pairs.

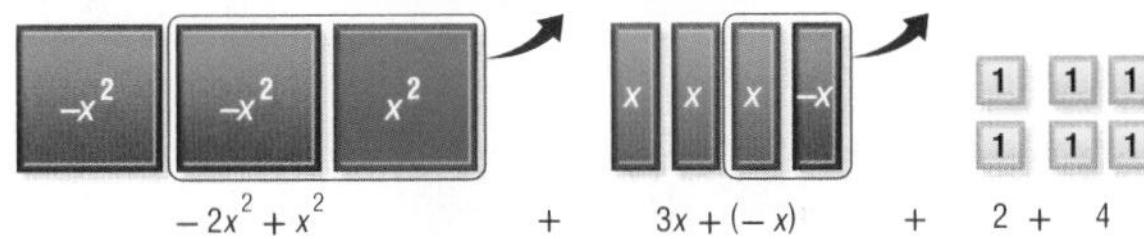

So, $(-2x^2 + 3x + 2) + (x^2 - x + 4) = -x^2 + 2x + 6$.

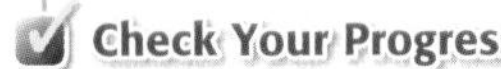

Check Your Progress

Add. Use models if needed. 2B. $-x^2 + x - 4$

2A. $(-3x^2 + 2x) + (3x^2 + 4x)$ $6x$

2B. $(x^2 - 4x - 1) + (-2x^2 + 5x - 3)$

Personal Tutor glencoe.com

Find Perimeter Polynomials can be used to find perimeter.

Real-World EXAMPLE 3 Use Polynomials to Find Perimeter

GEOMETRY The lengths of the sides of golden rectangles are in the ratio 1:1.62. So, the length of a golden rectangle is approximately 1.62 times greater than its width.

a. Write the formula for the perimeter of a golden rectangle.

$P = 2\ell + 2w$	Formula for the perimeter of a rectangle
$P = 2(1.62x) + 2x$	Replace ℓ with $1.62x$ and w with x.
$P = 3.24x + 2x$ or $5.24x$	Simplify.

The formula is $P = 5.24x$, where x is the measure of the width.

b. Find the perimeter of a golden rectangle if its width is 8.3 centimeters.

$P = 5.24x$	Perimeter of a golden rectangle
$= 5.24(8.3)$ or 43.492	Replace x with 8.3 and simplify.

The perimeter of the golden rectangle is 43.492 centimeters.

Check Your Progress

3. GEOMETRY A rectangle has side lengths of $(x^2 - 5x)$ units and $(2x^2 + x)$ units.

A. Write the formula for the perimeter of the rectangle. $P = 6x^2 - 8x$

B. Find the perimeter of the rectangle if the value of x is 5.4 units. 131.76 units

Personal Tutor glencoe.com

Real-World Link

The golden ratio has been incorporated in architecture from Ancient Greece to modern architecture.

Additional Example

Add $(-3x^2 + 4x + 2) + (x^2 - 2x + 1)$. $-2x^2 + 2x + 3$

Additional Examples also in Interactive Classroom PowerPoint® Presentations

IWB INTERACTIVE WHITEBOARD READY

Focus on Mathematical Content

Properties The Identity Property of Addition justifies the step of adding or removing a zero pair without changing the value of the set. The Inverse Property of Addition justifies the zero pair model.

Find Perimeter

Example 3 shows how to add polynomials to find the perimeter of a figure.

Additional Example

GEOMETRY A rectangle has a length of $4.6x$ units and a width of x units.

a. Find a formula for the perimeter of the rectangle. $P = 11.2x$

b. Find the perimeter of the rectangle if its width is 3.2 meters. 35.84 m

Differentiated Instruction

Visual Working in pairs, have each student write 4 polynomials in the form $ax^2 + bx + c$, where a, b, and c can be positive or negative numbers. Then have students add the polynomials, each student contributing one polynomial for each sum.

3 PRACTICE

Formative Assessment

Use Exercises 1–5 to check for understanding.

Use the chart at the bottom of this page to customize assignments for your students.

4 ASSESS

Crystal Ball Have students write how adding polynomials might connect with tomorrow's lesson on subtracting polynomials. Encourage students to look ahead to the first page of the next lesson, if needed.

Watch Out!

Preventing Errors Some students may find it helpful to mark through like terms as they combine them. They may also want to highlight the different like terms using different colored highlighters.

Check Your Understanding

Examples 1 and 2 pp. LA6–LA7

Add. Use models if needed. **3.** $x^2 + 3x + 5$ **4.** $-2x^2 - 6x + 6$

1. $(x + 5) + (2x + 3)$ $3x + 8$

2. $(x^2 - 4x) + (x^2 - 5x)$ $2x^2 - 9x$

3. $(2x^2 + 6) + (-x^2 + 3x - 1)$

4. $(x^2 - 7x + 2) + (-3x^2 + x + 4)$

Example 3 p. LA7

5. GEOMETRY Use the figure at the right.

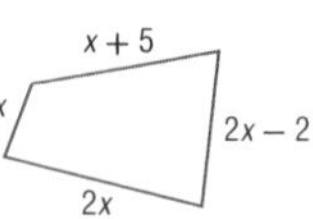

a. Write the formula for the perimeter of the figure. $P = 6x + 3$

b. Find the perimeter of the figure if $x = 4$. 27 units

Practice and Problem Solving

Examples 1 and 2 pp. LA6–LA7

Add. Use models if needed. **8.** $4x^2 - 8x + 1$ **9.** $6x^2 - 4x + 4$

6. $(7x + 5) + (x + 2)$ $8x + 7$

7. $(-x + 3) + (-5x + 6)$ $-6x + 9$

8. $(3x^2 - 7x + 1) + (x^2 - x)$

9. $(6x^2 + 5x) + (-9x + 4)$

10. $(-4x^2 - 2x) + (-x^2 + 2x + 10)$ $-5x^2 + 10$

11. $(-3x^2 + x - 1) + (x^2 + x - 4)$ $-2x^2 + 2x - 5$

Example 3 p. LA7

GEOMETRY For each of the figures, write a formula for the perimeter of the figure. Then find the perimeter of each figure if $x = 0.8$.

12.

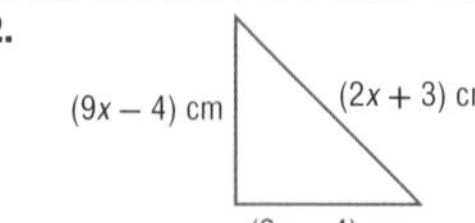

$P = 20x - 5$; 11 cm

13.

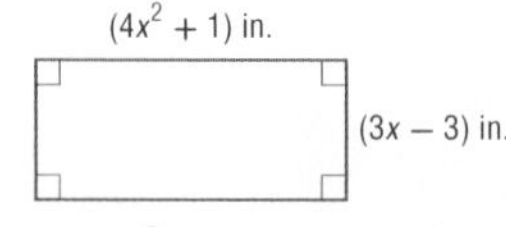

$P = 8x^2 + 6x - 4$; 5.92 in.

14a. $55x + 12$

14b. $68x + 15$

14c. $123x + 27$

18. Sample answer: $(5x^2 - 10x + 4)$ and $(-2x^2 + 2x - 4)$

20. Sample answer: Algebra tiles that represent like terms have the same size and shape. When adding polynomials, a red tile and tile of any other color with the same size and shape form a zero pair and may be removed. The result is the sum of the polynomials.

21. Sample answer: First, combine like terms. Then you can get rid of zero pairs and simplify.

B

14. NEWSPAPERS Anna and Cole each earn x cents per newspaper that they deliver, plus tips. Anna delivered 55 newspapers and earned \$12 in tips. Cole delivered 68 newspapers and earned \$15 in tips.

a. Write a polynomial expression to represent Anna's total earnings.

b. Write a polynomial expression to represent Cole's total earnings.

c. Write a polynomial expression to represent their total earnings.

15. GEOMETRY The angle measures of a triangle are $(x + 15)°$, $(2x - 20)°$, and $2x°$. What are the actual angle measures of the triangle? 52°, 54°, and 74°

C

Add. Use models if needed.

16. $(-2x^3 + 3x^2 + 6x + 1) + (x^3 - 10x^2 - 6x + 9)$ $-x^3 - 7x^2 + 10$

17. $(b^2 + a + 7 - 2b) + (4a^2 + 6b + 4b^2 - 8)$ $5b^2 + 4b + 4a^2 + a - 1$

H.O.T. Problems Use Higher-Order Thinking Skills

18. OPEN ENDED Write two polynomials that have a sum of $3x^2 - 8x$.

19. CHALLENGE What polynomial would you add to $3y^2 - 4y + 2$ to have a sum of $2y^2 + 5$? $-y^2 + 4y + 3$

20. REASONING Explain how algebra tiles represent like terms and zero pairs.

21. WRITING IN MATH Explain how to add polynomials without using numbers.

Differentiated Homework Options

Level	Assignment	Two-Day Option	
AL Basic	6–13, 18, 20, 21	7–13 odd	6–12 even, 18, 20, 21
OL Core	7–11 odd, 12–15, 17, 18, 20, 21	6–13	14–18, 20, 21
BL Advanced	14–21		

Subtracting Polynomials

Why?

A store had 14 video game systems and then received x more video game systems.

a. Write an expression for the total number of video game systems. $14 + x$

b. The store sold six of the systems. Write and simplify an expression to represent the number of systems the store has left. $14 + x - 6$; $8 + x$

Then
You have already subtracted algebraic equations. (Lesson 4-3)

Now
- Subtract polynomials.
- Solve real-world problems by subtracting polynomials.

Math Online
glencoe.com
- Extra Examples
- Personal Tutor
- Self-Check Quiz
- Homework Help
- Math in Motion

Subtracting Polynomials Just as you add like terms, you can also subtract like terms.

EXAMPLE 1 Subtract Polynomials

Subtract. Use models if needed.

a. $(5x + 4) - (3x + 2)$

Step 1 Model the polynomial $5x + 4$.

Step 2 To subtract $3x + 2$, remove three x-tiles and two 1-tiles.

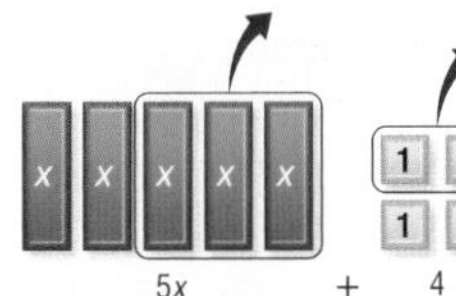

Step 3 Write the polynomial for the remaining tiles.

$(5x + 4) - (3x + 2) = 2x + 2$

b. $(x^2 - 4x - 6) - (-x - 3)$

Step 1 Model the polynomial $x^2 - 4x - 6$. $x^2 - 4x - 6 = x^2 + (-4x) + (-6)$

Step 2 To subtract $(-x - 3)$, remove 1 negative x-tile and 3 negative 1-tiles.

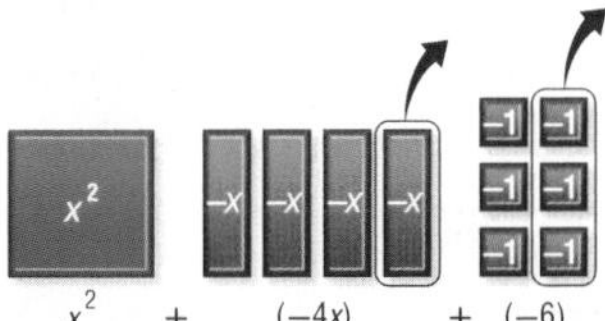

Step 3 Write the polynomial for the remaining tiles.

$(x^2 - 4x - 6) - (-x - 3) = x^2 - 3x - 3$

Check Your Progress 1B. $x^2 + 4x$

1A. $(7x - 5) - (2x - 1)$ $5x - 4$

1B. $(2x^2 + 6x - 4) - (x^2 + 2x - 4)$

Personal Tutor glencoe.com

Lesson Notes

1 FOCUS

Vertical Alignment

Before Lesson LA-3
Subtract algebraic equations.

Lesson LA-3
Subtract polynomials. Solve real-world problems by subtracting polynomials.

After Lesson LA-3
Multiply polynomials.

2 TEACH

Scaffolding Questions

Have students read the *Why?* section of the lesson and answer the questions.

Ask:

- How many game systems would the store have if they received six more? $14 + 6 = 20$
- What operation did you use to find the total? addition

Subtracting Polynomials

Examples 1 and 2 show how to use models to subtract polynomials.

Formative Assessment

Use the Check Your Progress exercises after each example to determine students' understanding of concepts.

Additional Example

Subtract. Use models if needed.

a. $(4x + 5) - (2x + 3)$ $2x + 2$

b. $(2x^2 - 3x - 5) - (-x - 1)$
$2x^2 - 2x - 4$

Additional Example

2 Find $(5x^2 + 4x + 2) - (x^2 - 3x)$. $4x^2 + 7x + 2$

Additional Examples also in Interactive Classroom PowerPoint® Presentations

IWB INTERACTIVE WHITEBOARD READY

Solve Problems

Example 3 shows how to solve a real-world problem by subtracting polynomials.

Additional Example

3 **PROFIT** The expression $9x + 27$ represents the total amount of money the band earned from selling x CDs.

a. If the band had to pay $(3x + 12)$ dollars in expenses, write an expression to represent their profit. $6x + 15$

b. If the band sold 125 CDs, what was their profit? \$765

Focus on Mathematical Content

Subtracting Polynomials When subtracting a polynomial, you must add its additive inverse. To find the additive inverse of a polynomial, multiply each of its terms by -1.

Math *in Motion,* Interactive Lab glencoe.com

EXAMPLE 2 Add Zero Pairs to Subtract Polynomials

Find $(2x^2 + 3x + 2) - (x^2 - 2x)$.

Step 1

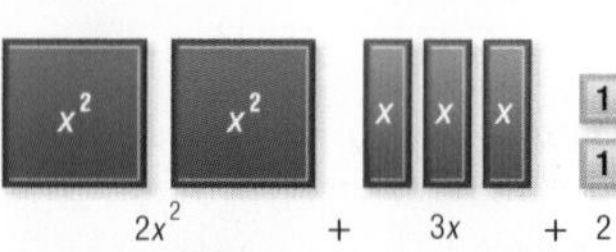

$2x^2 + 3x + 2$

Model the polynomial.

Step 2

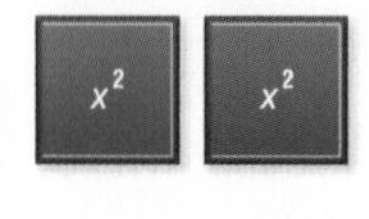

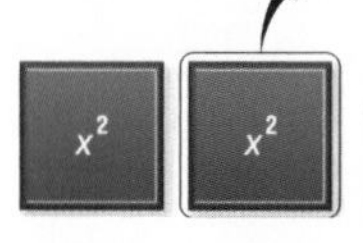

2 zero pairs

Since there are no negative x-tiles to remove, add 2 zero pairs of x-tiles.

Step 3

Remove 1 x^2-tile and 2 negative x-tiles.

So, $(2x^2 + 3x + 2) - (x^2 - 2x) = x^2 + 5x + 2$.

Check Your Progress

2. Find $(x - 5) - (2x - 1)$. $-x - 4$

Personal Tutor glencoe.com

Solve Problems You can solve real-world problems by subtracting polynomials.

Real-World EXAMPLE 3 Subtract Polynomials to Solve Problems

EXERCISE The expression $8x + 50$ represents the total amount of money the soccer team earned from selling x T-shirts.

a. If the team had to pay $(2x + 24)$ dollars in expenses, write an expression to represent their profit.

Total − Expenses	$= (8x + 50) - (2x + 24)$	Subtract.
	$= 8x + 50 - 2x - 24$	Distributive Property
	$= 6x + 26$	Simplify.

Watch Out! When subtracting $(2x + 24)$, subtract both $2x$ and 24, which is written as $-2x - 24$.

b. If the soccer team sold 54 T-shirts, what was their profit?

$6x + 26 = 6(54) + 26$	Replace x with 54.
$= 324 + 26$ or 350	Simplify.

So, the soccer team made \$350 profit.

Check Your Progress

3. **MONEY** After working x hours on Monday, Kay earns $9x$ dollars. On Tuesday, she earns earns $(7x + 3)$ dollars.

a. Write an expression to represent how much more she earned on Monday. $2x - 3$

b. If she worked for 5 hours each day, how much more did she earn on Monday? \$7

Personal Tutor glencoe.com

Differentiated Instruction AL OL

If students struggle with subtracting polynomials,

Then write a polynomial such as $-4x^2 - 5x - 2$ on the board. Have students state the opposite of each term. Next write a subtraction problem with the previous polynomial being subtracted. Have students verbally explain how they would complete the subtraction.

Check Your Understanding

Examples 1 and 2 pp. LA9, LA10

Subtract. Use models if needed. 2. $2x^2 - 2x + 2$

1. $(6x + 5) - (3x + 1)$ $3x + 4$
2. $(3x^2 - 4x + 2) - (x^2 - 2x)$
3. $(x^2 + 9x - 4) - (x^2 - 2x + 1)$ $11x - 5$
4. $(5x^2 + 7) - (x^2 + 2x + 4)$ $4x^2 - 2x + 3$

Example 3 p. LA10

5. **SHIPPING** The cost of shipping an item that weighs x pounds from Charlotte to Chicago is shown in the table.

Shipping Company	Cost ($)
Atlas Service	$4x + 2.80$
Mid-Atlantic Service	$3x + 1.25$

   a. Write an expression to represent how much more Atlas charges than Mid-Atlantic for shipping an item. $x + 1.55$

   b. If an item weighs 2 pounds, how much more does Atlas charge for shipping it? $3.55

Practice and Problem Solving

Examples 1 and 2 pp. LA9, LA10

Subtract. Use models if needed.

6. $(3x + 7) - (x + 5)$ $2x + 2$
7. $(2x^2 - 4x) - (x^2 - x)$ $x^2 - 3x$
8. $(x^2 + 8x - 9) - (3x - 1)$
9. $(-4x^2 + x + 7) - (-2x^2 + x + 2)$
10. $(5x + 6) - (x^2 + 2x)$ $-x^2 + 3x + 6$
11. $(-4x^2 + x + 5) - (x^2 + 2x + 3)$

8. $x^2 + 5x - 8$
9. $-2x^2 + 5$

Example 3 p. LA10

11. $-5x^2 - x + 2$

12. **EXERCISE** The expression $5x + 2$ represents the number of miles Celeste rode her bike, and $10x$ represents the number of miles that Kimiko rode her bike in x hours.

    a. Write an expression to show how many more miles Kimiko rode than Celeste. $5x - 2$

    b. If they each rode for 2 hours, how many more miles did Kimiko ride? 8 mi

13. **CARS** A car accelerates for t seconds. The expression $2t + t^2$ represents the distance the car travels in meters. Another car has twice the acceleration and travels $(2t + 2t^2)$ meters in t seconds. After 10 seconds, how much farther does the second car travel? 100 m

14. **MEASUREMENT** What is the difference in the areas of the rectangles shown? $x^2 + 8x - 6$

    $A = 2x^2 + 3x - 4$ $\qquad$ $A = x^2 - 5x + 2$

H.O.T. Problems — Use Higher-Order Thinking Skills

15. Sample answer: $5x + 4$ and $x + 3$

17. Sample answer: Write $2x^2 - (x^2 + 5x + 7)$. Simplify to get $x^2 - 5x - 7$.

C 15. **OPEN ENDED** Write two polynomials that have a difference of $4x + 1$.

16. **CHALLENGE** Suppose A and B represent polynomials. If $A + B = 3x^2 + 2x - 2$ and $A - B = -x^2 + 4x - 8$, find A and B. $A = x^2 + 3x - 5$; $B = 2x^2 - x + 3$

17. **WRITING IN MATH** Explain how to subtract $x^2 + 5x + 7$ from $2x^2$.

3 PRACTICE

Formative Assessment

Use Exercises 1–5 to check for understanding.

Use the chart at the bottom of this page to customize assignments for your students.

4 ASSESS

Ticket Out the Door Have students solve the problem $(4x^2 + 2x + 5) - (x^2 - 3x)$. Have them show their steps. $3x^2 + 5x + 5$

Differentiated Homework Options

Level	Assignment	Two-Day Option	
AL Basic	6–12, 15, 17	7–11 odd	6–12 even, 15, 17
OL Core	7–11 odd, 13–15, 17	6–12	13–15, 17
BL Advanced	13–17		

Lesson 3 Subtracting Polynomials LA11

Lesson Notes

FOCUS

Vertical Alignment

Before Lesson LA-4
Multiply monomials.

Lesson LA-4
Use models to multiply a binomial by a monomial. Multiply a binomial by a monomial to solve equations.

After Lesson LA-4
Multiply two binomials.

TEACH

Scaffolding Questions

Have students read the *Why?* section of the lesson and answer the questions.

Ask:

- What is the area of the original patio? x^2
- How do you find the area of a rectangle? multiply the length times the width

Additional Answer (Check Your Progress)

1. $4x^2 + 8x$

	x	x
x	x^2	x^2
x	x^2	x^2
1	x	x
1	x	x
1	x	x
1	x	x

Multiplying a Binomial by a Monomial

Then
You have already multiplied monomials. (Lesson 9-3)

Now
- Use models to multiply a binomial by a monomial.
- Multiply a binomial by a monomial to solve equations.

New Vocabulary
binomial

Math Online
glencoe.com
- Extra Examples
- Personal Tutor
- Self-Check Quiz
- Homework Help

Why?

A square patio has a side length of x meters. If you increase the length by 3 meters, what is the area of the new patio?

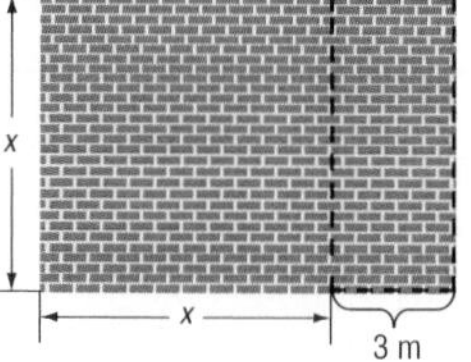

a. Write an expression to represent the new side length of the patio. $x + 3$

b. Write an expression to represent the area of the new patio. $x(x + 3)$

Binomials You can use algebra tiles to model **binomials**, a polynomial with two terms.

The algebra tiles shown form a rectangle with a width of x and a length of $x + 2$. They represent the product $x(x + 2)$.

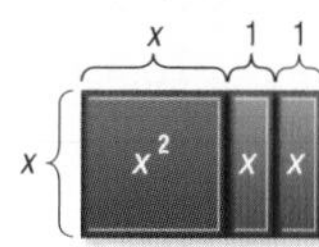

The area of the rectangle represents the product. Since the rectangle consists of one x^2-tile and two x-tiles, $x(x + 2) = x^2 + 2x$

EXAMPLE 1 Multiplying a Binomial by a Monomial

Use algebra tiles to find $x(x + 3)$.

Step 1 Make a rectangle with a width of x and a length of $x + 3$. Use algebra tiles to mark off the dimensions on a product mat.

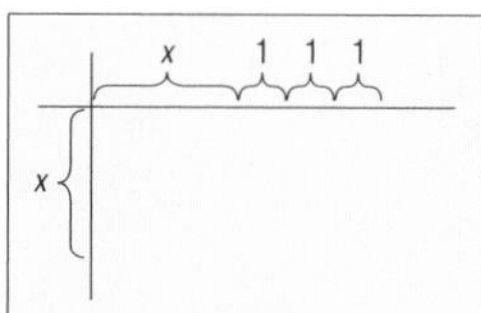

Step 2 Using the marks as a guide, fill in the rectangle with algebra tiles.

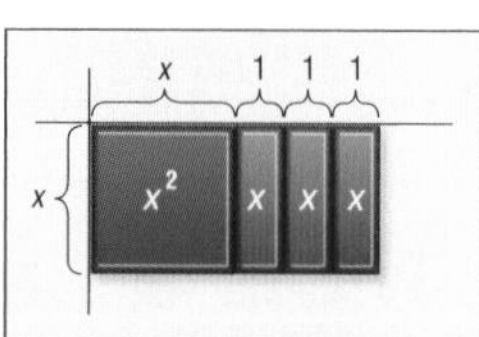

Step 3 The area of the rectangle is $x^2 + x + x + x$. In simplest form, the area is $x^2 + 3x$.

So, $x(x + 3) = x^2 + 3x$.

Check Your Progress

1. Use algebra tiles to find $2x(2x + 4)$. See margin.

Personal Tutor glencoe.com

In Example 1, each term in the binomial is multiplied by the monomial. This and other similar examples suggest that the Distributive Property can be used to multiply a binomial by a monomial.

Key Concept **Multiplying a Binomial by a Monomial** For Your FOLDABLE

Words To multiply a binomial by a monomial, use the Distributive Property.

Symbols $a(b + c) = ab + ac$

Model

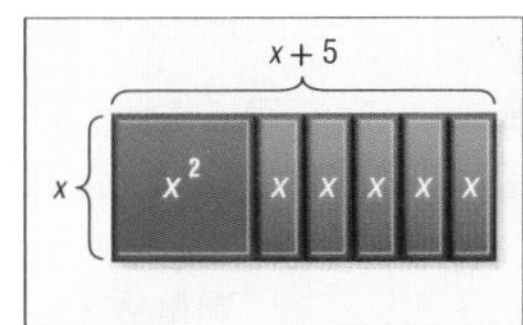

EXAMPLE 2 Multiplying a Binomial by a Monomial

Multiply. Use models if needed.

a. $x(x + 5)$

Method 1 Use a model.

$x + 5$, x: x^2 x x x x x

So, $x(x + 5) = x^2 + 5x$.

Method 2 Use the Distributive Property.

$x(x + 5) = x(x) + x(5)$ **Distributive Property**

$= x^2 + 5x$ **Simplify.**

So, $x(x + 5) = x^2 + 5x$.

b. $x(2x + 3)$

$x(2x + 3) = x(2x) + x(3)$

$= 2x^2 + 3x$

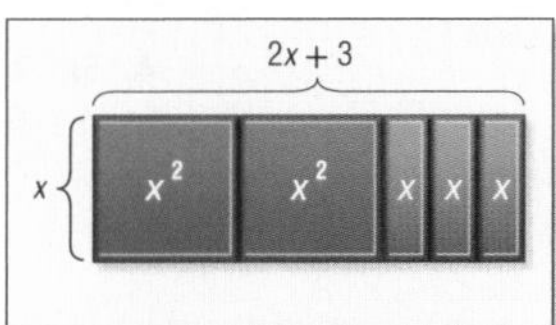

c. $3x^3(2x^2 - 5x)$

$3x^3(2x^2 - 5x) = 3x^3(2x^2) - 3x^3(5x)$ **Distributive Property**

$= 6x^5 - 15x^4$ **Simplify.**

StudyTip

Like Terms Recall that to multiply powers with the same base, add their exponents.

Check Your Progress

2A. $7(2x + 5)$ $14x + 35$ **2B.** $4x(3x^2 - 7)$ $12x^3 - 28x$ **2C.** $y^3(3y^2 + 2y)$ $3y^5 + 2y^4$

Personal Tutor glencoe.com

Differentiated Instruction

AL OL

If students have difficulty multiplying a binomial by a monomial,

Then have students work in pairs. One student should write down a monomial in terms of x on a piece of paper and model it with algebra tiles. The other student should write down a polynomial in terms of x on a piece of paper and model it with algebra tiles. Have students model the product of their monomial and polynomial and write the product as an expression.

Binomials

Example 1 shows how to use algebra tiles to multiply a binomial by a monomial. **Example 2** shows how to multiply a binomial by a monomial using a model and the Distributive Property. **Example 3** shows how to use multiplication of a binomial by a monomial to simplify an expression. **Example 4** shows how to use multiplication of a binomial by a monomial to solve a real-world problem.

Formative Assessment

Use the Check Your Progress exercises after each example to determine students' understanding of concepts.

Additional Examples

1 Use algebra tiles to find $x(x + 4)$. $x^2 + 4x$

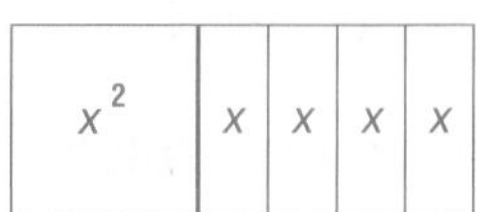

2 Multiply. Use models if needed.

a. $x(x + 6)$ $x^2 + 6x$

b. $x(4x + 1)$ $4x^2 + x$

c. $2x^3(3x^2 - 2x)$ $6x^5 - 4x^4$

Additional Examples also in Interactive Classroom PowerPoint® Presentations

IWB INTERACTIVE WHITEBOARD READY

Focus on Mathematical Content

Order of Operations When simplifying expressions involving products of monomials and polynomials, the order of operations must be followed. Multiplication precedes addition, unless parentheses indicate otherwise.

Additional Examples

3 Simplify $4x(x + 3) - 3x(x)$. $x^2 + 12x$

4 **BASKETBALL** The perimeter of a high school basketball court is 268 feet. The length of the court is 34 feet more than the width. What are the dimensions of the basketball court? 50 ft wide and 84 ft long

Watch Out!

Preventing Errors If students make mistakes with multiplying by a monomial, suggest that they draw arrows from the monomial to each term in the binomial.

3 PRACTICE

Formative Assessment

Use Exercises 1–11 to check for understanding.

Use the chart at the bottom of the next page to customize assignments for your students.

EXAMPLE 3 Simplifying Expressions

Simplify $5x(x + 2) - 2x(x)$.

$5x(x + 2) - 2x(x) = 5x(x) + 5x(2) - 2x(x)$ **Distributive Property**

$= 5x^2 + 10x - 4x^2$ **Multiply.**

$= x^2 + 10x$ **Simplify.**

Check Your Progress

3A. $-6a(a + 1) + 4a(2a)$ $2a^2 - 6a$

3B. $3n^2(n - 4) - 4(n^2 - 7)$ $3n^3 - 16n^2 + 28$

Personal Tutor glencoe.com

Real-World Link

The first youth hockey program was established in 1963 in Chicago, Illinois.

Source: *Chicago Encyclopedia*

Real-World EXAMPLE 4

SPORTS The length of a hockey rink is 115 feet longer than its width. If the perimeter of the rink is 570 feet, what are the dimensions of the rink?

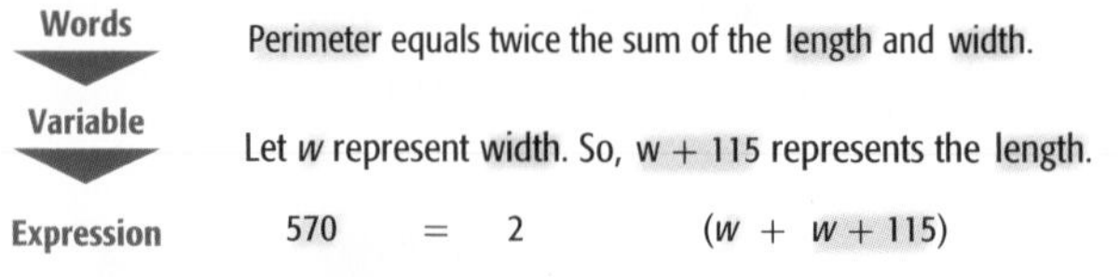

Words	Perimeter equals twice the sum of the length and width.
Variable	Let w represent width. So, $w + 115$ represents the length.
Expression	570 = 2 (w + $w + 115$)

$570 = 2(w + w + 115)$ **Write the equation.**

$570 = 2(2w + 115)$ **Combine like terms.**

$570 = 4w + 230$ **Distributive Property**

$340 = 4w$ **Subtract 230 from each side.**

$85 = w$ **Divide each side by 4.**

So, the width of the rink is 85 feet and the length is 85 + 115 or 200 feet.

Check Your Progress

4. SPORTS The perimeter of a tennis court is 228 feet. The length of the court is 6 feet more than twice the width. What are the dimensions of the court? 36 feet by 78 feet

Personal Tutor glencoe.com

Check Your Understanding

Examples 1 and 2 p. LA13

Find each product. Use models if needed.

1. $2(2x + 1)$ $4x + 2$
2. $x(2x + 2)$ $2x^2 + 2x$
3. $3a(a - 1)$ $3a^2 - 3a$
4. $-3n(5 - 2n)$ $-15n + 6n^2$
5. $4z(z^2 - 2z)$ $4z^3 - 8z^2$
6. $3(8y^3 + 3)$ $24y^3 + 9$

Example 3 p. LA14

Simplify.

7. $7x(x + 2) + 3x(x - 5)$ $10x^2 - x$

8. $4(y^2 - 8) + 10 - 2(y + 12)$ $4y^2 - 2y - 46$

9. $-3(2a - 4) + 9 - 3(a + 1)$ $-9a + 18$

10. $x(x + 3) + 5x + x(x + 5) + 9$ $2x^2 + 13x + 9$

Example 4 p. LA14

11. **SPORTS** One of the world's largest swimming pools is the Orthlieb Pool in Casablanca, Morocco. It is 30 meters longer than 6 times its width. If the perimeter of the pool is 1110 meters, what are the dimensions of the pool? **75 meters wide and 480 meters long.**

Practice and Problem Solving

Examples 1 and 2 p. LA13

Find each product. Use models if needed.

12. $2x(x + 4)$ $2x^2 + 8x$

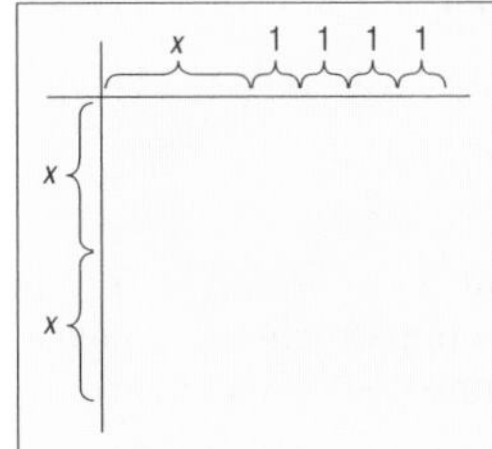

13. $2x(2x + 2)$ $4x^2 + 4x$

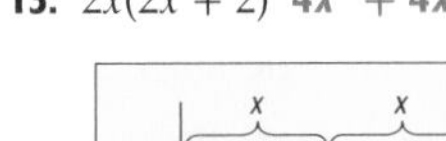

14. $4x(-2x + 7x^2)$ $-8x^2 + 28x^3$

15. $-5y(6 - 2y)$ $-30y + 10y^2$

16. $5d(d^2 + 3)$ $5d^3 + 15d$

17. $0.25x(4x - 8)$ $x^2 - 2x$

Example 3 p. LA14

Simplify.

18. $2a(a^2 - 5a) - 6(a^3 + 3a)$ $-4a^3 - 10a^2 - 18a$

19. $5t^2(t + 2) - 5t(4t^2 - 3t)$ $-15t^3 + 25t^2$

20. $3n^2(n - 4) + 6n(3n^2 + n - 7) - 4(n - 7)$ $21n^3 - 6n^2 - 46n + 28$

Example 4 p. LA14

21. **FOOTBALL** The perimeter of an arena football field is 188 yards. The perimeter of an NFL football field is 346 yards. Use the information in the table to find the length and width of each field. **See margin.**

FOOTBALL FIELDS

Measure	Arena	NFL
Width	$a - 38$	$n + 3$
Length	a	$2n + 20$

22. **MONUMENTS** The rectangular Reflecting Pool extends from the Lincoln Memorial to the World War II memorial in Washington, D.C. The length of the pool is 25 feet more than 12 times its width.

a. If the perimeter of the pool is 4392 feet, find the dimensions of the pool.

22a. **167 feet wide and 2029 feet long.**

b. Suppose the width of the pool is 83.5 times the depth. Find the volume of the pool. **677,686 ft³**

23. **SPORTS** A billiards table has a perimeter of 24 feet. The length of a billiards table is twice as long as its width. If the width of the billiards table is $4x - 1$, what are the dimensions of the table? **The width is 4 feet and the length is 8 feet.**

Tips for New Teachers

Monomial If students are having difficulty multiplying by a negative monomial, you may want to have them apply the negative first (by multiplying all terms by -1) and then multiply by the monomial in positive form.

Additional Answer

21. Arena football field: 28 yd wide by 66 yd long; NFL football field: 53 yd wide by 120 yd long

Differentiated Homework Options

Level	Assignment	Two-Day Option	
AL Basic	12–22, 30, 32–34	13–21 odd	12–22 even, 30, 32–34
OL Core	13–21 odd, 23–29 odd, 30, 32–34	12–22	23–30, 32–34
BL Advanced	23–34		

Watch Out!

Find the Error For Exercise 32, remind students to pay attention to the negative sign that precedes $4p$ in the expression.

4 ASSESS

Ticket Out the Door Have the students simplify $4x(x + 3) + 2x(x - 2)$. $6x^2 + 8x$

StudyTip

Properties of Equality You can use the same properties of equality from Chapter 4 to solve equations with polynomials.
For any numbers a, b, and c, if $a = b$ then
$a + c = b + c$
$a - c = b - c$
$ac = bc$ and
$\frac{a}{c} = \frac{b}{c}$ when $c \neq 0$

31. $4x$; Sample answer: Find the monomial that when multiplied by x^2 gives a product of $4x^3$. Then check to see that the other terms in the trinomial produce the desired product.
32. Carmen; Paul did not distribute the subtraction sign in the second set of parentheses.
33. First multiply $-2n$ by 3 and then multiply $-2n$ by $-5n$. Write as a polynomial $-6n + 10n^2$.
34. Place algebra tiles so that one side of the formed rectangle represents one factor and the other side represents the other factor. Fill in tiles to form a rectangle. Write a simplified polynomial of all algebra tiles present in the rectangle.

ALGEBRA Solve $w(w + 12) = w(w + 14) + 12$.

$w(w + 12) = w(w + 14) + 12$	**Write the equation.**
$w(w) + w(12) = w(w) + w(14) + 12$	**Distributive Property**
$w^2 + 12w = w^2 + 14w + 12$	**Simplify.**
$12w = 14w + 12$	**Subtract w^2 from each side.**
$-2w = 12$	**Subtract $14w$ from each side.**
$w = -6$	**Divide each side by -2.**

Solve each equation.

24. $4(y^2 - 3y) - 8 = 2y(2y + 4) + 32$ $y = -2$

25. $n(n - 7) = n^2 + 3(-2n + 1) - 1$ $n = -2$

26. $a(a + 2) + 3a = a(a - 3) + 8$ $a = 1$

27. $c(c + 8) - c(c + 3) - 23 = 3c + 11$ $c = 17$

28. $b(b + 10) + 6 = b(b + 6) - 2$ $b = -2$

29. RECREATION On the Caribbean island of Trinidad, children play a form of hopscotch called *Jumby*. The pattern for this game is shown at the right.

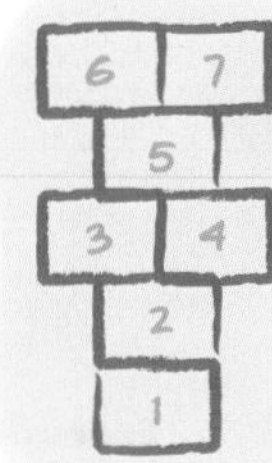

a. Suppose each rectangle is $y + 5$ units long and y units wide. Write an expression in simplest form for the area of the pattern. $7y^2 + 35y$

b. If y represents 10 inches, find the area of the pattern. 1050 square units

H.O.T. Problems Use Higher-Order Thinking Skills

30. OPEN ENDED Write three different multiplication problems for which the product is $6a^2 + 8a$. Sample answers: $2(3a^2 + 4a)$, $a(6a + 8)$, $2a(3a + 4)$

31. CHALLENGE The product of $x^2 - 2x + 1$ and a monomial is $4x^3 - 8x^2 + 4x$. What is the monomial? Explain your reasoning.

32. FIND THE ERROR Carmen and Paul are simplifying $5(p^2 + 2p - 2) - 4p(p - 1)$. Is either of them correct? Explain your reasoning.

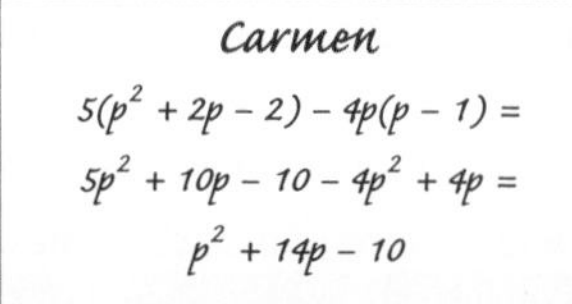

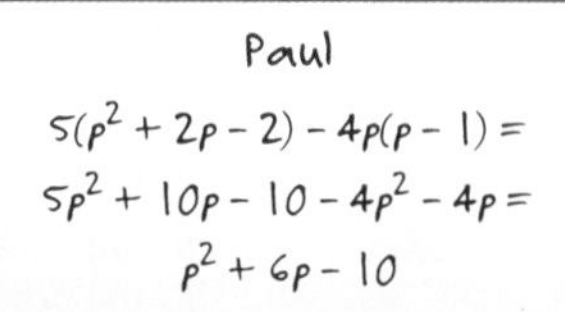

33. REASONING Explain how to multiply $-2n$ and $3 - 5n$.

34. WRITING IN MATH Describe how you can use models to multiply a monomial by a polynomial.

Differentiated Instruction BL

Extension Give students this problem: Norma multiplied a polynomial by a monomial and got $6x^8 - 3x^4 + 9x^2$. If the polynomial factor was $2x^6 - x^2 + 3$, what was the monomial factor? $3x^2$

Multiplying Two Binomials

Then

You have already multiplied a binomial by a monomial. (Looking Ahead 4)

Now

- Multiply two binomials by using models.
- Multiply two binomials by using the Distributive Property.

New Vocabulary

FOIL Method

Math Online

glencoe.com

- Extra Examples
- Personal Tutor
- Self-Check Quiz
- Homework Help

Why?

The local youth club has a stage for karaoke competitions. The main stage is a square. The technical crew needs to increase the length by 2 feet and the width by 1 foot for their equipment. A plan for the stage is shown below.

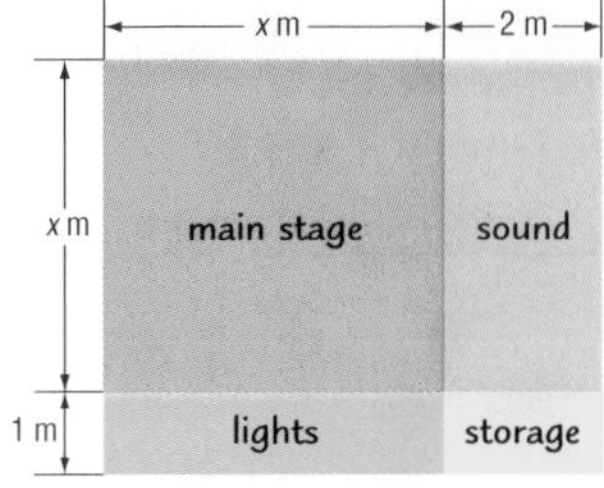

a. Write expressions for the area of each part of the stage.
main stage: x^2; sound: $2x$; lights: x; storage: 2

b. Write an expression for the total area of the stage. $x^2 + 3x + 2$

Multiply Binomials As with multiplying a monomial by a binomial, you can use algebra tiles to multiply two binomials. In the model, the length and width of a rectangle represent the two binomials. The area represents the product.

EXAMPLE 1 Modeling Multiplication of Binomials

Find $(x + 2)(x + 1)$.

Step 1 Make a rectangle with a width of $x + 1$ and a length of $x + 2$.

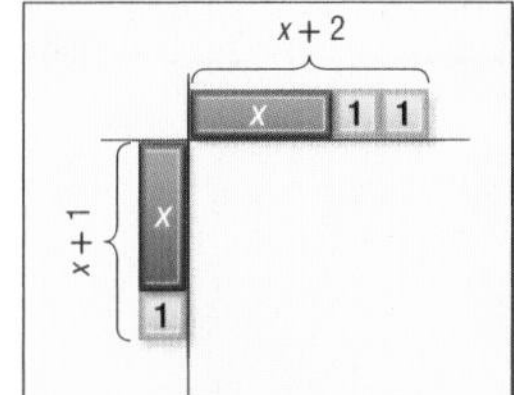

Step 2 Fill in the rectangle with algebra tiles. There is one x^2-tile, three x-tiles, and two 1-tiles.

So, $(x + 2)(x + 1) = x^2 + 3x + 2$.

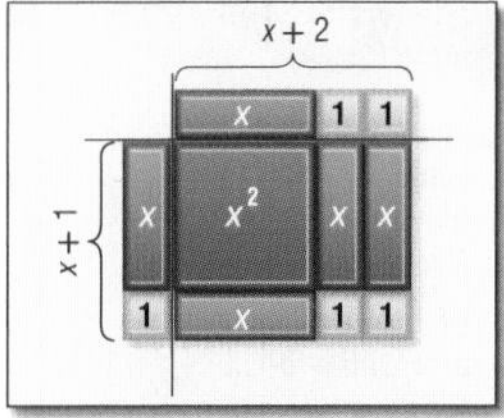

Check Your Progress

Multiply. Use a model. 1A–1B. See margin.

1A. $(x + 3)(x + 4)$ **1B.** $(2x + 1)(x + 3)$

Personal Tutor glencoe.com

Additional Answers (Check Your Progress)

1A. $x^2 + 7x + 12$

	x	1	1	1
x	x^2	x	x	x
1	x	1	1	1
1	x	1	1	1
1	x	1	1	1
1	x	1	1	1

1B. $2x^2 + 7x + 3$

	x	x	1
x	x^2	x^2	x
1	x	x	1
1	x	x	1
1	x	x	1

Looking 5 Ahead Lesson Notes

1 FOCUS

Vertical Alignment

Before Lesson LA-5
Multiply a binomial by a monomial.

Lesson LA-5
Multiply two binomials by using models. Multiply two binomials by using the Distributive Property.

After Lesson LA-5
Factor trinomials.

2 TEACH

Scaffolding Questions

Have students read the *Why?* section of the lesson and answer the questions.

Ask:

- What is the length of each side of the square? x m
- What are the dimensions of the storage area? 2 m by 1 m

Multiply Binomials

Example 1 shows how to use models to multiply two binomials.

Formative Assessment

Use the Check Your Progress exercises after each example to determine students' understanding of concepts.

Additional Example

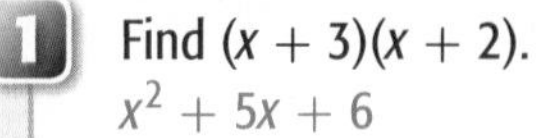

1 Find $(x + 3)(x + 2)$.
$x^2 + 5x + 6$

Additional Examples also in Interactive Classroom PowerPoint® Presentations

Distributive Property

Example 2 shows how to use the distributive property to find the product of two binomials. **Example 3** shows how to use the FOIL method to solve a real-world problem.

Additional Example

Find $(2x + 3)(x + 1)$. $2x^2 + 5x + 3$

Focus on Mathematical Content

Multiplying Other Polynomials The FOIL method only works for multiplying two binomials. To multiply any other polynomials, the Distributive Property must be used.

Distributive Property The Distributive Property can also be used to find the product of two binomials. The figure at the right shows the rectangle from Example 1 separated into four parts. Notice that each term from the first parentheses $(x + 2)$ is multiplied by each term from the second parentheses $(x + 1)$.

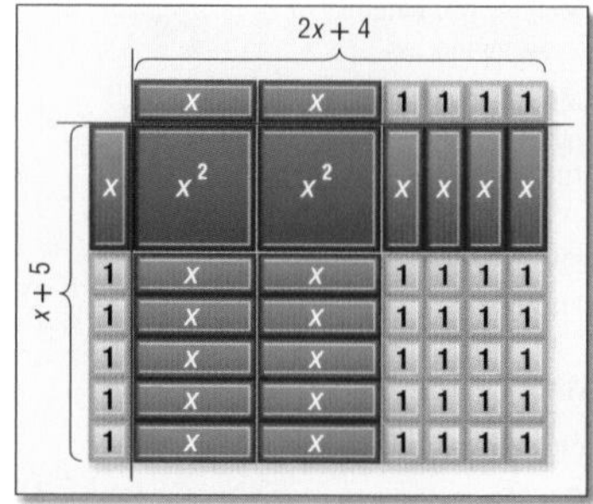

EXAMPLE 2 Use the Distributive Property

Find $(2x + 4)(x + 5)$.

Method 1 Use a model.

Method 2 Use the Distributive Property.

$(2x + 4)(x + 5) = 2x(x + 5) + 4(x + 5)$	Distributive Property
$= 2x^2 + 10x + 4x + 20$	Distributive Property
$= 2x^2 + 14x + 20$	Simplify.

So, $(2x + 4)(x + 5) = 2x^2 + 14x + 20$.

Watch Out!

Negative Signs If one or both of the binomials involve negatives or subtraction, remember to distribute the negatives.

Check Your Progress

Multiply. Use models if needed.

2A. $(3x + 2)(2x - 3)$ $6x^2 - 5x - 6$

2B. $(x + 6)(2x + 4)$ $2x^2 + 16x + 24$

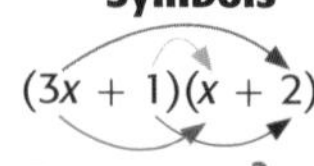

Personal Tutor glencoe.com

A shortcut version of the Distributive Property is the **FOIL method**.

StudyTip

Special Products Some pairs of binomial have products that follow a specific pattern.

$(a + b)^2 = a^2 + 2ab + b^2$

$(a - b)^2 = a^2 - 2ab + b^2$

$(a + b)(a - b) = a^2 - b^2$

Key Concept FOIL Method

For Your FOLDABLE

Words	Symbols
	$(3x + 1)(x + 2)$
F Multiply the **FIRST** terms.	$3x \cdot x$ or $3x^2$
O Multiply the **OUTER** terms.	$3x \cdot 2$ or $6x$
I Multiply the **INNER** terms.	$1 \cdot x$ or x
L Multiply the **LAST** terms.	$1 \cdot 2$ or 2

So, $(3x + 1)(x + 2) = 3x^2 + 6x + x + 2$ or $3x^2 + 7x + 2$.

Differentiated Instruction

AL OL

If students are less familiar with the Distributive Property,

Then you may want to show them how to use the vertical method for multiplying binomials because it is similar to multiplying two-digit numbers.

$$\begin{array}{r} x + 3 \\ (\times)\ x + 2 \\ \hline 2x + 6 \\ (+)\ x^2 + 3x \\ \hline x^2 + 5x + 6 \end{array}$$

Real-World EXAMPLE 3 Use FOIL to Multiply Binomials

GEOMETRY A shipping box is shaped like a rectangular prism. The volume V is equal to the area of the base B times the height h. Express the volume of the prism as a polynomial.

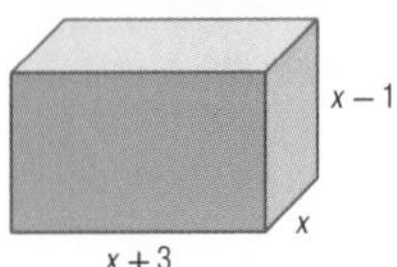

First, find the area of the rectangular base.

$B = \ell w$	Formula for area of a rectangle
$= (x + 3)(x)$	Replace ℓ with $x + 3$ and w with x.
$= x^2 + 3x$	Distributive Property

To find the volume, multiply the area of the base by the height.

$V = Bh$	Formula for volume of a prism
$= (x^2 + 3x)(x - 1)$	Replace B with $x^2 + 3x$ and h with $x - 1$.
F O I L	
$= x^2 \cdot x - x^2 \cdot 1 + 3x \cdot x - 3x \cdot 1$	Use the FOIL method.
$= x^3 - x^2 + 3x^2 - 3x$	Multiply.
$= x^3 + 2x^2 - 3x$	Simplify.

Check Your Progress

3. GIFTS Express the volume of the gift box at the right as a polynomial.
$2x^3 + 2x^2 - 24x$

Personal Tutor glencoe.com

Check Your Understanding

Example 1 p. LA17

Multiply. Use a model.

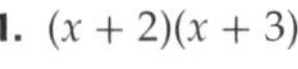

1. $(x + 2)(x + 3)$
2. $(x + 3)(x + 4)$
3. $(x + 1)(2x + 1)$

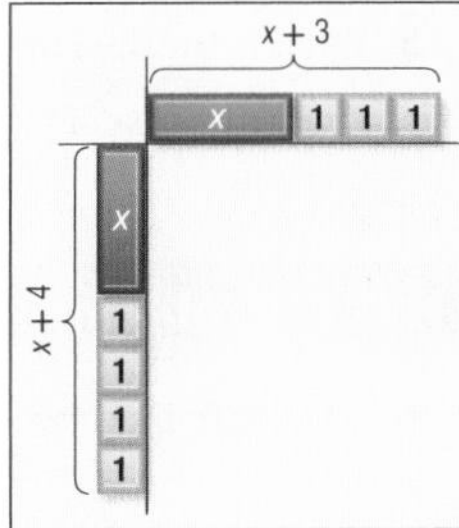

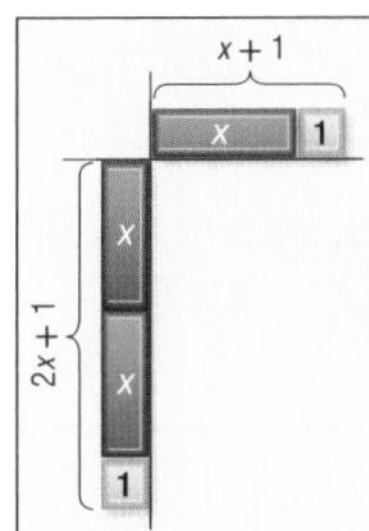

Multiply.

4. $(y + 4)(y - 2)$
5. $(m - 3)(m + 1)$
6. $(x - 5)(x - 2)$
7. $(3n + 2)(n - 2)$
8. $(2x - 5)(x - 4)$
9. $(4b - 3)(2b + 4)$

Example 3 p. LA19

10. **CEREAL** A cereal box has a length of $2x$ inches, a width of $x - 2$ inches, and a height of $2x + 5$ inches. Express the volume as a polynomial.
$4x^3 + 2x^2 - 20x$

1. $x^2 + 5x + 6$
2. $x^2 + 7x + 12$
3. $2x^2 + 3x + 1$
4. $y^2 + 2y - 8$
5. $m^2 - 2m - 3$
6. $x^2 - 7x + 10$
7. $3n^2 - 4n - 4$
8. $2x^2 - 13x + 20$
9. $8b^2 + 10b - 12$

Additional Example

3 **GEOMETRY** A shoebox is shaped like a rectangular prism. The volume V is equal to the area of the base B times the height h. Express the volume of the shoebox as a polynomial.
$2x^3 + 12x^2 - 14x$

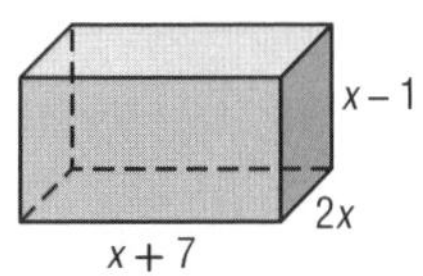

Tips for New Teachers

Multiplying Binomials Some students may have difficulty visualizing which tiles complete the product. Suggest students draw vertical and horizontal dashed lines at increment marks to more clearly define which tiles are needed.

3 PRACTICE

Formative Assessment

Use Exercises 1–10 to check for understanding.

Use the chart at the bottom of the next page to customize assignments for your students.

Differentiated Instruction

Extension Tell students that one way to multiply 25 and 18 mentally is to find (20 + 5) and (20 − 2). Have them show how the FOIL method can be used to find each product.

a. 35(19) (30 + 5)(10 + 9) = (30)(10) + (30)(9) + 5(10) + 5(9) = 300 + 270 + 50 + 45 = 665

b. (67)(102) (60 + 7)(100 + 2) = (60)(100) + (60)(2) + 7(100) + 7(2) = 6000 + 120 + 700 + 14 = 6834

4 ASSESS

Yesterday's News Have students write how yesterday's lesson on multiplying a binomial by a monomial helped them with today's lesson on multiplying binomials.

Additional Answers

38. $(x + 1)^2 = x^2 + 2x + 1$, $(x + 2)^2 = x^2 + 4x + 4$, $(x + 3)^2 = x^2 + 6x + 9$; Yes there is a pattern. There will always be an x^2, the middle term is the number value multiplied by $2x$, and the third term is the number value squared.; $(x + 6)^2 = x^2 + 12x + 36$; $(x + n)^2 = x^2 + 2nx + n^2$

39. no: Sample answer: $(x + 3)(x - 3) = x^2 - 9$

40. In multiplying a monomial by a binomial, only one term needs to be distributed. With multiplying binomials, two terms have to be distributed over two more terms, resulting in the FOIL method.

Practice and Problem Solving

Examples 1 and 2 pp. LA17–LA18

11. $x^2 + 12x + 32$
12. $r^2 - 10r + 21$
13. $z^2 + 2z - 24$

Example 3 p. LA19

14. $2a^2 - 9a - 35$
15. $5n^2 - 13n - 6$
16. $10x^2 + 31x + 15$
17. $2x^2 + x - 21$
18. $6a^2 + ab - b^2$
19. $n^2 - 16n + 55$
20. $25n^2 - 4p^2$
21. $9a^2 + 6a + 1$
22. $12h^2 - h - 6$
25. $y^3 + 3y^2 - 4y - 12$
26. $3x^4 + 8x^2 - 3$
27. $2y^3 + 2y^2 + y + 1$
28. $x^2 + 5xy + 6y^2$
29. $2a^2 - ab - 10b^2$
30. $m^4 + 3m^3 - 2m^2 - 6m$
31. $3x^2 - 10x - 8$
32. $6y^2 - 24yz + 24z^2$
33. $x^3 - 2x^2 + x - 2$
35. $s^2 + 9s + 20$
36a. $(a + b)(a + b)$
36b. a^2, ab, b^2
36c. $a^2 + 2ab + b^2$

Multiply.

11. $(x + 4)(x + 8)$	**12.** $(r - 3)(r - 7)$	**13.** $(z + 6)(z - 4)$
14. $(2a + 5)(a - 7)$	**15.** $(5n + 2)(n - 3)$	**16.** $(2x + 5)(5x + 3)$
17. $(2x + 7)(x - 3)$	**18.** $(3a - b)(2a + b)$	**19.** $(n - 11)(n - 5)$
20. $(5n - 2p)(5n + 2p)$	**21.** $(3a + 1)(3a + 1)$	**22.** $(4h - 3)(3h + 2)$

23. GEOMETRY A parcel box has a length of $3y$ centimeters, a width of $y + 3$ centimeters, and a height of $2y - 2$ centimeters. Express the volume of the package as a polynomial. $6y^3 + 12y^2 - 18y$

24. INTEREST Lauren deposited money into a savings account. The account earns an interest rate of $r\%$. For each dollar deposited, the amount in the account after two years is given by the formula $(1 + r)(1 + r)$. Find this product. $r^2 + 2r + 1$

B Find each product.

25. $(y + 3)(y^2 - 4)$	**26.** $(x^2 + 3)(3x^2 - 1)$	**27.** $(2y^2 + 1)(y + 1)$
28. $(x + 2y)(x + 3y)$	**29.** $(2a - 5b)(a + 2b)$	**30.** $(m^3 - 2m)(m + 3)$
31. $(x - 4)(3x + 2)$	**32.** $(2y - 4z)(3y - 6z)$	**33.** $(x^2 + 1)(x - 2)$

34. ENVELOPES The mailing envelope shown has a mailing label on the front.

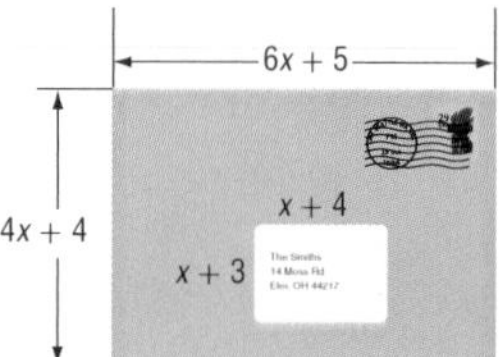

a. Find the area of the label. $x^2 + 7x + 12$

b. Find the area of the envelope not covered by the label. $23x^2 + 37x + 8$

35. GEOMETRY A square has sides of length s. C A rectangle is 5 inches longer and 4 inches wider than the square. Express the area of the rectangle as a polynomial.

36. GEOMETRY The model at the right represents the square of a binomial.

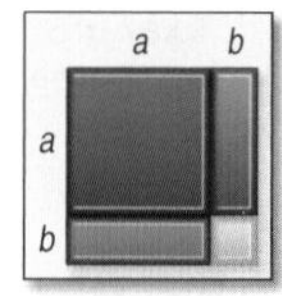

a. What product does this model represent?

b. What is the area of each tile?

c. Write the area of the square as a polynomial.

H.O.T. Problems

Use Higher-Order Thinking Skills

38–40. See margin.

37. OPEN ENDED Find two binomials that have $6x$ as one of the terms in their product. $(x + 4)(x + 2)$; $(x - 3)(x + 9)$

38. CHALLENGE Find $(x + 1)^2$, $(x + 2)^2$, and $(x + 3)^2$. Is there a pattern in the products of binomials? If so, use the pattern to find $(x + 6)^2$ and $(x + n)^2$.

39. REASONING Does the product of two binomials always have three terms? If so, explain why. If not, give a counterexample.

40. WRITING IN MATH Compare and contrast the procedure for multiplying two binomials and the procedure for multiplying a binomial by a monomial.

Differentiated Homework Options

Level	Assignment	Two-Day Option	
AL Basic	11–24, 37, 39, 40	11–23 odd	12–24 even, 37, 39, 40
OL Core	11–33 odd, 34–37, 39, 40	11–24	25–37, 39, 40
BL Advanced	25–40		

Dividing a Polynomial by a Monomial

Why?

Student Council is selling milkshakes at lunch as a fundraiser. Each milkshake requires $\frac{1}{8}$ gallon of ice cream. They had $6\frac{1}{2}$ gallons of ice cream. Then their advisor brought them 5 more gallons.

a. Find the number of milkshakes that can be sold with the amount of ice cream they now have. **92 milk shakes**

b. Describe two ways to find the number of milkshakes. **See margin.**

Then
You have already solved equations by dividing. (Lesson 4-4)

Now
- Divide polynomials by monomials.
- Solve problems using division of polynomials.

Math Online

glencoe.com
- Extra Examples
- Personal Tutor
- Self-Check Quiz
- Homework Help

Dividing Polynomials By Monomials To divide a polynomial by a monomial, divide each term of the polynomial by the monomial.

Key Concept Dividing Polynomials — For Your FOLDABLE

Words To divide a polynomial by a monomial, divide each term of the polynomial by the monomial.

Symbols $\frac{a+b}{c} = \frac{a}{c} + \frac{b}{c}$

EXAMPLE 1 Divide a Polynomial by a Monomial

Divide.

a. $(9b^2 - 15b) \div (3b)$

$(9b^2 - 15b) \div (3b) = \frac{9b^2 - 15b}{3b}$	Write as a rational expression.
$= \frac{9b^2}{3b} - \frac{15b}{3b}$	Divide each term by $3b$.
$= \frac{9}{3} \cdot \frac{b^2}{b} - \frac{15}{3} \cdot \frac{b}{b}$	Associative Property
$= 3 \cdot b^{2-1} - 5 \cdot 1$	Quotient of Powers and Identity Properties
$= 3b - 5$	Simplify.

b. $(6x^2 + 4x) \div (2x)$

$(6x^2 + 4x) \div (2x) = \frac{6x^2 + 4x}{2x}$	Write as a rational expression.
$= \frac{6x^2}{2x} + \frac{4x}{2x}$	Divide each term by $2x$.
$= \frac{6}{2} \cdot \frac{x^2}{x} + \frac{4}{2} \cdot \frac{x}{x}$	Associative Property
$= 3 \cdot x^{2-1} + 2 \cdot 1$	Quotient of Powers and Identity Properties
$= 3x + 2$	Simplify.

Check Your Progress

1A. $(10x^2y^2 + 5xy) \div (5xy)$ $2xy + 1$ **1B.** $(27x^2 - 21y^2) \div 3$ $9x^2 - 7y^2$

Personal Tutor glencoe.com

Lesson Notes

1 FOCUS

Vertical Alignment

Before Lesson LA-6
Solve equations by dividing.

Lesson LA-6
Divide polynomials by monomials. Solve problems using division of polynomials.

After Lesson LA-6
Factor trinomials.

2 TEACH

Scaffolding Questions

Have students read the *Why?* section of the lesson and answer the questions.

Ask:
- How many gallons of ice cream do they have in all? $11\frac{1}{2}$
- How can you determine how many eighths are in a number? divide the number by $\frac{1}{8}$

Dividing Polynomials by Monomials

Example 1 shows how to divide a polynomial by a monomial.

Formative Assessment

Use the Check Your Progress exercises after each example to determine students' understanding of concepts.

Additional Answer

b. Sample answer: Add the gallons of ice cream together and then divide by the amount of ice cream needed to make each milkshake. Divide the initial amount of ice cream by $\frac{1}{8}$ then divide the additional amount of ice cream by $\frac{1}{8}$. Then add the two values together.

Additional Example

1 Divide.

a. $(16a^2 - 8a) \div 4a$ $4a - 2$

b. $(10x^2 + 6x) \div 2x$ $5x + 3$

Additional Examples also in Interactive Classroom PowerPoint® Presentations

IWB INTERACTIVE WHITEBOARD READY

Solve Problems

Example 2 shows how to solve a real-world problem involving division of polynomials.

Additional Example

2 **GEOMETRY** The perimeter of an equilateral triangle is $18x^2 + 6x$. What is the length of one of its sides? $6x^2 + 2x$

3 PRACTICE

Formative Assessment

Use Exercises 1–12 to check for understanding.

Use the chart at the bottom of the next page to customize assignments for your students.

Focus on Mathematical Content

Quotient of Powers Property The Quotient of Powers Property justifies the step of subtracting exponents when dividing two terms with a variable. For example, $\frac{b^3}{b} = b^{3-1} = b^2$.

Watch Out!

Preventing Errors Encourage students to use multiplication to check their quotients: quotient × divisor = dividend.

Real-World Link

There are about 110 pandas in captivity. Only seven of these are in the United States. The majority of the other pandas in captivity are found in China.

Source: Panda Bear Facts

Solve Problems You can use division to solve real-world problems.

Real-World EXAMPLE 2 Solve Problems

ZOOS **Six friends visited the zoo to see the new panda exhibit. The group paid for admission and an additional \$12 for parking. The total cost of the visit can be shown by the expression \$6x + \$12. What was the cost of the visit for one person?**

$(6x + 12) \div 6 = \frac{6x + 12}{6}$ **Write as a rational expression.**

$= \frac{6x}{6} + \frac{12}{6}$ **Divide each term by 6.**

$= x + 2$ **Simplify.**

So, each person paid $x + 2$ dollars for admission to the zoo.

Check Your Progress

2. **GARDENS** The model at the right represents a garden. The total area of the garden shown can be represented by the expression $8x^2 + 12x$. If the width of the garden is $4x$, what is the length of the garden? $2x + 3$

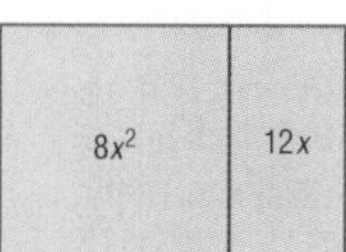

Personal Tutor glencoe.com

Check Your Understanding

Example 1 p. LA21

Divide.

1. $(5abc + c) \div c$ $5ab + 1$
2. $(14ab + 28b) \div (14b)$ $a + 2$
3. $(16x + 24xy) \div (8x)$ $2 + 3y$
4. $(25st - 35s) \div (5s)$ $5t - 7$
5. $(30mn - 9m) \div (3m)$ $10n - 3$
6. $(42q + 56) \div 7$ $6q + 8$
7. $(18x^2 + 32x) \div (2x)$ $9x + 16$
8. $(20k^2 - 35k) \div (5k)$ $4k - 7$
9. $(20b^3 + 40b) \div (20b)$ $b^2 + 2$
10. $(4x^3 + 2x^2 - 6x) \div (2x)$ $2x^2 + x - 3$

Example 2 p. LA22

11. **GEOMETRY** The area of the rectangle below can be shown by the expression $(16x + 4y)$ square feet. If the width of the rectangle is 4 feet, what is the length of the rectangle? $4x + y$

$A = 16x + 4y$

12. **GEOMETRY** The perimeter of the square below can be shown by the expression $12x^2 + 24x$. What is the length of each side of the square? $3x^2 + 6x$

$P = 12x^2 + 24x$

Differentiated Instruction AL OL BL

Kinesthetic Have students build a rectangle with algebra tiles and then determine the dimensions (length and width) of the rectangle. The length and width represent the factors of the polynomial.

Practice and Problem Solving

Example 1 p. LA21

Divide.

13. $(16x + 4y^2) \div 4$ $4x + y^2$

14. $(15a + 3b^2) \div 3$ $5a + b^2$

15. $(21a^2b - 14a^2) \div (7a^2)$ $3b - 2$

16. $(36st^2 - 9st) \div (9st)$ $4t - 1$

17. $(13r^2s - 26r^2) \div (13r^2)$ $s - 2$

18. $(32np + m^2np^2) \div (np)$ $32 + m^2p$

19. $(42c^3d^2 + 56c^2d - 14c) \div (7c)$ $6c^2d^2 + 8cd - 2$

20. $(81m^3n^2 - 45m^2n - 27n) \div (9n)$ $9m^3n - 5m^2 - 3$

Example 2 p. LA22

21. **CONSTRUCTION** A contractor built a basement for a new home. The volume of the rectangular basement shown at the right is represented by the expression $3x^3 + 6x^2 - 30x$. If the height of the basement is $3x$, what is the area of its base? $x^2 + 2x - 10$

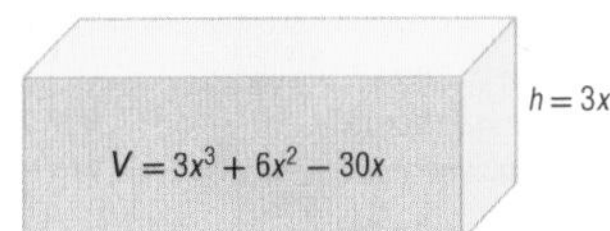

22. **BASKETBALL** The length of a basketball court is $6x^2 + 20x$. If the length is $2x$ times the width, what is the width of the court? $3x + 10$

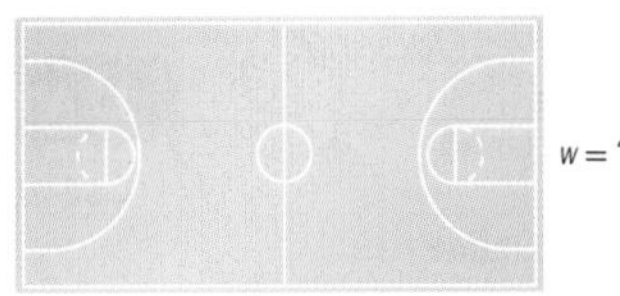

H.O.T. Problems
Use Higher-Order Thinking Skills

23. **OPEN ENDED** Write a polynomial and a monomial that have a quotient of $x^2 + 3x + 5$. Sample answer: $(x^3 + 3x^2 + 5x) \div x = x^2 + 3x + 5$

24. **CHALLENGE** The length and width of a rectangle are represented by $2x$ and $9 - 4x$. If x must be an integer, what are the only possible measures for the area of this rectangle? 10, 4

25. **FIND THE ERROR** George and Marilyn are finding the quotient of $(15x^3 + 12x^2 - 24x) \div (3x)$. Is either of them correct? Explain your reasoning.

George
$$= \frac{15x^3 + 12x^2 - 24x}{3x}$$
$$= \frac{15x^3}{3x} + \frac{12x^2}{3x} - \frac{24x}{3x}$$
$$= 5x^2 + 4x - 8$$

Marilyn
$$= \frac{15x^3 + 12x^2 - 24x}{3x}$$
$$= \frac{15x^3}{3x} + \frac{12x^2}{3x} - \frac{24x}{3x}$$
$$= 5x^3 + 4x^2 - 8x$$

26. **REASONING** Explain why dividing a polynomial by a monomial could be called factoring.

27. **WRITING IN MATH** Explain why $2y^2 + 3$ *cannot* be divided by $2y$ without using fractions.

25. George is correct because Marilyn divided her exponents incorrectly. She needs more practice with quotient of powers where you subtract exponents when you divide.
26. Since dividing requires dividing each term of the polynomial by the monomial you are actually finding the Greatest Common Factor and factoring it out of the polynomial.
27. It cannot be divided because $2y$ is a factor of $2y^2$ but not a factor of 3.

4 ASSESS

Ticket Out the Door Have students solve $(35g^2 - 15g) \div 5g$ and write the quotient on a slip of paper. Have them hand it to you as they walk out the door. $7g - 3$

Watch Out!

Find the Error For Exercise 25, remind students to divide not only the coefficients but also the variables.

Differentiated Homework Options

Level	Assignment	Two-Day Option	
AL Basic	13–22, 23, 25–27	13–21 odd	14–22 even, 23, 25–27
OL Core	13–21 odd, 23, 25–27	13–22	23, 25–27
BL Advanced	13–27		

Lesson Notes

FOCUS

Vertical Alignment

Before Lesson LA-7
Factor monomials.

Lesson LA-7
Use the greatest common factor to factor polynomials. Solve problems by using the greatest common factor to factor polynomials.

After Lesson LA-7
Factor trinomials.

TEACH

Scaffolding Questions

Have students read the *Why?* section of the lesson and answer the questions.

Ask:

- How do you find the area of a rectangle? multiply the length times the width
- If you know the area and the length of a rectangle, how can you find the width? divide the area by the length

Additional Answers (Check Your Progress)

1A. $3(x + 3)$

1B. $2(2x + 5)$

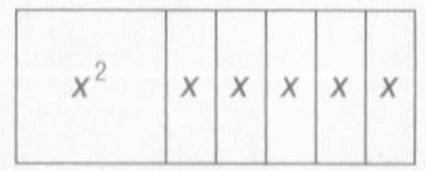

1C. $x(x + 5)$

x^2	x	x	x	x	x

1D. $x(3x + 4)$

x^2
x^2
x^2
x
x
x
x

Using the GCF to Factor Polynomials

Then
You have already factored monomials. (Lesson 9-2)

Now

- Use the Greatest Common Factor to factor polynomials.
- Solve problems by using the Greatest Common Factor to factor polynomials.

New Vocabulary
factoring
factored form

Math Online
glencoe.com

- Extra Examples
- Personal Tutor
- Self-Check Quiz
- Homework Help

Why?

A large area of an art classroom is shown at the right. The total area is represented by $A = 3x^2 + 9x$.

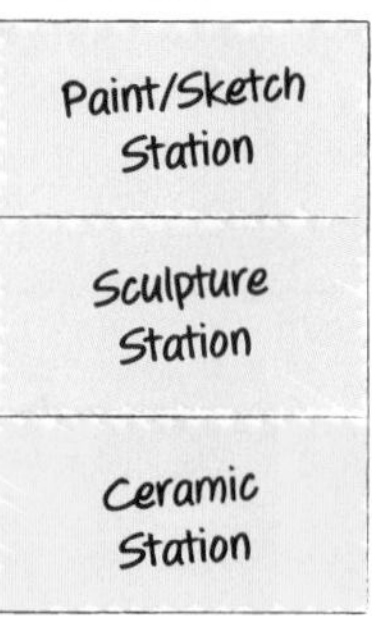

a. The teacher wants to create three rectangular work stations in the classroom that are x feet long. Each station has the same width. Write an expression for the width. $x + 3$ feet

b. If x is equal to 8 feet, what are the dimensions and area of the classroom? 24 feet by 11 feet; 264 ft^2

Factoring Sometimes, you know the product and are asked to find the factors. This process is called **factoring**. You can use algebra tiles to model factoring.

EXAMPLE 1 Using Algebra Tiles to Model Factoring

Use algebra tiles to factor $2x + 8$.

Step 1 Model the polynomial $2x + 8$.

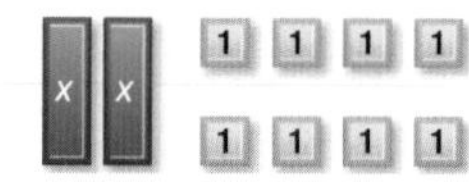

Step 2 Arrange the tiles into a rectangle. The total area of the tiles represents the product. Its length and width represent the factors. The rectangle has a width of 2 and a length of $x + 4$.

So, $2x + 8 = 2(x + 4)$.

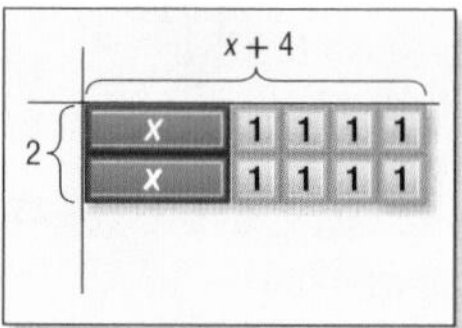

Check Your Progress

Factor. Use algebra tiles. 1A–1D. See margin.

1A. $3x + 9$ **1B.** $4x + 10$ **1C.** $x^2 + 5x$ **1D.** $3x^2 + 4x$

Personal Tutor glencoe.com

A polynomial is in **factored form** when it is expressed as the product of polynomials. To factor $8y^2 + 10y$, first find the greatest common factor (GCF) of each term.

$8y^2 = 2 \cdot 2 \cdot 2 \cdot y \cdot y$ **Write the prime factorization of $8y^2$ and $10y$.**

$10y = 2 \cdot 5 \cdot y$ **Circle the common factors.**

So, the GCF of $8y^2$ and $10y$ is $2y$.

Write each term as a product of the GCF and its remaining factors. Then use the Distributive Property.

$8y^2 + 10y = 2y(4y) + 2y(5)$

$= 2y(4y + 5)$ **Distributive Property**

StudyTip

Greatest Common Factor (GCF) Recall that the GCF is the greatest of the factors common to two or more numbers or terms.

EXAMPLE 2 Using GCF to Factor Polynomials

Factor $30x^2 + 12x$.

First, find the GCF of $30x^2$ and $12x$.

$30x^2 = 2 \cdot 3 \cdot 5 \cdot x \cdot x$ — Write the prime factorization of $30x^2$ and $12x$.

$12x = 2 \cdot 2 \cdot 3 \cdot x$ — Circle the common factors.

The GCF of $30x^2$ and $12x$ is $6x$. Write each term as a product of the GCF and its remaining factors.

$30x^2 + 12x = 6x(5x) + 6x(2)$

$= 6x(5x + 2)$ — Distributive Property

Check Your Progress

Factor each polynomial using the GCF.

2A. $15ab^2 - 25abc$ $5ab(3b - 5c)$

2B. $18x^2y + 12xy^2 + 6xy$ $6xy(3x + 2y + 1)$

Personal Tutor glencoe.com

Solve Problems You can solve some real-world problems by factoring.

Real-World EXAMPLE 3

ART Kiyoshi is planning to mat a square painting with a mat that is 6 inches wide. Let x represent the length and the width of the painting. Write an expression in factored form that represents the area of the mat.

x + 12

x + 12

Step 1 Find the total area.

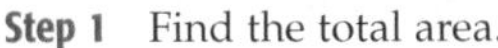

$A = \ell w$

$= (x + 12)(x + 12)$

$= x^2 + 24x + 144$

Step 2 Find the area of the mat alone.

Area of mat = Total Area − Area of painting

$= x^2 + 24x + 144 - x^2$

$= 24x + 144$

Step 3 Factor.

$24x = 2 \cdot 2 \cdot 2 \cdot 3 \cdot x$ — Write the prime factoriztion of $24x$ and 144.

$144 = 2 \cdot 2 \cdot 2 \cdot 2 \cdot 3 \cdot 3$ — Circle the common factors. The GCF is 24.

$24x + 144 = 24(x) + 24(6)$

$= 24(x + 6)$ — Distributive Property

So, the area of the mat is $24(x + 6)$ inches.

Check Your Progress

3. GEOMETRY If the area of a rectangle is $16y^2 + 48y$, write the expression in factored form. $16y(y + 3)$

Personal Tutor glencoe.com

Factoring

Example 1 shows how to use algebra tiles to factor a polynomial. **Example 2** shows how to factor a polynomial using the greatest common factor of the terms.

Formative Assessment

Use the Check Your Progress exercises after each example to determine students' understanding of concepts.

Additional Examples

1 Use algebra tiles to factor $3x + 6$. $3(x + 2)$

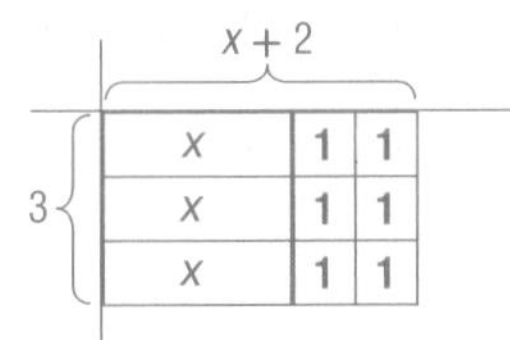

2 Factor $25y + 30y^2$. $5y(5 + 6y)$

Additional Examples also in Interactive Classroom PowerPoint® Presentations

Solve Problems

Example 3 shows how to use factoring to solve a real-world problem that involves polynomials.

Additional Example

3 **GEOMETRY** The area of a rectangle is $15d^2 - 18d$. Write the expression in factored form that represents the area of the rectangle. $3d(5d - 6)$

Focus on Mathematical Content

Greatest Common Factor Factoring using the Distributive Property requires expressing a polynomial as the product of the greatest common monomial factor of the polynomial's terms and a polynomial factor. To find the polynomial factor, each term of the polynomial is divided by the common monomial factor.

3 PRACTICE

Formative Assessment

Use Exercises 1–7 to check for understanding.

Use the chart at the bottom of this page to customize assignments for your students.

4 ASSESS

Crystal Ball Tell students that the next lesson is called *Factor Trinomials*. Ask them to write how today's lesson will connect with that lesson.

Additional Answers

17. To factor a polynomial is to find the factors of the polynomial and represent it as a product of those factors.

18. Sample answer: $x^2 + 3x$; $x^2 + y - xy$

19. Sample answer: The Distributive Property is used to factor out a common factor from the terms of an expression. $5xy + 10x^2y^2 = 5xy(1 + 2xy)$; $2a^2 + 8a + 10 = 2(a^2 + 4a + 5)$

Check Your Understanding

Example 1 p. LA24

Use algebra tiles to factor each binomial. **1–3. See students' work for models.**

1. $24y + 18y^2$ **$6y(4 + 3y)$**
2. $x^2 + 2x$ **$x(x + 2)$**
3. $5 + 5y^2$ **$5(1 + y^2)$**

Example 2 p. LA25

Factor each polynomial using the GCF.

4. $3x + 6$ **$3(x + 2)$**
5. $2x^2 + 4x$ **$2x(x + 2)$**
6. $12a^2b + 6a$ **$6a(2ab + 1)$**

Example 3 p. LA25

7. **GEOMETRY** The diagram represents a walkway that is 2 meters wide surrounding a rectangular garden. Write an expression in factored form that represents the area of the walkway. **$4(4 + 3x)$ square meters**

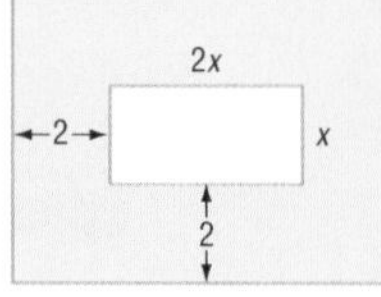

Practice and Problem Solving

Examples 1 and 2 pp. LA24, LA25

Factor each polynomial. If the polynomial cannot be factored, write *cannot be factored*. **9. $ab^2(7a + 3b)$ 10. $mn(36 - 11n)$**

8. $9x + 15$ **$3(3x + 5)$**
9. $7a^2b^2 + 3ab^3$
10. $36mn - 11mn^2$
11. $14mn^2 - 2mn$ **$2mn(7n - 1)$**
12. $24xy + 18xy^2 - 3y$ **$3y(8x + 6xy - 1)$**
13. $12axy - 14ay + 20ax$ **$2a(6xy - 7y + 10x)$**

Example 3 p. LA25

14. The figure at the right shows a walkway built around a statue with a square base.

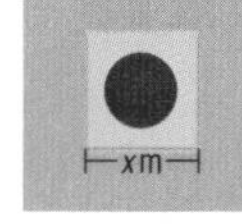

a. If the walkway is 3 meters wide, write an expression in factored form that represents the area of the walkway. **$12(x + 3)$ m^2**

b. If the base of the statue is 3 meters wide, find the area of the walkway. **72 m^2**

15. **MARINE BIOLOGY** In a pool at an aquarium, a dolphin jumps out of the water traveling at 20 feet per second. Its height h, in feet, above the water after t seconds is given by the formula $h = 20t - 16t^2$. Write an expression in factored form that represents the height. **$4t(5 - 4t)$**

H.O.T. Problems Use Higher-Order Thinking Skills

16. **CHALLENGE** The area of a circle is found using the formula $A = \pi r^2$, where r is the radius of the circle. Using π, write an expression in factored form that represents the area of the shaded region at the right. **$9x^2(25\pi - 9)$**

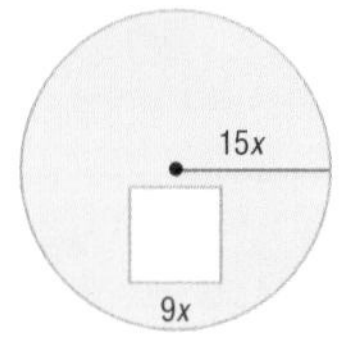

17–19. See margin.

17. **REASONING** Explain what it means to factor a polynomial.

18. **OPEN ENDED** Write a polynomial that can be factored. Write another polynomial that *cannot* be factored.

19. **WRITING IN MATH** Write a few sentences explaining how the Distributive Property is used to factor polynomials. Include at least two examples.

Differentiated Homework Options

Level	Assignment	Two-Day Option	
AL Basic	8–14, 17–19	9–13 odd	8–14 even, 17–19
OL Core	9–15 odd, 17–19	8–15	17–19
BL Advanced	8–19		

Factoring Trinomials

Why?

Alvin has enough bricks to make a patio with a perimeter of 34 feet and area of 72 square feet.

a. How could you find the dimensions of the patio? See margin.

b. Find the dimensions. 8 ft by 9 ft

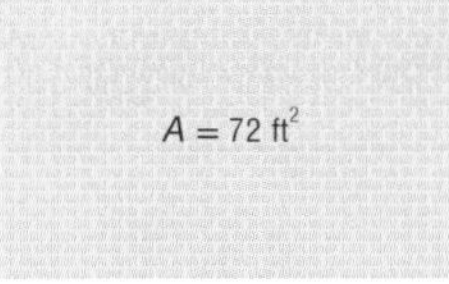

$P = 34$ ft

Then

You have already factored polynomials. (Looking Ahead 7)

Now

- Factor trinomials in the form $x^2 + bx + c$.
- Solve real-world problems by factoring trinomials.

New Vocabulary

trinomial

Math Online

glencoe.com

- Extra Examples
- Personal Tutor
- Self-Check Quiz
- Homework Help

You can also use algebra tiles to factor trinomials. A **trinomial** is a polynomial with three terms. Trinomials that are in the form $x^2 + bx + c$ can sometimes be factored into two binomials.

EXAMPLE 1 Factor Using Models

Factor.

a. $x^2 + 3x + 2$

Model the polynomial.

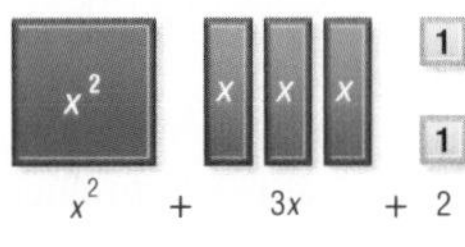

Try to form a rectangle with the tiles.

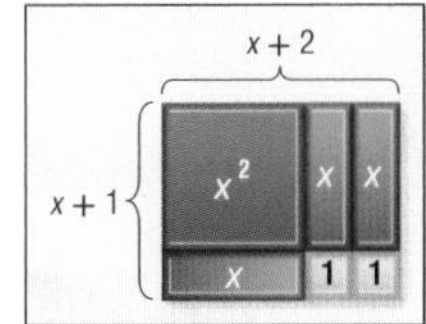

The rectangle has a width of $x + 1$ and a length of $x + 2$.

So, $x^2 + 3x + 2 = (x + 1)(x + 2)$.

b. $x^2 + 3x + 5$

Model the polynomial.

Try to form a rectangle with the tiles.

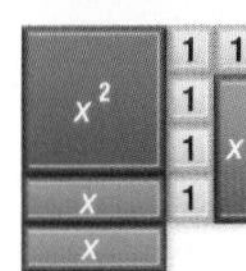

You cannot form a rectangle with the tiles.

So, $x^2 + 3x + 5$ cannot be factored.

Check Your Progress

Factor each trinomial.

1A. $x^2 + 7x + 10$ $(x + 2)(x + 5)$

1B. $x^2 + 7 + x$ Not factorable

Personal Tutor glencoe.com

Additional Answer

a. Sample answer: Find two numbers with a sum of 17 and a product of 72.

Lesson Notes

1 FOCUS

Vertical Alignment

Before Lesson LA-8
Factor polynomials.

Lesson LA-8
Factor trinomials in the form $x^2 + bx + c$. Solve real-world problems by factoring trinomials.

After Lesson LA-8
Solve quadratic equations by factoring.

2 TEACH

Scaffolding Questions

Have students read the *Why?* section of the lesson and answer the questions.

Ask:

- What is the formula for the perimeter of a rectangle? $P = 2l + 2w$
- What is the formula for the area of a rectangle? $A = lw$

Factor Trinomials

Example 1 shows how to factor a trinomial using a model. **Example 2** shows how to factor a trinomial using the FOIL method.

Formative Assessment

Use the Check Your Progress exercises after each example to determine students' understanding of concepts.

Additional Example

Factor each trinomial.

a. $x^2 + 4x + 3$ $(x + 3)(x + 1)$

b. $x^2 + 2x + 2$ Not factorable

Additional Example

2 Factor $x^2 + x - 12$.
$(x - 3)(x + 4)$

Additional Examples also in Interactive Classroom PowerPoint® Presentations

IWB INTERACTIVE WHITEBOARD READY

Solve Problems

Example 3 shows how to solve a real-world problem by factoring a trinomial.

Additional Example

3 **SHIPPING** The area designated for placing a rectangular shipping crate on a ship is $x^2 + 9x + 20$ ft^2.

a. What are the dimensions of the base of the shipping crate that will fit into the space in terms of x? $(x + 5)$ ft by $(x + 4)$ ft

b. If $x = 10$ feet, what are the dimensions of the shipping crate? How much area is being designated to store it? 15 ft by 14 ft; 210 ft^2

Focus on Mathematical Content

Factoring Trinomials A trinomial of the form $x^2 + bx + c$ may or may not be factorable into binomial factors. If the trinomial is factorable, then the factors of c must be two integers, m and n, such that $m + n = b$ and $mn = c$.

Use the FOIL method and guess-and-check to factor trinomials.

EXAMPLE 2 Factor Trinomials Using the Foil Method

Factor $x^2 + 6x + 8$.

Step 1 The x^2 term is the product of **F**irst terms. It only has one set of factors that are valid for two binomials.

$$x^2 + bx + c = (x + \blacksquare)(x + \blacksquare)$$

Step 2 The **L**ast two terms in each binomial must have a product of 8. Try several factor pairs of 8 until the sum of the products of the **O**uter and **I**nner terms is $6x$.

Try 1 and 8. $(x + 1)(x + 8) = x^2 + 8x + 1x + 8$
$= x^2 + 9x + 8$ — **9x is not the correct term.**

Try 2 and 4. $(x + 2)(x + 4) = x^2 + 4x + 2x + 8$
$= x^2 + 6x + 8$ ✓

So, $x^2 + 6x + 8 = (x + 2)(x + 4)$.

Check Your Progress

2A. $x^2 + 5x - 6$ $(x + 6)(x - 1)$ **2B.** $x^2 + 8x + 15$ $(x + 5)(x + 3)$

Personal Tutor glencoe.com

Real-World Link

In tennis, the service court fits inside the singles width of the court (27 feet) and extends back from the net 21 feet. The service court is divided in half with a center line marking the left and right service courts.

Source: SportsKnowHow

Solve Problems You can solve real-world problems by factoring trinomials.

Real-World EXAMPLE 3 Solve Problems By Factoring

SPORTS A doubles tennis court has an area represented by $x^2 + 78x + 1080$.

a. What are the dimensions of the court in terms of x?

$x^2 + 78x + 1080 = (x + \blacksquare)(x + \blacksquare)$ — **Write the expression.**

The factor pair of 1080 that has a sum of 78 is 18 and 60.

So, $x^2 + 78x + 1080 = (x + 18)(x + 60)$

The dimensions are $(x + 18)$ feet by $(x + 60)$ feet.

b. If the service court occupies 1134 ft^2 and $x = 18$ feet, how much of the court is not considered service court area?

$(x + 18)(x + 60) = (18 + 18)(18 + 60) - 1134$ — **Subtract the service area from the total area.**
$= (36)(78) - 1134$
$= 2808 - 1134$ or 1674 — **Subtract.**

So, 1674 square feet is *not* considered service court area.

Check Your Progress

3. SPORTS The platform on which table tennis is played has an area that can be represented by $y^2 - 2y - 3$.

A. What are the dimensions of the platform in terms of y? $(y - 3)$ ft by $(y + 1)$ ft

B. If $y = 8$ feet, what is the total platform area? 45 ft^2

Personal Tutor glencoe.com

Differentiated Instruction

AL OL

If students have difficulty factoring trinomials,

Then have students work in pairs. Have each student draw an algebra model for the product of two binomials. Then have the students trade papers and find the factors of their partner's model.

Check Your Understanding

Examples 1 and 2
p. LA26

Factor.

1. $x^2 + 5x + 6$ **$(x + 2)(x + 3)$**
2. $x^2 + 4x + 3$ **$(x + 1)(x + 3)$**
3. $x^2 + x + 2$ **not factorable**

4. $y^2 + 9y + 20$ **$(y + 4)(y + 5)$**
5. $a^2 - 5a + 4$ **$(a - 4)(a - 1)$**
6. $x^2 + 3x - 10$ **$(x + 5)(x - 2)$**

Example 3
p. LA26

7. **GEOMETRY** Refer to the figure at the right.
   a. Find the area of the shaded region. Express in factored form. **$(x - 8)(x + 3)$ units^2**
   b. If $x = 10$, what is the area? **26 units^2**

Practice and Problem Solving

Examples 1 and 2
p. LA26

Factor.

8. $m^2 - 4m - 21$
9. $b^2 - 9b + 20$
10. $x^2 - x - 12$
11. $b^2 + 5b + 4$
12. $a^2 + 3a + 5$
13. $x^2 - 8x + 15$
14. $d^2 - 11d + 28$
15. $c^2 + 2c - 3$
16. $m^2 - 2m - 24$
17. Express $x^2 + 24x + 95$ as the product of two binomials. **$(x + 19)(x + 5)$**

Example 3
p. LA26

18. **GEOMETRY** Refer to the figure.
   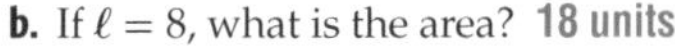
   a. Find the area of the shaded region. Express the area in factored form. **$(\ell - 6)(\ell + 1)$ units^2**
   b. If $\ell = 8$, what is the area? **18 units^2**

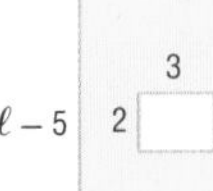

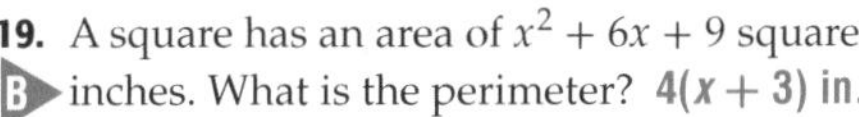

19. A square has an area of $x^2 + 6x + 9$ square inches. What is the perimeter? **$4(x + 3)$ in.**

Answers:
8. $(m - 7)(m + 3)$
9. $(b - 5)(b - 4)$
10. $(x - 4)(x + 3)$
11. $(b + 4)(b + 1)$
12. not factorable
13. $(x - 5)(x - 3)$
14. $(d - 7)(d - 4)$
15. $(c + 3)(c - 1)$
16. $(m - 6)(m + 4)$

H.O.T. Problems

Use **H**igher-**O**rder **T**hinking Skills

20. **CHALLENGE** The volume of a rectangular prism is $x^3 + 4x^2 + 3x$. Find the length, width, and height of the prism if each one can be written as a monomial or binomial. (*Hint*: Use the formula $V = \ell wh$.) **$\ell = x$; $w = x + 1$; $h = x + 3$**
21. **REASONING** Complete the trinomial $x^2 + 6x +$ ____ with a positive integer so that the resulting trinomial can be factored. (*Hint*: There is more than one solution.) **5, 8, or 9**
22. **CHALLENGE** The binomials $x^2 - 1$, $x^2 - 4$, $x^2 - 36$, and so on, can all be factored into the product of two binomials. What pattern do you notice? Make and test a conjecture about the factors $a^2 - b^2$. **See margin.**
23. **WRITING IN MATH** Explain why the trinomial $x^2 + x + 5$ *cannot* be factored. **There are no factors of 5 whose sum is 1.**

3 PRACTICE

Formative Assessment

Use Exercises 1–7 to check for understanding.

Use the chart at the bottom of this page to customize assignments for your students.

4 ASSESS

Ticket Out the Door Have students write the factors of $x^2 + 9x + 14$ and hand in their work as they leave. $(x + 2)(x + 7)$

Additional Answer

22. The factors will always be $(a + b)(a - b)$. For example, $x^2 - 49$. The factors would be $(x + 7)(x - 7)$.

Differentiated Homework Options

Level	Assignment	Two-Day Option	
AL Basic	8–18, 21, 23	9–17 odd	8–18 even, 21, 23
OL Core	9–23 odd	8–18	19–23 odd
BL Advanced	8–23		

Student Handbook

Built-In Workbooks

Reference

How to Use the Student Handbook

The Student Handbook includes additional skill and reference material and is located at the end of the text. This Handbook can help you answer these questions.

What If I Need More Practice?

You or your teacher may decide that working through some additional problems would be helpful. The **Extra Practice** section provides a set of problems for each lesson so you have ample opportunity to practice new skills.

What If I Have Trouble with Word Problems?

The **Mixed Problem Solving** section provides additional word problems that use the skills and concepts presented in each lesson. These problems are in real-world contexts so you can see how the mathematics is applied.

What If I Forget What I Learned Last Year?

Use the **Concepts and Skills Bank** to refresh your memory about things you have learned in other math classes. Here's a list of the topics covered in your book.

1. Factors
2. Greatest Common Factor
3. Least Common Multiple
4. Cube Roots
5. Linear Regression
6. Graphing Linear Inequalities
7. Geometric Figures
8. Geometric Constructions
9. Measuring and Drawing Angles
10. The Tangent Ratio
11. The Sine and Cosine Ratios
12. Accuracy and Precision
13. Geometric Probability
14. Displaying Data in Graphs
15. Misleading Graphs
16. Matrices

What If I Need to Recall a Specific Formula?

The **Key Concepts** section lists all of the important concepts that were highlighted in your text along with the pages where they appear.

What If I Need to Check an Answer?

The answers to odd-numbered problems are included in the **Selected Answers and Solutions** section. Check your answers to make sure you understand how to solve all of the assigned problems. Fully worked-out solutions to selected problems are also included in this section.

What If I Forget a Vocabulary Word?

The **Glossary/Glosario** provides a list of important or difficult words used throughout the textbook. It provides definitions in English and Spanish as well as the pages where the words were originally introduced.

What If I Need to Find Something Quickly?

The **Index** lists the subjects covered throughout the entire text alphabetically, along with the pages on which each subject can be found.

Where Can I Easily Find a List of Formulas and Symbols?

Inside the back cover of your math book are lists of **Symbols, Formulas,** and **Measurement Conversions** that are used throughout the text.

Extra Practice

Lesson 1-1 Words and Expressions (pp. 5–9)

Evaluate each expression.

1. $8 + 7 + 12 \div 4$ 18
2. $20 \div 4 - 5 + 12$ 12
3. $(25 \cdot 3) + (10 \cdot 3)$ 105
4. $36 \div 6 + 7 - 6$ 7
5. $30 \cdot (6 - 4)$ 60
6. $(40 \cdot 2) - (6 \cdot 11)$ 14
7. $\frac{86 - 11}{11 + 4}$ 5
8. $\frac{12 + 84}{11 + 13}$ 4
9. $\frac{5 \cdot 5 + 5}{5 \cdot 5 - 15}$ 3
10. $(19 - 8)4$ 44
11. $75 - 5(2 \cdot 6)$ 15
12. $81 \div 27 \times 6 - 2$ 16

Write a numerical expression for each verbal phrase.

13. three increased by nine $3 + 9$
14. fifteen divided by three $15 \div 3$
15. six less than ten $10 - 6$

Lesson 1-2 Variables and Expressions (pp. 11–16)

ALGEBRA Evaluate each expression if $a = 2$, $b = 4$, and $c = 3$.

1. $ba - ac$ 2
2. $4b + a \cdot a$ 20
3. $11 \cdot c - ab$ 25
4. $4b - (a + c)$ 11
5. $7(a + b) - c$ 39
6. $8a + 8b$ 48
7. $\frac{8(a + b)}{4c}$ 4
8. $36 - 12c$ 0
9. $\frac{9(b + a)}{c - 1}$ 27
10. $abc - bc$ 12
11. $28 - bc + a$ 18
12. $a(b - c)$ 2

Translate each phrase into an algebraic expression.

13. nine more than a $a + 9$
14. eleven less than k $k - 11$
15. three times p $3p$
16. the product of some number and five $5n$
17. twice Shelly's score decreased by 18 $2s - 18$
18. the quotient of 16 and n $16 \div n$

Lesson 1-3 Properties (pp. 18–23)

Name the property shown by each statement.

1. $1 \cdot 4 = 4$ Identity (×)
2. $6 + (b + 2) = (6 + b) + 2$ Associative (+)
3. $9(6n) = (9 \cdot 6)n$ Associative (×)
4. $8t \cdot 0 = 0 \cdot 8t$ Commutative (×)
5. $0(13n) = 0$ Multiplicative (0)
6. $7 + t = t + 7$ Commutative (+)

ALGEBRA Simplify each expression.

7. $(12 + x) + 9$ $x + 21$
8. $31 + (15 + c)$ $46 + c$
9. $d + (8 + 19)$ $d + 27$
10. $2 \cdot (6 \cdot m)$ $12m$
11. $(5 \cdot p) \cdot 3$ $15p$
12. $9(4f)$ $36f$

Lesson 1-4 Order Pairs and Relations (pp. 25–30)

Refer to the coordinate plane shown at the right. Write the ordered pair that names each point.

1. R (4, 8)
2. P (9, 7)
3. W (5, 1)
4. C (0, 6)
5. D (0, 8)
6. F (3, 4)

Express each relation as a table. Then determine the domain and range. 7–8. See Student Handbook Answer Appendix for tables.

7. {(3, 6), (4, 9), (5, 1)} D = {3, 4, 5}; R = {1, 6, 9}
8. {(2, 1), (4, 4), (6, 7), (4, 3)} D = {2, 4, 6}; R = {1, 3, 4, 7}

Lesson 1-5 Words, Equations, Tables, and Graphs (pp. 33–37)

Copy and complete each function table. Then state the domain and range of the function.

1. Each ticket cost $7.

Number of Tickets	Total Cost ($)
4	■ 28
8	■ 56
15	■ 105
20	■ 140

Domain: {4, 8, 15, 20}; Range: {28, 56, 105, 140}

2. Natalie has 3 less than twice as many CDs as Kilan.

Kilan's CDs	Natalie's CDs
Input (x)	Output (y)
5	■ 7
8	■ 13
13	■ 23
21	■ 39

Domain: {5, 8, 13, 21}; Range: {7, 13, 23, 39}

Lesson 1-6 Scatter Plots (pp. 40–46)

1–3. See Student Handbook Answer Appendix for explanations.

Determine whether a scatter plot of the data for the following might show a *positive, negative,* or *no* relationship. Explain your answer.

1. speed of airplane and miles traveled in three hours positive
2. weight and shoe size no
3. outside temperature and heating bill negative
4. **GAMES** The number of pieces in a jigsaw puzzle and the number of minutes required for a person to complete it is shown below.

Number of Pieces	100	60	500	750	1000	800	75
Time (min)	35	20	175	315	395	270	25

a. Make a scatter plot of the data. See Student Handbook Answer Appendix.

b. Does the scatter plot show any relationship? If so, is it positive or negative? Explain your reasoning. Positive; as the number of pieces increases, the time increases.

c. Suppose Dave purchases a puzzle having 650 pieces. Predict the length of time it will take him to complete the puzzle. 260 min

Extra Practice

Lesson 2-1 Integers and Absolute Value (pp. 61–66)

Replace each ● with <, >, or = to make a true sentence.

1. $-4 \bullet -8$ >
2. $-6 \bullet 3$ <
3. $0 \bullet -5$ >
4. $-12 \bullet -9$ <
5. $12 \bullet -25$ >
6. $3 \bullet -7$ >
7. $0 \bullet -2$ >
8. $-15 \bullet 12$ <
9. $5 \bullet -7$ >
10. $|6| \bullet -2$ >
11. $-2 \bullet |-3|$ <
12. $|-7| \bullet |-4|$ >

Order the integers in each set from least to greatest. 16. {−43, −40, −1, 8, 16, 27}

13. {−1, 2, −5} {−5, −1, 2}
14. {0, −2, 8, 5, −9} {−9, −2, 0, 5, 8}
15. {100, −34, −86, 21, 0} {−86, −34, 0, 21, 100}
16. {−1, 16, −43, 8, 27, −40}
17. {0, −23, 75, −15, 24} {−23, −15, 0, 24, 75}
18. {−6, 6, −5, 18} {−6, −5, 6, 18}

Evaluate each expression.

19. $|-3| + |9|$ 12
20. $|-18| - |5|$ 13
21. $|12 + 7|$ 19
22. $-|6|$ −6
23. $|-8| + |4|$ 12
24. $-|-20|$ −20
25. $|-6| \cdot |8|$ 48
26. $-|12| \cdot |9|$ −108
27. $-||-16| + |-22||$ −38

Lesson 2-2 Adding Integers (pp. 69–74)

Find each sum.

1. $5 + (-6)$ −1
2. $-17 + 24$ 7
3. $15 + (-29)$ −14
4. $-6 + 13$ 7
5. $50 + (-14)$ 36
6. $-21 + (-4)$ −25
7. $30 + (-7)$ 23
8. $(-3) + (-10)$ −13
9. $-15 + 26$ 11
10. $-11 + 15 + (-6)$ −2
11. $23 + (-64)$ −41
12. $-1 + 14 + (-13)$ 0
13. $33 + (-18) + 7$ 22
14. $-75 + (-13)$ −88
15. $26 + 14 + (-71)$ −31
16. $12 + (-20) + 16$ 8
17. $100 + (-54) + (-17)$ 29
18. $11 + (-22) + (-33)$ −44

Lesson 2-3 Subtracting Integers (pp. 76–80)

Find each difference.

1. $8 - 17$ −9
2. $-15 - 3$ −18
3. $10 - 21$ −11
4. $20 - (-5)$ 25
5. $5 - (-9)$ 14
6. $-12 - (-7)$ −5
7. $-19 - (-6)$ −13
8. $-16 - (-23)$ 7
9. $-56 - 32$ −88
10. $-49 - (-52)$ 3
11. $-6 - 9 - (-7)$ −8
12. $-6 - (-10) - 7$ −3
13. $17 - 33$ −16
14. $-21 - 19$ −40
15. $12 - (-24)$ 36
16. $-35 - (-18)$ −17
17. $-54 - 27$ −81
18. $32 - (-18)$ 50

ALGEBRA Evaluate each expression if $x = 6$, $y = -8$, $z = -3$, and $w = 4$.

19. $y - z$ −5
20. $3 - z$ 6
21. $y - 5$ −13
22. $x - y$ 14
23. $14 - y - x$ 16
24. $6 + x - z$ 15
25. $y + z + w$ −7
26. $w - z + 11$ 18

Lesson 2-4 Multiplying Integers (pp. 83–88)

Find each product.

1. $-4(2)$ −8
2. $-8(-5)$ 40
3. $13(-4)$ −52
4. $-5 \cdot 6 \cdot 10$ −300
5. $-6(-2)(-14)$ −168
6. $18(-3)(6)$ −324
7. $4(-10)(-3)$ 120
8. $-9(3)(2)$ −54
9. $12(-8)$ −96

ALGEBRA Simplify each expression.

10. $-3 \cdot 5x$ $-15x$
11. $7(-8m)$ $-56m$
12. $-10(-3k)$ $30k$
13. $-4y(-8z)$ $32yz$
14. $(-2r)(-3s)$ $6rs$
15. $6(-2m)(3n)$ $-36mn$

ALGEBRA Evaluate each expression.

16. $-6t$, if $t = 15$ −90
17. $7p$, if $p = -9$ −63
18. $-4k$, if $k = -16$ 64
19. aw, if $a = 0$ and $w = -72$ 0
20. dk, if $d = -12$ and $k = 11$ −132
21. st, if $s = -8$ and $t = -10$ 80
22. $3hp$, if $h = 9$ and $p = -3$ −81
23. $-5bc$, if $b = -6$ and $c = 2$ 60
24. $-4wx$, if $w = -1$ and $x = -8$ −32

Lesson 2-5 Dividing Integers (pp. 90–95)

Find each quotient.

1. $-36 \div 9$ −4
2. $112 \div (-8)$ −14
3. $-72 \div 2$ −36
4. $-26 \div (-13)$ 2
5. $-144 \div 6$ −24
6. $-180 \div (-10)$ 18
7. $304 \div (-8)$ −38
8. $-216 \div (-9)$ 24
9. $80 \div (-5)$ −16
10. $-105 \div 15$ −7
11. $120 \div (-30)$ −4
12. $-200 \div (-8)$ 25
13. $42 \div (-6)$ −7
14. $144 \div (-12)$ −12
15. $-360 \div 9$ −40
16. $-84 \div -6$ 14
17. $125 \div (-5)$ −25
18. $180 \div (-15)$ −12
19. $-400 \div 20$ −20
20. $72 \div (-9)$ −8
21. $-156 \div (-2)$ 78

ALGEBRA Evaluate each expression if $x = -5$, $y = -3$, $z = 2$, and $w = 7$.

22. $25 \div x$ −5
23. $-42 \div w$ −6
24. $3 \div y$ −1
25. $2x \div z$ −5
26. $-3x \div y$ −5
27. $x \div (-1)$ 5
28. $xyz \div 10$ 3
29. $yz \div 2$ −3
30. $\frac{3y}{-3}$ 3
31. $\frac{6-y}{y}$ −3
32. $\frac{w}{-7}$ −1
33. $\frac{w-x}{y}$ −4

Lesson 2-6 Graphing in Four Quadrants (pp. 96–100)

9–14. See Student Handbook Answer Appendix for Graph.

Name the ordered pair for each point graphed at the right.

1. D (−6, 8)
2. J (1, −2)
3. C (9, 2)
4. L (1, 4)
5. B (−3, −4)
6. N (2, 5)
7. K (3, 0)
8. M (5, −1)

Graph and label each point on a coordinate plane. Name the quadrant in which each point is located.

9. $H(-2, -5)$ III
10. $P(1, 5)$ I
11. $R(-3, 1)$ II
12. $M(4, -2)$ IV
13. $K(-4, 5)$ II
14. $G(3, -5)$ IV

Extra Practice

Lesson 2-7 Translations and Reflections on the Coordinate Plane (pp. 101–106)

1. The vertices of rectangle $ABCD$ are $A(-6, 5)$, $B(-2, 5)$, $C(-2, 2)$, and $D(-6, 2)$. What are the vertices of its image after a translation of 4 units to the right? **$A'(-2, 5)$, $B'(2, 5)$, $C'(2, 2)$, and $D'(-2, 2)$**
2. Rectangle $ABCD$ has vertices $A(2, 1)$, $B(5, 1)$, $C(5, 5)$, and $D(2, 5)$. Graph the rectangle and its image after a reflection over the x-axis. **See Student Handbook Answer Appendix for Graph.**
3. A triangle has vertices $A(-14, 12)$, $B(6, 7)$, and $C(-5, 0)$. Its image has vertices $A'(-9, 8)$, $B'(11, 3)$, and $C'(0, -4)$. Describe the transformation. **The transformation is a translation 5 right and 4 down.**

Use the coordinate plane at the right.

4. Find the coordinates of the vertices of the image of $\triangle ABC$ translated 3 units to the right and 4 units down. **$A'(2.5, 0)$, $B'(0, -5)$, $C'(5, -5)$**
5. Find the coordinates of the vertices of the image of $\triangle ABC$ reflected over the y-axis. **$A'(0.5, 4)$, $B'(3, -1)$, $C'(-2, -1)$**

Lesson 3-1 Fractions and Decimals (pp. 121–127)

Write each fraction as a decimal. Use a bar to show a repeating decimal.

1. $\frac{6}{10}$ **0.6**
2. $\frac{4}{25}$ **0.16**
3. $-\frac{1}{8}$ **−0.125**
4. $\frac{5}{6}$ **$0.8\overline{3}$**
5. $\frac{9}{20}$ **0.45**
6. $\frac{8}{11}$ **$0.\overline{72}$**
7. $-\frac{3}{16}$ **−0.1875**
8. $\frac{6}{15}$ **0.4**

Replace each ● with <, >, or = to make a true sentence.

9. $\frac{7}{8}$ ● $\frac{5}{6}$ **>**
10. 0.04 ● $\frac{5}{9}$ **<**
11. $\frac{1}{3}$ ● $\frac{2}{7}$ **>**
12. $\frac{3}{5}$ ● $\frac{12}{20}$ **=**
13. $\frac{1}{2}$ ● 0.75 **<**
14. 0.3 ● $\frac{1}{3}$ **<**
15. $\frac{2}{3}$ ● 0.64 **>**
16. $\frac{2}{20}$ ● 0.10 **=**
17. $0.\overline{5}$ ● $\frac{5}{9}$ **=**
18. $2.\overline{1}$ ● $2\frac{1}{10}$ **>**
19. $3\frac{7}{8}$ ● 3.78 **>**
20. $-\frac{6}{7}$ ● $-\frac{5}{6}$ **<**

Lesson 3-2 Rational Numbers (pp. 128–133)

Write each number as a fraction.

1. $3\frac{4}{5}$ **$\frac{19}{5}$**
2. $-1\frac{2}{9}$ **$-\frac{11}{9}$**
3. 15 **$\frac{15}{1}$**
4. $2\frac{3}{8}$ **$\frac{19}{8}$**
5. −13 **$-\frac{13}{1}$**
6. $2\frac{6}{7}$ **$\frac{20}{7}$**
7. 36 **$\frac{36}{1}$**
8. $-1\frac{3}{5}$ **$-\frac{8}{5}$**

Write each decimal as a fraction or mixed number in simplest form.

9. 0.6 **$\frac{3}{5}$**
10. 0.05 **$\frac{1}{20}$**
11. 0.38 **$\frac{19}{50}$**
12. 4.12 **$4\frac{3}{25}$**
13. 0.375 **$\frac{3}{8}$**
14. −3.24 **$-3\frac{6}{25}$**
15. 0.222… **$\frac{2}{9}$**
16. $-0.\overline{4}$ **$-\frac{4}{9}$**

Lesson 3-3 Multiplying Rational Numbers (pp. 134–139)

Find each product. Write in simplest form.

1. $\frac{2}{5} \cdot \frac{3}{16}$ **$\frac{3}{40}$**
2. $3\frac{1}{4} \cdot \frac{2}{11}$ **$\frac{13}{22}$**
3. $\frac{3}{5}\left(-\frac{5}{12}\right)$ **$-\frac{1}{4}$**
4. $\frac{5}{8} \cdot \frac{2}{3}$ **$\frac{5}{12}$**
5. $-\frac{9}{10} \cdot \frac{5}{24}$ **$-\frac{3}{16}$**
6. $\frac{1}{7} \cdot \frac{21}{22}$ **$\frac{3}{22}$**
7. $\frac{4}{5} \cdot \frac{1}{8}$ **$\frac{1}{10}$**
8. $2\frac{2}{6} \cdot 6\frac{2}{7}$ **$14\frac{2}{3}$**
9. $2\left(-\frac{7}{12}\right)$ **$-1\frac{1}{6}$**
10. $1\frac{3}{7}\left(-9\frac{4}{5}\right)$ **−14**
11. $-\frac{6}{7}\left(-\frac{6}{7}\right)$ **$\frac{36}{49}$**
12. $\frac{6c}{10} \cdot \frac{2}{c}$ **$1\frac{1}{5}$**
13. $\frac{p^3}{4} \cdot \frac{12}{p}$ **$3p^2$**
14. $\frac{ab}{9} \cdot \frac{3}{b^2}$ **$\frac{a}{3b}$**
15. $\frac{4x}{3y} \cdot \frac{12y^4}{x^2}$ **$\frac{16y^3}{x}$**

Lesson 3-4 Dividing Rational Numbers (pp. 141–146)

Find the multiplicative inverse of each number.

1. $\frac{4}{7}$ **$\frac{7}{4}$**
2. $-\frac{5}{9}$ **$-\frac{9}{5}$**
3. $\frac{1}{4}$ **4**
4. $5\frac{3}{8}$ **$\frac{8}{43}$**
5. 6 **$\frac{1}{6}$**
6. −18 **$-\frac{1}{18}$**
7. $\frac{7}{10}$ **$\frac{10}{7}$**
8. 2.35 **$\frac{20}{47}$**
9. −1.4 **$-\frac{5}{7}$**

Find each quotient. Write in simplest form.

10. $\frac{4}{5} \div \frac{2}{5}$ **2**
11. $-\frac{1}{3} \div \frac{6}{7}$ **$-\frac{7}{18}$**
12. $\frac{4}{9} \div \frac{1}{5}$ **$2\frac{2}{9}$**
13. $\frac{2}{3} \div \frac{1}{9}$ **6**
14. $\frac{4}{5} \div \left(-\frac{8}{15}\right)$ **$-1\frac{1}{2}$**
15. $\frac{1}{12} \div \frac{3}{4}$ **$\frac{1}{9}$**
16. $\frac{3}{4} \div \frac{15}{16}$ **$\frac{4}{5}$**
17. $16 \div 1\frac{7}{8}$ **$8\frac{8}{15}$**
18. $2\frac{1}{6} \div \left(-1\frac{1}{5}\right)$ **$-1\frac{29}{36}$**
19. $-11 \div 3\frac{1}{7}$ **$-3\frac{1}{2}$**
20. $\frac{8}{45} \div \frac{10}{27}$ **$\frac{12}{25}$**
21. $-22 \div \left(-5\frac{1}{2}\right)$ **4**
22. $\frac{w}{5} \div \frac{w}{35}$ **7**
23. $\frac{ab}{12} \div \frac{b}{16}$ **$\frac{4a}{3}$**
24. $\frac{21y}{8x^2} \div \frac{7y}{16x}$ **$\frac{6}{x}$**

Lesson 3-5 Adding and Subtracting Like Fractions (pp. 147–152)

Find each sum or difference. Write in simplest form.

1. $\frac{2}{7} + \frac{3}{7}$ **$\frac{5}{7}$**
2. $\frac{8}{15} - \frac{4}{15}$ **$\frac{4}{15}$**
3. $\frac{3}{7} + \frac{4}{7}$ **1**
4. $-\frac{8}{9} + \frac{1}{9}$ **$-\frac{7}{9}$**
5. $\frac{5}{6} - \frac{1}{6}$ **$\frac{2}{3}$**
6. $\frac{7}{12} - \frac{5}{12}$ **$\frac{1}{6}$**
7. $\frac{5}{12} + \frac{11}{12}$ **$1\frac{1}{3}$**
8. $-\frac{3}{14} - \frac{5}{14}$ **$-\frac{4}{7}$**
9. $3\frac{1}{4} + \left(-\frac{3}{4}\right)$ **$2\frac{1}{2}$**

ALGEBRA Find each sum or difference. Write in simplest form.

10. $\frac{n}{5} + \frac{3n}{5}$ **$\frac{4n}{5}$**
11. $\frac{15}{k} - \frac{8}{k}, k \neq 0$ **$\frac{7}{k}$**
12. $12\frac{7}{8}s - 7\frac{3}{8}s$ **$5\frac{1}{2}s$**
13. $-6\frac{4}{9}t - 3\frac{2}{9}t$ **$-9\frac{2}{3}t$**
14. $6\frac{1}{4}g + \left(-6\frac{3}{4}g\right)$ **$-\frac{1}{2}g$**
15. $7\frac{2}{5}n - \left(-4\frac{2}{5}n\right)$ **$11\frac{4}{5}n$**

Lesson 3-6 Adding and Subtracting Unlike Fractions (pp. 153–158)

Find each sum or difference. Write in simplest form.

1. $\frac{1}{5}+\frac{2}{7}$ $\frac{17}{35}$
2. $\frac{4}{5}+\frac{7}{9}$ $1\frac{26}{45}$
3. $\frac{1}{9}-\frac{7}{12}$ $-\frac{17}{36}$
4. $\frac{8}{11}-\frac{4}{5}$ $-\frac{4}{55}$
5. $\frac{7}{12}-\left(-\frac{4}{11}\right)$ $\frac{125}{132}$
6. $-\frac{9}{14}+\frac{15}{16}$ $\frac{33}{112}$
7. $-\frac{3}{8}+\left(-1\frac{5}{12}\right)$ $-1\frac{19}{24}$
8. $-\frac{2}{15}-3\frac{1}{5}$ $-3\frac{1}{3}$
9. $-5\frac{1}{3}+\left(-\frac{1}{6}\right)$ $-5\frac{1}{2}$
10. $3\frac{2}{5}+2\frac{4}{7}$ $5\frac{34}{35}$
11. $-4\frac{1}{8}+2\frac{5}{9}$ $-1\frac{41}{72}$
12. $11\frac{3}{5}-\left(-6\frac{5}{8}\right)$ $18\frac{9}{40}$

Lesson 4-1 The Distributive Property (pp. 171–176)

Use the Distributive Property to write each expression as an equivalent expression. Then evaluate the expression.

1. $2(4+5)$ $2 \cdot 4 + 2 \cdot 5$, 18
2. $4(5+3)$ $4 \cdot 5 + 4 \cdot 3$, 32
3. $3(7-6)$ $3 \cdot 7 - 3 \cdot 6$, 3
4. $(2+5)9$ $2 \cdot 9 + 5 \cdot 9$, 63
5. $(10-4)3$ $10 \cdot 3 - 4 \cdot 3$, 18
6. $-6(1+3)$ $-6 \cdot 1 - 6 \cdot 3$, -24

Use the Distributive Property to write each expression as an equivalent algebraic expression.

7. $3(m+4)$ $3m+12$
8. $(y+7)5$ $5y+35$
9. $-6(x+3)$ $-6x-18$
10. $(p-4)5$ $5p-20$
11. $-3(s-9)$ $-3s+27$
12. $5(x+y)$ $5x+5y$
13. $b(c+3d)$ $bc+3bd$
14. $(a-b)(-5)$ $-5a+5b$
15. $-6(v-3w)$ $-6v+18w$
16. $5(x+12)$ $5x+60$
17. $(m-6)(4)$ $4m-24$
18. $-2(a-b)$ $-2a+2b$
19. $(8-m)(-3)$ $-24+3m$
20. $8(p-3q)$ $8p-24q$
21. $(2x+3y)(4)$ $8x+12y$

Lesson 4-2 Simplifying Algebraic Expressions (pp. 179–183)

Identify the terms, like terms, coefficients, and constants in each expression.

1. $3+4x+x$
2. $5n+2-3n$
3. $6+1+7y$
4. $2c+c+8d$
5. $3a-9+b$
6. $2+6k+7-5k$

1–6. See Student Handbook Answer Appendix.

Simplify each expression.

7. $8k+2k+7$ $10k+7$
8. $3+2b+b$ $3+3b$
9. $t+2t$ $3t$
10. $9(3+2x)$ $27+18x$
11. $4(y+2)-2$ $4y+6$
12. $(6+3e)4$ $24+12e$
13. $4+9c+3(c+2)$ $12c+10$
14. $5(7+2s)+3(s+4)$ $13s+47$
15. $9(f+2)+14f$ $23f+18$
16. $5a-9a$ $-4a$
17. $-6+4x+9-2x$ $2x+3$
18. $6a+11+(-15)+9a$ $15a-4$
19. $2(8w-7)$ $16w-14$
20. $3(2d+5)+4d$ $10d+15$
21. $2+4p-6(p-2)$ $-2p+14$
22. $-3(b+4)$ $-3b-12$
23. $-6+3s+11-5s$ $-2s+5$
24. $3(x-5)+7(x+2)$ $10x-1$

Lesson 4-3 Solving Equations by Adding or Subtracting (pp. 184–189)

ALGEBRA Solve each equation. Check your solution and graph it on a number line.

1. $y+49=26$ -23
2. $d+31=-24$ -55
3. $q-8=16$ 24
4. $x-16=32$ 48
5. $40=a+12$ 28
6. $b+12=-1$ -13
7. $21=u+6$ 15
8. $-52=p+5$ -57
9. $-14=5-g$ 19
10. $121=k+(-12)$ 133
11. $-234=m-94$ -140
12. $110=x+25$ 85
13. $f-7=84$ 91
14. $y-864=652$ 1516
15. $475+z=-18$ -493
16. $x+12=-9$ -21
17. $15-h=11$ 4
18. $16=p+21$ -5
19. $-13+t=-2$ 11
20. $86=x+43$ 43
21. $y-11=-14$ -3

1–21. See student's work for number lines.

Lesson 4-4 Solving Equations by Multiplying or Dividing (pp. 191–196)

Solve each equation. Check your solution.

1. $-y=-32$ 32
2. $7r=-56$ -8
3. $\frac{t}{-3}=12$ -36
4. $4=\frac{s}{-14}$ -56
5. $\frac{b}{47}=-2$ -94
6. $64=-4n$ -16
7. $-144=12q$ -12
8. $\frac{r}{11}=-12$ -132
9. $-5g=-385$ 77
10. $-16x=-176$ 11
11. $-21=\frac{y}{-4}$ 84
12. $-372=31k$ -12
13. $84=\frac{k}{5}$ 420
14. $-b=19$ -19
15. $\frac{v}{112}=-9$ -1008
16. $-3x=-27$ 9
17. $\frac{p}{-12}=4$ -48
18. $5q=-100$ -20
19. $\frac{d}{11}=-8$ -88
20. $-9n=-45$ 5
21. $125=-25z$ -5

Lesson 4-5 Solving Two-Step Equations (pp. 199–204)

Solve each equation. Check your solution.

1. $3t-13=2$ 5
2. $-8j-7=57$ -8
3. $9d-5=4$ 1
4. $6-3w=-27$ 11
5. $\frac{k}{6}+8=12$ 24
6. $-4=\frac{q}{8}-19$ 120
7. $15-\frac{n}{7}=13$ 14
8. $44=-4+8p$ 6
9. $21-h=-32$ 53
10. $-19=11b-(-3)$ -2
11. $6=20+\frac{x}{3}$ -42
12. $9+3a=-3$ -4
13. $2x-8=10$ 9
14. $\frac{m}{4}-6=10$ 64
15. $-12+3p=3$ 5
16. $-18=6a-6$ -2
17. $\frac{t}{-3}+11=23$ -36
18. $3+2v=11$ 4
19. $16=\frac{k}{3}-11$ 81
20. $-6g-12=-60$ 8
21. $15-4c=-21$ 9

Lesson 4-6 Writing Equations (pp. 205–209)

Translate each sentence into an equation. Then find each number.

1. Five less than three times a number is 13. $3x - 5 = 13$; 6
2. The product of 2 and a number is increased by 9. The result is 17. $2p + 9 = 17$; 4
3. Ten more than four times a number is 46. $4z + 10 = 46$; 9
4. The quotient of a number and −8, less 5, is −2. $\frac{a}{-8} - 5 = -2$; −24
5. Three more than two times a number is 11. $2n + 3 = 11$; 4
6. The quotient of a number and six, increased by 2 is −5. $\frac{w}{6} + 2 = -5$; −42
7. The product of −3 and a number, decreased by 9 is 27. $-3x - 9 = 27$; −12
8. A number is divided by 2. The sum of the result and 6 is −2. $\frac{x}{2} + 6 = -2$; −16
9. The sum of 6 and a number divided by 3 is 7. $6 + \frac{n}{3} = 7$; 3

Lesson 5-1 Perimeter and Area (pp. 221–226)

Find the perimeter and area of each rectangle.

1. a rectangle 23 centimeters long and 9 centimeters wide 64 cm, 207 cm^2
2. a 16-foot by 14-foot rectangle 60 ft, 224 ft^2
3. a rectangle with a length of 31 meters and a width of 3 meters 68 m, 93 m^2
4. a square with sides 7 meters long 28 m, 49 m^2

Find the missing dimension of each rectangle.

	Length	Width	Area	Perimeter	
5.	9 ft	■	126 ft^2	46 ft	14 ft
6.	■	18 in.	108 in^2	48 in.	6 in.
7.	13 yd	■	273 yd^2	68 yd	21 yd
8.	■	12 cm	168 cm^2	52 cm	14 cm
9.	■	3 m	162 m^2	114 m	54 m

10. The area of a triangle is 50 square meters. Its base is 10 meters. Find the height. 10 m
11. The area of a triangle is 96 square inches. Its height is 12 inches. Find the base. 16 in.

Lesson 5-2 Solving Equations with Variables on Each Side (pp. 229–233)

Solve each equation. Check your solution.

1. $-7h - 5 = 4 - 4h$ −3
2. $5t - 8 = 3t + 12$ 10
3. $m + 2m + 1 = 7$ 2
4. $2y + 5 = 6y + 25$ −5
5. $3z - 1 = 23 - 3z$ 4
6. $5a - 5 = 7a - 19$ 7
7. $5x + 12 = 3x - 6$ −9
8. $3x - 5 = 7x + 7$ −3
9. $5c + 9 = 8c$ 3
10. $3p = 4 - 9p$ $\frac{1}{3}$
11. $6z + 5 = 4z - 7$ −6
12. $2a + 4.2 = 3a - 1.6$ 5.8
13. $3.21 - 7y = 10y - 1.89$ 0.3
14. $1.9s + 6 = 3.1 - s$ −1
15. $12b - 5 = 3b$ $\frac{5}{9}$
16. $9 + 11a = -5a + 21$ $\frac{3}{4}$

Lesson 5-3 Inequalities (pp. 234–239)

Write an inequality for each sentence.

1. To pass his math class, Manuel needs to earn a grade of at least 70%. $g \geq 70$
2. Children who weigh less than 40 pounds must ride in an approved car seat. $w < 40$
3. To train for the upcoming marathon race, Jeff must run at least 30 miles each week. $m \geq 30$
4. There are at least 315 students at Glenwood Elementary School. $s \geq 315$
5. A cell phone bill increased by \$10 is now more than \$60 per month. $b + 10 > 60$
6. Citizens who are 18 years of age or older can vote. $c \geq 18$

For the given value, state whether the inequality is true or false.

7. $16 < 2x - 4; x = 7$ false
8. $3 - y \geq 6; y = -5$ true
9. $-5 \geq 3 - 4a; a = 2$ true
10. $\frac{1}{2}m - 1 < -3; m = -6$ true
11. $-8 + 3c < 4; c = 4$ false
12. $-5k + 20 > 0; k = 8$ false

Graph each inequality on a number line. 13–18. See Student Handbook Answer Appendix.

13. $x > -3$
14. $2 > n$
15. $y \leq 4$
16. $m < -2$
17. $q \geq 1$
18. $-1 \leq a$

Lesson 5-4 Solving Inequalities (pp. 241–247)

Solve each inequality. Check your solution.

1. $m + 9 < 14$ $m < 5$
2. $k + (-5) < -12$ $k < -7$
3. $-15 < v - 1$ $-14 < v$
4. $-7 + f \geq 47$ $f \geq 54$
5. $r > -15 - 8$ $r > -23$
6. $18 \geq s - (-4)$ $14 \geq s$
7. $38 < r - (-6)$ $32 < r$
8. $z - 9 \leq -11$ $z \leq -2$
9. $-16 + c \geq 1$ $c \geq 17$
10. $d + 1.4 < 6.8$ $d < 5.4$
11. $-3 + x > 11.9$ $x > 14.9$
12. $-0.2 \geq 0.3 + y$ $y \leq -0.5$
13. $\frac{2}{3} \leq a - \frac{5}{6}$ $1\frac{1}{2} \leq a$
14. $-7.42 \leq d - 5.9$ $-1.52 \leq d$
15. $6p < 78$ $p < 13$
16. $\frac{m}{-3} > 24$ $m < -72$
17. $-18 < 3b$ $b > -6$
18. $-5k \geq 125$ $k \leq -25$
19. $-75 > \frac{a}{5}$ $-375 > a$
20. $\frac{w}{6} < -5$ $w < -30$
21. $8 < \frac{2}{3}c$ $12 < c$
22. $\frac{m}{1.3} \geq 0.5$ $m \geq 0.65$
23. $0.4y > -2$ $y > -5$
24. $-\frac{1}{2}d \leq -5\frac{1}{2}$ $d \geq 11$
25. The product of a number and −4 is greater than or equal to −20. What is the number? $n \leq 5$

Lesson 5-5 Solving Multi-Step Equations and Inequalities (pp. 248–253)

ALGEBRA Solve. Check your solution.

1. $6(m - 2) = 12$ 4
2. $4(x - 3) = 4$ 4
3. $5(2d + 4) = 35$ 1.5
4. $w + 6 = 2(w - 6)$ 18
5. $3(b + 1) = 4b - 1$ 4
6. $7w - 6 = 3(w + 6)$ 6
7. $4(k - 6) = 6(k + 2)$ −18
8. $3x - 0.8 = 3x + 4$ ∅
9. $\frac{5}{9}g + 8 = \frac{1}{6}g + 1$ −18
10. $2m + 1 < 9$ $m < 4$
11. $-3k - 4 \leq -22$ $k \geq 6$
12. $-2 > 10 - 2x$ $6 < x$
13. $-6a + 2 \geq 14$ $a \leq -2$
14. $3y + 2 < -7$ $y < -3$
15. $\frac{d}{4} + 3 \geq -11$ $d \geq -56$
16. $\frac{x}{3} - 5 < 6$ $x < 33$
17. $-5g + 6 < 3g + 26$ $g > -2.5$
18. $\frac{3(n + 1)}{7} \geq \frac{n + 4}{5}$ $n \geq 1.625$

Lesson 6-1 Ratios (pp. 265–269)

Express each ratio as a fraction in simplest form.

1. 15 vans out of 40 vehicles $\frac{3}{8}$
2. 6 pens to 14 pencils $\frac{3}{7}$
3. 12 dolls out of 18 toys $\frac{2}{3}$
4. 8 red crayons out of 36 crayons $\frac{2}{9}$
5. 18 boys out of 45 students $\frac{2}{5}$
6. 30 birds to 6 birds $\frac{5}{1}$
7. 98 ants to 14 ladybugs $\frac{7}{1}$
8. 140 dogs to 12 cats $\frac{35}{3}$
9. 321 pennies to 96 dimes $\frac{107}{32}$
10. 3 cups to 3 quarts $\frac{1}{4}$

Lesson 6-2 Unit Rates (pp. 270–274)

Express each rate as a unit rate. Round to the nearest tenth, if necessary.

1. 343.8 miles on 9 gallons 38.2 mi/gal
2. $7.95 for 5 pounds $1.59/lb
3. $52 for 8 tickets $6.50/ticket
4. $43.92 for 4 CDs $10.98/CD
5. 450 miles in 8 hours 56.3 mi/h
6. $3.96 for 12 cans of soda $0.33/can
7. $3.84 for 64 ounces $0.06/oz
8. 200 yards in 32.3 seconds 6.2 yd/s
9. **MONEY** Which costs more per notebook, a 4-pack of notebooks for $3.98 or a 5-pack of notebooks for $4.99? Explain. Since the 4-pack costs $0.995 per notebook and the 5-pack costs $0.998 per notebook, the 5-pack costs more per notebook.
10. **ANIMALS** A cheetah can run 70 miles in 1 hour. How many feet is this per second? Round to the nearest whole number. 103 ft/s

Lesson 6-3 Converting Rates and Measurements (pp. 275–280)

Complete each conversion. Round to the nearest hundredth if necessary.

1. 4 pt ≈ ■ L 1.89 L
2. 70 in. ≈ ■ cm 177.8 cm
3. 5 yd ≈ ■ m 4.57 m
4. 180 g ≈ ■ oz 6.3 oz
5. 1500 m ≈ ■ yd 1641 yd
6. 13 kg ≈ ■ lb 28.64 lb
7. 4 km ≈ ■ yd 4376 yd
8. 10 in ≈ ■ mm 254 mm
9. 35 fl oz ≈ ■ mL 1035.09 mL
10. A wildfire in Montana destroyed 240,000 acres in 3 days. At this rate, how many acres were destroyed per hour? 3333.33 acres
11. A new energy-efficient automobile can travel 34.4 miles on one gallon of gasoline. At this rate, how many feet per quart does the car average? 45,408 feet per quart
12. If a two-year old child consumes 48 ounces of milk each day, how many gallons does the child consume in a year? 136.88 gallons per year
13. Convert 60 miles per hour to feet per minute. 5280 feet per minute
14. Convert 40 kilometers per hour to miles per minute. 0.41 miles per minute
15. Convert 20 miles per gallon to kilometers per liter. 8.50 kilometers per liter
16. Convert 65 miles per hour to meters per second. 29.05 meters per second

Lesson 6-4 Proportional and Nonproportional Relationships (pp. 281–285)

Determine whether the set of numbers in each table is proportional. Explain.

1.

Baskets	2	4	6	8
Apples	10	20	30	40

yes; each rate is equal to $\frac{1}{5}$.

2.

Days	5	10	15	20
Grass Height (inches)	4	6	8	10

3.

Cups of Flour	2	4	6	8
Cups of Sugar	1.5	3	4.5	6

yes; each rate is equal to $\frac{4}{3}$.

4.

Men's Shoe Size	6	6.5	7	7.5
Women's Shoe Size	7.5	8	8.5	9

5.

Age (years)	5	10	15	20
Height (inches)	46	59	72	74

no; the rates are not equal.

6.

Temperature (°C)	0	25	60	100
Temparature (°F)	32	77	140	212

7.

Visitors	1	2	3	4
Shoes Left by the Door	2	4	6	8

yes; each rate is equal to $\frac{1}{2}$.

8.

Age (months)	8	10	14	20
Number of Teeth	2	6	12	16

2., 4., 6., 8.
no; the rates are not equal.

Lesson 6-5 Solving Proportions (pp. 287–292)

Solve each proportion.

1. $\frac{7}{k} = \frac{49}{63}$ 9
2. $\frac{s}{4.8} = \frac{30.6}{28.8}$ 5.1
3. $\frac{6}{11} = \frac{19.2}{g}$ 35.2
4. $\frac{8}{13} = \frac{b}{65}$ 40
5. $\frac{x}{12} = \frac{26}{24}$ 13
6. $\frac{21}{p} = \frac{3}{9}$ 63
7. $\frac{6.5}{8} = \frac{w}{20}$ 16.25
8. $\frac{10}{4.21} = \frac{7}{y}$ 2.947
9. $\frac{12}{x} = \frac{1}{2.54}$ 30.48

Write a proportion that could be used to solve for each variable. Then solve.

10. 6 plums at $1
    10 plums at d $\frac{6}{\$1.00} = \frac{10}{d}$; $1.67
11. 8 gallons at $9.36
    f gallons at $17.55 $\frac{8}{\$9.36} = \frac{f}{\$17.55}$; 15
12. 3 packages at $53.67
    7 packages at m $\frac{3}{\$53.67} = \frac{7}{m}$; $125.23
13. 10 cards at $7.50
    p cards at $18 $\frac{10}{\$7.50} = \frac{p}{\$18.00}$; 24
14. 12 cookies at $3.00
    16 cookies at s $\frac{12}{\$3.00} = \frac{16}{s}$; $4.00
15. 6 toy cars at $4.50
    c toy cars at $6.75 $\frac{6}{\$4.50} = \frac{c}{\$6.75}$; 9

Lesson 6-6 Scale Drawings and Models (pp. 294–299)

On a set of architectural drawings for a school, the scale is $\frac{1}{2}$ inch = 4 feet. Find the actual length of each room.

	Room	Drawing Distance (in.)	
1.	Classroom	5	40 ft
2.	Principal's Office	1.75	14 ft
3.	Library	$7\frac{1}{2}$	60 ft
4.	Cafeteria	$9\frac{1}{4}$	74 ft
5.	Gymnasium	12.2	97.6 ft
6.	Nurse's Office	1.3	10.4 ft

Lesson 6-7 Similar Figures (pp. 301–306)

The figures are similar. Find each missing measure.

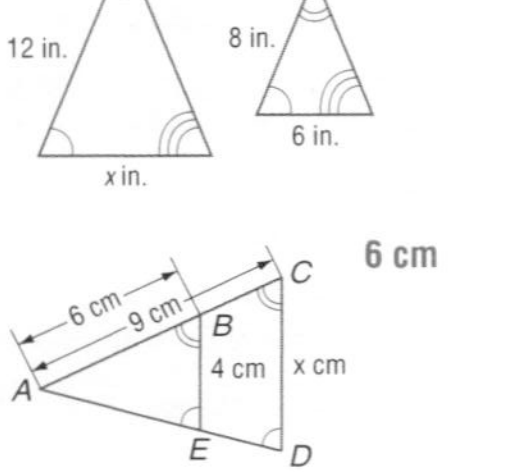

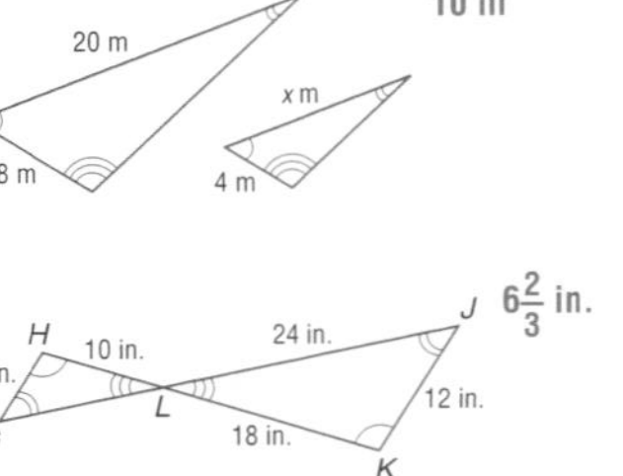

1. **9 in.**
2. **10 m**
3. **6 cm**
4. **$6\frac{2}{3}$ in.**

Lesson 6-8 Dilations (pp. 307–312)

1. A figure has vertices $A(-2, 1)$, $B(1, 3)$, $C(3, 2)$. Graph the figure and the image of the polygon after a dilation with a scale factor of 2. **See Student Handbook Answer Appendix.**
2. A quadrilateral has vertices $K(3, 1)$, $L(1, 4)$, $M(6, 6)$, and $N(11, 1)$. Find the coordinates of the figure after a dilation with a scale factor of 0.5. **$K'(1.5, 0.5)$, $L'(0.5, 2)$, $M'(3, 3)$, $N'(5.5, 0.5)$**
3. **BUSINESS** A $3\frac{1}{2}$ inch by 2 inch business card is being enlarged to $5\frac{1}{4}$ inches by 3 inches to use as an advertisement. What is the scale factor of the dilation? **1.5**

Lesson 6-9 Indirect Measurement (pp. 313–317)

1. **FLAGS** A flag pole casts a 5 foot shadow while a nearby sign post casts a $1\frac{1}{4}$ foot shadow. Find the height of the flagpole if the sign post is 4 feet high. **16 ft**
2. A 56 inch tall woman casts a shadow that is 16 inches long. How tall is her child if his shadow is 7 inches long? **24.5 in.**
3. In the figure, $\triangle ABC \sim \triangle EDC$. Find the width of the Olen River $(\overline{AB})$. **64 yd**

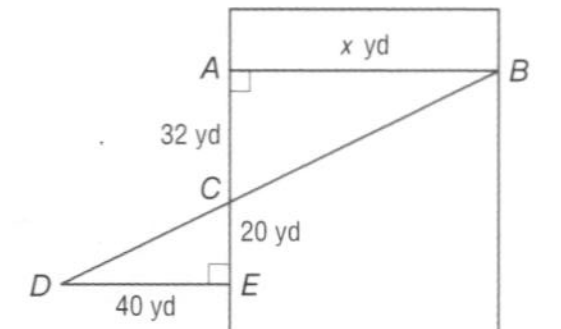

Lesson 7-1 Fractions and Percents (pp. 331–336)

Write each fraction as a percent. Round to the nearest hundredth.

1. $\frac{23}{25}$ **92%**
2. $\frac{48}{60}$ **80%**
3. $\frac{92}{96}$ **95.83%**
4. $\frac{17}{50}$ **34%**
5. $\frac{9}{25}$ **36%**
6. $\frac{12}{8}$ **150%**
7. $\frac{7}{40}$ **17.5%**
8. $\frac{11}{33}$ **33.33%**
9. $\frac{36}{27}$ **133.33%**

Write each percent as a fraction or mixed number in simplest form.

10. 32% $\frac{8}{25}$
11. 15% $\frac{3}{20}$
12. $88\frac{1}{2}\%$ $\frac{177}{200}$
13. 250% $\frac{5}{2}$ or $2\frac{1}{2}$
14. 21% $\frac{21}{100}$
15. 64% $\frac{16}{25}$
16. 25% $\frac{1}{4}$
17. 131% $\frac{131}{100}$ or $1\frac{31}{100}$
18. 72.5% $\frac{29}{40}$
19. $66\frac{2}{3}\%$ $\frac{2}{3}$
20. 0.06% $\frac{3}{5000}$
21. 315% $\frac{63}{20}$ or $3\frac{3}{20}$

Lesson 7-2 Fractions, Decimals, and Percents (pp. 337–342)

Write each percent as a decimal.

1. 72% **0.72**
2. 7% **0.07**
3. 380% **3.8**
4. 0.03% **0.0003**

Express each decimal or fraction as a percent. Round to the nearest tenth, if necessary.

5. 0.19 **19%**
6. 2.28 **228%**
7. 0.009 **0.9%**
8. 3.301 **330.1%**
9. $\frac{5}{18}$ **27.8%**
10. $\frac{3}{40}$ **7.5%**
11. $\frac{13}{1000}$ **1.3%**
12. $5\frac{3}{50}$ **506%**

13. **SPORTS** In a recent survey, 370 students said gymnastics was their favorite sport to watch. If 3500 students were surveyed, what percent chose gymnastics as their favorite sport to watch? Round to the nearest percent. **11%**

Lesson 7-3 Using the Percent Proportion (pp. 345–350)

Use the percent proportion to solve each problem. Round to the nearest tenth, if necessary.

1. What is 81% of 134? **108.5**
2. 52.08 is 21% of what number? **248**
3. 11.18 is what percent of 86? **13%**
4. What is 120% of 312? **374.4**
5. 140 is what percent of 400? **35%**
6. 430.2 is 60% of what number? **717**
7. 32 is what percent of 80? **40%**
8. What is 15% of 125? **18.8**
9. 22 is what percent of 110? **20%**
10. 9.4 is 40% of what number? **23.5**
11. What is 41.5% of 95? **39.4**
12. 17.92 is what percent of 112? **16%**

13. **FOOD** If 28 of the 50 soup cans on a shelf are chicken noodle soup, what percent of the cans are chicken noodle soup? **56%**
14. **SCHOOL** Of the students in a classroom, 60% are boys. If there are 20 students, how many are boys? **12**

Lesson 7-4 Find Percent of a Number Mentally (pp. 351–355)

Find the percent of each number mentally.

1. 40% of 60 **24**
2. 25% of 72 **18**
3. 50% of 96 **48**
4. $33\frac{1}{3}$% of 24 **8**
5. $37\frac{1}{2}$% of 80 **30**
6. 150% of 42 **63**
7. 200% of 125 **250**
8. $66\frac{2}{3}$% of 45 **30**

Estimate.

9. 60% of 49 **30**
10. 19% of 41 **8**
11. 82% of 60 **48**
12. 125% of 81 **100**
13. $\frac{1}{2}$% of 502 **2.5**
14. 31% of 19 **6**

Lesson 7-5 Using Percent Equations (pp. 357–362)

Solve each problem using a percent equation.

1. 9.28 is what percent of 58? **16%**
2. What number is 43% of 110? **47.3**
3. 80% of what number is 90? **112.5**
4. What number is 61% of 524? **319.64**
5. 126 is what percent of 90? **140%**
6. 52% of what number is 109.2? **210**
7. 62% of what number is 29.76? **48**
8. 54 is what percent of 90? **60%**
9. Find 78% of 125. **97.5**
10. What is 0.2% of 12? **0.024**
11. 66% of what number is 49.5? **75**
12. 36.45 is what percent of 81? **45%**

SHOPPING For each of the following, find the sales tax to the nearest cent.

13. $35 skirt, 7.5% sales tax **$2.63**
14. $108 lamp, 5.5% sales tax **$5.94**
15. $1585, 6% sales tax **$95.10**
16. $2934, 5.75% sales tax **$168.71**

Lesson 7-6 Percent of Change (pp. 364–369)

Find the percent of change. Round to the nearest tenth, if necessary. Then state whether each change is a *percent of increase* or a *percent of decrease*.

1. from $56 to $42 **−25%; decrease**
2. from $26 to $29.64 **14%; increase**
3. from $22 to $37.18 **69%; increase**
4. from $137.50 to $85.25 **−38%; decrease**
5. from $455 to $955.50 **110%; increase**
6. from $3 to $15 **400%; increase**
7. from $750.75 to $765.51 **2.0%; increase**
8. from $953 to $476.50 **−50%; decrease**
9. from $101.25 to $379.69 **275.0%; increase**
10. from $836 to $842.27 **0.8%; increase**
11. **BASEBALL CARDS** A baseball card collection contains 340 baseball cards. What is the percent of change if 25 cards are removed from the collection? Round to the nearest tenth. **−7.4%**

Lesson 7-7 Simple and Compound Interest (pp. 370–374)

Find the simple interest to the nearest cent.

1. $1,100 at 5% for 3 years **$165**
2. $850 at 6% for 2 years **$102**
3. $12,500 at 3.5% for 4 years **$1750**
4. $750 at $4\frac{1}{4}$% for 2 years **$63.75**
5. $140,700 at 5.4% for 6 years **$45,586.80**
6. $10,000 at $6\frac{1}{2}$% for 3 years **$1950**

Find the total amount in each account to the nearest cent if the interest is compounded annually.

7. $600 at 5% for 3 years **$694.58**
8. $2500 at 4% for 2 years **$2704**
9. $8240 at 10.5% for 4 years **$12,285.04**
10. $15,000 at 7.0% for 2 years **$17,173.50**
11. $10,500 at 3.75% for 3 years **$11,726.10**
12. $5075 at 6.25% for 1 year **$5392.19**
13. **LOAN** Mariah borrowed $1200 to buy a new computer system. She paid the simple interest loan off in 24 monthly payments of $56 each. What was the interest rate on this loan? **6%**
14. **FINANCIAL LITERACY** Zachary took out a simple interest loan at $7\frac{1}{2}$% for 4 years when he borrowed $8000 to pay for a used car. How much will his monthly payments be? **$216.67**
15. **INVESTMENT** Eduardo's great aunt left him some money in her will. Rather than spend the money right away, Eduardo put it into a certificate of deposit for 3 years earning 5% simple interest annually. At the end of the 3 years, the certificate had earned $375. How much money did Eduardo inherit from his great aunt? **$2500**

Lesson 7-8 Circle Graphs (pp. 376–381)

Fruit	Number of Votes
Apples	144
Bananas	152
Grapes	98
Raisins	51
Oranges	205

1. **FRUIT** During a recent lunch period, the cafeteria staff took a survey to find out which type of fruit the students preferred. The choices and results are listed in the table. Make a circle graph of the data. **See Student Handbook Answer Appendix.**
2. **PROJECTS** For a project, students charted their activities during a week's time and reported their results in a circle graph.
   a. Miguel said he studied for 16.8 hours. How many hours are there in a week? How many degrees would Miguel need to use for the central angle on his circle graph for the Study sector? **168 hours; 36°**
   b. If Gabriel used 25° for the central angle for the sector labeled Piano, how many hours did he spend practicing the piano during that week? Round to the nearest hundredth. **11.67 hours**
3. **SPORTS** The circle graph at the right shows the results of a survey about favorite sports to watch on TV. If 300 students were surveyed, how many more preferred to watch baseball rather than basketball? **21 students**

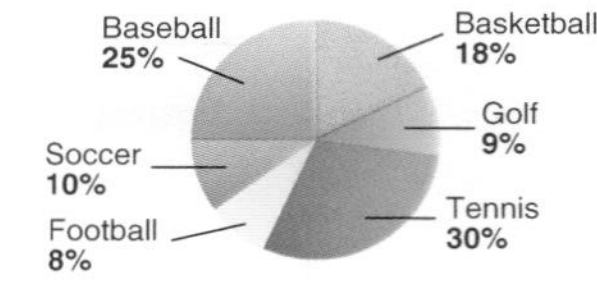

Lesson 8-1 Functions (pp. 395–400)

Determine whether each relation is a function.

1. $\{(4, -1), (2, -1), (0, 3), (5, -2)\}$ yes

2.

x	6	8	6	7
y	4	3	9	1

no

3. 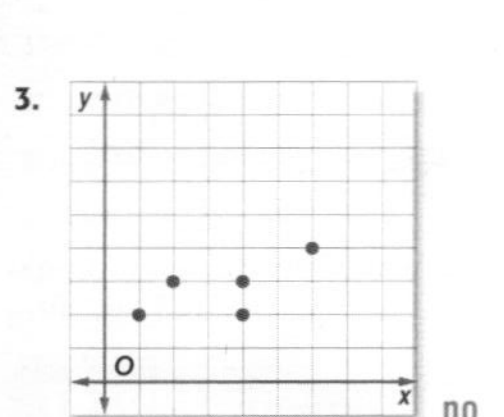

no

4. yes

If $f(x) = 3x - 1$, find each function value.

5. $f(-1)$ −4
6. $f(0)$ −1
7. $f(2)$ 5
8. $f(3)$ 8

If $g(x) = -6x$, find each function value.

9. $g(-12)$ 72
10. $g(15)$ −90
11. $g(-16)$ 96
12. $g(22)$ −132

Lesson 8-2 Sequences and Equations (pp. 401–405)

Describe each sequence using words and symbols. 1–14. See Student Handbook Answer Appendix.

1. 25, 50, 75, …
2. 39, 40, 41, …
3. 4, 8, 12, …
4. 1.5, 2.5, 3.5, …
5. $\frac{1}{2}, 1, 1\frac{1}{2}, \ldots$
6. 4, 7, 10, …

Write an equation that describes each sequence. Then find the indicated term.

7. 5, 10, 15, …; 23rd term
8. 18, 17, 16, …; 13th term
9. 2, 1, 0, …; 7th term
10. 3, 5, 7, …; 99th term
11. 6, 13, 20, …; 38th term
12. −6, −4, −2, …; 67th term
13. 0, 4, 8 …; 50th term
14. 5.5, 6, 6.5, …; 30th term

Lesson 8-3 Representing Linear Functions (pp. 406–411)

Find four solutions of each equation. Write the solutions as ordered pairs. 1–18. See Student Handbook Answer Appendix for sample answers.

1. $x = 4$
2. $y = 0$
3. $x + y = 2$
4. $y = 2x - 6$
5. $x - y = 5$
6. $3x - y = 8$
7. $y = \frac{1}{2}x - 3$
8. $y = \frac{1}{3}x + 1$
9. $2x + y = -2$
10. $2x + 3y = 12$
11. $x + 2y = -4$
12. $2x - 4y = 8$

Graph each equation.

13. $y = x + 4$
14. $y = 4x$
15. $x + y = 3$
16. $y = x - 3$
17. $y = -2x + 5$
18. $2x + y = 6$

Lesson 8-4 Rate of Change (pp. 412–417)

Find the rate of change for each linear function.

1. 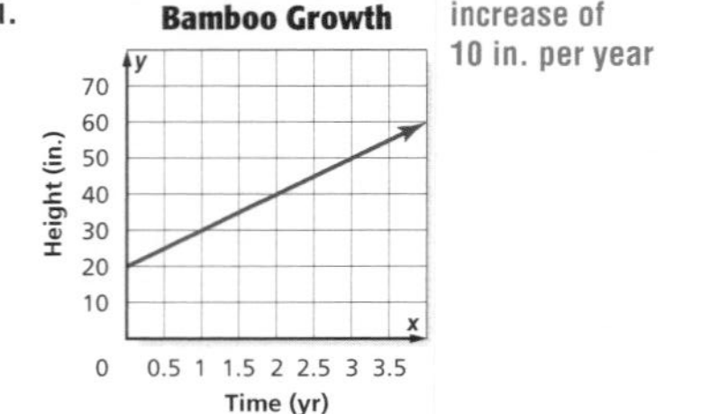

increase of 10 in. per year

2. Walking — increase of $\frac{1}{2}$ ft per s

3.

Sales ($)	1240	1580	2250	2885
Commission ($)	49.60	63.20	90.00	115.40

increase of $0.04 per $1 in sales

4.

Time (min)	10	30	40	90
Candle Height (in.)	5.9	5.7	5.6	5.1

decrease of 0.01 inch per minute

Lesson 8-5 Constant Rate of Change and Direct Variation (pp. 418–424)

Find the constant rate of change for each linear function and interpret its meaning.

1. 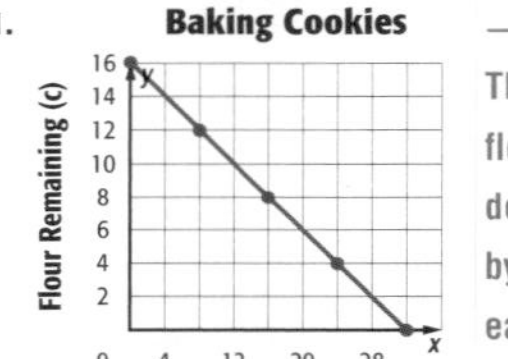

$-\frac{1}{2}$ c/cookies; The amount of flour remaining decreased by $\frac{1}{2}$ cup for each cookie.

2.

Time (min)	Volume (gal)
x	y
5	60
10	120
15	180
20	240

12 gal/min; water flows at 12 gallons per minute

3. **JOBS** Lee works at a job where her pay varies directly as the number of hours she works. Her pay for 6.5 hours is $49.40. Write a direct variation equation relating Lee's pay x to the hours worked y. Then find her pay if she works 25 hours in a week. $y = 7.6x$; $190

Lesson 8-6 Slope (pp. 427–431)

Find the slope of each line.

1. 3

2. 0

Find the slope of the line that passes through each pair of points.

3. $P(3, 8), Q(4, -3)$ −11
4. $D(4, 5), E(-3, -9)$ 2
5. $L(-1, 2), M(0, 5)$ 3
6. $J(6, 2), K(6, -4)$ undefined

Lesson 8-7 Slope-Intercept Form (pp. 433–438)

State the slope and the y-intercept of the graph of each equation.

1. $y = x + 9$ 1; 9
2. $y = 2x - 5$ 2; −5
3. $y = -6x$ −6; 0
4. $y = \frac{3}{2}x$ $\frac{3}{2}$; 0
5. $y = \frac{1}{3}x + 8$ $\frac{1}{3}$; 8
6. $x + 2y = 12$ $-\frac{1}{2}$; 6

Graph each equation using the slope and y-intercept. 7–12. Student Handbook Answer Appendix.

7. $y = 3x - 2$
8. $x - 3y = 9$
9. $y = \frac{1}{2}x + 4$
10. $y = -\frac{2}{3}x - 1$
11. $x - y = -4$
12. $2x + 4y = -4$

Lesson 8-8 Writing Linear Equations (pp. 441–447)

Write an equation in slope-intercept form for each line.

1. slope = 3, y-intercept = −4 $y = 3x - 4$
2. slope = $\frac{3}{4}$, y-intercept = 1 $y = \frac{3}{4}x + 1$
3. slope = $-\frac{1}{2}$, y-intercept = 0 $y = -\frac{1}{2}x$
4. slope = 0, y-intercept = −6 $y = -6$

Write an equation in slope-intercept form for the line passing through each pair of points.

5. (4, 7) and (0, 3) $y = x + 3$
6. (3, −6) and (−1, 2) $y = -2x$
7. (8, 7) and (0, 0) $y = \frac{7}{8}x$
8. (1, 4) and (3, −6) $y = -5x + 9$
9. (−2, 5) and (3, 9) $y = \frac{4}{5}x + \frac{33}{5}$
10. (3, −1) and (5, −1) $y = -1$

Lesson 8-9 Prediction Equations (pp. 448–452)

1. **COMPUTER SALES** The table shows the amount of sales of computers in the U. S. 1. See Student Handbook Answer Appendix.

Year	Computer Sales ($ billions)
1990	8.9
1994	18.0
1996	23.6
1998	28.6
2000	35.1

   a. Make a scatter plot of the computer sales and draw a line of fit.
   b. Use the line of fit to estimate the computer sales in 2010. about 60 billion dollars
   c. Write an equation in slope-intercept form using the points (1994, 18.0) and (1998, 28.6). $y = 2.65x - 5266.1$
   d. Use the equation to predict the amount of computer sales in 2020. 86.9 billion dollars

2. **HOUSING** The scatter plot and line of fit show the number of housing units for the U. S.

US Housing Units

Number of Houses (in millions): 12.0, 12.6, 13.2, 13.8, 14.4, 15.0, 15.6; Years Since 1998: 0, 2, 4, 6, 8; (2, 12.6), (7, 15)

   a. Write the equation in slope-intercept form for the line of fit. Round to the nearest tenth. $y = 0.48x + 11.64$
   b. Use the equation to estimate the number of housing units in 2014. 19.3 million houses

3. **JOBS** In 2006, 23.2% of the people between the ages of 65 and 74 were working. In 2000, only 19.6% of that age group was working.
   a. Write an equation in slope-intercept form for the line of fit for the data. $y = 0.6x - 1180.4$
   b. Use the equation to predict the percent of that age group that will be working in 2015. 28.6%

Lesson 8-10 Systems of Equations (pp. 453–457)

Solve each systems of equations by graphing. 1–4. Student Handbook Answer Appendix.

1. $x + y = -2$, $2x - 3y = -9$
2. $y = 2x - 1$, $y = x + 1$
3. $3x - 2y = 11$, $-x + 6y = 7$
4. $-x + 2y = 6$, $x + 4y = 24$

Solve each systems of equations by substitution.

5. $2x - y = -2$, $4x - y = -6$ (−2, −2)
6. $2x + 2y = 3$, $x - 4y = -1$ $(1, \frac{1}{2})$
7. $y = x - 4$, $4x + y = 26$ (6, 2)
8. $x - 2y = -25$, $3x - y = 0$ (5, 15)

Lesson 9-1 Powers and Exponents (pp. 471–475)

ALGEBRA Write each expression using exponents.

1. $8 \cdot 8 \cdot 8 \cdot 8$ 8^4
2. 9 9^1
3. $(-6)(-6)(-6)(-6)(-6)$ $(-6)^5$
4. $\left(\frac{1}{2}\right)\left(\frac{1}{2}\right)\left(\frac{1}{2}\right)\left(\frac{1}{2}\right)$ $\left(\frac{1}{2}\right)^4$
5. $(-0.4)(-0.4)(-0.4)$ $(-0.4)^3$
6. $s \cdot s \cdot s \cdot s \cdot s$ s^5
7. $(y \cdot y \cdot y) \cdot (y \cdot y \cdot y \cdot y)$ y^7
8. $a \cdot b \cdot b$ ab^2
9. $4 \cdot 4 \cdot 4 \cdot 4 \cdot x \cdot x \cdot x \cdot y$ 4^4x^3y
10. $3q \cdot 3q \cdot 3q \cdot 3q \cdot 3q \cdot 3q$ $(3q)^6$
11. $\underbrace{n \cdot n \cdot n \cdot \ldots \cdot n}_{17 \text{ factors}}$ n^{17}
12. $(x + y)(x + y)$ $(x + y)^2$

ALGEBRA Evaluate each expression if $m = 3$, $n = 2$, and $p = -4$.

13. $3m^2$ 27
14. $n^0 + m$ 4
15. 7^4 2401
16. -5^3 −125
17. p^3 −64
18. $2(m - p)^2$ 98
19. $-2n^3 + m$ −13
20. $m - p^2$ −13
21. $(m + n + p)^3$ 1
22. $5p - m^2$ −29
23. $(n + p)^4$ 16
24. $(m - n)^8$ 1

Lesson 9-2 Prime Factorization (pp. 476–480)

Determine whether each number is *prime* or *composite*.

1. 57 composite
2. 369 composite
3. 116 composite
4. 125 composite
5. 83 prime
6. 99 composite
7. 91 composite
8. 79 prime

Write the prime factorization of each number. Use exponents for repeated factors.

9. 21 $3 \cdot 7$
10. 44 $2^2 \cdot 11$
11. 51 $3 \cdot 17$
12. 65 $5 \cdot 13$
13. 30 $2 \cdot 3 \cdot 5$
14. 28 $2^2 \cdot 7$
15. 117 $3^2 \cdot 13$
16. 88 $2^3 \cdot 11$
17. 54 $2 \cdot 3^3$
18. 32 2^5
19. 300 $2^2 \cdot 3 \cdot 5^2$
20. 210 $2 \cdot 3 \cdot 5 \cdot 7$

ALGEBRA Factor each monomial.

21. $40y$ $2 \cdot 2 \cdot 2 \cdot 5 \cdot y$
22. $630a$ $2 \cdot 3 \cdot 3 \cdot 5 \cdot 7 \cdot a$
23. $187c^2$ $11 \cdot 17 \cdot c \cdot c$
24. $310p^2$ $2 \cdot 5 \cdot 31 \cdot p \cdot p$
25. $510xy$ $2 \cdot 3 \cdot 5 \cdot 17 \cdot x \cdot y$
26. $1589cd$ $7 \cdot 227 \cdot c \cdot d$
27. $-18ab^2$ $-1 \cdot 2 \cdot 3 \cdot 3 \cdot a \cdot b \cdot b$
28. $-117x^3$ $-1 \cdot 3 \cdot 3 \cdot 13 \cdot x \cdot x \cdot x$
29. $105j^2k^5$ $3 \cdot 5 \cdot 7 \cdot j \cdot j \cdot k \cdot k \cdot k \cdot k \cdot k$

Lesson 9-3 Multiplying and Dividing Monomials (pp. 481–485)

ALGEBRA Find each product or quotient. Express using exponents.

1. $r^4 \cdot r^2$ r^6
2. $\frac{2^9}{2^3}$ 2^6
3. $\frac{b^{18}}{b^5}$ b^{13}
4. $12^3 \cdot 12^8$ 12^{11}
5. $x \cdot x^9$ x^{10}
6. $(2s^6)(4s^2)$ $8s^8$
7. $w^3 \cdot w^4 \cdot w^2$ w^9
8. $(-2)^2(-2)^5(-2)$ $(-2)^8$
9. $\frac{4^7}{4^6}$ 4
10. $3(f^{17})(f^2)$ $3f^{19}$
11. $(5k)^2 \cdot k^7$ $25k^9$
12. $\frac{6m^8}{3m^2}$ $2m^6$
13. $(3x^4)(-6x)$ $-18x^5$
14. $(4k^4)(-3k)^3$ $-108k^7$
15. $\left(\frac{42}{-6}\right)\left(\frac{g^{10}}{g^3}\right)$ $-7g^7$

Lesson 9-4 Negative Exponents (pp. 486–491)

Write each expression using a positive exponent.

1. y^{-9} $\frac{1}{y^9}$
2. m^{-4} $\frac{1}{m^4}$
3. 5^{-3} $\frac{1}{5^3}$
4. 2^{-7} $\frac{1}{2^7}$
5. 6^{-3} $\frac{1}{6^3}$
6. a^{-11} $\frac{1}{a^{11}}$

Write each fraction as an expression using a negative exponent.

7. $\frac{1}{p^4}$ p^{-4}
8. $\frac{1}{b^9}$ b^{-9}
9. $\frac{1}{5^3}$ 5^{-3}
10. $\frac{1}{7^4}$ 7^{-4}
11. $\frac{1}{15^2}$ 15^{-2}
12. $\frac{1}{25}$ 5^{-2}
13. $\frac{1}{c^7}$ c^{-7}
14. $\frac{1}{64}$ $4^{-3}, 8^{-2}$, or 2^{-6}

Write each decimal using a negative exponent.

15. 0.01 10^{-2}
16. 0.00001 10^{-5}
17. 0.0001 10^{-4} or 100^{-2}
18. 0.001 10^{-3}
19. 0.1 10^{-1}
20. 0.000001 10^{-6} or 100^{-3}

Evaluate each expression if $x = 3$ and $y = -2$.

21. x^{-2} $\frac{1}{9}$
22. 9^y $\frac{1}{81}$
23. y^{-3} $-\frac{1}{8}$
24. x^{-3} $\frac{1}{27}$
25. y^{-4} $\frac{1}{16}$
26. $(xy)^{-2}$ $\frac{1}{36}$

Lesson 9-5 Scientific Notation (pp. 493–498)

Express each number in standard form.

1. 9.5×10^{-3} 0.0095
2. 8.245×10^{-4} 0.0008245
3. 8.2×10^4 82,000
4. 9.102040×10^2 910.2040
5. 4.02×10^3 4020
6. 1.6×10^{-2} 0.016
7. 2.41023×10^6 2,410,230
8. 4.21×10^{-5} 0.0000421
9. 1.0012×10^{-3} 0.0010012
10. 8.604×10^2 860.4

Express each number in scientific notation.

11. 9040 9.04×10^3
12. 0.015 1.5×10^{-2}
13. 6,180,000 6.18×10^6
14. 27,210,000 2.721×10^7
15. 0.00004637 4.637×10^{-5}
16. 0.00546 5.46×10^{-3}
17. 500,300,100 5.003001×10^8
18. 0.0000032 3.2×10^{-6}
19. 0.00047 4.7×10^{-4}
20. 10,471,300 1.04713×10^7

Lesson 9-6 Powers of Monomials (pp. 499–503)

Simplify.

1. $(3^2)^5$ 3^{10}
2. $(a^4)^3$ a^{12}
3. $(k^2)^{-4}$ k^{-8}
4. $(5^3)^3$ 5^9
5. $(m^{-5})^{-2}$ m^{10}
6. $(4^3)^{-1}$ 4^{-3}
7. $(2a)^3$ $8a^3$
8. $(-4c)^2$ $16c^2$
9. $(xy^3)^5$ x^5y^{15}
10. $(-3a^2b)^3$ $-27a^6b^3$
11. $(-x^2yz^3)^6$ $x^{12}y^6z^{18}$
12. $(-2ab^3)^5$ $-32a^5b^{15}$
13. $(-2m^4n^6)^3$ $-8m^{12}n^{18}$
14. $(-abc^3)^2$ $a^2b^2c^6$
15. $(-xy^6)^5$ $-x^5y^{30}$

GEOMETRY Express each measure as a monomial.

16. Volume of a cube. $8c^9d^{15}$

$2c^3d^5$

$2c^3d^5$

17. Area of square. $36m^4n^6$

$6m^2n^3$

$6m^2n^3$

Lesson 9-7 Linear and Nonlinear Functions (pp. 504–509)

Determine whether each graph, equation, or table represents a *linear* or *nonlinear* function. Explain. 1–11. See Student Handbook Answer Appendix.

1. 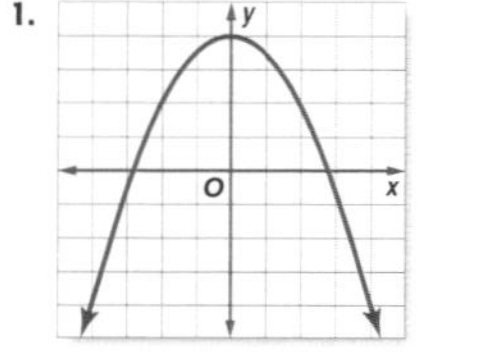

2. 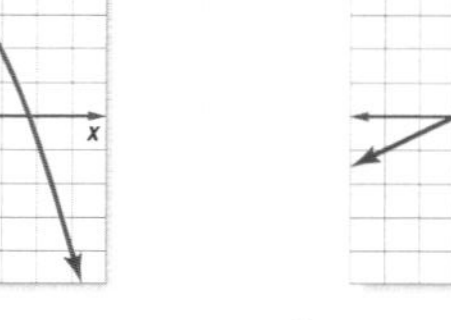

3. 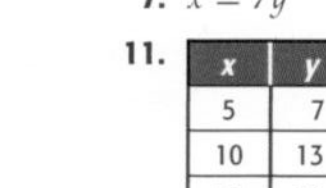

4. $y = -3x$
5. $y = 2x^3 - 5$
6. $-2x + 5y = 10$
7. $x = 7y$
8. $y = (-2)^x$
9. $y = \frac{6}{x}$
10. 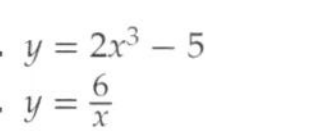

x	y
2	5
4	7
6	9
8	11

11. 

x	y
5	7
10	13
15	19
20	25

Lesson 9-8 Quadratic Functions (pp. 510–514)

Graph each function. 1–15. See Student Handbook Answer Appendix.

1. $y = 3x^2$
2. $y = -2x^2$
3. $y = \frac{1}{2}x^2$
4. $y = x^2 + 4$
5. $y = -0.5x^2 + 1$
6. $y = x^2 - 4x - 4$
7. $y = 5x^2 - 20x + 37$
8. $y = 3x^2 + 6x + 3$
9. $y = 2x^2 + 12x$
10. $y = x^2 - 6x + 5$
11. $y = x^2 + 6x + 9$
12. $y = -x^2 + 16x - 15$
13. $y = 4x^2 - 1$
14. $y = -2x^2 - 2x + 4$
15. $y = 6x^2 - 12x - 4$

Lesson 9-9 Cubic and Exponential Functions (pp. 516–520)

Graph each function. State the y-intercept. 1–15. See Student Handbook Answer Appendix.

1. $y = x^3$ 0
2. $y = 0.3x^3$ 0
3. $y = x^3 - 2$ −2
4. $y = 3^x + 1$ 2
5. $y = 2^x - 5$ −4
6. $y = 2^{x+3}$ 8
7. $y = 3^{x+1}$ 3
8. $y = \left(\frac{2}{3}\right)^x$ 1
9. $y = 5\left(\frac{2}{5}\right)^x$ 5
10. $y = 5(3^x)$ 5
11. $y = 4(5)^x$ 4
12. $y = 2(5)^x + 1$ 3
13. $y = \left(\frac{1}{2}\right)^{x+1}$ $\frac{1}{2}$
14. $y = \left(\frac{1}{3}\right)^x$ 1
15. $y = \left(\frac{3}{4}\right)^x - 2$ −1

Lesson 10-1 Squares and Square Roots (pp. 537–542)

Find each square root.

1. $\sqrt{36}$ 6
2. $-\sqrt{81}$ −9
3. $\sqrt{\frac{1}{4}}$ $\frac{1}{2}$
4. $-\sqrt{144}$ −12
5. $\sqrt{25}$ 5
6. $\sqrt{1.96}$ 1.4
7. $\sqrt{100}$ 10
8. $-\sqrt{0.49}$ −0.7
9. $\sqrt{400}$ 20

Estimate each square root to the nearest integer. Do not use a calculator.

10. $\sqrt{21}$ 5
11. $-\sqrt{85}$ −9
12. $\sqrt{7.3}$ 3
13. $\sqrt{1.99}$ 1
14. $-\sqrt{62}$ −8
15. $\sqrt{74.1}$ 9
16. $\sqrt{810}$ 28
17. $-\sqrt{88.8}$ −9
18. $\sqrt{1000}$ 32

Use a calculator to find each square root to the nearest tenth.

19. $\sqrt{21}$ 4.6
20. $\sqrt{99}$ 9.9
21. $-\sqrt{60}$ −7.7
22. $\sqrt{124}$ 11.1
23. $-\sqrt{350}$ −18.7
24. $\sqrt{18.6}$ 4.3
25. $-\sqrt{42}$ −6.5
26. $-\sqrt{84.2}$ −9.2
27. $\sqrt{182}$ 13.5

Lesson 10-2 The Real Number System (pp. 543–548)

Name all of the sets of numbers to which each real number belongs. Write *whole, integer, rational,* or *irrational.*

1. 15 whole, integer, rational
2. 0 whole, integer, rational
3. $\frac{3}{8}$ rational
4. 0.666… rational
5. 1.75 rational
6. $\sqrt{2}$ irrational
7. 5.14726… irrational
8. $-\sqrt{36}$ integer, rational
9. 0.3535… rational

Replace each ● with <, >, or = to make a true statement.

10. $3\frac{3}{4}$ ● $\sqrt{15}$ <
11. $-\sqrt{41}$ ● −6.8 >
12. 5.2 ● $\sqrt{27.04}$ =
13. $-\sqrt{110}$ ● −10.5 >

ALGEBRA Solve each equation. Round to the nearest tenth, if necessary.

14. $x^2 = 14$ 3.7, −3.7
15. $y^2 = 25$ 5, −5
16. $34 = p^2$ 5.8, −5.8
17. $55 = h^2$ 7.4, −7.4
18. $225 = k^2$ 15, −15
19. $324 = m^2$ 18, −18
20. $d^2 = 441$ 21, −21
21. $r^2 = 25{,}000$ 158.1, −158.1
22. $10{,}000 = x^2$ 100, −100

Lesson 10-3 Triangles (pp. 550–555)

Find the value of x in each triangle. Then classify each triangle by its angles and by its sides.

1. 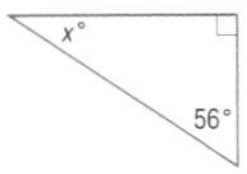 34; right scalene
2. 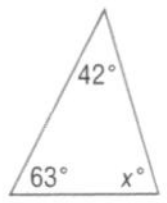 75; acute scalene
3. 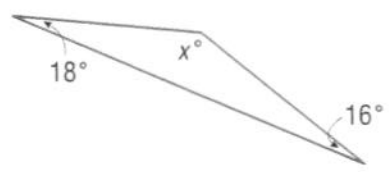 146; obtuse scalene
4. 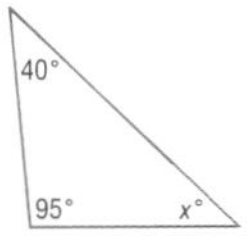 45; obtuse scalene
5. 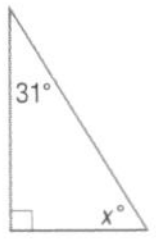 59; right scalene
6. 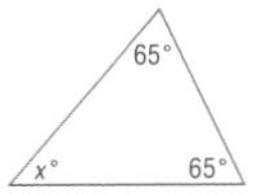 50; acute isosceles

7. The measure of the angles of a triangle are in the ratio 1:2:3. What is the measure of each angle? 30°; 60°; 90°
8. Determine the measures of the angles of $\triangle ABC$ if the measures of the angles of a triangle are in the ratio 1:1:2. 45°; 45°; 90°
9. Suppose the measures of the angles of a triangle are in the ratio 1:9:26. What is the measure of each angle? 5°; 45°; 130°

Lesson 10-4 The Pythagorean Theorem (pp. 558–563)

Find the length of the hypotenuse in each right triangle. Round to the nearest tenth, if necessary.

1. 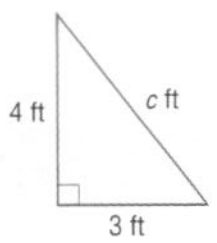 5 ft
2. 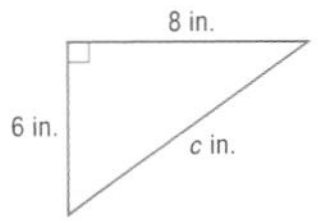 10 in.
3. 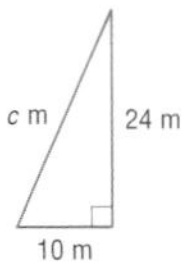 26 m

If c is the measurement of the hypotenuse, find each missing measure. Round to the nearest tenth, if necessary.

4. $a = 7$ m, $b = 24$ m 25 m
5. $a = 18$ in., $c = 30$ in. 24 in.
6. $b = 10$ ft, $c = 20$ ft 17.3 ft
7. $a = 3$ cm, $c = 9$ cm 8.5 cm
8. $b = 8$ m, $c = 32$ m 31.0 m
9. $a = 32$ yd, $c = 65$ yd 56.6 yd

Lesson 10-5 The Distance Formula (pp. 565–570)

Find the distance between each pair of points. Round to the nearest tenth, if necessary.

1. $A(2, 6), B(-4, 2)$ 7.2
2. $C(-3, 9), D(2, 4)$ 7.1
3. $E(6, -4), F(1, -6)$ 5.4
4. $G(0, -1), H(9, -1)$ 9
5. $I(-8, -3), J(2, 2)$ 11.2
6. $K(3, 0), L(-7, -2)$ 10.2
7. $M(3, 5), N(7, 1)$ 5.7
8. $O(-6, 2), P(0, 8)$ 8.5
9. $Q(4, -9), R(-2, 7)$ 17.1
10. $S(13, -1), T(-5, -3)$ 18.1

Lesson 10-6 Special Right Triangles (pp. 571–576)

Find each missing measure.

1. 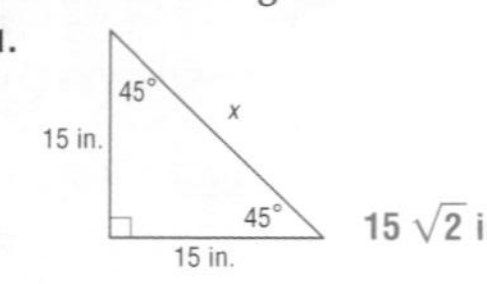

15 $\sqrt{2}$ in.

2. 

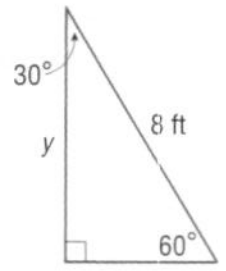

4 $\sqrt{3}$ ft

3. $x = 12.5$ m; $y = 12.5\sqrt{3}$ m

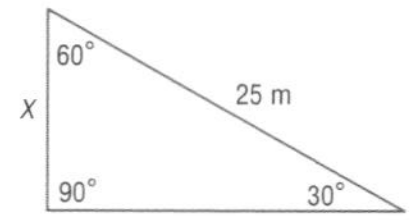

5. In a 45°-45°-90° right triangle, a leg is 36.4 inches long. Find the exact length of the hypotenuse. $(36.4)(\sqrt{2})$ in.

6. In a 30°-60°-90° right triangle, the shorter leg is 17 centimeters long. Find the length of the hypotenuse and the length of the longer leg to the nearest tenth of a centimeter. hypotenuse: 34 cm, longer leg: 29.4 cm

Lesson 11-1 Angle and Line Relationships (pp. 589–595)

In the figure at the right, $\ell \parallel m$ and p is a transversal. If the $m\angle 2$ is 38°, find the measure of each angle.

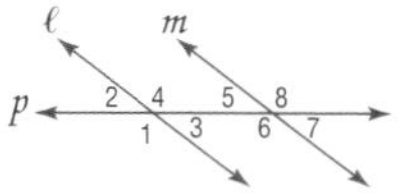

1. $\angle 1$ 142°
2. $\angle 4$ 142°
3. $\angle 3$ 38°
4. $\angle 6$ 142°
5. $\angle 5$ 38°
6. $\angle 8$ 142°

ALGEBRA Find the value of x in each figure.

7. 32
8. 162
9. 38

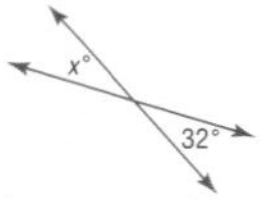

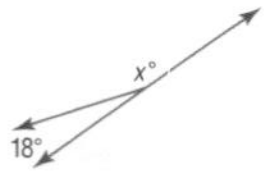

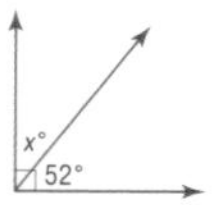

Lesson 11-2 Congruent Triangles (pp. 598–604)

Name the corresponding parts in each pair of congruent triangles. Then complete the congruence statement. 1–2. See Student Handbook Answer Appendix.

1. 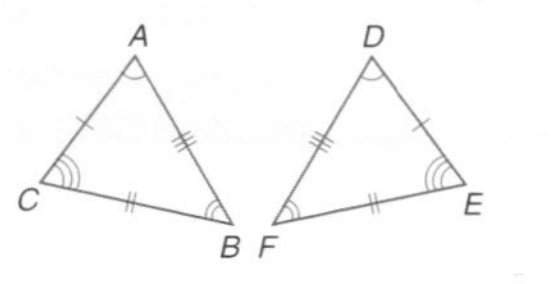

$\triangle ABC \cong \triangle$ __?__ DFE

2. 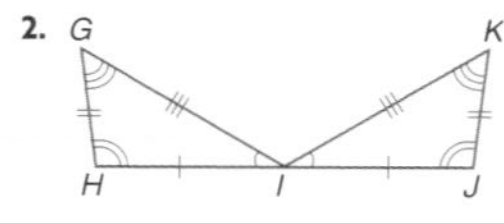

$\triangle GHI \cong \triangle$ __?__ KJI

Determine whether the triangles shown are congruent. If so, name the corresponding parts and write a congruence statement.

3. 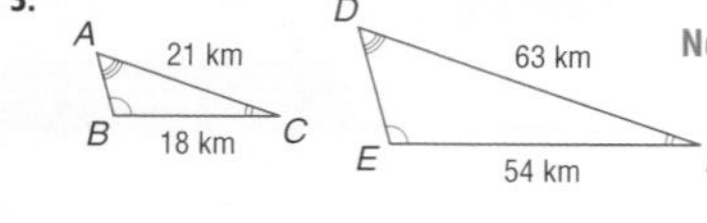

No

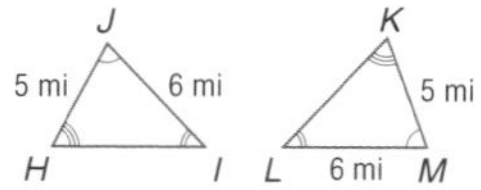

4. yes; $\angle J \cong \angle M$, $\angle I \cong \angle L$, $\angle H \cong \angle K$; $\overline{HJ} \cong \overline{KM}$, $\overline{JI} \cong \overline{ML}$, $\overline{HI} \cong \overline{KL}$; $\triangle HIJ \cong \triangle KLM$

Lesson 11-3 Rotations (pp. 605–610)

Figure *ABCDE* is shown. 1, 3. Student Handbook Answer Appendix

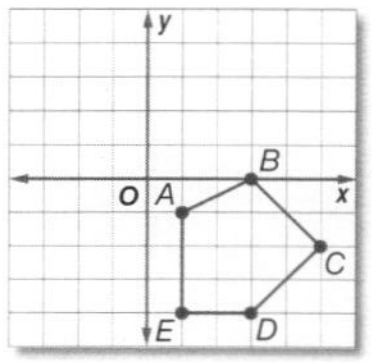

1. Graph the image of the figure after a 90° counterclockwise rotation about the origin.

2. Find the coordinates of the vertices of the figure after a 180° rotation about the origin. $A'(-1, 1)$, $B'(-3, 0)$, $C'(-5, 2)$, $D'(-3, 4)$, $E'(-1, 4)$

3. Graph the image of the figure after a 90° clockwise rotation about the origin.

4. **LETTERS** Determine whether the letter shown at the right has rotational symmetry. If it does, describe the angle of rotation. no

Lesson 11-4 Quadrilaterals (pp. 612–616)

ALGEBRA Find the value of x. Then find the missing angle measures.

1. 115; 115°
2. 110; 110°
3. 24; 48°
4. 88; 83°; 98°

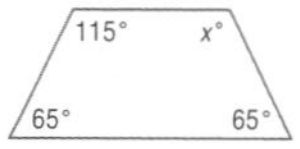

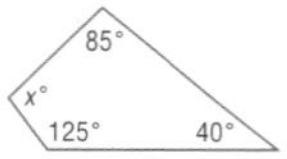

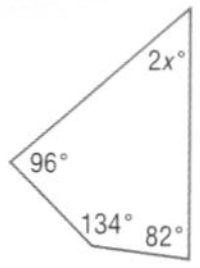

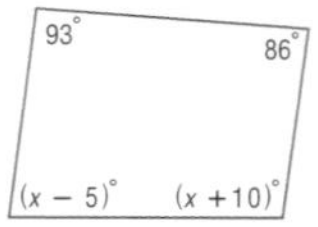

Lesson 11-5 Polygons (pp. 617–622)

Classify each polygon. Then determine whether it appears to be *regular* or *not regular*.

1. hexagon; regular
2. 11-gon; not regular

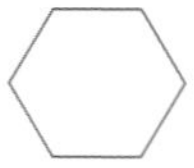

Find the sum of the measures of the interior angles of each polygon.

3. decagon 1440°
4. pentagon 540°
5. nonagon 1260°
6. hexagon 720°
7. octagon 1080°
8. 15-gon 2340°

Lesson 11-6 Area of Parallelograms, Triangles, and Trapezoids (pp. 624–630)

Find the area of each figure.

1. 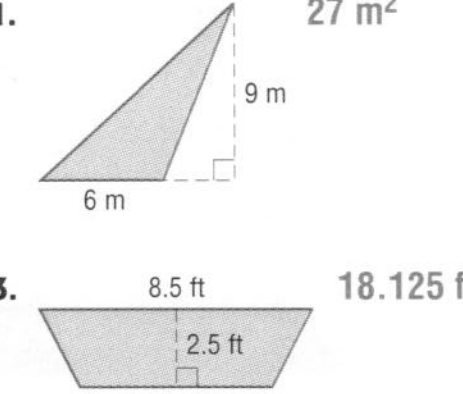

$27\ m^2$

2. 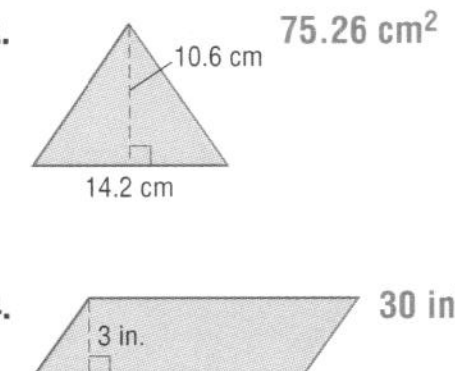

$75.26\ cm^2$

3. 8.5 ft, 2.5 ft, 6 ft — $18.125\ ft^2$

4. 3 in., 10 in. — $30\ in^2$

5. What is the height of a parallelogram with a base of 3.4 inches and an area of 32.3 square inches? 9.5 in.

6. The bases of a trapezoid measure 8 meters and 12 meters. Find the measure of the height if the trapezoid has an area of 70 square meters. 7 m

Lesson 11-7 Circles and Circumference (pp. 631–635)

Find the circumference of each circle. Round to the nearest tenth.

1. 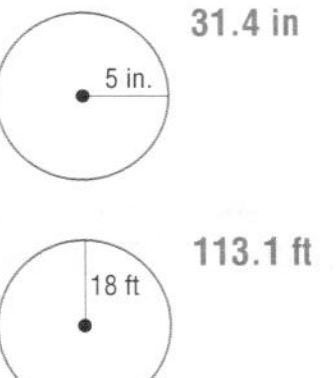

31.4 in

2. 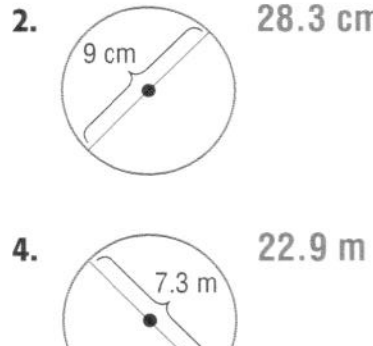

28.3 cm

3. 18 ft — 113.1 ft

4. 7.3 m — 22.9 m

5. Find the diameter of a circle if its circumference is 18.5 feet. Round to the nearest tenth. 5.9 ft

Lesson 11-8 Area of Circles (pp. 636–641)

Find the area of each circle. Round to the nearest tenth.

1. radius = 8.2 feet $211.2\ ft^2$
2. diameter = 1.3 yards $1.3\ yd^2$
3. diameter = 5.2 yards $21.2\ yd^2$
4. radius = 4.8 centimeters $72.4\ cm^2$
5. A circle has an area of 62.9 square inches. What is the radius of the circle? Round to the nearest tenth. 4.5 in.

Lesson 11-9 Area of Composite Figures (pp. 642–647)

Find the area of each figure. Round to the nearest tenth.

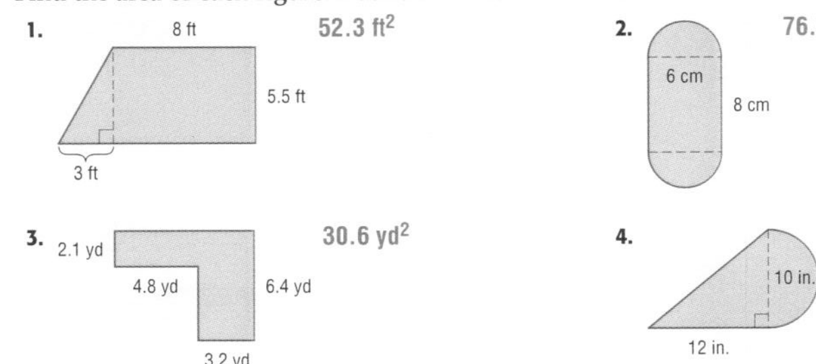

1. $52.3\ ft^2$
2. $76.3\ cm^2$
3. $30.6\ yd^2$
4. $99.3\ in^2$

Lesson 12-1 Three-Dimensional Figures (pp. 664–669)

Identify each figure. Name the bases, faces, edges, and vertices. 1–5. See Student Handbook Answer Appendix.

1. 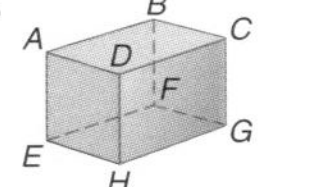

2. 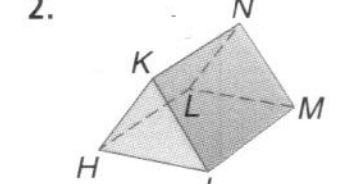

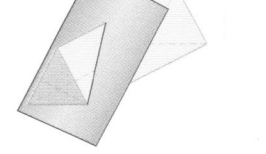

CROSS SECTIONS **Describe the shape resulting from each cross section.**

3. 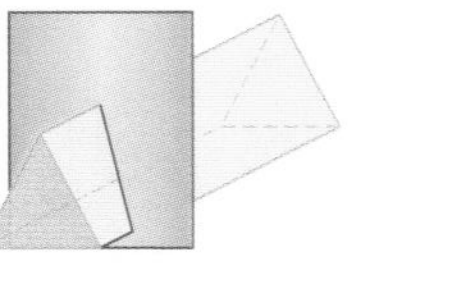

4. 

5. 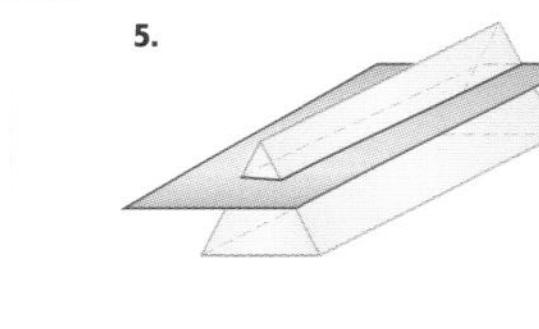

Lesson 12-2 Volume of Prisms (pp. 671–676)

Find the volume of each figure.

1. 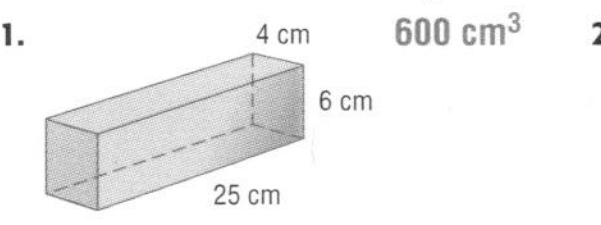

$600\ cm^3$

2. 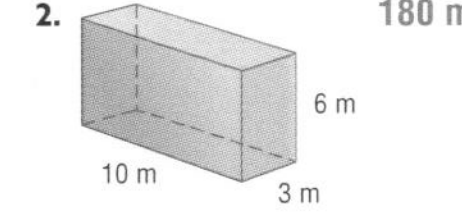
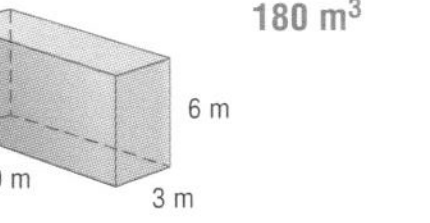

$180\ m^3$

3. 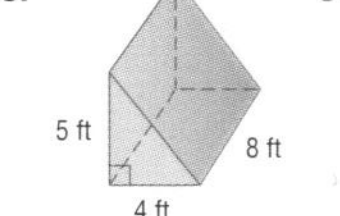

$80\ ft^3$

4. rectangular prism: length $2\frac{1}{2}$ yd, width 7 yd, height 12 yd $210\ yd^3$
5. triangular prism: base of triangle 3.1 cm, altitude of triangle 1.7 cm, height of prism 5.0 cm. Round to the nearest tenth. $13.2\ cm^3$

Lesson 12-3 Volume of Cylinders (pp. 677–681)

Find the volume of each cylinder. Round to the nearest tenth.

1. 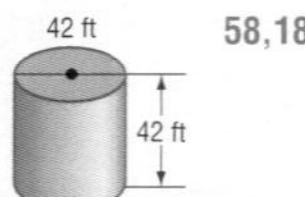

58,188.6 ft^3

2. 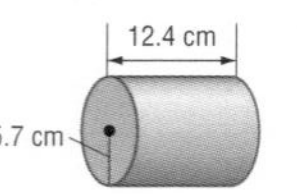

1265.7 cm^3

3. diameter: 6 mm
height: 13 mm
367.6 mm^3

Find the height of each cylinder. Round to the nearest tenth.

4. volume: 128.41 cm^3
radius: 2.4 cm 7.1 cm

5. volume: 208.81 cm^3
radius: 6.2 cm 1.7 cm

6. volume: 2575.2 cm^3
radius: 8.1 cm 12.5 cm

7. **PET CARE** Tina has an old fish tank in the shape of a cylinder. The tank is 2 feet in diameter and 6 feet high. How many cubic feet of water does it hold? Round to the nearest tenth. 18.8 ft^3

Lesson 12-4 Volume of Pyramids, Cones, and Spheres (pp. 683–688)

Find the volume of each figure. Round to the nearest tenth, if necessary.

1. 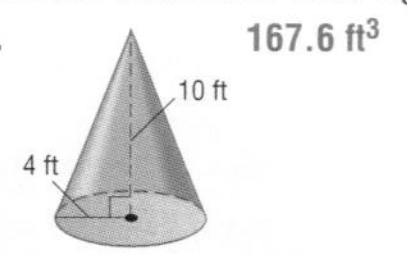

167.6 ft^3

2. 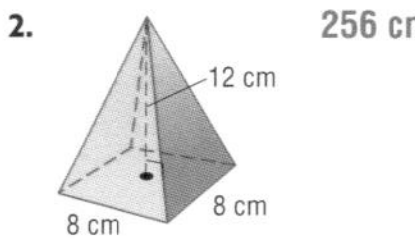

256 cm^3

3. sphere: radus 1.2 cm 7.2 cm^3
4. cone: diameter 10 yd, height 7 yd 183.3 yd^3
5. rectangular pyramid: length 6 in., width 6 in., height 9 in. 108 in^3
6. sphere: diameter 14.4 ft 1563.5 ft^3
7. square pyramid: length $3\frac{1}{4}$ ft, height 12 ft 42.3 ft^3
8. sphere: radius 3.1 cm 124.8 cm^3

Lesson 12-5 Surface Area of Prisms (pp. 691–695)

Find the lateral area and surface area of each prism. Round to the nearest tenth.

1. cube: side length 14 in. 784 in^2; 1176 in^2
2. rectangular prism: length 5 cm, width 9 cm, height 3 cm 84 cm^2; 174 cm^2
3. cube: side length 6 ft 144 ft^2; 216 ft^2
4. cube: side length 4.9 m 96.0 m^2; 144.1 m^2
5. rectangular prism: length 7.6 mm, width 8.4 mm, height 7.0 mm 224 mm^2; 351.7 mm^2
6. triangular prism: right triangle 3 in. by 4 in. by 5 in., height of prism 10 in. 120 in^2; 132 in^2

Lesson 12-6 Surface Area of Cylinders (pp. 697–701)

Find the lateral area and surface area of each cylinder. Round to the nearest tenth.

1. 6 in. 20 in. 754.0 in^2; 980.2 in^2

2. 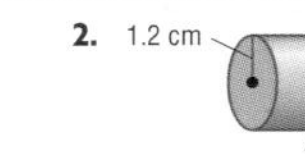

30.2 cm^2; 39.2 cm^2

3. radius of 4.2 m and a height of 10 m 263.9 m^2; 374.7 m^2
4. diameter of 8 m and a height of 12 m 301.6 m^2; 402.1 m^2
5. diameter of 5 cm and a height of 5 cm 78.5 cm^2; 117.8 cm^2
6. radius of 1.88 in. and a height of 3.9 in. 46.1 in^2; 68.3 in^2
7. radius of 4.3 mm and a height of 12.1 mm 326.9 mm^2; 443.2 mm^2
8. diameter of 4.5 yd and a height of 3.75 yd 53.0 yd^2; 84.8 yd^2

Lesson 12-7 Surface Area of Pyramids and Cones (pp. 702–707)

Find the lateral area and surface area of each figure. Round to the nearest tenth.

1. 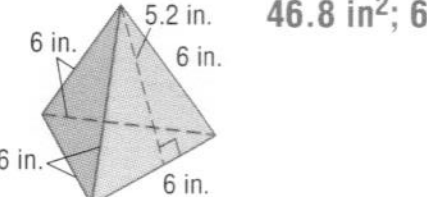

46.8 in^2; 62.4 in^2

2. 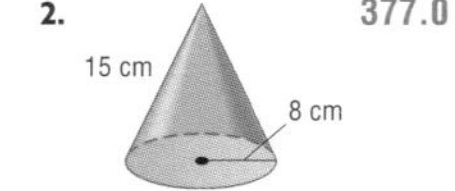

377.0 cm^2; 578.1 cm^2

3. 9 ft, 4 ft, 4 ft 72 ft^2; 88 ft^2

4. 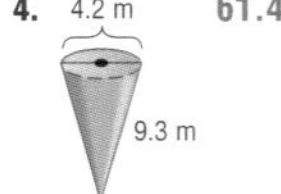

61.4 m^2; 75.2 m^2

5. square pyramid: base side length 1.8 mm, slant height 3.0 mm 10.8 mm^2; 14.0 mm^2
6. cone: radius 4 in., slant height 7 in. 88.0 in^2; 138.2 in^2
7. cone: diameter 15.2 cm, slant height 12.3 cm 293.7 cm^2; 475.1 cm^2

Lesson 12-8 Similar Solids (pp. 709–715)

Determine whether each pair of solids is similar.

1. 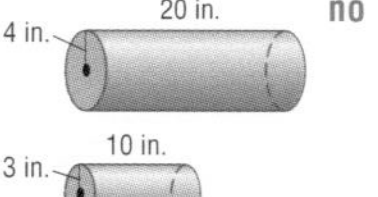

no

2. 

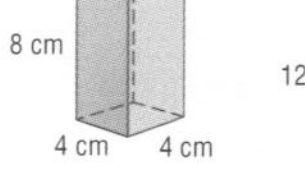

yes

Find the missing measure of each pair of similar solids.

3. 21 ft, 12 ft, x, 4 ft $x = 7$ ft

4. 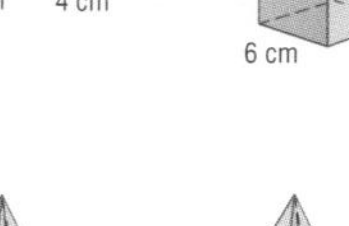

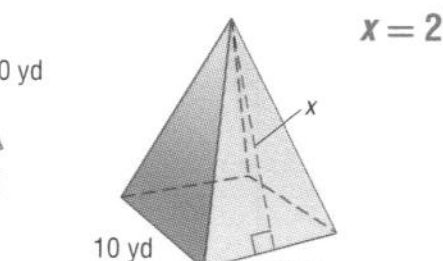

$x = 25$ yd

Lesson 13-1 Measures of Central Tendency (pp. 730–735)

Find the mean, median, and mode for each set of data. Round to the nearest tenth, if necessary.

1. quiz scores: 82, 79, 93, 91, 95 **88; 91; none**
2. ages of people in an aerobics class: 23, 32, 19, 27, 41, 21, 26, 32, 23 **27.1; 26; 23 and 32**
3. Students with Blue Eyes **11.7; 12; 11**

   8 9 10 11 12 13 14 15

4. Lengths of Snakes (meters) **0.4; 0.4; 0.3**

   0.1 0.2 0.3 0.4 0.5 0.6 0.7 0.8

7. **POPULATION** The population of the Canadian provinces and territories in 2006 is shown in the table. Find the mean, median, and mode of the data. Round to the nearest tenth, if necessary. **2500.0 thousand; 935.8 thousand; none**

Populations (thousands)						
3332.2	4292.2	1179.7	750.5	512.5	935.8	12,630.5
138.3	7636.7	989.0	42.2	31.1	29.8	

Lesson 13-2 Stem-and-Leaf Plots (pp. 737–742)

Display each set of data in a stem-and-leaf plot. **1–5. See Student Handbook Answer Appendix.**

1. ages of people in a store: 3, 26, 35, 8, 21, 24, 30, 39, 35, 5, 38
2. prices of bicycles: $172, $198, $181, $182, $193, $171, $179, $186, $181
3. number of vendors at craft shows: 17, 54, 37, 86, 24, 69, 77, 92, 21
4. science test scores: 73, 61, 89, 67, 82, 54, 93, 102, 59, 75, 83
5. **SPORTS** The stem-and-leaf plot shows the times in seconds of people in a race.

Race Times

Stem	Leaf
7	2 2 3 5 9
8	0 1 1 4 6 6 8 9
9	3 4 8

9 | 4 = 94 s

   a. What is the greatest value? **98 s**
   b. In which interval do most of the values occur? **80 s to 89 s**
   c. What is the median value? **82.5 s**

Lesson 13-3 Measures of Variation (pp. 743–749)

Find the range, interquartile range, and any outliers for each set of data.

1. cost of video games: 44, 37, 23, 35, 61, 95, 49, 96 **73; 42; none**
2. dollars in savings account: 271, 891, 181, 193, 711, 791, 861, 818 **710; 607.5; none**
3. **Ages of People in a Restaurant** **39; 20.5; none**

Stem	Leaf
2	0 1 1 2 4 7 9
3	3 3 6 8 8 8
4	2 4 5 7 9 9
5	2 9

3 | 6 = 36

4. **Typing Speeds (wpm)** **55; 32; none**

Stem	Leaf
4	0 2 2 3 4 5 6 6 7 8
5	1 2 5 5 5 9
6	4 7 8 8
7	0 0 1 4 9 9 9
8	1 7 9
9	0 0 1 3 5

8 | 7 = 87

Lesson 13-4 Box-and-Whiskers Plots (pp. 750–755)

Construct a box-and-whisker plot for each set of data. **1 and 2. See Student Handbook Answer Appendix.**

1. Ages of home owners: 42, 23, 31, 27, 32, 48, 37, 25, 19, 26, 30, 41, 32, 29
2. Price in dollars, of MP3 players: 124, 327, 215, 278, 109, 225, 186, 134, 251, 308, 179
3. **VOLLEYBALL** Use the box-and-whisker plot shown.

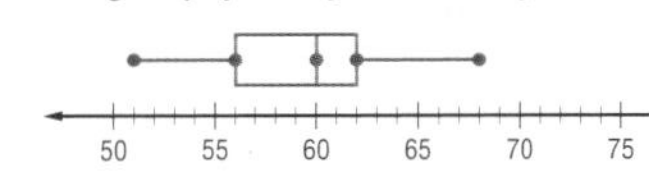

   a. What is the height of the tallest player? **68 in.**
   b. What percent of the players are between 56 and 68 inches tall? **75%**
   c. Explain what the length of the box-and-whisker plot tells us about the data. **The values are spread out.**

Lesson 13-5 Histograms (pp. 757–762)

Display each set of data in a histogram. **1 and 2. See Student Handbook Answer Appendix.**

1. **Weekly Exercise Time**

Time (h)	Tally	Frequency
0–2	𝍸 |||	8
3–5	||||	4
6–8	||	2
9–11	|||	3

2. **Weekly Grocery Bill**

Amount ($)	Tally	Frequency
0–49	𝍸 |	6
50–99	𝍸 𝍸 ||	12
100–149	𝍸 |||	8
150–199	||||	4
200–249	||	2

Lesson 13-6 Theoretical and Experimental Probability (pp. 765–770)

There are 4 blue marbles, 6 red marbles, 3 green marbles, and 2 yellow marbles in a bag. Suppose you select one marble at random. Find the probability of each outcome. Express each probability as a fraction and as a percent. Round to the nearest tenth of a percent if necessary.

1. $P(\text{green})$ $\frac{1}{5}$; **20%**
2. $P(\text{blue})$ $\frac{4}{15}$; **26.7%**
3. $P(\text{red})$ $\frac{2}{5}$; **40%**
4. $P(\text{yellow})$ $\frac{2}{15}$; **13.3%**
5. $P(\text{neither red nor green})$ $\frac{2}{5}$; **40%**
6. $P(\text{red or yellow})$ $\frac{8}{15}$; **53.3%**
7. $P(\text{not orange})$ **1; 100%**
8. $P(\text{neither blue nor yellow})$ $\frac{3}{5}$; **60%**
9. $P(\text{not red})$ $\frac{3}{5}$; **60%**
10. $P(\text{neither green nor yellow})$ $\frac{2}{3}$; **66.7%**
11. Suppose two number cubes are rolled. What is the probability of rolling a sum greater than 8? $\frac{5}{18}$ **or about 28%**
12. **COOKIES** A sample from a package of assorted cookies revealed that 20% of the cookies were sugar cookies. Suppose there are 45 cookies in the package. How many can be expected to be sugar cookies? **9 cookies**

Lesson 13-7 Using Sampling to Predict (pp. 771–776)

Identify each sample as *biased* or *unbiased* and describe its type. Explain your reasoning. 1–4. See Student Handbook Answer Appendix.

1. To determine the most popular kind of fish to eat, every third person coming out of a grocery store is interviewed.
2. To determine where to hold the senior prom, a survey is taken of the entire school.
3. To determine the popularity of blogging, members of the Blog Society are polled.
4. To determine whether a city's outerbelt should be widened, crews filmed traffic every six weeks at different times of day.

Lesson 13-8 Counting Outcomes (pp. 777–781)

Use the Fundamental Counting Principle to find the total number of outcomes in each situation.

1. Engagement rings come in silver, gold, and white gold. The diamond can weigh $\frac{1}{2}$ karat, $\frac{1}{3}$ karat, or $\frac{1}{4}$ karat. The diamond can have 4 possible shapes. 36
2. A dress can be long, tea-length, knee-length, or mini. It comes in 2 colors and the dress can have long sleeves or short sleeves. 16
3. The first digit of a 7-digit phone number is a 2. The last digit is a 3. 100,000
4. Three coins are tossed. What is the probability of three tails? $\frac{1}{8}$
5. Two six-sided dice are rolled. What is the probability of getting an odd sum? $\frac{1}{2}$
6. A ten-sided die is rolled and a coin is tossed. Find the probability of the coin landing on tails and the die landing on a number greater than 3. $\frac{7}{20}$

Lesson 13-9 Permutations and Combinations (pp. 783–788)

1. **STUDENT COUNCIL** Seven people are running for four seats on student council. How many ways can the students be elected? 35
2. **LETTERS** How many ways can the letters of the word ISLAND be arranged? 720
3. **CANDLES** How many ways can five candles be arranged in three candlesticks? 10
4. **RACES** How many ways can six students line up for a race? 720
5. **GEOMETRY** Determine the number of line segments that can be drawn between any two vertices of a pentagon. 10

Lesson 13-10 Probability of Compound Events (pp. 790–795)

A card is drawn from a deck of cards numbered 6–19. Find each probability.

1. P(13 or even) $\frac{4}{7}$
2. P(13 or less than 7) $\frac{1}{7}$
3. P(even or odd) 1
4. P(14 or greater than 20) $\frac{1}{14}$
5. P(even or less than 10) $\frac{9}{14}$
6. P(odd or greater than 10) $\frac{11}{14}$

Mixed Problem Solving

Chapter 1 The Tools of Algebra (pp. 2–57)

1. **FOOD** The Spanish Club is hosting a luncheon for all the students. The cost for each item is shown below. (Lesson 1-1)

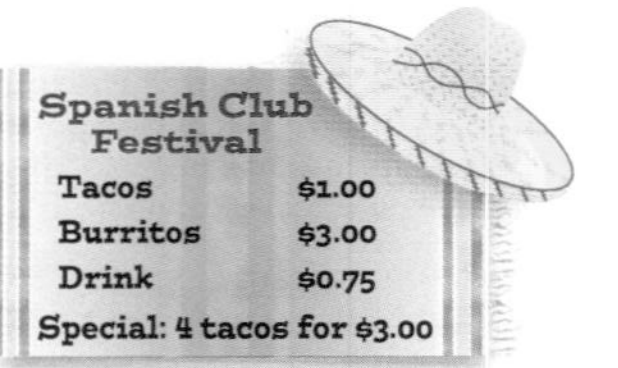

Spanish Club Festival
Tacos $1.00
Burritos $3.00
Drink $0.75
Special: 4 tacos for $3.00

   a. Write an expression for the cost of a meal that includes one of each item.
   b. Inez is buying lunch for her friends. If she buys 3 tacos, 2 burritos and 3 drinks, what is the total cost? 1a–b. See Student Handbook Answer Appendix.

2. **FOOTBALL** Admission to a high school football game is \$8. At the game, raffle tickets are sold for \$0.50 each. Write an expression showing the cost for admission and t tickets. Then find the total cost if 20 tickets are purchased. (Lesson 1-2) $8 + 0.50t$; \$18

3. **RIDES** The number of people who have ridden a ride and the number of ride tickets required at the fair are shown. (Lesson 1-2)

Rides	Number of People	Number of Tickets
Ferris wheel	f	3
Vortex	v	3
Hurricane	h	5

   a. Write an algebraic expression to show how many total ride tickets have been collected. $3f + 3v + 5h$
   b. Joseph rode the Ferris wheel twice, Vortex four times, and Hurricane three times. How many tickets did he use? 33 tickets

4. **HOMEWORK** After school, Morgan usually has a snack and works on her homework. Are the actions commutative? Explain. (Lesson 1-3) See Student Handbook Answer Appendix.

5. **MOVIES** The cost of renting one movie from an online movie rental company is \$3.50. (Lesson 1-4) a. See Student Handbook Answer Appendix.
   a. Make a table of ordered pairs in which the x-coordinate represents the number of movies and the y-coordinate represents the cost for renting 1, 2, 3, 4, and 5 movies.
   b. Graph the ordered pairs. Then describe the graph. The points appear to fall in a line. See Student Handbook Answer Appendix for graph.

6. **MULTIPLE REPRESENTATIONS** Pandas eat about 240 pounds of bamboo every three days. (Lesson 1-5) a. $p = 80d$
   a. **ALGEBRAIC** Write an equation that can be used to find the pounds of bamboo p a panda will eat in any number of days d.
   b. **TABULAR** Make a function table to find the pounds of bamboo a panda will eat in 5, 7, 10, and 13 days.
   c. **GRAPHICAL** Graph the ordered pairs.
   b–c. See Student Handbook Answer Appendix.

7. **SPORTS** The table shows the number of gold medals won by the United States Olympic team at the Summer Olympics from 1964 through 2004. (Lesson 1-6) 7a–b. See margin.

Year	1964	1968	1972	1976	1984
Number of Medals	36	45	33	34	83
Year	1988	1992	1996	2000	2004
Number of Medals	36	37	44	38	36

   a. Make a scatter plot of the data.
   b. Draw a conclusion about the type of relationship the data shows. Explain.
   c. Is it possible to predict the number of gold medals that will be won in 2016? Explain.
   7a–c. See Student Handbook Answer Appendix.

Chapter 2 Operations with Integers (pp. 58–115)

1. **PLANETS** The maximum surface temperatures for different planets are shown in the table below. Order the temperatures from least to greatest. (Lesson 2-1) **−216, −214, −148, −5, 58, 427**

Planet	Maximum Surface Temperature °C
Earth	58
Mars	−5
Mercury	427
Neptune	−214
Jupiter	−148
Uranus	−216

Source: NASA

2. **STOCKS** During a three-day period, a stock's price increased $2.03 the first day, then decreased $1.75 the second day and $0.89 the third day. Find the final price of the stock if the starting price was $97.86. (Lesson 2-2) **$97.25**

3. **BUSINESS SENSE** In January, Myers Construction Company had a net worth of −$12,061. By November of the same year, the company's net worth had increased by $33,385. What was the company's net worth in November? (Lesson 2-2) **$21,324**

4. **AVIATION** A commercial jet has a usual cruising altitude of 34,000 feet. Because of a storm, it climbs 2,500 feet and then descends 4,700 feet to its new cruising altitude. What is the jet's new cruising altitude? (Lesson 2-3) **31,800 ft**

5. **BANKING** Hasan wrote checks and made the deposits shown in his check registry. What was the change in his balance after these transactions? (Lesson 2-3) **−$283**

CK #	Name	Amt	Dep
145	Car Payment	$177	
	Deposit		$130
146	Cell Phone	$38	
147	Gasoline	$76	
	Deposit		$82
148	Rent	$204	

6. **ENVIRONMENT** The erosion rate at Emerald Isle in North Carolina is about 2 feet per year. If erosion continues at the current rate, what integer represents the amount of erosion at Emerald Isle in 13 years? (Lesson 2-4) **−26**

7. **MOUNTAINS** Every 1000 feet above Earth's surface, air temperature decreases 5°F. How much would the temperature change from sea level to the highest point on each mountain? (Lesson 2-4) **−101.6°, −90.04°, −87°**

Mountain	Highest Point (ft)
Mt. McKinley	20,320
Mt. St. Elias	18,008
Mt. Foraker	17,400

8. **AMUSEMENT PARK** After 6 seconds, the Dynamic Drop was −15 feet from the top of the ride. How many feet per second did the ride drop? (Lesson 2-5) **−2.5 feet per second**

9. **GOLF** The first round scores for a golf tournament are shown in the table below. What was the average score for the round? (Lesson 2-5) **−2.25**

Player	Score
Sara	−4
Cherylynn	−6
Juanita	+2
Mia	−1

10. **HOCKEY** A hockey team scored a total of 5 goals in the first two periods of play. (Lesson 2-6)
    a. If x represents the number of goals in the first period, and y represents the number of goals in the second period, make a function table of possible values for x and y.
    b. Graph the ordered pairs and describe the graph. **See Student Handbook Answer Appendix.**

11. **ANIMATION** Animators can use translations to show movement. Suppose the animator draws a ball with a center at (1, 5). Describe the translation if the next screen places the center of the ball at (0, −2). (Lesson 2-7) **The ball moved left 1 unit and down 7 units.**

Chapter 3 Operations with Rational Numbers (pp. 116–167)

1. **SCIENCE** A regular incandescent light bulb can have a life of 750 hours while a compact fluorescent bulb (CFB) can have a life of 10,000 hours. To the nearest thousandth, what part of the life of a CFB is the life of an incandescent bulb? (Lesson 3-1) **0.075**

2. **COOKING** The side of a cookie box lists the following nutritional information about one cookie:

Nutrition Facts
Serving Size 1 cookie
Amount per serving
Calories 67 Calories from fat 24

To the nearest hundredth, what part of the total Calories are Calories from fat? (Lesson 3-1) **0.36**

3. **BASKETBALL** At basketball practice yesterday, Zachary made $0.8\overline{6}$ of his free throw shots. What fraction of the shots did he miss? (Lesson 3-2) $\frac{2}{15}$

4. **BASEBALL** A player's batting average is found by dividing the number of hits by the total number of times at bat. A player has a batting average of .225. Write the player's batting average as a fraction in lowest terms. (Lesson 3-2) $\frac{9}{40}$

5. **RADIO STATIONS** In a recent survey $\frac{2}{3}$ of the people surveyed said they listen to Top 40 radio stations. Of these, $\frac{3}{4}$ said they listen to station WABC. What fraction of the people surveyed listen to station WABC? Write in simplest form. (Lesson 3-3) $\frac{1}{2}$

6. **MUSIC** Gracie has a collection of 32 CDs, each in its own case. Each CD case is $\frac{5}{8}$ inch thick. (Lesson 3-3)
    a. If Gracie puts them on a stack on the floor, how tall would the stack be? **20 inches tall**
    b. Can she store the CDs on a 2-foot shelf in her room? Explain your reasoning. **yes; the shelf is 24 inches long.**

7. **FOOD** A gallon of milk contains 128 ounces. Jung's favorite souvenir glass holds $10\frac{1}{2}$ ounces of milk. How many of these glasses of milk can Jung pour from one gallon? (Lesson 3-4) **12**

8. **COINS** A nickel is approximately $\frac{2}{25}$-inch thick. How many nickels will fit in a 4-inch storage tube? (Lesson 3-4) **50**

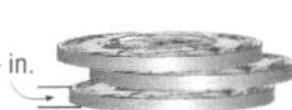

9. **MAIL** Mrs. Hamre wants to mail the packages shown. What is the total weight of the packages? Write in simplest form. (Lesson 3-5) **$13\frac{1}{2}$ oz**

Package	Weight (oz)
1	$8\frac{7}{16}$
2	$5\frac{1}{16}$

10. **SEWING** Kelli wants to sew trim around the sleeves and hem of a dance costume. She needs a piece of trim that is $8\frac{1}{8}$ inches long for the sleeves and a piece that is $40\frac{5}{8}$ inches long for the hem. If the package contains 5 feet of trim, how much trim will she have left after making the costume? (Lesson 3-5) **$11\frac{1}{4}$ in.**

11. **GARDENING** Kia wants to place a fence around her garden. The fencing material comes in a roll that is $40\frac{1}{2}$ feet long. If the width of the garden is $8\frac{7}{8}$ feet, what is the maximum length she can make her garden? (Lesson 3-6) **$11\frac{3}{8}$ ft**

12. **CONSTRUCTION** Members of the Drama Club are building a set for a play. Rob needs a piece of wood $7\frac{3}{4}$ feet long for the front and a piece $4\frac{5}{8}$ feet long for the side. The wood comes in 12-foot lengths. After he cuts off the piece for the front, will Rob have enough left over for the side? Explain your reasoning. (Lesson 3-6) **See Student Handbook Answer Appendix.**

Chapter 4 Expressions and Equations (pp. 168–217)

1. **MUSEUMS** A group of 10 friends are taking a trip to the Rock and Roll Hall of Fame. The cost of admission and transportation per person is \$20. Lunch will cost each person \$8.00. Use mental math to find the total amount they will spend. Justify your answer by using the Distributive Property. (Lesson 4-1)
\$280; $10(20 + 8) = 10 \cdot 20 + 10 \cdot 8$

2. **GEOMETRY** The perimeter of a triangle can be found by adding the lengths of its sides. (Lesson 4-2) **$4y + 18$**
   a. Write an expression for the perimeter of the triangle below.

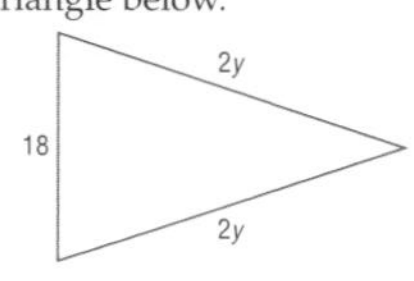

   b. If $y = 12$, what is the perimeter of the triangle? **66 units**

3. **SHOPPING** Pilar purchased a new computer. She made an initial payment of \$70 and will make monthly payments of \$45 for x months. Write an expression to show the total amount Pilar will pay for the computer. (Lesson 4-2) **$\$70 + \$45x$**

4. **TRAVEL** A city had an increase of 126,925 tourists from June to July. If there were 3.3 million tourists in July, how many were there in June? Write and solve an addition equation to find the number of tourists in June. (Lesson 4-3)
$v + 126{,}925 = 3{,}300{,}000$; 3,173,075 visitors in June

5. **SOCCER** During a recent season, Alex attempted 35 shots on goal and made 28 goals. Write and solve a subtraction equation to find the number of times he did not score. (Lesson 4-3)
$35 - m = 28$; 7 times

6. **MONEY** Hector wants to donate an equal amount of money to four different charities. As part of a fundraiser, he raised a total of \$420 for charity. Write and solve a multiplication equation to find how much each charity will receive. (Lesson 4-4)
$4x = 420$; \$105

7. **TIME** Sebastian spent 1.25 hours practicing the piano on Wednesday. Write and solve a division equation to find how many minutes he spent practicing on Wednesday. (Lesson 4-4) **$\frac{m}{60} = 1.25$; 75 min**

8. **MUSIC** An online music company advertises the rates shown in the table below. Sherita has \$30 to pay the membership fee and download songs. (Lesson 4-5)

Type of Fee	Cost (\$)
Membership	\$8.75
Song Download	\$0.85

   a. Solve the equation $0.85s + 8.75 = 30$ to find the number of songs she can download and have no money left over. **25 songs**
   b. If the membership fee increases to \$11.30, how many songs can she download? **22 songs**

9. **COLLECTIONS** Mathew and Aaron both collect baseball cards. Mathew has 66 cards in his collection which is 12 more than twice the number of cards in Aaron's collection. Solve the equation $12 + 2a = 66$ to find the number of cards in Aaron's collection. (Lesson 4-5) **27 cards**

10. **GEOMETRY** The perimeter of the figure below is 38 inches. Write and solve an equation to find the value of x. (Lesson 4-6)
$6x + 8 = 38$; 5 in.

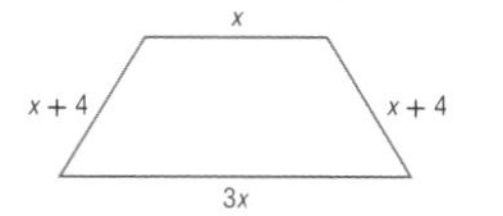

11. **CONSTRUCTION** The Trans-Pacific Express project involves laying 11,000 miles of telecommunications cable under the Pacific Ocean from China to the United States. The cost for the project will be approximately \$500 million. Write and solve an equation to find the cost per mile to the nearest dollar. (Lesson 4-6) **$500{,}000{,}000 = 11{,}000c$; about \$45,455 per mile**

Chapter 5 Multi-Step Equations and Inequalities (pp. 218–261)

1. **ARCHITECTURE** The Reflecting Pool in between the Washington Monument and the Lincoln Memorial is 167 feet wide and 2029 feet long. What is the perimeter of the Reflecting Pool? (Lesson 5-1) **4392 ft**

2. **FLOORS** The dining room in Mariah's house has a hardwood floor that is partially covered by a rug as shown below. If the rug measures 9 feet by 7.5 feet, how much of the hardwood floor is *not* covered by the area rug? (Lesson 5-1) **75.5 sq ft**

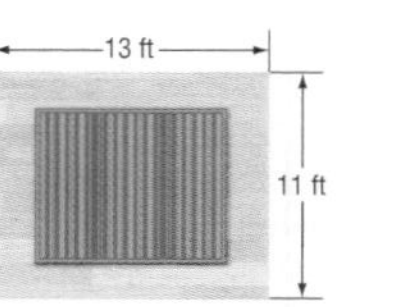

3. **SAVINGS** Theresa and Miranda are each saving money for a cruise. Theresa has already saved \$500 and plans to deposit \$40 each month. Miranda has \$200 in her account and will deposit \$60 each month. Write and solve an equation to find how many months it will take for them to have saved the same amount of money. (Lesson 5-2) **$500 + 40m = 200 + 60m$; 15 months**

4. **CELL PHONES** The Happy Talk Cell Phone company offers two different rate plans for teens. Write and solve an equation to determine for what number of minutes will the costs be equal. (Lesson 5-2)
$25 + 0.08m = 15 + 0.10m$; 500 min

Happy Talk Cell Phone Rates		
	Monthly Fee	Cost per Minute
Option A	\$25	\$0.08
Option B	\$15	\$0.10

5. **RAINFALL** Mt. Waialeale in Hawaii receives the most amount of rainfall with an average rainfall of at least 397 inches. Write an inequality to describe the amount of rainfall. (Lesson 5-3) **$r \geq 397$**

6. **TICKETS** The Student Council is planning a dance. The expenses for the dance are shown below. If they sell tickets for \$3.50, write and solve an inequality to find the minimum number of tickets they will have to sell to make a profit. (Lesson 5-4)
$3.5t > 590$; 169 tickets

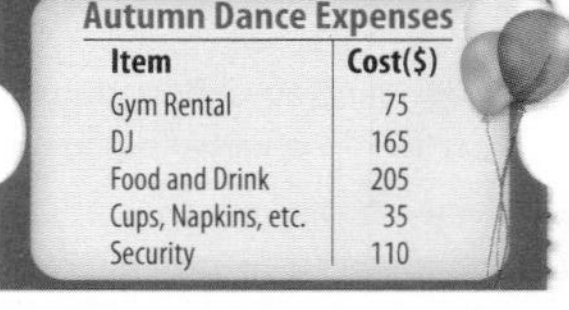

Autumn Dance Expenses	
Item	Cost(\$)
Gym Rental	75
DJ	165
Food and Drink	205
Cups, Napkins, etc.	35
Security	110

7. **MONEY** Jin earns \$2350 per month plus \$45 for each sale he completes. Write and solve an inequality to find how many sales he would have to make each month in order to earn at least \$3000. (Lesson 5-4)
$2350 + 45s \geq 3000$; 15 sales

8. **SHOPPING** The table below shows the cost of school supplies at a local store.

Item	Cost	Number Purchased
notebook	\$3.00	$2b$
box of pens	\$1.50	b
package of paper	\$2.00	$b + 1$

If Spencer spent a total of \$30.50 before tax, how many of each item did he purchase? (Lesson 5-5) **3 boxes of pens, 6 notebooks, and 4 packs of paper**

9. **TRAINING** Mimi is planning to run a marathon. To prepare for the race, she will follow the schedule below. She plans on running 11 hours per week. How many hours will she run each day? (Lesson 5-5)

Running Schedule	
Day	Length of Time
Monday	x hours
Tuesday	2 hours more than Monday
Thursday	same as Monday
Saturday	3 times as much as Monday

See Student Handbook Answer Appendix.

Chapter 6 Ratio, Proportion, and Similar Figures (pp. 262–327)

1. **BASKETBALL** The league statistics for a school basketball league are shown in the table below. Copy and complete the table. Express the ratios as fractions in simplest form. (Lesson 6-1) **See Student Handbook Answer Appendix.**

Team	Games	Win	Loss	W/L Ratio
Cougars	35	23	12	■
Bulldogs	36	30	6	■
Bears	33	22	11	■
Hawks	34	20	14	■
Sharks	36	26	10	■

2. **PET FOOD** Two stores have Munchies Dog Food on sale this week. Pets-a-lot sells a 17.6-pound bag for \$11.99. Doggie Haven sells the 31.8-pound bag for \$21.99. Which store has the lower price per pound of dog food? (Lesson 6-2) **Pets-a-lot**

3. **SPACE SHUTTLE** At an altitude of about 250 miles, the Space Shuttle can travel at approximately 17,500 mph in an orbit around Earth. In orbit, how many feet per second does the Shuttle travel? Round to the nearest foot. (Lesson 6-3) **25,667 feet per second**

4. **OLYMPICS** In the 2004 Olympics in Athens, Greece, Stefano Baldini from Italy won the 26.2 mile marathon in approximately 2 hours and 11 minutes. (Lesson 6-3)
   a. What was his average speed in miles per hour? Round to the nearest tenth. **12 miles per hour**
   b. What was his average speed in kilometers per hour? Round to the nearest tenth. **19.3 kilometers per hour**

5. **PIZZA** Is the cost of the pizza proportional to the size of the pizzas? Explain your reasoning. (Lesson 6-4) **See Student Handbook Answer Appendix.**

Papino's Pizza

Diameter (inches)	6	10	12	15
Cost	\$5	\$9	\$11	\$15

6. **COOKING** A soup recipe uses $3\frac{1}{2}$ cups of water for 8 bowls of soup. Find the amount of water Jacinda needs if she wants to make 12 bowls of soup. (Lesson 6-5) **$5\frac{1}{4}$ cups**

7. **MONEY** Jeff is preparing for a trip to China. The current exchange rate is 60 Chinese yuan for \$8 US. (Lesson 6-5)
   a. How many Chinese yuan are in \$1 US? **7.5 yuan**
   b. If Jeff's hotel in China charges 482 yuan per night, how much would that be in US dollars? **\$64.27**

8. **MODELS** Tony is making a scale model of his house for his granddaughter's doll's house. The front porch on Tony's house is 25 feet long. The front porch on the doll's house is 20 inches long. What is the scale of the model? (Lesson 6-6) **1 in. = 1.25 ft**

9. **PHOTOGRAPHS** A computer program can dilate photos so they print smaller or larger than the original. (Lesson 6-8)
   a. What scale factor should Jamie use to dilate a 4 inch by 6 inch photo so it will print as a 5 inch by 7.5 inch photo? **$1\frac{1}{4}$**
   b. What scale factor should he use to make a 2 inch by 3 inch print? **$\frac{1}{2}$**

10. **SHADOWS** Georgio wants to know how tall the tree is that grows in his backyard. His brother Mario is 4 feet tall and casts a shadow that measures 1.5 feet long. At the same time, the tree casts a shadow 4.5 feet long. How tall is the tree? (Lesson 6-9) **12 ft**

4 ft
1.5 ft
x ft
4.5 ft

Chapter 7 Percent (pp. 328–391)

1. **ALPHABET** The Hawaiian alphabet uses only 12 letters: A, E, H, I, K, L, M, N, O, P, U and W. What percentage of the English alphabet does the native Hawaiian alphabet use? Round to the nearest tenth of a percent. (Lesson 7-1) **46.2%**

2. **JOBS** A recent survey of students with part-time jobs showed that 33% worked in a grocery store, $\frac{7}{20}$ worked in fast food, and 0.27 worked in childcare. Which of these jobs has the largest percentage of student workers? (Lesson 7-2) **Fast food**

3. **EYES** The table below shows the eye colors of the students in Mr. Lehman's class. Use the percent proportion to find the percent of students with blue eyes. (Lesson 7-3) **37.5%**

Eye Color	Number of Students
blue	9
brown	5
green	6
hazel	4

4. **GRATUITY** The bill for the Morgan family at a restaurant was \$62.14. Mr. Morgan would like to leave their server a 20% tip. About how much of a tip will the server receive? (Lesson 7-4) **\$12.40**

5. **RECYCLING** In a community of 3200 homes, 72% of the households participate in the community recycling program. How many households is this? (Lesson 7-5) **2,304 households**

6. **ADS** An ad for a portable DVD player was listed in this week's newspaper.

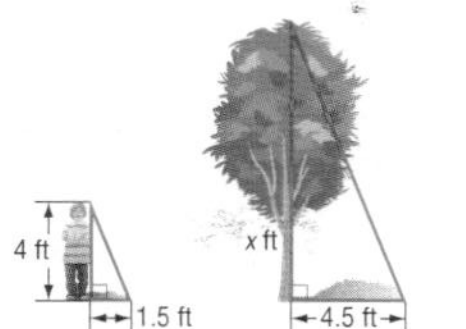

SPECIAL OFFER!
Portable DVD Player
Only \$99.99
*After \$20 in-store saving and \$20 mail-in rebate.

What percent will a shopper save by buying during this sale? (Lesson 7-6) **28.6%**

7. **HOMES** The figures for home sales for 2010 and 2011 in Shore County are shown. (Lesson 7-6)

Shore County Home Sales

Year	Number of Homes Sold	Average Selling Price
2010	18,328	\$220,988
2011	19,226	\$219,748

   a. Find the percent of change in the homes sold. Round to the nearest tenth. **4.9%; increase**
   b. Find the percent of change in the average selling price. Round to the nearest tenth. **0.6%; decrease**

8. **SAVINGS** Kira's parents started a college fund by depositing \$5500 in a savings account at an interest rate of 5.75% for 3 years. Find the simple interest. (Lesson 7-7) **\$948.75**

9. **MOVIES** Jacob surveyed his classmates to learn their favorite types of movies. Construct a circle graph of the data. (Lesson 7-8) **See Student Handbook Answer Appendix.**

Type of Movie	Number of Students
animated	3
comedy	10
drama	7
horror	4
romance	4

10. **PODCASTS** The circle graph shows the results of a survey about the ages of people who listen to podcasts. Suppose 1500 people were surveyed. How many more people aged 18–34 listen to podcasts than people aged 45 or older? (Lesson 7-8) **105 people**

Podcast Users

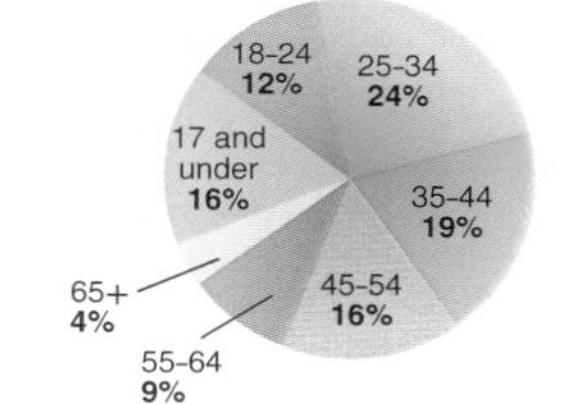

Source: Edison Media Research

Chapter 8 Linear Functions and Graphing (pp. 392–467)

1. **EXERCISE** Maria ran 17 miles at an average speed of 5 miles per hour. (Lesson 8-1)
   a. Use function notation to write an equation that gives the total distance she ran as a function of the total time. **$f(x) = 5x$**
   b. Use the function to find the total time she ran. **3.4 h**

2. **SALARY** Julio makes $215 per week at a shoe store plus an additional $5 for every pair of shoes he sells. (Lesson 8-2)
   a. Write an equation that describes the relationship between Julio's total earnings e and the number of pairs of shoes he sells s. **$e = 215 + 5s$**
   b. Determine how much money he would make if he sells 24 pairs of shoes. **$335**

3. **MOVIES** Lucia and her friends are going to Mario's Movies to rent m movies and buy b boxes of popcorn. Find three solutions of $5m + 1.25b = 20$. Explain each solution. (Lesson 8-3) **See Student Handbook Answer Appendix.**

4. **AIRPLANES** The table below shows the altitude of an airplane during take off. Find the rate of change. Round to the nearest hundredth. (Lesson 8-4)
3.77 ft/sec or increase of 3.77 ft/sec

Airplane Flight

Time (seconds)	Altitude (feet)
0	0
30	113
60	226

5. **WATER** The amount of water used in a community varies directly with the population. About 18 million people living in Florida use 2.4 trillion gallons of water a year. (Lesson 8-5)
   a. Write a direct variation equation relating the population p and the amount of water used w. **$w = 133{,}333p$**
   b. Estimate the amount of water that will be needed for 24 million people. **Sample answer: 3.2 trillion gal**

6. **CONSTRUCTION** A roofing contractor needed to find the slope of the roof on a house. The roof rises 24 inches for every horizontal change of 20 inches. Find the slope of the roof. (Lesson 8-6) $\frac{6}{5}$

7. **FITNESS** A gym charges a $59 initiation fee plus $7.70 per week that a person attends. The total cost y can be given by $y = 7.7x + 59$ for x weeks. (Lesson 8-7)
   a. Graph the equation using the slope and y-intercept.
   b. State the slope and y-intercept of the graph of the equation.
   c. Describe what the slope and y-intercept represent.
   See Student Handbook Answer Appendix.

8. **SCUBA DIVING** At a depth of 30 meters, a scuba diver noted the pressure was 58.8 pounds per square inch (psi). At a depth of 70 meters, the pressure was 117.6 psi. (Lesson 8-8)
   a. Write an equation in slope-intercept form to represent the data. **$y = 1.47x + 14.7$**
   b. Describe what the slope means. **the amount the pressure increases per meter**
   c. Find the diver's depth if the pressure is 107.3 psi. **63 m**

9. **CONCERTS** The table below shows attendance at an annual Fourth of July concert. (Lesson 8-9)
   a. Make a scatter plot and draw a line of fit.
   b. Use the equation for the line of fit to predict the number of attendees in 2010.

Year	2002	2003	2004	2005	2006
Attendees	850	925	1000	1200	1350

See Student Handbook Answer Appendix.

10. **SHOPPING** Elena spent $15 for 3 magazines and 2 puzzle books. At the same store, Christopher spent $16 for 2 magazines and 4 puzzle books. (Lesson 8-10)
   a. Write a system of equations to represent this situation. **$15 = 3m + 2p$ and $16 = 2m + 4p$**
   b. Solve the system of equations. Explain what the solution means. **Each magazine cost $3.50 and each puzzle book cost $2.25.**

Chapter 9 Powers and Nonlinear Functions (pp. 468–531)

1. **BUSINESS** A popular beverage company has about $(2^3)(3)(5^4)$ locations worldwide. How many locations do they have? (Lesson 9-1) **15,000 locations**

2. **DISTANCE** The state of Hawaii is located approximately 2,400 miles from the California coast and 3,850 miles from Japan. Write the prime factorization of each distance. (Lesson 9-2) **$2^5 \cdot 3 \cdot 5^2$; $2 \cdot 5^2 \cdot 7 \cdot 11$**

3. **TRAVEL** The table compares the number of people who drove to work versus the number of people who walked to work in Wyoming in a recent year. How many times more people drove than walked to work? (Lesson 9-3) **10^2 or 100 times**

Mode of Transportation	Number of People
Drove	10^5
Walked	10^3

4. **DIME** A dime has a thickness of approximately 0.001 meter. Write this decimal as a fraction and as a power of ten. (Lesson 9-4) **$\frac{1}{1000}$; 10^{-3}**

5. **PHYSICS** The length of an infrared light wave is approximately 0.0000037 meter. Write this number in scientific notation. (Lesson 9-5) **3.7×10^{-6} m**

6. **PLANETS** The table shows the mass of the planets. Arrange the planets in order from least to greatest. (Lesson 9-5)
See Student Handbook Answer Appendix.

Mass of the Planets

Planet	Mass (kg)
Mercury	3.303×10^{23}
Venus	4.869×10^{24}
Earth	5.976×10^{24}
Mars	6.421×10^{23}
Jupiter	1.900×10^{27}
Saturn	5.688×10^{26}
Uranus	8.686×10^{25}
Neptune	1.024×10^{26}

7. **HAIR** The average width of a human hair is 4×10^{-3} centimeter. If the cross section of the average hair is round, use the formula $A = 3.14 \cdot r^2$ to find the area of the cross section of a hair. Write your answer in scientific notation. (Lesson 9-6) **1.26×10^{-5} cm²**

8. **SAVINGS** Contessa makes monthly deposits in her savings account. A record of her deposits is shown below. Do these data represent a *linear* or *nonlinear* function? Explain. (Lesson 9-7) **linear; Sample answer: The change in the deposit amount each month is constant.**

Month	Deposit
January	30
February	35
March	40
April	45
May	50

9. **FLOWER BED** Teresa is planning to make a rectangular flower garden. She wants the length of the garden to be 1.5 times the width. (Lesson 9-8)

x ft
1.5x ft

   a. Write and graph a function that gives the area of the garden for different widths and lengths. **See Student Handbook Answer Appendix.**
   b. What is the area of the garden if it is 6 feet wide? **54 ft²**

10. **MAIL** Monique sent a chain letter to three of her friends. Each of her three friends sends the letter to three of their friends. Each of those friends sends it to three friends, and so on. The function $N = 3^x$ represents the total number of letters sent, where x is the stage of letters. (Lesson 9-9)
   a. Make a table showing the number of people that will have received the letter after 1, 2, 3, and 4 stages.
   b. Graph the function. **a–b. See Student Handbook Answer Appendix.**
   c. After how many stages will 243 people receive the letter? **5 stages**

Chapter 10 Real Numbers and Right Triangles (pp. 532–585)

1. **HORIZON** The formula $d = \sqrt{\frac{h}{0.57}}$ where h represents the number of feet above sea level can be used to find the distance d in miles to the horizon. Ella, standing on a deck of a cruise ship, is approximately 80 feet above sea level. Estimate how far out to the horizon she can see. (Lesson 10-1) **11.8 m**

2. **BELL TOWER** The Bell Tower in the Piazza San Marco in Venice, Italy is 99 meters tall. If a person drops a coin from the top of the tower, how many seconds would it take the coin to reach the ground? Use the formula $t = \sqrt{\frac{d}{4.9}}$ where t is the time in seconds and d is the distance in meters. Round your answer to the nearest tenth. (Lesson 10-1) **4.5 s**

3. **EARTH** If you could cut Earth into two pieces at the equator, the area of a cross section of Earth would be approximately 127,796,483 square kilometers. Use the formula $A = \pi r^2$ to find the radius of Earth. (Lesson 10-2) **6378 km**

4. **TRAVEL** The table shows the distance between Cincinnati, Ohio, and two other cities. Suppose a triangle was formed by drawing a line between each pair of cities. Classify the triangle by its sides. (Lesson 10-3) **isosceles**

Distance from Cincinnati

City	Distance (mi)
Minneapolis	692
Omaha	692

5. **POOL TABLE** The playing surface on a regulation 8-foot billiards table measures 88 inches by 44 inches. How far would a ball travel from one corner to the opposite corner? (Lesson 10-4) **98.4 in.**

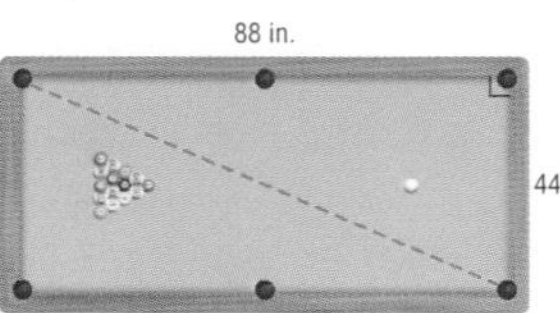

6. **TELEVISION** Katy learned that the 21-inch dimension on a television is the approximate diagonal of the screen. About how tall would the screen on a 21-inch television be if the screen is 16.5 inches wide? Round your answer to the nearest tenth. (Lesson 10-4) **13 in.**

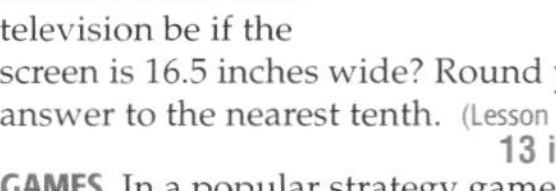
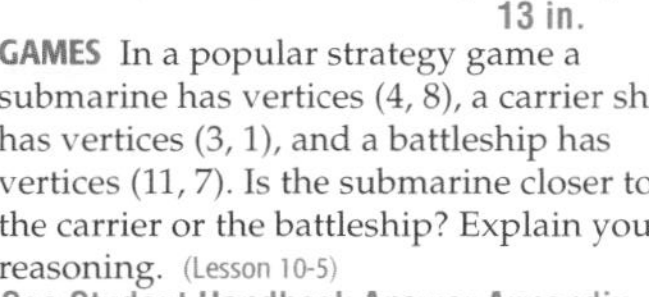

7. **GAMES** In a popular strategy game a submarine has vertices (4, 8), a carrier ship has vertices (3, 1), and a battleship has vertices (11, 7). Is the submarine closer to the carrier or the battleship? Explain your reasoning. (Lesson 10-5) **See Student Handbook Answer Appendix.**

8. **DISTANCE** Trey's home is at (4, 9) on the map. His friend Nicolas' home is at (6, 3) on the same map. If each unit on the map is 1 mile, how far do the two friends live from each other? Round to the nearest tenth. (Lesson 10-5) **6.3 mi**

9. **CONSTRUCTION** The diagram below shows the basic outline of the trusses that support a roof. The two sides of a truss meet in a 90° angle. How long will the base of the truss need to be if each of the sides measure 18 feet? Round your answer to the nearest tenth of a foot. (Lesson 10-6) **25.5 feet**

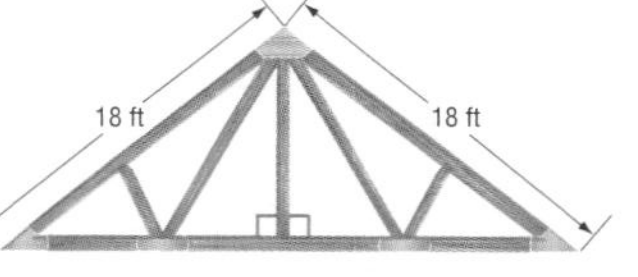

10. **UTILITIES** A telephone pole is braced by a cable attached at the top and anchored in the ground. If the angle between the cable and the ground is 60°, find the length of the cable to the nearest tenth. (Lesson 10-6) **86.6 feet**

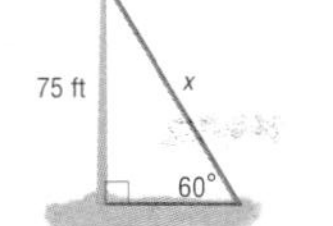

Chapter 11 Distance and Angles (pp. 586–659)

1. **FLOORING** A decorative floor has the tiling pattern shown below.

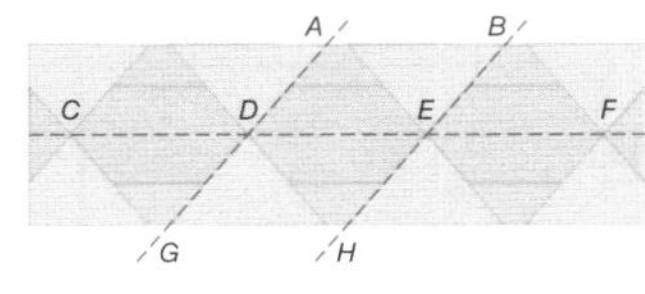

The horizontal lines are all parallel. Lines AG and BH are parallel and are transversals of the horizontal lines. If the measure of $\angle GDE = 130°$, find the measures of $\angle ADE$, $\angle ADC$, $\angle DAB$, $\angle ABE$, $\angle BEF$, and $\angle BED$. (Lesson 11-1) **See Student Handbook Answer Appendix.**

2. **GEOMETRY** Triangle PQR is congruent to triangle MLK. In the figures, $m\angle P = 32°$ and $m\angle K = 56°$. What are the measures of the other angles? (Lesson 11-2) **$m\angle L = 92°$; $m\angle R = 56°$; $m\angle Q = 92°$; $m\angle M = 32°$**

3. **QUILTS** Determine whether the quilt pattern shown has rotational symmetry. If so, describe the angle of rotation. (Lesson 11-3) **yes; 90°**

4. **ALGEBRA** What is the measure of $\angle A$ in quadrilateral $ABCD$ if $m\angle B = 68°$, $m\angle C = 136°$, and $\angle D$ is a right angle? (Lesson 11-4) **66°**

5. **WINDOWS** Jamie is making a stained glass window from a tessellation of 12 isosceles triangles. What is the measure of $\angle x$ and $\angle y$? (Lesson 11-5) **75°; 30°**

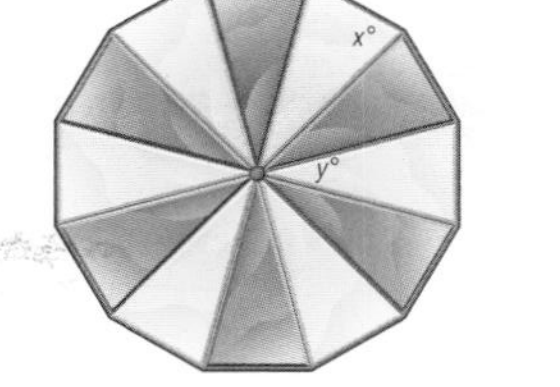

6. **SAILS** Mr. Johnson wants to replace the sail on his sailboat. What is the area of the sail shown below? (Lesson 11-6) **301.04 ft²**

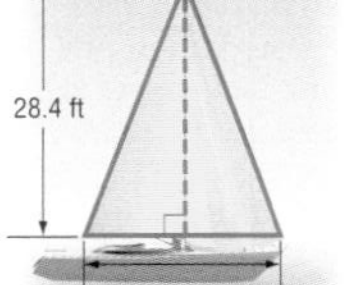

7. **FOUNTAINS** A landscape architect is designing a circular fountain to be placed in front of an office building. The fountain will have a decorative stone path around the outside of the fountain as shown.

   a. What is the circumference of the space occupied by the fountain and the path to the nearest tenth? (Lesson 11-7) **75.4 ft**

   b. How many square feet of space are needed to build the fountain and the path? Round to the nearest tenth. (Lesson 11-8) **452.4 ft²**

   c. If the stone for the path costs $1.75 per square foot, what is the total cost of stone for the walkway? (Lesson 11-9) **$439.78**

8. **FLOORING** Nigel wants to buy new outdoor carpeting for his wrap-around porch. A model of his porch is shown. (Lesson 11-9)

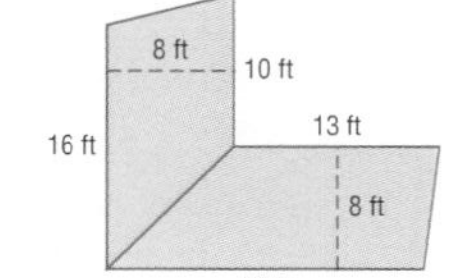

   a. Find the area of the porch. **236 ft²**

   b. If the carpet costs $1.25 per square foot, how much will it cost to carpet the entire porch? **$295**

Chapter 12 Surface Area and Volume (pp. 660–725)

1. **CAMPING** Jack uses the tent shown when he goes camping.

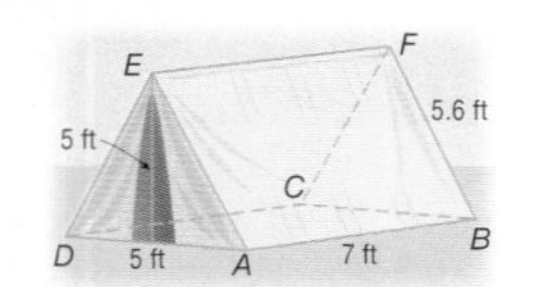

a. See Student Handbook Answer Appendix.

   a. Identify the solid. Then name the bases, faces, edges, and vertices. (Lesson 12-1)
   b. Find the volume of the tent. (Lesson 12-2) 87.5 ft³
   c. How much fabric was needed to make the tent? (Lesson 12-5) 138.4 ft²

2. **GARDENING** Alexa wants to buy a greenhouse like the one shown below for her backyard. What is the volume of the greenhouse to the nearest foot? (Lesson 12-2) 1634 ft³

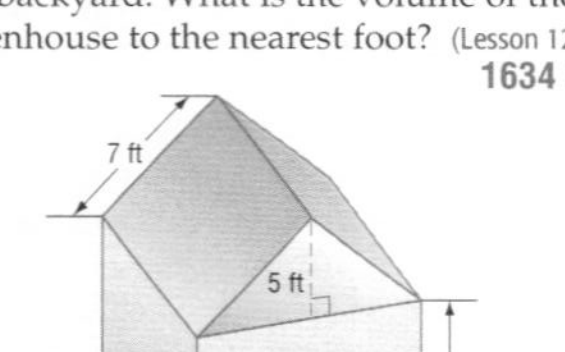

3. **AVIARY** The bird aviary shown is shaped like a cylinder with a flat top.
   a. What is the volume of the aviary to the nearest tenth of a foot? (Lesson 12-3) 226.2 ft³
   b. What is the surface area of the aviary to the nearest tenth of a foot? (Lesson 12-6) 207.3 ft²

8 ft

3 ft

4. **BALLOONS** A giant inflatable balloon used for a parade is spherical in shape. If the balloon has a diameter of 45 feet, how many cubic feet of helium are needed to fill the balloon? Round to the nearest tenth. (Lesson 12-4) 47,712.9 ft³

5. **ART** George is making a model of the Great Pyramid of Giza for a social studies project. The model has a square base with sides that measure 10 inches and a height of 6 inches.
   a. What is the volume of the model? (Lesson 12-4) 200 in³
   b. Suppose George wants to paint the sides of the pyramid. If the slant height of the pyramid is 7.8 inches, what is the total area of the sides of the pyramid? (Lesson 12-7) 156 in²

6. **SNOW SALT** The cone-shaped pile of snow salt shown has a base with a diameter of 12 meters and a height of 8 meters.

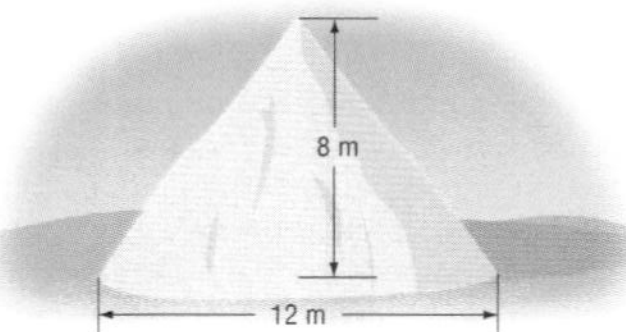

   a. How many cubic meters of snow salt are in the pile? Round to the nearest tenth. (Lesson 12-4) 301.6 m³
   b. The pile of salt is covered with a tarp when the salt is not being used. What is the area of the smallest possible tarp needed to cover the entire pile of salt? Round to the nearest tenth. (Lesson 12-7) 188.5 m²

7. **MODELS** Mr. Walker is renovating an old farmhouse. He wants to build a model of the farmhouse to use for his planning process. The main part of the original farm house is 25 feet wide, 30 feet deep and 20 feet tall. The model of the farm house will be 2 feet deep. (Lesson 12-8)
   a. What is the scale factor between the model and the actual house? $\frac{1}{15}$
   b. Find the width of the model. $1\frac{2}{3}$ ft
   c. Find the height of the model. $1\frac{1}{3}$ ft
   d. Find the volume of the house. 15,000 ft³
   e. Find the volume of the model. $4\frac{4}{9}$ ft³

Chapter 13 Statistics and Probability (pp. 726–807)

1. **TESTS** Mrs. Thomas teaches two Pre-Algebra classes. The scores for the two classes are shown below.
a–b. See Student Handbook Answer Appendix.

First Period									
92	98	96	84	90	82	64	76	70	80
72	90	90	98	74	72	86	88	90	82
Second Period									
90	98	76	74	92	80	82	84	92	74
70	60	80	92	94	78	80	90	78	82

   a. Find the mean, median and mode for each class. (Lesson 13-1)
   b. Make a back-to-back stem-and-leaf plot for the data. (Lesson 13-2)
   c. Find the measures of variation for the two classes. (Lesson 13-3) First Period: range, 34; median, 85; UQ, 90; LQ, 75. Second Period: range, 38; median 81; UQ, 91; LQ, 77

2. **OLYMPICS** The table below shows the number of gold and silver medals won by athletes in past summer Olympic games. (Lesson 13-4)
a. See Student Handbook Answer Appendix.

United States Summer Olympic Medals								
Gold	35	40	44	37	36	83	34	33
Silver	39	24	32	34	31	61	35	31

   a. Draw box-and-whisker plots for the gold and silver medals.
   b. Which set of data has the greatest range? b. gold medals, 50
   c. In what percent of the years did the U.S. earn more than 40 gold medals? 25%

3. **SUMMER WAGES** The table below shows the results of a survey about wages earned by students during the summer. (Lesson 13-5)
3a. See Student Handbook Answer Appendix.

Hourly Rate ($)	Number of Students
6–7.99	6
8–9.99	29
10–11.99	23
12–13.99	12
14–15.99	10

   a. Construct a histogram of the data.
   b. About what percent of the students made $10 or more per hour? 56.25%
   c. Which hourly rate accounts for about 15% of the data? 12–13.99

4. **SOCKS** Of the 28 socks in Becca's sock drawer, 8 are black, 6 are brown, 4 are gray, and the rest are white. What is the probability she will pull a white sock out of the drawer without looking? Write in simplest form. (Lesson 13-6) $\frac{5}{14}$

5. **PIZZA** The Walnut Springs Middle School cafeteria staff wants to know which types of pizza to serve. They survey every 5th student in the cafeteria line about their pizza preference. Is this sample biased or unbiased? Then describe the sample's type. (Lesson 13-7) Unbiased; systematic random sample

6. **TRAVEL** You want to go on a summer vacation. A travel agency offers a vacation package allows you to choose one hotel, one car, and two activities from the list below. How many ways can you plan your vacation? (Lesson 13-8) 36

Hotels	Cars	Activities
Sandy Beach	SUV	Parasailing
Ocean Waves	Convertible	Fishing
The Dunes		Surfboarding
		Snorkeling

7. **BASKETBALL** Coach Camaruca has 14 players on her junior varsity basketball team. She wants to try different groups of players to see how they work together. In how many ways can she pick her team of 5? (Lesson 13-9) 2002

8. **ALPHABET** The Hawaiian alphabet consists of 12 letters: A, E, H, I, K, L, M, N, O, P, U, and W. Each letter is written on a block and placed in a bag. A block is randomly chosen from the bag and not replaced. Find the probability of each outcome. Write in simplest form. (Lesson 13-10)
   a. P(vowel) $\frac{5}{12}$
   b. P(vowel or L) $\frac{1}{2}$
   c. three vowels in a row $\frac{1}{22}$
   d. three consonants in a row $\frac{7}{44}$
   e. one consonant followed by two vowels $\frac{7}{66}$

Lesson 1

1 FOCUS

Vertical Alignment

Lesson 1
Find the factors of a number.

After Lesson 1
Find the prime factorization of numbers. Find the greatest common factor (GCF) of two or more numbers.

2 TEACH

Example 1 shows how to determine whether numbers are divisible by 2, 3, 5, 6, or 10. **Example 2** shows how to find the factors of a number.

Additional Example

1 Determine whether each number is divisible by 2, 3, 5, 6, or 10.

a. 140 2, 5, 10

b. 2790 2, 3, 5, 6, 10

Concepts and Skills Bank

1 Factors

Two or more numbers that are multiplied to form a product are called **factors.**

$4 \times 9 = 36$ ← product
factors (4 and 9)

So, 4 and 9 are factors of 36 because they each divide 36 with a remainder of 0. We can say that 36 is **divisible** by 4 and 9. However, 5 is not a factor of 36 because $36 \div 5 = 7$ with a remainder of 1.

Sometimes you can test for divisibility mentally. The following rules can help you determine whether a number is divisible by 2, 3, 5, 6, or 10.

Divisibility Rules

A number is divisible by...	Examples	Reasons
2 if the ones digit is divisible by 2.	54	4 is divisible by 2.
3 if the sum of its digits is divisible by 3.	72	$7 + 2 = 9$, and 9 is divisible by 3.
5 if the ones digit is 0 or 5.	65	The ones digit is 5.
6 if the number is divisible by 2 and 3.	48	48 is divisible by 2 and 3.
10 if the ones digit is 0.	120	The ones digit is 0.

EXAMPLE 1

Determine whether each number is divisible by 2, 3, 5, 6, or 10.

a. 138

Number	Divisible?	Reason
2	yes	8 is divisible by 2.
3	yes	$1 + 3 + 8 = 12$, and 12 is divisible by 3.
5	no	The ones digit is 8, not 0 or 5.
6	yes	138 is divisible by 2 and 3.
10	no	The ones digit is not 0.

So, 138 is divisible by 2, 3, and 6.

b. 3050

Number	Divisible?	Reason
2	yes	0 is divisible by 2.
3	no	$3 + 0 + 5 + 0 = 8$, and 8 is not divisible by 3.
5	yes	The ones digit is 0.
6	no	3050 is divisible by 2, but not 3.
10	yes	The ones digit is 0.

So, 3050 is divisible by 2, 5, and 10.

You can also use the rules for divisibility to find the factors of a number.

Concepts and Skills Bank

EXAMPLE 2

List all the factors of 72.

Use the divisibility rules to determine whether 72 is divisible by 2, 3, 5, and so on. Then use division to find other factors of 72.

Number	72 Divisible by Number?	Factor Pairs
1	yes	1 • 72
2	yes	2 • 36
3	yes	3 • 24
4	yes	4 • 18
5	no	
6	yes	6 • 12
7	no	
8	yes	8 • 9
9	yes	9 • 8

Use division to find the other factor in each factor pair. $72 \div 2 = 36$

You can stop finding factors when the numbers start repeating.

So, the factors of 72 are 1, 2, 3, 4, 6, 8, 9, 12, 18, 24, 36, and 72.

Exercises

Use divisibility rules to determine whether each number is divisible by 2, 3, 5, 6, or 10.

1. 39 3
2. 135 3, 5
3. 82 2
4. 120 2, 3, 5, 6, 10
5. 250 2, 5, 10
6. 118 2
7. 378 2, 3, 6
8. 955 5
9. 5010 2, 3, 5, 6, 10
10. 684 2, 3, 6
11. 10,523 none
12. 24,640 2, 5, 10

List all the factors of each number.

13. 75 1, 3, 5, 15, 25, 75
14. 114 1, 2, 3, 6, 19, 38, 57, 114
15. 57 1, 3, 19, 57
16. 65 1, 5, 13, 65
17. 90 1, 2, 3, 5, 6, 9, 10, 15, 18, 30, 45, 90
18. 124 1, 2, 4, 31, 62, 124
19. 102 1, 2, 3, 6, 17, 34, 51, 102
20. 135 1, 3, 5, 9, 15, 27, 45, 135

21. **MUSIC** The band has 72 students who will march during halftime of the football game. For one drill, they need to march in rows with the same number of students in each row.

a. Can the whole band be arranged in rows of 7? Explain. No. Sample answer: 7 is not a factor of 72.

b. How many different ways could students be arranged? Describe the arrangements. 12 different ways:

Rows	Students in Each Row
1	72
2	36
3	24
4	18
6	12
8	9
9	8
12	6
18	4
24	3
36	2
72	1

22. **CALENDARS** Years that are divisible by 4, called *leap years,* are 366 days long. Also, years ending in "00" that are divisible by 400 are leap years. Use the rule given below to determine whether 2000, 2004, 2015, 2018, 2022, and 2032 are leap years. 2000 yes; 2004, yes; 2015, no; 2018, no; 2022, no; and 2032, yes.

If the last two digits form a number that is divisible by 4, then the number is divisible by 4.

Additional Example

List all the factors of 84. 1, 2, 3, 4, 6, 7, 12, 14, 21, 28, 42, 84

Tips for New Teachers

Divisibility Rules Students may find it useful to know that a number is divisible by 9 if the sum of the digits of the number is divisible by 9. For example, the sum of the digits of 261 is 2 + 6 + 1 or 9, so 261 is divisible by 9.

3 ASSESS

Formative Assessment

Use Exercises 1–22 to assess whether students understand how to use divisibility rules and division to find the factors of a number.

Crystal Ball Ask students how they think today's lesson on factors will help them with the next lesson on the greatest common factor.

Lesson 2

1 FOCUS

Vertical Alignment

Lesson 2
Find the greatest common factor (GCF) of two or more numbers or two or more monomials.

After Lesson 2
Use the GCF to simplify algebraic fractions.

2 TEACH

Example 1 shows how to find the GCF of two numbers. **Example 2** shows how to use the GCF to solve a real-world problem. **Example 3** shows how to find the GCF of monomials.

Additional Examples

1. Find the GCF of 32 and 48. 16
2. **SUPPLIES** A middle school has 120 boxes of colored pencils and 168 boxes of markers to distribute to classrooms.
   a. What is the greatest number of classrooms that will get pencils and markers if each classroom gets the same number of boxes of each type of supply? 24
   b. How many boxes of colored pencils and boxes of markers will be distributed to each classroom? 5 boxes of colored pencils; 7 boxes of markers
3. Find the GCF of $18a^2b$ and $24ab^2$. $6ab$

Concepts and Skills Bank

2 Greatest Common Factor

Often, numbers have some of the same factors. The greatest number that is a factor of two or more numbers is called the **greatest common factor (GCF).**

EXAMPLE 1 Find the GCF

Find the GCF of 12 and 20.

Method 1 List the factors.

factors of 12: 1, 2, 3, (4), 6, 12

factors of 20: 1, 2, (4), 5, 10, 20

The common factors of 12 and 20: 1, 2, 4. The greatest one is 4.

Method 2 Use prime factorization.

$12 = (2) \cdot (2) \cdot 3$
$20 = (2) \cdot (2) \cdot 5$

The common prime factors of 12 and 20: 2, 2

The GCF is the product of the common prime factors.

$2 \cdot 2 = 4.$

The greatest common factor of 12 and 20 is 4.

EXAMPLE 2 Find the GCF

TRACK AND FIELD There are 208 boys and 240 girls participating in a field day competition.

a. What is the greatest number of teams that can be formed if each team has the same number of girls and each team has the same number of boys?

Find the GCF of 208 and 240.

$208 = (2) \cdot (2) \cdot (2) \cdot (2) \cdot 13$
$240 = (2) \cdot (2) \cdot (2) \cdot (2) \cdot 3 \cdot 5$

Write the prime factorization of each number. The common prime factors are 2, 2, 2, and 2.

The greatest common factor of 208 and 240 is $2 \cdot 2 \cdot 2 \cdot 2$ or 16. So, 16 teams can be formed.

b. How many boys and girls will be on each team?

$208 \div 16 = 13$ and $240 \div 16 = 15$

So, each team will have 13 boys and 15 girls

Factor Algebraic Expressions You can also find the GCF of two or more monomials by finding the product of their common prime factors.

EXAMPLE 3 Find the GCF of Monomials

Find the GCF of $16xy^2$ and $30xy$.

Completely factor each expression.

$16xy^2 = (2) \cdot 2 \cdot 2 \cdot 2 \cdot (x) \cdot (y) \cdot y$
$30xy = (2) \cdot 3 \cdot 5 \cdot (x) \cdot (y)$

Circle the common factors.

The GCF of $16xy^2$ and $30xy$ is $2 \cdot x \cdot y$

Exercises

Find the GCF of each set of numbers or monomials.

1. 6, 8 2	**2.** 12, 8 4	**3.** 3, 9 3
4. 24, 40 8	**5.** 21, 45 3	**6.** 16, 56 8
7. 28, 42 14	**8.** 21, 14 7	**9.** 20, 30 10
10. 12, 18 6	**11.** 42, 56 14	**12.** 30, 35 5
13. 9, 15, 24 3	**14.** 12, 24, 36 12	**15.** 6, 15, 24 3
16. 66, 90, 150 6	**17.** 20, 21, 25 1	**18.** 20, 28, 36 4
19. 18, $45mn$ 9	**20.** $24t^2$, 32 8	**21.** $12x$, $40x^2$ $4x$
22. $4st$, $10s$ $2s$	**23.** $5ab$, $6b^2$ b	**24.** $7x^2$, $15xy$ x
25. $14b$, $56b^2$ $14b$	**26.** $25k$, $35j$ 5	**27.** $21x^2y$, $63xy^2$ $21xy$

28. The Venn diagram shows the factors of $10x$ and $18x^2$. What is the greatest common factor of the two monomials? $2x$

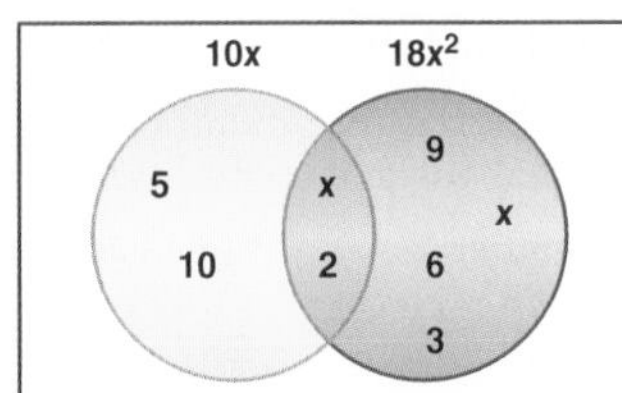

29. **FOOD** Marta is cutting a 16-inch and a 28-inch submarine sandwich for a party.

a. How long is the longest possible piece if she cuts them to be the same length? 4 in.

b. How many total pieces are there? 11

30. **DESIGN** Lauren is covering the surface of an end table with equal-sized ceramic tiles. The table is 30 inches long and 24 inches wide.

a. What is the largest square tile that Lauren can use and not have to cut any tiles? 6-in. squares

b. How many tiles will Lauren need? 20 tiles

31. **PARADES** In the parade, 36 members of the color guard are to march in front of 120 members of the high school marching band. Both groups are to have the same number of students in each row.

a. Find the greatest number of students that could be in each row. 12 students

b. How many rows will each group have? 3;10

32. **QUILTING** Suki is making a quilt from two different kinds of fabrics. One is 48 inches wide and the other is 54 inches wide. What are the dimensions of the largest squares she can cut from both fabrics so there is no wasted fabric? 6 in. by 6 in.

33. **CARPENTRY** Tamika is helping her father make shelves to store her sports equipment in the garage. How many shelves measuring 12 inches by 16 inches can be cut from a 48-inch by 72-inch piece of plywood so that there is no waste? 18 shelves

34. **DECORATIONS** Terrell is cutting paper streamers to decorate for a party. He has a blue roll of paper 144 inches long, a red roll 192 inches long, and a yellow roll 360 inches long.

a. If he wants to have all colors the same length, what is the longest length that he can cut? 24 in.

b. How many total streamers will he have? 29

Concepts and Skills Bank

Tips for New Teachers

GCF and Monomials Remind students that the GCF of two or more monomials includes only those factors that appear in all of the monomials. For example, in the monomials xy^2 and y, the GCF does not include the variable x because x does not appear in both. Point out that the GCF of the monomials is y and that y is the least power of y that appears in both expressions.

3 ASSESS

Formative Assessment

Use Exercises 1–34 to assess whether students understand how to find the GCF of numbers and monomials.

Name the Math Have students explain the procedure for finding the GCF of two or more numbers.

Concepts and Skills Bank

Lesson 3

1 FOCUS

Vertical Alignment

Lesson 3
Find the least common multiple (LCM) of two or more numbers or two or more monomials.

After Lesson 3
Use the LCM to find the least common denominator of unlike fractions and unlike algebraic fractions.

2 TEACH

Example 1 shows how to find the LCM of two numbers. **Example 2** shows how to use the LCM to solve a real-world problem. **Example 3** shows how to find the LCM of two monomials.

Additional Examples

1. Find the LCM of 25 and 30. 150
2. **NUTRITION** Anna orders vitamins every 8 weeks and protein powder every 12 weeks. If she places an order today for both vitamins and protein powder, in how many weeks will she again order them on the same day? 24 weeks

Concepts and Skills Bank

3 Least Common Multiple

A **multiple** of a number is a product of that number and a whole number. Sometimes numbers have some of the same multiples. These are called **common multiples.**

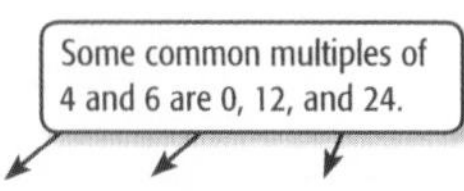

multiples of 4: 0, 4, 8, 12, 16, 20, 24, 28, . . .
multiples of 6: 0, 6, 12, 18, 24, 30, 36, 42, . . .

Some common multiples of 4 and 6 are 0, 12, and 24.

The least of the *nonzero* common multiples is called the **least common multiple (LCM).** So, the LCM of 4 and 6 is 12.

You can use prime factorization to find the least common multiple.

EXAMPLE 1 Find the LCM

Find the LCM of 108 and 240.

The LCM is the product of the prime factors, with each one raised to the *highest* power it occurs in *either* prime factorization.

Number	Prime Factorization	Exponential Form
108	$2 \cdot 2 \cdot 3 \cdot 3 \cdot 3$	$2^2 \cdot 3^3$
240	$2 \cdot 2 \cdot 2 \cdot 2 \cdot 3 \cdot 5$	$2^4 \cdot 3 \cdot 5$

The prime factors of both numbers are 2, 3, and 5. Multiply the greatest power of 2, 3, and 5 appearing in either factorization.

LCM = $2^4 \cdot 3^3 \cdot 5$ or 2160

So, the LCM of 108 and 240 is 2160.

EXAMPLE 2 Use the LCM to Solve Problems

ANIMALS The scales show the average weight of three different kinds of fish.

a. At what minimum weight will the scales show equal weights for each fish?

Find the LCM using prime factors.

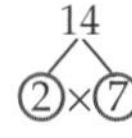

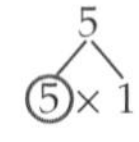

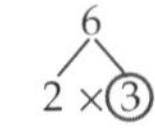

The scales will show the same weight at $2 \times 7 \times 5 \times 3$ or 210 pounds.

b. How many of each type of fish will show that weight?

You can find the number of fish by multiplying the prime factors that appear in the weight of the scale and *do not* appear in the weight of the fish.

Pink Salmon: 2×7 pounds — Scale: $2 \times 3 \times 5 \times 7$ pounds
You would need 3×5 or 15 pink salmon.

Bluegill: 1×5 pounds — Scale: $2 \times 3 \times 5 \times 7$ pounds
You would need $2 \times 3 \times 7$ or 42 bluegill.

Artic Grayling: 2×3 pounds — Scale: $2 \times 3 \times 5 \times 7$ pounds
You would need 5×7 or 35 Arctic grayling

The LCM of two or more monomials is found in the same way as the LCM of two or more numbers.

EXAMPLE 3 Find the LCM of Monomials

Find the LCM of $18xy^2$ and $10y$.

$18xy^2 = 2 \cdot 3^2 \cdot x \cdot y^2$

$10y = 2 \cdot 5 \cdot y$

$\text{LCM} = 2 \cdot 3^2 \cdot 5 \cdot x \cdot y^2$ **Multiply the greatest power of each prime factor.**

$= 90xy^2$

The LCM of $18xy^2$ and $10y$ is $90xy^2$.

Exercises

Find the least common multiple (LCM) of each pair of numbers or monomials.

1. 6, 8 24
2. 7, 9 63
3. 10, 14 70
4. $36ab$, $4b$ $36ab$
5. $5x^2$, $12y^2$ $60x^2y^2$
6. $14e^3$, $8e^2$ $56e^3$
7. 4, 10 20
8. 20, 12 60
9. 2, 9 18
10. 16, 3 48
11. 15, 75 75
12. 21, 28 84
13. 14, 28 28
14. 20, 50 100
15. 18, 32 288
16. 24, 32 96
17. $20c$, $12c$ $60c$
18. $16a^2$, $14ab$ $112a^2b$
19. $7x$, $12x$ $84x$
20. $75n^2$, $25n^4$ $75n^4$
21. $20ef$, $52f^3$ $260ef^3$
22. **AUTO RACING** One driver can circle a one-mile track in 30 seconds. Another driver takes 20 seconds. If they both start at the same time, in how many seconds will they be together again at the starting line? 60 s
23. **LIGHTS** Sahale decorated his house with two strands of holiday lights. The red lights strand blinks every 4 seconds, and the green lights strand blinks every 6 seconds. How many seconds will go by until both strands blink at the same time? 12 s
24. **TIME** If train A and train B both leave the station at 9:00 A.M., at what time will they next leave the station together? 9:24 A.M.

Train Schedule	
Train	**Departs**
A	every 8 minutes
B	every 6 minutes

25. **PRIZES** A radio station is giving away 2 concert tickets to every sixteenth caller and a dinner for two to every twentieth caller. Which caller will receive both the concert tickets and the dinner? 80th
26. **SCIENCE** The cycle for the appearance of cicadas and tent caterpillars is shown. Suppose the peak cycles of these two insects coincided in 1998. What will be the next year in which they will coincide? 2100

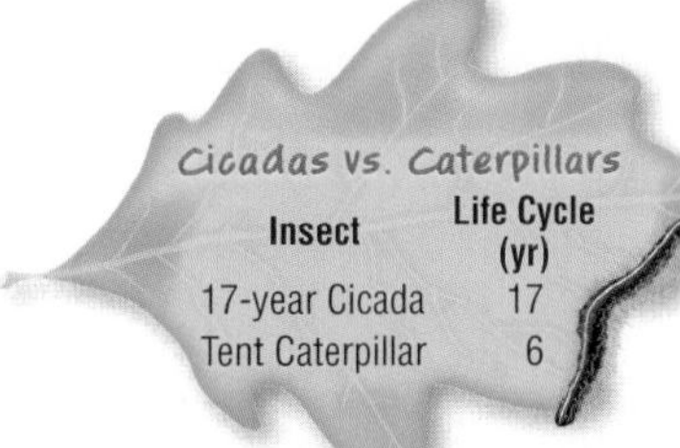

Cicadas vs. Caterpillars

Insect	Life Cycle (yr)
17-year Cicada	17
Tent Caterpillar	6

Additional Example

Find the LCM of $9m^2$ and $12mn$. $36m^2n$

Tips for New Teachers

Least Common Multiple When finding the LCM, students can first check whether the lesser number divides into the greater with no remainder. If yes, the greater number is the LCM. If no, students can list multiples or use prime factorization. Sometimes the LCM is the product of the numbers or monomials.

3 ASSESS

Formative Assessment

Use Exercises 1–26 to assess whether students understand how to find the LCM of numbers or monomials.

Ticket Out the Door Ask students to find the LCM of $4xy$ and $14y$. $28xy$

Lesson 4

1 FOCUS

Vertical Alignment

Lesson 4
Find and estimate cube roots.

After Lesson 4
Use cube roots to solve problems in geometry.

2 TEACH

Example 1 shows how use a calculator to find cube roots. **Example 2** shows how to estimate cube roots.

Additional Example

1 Use a calculator to find each cube root to the nearest tenth.

a. $\sqrt[3]{228}$ 6.1

b. $\sqrt[3]{-56}$ −3.8

4 Cube Roots

Numbers like 27, 125, and 1000 are perfect cubes because they are the cubes of integers.

$27 = 3 \times 3 \times 3$ or 3^3

$125 = 5 \times 5 \times 5$ or 5^3

$1000 = 10 \times 10 \times 10$ or 10^3

A **cube root** of a number is one of three equal factors of the number.

Key Concept Cube Roots — For Your FOLDABLE

Words A cube root of a number is one of its three equal factors.

Symbols If $x^3 = y$, then $x = \sqrt[3]{y}$.

Examples Since $2 \times 2 \times 2$ or $2^3 = 8$, 2 is a cube root of 8.
Since $-6 \times (-6) \times (-6) = -216$, −6 is a cube root of −216.

Recall that a negative number has no real-number square root because the square of a number cannot be negative. The multiplication problem $(-6) \times (-6) \times (-6) = (-216)$ suggests that $\sqrt[3]{-216} = -6$

Every integer has exactly one cube root.

- The cube root of a positive number is positive.
- The cube root of zero is zero.
- The cube root of a negative number is negative.

EXAMPLE 1

Use a calculator to find each cube root to the nearest tenth.

a. $\sqrt[3]{150}$

MATH 4 150 ENTER 5.313292846 — Use a calculator.

Round to the nearest tenth.

$\sqrt[3]{150} \approx 5.3$ — Check Since $5^3 = 125$, the answer is reasonable.

b. $\sqrt[3]{-32}$

MATH 4 (−)32 ENTER −3.174802104 — Use a calculator.

Round to the nearest tenth.

$\sqrt[3]{-32} \approx -3.2$ — Check Since $(-3)^3 = -27$, the answer is reasonable.

You can also estimate cube roots mentally by using perfect cubes. The first twelve perfect cubes are shown at the right.

$1 = 1^3$	$64 = 4^3$	$343 = 7^3$	$1000 = 10^3$
$8 = 2^3$	$125 = 5^3$	$512 = 8^3$	$1331 = 11^3$
$27 = 3^3$	$216 = 6^3$	$729 = 9^3$	$1728 = 12^3$

862 Concepts and Skills Bank

EXAMPLE 2

Estimate each cube root to the nearest tenth. Do not use a calculator.

a. $\sqrt[3]{83}$

The first perfect cube less than 83 is 64. $\sqrt[3]{\mathbf{64}} = \mathbf{4}$

The first perfect cube greater than 83 is 125. $\sqrt[3]{\mathbf{125}} = \mathbf{5}$

Approximate the placement of $\sqrt[3]{83}$ on a number relative to 4 and 5. Since 83 is closer to 64 than 125, $\sqrt[3]{83}$ will be closer to 4.

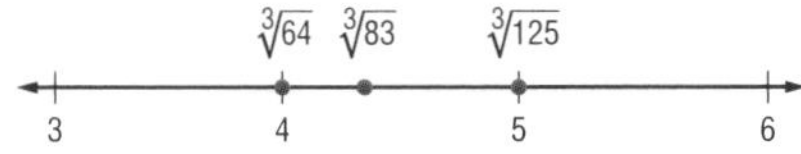

On the graph, it appears to be about 4.4. **Check** $4.4^3 = 4.4 \cdot 4.4 \cdot 4.4 = 85.184$

Since 83 is close to 85.184, the answer is reasonable.

b. $\sqrt[3]{-195}$

The first perfect cube less than −195 is −216. $\sqrt[3]{-216} = -6$

The first perfect cube greater than −195 is −125. $\sqrt[3]{-125} = -5$

Approximate the placement of $\sqrt[3]{-195}$ on a number relative to −6 and −5. Since −195 is closer to −216 than −125, $\sqrt[3]{-195}$ will be closer to −6.

∛−216 ∛−195 ∛−125
3 −6 −5 −4

On the graph, it appears to be about −5.8. **Check** $-5.8^3 = (-5.8) \cdot (-5.8) \cdot (-5.8) = -195.112$

Since −195 is close to −195.112, the answer is reasonable.

Exercises

Use a calculator to find each cube root to the nearest tenth.

1. $\sqrt[3]{20}$ 2.7 **2.** $\sqrt[3]{35}$ 3.3 **3.** $\sqrt[3]{-113}$ −4.8

4. $\sqrt[3]{-92}$ −4.5 **5.** $\sqrt[3]{563}$ 8.3 **6.** $\sqrt[3]{854}$ 9.5

7. $\sqrt[3]{1236}$ 10.7 **8.** $\sqrt[3]{2024}$ 12.6 **9.** $\sqrt[3]{4635}$ 16.7

Estimate each cube root to the nearest tenth. Do not use a calculator.

10. $\sqrt[3]{74}$ 4.2 **11.** $\sqrt[3]{39}$ 3.4 **12.** $\sqrt[3]{499}$ 7.9

13. $\sqrt[3]{576}$ 8.3 **14.** $\sqrt[3]{-636}$ −8.6 **15.** $\sqrt[3]{-879}$ −9.6

16. Express the length of one side of a cube whose volume is 350 cubic meters. Round to the nearest tenth. 7.0 m

Concepts and Skills Bank

Additional Example

2 Estimate each cube root to the nearest tenth. Do not use a calculator.

a. $\sqrt[3]{44}$ 3.5

b. $\sqrt[3]{-412}$ −7.4

Tips for New Teachers

Roots and Negative Numbers Some students may be confused because you can find the cube root of a negative number, but not the square root of a negative number. Remind students that you cannot multiply two negative numbers together and get a negative number, but you can multiply three numbers together and get a negative number. Explain that the same reasoning applies to any even or odd root, such as the fourth root or the fifth root.

3 ASSESS

Formative Assessment

Use Exercises 1–15 to assess whether students understand how to find and estimate cube roots.

Name the Math Ask students to describe the procedure for estimating cube roots.

Concepts and Skills Bank

Lesson 5

1 FOCUS

Vertical Alignment

Lesson 5
Use a graphing calculator to find a linear regression equation for a line of best-fit.

After Lesson 5
Use linear regression equations to find missing values.

2 TEACH

Activities 1 and **2** show how to find a linear regression equation for a line of best fit, and how to use the equation to make a prediction.

Additional Example

1 NEWSPAPERS The table shows the number of U. S. morning edition newspapers from 1995 to 2006. Find and graph a linear regression equation. Then predict the number of morning newspapers in 2015. Sample answer: $y = 15.22x - 29{,}685.01$; about 977

Year	Number
1995	656
1996	686
1997	705
1998	721
1999	736
2000	766
2001	776
2002	777
2003	787
2004	814
2005	817
2006	833

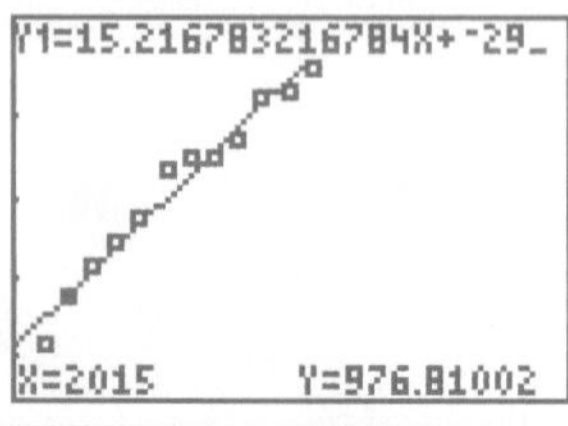

5 Linear Regression

Recall that a line of fit is a line that is very close to most of the data points in a scatter plot. A **linear regression equation** is an approximate equation describing a line of fit. You can use a graphing calculator to find a linear regression equation for a line of best-fit.

ACTIVITY 1

POSTAGE The table shows the cost to mail a first-class letter from 1978 to 2007. Find and graph a linear regression equation. Then predict the cost of a stamp in the year 2015.

Year	1978	1981	1985	1988	1991	1995	1999	2001	2002	2006	2007
Cost (¢)	15	20	22	25	29	32	33	34	37	39	41

Step 1 Find a regression equation.

- Clear any existing list.

  KEYSTROKES: STAT ENTER ▲ CLEAR ENTER

- Enter the years in L1 and the cost in L2. Find the regression equation.

  KEYSTROKES: STAT ENTER 1978 ENTER . . . 2007 ENTER ▶ 15 ENTER . . . 41 ENTER STAT ▶ 4 ENTER

The equation is about $y = 0.82x - 1613.91$.

Step 2 Graph the regression equation.

- Use STAT PLOT to graph the scatter plot.

  KEYSTROKES: 2nd [STAT PLOT] ENTER ENTER

- Copy the equation to the Y= list and graph.

  KEYSTROKES: Y= VARS 5 ▶ ▶ 1 GRAPH

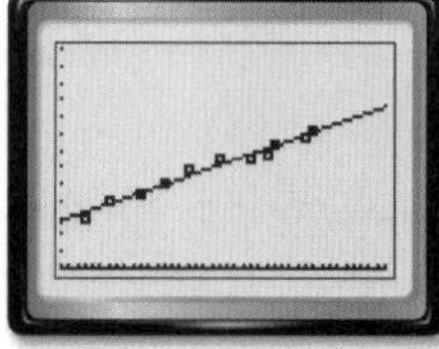

Step 3 Predict using the regression equation.

- Find y when $x = 2015$.

  KEYSTROKES: 2nd [CALC] 1 2015 ENTER

According to the regression equation, in 2015 a first-class stamp will cost about 47 cents.

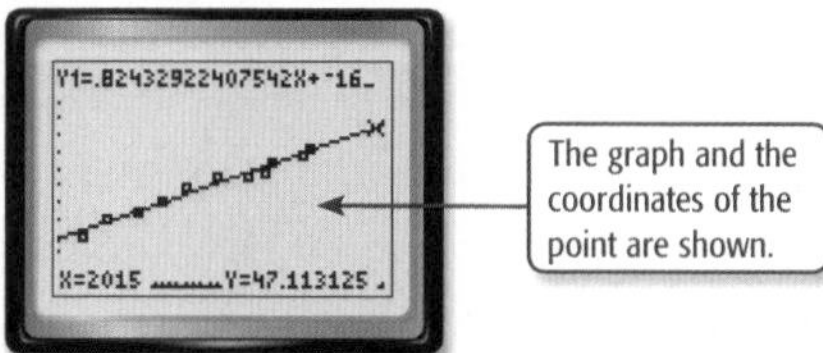

ACTIVITY 2

SWIMMING **The table shows the winning times for the women's 4 by 100-meter freestyle swimming relay in the summer Olympics from 1964–2004. Find and graph a linear regression equation. Then predict the winning time in the year 2016.**

Year	1964	1968	1972	1976	1980	1984	1988	1992	1996	2000	2004
Time (min)	4.06	4.04	3.92	3.75	3.71	3.72	3.68	3.66	3.35	3.6	3.6

Source: *ESPN Sport Almanac*

Step 1 **Find a regression equation.**

- Clear any existing list.

  KEYSTROKES: STAT ENTER ▲ CLEAR ENTER

- Enter the years in L1 and the times in L2. Find the regression equation.

  KEYSTROKES: STAT ENTER 1964 ENTER . . . 2004 ENTER ▶ 4.06 ENTER . . . 3.6 ENTER STAT ▶ 4 ENTER

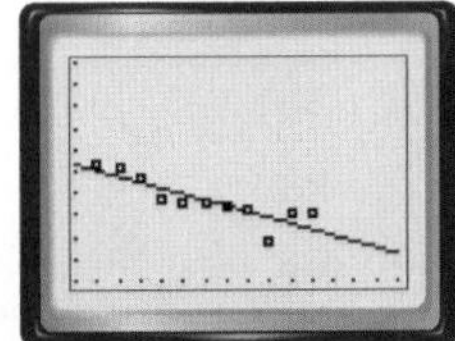

The equation is about $y = -0.01x + 30.70$.

Step 2 **Graph the regression equation.**

- Use STAT PLOT to graph the scatter plot.

  KEYSTROKES: 2nd [STAT PLOT] ENTER ENTER

- Copy the equation to the Y= list and graph.

  KEYSTROKES: Y= VARS 5 ▶ ▶ 1 GRAPH

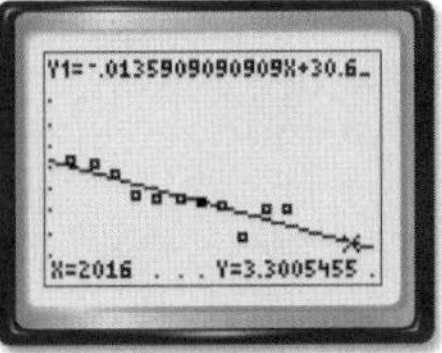

Step 3 **Predict using the regression equation.**

- Find y when $x = 2016$.

  KEYSTROKES: 2nd [CALC] 1 2016 ENTER

According to the regression equation, in 2016 the winning time for the 4 × 100 freestyle relay will be about 3.30 minutes.

Additional Example

2 **MOVIES** The table shows the average cost of movie tickets from 1996 to 2007. Find and graph a linear regression equation. Then predict the cost of a movie ticket in 2015. Sample answer: $y = 0.23x - 445.46$; \$8.69

Year	Number
1996	4.42
1997	4.59
1998	4.69
1999	5.08
2000	5.39
2001	5.66
2002	5.81
2003	6.03
2004	6.21
2005	6.41
2006	6.55
2007	6.88

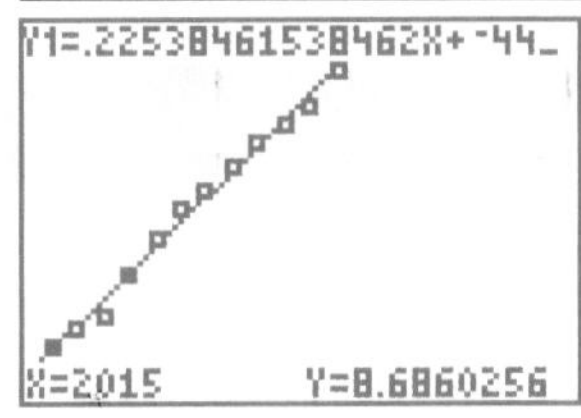

Exercises

1. **CELL PHONES** The table below shows the number of cellular phone users in the United States from 1985 to 2007. Find and graph a linear regression equation. In what year will the number of cell phone users reach 300 million? Sample answer: $y = 11.29x - 22{,}450.82$; 2016 See margin for graph.

Cell Phone Users in the United States (millions)												
Year	1985	1987	1989	1991	1993	1995	1997	1999	2001	2003	2005	2007
Users	0.3	1.2	3.5	7.6	16.0	33.8	55.3	86.0	128.4	158.7	207.9	243.4

Tips for New Teachers

Correlation Coefficient Explain to students that the calculator will show a correlation coefficient r. The closer r is to 1, the closer the fit between the equation and the data.

Additional Answer

1. 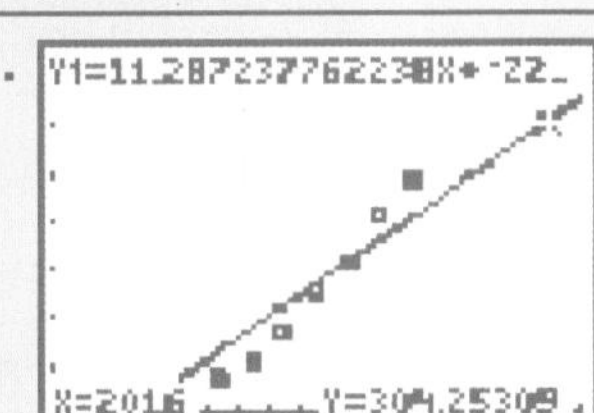

3 ASSESS

Formative Assessment

Use Exercise 1 to assess whether students understand how to find and graph a linear regression equation for a best-fit line and use it to make a prediction.

Yesterday's News Ask students to explain how previous lessons on finding a line of fit helped with understanding today's lesson on finding a linear regression equation for a line of best fit.

Lesson 6

1 FOCUS

Vertical Alignment

Lesson 6
Graph linear inequalities in two variables on a coordinate plane.

After Lesson 6
Graph linear inequalities on a coordinate plane to solve real-world problems

2 TEACH

Example 1 shows how to graph a linear inequality when the boundary is a solid line. **Example 2** shows how to graph a linear inequality when the boundary is a dashed line.

Additional Example

1 Graph $y \geq x + 5$.

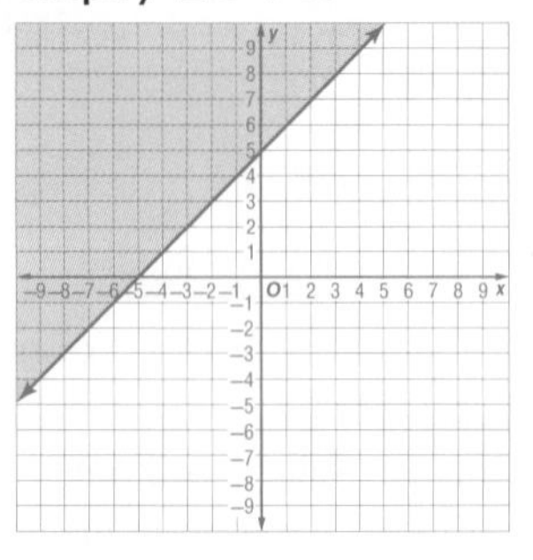

Concepts and Skills Bank

6 Graphing Linear Inequalities

Like a linear equation in two variables, the solution set of an inequality in two variables is graphed on a coordinate plane. The solution set for an inequality in two variables contains many ordered pairs when the domain and range are the set of real numbers. The graphs of all of these ordered pairs fill a region on the coordinate plane called a **half-plane**. An equation defines the **boundary** or edge for each half-plane.

Key Concept Half-Planes and Boundaries — For Your FOLDABLE

Words Any line in the plane divides the plane into two regions called half-planes. The line is called the boundary of each of the two half-planes.

Model

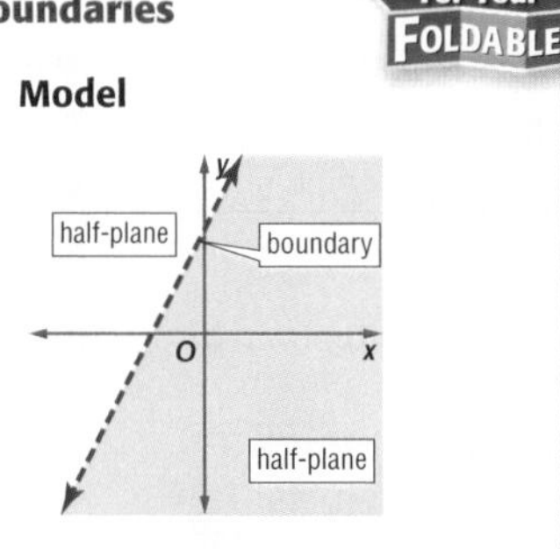

EXAMPLE 1

Graph $y \leq 2x - 1$.

Step 1 Graph $y = 2x - 1$. Since $y \leq 2x - 1$ means $y < 2x - 1$ or $y = 2x - 1$, the boundary is included in the solution set. The boundary should be drawn as a solid line.

Step 2 Select a point in one of the half-planes and test it. Let's use (0, 0).

$y \leq 2x - 1$	**Original inequality**
$0 \leq 2(0) - 1$	$x = 0, y = 0$
$0 \leq -1$	**false**

Since the statement is false, the half-plane containing the origin is *not* part of the solution. Shade the other half-plane.

Check Test a point in the other half-plane, such as (2, –2).

$y \leq 2x - 1$	**Original inequality**
$-2 \leq 2(2) - 1$	$x = 2, y = -2$
$-2 \leq 3$	**Simplify.** ✓

Since the statement is true, the half-plane containing (2, −2) should be shaded. The graph of the solution is correct.

In Example 1, the boundary was a solid line because $y < 2x - 1$ or $y = 2x - 1$. When the inequality symbol does not contain an "=", a dashed line on a coordinate plane indicates that the boundary is *not* part of the solution set.

EXAMPLE 2

Graph $y > \frac{1}{2}x + 2$.

Step 1 Graph $y = \frac{1}{2}x + 2$. Since $y > \frac{1}{2}x + 2$ does *not* contain an equality, the boundary is *not* included in the solution set.
The boundary should be drawn as a dashed line.

Step 2 Select a point in one of the half-planes and test it, such as (0, 0).

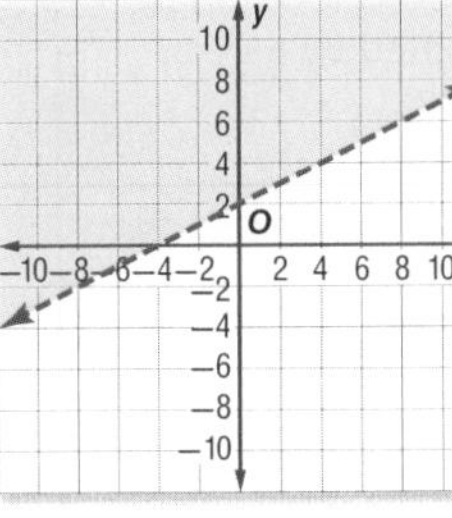

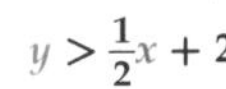

$y > \frac{1}{2}x + 2$	**Original inequality**
$0 > \frac{1}{2}(0) + 2$	**$x = 0, y = 0$**
$0 > 2$	**false**

Since the statement is false, the half-plane containing the origin is *not* part of the solution. Shade the other half-plane.

Check Test a point in the other half-plane, such as (–8, 1).

$y > \frac{1}{2}x + 2$	**Original inequality**
$1 > \frac{1}{2}(-8) + 2$	**$x = -8, y = 1$**
$1 > -2$	**Simplify.** ✓

Since the statement is true, the half-plane containing (–8, 1) should be shaded. The graph of the solution is correct.

Exercises

Graph each inequality on a coordinate plane. **1–10. See Student Handbook Answer Appendix.**

1. $y \leq x - 3$

2. $y \geq x - 1$

3. $y > \frac{1}{3}x$

4. $y < \frac{3}{4}x$

5. $y \geq -3x + 3$

6. $y \leq -x + 5$

7. $-4x + y < 6$

8. $4x + y \geq 5$

9. $2y \geq -9$

10. $-3y < -16$

Additional Example

2 Graph $y < 3x + 1$.

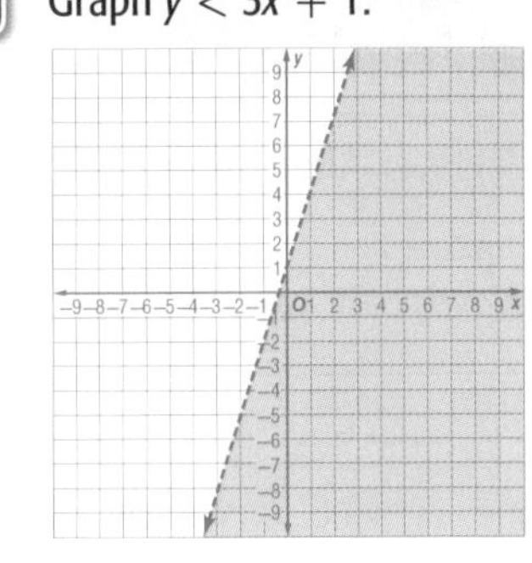

Tips for New Teachers

Graphing Linear Inequalities Students may need a quick review on graphing linear equations in slope-intercept form. Recall for them that the form is $y = mx + b$. Review that they graph the y-intercept point and then use the slope to find a second point. Next, they draw a line through the points and extend the line. Caution that they need to determine whether the line is solid or dashed. Have students write equations in slope-intercept form, if necessary.

3 ASSESS

Formative Assessment

Use Exercises 1–10 to assess whether students understand how to graph inequalities on the coordinate plane.

Name the Math Have students describe the procedure for graphing an inequality on a coordinate plane. Ask them to include the conditions that determine whether the boundary is a solid or dashed line.

Concepts and Skills Bank

Lesson 7

Vertical Alignment

Lesson 7
Identify basic geometric figures.

After Lesson 7
Solve problems involving lines, line segments, and angles.

Tips for New Teachers

Planes Explain to students that a plane can be named by three points on the plane, but the points cannot lie on the same line. Planes sometimes are named by a single, uppercase script letter. A plane has length and width, but no thickness.

7 Geometric Figures

The table below shows the basic geometric figures.

Key Concept Geometric Figures — For Your FOLDABLE

Definition	Model
A **point** is an exact location in space, represented by a dot.	A **Words** point *A*
A **line** is a set of points that form a straight path that goes in opposite directions without ending.	M N **Words** line *MN* or line *NM* **Symbols** $\overleftrightarrow{MN}$ or $\overleftrightarrow{NM}$, line ℓ
A **ray** is part of a line that has an endpoint and goes in one direction without ending.	Y Z **Words** ray *YZ* **Symbols** $\overrightarrow{YZ}$
A **line segment** is part of a line between two endpoints.	C D **Words** line segment *CD* or line segment *DC* **Symbols** $\overline{CD}$ or $\overline{DC}$
A **plane** is a flat surface that goes on forever in all directions.	D F E **Words** plane *DEF*, plane *FDE*, plane *EDF*, plane *DFE*, plane *FED*, plane *EFD*
An **angle** is formed by two rays with a common endpoint. The two rays that make up the angle are called the sides of the angle. The common endpoint is called the **vertex**.	R side S vertex side T **Words** angle *RST* or angle *TSR*, angle *S* **Symbols** $\angle RST$ or $\angle TSR$, $\angle S$

EXAMPLE Name Geometric Figures

Use the figure to name each of the following.

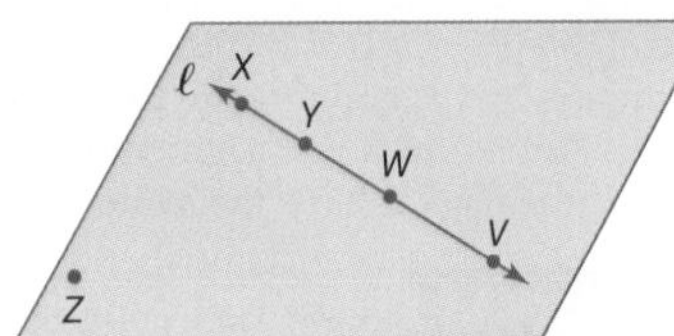

a. a line containing point *X*

There are four points on the line. Any two of the points can be used to name the line.

$\overleftrightarrow{XY}$ $\overleftrightarrow{YX}$ $\overleftrightarrow{XW}$ $\overleftrightarrow{WX}$ $\overleftrightarrow{XV}$ $\overleftrightarrow{VX}$
$\overleftrightarrow{YW}$ $\overleftrightarrow{WY}$ $\overleftrightarrow{YV}$ $\overleftrightarrow{VY}$ $\overleftrightarrow{WV}$ $\overleftrightarrow{VW}$

b. a line segment

There are 6 line segments: $\overline{XY}$, $\overline{XW}$, $\overline{XV}$, $\overline{YW}$, $\overline{YV}$, $\overline{WV}$

Exercises

For Exercises 1–5, refer to the figure at the right.

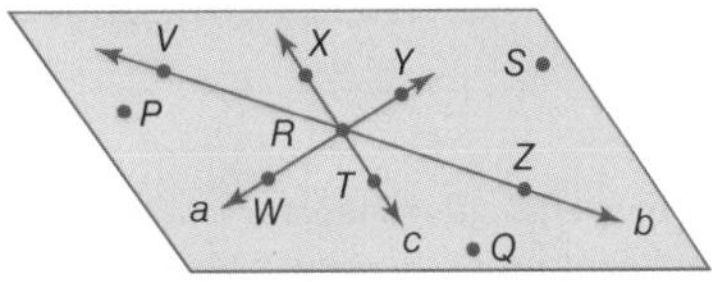

1. Name a line containing point *Z*. **Sample answer: line *b***
2. Identify two rays. **Sample answer: ray *WY* and ray *TX***
3. What is another name for ∠*YRV*? **∠*VRY***
4. Name the plane shown. **Sample answer: plane *PQS***
5. List 3 line segments. **Sample answer: $\overline{VZ}$, $\overline{WY}$, $\overline{XT}$**

For Exercises 6–10, refer to the figure at the right.

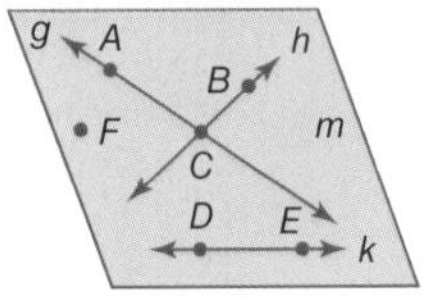

6. Name a line that contains point *B*. **Sample answer: $\overleftrightarrow{BC}$**
7. Identify two angles. **Sample answer: ∠*BCE* and ∠*BCA***
8. List 3 line segments. **Sample answer: $\overline{AC}$, $\overline{BC}$, $\overline{DE}$**
9. Name a point *not* contained in lines *g*, *h*, or *k*. **point *F***
10. What is another name for line *g*? **Sample answer: $\overleftrightarrow{AC}$**

Draw and label a figure for each of the following. **11–14. See Student Handbook Answer Appendix.**

11. point *G*
12. $\overline{XY}$
13. $\overrightarrow{XY}$ and $\overrightarrow{YZ}$
14. plane *ABC*

Name the geometric term(s) modeled by each object. **15–20. Sample answer given.**

15. 
angles

16. 
lines

17. 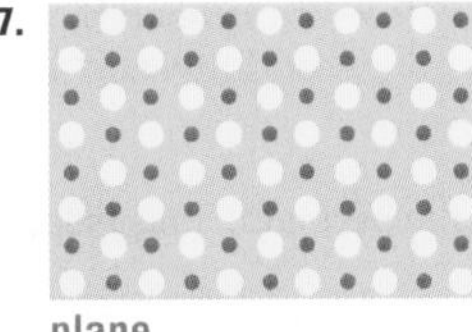
plane

18. a napkin **plane**
19. the end of a pencil **point**
20. woven threads in a blanket **lines**
21. Describe a real-life example of a plane containing points, lines, and angles. **See student's work.**

2 TEACH

Example 1 shows how to name geometric figures.

Additional Example

1 Use the figure to name each of the following.

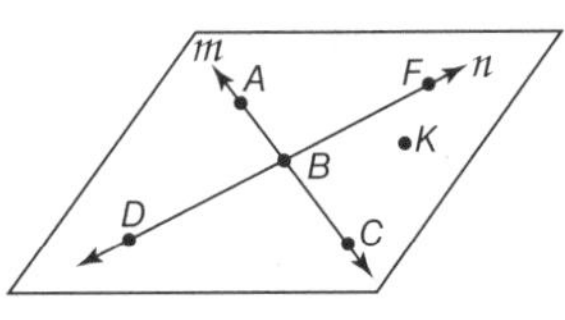

a. the plane Sample answer: *AFK*

b. two angles Sample answer: ∠*ABF* and ∠*CBD*

Concepts and Skills Bank 869

Lesson 8

1 FOCUS

Vertical Alignment

Lesson 8
Use a compass and straightedge to construct congruent segments, perpendicular bisectors, congruent angles, and angle bisectors.

After Lesson 8
Use constructions to explore the properties of geometric figures.

2 TEACH

Activities 1–4 show how to construct congruent segments, perpendicular bisectors, congruent angles, and angle bisectors.

Additional Examples

1 Draw $\overline{PR}$. Then construct a line segment congruent to $\overline{PR}$. Sample answer and construction: $\overline{SU}$ is congruent to $\overline{PR}$.

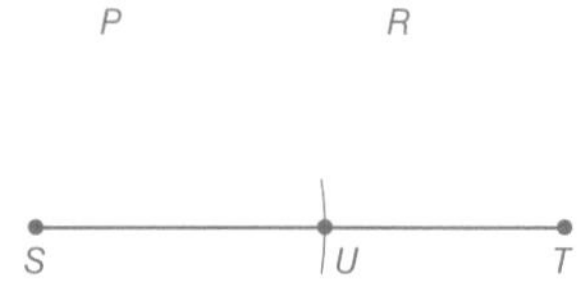

2 Draw $\overline{CD}$. Then construct the perpendicular bisector of $\overline{CD}$. Sample answer and construction: $\overline{EF}$ is the perpendicular bisector of $\overline{CD}$.

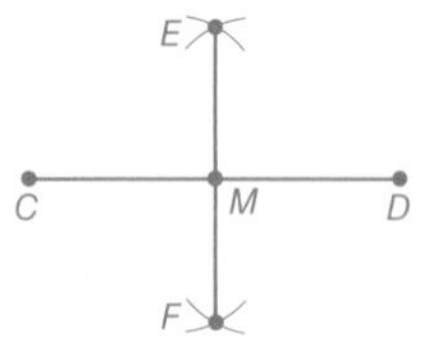

Concepts and Skills Bank

8 Geometric Constructions

A compass is a drawing instrument used for drawing circles and arcs. A straightedge, such as a ruler, is used to draw segments. You can use a compass and a straightedge to construct basic elements of geometric figures. You know a line segment is part of a line with two endpoints. Line segments that have the same length are called **congruent segments**.

ACTIVITY 1 Construct Congruent Segments

Step 1 Draw $\overline{JK}$. Then use a straightedge to draw a line segment longer than $\overline{JK}$. Label it $\overline{LM}$.

Step 2 Place the compass at J and adjust the compass setting so you can place the pencil tip on K. The compass setting equals the length of $\overline{JK}$.

Step 3 Using this setting, place the compass tip at L. Draw an arc to intersect $\overline{LM}$. Label the intersection P.

$\overline{LP}$ is congruent to $\overline{JK}$.

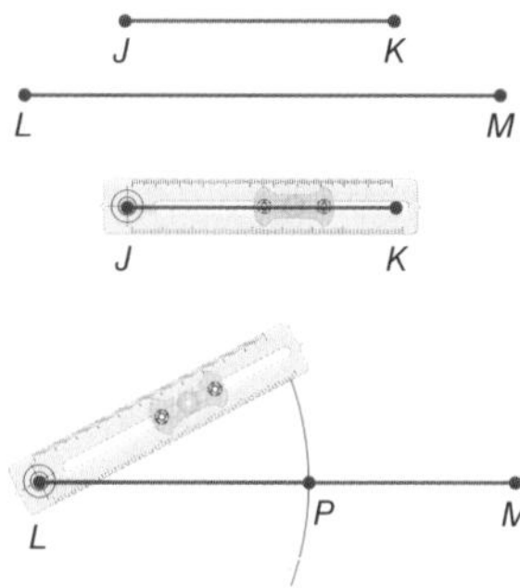

A **perpendicular bisector** is a perpendicular line that divides a line segment into two congruent segments.

ACTIVITY 2 Construct Perpendicular Bisectors

Step 1 Draw $\overline{AB}$. Then place the compass at point A. Using a setting greater than one half the length of $\overline{AB}$, draw an arc above and below $\overline{AB}$.

Step 2 Using this setting, place the compass at point B. Draw another set of arcs above and below $\overline{AB}$ as shown.

Step 3 Label the intersection of these arcs X and Y as shown.

Step 4 Draw $\overline{XY}$. Label the intersection of $\overline{AB}$ and this new line M.

$\overline{XY}$ is the perpendicular bisector of $\overline{AB}$.

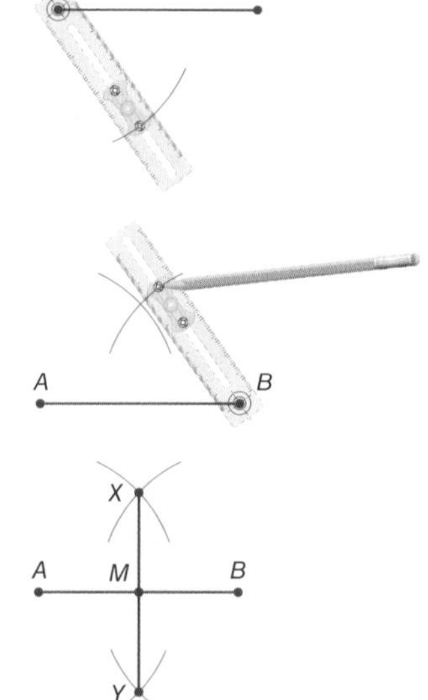

Tips for New Teachers

Students can construct an equilateral triangle by using a technique similar to Activity 1.

1. Draw $\overline{AB}$. Place the compass at A and adjust the compass setting so you can place the pencil tip on B. The compass setting equals the length of $\overline{AB}$. Then draw an arc.
2. Using this same setting, place the compass at point B. Draw another arc above $\overline{AB}$ as shown.
3. Label the intersection of these arcs C. Using a straightedge, draw $\overline{AC}$ and $\overline{BC}$. Since the sides are congruent segments, the triangle is equilateral.

Two angles that have the same measure are **congruent angles**. You can use a protractor to construct congruent angles.

ACTIVITY 3 Construct Congruent Angles

Step 1 Draw $\angle ABC$.

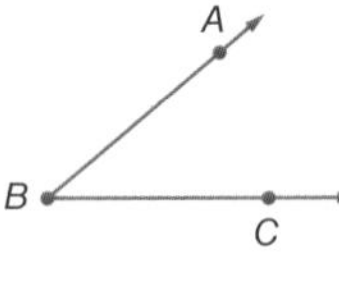

Step 2 Use a straightedge to draw $\overrightarrow{LK}$.

Step 3 With the compass at point *B*, draw an arc that intersects both sides of $\angle ABC$. Label the two points of intersection as *X* and *Y*.

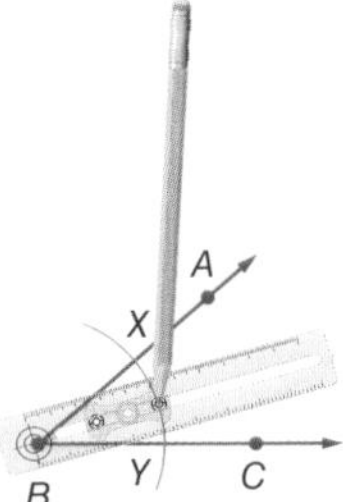

Step 4 With the same setting on your compass, place your compass at point *L*. Draw another arc. Label the intersection *R*.

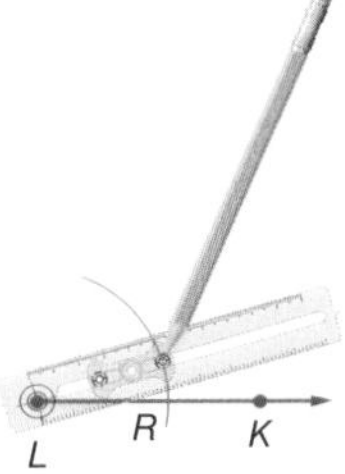

Step 5 Open your compass to the same width as the distance between points *X* and *Y*. Then place the compass at point *R*. Draw an arc that intersects the arc you drew in Step 4. Label this point of intersection *S*.

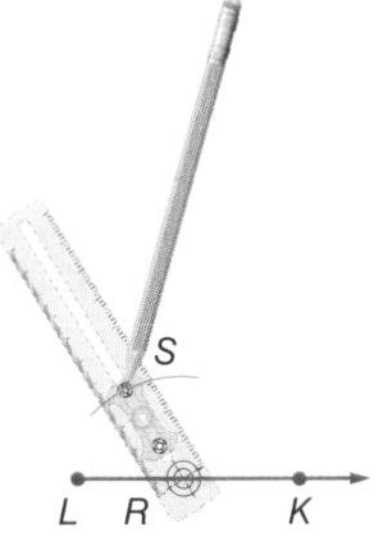

Step 6 Draw $\overrightarrow{LM}$ through point S. Angle *MLK* is congruent to $\angle ABC$.

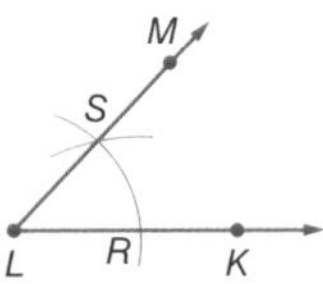

Concepts and Skills Bank

Additional Example

3 Draw $\angle STU$. Then construct an angle congruent to $\angle STU$. Sample answer and construction: $\angle PQR$ is congruent to $\angle STU$.

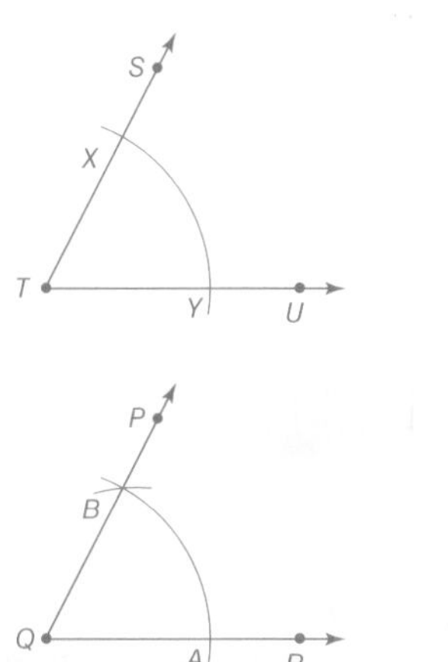

Tips for New Teachers

Constructions Encourage students to discuss each construction and to verify that line segments and angles are congruent. Ask students to describe the angles formed by the perpendicular bisector and the angle bisector.

Concepts and Skills Bank

Concepts and Skills Bank **871**

Additional Example

4 Draw $\angle DEF$. Then construct the angle bisector of $\angle DEF$. Sample answer and construction: $\overrightarrow{EG}$ is the bisector of $\angle DEF$.

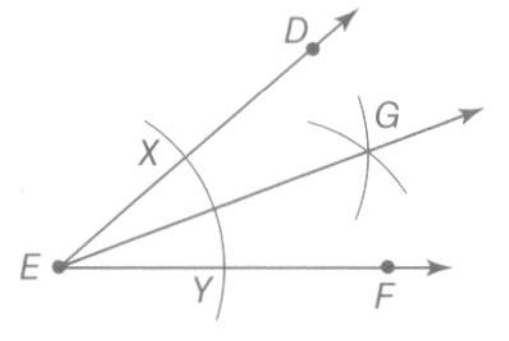

3 ASSESS

Formative Assessment

Use Exercises 1–12 to assess whether students understand how to use a compass and straightedge to construct congruent segments, perpendicular bisectors, congruent angles, and angle bisectors.

Name the Math Ask students to describe in their own words the steps they would use to construct one of the following: congruent segment, perpendicular bisector, congruent angle, or angle bisector.

Concepts and Skills Bank

An **angle bisector** is a ray that divides an angle into two congruent angles.

ACTIVITY 4 Construct an Angle Bisector

Step 1 Draw $\angle JKL$.

Step 2 Place the compass at point K and draw an arc that intersects both sides of the angle. Label the intersections X and Y.

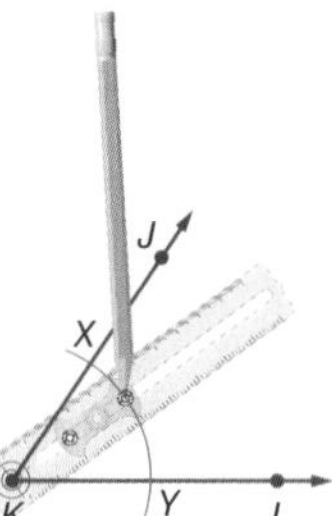

Step 3 With the compass at point X, draw an arc in the interior of $\angle JKL$.

Step 4 Using this setting, place the compass at point Y. Draw another arc.

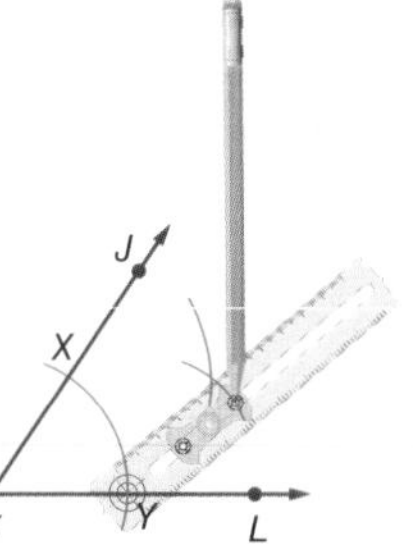

Step 5 Label the intersection of these arcs H. Then draw $\overrightarrow{KH}$.

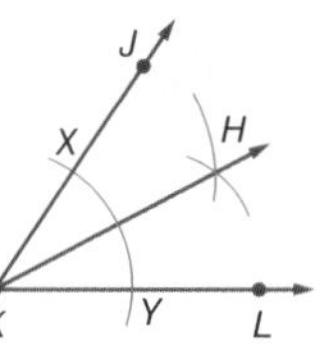

$\overrightarrow{KH}$ is the bisector of $\angle JKL$.

Exercises

For Exercises 1–12, see students' work.

Trace each segment. Then construct a segment congruent to it.

1. 2. 3.

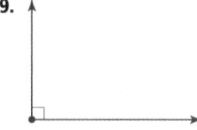

Trace each segment. Then construct the segment's perpendicular bisector.

4. 5. 6.

Trace each angle. Then construct an angle congruent to it.

7. 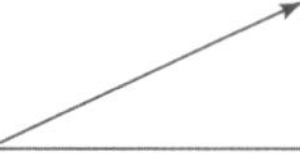

8. 

9. 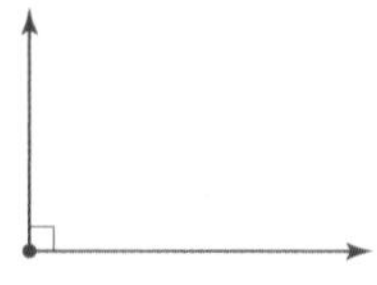

10. Construct the angle bisector for Exercise 7.
11. Construct the angle bisector for Exercise 8.
12. Construct the angle bisector for Exercise 9.

9 Meauring and Drawing Angles

Recall a ray is part of a line that has an endpoint and goes in one direction without ending. Two rays that have the same endpoint form an angle. The common endpoint is called the vertex, and the two rays that make up the angle are called the **sides** of the angle.

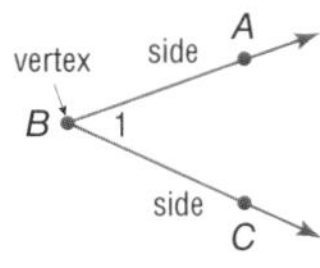

The symbol ∠ represents angle. There are several ways to name the angle shown above.

- Use the vertex and a point from each side. The vertex is always the middle letter. — $\angle ABC$ or $\angle CBA$
- Use the vertex only. — $\angle B$
- Use a number. — $\angle 1$

The most common unit of measure for angles is the **degree** (°). Angles are most often classified by their measures. The following are four types of angles.

Acute angle	Obtuse angle	Right angle	Straight angle
less than 90°	between 90° and 180°	exactly 90°	exactly 180°

You can use a **protractor** to measure angles.

EXAMPLE 1 Find Angle Measures

Use a protractor to find the measure of angle ∠CDE. Then classify each angle as *acute*, *obtuse*, *right*, or *straight*.

Step 1 Place the center point of the protractor's base on vertex *D*. Align the straight side with side $\overrightarrow{DE}$ so that the marker for 0° is on one of the rays.

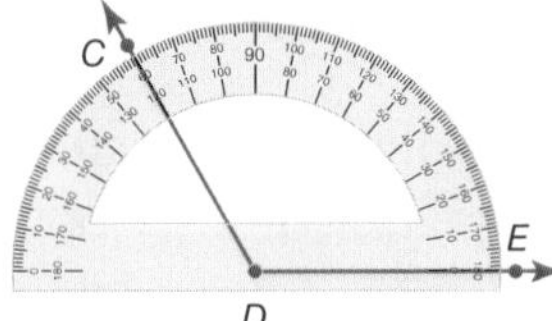

Step 2 Use the scale that begins with 0° at $\overrightarrow{DE}$. Read where the other side of the angle, $\overrightarrow{DC}$, crosses this scale.

The measure of angle *CDE* is 120°. Using symbols, $m\angle CDE = 120°$.

The angle is between 90° and 180°, so it is an obtuse angle.

Lesson 9

1 FOCUS

Vertical Alignment

Lesson 9
Measure and draw angles.

After Lesson 9
Use the properties of angles to solve real-world problems.

2 TEACH

Example 1 shows how to use a protractor to measure an angle. Example 2 shows how to draw an angle.

Additional Example

1 Use a protractor to find the measure of ∠*RST.* Then classify the angle as *acute, obtuse, right,* or *straight.* 75°; acute

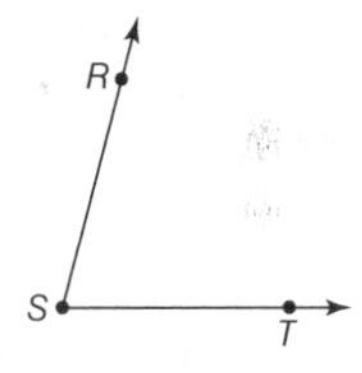

Additional Example

2 Draw $\angle A$ having a measure of 135°.

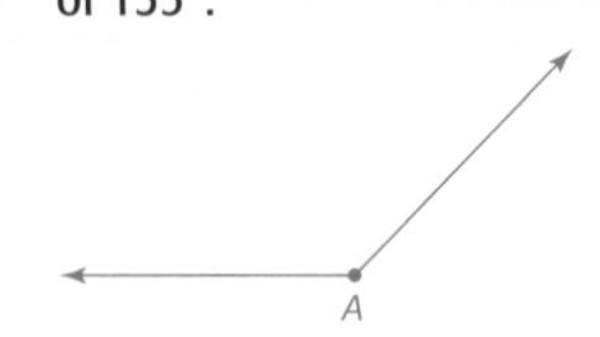

Tips for New Teachers

Using the Protractor Some students may use the wrong scale on a protractor. Encourage students who make this error to first estimate the size of the angle or determine whether the angle is acute or obtuse. Then have them identify whether they should use the inner or outer scale to measure the angle.

3 ASSESS

Formative Assessment

Use Exercises 1–24 to assess whether students understand how to measure and draw angles.

Yesterday's News Ask students how the previous lesson on geometric constructions helped with today's lesson on measuring and drawing angles.

Protractors can also be used to draw an angle of a given measure.

EXAMPLE 2 Draw Angles

Draw $\angle X$ having a measure of 85°.

Step 1 Draw a ray with endpoint X.

Step 2 Place the center point of the protractor on X. Align the mark labeled 0 with the ray.

Step 3 Use the scale that begins with 0. Locate the mark labeled 85. Then draw the other side of the angle.

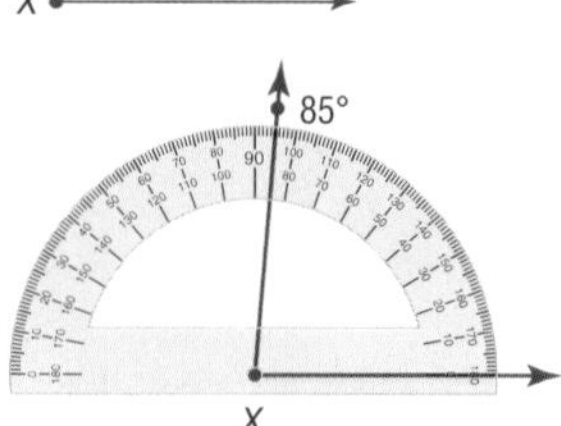

Exercises

1–11. See students' work for estimates.

Estimate the measure of each angle. Then use a protractor to find the actual measure. Classify each angle as *acute, obtuse, right,* or *straight*.

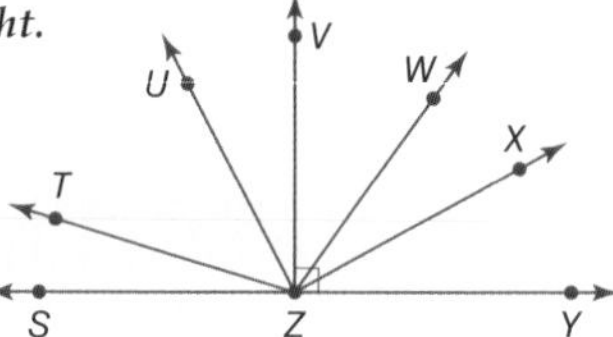

1. $\angle XZY$ 30°; acute
2. $\angle SZT$ 15°; acute
3. $\angle SZY$ 180°; straight
4. $\angle UZX$ 85°; acute
5. $\angle TZW$ 110°; obtuse
6. $\angle XZT$ 135°; obtuse
7. $\angle UZV$ 25°; acute
8. $\angle WZU$ 60°; acute

Estimate the measure of each angle. Then use a protractor to find the actual measure.

9.  45°
10.  90°
11.  60°

Use a protractor to draw an angle having each measurement. Then classify each angle as *acute, obtuse, right,* or *straight*.

12. 40° acute
13. 70° acute
14. 65° acute
15. 85° acute
16. 95° obtuse
17. 180° straight
18. 155° obtuse
19. 140° obtuse
20. 38° acute
21. 90° right
22. 127° obtuse
23. 174° obtuse

12–23. See Student Handbook Answer Appendix for drawings.

24. **SCHOOL** The graph at the right shows the amount of money spent on school clothes.
    a. Find the measure of each angle of the circle graph to the nearest degree. 21%: 76°; 10%: 36°; 20%: 72°; 49%: 176°
    b. Suppose 500 adults were surveyed. How many would you expect to spend between \$250 and \$349? 105

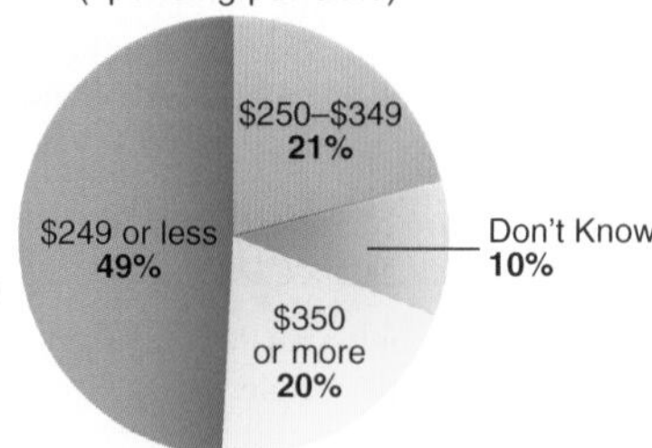

⑩ The Tangent Ratio

The study of the properties of triangles is called **trigonometry**. The word trigonometry means *angle measure.*

A **trigonometric ratio** is a ratio of the lengths of two sides of a right triangle. The **tangent** compares the measure of the leg opposite an angle with the measure of the leg adjacent to that angle. The symbol for the tangent of angle A is tan$A$.

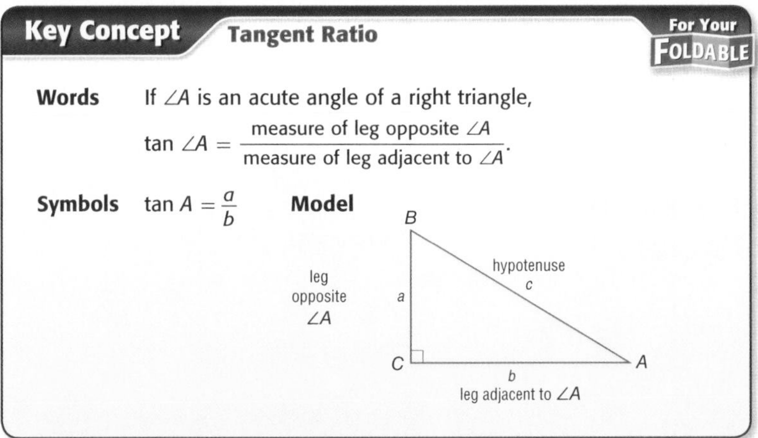

Key Concept Tangent Ratio — For Your FOLDABLE

Words If $\angle A$ is an acute angle of a right triangle,

$$\tan \angle A = \frac{\text{measure of leg opposite } \angle A}{\text{measure of leg adjacent to } \angle A}.$$

Symbols $\tan A = \frac{a}{b}$

Model

You can use the tangent ratio to solve real-world problems.

Real-World EXAMPLE 1 Find Length

ARCHITECTURE The Leaning Tower of Pisa in Pisa, Italy, tilts about 5.2° from vertical. If the top of the tower is 55 meters from the ground, about how far has its top shifted from its original position?

Angle A measures 5.2°, and you know the length of the side adjacent to $\angle A$. You want to find the length of the side opposite to $\angle A$.

Use the tangent ratio.

$\tan \angle A = \frac{\text{measure of leg opposite } \angle A}{\text{measure of leg adjacent to } \angle A}$	Write the tangent ratio.
$\tan 5.2° = \frac{x}{55}$	Substitution
$55(\tan 5.2°) = 55 \cdot \frac{x}{55}$	Multiply each side by 55.
55 [x] [TAN] 5.2 [ENTER] 5.00539211	Use a calculator.
$x \approx 5.0$ m	Simplify.

So, the top of the tower has shifted about 5.0 meters from its original position.

Lesson 10

1 FOCUS

Vertical Alignment

Lesson 10
Use the tangent ratio to find missing side measures and missing angle measures.

After Lesson 10
Use the sine and cosine ratios to find missing measures.

2 TEACH

Example 1 shows how to use the tangent ratio to find a missing side measure. **Example 2** shows how to use tangent to find an angle measure.

Additional Example

1 **RAMPS** A company is installing a wheelchair ramp that rises 2 feet to the entrance of the building. If the ramp forms a 4.8° angle with the ground, about how far should the start of the ramp be from the entrance? about 23.8 feet

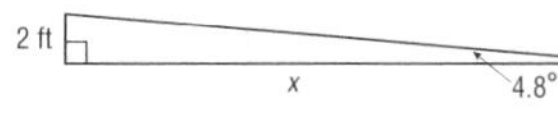

Tips for New Teachers

Tangent Ratio Some students may confuse the legs of the triangle and try to solve for the wrong leg. Point out that if the unknown leg is adjacent to $\angle A$, then students will need to divide by tan$A$ to solve for x rather than multiply.

Additional Example

2 Find the measure of $\angle B$ to the nearest degree. about 70°

C, 9 cm, 25 cm, B, A

3 ASSESS

Formative Assessment

Use Exercises 1–9 to assess whether students understand how to use the tangent ratio to find missing side measures and missing angle measures.

Crystal Ball Ask students how they think today's lesson on the tangent ratio will help with the next lesson on the sine and cosine ratios.

Concepts and Skills Bank

You can use the $\tan^{-1}$ function on your calculator to find the measure of an angle when you know the measures of the two legs.

EXAMPLE 2 Find Angle Measures

Find the measure of $\angle B$ to the nearest degree.

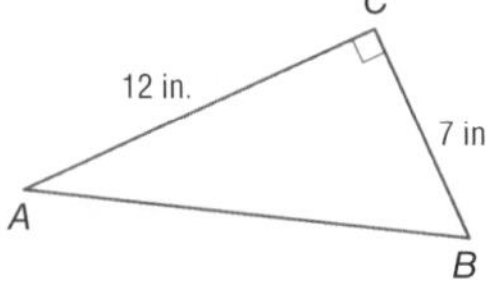

From the figure, you know the measures of the two legs. Use the definition of tangent.

$$\tan B = \frac{\text{opposite leg}}{\text{adjacent leg}}$$

$$\tan B = \frac{12}{7}$$

Use your calculator to find the measure of $\angle B$.

[2nd] [TAN^{-1}] 12 [÷] 7 [ENTER] 59.74356284

The measure of $\angle B$ is about 60°.

Exercises

Find each missing measure to the nearest tenth.

1. 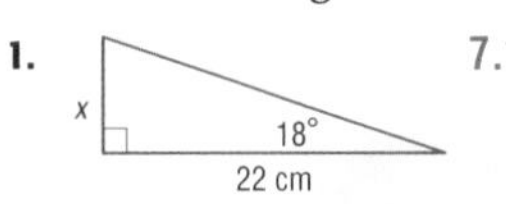

7.1 cm

2. 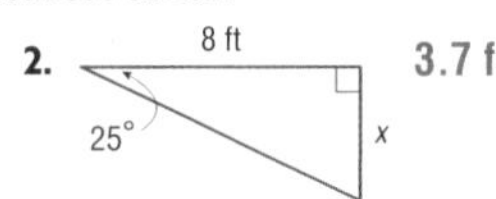

3.7 ft

3. 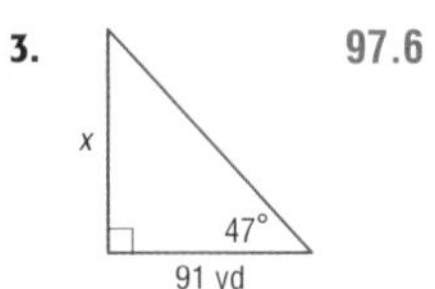

97.6 yd

4. 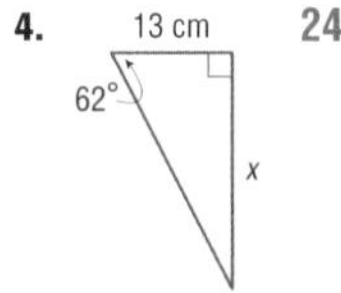

24.4 cm

5. 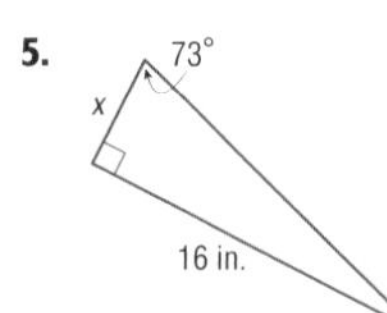

4.9 in.

6. 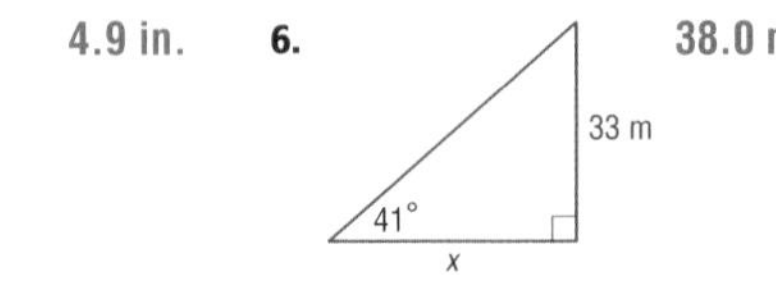

38.0 m

Find each missing angle measure to the nearest degree.

7. 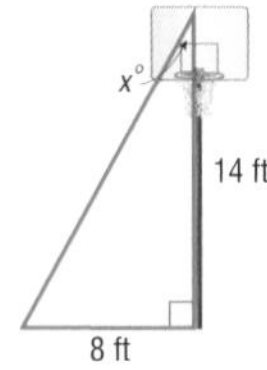

30°

8. 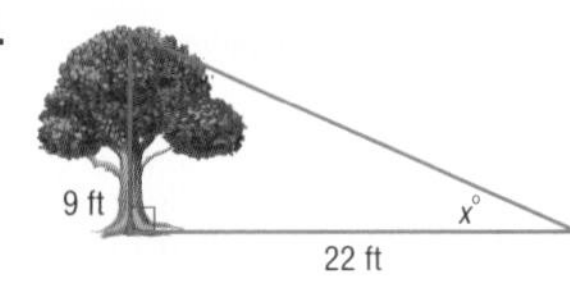

22°

9. 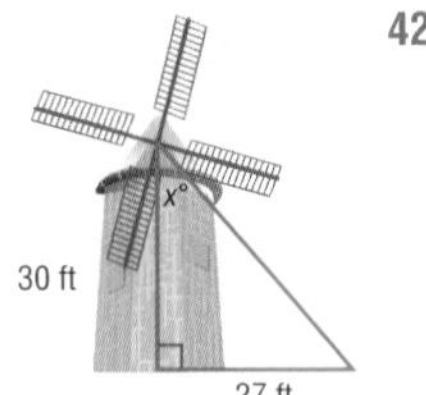

42°

876 Concepts and Skills Bank

⑪ The Sine and Cosine Ratios

Some problems involving right triangles give the measures of one leg and the hypotenuse. You could use the Pythagorean Theorem to find the measure of the remaining leg or you could use the sine or cosine ratios.

For an acute angle of a right triangle,

- the **cosine** is the ratio of the measure of the leg adjacent to the acute angle to the measure of the hypotenuse.
- the **sine** is the ratio of the measure of the leg opposite the acute angle to the measure of the hypotenuse.

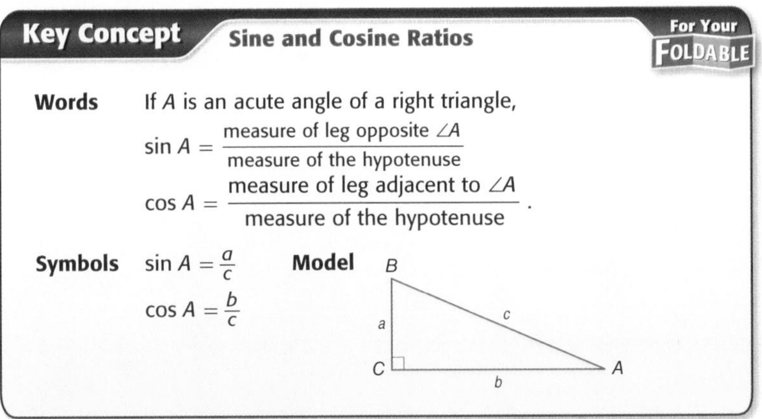

Key Concept Sine and Cosine Ratios — For Your FOLDABLE

Words If A is an acute angle of a right triangle,

$$\sin A = \frac{\text{measure of leg opposite } \angle A}{\text{measure of the hypotenuse}}$$

$$\cos A = \frac{\text{measure of leg adjacent to } \angle A}{\text{measure of the hypotenuse}}.$$

Symbols $\sin A = \frac{a}{c}$ $\cos A = \frac{b}{c}$

Model

You can use the sine and cosine ratios to find missing lengths of sides or angle measures in a right triangle.

EXAMPLE 1 Find Length

Use $\triangle ABC$ to find the length of BC.

Angle A measures 28° and you know the length of the hypotenuse. You want to find the length of the side adjacent to ∠A.

Use the cosine ratio.

$\cos \angle A = \frac{\text{measure of leg opposite } \angle A}{\text{measure of the hypotenuse}}$ **Write the cosine ratio.**

$\cos 28° = \frac{x}{17}$ **Substitution**

$17(\cos 28°) = 17 \cdot \frac{x}{17}$ **Multiply each side by 17.**

17 [×] [cos] 28 [ENTER] 15.01010908 **Use a calculator.**

$x \approx 15$ m **Simplify.**

So, the length of $\overline{BC}$ is about 15 meters.

Lesson 11

1 FOCUS

Vertical Alignment

Lesson 11
Use the sine and cosine ratios to find side lengths and angle measures.

After Lesson 11
Use trigonometric ratios to solve real-world problems.

2 TEACH

Example 1 shows how to use the sine or cosine ratio to find a side length. **Example 2** shows how to use the sine or cosine ratio to find an angle measure.

Additional Example

1 Use $\triangle JKL$ to find the length of BC. about 13.4 in.

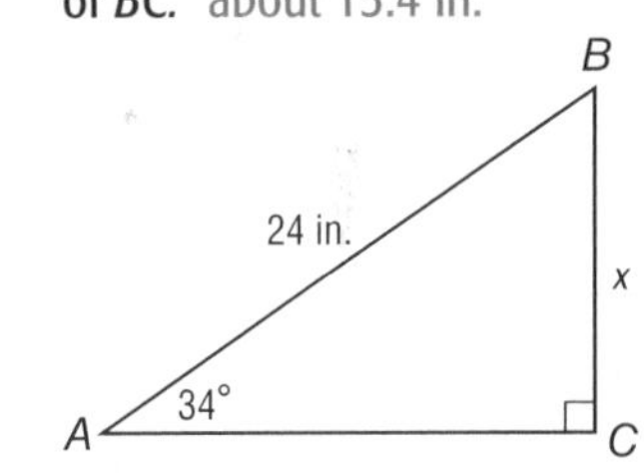

Concepts and Skills Bank **877**

Additional Example

2 **CANOPIES** Kara attached a 12-foot rope to the top of a canopy pole. The rope is anchored to the ground 8 feet from the pole. What is the angle of elevation between the anchor and the top of the rope attached to the pole? about 48°

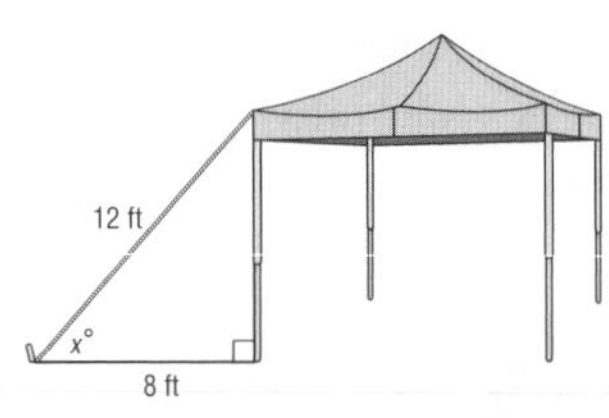

Tips for New Teachers

Sine, Cosine, and Tangent Ratios Students often confuse the sine, cosine, and tangent ratios. Suggest that they make study cards to use as a reference until they are familiar with the ratios. Encourage students to use or create a mnemonic device to remember the ratios, such as the well-known SOH-CAH-TOA: sine: opposite/hypotenuse; cosine: adjacent/hypotenuse; tangent: opposite/adjacent.

3 ASSESS

Formative Assessment

Use Exercises 1–8 to assess whether students understand how to use the sine and cosine ratios to find missing side lengths and missing angle measures.

Name the Math Have students describe when and how they would use the sine or cosine ratio to find a missing angle measure.

You can use the $\sin^{-1}$ or $\cos^{-1}$ function on your calculator to find the measure of an angle when you know the measures of the two legs.

Real-World EXAMPLE 2 Find Angle Measures

SPORTS **A parasailer is 30 feet above the water. The tow rope is 65 feet long. Find the angle of elevation between the parasailer and the surface of the water.**

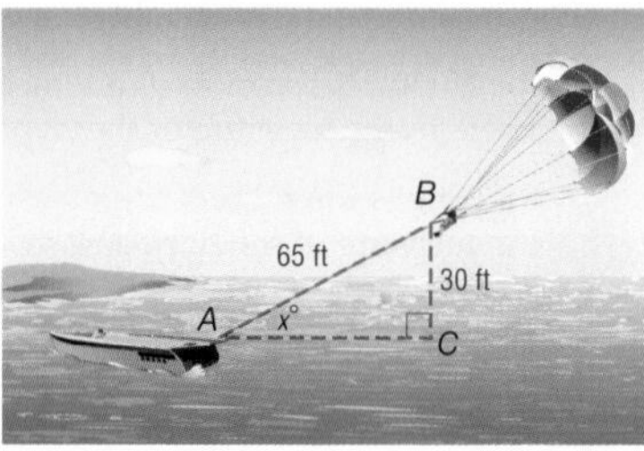

You know the side opposite the angle and the hypotenuse. You want to know the angle measure.

Use the sine ratio.

$\sin \angle A = \dfrac{\text{measure of leg opposite } \angle A}{\text{measure of the hypotenuse}}$ **Write the sine ratio.**

$\sin x° = \dfrac{30}{65}$ **Substitution**

Use your calculator to find the measure of $\angle A$.

[2nd] [$\sin^{-1}$] 30 [÷] 65 [ENTER] 27.48642625

The measure of $\angle A$ is about 27.5°.

Exercises

Find each missing measure to the nearest tenth or nearest degree.

1. 12 yd

(13 yd; x yd; 67°)

2. 6.9 m

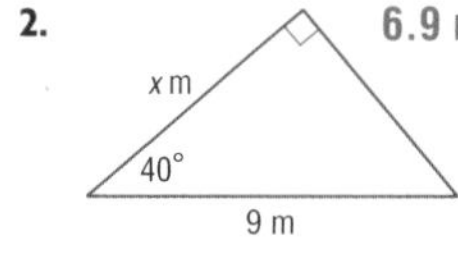

3. 21.2 in.

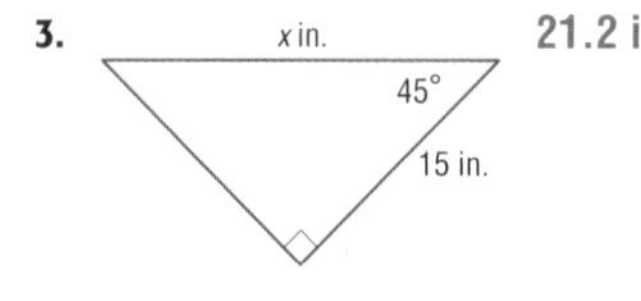

4. 14.6 m **5.** 58°

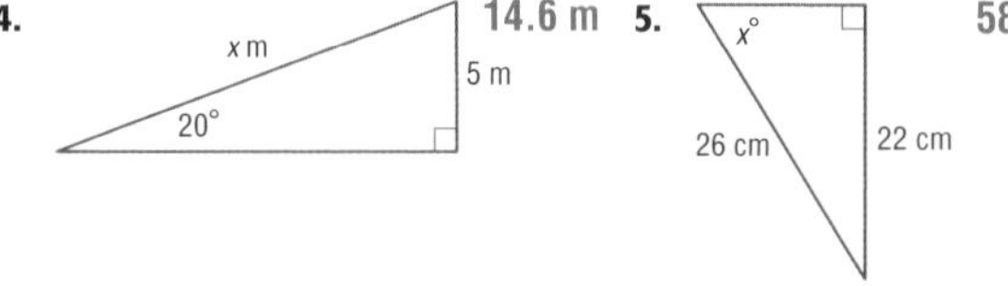

6. 63°

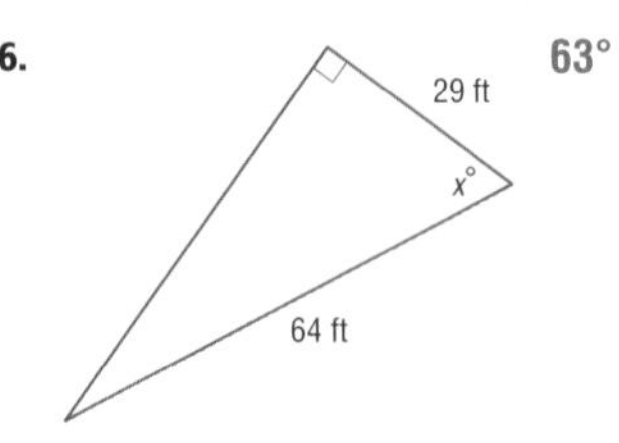

7. **HOME IMPROVEMENT** A painter props a 20-foot ladder against a house. The angle it forms with the ground is 65°. To the nearest foot, how far up the side of the house does the ladder reach? 18 ft

8. **TRANSPORTATION** The end of an exit ramp from an interstate highway is 22 feet higher than the highway. If the ramp is 630 feet long, what angle does it make with the highway? Round to the nearest degree. 2°

878 Concepts and Skills Bank

12 Accuracy and Precision

All measurements taken in the real world are approximations. The greater the care in which a measurement is taken, the more accurate it will be.

Accuracy is the degree of conformity of a measurement with the true value.
Precision is the degree of perfection in which a measurement is made.

EXAMPLE 1 **Determine Precision**

Which is a more precise measurement of the line segment shown, 2 centimeters or 1.8 centimeters?

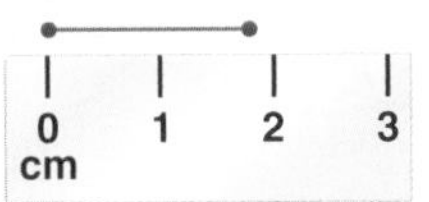

0 1 2 3
cm

Estimate 2 cm	**Estimate** 2 cm
measurement: 2 cm	measurement: 1.8 cm
precision: 1 cm	precision: 0.1 cm

So, 1.8 centimeters is a more precise measurement.

Exercises

Choose the correct term(s) to determine the degree of precision needed in each measurement situation.

1. In a pharmacy, the mass of one drop of a medicine is found to the nearest 0.01 (gram, kilogram). gram
2. The weight of a puppy in a veterinarian's office would be given to the nearest (tenth of a pound, tenth of an ounce). tenth of a pound
3. On a cruise, the length of a tour on an island would be described in (minutes, hours). hours
4. A person making a sweater measures the fabric to the nearest (inch, eighth of an inch). eighth of an inch

Estimate and then measure the length of each line segment to the nearest half, quarter, eighth, or sixteenth inch. State the measurement that is the most precise.

5. $1\frac{3}{4}$ in.
6. 1 in.
7. **GEOMETRY** Draw a line segment. Estimate the length of the line segment. Then measure using two different units. Which measuring unit gave the more precise measurement? Sample answer: 0.9 cm is more precise than 1 in. See Student Handbook Answer Appendix for line segment.
8. **CONSTRUCTION** A construction company is ordering cement to pour the garage floor for a new house. Would you say that precision or accuracy is more important in the completion of their order? Explain. Sample answer: Accuracy, because it is more important to have approximately the correct amount of cement than it is to have a very precise amount.

Lesson 12

1 FOCUS

Vertical Alignment

Lesson 12
Determine the accuracy and precision of measurements.

After Lesson 12
Use accuracy and precision in solving problems involving measurements.

2 TEACH

Example 1 shows how to determine precision.

Additional Example

1. Which measurement of the line segment is more precise: $1\frac{1}{2}$ inches or $1\frac{3}{8}$ inches?

$1\frac{3}{8}$ inches

Tips for New Teachers

Line Segments Remind students to align the segment with 0 on the ruler.

3 ASSESS

Formative Assessment
Use Exercises 1–8 to assess whether students understand accuracy and precision in measurements.

Yesterday's News Ask students how previous lessons on measuring objects helped with today's lesson on accuracy and precision.

Lesson 13

1 FOCUS

Vertical Alignment

Lesson 13
Find probabilities using area models.

After Lesson 13
Use geometric probability to solve real-world problems and estimate areas.

2 TEACH

Example 1 shows how to find probability using area models.

Additional Example

1 **A.** Find the probability that a token dropped on the board will land within the shaded region.

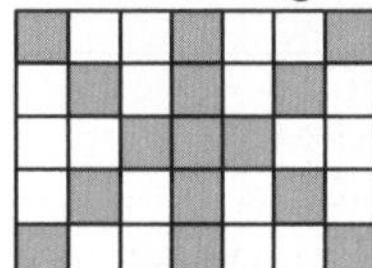

$\frac{15}{35}$ or $\frac{3}{7}$, ≈ 0.43, or 43%

B. Tyson will win a prize if a dart thrown at random lands on the 2-inch green square. What is the probability that a dart will land on the square?

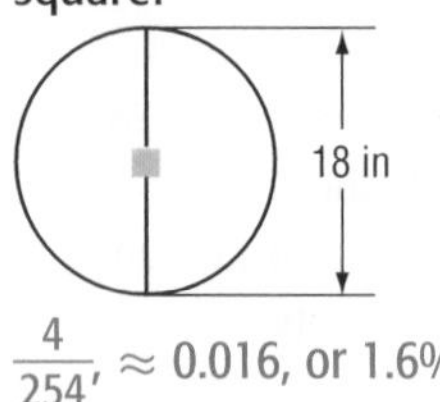

$\frac{4}{254}$, ≈ 0.016, or 1.6%

Concepts and Skills Bank

13 Geometric Probability

Recall that the probability of an event is defined as the ratio of the number of ways something can happen to the total possible outcomes. Probability can also be related to the area of a figure.

Key Concept **Probability and Area** *For Your FOLDABLE*

Words The probability of landing in a specific region of a target is the ratio of the area of the specific region to the area of the target.

Symbols $P(\text{specific region}) = \frac{\text{area of specific region}}{\text{area of the target}}$

You can find probability using an area model.

EXAMPLE 1 Find Probability Using Area Models

a. Find the probability that a coin dropped on the board will land within the shaded region.

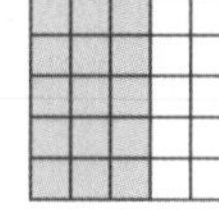

$P(\text{shaded region}) = \frac{\text{area of shaded region}}{\text{area of the target}}$

$= \frac{15}{25}$ or $\frac{3}{5}$

So, the probability is $\frac{3}{5}$, 0.6, or 60%.

b. To win a game at the school carnival, a thrown dart must land in the red section of the square board. What is the probability that a dart thrown at random will land in the red section?

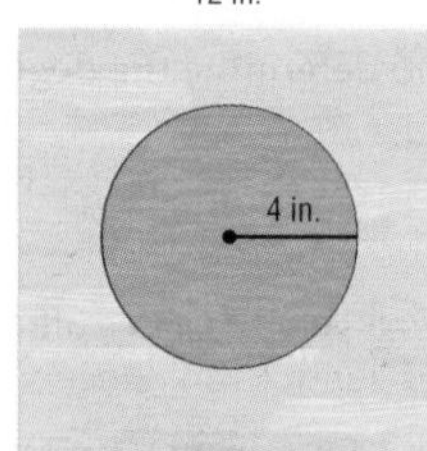

To find the probability of landing in the red section, you need to know the area of the red section and the area of the entire board.

Area of red section	$= \pi \cdot r^2$	**Area of a circle**
	$= \pi \cdot 4^2$	**Replace *r* with 4.**
	$= 16\pi$	**Multiply 4 by 4.**
	≈ 50.27	**Simplify.**

The area of the red circle is about 50.27 square inches.

Area of the square $= s^2$

$= 12^2$ or 144

Now find the probability.

$P(\text{landing in the red section}) = \frac{\text{area of red section}}{\text{total area}}$

$\approx \frac{50.27}{144}$ or about 0.35

So, the probability of a dart landing in the red section is about 0.35 or 35%.

Exercises

Find the probability that a randomly thrown dart will land in the shaded region of each dartboard. Round to the nearest hundredth, if necessary.

1. 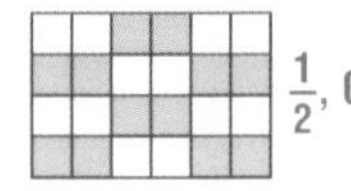 $\frac{1}{2}$, 0.5, or 50%

2. 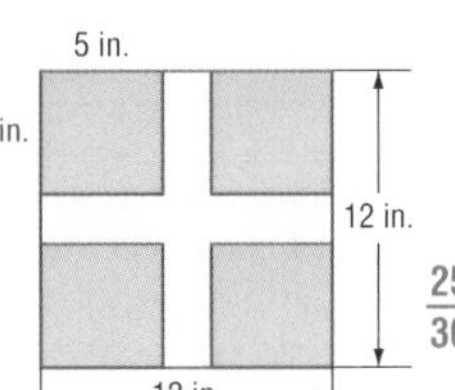

$\frac{25}{36}$, 0.69, or 69%

3. 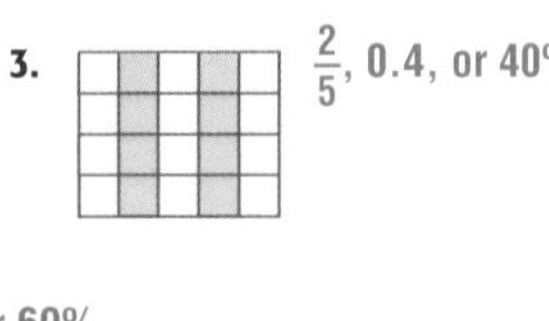 $\frac{2}{5}$, 0.4, or 40%

4. 0.38 or 38%

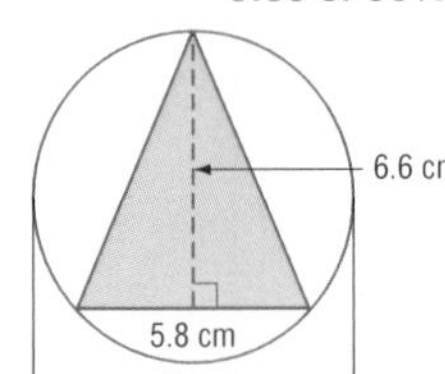

5. 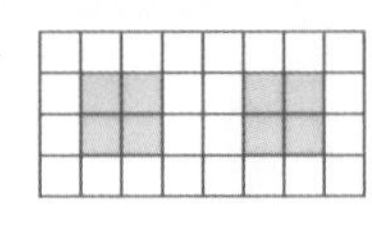 $\frac{1}{4}$, 0.25, or 25%

6. 0.56 or 56%

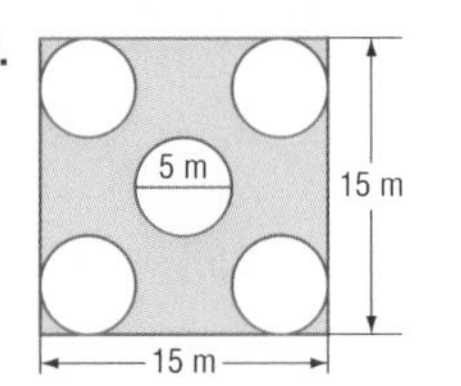

7. GAMES A popular game involves tossing a bean bag through a hole in a wooden board like the one shown. What is the probability of tossing the bean bag through the hole? 0.02 or 2%

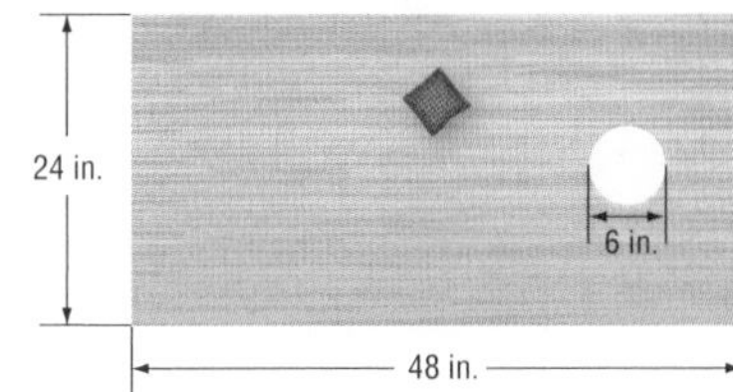

8. PATIOS A square patio is 10 feet by 10 feet. At the center of the patio is a rectangular rug 5 feet by 6 feet. If a coin is dropped somewhere on the patio, what is the probability that the coin lands on the rug? $\frac{3}{10}$, 0.3, or 30%

9. PRIZES To win a prize, a coin must land on an odd number on the triangular board shown. It is equally likely that the coin will land anywhere on the board. What is the probability of winning a prize? $\frac{5}{9}$, $0.\overline{5}$, or $55.\overline{5}$%

1 3 2 4 6 8 5 7 9

21 in.

24 in.

10. FOUNTAINS A circular flower garden has a diameter of 16 feet. At the center of the garden is a fountain 5 feet in diameter. If a coin is tossed at random into the garden, what is the probability that the coin will land in the fountain? $\frac{25}{256}$, 0.097, or 9.7%

11. DARTS Draw a dartboard in which the probability of a dart landing in the shaded area is 60%. See Student Handbook Answer Appendix.

12. GAMES It is equally likely that a thrown dart will land anywhere on the dartboard shown at the right. Find the probability of a randomly thrown dart landing inside the target region. 0.26 or 26%

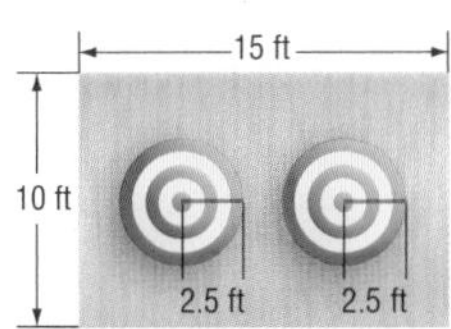

Concepts and Skills Bank

Tips for New Teachers

Simple Probability and Geometric Probability It may be helpful to review simple probability at the start of this lesson so that students make the connection between finding the probability of an event and finding the geometric probability of an event. Remind students that

$$P(\text{event}) = \frac{\text{number of favorable outcomes}}{\text{number of possible outcomes}}.$$

Explain that the concepts of simple probability and geometric probability are the same, except that geometric probability involves the ratio of the area of a region to the total area.

3 ASSESS

Formative Assessment

Use Exercises 1–12 to assess whether students understand how to find the geometric probability of an event.

Ticket Out the Door Tell students that a 3-inch square is in the center of a 10-inch × 15-inch rectangular board. Ask them to find the probability that a coin dropped on the board will land in the square. Have them turn in the answer as they go out the door. $\frac{9}{150}$, 0.06, or 6%

Concepts and Skills Bank

Lesson 14

1 FOCUS

Vertical Alignment

Lesson 14
Select an appropriate graph for a set of data.

After Lesson 14
Analyze data in graphs and recognize misleading graphs.

2 TEACH

Example 1 shows how to select an appropriate graph to display data.

Tips for New Teachers

Choosing Graphs to Display Data Remind students that there is often more than one way to represent data. However, sometimes one type of graph will represent the data better than another type. Encourage students to think about the reasons for displaying the data, and then choose the type of graph that is *most* appropriate. Have them explain why their choice better represents the data than the other choices.

Concepts and Skills Bank

14 Displaying Data in Graphs

Statistics involves collecting, analyzing, and presenting information. The information that is collected is called data. Displaying data in graphs makes it easier to visualize the data.

- **Bar graphs** are used to compare the frequency of data. The bar graph at the right compares the amounts of recycled materials.

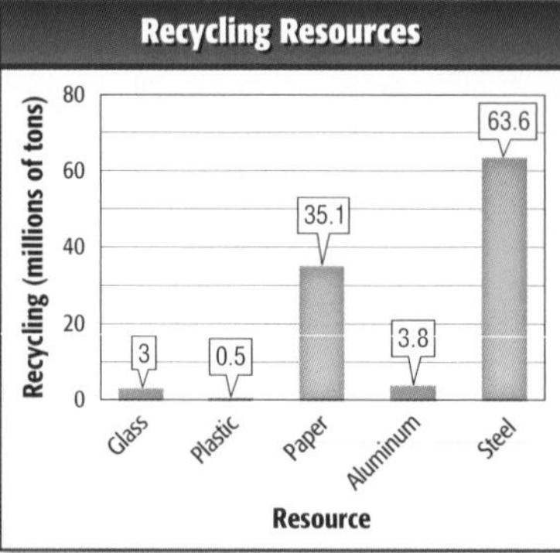

- **Double bar graphs** compare two sets of data. The double bar graph at the left shows movie preferences for men and women.

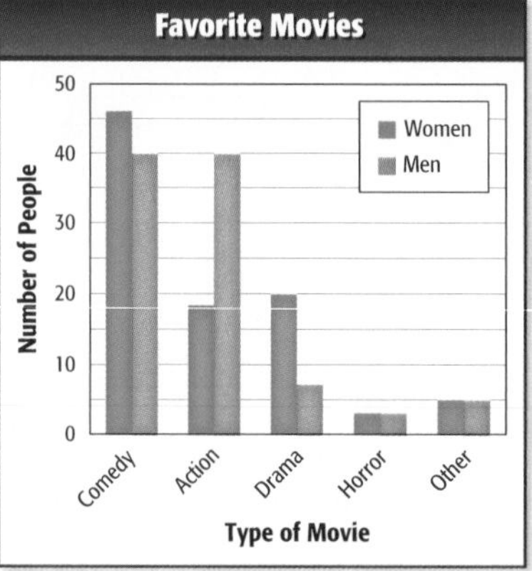

- **Line graphs** usually show how values change over a period of time. The line graph at the right shows the results of the women's Olympic Long Jump event from 1972 to 2004.

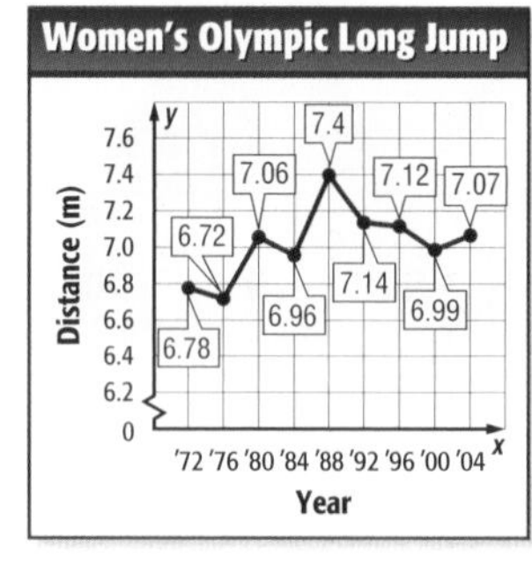

- **Double line graphs**, like double bar graphs, show two sets of data. The double line graph below compares the number of boys and the number of girls participating in high school athletics.

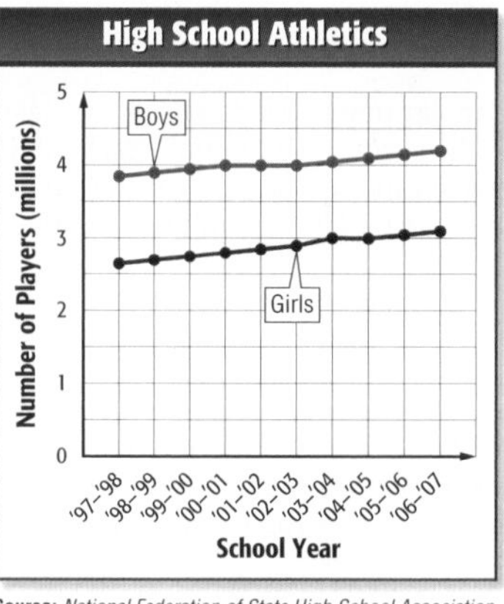

Source: *National Federation of State High School Association*

- **Circle graphs** show how parts are related to the whole. The circle graph below shows how electricity is generated in the United States.

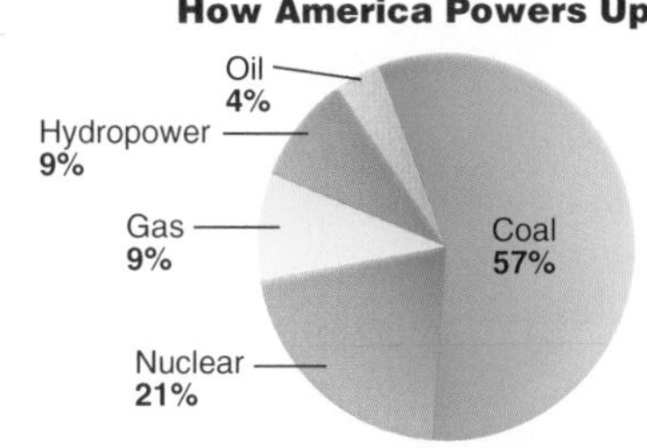

- **Line plots** organize data using a number line. The line plot below shows the number of Calories in a single serving of different brands of yogurt.

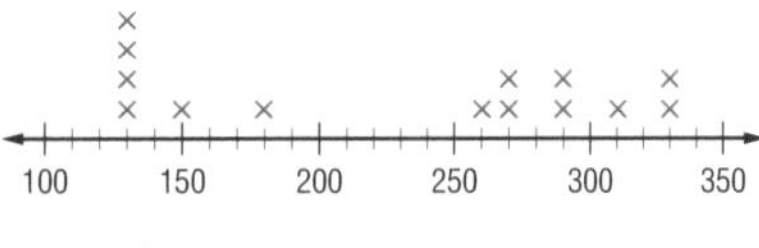

EXAMPLE 1 Select a Display

A newspaper wants to display the high temperature of the past week. Should they use a line graph, circle graph, or double bar graph?

Since the data would show change over time, a line graph would give the reader a clear picture of changes in temperature.

Exercises

Determine whether a bar graph, double bar graph, line graph, double line graph, line plot, or circle graph is the best way to display each sets of data. Explain.

1. the number of people who have different kinds of pets
Sample answer: A bar graph would show the different frequencies of the data.
2. the percent of students in class who have 0, 1, 2, 3, or more than 3 siblings
Sample answer: A circle graph would show how each category compares to the whole class.
3. the number of teens who attended art museums, symphony concerts, rock concerts, and athletic events in 1990 compared to the number who attended the same events this year
Sample answer: A double bar graph would make a side-by-side comparison of the two sets of data.
4. the minimum wage every year from 1980 to the present
Sample answer: A line graph would show the wage's increase during those years.
5. the number of boys and the number of girls participating in volunteer programs each year from 1995 to the present
Sample answer: A double line graph would show the changes in boys' and girls' participation over time.
6. The table below shows the number of events at recent Olympic games. Sample answer: Line graph would show an increase in the events over time.

Olympic Year	1968	1972	1976	1980	1984	1988	1992	1996	2000	2004
Number of Events	172	196	199	200	223	237	257	271	300	296

7. The prices of lawn seats at events held at an amphitheater are shown in the chart below.

Lawn Seat Prices ($)							
23	29	31	34	19	28	35	37
22	28	26	33	35	39	26	27

Sample answer: A line plot would be the best display for the prices because there are prices that overlap.

Additional Example

1 A conservation organization wants to display last year's contributions, in dollars, made to four of their projects, including funds for wildlife, soil erosion, wetlands, and water reclamation. Should they use a line graph, line plot, bar graph, or circle graph? Sample answer: They should use a bar graph since it would compare the amounts of contributions for all four categories of projects.

3 ASSESS

Formative Assessment

Use Exercises 1–7 to assess whether students understand how to choose an appropriate display for data.

Crystal Ball Ask students how they think today's lesson on displaying data will help with the next lesson on misleading graphs.

Lesson 15

1 FOCUS

Vertical Alignment

Lesson 15
Identify and evaluate misleading graphs.

After Lesson 15
Use graphs to represent, compare, and analyze data.

2 TEACH

Example 1 shows how to compare two graphs that may be misleading. **Example 2** shows how to evaluate conclusions based on misleading graphs.

Additional Example

1 **WEATHER** The graphs show the average January rainfall in Seattle.

GRAPH A
January Rainfall in Seattle

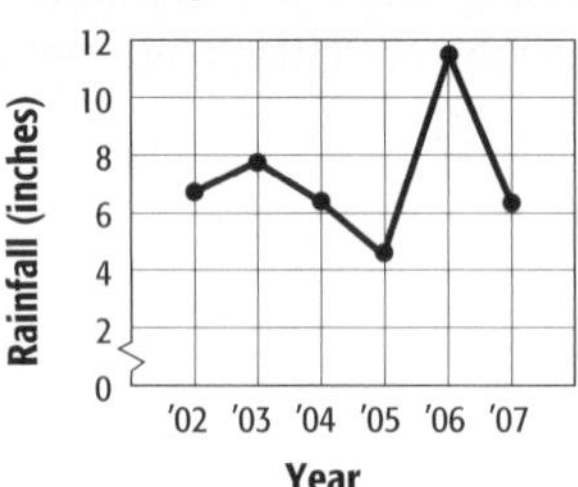

GRAPH B
January Rainfall in Seattle

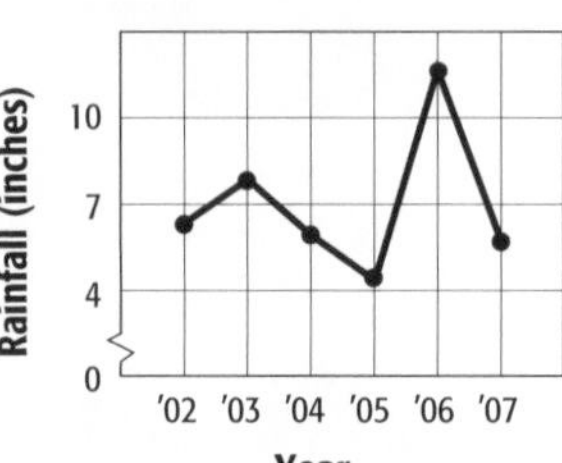

a. Why do the graphs look different?

b. Which graph appears to show greater fluctuations in rainfall?

Concepts and Skills Bank

15 Misleading Graphs

Two graphs that represent the same data may look quite different. If different vertical scales are used, each graph will give a different visual impression.

EXAMPLE 1 Misleading Graphs

TRAVEL The graphs show domestic traveler spending in the U.S.

Graph A

Graph B

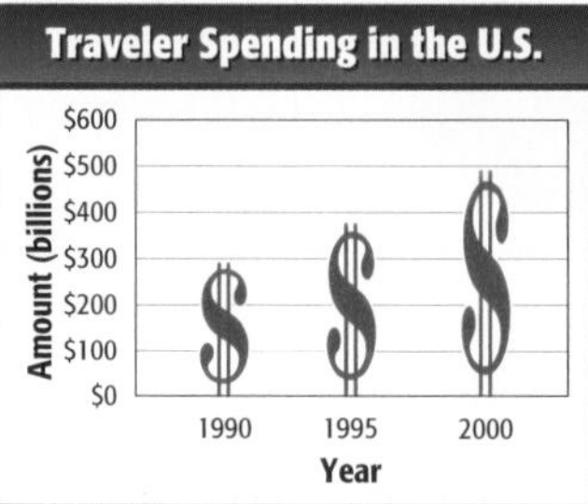

a. Why do the graphs look different?

The vertical scales differ.

b. Which graph appears to show a greater increase in the growth of traveler spending?

Graph A; the size of the dollar sign makes the increase appear more dramatic because both the height and width of the dollar sign are increasing.

When reading a statistical graph, you must interpret the information carefully and determine whether the inference made from the data is valid.

EXAMPLE 2 Accuracy of Predictions and Conclusions

SCOOTERS The graph displays units sold during the life of a scooter company. According to the graph, the number of scooters did not increase as fast in the 2000s as they did from 1970–2000. Determine whether this statement is accurate. Justify your reasoning.

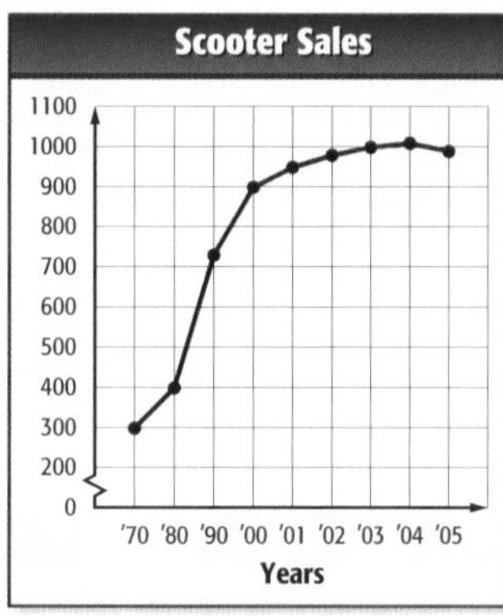

No, the statement is not accurate. The horizontal scale is inconsistent; from 1970 to 2000, the interval is 10 years, but the interval is 1 year from 2000 to 2005. Also, the graph only goes through 2005. You would have to wait until 2010 to know the number of scooters sold and compare the rate of change from 2000 to 2010 to the rate of increase from 1970 to 2000.

Additional Example Answers

1a. The vertical scale on A starts at 0 with intervals of 2; the scale on B starts at 4 with intervals that are not equal: 4 to 7, 7 to 10, 10 to 12.

1b. Graph B because of the vertical axis.

Exercises

1. **MOVIES** The graphs below show the dollars earned by the top five all time movies.

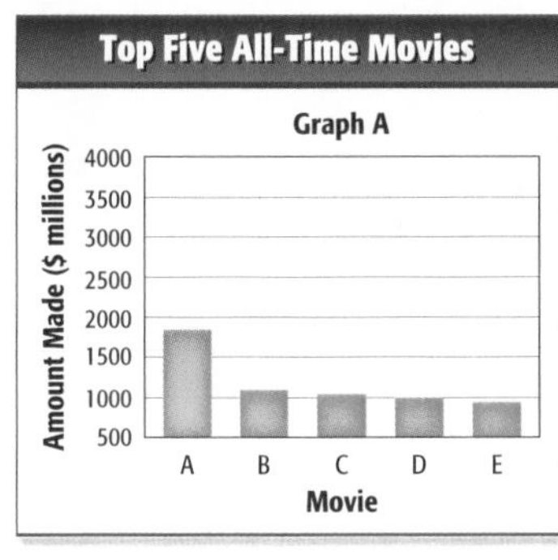

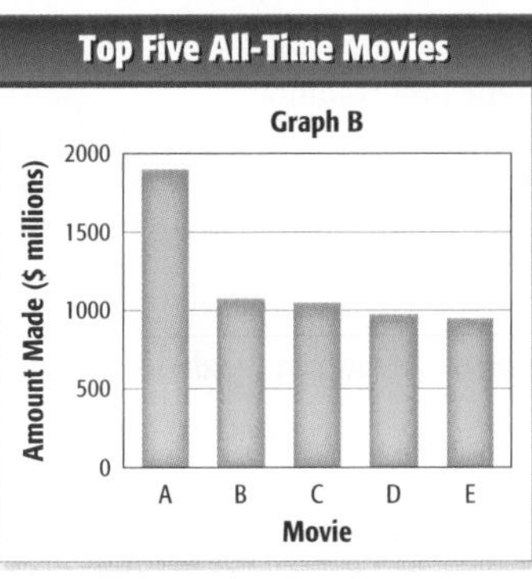

a. Which graph gives the impression that the top all-time movie made far more money than any other top all-time movie? **Graph B**

b. Which graph shows that the bottom four movies earned about the same amount? **Graph A**

2. **TRAVEL** The distance adults drive each week is shown in the graph below.

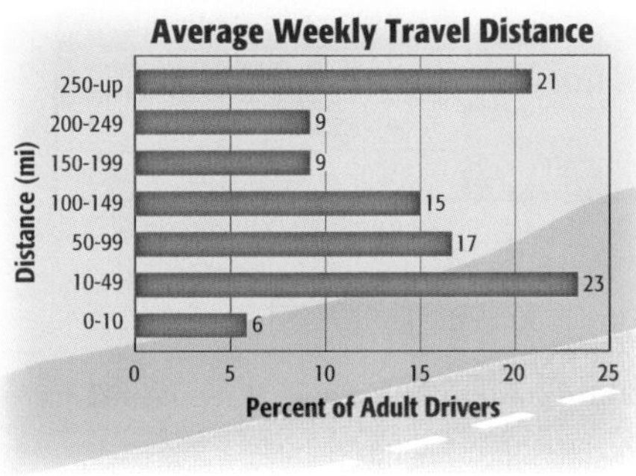

2a. The vertical scale is not equally labeled. The scale goes from 0–10 and then 10–49. The rest of the distances are broken up into groups of 50 miles. They should be equally broken up.

a. Is the graph misleading? Explain your reasoning.

b. Create a new graph. Change the scale to appropriately fit the data. **See students' work.**

3. **HOCKEY** The graph at the right shows the number of wins after an 82-game schedule. According to the graph, Detroit had about 4 times as many wins as Chicago. Determine whether this statement is accurate. Justify your reasoning. **See Student Handbook Answer Appendix.**

4. How can graphs be misleading? Give an example of a graph that is misleading and explain how to redraw the graph so it is not misleading. **See Student Handbook Answer Appendix.**

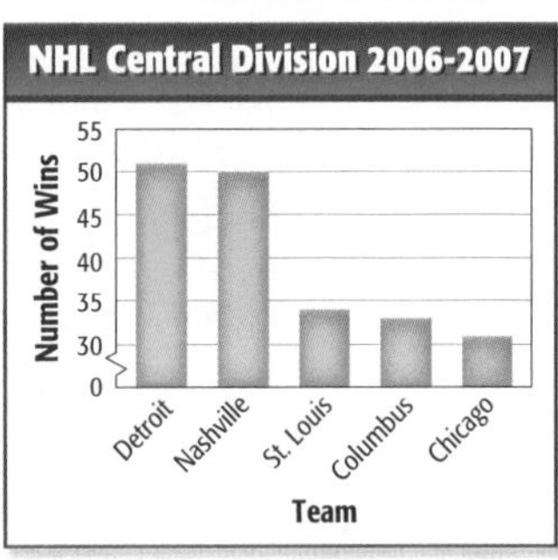

Additional Example

2 **TRANSPORTATION** The bar graph shows the results of a survey on school transportation. According to the graph, 6 times as many students ride the bus as walk. Determine whether this statement is accurate. Justify your reasoning.

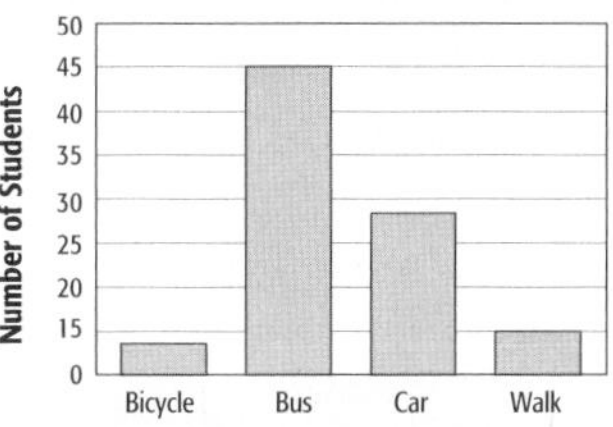

Sample answer: No; the broken scale makes it appear that 6 times as many rode the bus as walked, but that would mean that 6×15 or 90 students would have taken the bus and only 45 did; 45 is 3 times as many as the 15 who walked, not 6 times.

Tips for New Teachers

Misleading Graphs Discuss other signs of misleading graphs such as no titles, no labels, and a vertical axis that does not start at zero.

3 ASSESS

Formative Assessment

Use Exercises 1–4 to assess whether students can identify and evaluate misleading graphs.

Yesterday's News Ask students how previous lessons on displaying data helped with this lesson on evaluating misleading graphs.

Lesson 16

1 FOCUS

Vertical Alignment

Lesson 16
Use matrices to organize data and to find sums and differences.

After Lesson 16
Multiply a matrix by a scalar. Use matrices to solve systems of equations.

2 TEACH

Example 1 shows how to identify the dimensions and elements of a matrix. **Example 2** shows how to organize data in a matrix. **Example 3** shows how to add and subtract matrices.

Additional Examples

1 State the dimensions of the matrix. Then identify the position of the circled element.

[3 ④ 6 2]

1 by 4; first row, second column

2 **HIKING** The table shows the number of miles Ana and Kai hiked.

Hiker	Miles				
Ana	2	1.5	3.2	1.8	3
Kai	2.5	2	3	1.5	3.4

a. Organize the information in a matrix.

$$\begin{bmatrix} 2 & 1.5 & 3.2 & 1.8 & 3 \\ 2.5 & 2 & 3 & 1.5 & 3.4 \end{bmatrix}$$

b. Name the element in the second row, fourth column. What does it represent? 1.5; the miles Kai hiked

Concepts and Skills Bank

16 Matrices

A rectangular arrangement of numerical data in rows and columns is called a **matrix**. Each number in a matrix is called an **element**.

$$\begin{bmatrix} 9 & 0 \\ 2 & 6 \\ 1 & 3 \end{bmatrix} \text{3 rows}$$

2 columns

- This matrix has 3 rows and 2 columns.
- The number 1 is an element in the third row and the first column.

A matrix is described by its **dimensions**, or the number of rows and columns, with the number of rows stated first. The dimensions of the matrix above are 3 by 2.

EXAMPLE 1 Identify Dimensions and Elements

State the dimensions of the matrix $\begin{bmatrix} 14 & ⑦ & 4 \\ 10 & 19 & 9 \end{bmatrix}$. Then identify the position of the circled element.

The matrix has 2 rows and 3 columns. So, the dimensions of the matrix are 2 by 3. The circled element is in the first row, second column.

$$\begin{bmatrix} 14 & ⑦ & 4 \\ 10 & 19 & 9 \end{bmatrix} \text{2 rows}$$

3 columns

Real-World EXAMPLE 2 Use a Matrix to Organize Data

TRACK AND FIELD The table shows the times of two athletes at a track and field meet.

Athlete	Event			
	100m	200m	400m	800m
Katherine	12.50	25.50	56.45	1:53.75
Brianne	12.25	25.55	57.65	1:54.35

a. Organize the information in a matrix.

$$\begin{bmatrix} 12.50 & 25.50 & 56.45 & 1{:}53.75 \\ 12.25 & 25.55 & 57.65 & 1{:}54.35 \end{bmatrix}$$ The matrix has 2 rows and 4 columns, like the information in the table.

b. Name the element in the first row, third column. What does it represent?

The element is 56.45. It is Katherine's time for the 400m event.

Key Concept Add or Subtract Matrices

For Your FOLDABLE

Words Two matrices with the same dimensions can be added or subtracted by adding or subtracting their corresponding elements.

Symbols

$$\begin{bmatrix} a & b \\ c & d \end{bmatrix} + \begin{bmatrix} e & f \\ g & h \end{bmatrix} = \begin{bmatrix} a+e & b+f \\ c+g & d+h \end{bmatrix}$$

$$\begin{bmatrix} a & b \\ c & d \end{bmatrix} - \begin{bmatrix} e & f \\ g & h \end{bmatrix} = \begin{bmatrix} a-e & b-f \\ c-g & d-h \end{bmatrix}$$

Example

$$\begin{bmatrix} 1 & 4 \\ 0 & 2 \end{bmatrix} + \begin{bmatrix} 5 & 5 \\ 1 & 3 \end{bmatrix} = \begin{bmatrix} 1+5 & 4+5 \\ 0+1 & 2+3 \end{bmatrix} \text{ or } \begin{bmatrix} 6 & 9 \\ 1 & 5 \end{bmatrix}$$

EXAMPLE 3 Add and Subtract Matrices

Add or subtract. If there is no sum or difference, write *impossible*.

a. $\begin{bmatrix} 7 & -6 & 2 \\ 4 & 6 & 8 \end{bmatrix} + \begin{bmatrix} 10 & 4 \\ -1 & 7 \end{bmatrix}$

The first matrix is 2 by 3. The second matrix is 2 by 2. Since the matrices do not have the same dimensions, it is impossible to add them.

b. $\begin{bmatrix} 0 & 2 \\ -3 & 4 \\ 1 & 4 \end{bmatrix} + \begin{bmatrix} 7 & 5 \\ 2 & 1 \\ -3 & 5 \end{bmatrix}$

$$\begin{bmatrix} 0 & 2 \\ -3 & 4 \\ 1 & 4 \end{bmatrix} + \begin{bmatrix} 7 & 5 \\ 2 & 1 \\ -3 & 5 \end{bmatrix} = \begin{bmatrix} 0+7 & 2+5 \\ -3+2 & 4+1 \\ 1+(-3) & 4+5 \end{bmatrix} = \begin{bmatrix} 7 & 7 \\ -1 & 5 \\ -2 & 9 \end{bmatrix}$$

c. $\begin{bmatrix} 12 & 5 & 2 \\ 0 & 1 & -1 \end{bmatrix} - \begin{bmatrix} 3 & 5 & 1 \\ 9 & -6 & 0 \end{bmatrix}$

$$\begin{bmatrix} 12 & 5 & 2 \\ 0 & 1 & -1 \end{bmatrix} - \begin{bmatrix} 3 & 5 & 1 \\ 9 & -6 & 0 \end{bmatrix} = \begin{bmatrix} 12-3 & 5-5 & 2-1 \\ 0-9 & 1-(-6) & -1-0 \end{bmatrix} = \begin{bmatrix} 9 & 0 & 1 \\ -9 & 7 & -1 \end{bmatrix}$$

Exercises

1. **WEATHER** The table shows the high and low temperatures in a city for five days.

Temperature (°F)	Mon.	Tues.	Wed.	Thurs.	Fri.
High	76	79	71	69	74
Low	46	51	43	53	48

a. Organize the data in a matrix. $\begin{bmatrix} 76 & 79 & 71 & 69 & 74 \\ 46 & 51 & 43 & 53 & 48 \end{bmatrix}$

b. What are the dimensions of the matrix? **2 by 5**

c. What is the element in the first row, fourth column? What does it represent? **69; the high temperature on Thursday**

Add or subtract. If there is no sum or difference, write *impossible*.

2. $\begin{bmatrix} 3 & 2 \\ -2 & 8 \end{bmatrix} + \begin{bmatrix} 5 & -2 \\ 5 & 1 \end{bmatrix}$ $\begin{bmatrix} 8 & 0 \\ 3 & 9 \end{bmatrix}$

3. $\begin{bmatrix} 11 \\ 16 \\ 4 \end{bmatrix} - \begin{bmatrix} 7 \\ 19 \\ 2 \end{bmatrix}$ $\begin{bmatrix} 4 \\ -3 \\ 2 \end{bmatrix}$

4. $\begin{bmatrix} 4 & 6 & 5 \end{bmatrix} - \begin{bmatrix} 6 & 14 & 7 \\ 5 & -3 & 8 \end{bmatrix}$ **impossible**

5. $\begin{bmatrix} 4 & 7 & 2 \\ 6 & 2 & -4 \end{bmatrix} + \begin{bmatrix} 1 & 3 & 6 \\ -4 & 5 & 7 \end{bmatrix}$ $\begin{bmatrix} 5 & 10 & 8 \\ 2 & 7 & 3 \end{bmatrix}$

6. $\begin{bmatrix} -1 & 2 & 6 & 8 \end{bmatrix} + \begin{bmatrix} 3 & 6 & -2 & 4 \end{bmatrix}$ $\begin{bmatrix} 2 & 8 & 4 & 12 \end{bmatrix}$

7. $\begin{bmatrix} 1 & 3 & 1 \\ 2 & 7 & 0 \end{bmatrix} + \begin{bmatrix} 3 & -7 \\ 15 & 9 \end{bmatrix}$ **impossible**

8. $\begin{bmatrix} 12 & 6 \\ -3 & 2 \end{bmatrix} - \begin{bmatrix} 3 & 11 \\ 4 & 9 \end{bmatrix}$ $\begin{bmatrix} 9 & -5 \\ -7 & -7 \end{bmatrix}$

9. $\begin{bmatrix} 2 & -3 \\ 10 & 11 \\ 15 & -4 \end{bmatrix} + \begin{bmatrix} -1 & -6 \\ 2 & -3 \\ -7 & 3 \end{bmatrix}$ $\begin{bmatrix} 1 & -9 \\ 12 & 8 \\ 8 & -1 \end{bmatrix}$

10. **ACTIVITIES** Janice practices trumpet 1.5 hours on Monday, 1 hour on Tuesday, and 0.5 hour on Wednesday. She practices soccer 2 hours on Monday, 1.5 hours on Tuesday, and 2 hours on Wednesday.

a. Organize this information in a matrix. $\begin{bmatrix} 1.5 & 1 & 0.5 \\ 2 & 1.5 & 2 \end{bmatrix}$

b. Name the element in the second row, third column and describe what it represents. **2; Janice practices soccer 2 hours on Wednesday.**

Concepts and Skills Bank

Additional Example

3 Add or subtract. If there is no sum or difference, write *impossible.*

a. $\begin{bmatrix} 5 & -2 \\ 10 & -5 \end{bmatrix} + \begin{bmatrix} 4 & 7 \\ -8 & 4 \end{bmatrix}$ $\begin{bmatrix} 9 & 5 \\ 2 & -1 \end{bmatrix}$

b. $\begin{bmatrix} 4 & 12 \\ -9 & 6 \\ 0 & 5 \end{bmatrix} + \begin{bmatrix} 3 & -7 & 1 \\ -4 & 4 & 10 \end{bmatrix}$ impossible

c. $\begin{bmatrix} 6 & 0 & 2 \\ -8 & 5 & 8 \end{bmatrix} - \begin{bmatrix} 3 & -4 & 5 \\ -1 & 6 & 7 \end{bmatrix}$ $\begin{bmatrix} 3 & 4 & -3 \\ -7 & -1 & 1 \end{bmatrix}$

Tips for New Teachers

Adding and Subtracting Matrices Some students may easily add and subtract matrices using mental math, while others may struggle to keep the rows and columns of numbers straight. Until they are familiar with matrices, encourage students to use the step-by-step method for adding and subtracting as shown in the examples, or some other method, such as circling and crossing off elements.

3 ASSESS

Formative Assessment

Use Exercises 1–10 to assess whether students understand how to organize data in a matrix and add and subtract matrices.

Ticket Out the Door Ask students to write two 3 by 2 matrices and then find their sum or difference. Have them turn in the matrices as they leave the classroom.

Concepts and Skills Bank

Page 811, Extra Practice (Lesson 1-4)

7.

x	y
3	6
4	9
5	1

8.

x	y
2	1
4	4
6	7
4	3

Page 811, Extra Practice (Lesson 1-6)

1. the faster an airplane travels, the more miles it will cover in three hours
2. there is no relationship between weight and shoe size
3. as the outside temperature increases, the heating bill decreases; as the outside temperature decreases, the heating bill increases

4a.

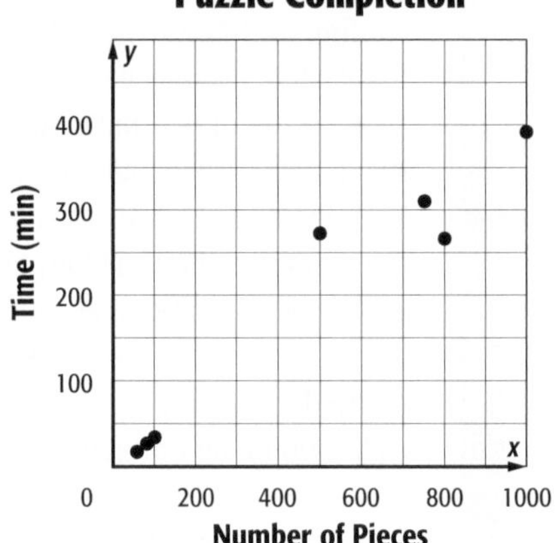

Page 813, Extra Practice (Lesson 2-6)

9-14.

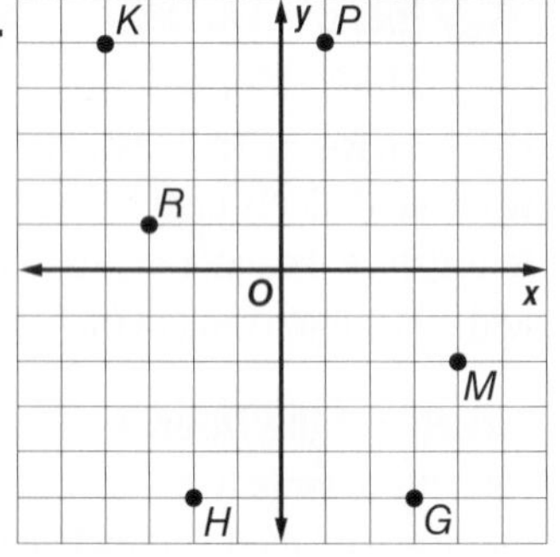

Page 814, Extra Practice (Lesson 2-7)

2.

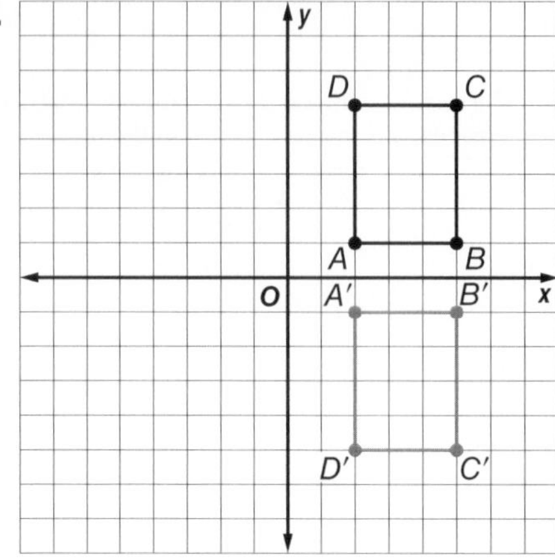

Page 816, Extra Practice (Lesson 4-2)

1. terms: 3, 4*x*, *x;* like terms: 4*x*, *x;* coefficients: 4, 1; constant: 3
2. terms: 5*n*, 2, −3*n;* like terms: 5*n*, −3*n;* coefficients: 5, −3; constant: 2
3. terms: 6, 1, 7*y;* like terms: 6, 1; coefficient: 7; constants: 6, 1
4. terms: 2*c*, *c*, 8*d;* like terms: 2*c*, *c;* coefficients: 2, 1, 8; constants: none
5. terms: 3*a*, −9, *b;* like terms: none; coefficients: 3, 1; constant: −9
6. terms: 2, 6*k*, 7, −5*k;* like terms: 2, 7 and 6*k*, −5*k;* coefficients: 6, −5; constants: 2, 7

Page 819, Extra Practice (Lesson 5-3)

13.

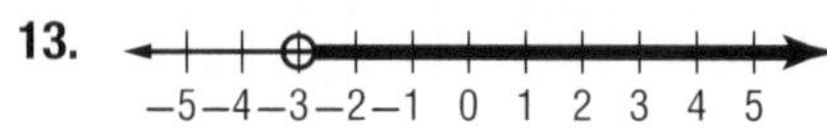

14. −5 −4 −3 −2 −1 0 1 2 3 4 5

15. −5 −4 −3 −2 −1 0 1 2 3 4 5

16. −5 −4 −3 −2 −1 0 1 2 3 4 5

17. −5 −4 −3 −2 −1 0 1 2 3 4 5

18. −5 −4 −3 −2 −1 0 1 2 3 4 5

Page 822, Extra Practice (Lesson 6-8)

1. 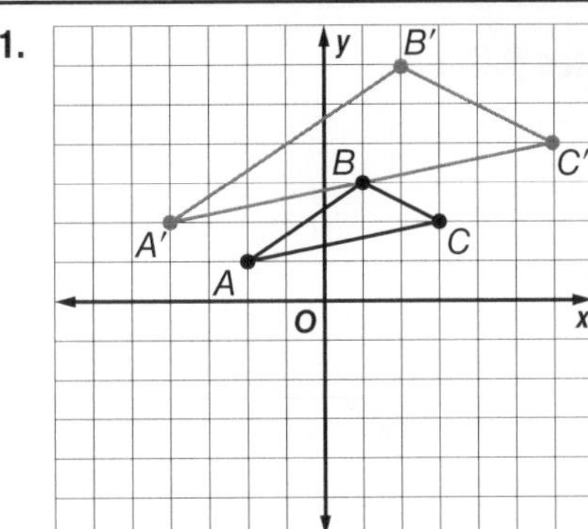

Page 825, Extra Practice (Lesson 7-8)

1. 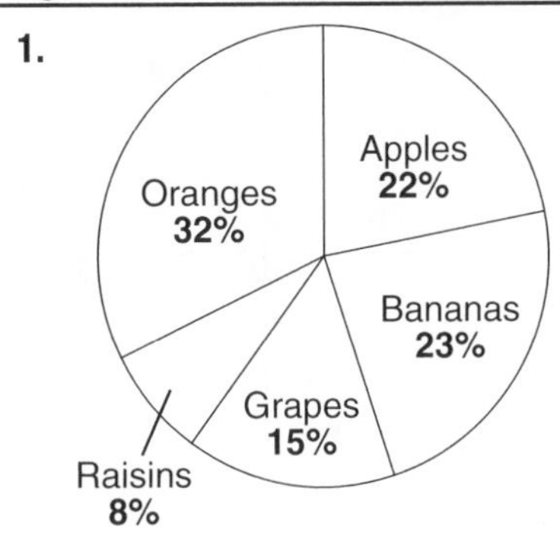

Page 826, Extra Practice (Lesson 8-2)

1. The terms have a common difference of 25. A term is 25 times the term number. $t = 25n$
2. The terms have a common difference of 1. A term is 38 more than the term number. $t = 38 + n$
3. The terms have a common difference of 4. A term is 4 times the term number. $t = 4n$
4. The terms have a common difference of 1. A term is 0.5 more than the term number. $t = 0.5 + n$
5. The terms have a common difference of $\frac{1}{2}$. A term is $\frac{1}{2}$ times the term number. $t = \frac{1}{2}n$
6. The terms have a common difference of 3. A term is 3 times the term number, plus 1. $t = 3n + 1$
7. $t = 5n$; 115
8. $t = 19 - n$; 6
9. $t = 3 - n$; -4
10. $t = 2n + 1$; 199
11. $t = 7n - 1$; 265
12. $t = -8 + 2n$; 126
13. $t = 4n - 4$; 196
14. $t = \frac{1}{2}(n) + 5$; 20

Page 826, Extra Practice (Lesson 8-3)

1.

x	y
4	2
4	3
4	5
4	6

2.

x	y
1	0
5	0
6	0
0	0

3.

x	y
2	0
1	1
0	2
−1	3

4.

x	y
0	−6
1	−4
2	−2
3	0

5.

x	y
8	3
7	2
6	1
5	0

6.

x	y
3	1
4	4
0	−8
2	−2

7.

x	y
0	−3
2	−2
4	−1
6	0

8.

x	y
0	1
3	2
−3	0
6	3

9.

x	y
1	−4
0	−2
−1	0
−2	2

10.

x	y
6	0
0	4
3	2
−3	6

11. 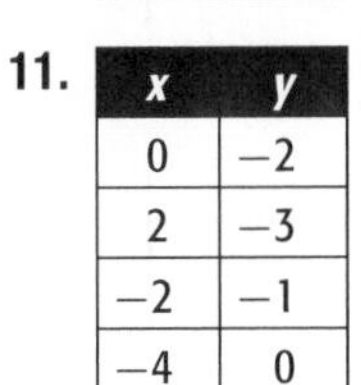

x	y
0	−2
2	−3
−2	−1
−4	0

12. 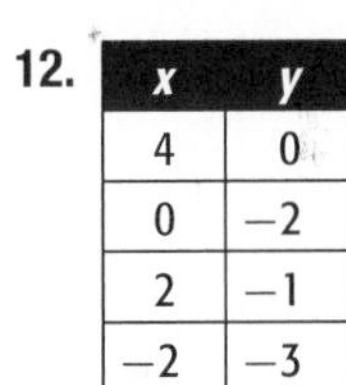

x	y
4	0
0	−2
2	−1
−2	−3

13. 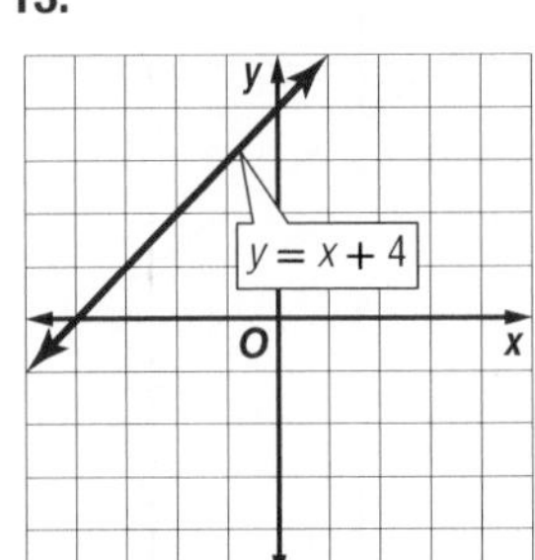

14. 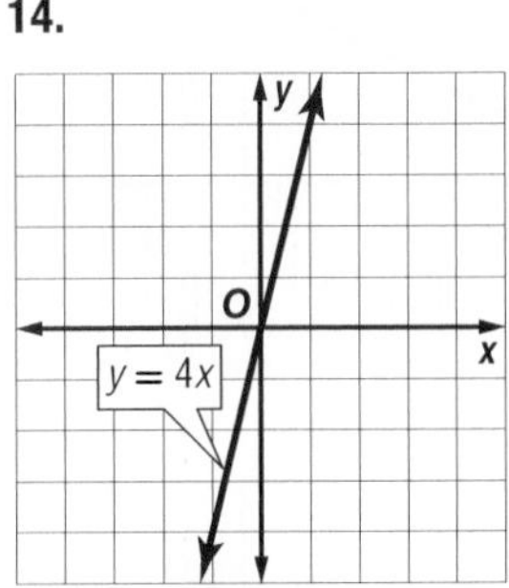

15.

$x + y = 3$

16.

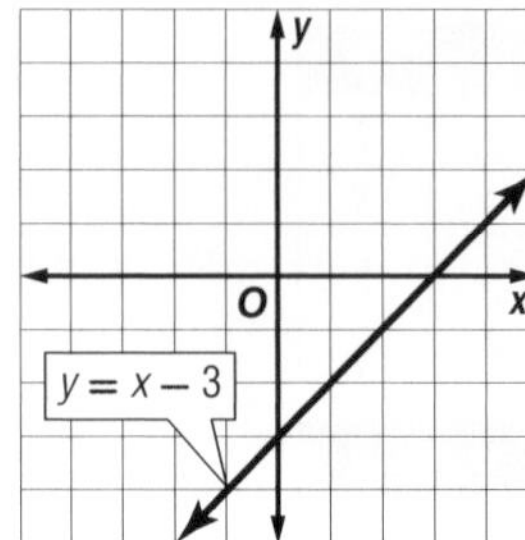

17.

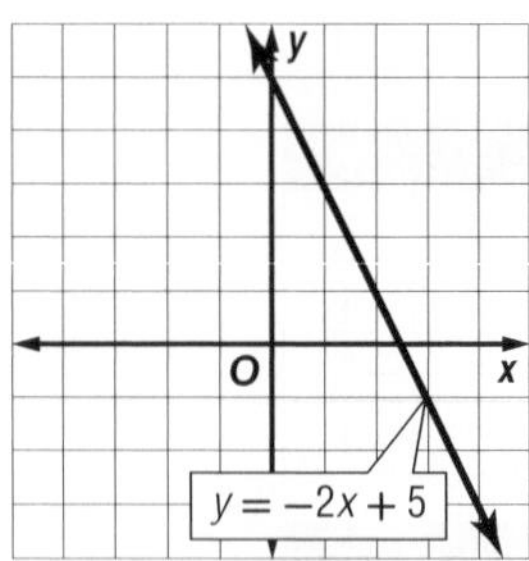

18.

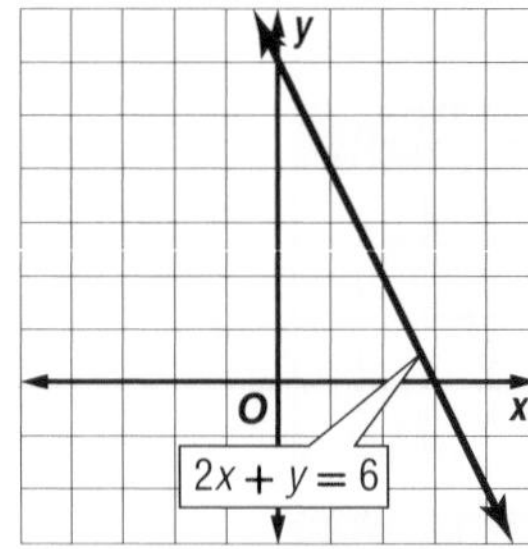

Page 828, Extra Practice (Lesson 8-7)

7.

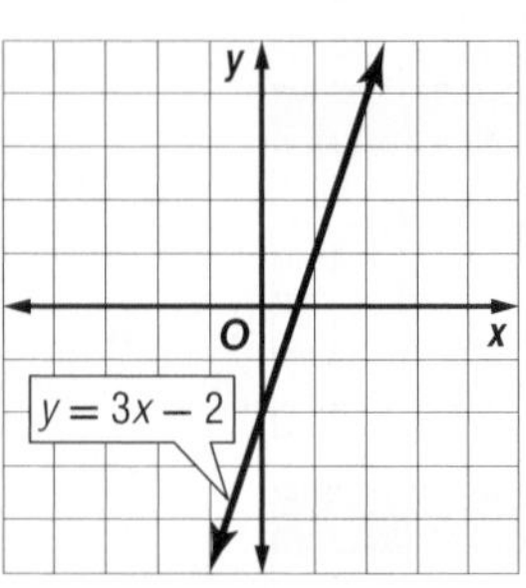

8.

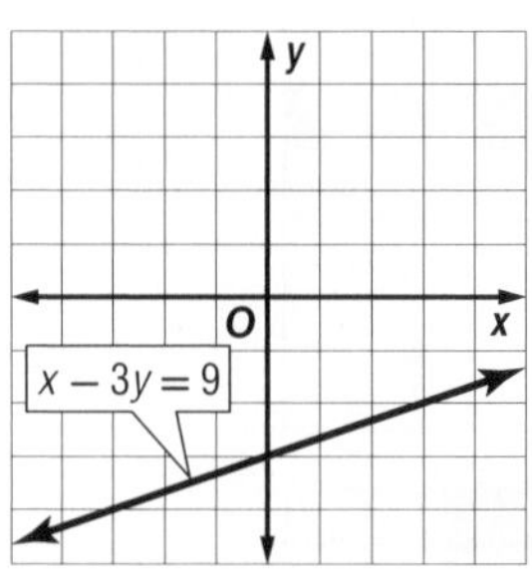

9.

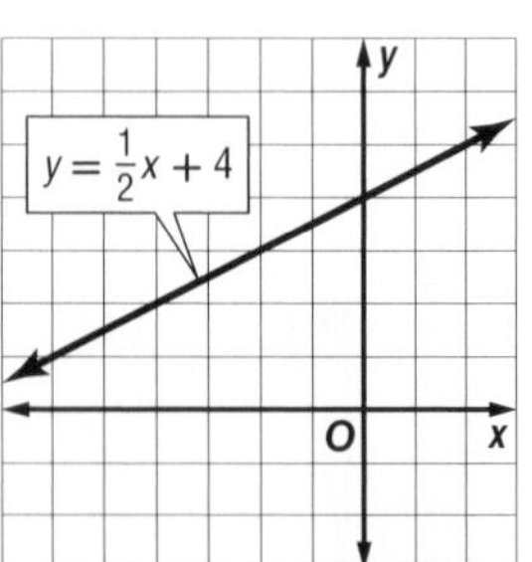

10.

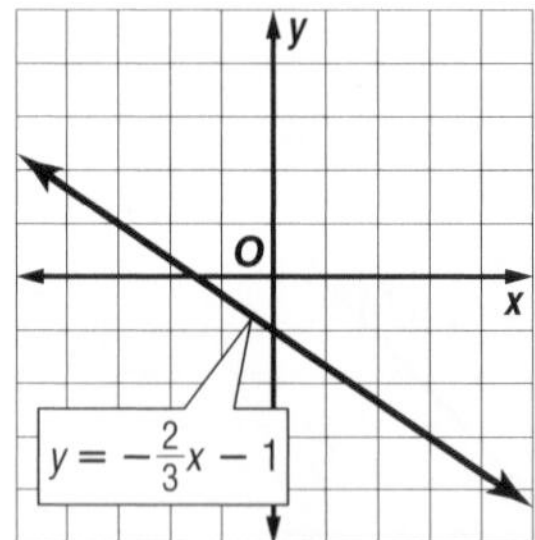

11.

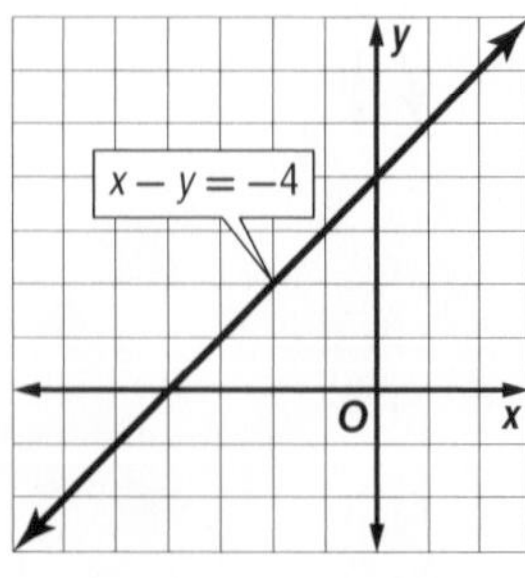

12.

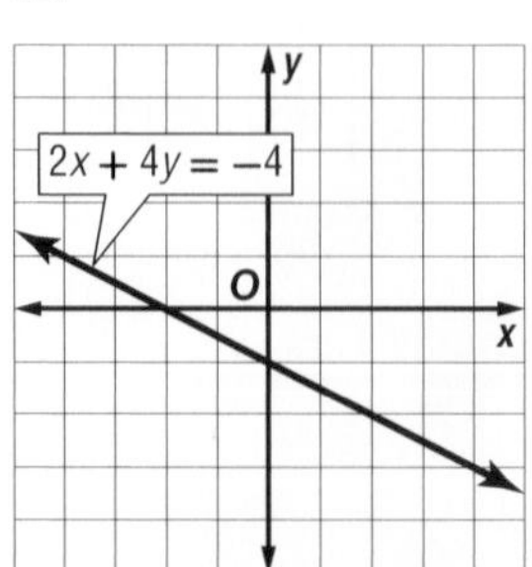

Page 828, Extra Practice (Lesson 8-9)

1a.

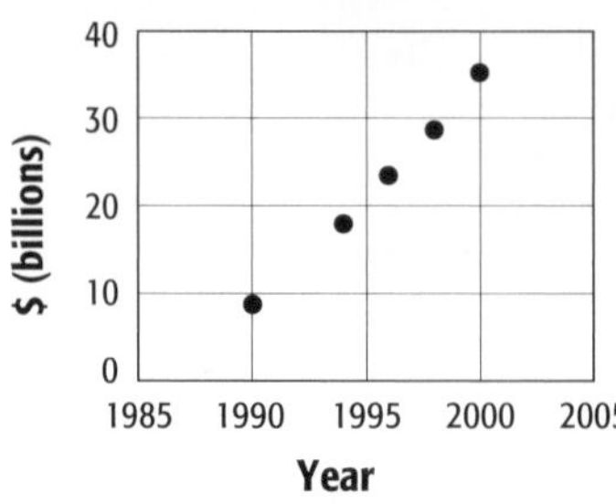

Page 829, Extra Practice (Lesson 8-10)

1.

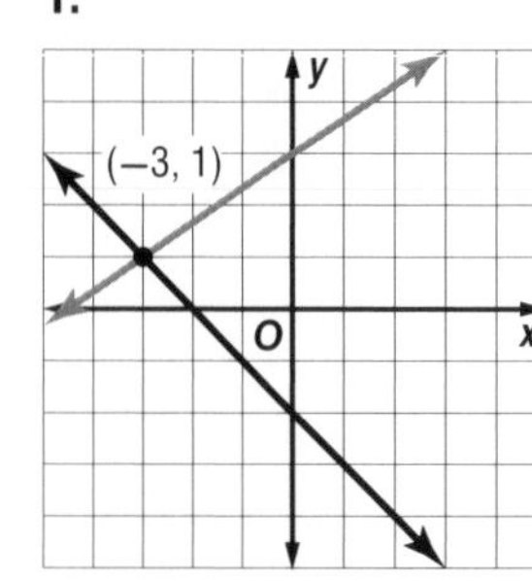

2.

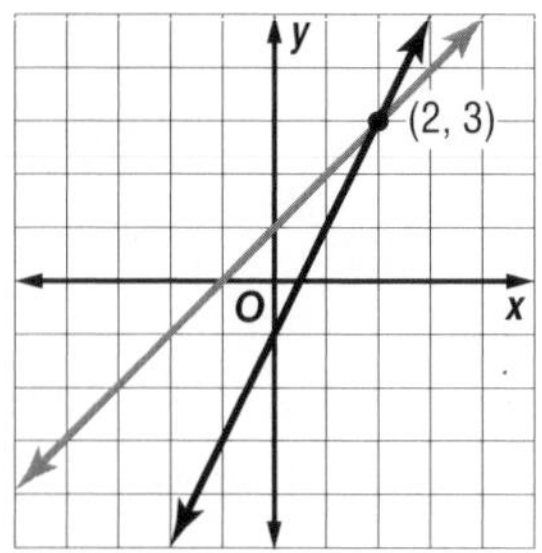

3.

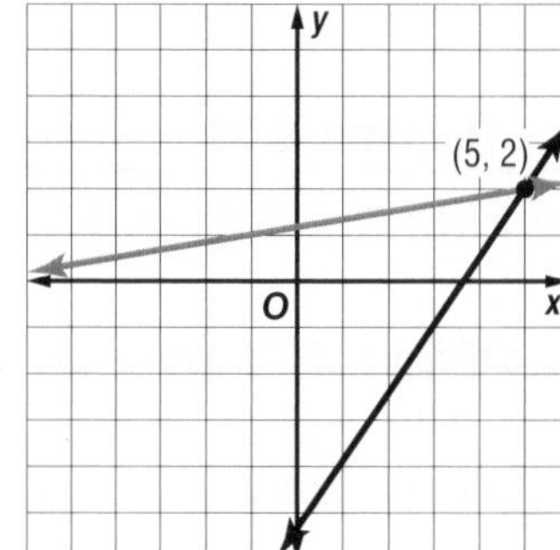

4.

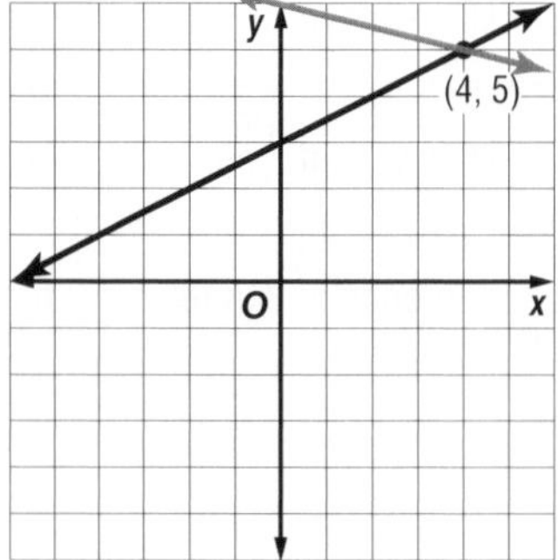

Page 831, Extra Practice (Lesson 9-7)

1. Nonlinear; the graph is a curve.
2. Linear; the graph is a straight line.
3. Nonlinear; the graph is a curve.
4. Linear; the graph is a straight line.
5. Nonlinear; the graph is a curve.
6. Linear; the graph is a straight line.
7. Linear; the graph is a straight line.
8. Nonlinear; the graph is a curve.
9. Nonlinear; the graph is a curve.
10. Linear; as x increases by 2, y increases by 2.
11. Linear; as x increases by 5, y increases by 6.

Page 831, Extra Practice (Lesson 9-8)

1. 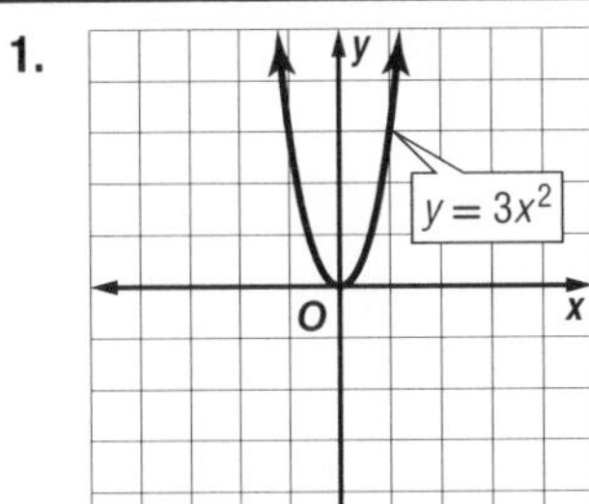

2. 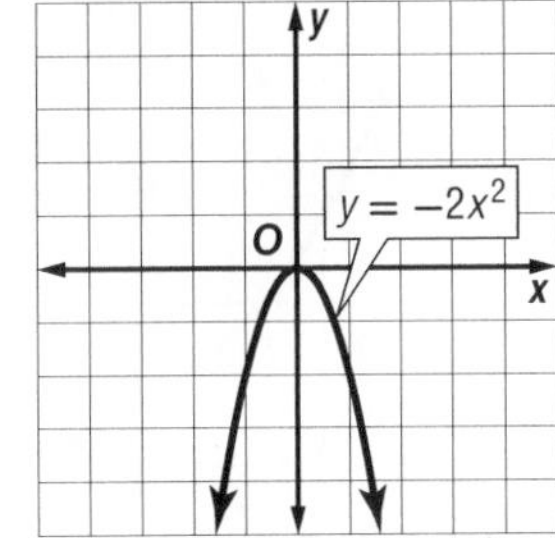

3. 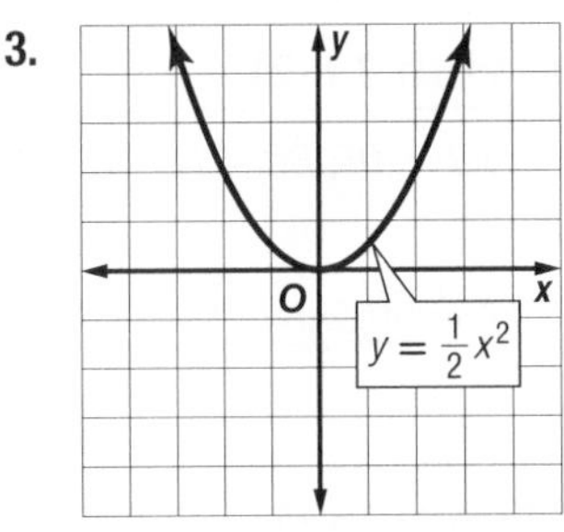

4. 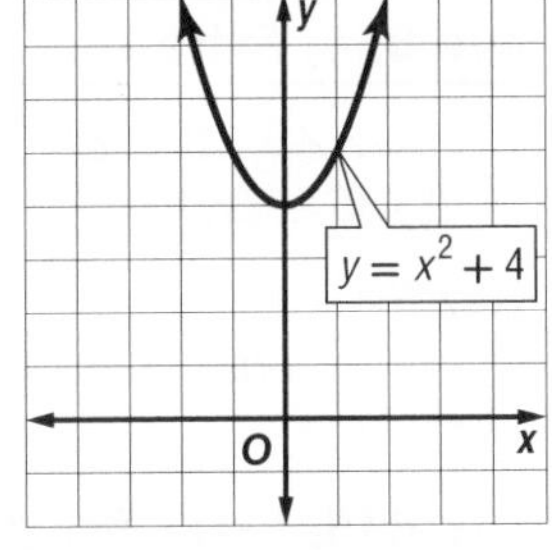

5. 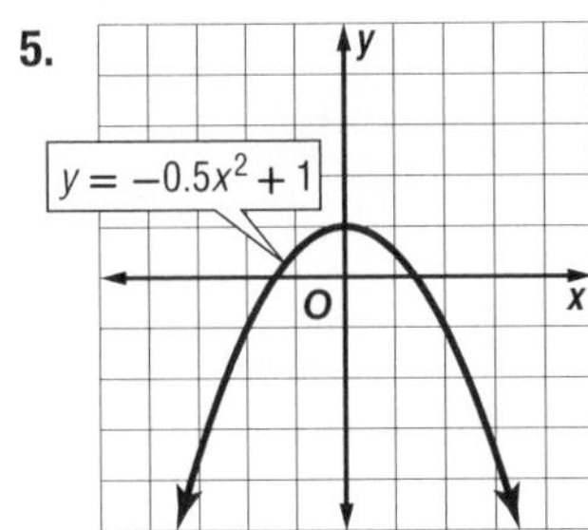

6. 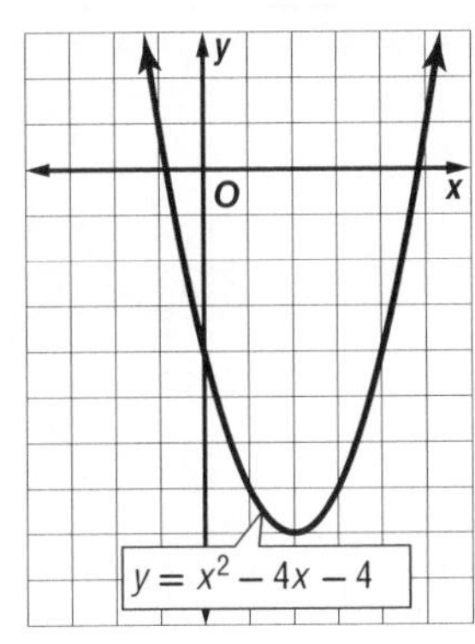

7. 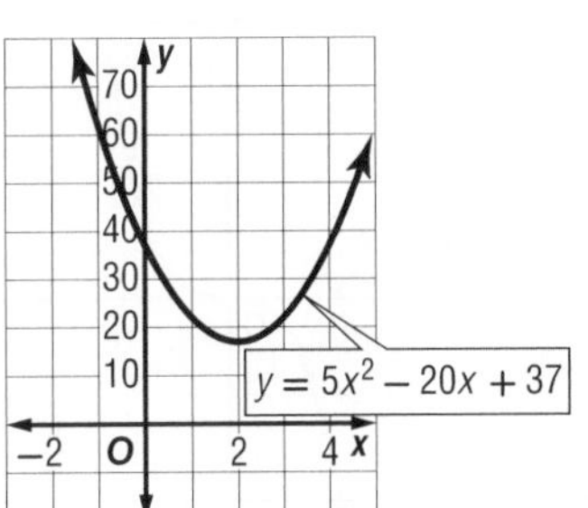

8. 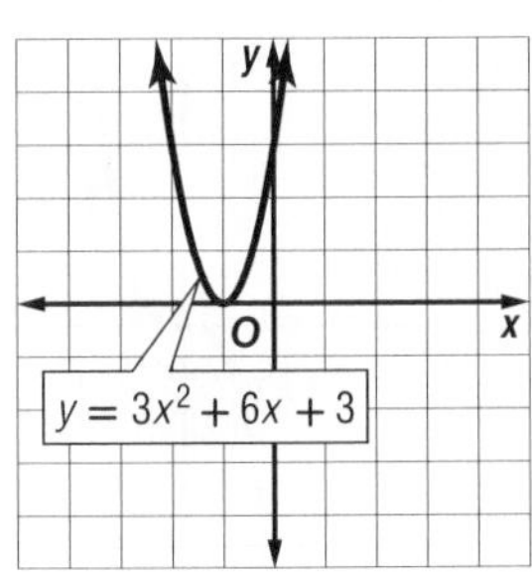

9. 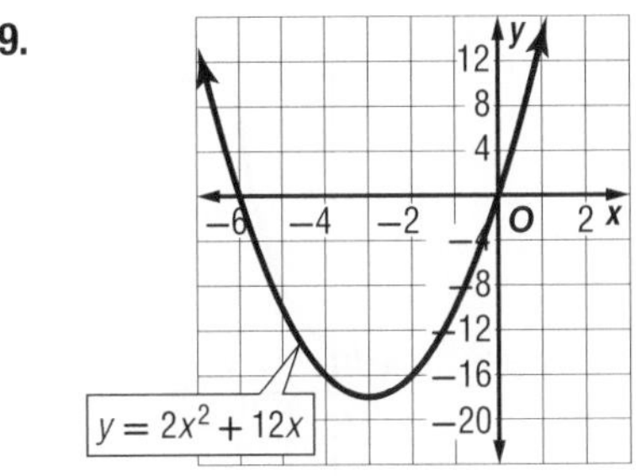

10. 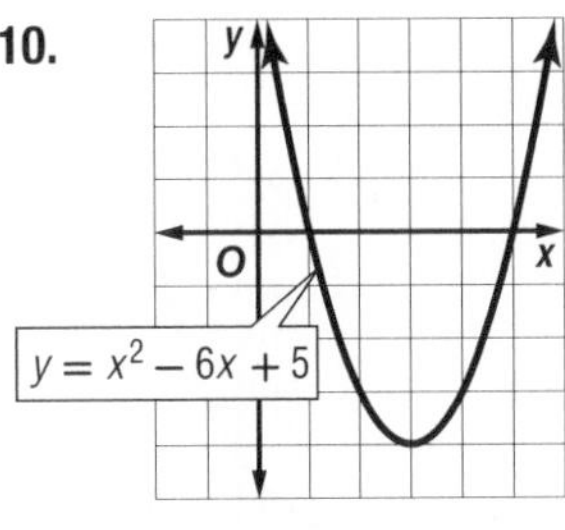

11. 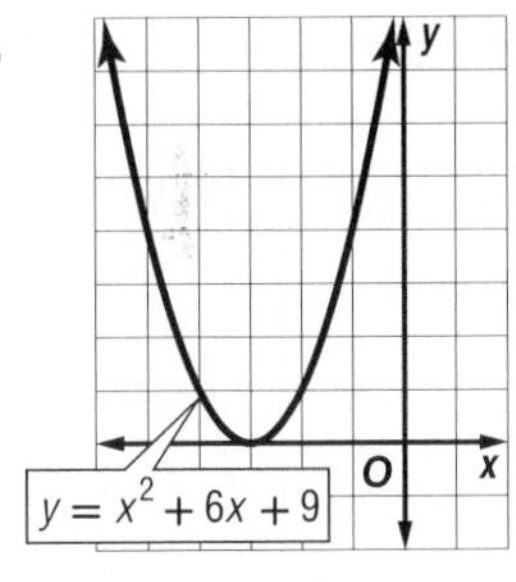

12. 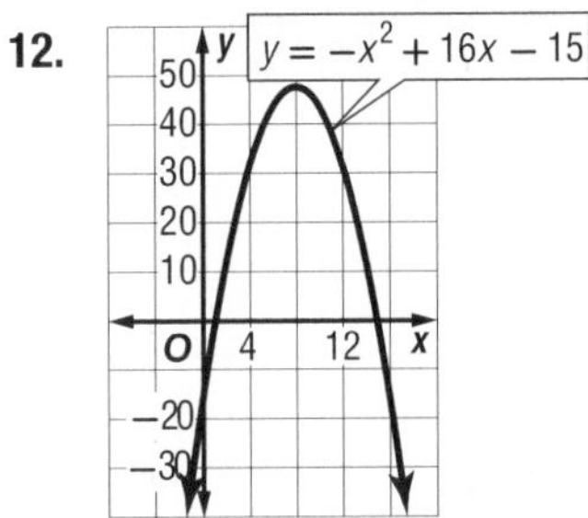

13. 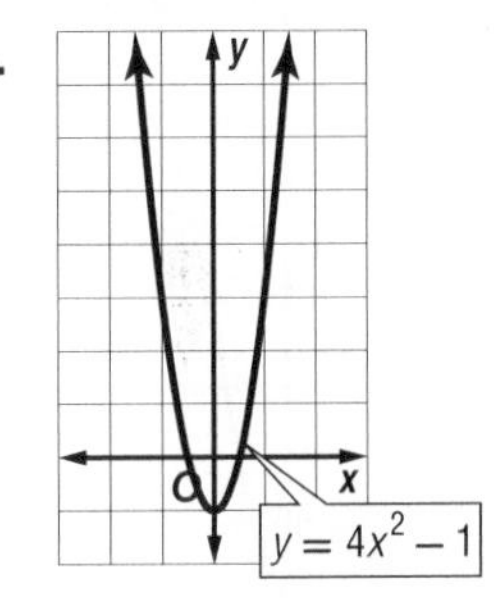

14. 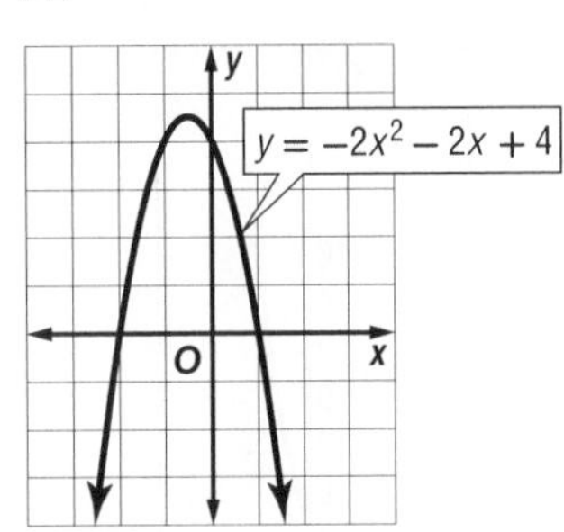

15. 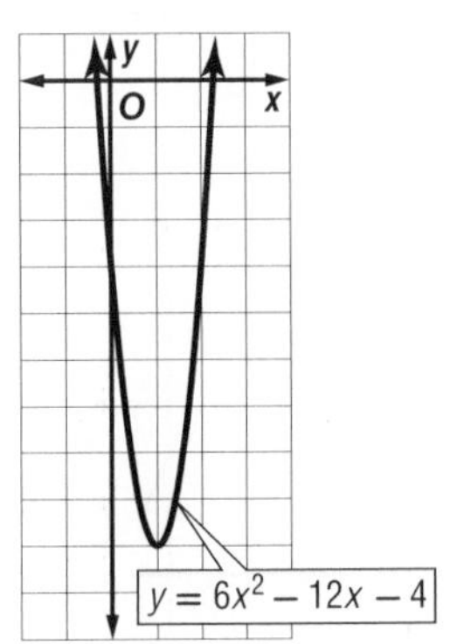

Page 832, Extra Practice (Lesson 9-9)

1.

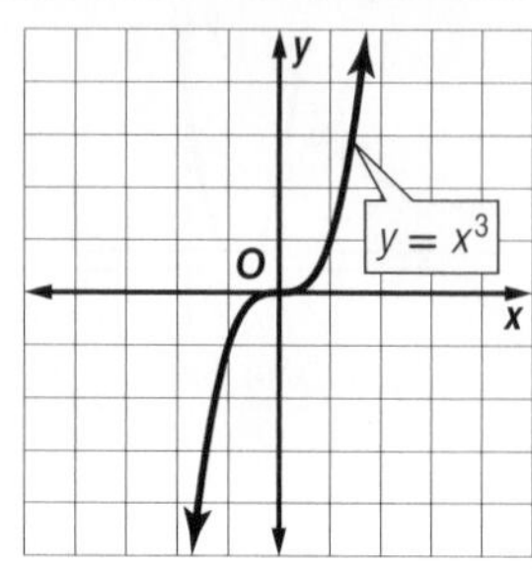

2.

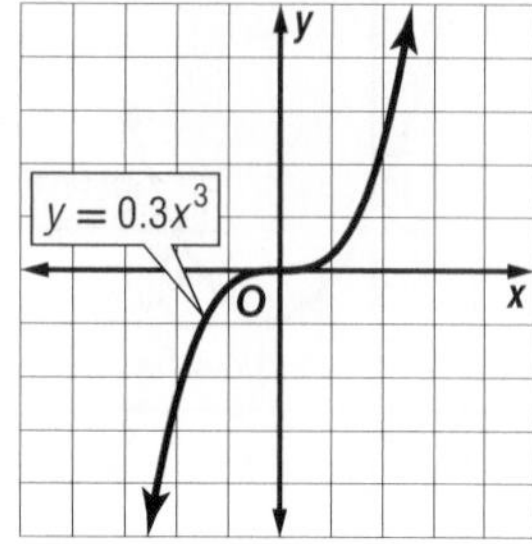

3.

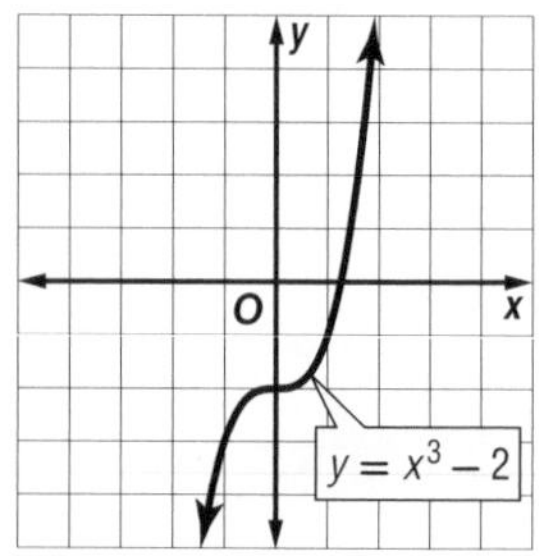

4.

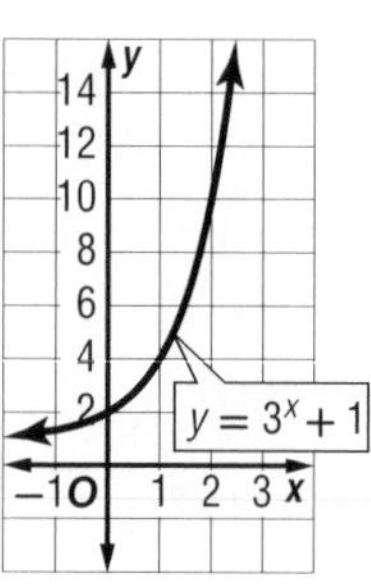

5.

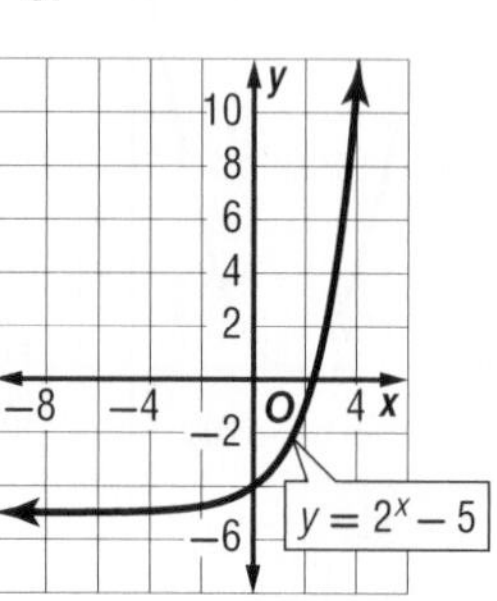

6.

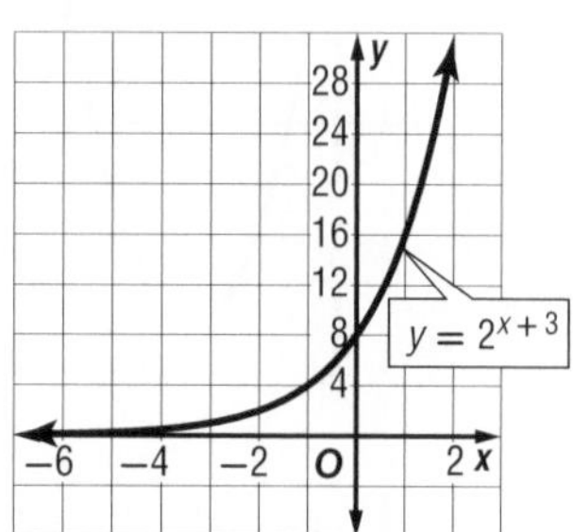

7.

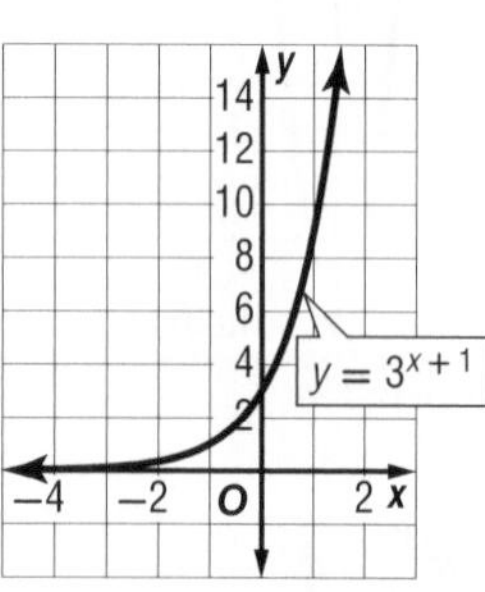

8.

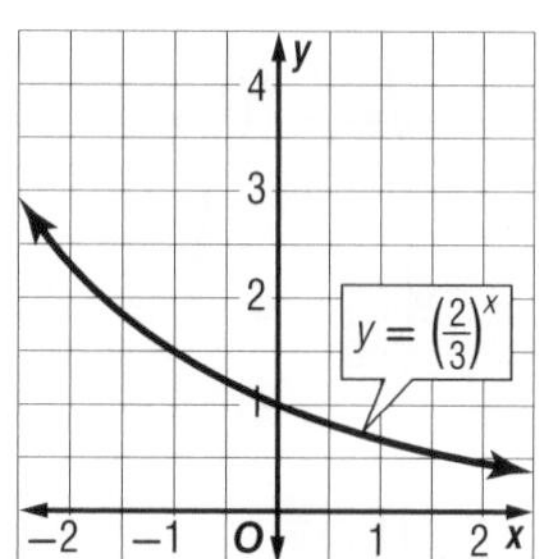

9.

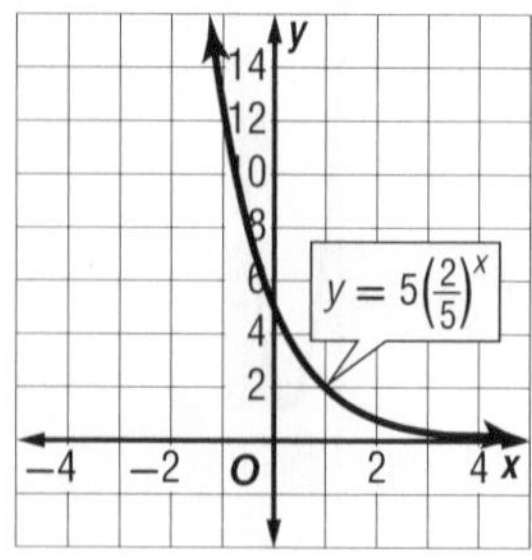

10.

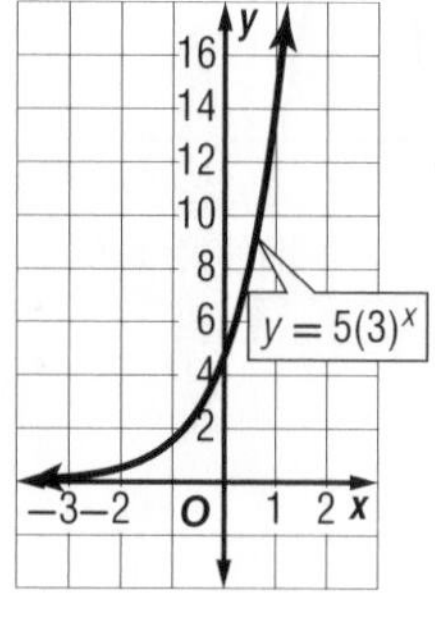

11.

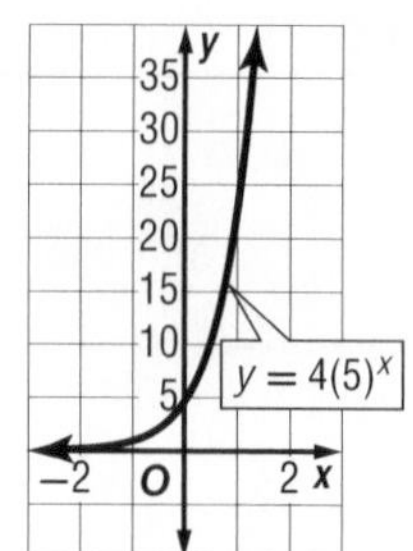

12.

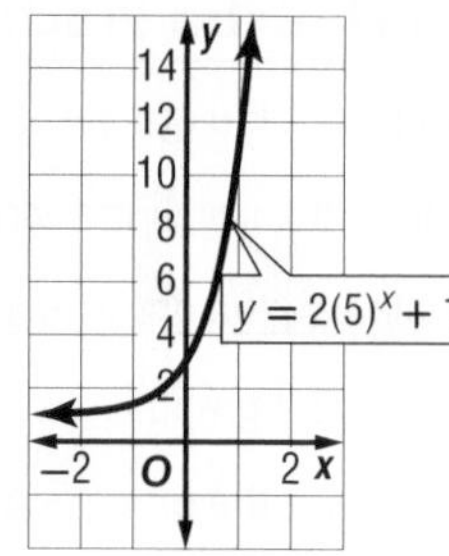

13.

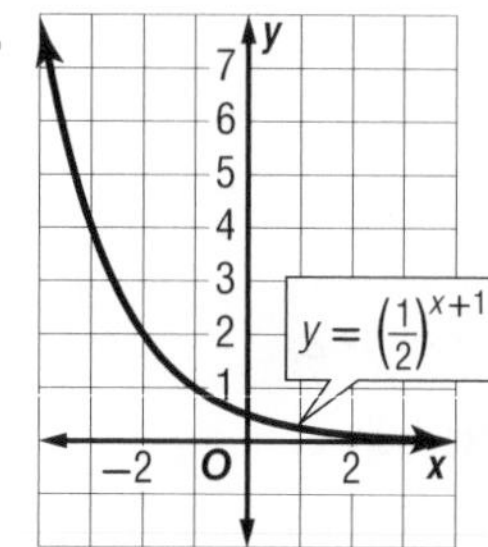

14.

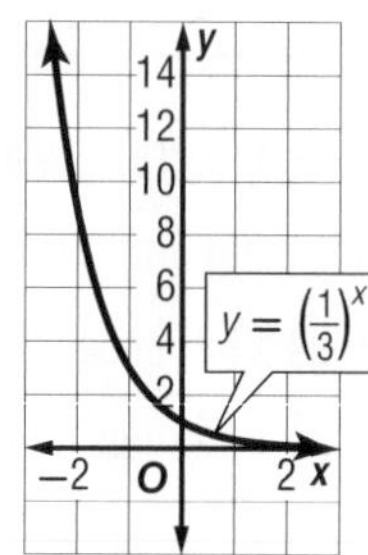

15.

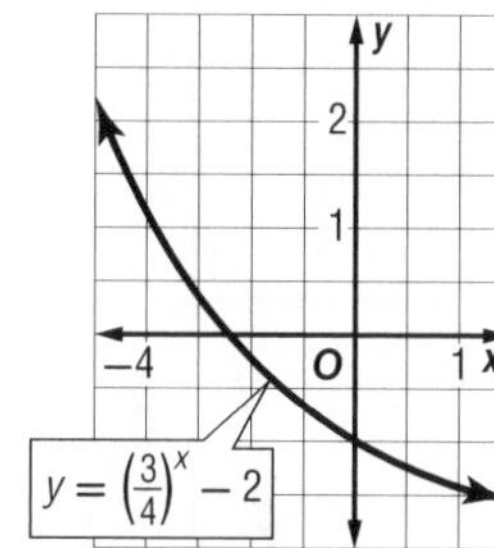

Page 834, Extra Practice (Lesson 11-2)

1. $\angle A \cong \angle D; \angle B \cong \angle F; \angle C \cong \angle E; \overline{AB} \cong \overline{DF}, \overline{BC} \cong \overline{FE}, \overline{AC} \cong \overline{DE}; \triangle ABC \cong \triangle DFE$

2. $\angle G \cong \angle K; \angle H \cong \angle J; \angle GIH \cong \angle KIJ; \overline{GH} \cong \overline{KJ}, \overline{HI} \cong \overline{JI}, \overline{GI} \cong \overline{KI}; \triangle GHI \cong \triangle KJI$

Page 835, Extra Practice (Lesson 11-3)

1.

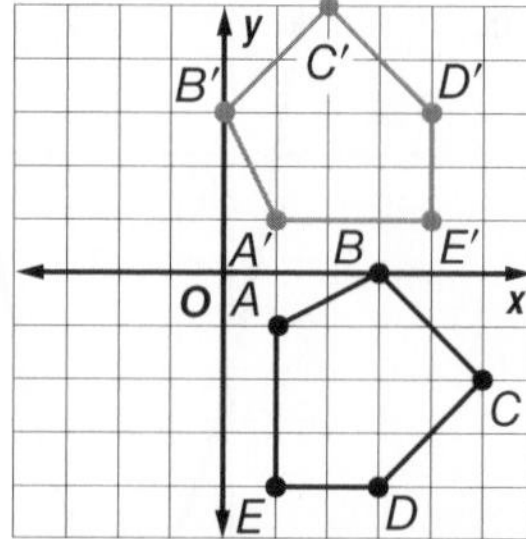

3.

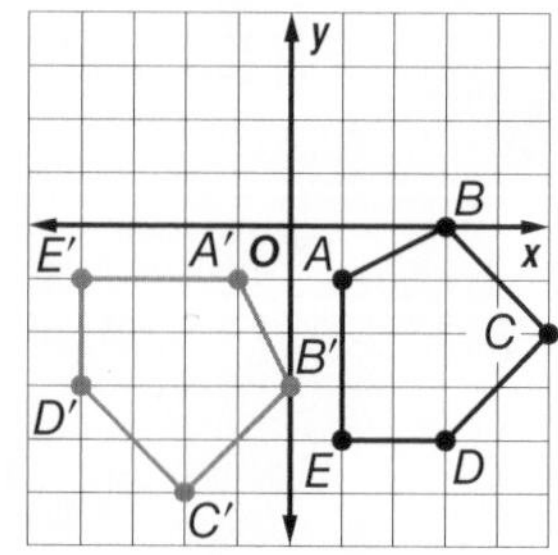

Page 837, Extra Practice (Lesson 12-1)

1. rectangular prism; bases: *ABCD, EFGH*, or *ADHE, BCGF*, or *ABFE, DCGH;* faces: *ABCD, ADHE, DHGC, BCGF, ABFE, EFGH;* edges: $\overline{AB}$, $\overline{BC}$, $\overline{CD}$, $\overline{DA}$, $\overline{EF}$, $\overline{FG}$, $\overline{GH}$, $\overline{HE}$, $\overline{AE}$, $\overline{DH}$, $\overline{CG}$, $\overline{BF}$; vertices: *A, B, C, D, E, F, G, H*
2. triangular prism; bases: *HJK, LMN;* faces: *HJK, LMN, HJML, KJMN, HLNK;* edges: $\overline{HJ}$, $\overline{JK}$, $\overline{KH}$, $\overline{LM}$, $\overline{MN}$, $\overline{NL}$, $\overline{JM}$, $\overline{HL}$, $\overline{KN}$; vertices: *H, J, K, L, M, N*
3. equilateral triangle
4. isosceles triangle
5. rectangle

Page 840, Extra Practice (Lesson 13-2)

1. **Ages of People**

Stem	Leaf
0	3 5 8
1	
2	1 4 6
3	0 5 5 8 9

2 | 1 = 21 years

2. **Prices of Bicycles**

Stem	Leaf
17	1 2 9
18	1 1 2 6
19	3 8

18 | 6 = $186

3. **Number of Vendors**

Stem	Leaf
1	7
2	1 4
3	7
4	
5	4
6	9
7	7
8	6
9	2

8 | 6 = 86 vendors

4. **Test Scores**

Stem	Leaf
5	4 9
6	1 7
7	3 5
8	2 3 9
9	3
10	2

6 | 7 = 67 points

Page 841, Extra Practice (Lesson 13-4)

1. **Ages of Home Owners**

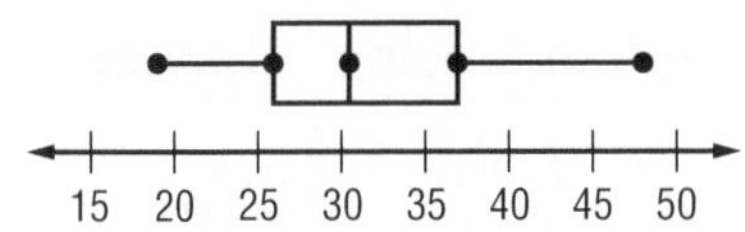

2. **Price of MP3 Players ($)**

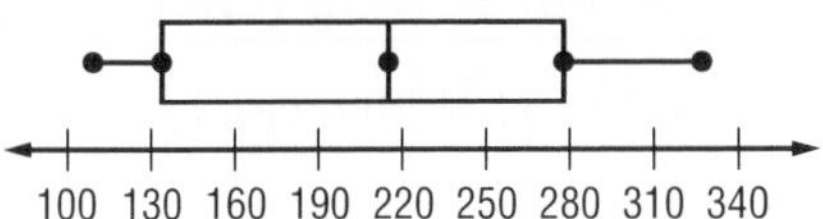

Page 841, Extra Practice (Lesson 13-5)

1. **Weekly Exercise Time**

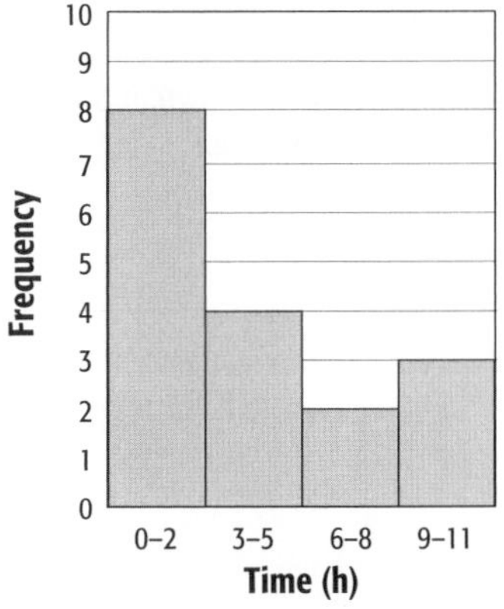

2. **Weekly Grocery Bill**

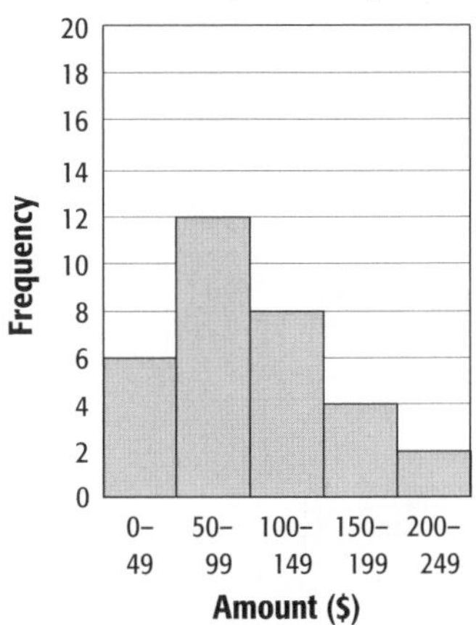

Page 842, Extra Practice (Lesson 13-7)

1. Unbiased; systematic random sample; because everyone goes to a grocery store, interviewing every third person ensures a random sample.
2. Biased; convenience sample; while it may be easiest to survey the entire school, only the seniors' opinion should matter.
3. Biased; voluntary response sample; members of the Blog Society would probably find blogging popular.
4. Unbiased; stratified random sample; this would show the flow of traffic over time.

Page 843, Mixed Problem Solving (Chapter 1)

1a. $\$1 + \$3 + \$0.75$

1b. $\$1 \times 3 + \$3 \times 2 + \$0.75 \times 3$; \$11.25

4. Sample answer: Yes, the actions are commutative. It does not matter in what order the actions are completed.

5a.

x	*y*	*(x, y)*
1	3.5	(1, 3.5)
2	7	(2, 7)
3	10.5	(3, 10.5)
4	14	(4, 14)
5	17.5	(5, 17.5)

5b.

Movie Rentals

Total Cost ($)

Number of Movies

6b.

Input *(x)*	80*d*	Output *(y)*
5	80(5)	400
7	80(7)	560
10	80(10)	800
13	80(13)	1040

6c.

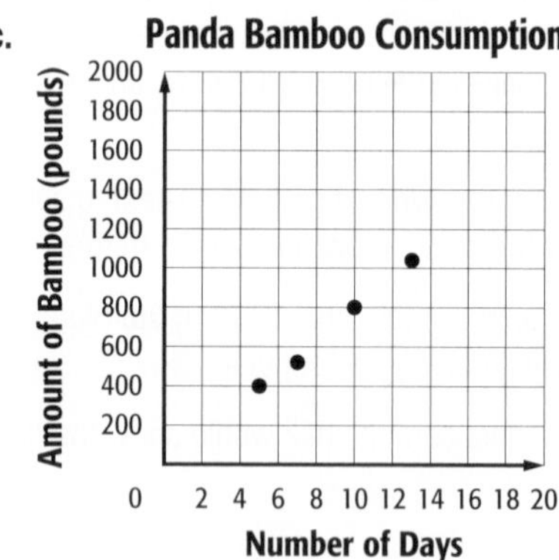

7a.

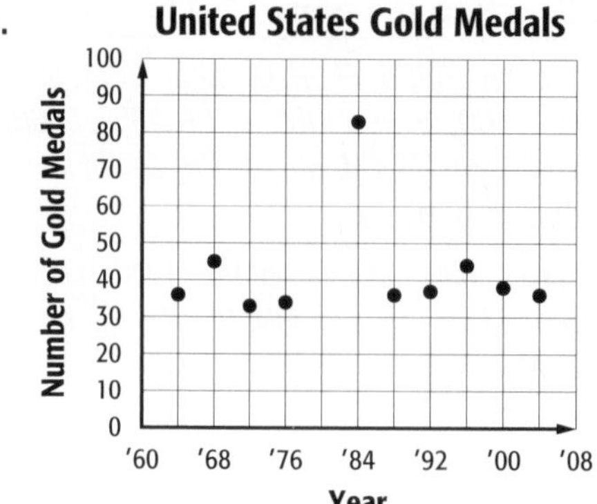

7b. Sample answer: The graph does not show a positive or negative relationship.

7c. Sample answer: There is not a positive or negative relationship, but the number of medals is around 40 each year. You could reasonably predict the number of gold medals in 2010 would be around 40.

Page 844, Mixed Problem Solving (Chapter 2)

10a.

$x + y = 5$		
x	*y*	*(x, y)*
0	5	(0, 5)
1	4	(1, 4)
2	3	(2, 3)
3	2	(3, 2)
4	1	(4, 1)
5	0	(5, 0)

10b.

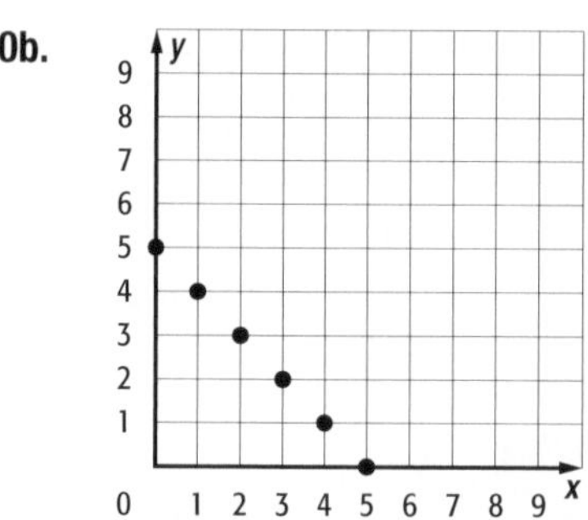

The graph will be a series of 6 points in a straight line crossing the x-axis at 5 and the y-axis at 5.

Page 845, Mixed Problem Solving (Chapter 3)

12. No, the left over piece is $4\frac{1}{4}$ ft long and $4\frac{5}{8} > 4\frac{1}{4}$.

Page 847, Mixed Problem Solving (Chapter 5)

9. Monday: $1\frac{1}{2}$ hr; Wednesday: $3\frac{1}{2}$ hr; Thursday: $1\frac{1}{2}$ hr; Saturday: $4\frac{1}{2}$ hr

Page 848, Mixed Problem Solving (Chapter 6)

1.

Team	Games	Win	Loss	W/L Ratio
Cougars	35	23	12	$\frac{23}{12}$
Bulldogs	36	30	6	$\frac{5}{1}$
Bears	33	22	11	$\frac{2}{1}$
Hawks	34	20	14	$\frac{10}{7}$
Sharks	36	26	10	$\frac{13}{5}$

5. No; the rates are not equal.

Page 849, Mixed Problem Solving (Chapter 7)

9.

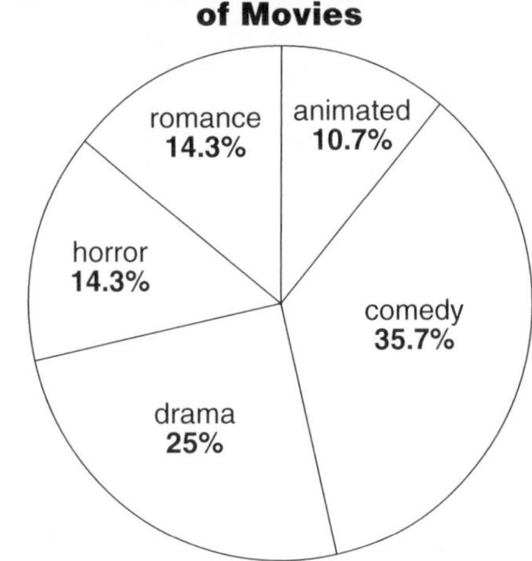

Page 850, Mixed Problem Solving (Chapter 8)

3. Sample answer: (1, 12) means they can get 1 movie and 12 boxes of popcorn. (2, 8) means they can get 2 movies and 8 boxes of popcorn. (3, 4) means they can get 3 movies and 4 boxes of popcorn.

7a.

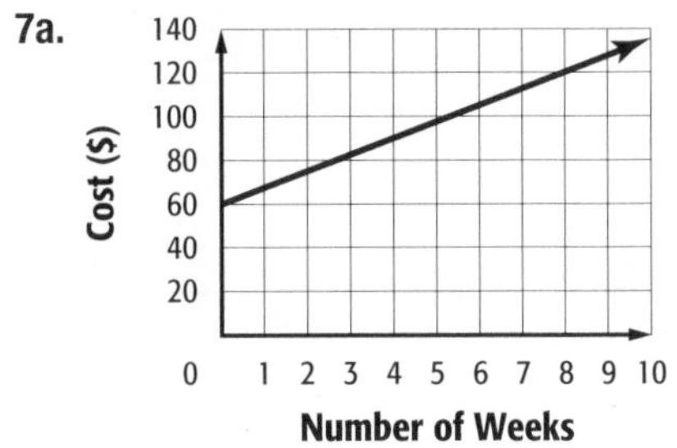

7b. The y-intercept is 59 and the slope is 7.7.

7c. The y-intercept represents the initiation fee of the club and the slope represents the weekly cost of using the club.

9a.

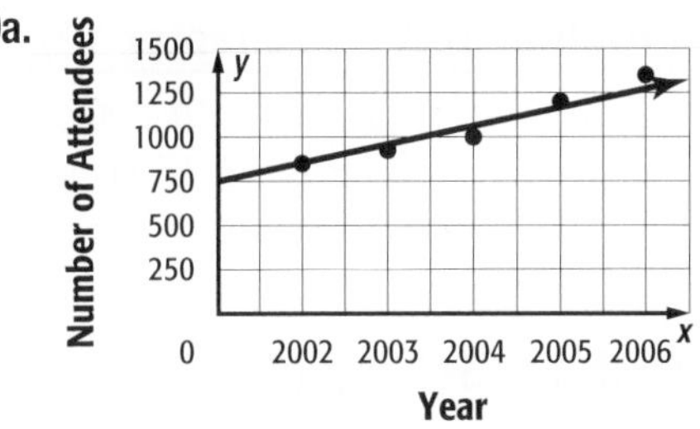

9b. $y = 100x - 199{,}350$; 1650 attendees

Page 851, Mixed Problem Solving (Chapter 9)

6. Mercury, Mars, Venus, Earth, Uranus, Neptune, Saturn, Jupiter

9a.

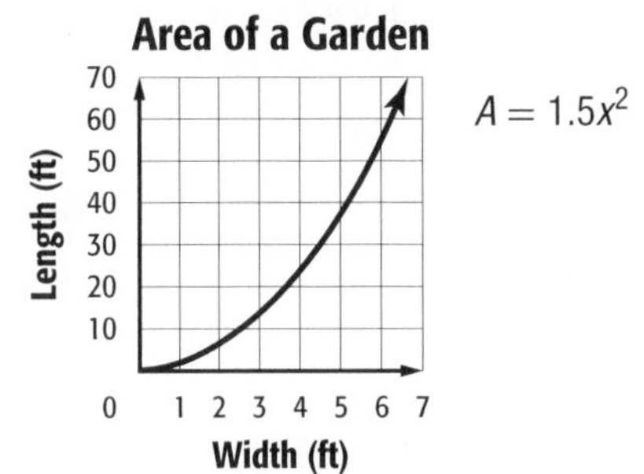

$A = 1.5x^2$

10a.

x	$N = 3^x$	(x, N)
1	$N = 3^1$	(1, 3)
2	$N = 3^2$	(2, 9)
3	$N = 3^3$	(3, 27)
4	$N = 3^4$	(4, 81)

10b.

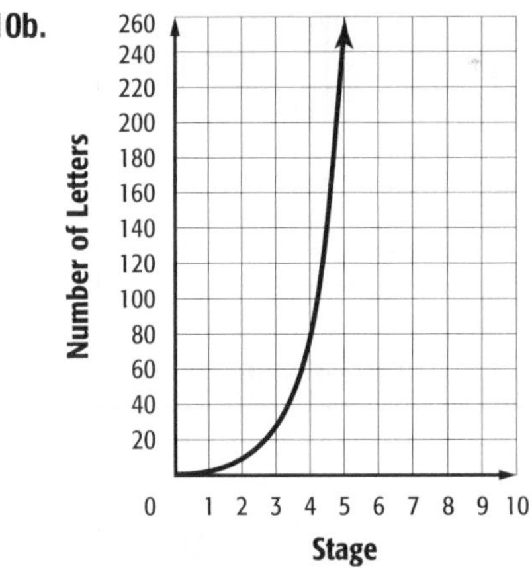

Page 852, Mixed Problem Solving (Chapter 10)

7. Neither; the distance between the submarine and the carrier is the same as the distance between the submarine and the battleship.

Page 853, Mixed Problem Solving (Chapter 11)

1. $m\angle ADE = 50°$, $m\angle ADC = 130°$, $m\angle DAB = 130°$, $m\angle ABE = 50°$, $m\angle BEF = 50°$, and $m\angle BED = 130°$

Page 854, Mixed Problem Solving (Chapter 12)

1a. triangular prism; bases: *ADE, BCF;* faces: *ABFE, CDEF, ABCD, ADE, BCF;* edges: $\overline{AB}$, $\overline{BC}$, $\overline{CD}$, $\overline{AD}$, $\overline{AE}$, $\overline{DE}$, $\overline{EF}$, $\overline{CF}$, $\overline{BF}$; vertices: *A, B, C,D, E, F*

Page 855, Mixed Problem Solving (Chapter 13)

1a. 1st Period: mean, 83.7; median, 85; mode, 90;
2nd Period: mean, 82.3; median, 81; mode, 80 and 92

1b.

1st Period	Stem	2nd Period
4	6	0
6 4 2 2 0	7	0 4 4 6 8 8
8 6 4 2 2 0	8	0 0 0 2 2 4
8 8 6 2 0 0 0 0	9	0 0 2 2 2 4 8

2 | 8 = 82% *7 | 8 = 78%*

2a. U.S. Summer Olympic Medals

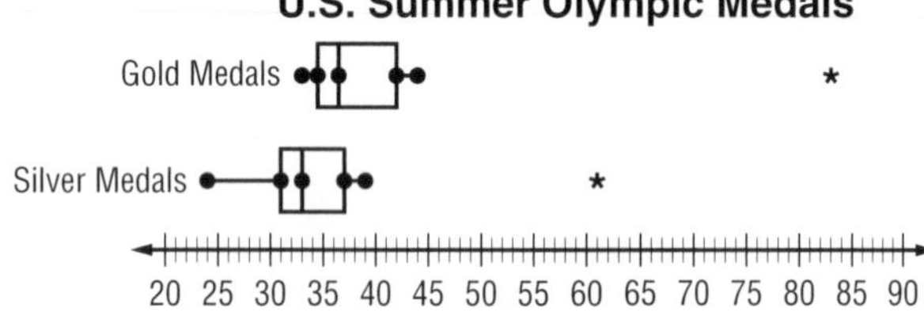

3a.

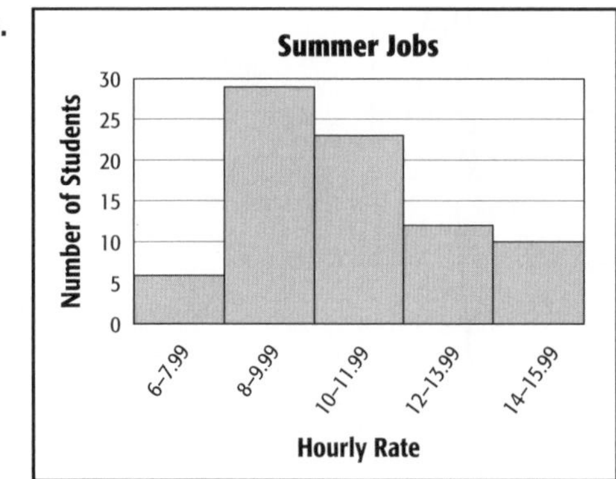

Page 867, Concepts and Skills Bank 6

1.

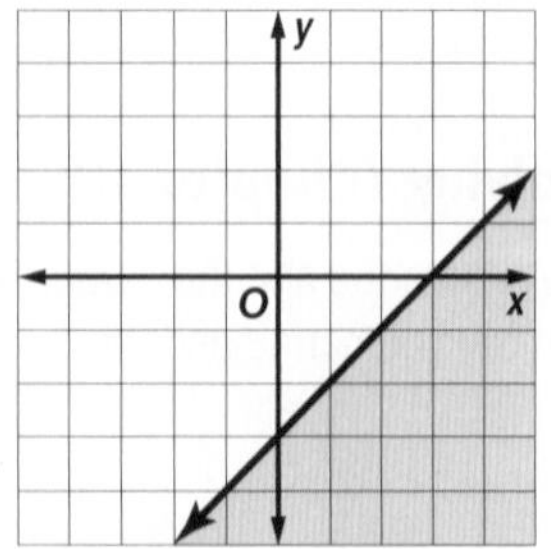

2.

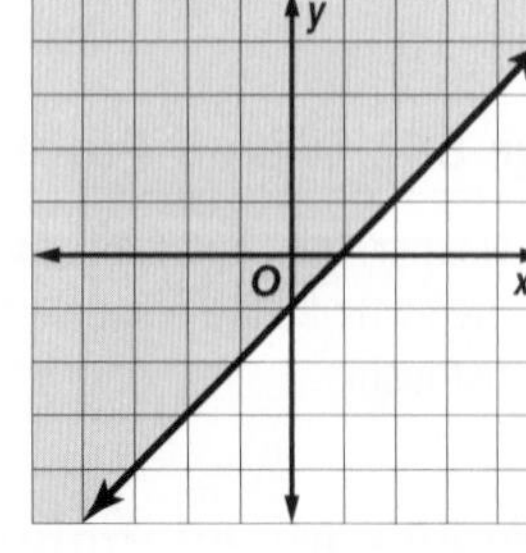

3.

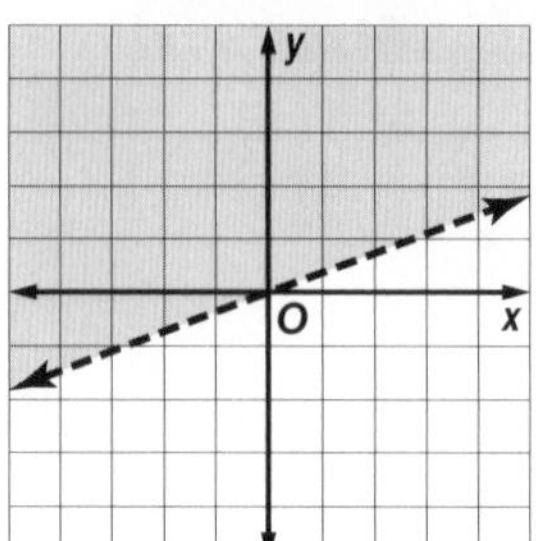

4.

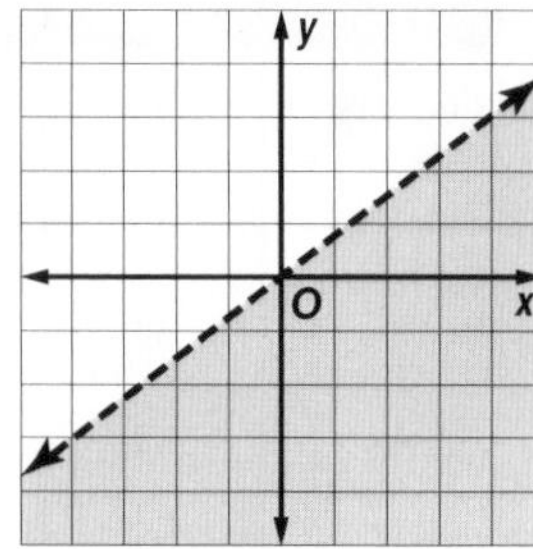

5.

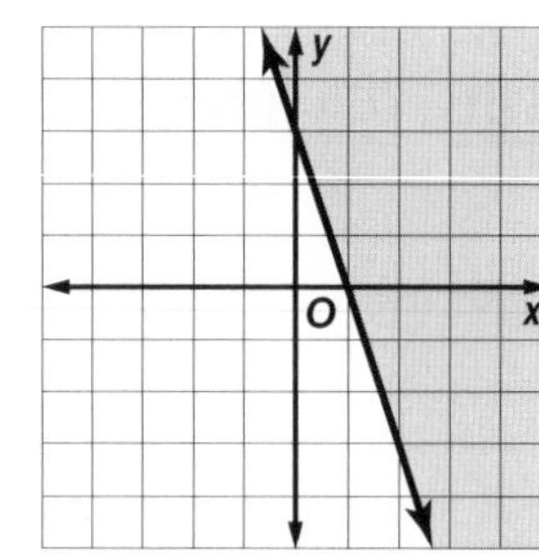

6.

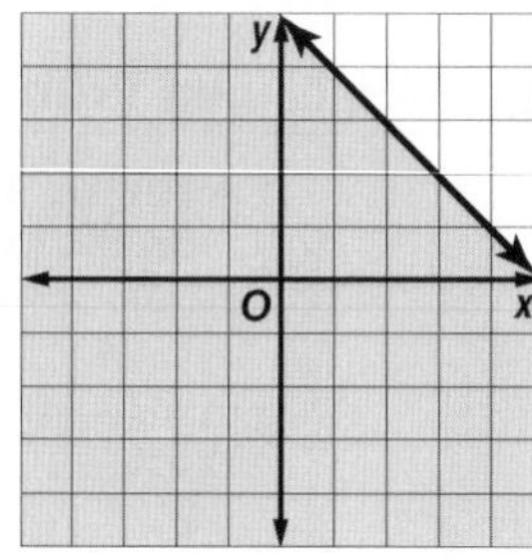

7.

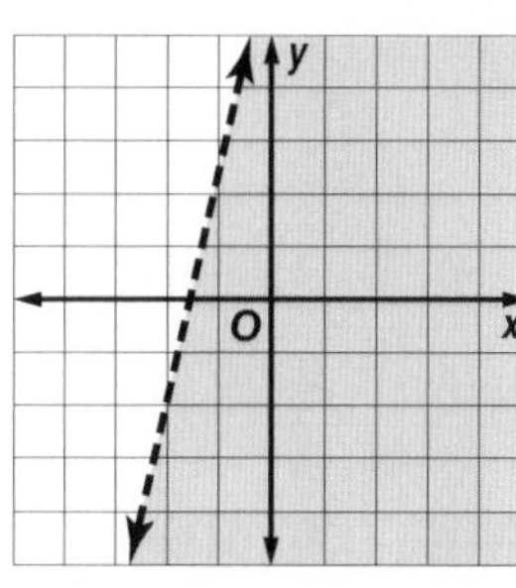

8.

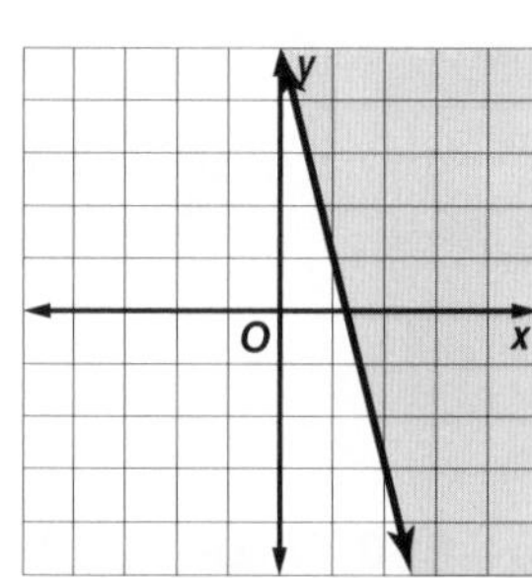

9.

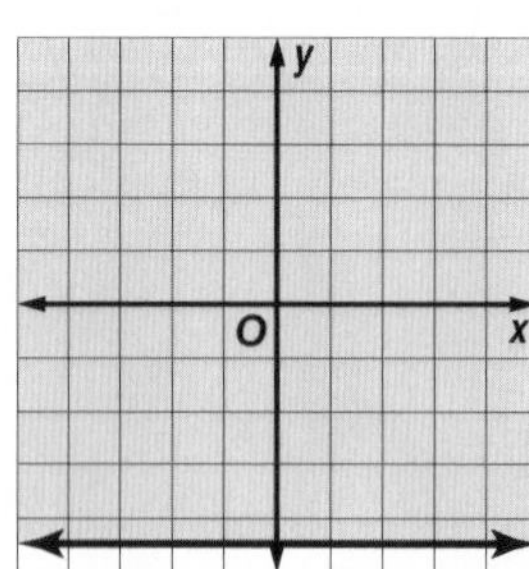

10.

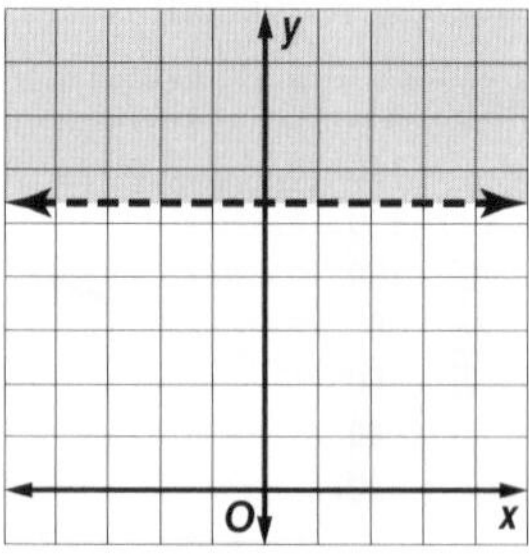

Page 869, Concepts and Skills Bank 7

11. ● *G*

12. *X* *Y*

13. 

14. 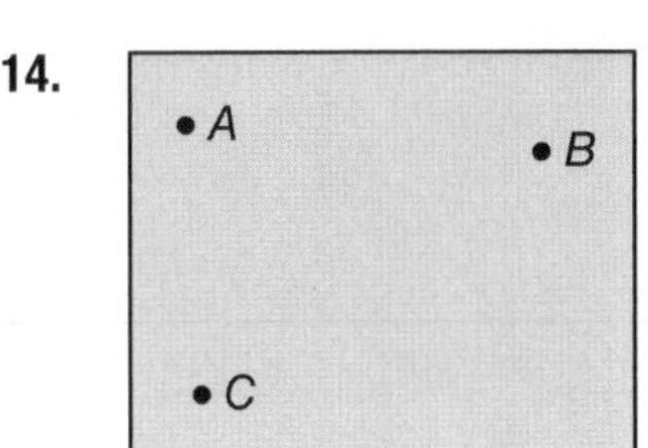

Page 874, Concepts and Skills Bank 9

12. C 40° A B

13. 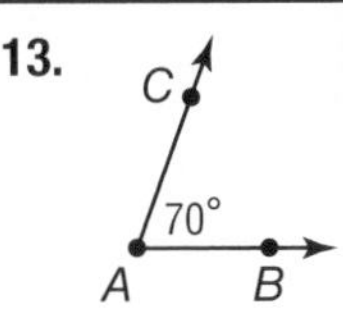

14. C 65° A B

15. 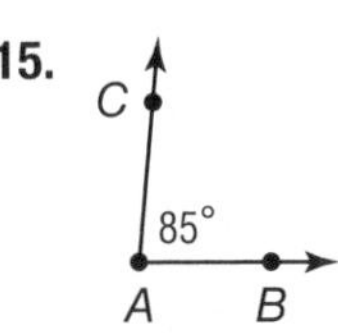

16. 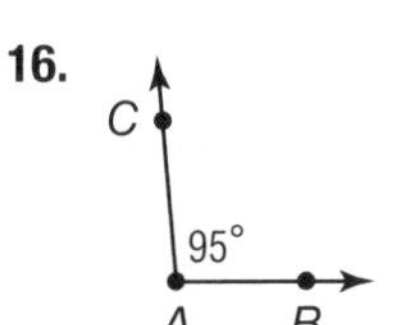

17. 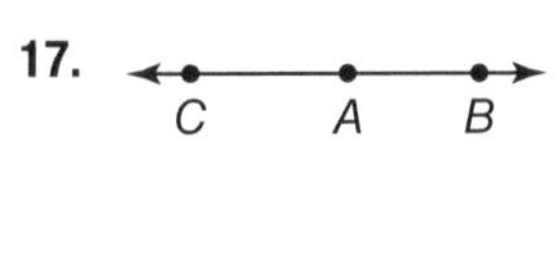

18. 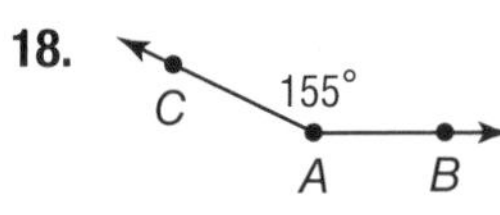

19. 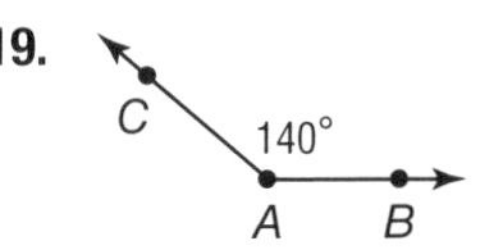

20. 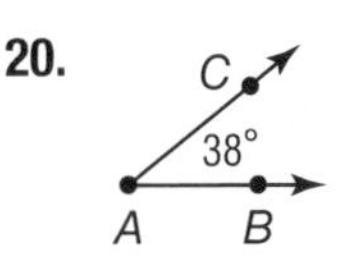

21. 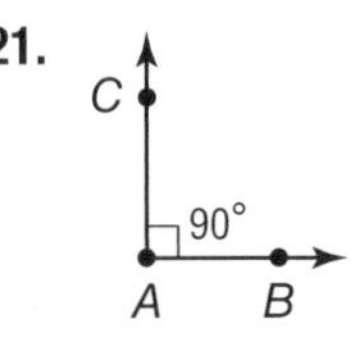

22. 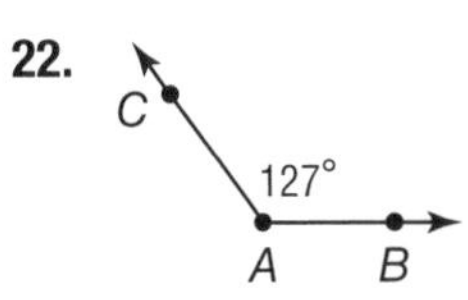

23. 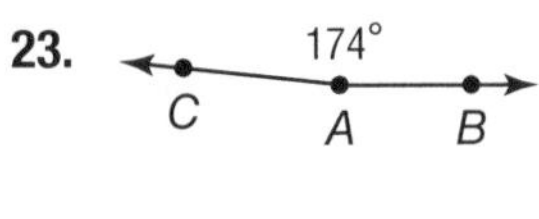

Page 881, Concepts and Skills Bank 13

11. Sample answer:

Page 885, Concepts and Skills Bank 15

3. No, the statement is not accurate. There is a break in the vertical axis giving the impression that Detroit won 4 times as many games as Chicago. However, Detroit won 51 games and Chicago won 31 games; Detroit won less than twice as many games as Chicago.

4. The use of inconsistent scales, broken scales, expanded and shortened axes will make the graph misleading. Answers should include the following.

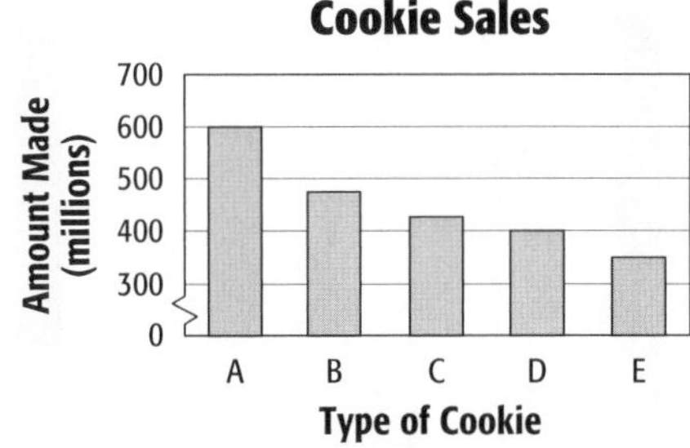

This graph is misleading because the vertical axis does not start at zero. To redo the graph so that it is not misleading, you can redraw the vertical axis so that it does include zero and the intervals of the vertical axis are equal.

Key Concepts

Chapter 1

The Tools of Algebra

Order of Operations (p. 6)

Step 1 Evaluate the expressions inside grouping symbols.
Step 2 Multiply and/or divide in order from left to right.
Step 3 Add and/or subtract in order from left to right.

Substitution Property of Equality (p. 12)

If two quantities are equal, then one quantity can be replaced by the other.

Commutative Properties (p. 18)

For any numbers a and b, $a + b = b + a$.
For any numbers a and b, $a \cdot b = b \cdot a$.

Associative Properties (p. 18)

For any numbers a, b, and c, $(a + b) + c = a + (b + c)$.
For any numbers a, b, and c, $(a \cdot b) \cdot c = a \cdot (b \cdot c)$.

Numbers Properties (p. 19)

Property	Words	Symbols	Examples
Additive Identity	When 0 is added to any number, the sum is the number.	For any number a, $a + 0 = 0 + a = a$.	$5 + 0 = 5$ $0 + 5 = 5$
Multiplicative Identity	When any number is multiplied by 1, the product is the number.	For any number a, $a \cdot 1 = 1 \cdot a = a$.	$8 \cdot 1 = 8$ $1 \cdot 8 = 8$
Multiplicative Property of Zero	When any number is multiplied by 0, the product is 0.	For any number a, $a \cdot 0 = 0 \cdot a = 0$	$3 \cdot 0 = 0$ $0 \cdot 3 = 0$

Chapter 2

Operations with Integers

Absolute Value (p. 63)

The absolute value of a number is the distance the number is from zero on the number line. The absolute value of a number is always greater than or equal to zero.

Adding Integers with the Same Sign (p. 69)

To add integers with the same sign, add their absolute values. The sum is:
- positive if both integers are positive.
- negative if both integers are negative.

Adding Integers with Different Signs (p. 70)

To add integers with different signs, subtract their absolute values. The sum is:
- positive if the positive integer's absolute value is greater.
- negative if the negative integer's absolute value is greater.

Additive Inverse Property (p. 71)

The sum of any number and its additive inverse is zero.

Subtracting Integers (p. 76)

To subtract an integer, add its additive inverse.

Multiplying Two Integers with Different Signs (p. 83)
The product of two integers with different signs is negative.

Multiplying Two Integers with the Same Sign (p. 84)
The product of two integers with the same sign is positive.

Dividing Integers with Different Signs (p. 90)
The quotient of two integers with different signs is negative.

Dividing Integers with the Same Sign (p. 91)
The quotient of two integers with the same sign is positive.

Chapter 3

Operations with Rational Numbers

Multiplying Fractions (p. 134)
To multiply fractions, multiply the numerators and multiply the denominators.

Inverse Property of Multiplication (p. 141)
The product of a number and its multiplicative inverse is 1.

Dividing Fractions (p. 142)
To divide by a fraction, multiply by its multiplicative inverse.

Adding Like Fractions (p. 147)
To add fractions with like denominators, add the numerators and write the sum over the denominator.

Subtracting Like Fractions (p. 148)
To add fractions with like denominators, add the numerators and write the sum over the denominator.

Adding Unlike Fractions (p. 153)
To add fractions with unlike denominators, rename the fractions with a common denominator. Then add and simplify as with like fractions.

Subtracting Unlike Fractions (p. 154)
To subtract fractions with unlike denominators, rename the fractions with a common denominator. Then subtract and simplify as with like fractions.

Chapter 4

Expressions and Equations

Distributive Property (p. 171)
$a(b + c) = ab + ac$ $(b + c)a = ba + ca$
$a(b - c) = ab - ac$ $(b - c)a = ba - ca$

Addition Property of Equality (p. 184)
If you add the same number to each side of an equation, the two sides remain equal.

Subtraction Property of Equality (p. 185)
If you subtract the same number from each side of an equation, the two sides remain equal.

Division Property of Equality (p. 191)
When you divide each side of an equation by the same nonzero number, the two sides remain equal.

Multiplication Property of Equality (p. 193)
When you multiply each side of an equation by the same number, the two sides remain equal.

Chapter 5

Multi-Step Equations and Inequalities

Perimeter (p. 221)
Words The perimeter of a rectangle is the sum of the measures of all four sides.
Symbols $P = \ell + \ell + w + w$
$P = 2\ell + 2w$ or $P = 2(\ell + w)$
Words The perimeter of a triangle is the sum of the measure of all three sides.
Symbols $P = a + b + c$

Area (p. 222)
Words The area of a rectangle is the product of the length and width.
Symbols $A = \ell w$

Addition and Subtraction Properties of Inequalities (p. 241)
When you add or subtract the same number from each side of an inequality, the inequality remains true.

Multiplication and Division Properties of Inequalities (p. 242)
When you multiply or divide each side of an inequality by the same positive number, the inequality remains true.

When you multiply or divide each side of an inequality by the same negative number, the inequality symbol must be reversed for the inequality to remain true.

Chapter 6

Ratio, Proportion, and Similar Figures

Ratio (p. 265)
Words A ratio is a comparison of two quantities by division.
Examples Numbers: 3 to 9 3:9 $\frac{3}{9}$ Algebra: a to b $a{:}b$ $\frac{a}{b}$

Property of Proportions (p. 287)
Words The cross products of a proportion are equal.
Symbols If $\frac{a}{b} = \frac{c}{d}$, then $ad = cb$. If $ad = cb$, then $\frac{a}{b} = \frac{c}{d}$ if $b \neq 0$ and $d \neq 0$.

Corresponding Parts of Similar Triangles (p. 301)
Words If two figures are similar, then
- the corresponding angles are congruent, or have the same measure, and
- the corresponding sides are proportional and opposite corresponding angles

Symbols $\triangle ABC \sim \triangle XYZ$: $\angle A \cong \angle X$, $\angle B \cong \angle Y$, $\angle C \cong \angle Z$ and $\frac{AB}{XY} = \frac{BC}{YZ} = \frac{AC}{XZ}$

Scale Factor (p. 308)
A dilation with a scale factor of k will be:
- an enlargement if $k > 1$,
- a reduction if $0 < k < 1$,
- the same as the original figure if $k = 1$.

Key Concepts

Chapter 7

Percent

Percent (p. 331)

Words A percent is a part to whole ratio that compares a number to 100.

Examples 80% 80 out of 100 $\frac{80}{100}$

Percents and Decimals (p. 337)

To write a percent as a decimal, divide by 100 and remove the percent symbol. To write a decimal as a percent, multiply by 100 and add the percent symbol.

Percent Proportion (p. 345)

$\frac{a}{b} = \frac{p}{100}$, where a is the part, b is the whole or base and p is the percent.

Types of Percent Problems (p. 346)

Type	Example	Proportion
Find the Percent	1 is what percent of 5? or What percent of 5 is 1?	$\frac{1}{5} = \frac{p}{100}$
Find the Part	What number is 20% of 5?	$\frac{a}{5} = \frac{20}{100}$
Find the Base or Whole	1 is 20% of what number?	$\frac{1}{b} = \frac{20}{100}$

The Percent Equation (p. 358)

Type	Example	Equation
Find the Part	What number (part) is 25% of 60?	$a = 0.25(60)$
Find the Percent	15 is what percent (percent) of 60?	$15 = p(60)$
Find the Whole	15 is 25% of what number? (whole)	$15 = 0.25b$

Percent of Change (p. 364)

$$\text{percent of change} = \frac{\text{amount of change}}{\text{original amount}}$$

Chapter 8

Linear Functions and Graphing

Representing Functions (p. 408)

Equation	Ordered Pairs	Words	Table
$y = -2x$	(−1, 2), (0, 0), (1, −2)	The value of y is −2 times the corresponding value of x.	x: −1, 0, 1; y: 2, 0, −2

Direct Variation (p. 420)

A direct variation is a relationship in which the ratio of y to x is a constant, k. We say y varies directly with x.

Proportional Linear Relationships (p. 421)

Two quantities a and b have a proportional linear relationship if they have a constant ratio and a constant rate of change.

Slope (p. 428)

Words The slope m of a line passing through points at (x_1, y_1) and (x_2, y_2) is the ratio of the difference in y-coordinates to the corresponding difference in x-coordinates.

Symbols $m = \frac{y_2 - y_1}{x_2 - x_1}$, where $x_2 \neq x_1$

Slope-Intercept Form (p. 433)

Words The slope-intercept form of an equation is $y = mx + b$, where m is the slope and b is the y-intercept.

Symbols $y = mx + b$ (m ↑ slope, b ↑ y-intercept)

Write a Linear Equation (p. 444)

From Slope and y-Intercept	• Substitute the slope m and y-intercept b in $y = mx + b$.
From a Graph	• Find the y-intercept b and the slope m from the graph. • Substitute the slope and y-intercept in $y = mx + b$.
From Two Points	• Use the coordinates of the two points to find the slope. • Substitute the slope and coordinates of one of the points in $y - y_1 = m(x - x_1)$
From a Table	• Use the coordinates of the two points to find the slope. • Substitute the slope and coordinates of one of the points in $y - y_1 = m(x - x_1)$

Chapter 9

Powers and Nonlinear Functions

Order of Operations (p. 472)

Step 1 Simplify the expressions inside grouping symbols first.
Step 2 Evaluate all powers
Step 3 Do all multiplications or divisions in order from left to right.
Step 4 Do all additions or subtractions in order from left to right.

Product of Powers Property (p. 481)

Words Multiply powers with the same base by adding their exponents.

Symbols $a^m \cdot a^n = a^{m+n}$

Quotient of Powers Property (p. 482)

Words Divide powers with the same base by subtracting their exponents.

Symbols $a^m \div a^n = a^{m-n}$

Negative and Zero Exponents (p. 486)
For $a \neq 0$ and any whole number n, $a^{-n} = \frac{1}{a^n}$.
For $a \neq 0$, $a^0 = 1$.

Scientific Notation (p. 493)
Words A number is expressed in scientific notation when it is written as the product of a factor and a power of 10. The factor must be greater than or equal to 1 and less than 10.
Examples $3{,}500{,}000 = 3.5 \times 10^6$ $\quad 0.00004 = 4.0 \times 10^{-5}$

Power of a Power Property (p. 499)
Words To find the power of a power, multiply exponents.
Symbols $(a^m)^n = a^{m \cdot n}$

Power of a Product Property (p. 500)
Words To find the power of a product, find the power of each factor and multiply.
Symbols $(ab)^m = a^m b^m$, for all numbers a and b and any integer m

Quadratic Function (p. 510)
A quadratic function can be described by an equation of the form $y = ax^2 + bx + c$, where $a \neq 0$.

Chapter 10

Real Numbers and Right Triangles

Square Root (p. 537)
Words A square root of a number is one of its two equal factors.
Symbols If $x^2 = y$, then x is a square root of y.

Irrational Number (p. 543)
An irrational number is a number that cannot be expressed as $\frac{a}{b}$, where a and b are integers and $b \neq 0$.

Angles of a Triangle (p. 550)
The sum of the measures of the angles of a triangle is 180°.

Pythagorean Theorem (p. 558)
Words In a right triangle, the sum of the squares of the lengths of the legs is equal to the square of the length of the hypotenuse.
Symbols $a^2 + b^2 = c^2$

Distance Formula (p. 565)
The distance d between two points with coordinates (x_1, y_1) and (x_2, y_2) is given by $d = \sqrt{(x_2 - x_1)^2 + (y_2 - y_1)^2}$.

45°-45°-90° Triangles (p. 572)
In a 45°-45°-90° triangle, the length of the hypotenuse is $\sqrt{2}$ times the length of a leg.

30°-60°-90° Triangles (p. 573)
In a 30°-60°-90° triangle,
- the length of the hypotenuse is 2 times the length of the shorter leg, and
- the length of the longer leg is $\sqrt{3}$ times the length of the shorter leg.

Chapter 11

Distance and Angle

Pairs of Angles (p. 589)
When two lines intersect, they form two pairs of opposite angles, called *vertical angles*. Vertical angles are congruent.
Two angles that have the same vertex, share a common side, and do not overlap are called *adjacent angles*.
If the sum of the measures of two angles is 90°, the angles are called *complementary angles*.
If the sum of the measures of two angles is 180°, the angles are called *supplementary angles*.

Names of Special Angles (p. 590)
When a transversal intersects two parallel lines, eight angles are formed.
- *Interior angles* lie inside the parallel lines.
- *Exterior angles* lie outside the parallel lines.

The following pairs of angles have the same measure, or are *congruent*.
- *Alternate interior angles* are on opposite sides of the transversal and inside the parallel lines.
- *Alternate exterior angles* are on opposite sides of the transversal and outside the parallel lines.
- *Corresponding angles* are in the same position on the parallel lines in relation to the transversal.

Corresponding Parts of Congruent Triangles (p. 598)
If two triangles are congruent, their corresponding sides are congruent and their corresponding angles are congruent.

Angles of a Quadrilateral (p. 611)
The sum of the measures of the angles of a quadrilateral is 360°.

Interior Angles of a Polygon (p. 618)
If a polygon has n sides, then $n - 2$ triangles are formed. The sum of the degree measures of the interior angles of the polygon is $(n - 2)180$.

Area of Parallelogram (p. 624)
Words The area A of a parallelogram in square units is $A = bh$, where b is the base of the parallelogram and h is the height.
Symbols $A = bh$

Area of Triangle (p. 625)
Words The area A of a triangle in square units is $A = bh$, where b is the base of the triangle and h is the height.
Symbols $A = \frac{1}{2}bh$

Area of Trapezoid (p. 626)
Words The area A of a trapezoid equals half the product of the height h and the sum of the bases $b_1 + b_2$.
Symbols $A = \frac{1}{2}h(b_1 + b_2)$

Circumference of a Circle (p. 631)
Words The circumference C of a circle is equal to its diameter times π, or 2 times its radius times π.
Symbols $C = \pi d$ or $C = 2\pi r$

Area of a Circle (p. 636)
Words The area A of a circle equals π times the square of its radius r.
Symbols $A = \pi r^2$

Key Concepts

Key Concepts

Area of a Sector (p. 638)
Words The area A of a sector is $A = \frac{N}{360}(\pi r^2)$, where N is the degree measure of the central angle of the circle and r is the radius.
Symbols $A = \frac{N}{360}(\pi r^2)$

Chapter 12 Surface Area and Volume

Volume of a Prism (p. 671)
Words The volume V of a prism is the area of the base B times the height h.
Symbols $V = Bh$

Volume of a Cylinder (p. 677)
Words The volume V of a circular cylinder with radius r is the area of the base B times the height h.
Symbols $V = Bh$, where $B = \pi r^2$ or $V = \pi r^2 h$

Volume of a Pyramid (p. 683)
Words The volume V of a pyramid is one-third the area of the base B times the height h.
Symbols $V = \frac{1}{3}Bh$

Volume of a Cone (p. 684)
Words The volume V of a cone with radius r is one-third the area of the base πr^2 times the height h.
Symbols $V = \frac{1}{3}Bh$, where $B = \pi r^2$ or $V = \frac{1}{3}\pi r^2 h$

Volume of a Sphere (p. 685)
Words The volume V of a sphere with radius r is four-thirds times π times the radius cubed.
Symbols $V = \frac{4}{3}\pi r^3$

Surface Area of Prisms (p. 702)
Words The surface area S of a prism is the lateral area L plus the area of the two bases $2B$.
Symbols $S = L + 2B$ or $S = Ph + 2B$

Surface Area of Cylinders (p. 697)
Words The surface area S of a cylinder is the lateral area L plus the area of the two bases $(2\pi r^2)$.
Symbols $S = L + 2B$ or $S = 2\pi rh + 2\pi r^2$

Lateral Area and Surface Area of a Pyramid (p. 702)
Words The lateral area L of a regular pyramid is half the perimeter P of the base times the slant height ℓ.
Symbols $L = \frac{1}{2}P\ell$
Words The total surface area S of a regular pyramid is the lateral area L plus the area of the base B.
Symbols $S = L + B$ or $S = \frac{1}{2}P\ell + B$

Lateral Area and Surface Area of a Cone (p. 704)
Words The lateral area L of a cone is π times the radius times the slant height ℓ.
Symbols $L = \pi r\ell$
Words The surface area S of a cone with slant height ℓ and radius r is the lateral area plus the area of the base.
Symbols $S = L + \pi r^2$

Ratio of Surface Area and Volume of Similar Solids (p. 712)
If two solids are similar with a scale factor of $\frac{a}{b}$, then the surface areas have a ratio $\left(\frac{a}{b}\right)^2$ and the volumes have a ratio $\left(\frac{a}{b}\right)^3$.

Chapter 13 Statistics and Probability

Measures of Central Tendency (p. 730)
mean sum of the data divided by the number of items in the data set
median middle number of the data ordered from least to greatest, or the mean of the middle two numbers
mode number or numbers that occur most often

Interquartile Range (p. 744)
Words The interquartile range is the range of the middle half of a set of data. It is the difference between the upper quartile and the lower quartile.
Symbols Interquartile range $= UQ - LQ$

Probability (p. 765)
Words The probability of an event is a ratio that compares the number of favorable outcomes to the number of possible outcomes.
Symbols $P(\text{event}) = \frac{\text{number of favorable outcomes}}{\text{number of possible outcomes}}$

Unbiased Samples (p. 771)

Simple Random Sample
a sample where each item or person in a population is as likely to be chosen as any other

Stratified Random Sample
a sample in which the population is divided into similar, nonoverlapping groups. A simple random sample is then selected from each group

Systematic Random Sample
a sample in which the items or people are selected according to a specific time or item interval

Convenience Sample
a sample which includes members of the population that are easily accessed

Voluntary Response Sample
a sample which involves only those who want to participate in the sampling.

Fundamental Counting Principle (p. 777)
If event M can occur in m ways and is followed by event N that can occur in n ways, then the event M followed by N can occur in $m \cdot n$ ways.

Probability of Two Independent Events (p. 790)
Words The probability of two independent events is found by multiplying the probability of the first event by the probability of the second event.
Symbols $P(A \text{ and } B) = P(A) \cdot P(B)$

Probability of Two Dependent Events (p. 791)

Words If two events, A and B, are dependent, then the probability of both events occurring is the product of the probability of A and the probability of B after A occurs.

Symbols $P(A \text{ and } B) = P(A) \cdot P(B \text{ following } A)$

Probability of Mutually Exclusive Events (p. 792)

Words The probability of one or the other of two mutually exclusive events can be found by adding the probability of the first event to the probability of the second event.

Symbols $P(A \text{ or } B) = P(A) + P(B)$

Selected Answers and Solutions

For Homework Help, go to Hotmath.com
Complete, step-by-step solutions of most odd-numbered exercises are provided free of charge.

Chapter 0 Start Smart: Preparing for Pre-Algebra

Pages P3–P4 *Chapter 0* *Pretest*

1. 5 postcards and 5 letters **3.** 25 min **5.** 80 chairs **7.** 24.71 **9.** 81.85 **11.** 3568.87 **13.** 44.08 **15.** 26.95 **17.** 524.72 **19.** 47 **21.** 229.32 **23.** 221.652 **25.** 2.48 **27.** 5.67 **29.** 300.96 **31.** about 1.5 times **33.** Sample answer: the money earned is equal to 5 times the number of cars washed plus five; $55. **35.** Sample answer: the value of the term is equal to one less than five times the term number; 49. **37.** 101 cm **39.** inch **41.** mile **43.** 3.5 **45.** 135 **47.** $6\frac{2}{3}$ **49.** 6400 **51.** 430 **53.** 148 tickets

Page P6 *Lesson 0-1*

1. 16 pizzas **3.** $10 \times 10 \times 10$

Pages P9–P10 *Lesson 0-2*

1. 28 **3.** 27 and 29

5. 45 cards

Total Number of Cards	Amount Traded	Amount Received	New Total
55	8	5	52
52	6	4	50
50	5	3	48
48	12	9	45

7. $8 **9.** Sample answer: 125 candy bars and 105 pretzels **11.** 10 **13.** 12

15. 16 combinations

First Spin	Second Spin	First Spin	Second Spin
red	red	green	red
red	blue	green	blue
red	green	green	green
red	yellow	green	yellow
blue	red	yellow	red
blue	blue	yellow	blue
blue	green	yellow	green
blue	yellow	yellow	yellow

17. $119 **19.** Sample answer: 3 $5 bills, 2 $10 bills, and 7 $20 bills

Page P12 *Lesson 0-3*

1. 40.09 **3.** 20.411 **5.** 71.8 **7.** 2.918 **9.** $207.94 **11.** $12.39 **13.** 53.58 **15.** 105.35 **17.** 2.1 **19.** 3993 **21.** 1.15354 **23.** 7 **25.** 7.72 in.

Page P14 *Lesson 0-4*

1. Sample answer: the number of bracelets made is equal to 25 times the number of hours; 500 bracelets. **3.** Sample answer: the value of the term is equal to three more than the term number; 23.

5a.

Number of Tickets	1	2	3	4	5
Total Cost ($)	6.50	13.00	19.50	26.00	32.50

5b. Sample answer: The total cost is 6.5 times the number of tickets. **5c.** $52.00

7a.

Term Number	1	2	3
Number of Cubes	8	12	16

7b. Sample answer: The number of cubes is four more than four times the term number.

7c. 44 cubes

Page P16 *Lesson 0-5*

1. 33 in. **3.** 128 m **5.** $11\frac{1}{4}$ ft **7.** 76 mm

9. 93 mm **11.** $3\frac{3}{16}$ in. **13a.** 8

13b.

Side Length	Perimeter
1 in.	4 in.
2 in.	8 in.
3 in.	12 in.
4 in.	16 in.

13c. it doubles; it triples; it quadruples

13d. 32 in.

Page P18 *Lesson 0-6*

1. in. **3.** mi **5.** cm **7.** km **9.** $1\frac{1}{2}$ in.; $1\frac{1}{4}$ in.

11. 1.75 **13.** 63 **15.** 153 **17.** 750 **19.** 540 **21.** 7.4

Page P22 *Lesson 0-7*

1. 4 students **3.** Sample answer: Which homeroom had the greatest number of students with their driver's permit? Homeroom 16
5. Sample answer: 1300 pounds

7. Sample answer: There are about the same number of malls in New York and Ohio.

Pages P22–P23 *Chapter 0* *Posttest*

1. 7587 ft **3.** 204 squares **5.** 29 ways **7.** 8.8 **9.** 136.88 **11.** 603.247 **13.** 0.6 **15.** 280.94 **17.** 472.33 **19.** \$35.60 **21.** 28.2 **23.** 3341.94 **25.** 555.744 **27.** 7.2 **29.** 15.84 **31.** 294.212963 **33.** about 2 times **35.** Sample answer: the bracelets made are equal to 10 times the number of people plus five; 105 bracelets. **37.** Sample answer: the value of the term is equal to one more than five times the term number; 51. **39.** 56 in. **41.** centimeter **43.** kilometer **45.** 4 **47.** 216 **49.** 6160 **51.** 165.6 **53.** 6.2 **55.** 430 **57.** 1.4 times

Chapter 1 The Tools of Algebra

Page 3 *Chapter 1* *Get Ready*

1. 10 **3.** 3.9 **5.** 7.5 **7.** \$4.50 **9.** Sample answer: 1790 **11.** Sample answer: 7200 **13.** Sample answer: 200 mi **15.** 1 **17.** 4 **19.** (number line 28–39, point at 32)

Pages 7–9 *Lesson 1-1*

1. 6×8 **3.** 26 **5.** 33 **7.** 36 **9.** 5 **11.** $75 + 6(25)$; \$225

Number of Passengers	Expression	Cost (\$)
25	75 + 6(25)	225
30	75 + 6(30)	255
35	75 + 6(35)	285
40	75 + 6(40)	315

13. $8 + 4$ **15.** 9×3 **17.** $15 - 10$ **19.** 10

21 $2[3 + 7(4)] = 2[3 + 28]$
$= 2[31]$
$= 62$

23. 76 **25.** 16 **27.** 28 **29.** 2

31 Words: \$8 plus 6 times \$0.75 per line
Expression: $8 + 6(0.75)$
$8 + 6(0.75) = 8 + 4.50$
$= \$12.50$

Number of Lines	Expression	Cost (\$)
6	8 + 6(0.75)	12.50
10	8 + 10(0.75)	15.50
14	8 + 14(0.75)	18.50
18	8 + 18(0.75)	21.50

33a.

Term Number	Number of Toothpicks
1	4
2	6
3	8

33b. The number of toothpicks is two more than twice the term number. **35a.** around $(64 - 20)$ **35b.** $64 - (20 \div 4) + 6 = 64 - 5 + 6$
$= 59 + 6$
$= 65$

37a. 200(2.54); 508 cm **37b.** $508 + 350 = 858$ cm **37c.** 90 in. $\approx$ 90(2.54) or about 230 cm; $858 \div 230 \approx 3.73$; about 4 packages of 90-in. trim **39.** C **41.** B

Pages 14–16 *Lesson 1-2*

1. $c - 4$ **3.** $10h$ **5.** 25 **7.** 16 **9.** 12 **11a.** $16p$ **11b.** 80 fl oz

13 Words: twenty-four divided among some students
Variable: Let s represent some students.
Expression: $24 \div s$

15. $12n$ **17.** $10n - 4$ **19.** 4 **21.** 34 **23.** 18 **25.** 6 **27.** 18 **29.** 72 **31.** $\frac{w}{231}$ **33.** 13 **35.** 50 **37.** 58

39 Words: 42 pounds per bushel
Expression: $42b$
To find the number of pounds in 100 trees that each produce 6 bushels, find $100 \cdot 42 \cdot 6 = 25{,}200$ pounds.

41. $6a + c$; $a = 4$; $c = 8$; \$32 total cost for 4 items costing \$6 each and an \$8 item **43.** $2n + 4$; $2(n + 2)$; Sample answer: The first expression represents the top multiplied by two to give the top and bottom, then add 4 for the sloped sides. The second expression represents half of the figure, then multiply by two to get the whole figure. **45.** C **47.** B **49.** 14 **51.** 15 **53.** 2 **55.** 9 **57.** 48 **59.** 43 points **61.** 23 **63.** 32

Pages 21–23 *Lesson 1-3*

1. no; $10 - 6 \neq 6 - 10$ **3.** Identity (×) **5.** Identity (+) **7.** Associative (×) **9.** $11 + k$ **11.** $40x$ **13.** $72a$ **15.** no; $13 + 15 = 28$ **17.** Identity (+) **19.** Commutative (+) **21.** Multiplicative (0) **23.** Commutative (+) **25.** $d + 28$

27 $(54 + p) + 16 = (54 + 16) + p$
$= 70 + p$

29. $72s$ **31.** $44t$ **33.** $72c$ **35.** $30 + t$ **37.** $1978 + f$

39 Words: the sum of two times a number and five added to six times a number

Expression: $2n + 5 + 6n$
Simplify: $2n + 5 + 6n = 8n + 5$

41. $8 + 6n + 9n + 1$; $15n + 9$ **43a.** $\$5x + \$61.25$ **43b.** \$79 **45.** false; $15 + (4 \cdot 6) = 39$ and $(15 + 4) \cdot 6 = 114$; Since $39 \neq 114$, the statement is false. **47a.** No; $2 - 3 = -1$ and -1 is not a whole number. **47b.** No; $1 + 1 = 2$ and 2 is not a member of the set. **47c.** The Closure Property for Multiplication states that because the product of two whole numbers is also a whole number, the set of whole numbers is closed under multiplication. **47d.** Yes. $0 \cdot 0 = 0$, $0 \cdot 1 = 0$, $1 \cdot 0 = 0$, and $1 \cdot 1 = 1$. **49.** D **51.** B **53.** $s + 200$ **55.** $h - 6$ **57a.** 71°F **57b.** 62°F **59.** 45 **61.** 24 **63.** 210 **65.** 405 **67.** 54 **69.** 336 **71.** 5117

Pages 28–30 *Lesson 1-4*

1–4. (graph with points A, Z, W, F)

5. (3, 4) **7.** (5, 2)

9.

x	y
3	4
1	5
4	2

$D = \{1, 3, 4\}$, $R = \{2, 4, 5\}$

11a.

x	y	(x, y)
1	2	(1, 2)
2	4	(2, 4)
3	6	(3, 6)
4	8	(4, 8)

11b.

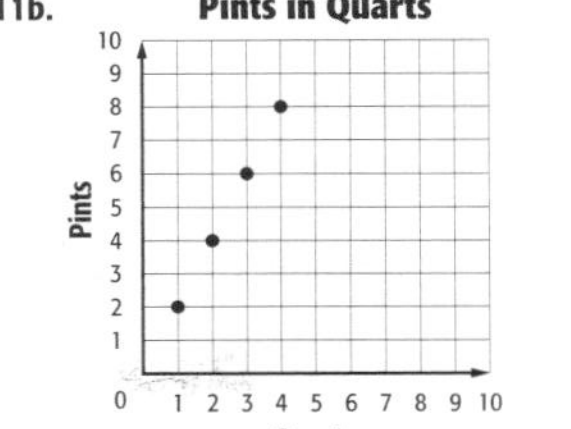

The points appear to lie in a line.

For Homework Help, go to Hotmath.com

12–19. (graph with points A, B, C, D, F, G, H, J)

21. (6, 4) **23.** (5, 2) **25.** (7, 2) **27.** (4, 5)

29

x	y
0	2
2	2
4	1
3	5

The domain is the set of x-values. $D = \{0, 2, 3, 4\}$
The range is the set of y-values. $R = \{1, 2, 5\}$

31.

x	y
5	1
3	7
4	8
5	7

$D = \{3, 4, 5\}$, $R = \{1, 7, 8\}$

33a.

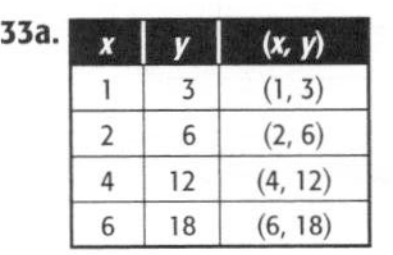

x	y	(x, y)
1	3	(1, 3)
2	6	(2, 6)
4	12	(4, 12)
6	18	(6, 18)

33b.

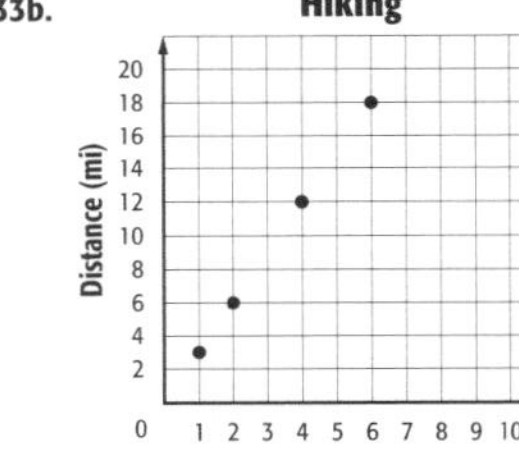

35 a.

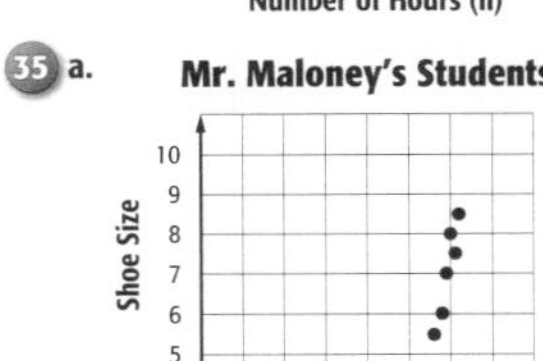

b. Sample answer: The graph is not linear like the other graph.

37a. {(1, 4), (2, 7), (3, 10), (4, 13)}

37b. Arithmetic Sequence

37c. The graph shows a positive, linear relationship. **37d.** 3 times the x value plus 1 to get the y-value; 61 **39.** Exercise 33; Sample answer: By connecting the points on the graph in Exercise 33, you could determine how far he will have hiked at any time other than hours. In Exercise 32, the points do not need to be connected because you wouldn't need to know how much a portion of a pizza would cost.
41. C **43.** A **45.** Commutative (×)
47. Identity (+) **49.** no; $(100 \div 10) \div 2 \neq 100 \div (10 \div 2)$ **51a.** $3s + 16$ **51b.** \$91
53. 7 **55.** 16 **57.** 14

Pages 35–37 *Lesson 1-5*

1.

Number of Touchdowns	Number of Points
Input (x)	Output (y)
1	6
2	12
5	30
7	42

D:{1, 2, 5, 7}; R:{ 6, 12, 30, 42}
3a. $z = 16p$
3b.

Input (p)	$16p$	Output (z)
5	16(5)	80
8	16(8)	128
11	16(11)	176
13	16(13)	208

3c.

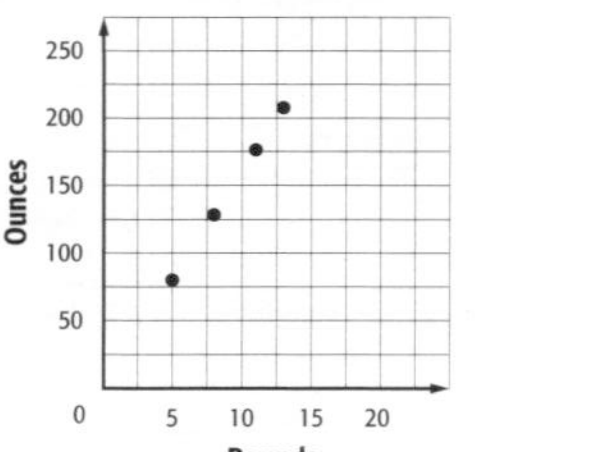

5.

Weight of Cat (lb)	Weight of Dog (lb)
Input (x)	Output (y)
3	7
6	10
9	13
12	16

D: {3, 6, 9, 12}; R: {7, 10, 13, 16}

7 Step 1: Create a function table showing the input and output. Step 2: The rule "five less than four times as many baseball cards." This translates into $4x - 5$. Use the rule to fill in the table. The domain is {3, 7, 11, 15}; the range is {7, 23, 39, 55}.

Ben's Cards	Casey's Cards
Input (x)	Output (y)
3	7
7	23
11	39
15	55

9 **a.** Words: area = side × side
Expression: $A = 10 \cdot s \cdot s$

b.

Input (x)	$10 \cdot s \cdot s$	Output (y)
6	$10 \cdot 6 \cdot 6$	360
12	$10 \cdot 12 \cdot 12$	1440
15	$10 \cdot 15 \cdot 15$	2250
24	$10 \cdot 24 \cdot 24$	5760

c. Plot the ordered pairs on a coordinate grid.

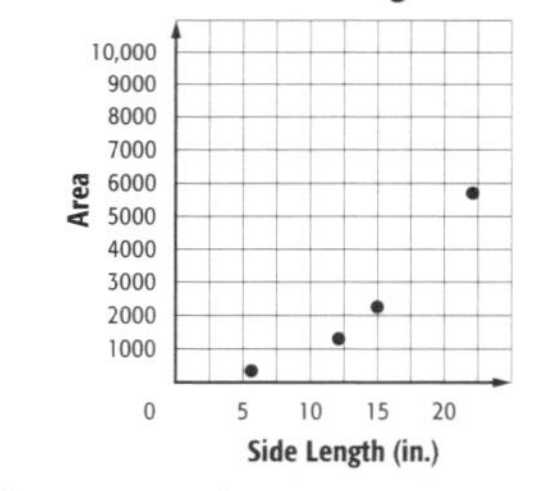

11a.

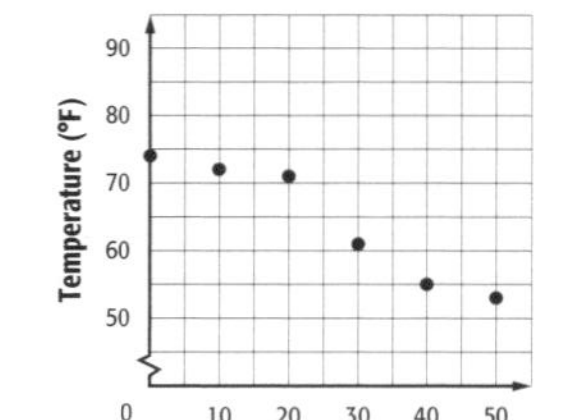
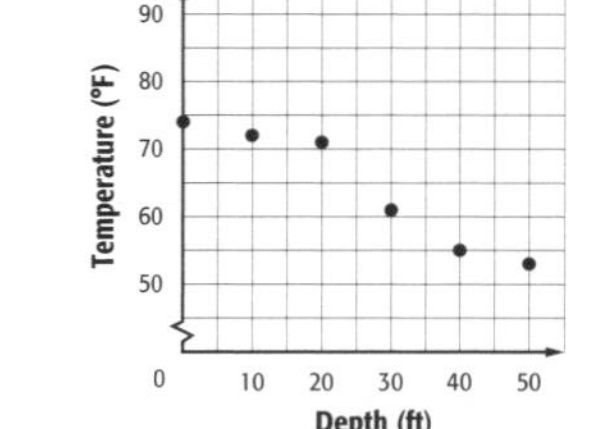
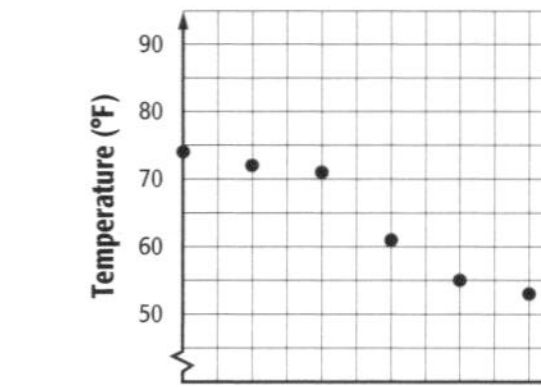

11b. No; the change in temperature is not constant so one equation cannot be used to find any temperature value. **11c.** yes; Sample answer: Each depth is paired with only one temperature.
13. $2(x + 4)$ **15a.** 26, 32 **15b.** $3x + 2$ **17.** J
19. (1, 7) **21.** (0, 4) **23.** (2, 1) **25.** $m + 12$
27. $37 + k$ **29.** $16y$ **31a.** $20n$ **31b.** 140 nickels
33. 14 **35.** 15

Pages 42–46 *Lesson 1-6*

1 **a.** Text Messages

Let the x-axis represent the number of friends. Let the y-axis represent the number of text messages. Then graph the ordered pairs.
b. As the number of friends increases, the number of messages increases. There is a positive relationship between the number of friends and the number of messages.
c. By looking at the pattern in the graph, you can determine that a group of 8 friends will have around 300 messages.

3 Let the x-axis represent the year. Let the y-axis represent the winning times. Then graph the ordered pairs.

Women's Olympic 100-meter Run

5. Negative; candle burn time increases as the height of the candle decreases. **7.** Positive; as the distance increases, the number of gallons increases. **9.** Positive; as the lawn size increases, the amount of water used increases.

11 **a.** Let the x-axis represent the month. Let the y-axis represent the temperature. Then graph the ordered pairs.

Average High Temperature for Lousiville, Kentucky

b. Sample answer: There is a positive relationship from January through July then a negative relationship for the rest of the year.

13a.

x	y
1	5
1	6
1	7
2	6
2	8
2	9
3	11
4	10
4	12

13b. Sample answer: The x-value could represent the number of people that went out to lunch and the y-value could represent the total cost of lunch.
13c. Sample answer: Overall, the data shows a positive relationship between the x and y values.

15a. Sample answer:

Length (in.)	Width (in.)
2	18
4	9
6	6
12	3
18	2

15b. Area of a Rectangle

15c. about 5 in. **17.** negative **19.** Sample answer: Because both are warm weather activities, the scatter plot would show a positive relationship. They are both independent events, so they do not affect each other. **21.** No; Sample answer: The table does represent a function.

Sonya is incorrect because even though it shows a negative relationship, it is still a function. Melisa is incorrect because each x-value can be paired with only 1 y-value, but y-values can be paired with any number of x-values.
23. C **25.** B **27a.** $32.50 + 4.95c$
27b.

Number of Channels	Total Cost
0	32.50
1	37.45
2	42.40
3	47.35
4	52.30

27c. Cable Costs

28–33.

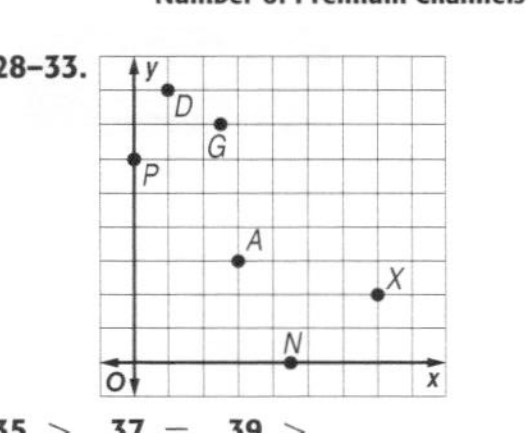

35. > **37.** = **39.** >

Pages 49–52 *Study Guide and Review*

1. true **3.** true **5.** true **7.** true **9.** false; scatter plot **11.** 45 **13.** \$130 **15.** 20 **17.** 33 **19.** $\frac{x}{36}$
21. Associative Property (×) **23.** $12 + v$
25.

x	y
2	3
2	6
2	5

D = {2}; R = {3, 5, 6}

27a.

x	y
4	8
8	16
12	24
16	32

27b. Cost to Ride the Ferris Wheel

The points appear to fall in a line.

29. Health Care

Chapter 2 Operations with Integers

Page 59 *Chapter 2* *Get Ready*

1. 18 **3.** 21 **5.** 40 **7.** 60 **9.** (1, 6) **11.** (2, 4) **13.** (3, 0) **15.** (5, 2)

Pages 64–66 *Lesson 2-1*

1. −500

3. $2 > -5$; $-5 < 2$ **5.** $1 > -1$; $-1 < 1$ **7.** <
9. −80, −48, −45, −39, −34, −27, −23, −2, 12
11. 17 **13.** 9 **15.** 18

17. −200

19. 0

21. $14 > -8$; $-8 < 14$ **23.** $-11 > -12$; $-12 < -11$
25. $4 > 0$; $0 < 4$ **27.** $30 > 27$; $27 < 30$ **29.** >
31. < **33.** > **35.** =
37 Graph each score on a number line.

So, the scores from least to greatest are −4, −3, −2, −1, +1, +2, +3, +4, +5, +6
39. 17 **41.** −15
43 $-|-7| + |12| = -7 + 12$
$= 5$
45. 26 **47.** 7 **49.** 21 **51.** 23 **53.** Movie F; The absolute value of −8 is 8 and 8 is greater than any other value in the table. **55.** −272, −249, −201, −157, −101 **57.** Saturn; $-218 < -162$
59. 5, 0, −5, −13 **61.** 62, 20, −28, −35, −59
63. 232, 88, −72, −83, −94, −165
65. Always; The absolute value of a non-zero number is always positive. **67.** Sometimes; when $x = 0$, $|-0| = -|0|$, but when $x = 1$, $|-1| \neq -|1|$. **69.** 1 **71.** D **73.** −10, −9, −4, 0, 5, 7; Sample answer: Graph each integer on a number line. Then write the numbers as they appear from left to right. The integers −10, −9, −4, 0, 5, and 7 are in order from least to greatest. **75.** Positive; As the number of hours increases, the number of homeruns increases. Thus, the scatter plot shows a positive relationship. **77a.** $y = 3x$
77b.

x	y
3	9
4	12
5	15
6	18

77c. Wrapping Paper

79. 438 **81.** 1025 **83.** 181

Pages 72–74 *Lesson 2-2*

1. −11 **3.** −7 **5.** $-1500 + (-1250) = p$; −2750
7. −1 **9.** −10 **11.** 9 **13.** −5 **15.** 6
17. $6 + (-10) = x$; −4 yards **19.** 10 **21.** −16
23 $8 + (-11) + (-19) + 11 = (8 + 11) + (-11 + -19)$
$= 19 + (-30)$
$= -11$
25. −128 ft **27.** 11 **29.** 8 **31.** 35
33 **a.** Rock: 33 + 1 = 34%; Rap: 10 + 2 = 12%; Pop: 9 − 2 = 7%; Country: 14 − 1 = 13%
b. 1 + 2 + (−2) + (−1) = 0%
35. −20 **37.** Sample answer: At midnight the temperature was 0°F. From midnight to 3:00 A.M. the temperature dropped 5°. From 3:00 A.M. to 6:00 A.M. the temperature raised 4°. What was the temperature at 6:00 A.M.? **39.** Commutative Property (×) **41.** −22 + (28) equals positive 6, while the sum of the other expressions is negative 6. **43.** $4 - 3y$ **45.** A **47.** H
49. −54 **51.** no relationship **53.** Commutative Property (×) **55.** Identity Property (×)
57. 18 **59.** 51 **61.** 3 **63.** 49

Pages 78–80 *Lesson 2-3*

1. −2 **3.** −24 **5.** 31 **7.** 4 **9.** −16 in. **11.** −9
13. −1 **15.** −7 **17.** 15
19 $-12 - (-11) = -12 + 11$
$= -1$
21. 10 **23.** −60 **25.** −\$13 **27.** −1 **29.** −12
31. −20 **33.** 17 **35a.** +11,000; −3000; +4000; +26,000; −2000; −1000; +9000 **35b.** 44,000
37. −214
39 **a.** 30.59 − 33.30 = \$−2.71; 31.04 − 30.59 = \$0.45; 31.97 − 31.04 = \$0.93; 30.15 − 31.97 = \$−1.82
b. highest: \$0.93;
lowest: −2.71; 0.93 −2.71 = 0.93 + 2.71
= \$3.64
41. Sample answer: 4 − (−7); 11 **43.** false; 2 − (−2) = 4 and (−2) − 2 = −4 **45.** C **47.** 5765
49. 4 + (−5) = −1 **51.** > **53a.** $y = 6x$

53b.

Input (x)	6x	Output (y)
2	6(2)	12
4	6(4)	24
5	6(5)	30
7	6(7)	42

53c. Movie Tickets

55. $r - 5$ **57.** $7 + n \div 8$ **59.** 56 **61.** 420

Pages 86–88 *Lesson 2-4*

1. −42 **3.** 120 **5.** −\$40 **7.** $-21ab$ **9.** −88
11 3(−9) = −27; The factors have different signs. The product is negative.
13. 75 **15.** 49 **17.** −336 **19.** −12°F **21.** $-30m$
23. $81mn$ **25.** $-36ab$ **27.** $-54efg$ **29.** −100
31. −72 **33.** $y = -2x$ **35.** $y = -4x$ **37.** < **39.** >
41 Team 1 answered 12 questions correctly, 3 questions incorrectly, and passed on 1 question. So, Team 1 earned 12(5) + 3(−8) + 1(−2) or 34 points. Team 2 answered 13 questions correctly, 2 questions incorrectly, and passed on 7 questions. So, Team 2 earned 13(5) + 2(−8) + 7(−2) or 35 points. Since 34 < 35, Team 2 won.
43. Sample answer: 2 and −7 **45.** 22
47. false; Sample answer: −3(−2)(−2)= −12
49. Sample answer: The sign of the product will be negative if there is an odd number of negative integers; otherwise the sign will be positive. **51.** J **53.** 62.5 **55.** 6 **57.** −3
59a. −54 > −70 **59b.** −54°, −70°, −80°
61. 9 **63.** 13

Pages 92–95 *Lesson 2-5*

1 40 ÷ −10 = −4; The quotient of two integers with different signs is negative.
3. $8.\overline{6}$ **5.** −16 **7.** −9 **9.** −4 **11.** −7 **13.** −3
15. 18 **17.** −15 **19.** 14 **21.** −110 **23.** 5
25. 14 **27.** −36 **29.** 12
31 To find the mean, add the amount of the transactions and divide by the number of transactions.
$\frac{250 + (-60) + (-94) + 300 + (-186)}{5} = \frac{210}{5}$
$= 42$
The mean transaction amount is \$42.
33. −184.4°C **35.** −\$300; Sample answer:

Every month, the company spends \$300 more than they earn. **37.** < **39.** >

41 $22 = x \div (-34)$
Use guess and check.
$22 \stackrel{?}{=} (-714) \div (-34)$
$22 \stackrel{?}{=} 21$ too low
$22 \stackrel{?}{=} (-748) \div (-34)$
$22 \stackrel{?}{=} 22$ ✓
$x = -748$

43. −13 **45.** −40 ÷ 8; −5°F; Each hour the temperature dropped 5°F. **47a.** −244.8 m **47b.** −234.8 m; The mean would be 10 meters higher. **49.** Sample answer: −110 ÷ 5 = −22 **51.** 4, −1; Divide the previous term by −4 **53.** Sample answer: The Associate Property is not true for the division of integers because how the integers are grouped affects the solution. [24 ÷ (−6)] ÷ 2 = −2; 24 ÷ [(−6 ÷ 2) = −8; The Commutative Property is not true for the division of integers because the order of the integers effects the solution. −2 ÷ 10 = −0.2; 10 ÷ −2 = −5 **55.** J **57a.** −5°F **57b.** $-5h$

57c.

Input (x)	$300m$	Output (y)
1	5(1)	5
3	5(3)	15
5	5(5)	25

59. −5 **61.** −7 **63.** 3 **65.** −\$7 **67.** (5, 1) **69.** (5, 4)

Pages 98–100 *Lesson 2-6*

1. (−5, 2) **3.** (5, 2) **5.** II **7.** III

9.

$x - y = 4$		
x	y	(x, y)
6	2	(6, 2)
5	1	(5, 1)
4	0	(4, 0)
−1	−5	(−1, −5)
−2	−6	(−2, −6)

The points are along a diagonal line that crosses the y-axis at $y = 4$ and the x-axis at $x = 4$.

11. (−3, 1) **13.** (3, 5) **15.** (−4, −3) **17.** (5, −3) **19.** (0, 3)

20–31.

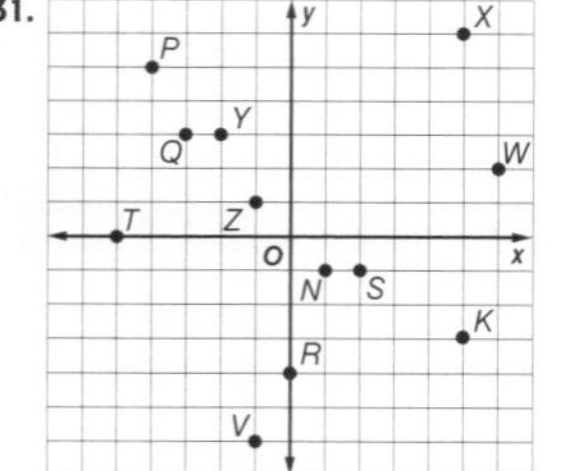

21 To graph (−2, 3), move left from the origin 2 units and then up 3 units. Draw a dot and label. The point is in quadrant II.

23. I **25.** IV **27.** none **29.** II **31.** IV

33.

$x - y = 10$		
x	y	(x, y)
30	20	(30, 20)
20	10	(20, 10)
10	0	(10, 0)
−20	−30	(−20, −30)
−30	−40	(−30, −40)

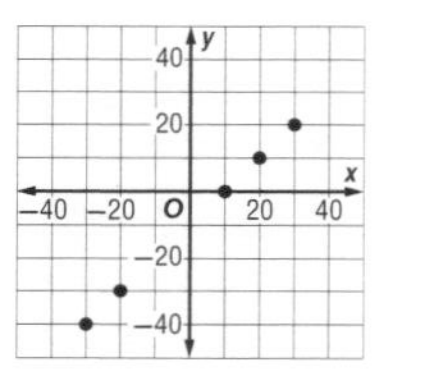

The points on the graph are in a line that slants downward to the left. The line crosses the x-axis at $x = 10$. **35.** IV **37.** IV

39 Graph each ordered pair on a coordinate plane.

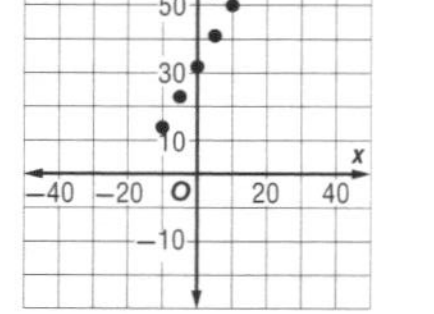

41.

Input	Rule: $x - 4$	Output
−2	−2 − 4	−6
−1	−1 − 4	−5
0	0 − 4	−4
1	1 − 4	−3
2	2 − 4	−2

43–46.

47. Sample answer: (−3, 1) **49a.** Sample answer: Never; both coordinates are positive. **49b.** Sample answer: Sometimes; both (−2, 0) and (2, 0) lie on the x-axis. **51.** C **53.** D **55.** 3 **57.** −50 **59.** −11 s **61.** 6 **63.** *B* **65.** *D* **67.** *C*

Pages 104–106 *Lesson 2-7*

1. A

3

original		translation		image
$X(0, 4)$	+	(4, −5)	→	$X'(4, -1)$
$Y(-2, 0)$	+	(4, −5)	→	$Y'(2, -5)$
$Z(2, 0)$	+	(4, −5)	→	$Z'(6, -5)$

5.

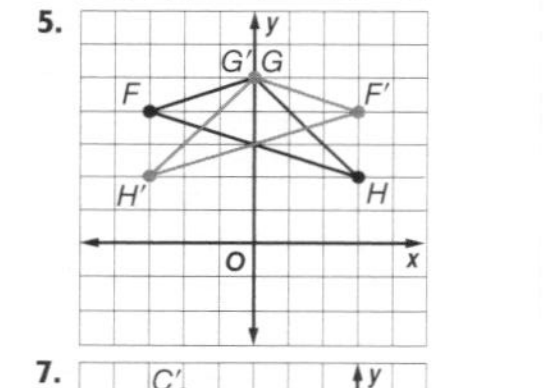

7.

9. 5 units left and 3 units up

11 Since the letter T is flipped, it shows a reflection. It is reflected over the x-axis.

13. The translation is to the left 5 units and down 4 units. **15.** $S'(-14, 2)$, $T'(0, 9)$; The translation is to the left 6 units and up 2 units.

17. MATH (reflected); y-axis **19.** No; For example, the vertices of $\triangle ABC$ are $A(1, 3)$, $B(7, 3)$, and $C(1, 6)$. The image's vertices reflected over the x-axis and y-axis would be $A'(-1,-3)$, $B'(-7, -3)$, and $C'(-1, -6)$. **21.** No single transformation is equivalent to the original two. The new figure is a reflection of the original but moved up and over to the right. **23.** D **25.** H **27.** (−4, 4) **29.** (−3, −2) **31.** 49 points **33.** $3n$ **35.** 0.2 **37.** 0.625

Pages 107–110 *Study Guide and Review*

1. true **3.** false, flip **5.** true **7.** true **9.** false; mean **11.** true **13.** 0 > −5; −5 < 0 **15.** = **17.** > **19.** 4 **21.** 13 **23.** −6 **25.** 4 **27.** 5 **29.** −13 **31.** −25 + (−50); −75 points **33.** 6 **35.** 11 **37.** −10 **39.** 20,602 ft **41.** −30 **43.** 48 **45.** −140 **47.** 4 **49.** −6 **51.** 8 **53.** 13.4 s

54–57.

55. II **57.** III **59.** $A'(1, 3)$, $B'(4, 3)$, $C'(1, 1)$, and $D'(-2, 1)$ **61.** translation

Chapter 3 Operations with Rational Numbers

Page 117 *Chapter 3* *Get Ready*

1. 0.6 **3.** 0.2 **5.** 0.5 **7.** −1.8 **9.** 29 bricks **11.** $\frac{4}{5}$ **13.** $\frac{3}{20}$ **15.** simplified **17.** −4 **19.** −7 **21.** +9 miles

Pages 124–127 *Lesson 3-1*

1. 0.6

3 $-20\overline{)3.00}$ = −0.15

5. $-0.\overline{6}$ **7.** 0.8 **9.** < **11.** > **13.** < **15.** test 1 **17.** 0.35 **19.** −0.1875 **21.** 0.36 **23.** −0.4375 **25.** $0.7\overline{3}$ **27.** $-0.\overline{2}$

29 955 ÷ 1028. Use a calculator:
955 ÷ 1028 ENTER 0.929

31. < **33.** = **35.** < **37.** < **39.** more than; $\frac{1}{4} = 0.25$ and $0.28 > 0.25$ **41.** < **43.** > **45.** > **47.** $\frac{3}{32}, \frac{5}{16}, \frac{3}{8}, \frac{1}{2}, \frac{3}{4}$ **49.** $2\frac{3}{5}, 2\frac{2}{3}, 2.67$ **51.** $\frac{1}{13}, \frac{2}{25}, 0.089$

53 Place a bar over the part that repeats. $0.999993... = 0.\overline{9}$

55. $-10.3\overline{4}$ **57.** Sample answer: A: $\frac{7}{9}$; B: $\frac{9}{10}$; C: $1\frac{1}{5}$; D: $1\frac{3}{10}$; E: $1\frac{3}{5}$; $\frac{7}{9} < \frac{9}{10}$ **59.** Sample answer: fractional form: customary measurement; decimal form: stock price **61.** $\frac{1}{3} = 0.\overline{3}$, $\frac{1}{6} = 0.1\overline{6}$, $\frac{1}{7} = 0.\overline{142857}$, $\frac{1}{9} = 0.\overline{1}$ **63.** $0.\overline{1}$, $0.\overline{23}$, and $0.\overline{75}$. Sample answer: When the denominator is a 9 or 99, the numerator repeats. **65.** C **67.** B **69.** 240 **71.** 9 **73.** 24 m below the surface **75.** 15 **77.** 13 **79.** thirty-four hundredths **81.** three tenths

Pages 130–133 *Lesson 3-2*

1. $\frac{15}{4}$

3 $-1\frac{3}{4} = -\frac{1(4) + 3}{4}$
$= -\frac{4+3}{4}$
$= -\frac{7}{4}$

5. $-3\frac{85}{99}$ **7.** $2\frac{27}{50}$ **9.** rational **11.** $\frac{11}{6}$ **13.** $-\frac{87}{8}$

15. $3\frac{5}{8}$ **17.** $-5\frac{9}{25}$ **19.** $-1\frac{3}{10}$

21 $0.506 = \frac{506}{1000}$
$= \frac{506 \div 2}{1000 \div 2}$
$= \frac{253}{500}$

23. $-2\frac{5}{9}$ **25.** $\frac{16}{99}$ **27.** $-\frac{1}{11}$ **29.** integer, rational **31.** rational **33.** irrational **35.** Yes; $\frac{5}{8} = 0.625$, and $0.625 > 0.6$, so the bead will fit.

37. > **39.** < **41.** > **43.** $\frac{652}{999}$ **45.** $\frac{163}{225}$

47. $9\frac{241}{990}$ **49a.** 3.1415927

3.14 3.1415927 $\frac{22}{7}$ 3.145
3.1 3.2

49b. $3.14 < \pi < \frac{22}{7}$ **49c.** Sample answer: If the diameter is a multiple of 7, use $\frac{22}{7}$. Otherwise, use 3.14.

51 To compare the numbers, rewrite the fractions as decimals. $3\frac{4}{11} = 3.\overline{36}$

On a number line, $-3.\overline{42}$ is to the left of -3.4 which is to the left of $3.\overline{36}$ which is to the left of 3.38. So, the order from least to greatest is $-3.\overline{42}$, -3.4, $3\frac{4}{11}$, 3.38.

53. $-1.95, -1\frac{13}{14}, -1.9, -1\frac{9}{11}$ **55.** $\frac{7}{9}, \frac{5}{8}, \frac{5}{8} < \frac{5}{7} < \frac{7}{9}$

57. Sample answer: Since $0.\overline{76} = 0.76767676\ldots$ and $0.76 = 0.76000000\ldots$, $0.\overline{76}$ is greater than 0.76. **59a.** true; Sample answer: Integers include all whole numbers and their opposites. Therefore, they belong to the set of rational numbers. **59b.** true; Sample answer: All whole numbers and their opposites belong to the set of integers. **59c.** false: Sample answer: $\frac{1}{2}$ is not an integer **59d.** true: Sample answer: All natural numbers are rational because they can be expressed as fractions. **61.** B **63.** C **65.** -0.625

67. -0.2

69.

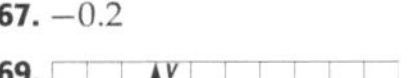

71.

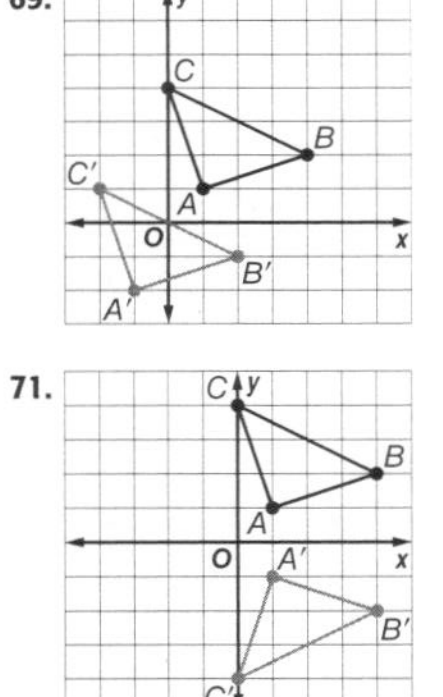

73. D = {0, 3, 4, 8}; R = {0, 2, 6, 12} **75.** 6050 m

77. 0 **79.** -280

Pages 136–139 *Lesson 3-3*

1 $\frac{7}{8} \cdot \frac{1}{2} = \frac{7 \cdot 1}{8 \cdot 2}$
$= \frac{7}{16}$

3. $-\frac{1}{8}$ **5.** 5 **7.** $-\frac{98}{75}$ or $-1\frac{23}{75}$ **9.** $-\frac{2}{5}$

11. $-\frac{28}{5}$ or $-5\frac{3}{5}$ **13.** 140 towns **15.** $\frac{3}{32}$ **17.** $\frac{8}{27}$

19. $\frac{1}{9}$ **21.** $\frac{2}{39}$ **23.** $-\frac{2}{3}$ **25.** -1 **27.** $\frac{5}{2}$ or $2\frac{1}{2}$

29. $-\frac{8}{5}$ or $-1\frac{3}{5}$ **31.** -10

33 $\frac{3}{5}(145) = \frac{3}{5} \cdot \frac{145}{1}$
$= \frac{3}{1} \cdot \frac{29}{1}$
$= \frac{3 \cdot 29}{1 \cdot 1}$
$= 87$ lb

35. $\frac{1}{21}$ **37.** -3 **39.** -2 **41.** 5 bags **43.** 12

45. 10 **47.** 4

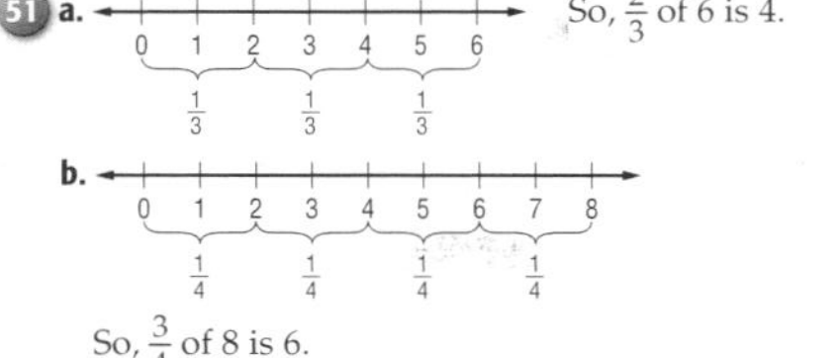

51 a. So, $\frac{2}{3}$ of 6 is 4.

b. So, $\frac{3}{4}$ of 8 is 6.

c. So, $\frac{1}{2}$ of $\frac{2}{3}$ is $\frac{1}{3}$.

d. So, $\frac{1}{2}$ of 2 is 1.

e. So, $\frac{2}{3}$ of $\frac{3}{2}$ is 1.

f. So, $\frac{3}{7}$ of $\frac{7}{3}$ is 1.

g. When a number is multiplied by its reciprocal, the result is 1.

h. $\frac{a}{b} \cdot \frac{b}{a} = \frac{ab}{ba}$
$= \frac{1}{1}$
$= 1$

53. Marina; Kelly did not write the mixed numbers as improper fractions before multiplying.

55. $-\frac{5}{6}$ **57.** always; Sample answer: When you multiply a fraction by a whole number or mixed number, you are finding a part of that whole number or mixed number. Since you are finding a part, the product will always be less than the whole number or mixed number.

59. A **61.** B **63.** $4\frac{1}{50}$ **65.** $-5\frac{1}{8}$ **67.** $4\frac{5}{9}$ **69.** >

71. = **73.** < **75.** The group that goes to sleep at 12 A.M. or later. **77.** 88 **79.** 1440 **81.** -192 **83.** 84

Pages 144–146 *Lesson 3-4*

1. $\frac{7}{6}$ **3.** $-\frac{1}{63}$ **5.** $-\frac{25}{2}$ or $-12\frac{1}{2}$ **7.** $-\frac{1}{18}$

9. $-\frac{16}{3}$ or $-5\frac{1}{3}$ **11.** $\frac{8b}{3}$ **13.** $\frac{5x}{2yz}$

15 The multiplicative inverse of $\frac{10}{19}$ is $\frac{19}{10}$ or $1\frac{9}{10}$.

17. $-\frac{7}{30}$ **19.** $-\frac{1}{54}$ **21.** $-\frac{5}{8}$ **23.** $\frac{1}{54}$ **25.** $-\frac{5}{3}$ or $-1\frac{2}{3}$ **27.** $\frac{57}{28}$ or $2\frac{1}{28}$ **29.** 12 costumes **31.** $\frac{1}{14}$

33. $\frac{15}{2}$ or $7\frac{1}{2}$

35 $405 \div \left(4\frac{1}{2}\right) = 4.0 \div \frac{9}{2}$
$= 405 \cdot \frac{2}{9}$
$= \frac{810}{9}$
$= 90$ mph

37. $-\frac{3}{25}$ **39.** $-\frac{3}{4}$ **41.** The quotient decreases; $\frac{3}{4} \div \frac{1}{8} = 6$. **43.** The quotient of $\frac{1}{2} \div \frac{3}{4}$ is $\frac{2}{3}$. The fraction $\frac{2}{3}$ is not a whole number. **45.** always

47. C **49.** A **51.** $\frac{9}{8}$ or $1\frac{1}{8}$ **53.** $-\frac{3}{22}$ **55.** 1

57. $\frac{7}{250}$ mi^2 **59.** -72 **61.** 48 **63.** -68 **65.** $3n$

67. $-5n$

Pages 150–152 *Lesson 3-5*

1. $1\frac{1}{3}$ **3.** $-\frac{1}{2}$ **5.** 10 **7.** $\frac{5}{7}$ **9.** $7\frac{6}{7}$ **11.** $-\frac{2x}{y}$

13. $-\frac{12c}{ab}$ **15.** $-\frac{1}{3}$ **17.** $\frac{3}{7}$ **19.** $13\frac{2}{3}$ **21.** $-\frac{17}{5}$ or $-3\frac{2}{5}$ **23.** $-\frac{2}{11}$

25 $-\frac{7}{20} - \frac{7}{20} = -\frac{7}{20} + \left(\frac{-7}{20}\right)$
$= \frac{-14}{20}$
$= -\frac{7}{10}$

27. $-2\frac{1}{9}$ **29.** $-6\frac{4}{9}$ **31.** $4\frac{1}{2}c$ **33.** $\frac{9m}{5}$ **35.** $\frac{5p}{14}$

37. $-2\frac{8}{9}$

39 a. $19\frac{4}{8} - 18\frac{3}{8} = 19 - 18\frac{4-3}{8}$
$= 1\frac{1}{8}$ lb
$20\frac{7}{8} - 17\frac{2}{8} = 20 - 17\frac{7-2}{8}$
$= 3\frac{5}{8}$ lb

b. $20\frac{7}{8} + 1\frac{3}{8} + 1\frac{3}{8} = 20 + 1 + 1 + \frac{7+3+3}{8}$
$= 22\frac{13}{8}$
$= 23\frac{5}{8}$ lb

41. $\frac{9pr}{2n}$ **43.** Sample answer: $\frac{1}{3} - 1 = -\frac{2}{3}$

45. No; he did not add the fraction part of the mixed numbers correctly. **47.** Sample answer: A recipe requires $\frac{3}{4}$ cup of milk and $1\frac{1}{4}$ cups of water. How much liquid is in the recipe? 2 cups.

49. J **51.** $-6\frac{1}{3}$ **53.** -10 **55.** $\frac{2}{35}$ **57.** $\frac{5}{9}$

59. 17 yard line **61.** 60 **63.** 45 **65.** x^2y

Pages 155–158 *Lesson 3-6*

1. $\frac{2}{3}$

3 $\frac{7}{8} + \left(-\frac{2}{7}\right) = \frac{49}{56} + \left(-\frac{16}{56}\right)$
$= \frac{49 + (-16)}{56}$
$= \frac{33}{56}$

5. $-9\frac{5}{6}$ **7.** $-1\frac{1}{36}$ **9.** $\frac{1}{24}$ **11.** $8\frac{1}{12}$ **13.** $\frac{7}{12}c$
15. $\frac{5}{21}$ **17.** $-1\frac{8}{33}$ **19.** $-\frac{23}{42}$ **21.** $-\frac{11}{30}$

23 $\frac{2}{3} - \frac{7}{15} = \frac{2}{3} + \frac{-7}{15}$
$= \frac{10}{15} + -\frac{7}{15}$
$= \frac{3}{15}$
$= \frac{1}{5}$

25. $12\frac{3}{10}$ **27.** $4\frac{1}{2}$ **29.** $-11\frac{7}{9}$ **31.** $4\frac{19}{48}$ **33.** $-17\frac{3}{14}$

35. $\frac{3}{4}c$ **37a.** Sample answer:

Perimeter of 20	
Length	Width
8	2
7	3
6	4
5	5

37b. (8, 2), (7, 3), (6, 4), (5, 5)

Width (units)
Length (units)

37c. $4\frac{1}{2}$ in.

41 $-19\frac{3}{8} - \left(-4\frac{3}{4}\right) = \frac{-155}{8} + \left(\frac{19}{4}\right)$
$= \frac{-155}{8} + \frac{38}{8}$
$= \frac{-117}{8}$
$= -14\frac{5}{8}$

43. $-59\frac{1}{6}$ **45.** $36\frac{67}{99}$ **47.** Sample answer: $\frac{2}{3} - \frac{5}{8} = \frac{1}{24}$

49. Sample answer: One way to respond is to use a diagram similar to the one given in the lesson opener to show that the fractions have to have the same "unit" (parts of a whole) to be added or subtracted. **51.** Sample answer: Fill the $\frac{1}{2}$-cup. From the $\frac{1}{2}$-cup, fill the $\frac{1}{3}$-cup. $\frac{1}{6}$ cup will be left in the $\frac{1}{2}$-cup because $\frac{1}{2} - \frac{1}{3} = \frac{1}{6}$. **53.** D **55.** H
57. $14\frac{1}{2}$ **59.** $\frac{3}{4}$ **61.** $\frac{2}{3}$ **63.** 6 **65.** $\frac{39}{1{,}000{,}000}$
67. 50

Pages 159–162 Study Guide and Review

1. false; rational **3.** false; unlike **5.** true
7. false; denominator **9.** false; add or subtract
11. 0.3 **13.** $-0.\overline{083}$ **15.** 0.625 **17.** > **19.** >
21. < **23.** 5.3125 **25.** $-\frac{9}{20}$ **27.** $-\frac{14}{25}$ **29.** $-2\frac{1}{33}$
31. $10\frac{3}{11}$ **33.** rational **35.** rational **37.** $\frac{3}{20}$
39. $3\frac{1}{3}$ **41.** $6\frac{1}{4}$ in. **43.** $-\frac{1}{16}$ **45.** $\frac{5}{19}$ **47.** $-2\frac{11}{12}$
49. $\frac{2}{3}$ **51.** 8 days **53.** $-\frac{5}{12}$ **55.** $8\frac{2}{7}$ **57.** $11\frac{1}{2}c$
59. $-6\frac{1}{3}$ **61.** $\frac{17}{40}$ **63.** $9\frac{1}{8}$ **65.** $-3\frac{5}{12}$
67. $166\frac{17}{20}$ miles or 166.85 miles

Chapter 4 Expressions and Equations

Page 169 Chapter 4 Get Ready

1. -9 **3.** 28 **5.** 88 **7.** $10.25 decrease
9. $4 + (-10)$ **11.** $-19 + (-10)$ **13.** -1
15. 0 **17.** -21 **19.** -22 ft

Pages 173–176 Lesson 4-1

1 $7(9 + 3) = 7 \cdot 9 + 7 \cdot 3$
$= 63 + 21$
$= 84$

3. $7 \cdot 2 + 8 \cdot 2$; 30 **5.** $6.50; $5(\$1 + \$0.30) = 5 \cdot 1 + 5 \cdot 0.30$ **7.** $5p + 20$ **9.** $9a - 90$ **11.** $8 \cdot 8 + 8 \cdot 5$; 104 **13.** $5 \cdot 12 + 5 \cdot 7$; 95 **15.** $3 \cdot 15 - 3 \cdot 5$; 30 **17.** $-7 \cdot 16 - (-7)8$; -56 **19.** $65.70; $2(\$32.85) = 2(\$33 - \$0.15)$ **21.** $4y + 28$

23 $(a + 9)6 = 6 \cdot a + 6 \cdot 9$
$= 6a + 54$

25. $5t - 30$ **27.** $-d + 10$ **29.** $-7x + 21$
31. 176 **33.** 779 **35.** 3000 **37.** 441 **39.** 1815
41. $2(\$8 + \$7), 2(\$8) + 2(\$7)$; $30
43. $5 \cdot 4 + 5 \cdot \frac{1}{5}$; 21 **45.** $6 \cdot 4 + 6 \cdot \frac{2}{3}$; 28

47 $9(2 + \frac{1}{3}) = 9 \cdot 2 + 9 \cdot \frac{1}{3}$
$= 18 + 3$
$= 21$ yd

49. $-5e - 5f$ **51.** $-4j + 4k$ **53.** $8u - 8w$
55. Sample answer: $2(3 + 4) = 2 \cdot 3 + 2 \cdot 4$
57. no; $3 + (4 \cdot 5) = 23$, $(3 + 4)(3 + 5) = 56$
59. C **61.** C **63.** $\frac{1}{8}$ **65.** $\frac{17}{30}$ **67.** $20\frac{1}{8}$ yd
69. 120 **71.** 17 **73.** $9 + (-12)$ **75.** $-10 + 3$

Pages 180–183 Lesson 4-2

1. terms: $-2a$, $3a$, $5b$; like terms: $-2a$, $3a$; coefficients: -2, 3, 5; constant: none
3. terms: mn, $4m$, $6n$, $2mn$; like terms: mn, $2mn$; coefficients: 1, 4, 6, 2; constant: none

5 The terms are $3x$, $4x$, and $5y$. The like terms are $3x$ and $4x$ because they have the same variables. The coefficients are 3, 4, and 5. There is no constant in the expression.

7. $8x + 3$ **9.** $2x - 4$ **11.** $m + 5$ **13.** $2x + 7$
15. terms: $3a$, 2, $3a$, 7; like terms: $3a$, $3a$; coefficients: 3, 3; constants: 2, 7 **17.** terms: $3c$, $4d$, $5c$, 8; like terms: $3c$, $5c$; coefficients: 3, 4, 5; constant: 8 **19.** terms: $4x$, $4y$, $4z$, 4; like terms: none; coefficients: 4, 4, 4; constant: 4 **21.** $7a$
23. $-4m + 5$ **25.** $11p + 8$ **27.** $-3a - 6b$
29. $6x + 30$ **31.** $-18 + 3r$ **33.** $2y - 5$

35 first game: x; second game: $3x$;
third game: $3x + 6$
Total $= x + 3x + 3x + 6$
$= 7x + 6$

37. $5x - 2y$ **39.** $-17m - 8n + y$ **41.** $-\frac{3}{4}m + \frac{3}{2}n$
43. $\frac{22}{15}a + \frac{14}{15}b$
45a. $7 + 4x + (-4) + (-2x) + 3$

1 1 1 / 1 1 1 + x x
6 + 2x

45b. $-8 + (-3x) + 2 + (-5x) + 2x + 4$

−1 / −1 + −x −x −x −x −x −x
−2 + (−6x)

47. $6c - 8$

49 $16 \cdot (-31) + 16 \cdot 32$
$= 16(-31 + 32)$ Distributive Property
$= 16(1)$ Add −31 and 32.
$= 16$ Multiplicative Identity

51. $24 \cdot (-15) + 36 \cdot 15$
$= (-24 + 36)15$ Distributive Property
$= (12)15$ Simplify.
$= (10 + 2)15$ Distributive Property
$= 150 + 30$ or 180 Simplify.

53. $4x + 2$ **55.** $5x + xy + 2y + 10$ **57.** $-6x - 12$; the other expressions are equivalent to $-6x + 12$.
59. Sample answer: The friend multiplied 5 by +2 instead of −2.
$4x - 2(x + 5) = 4x - 2x - 10$
$= 2x - 10$

61. G **63.** $9a - 9b - 6$ **65.** $-5a + 30$
67. 4($7 + $3), 4($7) + 4($3); $40
69. $-6 < -2$; $-2 > -6$ **71.** $0 > -9$; $-9 < 0$
73. $|15| < |18|$; $|18| > |15|$ **75.** 23 **77.** 3 **79.** 74

Pages 187–189 Lesson 4-3

1. 39 **3.** $\frac{1}{2}$ **5.** -32 **7.** 1.44 **9.** 3.5
11. $29.15 + x = 28.79$; -0.36 in.

13 $x - 24 = 73$
$x - 24 + 24 = 73 + 24$
$x = 97$

15. 5 **17.** 39 **19.** $-1\frac{1}{4}$ **21.** 134.9 **23.** -4.1
25. $-\frac{7}{8}$ **27.** $65 = m - 25$; $90 **29.** -41 **31.** 0.1
33. -1 **35.** $\frac{7}{20}$ or 0.35 **37.** $97 - 9 = d$, $d - 13 = w$; Damon scored 88 points and Wes scored 75 points.

39 Words: The Gates of Arctic National Park is 2.78 million larger than Denali National Park.
Equation: $7.52 = 2.78 + x$
$7.52 = 2.78 + x$
$7.52 - 2.78 = 2.78 - 2.78 + x$
$4.74 = x$
4.74 million acres

41a. $y = 8 - x$ or $x + y = 8$
41b.

41c. Sample answer: Together, Melinda and Ariana sold 8 t–shirts for the school fundraiser.
41d. The equation $x + y = 8$ has an infinite number of solutions. If $y = 3$, there is only one solution, 5. **43.** Sample answer: $x - (-1.2) = -1.2$ **45.** Sample answer: The small numbers allow you to use algebra tiles to solve the problem. $x - 5 = -9$; place an x–tile and 5 negative tiles on the left side of the mat and 9 negative tiles on the right side of the mat. Then remove 5 negative tiles from each side. The x-tile remains on the left side and four negative tiles remain on the right side. So, Jaime shot a −4 on the previous day. **47.** Sample answer: Peggy paid $3.25 for a new notebook that was on sale. The sale price was $2.70 less than the original price. Find the original price of the notebook.
49. H **51.** B **53.** $6r - 30$ **55.** $3c - 32$
57. $8 - 4x$ **59.** Fate: $\frac{9}{500}$; McLendon-Chisholm: $\frac{1}{50}$; Rockwall: $\frac{21}{50}$; Royse City: $\frac{7}{100}$ **61.** -7
63. 4 **65.** 125

Pages 194–196 Lesson 4-4

1. -13 **3.** 12 **5.** -36 **7.** -8.5 **9.** 60
11. $\frac{x}{6} = 54$; 324 lb **13.** -12

15 $-72 = 3y$
$\frac{-72}{3} = \frac{3y}{3}$
$-24 = y$
CHECK: $-72 = 3(-24)$
$-72 = -72$

17. 16.5 **19.** 392 **21.** −64 **23.** 24 **25.** −80
27. $\frac{5}{6}x = 420$; 504 strawberries **29.** −4
31. −12 **33.** −64 **35.** $\frac{2}{3}$ **37.** 0.9 or $\frac{9}{10}$
39. $-\frac{7}{27}$ **41.** 70 bpm

43 **a.** Words: 50 miles per day for t days
Expression: $50 \cdot t$
The equation is $d = 50t$.
b. Multiply each input value by 50 to get the output value.

Time	1	2	3	4	5	6
Distance	50	100	150	200	250	300

c. Plot each ordered pair on a coordinate grid.

d. Using the graph, it looks like it should take 9 days to travel 450 miles.
e. $50t = 2500$
$\frac{50t}{50} = \frac{2500}{50}$
$t = 50$ It will take 50 days.

45. Sample answer: A shirt was on sale for half off. If the sale price was \$15.60, find the original price; \$31.20 **47.** Rachel; to undo division, you multiply. **49.** Sample answer: Yes; he can multiply each side of the equation by $\frac{1}{3}$ instead of dividing by 3. **51.** J **53a.** $c = \frac{64}{2}$ **53b.** \$32
55. −3 **57.** −0.7 **59.** −8 **61.** $-\frac{1}{2}$ **63.** $5t + 15$
65. $12p + 4$ **67.** $-4x - 5$
69.

x	−2	−1	0	1
y	8	4	0	−4

71. 25 **73.** −19 **75.** 43

Pages 202–204 *Lesson 4-5*
1. 4 **3.** −4 **5.** −12 **7.** −3 **9.** 5 **11.** 1.2
13. C **15.** 4

17 $4d - 18 = -34$
$4d - 18 + 18 = -34 + 18$
$4d = -16$
$\frac{4d}{4} = -\frac{16}{4}$
$d = -4$

19. 45 **21.** 40 **23.** 8 **25.** 30 **27.** −11
29. 15 months **31.** 1.3 **33.** $\frac{5}{12}$ **35.** 30.4

37 $6s - 1.5s + 2.25s = 40.50$
$6.75s = 40.50$
$\frac{6.75s}{6.75} = \frac{40.50}{6.75}$
$s = 6$

39. 15.1 **41.** −14.5 **43.** Sample answer: You spent \$7 at the bookstore and bought lunch for 2 days. You spent a total of \$15. How much was lunch? \$4 **45.** Sample answer: When solving equations you may have to combine like terms as a first step. Combining like terms is one way to simplify expressions. Also, after you use the addition property or the multiplication property, you will need to combine terms again. Throughout the entire equation solving process, you have to know how to simplify expressions. **47.** Sample answer: The problems both involve multiplying by 3 and adding 5. They are different because $3(2) + 5$ is an expression while $3x + 5 = 11$ is an equation in which you solve by subtracting 5 then dividing by 3. **49.** G **51.** 19 **53.** 56 **55.** −32
57. 3.83 **59.** $2x + 40$ **61.** 4 **63.** 8 **65.** −8

Pages 207–209 *Lesson 4-6*
1. $\frac{n}{3} - 8 = 16$ **3.** $5t - 12 = 98$
5. $2x - 14 = 96$; 41 cars

7 Words: Eighteen more than twice a number is 8.
Variables: Let x represent the number.
Equation: $18 + 2x = 8$
The equation is $18 + 2x = 8$.
$18 + 2x = 8$
$18 - 18 + 2x = 8 - 18$
$2x = -10$
$\frac{2x}{2} = \frac{-10}{2}$
$x = -5$

9. $3x - 3 = 48$, 17 teams **11.** $2g + 37 = 497$; 230 field goals **13.** $\frac{x}{3} + 8.50 = 13.25$; \$14.25
15. $6d + 0.90 = 2.40$; \$0.25

17 Words: Eight more than twice as many action movies is the number of animated movies.
Variables: Let n represent the number of action movies.

Equation: $8 + 2n = 24$
$8 + 2n = 24$
$8 - 8 + 2n = 24 - 8$
$2n = 16$
$\frac{2n}{2} = \frac{16}{2}$
$n = 8$

19a. $47 + 15w$

Number of weeks	Amount of savings (\$)
1	62
2	77
3	92
4	107

19b.

Weekly Savings

Draw a straight line through the plotted points. Then go to the point that has 212 as its y-value and find the corresponding x-value.
19c. $47 + 15w = 212$; 11 weeks **19d.** The scatter plot is less accurate and will take a longer time to find because the plot will be large. Solving an equation is quick and ends with an exact answer. **21.** 8, 10 ,12 **23.** 24 years old **25.** D
27a. $60 + 6d = 180$ **27b.** \$20 per month **29.** −22
31. −10 **33.** 4 **35.** $n(t + h + s)$ **37.** 40 customers
39. $8y - 16$ **41.** $18 + 2p$

Pages 210–212 *Study Guide and Review*
1. equivalent expressions **3.** constant
5. solution **7.** Distributive Property
9. inverse operations **11.** $7y + 21$ **13.** $-b + 9$
15. \$30; $5(2.50 + 3.50)$; $5 \cdot 2.50 + 5 \cdot 3.50$;
17. $9x$ **19.** $8x + 2$ **21.** $5b + 6$ **23.** $x = 6$
25. $x = -1\frac{1}{20}$ **27.** $p = 18$ **29.** $x + 13 = 37$; 24 pages **31.** $x = 20$ **33.** $x = 5$ **35.** $x = -24$
37. 3 **39.** 9 **41.** $-\frac{1}{7}$ **43.** 35 books
45. $2n - 6 = -22$; −8

Chapter 5 Multi-Step Equations and Inequalities

Page 219 *Chapter 5* *Get Ready*
1. −6 **3.** 90 **5.** −7 **7.** \$75 **9.** −37 **11.** −73
13. 0 **15.** −40 **17.** 120 **19.** −4 **21.** −36°F

Pages 223–226 *Lesson 5-1*
1. 28 cm; 24 cm^2

3 $A = \ell w$
$117 = \ell(9)$
$\frac{117}{9} = \frac{9\ell}{9}$
$13 = \ell$
She will use 13 squares along the length of the quilt

5. 22 cm, 24cm^2 **7.** 30in, 30 in^2 **9.** $50\frac{3}{4}$ ft

11 $A = \ell w$
$432 = 36w$
$\frac{432}{36} = \frac{36w}{36}$
$12 = w$ The answer is 12 cm.

13. 527.52 in. **15a.** 74 ft **15b.** 3

17 $\ell = 4$ units; $w = 7$ units
$A = \ell w$
$= 4(7)$
$= 28$ square units

19. $\frac{V}{A} = h$ **21.** $r - st = p$ **23.** $\frac{2A}{h} = b$
25. Sample answer: The dimensions of a lacrosse field are 330 ft by 180 ft. What is the perimeter and area of the field? $P = 1020$ ft
$A = 59{,}400$ ft^2
27. $\ell = 10$ ft, $w = 10$ ft **29.** C
31. C **33.** $17 + 3x = 32$; 5 h **35.** 21 **37.** $12f = 132$; 11 ft **39.** $5280m = 10{,}560$; 2mi **41.** −8 **43.** −3

Pages 231–233 *Lesson 5-2*
1. 3 **3.** 4 **5.** 28 **7.** $50 + 1.99m = 3.99m$; 25 DVDs

9 $8 - v = 7v$
$8 - v + v = 7v + v$
$8 = 8v$
$\frac{8}{8} = \frac{8v}{8}$
$1 = v$

11. $\frac{3}{2}$ **13.** −3 **15.** $\frac{2}{5}$ **17.** $5 + 0.5s = s$; 10 songs
19. −0.75 **21.** −0.5 **23.** −80
25. 100 text messages

27 Words: 118 miles shorter than 4 times the coastline of Texas is 983 miles longer than the coastline of Texas.
Variables: Let x represent the length of the coastline of Texas.
Equation: $4x - 118 = x + 983$
$4x - 118 = x + 983$
$4x - 118 + 118 = x + 983 + 118$
$4x = x + 1101$
$4x - x = 1101$
$3x = 1101$
$\frac{3x}{3} = \frac{1101}{3}$
$x = 367$

The length of the coastline of Texas is 367 miles. The length of the coastline of Florida is 367 + 983 = 1350 miles.

29. Sample answer: Use the information in the figure to write and solve an equation.; $w = 55$ ft, $w + 40 = 95$ ft, $w + 45 = 100$ ft **31.** 7, 8, 9

33. She is incorrect. In the third step, the 4 should be negative, not positive; $x = -5$ **35.** B **37.** −2

39. 16 m; 12 m^2 **41.** 12 lessons **43.** $9b$ **45.** 2006: 0.36; 2003: 0.53; 2000: 0.34; 1997: 0.37 **47.** 53 **49.** 24

Pages 237–239 Lesson 5-3

1. $x \le 45$ **3.** $f > 8000$ **5.** true

7. 0 1 2 3 4 5 6 7 8 9 10

9. −3 −2 −1 0 1 2 3 4 5 6 7

11. $y > 5$

13 Words: children under the age of 2
Symbols: Let c represent the age of the children.
Inequality: $c < 2$

15. $s \le 50$ **17.** $\ell \le 15$ **19.** false **21.** false

23. true

25. −3 −2 −1 0 1 2 3 4 5 6 7

27. 1 2 3 4 5 6 7 8 9 10 11

29. −7 −6 −5 −4 −3 −2 −1 0 1 2 3

31. $x > 2$ **33.** $x \le 0$ **35.** $x > -4$

37 Words: 4418 is at most 500 yards more than Brett Favre's passing yards.
Symbols: Let f represent Brett Favre's passing yards.
Inequality:
$$4418 \le 500 + f$$
$$4418 \le 500 + f$$
$$4418 - 500 \le 500 - 500 + f$$
$$3918 \le f$$

39. −13, −14, −15; −17 −15 −13 −11 −9 −7

41. Sample answer: $-\frac{1}{2}$ **43.** The Wilson family spent more than $20.50 on groceries.

45. −5 −4 −3 −2 −1 0 1 2 3 4 5

47. D **49.** 4 **51.** −4 **53.** 180 min **55.** 1

57. $-1\frac{3}{8}$ **59.** $11\frac{3}{10}$ **61.** −21 **63.** −15 **65.** −1.8

Pages 244–247 Lesson 5-4

1. $y \le 5$

3
$$-7 < x + (-3)$$
$$-7 + 3 < x + (-3) + 3$$
$$-4 < x$$
CHECK: Try any number less than −4.
$$-7 < -5 + (-3)$$
$$-7 < -8 \checkmark$$

5. $f < 4$ −1 0 1 2 3 4 5 6 7 8 9

7. $7.5t \ge 120$; at least 16 hours

9. $z \ge 3$ −2 −1 0 1 2 3 4 5 6 7 8

11. $a < 22$ **13.** $y \le 10.7$ **15.** $p > 26$ **17.** $n \le 1.5$

19. $c \le 24.1$ **21.** $b > 15\frac{3}{4}$ **23.** $0.75y \le 10$; at most 13 games.

25. $x > -9$ −14 −12 −10 −8 −6 −4

27. $m \le -3$ −8 −7 −6 −5 −4 −3 −2 −1 0 1 2

29. $r \le -4.5$ −9 −8 −7 −6 −5 −4 −3 −2 −1 0 1

31. $y > 18$ 12 13 14 15 16 17 18 19 20 21 22 23

33. $b \le 2$ −3 −2 −1 0 1 2 3 4 5 6 7

35. $c \le -\frac{9}{5}$ or $-1\frac{4}{5}$ −7 −6 −5 −4 −3 −2 −1 0 1 2 3

37 Words: $\frac{3}{4}$ of an hour plus the time on the history project is at most 3 hours
Symbols: Let h represent the time spent on the history project.
Inequality:
$$\frac{3}{4} + h \le 3$$
$$\frac{3}{4} + h \le 3$$
$$\frac{3}{4} - \frac{3}{4} + h \le 3 - \frac{3}{4}$$
$$h \le 2\frac{1}{4}$$
She spends at most $2\frac{1}{4}$ hours or 2 hours and 15 minutes.

39. $a < 3.9$ **41.** $c \le -21$ **43.** $r \le 3$ **45.** $t \le 8.5$

47. $g \ge \frac{3}{2}$ **49.** $\frac{n}{-3} > \frac{5}{6}$; $n < -\frac{5}{2}$

51. $n - 15 \le -8$; $n \le 7$

53
$$4a - 7 \ge 21$$
$$4a - 7 + 7 \ge 21 + 7$$
$$4a \ge 28$$
$$\frac{4a}{4} \ge \frac{28}{4}$$
$$a \ge 7$$
CHECK: Try any number greater than 7.
$$4(8) - 7 \ge 21$$
$$32 - 7 \ge 21$$
$$25 \ge 21 \checkmark$$

55. $b \ge 4$ **57.** $d \le -20$ **59.** $g > -3$ **61.** $q \ge -2$

63. −4 −3 −2 −1 0 1 2 3 4 5 6

65. 5 6 7 8 9 10 11 12 13 14 15 16

67. $\frac{x}{-5} + 4 \le 8$; $x \ge -20$; Sample answers: −18, 0, 18 because they are all greater than −20.

69. 50 **71.** Sometimes; if $x = 21$ and $y = 21$ then $x \le y$ is true but $y > x$ is not true. **73.** B **75.** D **77.** $\ell \ge 45$ **79.** $b \ge 86$ **81.** 7.5 **83.** 13 **85.** −13 **87.** 2 **89.** 4 **91.** 8

Pages 251–253 Lesson 5-5

1. 6 **3.** 11

5
$$7(x + 2) = 2(x + 2)$$
$$7x + 14 = 2x + 4$$
$$7x - 2x + 14 = 2x - 2x + 4$$
$$5x + 14 = 4$$
$$5x + 14 - 14 = 4 - 14$$
$$5x = -10$$
$$x = -2$$
CHECK: $7(-2 + 2) = 2(-2 + 2)$
$$7(0) = 2(0)$$
$$0 = 0 \checkmark$$

7. null set; no solution **9.** Identity; all numbers

11. B

13. $r \le -8$ −13 −12 −11 −10 −9 −8 −7 −6 −5

15. $p \ge 5$ −1 0 1 2 3 4 5 6 7 8

17. $p \ge 7$ 2 4 6 8 10 12

19. 2 **21.** 4 **23.** null set; no solution

25. null set; no solution **27.** Identity; all numbers

29. 6 granola bars and 6 magazines

31. $h \ge -2$ −5 −4 −3 −2 −1 0 1 2 3 4 5

33. $s < -5$ −7 −6 −5 −4 −3 −2 −1 0 1 2 3

35. $h \le -7$ −9 −8 −7 −6 −5 −4 −3 −2 −1 0 1

37. $t < 10$ 5 6 7 8 9 10 11 12 13 14 15

39. 7 **41.** $x > 8$ **43.** 6

45 Words: three times her daily distance is at least 26.2 miles
Symbols: Let m represent the daily distance.
Inequality: $3m \ge 26.2$
$$3m \ge 26.2$$
$$\frac{3m}{3} \ge \frac{26.2}{3}$$
$$m \ge 8.73$$
So, she needs to increase her distance by 8.73 − 4 or 4.73 miles.

47. −16

$4(y - 3) = 2(3y + 10)$	Write the equation.
$4y - 12 = 6y + 20$	Distributive Property
$4y - 12 + 12 = 6y + 20 + 12$	Addition Property (=)
$4y = 6y + 32$	Simplify.
$4y - 6y = 6y + 32 - 6y$	Subtraction Property (=)
$-2y = 32$	Simplify.
$y = -16$	Division Property (=)

49. $w \ge 6.25$

$-1.2(w + 1.1) \le 6.18$	Write the Inequality.
$-1.2w - 1.32 \le 6.18$	Distributive Property
$-1.2w - 1.32 + 1.32 \le 6.18 + 1.32$	Addition Property
$-1.2w \le 7.5$	Simplify.
$\frac{-1.2w}{-1.2} \ge \frac{7.5}{-1.2}$	Division Property
$w \ge -6.25$	Simplify.

51. Sample answer: $10y - 3 \le -12$

53. Neither girl is correct. Jada did not distribute the 5 in the second step. Liu did not switch the inequality sign when she divided by −2 in the last step. **55.** Sample answer: If you get an answer like 5 = 5 which is always true, all numbers are solutions. If you get an answer like 5 = 9 which is never true, there are no solutions. If you get an answer like $x = 8$, there is one solution. **57.** 12 **59.** D

61. $q < 24$ 21 22 23 24 25 26 27 28 29

63. $x \le -5$ −7 −6 −5 −4 −3 −2 −1 0 1

65. $a \ge 2\frac{1}{2}$ 0 1 2 3 4

67. $86 > w$ **69.** −0.625 **71.** $0.\overline{1}$ **73.** $-0.\overline{45}$

75. 3.6 **77.** $7.40

Pages 254–256 Study Guide and Review

1. inequality **3.** negative **5.** greater than

7. product **9.** area **11.** 20 ft; 25 ft^2

13. 12 cm; 6 cm^2 **15.** 15 ft **17.** 1 **19.** 16

21. 0 **23.** $j \le 15$ **25.** true **27.** true

29. false

31. $x < 12$ 6 7 8 9 10 11 12 13 14 15 16 17

33. $a \le 18$ 12 13 14 15 16 17 18 19 20 21 22 23

35. $z \ge 8$ 2 3 4 5 6 7 8 9 10 11 12 13

37. $x > \frac{13}{5}$ −1 0 1 2 3 4 5 6 7 8 9

39. $20x \le 120$; $x \le 6$ **41.** $n = 7$ **43.** $a = 4$

45. $m < 5$ **47.** $k < -6$

Chapter 6 Ratio, Proportion, and Similar Figures

Page 263 Chapter 6 Get Ready

1. $\frac{4}{5}$ **3.** $\frac{2}{3}$ **5.** $\frac{2}{3}$ **7.** $\frac{3}{4}$ students **9.** 120 **11.** 4

13. 4000 **15.** 13,000 **17.** $\frac{1}{5}$ **19.** 2.5 **21.** 2

23. 81 books

Pages 266–269 Lesson 6-1

1
$$\frac{12}{16} = \frac{12 \div 4}{16 \div 4}$$
$$= \frac{3}{4}$$

This means that for every 3 boys there are 4 girls. **3.** $\frac{3}{7}$ **5.** $\frac{5}{8}$; For every 8 students, 5 participate in sports. **7.** $\frac{16}{3}$ **9.** $\frac{8}{1}$ **11.** $\frac{5}{9}$ **13.** $\frac{3}{4}$ **15.** $\frac{32}{1}$

17. $\frac{2}{3}$; For every 3 tables, 2 are booths or $\frac{2}{3}$ of the tables are booths.

19 $\frac{4 \text{ ounces}}{2 \text{ pounds}} = \frac{4 \text{ ounces}}{32 \text{ ounces}} = \frac{4}{32} = \frac{4 \div 4}{32 \div 4} = \frac{1}{8}$

21. $\frac{36}{7}$ **23a.** $\frac{7}{4}$ **23b.** $\frac{3}{4}$ **23c.** $\frac{11}{15}$ **23d.** $\frac{11}{4}$

25a. horse, cow, cat, hamster **25b.** horse; Sample answer: For every 27,272 grams a horse's heart will beat 1 time.

27 The turkey should be cooked at the ratio of 1 hour per four pounds which simplifies to $\frac{1}{4}$ hours per pound. The 18 pound turkey should be cooked for $18\left(\frac{1}{4}\right) = 4\frac{1}{2}$ hours. So it was not cooked long enough.

29. $\frac{27}{9} = \frac{45}{15}$ **31.** $\frac{6}{48} < \frac{14}{88}$ **33.** Sample answers: number of girls to boys in a class, number of apples to bananas in a fruit basket, a sale price of 3 for $8 **35.** 10 **37.** always; Sample answer: No matter what is used to measure the dimensions of the table, the actual dimensions will never change so the ratio will always be the same.

39. C **41.** B

43. $x \leq 9$ (number line: 5 6 7 8 9 10 11 12 13)

45. $y \leq -1$ (number line: −4 −3 −2 −1 0 1 2 3 4)

47. $n \leq -3$ (number line: −7 −6 −5 −4 −3 −2 −1 0 1)

49. $a > 2500$ **51.** (2, −1) **53.** (3, 4) **55.** (4, −4) **57.** $1.44 **59.** $0.28

Pages 272–274 *Lesson 6-2*

1. $24 per day **3.** 21.1 points per game **5.** 4.3 gallons per minute **7.** Mr. Nut; Sample answer: Barrel costs $0.34 cents per ounce, Mr. Nut costs $0.32 cents per ounce, and Chip's costs $0.35 cents per ounce.

9 $\frac{156 \text{ students}}{6 \text{ classes}} = \frac{156 \div 6}{6 \div 6} = \frac{26}{1}$ = 26 students per class

11. 59 miles per hour **13.** $77 per ticket

15. 1 pizza for $6.50 **17.** Party Time **19.** $12.25 **21.** Jenny **23a.** Alicia ran 8 feet per second, Jermaine ran 6 feet per second **23b.** Alicia: 660 s or 11 min; Jermaine: 880 s or 14 min 40 s **23c.** His line would be just below Jermaine's because he ran at a slower rate than him.

25 $\frac{525 \text{ grams}}{15 \text{ kilograms}} = \frac{525 \text{ grams}}{15000 \text{ grams}} = \frac{525 \div 15000}{15000 \div 15000} = \frac{0.035}{1} = \frac{0.035 \text{ grams salt}}{1 \text{ gram water}}$

27. situation b; Sample answer: $\frac{120 \text{ mi}}{2 \text{ hr}} = 60$ mi/hr, $\frac{120 \text{ mi}}{3 \text{ hr}} = 40$ mi/hr **29.** $6.40; Sample answer: The unit rate for the 96 ounce container is $0.05 per ounce. So, 128 ounces would cost $0.05 × 128 or $6.40. **31.** B **33a.** x-small **33b.** Large; It has the least cost per ounce. **35.** $\frac{31}{15}$ **37.** $\frac{4}{1}$

39. 700 clicks **41.** 8 **43.** 144 **45.** 0.04 **47.** 3500

Pages 278–280 *Lesson 6-3*

1. 28,800 acres **3.** 20.32 **5.** 425.25 **7.** 4.26 **9.** 138.72 grams per minute **11.** 1 billion cans per week **13.** 80.67 feet per second

15 16 in. · $\frac{2.54 \text{ cm}}{1 \text{ in.}} = 40.64$ cm

17. 7.31 **19.** 1.85 **21.** 4.58 **23.** 3250.68 miles per hour **25.** 203.2 **27.** 2188 **29.** 6.02 **31a.** 2.60 meters per second **31b.** 12.27 miles per hour **33.** 7 yd/min, 500 m/h, 6 in./s **35.** 18 lb/min, 500 kg/h, 5 oz/s **37.** 72.79 liters per week **39.** <

41 150 dollars · $\frac{0.729 \text{ euro}}{1 \text{ dollar}} = 109.35$ euro

43. 10,997.82 yen **45.** Sample answers: 600 cm/min, 360 m/h **47.** 500 ft/min; Sample answer: All of the other rates are equal to 60 mi/h. **49.** Identity Property; the conversion factor is equal to 1. **51.** C **53.** A **55.** $45.75 per ticket **57.** 24.2 miles per gallon **59.** The 6-pack of soda costs about $0.37 per can. The 12-pack of soda costs about $0.35 per can. So, the 12-pack is less expensive. **61.** $\frac{1}{4}$ **63.** $\frac{2}{5}$

65. −0.8 **67.** $7\frac{5}{14}$ **69.** $\frac{1}{4}$ **71.** $\frac{4}{5}$ **73.** $\frac{3}{13}$

Pages 283–285 *Lesson 6-4*

1. No; The rates are not equal. **3.** $c = 3.19g$; $59.02

5 $\frac{1}{8}, \frac{2}{15}, \frac{3}{30} = \frac{1}{10}, \frac{4}{42} = \frac{2}{21}$

The rates are not equal, so the set of numbers is not proportional.

7. Yes; Each rate is equal to $\frac{1}{7}$ **9.** no; The rates are not equal. **11.** $p = \$18\ell$; $126 **13.** no

Number of Rides	2	3	4	5	6
Cost	$5.50	$7.00	$8.50	$10.00	$11.50

15 **a.** Yes; sample answer:

Hot Dog Packages	1	2	3	4
Hot Dogs	8	16	24	32

The hot dog packages to hot dogs ratio for hot dog packages of 1, 2, 3, and 4 units is $\frac{1}{8}, \frac{2}{16}$ or $\frac{1}{8}, \frac{3}{24}$ or $\frac{1}{8}$, and $\frac{4}{32}$ or $\frac{1}{8}$. Since these ratios are all equal to $\frac{1}{8}$, the number of hot dog packages is proportional to the number of hot dogs.

b. Yes; sample answer:

Hot Dogs	8	16	24	32
Hot Dog Buns	10	20	30	40

The hot dogs to hot dog buns ratio for hot dog packages of 1, 2, 3, and 4 units is $\frac{8}{10}$ or $\frac{4}{5}, \frac{16}{20}$ or $\frac{4}{5}, \frac{24}{30}$ or $\frac{4}{5}$, and $\frac{32}{40}$ or $\frac{4}{5}$. Since these ratios are all equal to $\frac{4}{5}$, the number of hot dogs is proportional to the number of hot dog buns.

17. Sample answer: If the ratio of red to pink flowers is $\frac{2}{8}$; $r = 0.25p$ for r red flowers and p pink flowers. At store A, there are always 2 red flowers for every 8 pink flowers in the bouquet. At store B, their signature bouquet will always have 3 more pink flowers than red flowers. The bouquet for store A is proportional while the bouquet for Store B is nonproportional. Store A: If $\frac{2}{10}$ of the flowers are red, $r = 0.25p$ for r red flowers and p pink flowers. Store B: $r = p - 3$ for r red flowers and p pink flowers. **19b.** The ratios should be close in value. **19c.** Sample answer: Pyramid of Khufu in Giza, Egypt; The Taj Mahal in India; The Lincoln Memorial in Washington, D.C. **21.** A **23.** D **25.** 10.16 **27.** 681 **29.** 23.3 miles per gallon **31.** 52.6 miles per day **33.** 12($15 + $10 + $8), 12($15) + 12($10) + 12($8); $396 **35.** 18 **37.** 7 **39.** 7

Pages 290–292 *Lesson 6-5*

1. 24 **3.** 34 **5.** 29 **7.** 27 in.

9 $\frac{6}{8} = \frac{z}{48}$
$6(48) = 8 \cdot z$
$288 = 8z$
$\frac{288}{8} = \frac{8z}{8}$
$36 = z$

11. 24 **13.** 12 **15.** 14 **17.** 0.96 **19.** 23 **21.** 28 gal **23.** $d = 15.46t$; 927.6 ft; 1391.4 ft **25a.** 10 oz **25b.** 27 oz **25c.** 190.67 oz **27.** $\frac{s}{0.54} = \frac{4.55}{1.89}$; 1.3 **29.** $\frac{20}{4} = \frac{b}{20}$; 100 **31.** 0.8 **33.** 15 **35.** 7

37 **a.** $c = \frac{2.67}{3n}$ or $0.89n$; $c = \frac{9.50}{2n}$ or $4.75n$; $c = \frac{11.96}{4n}$ or $2.99n$; $c = \frac{10.35}{3n}$ or $3.45n$

b. Cost of Craft Supplies

c. 18 inches is 1.5 feet which is $\frac{1}{2}$ yard.

The cost is: $c = 0.89\left(\frac{1}{2}\right) = \$0.45$

$10 \text{ m} \cdot \frac{1 \text{ yard}}{0.914 \text{ m}} = 10.94$ yard
$c = 4.75(10.94)$
$= \$51.97$

39. 45 **41.** Trey; Sample answer: Morgan cross multiplied incorrectly. **43.** Sample answer: It is easier to use the constant of proportionality if you are solving the proportion for several unknowns. It is easy to find a unit rate and then multiply the amounts needed to find the equivalent amounts. No, because no matter how you set up and solve a proportion, you will also arrive at the same answer. **45.** J **47a.** $\frac{100}{258} = \frac{s}{645}$ **47b.** 250 students **47c.** $\frac{25}{258} = \frac{s}{220}$; about 21 students **49.** 12.7 **51.** 10.36 **53.** $\frac{8}{27}$ **55.** $\frac{9}{20}$

Pages 297–299 *Lesson 6-6*

1. 1 in. = 2 ft

3.

5 $\frac{255 \text{ ft}}{4 \text{ in.}} = \frac{x \text{ ft}}{1 \text{ in.}}$

$255 = 4x$

$63.75 = x$

1 in. = 63.75 ft

7a. $\frac{1}{2}$ in. by $\frac{5}{8}$ in. **7b.** $\frac{3}{4}$ in. by $\frac{3}{8}$ in.
7c. $\frac{1}{2}$ in. by $\frac{3}{8}$ in.

11 $\frac{6 \text{ in.}}{10 \text{ ft}} = \frac{6 \text{ in.}}{120 \text{ in.}}$

$= \frac{6 \div 6}{120 \div 6}$

$= \frac{1}{20}$

13. $\frac{1}{72}$ **15.** $\frac{16}{1}$ **17a.** Sample answer: $\frac{1}{4}$ in. = 3.0×10^7 mi **17b.**

21. Always; Sample answer: A scale factor of $\frac{3}{1}$ means that 3 units is equal to 1 unit so the scale drawing or model will be larger than the actual object. **23.** Sample answer: The model is larger than the actual insect. The scale factor is $\frac{2.5}{1}$ which means the model is 2.5 times as large as the insect. **25.** B **27.** H **29.** 4 **31.** 16 **33.** 1.4 **35.** $h = 35d$; 105 in. **37.** 9 **39.** 18.4 **41.** 2.6

Pages 303–306 Lesson 6-7

1 $\frac{5}{x} = \frac{12}{8}$

$t(8) = 12x$

$40 = 12x$

$\frac{40}{12} = \frac{12x}{12}$

$3\frac{1}{3} = x$

3. 2 units

5 $\frac{25}{10} = \frac{x}{6}$

$25(6) = 10x$

$150 = 10x$

$\frac{150}{10} = \frac{10x}{10}$

$15 = x$

7. 2.125 cm **9.** 27 in.
11. (rectangle ABCD: 6 cm by 4) **13.** 102 m

15 **a.** $a + b + c$
b. The new sides will be the original sides multiplied by d. ad, bd, cd.
c. $ad + bd + cd$
d. $ad + bd + cd = d(a + b + c)$; This expression means that the perimeter of the original figure can be multiplied by d to find the perimeter of the new figure.
e. The perimeter of the original is $3 + 4 + 5 = 12$ and the scale factor is 2, so the perimeter of the new figure is $12(2) = 24$ inches.
f. If the figures are similar, then the perimeter is also similar. So, the perimeters are proportional.

17. Sometimes; Sample answer: Even though all rectangles have equal corresponding angles, the sides of one rectangle are not always proportional to the sides of another rectangle. **19.** No; Sample answer: Both of them incorrectly set up the proportions. The proportion should be set up as $\frac{BC}{EF} = \frac{AB}{DE}$ or $\frac{16}{12} = \frac{x}{18}$. **21.** Triangle B is the original triangle. Since the scale factor is less than 1, the original triangle is being reduced, which means that the scaled triangle will be smaller. The measures of the sides of triangle A are less than the measures of the sides of triangle B, so triangle B must be the original triangle. **23.** J **25.** 8 **27.** 16 bags **29.** 4 **31.** 4

Pages 309–312 Lesson 6-8

1. $A'(-1, 0.5)$, $B'(0.5, 1)$, $C'(1.5, -1)$

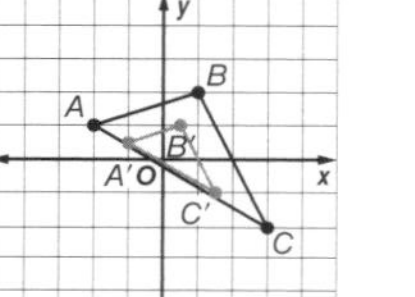

3 $M(0, 0)$, $N(3, -3)$, $O(0, -6)$, $P(-3, -3)$ yields $M'(0 \cdot 2.5, 0 \cdot 2.5)$, $N'(3 \cdot 2.5, -3 \cdot 2.5)$, $O'(0 \cdot 2.5, -6 \cdot 2.5)$, $P'(-3 \cdot 2.5, -3 \cdot 2.5) =$ $M'(0, 0)$, $N'(7.5, -7.5)$, $O'(0, -15)$, $P'(-7.5, -7.5)$ The correct answer choice is A.

5. $P'(4, 4)$, $Q'(8, 12)$, $R'(12, 4)$

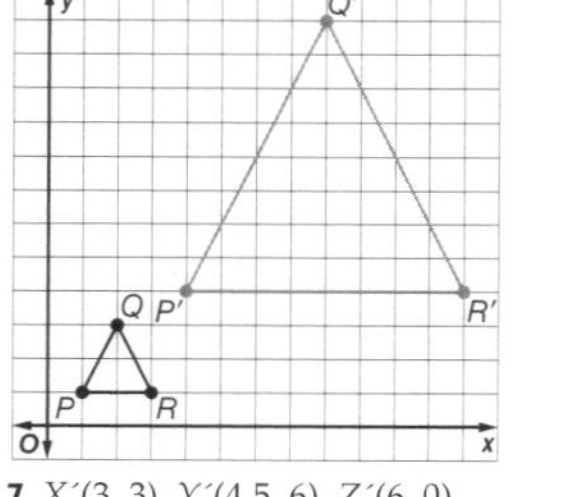

7. $X'(3, 3)$, $Y'(4.5, 6)$, $Z'(6, 0)$

9. $G'(-2, 2)$, $H'(4, 2)$, $J'(6, -4)$, $K'(-4, -4)$

11. $R'(-3, 6)$, $S'(3, 12)$, $T'(3, 3)$

13. 200

15 **a.** $640\ (1.5) = 960$; $460(1.5) = 720$ The image is 960×720 pixels.
b. $\frac{32}{640} = \frac{1}{20}$
c. $\frac{600}{480} = \frac{1.25}{1}$ The scale factor is 1.25.

17 The length of side DC is 3 units and the length of $D'C'$ is 2 units, so the scale factor is $\frac{2}{3}$. It is a reduction since the image is smaller than the original figure.

19. Sample answer:

21a. $A'(0, 4)$, $B'(0, 0)$, $C'(8, 4)$ **21b.** $A'(0, 4)$, $B'(0, 0)$, $C'(8, 4)$ **21c.** $A'(0, 2.5)$, $B'(0, 0)$, $C'(5, 2.5)$
21d. $A'(0, 2.5)$, $B'(0, 0)$, $C'(5, 2.5)$ **23.** $C(2, 5)$, $C'(4, 7)$; Sample answer: Dilations involve multiplying the coordinates by the scale factor. In the points $C(2, 5)$ and $C'(4, 7)$, 2 is added to each coordinate. **25.** C **27.** B **29.** 2.1 **31.** 240 mi **33.** 9.6 **35.** 0.94

For Homework Help, go to Hotmath.com

Pages 314–317 Lesson 6-9

1 $\frac{8}{4.5} = \frac{x}{5.5}$

$8(5.5) = 4.5x$

$44 = 4.5x$

$\frac{44}{4.5} = \frac{4.5x}{4.5}$

$9.8 \text{ ft} \approx x$

3. 45 ft **5.** 120 yd

7 $\frac{157.5}{60} = \frac{5.25}{x}$

$157.5x = 60(5.25)$

$157.5x = 315$

$\frac{157.5x}{157.5} = \frac{315}{157.5}$

$x = 2$ ft

9a. Sample answer:

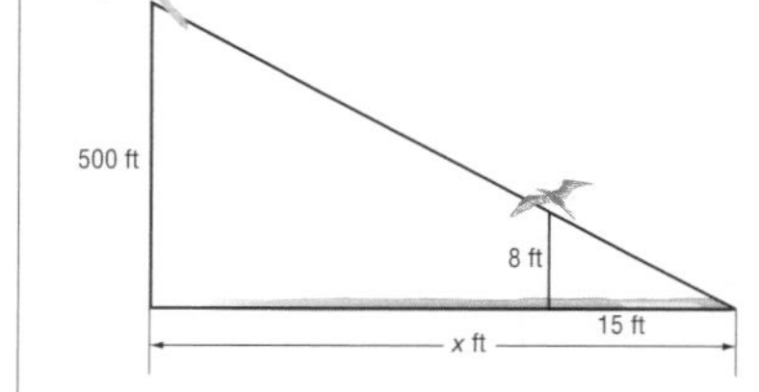

9b. $\frac{500}{8} = \frac{x}{15}$; 937.5 ft

11 $\frac{4}{d} = \frac{5\frac{1}{3}}{16}$

$4 \cdot 16 = d \cdot 5\frac{1}{3}$

$64 = 5\frac{1}{3}d$

$12 \text{ ft} = d$

13. $\frac{37.5}{1.5} = \frac{150}{x}$; 6 ft **17.** False; Sample answer: You also need to know if the angles created by the two sides are congruent as well. **19.** D **21.** 10 km
23.

25. 18 pieces **27.** $0.58\overline{3}$ **29.** 0.6

Pages 318–322 Study Guide and Review

1. proportion **3.** constant of proportionality **5.** similar figures **7.** dimensional analysis

9. $\frac{5}{12}$ **11.** $\frac{45}{1}$ **13.** $\frac{3}{4}$; For every 4 times at bat, Jean got 3 hits or on $\frac{3}{4}$ of his at bats, he got a hit. **15.** 80 meters per minute **17.** 0.6 miles per minute **19.** 17.78 **21.** 739.35 **23.** 8.51 **25.** 318.75 mi **27.** Yes; Each rate is equal to $\frac{1}{8}$. **29.** $c = 0.25r$, 11 rings cost \$2.75; 20 rings cost \$5 **31.** 7.2 **33.** 7 **35.** 120 ft **37.** 150 ft **39.** 7.2 in. **41.** 3.5 cm

43.

$Q'(-6, 9), R'(3, 6), S'(9, -3), T'(-6, -6)$

45.

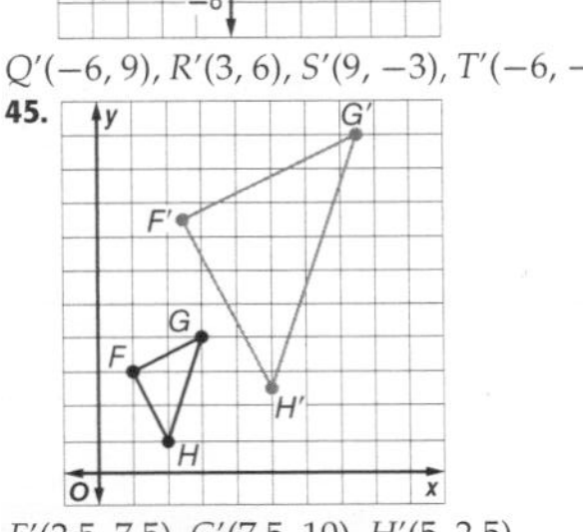

$F'(2.5, 7.5), G'(7.5, 10), H'(5, 2.5)$

47. 31 in. **49.** 70 m

Chapter 7 Percent

Page 329 *Chapter 7* *Get Ready*

1. 0.25 **3.** 0.375 **5.** 0.67 **7.** 15 **9.** 44 **11.** 2 **13.** 5 **15.** 129 songs

Pages 334–336 *Lesson 7-1*

1. 25 **3.** 112 **5.** 95% **7.** 94.44% **9.** 43.75% **11.** $\frac{61}{100}$ **13.** $\frac{31}{150}$ **15.** $\frac{29}{25}$ or $1\frac{4}{25}$ **17.** $\frac{3}{500}$ **19.** $\frac{5}{8}$ **21.** $\frac{3}{250}$

23 $140\% = \frac{140}{100}$
$= \frac{7}{5}$
$= 1\frac{2}{5}$

25. 25% **27.** 450% **29.** 87.5% **31.** 71.43% **33.** 62.5% **35.** 550% **37.** figure A: $\frac{1}{4}$, 25%; figure B: $\frac{7}{10}$, 70%; figure C: $\frac{3}{4}$, 75%; figure C

39 $75\% = \frac{75}{100}$
$= \frac{3}{4}$ and $\frac{36}{48} = \frac{3}{4}$; So, they are equal.

41. < **43.** > **45.** Sample answer: 76%; $\frac{3}{4} = 0.75$ or 75% and $\frac{7}{9} \approx 77.8\%$. So, 76% is between 75% and 77.8%.

47. 750% **49.** 5; $\frac{5}{5+5} = 50\%$ **51.** B **53.** A **55.** 76 ft

57.

$A'(-1, 0.5), B'(0.5, 1), C'(1.5, -1)$

59. $y \geq -7$ **61.** a > 11 **63.** 1820 **65.** 0.333

Pages 340–342 *Lesson 7-2*

1. 0.45 **3.** 0.006 **5.** 3% **7.** 60% **9.** dog **11.** 0.75 **13.** 0.03 **15.** 0.0091 **17.** 2.84

19 0.43 = 0.43 = 43% **21.** 28.6% **23.** 3.5% **25.** 80% **27.** 620% **29.** 366.7% **31.** 0.2% **33.** 0.02% **35.** action **37.** $\frac{5}{22}$, 2.2, 227% **39a.** 54 students **39b.** 100 students

41 $0.04x = 1$ is solved to show that there are 25 questions on the test. If Luther answered 1 incorrectly then he answered 24 questions correctly.

43. Sample answer: 9%; 0.09; $\frac{9}{100}$ **45.** Len; Carlita divided by 100 and she should have multiplied by 100 **47.** Sample answer: Greater than; by dividing by 100 and removing the % symbol, 0.005 > 0.0005. Since 0.005 > 0.0005, 0.5% > 0.0005. **49.** J **51.** 45 **53.** $\frac{1}{8}$ **55.** 80 m **57.** $8a + 4$ **59.** $3x + 6y$ **61.** $(3 \times 24) + (2 \times 12)$ is 96. So, the luggage is within the limit. **63.** 900 **65.** 0.42 **67.** 240

Pages 347–350 *Lesson 7-3*

1. 25% **3.** 41.44 **5.** 400% **7.** 39%

9 $\frac{21}{50} = \frac{p}{100}$
$21(100) = 50p$
$2100 = 50p$
$42 = p$
42%

11. 55% **13.** 100 **15.** 166 **17.** 170 **19.** 375 **21.** 500 gumballs

23 **a.** $\frac{a}{2947} = \frac{33}{100}$
$100a = 2947(33)$
$100a = 97251$
$a = 972.51$
about 973 people

b. $\frac{a}{2947} = \frac{26}{100}$
$100a = 2947(26)$
$100a = 76622$
$a = 766.22$
about 766 people

25a. The percent is increased by a factor of 2 and the whole is halved. Each answer is 2. **25b.** 32% of 6.25 = 2 **27.** 300% **29.** 4.1 **31.** 2.2 **33.** 88.9%

35 **a.** Let x be the number of phones to add.
$\frac{45 + x}{120 + x} = \frac{40}{100}$
$40(120 + x) = 100(45 + x)$
$4800 + 40x = 4500 + 100x$
$300 + 40x = 100x$
$300 = 60x$
5 cell phones = x

b. There will be 120 + 5 or 125 cell phones in stock.

37. 5% of 80, 25% of 80, 25% of 160; If the percent is the same but the whole is bigger, then the part is greater. If the whole is the same but the percent is greater, then the part is greater. **39.** 3 **41.** Always; Sample answer: To solve for x% of y, find $\frac{x}{100} = \frac{n}{y}$. So, $n = \frac{xy}{100}$. To solve for y% of x, find $\frac{y}{100} = \frac{n}{x}$. So, $n = \frac{xy}{100}$. **43.** C **45.** C **47.** daily newspaper **49.** $1\frac{1}{5}$ **51.** $\frac{5}{6}$ **53.** $\frac{2}{3}$ **55.** $-\frac{3}{10}$ **57.** $\frac{11}{36}$ **59.** 3 **61.** 19

Pages 353–355 *Lesson 7-4*

1 75% of $16 = \frac{3}{4}(16)$
$= 3(4)$
$= 12$

3. 3.7 **5.** 0.72 **7.** 12 exercises **9.** 10; 53% is about 50% or $\frac{1}{2}$, $\frac{1}{2} \cdot 20 = 10$ **11.** 36; 87% is about 90% or $\frac{9}{10}$, $\frac{9}{10} \cdot 40 = 36$ **13.** 44; 39 is about 40, 100% of 40 is 40 and 10% of 40 is 4, 40 + 4 = 44 **15.** 32 **17.** 70 **19.** 9 **21.** 6 **23.** 12.5 **25.** 0.3 **27.** \$7.50 **29.** 63; 73% is about 75% or $\frac{3}{4}$, $\frac{3}{4} \cdot 84 = 63$ **31.** 12.5; 49 is about 50, $\frac{1}{4} \cdot 50 = 12.5$ **33.** 0.5; 1% of 295 is about 3, $\frac{1}{6} \cdot 3 = 0.5$ **35.** 22; 276% is about 275%, 100% of 8 is 8 and 75% of 8 is 6, 8 • 2 + 6 = 22 **37.** 0.24; 1% of 30 is 0.3, $\frac{4}{5} \cdot 0.3 = 0.24$ **39.** 30; 194% is about 200%, 100% of 15 is 15, 15 • 2 = 30

41 $81\% \approx 80\% = \frac{4}{5}$
$\frac{4}{5}(6700) = 5360$ teens

43a. Sample answer: 155 mi **43b.** Sample answer: 90 mi **43c.** Sample answer: 65 mi **45.** Sample answer: 60 and 600; These numbers are divisible by 3, making it easy to find $66\frac{2}{3}\%$ or $\frac{2}{3}$ of each number. **47.** Sample answer: One way is to use a fractional equivalent. 20% = $\frac{1}{5}$ and $\frac{1}{5} \cdot 60 = 12$. Another way is to find 10% of 60 and multiply the result by 2. 10% • 60 = 6, 6 • 2 = 12 **49.** G **51a.** \$2.10; Sample answer: \$28 is about \$30. Since 1% of \$30 is \$0.30, then 7% of \$30 is 7 • 0.30 or \$2.10 **51b.** \$30.10; \$28 + \$2.10 = \$30.10 **51c.** \$4.50; Sample answer: \$30.10 is about \$30. 10% of \$30 is \$3 and 5% of 30 is \$1.50. \$3 + \$1.50 = \$4.50 **51d.** yes; Sample answer: The total bill with tax will be around \$30.10. The tip is \$4.50. \$30.10 + \$4.50 = \$34.60 **53.** $\frac{37}{1000}$ **55.** 4 **57.** 7.5 in. **59.** 0.25 **61.** 0.05 **63.** 0.35

Pages 360–362 *Lesson 7-5*

1. 30 **3.** $33\frac{1}{3}\%$ **5.** 275 **7.** 114 boxes

9 Part = Percent • Whole
= 16% • 64
= 0.16(64)
= 10.24

11. 20% **13.** 64 **15.** 78 **17.** 5.5% **19.** 39.9 **21.** 26% **23.** \$2500

25 **a.** 120% of 120 = 1.2(120)
= 144 cars
144 − 120 = 24
They will need to add 24 cars.

b.

Percent	Equation	Number of Cars
5	1.05(120)	126
15	1.15(120)	138
25	1.25(120)	150
35	1.35(120)	162

27a. $s = 1.06 \cdot 500$; \$530

27b.

x	2010	2011	2012	2013	2014	2015
y	\$500.00	\$530.00	\$561.80	\$595.51	\$631.24	\$669.11

27c. Sample answer: No; The base amount is different each year so the part changes even though the percent remains constant. **29.** 96 **31.** Sample answer: The percent is greater than 100% because otherwise the part would be less than or equal to the whole. **33.** No; Suppose an item costs \$100. A 10% discount would be a discount of \$10, so the discounted price would be \$90. Adding a 10% sales tax adds \$9. So, \$90 + \$9 is not \$100. **35.** B **37.** A **39.** 48 **41.** 9 **43.** chocolate pieces: 2 c; peanuts: 3 c **45.** 26.4 **47.** 19.2 **49.** 37% **51.** 182% **53.** 5% **55.** 0.7%

Pages 366–369 *Lesson 7-6*

1. −20%; decrease

3 Step 1: Find the change in sales:
$900 - 1300 = -400$
Step 2: Divide the change by the original number:
$\frac{-400}{1300} = -0.308$
Step 3: Write the decimal as a percent:
$-0.308 = -30.8\%$; decrease

5. \$58.95

7 Step 1: Find the change in inches:
$26 - 14 = 12$
Step 2: Divide the change by the original number:
$\frac{12}{14} = 0.857$
Step 3: Write the decimal as a percent:
$0.857 = 85.7\%$; increase

9. −9.8%; decrease **11.** −12.5%; decrease **13.** 41.4%; increase **15.** 13.2%; increase **17.** \$76.80 **19.** \$33.00 **21.** \$18.85 **23.** \$598.80 **25.** \$7.50 **27.** 3088 calls **29.** −11.7%; decrease

31 Juliette's time will be 85% of Torie's since she is 15% faster.
85% of 74 is 0.85(74) = 62.9 seconds
62.9 < 74

33a.

City	Population 2000	Population 2006	Amount of Change	%
Raleigh, NC	276,093	356,321	80,228	29%
Columbia, SC	116,278	119,961	3683	3%
Frankfort, KY	27,741	27,077	−664	−2%
Columbus, OH	711,470	733,203	21,733	3%

33b. Sample answer: The percents of change were the same but the amount of change for Columbus was much greater than the amount of change for Columbia. The percents were the same because the original amounts for each city were very different. **35.** Sample answer: from 80 mi to 160 mi; 100% increase **37a.** false; Sample answer: Suppose the cost of an item is \$25 and you want to mark it up 125% of the cost. So, multiply \$25 by 125% or 1.25. The new price is \$25 + \$31.25 or \$56.25. **37b.** true **39.** Sample answer: An internet service provider offers a plan for \$40 per month. If this month the plan is 45% off, what is the cost of the plan?; \$22 **41.** H **43.** \$855 **45.** 63 **47.** 14.52 **49.** 13 angelfish **51.** $\frac{2}{9}$ **53.** 0.875 **55.** 0.3

Pages 372–374 Lesson 7-7

1. \$567 **3.** \$117.81 **5.** 3.23% **7.** \$643.71 **9.** \$3512.55

11 $I = prt$
$= (620)(0.0625)(5)$
$= \$193.75$

13. \$242.40 **15.** \$919.80 **17.** \$4264.86 **19.** \$683.88 **21.** \$15,700.17 **23.** 42 months **25.** option A; Sample answer: After 3 years, the interest earned with option A is \$281.25. With option B, the interest earned is \$273.91. **27.** \$15,496.72 **29.** \$1123.16

31 #4 \$182.99(1.015) = \$185.73 − 50 = \$135.73
#5 \$135.73(1.015) = \$137.77 − 50 = \$87.77
#6 \$87.77(1.015) = \$89.08 − 50 = \$39.08
#7 \$39.08(1.015) = \$39.67
The bill amounts for the 5th and 7th months are \$137.77 and \$39.67.

33. Sample answer: \$2000 at 1%. Using the simple interest formula $I = \$2000 \cdot 0.01 \cdot 4$ or \$80 **35.** no; Sabino did not convert the time to years and Mya did not change the percent to a decimal correctly. **37.** Sample answer: With simple interest, the amount of money earned will be the same each year because it is always applied to the initial amount. With compound interest, the amount of interest will increase each year because it is being applied to the new total after the interest is added each year. **39.** J **41.** 6.5% compounded annually; Sample answer: The investment of \$500 at a 6.75% simple interest will earn \$168.75 and the investment at a 6.5% rate compounded annually will earn \$185.04. **43.** 3% **45a.** $\frac{1}{4} \times 7$ or 1.75 billion **45b.** $\frac{1}{5} \times 7$ or 1.4 billion **47.** $\frac{5a}{c}$ **49a.** $m = 8w - 1$ **49b.** 71 min **51.** 1.47

Pages 378–381 Lesson 7-8

1. **Atmospheric Composition**

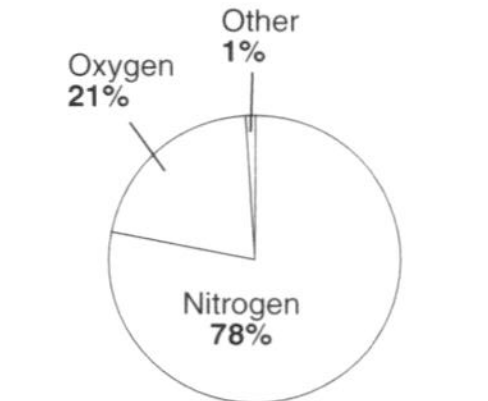

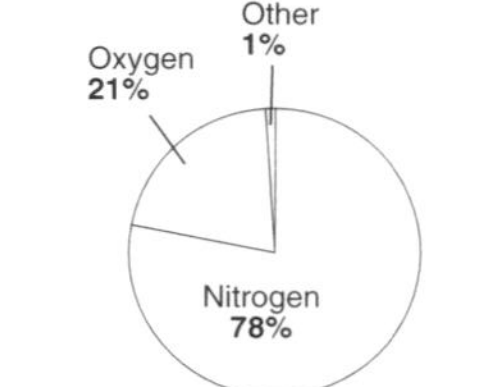

Source: *NASA*

3 Mystery: 0.18(600) = 108
Historical Fiction: 0.10(600) = 60
108 − 60 = 48 people

5. **Layers of the Atmosphere (km)**

Troposphere 1.5%
Stratosphere 6.7%
Mesosphere 11.4%
Thermosphere 80.4%

7 To find the angle measure for each category, multiply the entire circle, 360°, by the percent.

Type	Percent	Angle Measure in Graph
metal	8%	$0.08 \cdot 360 \approx 29°$
plastic	24%	$0.24 \cdot 360 \approx 86°$
food and yard waste	11%	$0.11 \cdot 360 \approx 40°$
rubber and leather	6%	$0.06 \cdot 360 \approx 21°$
other	21%	$0.21 \cdot 360 \approx 76°$
paper	30%	$0.30 \cdot 360 = 108°$

Use a compass to draw a circle and a radius. Then use a protractor to draw a 29° angle. Repeat for each of the remaining angles.

U.S. Landfill Composition

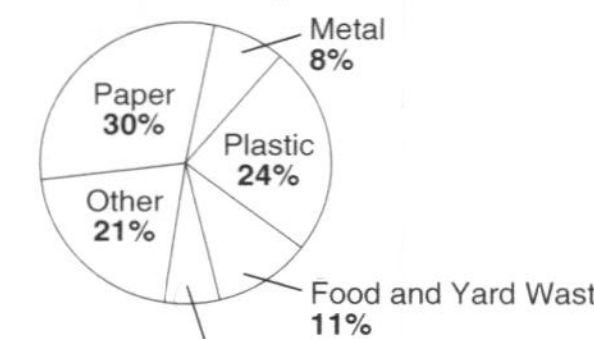

9. 45 households

11 $\frac{54}{360} = \frac{75}{x}$
$54x = 360(75)$
$54x = 27000$
$x = 500$
500 people were surveyed.

13a. **Sampras's Grand Slam Wins**

Australian Open 14%
U.S. Open 36%
Wimbledon 50%

Graf's Grand Slam Wins

Australian Open 18%
U.S. Open 23%
Wimbledon 32%
French Open 27%

13b. No, even though they each have 5 U.S. Grand Slam wins, the total number of Grand Slam wins for each is different, therefore giving a different percentage for each. **15.** Sample answer: The percentages exceed 100% **17.** True; Sample answer: You can write a proportion comparing parts to wholes and use 360 as the whole in one of the ratios. **19.** Sample answer: Change each percent to a decimal. Then multiply each decimal by 360° to find the measure of each angle. Draw a circle and use a protractor to mark each angle. Label each section and add a title. **21.** H

23.

Color	Number of Cars	Angle Measure
Red	5	18°
White	10	36°
Green	15	54°
Blue	30	108°
Other	40	144°

25. \$558.90 **27.** Domain: {4, −7, 0}, Range: {2, 9, −1} **29.** Domain: {18, 14, −6}, Range: {0, −9, 6}

Pages 382–385 Study Guide and Review

1. markup **3.** percent of change **5.** principal **7.** percent **9.** $\frac{3}{10}$ **11.** $\frac{23}{25}$ **13.** $\frac{3}{500}$ **15.** $1\frac{2}{5}$ **17.** 25% **19.** 60% **21.** 33.33% **23.** 36% **25.** 80% **27.** 0.072 **29.** 0.0048 **31.** 240% **33.** 77.5% **35.** 20% **37.** 35 **39.** 18 **41.** 9 **43.** 10; 24% is about 25% or $\frac{1}{4}$, $\frac{1}{4} \cdot 40 = 10$ **45.** 0.5; 1% of 298 is about 3, $3 \div 6 = 0.5$ **47.** 200 free throws; 77% is about 80% or $\frac{4}{5}$ and 244 is about 250, $\frac{4}{5} \cdot 250 = 200$ **49.** 4 **51.** 150% **53.** No, the jersey is now 75% off the original price. If the jersey was originally \$100, after the first markdown it is \$50. Then the manager takes 50% off of \$50 making the jersey \$25, or 75% off the original price. **55.** 34.5%; increase **57.** \$204 **59.** 25% **61.** \$6375.00 **63.** \$1898.44

65. Daily Nutrition

Fats & Oils 19%; Fluids 25%; Breads 19%; Vegetables 13%; Fruits 9%; Dairy 9%; Meat/Fish/Poultry 6%

67. 2 championships

Chapter 8 Linear Functions and Graphing

Page 393 *Chapter 8* *Get Ready*

1. 17 **3.** 20 **5.** 5th week **7.** A **9.** Sample answer: Walk north 10 blocks then west 5 blocks. **11.** 65 mph

Pages 397–400 *Lesson 8-1*

1 This relation is a function because each element of the domain is paired with exactly one element of the range.
3. The graph represents a relation that is not a function because it does not pass the vertical line test. At least one input value has more than one output value. By examining the graph, you can see that when $x = 3$, there are two different y values. **5.** 14 **7.** 44 **9a.** $c(p) = 125 + 15p$
9b. 6 people **11.** This is not a function because 24 is paired with two range values, 16 and 17.
13. This is not a function because 3 is paired with 4 range values, 1, 3, 7, and 9. **15.** This relation is a function because each element of the domain is paired with exactly one element of the range.
17. This graph is a function because the vertical line test shows that it passes through no more than one point on the graph for each value of x.

19 $f(9) = 3(9) - 9$
$= 27 - 9$
$= 18$

21. −54 **23.** 0 **25.** −42 **27.** 74 **29.** −86 **31.** 254 **33.** −66 **35a.** $c(m) = 50 + 0.55m$ **35b.** 142 mi

37 **a.** {(1970, 37), (1980, 35), (1990, 34), (2000, 34)} Sample answer: The data represent a function because the x values or years are not repeated.
b. {(37, 1970), (35, 1980), (34, 1990), (34, 2000)} Sample answer: The inverse does not represent a function because the x-value of 34 has two different y-values.

39a. −3

39b.

Term Number	Term
1	36
2	33
3	30
4	27
5	24
6	21
7	18

The set of ordered pairs is a function because each input is paired with only one output.

39c. [graph]

There is a negative relationship.
41. 138 **43.** 362 **45.** −982 **47.** A
49a. $c(s) = 15 + 1.75s$ **49b.** $41.25

49c.

s	c(s) + 15 = 1.75s	c(s)
15	15 + 1.75(15)	41.25
20	15 + 1.75(20)	50.00
25	15 + 1.75(25)	58.75
30	15 + 1.75(30)	67.50

51. Favorite Rides

Tilt-a-Whirl 10%; Ferris Wheel 10%; Carousel 3%; Bumper Cars 29%; Roller Coaster 48%

53. $\frac{6}{7}$ **55.** $-\frac{7}{20}$ **57.** $\frac{8}{9}$ **59.** $\frac{27}{25}$ or $1\frac{2}{25}$ **61.** 40 **63.** 52

Pages 403–405 *Lesson 8-2*

1. The terms have a common difference of 1. A term is 1 more than the term number; $t = 1 + n$.
3. The terms have a common difference of 3. A term is 3 times the term number; $t = 3n$.
5. $t = 9 + n$; 19 **7.** $t = 3n + 1$; 70 **9.** 15 **11.** The terms have a common difference of 1. A term is 7 more than the term number; $t = 7 + n$. **13.** The terms have a common difference of 1. A term is 14 more than the term number; $t = 14 + n$.

15. The terms have a common difference of 8. A term is 8 times the term number; $t = 8n$.
17. The terms have a common difference of 20. A term is 20 times the term number; $t = 20n$.
19. $t = 15 + n$; 38 **21.** $t = 4n$; 52 **23.** $t = 3n + 4$; 64 **25.** $t = 4n - 3$; 353

27 **a.** Make a table to organize the sequence and find a rule. Each term is 2 more than the one before it. This would indicate that the rule should be $t = 2n$. However, you need to add 1 to get to the value of t. So, the rule is $t = 2n + 1$.

Term Number (n)	1	2	3	4
Term (t)	3	5	7	9

b. Use the rule to find to number of triangles if there are 27 beams.
$t = 2n + 1$
$27 = 2n + 1$
$26 = 2n$
$\frac{26}{2} = \frac{2n}{2}$
$13 = n$
There will be 13 triangles.

29. $d = 9s$; 108 ft

31 Make a table to organize the sequence. The terms have a common difference of 2. This would indicate that the rule should be $t = 2n$. However, you need to add 2 to get to the value of t. A term is 2 times the term number, plus 2. So, the rule is $t = 2n + 2$.

Term Number (n)	1	2	3	4	5
Term (t)	4	6	8	10	12

33. The terms have a common difference of 5. A term 5 times the term number, minus 1; $t = 5n - 1$. **35.** 665 seats **37.** Sample answer: 3, −5, −13, −21, . . . **39.** Sample answer: The pattern can be used to create an algebraic expression or equation that is a rule for the sequence. The expression or equation is then used to find values that continue the pattern, and it allows you to make predictions. **41.** $t = n + 6$; In both the function and the sequence, the input values are 1, 2, 3, 4 and the output values are 7, 8, 9, 10. **43.** 59

45a.

x	y
1	5
2	7
3	9
4	11
5	13

45b. $y = 2x + 3$

47. $252 **49.** 10 **51.** 5

Pages 409–411 *Lesson 8-3*

1.

x	y = x + 7	y
−1	y = −1 + 7	6
0	y = 0 + 7	7
1	y = 1 + 7	8
2	y = 2 + 7	9

(−1, 6), (0, 7), (1, 8), (2, 9)

3. Sample answer: (−1, 4), (0, 5), (1, 6), (2, 7)
5. Sample answer: (−1, 3), (0, 6), (1, 9), (2, 12)
7. Sample answer: (1, 10) means that she earns $10 for working 1 hour; (2, 20) means that she earns $20 for working 2 hours.

9. [graph: $y = 3x$]

11. [graph: $x + y = 6$]

13.

x	y = x + 7	y
−1	y = −2(−1)	2
0	y = −2(0)	0
1	y = −2(1)	−2
2	y = −2(2)	−4

(−1, 2), (0, 0), (1, −2), (2, −4)

15.

x	y = −2x + 8	y
−1	y = −2(−1) + 8	10
0	y = −2(0) + 8	8
2	y = −2(2) + 8	4
4	y = −2(4) + 8	0

(−1, 10), (0, 8), (2, 4), (4, 0)

17 Choose four values for x and substitute each value into the equation. We chose −1, 0, 1, and 2. Evaluate the expression to find the value of y. Write the solution as ordered pairs. Sample answer: (−1, 2), (0, 0), (1, −2), (2, −4).

x	2x	y	(x, y)
−1	−2(−1)	2	(−1, 2)
0	−2(0)	0	(0, 0)
1	−2(1)	−2	(1, −2)
2	−2(2)	−4	(2, −4)

19. Sample answer: (−1, 4), (0, 3), (1, 2), (2, 1) **21.** Sample answer: (−1, −1), (0, −4), (1, −7), (2, −10) **23.** Sample answer: (−1, 11), (0, 9), (1, 7), (2, 5) **25.** Sample answer: (1, 9) means they can ride 1 regular ride and 9 children's rides; (2, 6) means they can ride 2 regular rides and 6 children's rides; (3, 3) means they can ride 3 regular rides and 3 children's rides.

27.

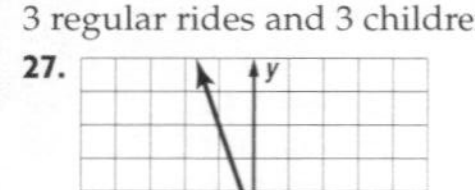

29.

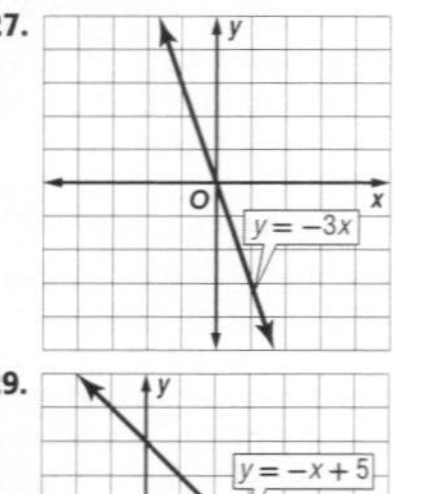

31.

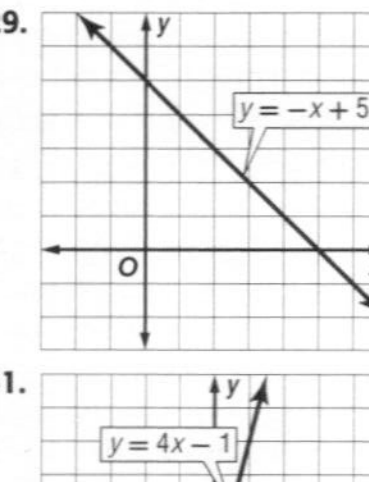

33.

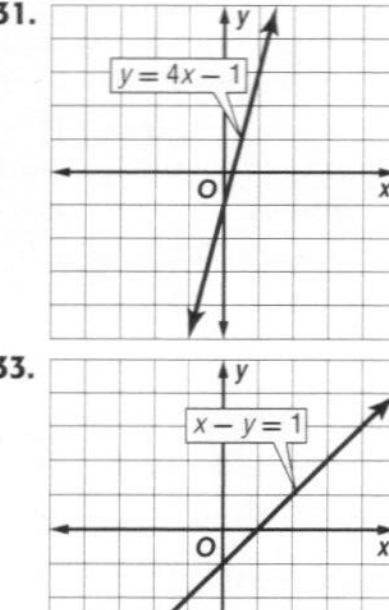

35 **a.** $P = 2w + 2\ell$ Perimeter of a rectangle
$16 = 2x + 2y$ Replace P with 16, w with x, and ℓ with y.

x	16 = 2x + 2y	y	(x, y)
1	16 = 2(1) + 2y	7	(1, 7)
2	16 = 2(2) + 2y	6	(2, 6)
3	16 = 2(3) + 2y	5	(3, 5)

b. Choose three values for x and substitute each value into the equation. We chose 1, 2, and 3. Solve the equation to find the value of y. Write the solution as ordered pairs. Sample answer: (1, 7), (2, 6), (3, 5).

c. Plot the ordered pairs on a coordinate plane.

Perimeter of a Rectangle

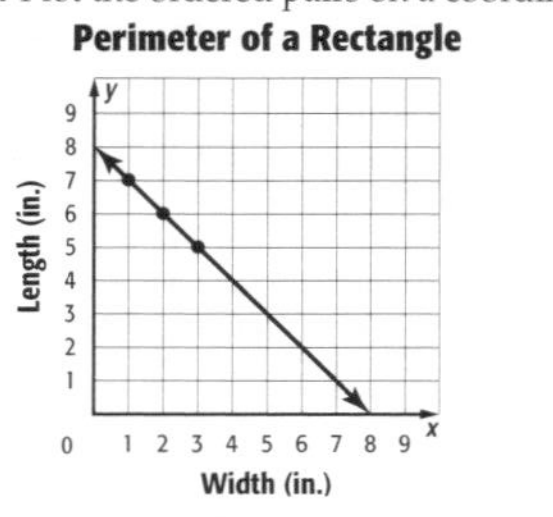

d. (−4, 12): $16 \stackrel{?}{=} 2(-4) + 2(12)$
$16 \stackrel{?}{=} -8 + 24$
$16 \stackrel{?}{=} 16$ ✓

(−4, 12) is a solution. It does not make sense because the width of a rectangle cannot have a negative value.

37. Sample answer: $y = x - 5$; (1, −4) **39.** Sample answer: Infinitely many values can be substituted for x, or the domain. A table and a graph show some of the solutions. An equation represents all the solutions of a function. **41.** Sample answer: Linear equations use variables to show the relationship between the domain values and the range values of a function. Functions can be represented using a table, a graph, a verbal description, or an equation. **43.** F **45a.** Water weighs 64 pounds per cubic foot.

45b. Sample answer:

x	y
1	64
2	128
3	192
4	256

45c. Sample answer: (1, 64) means that 1 cubic foot of water weighs 64 pounds; (2, 128) means that 2 cubic feet of water weighs 128 pounds.

45d. Sample answer:

Weight of Water

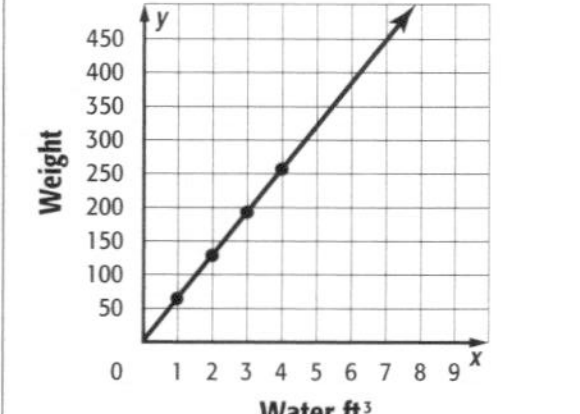

47. $t = 4n + 2$; 94 **49.** No; −0.1 in the domain is paired with 5 and −5 in the range. **51.** 2 **53.** 6

Pages 415–417 Lesson 8-4

1. increase of 0.5 h/lb **3.** −0.8 ft/min or decrease of 0.8 ft/min **5.** increase of 15 miles/h

7 rate of change $= \dfrac{\text{change in temperature}}{\text{change in time}}$
$= \dfrac{30 - 20}{2 - 1}$
$= \dfrac{10}{1}$

The rate of change is an increase of 10 jumps per minute.

9 rate of change $= \dfrac{\text{change in temperature}}{\text{change in time}}$
$= \dfrac{45 - 48}{2 - 1}$
$= \dfrac{-3}{1}$

The rate of change is a decrease of 3° per hour or −3°/h.

11. Mosquito: 600 beats/s; honey bee: 200 beats/s; the number of times a mosquito's wings beats increases at a faster rate than the number of times a honey bee's wings beat. **13.** 3 times/day, 2 times/day, 1 time/day; A puppy less than 6 months old should be fed 3 times a day. A puppy between 6 and 12 months old should be fed twice a day. A puppy older than 12 months should be fed once a day. **15.** Sample answer: The steeper the line, the greater the rate of change. **17.** Sample answer: For a horizontal line, as x increases, y does not change. So, the rate of change is 0. For a vertical line, x does not change. So, it cannot represent a rate of change. **19.** D **21.** C

23. Sample answer:

x	y
−1	−8
0	−7
1	−6
2	−5

25. Sample answer:

x	y
−1	−13
0	−10
1	−7
2	−4

27. The difference of the term numbers is 1. The terms have a common difference of 3. The term is 3 times the term number, minus 2. $t = 3n - 2$. **29.** $4n + 1$; figure 11 **31.** 25 ft/s **33.** $y = -2x$ **35.** $y = \frac{1}{3}x$

Pages 422–424 Lesson 8-5

1. $\frac{1}{2}$ in./wk; The plant grows $\frac{1}{2}$ inch per week.

No; the ratio $\frac{\text{height}}{\text{time}}$ is not the same for every pair of values. **3a.** $y = 0.25x$ **3b.** 5 in.

5 rate of change $= \dfrac{\text{change in distance}}{\text{change in time}}$
$= \dfrac{2000 \text{ mi} - 1000 \text{ mi}}{4\,h - 2\,h}$
$= \dfrac{1000 \text{ mi}}{2\,h}$
= 500 mih

The airplane travels 500 miles per hour. To determine if the quantities are proportional, find $\frac{\text{distance } m}{\text{time } h}$ for points on the graph. $\frac{1000}{2} = 500$ mi/h; $\frac{2000}{4} = 500$ mi/h; $\frac{3000}{6} = 500$ mi/h

Since the ratio $\frac{\text{distance}}{\text{time}}$ is the same for every pair of values, the relationship is proportional.

7. −1 ticket available/ticket sold; For each ticket sold, there is 1 less ticket available to buy. No; the ratio $\frac{\text{tickets available}}{\text{tickets sold}}$ is not the same for every pair of values.

9 **a.** Use the equation $k = \frac{y}{x}$ to find the constant of variation; $k = \frac{14.7}{33}$ or 0.4; So, the equation is $y = 0.4x$ to the nearest tenth.
b. $y = 0.4x$
$y = 0.4(900)$
$y = 360$ psi

11. True; the ratio $\frac{\text{total cost}}{\text{number of rooms}}$ is not the same for every pair of values. **13.** False; the graph of a direct variation always passes through the origin. **15.** Keyshawn; Ramiro found the constant rate of change rather than finding the ratios $\frac{y}{x}$ for each point. **17.** It increases the distance. **19.** C **21.** B **23a.** $12/person **23b.** The cost of admission is $12 per person. **25.** Sample answer: $\left(-1, -\frac{1}{2}\right)$, (0, 0), $\left(1, \frac{1}{2}\right)$, (2, 1) **27.** −24 **29.** 0

Pages 429–431 Lesson 8-6

1. 6 **3.** $\frac{1}{2}$

5 slope $= \dfrac{y_2 - y_1}{x_2 - x_1}$
$= \dfrac{1 - (-4)}{7 - (-2)}$
$= \dfrac{1 + 4}{7 + 2}$
$= \dfrac{5}{9}$

7. 0

9 slope $= \frac{\text{rise}}{\text{run}}$
$= \frac{5}{45}$
$= \frac{1}{9}$

11. −2 **13.** $\frac{1}{5}$ **15.** $-\frac{3}{5}$ **17.** undefined
19. −2 **21.** Sample answer: (2, 1) and (10, 6)
23. False; the graph of $y = 100x$ is as steep as the graph of $y = -100x$. **25.** C **27.** D
29. Yes; the ratio $\frac{\text{circumference}}{\text{radius}}$ is the same for every pair of values. **31.** 60 **33.** 667
35. $y = -3x + 1$ **37.** $y = 14x + 10$

Pages 435–438 *Lesson 8-7*

1 The equation $y = 2x + 6$ is written in the form $y = mx + b$. So, the slope is 2 and the y-intercept 6.
3. −7; 0
5. $y = \frac{1}{3}x + 1$
7. $y = 2x - 4$
9a. Flying a Kite
$y = -x + 60$
Altitude (ft); Time (s)

9b. The y-intercept 60 represents the initial height of the kite. The slope −1 represents the descent of 1 foot per second. **11.** $-\frac{5}{2}$; −2 **13.** −9; 0
15. −4; 0 **17.** $\frac{1}{2}$; 6

19. $y = 3x + 4$
21. $y = \frac{3}{2}x - 3$
23. $y = -\frac{4}{3}x + 5$

25 **a.** The slope is −50 and the y-intercept is 300. Plot the y-intercept and use the slope to find the next point. Connect the points with a line.

A Flying Albatross
$y = 300 - 50x$
Altitude (ft); Time (min)

b. 300 is the y-intercept which represents the original height. The slope is −50 which represents descending at 50 ft/min.
27a. $y = 15x + 18$; $y = 15x + 12$
27b.

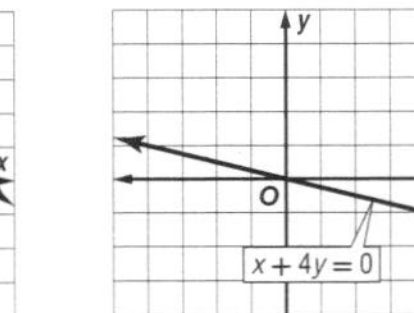

27c. No; the lines are parallel and parallel lines do not intersect. **27d.** Each line has a slope of 15.
29. $3x + 4y = 12$ **31.** $x + 4y = 0$

33 slope $= \frac{y_2 - y_1}{x_2 - x_1}$
$= \frac{6 - 0}{1 - (-2)}$
$= \frac{6}{3}$ or 2

35. $y = 2x + 4$ **37.** Sample answer: A photographer charges a \$50 sitting fee to come to your house to take family portraits and then \$15 for each 5 × 7 portrait. The total cost y can be represented by the equation $y = 50 + 15x$, where x represents the number of portraits ordered. A family has \$300 to spend on the portraits. How many portraits can they purchase?; 16 **39.** The graph becomes less steep. **41.** Sample answer: Graph the y-intercept point. Then use the slope to locate a second point on the line. Draw a line through the two points. **43.** J
45a. Total Cost ($); Number of Times

45b. The y-intercept 35 is the initial cost of the pass and the slope 25 is the cost per time of skiing. **47.** \$2.80/lb; The birdseed costs \$2.80 per pound. **49.** $\frac{5}{12}$ **51.** −22 **53.** 2 **55.** 32

Pages 444–447 *Lesson 8-8*

1. $y = 2x + 4$ **3.** $y = -\frac{3}{4}x$ **5.** $y = x + 2$
7. $y = \frac{1}{2}x$

9 First, find the slope.
$m = \frac{y_2 - y_1}{x_2 - x_1}$
$m = \frac{-4 - 5}{3 - 2}$
$m = \frac{-9}{1}$ or −9
Use the point (5, 2) to write an equation for the line in point-slope form.
$y - y_1 = m(x - x_1)$
$y - 5 = -9(x - 2)$
You can also use the point (3, −4) to write an equation in point-slope form.
$y - y_1 = m(x - x_1)$
$y + 4 = -9(x - 3)$
Slope either point-slope equation for y to write the equation in slope-intercept form.
$y + 4 = -9(x - 3)$
$y + 4 = -9x + 27$
$y = -9x + 23$

11. Sample answer: $y - 2 = 4(x - 1)$
13a. $y = 2.4x$; The speed of the rip current is 2.4 feet per second. **13b.** 144 ft **15.** $y = x - 4$
17. $y = 2x$ **19.** $y = -7$ **21.** $y = -\frac{5}{3}x - 6$

23 The slope is $\frac{1}{2}$ and the y-intercept is (0, 2). The equation is $y = \frac{1}{2}x + 2$.
25. $y = -\frac{4}{3}x - 5$ **27.** $y = 6$
29. $y + 2 = \frac{1}{2}(x - 2)$ or $y + 1 = \frac{1}{2}(x - 4)$ or $y = \frac{1}{2}x - 3$
31. $y + 6 = 0(x - 3)$ or $y + 6 = 0(x - 5)$ or $y = -6$
33. $y - 9 = -5(x + 1)$ or $y + 6 = -5(x - 2)$ or $y = -5x + 4$
35. Sample answer: $y + 2 = 2(x + 1)$
37. Sample answer: $y - 5 = \frac{2}{5}(x - 10)$

39 **a.** First, find the slope.
slope $= \frac{y_2 - y_1}{x_2 - x_1}$
$= \frac{150 - 120}{4 - 3}$
$= \frac{30}{1}$ or 30
Now, use the point-slope form.
$y - y_1 = m(x - x_1)$
$y - 120 = 30(x - 3)$
$y - 120 = 30x - 90$
$y - 120 + 120 = 30x - 90 + 120$
$y = 30x + 30$
The height of the fireworks increases 30 meters per 1-inch increase in shell radius.
b. $y = 30x + 30$
$y = 30(9) + 30$
$y = 270 + 30$
$y = 300$ m

41a. $y = 34.95x$; The slope \$34.95 is the cost per person. **41b.** \$314.55 **43.** Sample answer: (−1, 2) and (−4, 5); $y - 5 = -1(x + 4)$
45. Daniel; Kayla incorrectly calculated the slope by dividing the change in x by the change in y. Also, the y-intercept is 5, not 0. **47.** Sample answer: When using an equation in the form $y = mx + b$, the slope is m and the y-intercept is b. When using a table, choose two pairs of x- and y-coordinates to find the slope. The y-intercept is

the y value in the table when the corresponding x value is 0. When using a graph, choose two points on the line to find the slope. The y-intercept is the y-coordinate of the point where the graph crosses the y-axis. **49.** F

51. $d = 320 - 65s$

53.

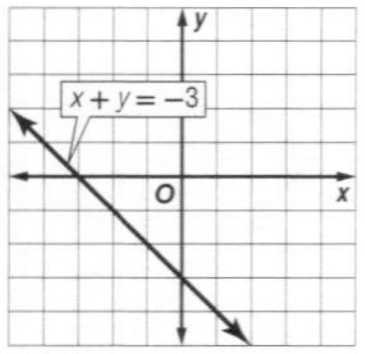

$x + y = -3$

55. 1 **57.** 16%

59. negative; As the temperature decreases, heating costs increase.

Pages 450–452 Lesson 8-9

1a. Sample answer:

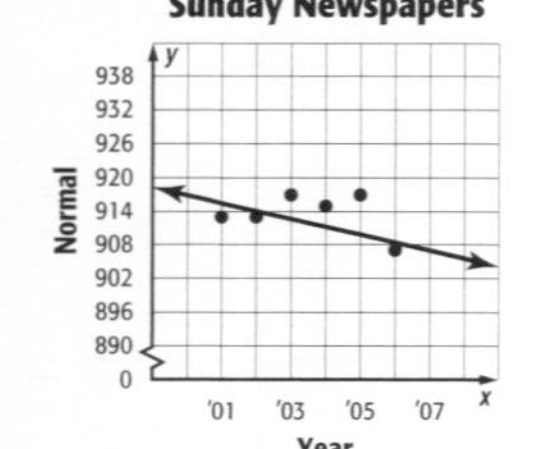

1b. Sample answer: 898

3 **a.** Plot the data points on a coordinate grid and draw a line that best fits the points. Sample answer:

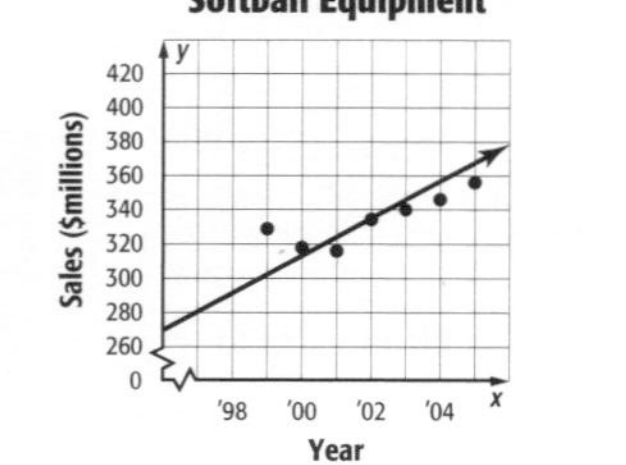

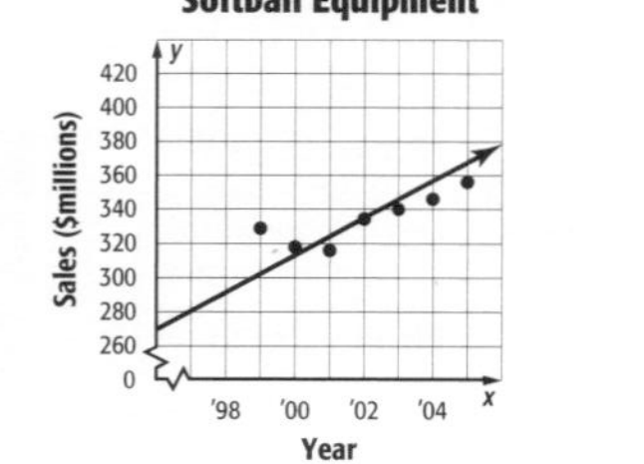

b. Extend the line to estimate the sales for 2015. Sample answer: $492 million

c. Plot the data points on a coordinate grid and draw a line that best fits the points. Sample answer:

Tennis Equipment

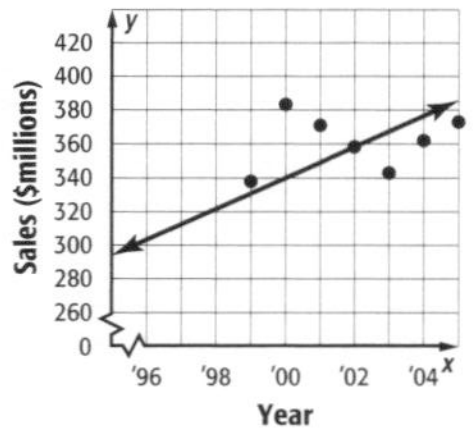

d. Extend the line to estimate the sales for 2015. Sample answer: $490 million

5 **a.** Use the points shown to find the slope of the line.

$$\text{slope} = \frac{y_2 - y_1}{x_2 - x_1} = \frac{14.8 - 13.5}{7 - 4} = \frac{1.3}{3} \approx 0.4$$

Now, use the point-slope form.

$$y - y_1 = m(x - x_1)$$
$$y - 13.5 = 0.4(x - 4)$$
$$y - 13.5 = 0.4x - 1.6$$
$$y - 13.5 + 13.5 = 0.4x - 1.6 + 13.5$$
$$y = 0.4x + 11.9$$

Sample answer: $y = 0.4x + 11.9$

b. $y = 0.4x + 11.9$
$y = 0.4(18) + 11.9$
$y = 7.2 + 11.9$
$y = 19.1$
Sample answer: $19.1 billion

7a.

Population of Illinois

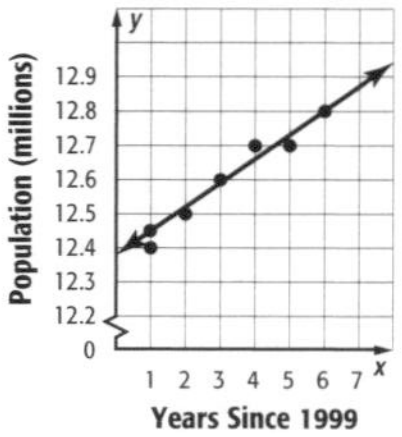

Population of Pennsylvania

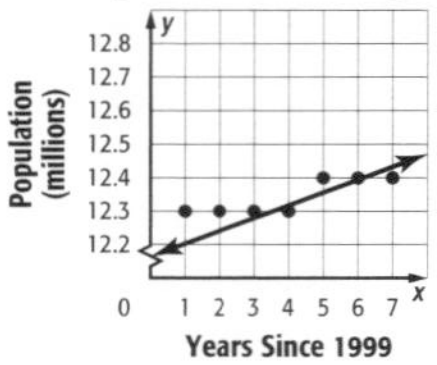

Sample answer: The slope of the line for the population of Illinois means that the population grows by 0.07 million (70,000) people every year. The slope of the line for the population of Pennsylvania means that the population grows by 0.03 million (30,000) people every year. **7b.** Illinois' population; the line of fit is steeper than the line of fit representing the growth of Pennsylvania's population. The intersection would represent the year in which the populations were equal. **7c.** Sample answer: Illinois: $y = 0.07x + 12.31$; Pennsylvania: $y = 0.03x + 12.22$; the slope of the Illinois equation is greater than the slope of the Pennsylvania equation. So, it is true that Illinois' population is growing at a faster rate. **7d.** Sample answer: Illinois 13.43 million; Pennsylvania 12.7 million **9.** Sample answer: It is reasonable to make a prediction when the data have either a positive or a negative relationship. It is not reasonable if there is no noticeable relationship between the data. **11.** Sample answer: a scatter plot in which the data do not appear to be linear **13.** B **15.** A

17a.

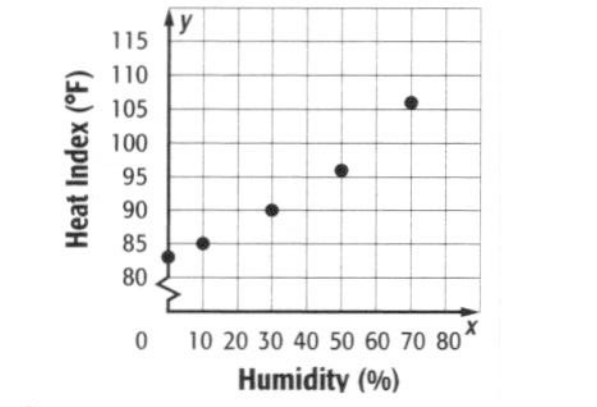

17b. Sample answer: $y = 0.35x + 81.5$

17c. 116.5°F **19.** $y = \frac{2}{5}x$

21.

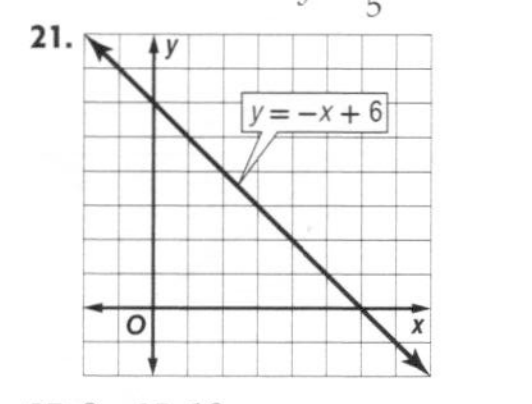

23. 9 **25.** 18

Pages 455–457 Lesson 8-10

1. (2, −2)

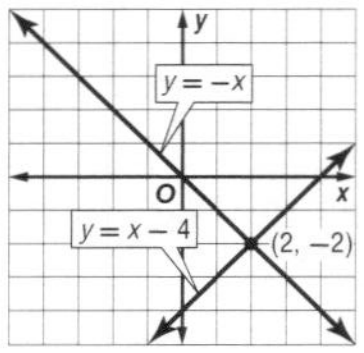

3. infinitely many solutions **5.** (5, 3)

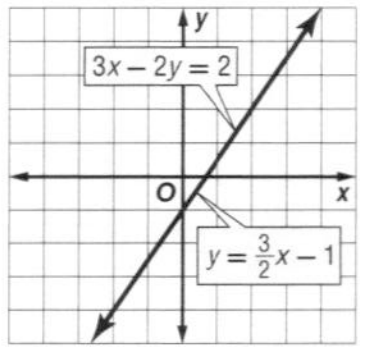

7
$y = 2x + 3$
$y = 1$
$1 = 2x + 3$
$-2 = 2x$
$-1 = x$ The solution is $(-1, 1)$.

9. (2, 2)

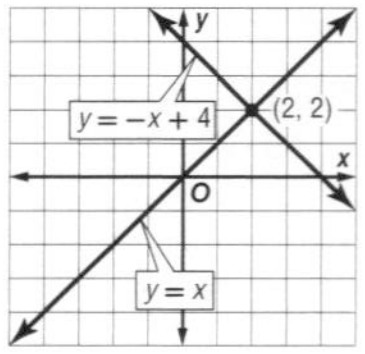

11. infinitely many solutions

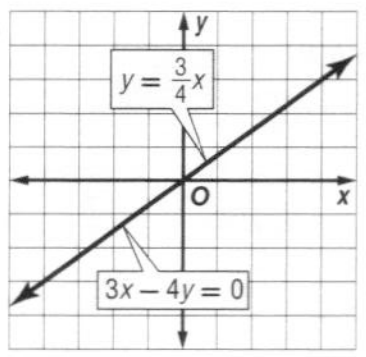

13. (−3, 0)

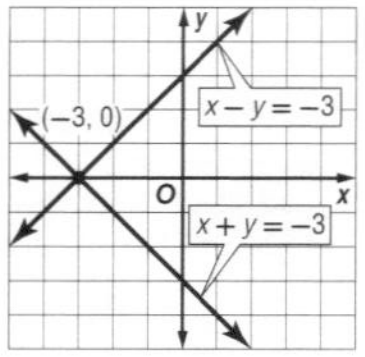

15 **a.** Let y represent the number of baseball cards after x months. Ling starts out with 50 baseball cards and *collects* 5 per month:

$y = 5x + 50$. Jonathon starts out with 90 baseball cards and *sells* 5 per month: $y = -5x + 90$.

b. Graph each equation on the same coordinate grid.

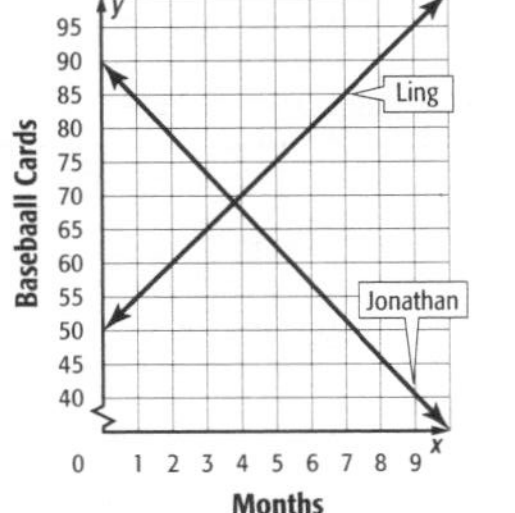

The equation intersects at (4, 70). The solution (4, 70) means that after 4 months, they will have the same number of cards (70).

17. $(-4, 0)$ **19.** $(2, -6)$ **21.** $(5, -1)$
23. Sample answer: $y = x + 6$ and $y = 8x - 1$
25. $(-6, -6)$ **27.** $(2, -2)$ **29.** Sample answer: If a system of equations has 1 solution, the graphs are intersecting lines. If the system has no solution, the graphs are parallel lines. If the system has infinitely many solutions, then the graphs are the same line. **31.** G **33.** 12
35. $y = 4x - 3$ **37.** 64 **39.** 32

Pages 458–462 *Study Guide and Review*

1. slope **3.** sequence **5.** y-intercept
7. independent variable **9.** system of equations
11. No; The domain value 4 is paired with 2 range values, 1 and 2. **13.** The terms have a difference of 6. A term is 6 times the term number; $t = 6n$. **15.** $t = 7n$; 350 **17.** Sample answer: $(-1, 5)$, $(0, 0)$, $(1, -5)$, $(2, -10)$
19. Sample answer: $(-1, 8)$, $(0, 9)$, $(1, 10)$, $(2, 11)$

21.

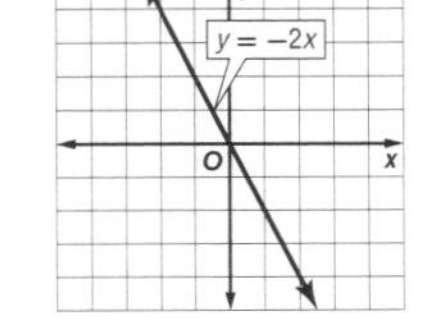

23. Sample answer: (0, 4) means she can buy 0 small smoothies and 4 large smoothies with \$12; (6, 1) means she can buy 6 small smoothies and 1 large smoothie with \$12. **25.** Adults: \$18/person; children: \$12.50/person; the cost for adults increases at a faster rate than the cost for children.

27. $\frac{1}{2}$ **29.** -1 **31.** $\frac{1}{6}$ **33.** $-\frac{4}{3}$; 0 **35.** 1; -8

37. $y = 2x - 6$

39. $y = -\frac{1}{4}x + 5$

41. $y = -2x + 5$ **43.** $y = 4x$ **45.** $y - 5 = 3(x - 1)$

47a. Sample answer:

47b. Sample answer: \$362,000

49. $(-2, -2)$

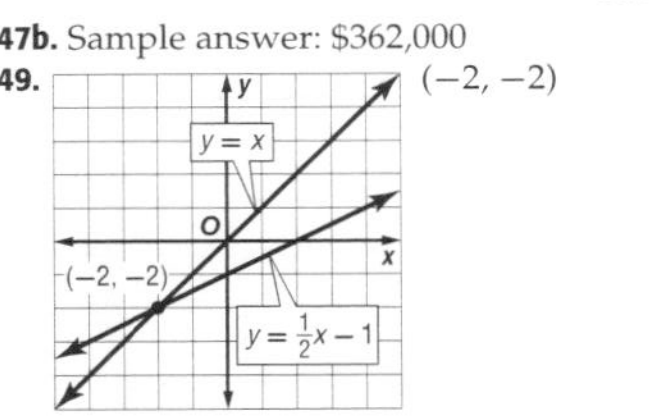

51. (1, 4) **53.** Sample answer: $x + y = 9$, $x - y = 1$; 5 and 4; $x = 5$; $y = 4$

Chapter 9 Powers and Nonlinear Functions

Page 469 *Chapter 9* *Get Ready*

1. 22 **3.** 7 **5.** -11 **7.** \$120 **9.** -7 **11.** 6
13. -19 **15.** 4 **17.** 70 **19.** 167.8 **21.** 5.6
23. 0.9718 **25.** \$15.90

Pages 473–475 *Lesson 9-1*

1. 2^6 **3.** $\left(-\frac{1}{4}\right)^3$ **5.** $(y - 3)^3$

7. 16 cm **9.** 29 **11.** 28.25

13 The base 3 is a factor 5 times, so the exponent is 5, $3 \cdot 3 \cdot 3 \cdot 3 \cdot 3 = 3^5$ **15.** $(-14)^3$
17. $(-1.5)^3$ **19.** $5p^3q^3$ **21.** $8(c + 4)^2$
23. $(2x + 3y)^2$ **25.** 81 **27.** 28 **29.** 4.25
31. 21.625 **33.** 23 **35.** 243

37 a. Field Hockey: $2^6 \cdot 10^3 = 64 \cdot 1000 = 64{,}000 \text{ ft}^2$

Men's Lacrosse: $3^2 \cdot 7 \cdot 10^3 = 9 \cdot 7 \cdot 1000 = 63 \cdot 1000 = 63{,}000 \text{ ft}^2$

Women's Soccer: $2^4 \cdot 5^2 \cdot 7 \cdot 13 = 16 \cdot 25 \cdot 7 \cdot 13 = 400 \cdot 7 \cdot 13 = 36{,}400 \text{ ft}^2$

b. The order from least to greatest is 36,400 ft^2; 63,000 ft^2; 64,000 ft^2
c. $64{,}000 - 63{,}000 = 1{,}000 \text{ ft}^2$

39. 1331 **41.** 625 **43.** 512 **45.** 2430 **47.** 1372
49. 820.125 **51.** > **53.** < **55.** Sample answer: 6^2, 4^3; 2304 **57.** 10^8; Sample answer: 10^7 = 10,000,000 and 10^8 = 100,000,000. 100,000,000 is much closer to 230,000,000 than 10,000,000.
59. Using exponents is a more efficient way to describe and compare numbers.
61. 512 **63.** B **65.** $(0, -5)$

67a.

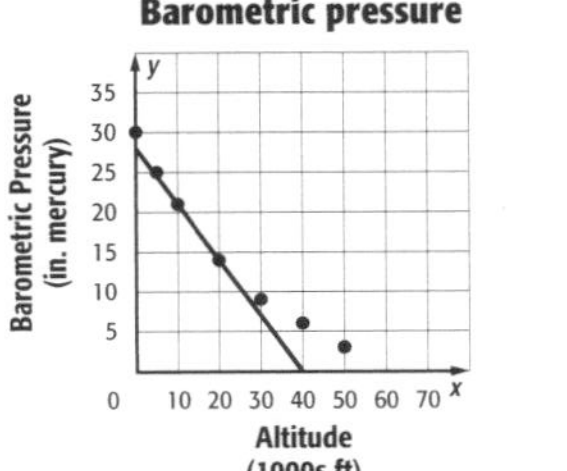

67b. Sample answer: Using (10,000, 21) and (30,000, 9), $y = -0.0006x + 27$; -9; this is not reasonable because barometric pressure cannot be negative. **67c.** No, the equation gives a negative value for barometric pressure, which is not possible. Also, the data in the scatter plot do not appear to be linear. **69.** 4 out of 5
71. $\frac{10}{11}$ **73.** 1, 3, 5, 15 **75.** 1, 2, 4, 5, 8, 10, 20, 40

Pages 478–480 *Lesson 9-2*

1. composite **3.** composite **5.** $2 \cdot 7 \cdot a \cdot a \cdot a$
7. $2 \cdot 2 \cdot 5 \cdot x \cdot x \cdot y$ **9.** prime **11.** composite
13. prime **15.** composite

17 Factor tree: 243 = 3 · 81; 81 = 3 · 27; 27 = 3 · 9; 9 = 3 · 3

So, $243 = 3 \cdot 3 \cdot 3 \cdot 3 \cdot 3 = 3^5$
19. $2^3 \cdot 7$ **21.** $2^2 \cdot 7^2$ **23.** $2 \cdot 3^2 \cdot 11$
25. $2 \cdot 3 \cdot n \cdot n$ **27.** $-1 \cdot 11 \cdot n \cdot n \cdot n$
29. $2 \cdot 2 \cdot 5 \cdot q \cdot r \cdot s$ **31.** $-1 \cdot 5 \cdot 7 \cdot c \cdot c \cdot c \cdot d \cdot d$
33a. $2 \cdot 3 \cdot 5$ **33b.** $2 \cdot 5^2$ **33c.** $2^3 \cdot 3 \cdot 5$
33d. $2 \cdot 3 \cdot 5^2$ **35a.** 4 rectangles **35b.** 3 rectangles

37 $27 = 3 \cdot 9$ (not the product of two primes)
29 is prime, not the product of two primes
31 is prime, not the product of two primes
$33 = 3 \cdot 11$ which is the product of two primes
So, 33 could be N.

39. Sample answer: $10a^2$, $10a^2b$, $20a^2$ **41.** Both are incorrect; Filipe did not consider numbers like 9, 15, and 21 and Ledell did not consider 2 as a prime number. **43.** Sample answer: The number $2n$ is never prime. Since you are multiplying a number by 2, you have an additional set of factor pairs, 2 and n.

45. 1 ft × 36 ft; 2 ft × 18 ft; 3 ft × 12 ft; 4 ft × 9 ft; 6 ft × 6 ft

47. C **49.** -9 **51.** 45 **53.** 13 **55.** 14 pizzas
57. $-5 + n = -15$; -10 **59.** $(3 \cdot 5)(a^4)$ **61.** $(b \cdot b^4)(5 \cdot 10)$ **63.** $(-8 \cdot 2)(b^3)(c^2 \cdot c^3)(d^3)$

Pages 483–485 *Lesson 9-3*

1. 2^{10} **3.** x^{16} **5.** 4^2 **7.** r^4 **9.** 2^3 or 8 times
11 $(-2)^3 \cdot (-2)^2 = (-2)^{3+2} = (-2)^5$
13. t^6 **15.** $54p^{14}$ **17.** $24s^7$ **19.** 7^5
21. k^3 **23.** 8^6 **25.** $(-n)^2$

27 $5^3 \cdot 5 = 5^3 \cdot 5^1$
$= 5^{3+1}$
$= 5^4$
$= 5 \cdot 5 \cdot 5 \cdot 5$
$= 625$
5^4 or 625 lb

29. $\frac{484}{1}$; Sample answer: For every 484 red blood cells, there is 1 white blood cell. **31.** 5 **33.** 12 **35.** 2 **37.** $8a^3b^{10}$ **39.** n^6 **41.** Sample answer: x^7, x^2 **43.** Sample answer: By the Quotient of Powers, $\frac{a^n}{a^n} = a^{n-n}$ or a^0 for $a \neq 0$. Since $\frac{a^n}{a^n} = 1$, then $a^0 = 1$. So, any nonzero number raised to the zero power must equal 1. **45.** Sample answer: Write the numbers as powers with the same base. Then subtract the exponents. **47.** F

49. $A = \frac{1}{2}bh$
$A = \frac{1}{2}(4x^3)(3x^5)$
$A = \frac{1}{2} \cdot 4 \cdot 3 \cdot x^3 \cdot x^5$
$A = \frac{1}{2} \cdot 4 \cdot 3 \cdot x^8$
$A = 6x^8$

51. 3^4 **53.** $2 \cdot 3 \cdot 5^2$ **55.** $2 \cdot 3 \cdot 3 \cdot 3 \cdot a \cdot a \cdot a \cdot a \cdot a \cdot a$ **57.** $-1 \cdot 3 \cdot 11 \cdot t \cdot t \cdot t \cdot t \cdot t$ **59.** \$6900 **61.** $-\frac{1}{8}$ **63.** $-\frac{1}{21}$ **65.** $\frac{1}{15}$

Pages 488–491 Lesson 9-4

1. $\frac{1}{6^2}$ **3.** $\frac{1}{x^5}$ **5.** 2^{-6} **7.** 3^{-2} **9.** 10^{-3} **11.** $-\frac{1}{64}$ **13.** $\frac{1}{2}$

15 $7^{-1} = \frac{1}{7^1}$
$= \frac{1}{7}$

17. $\frac{1}{(-5)^4}$ **19.** $\frac{1}{k^8}$ **21.** $\frac{1}{r^{20}}$ **23.** 10^{-3} **25.** 6^{-5} **27.** 7^{-2} **29.** 5^{-3}

31 $0.00000001 = \frac{1}{100,000,000}$
$= \frac{1}{10^8}$
$= 10^{-8}$

33. $\frac{1}{144}$ **35.** $-\frac{1}{6}$ **37.** $\frac{1}{64}$ **39.** $-\frac{2}{9}$ **41a.** 10^3 or 1000 times **41b.** 10^4 or 10,000 **41c.** 10^6 or 1,000,000 times **43a.** coffee, 10^3 or 1,000 **43b.** milk **43c.** It is divided by 10. **43d.** 10^2 or 100 times

45a.

Power	Fraction	Decimal
10^{-1}	$\frac{1}{10}$	0.1
10^{-2}	$\frac{1}{100}$	0.01
10^{-3}	$\frac{1}{1000}$	0.001
10^{-4}	$\frac{1}{10000}$	0.0001
10^{-5}	$\frac{1}{100000}$	0.00001

45b. yes; Sample answer: As the exponents decrease, the number of zeros in the decimal places increase. **45c.** Sample answer: The number of zeros in the decimal equivalent is equal to one less than the absolute value of the negative exponent. For example, $10^{-3} = 0.001$. **45d.** $10^{-12} = 0.000000000001$ **47.** a^{-6} or $\frac{1}{a^6}$

49 $x^{-3}y^4 \div x^{-2}y^2 = x^{-3-(-2)}y^{4-2} = x^{-1}y^2$ or $\frac{y^2}{x}$

51. Sample answer: $5^{-2} = \frac{1}{5^2} = \frac{1}{5 \cdot 5} = \frac{1}{25}$ **53a.** $2^{-2} = \frac{1}{4}$, $(-2)^{-2} = \frac{1}{4}$, $(-2)^2 = 4$, $2^2 = 4$; $2^{-2} = (-2)^{-2}$ and $(-2)^2 = 2^2$ **53b.** $2^{-3} = \frac{1}{8}$, $(-2)^{-3} = -\frac{1}{8}$, $(-2)^3 = -8$, $2^3 = 8$; none of the expressions are equal **53c.** Sample answer: When you square either a positive or a negative value, the answer is positive. When you cube a positive value, you get a positive and when you cube a negative value, you get a negative. **53d.** x is an even number **53e.** x is an even number **55.** Sample answer: If $n = 3$, $\frac{1}{2^n} = \frac{1}{2^3}$ or $\frac{1}{8}$. If $n = 4$, $\frac{1}{2^n} = \frac{1}{2^4}$ or $\frac{1}{16}$. **57.** C **59.** D **61a.** 224 pieces **61b.** 1024 in. or $85\frac{1}{3}$ ft **63.** $-1 \cdot r \cdot r \cdot s \cdot t$ **65.** -2; -3 **67.** 0; 4 **69.** 0.025 **71.** 0.038 **73.** 76,000

Pages 495–498 Lesson 9-5

1. 4160 **3** $1.075 \times 10^5 = 1.075 \times 100,000$
$= 107,500$

5. 1.35×10^5 **7.** 3.27×10^6 mi **9.** 6.1×10^{-2}, 6.5×10^3, 6.01×10^4, 6.12×10^5 **11.** 0.00015 **13.** 0.00951 **15.** 792.4 **17.** 171,000,000,000

19 $32,000,000 = 3.2 \times 10,000,000$
$= 3.2 \times 10^7$

21. 9.18×10^{-4} **23.** 6.752×10^{-3} **25.** 2.4×10^{-2}, 2.45×10^{-2}, 2.4×10^2, 2.45×10^2 **27.** 5.1×10^{-3}, 5.9×10^4, 5.01×10^5, 5.9×10^6 **29a.** 0.0000125 cm **29b.** $1.25\text{ cm}^3 \times 10^{-6}$ **31.** 1.24×10^8

33 $(3.84 \times 10^5) \div (3 \times 10^5) = (3.84 \div 3) \times (10^5 \div 10^5)$
$= 1.28 \times 10^{5-5}$
$= 1.28 \times 10^0$
$= 1.28$ seconds

35. = **37.** < **39.** 2.763×10^7; 27,630,000 **41.** 5.642×10^6; 5,642,000 **43.** Sample answer: 2×10^2 and 4×10^3; sum: 4.2×10^3; difference: 3.8×10^3; product: 8×10^5; quotient: 5×10^{-2} **45a.** 3.8×10^6; 3.8×10^4 is only about 40,000 people, which is not very many for the second largest city in Florida **45b.** Sample answer: 3,800,000 or 3.8 million **45c.** Sample answer: 3.8 million is easier to read and understand than the standard form (3,800,000) or scientific notation (3.8×10^6) of the number. **47.** Sample answer: 7.8×10^3 is greater than 6.5×10^2 because the exponent of 3 is greater than the exponent of 2. **49.** G **51a.** $(1.832 \times 10^2)(2 \times 10^3) = 3.664 \times 10^5$ **51b.** $(1.832 \times 10^2)(2 \times 10^3) / (4.5 \times 10^1) = 8.142 \times 10^3$ **51c.** 8142 lb **53.** a^6 **55.** $-12x^5$ **57a.** 5450 ft^2 **57b.** 3 bags **59.** 4^5 **61.** $2^3 \cdot 3^2$

Pages 501–503 Lesson 9-6

1. 6^8 **3** $(r^6)^{-2} = r^{6 \cdot -2}$
$= r^{-12}$
$= \frac{1}{r^{12}}$

5. $16m^4n^2$ **7.** $121n^{12}p^4$ **9.** 2^6 **11.** 3^{15} **13.** b^{28} **15.** $256y^{16}$ **17.** $81s^4t^{12}$ **19.** $-1024n^{10}p^{20}$ **21.** $16a^6b^{14}$ **23.** 2.9×10^9 km^2

25 $10(4^9)^2 = 10(4^{9 \cdot 2})$
$= 10(4^{18})$
$= 10(68,719,476,736)$
$= 687,194,767,360$ or 6.87×10^{11} stars

27. 3^{24} **29.** $\frac{1}{16}t^{16}v^{12}$ **31a.** $4x^4$ and $16x^8$

31b.

31c. Sample answer: All three graphs are shaped like "U". As the coefficient and exponent increase, the graph gets narrower and flatter on the bottom. **33.** $x = 5$; $(8^{2x})^3 = 8^{6x}$, so $6x = 30$ or $x = 5$ **35.** Sample answer: To find the power of a power, multiply exponents. To find the power of a product, find the power of each factor and multiply. **37.** C **39.** D **41.** 57,200

43. 2×10^6 **45.** 6×10^{-3} **47.** \$1.20

49.

x	$3x^2 - 2$	(x, y)
0	$3(0)^2 - 2$	(0, −2)
1	$3(1)^2 - 2$	(1, 1)
2	$3(2)^2 - 2$	(2, 10)

Pages 506–509 Lesson 9-7

1 The graph is a straight line, so it represents a linear function.

3. Linear; the equation is written in the form $y = mx + b$. **5.** Linear; as x increases by 1, y increases by 3. **7.** Nonlinear; the rate of change is not constant. **9.** Linear; graph is a straight line.

11 Nonlinear; graph is a curve

13. Linear; the equation is written in the form $y = mx + b$. **15.** Nonlinear; the equation cannot be written in the form $y = mx + b$. **17.** Nonlinear; as x increases by 2, y increases by a different amount each time. **19.** Linear; as x increases by 1, y increases by 2. **21.** Nonlinear; the amount of change in price each year is not constant.

23a.

Radius r	Circumference C	Area A
1	6.28	3.14
2	12.56	12.56
3	18.84	28.26
4	25.12	50.24
5	31.4	78.5

23b.

23c.

23d. Yes, the circumference is a linear relationship. The slope is 6.28.

25 Make a table of values.

Inches	1	2	3	4
Centimeters	2.54	5.08	7.62	10.16

+1 +1 +1

+2.54 +2.54 +2.54

Since the rate of change is constant, 2.54, the function is linear. **27.** Sample answer: Ben's pay from Mrs. Rodriquez is a linear relationship. As his hours increase, his pay increases by $10. His pay does not increase when he works for Mrs. Benson. **31.** $xy = 3$ because it is not a linear equation. **33.** Sample answer: Functions can be represented using graphs, equations, or tables. A graph that is a straight line represents linear function. An equation that can be written in the form $y = mx + b$ is a linear function. If a table of values shows a constant defined rate of change, the function is linear.
35. The equation for the area of a square $A = s^2$ represents a nonlinear function. You can construct a table of values and graph the points (s, A) to see that the graph is a curve.

Side	Area
1	1
2	4
3	9
4	16

37. B **39.** $-216p^6$ **41.** 8×10^7 **43.** 5.9×10^{-2}
45. About $3.60

47.

x	y
−1	4
0	5
1	6

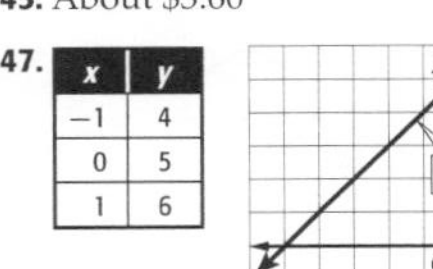

49.

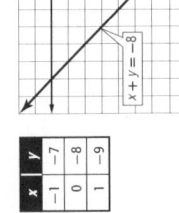

x	y
−1	−7
0	−8
1	−9

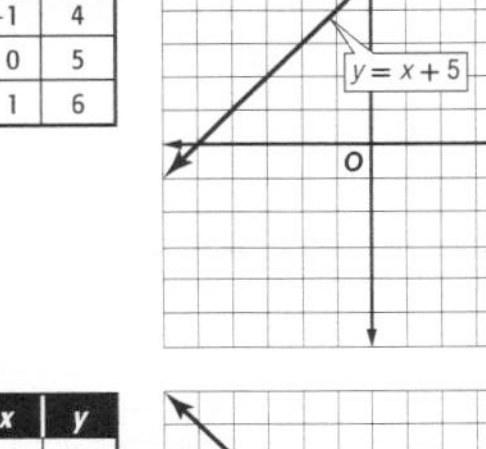

51.

x	y
−3	11
0	9
3	7

$y = -\frac{2}{3}x + 9$

Pages 512–514 *Lesson 9-8*

1. $y = 2x^2$

3. $y = \frac{1}{2}x^2$

5. $y = \frac{1}{4}x^2 + 1$

7a. Height of a Soccer Ball

$h = -16t^2 + 40t + 2$

18 ft

As the time increases up to about 1.5 seconds, the height of the ball increases. Then, the height of the ball decreases until it reaches 0 feet at about 2.5 seconds; 18 ft.

7b. Sample answer: Any negative values because height and time cannot be negative.

9 $y = x^2 + 1$
Make a table of values and plot the points.
Then connect the points with a smooth curve.

x	$y = x^2 + 1$	(x, y)
−2	$(-2)^2 + 1$	(−2, 5)
−1	$(-1)^2 + 1$	(−1, 2)
0	$(0)^2 + 1$	(0, 1)
1	$(1)^2 + 1$	(1, 2)
2	$(2)^2 + 1$	(2, 5)

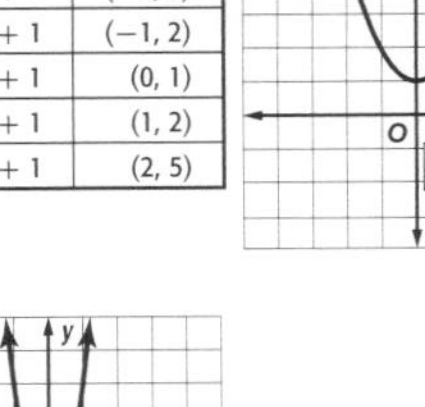

11.

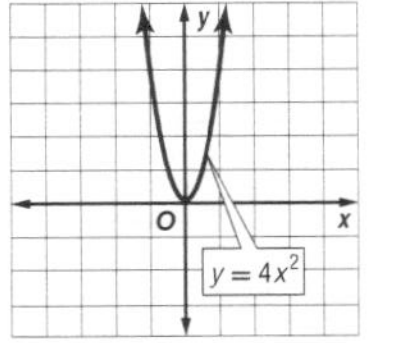

13.

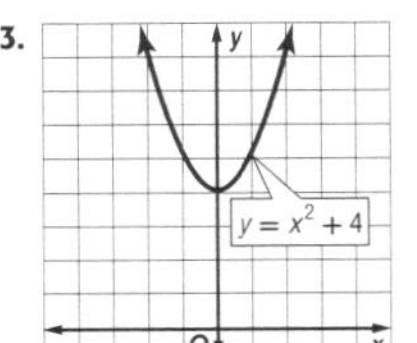

15.

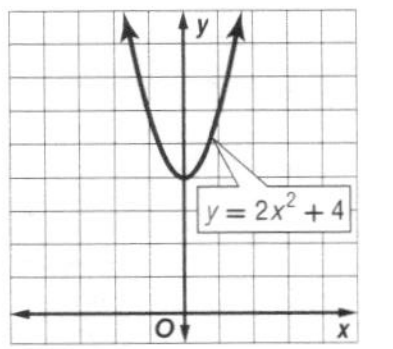

17.

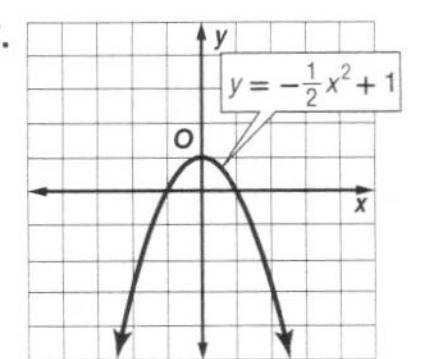

19.

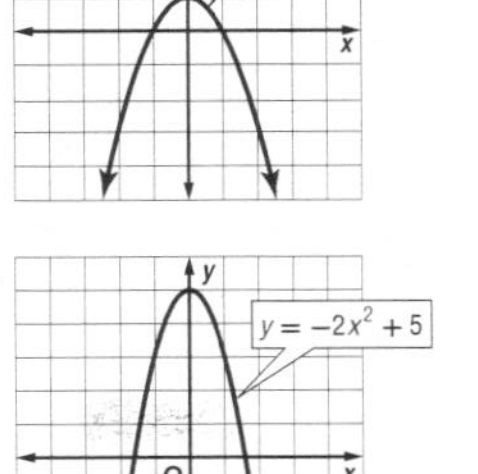

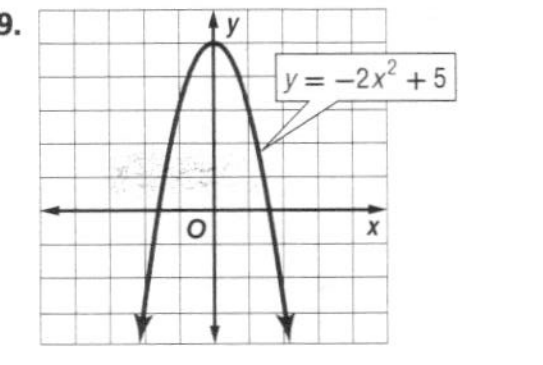

21a. Cars

21b. about 6 seconds

23 a. $P = 4s$; $A = s^2$

b.

s	$P = 4s$	$A = s^2$
0	$4 \cdot 0 = 0$	$0^2 = 0$
1	$4 \cdot 1 = 4$	$1^2 = 1$
2	$4 \cdot 2 = 8$	$2^2 = 4$
3	$4 \cdot 3 = 12$	$3^2 = 9$
4	$4 \cdot 4 = 16$	$4^2 = 16$

c. Perimeter and Area

Graph the points (1, 4), (2, 8), (3, 12), and (4, 16). Then connect the points.
Graph the points (1, 1), (2, 4), (3, 9), and (4, 16). Then connect the points.
Since the points on the graph for the perimeter are in a straight line, it is a linear function. The points on the graph for the area follow a parabolic shape. So, it is a quadratic function.

d. Yes, when the side length is 4 units both the perimeter and area are 16. In the table, the values are the same. On the graph, it is where the two functions intersect.

25. Sample answer:

27. (0, 7)

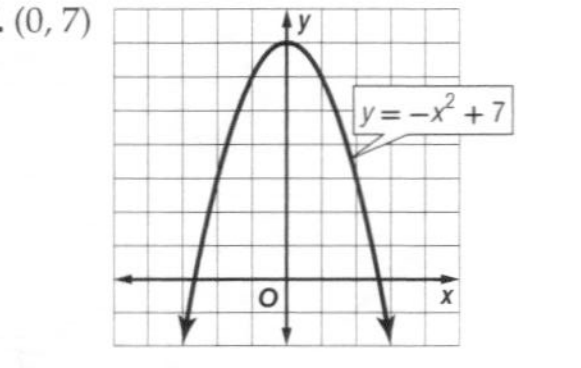

29. Sample answer: Formulas and tables can be used to make graphs. Tables and graphs can be used to write rules. To make a graph, use a rule to make a table of values. Then plot the points. To write a rule, find points that lie on the graph and make a table using the coordinates. Look for a pattern and write a rule that describes the pattern. **31.** G

33a.

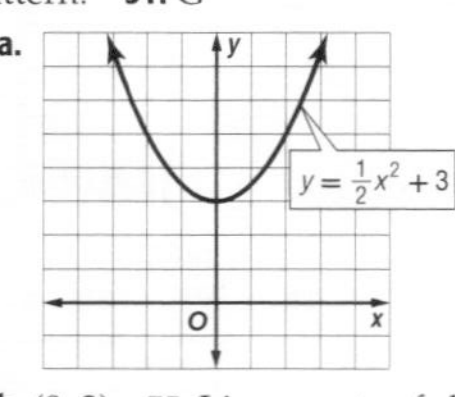

33b. (0, 3) **35.** Linear; rate of change is constant. **37.** 7^8 or 5,764,801 **39.** $8c^{15}d^3$ **41.** −14.3% **43.** 216 **45.** 128

Pages 518–520 Lesson 9-9

1.

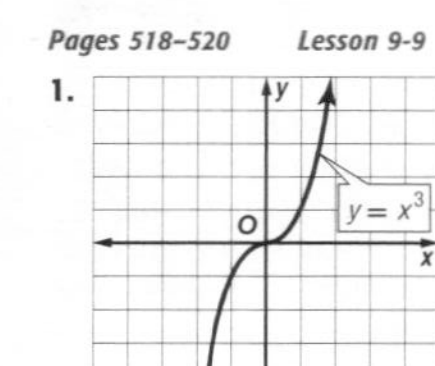

3.

5a.

Years	Money Spent (in millions)
1	13.4
2	15.1
3	16.9
4	18.9

5b.

5c. \$12 million sales in 2005

7.

x	$y = 2^x - 3$	(x, y)
0	$y = 2^0 - 3 = -2$	(0, −2)
1	$y = 2^1 - 3 = -1$	(1, −1)
2	$y = 2^2 - 3 = 1$	(2, 1)
3	$y = 2^3 - 3 = 5$	(3, 5)

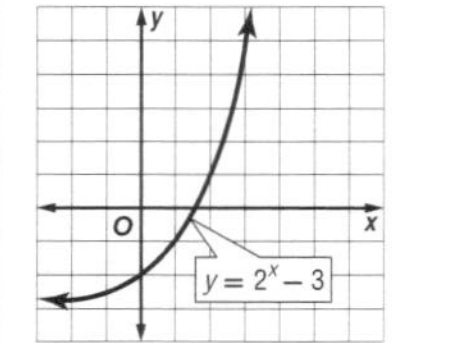

9.

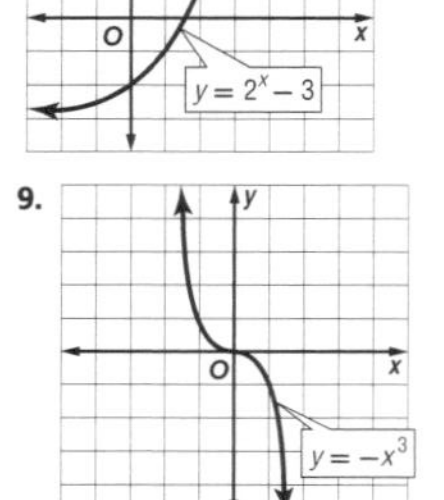

11.

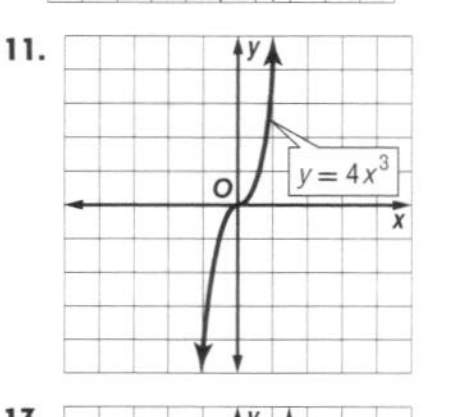

13.

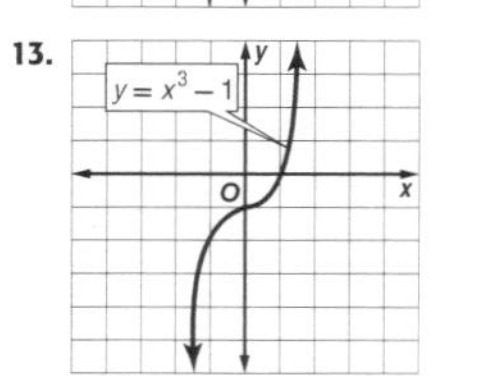

15.

17 a.

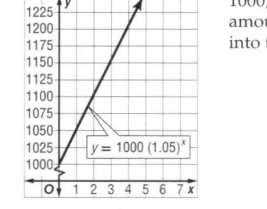

x	$y = 1000(1.05)^x$	(x, y)
0	$y = 1000(1.05)^0 = 1000$	(0, 1000)
1	$y = 1000(1.05)^1 = 1050$	(1, 1050)
2	$y = 1000(1.05)^2 = 1102.50$	(2, 1102.50)
3	$y = 1000(1.05)^3 = 1157.63$	(3, 1157.63)

1000; The initial amount of money put into the account.

b. The balance will be greater than \$2000 after 15 years.

19. label: $y = 2^x + 2$

21.

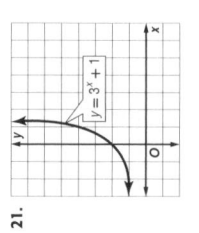

23.

25. quadratic **27.** exponential **29.** linear **31.** Sample answer: $y = 3x$, $y = 3^x$; the linear function has a constant rate of change. The exponential function has a greater rate of change. **33.** $y + 3x = 5$; This equation represents a linear function and the others represent exponential functions. **35.** Sample answer: The graph begins almost flat, but then for increasing x values, it becomes more steep. **37.** J

39a.

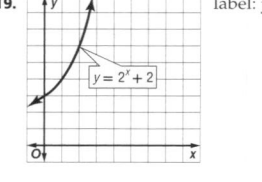

x	y
−2	$-\frac{8}{9}$
−1	$-\frac{2}{3}$
0	0
1	2
2	8

39b.

39c. Exponential; The variable is the exponent. **41.** Linear; graph is a straight line. **43.** Nonlinear; the graph is a curve. **45.** 140 **47.** 256 **49.** 81

Study Guide and Review

1. true **3.** false; exponent **5.** true **7.** true **9.** false; multiply **11.** 6^5 **13.** x^3 **15.** 243 **17.** 10 **19.** −248 **21.** 32 teeth **23.** $2^3 \cdot 5$ **25.** $3^2 \cdot 5^2$ **27.** $2 \cdot 5 \cdot r \cdot r$ **29.** $-1 \cdot 5 \cdot 5 \cdot a \cdot b \cdot b$ **31.** 3^7 **33.** m^9 **35.** $12h^8$ **37.** 9^1 or 9 **39.** about 10 times **41.** $\frac{1}{(-10)^2}$ **43.** 6^{-3} **45.** 5^{-3} **47.** 5820 **49.** 0.00034 **51.** 3.79×10^2 **53.** 1.4×10^{-3} **55.** 1,988,920,000,000,000 exagrams **57.** r^{16} **59.** $64n^{24}$ **61.** $125w^{15}x^{24}$ **63.** Nonlinear; the graph is a curve. **65.** Linear; the equation is written in the form $y = mx + b$. **67.** Linear; as x increases by 1, y decreases by 2. **69.** No; the equation cannot be written in $y = mx + b$ form.

71.

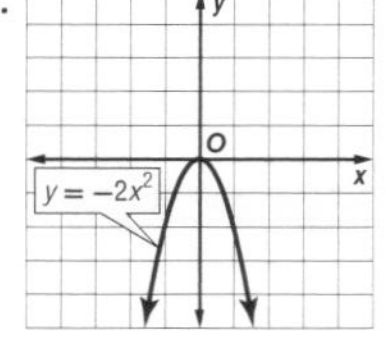

73.

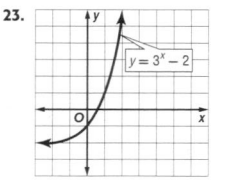

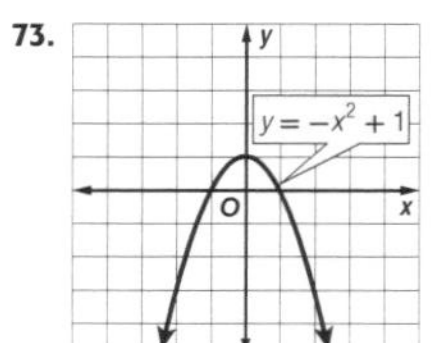

75. 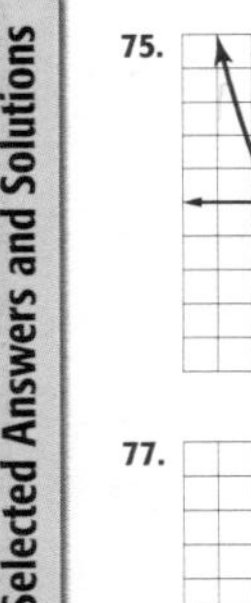
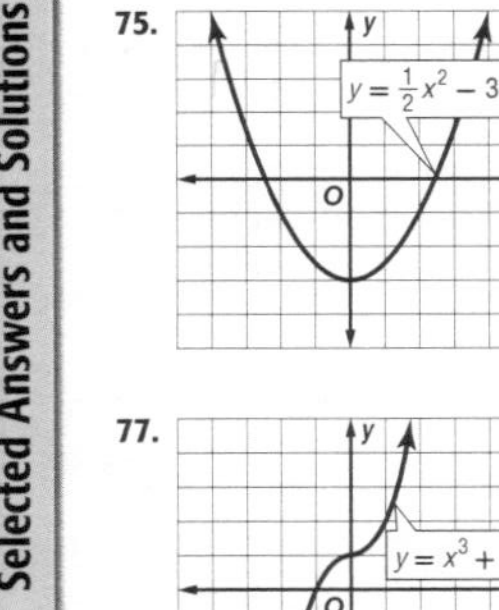

77. 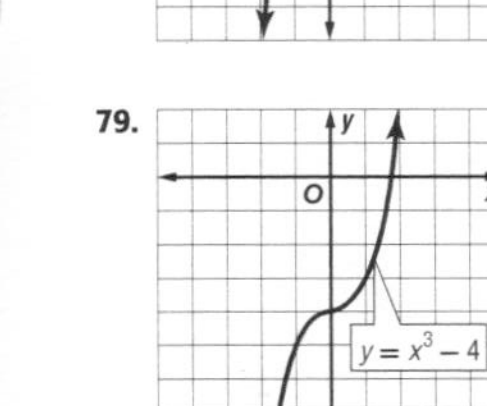

79. 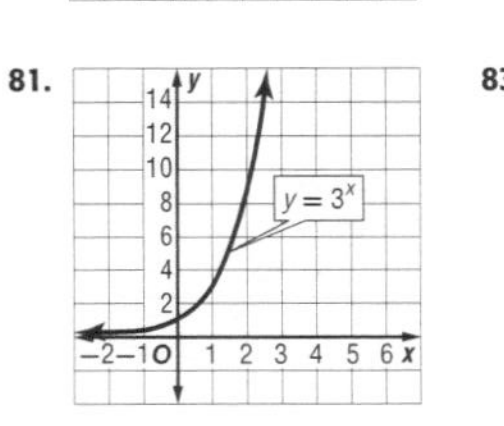

81. 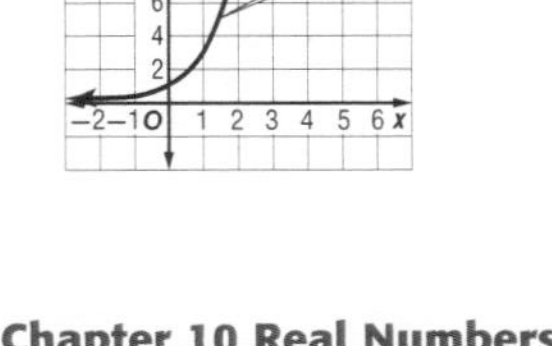

83. 4000

Chapter 10 Real Numbers and Right Triangles

Page 533 *Chapter 10* *Get Ready*

1. > **3.** = **5.** < **7.** 0.601, 0.594, 0.546, 0.523, 0.509 **9.** 12 **11.** 9 **13.** 3 **15.** 34 **17.** 101 **19.** 185

Pages 540–542 *Lesson 10-1*

1. 4 **3.** ±9 **5.** −7 **7.** 4.6 **9.** ±6.1 **11.** 6 **13.** −13 **15.** No real solution

17 The first perfect square integer less than 83 is 81. The first perfect square greater than 83 is 100. The square root of 83 is between 9 and 10. Since 83 is closer to 81, the square root of 83 is closer to 9.

19. −10 **21.** ±9 **23.** 2.6 **25.** ±8.4 **27.** −12.4 **29.** 17.6 **31a.** 21.5 mi **31b.** 15.5 mi **31c.** 7.5 mi

33 $A = s^2$ $P = 4s$
$215 = s^2$ $= 4(14.7)$
$\sqrt{215} = s$ $= 58.8$ cm
$14.7 \text{ cm} \approx s$

35. $\sqrt{79}$; Sample answer: $\sqrt{79}$ is between $\sqrt{64}$ and $\sqrt{81}$, which is greater than 8. **37.** 9 and 10

39a.

x	x^2
−2	4
−1	1
0	0
1	1
2	4

x	$\sqrt{x}$
4	2, −2
2.25	1.5, −1.5
1	1, −1
0.25	0.5, −0.5
0	0

39b. 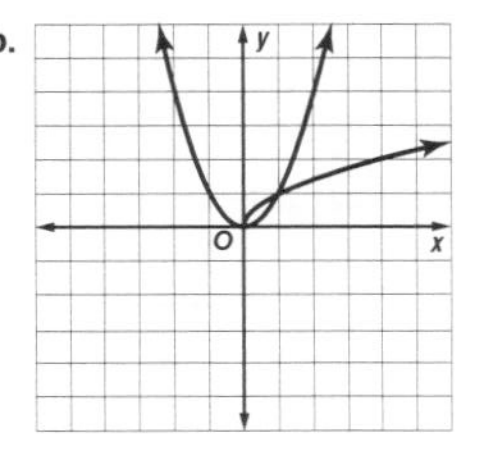

39c. Sample answer: For $0 < x < 1$, the graph for $y = x^2$ has a gradual climb then gets steeper as it approaches 1. The graph for $y = \sqrt{x}$ starts out steeper, then begins to flatten out. At $x = 1$, the graphs intersect. When $x > 1$, the first graph continues to get steeper while the second graph levels out. **39d.** Sample answer: The graph for $y = x^2$, it is steeper for most of the graph. **41a.** 246 **41b.** 811 **41c.** 732 **41d.** finding the square root of a number **43.** Sample answer: The exact value of a square root is given using the square root symbol, such as $\sqrt{13}$. An approximation is a decimal value, such as $13 \approx 3.6$. **45.** 60 units **47.** C

49. 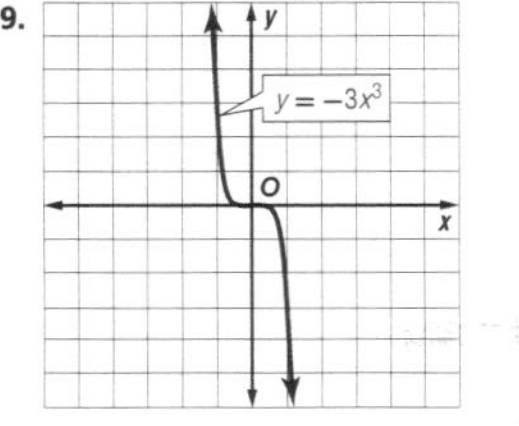

51a. (graph: $h = -16t^2 + 8t + 4$)

51b. about 0.85 s **55.** natural, whole, integer, rational **57.** rational **59.** rational **61.** not rational

Pages 546–548 *Lesson 10-2*

1. whole, integer, rational **3.** irrational **5.** > **7.** > **9.** 10.15, $10\frac{1}{5}$, $\sqrt{110}$, $10.\overline{5}$ **11.** 8.6, −8.6 **13.** 61.3 ft **15.** rational **17.** irrational **19.** rational **21.** integer, rational **23.** whole, integer, rational **25.** rational **27.** > **29.** = **31.** < **33.** $\frac{15}{2}$, $\sqrt{64}$, $8.\overline{14}$, $8\frac{1}{7}$ **35.** $-\frac{31}{6}$, $-\sqrt{26}$, −5, $-\frac{5}{6}$

37 $130 = n^2$
$\pm\sqrt{130} = n$
$11.4 \text{ and } -11.4 \approx n$

39. 9, −9 **41.** 1.3, −1.3

43 $h = 16t^2$
$60 = 16t^2$
$3.75 = t^2$
$\pm\sqrt{3.75} = t$
$1.9 \text{ and } -1.9 = t$

Since −1.9 seconds does not make sense, the answer is 1.9 seconds.

45. sometimes; Sample answer: $\frac{4}{9}$ can be written as $0.\overline{4}$, but $\frac{1}{2}$ is written as 0.5. **47.** always; Sample answer: All whole numbers are integers. **49.** Rational; $\sqrt{49}$ is rational. **51.** Irrational; π is irrational. **53.** Sample answer: 6.4; $\sqrt{40} \approx 6.32$ **55.** false; $\sqrt{16}$ is rational **57.** 5.6 or −5.6 **59.** If a square has an area that is not a perfect square, the lengths of the sides will be irrational. Sample answer: A square with an area of 25 square units has sides that are rational. A square with an area of 26 square units has sides that are irrational. **61.** F **63.** 43.3 **65.** 10 **67.** −11 **69.** ±20

71. (graph: $y = -2x^3 - 3$)

For Homework Help, go to Hotmath.com

73. 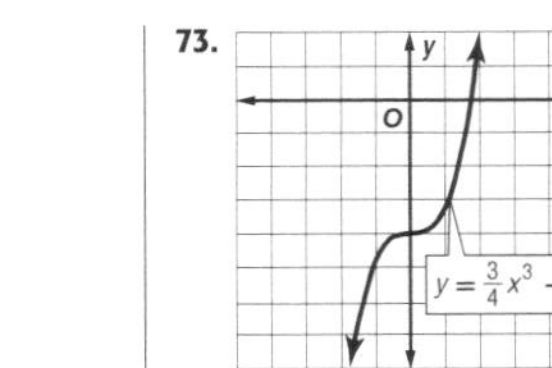

75. 105 **77.** 71 **79.** 20

Pages 553–555 *Lesson 10-3*

1. 45; acute scalene **3.** 45; right isosceles **5.** straight **7.** 30; obtuse isosceles **9.** 75; right scalene **11.** 70; acute isosceles **13.** 12°, 72°, 96°

15 At 6:00 the hands form an angle that measures 180°, so the angle is a straight angle.

17. acute **19.** acute **21.** obtuse **23.** acute **25.** obtuse **27a.** ∠E **27b.** ∠G from 100,000 years ago

29 $x + x + 2x = 180$
$4x = 180$
$x = 45$

So, the angle measures are 45°, 45°, and 90°.

31. 27°, 36°, 117° **33.** equilateral

35a. 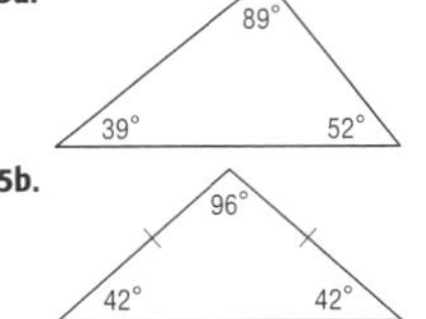

35b. 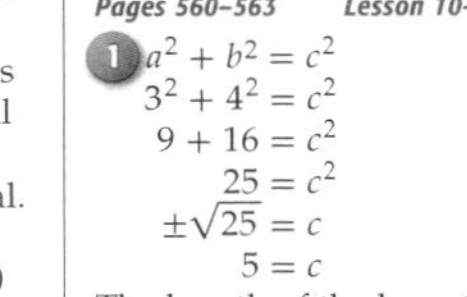

35c. not possible **35d.** not possible **37.** 50; 80 **39.** True; Sample answer: There can be at most one right or one obtuse angle. So, the sum of the two remaining angles must be ≤ 90°. **41.** F **43a.** 56 **43b.** 90 + 34 = 124, 180 − 124 = 56 **43c.** right scalene **45.** 14, −14 **47.** 10.1, −10.1 **49.** −4 **51.** 12 **53.** 121 **55.** 256

Pages 560–563 *Lesson 10-4*

1 $a^2 + b^2 = c^2$
$3^2 + 4^2 = c^2$
$9 + 16 = c^2$
$25 = c^2$
$\pm\sqrt{25} = c$
$5 = c$

The length of the hypotenuse is 5 feet.

3. 56.6 ft **5.** yes **7.** no **9.** 34 cm **11.** 12.0 in. **13.** 110.8 mi

15 $a^2 + b^2 = c^2$
$35^2 + 35^2 = c^2$
$1225 + 1225 = c^2$
$2450 = c^2$
$\pm\sqrt{2450} = c$
$49.5 \approx c$

The length of the walkway is 49.5 feet.

17. yes **19.** no **21.** 42 in.

23 $a^2 + b^2 = c^2$
$9^2 + b^2 = 12^2$
$81 + b^2 = 144$
$b^2 = 63$
$b = \pm\sqrt{63}$
$b \approx 7.9$ m

25. 24.2 ft **27.** 8.8 mi **29.** 19 ft **31a.** 624.5 ft **31b.** 2500 ft

33a. [graph with points A, B, C, O]

33b. Sample answer: Find the length of the legs using the units on the coordinate plane. Then use the Pythagorean Theorem to find the length of the hypotenuse. **33c.** $\overline{AB} = 6$ units, $\overline{BC} = 4$ units, $\overline{AC} \approx 7.2$ units **33d.** $P = 17.2$ units, $A = 12$ units^2 **35.** 19.7 units

37. $c^2 = a^2 + b^2$ Pythagorean Theorem
$10^2 = x^2 + x^2$ Replace c with 10, a with x and b with x.
$100 = 2x^2$ Simplify.
$50 = x^2$ Divide each side by 2.
$\sqrt{50} = x$ Take the square root of each side.
So, the length of the legs is $\sqrt{50}$ or about 7.1 in.

39. D **41.** G **43.** 27; right scalene **45.** 66; acute scalene **47.** rational **49.** rational **51.** 65 **53.** 136

Pages 568–570 Lesson 10-5

1. 8 **3.** 33.5 ft **5.** scalene; 22.7

7 $d = \sqrt{(x_2 - x_1)^2 + (y_2 - y_1)^2}$
$= \sqrt{(8-5)^2 + (4-1)^2}$
$= \sqrt{(3)^2 + (3)^2}$
$= \sqrt{9+9}$
$= \sqrt{18}$
≈ 4.2

9. 7.8 **11.** 8.6 **13.** 91 mi **15.** isosceles; 17.1 **17.** scalene; 36.1

19 $a^2 + b^2 = c^2$
$2^2 + 7^2 = c^2$
$4 + 49 = c^2$
$53 = c^2$
$\pm\sqrt{53} = c$
7.3 in. $\approx c$

21. 10 square units **23.** 4.8 **25.** 13.1

27. Sample answer: (1, 3) and (5, 6) **29.** Mental math; the cup is located at (0, 0) on a coordinate system with points at (−2, −3) and (1, 4). You can use mental math to find the distance between the cup and the two balls; $\sqrt{(-2)^2 + (-3)^2} = \sqrt{13}$; $\sqrt{(1)^2 + (4)^2} = \sqrt{17}$. Since $\sqrt{13} < \sqrt{17}$, Joan's ball is closer to the cup. **31.** Sample answer: To use the Pythagorean Theorem, connect the points. Then draw vertical and horizontal lines so that a right triangle is formed. Determine the lengths of the legs. Then use the Pythagorean Theorem formula to find the length of the hypotenuse. To use the Distance Formula, replace (x_1, y_1) and (x_2, y_2) in the formula with the coordinates of the two points. Then simplify. **33.** H **35.** B **37.** 51 **39.** 20°, 60°, 100° **41.** −12

Pages 574–576 Lesson 10-6

1. $14\sqrt{2}$ mm **3.** $x = 20$ in.; $y = 10\sqrt{3}$ in. **5.** $2\sqrt{2}$ cm **7.** 69.3 in. **9.** $x = 12\sqrt{2}$ in. **11.** $x = 17$ in., $y = 17\sqrt{3}$ in. **13.** $20\sqrt{2}$ cm

15 In a 45°-45°-90° triangle, the length of the hypotenuse is $\sqrt{2}$ times the length of a leg. So, the length of the hypotenuse is $15\sqrt{2}$ inches.

17 In a 30°-60°-90° triangle, the length of the hypotenuse is 2 times the length of the shorter leg. So, the length of the hypotenuse is 2(12) or 24 feet.

19a.

Leg Length	Hypotenuse
1	1.4
2	2.8
3	4.2
4	5.7
5	7.1

19b. 45°-45°-90° Triangles [graph: Hypotenuse (units) vs. Leg length (units)]

The points lie in a straight line.

19c. $y = x\sqrt{2}$ **21.** $x = 11$, $y = 11$ **25.** Yes; the legs are 21 cm and 36.4 cm and the hypotenuse is 42 cm. Since 21 • 2 = 42, the hypotenuse is twice the shorter leg. Since $21 \cdot \sqrt{3} \approx 36.4$, the longer leg is $\sqrt{3}$ times the length of the shorter leg. **27.** The hypotenuse is twice the length of the shorter leg. The longer leg is $\sqrt{3}$ times the length of the shorter leg. **29.** H **31a.** $x = 20$, $y = 45$, $z = 20\sqrt{2}$ **31b.** First solve for y to determine the triangle is an isosceles triangle. Since the triangle is isosceles, both legs are congruent so find x. Use the properties of 45-45-90 triangles to find z. **33.** 14.3 **35.** 10.6 **37.** 12 **39.** 12.1 **41.** 90 **43.** 45 **45.** 35 **47.** 101

Pages 577–580 Study Guide and Review

1. perfect square **3.** irrational numbers **5.** acute triangle **7.** congruent **9.** radical sign **11.** 13 **13.** ±1 **15.** 4 **17.** −9 **19.** 3.14 s **21.** rational **23.** rational **25.** < **27.** < **29.** 1.2, −1.2 **31.** 45; acute scalene **33.** 45; right isosceles **35.** acute equilateral **37.** 7.8 ft **39.** 37.2 m **41.** 5 **43.** 12.7 **45.** 15.4 **47.** $6\sqrt{2}$ cm **49.** $x = 30$ in.; $y = 15\sqrt{3}$ in. **51.** $9\sqrt{2}$ in.

Chapter 11 Distance and Angle

Page 587 Chapter 11 Get Ready

1. −92 **3.** 35 **5.** 70 **7.** 5 mi **9.** 16.6 **11.** 9.6 **13.** 8.9 **15.** $9\frac{7}{15}$ **17.** $6\frac{1}{12}$ **19.** $8\frac{1}{12}$ **21.** $20\frac{23}{24}$ lb

Pages 592–595 Lesson 11-1

1. supplementary angles; 34 **3.** supplementary angles; 75 **5.** 128°; ∠1 and ∠8 are alternate exterior angles, so they are congruent. **7a.** the angles are alternate interior angles **7b.** 117 **9.** $x = 9.15$, $m\angle Q = 71.7°$, $m\angle R = 18.3°$

11 Since the two angles form a 180° angle, they are supplementary angles.
$58.9 + m\angle x = 180$
$m\angle x = 121.1°$

13a. complementary angles **13b.** 66° **15.** 52.6°; ∠6 and ∠5 are corresponding angles, so they are congruent. **17.** 127.4°; ∠6 and ∠8 are supplementary angles, so the sum of their measures is 180°. **19.** 127.4°; Sample answer: ∠6 and ∠8 are supplementary angles, so $m\angle 8 = 127.4$. ∠8 and ∠1 are alternate exterior angles, so $m\angle 1 = 127.4$. **21.** 30° **23.** $x = 38.66$; $m\angle D = 49.96°$ **25.** $x = 5$, $m\angle 4 = 75°$, $m\angle 2 = 75°$ **27.** $m\angle B = 35°$, $m\angle C = 35°$

29 **a.** The two angles are supplementary, so $2x + 6x = 180$.
$2x + 6x = 180$
$8x = 180$
$\frac{8x}{8} = \frac{180}{8}$
$x = 22.5$

b. Since $x = 22.5$, substitute to find each angle measure.
$2x = 2(22.5)$
$= 45°$
$6x = 6(22.5)$
$= 135°$

31 **a.** $m\angle WXY = 60°$ because it is 1/3 of a straight angle which is 180°. $m\angle YXZ = 120°$ because $120° + 60° = 180°$
b. Sample answer: 6:00 and 15 seconds

33. Sample answer: [diagram: 40°, 50°]

35. The sum of their measures is 180°. The interior angles on the same side of a transversal are supplementary. **37.** C **39.** A **41.** hypotenuse: 24 ft., leg $12\sqrt{3}$ **43.** 9.3%; increase **45.** $a < -6$ **47.** [diagram: 35°] **49.** [diagram: 85°]

51. [diagram: 180°]

Pages 601–604 Lesson 11-2

1. $\angle L \cong \angle X$, $\angle M \cong \angle Y$, $\angle N \cong \angle Z$, $\overline{LM} \cong \overline{XY}$, $\overline{MN} \cong \overline{YZ}$, $\overline{NL} \cong \overline{ZX}$; $\triangle MNL$

3a. 67.5° **3b.** 12 in. **5.** no

7 Use the matching arcs and tick marks to identify the corresponding angles and segments.
corresponding angles: $\angle S \cong \angle Y$, $\angle STZ \cong \angle YTW$, $\angle Z \cong \angle W$
corresponding sides: $\overline{ST} \cong \overline{YT}$, $\overline{TZ} \cong \overline{TW}$, $\overline{ZS} \cong \overline{WY}$
$\triangle STZ \cong \triangle YTW$

9. $\angle N \cong \angle D$, $\angle P \cong \angle E$, $\angle Q \cong \angle F$, $\overline{NP} \cong \overline{DE}$, $\overline{PQ} \cong \overline{EF}$, $\overline{QN} \cong \overline{FD}$; $\triangle PQN$

11. 8.55 mm **13.** no **15.** yes; $\angle J \cong \angle P$, $\angle L \cong \angle R$, $\angle K \cong \angle Q$, $\overline{JL} \cong \overline{PR}$, $\overline{JK} \cong \overline{PQ}$, $\overline{LK} \cong \overline{RQ}$; Sample answer: $\triangle JLK \cong \triangle PRQ$

17 $\angle M \cong \angle N = 60°$
$\angle OPN = 50°$
Let the missing angle be x
$60° + 50° + x = 180°$
$110° + x = 180°$
$x = 70°$

19. 3.6 cm

21. Sample answer: [butterfly diagram with points G, H, I, J, K, L, M, N, O, P, Q, R]

$\triangle GHI \cong \triangle JKL$, $\triangle MNO \cong \triangle PQR$

23 Since $\overline{PZ} \cong \overline{NZ}$, $18 = 4x - 9$
$19 = 4x - 9$
$28 = 4x$
$7 = x$

25. No; corresponding vertices must be written in the same order, so $\angle YXZ \cong \angle SRT$, not $\angle STR$, and $\overline{ST} \cong \overline{YZ}$ not $\overline{ZY}$ **27.** The scale factor is 1:1 or 1. **29.** B **31.** D **33.** 24.3° **35.** $\frac{1}{5^4}$

37–40.

Pages 608–610 *Lesson 11-3*

1. **3.**

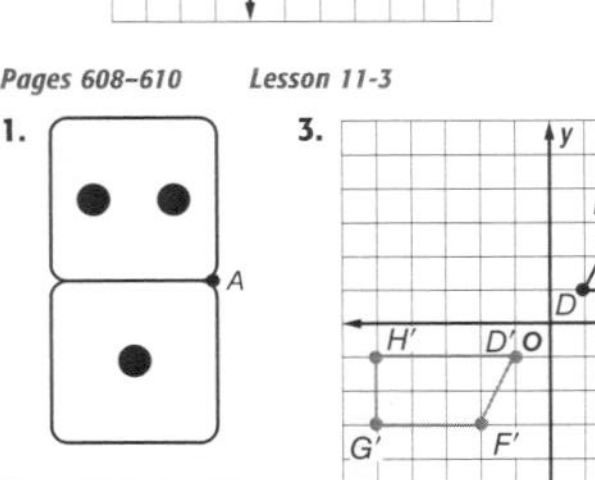

5.

7 **a.** Step 1: graph the original figure. Then graph the vertex H' after a 90° rotation about vertex G.
Step 2: Graph the remaining vertex after a 90° rotation about vertex G. Connect the vertices to form $G'H'J'$.
b. $G'(1, 1)$, $H'(-3, -1)$, $J'(-3, 1)$

9.

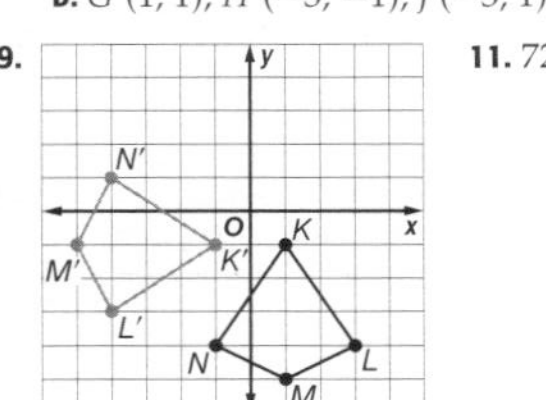

11. 72°

13 The formation has rotational symmetry. The angle of rotation is 180° because if the image is rotated 180° it looks like the original.

15. Sample answer:
90° clockwise; 270° clockwise; 180°

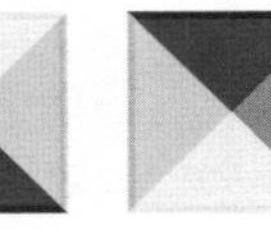

17. Sample answer: 90°

19. $R(1, 5)$, $S(0, -2)$, $T(-6, 3)$ **21.** With both transformations, the original figure and the image are congruent. In a reflection, a figure is reflected across a line. In a rotation, a figure is rotated around a point. **23.** J **25.** C **27.** 73° **29.** 21.5 **31.** 35

Pages 614–616 *Lesson 11-4*

1. 57; 57°, 114° **3.** rhombus **5.** rectangles

7 $115° + 94° + 107° + 2x = 360°$
$316° + 2x = 360°$
$2x = 44°$
$x = 22$

The missing angle is $2(22) = 44°$

9. 33; 132°, 38° **11.** square, rectangles **13.** trapezoid **15.** rhombus **17.** quadrilateral

19 Sample answer: The top of a coffee table is shaped like a rectangle or a square.

21. always **23.** sometimes
25a. $x + x + 70 + 70 = 360$; 110°; 110°
25b. Sample answer:

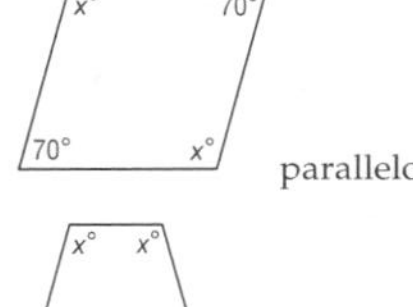

parallelogram

trapezoid

27. Yes; sample answer: quadrilateral with angles that measure 60°, 60°, 120°, and 120°.
29. A square and a rectangle both have four right angles. A square and a rhombus both have four congruent sides. **31.** 50 **33.** C **35.** $\angle L$
37. $\overline{QR}$ **39.** $2(x + 3) + (x + 3) = 90$
41. 21.6 **43.** 3 **45.** 27

Pages 620–622 *Lesson 11-5*

1. The figure is not a polygon because it is an open figure. Two of the sides are not connected. **3.** The figure has 5 sides that only intersect at their endpoints. It is a pentagon.
5. 154.3° **7.** The figure has 5 sides that only intersect at their endpoints. It is a pentagon.
9. The figure has 6 sides that only intersect at their endpoints. It is a hexagon. **11.** The figure has 9 sides that only intersect at their endpoints. It is a nonagon. **13.** 1440° **15.** 2520°

17 A hexagon has 6 sides, so the sum of the measures of the interior angles is $(6 - 2)180 = 4(180)$ or 720. The measure of one interior angle is $720 \div 6 = 120°$.

19. yes **21.** no; Each interior angle of a regular 15-gon measures 156° and 360° is not evenly divisible by 156°. **23.** octagon **25.** 20-gon
27. He used translations of the image of the bird and fish to make the tessellating pattern.

29.

31 In a regular triangle, each interior angle has a measure of 60°. So, the exterior angle has a measure of 180° − 60° or 120°. **33.** 36°

35. Sample answer:

regular hexagons, equilateral triangles; translations, reflections, or rotations
37. Jacinta; the interior angles of a polygon do not have to be congruent in order to create a tessellation. The sum of their measures at a vertex must equal 360°. **39.** Sample answer: A regular polygon has all sides congruent and all angles congruent. A polygon that is not regular has different side lengths, different angle measures, or both. To find the interior angle measure of a regular polygon, subtract 2 from the number of sides, multiply the result by 180, then divide that result by the number of angles.
41. G **43.** 162° **45.** Sometimes **47.** Always

49. yes, $\angle M \cong O$, $\angle L \cong \angle PNO$, $\angle LNM \cong \angle P$, $\overline{NM} \cong \overline{PO}$, $\overline{ML} \cong \overline{ON}$, $\overline{LN} \cong \overline{NP}$, $\triangle LMN \cong \triangle NOP$
51. $x \geq 9.6$ (number line: 9.2, 9.4, 9.6, 9.8, 10)
53. −6 **55.** −10 **57.** 900 **59.** 1260

Pages 627–630 *Lesson 11-6*

1. 30.5 ft² **3.** 275 cm² **5.** 85.6 in²

7 $A = bh$
$= (15)(11.5)$
$= 172.5 \text{ yd}^2$

9. 93.1 mi² **11.** 25.5 mm² **13.** 972.4 m² **15.** 33 cm² **17a.** 6.25 ft² **17b.** 12.5 ft² **19.** 19.2 m² **21.** 9 cm **23.** 11.6 ft **25.** 81 mm² **27.** 15 units² **29.** 60 in.; 213.75 in²

31 $A = \frac{1}{2}h(b_1 + b_2) - \ell w$
$= \frac{1}{2}(9)(12 + 8) - (2)(3)$
$= \frac{1}{2}(9)(20) - 6$
$= \frac{1}{2}(180) - 6$
$= 90 - 6$
$= 84 \text{ ft}^2$

33 $A = \frac{1}{2}h(b_1 + b_2)$
$= \frac{1}{2}(11.2)(24 + 14)$
$= \frac{1}{2}(11.2)(38)$
$= \frac{1}{2}(425.6)$
$= 212.8 \text{ ft}^2$

Divide by 9 to determine the area in square yards. $212.8 \div 9 \approx 23.6 \text{ yd}^2$

35. Sample answer: a triangle with a base of 8 units and a height of 3 units has the same area as a parallelogram with a base of 4 units and a height of 3 units, 12 units². **37a.** Sample answer: a parallelogram with base 10 in., height 12 in., and sides 13 in.; 46 in., 120 in² **37b.** Sample answer: a parallelogram with base 11 in., height 11 in., and sides 13 in.; 48 in., 121 in²
39. In the formula for the area of a triangle, $\frac{1}{2}$ is multiplied by the base and the height. The formula for the area of a trapezoid is the same, except that the sum of the bases is multiplied rather than a single base. **41a.** She would need to determine the area of the lawn that she is going to fertilize. After finding the total area, she will then divide that by 1000 square feet to determine how many bags she needs to buy. **41b.** $90 \cdot 150 = 13{,}500$. $13{,}500 \div 1000 = 13.5$ so she would need to buy 14 bags of fertilizer. **43.** B **45.** about 128.6° **47.** 150°
49. $x = 100$ **51.** \$73.35 **53.** \$16.25 **55.** 33.9
57. 13.5

Pages 633–635 **Lesson 11-7**

1. 37.7 in. **3.** 50.9 cm **5.** 22.6 km

7 $d = 7$
$C = \pi d$
$= \pi(7)$
≈ 22.0 m

9. 62.8 ft **11.** 17.9 cm **13.** 29.5 m **15.** 70.7 ft
17. Sample answer: Small sand dollar: $C \approx 3.9$ in., large sand dollar: $C \approx 7.9$ in.; the circumference of the small sand dollar is half the circumference of the large sand dollar. **19a.** 49.76 m
19b. 12.44 m **19c.** 143.06 m

21 current fountain:
$C = \pi d$
$= \pi(8)$
≈ 25.1327 ft
new fountain:
$25.1237 \times 4 \approx 100.5$ ft

23a.

Radius (in.)	Circumference (in.)
1	6.3
2	12.6
3	18.8
4	25.1
5	31.4

23b. Sample answer:

Circles
Circumference (in.)
Radius (in.)

23c. 2π; Since the formula for the circumference of a circle, $C = 2\pi r$, is in the form of $y = mx$, 2π is the slope. **25.** Sample answer: A glass with a diameter of 7 centimeters has a circumference of about 22.0 centimeters. **27.** Circumference of one circle; ℓ equals $3d$ and the circumference of one circle is approximately $3.14d$
29. Circumference is 2π or about 6.3 times the radius. The circumference increases as the radius increases. The radius decreases as the circumference decreases. **31.** F **33a.** 15π
33b. 47 ft **35.** 52.5 ft² **37.** 720°
39.

41a. $C = 15n$ **41b.** \$180 **43.** 153.86

Pages 638–641 **Lesson 11-8**

1 $A = \pi r^2$
$= \pi(7)^2$
$= \pi(49)$
≈ 153.9 m²

3. 132.7 ft² **5.** 86.6 cm² **7.** 2.1 in² **9.** 50.3 cm²
11. 78.5 mi² **13.** 66.5 cm² **15.** 289.5 ft²
17. 103.9 yd²

19 $A = \pi r^2 - \ell w$
$= \pi(12)^2 - (3)(6)$
$= 144\pi - 18$
≈ 434.4 ft²

21. 39.3 m² **23.** 5.7 mm² **25.** 4 in. **27.** 837.7 ft²

29 $C = \frac{1}{2}\pi d + 10$ $\quad A = \frac{1}{2}\pi r^2$
$= \frac{1}{2}\pi(10) + 10$ $\quad = \frac{1}{2}\pi(5)2$
$= 5\pi + 10$ $\quad = \frac{1}{2}\pi(25)$
≈ 25.7 ft $\quad \approx 39.3$ ft²

31a.

Radius (cm)	Area (cm²)
3	28.3
6	113.1
12	452.4
24	1809.6
48	7238.2

31b. The area is multiplied by 4.
31c. Sample answer: Since $96 = 48 \cdot 2$, the area should be $4 \cdot 7238.2$ or 28,952.8 cm²; actual area $\approx 28{,}952.9$ cm². **33.** Circumference measures the distance around a circle and is given in units. Area measures the surface enclosed by the circle and is given in square units. The formulas for both measures involves π and the radius. The formula for circumference is $C = 2\pi r$ and the formula for area is $A = \pi r^2$. **35.** 2 units; if $r = 2$, then $C = 2\pi(2)$ or 4π units and $A = \pi(2)^2$ or 4π units². **37.** A **39.** A **41.** 50.3 in. **43.** 66.0 cm
45. 90 cm² **47.** $\frac{8}{45}$ **49.** 533.71 **51.** 138.45

Pages 644–647 **Lesson 11-9**

1. 38.4 cm² **3.** 18.9 cm² **5a.** 58 ft²
5b. 10 cases; \$250

7 $A = \frac{1}{2}bh + \ell w$
$= \frac{1}{2}(18)(12) + (22)(6)$
$= \frac{1}{2}(216) + 132$
$= 108 + 132$
$= 240$ in²

9. 7.3 mm² **11.** 257.1 ft² **13a.** 354 ft²
13b. \$796.50 **15a.** 73.1 in² **15b.** 104.5 in²

17 $A = \frac{1}{2}(1.5)(6 + 5) + \frac{1}{2}(9)(6)$ or 35.25 ft²

19. 40.8 m²

21 $A = 5(8) - \frac{1}{2}\pi r^2$
$= 40 - 9.8$
≈ 30.2 in²

23. Sample answer: states, parks, shopping malls
25. Sample answer: Use polygons to approximate the shape of the curved side. **27.** 429.7 **29.** J
31. 37.7 cm; 113.1 cm² **33.** 125.7 in, 1256.6 in²
35. 18 cm² **37.** pentagon **39.** triangle

Pages 650–654 **Study Guide and Review**

1. true **3.** false; base **5.** true **7.** false; supplementary angles **9.** false; rotation
11. 112°; ∠4 and ∠2 are vertical angles, so they are congruent. **13.** 68°; ∠4 and ∠1 are a linear pair of angles, so they are supplementary.
15. $\angle F \cong \angle L$, $\angle G \cong \angle M$, $\angle H \cong \angle N$; $\overline{FG} \cong \overline{LM}$, $\overline{GH} \cong \overline{MN}$, $\overline{HF} \cong \overline{NL}$; $\triangle LMN$
17.

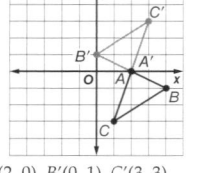

$A'(2, 0)$, $B'(0, 1)$, $C'(3, 3)$

19.

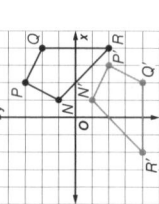

21. 98; 98°, 100° **23.** rhombus **25.** The figure has 5 sides that only intersect at their endpoints. It is a regular pentagon. **27.** 160° **29.** 120 ft²
31. about \$76.25 **33.** 44.0 yd **35.** 84.8 mm
37. 201.1 cm² **39.** 63.6 in² **41.** about 14,055 ft²

Chapter 12 Surface Area and Volume

Page 661 **Chapter 12** **Getting Ready**

1. yes; parallelogram **3.** octagon **5.** 35 **7.** 330
9. no **11.** no **13.** yes; $\frac{1}{1.25} = \frac{2}{2.5} = \frac{3}{3.75} = \frac{4}{5}$

Pages 667–669 **Lesson 12-1**

1. rectangular prism; *EIJF* and *HLKG*, or *EILH* and *FGKJ*, or *IJKL* and *EFGH*; *EFGH*, *EFJI*, *GHLK*, *JFGK*, *EHLI*, *IJKL*, *E*, *F*, *G*, *H*, *I*, *J*, *K*, *L*

3. parallelogram; **5.** rectangle;

7. triangular prism, bases: *DEF*, *ABC*; faces: *ABEF*, *BCDE*, *ACDF*, *FED*, *ABC*; edges: $\overline{AB}$, $\overline{AC}$, $\overline{AF}$, $\overline{BC}$, $\overline{BE}$, $\overline{DF}$, $\overline{CD}$, $\overline{ED}$, $\overline{EF}$; vertices: *A*, *B*, *C*, *D*, *E*, *F*

9 This figure has one rectangular base, *ABCD*, so it is a rectangular pyramid; faces: *BEC*, *BEA*, *AED*, *CED*, *ABCD*; edges: $\overline{AB}$, $\overline{BC}$, $\overline{CD}$, $\overline{AD}$, $\overline{AE}$, $\overline{BE}$, $\overline{CE}$, $\overline{DE}$; vertices: *A*, *B*, *C*, *D*, *E*

11. hexagonal pyramid; base: *BCDEFG*; faces: *ABC*, *ACD*, *ADE*, *AEF*, *AFG*, *AGB*, *BCDEFG*; edges: $\overline{AB}$, $\overline{AC}$, $\overline{AD}$, $\overline{AE}$, $\overline{AF}$, $\overline{AG}$, $\overline{BC}$, $\overline{CD}$, $\overline{DE}$, $\overline{EF}$, $\overline{FG}$, $\overline{GB}$; vertices: *A*, *B*, *C*, *D*, *E*, *F*, *G*

13. circle; **15.** square;

17a.

17b. base: *BCDE*; faces: *ABC*, *BCDE*, *ABE*, *ACD*, *ADE*; edges: $\overline{AB}$, $\overline{AC}$, $\overline{AD}$, $\overline{AE}$, $\overline{BC}$, $\overline{CD}$, $\overline{DE}$, $\overline{EB}$
17c. triangle, triangle or trapezoid, square

17d. top-triangle
base-trapezoid

19. Top Side Cross section

triangle and circle

21 **a.** The first figure is a triangular pyramid. It will have four triangular faces. The second figure is a square pyramid. It will have a square base and four triangular faces. The third figure is a pentagonal pyramid. It will have a pentagonal base and five triangular faces. From this information, you can complete the table.

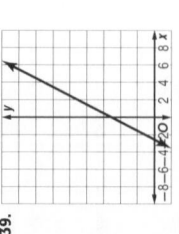

Name	Triangular Pyramid	Square Pyramid	Pentagonal Pyramid
Figure			
Vertices	4	5	6
Faces	4	5	6
Edges	6	8	10

b. Sample answer: The number of vertices is equal to the number of faces. The number of edges increases by 2 as the number of vertices of the pyramid increases by 1.
c. The sum of the number of vertices V and the number of faces F is equal to the number of edges E plus 2. So, $V + F = E + 2$.
23. never **25.** sometimes **27.** Sample answer: Examine the base of the object; it is a hexagon. Since it has two parallel, congruent bases, it is also a prism. The figure is a hexagonal prism. **29.** D
31. The shape resulting from a vertical cross section is a rectangle. **33.** 72 ft² **35.** 56.1 cm² **37.** 21.6 in² **39.** 156.4 ft²

Pages 673–676 Lesson 12-2

1. 36 mm³ **3.** 1000 in³
5 The figure is made of three rectangular prisms.
V(figure) = V(rectangular prism 1) + V(rectangular prism 2) + V(rectangular prism 3)
$V(\text{figure}) = \ell wh + \ell wh + \ell wh$
$= (10 \cdot 10 \cdot 4) + (6 \cdot 6 \cdot 4) + (2 \cdot 2 \cdot 2)$
$= 400 + 144 + 8$
$= 552$ cubic inches
The answer is B.
7. 260 ft³ **9.** 54 in³
11 $V = Bh$
$= (\frac{1}{2} \cdot 3 \cdot 10)(8)$
$= 15 \cdot 8$
$= 120 \text{ cm}^3$
13. $1\frac{1}{2}$ in³ **15.** 6 yd **17.** 3888 in³ **19.** 10 ft **21.** 972 m³ **23.** 180 ft³
25 $V = Bh$
The base of the figure is a trapezoid.
So, $B = \frac{1}{2}(b_1 + b_2)h$.
$V = \left[\frac{1}{2}(b_1 + b_2)h\right]h$
$= \left[\frac{1}{2}(1.5 + 1)0.5\right](3)$
$= \frac{1}{2}(2.5)(0.5)(3)$
$= 1.875 \text{ in}^3$
27a. 42 cm³ **27b.** The volume is multiplied by 2 because $V = \ell w(2h) = 2(\ell wh)$; The original volume is multiplied by 2^2 or 4 because $V = \ell(2w)(2h) = 4(\ell wh)$; The original volume is multiplied by 2^3 or 8 because $V = (2\ell)(2w)(2h) = 8(\ell wh)$. **27c.** When one dimension is tripled, the volume is multiplied by 3. When two dimensions are tripled, the original volume is multiplied by 3^2. When three dimensions are tripled, the original volume is multiplied by 3^3.
27d. 9072 cm³ **29.** Sample answer: base length 4, base height 2, prism height 11. **31.** 35
33. Sample answer: The volume of the box is changed by 2^3 or 8. **35.** 12 **37.** C
39. rectangular prism; bases: $ABCD$ and $EFGH$, or $BCGF$ and $ADHE$, or $ABFE$ and $DCGH$; faces: $ABCD$, $EFGH$, $BCGF$, $ADHE$, $ABFE$, $DCGH$; edges: $\overline{AB}, \overline{DC}, \overline{HG}, \overline{EF}, \overline{AD}, \overline{BC}, \overline{EH}, \overline{FG}, \overline{AE}, \overline{BF}, \overline{DH}, \overline{CG}$ **41.** 228.5 mm² **43.** 12.6 in² **45.** 78.5 mi²

Pages 679–681 Lesson 12-3

1. 25.1 ft³ **3.** 10.0 in. **5.** 22.0 cm³ **7.** 254.5 m³
9 $V = Bh$
$= \pi r^2 h$
$= \pi(2.2)^2(3)$
$\approx 45.6 \text{ cm}^3$
11. 101.4 m³ **13.** 5.5 m **15.** 69.1 in³
17. 2628.1 cm³
19 $V = \pi r_1{}^2 h_1 - \pi r_2{}^2 h_2$
$= \pi(6.5)^2(28) - \pi(2.25)^2(28)$
$\approx 3271.2 \text{ cm}^3$
21. 101.3 gal **23.** Sample answer: Changing the packaging size of a drink; changing the size of a garbage can to fit in a narrower but taller space. **25a.** 2:1 **25b.** 4:1 **27.** B **29a.** 77.8 in³ **29b.** 699.8 in³ **31.** 5200 ft³ **33.** 120 in³
35. triangular prism: bases ACE and BDF; faces: $ABFE$, $EFDC$, $ABCD$, ACE, BDF; edges: $\overline{AB}, \overline{EF}, \overline{CD}, \overline{AC}, \overline{CE}, \overline{EA}, \overline{BF}, \overline{FD}, \overline{DB}$; vertices: A, B, C, D, E, F
37. 160 **39.** 35 **41.** $3\frac{1}{3}$

Pages 686–688 Lesson 12-4

1. 115.5 in³ **3.** 74.2 cm³ **5.** 268.1 mm³ **7.** 392.7 ft³ **9.** 6 ft³ **11.** 4.3 in³ **13.** 10.5 ft³ **15.** 1563.5 km³
17 **a.** $V = \frac{1}{3}\pi r^2 h$
$= \frac{1}{3}\pi(0.75)^2(2.5)$
$\approx 1.5 \text{ ft}^3$
b. Use a proportion.
$\frac{0.1 \text{ ft}^3}{5 \text{ m}} = \frac{1.5 \text{ ft}^3}{x \text{ m}}$
$0.1x = 5 \cdot 1.5$
$\frac{0.1x}{0.1} = \frac{7.5}{0.1}$
$x = 75$
It will take about 75 minutes or 1 hour 15 minutes for the icicle to melt.
19. 18.3 ft
21 $V = \frac{1}{3}\pi r_1{}^2 h_1 + \frac{1}{3}\pi r_2{}^2 h_2$
$= \frac{1}{3}\pi(3)^2(15) + \frac{1}{3}\pi(3)^2(7)$
$\approx 207.3 \text{ in}^3$

23. 4656.8 g **25.** 140.4 cm³ **27.** 3 units
29. True. The volumes are equal if both heights and both bases are equal. Changing the shape of the base will not affect the volume.
31. Changing the shape of the packaging. If the volumes remained the same and they have congruent bases, the cone's height would be 3 times the height of the cylinder. **33.** H
35. D **37.** 748 cm³ **39.** 24.6 mi **41.** $575p = 15$; 2.6 lb **43.** 3772 m²

Pages 693–695 Lesson 12-5

1. 108 in²; 268 in² **3.** 360 yd²; 464.5 yd² **5.** 3.84 cm²; 4.8 cm² **7.** 8.4 m²; 10.08 m²
9 $L = Ph$
$= (2\ell + 2w)h$
$= (2(2.2) + 2(1.4))(9)$
$= 64.8 \text{ cm}^2$
$S = L + 2B$
$= 64.8 + 2(2.2)(1.4)$
$= 70.96 \text{ cm}^2$
11. 334 in² **13.** 528 m²
15 **a.** $S = 2(\ell h + wh + \ell w)$
$= 2(5 \cdot 5 + 5 \cdot 5 + 5 \cdot 5)$
$= 150 \text{ in}^2$
b.

Scale Factor of Dilation	Original	×2	×3
Length of Side	5	10	15
Surface Area	150	600	1350

$S = 2(\ell h + wh + \ell w)$
$= 2(10 \cdot 10 + 10 \cdot 10 + 10 \cdot 10)$
$= 600 \text{ in}^3$
$S = 2(\ell h + wh + \ell w)$
$= 2(15 \cdot 15 + 15 \cdot 15 + 15 \cdot 15)$
$= 900 \text{ in}^3$
c. Sample answer: The surface area after a dilation of scale factor of 2 is four times the original; The surface area after a dilation of a scale factor of 3 is 9 times the original.
d. Yes. The original formula for surface area is $S = Ph + 2B$. After doubling the sides, the new formula would be $S = (2P)(2h) + 2(4B)$ which simplifies to $S = 4(Ph + 2B)$. Remember, the B is four times as much because both base and height are doubled.
17. The rectangular prism would be more expensive to make. The surface area of the rectangular prism is 36.64 in², which would cost \$47.63 to make. The surface area of the cube is 34.56 in², which would cost \$44.93 to make.
19. The box is a cube that measures 6 cm on each side. **21.** See students' work. Sample answer: Prism A with dimensions 3 by 3 by 3 and Prism B with dimensions 10 by 2 by 1. Prism A has the larger volume while Prism B has the larger surface area. **23.** D **25.** J **27.** 268.1 cm³ **29.** 251.3 m³ **31.** 625 **33.** 722 **35.** 153.9 yd² **37.** 1240.9 m²

Pages 699–701 Lesson 12-6

1. 1492.3 mm²; 2059.3 mm²
3. 102.9 m²; 130.6 m²
5 $L = 2\pi rh$
$= 2\pi(3.1)(2)$
$= 12.4\pi$
$\approx 39.0 \text{ yd}^2$
$S = L + 2\pi r^2$
$= 12.4\pi + 2\pi(3.1)^2$
$\approx 99.3 \text{ yd}^2$
7. 125.7 in²; 150.8 in² **9.** 121.0 ft²; 205.4 ft²
11. The box has surface area of 1296 in² and the tube has a surface area of 1288.1 in². So the tube has a smaller surface area.
13 Exterior of Pipe:
$S = 2\pi rh$
$= 2\pi(1.6)(10)$
$= 32\pi$
$\approx 100.5 \text{ in}^2$
Interior of Pipe:
$S = 2\pi rh$
$= 2\pi(1.5)(10)$
$= 30\pi$
$\approx 94.2 \text{ in}^2$
So, the surface area of the pipe is about 100.5 + 94.2 or 194.7 in².
15. 6121.0 cm² **17.** The cylindrical popcorn container because it uses less material (surface area) and holds about the same amount of popcorn (volume). Rectangular Prism: V = 275 in³ S.A. = 237.5 in²; Cylinder: V = 274.3 in³ S.A. = 211.1 in²
19. Sample answer: surface area of the cylinder:
$S = 2\pi rh + 2\pi r^2$
$= 2(3)(5)15 + 2(3)5^2$
$= 150 + 450$
$= 600 \text{ ft}^2$
A cube measuring 10 ft would have a surface area of 600 square feet.
$S = 6s^2$
$600 = 6s^2$
$100 = s^2$
$s = 10$
21. The ice cube in the shape of a half cylinder would melt at a faster rate because it has a greater total surface area exposed to the air. **23.** G
25. D **27.** 114 in²; 282 in² **29.** 4356 m³
31. straight **33.** obtuse **35.** \$918.75 **37.** \$9135
39. 48 **41.** 58.75 **43.** $\frac{14}{15}$

Pages 705–707 Lesson 12-7

1. 364 m²; 533 m² **3.** 192 mm²; 336 mm²
5 $L = \frac{1}{2}P\ell$
$= \frac{1}{2}(4 \times 10)(12)$
$= 240 \text{ in}^2$
$S = L + B$
$= 240 + 10(10)$
$= 340 \text{ in}^2$
7. 105.3 mm²; 140.4 mm² **9.** 339.3 mm²
11. 125.7 cm²; 175.9 cm² **13.** 427.3 ft²; 628.3 ft²
15. 471.2 cm²
17 $C = 2\pi r$
$22 = 2\pi r$
$3.5 = r$
$a^2 + b^2 = c^2$
$(3.5)^2 + (18) = c^2$
$12.25 + 324 = c^2$

$S = \pi r\ell$
$= \pi(3.5)(18.3)$
≈ 201.2
$8(201.2) = 1609.8 \text{ in}^2$
$18.3 \approx c$

19. lateral area = 130.5 m^2; surface area = 174 m^2 **21.** 48.7 feet **25.** 4 **27.** C **29.** B **31.** 386.4 in^2; 612.6 in^2 **33.** 120 ft^2; 244.8 ft^2 **35.** 50° **37.** $2\frac{1}{7}$ **39.** 6 **41.** 5.5

Pages 712–715 *Lesson 12-8*

1. yes

3 $\frac{2}{6} = \frac{d}{12}$
$2 \cdot 12 = 6 \cdot d$
$24 = 6d$
$\frac{24}{6} = \frac{6d}{6}$
$4 = d$
$d = 4$ yd

5. 450 ft^2 **7.** no **9.** no

11 $\frac{10}{6} = \frac{8}{x}$
$10 \cdot x = 6 \cdot 8$
$10x = 48$
$\frac{10x}{10} = \frac{48}{10}$
$x = 4.8$ in.

13. 4800 mm^2 **15a.** 4:1 **15b.** 4.25 inches **15c.** large wheel volume = 30,762.5 in^3; small wheel volume 480.7 in^3 **15d.** 64 times greater

17 $V = \frac{4}{3}\pi r^3$
$= \frac{4}{3}\pi(33)^3$
$\approx 150{,}536.3 \text{ ft}^3$

19. 3.3 in. **21a.** $\frac{4}{9}, \frac{8}{27}$ **21b.** 90 ft^2 **21c.** 16 ft^3

23. True. Spheres have only one measurement, the radius. **25.** The surface area quadruples. **29.** G **31.** 13.75 **33.** 201.1 in^2; 603.2 in^2 **35.** $\frac{25}{4}$ **37.** 475

Pages 716–720 *Chapter 12* *Study Guide and Review*

1. true **3.** true **5.** false; pyramid **7.** false; cylinder or prism **9.** rectangular prism; bases: *AFGD, BEHC*; faces: *ABCD, EFGH, BEFA, CHGD*; edges: $\overline{AB}, \overline{BC}, \overline{CD}, \overline{AD}, \overline{EF}, \overline{EH}, \overline{FG}, \overline{GH}, \overline{EB}, \overline{HC}, \overline{AF}, \overline{GD}$; vertices: *A, B, C, D, E, F, G, H* **11.** square pyramid; bases: *LMNO* faces: *LPM, LPO, NPO, NPM*; edges: $\overline{LM}, \overline{MN}, \overline{NO}, \overline{OL}, \overline{LP}, \overline{MP}, \overline{NP}, \overline{OP}$; vertices: *L, M, N, O, P*

13. Top View Side View Cross Section

A vertical cross section of the drum is a rectangle.

15. 60 cm^3 **17.** 445.3 cm^3 **19.** 18.9 in^3 **21.** 8 in^3 **23.** 15 ft^3 **25.** 68 cm^2; 101 cm^2 **27.** 143.6 m^2; 166.4 m^2 **29.** 288 in^2 **31.** 298.5 ft^2; 865.5 ft^2 **33.** 202.3 mm^2; 335.3 mm^2 **35.** 244.8 cm^2; 308.8 cm^2 **37.** 131.9 cm^2; 182.2 cm^2 **39.** 1980 ft^2 **41.** 5 m

Chapter 13 Statistics and Probability

Page 727 *Chapter 13* *Get Ready*

1. $15.33 **3.** 5000 visitors **5.** 6 **7.** 12 **9.** $\frac{12}{25}$ **11.** 1 **13.** $\frac{5}{8}$

Pages 733–735 *Lesson 13-1*

1. mean: 151.4 mph; median: 157 mph; mode: 157 mph **3.** A **5.** mean or median; Sample answer: The mean and median both show longer amounts of time.

7 mean
Add the data values and divide by the number of data values.
$\frac{250 + 200 + 320 + 235 + 265 + 200}{6} = \frac{1470}{6}$ or $245
median
List the data values in ascending order.
200, 200, 235, 250, 265, 320
Since there is an even number of data values, find the mean of the two middle numbers.
$\frac{235 + 250}{2} = \frac{485}{2}$ or $242.50
mode
Find the data value(s) which occur the most.
$200

9. Median; 869 is an extreme value that shifts the mean upward.

11 mean
Add the data values and divide by the number of data values.
$\frac{50 + 76 + 94 + 90 + 88 + 92 + 88 + 96}{8} = \frac{704}{8}$ or $88
median
List the data values in ascending order.
76, 80, 88, 88, 90, 92, 94, 96
Since there is an even number of data values, find the mean of the two middle numbers.
$\frac{88 + 90}{2} = \frac{178}{2}$ or 89
mode
Find the data value(s) which occur the most.
88
The measure of central tendency that makes his score look best is the median, 89.

13. mode; Sample answer: More students have 2 siblings than any other number. It is the best representation of the data.

15. Sample answer:

Student's Heights

Height (in.) 54 56 58 60 62 64 66

mean: 60.45; median: 60; mode: 60; any of them. Each measure is around 60 inches.

17. Sometimes; For example, the data set: $3, $5, $5, $5, and $7. The mean is $5, the median is $5, and the mode is $5.

19. Sample answer: The median home price would be useful because it is not affected by the cost of the very expensive homes. The cost of half the homes in the county would be greater than the median cost and half would be less.

21. Sample answer:

Completed Passes in the NFL

Player	Number of Passes
Jon Kitna	372
Peyton Manning	362
Carson Palmer	324
Steve McNair	295
Jake Plummer	175

Source: National Football League

The median; the mean is affected by the extreme value of 175, and there is no mode. The median is 324 passes.

23. J **25a.** 155 **25b.** 140 **27.** yes

29. **Ages of Basketball Players**

Age (years) 15 16 17 18 19 20 21 22

Pages 739–742 *Lesson 13-2*

1. **Test Scores**

Stem	Leaf
7	2 3 6 6 9
8	0 0 1 4
9	9

8|1 = 81

3a. 14.5 lb; **3b.** 15lb **3c.** 56 lb

5 Step 1: Find the least and greatest number. Then identify the greatest place value in each number. The least number, 18, has 1 in the tens place. The greatest number, 55, has 5 in the tens place.
Step 2: Write the stems 1-5 in the Stem column from least to greatest. Write the ones digit to the right of each corresponding stem in the Leaf column.
Step 3: Order the leaves from least to greatest and write a key that explains how to read the stems in the Leaf column. Include a title.

Ages of People in Spinning Class

Stem	Leaf
1	8
2	0 1 2 2 3 6 7 7
3	0 3 5 9
4	0 2 9
5	5

2|8 = 28 years

7. **Tennis Shoe Cost**

Stem	Leaf
5	0 9
6	0 5 5
7	0 5 6 8
8	0 0
9	6

5|9 = $59

9 **a.** List numbers in ascending order: 31, 35, 35, 37, 37, 39, 42, 44, 44, 46, 46, 48, 48, 50, 50, 50, 53, 54, 56, 56, 57, 61, 66, 67, 68, 68, 88 and determine the middle number; 50 pages
b. Observe data and determine which number occurs most often; 50 pages
c. 88 – 31 = 57 pages

11 **a.** Look at the overall data. Troop 60 members generally sold 30 to 40 boxes and Troop 122 members generally sold 50 to 60 boxes. So, Troop 122 sold more boxes.
b. Troop 122 sales are more spread out. Troop 60 are more clustered.

13. Sample answer: The person who came in first beat the other runners by almost 2 seconds. An average time is about 17.8 seconds.

100 Meter Times

Stem	Leaf
14	3
15	
16	2 5
17	4 7 9
18	0 7
19	2 9

18|0 = 18.0 s

15 **a.** Step 1: Find the least and greatest number. Then identify the greatest place value in each number. The least number, 6, has 0 in the tens place. The greatest number, 80, has 8 in the tens place.
Step 2: Write the stems 0-8 in the Stem column from least to greatest. Write the ones digit to the right of each corresponding stem in the Leaf column.
Step 3: Order the leaves from least to greatest and write a key that explains how to read the stems in the Leaf column. Include a title.

Test Scores

Stem	Leaf
0	6
1	3 9
2	0 3
3	2 4 6 8 9
4	6 8 9
5	6 6 9 9 9
6	2 2 3 4 7 8
7	3 3 5 6 6 8 8 8 9 9
8	0 0

b. mean: Find the sum of the data and divide by the total number of values.
$\frac{2003}{36} = 55.6$
median: Find the middle number of the data.
$\frac{62 + 59}{2} = 60.5$
mode: 59, 78

c.

Stem	Leaf
0	6
1	3 9
2	0 3
3	2 4 6 8 9
4	6 8 9
5	6 6 9 9 9
6	2 2 3 4 7 8
7	3 3 5 6 6 8 8 8 9 9
8	0 0

d. Sample answer: There are two main peaks in the graph with one valley. The graph is not symmetric since the shape is not the same on each side of the graph.

e. Sample answer: The data set is skewed. Most of the data is on the right side of the graph.

17. Sample answer:

Stem	Leaf
1	0 0 2 3 6 7 8
2	2 5 6 9 9
3	1 2 8

2|6 = 26

19. Neither; Sample answer: The median is 32. J'vonté divided wrong, and Paolo forgot to divide 64 by 2.

21. Sample answer: Stem-and-leaf plots can help you see how the winning speeds are distributed. You can identify the fastest and slowest winning speeds, the mean speed, the mode speed, and the median speed. **23.** D **25.** B **27.** $33\frac{1}{3}$ ft **29.** 36 **31.** 8 **33.** 7.5

Pages 747–749 Lesson 13-3

1. R: 145; UQ: 145; LQ: 90; M: 115; IR 55; none
3a. The fruits' range is 30. The vegetables' range is 20. So, the number of Calories in fruits varies more than the number of Calories in vegetables.
3b. 80; With the outlier, the mean increased by 57.5–54.3 or 3.2, the median increased by 55–50 or 5, and the mode did not change.

5 The range is 30 – 15 or 15.
The median is $\frac{21}{2}$ or 21.5.
lower quartile: 15 17 18 18 10 21
LQ is 18
upper quartile: 22 23 25 25 27 30
UQ is 25
The interquartile range is 25 – 18 = 7
To find an outlier, multiply the interquartile range by 1.7.
$7 \cdot 1.5 = 10.5$
Add 10.5 to the lower quartile and the upper quartile to find any outliers
18 – 10.5 = 7.5 25 + 10.5 = 35.5
There are no outliers.
7a. Room 110: 91; Room 100: 94 **7b.** Room 100
7c. Room 100 has an outlier, 64. The outlier makes the range greater by 24 points.

9 **a.** Antelope, MT: 84 – 21 = 63
Augusta, ME: 80 – 28 = 52
Antelope has the greater range.
b. Antelope:
The median is $\frac{58 + 58}{2} = 58$.
lower quartile: 21 24 30 37 42 58
LQ is 33.5
upper quartile: 58 70 72 79 84 84
UQ is 75.5
The interquartile range is 75.5 – 33.5 = 42
Augusta:
The median is $\frac{53 + 58}{2} = 55.5$.
lower quartile: 28 32 34 41 46 53
LQ is 37.5
upper quartile: 58 66 70 75 79 80
UQ is 72.5
The interquartile range is 72.5 – 37.5 = 35
c. The median for Antelope is higher. The lower quartile for Augusta is higher and the upper quartile for Antelope is higher.
d. The median is the best measure of central tendency because it best describes the data.
e. The average temperature of the two cities is similar, although Antelope has the greater median and range. This means that the temperature varies more in Antelope than it does in Augusta.

11. Sample answer: Mean: 24.38; Interquartile Range: 6; Mean: 20.43; Interquartile Range: 6; Without the outlier, the mean price is lower and the prices vary less.

Colorado 1-day Lift Ticket Prices for Kids

Ski Area	Child Price
Arapahoe Basin	$24
Aspen Highlands	$52
Howelsen	$10
Loveland	$23
Monarch	$19
Ski Cooper	$18
SolVista	$24
Wolf Creek	$25

13. Always; the range is the difference between the greatest and least value. An outlier is an extreme value, therefore will always effect the range.
15. true **17.** D **19.** A **21.**

Cost of DVDs

Stem	Leaf
0	9
1	2 4 5 8
2	1 7
3	7

3|7 = $37

23. 4.3; 4.2; 4.1 and 4.2 **25.** yes **27.** 120.1 yd³
29. 6.7, 6.8, 6.9, 7.0, 7.8, 8.7

Pages 752–755 Lesson 13-4

1 Step 1: Draw a number line that includes the least and greatest numbers in the data.
Step 2: Mark the median, and the upper and lower quartile above the number line. Check for outliers. If an outlier exists, mark the greatest value that is not an outlier. Then mark the outlier with an asterisk.
Step 3: Draw the box and whiskers. Add a title.

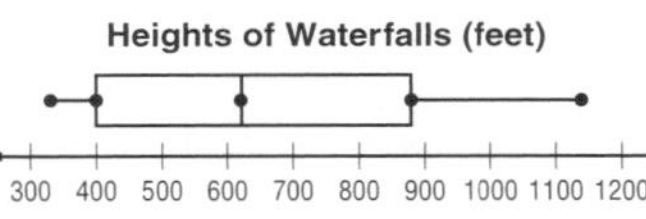

3. Sample answer: Half the time the Cougars scored between 18 and 31 points. Half the time the Falcons scored between 14 and 21 points. So, the Cougars usually scored more points per game than the Falcons.

5. Price of Paintings
170 210 250 290 330 370

7. Age of Students
18 20 22 24 26 28 30 32 34 36 38 40

9 **a.** 50%
b. Sample answer: The median divides the data in the box into unequal parts. The left whisker is significantly shorter than the right whisker so the data below the lower quartile is more concentrated than the data above the upper quartile. The data below the upper quartile is more spread out.

11 Step 1: Draw a number line that includes the least and greatest numbers in the data.
Step 2: Mark the median, and the upper and lower quartile above the number line. Check for outliers. If an outlier exists, mark the greatest value that is not an outlier.
Step 3: Draw the box and whiskers. Add a title.

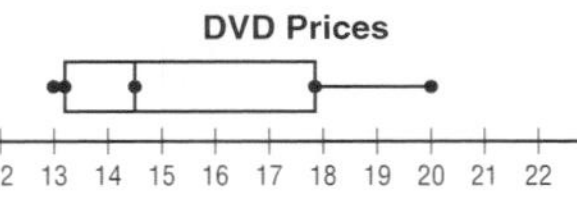

13. Sample answer: Data set A {21, 21, 22, 26, 26, 27, 28, 28, 28, 29, 30, 30, 30, 30, 31} Data set B {18, 18, 18, 22, 22, 22, 26, 26, 26, 26, 31, 31, 31, 33}
15a. 28, 29, 30, 30, 31, 35, 38, 39, 41, 42, 42, 47, 48
15b. at least 21; Sample answer: since 6 students have scores ranging from 38 to 42, there are at most 4 students with scores between 38 and 42. If the measures of variation above are constant, there are at most 4 students with scores between 28 and 30, 30 and 38, 38 and 42, and 42 and 48. Therefore, 16 students are accounted for in these scores, plus the minimum, lower quartile, median,

upper quartile, and maximum scores gives a minimum of 21 students. **17.** 4 **19.** H **21a.** Rose Bowl: 39, 27, 38, 17.5, 20.5, no outliers; .Cotton Bowl: 48, 28, 35, 17, 18, no outliers **21b.** Sample answer: The winners of the Cotton Bowl scored more points on average than the winners of the Rose Bowl. The number of points scored by the Cotton Bowl winners varies greater than the number of points scored by the Rose Bowl winners. The Rose Bowl data in the middle are more spread out than the Cotton Bowl data.

Pages 759–762 *Lesson 13-5*

1 Step 1: Draw and label a horizontal and vertical axis as shown. Include a title.
Step 2: Show the intervals from the frequency table on the horizontal axis and the frequency on the vertical axis.
Step 3: For each interval, draw a bar whose height is given by the frequency.

Age of Indianapolis 500 Winners

Frequency: 0, 2, 4, 6, 8, 10
20–25 26–30 31–35 36–40 41–45 46–50
Ages (years)

3a. about 24% **3b.** Not very likely. Only 3 temperatures out of 51are 125°F or higher. **3c.** This information cannot be determined from the data presented in the graph. We only know the highest temperature is between 130–134 degrees Fahrenheit and the lowest is between 100–104.

5.

Calories of Fruit Bars

Number of Bars: 0, 2, 4, 6, 8, 10
0–39 40–79 80–119 120–159 160–199
Calories

7 **a.** Find the value for each interval, then add.
$12 + 8 = 20$
b. Find the value for each interval, then add to find the total.
$16 + 10 + 7 = 33$

Write a ratio comparing the part to the base.
$\frac{33}{53} \approx 0.62$ or 62%
c. The tallest bar is 60–69.99, so that is the price most shoes are likely to cost.

9a. Sample answer: By counting the heights of the bars, there are 75 students represented in the graph. You can find the number of students in each 10-minute span. The students in the survey spent at least 11 minutes on the Internet. Eighty percent of students spent at least 31 minutes on the Internet. **9b.** Since exact data values are not listed, you are not able to find any measure of central tendency. However, the median is located in the 41-50 minute time period by counting the number of students in each time period.

11 **a.** There have been 25 summer Olympic games. In 52% of the games, the country that won the medal count won at least 100 medals.
b. The intervals along the x-axis are not equal. Because the intervals are not equal, the data is distributed unevenly.
c. The data could be rearranged into intervals of 50. Then the histogram would give a more accurate representation of the data.

13. Sample answer: 10, 12, 15, 19, 20, 25, 26, 31, 31, 31, 33, 36, 50, 52, 55, 57, 58, 59

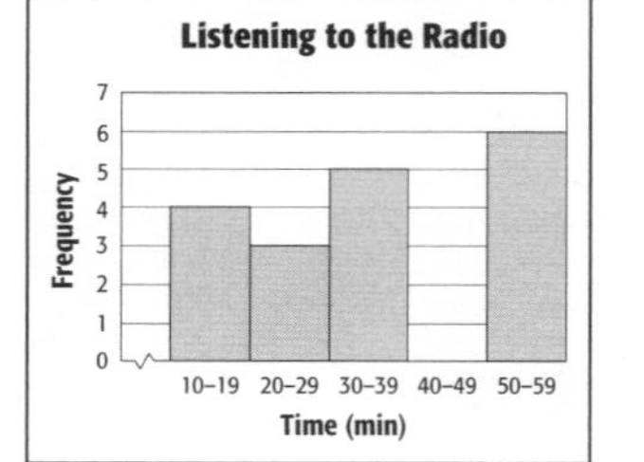

17. D

19.

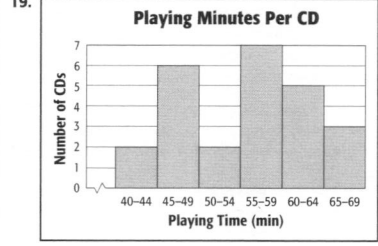

Playing Minutes Per CD

Number of CDs: 0, 1, 2, 3, 4, 5, 6, 7
40–44 45–49 50–54 55–59 60–64 65–69
Playing Time (min)

21.

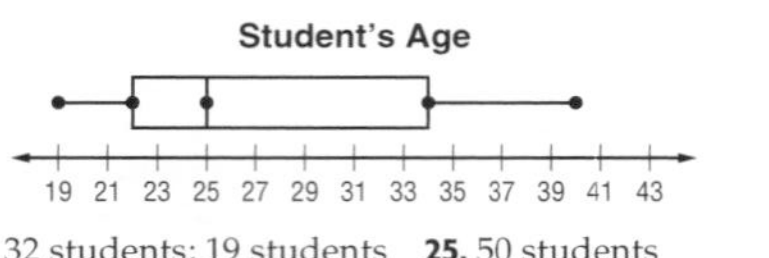

23. 32 students; 19 students **25.** 50 students

Pages 768–770 *Lesson 13-6*

1. $\frac{1}{10}$ or 10%. **3.** $\frac{2}{5}$ or 40%. **5.** $\frac{1}{4}$ or 25% **7.** 5:21

9 $P(20) = \frac{\text{number of sections labeled 20}}{\text{total number of sections}}$
$= \frac{1}{20}$
$= 5\%$

11. $\frac{1}{2}$ or 50% **13.** $\frac{1}{5}$ or 20%

15a.

(1, 1)	(1, 2)	(1, 3)	(1, 4)
(2, 1)	(2, 2)	(2, 3)	(2, 4)
(3, 1)	(3, 2)	(3, 3)	(3, 4)
(4, 1)	(4, 2)	(4, 3)	(4, 4)

15b. $\frac{1}{2}$ or 50% **15c.** $\frac{1}{4}$ or 25% **17.** 2:1 **19a.** 1140

19b. 1380

21 **a.** First, find the total number of students.
$8 + 6 + 4 + 15 + 7 = 40$
15 of the 40 students' favorite sport is skateboarding.
$\frac{15}{40} = \frac{3}{8}$ or 37.5%

b. Use the percent proportion.
$\frac{6}{40} = \frac{p}{100}$
$6 \cdot 100 = 40 \cdot p$
$600 = 40p$
$15 = p$
15% of the students chose inline skating. Use the percent proportion to predict.
$\frac{p}{800} = \frac{15}{100}$
$p \cdot 100 = 800 \cdot 15$
$100p = 12{,}000$
$p = 120$
120 students should chose inline skating.

c. Use the percent proportion.
Students that prefer BMX:
$\frac{8}{40} = \frac{p}{100}$
$8 \cdot 100 = 40 \cdot p$
$800 = 40p$
$20 = p$
20% of the students chose inline skating. Use the percent proportion to predict.
$\frac{p}{800} = \frac{20}{100}$
$p \cdot 100 = 800 \cdot 20$
$100p = 16{,}000$
$p = 160$
160 students should chose BMX. Students that prefer MotoX:
$\frac{4}{40} = \frac{p}{100}$
$4 \cdot 100 = 40 \cdot p$
$400 = 40p$
$10 = p$
20% of the students chose inline skating. Use the percent proportion to predict.
$\frac{p}{800} = \frac{10}{100}$
$p \cdot 100 = 800 \cdot 10$
$100p = 8{,}000$
$p = 80$
80 students should chose MotoX.
$160 - 80 = 80$
So, 80 more students prefer BMX.

23. 48 **25.** Sample answer: The theoretical probability is $\frac{7}{35}$ or 20%. So, she would expect to select a navy pair of sock 4 out of 20 times. Since she selected a navy pair 6 times, her probability experimental of $\frac{6}{20}$ or 30%, exceeded her theoretical probability. **27.** F **29.** D **31a.** Since SUVs average the least miles per gallon, they tend to be less fuel-efficient. **31b.** The most fuel-efficient SUV and the least fuel-efficient sedan both average 22 miles per gallon. **33.** 900 **35.** 12,960

Pages 773–776 *Lesson 13-7*

1 This sample is biased and is a convenience sample because it is easy to survey students on one bus.

3. unbiased, stratified random sample; the shoppers are first divided into non-overlapping groups and then 1 male and 1 female is selected randomly from each group **5.** unbiased, simple random sample; the students are randomly selected

7 This sample is biased and is a voluntary response survey because those teenagers who are interested in participating in the survey are part of the sample.

9. This sampling method is not valid because it will include students who do not attend your school. So, the results can not lead to a reasonable conclusion. **11.** Yes; this is a systematic random survey because the sample is selected according to an interval; 1225 **13.** No; only 80 out of 300 customers agree. From this random survey, you can predict that only about 27% of the customers would like a foreign movie section, so the store should not add such an area.

15 a. Sample answer: Send out a survey to all students is the school.
b. Sample Answer:
1. What is your favorite carnival game?
2. Which game would you play first?
3. If you could only play one game, which one would it be?

c. They could determine which games most students would play and which would raise the most money.

17. Sample answer: unbiased survey: Survey your classmates about their favorite sport.; See student's work. **19.** yes: Sample answer: If questions are asked in a neutral tone, then a more accurate answer can be expected. However, if the person asking the questions changes their tone of voice it can persuade someone to give an inaccurate response. **21.** B **23.** J **25.** $\frac{1}{6}$; 16.7% **27.** 146.9%; increase **29.** 23.9 **31.** 75% **33.** $66\frac{2}{3}$%

Pages 779–781 *Lesson 13-8*

1. 6 pairs

Color	Size	Outcome
white	6	white, 6
	7	white, 7
	8	white, 8
grey	6	grey, 6
	7	grey, 7
	8	grey, 8

3. 144 **5.** $\frac{1}{64}$

7 8 outcomes

Question 1	Question 2	Question 3	Outcome
T	T	T	T, T, T
		F	T, T, F
	F	T	T, F, T
		F	T, F, F
F	T	T	F, T, T
		F	F, T, F
	F	T	F, F, T
		F	F, F, F

9. 24 **11.** 1000

13 a. P(same number on both dice) = P(1 on both dice) + P(2 on both dice) + P(3 on both dice) + P(4 on both dice) + P(5 on both dice) + P(6 on both dice)

P(1 on both dice)
$$= \frac{1}{10} \cdot \frac{1}{6} \text{ or } \frac{1}{60}$$
So, P(same number on both dice)
$$= \frac{1}{60} + \frac{1}{60} + \frac{1}{60} + \frac{1}{60} + \frac{1}{60} + \frac{1}{60}$$
$$= \frac{6}{60} \text{ or } \frac{1}{10}$$

b. P(odd, even) or P(odd, even)
$$= \frac{5}{10} \cdot \frac{3}{6} + \frac{5}{10} \cdot \frac{3}{6}$$
$$= \frac{1}{4} + \frac{1}{4}$$
$$= \frac{1}{2}$$

15a. $\frac{7}{16}$ **15b.** $\frac{1}{4}$ **17.** Neither girl is correct. Cameron added the possibilities and she should have multiplied them. Lisa multiplied the wrong possibilities. **19.** 5^x **21.** A **23.** C **25.** No; this is a biased sample. The students who participate in band are more likely to enjoy music, so more of them may say music is their favorite class, than compared to the entire school population. **27a.** 20; 36 **27b.** Chicken; whereas chicken sandwiches have 8–20 grams of fat, burgers have 10–36 grams of fat **27c.** chicken: R: 12; UQ: 18.5; LQ: 13; M: 15; IE: 5.5; outliers: none; burgers: R: 26; UQ: 31.5; LQ: 17; M: 23; IR: 14.5; outliers: none **29.** 6 **31.** 12

Pages 785–788 *Lesson 13-9*

1. 1,320 ways

3 Label her books A, B, C, D, E, and F
List all possibilities:

AB	AC	AD	AE	AF
~~BA~~	BC	BD	BE	BF
~~CA~~	~~CB~~	CD	CE	CF
~~DA~~	~~DB~~	~~DC~~	DE	DF
~~EA~~	~~EB~~	~~EC~~	~~ED~~	EF
~~FA~~	~~FB~~	~~FC~~	~~FD~~	~~FE~~

Cross out those that are the same. There are 15 possible ways.
5. 120 **7.** 504 ways **9.** 10 **11.** $\frac{1}{120}$ **13.** 360

15 $C(7, 7) = \frac{7 \cdot 6 \cdot 5 \cdot 4 \cdot 3 \cdot 2 \cdot 1}{7 \cdot 6 \cdot 5 \cdot 4 \cdot 3 \cdot 2 \cdot 1} = 1$

17. 240,240 **19.** 12,650 **21.** combination; 66
23. permutation; 5040 **25.** $\frac{1}{5}$

27 best of three: win first 2, win last 2, win first and last or $C(3, 2)$: 3 ways

best of five: $C(5, 3)$: $\frac{5 \cdot 4 \cdot 3}{3 \cdot 2 \cdot 1} = 10$ ways

best of seven: $C(7, 4)$: $\frac{7 \cdot 6 \cdot 5 \cdot 4}{4 \cdot 3 \cdot 2 \cdot 1} = 35$ ways

29a. 10,000 **29b.** Since there are 10,000 different PINs, there is only a $\frac{1}{10,000}$ chance that someone could guess the PIN. **31.** 15 teams **33.** Sample answer: the number of five-person committees that could be formed from a group of 15 people. **35.** mental math; P(10, 10) = 10 • P(9, 9) so 10 × 362,880 = 3,628,800. **37.** Sample answer: A combination could be used to find 9 batters from a baseball team with 20 players. A permutation would be used if the 9 batters are to bat in a particular order. in the first situation, the batters would hit in any order, while in the second they would hit in a determined order. **39.** G **41.** permutation; 154,440 **43.** biased, convenience sample; Sara is only surveying people who probably like chocolate and not other types of desserts

45. $a \geq 6$ (number line: 3 4 5 6 7 8 9 10)

47. $y > -3$ (number line: −6 −5 −4 −3 −2 −1 0 1 2)

49. $\frac{1}{18}$ **51.** $\frac{1}{27}$

Pages 793–795 *Lesson 13-10*

1. $\frac{1}{10}$ **3.** $\frac{7}{80}$

5 $P(\text{heads and } 4) = \frac{1}{2} \cdot \frac{1}{6} = \frac{1}{12}$

7. $\frac{1}{3}$ **9.** $\frac{1}{56}$ **11.** $\frac{1}{12}$ **13.** $\frac{1}{20}$ **15.** $\frac{4}{7}$ **17.** $\frac{1}{7}$

19. $\frac{1}{91}$

21 P(they match) = P(2 blue socks) + P(2 black socks) + P(2 white socks)
$$= \frac{6}{24} \cdot \frac{5}{23} + \frac{8}{24} \cdot \frac{7}{23} + \frac{10}{24} \cdot \frac{9}{23}$$
$$= \frac{176}{552} \text{ or } \frac{22}{69}$$

23a. 0.2401 **23b.** 0.0576 **23c.** Independent; Making one field goal does not typically affect making another one.

25.

First	Second
R	R Y B G
Y	R Y B G
B	R Y B G
G	R Y B G

$\frac{1}{16}$; independent event **27.** 37.5% **29.** Shannon; rolling a difference of 0 or 1 are mutually exclusive events so the probability of rolling a difference of 0 must be added to the probability of rolling a difference of 1. **31.** A **33.** G **35.** P; 720 ways **37.** C; 210 ways **39a.** 9 **39b.** $\frac{1}{9}$

Pages 798–802 *Study Guide and Review*

1. mean **3.** tree diagram **5.** box-and-whisker plot **7.** range **9.** 22.4; 22; 22
11. 2.1; 2; 1.5, 2, 2.5
13. **Heights of Football Players**

Stem	Leaf
6	8 9
7	0 1 1 2 2 3 3 4 5 6

6|8 = 68 in.

15. Frank; whereas Frank's times range from 0.8-2.0 minutes, Shandra's times range from 1.3-2.1 minutes. **17.** R: 4; UQ: 8; LQ: 6; M: 6.5; IR 2; none **19.** The spread of the data is 41 points. The median is 82 points. One fourth of the students, earned 76 points or less. One fourth of the students earned 87.5 points or more. Half of the students earned between 76 and 87.5 points.

21.

Number of Siblings

Frequency: 0 2 4 6 8 10 12 14 16 18 20
Number of Siblings: 0–1 2–3 4–5

23. $\frac{1}{3}$ **25.** $\frac{13}{15}$ **27.** Biased, convenience sample; Diners at a steakhouse are more likely to choose steak as their favorite meal. **29.** 4 **31.** 216 **33.** 12 **35.** 59,280 combinations **37.** 26,334
39. $\frac{28}{153}$ **41.** $\frac{10}{153}$

For Homework Help, go to Hotmath.com

Photo Credits

Cover i: (c) SW Productions/Brand X/CORBIS, (bkgd) Jason Reed/Photodisc/Getty Images; **v** Creatus/Punchstock; **P1** Jack Sullivan/Alamy; **P2** Jack Sullivan/Alamy; **P7** BananaStock/Jupiter Images; **P9** Bill Aron/PhotoEdit; **P10** Guy Motil/CORBIS; **P11** Robert W. Ginn/Alamy; **P12** Rick Rickman/NewSport/CORBIS; **P13** Matt King/Getty Images; **P15** Erik Dreyer/Taxi/Getty Images; **P16** H. Mark Weidman Photography/Alamy; **P21** Mira/Alamy; **2-3** Ron Chapple/Jupiter Images; **7** Ted Soqui/CORBIS; **11** Don Farrall/Getty Images; **12** Franck Guiziou/Hemis/CORBIS; **13** moodboard/CORBIS; **15** Anthony-Masterson/Getty Images; **18** ed-imaging; **22** Jason Reed/Reuters/CORBIS; **27** Stephen Frink/Getty Images; 29 Lee Foster/Alamy; **31** (l) G.K. & Vikki Hart/Getty Images, (r) Photodisc/PunchStock; **33** Stephen Frink/Science Faction/Getty Images; **34** vario images GmbH & Co. KG/Alamy; **36** Jeff Greenberg/PhotoEdit; **39** Laura Sifferlin; **41** ThinkStock LLC/Index Stock Imagery; **42** Dex Image/CORBIS; **44** Radius Images/Jupiter Images; **45** Superstudio/ Iconica/Getty Images; **54** Colin Young-Wolff/PhotoEdit, Inc.; **58-59** Photo Network/Alamy; **62** Cosmo Condina/Stock Connection/Jupiter Images; **65** Erik Dreyer/Stone/Getty Images; **71** FLIP NICKLIN/MINDEN PICTURES; **73** Masterfile; **76** Brand X Pictures/PunchStock; **77** Cindy Charles/PhotoEdit; **79** David Stoecklein/CORBIS; **83** Stephen Frink/zefa/CORBIS; **84** © DoD/Roger-Viollet/The Image Work; **87** Visions of America/Joe Sohm/Getty Images; **90** Tyler Stableford/The Image Bank/Getty Images; **94** Peter Johnson/CORBIS; **97** Leonard de Selva/CORBIS; **99** Inti St Clair/Getty Images; **101** Bryan Rinnert/3Sight Photography; **105** AP Images; **116-117** David Papazian/Beateworks/CORBIS; (bkgd) Stockbyte/PunchStock; **121** Ed Kashi/IPN; **123** USDA; **124** Steve Hockstein/Star Ledger/CORBIS; **126** Eddie Gerald/Alamy; **132** British Museum, London, UK/Bridgeman Art Library; **136** KVLY; **137** AP Images; **143** Somos Images/CORBIS; **145** (l) Jeff Greenberg/PhotoEdit, (c and r) Larry Williams/CORBIS; **149** George Tiedemann/GT Images/CORBIS; **151** AP Images; **153** Dorling Kindersley/Getty Images; **155** Sonda Dawes/The Image Works; **157** Ian Shive/Aurora/Getty Images; **168-169** AP Images; **172** Gregg Newton/CORBIS; **175** Alan Schein Photography/CORBIS; **178** Duomo/CORBIS; **179** Pictorial Parade/Hulton Archive/Getty Images; **180** JupiterImages/Thinkstock/Alamy; **184** Thomas Northcut/Digital Vision/Getty Images; **186** Michael Newman/PhotoEdit; **188** Bill Heinsohn/Photographer's Choice/Getty Images; **191** Creatas/Jupiter Images; **192** Jeremy Woodhouse/Getty Images; **195** Howie Garber/Photographer's Choice/Getty Images; **199** Marvin E. Newman/Photographer's Choice/Getty Images; **201** Mario Tama/Getty Images; **203** Bob Daemmrich/PhotoEdit; **205** Edward Pond/Masterfile; **208** Kayte M. Deioma/PhotoEdit; **214** ed-imaging; **218-219** Picturenet/Blend Images/Getty Images; **221** David Madison/Getty Images; **222** The British Library/HIP/The Image Works; **224** Jeff Pape/New Bremen Giant Pumpkin Growers; **230** Bob Daemmrich/PhotoEdit; **232** Alaska Stock; **235** David McNew/Getty Images; **238** David Stluka/Getty Images; **243** Robert Harding/Getty Images; **245** Courtesy Ohio Expo Center; **246** Peter Dazeley/Photographer's Choice/Getty Images; **248** Tetra Images/Alamy; **249** Chris Farina/CORBIS; **252** AP Images; **258** Kelly Redinger/Design Pics/CORBIS; **262-263** Martin Beddall/Alamy; **267** (l) Buzzshotz/Alamy; (r) Martin Barraud/Riser/Getty Images; **268** Elsa/Getty Images; **270** AP Images; **271** Stuart Westmorland/Getty Images; **273** Karl Weatherly/CORBIS; **275** Nation Bill/CORBIS SYGMA; **277** Kevin Schafer/Riser/Getty Images; **279** Ralf-Finn Hestoft/CORBIS; **283** Michael Newman/PhotoEdit, Inc.; **289** moodboard/CORBIS; **291** Julie Hollern; **294** Steffen Schmidt/epa/CORBIS; **296** Dennis MacDonald/PhotoEdit; **297** Bob Thomas/CORBIS; **298** Thinkstock/Jupiter Images; **301** Digital Art/CORBIS; **301** Digital Art/CORBIS; **305** CORBIS; **307** David Young-Wolff/PhotoEdit; **310** Fendis/zefa/CORBIS; **315** Bettmann/CORBIS; **328-329** John Capella/Sports Imagery/Getty Images; **331** Photodisc/Getty Images; **332** The Stapleton Collection/The Bridgeman Art Library International; **333** Radius Images/Alamy; **335** Glowimages/Getty Images; **337** PureStock/Jupiter Images; **339** Don Mason/CORBIS; **341** SERGIO MORAES/Reuters/CORBIS; **345** Dasha Wright/Jupiter Images; **347** WireImage/Getty Images; **348** David Young-Wolff/PhotoEdit; **349** Joe Murphy/NBAE via Getty Image; **351** Comstock Images/Alamy; **352** ed-imaging; **353** Gabe Palmer/Alamy; **354** K. & H. Benser/zefa/CORBIS; **357** STAN HONDA/AFP/Getty Images; **359** Getty Images; **360** Brand X Pictures/Jupiter Images; **361** Bruno de Hogues/Sygma/CORBIS; **364** PhotoLink/Getty Images; **366** Robert Laberge/Getty Images; **367** Clive Rose/Getty Images; **368** Arthur Pollock/America 24-7/Getty Images; **370** David Young-Wolff/PhotoEdit; **373** ML Harris/Getty Images; **377** John Zoiner/Workbook Stock/Jupiter Images; **380** Clive Mason/Getty Images; **388** ed-imaging; **392-393** Art Wolfe/Getty Images; **396** State Central Artillery Museum, St. Petersburg, Russia Bridgeman Art Library; **399** Colin Young-Wolff/PhotoEdit; **401** Ablestock/Images.com/IPN; **402** Peter Mason/Getty Images; **404** AP Images; **406** CORBIS/PunchStock; **407** Michael Newman/PhotoEdit; **410** Lee Snider/The Image Works; **412** Darryl Leniuk/Getty Images; **413** STAN HONDA/AFP/Getty Images; **414** ed-imaging; **416** Colin Gray/Getty Images; **418** IPS Co., Ltd./Beateworks/CORBIS; **420** Envision/CORBIS; **423** GERARD LACZ/Animals Animals - Earth Scenes; **426** Horizons Companies; **427** Paul A. Souders/CORBIS; **429** Corey Rich/Aurora Photos; **433** Photo by Getty Images for John Deere; **435** Terry Whittaker/Photo Researchers, Inc.; **437** AP Images; **438** Clayton Sharrard/PhotoEdit; **439** Kevin

401 Ablestock/Images.com/IPN; **402** Peter Mason/Getty Images; **404** AP Images; **406** CORBIS/PunchStock; **407** Michael Newman/PhotoEdit; **410** Lee Snider/The Image Works; **412** Darryl Leniuk/Getty Images; **413** STAN HONDA/AFP/Getty Images; **414** ed-imaging; **416** Colin Gray/Getty Images; **418** IPS Co., Ltd./Beateworks/CORBIS; **420** Envision/CORBIS; **423** GERARD LACZ/Animals Animals - Earth Scenes; **426** Horizons Companies; **427** Paul A. Souders/CORBIS; **429** Corey Rich/Aurora Photos; **433** Photo by Getty Images for John Deere; **435** Terry Whittaker/Photo Researchers, Inc.; **437** AP Images; **438** Clayton Sharrard/PhotoEdit; **439** Kevin Dodge/CORBIS; **443** Frances M. Roberts/Alamy; **446** Jon Hicks/CORBIS; **449** Benjamin Collier/Aurora Photos; **453** Kitt Cooper-Smith/Alamy; **456** David Young-Wolff/PhotoEdit; **468–469** Antonio M. Rosario/Stone/Getty Images; **471** ERWIN & PEGGY BAUER/Animals Animals - Earth Scenes; **472** AP Images; **474** AP Images; **476** BananaStock/Jupiter Images; **476** DreamPictures/Pam Ostrow/Blend; **479** The Granger Collection, New York; **481** RubberBall/Alamy; **483** Courtesy NSSDC Goddard Space Flight Center/NASA; **484** David Wrobel/Visuals Unlimited/Getty Images; **486** Brand X Pictures/PunchStock; **487** Art Wolfe/Stone/Getty Images; **489** Dana White/PhotoEdit; **490** Peter Miller/Iconica/Getty Images; **493** NASA; **494** MICHAEL & PATRICIA FOGDEN/Minden Pictures; **496** C Squared Studios/Getty Images; **497** Image Source/PunchStock; **501** Micro Discovery/CORBIS; **506** Hans Neleman/Stone/Getty Images; **513** James Marshall/CORBIS; **516** GK Hart/Vikki Hart/Getty Images; **517** Sean Justice/Riser/Getty Images; **519** S. Lowry/Univ Ulster/Stone/Getty Images; **521** ed-imaging; **528** ed-imaging; **532–533** Mark A. Johnson/CORBIS; **537** Brad Perks Lightscapes/Alamy; **538** Courtesy of Inter University Centre for Astronomy and Astrophysics/Dinodia; **539** dk/Alamy; **540** Cedar Point Amusement Park/Resort; **541** AP Images; **543** Cedar Point Amusement Park/Resort; **545** Peter Poby/zefa/CORBIS; **547** Getty Images; **550** Steve Vidler/SuperStock; **551** DEA PICTURE LIBRARY/Getty Images; **553** Martin Harvey/Alamy; **554** REUTERS/Mike Blake; **562** Chris A Crumley/Alamy; **566** Bilderbuch/Design Pics/CORBIS; **569** Jeff Greenberg/Alamy; **573** Todd Bigelow/Aurora Photos; **575** david pearson/Alamy; **579** Photodisc/Getty Images **582** ed-imaging; **586–587** Creatas Images/Jupiter Images; **593** (l) AP Images; **593** (r) Richard Cummins/SuperStock; **594** Comstock Images/PunchStock; **598** Tim Gainey/Alamy; **600** (l) Inmagine/Jupiter Images, (r) Darren Baker/Alamy; **602** (l) Robert Harding/Getty Images, (r) Courtesy National Gallery of Art, Washington DC; © 2010 Estate of Tony Smith/Artist Rights Society, NY; **603** UpperCut Images/Alamy; **605** Eric Nathan/PhotoShelter; **609** (l) Al Bello/Getty Images, (cl) Dennis O'Clair/Stone/Getty Images, (cr) Mike Powell/Getty Images, (r) Pete Saloutos/UpperCut Images/Getty Images; **613** John Kolesidis/Reuters/CORBIS; **615** (l) Oxford Scientific/Jupiter Images, (r) Hugh Lansdown/Alamy; **619** Comstock Images/Alamy; **621** The Granger Collection, New York; **627** Adam Crowley/Getty Images; **633** Stuart Westmorland/Riser/Getty Images; **634** Gregory Dunham; **636** plainpicture/Bornkessel, E./Jupiter Images; **637** David Stluka/Getty Images; **640** PureStock/Jupiter Images; **642** Stockbyte; **645** Hiep Vu/Masterfile; **646** Leo Keeler/Alamy; **652–653** Photodisc/Getty Images; **653** Photodisc Collection/Getty Images; **656** Bob Rowan; Progressive Image/CORBIS; **660–661** Andrea Jones/Alamy; **664** Kelly Redinger/Design Pics/CORBIS; **666** (l) Classic Image/Alamy, (r) Lester V. Bergman/CORBIS; **668** (t) Brand X Pictures/PunchStock, (bl) SuperStock, Inc./SuperStock/The Isamu Noguchi Foundation and Garden Museum, NY Artist Rights Society, NY, (bc) CORBIS/SuperStock, (br) Walter Bibikow/CORBIS; **670** ed-imaging; **672** EPA; **675** Brand X Pictures/Jupiter Images; **677** WidStock/Alamy; **678** James P. Blair/CORBIS; **679** Chloe Johnson/Alamy; **681** (l) Focal Depth/Alamy, (r) Matthias Kulka/zefa/CORBIS; **685** Frances Roberts/Alamy; **686** (l) Design and Photo © Barbara Butler; www.barbarabutler.com, (c) Getty Images/Photodisc, (r) FoodPhotography Eising/Stockfood; **687** Ed-Imaging; **692** Duomo/CORBIS; **694** Image Source Black/Alamy; **698** AP Images; **699** (t) Tannen Maury/epa/CORBIS, (b) Stockbyte Silver/Alamy; **700** CORBIS; **702** Jack Sullivan/Alamy; **703** The Granger Collection, New York; **706** Ron Chapple Stock/Alamy; **709** Rodolfo Arpia/Alamy; **712** Nik Wheeler/CORBIS; **713** Burke/Triolo Productions/Getty Images; **714** Tania Reinicke/Bilderberg/Aurora Photos; **722** Will & Deni McIntyre/CORBIS; **726–727** Elizabeth Kreutz/NewSport/CORBIS; **729** CORBIS/PunchStock; **732** Richard Klune/CORBIS; **734** Neal Preston/CORBIS; **738** Greg Von Doersten/Aurora/Getty Images; **740** William Perlman/Star Ledger/CORBIS; **741** Michael Zito/SportsChrome, Inc; **745** Hemera Technologies/Jupiter Images; **746** Geoff du Feu/Alamy; **748** Toshio Hoshi/Jupiter Images; **752** Bruce Bennett/Getty Images; **753** StockTrek/Getty Images; **754** Reuters/CORBIS; **760** Spencer Grant/PhotoEdit; **761** BOCOG - HANDOUT/epa/CORBIS; **765** Brian Hagiwara/Jupiter Images; **766** Roger-Viollet/The Image Works; **769** Jeff Gross/Getty Images; **772** David Young-Wolff/PhotoEdit; **774** Lester Lefkowitz/CORBIS; **775** MIXA/Getty Images; **778** Marc Romanelli/Photographer's Choice/Getty Images; **780** Raquel Ramirez/PhotoEdit; **784** Brand X Pictures; **787** Jeff Gross/Getty Images; **792** AP Images; **794** Zefa RF/Alamy; **796** ed-imaging; **804** ed-imaging; **808** Eclipse Studios; **LA0–LA1** TOM MARESCHAL/Alamy; **LA2** Burke/Triolo/Brand X Pictures/Jupiterimages, (inset) Ryan McVay/Getty Images, (inset) The McGraw-Hill Companies, Inc./Ken Cavanagh photographer; **LA6** Steve Hamblin/Alamy; **LA7** Ingolf Pompe/Aurora Photos; **LA9** David Young-Wolff/PhotoEdit; **LA14** Don Hammond/DesignPics/IPN; **LA21** Lew Robertson/Brand X/CORBIS; **LA22** John W. Banagan/Getty Images; **LA28** Christian Liewig/Liewig Media Sports/CORBIS

Glossary/Glosario

Math Online

A mathematics multilingual eGlossary is available at glencoe.com. The glossary includes the following languages:

Arabic	Haitian Creole	Portuguese	Tagalog
Bengali	Hmong	Russian	Urdu
Cantonese	Korean	Spanish	Vietnamese
English			

Cómo usar el glosario en español:

1. Busca el término en inglés que desees encontrar.
2. El término en español, junto con la definición, se encuentran en la columna de la derecha.

English	Español
A	
absolute value (p. 63) The distance a number is from zero on the number line.	**valor absoluto** Distancia que un número dista de cero en la recta numérica.
accuracy (p. 879) The degree of conformity of a measurement with the true value.	**exactitud** Grado de conformidad de una medida con el valor verdadero.
acute angle (p. 551) An angle with a measure greater than 0° and less than 90°.	**ángulo agudo** Ángulo con una medida mayor que 0° y menor que 90°.
acute triangle (p. 552) A triangle that has three acute angles.	**triángulo acutángulo** Triángulo que posee tres ángulos agudos.
Addition Property of Equality (p. 184) If you add the same number to each side of an equation, the two sides remain equal.	**Propiedad de adición de la igualdad** Si sumas el mismo número a ambos lados de una ecuación, los dos lados permanecen iguales.
additive inverses (p. 71) An integer and its opposite.	**inverso aditivo** Un entero y su opuesto.
adjacent angles (p. 590) Two angles that have the same vertex, share a common side, and do not overlap.	**ángulos adyacentes** Dos ángulos que poseen el mismo vértice, comparten un lado y no se traslapan.
algebra (p. 11) A branch of mathematics dealing with symbols.	**álgebra** Rama de las matemáticas que tiene que ver con signos.
algebraic expression (p. 11) An expression that contains sums and/or products of variables and numbers.	**expresión algebraica** Expresión que contiene sumas y/o productos de números y variables.
alternate exterior angles (p. 590) Nonadjacent exterior angles found on opposite sides of the transversal. In the figure below, $\angle 1$ and $\angle 7$, $\angle 2$ and $\angle 8$ are alternate exterior angles.	**ángulos alternos externos** Ángulos exteriores no adyacentes que se encuentran en lados opuestos de una transversal. En la siguiente figura, $\angle 1$ y $\angle 7$, $\angle 2$ y $\angle 8$ son ángulos alternos externos.

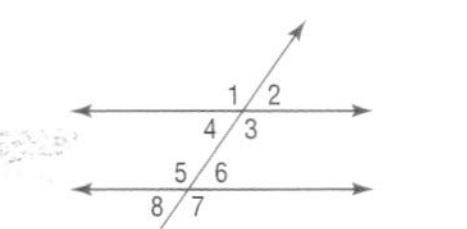

alternate interior angles (p. 590) Nonadjacent interior angles found on opposite sides of the transversal. In the figure on page R63, $\angle 4$ and $\angle 6$, $\angle 3$ and $\angle 5$ are alternate interior angles.

ángulos alternos internos Ángulos interiores no adyacentes que se encuentran en lados opuestos de una transversal. En la figura anterior, $\angle 4$ y $\angle 6$, $\angle 3$ y $\angle 5$ son ángulos alternos internos.

altitude (p. 624) A line segment that is perpendicular to the base of a figure with endpoints on the base and the side opposite the base.

altura Segmento de recta perpendicular a la base de una figura y cuyos extremos yacen en la base y en el lado opuesto de la base.

angle (p. 868) Two rays with a common endpoint form an angle. The rays and vertex are used to name an angle. The angle below is $\angle ABC$.

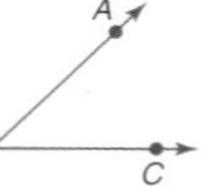

ángulo Dos rayos con un punto común forman un ángulo. Los rayos y el vértice se usan para identificar el ángulo. El siguiente ángulo es $\angle ABC$.

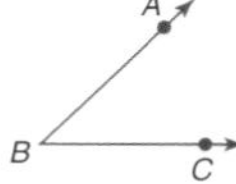

angle bisector (p. 872) A ray that divides an angle into two congruent angles.

bisectriz de un ángulo Semirrecta que divide un ángulo en dos ángulos congruentes.

area (p. 222) The measure of the surface enclosed by a geometric figure.

área Medida de la superficie que encierra una figura geométrica.

arithmetic sequence (p. 401) A sequence in which the difference between any two consecutive terms is the same.

sucesión aritmética Sucesión en que la diferencia entre dos términos consecutivos cualesquiera es siempre la misma.

Associative Property (p. 18) The way in which numbers are grouped when added or multiplied does not change the sum or product.

Propiedad asociativa La forma en que se suman o multiplican dos números no altera su suma o producto.

average (p. 92) The sum of data divided by the number of items in the data set, also called the mean.

promedio Suma de los datos dividida entre el número de elementos en el conjunto de datos. También llamado media.

B

back-to-back stem-and-leaf plot (p. 738) Used to compare two sets of data. The leaves for one set of data are on one side of the stem and the leaves for the other set of data are on the other side.

diagrama de tallo y hojas consecutivo Se usa para comparar dos conjuntos de datos. Las hojas de uno de los conjuntos de datos aparecen en un lado del tallo y las del otro al otro lado de éste.

bar graph (p. 882) A graphic form using bars to make comparisons of statistics.

gráfica de barras Tipo de gráfica que usa barras para comparar estadísticas.

bar notation (p. 122) In repeating decimals, the line or bar placed over the digits that repeat. For example, $2.\overline{63}$ indicates the digits 63 repeat.

notación de barra En decimales periódicos, la línea o barra que se escribe encima de los dígitos que se repiten. Por ejemplo, en $2.\overline{63}$ la barra encima del 63 indica que los dígitos 63 se repiten.

base (p. 471) In 2^4, the base is 2. The base is used as a factor as many times as given by the exponent (4). That is, $2^4 = 2 \times 2 \times 2 \times 2$.

base En 2^4, la base es 2. La base se usa como factor las veces que indique el exponente (4). Es decir, $2^4 = 2 \times 2 \times 2 \times 2$.

base (p. 624) The base of a parallelogram or a triangle is any side of the figure. The bases of a trapezoid are the parallel sides.

base La base de un paralelogramo o de un triángulo es cualquier lado de la figura. Las bases de un trapecio son los lados paralelos.

base (p. 665) The bases of a prism are any two parallel congruent faces.

base Las bases de un prisma son cualquier par de caras paralelas y congruentes.

biased sample (p. 771) A sample that is not representative of a population.

muestra sesgada Una muestra que no es representativa de una población.

binomial (p. LA12) A polynomial with exactly two terms.

binomio Polinomio con exactamente dos términos.

boundary (p. 866) A line or curve that separates the coordinate plane into regions.

frontera Recta o curva que divide el plano de coordenadas en regiones.

box-and-whisker plot (p. 750) A diagram that divides a set of data into four parts using the median and quartiles. A box is drawn around the quartile values and whiskers extend from each quartile to the extreme data points.

diagrama de caja y patillas Diagrama que divide un conjunto de datos en cuatro partes usando la mediana y los cuartiles. Se dibuja una caja alrededor de los cuartiles y se extienden patillas de cada uno de ellos a los valores extremos.

C

cell (p. 17) A box within a spreadsheet.

celda Casilla dentro de una hoja de cálculos.

center (p. 631) The given point from which all points on the circle are the same distance.

centro Punto dado del cual equidistan todos los puntos de un círculo.

center of rotation (p. 605) A fixed point around which shapes move in a circular motion to a new position.

centro de rotación Punto fijo alrededor del cual una figura gira con un movimiento circular hasta alcanzar una nueva posición.

central angle (p. 638) An angle whose vertex is the center of a circle and whose sides intersect the circle.

ángulo central Ángulo cuyo vértice es el centro de un círculo y cuyos lados intersecan el círculo.

chord (p. 631) A segment with endpoints that are on a circle.

cuerda Segmento cuyos extremos están sobre un círculo.

circle (p. 631) The set of all points in a plane that are the same distance from a given point called the center.

círculo Conjunto de todos los puntos del plano que están a la misma distancia de un punto dado del plano llamado centro.

circle graph (p. 376) A type of statistical graph used to compare parts of a whole.

gráfica circular Tipo de gráfica estadística que se usa para comparar las partes de un todo.

circumference (p. 631) The distance around a circle.

circunferencia Longitud del contorno de un círculo.

coefficient (p. 178) The numerical part of a term that contains a variable.

coeficiente Parte numérica de un término que contiene una variable.

combination (p. 784) An arrangement or listing in which order is not important.

combinación Arreglo o lista en que el orden no es importante.

common difference (p. 401) The difference between any two consecutive terms in an arithmetic sequence.

diferencia común Diferencia entre dos términos consecutivos cualesquiera de una sucesión aritmética.

common multiples (p. 860) Multiples that are shared by two or more numbers. For example, some common multiples of 4 and 6 are 0, 12, and 24.

múltiplos comunes Múltiplos compartidos por dos o más números. Por ejemplo, algunos múltiplos comunes de 4 y 6 son 0, 12 y 24.

Commutative Property (p. 18) The order in which numbers are added or multiplied does not change the sum.

Propiedad conmutativa La forma en que se suman o multiplican dos números no altera su suma o producto.

complementary angles (p. 589) Two angles are complementary if the sum of their measures is 90°.

composite figure (p. 644) A figure that is made up of two or more shapes.

composite number (p. 476) A whole number that has more than two factors.

compound event (p. 790) Two or more simple events.

compound interest (p. 371) Interest paid on the initial principal and on interest earned in the past.

cone (p. 665) A three-dimensional figure with one circular base. A curved surface connects the base and vertex.

congruent (p. 301, 552, 598) Line segments that have the same length, or angles that have the same measure, or figures that have the same size and shape.

congruent angles (p. 871) Two angles that have the same measure.

congruent segments (p. 870) Line segments that have the same length.

constant (p. 178) A term without a variable.

constant of proportionality (p. 282) A constant ratio or unit rate of a proportion.

constant of variation (p. 420) The slope, or rate of change, in the equation $y = kx$, represented by k.

constant rate of change (p. 418) The rate of change between any two data points in a linear relationship is the same or constant.

convenience sample (p. 772) A sample which includes members of the population that are easily accessed.

converse (p. 560) The statement formed by reversing the phrases after *if* and *then* in an if-then statement.

converse of the Pythagorean Theorem (p. 560) The reversal of the *if* and *then* statement that forms the Pythagorean Theorem.

coordinate (p. 62) A number that corresponds with a point on a number line.

ángulos complementarios Dos ángulos son complementarios si la suma de sus medidas es 90°.

figura compleja Figura compuesta de dos o más formas.

número compuesto Número entero que posee más de dos factores.

evento compuesto Dos o más eventos simples.

interés compuesto Interés que se paga sobre el capital inicial y sobre el interés que se haya ganado en el pasado.

cono Figura tridimensional con una base circular, la cual posee una superficie curva que une la base con el vértice.

congruentes Segmentos de recta que tienen la misma longitud o ángulos que tienen la misma medida o figuras que poseen la misma forma y tamaño.

ángulos congruentes Ángulos que tienen la misma medida.

segmentos congruentes Segmentos de recta que tienen la misma longitud.

constante Término sin variables.

constante de proporcionalidad La razón constante o tasa unitaria de una proporción.

constante de variación La pendiente, o tasa de cambio, en la ecuación $y = kx$, representada por k.

tasa constante de cambio La tasa de cambio entre dos puntos cualesquiera en una relación lineal permanece constante o igual.

muestra de conveniencia Muestra que incluye miembros de una población fácilmente accesibles.

recíproca Un enunciado que se forma intercambiando los enunciados que vienen a continuación de *si-entonces* en un enunciado *si-entonces*.

recíproco del Teorema de Pitágoras El intercambio de las frases del enunciado *si-entonces* que forman el Teorema de Pitágoras.

coordenada Número que corresponde a un punto en la recta numérica.

coordinate plane (p. 25) Another name for the coordinate system.

coordinate system (p. 25) A coordinate system is formed by the intersection of two number lines that meet at right angles at their zero points, also called a coordinate plane.

corresponding angles (p. 590) Angles that have the same position on two different parallel lines cut by a transversal. In the figure, ∠1 and ∠5, ∠2 and ∠6, ∠3 and ∠7, ∠4 and ∠8 are corresponding angles.

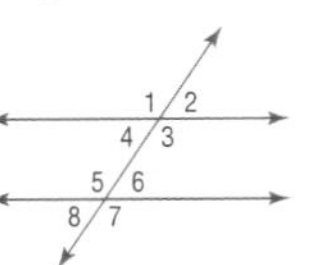

corresponding parts (pp. 301, 598) Parts of congruent or similar figures that match.

cosine (p. 877) For an acute angle of a right triangle, the ratio of the measure of the leg adjacent to the acute angle to the measure of the hypotenuse.

counterexample (p. 19) An example that shows a conjecture is not true.

cross products (p. 287) If $\frac{a}{c} = \frac{b}{d}$, then $ad = bc$. If $ad = bc$, then $\frac{a}{c} = \frac{b}{d}$.

cross section (p. 666) The intersection of a solid and a plane.

cube root (p. 862) A number that can be raised to the third power to create another number.

cubic function (p. 516) A function that can be described by an equation of the form $y = ax^3 + bx^2 + cx + d$, where $a \neq 0$.

cylinder (p. 665) A solid that has two parallel, congruent bases (usually circular) connected with a curved side.

plano de coordenadas Otro nombre para el sistema de coordenadas.

sistema de coordenadas Un sistema de coordenadas se forma de la intersección de dos rectas numéricas perpendiculares que se intersecan en sus puntos cero. También llamado plano de coordenadas.

ángulos correspondientes Ángulos que tienen la misma posición en dos rectas paralelas distintas cortadas por una transversal. En la figura, ∠1 y ∠5, ∠2 y ∠6, ∠3 y ∠7, ∠4 y ∠8 son ángulos correspondientes.

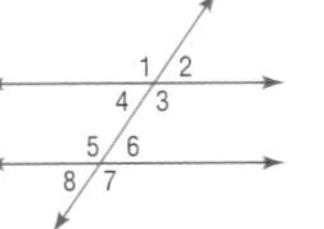

partes correspondientes Partes de figuras congruentes o semejantes que se corresponden mutuamente.

coseno Para un ángulo agudo de un triángulo rectángulo, la razón de la medida del cateto adyacente al ángulo agudo la medida de la hipotenusa.

contraejemplo Ejemplo que muestra que una conjetura no es verdadera.

productos cruzados Si $\frac{a}{c} = \frac{b}{d}$, entonces $ad = bc$. Si $ad = bc$, entonces $\frac{a}{c} = \frac{b}{d}$.

seccion transversal Intersección de un sólido con up plano.

raíz cúbica Número que se puede elevar a la tercera potencia para crear otro número.

función cúbica Función que puede describirse por una ecuación de la forma $y = ax^3 + bx^2 + cx + d$, donde $a \neq 0$.

cilindro Sólido que posee dos bases congruentes y paralelas (por lo general circulares) unidas por un lado curvo.

D

data (p. 882) Pieces of information, which are often numerical.

datos Información, la cual a menudo se presenta de manera numérica.

deductive reasoning (p. 20) The process of using facts, properties, or rules to justify reasoning or reach valid conclusions.

razonamiento deductivo Proceso de usar hechos, propiedades o reglas para justificar un razonamiento o para sacar conclusiones válidas.

defining a variable (p. 11) Choosing a variable and a quantity for the variable to represent in an equation.

definir una variable Seleccionar una variable y una cantidad para la variable que represente en la ecuación.

degree (p. 873) The most common unit of measure for angles.

grado La unidad de medida angular más común.

dependent events (p. 791) Two or more events in which the outcome of one event does affect the outcome of the other event(s).

eventos dependientes Dos o más eventos en que el resultado de uno de ellos afecta el resultado del otro o de los otros eventos.

dependent variable (p. 395) The variable in a relation with a value that depends on the value of the independent variable.

variable dependiente La variable en una relación cuyo valor depende del valor de la variable dependiente.

diagonal (p. 618) A line segment that joins two nonconsecutive vertices of a polygon.

diagonal Segmento de recta que une dos vértices no consecutivos de un polígono.

diameter (p. 631) The distance across a circle through its center.

diámetro La distancia a través de un círculo pasando por el centro.

dilation (p. 307) A transformation that alters the size of a figure but not its shape.

homotecia Transformación que altera el tamaño de una figura, pero no su forma.

dimensional analysis (p. 275) The process of including units of measurement when computing.

análisis dimensional Proceso que incorpora las unidades de medida al hacer cálculos.

dimensions (p. 886) The number of rows and columns in a matrix, with the number of rows stated first.

dimensiones El numero de filas y columnas que hay en una matriz, con el número de filas indicó primero.

direct variation (p. 420) A special type of linear equation that describes rate of change. A relationship such that as x increases in value, y increases or decreases at a constant rate.

variación directa Tipo especial de ecuación lineal que describe tasas de cambio. Relación en que a medida que x aumenta de valor, y aumenta o disminuye a una tasa constante.

discount (p. 366) The amount by which the regular price of an item is reduced.

descuento Cantidad por la que se reduce el precio normal de un artículo.

Distance Formula (p. 565) The distance between two points, with coordinates (x_1, y_1) and (x_2, y_2), is given by $d = \sqrt{(x_2 - x_1)^2 + (y_2 - y_1)^2}$.

Fórmula de la distancia La distancia entre dos puntos, con coordenadas (x_1, y_1) y (x_2, y_2), se calcula con $d = \sqrt{(x_2 - x_1)^2 + (y_2 - y_1)^2}$.

Distributive Property (p. 171) To multiply a sum by a number, multiply each number in parentheses by the number outside the parentheses.

Propiedad distributiva Para multiplicar una suma por un número, multiplica cada número en paréntesis por el número fuera del paréntesis.

divisible (p. 856) A number is divisible by another if, upon division, the remainder is zero.

divisible Un número es divisible entre otro si, al dividirlos, el residuo es cero.

Division Property of Equality (p. 191) When you divide each side of an equation by the same nonzero number, the two sides remain equal.

Propiedad de igualdad de la división Cuando divides ambos lados de una ecuación entre el mismo número no nulo, los dos lados permanecen iguales.

domain (p. 27) The domain of a relation is the set of all x-coordinates from each pair.

dominio El dominio de una relación es el conjunto de coordenadas x de todos los pares.

E

edge (p. 664) Where two planes intersect in a line.

arista Recta en donde se intersecan dos planos.

element (p. 886) Each entry in a matrix.

elemento Cada entrada de una matriz.

equation (pp. 34, 184) A mathematical sentence that contains an equals sign (=).

ecuación Enunciado matemático que contiene el signo de igualdad (=).

equilateral triangle (p. 552) A triangle with all sides congruent.

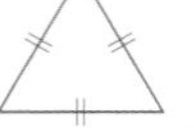

triángulo equilátero Un triángulo cuyos lados son todos congruentes.

equivalent equations (p. 184) Two or more equations with the same solution. For example, $x + 4 = 7$ and $x = 3$ are equivalent equations.

ecuaciones equivalentes Dos o más ecuaciones con las mismas soluciones. Por ejemplo, $x + 4 = 7$ y $x = 3$ son ecuaciones equivalentes.

equivalent expressions (p. 171) Expressions that have the same value.

expresiones equivalentes Expresiones que tienen el mismo valor.

evaluate (p. 6) Find the numerical value of an expression.

evaluar Calcular el valor numérico de una expresión.

experimental probability (p. 766) What actually occurs in a probability experiment.

probabilidad experimental Lo que realmente sucede en un experimento probabilístico.

exponent (p. 471) In 2^4, the exponent is 4. The exponent tells how many times the base, 2, is used as a factor. So, $2^4 = 2 \times 2 \times 2 \times 2$.

exponente En 2^4, el exponente es 4. El exponente indica cuántas veces se usa la base, 2, como factor. Así, $2^4 = 2 \times 2 \times 2 \times 2$.

exponential function (p. 516) A function that can be described by an equation of the form $y = a^x$, where $a > 0$ and $a \neq 1$.

función exponencial Función que puede describirse mediate una ecuación de la forma $y = a^x$, donde $a > 0$ y $a \neq 1$.

exterior angles (p. 590) Four of the angles formed by the transversal and two parallel lines. Exterior angles lie outside the two parallel lines.

ángulos exteriores Cuatro de los ángulos formados por una transversal y dos rectas paralelas. Los ángulos exteriores yacen fuera de las dos rectas paralelas.

F

face (p. 664) A flat surface, the side or base of a prism.

cara plana, el lado o la base de un prisma.

factor (p. 478) To write a number as a product of its factors.

factorizar Escribir un número como el producto de sues propios factores.

factored form (p. LA24) A monomial expressed as a product of prime numbers and variables and no variable has an exponent greater than 1.

forma reducida Monomio escrito como el producto de números primos y variables y en el que ninguna variable tiene un exponente mayor que 1.

factoring (p. LA24) To express a polynomial as the product of monomials and polynomials.

factorización La escritura de un polinomio como producto de monomios y polinomios.

factors (p. 856) Two or more numbers that are multiplied to form a product.

factores Dos o más números que se multiplican para formar un producto.

factor tree (p. 477) A way to find the prime factorization of a number. The factors branch out from the previous factors until all the factors are prime numbers.

family of functions (p. 439) A set of functions that is related in some way.

FOIL method (p. LA18) To multiply two binomials, find the sum of the products of the *F*irst terms, the *O*uter terms, the *I*nner terms, and the *L*ast terms.

formula (p. 221) An equation that shows a relationship among certain quantities.

frequency table (p. 757) A chart that indicates the number of values in each interval.

function (p. 33) A function is a special relation in which each element of the domain is paired with exactly one element in the range.

function notation (p. 396) A way to name a function that is defined by an equation. In function notation, the equation $y = 3x - 8$ is written as $f(x) = 3x - 8$.

function rule (p. 33) The operation performed on the input of a function.

function table (p. 33) A table organizing the input, rule, and output of a function.

Fundamental Counting Principle (p. 777) If event M can occur in m ways and is followed by event N that can occur in n ways, then the event M followed by event N can occur in $m \cdot n$ ways.

árbol de factores Forma de encontrar la factorización prima de un número. Los factores se ramifican de los factores anteriores hasta que todos los factores son números primos.

familia de funciones Conjunto de funciones con características similares.

método FOIL Para multiplicar dos binomios, busca la suma de los productos de los primeros (*F*irst) términos, los términos exteriores (*O*uter), los términos interiores (*I*nner) y los últimos términos (*L*ast).

fórmula Ecuación que muestra la relación entre ciertas cantidades.

tabla de frecuencias Tabla que indica el número de valores en cada intervalo.

función Una función es una relación especial en que a cada elemento del dominio le corresponde un único elemento del rango.

notación funcional Una manera de nombrar una función definida por una ecuación. En notación funcional, la ecuación $y = 3x - 8$ se escribe $f(x) = 3x - 8$.

regla de función Operación que se efectúa en el valor de entrada.

tabla de funciones Tabla que organiza las entradas, la regal y las salidas de una función.

Principio fundamental de contar Si el evento M puede ocurrir de m maneras y lo sigue un evento N que puede ocurrir de n maneras, entonces el evento M seguido del evento N puede ocurrir de $m \cdot n$ maneras.

G

graph (p. 26) A dot at the point that corresponds to an ordered pair on a coordinate plane.

greatest common factor (GCF) (p. 858) The greatest number that is a factor of two or more numbers.

gráfica Marca puntual en el punto que corresponde a un par ordenado en un plano de coordenadas.

máximo común divisor (MCD) El número mayor que es factor de dos o más números.

H

half-plane (p. 866) The region of the graph of an inequality on one side of a boundary.

histogram (p. 757) A histogram uses bars to display numerical data that have been organized into equal intervals.

semiplano Región de la gráfica de una desigualdad en un lado de la frontera.

histograma Un histograma usa barras para exhibir datos numéricos que han sido organizados en intervalos iguales.

hypotenuse (p. 558) The side opposite the right angle in a right triangle.

hypotenuse

hipotenusa Lado opuesto al ángulo recto en un triángulo rectángulo.

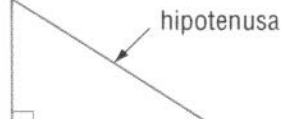

I

identity (p. 250) An equation that is true for every value of the variable.

image (p. 101) Every corresponding point on a figure after its transformation.

independent events (p. 790) Two or more events in which the outcome of one event does not influence the outcome of the other event(s).

independent variable (p. 395) The variable in a function with a value that is subject to choice.

indirect measurement (p. 313) Using the properties of similar triangles to find measurements that are difficult to measure directly.

inequality (pp. 62, 234) A mathematical sentence that contains $<, >, \neq, \leq$, or $\geq$.

integer (p. 61) The whole numbers and their opposites.

$$\ldots, -3, -2, -1, 0, 1, 2, 3, \ldots$$

interest (p. 370) The amount of money paid or earned for the use of money.

interior angle (p. 618) An angle inside a polygon.

interior angles (p. 590) Four of the angles formed by the transversal and two parallel lines. Interior angles lie between the two parallel lines.

interquartile range (p. 744) The range of the middle half of a set of data. It is the difference between the upper quartile and the lower quartile.

inverse operation (p. 184) Operation that undoes another, such as addition and subtraction.

inverse proportion (p. 293) A relationship formed when the product of two variables is a constant.

irrational number (p. 543) A number that cannot be expressed as $\frac{a}{b}$, where a and b are integers and b does not equal 0.

identidad Ecuación que es verdadera para cada valor de la variable.

imagen Todo punto correspondiente de una figura después de ser transformación.

eventos independientes Dos o más eventos en que el resultado de uno de ellos no afecta el resultado del otro o de los otros eventos.

variable independiente La variable de una función sujeta a elección.

medición indirecta Uso de las propiedades de triángulos semejantes para hacer mediciones que son difíciles de realizar directamente.

desigualdad Enunciado matemático que contiene $<, >, \neq, \leq$, o $\geq$.

enteros Los números enteros y sus opuestos.

$$\ldots, -3, -2, -1, 0, 1, 2, 3, \ldots$$

interés Cantidad que se cobra o se paga por el uso del dinero.

ángulo interno ángulo ubicado dentro de un polígono.

ángulos interiores Cuatro de los ángulos formados por una transversal y dos rectas paralelas. Los ángulos interiores están entre las dos rectas paralelas.

amplitud intercuartílica Amplitud de la mitad central de un conjunto de datos. Es la diferencia entre el cuartil superior y el inferior.

operaciones inversas Operaciones que se anulan mutuamente, como la adición y la sustracción.

proporción inversa Una relación formó cuando el producto de dos variables es una constante.

número irracional Número que no puede escribirse como $\frac{a}{b}$, donde a y b son enteros y b no es igual a 0.

isosceles triangle (p. 552) A triangle that has at least two congruent sides.

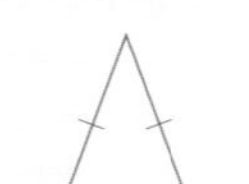

L

lateral area (p. 691) The sum of the areas of the lateral faces of a solid.

lateral faces (p. 691) The lateral faces of a prism, cylinder, pyramid, or cone are all the surfaces of the figure except the base or bases.

least common multiple (LCM) (p. 860) The least of the nonzero common multiples of two or more numbers. The LCM of 4 and 6 is 12.

leaf (p. 737) In a stem-and-leaf plot, the next greatest place value of the data after the stem forms the leaves.

legs (p. 558) The sides that are adjacent to the right angle of a right triangle.

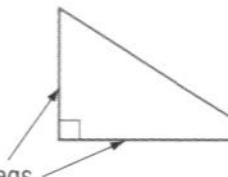

like fractions (p. 147) Fractions that have the same denominator.

like terms (p. 178) Expressions that contain the same variables to the same power, such as $2n$ and $5n$ or $6xy^2$ and $4xy^2$.

line (p. 868) A never-ending straight path.

line graph (p. 882) A type of statistical graph used to show how values change over a period of time.

line of fit (p. 448) On a scatter plot, a line drawn that is very close to most of the data points. The line that best fits the data.

line of symmetry (p. 101) Each half of a figure is a mirror image of the other half when a line of symmetry is drawn.

line plot (p. 550) A diagram that shows the frequency of data on a number line.

line segment (p. 550) Part of a line containing two endpoints and all the points between them.

triángulo isósceles Triángulo que posee por lo menos dos lados congruentes.

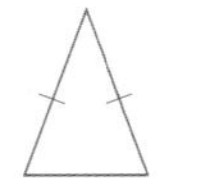

área lateral Suma de las áreas de las caras laterales de un sólido.

caras laterales Las caras laterales de un prisma, cilindro, pirámide o cono son todas las superficies de la figura, excluyendo la base o las bases.

mínimo común múltiplo (mcm) El menor de los múltiplos comunes no nulos de dos o más números. El MCM de 4 y 6 es 12.

hojas En un diagrama de tallo y hojas, las hojas las forma el segundo valor de posición mayor después del tallo.

catetos Lados adyacentes al ángulo recto de un triángulo rectángulo.

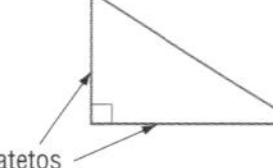

fracciones semejantes Fracciones con el mismo denominador.

términos semejantes Expresiones que tienen las mismas variables elevadas a los mismos exponentes, como $2n$ y $5n$ ó $6xy^2$ y $4xy^2$.

recta Trayectoria rectilínea interminable.

gráfica lineal Tipo de gráfica estadística que se usa para mostrar cómo cambian los valores durante un período de tiempo.

recta de ajuste En una gráfica de dispersión, una recta que está muy cercana a la mayoría de los puntos de datos. La recta que mejor se ajusta a los datos.

eje de simetría Cuando se traza un eje de simetría, cada mitad de una figura es una imagen especular de la otra mitad.

esquema lineal Diagrama que muestra la frecuencia de los datos sobre una recta numérica.

segmento de recta Parte de una recta que contiene dos extremos y todos los puntos entre éstos.

linear equation (p. 406) An equation in which the variables appear in separate terms and neither variable contains an exponent other than 1. The graph of a linear equation is a straight line.

linear regression equation (p. 864) One type of equation for a line of fit.

linear relationships (p. 418) Relationships that have straight line graphs.

lower quartile (p. 744) The median of the lower half of a set of data, indicated by LQ.

ecuación lineal Ecuación en que las variables aparecen en términos separados y en la cual ninguna de ellas tiene un exponente distinto de 1. La gráfica de una ecuación lineal es una recta.

ecuación de la regresión linear Tipo de ecuación para una recta de regresión.

relación lineal Relación que al ser graficada forma una línea recta.

cuartil inferior Mediana de la mitad inferior de un conjunto de datos, se denota con CI.

M

markup (p. 365) The amount the price of an item is increased above the price of the store paid for an item.

matrix (p. 886) A rectangular arrangement of numerical data in rows and columns.

mean (pp. 92, 730) The sum of data divided by the number of items in the data set, also called the average.

measures of central tendency (p. 730) For a list of numerical data, numbers that can represent the whole set of data.

measures of variation (p. 743) Used to describe the distribution of statistical data.

median (p. 274) In a set of data, the middle number of the ordered data, or the mean of the two middle numbers.

mode (p. 274) The number or numbers that occur(s) most often in a set of data.

monomial (p. 477) An expression that is a number, a variable, or a product of numbers and/or variables.

Multiplication Property of Equality (p. 193) When you multiply each side of an equation by the same number, the two sides remain equal.

multiplicative inverse (p. 141) Two numbers whose product is 1.

multiple (p. 860) The product of a number and a whole number.

mutually exclusive events (p. 792) Two or more events that cannot happen at the same time.

margen de utilidad Cantidad de aumento en el precio de un artículo por encima del precio que paga la tienda por dicho artículo.

matriz Disposición rectangular de números colocados en filas y columnas.

media Suma de los datos dividida entre el número de elementos en el conjunto de datos. También llamada promedio.

medidas de tendencia central Números que pueden representar todo el conjunto de datos en una lista de datos numéricos.

medidas de variación Se usan para describir la distribución de datos estadísticos.

mediana En un conjunto de datos, el número central de los datos ordenados numéricamente o la media de los dos números centrales.

moda Número o números de un conjunto de datos que aparecen más frecuentemente.

monomio Expresión que es un número, una variable y/o un producto de números y variables.

Propiedad de multiplicación de la igualdad Cuando multiplicas ambos lados de una ecuación por el mismo número, los dos lados permanecen iguales.

inversos multiplicativos Dos números cuyo producto es igual a uno.

múltiplo Producto de un número por un número entero.

eventos mutuamente exclusivos Dos o más eventos que no pueden ocurrir simultáneamente.

N

negative number (p. 61) A number less than zero.

número negativo Número menor que cero.

net (p. 690) A two-dimensional pattern for a three-dimensional figure.

redes Patrón bidimensional de una figura tridimensional.

nonlinear function (p. 504) A function with a graph that is not a straight line.

función no lineal Función cuya gráfica no es una recta.

nonproportional (p. 281) A relationship in which two ratios are not equal.

relación no proporcional Relación en la que dos razones no son iguales.

null set or empty set (p. 250) A set with no elements shown by the symbol { } or Ø.

conjunto vacío Conjunto que carece de elementos y que se denota con el símbolo { } o Ø.

numerical expression (p. 5) A combination of numbers and operations such as addition, subtraction, multiplication, and division.

expresión numérica Combinación de números y operaciones, como adición, sustracción, multiplicación y división.

O

obtuse angle (p. 551) An angle with a measure greater than 90° but less than 180°.

ángulo obtuso Ángulo que mide más de 90°, pero menos de 180°.

obtuse triangle (p. 552) A triangle with one obtuse angle.

obtuse angle

triángulo obtusángulo Triángulo que posee un ángulo obtuso.

ángulo obtuso

odds against (p. 767) The ratio that compares the number of ways the event *cannot* occur to the number of ways that the event *can* occur.

probabilidad en contra Como la razón entre el número de casos desfavorables y el número de caso favorables.

odds in favor (p. 767) The ratio that compares the number of ways the event *can* occur to the number of ways that the event *cannot* occur.

probabilidad a favor Como la razon entre el número de casos favorables y el número de casos desfavorables.

opposites (p. 71) Two numbers with the same absolute value but different signs.

opuestos Dos números que tienen el mismo valor absoluto, pero que tienen distintos signos.

order of operations (p. 6) The rules to follow when more than one operation is used in an expression.

1. Do all operations within grouping symbols first; start with the innermost grouping symbols.
2. Evaluate all powers before other operations.
3. Multiply and divide in order from left to right.
4. Add and subtract in order from left to right.

orden de las operaciones Reglas a seguir cuando se usa más de una operación en una expresión.

1. Primero ejecuta todas las operaciones dentro de los símbolos de agrupamiento
2. Evalúa todas las potencias antes que las otras aperaciones.
3. Multiplica y divide en orden de izquierda a derecha.
4. Suma y resta en orden de izquierda a derecha.

ordered pair (p. 25) A pair of numbers used to locate any point on a coordinate plane.

par ordenado Par de números que se usa para ubicar cualquier punto en un plano de coordenadas.

origin (p. 25) The point at which the number lines intersect in a coordinate system.

origen Punto de intersección de las rectas numéricas de un sistema de coordenadas.

outcome (p. 765) Possible result of a probability experiment.

resultado Resultados posibles de un experimento probabilístico.

outlier (p. 745) Data that are more than 1.5 times the interquartile range beyond the quartiles.

valores atípicos Datos que distan de los cuartiles más de 1.5 veces la amplitud intercuartílica.

P

parabola (p. 510) The graph of a quadratic function.

parábola La gráfica de una función cuadrática.

parallel lines (p. 590) Two lines in the same plane that do not intersect.

rectas paralelas Dos rectas en el mismo plano que no se intersecan.

parallelogram (p. 612) A quadrilateral with opposite sides parallel and congruent.

paralelogramo Cuadrilátero con lados opuestos congruentes y paralelos.

part (p. 345) In a percent proportion, the number being compared to the whole quantity.

parte En una proporción porcentual, el número que se compara con la cantidad total.

percent (p. 331) A ratio that compares a number to 100.

por ciento Razón que compara un número con 100.

percent equation (p. 357) An equivalent form of the percent proportion, where % is written as a decimal.

$$\text{Part} = \text{Percent} \times \text{Whole}$$

ecuación porcentual Forma equivalente a la proporción porcentual en la cual el % se escribe como decimal.

$$\text{Parte} = \text{Por ciento} \times \text{Entero}$$

percent of change (p. 364) The ratio of the increase or decrease of an amount to the original amount.

porcentaje de cambio Razón del aumento o disminución de una cantidad a la cantidad original.

percent of decrease (p. 364) The ratio of an amount of decrease to the previous amount, expressed as a percent. A negative percent of change.

porcentaje de disminución Razón de la cantidad de disminución a la cantidad original, escrita como por ciento. Un por ciento de cambio negativo.

percent of increase (p. 364) The ratio of an amount of increase to the original amount, expressed as a percent.

porcentaje de aumento Razón de la cantidad de aumento a la cantidad original, escrita como por ciento.

percent proportion (p. 345)

$$\frac{\text{part}}{\text{whole}} = \frac{\text{percent}}{100} \text{ or } \frac{a}{b} = \frac{p}{100}$$

proporción porcentual

$$\frac{\text{parte}}{\text{todo}} = \frac{\text{por ciento}}{100} \text{ or } \frac{a}{b} = \frac{p}{100}$$

perfect square (p. 537) Rational number whose square root is a whole number. 25 is a perfect square because $\sqrt{25} = 5$.

cuadrados perfectos Números racionales cuyas raíces cuadradas son números racionales. 25 es un cuadrado perfecto porque $\sqrt{25} = 5$.

perimeter (p. 221) The distance around a geometric figure.

perímetro Longitud alrededor de una figura geométrica.

permutation (p. 783) An arrangement or listing in which order is important.

permutación Arreglo o lista en que el orden es importante.

perpendicular bisector (p. 870) A perpendicular line that divides a line segment into two congruent segments.

bisector perpendicular Línea perpendicular que divide una línea segmento en dos segmentos congruentes.

perpendicular lines (p. 589) Lines that intersect to form a right angle.

perspective (p. 663) A point of view.

pi, π (p. 631) The ratio of the circumference of a circle to the diameter of the circle. Approximations for π are 3.14 and $\frac{22}{7}$.

plane (p. 664) A two-dimensional flat surface that extends in all directions and contains at least three noncollinear points.

point (p. 868) An exact location in space that is represented by a dot.

point-slope form (p. 441) An equation of the form $y - y_1 = m(x - x_1)$, where m is the slope and (x_1, y_1) is a given point on a nonvertical line.

polygon (p. 617) A simple closed figure in a plane formed by three or more line segments.

polyhedron (p. 664) A solid with flat surfaces that are polygons.

polynomial (p. LA2) An algebraic expression that contains the sums and/or products of one or more monomials.

population (p. 771) A larger group used in statistical analysis.

positive number (p. 61) Any number that is greater than zero.

power (p. 471) A number that is expressed using an exponent.

precision (p. 879) The degree of perfection in which a measurement is made.

prime factorization (p. 477) A composite number expressed as a product of prime factors. For example, the prime factorization of 63 is $3 \times 3 \times 7$.

prime number (p. 476) A whole number that has exactly two factors, 1 and itself.

principal (p. 370) The amount of money in an account.

rectas perpendiculares Rectas que se intersecan formando un ángulo recto.

perspective Un punto de vista.

pi, π Razón de la circunferencia de un círculo al diámetro del mismo. 3.14 y $\frac{22}{7}$ son aproximaciones de π.

plano Superficie plana bidimensional que se extiende en todas direcciones y que contiene por lo menos tres puntos no colineales.

punto Ubicación exacta en el espacio que se representa con un marca puntual.

forma punto-pendiente Ecuación de la forma $y - y_1 = m(x - x_1)$, donde m es la pendiente y (x_1, y_1) es un punto dado de una recta no vertical.

polígono Figura simple y cerrada en el plano formada por tres o más segmentos de recta.

poliedro Sólido con superficies planas que son polígonos.

polinomio Expresión algebraica que contiene sumas y/o productos de uno o más monomios.

población Grupo grande que se utiliza en análisis estadísticos.

número positive Todo número mayor que cero.

potencia Número que puede escribirse usando un exponente.

precisión Grado de perfección el cual se hace una medida.

factorización prima Número compuesto escrito como producto de factores primos. Por ejemplo, la factorización prima de 63 es $3 \times 3 \times 7$.

número primo Número entero que sólo tiene dos factores, 1 y sí mismo.

capital Cantidad de dinero en una cuenta.

prism (p. 665) A polyhedron that has two parallel, congruent bases in the shape of polygons.

rectangular prism triangular prism

probability (p. 765) The ratio of the number of ways a certain event can occur to the number of possible outcomes.

$$P(\text{event}) = \frac{\text{number of favorable outcomes}}{\text{number of possible outcomes}}$$

properties (p. 18) Statements that are true for any numbers.

proportion (p. 287) A statement of equality of two or more ratios.

proportional (p. 281) The ratios of related terms are equal.

protractor (p. 873) An instrument used to measure angles.

pyramid (p. 665) A polyhedron that has a polygon for a base and triangles for sides.

Pythagorean Theorem (p. 558) If a triangle is a right triangle, then the square of the length of the hypotenuse is equal to the sum of the squares of the lengths of the legs or $c^2 = a^2 + b^2$.

Pythagorean Triple (p. 557) The sides of right triangle represented by a, b, and c, when $a^2 + b^2 = c^2$.

prisma Poliedro que posee dos bases congruentes y paralelas en forma de polígonos.

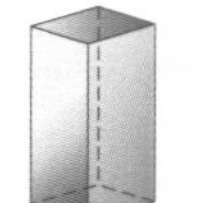

prisma rectangular prisma triangular

probabilidad La razón del número de maneras en que puede ocurrir el evento al número de resultados posibles.

$$P(\text{evento}) = \frac{\text{número de resultados favorables}}{\text{número de resultados posibles}}$$

propiedades Enunciados que son verdaderos para cualquier número.

proporción Enunciado de la igualdad de dos o más razones.

proporcional Relación en la que la razón entre los términos relacionados permanece igual.

transportador Instrumento que se usa para medir ángulos.

pirámide Poliedro cuya base es un polígono y cuyos lados son triángulos.

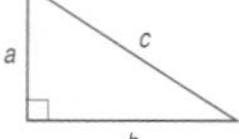

Teorema de Pitágoras Si un triángulo es rectángulo, entonces el cuadrado de la longitud de la hipotenusa es igual a la suma de los cuadrados de las longitudes de los catetos, o $c^2 = a^2 + b^2$.

Triple pitagórico Los lados de un triángulo rectángulo representados por a, b y c, cuando $a^2 + b^2 = c^2$.

Q

quadrant (p. 97) One of four regions into which the x-axis and y-axis separate the coordinate plane.

quadratic function (p. 510) A function that can be described by an equation of the form $y = ax^2 + bx + c$, where $a \neq 0$.

cuadrantes Las cuatro regiones en que los ejes x y y dividen el plano de coordenadas.

función cuadrática Función que puede describirse por una ecuación de la forma $y = ax^2 + bx + c$, donde $a \neq 0$.

quadrilateral (p. 612) A closed figure with four sides and four vertices, including squares, rectangles, and trapezoids.

quartile (p. 744) The values that divide a set of data into four equal parts.

R

radical sign (p. 537) The symbol $\sqrt{}$ used to indicate a nonnegative square root.

radius (p. 631) The distance from the center to any point on the circle.

random (p. 766) Outcomes occur at random if each outcome is equally likely to occur.

range (p. 27) The range of a relation is the set of all y-coordinates from each ordered pair.

range (p. 743) A measure of variation that is the difference between the least and greatest values in a set of data.

rate (p. 270) A ratio of two measurements having different units.

rate of change (p. 412) A change in one quantity with respect to another quantity.

ratio (p. 265) A comparison of two numbers by division. The ratio of 2 to 4 can be stated as 2 out of 4, 2 to 4, 2 : 4, or $\frac{2}{4}$.

rational number (p. 128) A number that can be written as a fraction in the form $\frac{a}{b}$, where a and b are integers and $b \neq 0$.

ray (p. 868) A part of a line that extends indefinitely in one direction.

real numbers (p. 543) The set of rational numbers together with the set of irrational numbers.

reciprocal (p. 141) Another name for a multiplicative inverse.

rectangle (p. 613) A parallelogram with four right angles.

reflection (p. 101) A transformation where a figure is flipped over a line. Also called a flip.

regular polygon (p. 619) A polygon having all sides congruent and all angles congruent.

regular pyramid (p. 702) A pyramid whose base is a regular polygon.

relation (p. 27) A set of ordered pairs.

repeating decimal (p. 122) A decimal whose digits repeat in groups of one or more without end. Examples are 0.181818… and 0.8333….

cuadrilátero Figura cerrada de cuatro lados y cuatro vértices, incluyendo cuadrados, rectángulos y trapecios.

cuartiles Valores que dividen un conjunto de datos en cuatro partes iguales.

signo radical El símbolo $\sqrt{}$ que se usa para indicar la raíz cuadrada no negativa.

radio Distancia del centro a cualquier punto de un círculo.

aleatorio Los resultados son aleatorios si todos son equiprobables.

rango El rango de una relación es el conjunto de coordenadas y de todos los pares.

amplitud Medida de variación que es la diferencia entre los valores máximo y mínimo de un conjunto de datos.

tasa Razón de dos medidas que tienen unidades distintas.

tasa de cambio Cambio de una cantidad con respecto a otra.

razón Comparación de dos números mediante división. La razón de 2 a 4 puede escribirse como 2 de cada 4, 2 a 4, 2 : 4 ó $\frac{2}{4}$.

número racional Número que puede escribirse como una fracción de la forma $\frac{a}{b}$ donde a y b son enteros y $b \neq 0$.

rayo Parte de una recta que se extiende indefinidamente en una dirección.

números reales El conjunto de los números racionales junto con el de números irracionales.

recíproco Otro nombre del inverso multiplicativo.

rectángulo Paralelogramo con cuatro ángulos rectos.

reflexión Transformación en que una figura se voltea a través de una recta.

polígono regular Polígono cuyos lados son todos congruentes y cuyos ángulos son también todos congruentes.

pirámide regular Pirámide cuya base es un polygon regular.

relación Conjunto de pares ordenados.

decimal periódico Decimal cuyos dígitos se repiten en grupos de uno o más. 0.181818… y 0.8333… son ejemplos de este tipo de decimales.

rhombus (p. 613) A parallelogram with four congruent sides.

right angle (p. 551) An angle that measures 90°.

right triangle (p. 552) A triangle with one right angle.

rotation (p. 605) A transformation where a figure is turned around a fixed point. Also called a turn.

rotational symmetry (p. 607) A figure has rotational symmetry if it can be turned less than 360° about its center and still look like the original.

rombo Paralelogramo con cuatro lados congruentes.

ángulo recto Ángulo que mide 90°.

triángulo rectángulo Triángulo que tiene un ángulo recto.

rotación Transformación en que una figura se hace girar alrededor de un punto fijo. También se llama vuelta.

simetría rotacional Una figura posee simetría rotacional si se puede girar menos de 360° en torno a su centro sin que esto cambia su apariencia con respecto a la figura original.

S

sample (p. 771) A subgroup or subset of a population used to represent the whole population.

sample space (p. 766) The set of all possible outcomes.

scale (p. 294) The relationship between the measurements on a drawing or model and the measurements of the real object.

scale drawing (p. 294) A drawing that is used to represent an object that is too large or too small to be drawn at actual size.

scale factor (p. 295) The ratio of a length on a scale drawing or model to the corresponding length on the real object.

scale model (p. 294) A model used to represent an object that is too large or too small to be built at actual size.

scalene triangle (p. 552) A triangle with no congruent sides.

scatter plot (p. 40) The relationship between a set of data with two variables, graphed as ordered pairs on a coordinate plane.

scientific notation (p. 493) A number in scientific notation is expressed as $a \times 10n$, where $1 \leq a < 10$ and n is an integer. For example, $5{,}000{,}000 = 5.0 \times 10^6$.

sector (p. 638) A pie-shaped part of a circle bound by the radius of a circle and an arc.

muestra Subgrupo o subconjunto de una población que se usa para representarla.

espacio muestral Conjunto de todos los resultados posibles.

escala Relación entre las medidas de un dibujo o modelo y las medidas de la figura verdadera.

dibujo a escala Dibujo que se usa para representar una figura que es demasiado grande o pequeña como para ser dibujada de tamaño natural.

factor de escala Razón de la longitud en un dibujo a escala o modelo a la longitud correspondiente en la figura verdadera.

modelo a escala Modelo que se usa para representar una figura que es demasiado grande o pequeña como para ser construida de tamaño natural.

triángulo escaleno Triángulo que no tiene lados congruentes.

gráfica de dispersión Es un diagrama que muestra la relación entre un conjunto de datos con dos variables, graficados como pares ordenados en un plano coordenadas.

notación científica Un número en notación científica se escribe como $a \times 10n$, donde $1 \leq a < 10$ y n es un entero. Por ejemplo, $5{,}000{,}000 = 5.0 \times 10^6$.

sector Una parte empanada-formada de un círculo limita por el radio de un círculo y de un arco.

selling price (p. 365) The amount a customer pays for an item.

sequence (p. 401) An ordered list of numbers, such as, 0, 1, 2, 3, or 2, 4, 6, 8.

sides (p. 868) The two rays that make up an angle.

similar figures (p. 301) Figures that have the same shape but not necessarily the same size.

similar solids (p. 709) Solids that have the same shape but not necessarily the same size.

simple event (p. 765) One outcome or a collection of outcomes.

simple interest (p. 370) The amount of money paid or earned for the use of money.

$I = prt$ (Interest = principal × rate × time)

simple random sample (p. 771) A sample where each item or person in the population is as likely to be chosen as any other.

simplest form (p. 179) An algebraic expression in simplest form has no like terms and no parentheses.

simplify (p. 20) To write an expression in a simpler form.

simplify the expression (p. 179) To use distribution to combine like terms.

sine (p. 877) For an acute angle of a right triangle, the ratio of the measure of the leg opposite the acute angle to the measure of the hypotenuse.

slant height (p. 702) The length of the altitude of a lateral face of a regular pyramid or cone.

slope (p. 427) The ratio of the rise, or vertical change, to the run, or horizontal change. The slope describes the steepness of a line.

$$\text{slope} = \frac{\text{rise}}{\text{run}}$$

slope-intercept form (p. 433) A linear equation in the form $y = mx + b$, where m is the slope and b is the y-intercept.

solid (p. 664) Three-dimensional figure.

solution (p. 184) A value for the variable that makes an equation true. For $x + 7 = 19$, the solution is 12.

precio de venta Cantidad de dinero que paga un consumidor por un artículo.

sucesión Lista ordenada de números, como 0, 1, 2, 3 ó 2, 4, 6, 8.

lados Los dos rayos que forman un ángulo.

figuras semejantes Figuras que tienen la misma forma, pero no necesariamente el mismo tamaño.

sólidos semejantes Sólidos que tienen la misma forma, pero no necesariamente el mismo tamaño.

evento simple Resultado o colección de resultados.

interés simple Cantidad que se paga o que se gana por usar el dinero.

$I = crt$ (Interés = capital × rédito × tiempo)

muestra aleatoria simple Muestra de una población que tiene la misma probabilidad de escogerse que cualquier otra.

forma reducida Una expresión algebraica reducida no tiene ni términos semejantes ni paréntesis.

reducir Escribir una expresión en forma más simple.

reducir la expresión Usar la distribución para combinar términos semejantes.

seno Es la razón entre la medida del cateto opuesto al ángulo agudo y la medida de la hipotenusa de un triángulo rectángulo.

altura oblicua En una pirámide regular o un cono, la longitud de la altura de una cara lateral.

pendiente Razón de la elevación o cambio vertical al desplazamiento o cambio horizontal. La pendiente describe la inclinación de una recta.

$$\text{pendiente} = \frac{\text{elevación}}{\text{desplazamiento}}$$

forma pendiente-intersección Una ecuación lineal de la forma $y = mx + b$, donde m es la pendiente y b es la intersección y.

sólido Figura tridimensional.

solución Valosss y que posee cuatro ángulos rectos.

solving a right triangle (p. 559) Using the Pythagorean Theorem to find the length of the third side of a right triangle, if the lengths of the other two sides are known.

solving the equation (p. 184) The process of finding a solution to an equation.

sphere (p. 684) The set of all points in space that are a given distance, r, from the center.

spreadsheet (p. 17) A table that performs calculations.

square (p. 613) A parallelogram with all sides congruent and four right angles.

square root (p. 537) One of the two equal factors of a number. The square root of 25 is 5 since $5^2 = 25$.

standard form (p. 493) A number is in standard form when it does not contain exponents. The standard form for seven hundred thirty-nine is 739.

statistics (p. 882) The branch of mathematics that deals with collecting, organizing, and interpreting data.

stem (p. 737) The greatest place value common to all the data values is used for the stem of a stem-and-leaf plot.

stem-and-leaf plot (p. 737) A system used to condense a set of data where the greatest place value of the data forms the stem and the next greatest place value forms the leaves.

straight angle (p. 551) An angle with a measure equal to 180°.

stratified random sample (p. 771) A sampling method in which the population is divided into similar, non-overlapping groups. A simple random sample is then selected from each group.

substitution (p. 455) Use algebraic methods to find an exact solution of a system of equations.

Subtraction Property of Equality (p. 185) If you subtract the same number from each side of an equation, the two sides remain equal.

supplementary angles (p. 589) Two angles are supplementary if the sum of their measures is 180°.

surface area (p. 691) The sum of the areas of all the surfaces (faces) of a 3-dimensional figure.

system of equations (p. 453) A set of two or more equations with the same variables.

resolver un triángulo rectángulo Uso del Teorema de Pitágoras para hallar la longitud de un tercer lado de un triángulo rectángulo, si se conocen las longitudes de los otros dos lados.

resolver la ecuación Proceso de hallar una solución a una ecuación.

esfera El conjunto de todos los puntos en el espacio que se hallan a una distancia r del centro.

hoja de cálculos Tabla que realiza cálculos.

cuadrado Paralelogramo cuyos lados son todos congruentes y que posee cuatro ángulos rectos.

raíz cuadrada Uno de los dos factores iguales de un número. Una raíz cuadrada de 25 es 5 porque $5^2 = 25$.

forma estándar Un número está en forma estándar si no contiene exponentes. Por ejemplo, la forma estándar de setecientos treinta y nueve es 739.

estadística Rama de las matemáticas cuyo objetivo primordial es la recopilación, organización e interpretación de datos.

tallo Máximo valor de posición común a todos los datos que se usa como el tallo en un diagrama de tallo y hojas.

diagrama de tallo y hojas Sistema que se usa para condensar un conjunto de datos, en que el valor de posición máximo de los datos forma el tallo y el segundo valor de posición máximo forma las hojas.

ángulo llano Ángulo que mide 180°.

muestra aleatoria estratificada Método de muestreo en que la población se divide en grupos semejantes que no se sobreponen. Luego se selecciona una muestra aleatoria simple de cada grupo.

sustitución Usa métodos algebraicos para hallar una solución exacta a un sistema de ecuaciones.

Propiedad de sustracción de la igualdad Si restas el mismo número de ambos lados de una ecuación, los dos lados permanecen iguales.

suplementarios ángulos Dos ángulos son suplementarios si sus medidas suman 180°.

área de superficie Suma de las áreas de todas las superficies (caras) de una figura tridimensional.

sistema de ecuaciones Sistema de ecuaciones con las mismas variables.

T

tangent (p. 875) For an acute angle of a right triangle, the ratio of the measure of the leg opposite the acute angle to the measure of the leg adjacent to the acute angle.

term (p. 178) When plus or minus signs separate an algebraic expression into parts, each part is a term.

term (p. 401) Each number within a sequence is called a term.

terminating decimal (p. 121) A decimal whose digits end. Every terminating decimal can be written as a fraction with a denominator of 10, 100, 1000, and so on.

tessellation (p. 619) A pattern formed by repeating figures that fit together without gaps or overlaps.

theoretical probability (p. 766) What should occur in a probability experiment.

transformation (p. 101) A movement of a geometric figure.

translation (p. 101) A transformation where a figure is slid from one position to another without being turned. Also called a slide.

transversal (p. 590) A line that intersects two parallel lines to form eight angles.

trapezoid (p. 612) A quadrilateral with exactly one pair of parallel sides.

tree diagram (p. 777) A diagram used to show the total number of possible outcomes.

triangle (p. 550) A figure having three sides.

trigonometric ratio (p. 875) A ratio of the lengths of sides of a right triangle.

trigonometry (p. 875) The study of the properties of triangles and trigonometric functions and their applications.

trinomial (p. LA25) A polynomial with three terms.

two-step equation (p. 199) An equation that contains two operations.

tangente La razón entre la medida del cateto opuesto al ángulo agudo y la medida del cateto adyacente al ángulo agudo de un triángulo rectángulo.

término Cada una de las partes de una expresión algebraica separadas por los signos de adición o sustracción.

término Cada número de una sucesión se llama término.

decimal terminal Decimal cuyos dígitos terminan. Todo decimal terminal puede escribirse como una fracción con un denominador de 10, 100, 1000, etc.

teselado Patrón formado por figuras repetidas que no se traslapan y que no dejan espacios entre sí.

probabilidad teórica Lo que debería ocurrir en un experimento probabilístico.

transformación Desplazamiento de una figura geométrica.

translación Transformación en que una figura se desliza sin girar, de una posición a otra. También se llama deslizamiento.

transversal Recta que interseca dos rectas paralelas formando ocho ángulos.

trapecio Cuadrilátero con sólo un par de lados paralelos.

diagrama de árbol Diagrama que se usa para mostrar el número total de resultados posibles.

triángulo Figura de tres lados.

razón trigonométrica Razón de las longitudes de las lados de un triángulo rectángulo.

trigonometría Estudio de las propiedades de los triángulos y de las funciones trigonométricas y sus aplicaciones.

trinomio Polinomio de tres términos.

ecuación de dos pasos Ecuación que contiene dos operaciones.

U

unbiased sample (p. 771) A random sample that is representative of a larger sample.

unlike fractions (p. 153) Fractions with different denominators.

unit rate (p. 270) A rate simplified so that it has a denominator of 1.

upper quartile (p. 744) The median of the upper half of a set of data, indicated by UQ.

muestra insesgada Muestra aleatoria que es representativa de una muestra más grande.

fracciones con distinto denominador Fracciones cuyos denominadores son diferentes.

tasa unitaria Tasa reducida que tiene denominador igual a 1.

cuartil superior Mediana de la mitad superior de un conjunto de datos, denotada por CS.

V

variable (p. 11) A placeholder for any value.

vertex (p. 550) A vertex of a polygon is a point where two sides of the polygon intersect.

vertex (p. 664) Where three or more planes intersect in a point.

vertex (p. 868) The common endpoint of the rays forming an angle.

vertical angles (p. 589) Two pairs of opposite angles formed by two intersecting lines. The angles formed are congruent. In the figure, the vertical angles are $\angle 1$ and $\angle 3$, $\angle 2$ and $\angle 4$.

vertical line test (p. 396) If any vertical line drawn on the graph of a relation passes through no more than one point on the graph for each value of x in the domain, then the relation is a function.

volume (p. 671) The measure of space occupied by a solid region.

voluntary response sample (p. 772) A sample which involves only those who want to participate in the sampling.

variable Marcador de posición para cualquier valor.

vértice El vértice de un polígono es un punto en que se intersecan dos lados del mismo.

vértice Punto en que se intersecan tres o más planos.

vértice Extremo común de los rayos que forman un ángulo.

ángulos opuestos por el vértice Dos pares de ángulos opuestos formados por dos rectas que se intersecan. Los ángulos que resultan son congruentes. En la figura, los ángulos opuestos por el vértice son $\angle 1$ y $\angle 3$, $\angle 2$ y $\angle 4$.

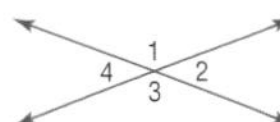

prueba de la recta vertical Si todas las rectas verticales trazadas en la gráfica de una relación no pasan por más un punto para cada valor de x en el dominio, entonces la relación es una función.

volumen Medida del espacio que ocupa un sólido.

muestra de respuesta voluntaria Muestra que involucra sólo aquellos que quieren participar en el muestreo.

W

whole (p. 345) In a percent proportion, the whole quantity, or the number to which the part is being compared.

$$\frac{\text{part}}{\text{whole}} = \frac{\text{percent}}{100}$$

entero o base En una proporción porcentual, toda la cantidad o número al que se compara la parte.

$$\frac{\text{parte}}{\text{todo}} = \frac{\text{porciento}}{100}$$

X

***x*-axis** (p. 25) The horizontal number line which helps to form the coordinate system.

***x*-coordinate** (p. 25) The first number of an ordered pair.

***x*-intercept** (p. 407) The x-coordinate of a point where a graph crosses the x-axis.

eje *x* Recta numérica horizontal que forma parte de un sistema de coordenadas.

coordenada *x* El primer número de un par ordenado.

intersección *x* La coordenada x de un punto en que una gráfica interseca el eje x.

Y

***y*-axis** (p. 25) The vertical number line which helps to form the coordinate system.

***y*-coordinate** (p. 25) The second number of an ordered pair.

***y*-intercept** (p. 407) The y-coordinate of a point where a graph crosses the y-axis.

eje *y* Recta numérica vertical que forma parte de un sistema de coordenadas.

coordenada *y* El segundo número en un par ordenado.

intersección *y* La coordenada y de un punto en que una gráfica interseca el eje y.

Z

zero pair (p. 67) A positive tile paired with a negative tile.

par nulo Ficha positiva apareada con una negativa.

Glossary/Glosario

R94 Glossary

Index

A

Index

Index

Index

D

Index

E

Index

G

Index

H

I

Index

L

M

N

Index

Q

S

Index

T

X

Y

Z

Curriculum Focal Points and Connections for Grade 7

The Curriculum Focal Points identify key mathematical ideas for this grade. They are not discrete topics or a checklist to be mastered; rather, they provide a framework for the majority of instruction at a particular grade level and the foundation for future mathematics study. The complete document may be viewed at www.nctm.org/focalpoints.

KEY

G7-FP1 Grade 7 Focal Point 1

G7-FP2 Grade 7 Focal Point 2

G7-FP3 Grade 7 Focal Point 3

G7-FP4C Grade 7 Focal Point 4 Connection

G7-FP5C Grade 7 Focal Point 5 Connection

G7-FP6C Grade 7 Focal Point 6 Connection

G7-FP7C Grade 7 Focal Point 7 Connection

G7-FP1 Number and Operations and Algebra and Geometry: **Developing an understanding of and applying proportionality, including similarity**

Students extend their work with ratios to develop an understanding of proportionality that they apply to solve single and multistep problems in numerous contexts. They use ratio and proportionality to solve a wide variety of percent problems, including problems involving discounts, interest, taxes, tips, and percent increase or decrease. They also solve problems about similar objects (including figures) by using scale factors that relate corresponding lengths of the objects or by using the fact that relationships of lengths within an object are preserved in similar objects. Students graph proportional relationships and identify the unit rate as the slope of the related line. They distinguish proportional relationships $\left(\frac{y}{x} = k, \text{ or } y = kx\right)$ from other relationships, including inverse proportionality $\left(xy = k, \text{ or } y = \frac{k}{x}\right)$.

G7-FP2 Measurement and Geometry and Algebra: **Developing an understanding of and using formulas to determine surface areas and volumes of three-dimensional shapes**

By decomposing two- and three-dimensional shapes into smaller, component shapes, students find surface areas and develop and justify formulas for the surface areas and volumes of prisms and cylinders. As students decompose prisms and cylinders by slicing them, they develop and understand formulas for their volumes (*Volume* = *Area of base* × *Height*). They apply these formulas in problem solving to determine volumes of prisms and cylinders. Students see that the formula for the area of a circle is plausible by decomposing a circle into a number of wedges and rearranging them into a shape that approximates a parallelogram. They select appropriate two- and three-dimensional shapes to model real-world situations and solve a variety of problems (including multistep problems) involving surface areas, areas and circumferences of circles, and volumes of prisms and cylinders.

G7-FP2 Number and Operations and Algebra: **Developing an understanding of operations on all rational numbers and solving linear equations**

Students extend understandings of addition, subtraction, multiplication, and division, together with their properties, to all rational numbers, including negative integers. By applying properties of arithmetic and considering negative numbers in everyday contexts (e.g., situations of owing money or measuring elevations above and below sea level), students explain why the rules for adding, subtracting, multiplying, and dividing with negative numbers make sense. They use the arithmetic of rational numbers as they formulate and solve linear equations in one variable and use these equations to solve problems. Students make strategic choices of procedures to solve linear equations in one variable and implement them efficiently, understanding that when they use the properties of equality to express an equation in a new way, solutions that they obtain for the new equation also solve the original equation.

Connections to the Focal Points

G7-FP4C **Measurement and Geometry:** Students connect their work on proportionality with their work on area and volume by investigating similar objects. They understand that if a scale factor describes how corresponding lengths in two similar objects are related, then the square of the scale factor describes how corresponding areas are related, and the cube of the scale factor describes how corresponding volumes are related. Students apply their work on proportionality to measurement in different contexts, including converting among different units of measurement to solve problems involving rates such as motion at a constant speed. They also apply proportionality when they work with the circumference, radius, and diameter of a circle; when they find the area of a sector of a circle; and when they make scale drawings.

G7-FP5C **Number and Operations:** In grade 4, students used equivalent fractions to determine the decimal representations of fractions that they could represent with terminating decimals. Students now use division to express any fraction as a decimal, including fractions that they must represent with infinite decimals. They find this method useful when working with proportions, especially those involving percents. Students connect their work with dividing fractions to solving equations of the form $ax = b$, where a and b are fractions. Students continue to develop their understanding of multiplication and division and the structure of numbers by determining if a counting number greater than 1 is a prime, and if it is not, by factoring it into a product of primes.

G7-FP6C **Data Analysis:** Students use proportions to make estimates relating to a population on the basis of a sample. They apply percentages to make and interpret histograms and circle graphs.

G7-FP7C **Probability:** Students understand that when all outcomes of an experiment are equally likely, the theoretical probability of an event is the fraction of outcomes in which the event occurs. Students use theoretical probability and proportions to make approximate predictions.

Formulas

Perimeter

square	$P = 4s$		
rectangle	$P = 2\ell + 2w$ or $P = 2(\ell + w)$		

Circumference

circle	$C = 2\pi r$ or $C = \pi d$		

Area

square	$A = s^2$	**triangle**	$A = \frac{1}{2}bh$
rectangle	$A = \ell w$	**trapezoid**	$A = \frac{1}{2}h(b_1 + b_2)$
parallelogram	$A = bh$	**circle**	$A = \pi r^2$

Surface Area

cube	$S = 6s^2$	**cylinder**	$S = 2\pi rh + 2\pi r^2$
rectangular prism	$S = 2\ell w + 2\ell h + 2wh$	**pyramid**	$S = L + B$ or $S = \frac{1}{2}P\ell + B$

Volume

cube	$V = s^3$	**pyramid**	$V = \frac{1}{3}Bh$
prism	$V = \ell wh$ or Bh	**cone**	$V = \frac{1}{3}\pi r^2 h$ or $\frac{1}{3}Bh$
cylinder	$V = \pi r^2 h$ or Bh		

Pythagorean Theorem

right triangle	$a^2 + b^2 = c^2$		

Temperature

Fahrenheit to Celsius	$C = \frac{5}{9}(F - 32)$	**Celsius to Fahrenheit**	$F = \frac{9}{5}C + 32$

Slope

line	$m = \frac{\text{rise}}{\text{run}}$ or $m = \frac{\text{change in } y}{\text{change in } x}$ or $m = \frac{y_2 - y_1}{x_2 - x_1}$		

Measures

Metric	Customary
Length	
1 kilometer (km) = 1,000 meters (m)	1 foot (ft) = 12 inches (in.)
1 meter = 100 centimeters (cm)	1 yard (yd) = 3 feet or 36 inches
1 centimeter = 10 millimeters (mm)	1 mile (mi) = 1,760 yards or 5,280 feet
Volume and Capacity	
1 liter (L) = 1,000 milliliters (mL)	1 cup (c) = 8 fluid ounces (fl oz)
1 kiloliter (kL) = 1,000 liters	1 pint (pt) = 2 cups
	1 quart (qt) = 2 pints
	1 gallon (gal) = 4 quarts
Weight and Mass	
1 kilogram (kg) = 1,000 grams (g)	1 pound (lb) = 16 ounces (oz)
1 gram = 1,000 milligrams (mg)	1 ton (T) = 2,000 pounds
1 metric ton = 1,000 kilograms	

Measures (cont.)

Time

1 minute (min) = 60 seconds (s)
1 hour (h) = 60 minutes
1 day (d) = 24 hours
1 week (wk) = 7 days
1 year (yr) = 12 months (mo) or 52 weeks or 365 days
1 leap year = 366 days

Metric to Customary

1 meter ≈ 39.37 inches
1 kilometer ≈ 0.62 mile
1 centimeter ≈ 0.39 inch
1 kilogram ≈ 2.2 pounds
1 gram ≈ 0.035 ounce
1 liter ≈ 1.057 quarts

Symbols

Number and Operations

$+$	plus or positive
$-$	minus or negative
$a \cdot b$	a times b
$a \times b$	a times b
ab or $a(b)$	a times b
$\div$	divided by
$\pm$	plus or minus
$=$	is equal to
$\neq$	is not equal to
$>$	is greater than
$<$	is less than
$\geq$	is greater than or equal to
$\leq$	is less than or equal to
$\approx$	is approximately equal to
%	percent
$a : b$	the ratio of a to b, or $\frac{a}{b}$
$0.7\overline{5}$	repeating decimal 0.75555 . . .

Algebra and Functions

$-a$	opposite or additive inverse of a
a^n	a to the nth power
a^{-n}	$\frac{1}{a^n}$
$\lvert x \rvert$	absolute value of x
$\sqrt{x}$	principal (positive) square root of x
$f(n)$	function, f of x

Geometry and Measurement

$\cong$	is congruent to
$\sim$	is similar to
$^\circ$	degree(s)
$\overleftrightarrow{AB}$	line AB
$\overrightarrow{AB}$	ray AB
$\overline{AB}$	line segment AB
AB	length of $\overline{AB}$
∟	right angle
$\perp$	is perpendicular to
$\parallel$	is parallel to
$\angle A$	angle A
$m\angle A$	measure of angle A
$\triangle ABC$	triangle ABC
(a, b)	ordered pair with x-coordinate a and y-coordinate b
O	origin
π	pi (approximately 3.14 or $\frac{22}{7}$)

Probability and Statistics

$P(A)$	probability of event A